Volume 2

I.I.T. MATHEMATICS

For JEE Main & Advanced

and many other Engineering Entrance Examinations

PROF. M.L. KHANNA
Head of Mathematics Department (Retd.)
Meerut College, MEERUT

PROF. J.N. SHARMA
Senior Lecturer, Mathematics Department (Retd.)
Meerut College, MEERUT

Revised by

DR. SUDHIR K. PUNDIR
Associate Professor
Department of Mathematics
S.D. (P.G.) College, MUZAFFARNAGAR

Er. Ajay Khanna (I.I.T Roorkee) | Er. Atul Khanna (I.I.T Delhi)

Newly Revised & Enlarged Edition

PUBLISHED BY:
JAI PRAKASH NATH & CO.
EDUCATIONAL PUBLISHERS
MEERUT
A DHARMENDRA NATH GUPTA GROUP

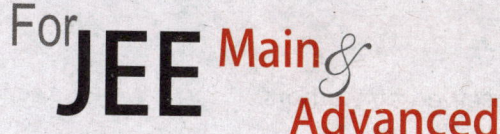

Published by :

JAI PRAKASH NATH & CO.

Head Office

Gandhi Ashram Crossing, Garh Road
Meerut City - 250 002 (U.P.) INDIA
Tel. : Off. : 0121-4004414, 6549111
Fax : : 0121-2600013
email : jpn1914@gmail.com
Like us at : facebook.com/jpnco1914
WEBSITE : www.jpncobooks.com

A DHARMENDRA NATH GUPTA GROUP

Newly Revised Edition, 2016-17

I.S.B.N. : 978-81-929005-2-0

Price : ₹ [redacted]**.00** only

(Combined Price for Vol-1 and Vol-2)
Not to be sold separately.

Typesetted at :

BALAJI Computers
Meerut.

Printed at :

Sunny Offset
Meerut.

Contents

Volume 2

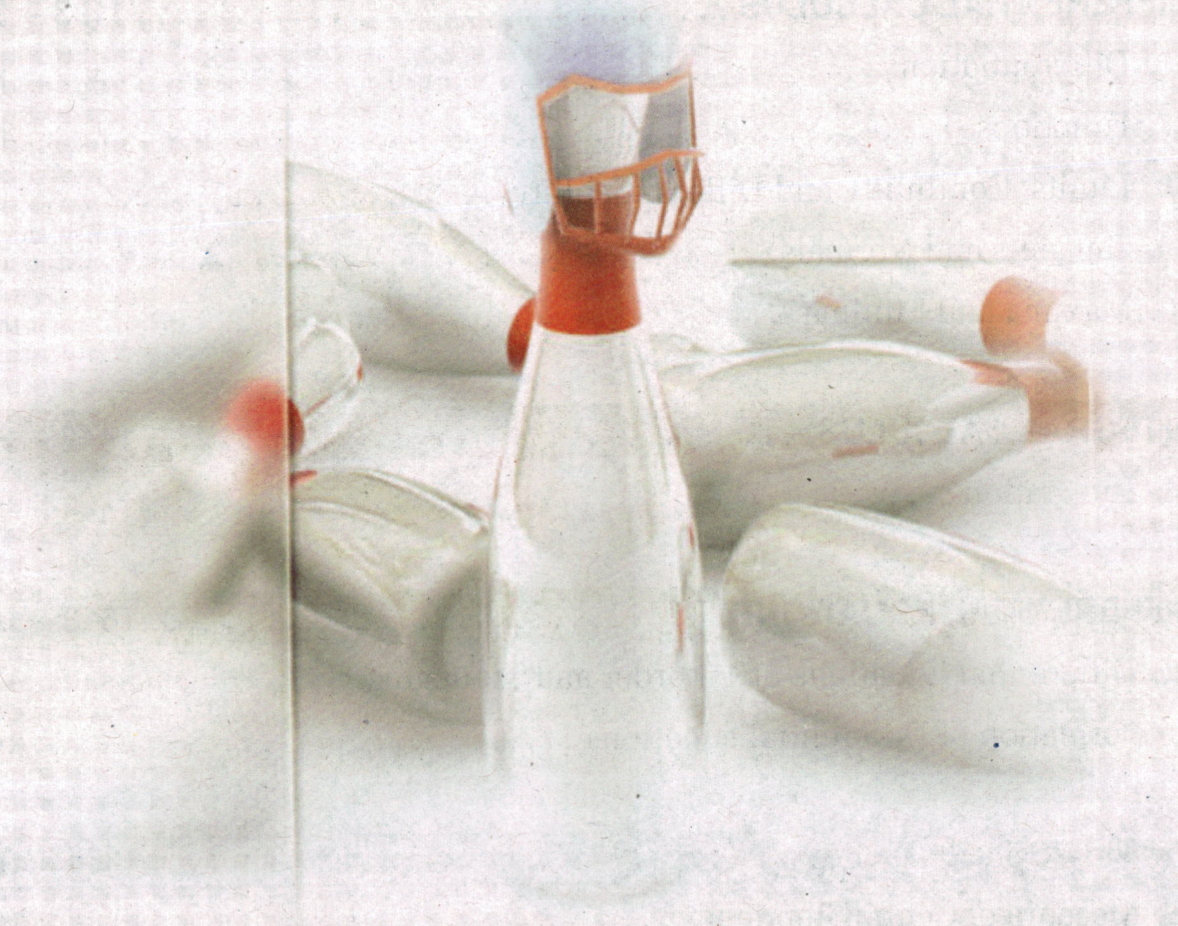

CHAPTER 20

Co-ordinates Geometry

The Parabola

§1 Conic Section

(a) Definition : The locus of a moving point P such that its distance from a fixed point S called **focus** bears a constant ratio 'e' to its distance from a fixed line MZ called **directrix** is called conic section. This ratio e is its **eccentricity**, *i.e.*

$$PS = e \, . \, PM.$$

This conic section is called **parabola, ellipse** or **hyperbola** according as $e = 1, < 1, > 1$ respectively.

(b) Define a parabola and find its equation in standard form.

Definition : A parabola is the locus of a point which moves so that its distance from a fixed point called focus is equal to its distance from a fixed straight line called directrix.

Equation of the parabola in standard form.

Let S be the given focus, MZ the directrix and P any moving point (x, y). From S draw SZ perpendicular to the directrix MZ and bisect it at

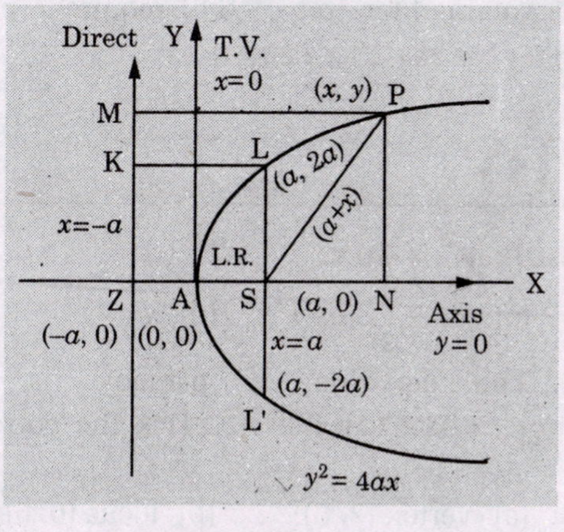

Fig. 1

A so that $AS = AZ$. Now A is such a point that its distance from the focus S is equal to its distance from directrix MZ and as such by definition it will be on the parabola.

Take the point A as origin and the line ASX as x-axis and a line through A perpendicular to AX as y-axis. If $AS = a = AZ$ then the **co-ordinates of S are $(a, 0)$ and of Z will be $(-a, 0)$.**

Now if P be any moving point (x, y) then by definition, we have

$$SP = PM \quad \text{or} \quad PS = ZN$$

or $\quad \boldsymbol{PS = AZ + AN = a + x}$ ...(1)

$\therefore$ **Focal distance of a point $P(x, y)$ $= a +$ abscissa of P.**

Again SP is the distance of (x, y) from $S(a, 0)$.

$\therefore \quad SP = \sqrt{[(x-a)^2 + y^2]}$ ...(2)

Equating the values of SP from (1) and (2), we get

$\sqrt{[(x-a)^2 + y^2]} = a + x.$ Square

$$(x-a)^2 + y^2 = (a+x)^2$$

or $\quad y^2 = (a+x)^2 - (x-a)^2$

or $\quad \boldsymbol{y^2 = 4ax}$ or $\boldsymbol{PN^2 = 4AS \, . \, AN}$ ...(3)

The point A is called vertex and the line AX is called the axis of the parabola and the line AY is called **tangent at the vertex.**

The line through focus S and perpendicular to axis of the parabola meets it in L and L', then LSL' is called the latus rectum of the parabola. Further L being a point on the curve its distance from S is equal to its distance from directrix MZ.

$\therefore \quad LS = LK = SZ = 2a.$

$\therefore \quad LS = L'S = 2a$

Hence,

$\boldsymbol{LL' = 4a =}$ **Latus rectum of the parabola.**

The co-ordinates of the extremities of latus rectum are

$$\boldsymbol{L(a, 2a)} \quad \text{and} \quad \boldsymbol{L'(a, -2a)}$$

(c) Some important results connected with the equation $y^2 = 4ax$ of the parabola to be committed to memory.

1. **Vertex** $A(0, 0)$.
2. **Focus** $S(a, 0)$
3. **Foot of directrix** $Z(-a, 0)$.
4. **Eq. of directrix** $x = -a$; **Eq. of L.R.** $x = a$

5. **Eq. of axis** $y = 0$.
6. **Eq. of tangent at vertex** $x = 0$.
7. **Length of L.R.** $= 4a$.
8. **Extremities of L.R.** $(a, 2a)$ **and** $(a, -2a)$.
9. **Focal distance of any point (x, y) is** $a + x$.

(V. Imp.)

Note : Two parabolas are said to be equal when their latus rectum are equal.

(d) General Equation of a parabola

In case the directrix of the parabola be given to be the line $ax + by + c = 0$ and its focus is the point (h, k) and if $P(x, y)$ be any point on the parabola then by definition, the distance of P from focus is equal to its distance from directrix.

i.e. $SP = PM$ or $SP^2 = PM^2$

$$\therefore \quad (x-h)^2 + (y-k)^2 = \left(\frac{ax+by+c}{\sqrt{(a^2+b^2)}}\right)^2$$

or $$(a^2+b^2)[x^2+y^2-2hx-2ky + h^2+k^2] = (ax+by+c)^2$$

On simplification it will be seen that **second degree terms** are

$$b^2x^2 + a^2y^2 - 2abxy \quad i.e. \quad (bx-ay)^2$$

i.e. **they form a perfect square.**

Above is the characteristic property of the equation of the parabola.

Another form : $x^2 = 4ay$.

The shape of the parabola $x^2 = 4ay$ is shown in figure. Vertex (0, 0), Focus $(0, a)$, Directrix $y = -a$, Axis $x = 0$. Tangent at vertex $y = 0$, Extremities of L.R. $(2a, a), (-2a, a)$.

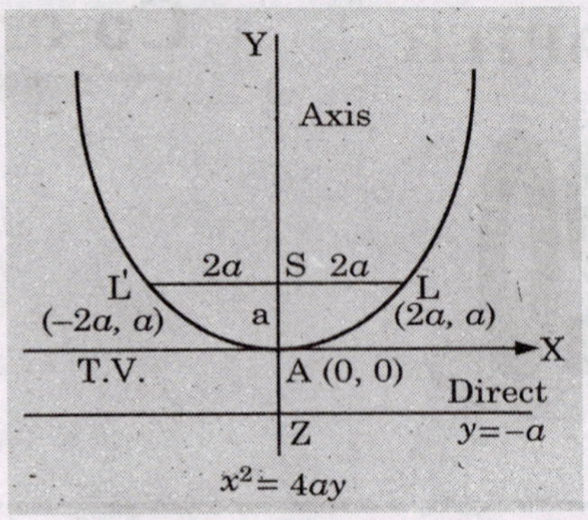

Fig. 2

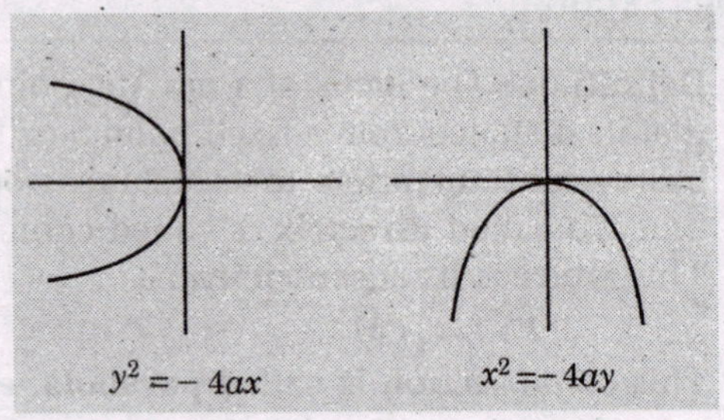

Fig. 3

Other forms : $y^2 = -4ax$, $x^2 = -4ay$

The general equation of a parabola with axis parallel to x-axis is of the form

$$ay^2 + by + c = x \quad ...(1)$$

as it reduces to the form

$$(y-k)^2 = 4A(x-h)$$

i.e. the parabola passing through the points $(-1, 3)$, $(1, 2)$ and $(-2, 1)$ and whose axis is parallel to x-axis. Putting the above three points in (1) and solving for a, b, c the required parabola is $5y^2 + 2x - 21y + 20 = 0$

Problem Set (1)

Standard equation of a parabola $y^2 = 4ax$.

1. Find the vertex, focus, directrix, latus rectum and tangent at the vertex for the following parabolas :

(a) $4y^2 - 6x - 4y = 5$

(b) $(y-4)^2 = 12(x-2)$,

(c) $y^2 + 4x - 6y + 13 = 0$

(d)* $9y^2 - 16x - 12y - 57 = 0$ **(M.N.R. 1995)**

2. (a)* $5x^2 + 30x + 2y + 59 = 0$

(b) $(x-h)^2 = -4a(y-k)$.

3. (a) The equation of the directrix of the parabola $y^2 + 4y + 4x + 2 = 0$ is

(a) $x = -1$ (b) $x = 1$

(c) $x = -\frac{3}{2}$ (d) $x = \frac{3}{2}$ **(I.I.T. Sc. 2001)**

(b) The equation of parabola is given by $y^2 + 8x - 12y + 20 = 0$. Tick the correct options given below :

(a) vertex (2, 6) (b) focus (0, 6)

(c) latus rectum 4 (d) axis $y = 6$

4. (a) Find the equation of the parabola whose focus is the point (2, 3) and directrix is the line $x - 4y + 3 = 0$. Also find the length of its latus rectum.

(b) If the line $x - 1 = 0$ is the directrix of the parabola $y^2 - kx + 8 = 0$, then one of the values of k is –

(a) 1/8 (b) 8
(c) 4 (d) 1/4 **(I.I.T. Sc. 2000)**

(c) Find the equation of parabola whose focus is the point $(-6, -6)$ and vertex is at $(-2, 2)$.

(d) The extremities of the latus rectum of the parabola are $(7, 5)$ and $(7, 3)$. Find its equation and the points where it meets the axes.

(e) Equation of the parabola whose axis is $y = x$ distance from origin to vertex is $\sqrt{2}$ and distance from origin to focus is $2\sqrt{2}$, is (Focus and vertex lie in Ist quadrant) :

(a) $(x+y)^2 = 2(x+y-2)$

(b) $(x-y)^2 = 8(x+y-2)$

(c) $(x-y)^2 = 4(x+y-2)$

(d) $(x+y)^2 = 4(x+y-2)$ **(I.I.T. 2006)**

5. (a)* Find the equation of the parabola whose focus is at the origin.

(b) Write down the co-ordinates of the foci of the parabolas $y^2 = 4a(x-a)$ and $x^2 = 4ay$ and hence the equation of the circle on the join of these foci as diameter.

(c) Find the equations of the parabolas the extremities of whose L.R. are (3, 5) and (3, – 3).

(d) Find the equation of the parabola whose axis is parallel to y-axis and which passes through the points $(0, 4), (1, 9)$ and $(-2, 6)$.

6.* (a) Find the equation of the parabola whose vertex and focus lie on the axis of x at distances a and a_1 from the origin respectively.

(b) If (2, 0) is the vertex and y-axis the directrix of a parabola, then its focus is (4, 0).

7. (a) Find the co-ordinates of a point on the parabola $y^2 = 8x$ whose focal distance is 4. What will be the co-ordinates if the focal distance of a point on it be 8 ?

(b)* Consider a circle with centre lying on the focus of the parabola $y^2 = 2px$ such that it touches the directrix of the parabola. Then points of intersection of the circle and the parabola are $(p/2, p)$ and $(p/2, -p)$ **(I.I.T. 1995)**

(c) The focal chord of $y^2 = 16x$ is tangent to $(x-6)^2 + y^2 = 2$, then the possible values of the slope of this chord, are

(a) $1, -1$ (b) $-1/2, 2$
(c) $-2, 1/2$ (d) $1/2, 2$ **(Screening 2003)**

8. (a) An equilateral triangle is inscribed in the parabola $y^2 = 4ax$ whose vertex is at the vertex of the parabola. Find the length of its side.

(b) Prove that in the parabola $y^2 = 4ax$, the length of the chord passing through the vertex and inclined to the x-axis at an angle θ is $(4a\cos\theta)/\sin^2\theta$.

(c)* If r_1 and r_2 are the lengths of perpendicular chords of the parabola drawn through the vertex, then $(r_1 r_2)^{4/3} = 16a^2\,(r_1^{2/3} + r_2^{2/3})$.

9. Find the length and equation of a perpendicular dropped from the focus of the parabola $y = -\dfrac{x^2}{8}$ onto a straight line cutting off the intercepts $a = b = 2$ on the co-ordinate axes.

10.* From the focus of the parabola $y^2 = 2px$ as centre a circle is described so that a common chord of the curves is equidistant from the vertex and the focus of the parabola. Write the equation of the circle.

11. (a) The x and y-co-ordinates of a point P in the $x-y$ plane are given by

$$x = (v\cos\alpha)\,t,\ y = (v\sin\alpha)\,t - \frac{1}{2}gt^2,$$

where t is a parameter, g, v and α are given constants. Show that the locus of the point P is a parabola. Find the co-ordinates of the vertex of the parabola.

(b) The path of a projectile in vacuum is a

(a) straight line (b) circle
(c) ellipse (d) parabola.

12. (a) The curve described parametrically by $x = t^2 + t + 1, y = t^2 - t + 1$ represents

(a) a pair of straight lines
(b) an ellipse
(c) a parabola
(d) a hyperbola **(I.I.T. 1999)**

(b) The locus of the mid-point of the line segment joining the focus to a moving point on the parabola $y^2 = 4ax$ is another parabola with directrix

(a) $x = -a$ (b) $x = -\dfrac{a}{2}$
(c) $x = 0$ (d) $x = \dfrac{a}{2}$ **(I.I.T. Sc. 2002)**

13. (a) Prove that

$$9x^2 - 24xy + 16y^2 - 20x - 15y - 60 = 0$$

represents a parabola. Find its focus and directrix.

(b) The locus of the vertices of the family of parabolas $y = \dfrac{a^3x^2}{3} + \dfrac{a^2x}{2} - 2a$ is

(a) $xy = \dfrac{3}{4}$ (b) $xy = \dfrac{35}{16}$
(c) $xy = \dfrac{64}{105}$ (d) $xy = \dfrac{105}{64}$ **(AIEEE 2006)**

14. (a) If $a \neq 0$ and the line $2bx + 3cy + 4d = 0$ passes through the points of intersection of the parabolas $y^2 = 4ax$ and $x^2 = 4ay$, then

(a) $d^2 + (2b+3c)^2 = 0$

(b) $d^2 + (3b+2c)^2 = 0$

(c) $d^2+(2b-3c)^2=0$

(d) $d^2+(3b-2c)^2=0$ **(AIEEE 2004)**

(b) Let P be the point $(1,0)$ and Q a point on the locus $y^2=8x$. The locus of mid-point of PQ is

(a) $x^2+4y+2=0$ (b) $x^2-4y+2=0$

(c) $y^2-4x+2=0$ (d) $y^2+4x+2=0$

(AIEEE 2005)

15. Consider the two curves $C_1: y^2=4x, C_2: x^2+y^2-6x+1=0$. Then,

(a) C_1 and C_2 touch each other only at one point

(b) C_1 and C_2 touch each other exactly at two points

(c) C_1 and C_2 intersect (but do not touch) at exactly two points

(d) C_1 and C_2 neither intersect nor touch each other

(I.I.T. 2008)

Solutions to Problem Set (1)

1. (a) $4y^2-6x-4y=5$

or $4(y^2-y)=6x+5.$ Make perfect square.

$$4\left(y^2-y+\frac{1}{4}\right)=6x+5+4\cdot\frac{1}{4}=6(x+1)$$

or $\left(y-\frac{1}{2}\right)^2=\frac{3}{2}\cdot(x+1).$

Above is of the form $Y^2=4AX.$

where $Y=y-1/2,\ X=x+1,\ 4A=3/2$

$\therefore$ $A=3/8.$

Vertex : $X=0, Y=0$ or $x+1=0,\ y-1/2=0$

or $(-1, 1/2)$

Focus : $X=A, Y=0$ or $x+1=3/8, y-1/2=0$

or $(-5/8, 1/2)$

Directrix : $X=-A$ or $x+1=-3/8$

or $x=-11/8$

L.R. : $X=A$ or $x+1=3/8$ or $x=-5/8$

and length $4A=3/2$

Axis : $Y=0$ or $y-1/2=0$

or $y=1/2$

T.V. : $X=0$ or $x+1=0$

or $x=-1$

(b) Vertex (2, 4), Focus (5, 4), Directrix $x+1=0$, Axis $y-4=0$, L.R. = 12.

(c) $y^2+4x-6y+13=0$ or $(y-3)^2=-4(x+1)$

Vertex (–1, 3), Focus (–2, 3), Directrix $x=0$, T.V. $x+1=0$. Axis $y-3=0$, L.R. $=4A=4$.

(d) $\left(y-\frac{2}{3}\right)^2=\frac{16}{9}\left(x+\frac{61}{16}\right)$

$A\left(-\frac{61}{16},\frac{2}{3}\right), S\left(-\frac{485}{144},\frac{2}{3}\right)$

Axis $3y-2=0$, T.V. $16x+61=0$

2. (a) $5x^2+30x+2y+59=0$

$5(x^2+6x+9)=(-2y-59)+45=-2(y+7)$

or $(x+3)^2=-\frac{2}{5}.(y+7)$

Above is of the form $X^2=4AY$

where $X=x+3, Y=y+7, 4A=-2/5,$

or $A=-1/10$

Vertex : $X=0, Y=0$ or $x+3=0, y+7=0$

or $(-3,-7)$

Focus : $X=0, Y=A$ or $x+3=0,\ y+7=-\frac{1}{10}$

or $\left(-3,\frac{-71}{10}\right)$

Directrix : $Y=-A$ or $y+7=-\left(-\frac{1}{10}\right)$ or $y=-\frac{69}{10}$

L.R. : $Y=A$ or $y+7=-\frac{1}{10}$

or $y=-\frac{71}{10}$ and length $=4A=\frac{2}{5}$

Axis : $X=0$ or $x+3=0$ or $x=-3$

T.V. : $Y=0$ or $y+7=0$ or $y=-7.$

(b) $(h,k),(h,k-a), y=k+a$ etc.

3. (a) Ans. (d).

The given equation can be written as

$$(y+2)^2=4\left(x-\frac{1}{2}\right)$$

Form $Y^2=4AX$ where $4A=-4$ or $A=-1$

The directrix is $X=-A$ or $x-\frac{1}{2}=-(-1)$

or $x=\frac{3}{2}$

(b) Ans. (a), (b), (d).

$y^2-12y=-8x-20$

Add 36 to both sides

$\therefore$ $(y-6)^2=-8(x-2)$

or $Y^2=4AX$ where $A=-2$

Axis is $Y=0$ or $y-6=0$ or $y=6$

Vertex $X=0, Y=0$ *i.e.* $(2,6)$

Focus $X=A, Y=0$ or $x-2=-2, y-6=0$

or $x=0, y=6\ \therefore\ (0,6)$

Length of latus rectum $=4A=-8=8$

4. (a) By definition the distance of any point on the parabola from the focus is equal to its distance from the directrix.

$\therefore$ $\sqrt{\{(x-2)^2+(y-3)^2\}}=\frac{x-4y+3}{(1+16)^{1/2}}$. Square.

$17(x^2+y^2-4x-6y+13)=x^2+16y^2+9$
$-8xy-24y+6x$

or $\quad 16x^2 + y^2 + 8xy - 74x - 78y + 212 = 0$

We know L.R. $= 4a = 2\,(2a)$ where $2a$ is the distance between the focus and directrix

$$= 2\,\frac{2 \cdot 1 - 4 \cdot 3 + 3}{(1+16)^{1/2}} = \frac{14}{\sqrt{(17)}}.$$

(b) Ans. (c).

Parabola is $y^2 = k\,(x - 8/k)$

or $\quad Y^2 = 4AX$, where $4A = k, Y = y, X = x - 8/k$

Its directrix is $X = -A$ or $x - 8/k = -k/4$

or $\quad x = \dfrac{8}{k} - \dfrac{k}{4}$

Comparing with $x = 1$, we get $1 = \dfrac{32 - k^2}{4k}$

or $\quad k^2 + 4k - 32 = 0$

$(k+8)\,(k-4) = 0 \quad \therefore\ k = 4$

$k = -8$ is also true but it is not given in any of the four choices.

(c) Directrix will be a line through Z and perpendicular to SA whose slope is $\dfrac{-6-2}{-6+2} = 2$

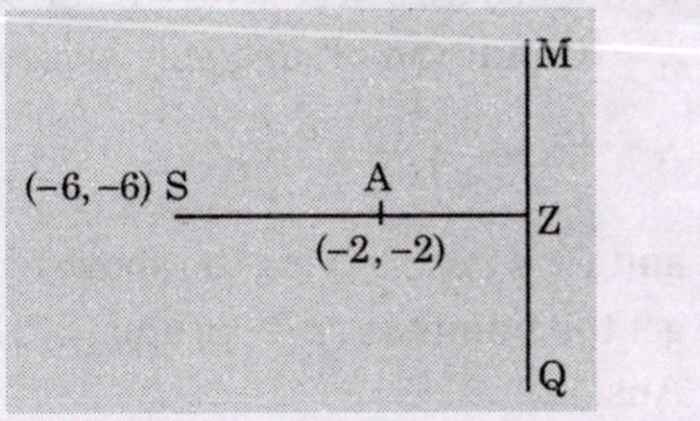

Fig. 4

If $Z\,(h, k)$ be the foot of directrix then A is mid-point of SZ

$\therefore \quad \dfrac{-6+h}{2} = -2, \quad \dfrac{-6+k}{2} = 2$

$\therefore \quad Z = (h, k) = (2, 10)$

$\therefore \quad MZ$ is $y - 10 = -\dfrac{1}{2}(x - 2)$

or $\quad x + 2y - 22 = 0$

By definition if $P\,(x, y)$ be any point on the parabola then $SP = PM$

$$\therefore \quad \sqrt{(x+6)^2 + (y+6)^2} = \frac{x + 2y - 22}{\sqrt{5}}$$

Square both sides and simplify, we get

$$4x^2 + y^2 - 4xy + 104x + 148y - 124 = 0$$

or $\quad (2x - y)^2 + 104x + 148y - 124 = 0$

Note : Second degree terms form perfect square.

(d) Equation of L.R. is

$$y - 3 = \frac{2}{0}(x - 7) \ \ i.e.\ \ x = 7, \quad m = \infty$$

Also focus is mid-point of L.R. is (7, 4).

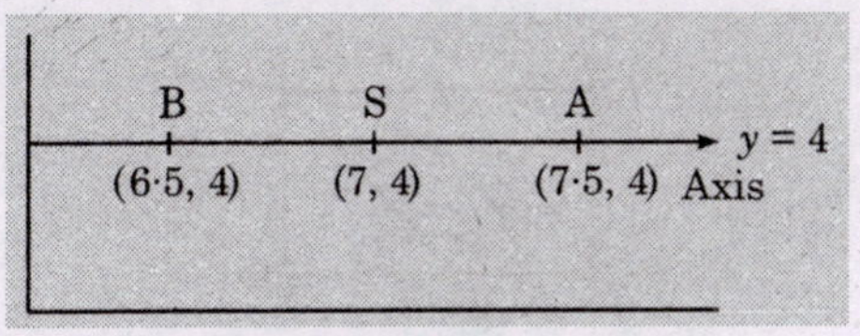

Fig. 5

$\therefore$ Equation of axis is $y - 4 = 0\,(x - 7)$, $m = 0$ as it is $\perp$ to L.R. $\therefore\ y = 4$ is the equation of axis and length of L.R. $= 2 = 4a \quad \therefore\ a = \dfrac{1}{2}$

Hence its vertex is at a distance $a = \dfrac{1}{2}$ from focus S on the axis $y = 4$.

$\therefore \quad$ Vertex is $\left(7 \pm \dfrac{1}{2}, 4\right)$ or $\left(7\dfrac{1}{2}, 4\right)$ and $\left(6\dfrac{1}{2}, 4\right)$

Hence its equation is $Y^2 = 4AX$ or $Y^2 = -4AX$

where $\quad Y = y - 4, X = x - 6\cdot 5$ or $x - 7 \cdot 5$ and $4A = 2$

$(y-4)^2 = 2\,(x - 6 \cdot 5)$ or $(y-4)^2 = -2\,(x - 7 \cdot 5)$
focus is right of A $\qquad$ focus is left of A

(e) Ans. (b).

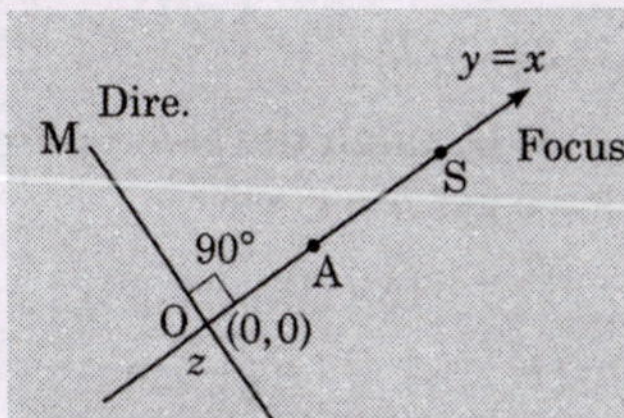

Fig. 6

The equation of axis of the parabola is

$$\frac{x - 0}{\cos 45^\circ} = \frac{y - 0}{\sin 45^\circ} = \sqrt{2} \text{ for } A, 2\sqrt{2} \text{ for } S$$

$\therefore\ A$ is (1, 1) and S is (2, 2) and foot of directrix be Z, then A is mid-point of SZ

$\therefore \quad \dfrac{x+2}{2} = 1, \dfrac{y+2}{2} = 1 \quad \therefore \quad Z$ is (0, 0).

Equation of directrix is

$$y - 0 = -1\,(x - 0) \text{ or } x + y = 0$$

By definition if $P\,(x, y)$ be any point on the parabola then $SP = PM$

or $\quad (x-2)^2 + (y-2)^2 = \left[\dfrac{x+y}{\sqrt{2}}\right]^2$

$$2\,[x^2 + y^2 - 4x - 4y + 8] = (x+y)^2$$

or $\quad x^2 + y^2 - 2xy = 8\,(x + y - 2)$

5. (a) Suppose that $SZ = 2a$ then Z is $(-2a, 0)$. Its mid-point $A\,(-a, 0)$ is vertex. By definition,

$$SP = PM = ZN = 2a + x$$

or $\quad \sqrt{(x^2 + y^2)} = 2a + x$

Square

$$x^2 + y^2 = 4a^2 + 4ax + x^2 \text{ or } y^2 = 4a\,(x + a)$$

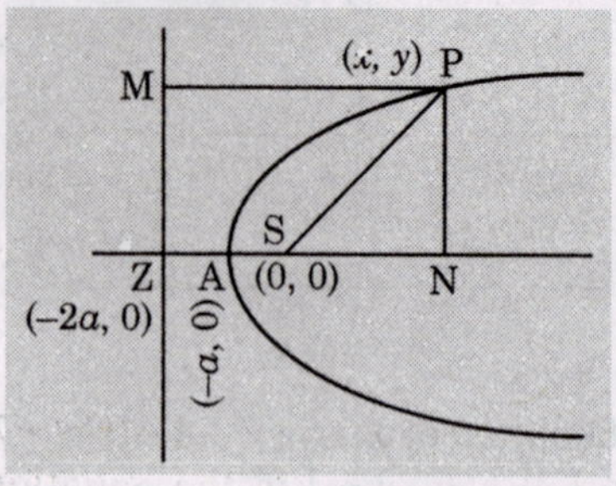

Fig. 7

Alt. : Shift the origin to focus $(a, 0)$ in $y^2 = 4ax$

$\therefore \quad y^2 = 4a(x + a)$.

(b) $Y^2 = 4AX$, focus S_1 is $X = a, Y = 0$

or $x - a = a, y = 0$

$\therefore \quad S_1$ is $(2a, 0)$ and $S_2 = (0, a)$.

Circle on S_1S_2 as diameter is

$x(x - 2a) + y(y - a) = 0$

or $x^2 + y^2 - 2ax - ay = 0$

(c) Clearly L.R. is parallel to y-axis therefore axis is parallel to x-axis.

L.R. $= 4a = \pm 8$. If its vertex be (h, k), then $(y - k)^2 = 8(x - h)$

Make it pass through the given points and solving for (h, k), we get $h = k = 1$

$\therefore \quad (y - 1)^2 = 8(x - 1)$.

Similarly $(y - 1)^2 = -8(x - 5)$

(d) Let the vertex of the parabola be the point (h, k) and length of its L.R. be $4a$. Since its axis is parallel to y-axis its equation can be written as

$(x - h)^2 = 4a(y - k)$ ...(1)

It passes through the given points.

$(0 - h)^2 = 4a(4 - k)$ or $h^2 = 4a(4 - k)$ ...(2)

$(1 - h)^2 = 4a(9 - k)$

or $1 - 2h + h^2 = 4a(9 - k)$ ...(3)

$(-2 - h)^2 = 4a(6 - k)$

or $4 + 4h + h^2 = 4a(6 - k)$ ...(4)

Subtracting (2), (3) and (3), (4), we have

$1 - 2h = 20a$ and $3 + 6h = -12a$

or $1 + 2h = -4a$

$\therefore \quad a = \frac{1}{8}$ and $h = -\frac{3}{4}$. Putting in any, $k = \frac{23}{8}$.

Putting in (1), the equation of parabola is

$$\left(x + \frac{3}{4}\right)^2 = 4 \cdot \frac{1}{8}\left(y - \frac{23}{8}\right)$$

Its vertex is the point $\left(-\frac{3}{4}, \frac{23}{8}\right)$ and L.R. $= \frac{1}{2}$.

6. (a) A is $(a, 0)$, $S = (a_1, 0)$

$\therefore \quad AS = a_1 - a = A$

$\therefore \quad$ L. R. $= 4\,AS = 4(a_1 - a)$.

Since the axis is the axis of x and vertex is the point $(a, 0)$, hence by definition its equation is $Y^2 = 4AX$

or $(y - 0)^2 = 4(a_1 - a)(x - a)$

or $y^2 = 4(a_1 - a)(x - a)$.

(b) Distance of vertex from directrix y-axis is 2 and it is half the distance of focus from directrix.

$\therefore \quad$ Focus is $(4, 0)$.

7. (a) If the co-ordinates of a point on the parabola be (x, y), then its distance from the focus is $\boldsymbol{SP = a + x}$

$\therefore \quad 4 = 2 + x \qquad \because 4a = 8$ given.

$\therefore \quad x = 2$.

Hence $\quad y^2 = 8x = 8.2 = 16$

$\therefore \quad y = \pm 4$.

Thus the co-ordinates of the points are $(2, \pm 4)$.

In the second case points are $(6, \pm 4\sqrt{3})$.

(b) $4a = 2p \quad \therefore \quad a = p/2$

Centre $(a, 0) = (p/2, 0)$

Eq. of circle is $(x - p/2)^2 + y^2 = r^2$

It touches directrix $x + a = 0$ or $x + p/2 = 0$

$\therefore \quad$ Condition of tangency gives $r = p$

$$\therefore \quad \left(x - \frac{p}{2}\right)^2 + y^2 = p^2$$

and $y^2 = 2px$. Solving the above two equations we get the points as $(p/2, p)$ and $(p/2, -p)$.

(c) Ans. (a).

Focus $(a, 0)$ is $(4, 0)$. Any focal chord is

$y - 0 = m(x - 4)$

or $mx - y - 4m = 0$.

Apply the condition of tangency $p = r$ with circle $(6, 0)$, $\sqrt{2}$.

$$\frac{6m - 4m}{\sqrt{m^2 + 1}} = \sqrt{2} \text{ or } 2m = \sqrt{2}\,.\sqrt{m^2 + 1}$$

or $2m^2 = m^2 + 1 \Rightarrow m^2 = 1$

$\therefore \quad m = \pm 1$.

8. (a) We know that each angle of an equilateral triangle is 60°. A is $(0, 0)$ and $AB = l$, then

$x = AM = l \cos 30^\circ = l \,.\, \sqrt{3}/2$.

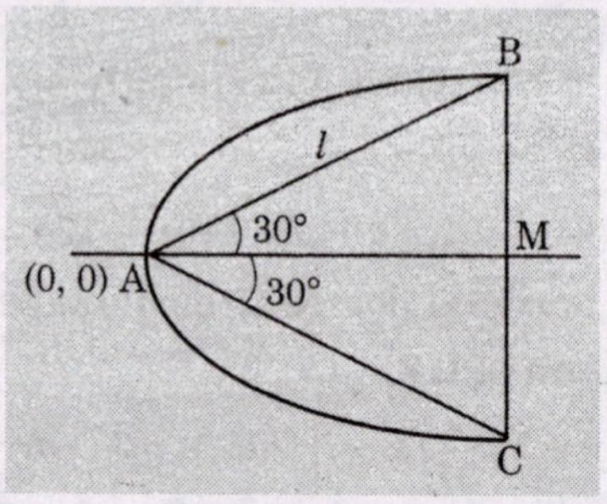

Fig. 8

$y = BM = l \sin 30^\circ = l/2.$

Also $\quad y^2 = 4ax$

$\dfrac{l^2}{4} = 4a \cdot \dfrac{\sqrt{3}}{2} \cdot l \quad \therefore \quad l = 8a\sqrt{3}.$

(b) As in part (a), $x = l\cos\theta,\ y = l\sin\theta$

Putting in $y^2 = 4ax$ we get the value of l as given.

(c) As in part (b),

$$r_1 = \frac{4a\cos\theta}{\sin^2\theta}$$

Replacing θ by $90^\circ - \theta$ for perpendicular chord,

$$r_2 = \frac{4a\sin\theta}{\cos^2\theta}$$

$$\therefore \quad r_1 r_2 = \frac{16a^2}{\sin\theta\cos\theta}$$

$$\therefore \quad (r_1 r_2)^{4/3} = \frac{(4a)^{8/3}}{(\sin\theta\cos\theta)^{4/3}}$$

$$\text{R.H.S.} = 16a^2\,(4a)^{2/3}\left[\frac{\cos^{2/3}\theta}{\sin^{4/3}\theta} + \frac{\sin^{2/3}\theta}{\cos^{4/3}\theta}\right]$$

$$= \frac{(4a)^{8/3}\,.1}{(\sin\theta\cos\theta)^{4/3}} = \text{L.H.S.}$$

$\because \quad \sin^2\theta + \cos^2\theta = 1$

9. Equation of the line is

$\dfrac{x}{2} + \dfrac{y}{2} = 1 \quad \text{or} \quad x + y = 2 \qquad ...(1)$

Parabola is $x^2 = -8y$. Its focus is $(0, -2)$

$\therefore \quad p = \dfrac{2+2}{\sqrt{2}} = 2\sqrt{2}.$ Now line $\perp$ to (1) and passing through $(0, -2)$ is $x - y = 2$

10. $y^2 = 2px;\quad S$ is $(p/2, 0)$.

Circle with centre $(p/2, 0)$ is

$(x - p/2)^2 + y^2 = r^2$

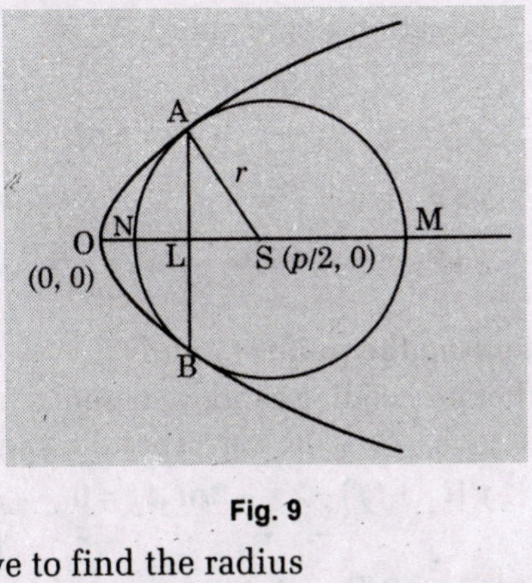

Fig. 9

We have to find the radius

AB is the common chord, $(p/4, 0)$ is mid-point

$LS = p/4 = OL = x$

$AL^2 = y^2$ where $y^2 = 2p \cdot \dfrac{p}{4} = \dfrac{p^2}{2}$

$\therefore \quad r^2 = AL^2 + SL^2 = \dfrac{p^2}{2} + \dfrac{p^2}{16} = \dfrac{9p^2}{16} \quad \therefore \quad r = \dfrac{3p}{4}$

Hence the circle is $\left(x - \dfrac{p}{2}\right)^2 + y^2 = \dfrac{9p^2}{16}$

11. (a) Eliminating the parameter t, we get

$$y = x\tan\alpha - \frac{1}{2}g\frac{x^2}{u^2\cos^2\alpha}$$

or $\quad x^2 - x.\dfrac{\sin\alpha}{\cos\alpha}.\dfrac{2u^2\cos^2\alpha}{g}$

$$= -\frac{2u^2\cos^2\alpha}{g}.y$$

or $\quad x^2 - 2x\dfrac{u^2\sin\alpha\cos\alpha}{g} = \dfrac{-2u^2\cos^2\alpha}{g}y$

Add $\dfrac{u^4\sin^2\alpha\cos^2\alpha}{g^2}$ in both sides, we get

$$\left(x - \frac{u^2\sin\alpha\cos\alpha}{g}\right)^2$$

$$= \frac{-2u^2\cos^2\alpha}{g}\left(y - \frac{u^2\sin^2\alpha}{2g}\right)$$

$X^2 = -4AY.$

It represents a parabola whose vertex is given by $X = 0, Y = 0.$

$$\left(\frac{u^2\sin\alpha\cos\alpha}{g}, \frac{u^2\sin^2\alpha}{2g}\right).$$

(b) Ans. (d).

12. (a) Ans. (c).

$\dfrac{x+y}{2} = t^2 + 1,\quad \dfrac{x-y}{2} = t$

Eliminating t, $2(x+y) = (x-y)^2 + 4$

Since 2nd degree terms form a perfect square, it represents a parabola.

(b) Ans. (c).

$S(a, 0), P(at^2, 2at)$. If (h, k) be mid-point, then

$2h = a(1 + t^2), 2k = 2at$ or $k = t$

$\therefore \quad 2x = a(1 + y^2)$ or $y^2 = 2a(x - a/2)$

or $\quad Y^2 = 4AX$

Directrix is $X = -A$ or $x - \dfrac{a}{2} = -\dfrac{2a}{4}$ or $x = 0$

13. (a) $(3x - 4y)^2 = 5(4x + 3y + 12) = 0$

or $\quad \left(\dfrac{3x - 4y}{\sqrt{(3^2 + 4^2)}}\right)^2 .25 = 5\left(\dfrac{4x + 3y + 12}{\sqrt{(4^2 + 3^2)}}\right).5$

Above is of the form $Y^2 = 4AX,$

where $Y = \dfrac{3x - 4y}{5}$ and $X = \dfrac{4x + 3y + 12}{5}$

and $4A = 1$

Directrix is $X = -A$ or $\dfrac{4x+3y+12}{5} = -\dfrac{1}{4}$

or $\quad 4x+3y+\dfrac{53}{4} = 0$

Focus is $X = -A, Y = 0$, *i.e.*, $4x+3y+\dfrac{53}{4} = 0$ and

$3x-4y = 0$

Solving, the focus is the point $\left(-\dfrac{43}{25}, -\dfrac{129}{100}\right)$

(b) Ans. (d).

$$y+2a = \frac{a^3}{3}\left[x^2+\frac{3x}{2a}+\frac{9}{16a^2}-\frac{9}{16a^2}\right]$$

or $\quad y+2a+\dfrac{a^3}{3}\cdot\dfrac{9}{16a^2} = \dfrac{a^3}{3}\left[x+\dfrac{3}{4a}\right]^2$

or $\quad \left(x+\dfrac{3}{4a}\right)^2 = \dfrac{3}{a^3}\left(y+2a+\dfrac{3a}{16}\right)$

or $\quad \left(x+\dfrac{3}{4a}\right)^2 = \dfrac{3}{a^3}\left(y+\dfrac{35a}{16}\right)$

If (h, k) be the vertex, then

$$h = -\frac{3}{4a}, k = -\frac{35a}{16}$$

Eliminate the variable a, we have

$$hk = \frac{105}{64} \quad \text{or} \quad xy = \frac{105}{64}.$$

14. (a) Ans. (a).

The two parabolas meet at $(0,0)$ and $(4a, 4a)$. Putting in the given line, we have $d = 0$ and $2ba+3ac = 0 \Rightarrow 2b+3c = 0$. Both the above satisfy (a).

(b) Ans. (c).

Any point on the parabola is $(at^2, 2at), a = 2$.

Q is $(2t^2, 4t)$ and P is $(1, 0)$.

If (h, k) be the mid-point of PQ, then

$$2h = 2t^2+1, 2k = 4t \quad \therefore \quad t = k/2$$

$$\therefore \quad 2h = \frac{k^2}{2}+1$$

$\therefore \quad$ Locus is $y^2-4x+2 = 0 \Rightarrow$ (c)

15. Ans. (b).

For points of intersection of circle and parabola, put $y^2 = 4x$ in the equation of the circle, we get $x^2+4x-6x+1 = 0$ or $(x-1)^2 = 0$ *i.e.*, they intersect at

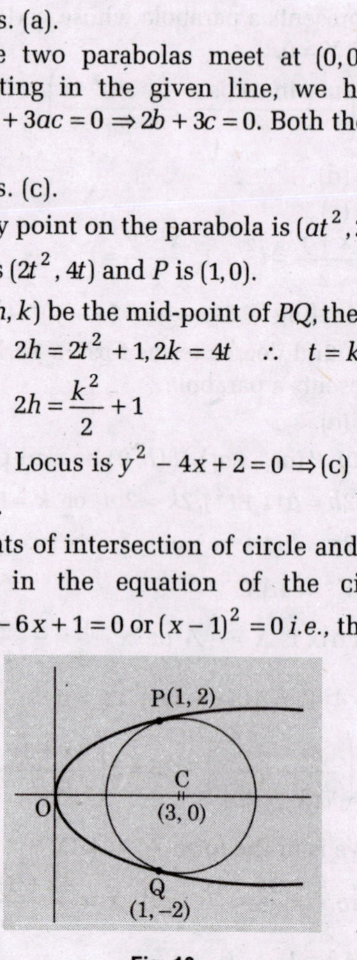

Fig. 10

two coincident points given by $x = 1$ and hence from parabola $y^2 = 4$

$\therefore \quad y = 2, -2$

Hence the two curves cut at two coincident points $P(1, 2)$ and $Q(1, -2)$. Thus they touch at the above two points.

§2 Points on a parabola, Chord, Tangent and Normal to a parabola.

(a) Points on a parabola :

If (x_1, y_1) be any point on the parabola $y^2 = 4ax$ then $y_1^2 = 4ax_1$ or $x_1 = y_1^2/4a$.

Hence in terms of the ordinate the co-ordinates of any point on the parabola are $\left(\dfrac{y_1^2}{4a}, y_1\right)$ and we shall call it as the point y_1. Similarly for all values of t the point $(at^2, 2at)$ satisfies the equation of the parabola. We shall call this point as the point 't'.

Relation between y_1 and t_1 :

The point y_1 is $\left(\dfrac{y_1^2}{4a}, y_1\right)$ and t_1 is $(at_1^2, 2at_1)$

$$\therefore \quad y_1 = 2at_1 \quad \text{or} \quad t_1 = \frac{y_1}{2a}.$$

(b) Equation of the chord joining two points y_1 and y_2 :

Let $P\left(\dfrac{y_1^2}{4a}, y_1\right)$ and $Q\left(\dfrac{y_2^2}{4a}, y_2\right)$ be two points on the parabola $y^2 = 4ax$.

The slope of the line joining P and Q is

$$\frac{y_2-y_1}{\dfrac{y_2^2-y_1^2}{4a}} = \frac{4a}{y_1+y_2}$$

$\therefore \quad$ Equation to the chord PQ is

$$y-y_1 = \frac{4a}{y_1+y_2}\left(x-\frac{y_1^2}{4a}\right)$$

or $\quad y(y_1+y_2)-y_1(y_1+y_2) = 4ax-y_1^2$

*or $\quad \boldsymbol{y(y_1+y_2)-4ax-y_1y_2 = 0}$ ...(1)

(Remember)

Chord joining the points t_1 and t_2.

Either proceeding as above or replacing y_1 by $2at_1$ and y_2 by $2at_2$ the corresponding equation is

$$\boldsymbol{y(t_1+t_2)-2x-2at_1t_2 = 0} \quad ...(2)$$

(Remember)

Its slope $= 2/(t_1+t_2)$.

(c)* Condition for a focal chord.

If the chord PQ be a focal chord then it passes through focus $(a, 0)$. Hence from (1) and (2) above the required condition is

$y_1 y_2 = -4a^2$ or $t_1 t_2 = -1$ ...(3)

(c_1)* Condition for the chord *PQ* to subtend a right angle at the vertex of the parabola.

Since *PQ* subtends a right angle at vertex *O* (0, 0), *OP* and *OQ* are perpendicular, *i.e.*, $m_1 m_2 = -1$.

$$\frac{2at_1}{at_1^2} \cdot \frac{2at_2}{at_2^2} = -1$$

$\therefore$ $t_1 t_2 = -4$ **(Remember)**

(d) Equation of tangent at the point *P* 'y_1' or 't_1'.

The tangent at *P* is the limiting position of chord *PQ* when $Q \to P$, *i.e.* $y_2 \to y_1$ or $t_2 \to t_1$. Hence from (1) and (2) above the equation of the tangent is

$$y(2y_1) - 4ax - y_1^2 = 0$$

or $y(2t_1) - 2x - 2at_1^2 = 0$

Put $y_1^2 = 4ax_1$

$\therefore$ $2yy_1 - 4ax - 4ax_1 = 0$ or $t_1 y = x + at_1^2$

*or $\boldsymbol{yy_1 = 2a(x + x_1)}$ or $\boldsymbol{t_1 y = x + at_1^2}$ ...(4)

(e) Tangent in terms of its slope *m*.

From equation (4) the slope of the tangent is

$$\frac{2a}{y_1} = m \quad \text{or} \quad \frac{1}{t_1} = m.$$

$$\therefore \quad y_1 = \frac{2a}{m}, x_1 = \frac{y_1^2}{4a} = \frac{a}{m^2}, \quad \therefore \quad t_1 = \frac{1}{m}.$$

Putting in (4) the equation of tangent is

$$y \cdot \frac{2a}{m} = 2a\left(x + \frac{a}{m^2}\right)$$

or $\frac{1}{m} y = x + a \cdot \frac{1}{m^2}$

*or $\boldsymbol{y = mx + a/m}$ ...(5)

The point of contact (x_1, y_1) or $(at_1^2, 2at_1)$ becomes

* $\left(\boldsymbol{\frac{a}{m^2}, \frac{2a}{m}}\right)$ ...(6)

(f) Condition for the line $y = mx + c$ to be a tangent to the parabola.

Solving $y = mx + c$ with $y^2 = 4ax$, we get

$$(mx + c)^2 = 4ax$$

or $m^2x^2 + 2(mc - 2a)x + c^2 = 0$ ...(A)

Above is a quadratic equation in *x* and will give us two values of *x*. But if the given line is to be a tangent to the parabola then both the values of *x* given by above quadratic should be equal and as such its discriminant $B^2 - 4AC = 0$.

$\therefore$ $4(mc - 2a)^2 - 4m^2c^2 = 0$

or $m^2c^2 - 4amc + 4a^2 - m^2c^2 = 0$

$\therefore$ $\boldsymbol{c = a/m}$. ...(7)

is the required condition. Putting $c = a/m$ in (A), it becomes

$$m^2x^2 + 2(a - 2a)x + a^2/m^2 = 0$$

or $(mx - a/m)^2 = 0$

$\therefore$ $x = a/m^2$

and $y = mx + c = m \cdot a/m^2 + a/m = 2a/m$.

***Hence the line $y = mx + a/m$ is always a tangent to the parabola $y^2 = 4ax$ and its point of contact is $(a/m^2, 2a/m)$.**

Note : General Method for proving any line to be a tangent to any given curve.

Solve the curve with the equation of line by eliminating *y* and thus you will have a quadratic in *x*. If the line is a tangent, then this quadratic must have equal roots as the tangent cuts the curve in two coincident points.

See Q. 1, 2 P. 968-969.

Any tangent to $x^2 = 4ay$

We know that $y = mx + a/m$ is a tangent to $y^2 = 4ax$. Interchanging *x* and *y*, $\boldsymbol{x = my + a/m}$ is a tangent to $x^2 = 4ay$ at $\left(\frac{2a}{m}, \frac{a}{m^2}\right)$.

(g) Normal to the parabola $y^2 = 4ax$.

Tangent at any point (x_1, y_1) is $yy_1 = 2a(x + x_1)$

Its slope is $\frac{2a}{y_1}$ and hence slope of normal which is perpendicular to the tangent will be $-y_1/2a$. Hence its equation is

$$y - y_1 = -\frac{y_1}{2a}(x - x_1) \quad \text{...(8)}$$

Normal in terms of slope *m*.

The equation of the normal at (x_1, y_1) is given by (8).

Its slope $\frac{-y_1}{2a} = m$, say $\therefore$ $y_1 = -2am$.

Also $x_1 = \frac{y_1^2}{4a} = \frac{4a^2m^2}{4a} = am^2$

Hence the required equation of normal by (8) in terms of *m* is

$$y - (-2am) = m(x - am^2)$$

*or $\boldsymbol{y = mx - 2am - am^3}$ at $\boldsymbol{(am^2, -2am)}$ ...(9)

Normal at the point $(at^2, 2at)$.

Tangent at $(at^2, 2at)$ is $ty = x + at^2$

Its slope is $\frac{1}{t}$ and hence that of normal will be $-t$.

Hence its equation is $y - 2at = -t(x - at^2)$

*or $\boldsymbol{y = -tx + 2at + at^3}$. ...(10)

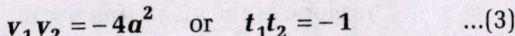

It may be observed that if we replace m by $-t$ in equation (9), we get the equation of the normal (10).

Normal to $x^2 = 4ay$

Interchanging x and y in (9) the equation of normal is

$$x = my - 2am - am^3 \text{ at } (-2am, am^2)$$

(h)* Condition for the line $y = mx + c$ to be normal.

The slope of the given line $y = mx + c$ is m.

The equation of the normal whose slope is m is

$$y = mx - 2am - am^3.$$

Comparing the two we get the required condition as

$$c = -2am - am^3,$$

and the foot of the normal is $(am^2, -2am)$.

Problem Set (2)

Tangents and Normals

1. (a) Prove that the line $lx + my + n = 0$ will touch the parabola $y^2 = 4ax$ if $ln = am^2$.

(b) The line $y = mx + 1$ is a tangent to the parabola $y^2 = 4x$ if

(a) $m = 1$ (b) $m = 2$
(c) $m = 4$ (d) $m = 3$. **(M.N.R. 1990)**

2. (a) Prove that the line $x + my + am^2 = 0$ touches the parabola $y^2 = 4ax$. Find also the co-ordinates of the point of contact.

(b) The point, on the curve $y^2 = x$, the tangent at which makes an angle $45°$ with x-axis is $\left(\frac{1}{4}, \frac{1}{2}\right)$.

3.* Prove that the line $y = mx + c$ is a tangent to the parabola $y^2 = 4a(x + a)$ if $c = ma + a/m$.

4. (a) Prove that the straight line $y = x + 2a$ touches the parabola $y^2 = 4a(x + a)$ and find its point of contact.

(b) If the line $2x + 3y = 1$ touches the parabola $y^2 = 4ax$ at the point P, then prove that the focal distance of point P is $13/18$.

5. (a) Find the equation of tangents drawn to $y^2 + 12x = 0$ from the point $(3, 8)$.

(b)* The angle between the tangents drawn from the origin to the parabola $y^2 = 4a(x - a)$ is

(a) $90°$ (b) $30°$
(c) $\tan^{-1}\frac{1}{2}$ (d) $45°$ **(M.N.R. 1994)**

(c) Angle between tangents drawn from the point $(1, 4)$ to the parabola $y^2 = 4x$ is

(a) $\frac{\pi}{6}$ (b) $\frac{\pi}{4}$
(c) $\frac{\pi}{3}$ (d) $\frac{\pi}{2}$ **(Screening 2004)**

6. (a) Find the equations of tangents to the parabola $y^2 = 16x$ which are parallel and perpendicular to the line $2x - y + 5 = 0$. Find also the co-ordinates of their points of contact.

(b)* Find the equation of tangent to the parabola $y^2 = 4x + 5$ which is parallel to the line $y = 2x + 7$.

(c)* Find the equations of tangents to the parabola $y^2 = 12x$ which make an angle of $45°$ with the line $y = 3x + 7$.

7. Two straight lines are perpendicular to each other. One of them touches the parabola $y^2 = 4a(x + a)$ and the other touches $y^2 = 4b(x + b)$. Prove that the point of intersection of the lines lie on the line $x + a + b = 0$.

8. (a) Find the equation of the common tangent to the parabolas $y^2 = 4ax$ and $x^2 = 4by$.

(b)* Find the equation to the common tangent to the parabolas $y^2 = 2x$ and $x^2 = 16y$.

(c) Find the equations of the common tangents of the circle $x^2 + y^2 - 6y + 4 = 0$ and the parabola $y^2 = x$. **(Roorkee 1999)**

(d) The equation of the common tangent touching the circle $(x - 3)^2 + y^2 = 9$ and the parabola $y^2 = 4x$ above the x-axis is

(a) $\sqrt{3}y = 3x + 1$ (b) $\sqrt{3}y = -(x + 3)$
(c) $\sqrt{3}y = x + 3$ (d) $\sqrt{3}y = -(3x + 1)$ **(I.I.T. Sc. 2001)**

(e) The common tangent(s) of $y = x^2$ and $y = -x^2 + 4x - 4$ is (are) :

(a) $y = 4(x - 1)$ (b) $y = -4(x - 1)$
(c) $y = 0$ (d) $y = 30x - 20$ **(I.I.T. 2006)**

9. (a) Find the equations of common tangents to the parabolas $y^2 = 16x$ and the circle $x^2 + y^2 = 8$.

(b) A is the vertex and S is focus of the parabola $y^2 = 4ax$. A circle with centre at A and radius $\frac{3}{2}a$ cuts the parabola in P and Q. Prove that PQ is right bisector of AS.

(c) The equation of the common tangent to the curves $y^2 = 8x$ and $xy = -1$ is

(a) $3y = 9x + 2$ (b) $y = 2x + 1$
(c) $2y = x + 8$ (d) $y = x + 2$ **(I.I.T. Sc. 2002)**

(d) A tangent and a normal are drawn at the point $P(16, 16)$ of the parabola $y^2 = 16x$ which cut the axis of the parabola at the points A and B respectively. If the centre of the circle through

P, A and B is C, then angle between PC and axis of x is :

(a) $\tan^{-1}\frac{1}{2}$ (b) $\tan^{-1} 2$

(c) $\tan^{-1}\frac{3}{4}$ (d) $\tan^{-1}\frac{4}{3}$

10.* Prove that the two parabolas $y^2 = 4ax$ and $x^2 = 4by$ intersect at an angle $\tan^{-1}\frac{3a^{1/3}b^{1/3}}{2(a^{2/3}+b^{2/3})}$.

11. (a) Find the points of intersection of parabolas $y^2 = 4ax$ and $x^2 = 4ay$; also find the angle between the tangents to both at these points.

(b) Prove that a circle cuts a parabola $y^2 = 4ax$ in four points such that the line joining one pair of these four points is equally inclined to the line joining the other two points.

12. Prove that the distance between a tangent to the parabola $y^2 = 4ax$ and a parallel normal is $a \operatorname{cosec}\alpha \sec^2\alpha$ where α is the inclination of either to the axis.

13. If perpendiculars be drawn from any two fixed points on the axis of a parabola equidistant from the focus on any tangent to it, show that the difference of their squares is constant.

14. Two perpendicular straight lines through the focus of the parabola $y^2 = 4ax$ meet its directrix in T and T' respectively. Show that the tangents to the parabola parallel to the perpendicular lines intersect in the mid-point of TT'.

15. (a)* Prove that the chord of the parabola $y^2 = 4ax$ whose equation is $y - x\sqrt{2} + 4a\sqrt{2} = 0$ is a normal to it and its length is $6\sqrt{3}a$.

(b) Show that the line $x + y = 3$ is normal to the parabola $y^2 = 4x$ and find the length of the chord cut off by the line from the parabola.

(c) If $x + y = k$ is normal to $y^2 = 12x$, then k is

(a) 3 (b) 9

(c) -9 (d) -3 **(I.I.T. Sc. 2000)**

16. If the normal at $P(18, 12)$ to the parabola $y^2 = 8x$ cuts it again at Q, show that $9PQ = 80\sqrt{(10)}$.

17. (a) Find the equation of tangent and normal to the parabola $y^2 = 6x$, at the point whose ordinate is 6.

(b) Equation of normal to the parabola $y = x^2 - 6x + 6$ which is perpendicular to the straight line joining the origin to the vertex of the parabola is :

(a) $4x - 4y - 11 = 0$ (b) $4x - 4y + 21 = 0$

(c) $4x - 4y + 1 = 0$ (d) $4x - 4y - 21 = 0$

18. (a) Find the equations of the normal and tangent to the parabola $y^2 = 4ax$, at the extremities of the latus rectum and show that tangents at the ends of latus rectum meet at right angles on the directrix.

(b)* The point of intersection of the tangents at the ends of the latus rectum of the parabola $y^2 = 4x$ is .... **(I.I.T. 1994)**

19. Show that the normals at the points $(4a, 4a)$ and at the upper end of the latus rectum of the parabola $y^2 = 4ax$ intersect on the same parabola.

20.* Show that whatever be the value of θ, the line

$y = (x - 11)\cos\theta - \cos 3\theta$ is a normal

to the parabola $y^2 = 16x$.

21. Show that latus rectum of a parabola bisects the angle between the tangent and normal at either extremity.

22. Three normals to $y^2 = 4x$ pass through the point $(15, 12)$; show that one of the normals is given by $y = x - 3$ and find the equations of the others.

23. Prove that the locus of the mid-point of the portion of the normal to the parabola $y^2 = 4ax$ intercepted between the curve and the axis is another parabola. Find its vertex and length of latus rectum.

24.* Through the vertex O of the parabola $y^2 = 4ax$ a perpendicular is drawn to any tangent meeting it at P and the parabola at Q. Show that $OP.OQ$ = constant.

25.* Find the centre and radius of the smaller of the two circles that touch the parabola $75y^2 = 64(5x - 3)$ at $\left(\frac{6}{5}, \frac{8}{5}\right)$ and the x-axis. **(M.N.R. 1994)**

26.* If the tangent to the parabola $y^2 = 4ax$ meets the axis in T and the tangent at the vertex A in Y, and the rectangle $TAYG$ is completed, show that the locus of G is $y^2 + ax = 0$.

27.* A ray of light is coming along the line $y = b$ from the positive direction of x-axis and strikes a concave mirror whose intersection with the xy-plane is a parabola $y^2 = 4ax$. Find the equation of the reflected ray and show that it passes through the focus of the parabola. Both a and b are positive. **(Roorkee 1995)**

28. At any point P on the parabola $y^2 - 2y - 4x + 5 = 0$, a tangent is drawn which meets the directrix at Q. Find the locus of point R which divides QP externally in the ratio $\frac{1}{2} : 1$. **(I.I.T. 2004)**

Solutions to Problem Set (2)

1. (a) Condition of tangency is $C = \frac{A}{M}$

Rule (f), Page 195

$$A = a,\ lx + my + n = 0 \text{ is}$$

$$y = -\frac{l}{m}x - \frac{n}{m} \quad \therefore \quad C = -\frac{n}{m}, M = -\frac{l}{m}.$$

$\therefore \quad -\frac{n}{m} = \frac{a}{-l/m} = -\frac{am}{l}$

$\therefore \quad ln = am^2$ is the required condition.

Alt. : Find points of intersection by eliminating x.

Put $x = -\frac{(m+y)}{l} \quad \therefore \quad y^2 = -4a\frac{(my+n)}{l}$

or $\quad ly^2 + 4amy + 4an = 0$

If the line is a tangent, the above quadratic must have equal roots. $\quad \therefore \ \Delta$ *i.e.*, $B^2 - 4AC = 0$

or $\quad 16a^2m^2 - 16aln = 0$ or $\ ln = am^2$

as found above. In numerical questions you will get the point of contact as well, as shown in **Q. 2 (a).**

(b) Ans. (a).

2. (a) Solving the parabola $y^2 = 4ax$ with the line

$x + my + am^2 = 0$, we get

$y^2 = 4a(-my - am^2)$

or $\quad y^2 + 4amy + 4a^2m^2 = 0$

or $\quad (y + 2am)^2 = 0.$

Since above is a perfect square therefore both the values of y are equal. Hence the given line is a tangent to the parabola and the ordinate of the point of contact is $-2am$ from $y + 2am = 0$. Putting the value of y in the equation of the line we get $x = am^2$. Hence the point of contact is $(am^2, -2am)$.

(b) **Hint** : Here $m = \tan 45^\circ = 1$ and $a = 1/4$

Point is $(a/m^2, 2a/m)$ or $\quad (1/4, 1/2)$

by (f), P. 967.

3. Solving the two, we get

$\frac{y-c}{m} = x, \ y^2 = 4ax + 4a^2$

or $\quad y^2 = 4a\left(\frac{y-c}{m}\right) + 4a^2$

or $\quad my^2 - 4ay + 4ac - 4a^2m = 0. \qquad$ ...(1)

Above is a quadratic in y and gives the values of y corresponding to the two points of intersection of the lines and the parabola. If the line is to be a tangent to the parabola then the two values of y should be equal. $\ \therefore \ B^2 - 4AC = 0$

i.e. $\quad 16a^2 - 4m(4ac - 4a^2m) = 0$

or $\quad a = mc - am^2 \qquad$ or $\quad mc = a + am^2$

$\therefore \quad c = \frac{a}{m} + am$ is the required condition.

4. (a) Proceed as in Q. 2. $(0, 2a)$ is the point of contact

(b) Let P be $(at^2, 2at)$ whose focal distance is

$SP = a + x = a + at^2 = a(1 + t^2) \qquad$ ...(1)

Tangent at P is $ty = x + at^2$

Compare with given line $3y = -2x + 1$

$\therefore \quad \frac{t}{3} = \frac{1}{-2} = \frac{at^2}{1} \quad \therefore \ t = -\frac{3}{2}$ and $a = -\frac{2}{9}$

$SP = \frac{-2}{9}\left(1 + \frac{9}{4}\right) = \left|-\frac{13}{18}\right| = \frac{13}{18}$

5. (a) $y^2 + 12x = 0 \quad \therefore \quad y^2 = -12x$

or $\quad 4a = -12 \quad \therefore \quad a = -3.$

Any tangent to the parabola $y^2 = 4ax$ is

$y = mx + \frac{a}{m} \quad$ or $\quad y = mx - \frac{3}{m}$

$\because \quad a = -3$ and m is unknown

Since the tangent passes through the point (3, 8), we have

$8 = 3m - \frac{3}{m} \quad$ or $\quad 3m^2 - 8m - 3 = 0$

or $\quad (m-3)(3m+1) = 0 \quad \therefore \quad m = 3, -\frac{1}{3}.$

Above gives two values of m and hence there will be two tangents through the point (3, 8). On putting the values of m the two tangents are

$3x - y - 1 = 0$ and $x + 3y - 27 = 0.$

They are perpendicular.

(b) Ans (a). Any line through origin is $y = mx$. Since it is a tangent to $y^2 = 4a(x - a)$, it will cut it in two coincident points.

$\therefore \quad$ Roots of $m^2x^2 - 4ax + 4a^2$ are equal

$\therefore \quad 16a^2 - 16a^2m^2 = 0 \quad$ or $\quad m^2 = 1$

or $\quad m = 1, -1.$

Product of slopes $= -1.$

Hence a right angle.

(c) Ans. (c).

Any tangent to parabola $y^2 = 4x$ is

$y = mx + \frac{1}{m}$ as $a = 1$. It passes through (1, 4)

$\therefore \quad m^2 - 4m + 1 = 0$

$\therefore \quad \tan\theta = \frac{m_1 - m_2}{1 + m_1m_2} = \frac{\sqrt{16-4}}{1+1} = \sqrt{3}$

$\therefore \quad \theta = \frac{\pi}{3}$

6. (a) We know that $y = mx + \frac{a}{m}$ is a tangent to the parabola $y^2 = 4ax$ and the point of contact is $\left(\frac{a}{m^2}, \frac{2a}{m}\right)$.

Here $y^2 = 16x \quad \therefore \quad 4a = 16 \quad$ or $\quad a = 4.$

Slope of the line $2x - y + 5 = 0$ is 2.

Any tangent parallel to it will have its slope 2 and $\perp$ to it will have slope $-\frac{1}{2}$.

Hence putting $a = 4, m = 2$ and $= -\frac{1}{2}$ the tangents are $2x - y + 2 = 0$ at $(1, 4)$ and $x + 2y + 16 = 0$ at $(16, -16)$.

(b) Any line parallel to given line is $y = 2x + \lambda$. If it is a tangent to the parabola then it will meet it in two coincident points. Eliminating x,

$$y^2 - 5 = 4x = 2.2x = 2(y - \lambda)$$

or $y^2 - 2y + 2\lambda - 5 = 0$. Its roots are equal

$\therefore$ $B^2 - 4AC = 0$ gives $4 - 4(2\lambda - 5) = 0$

or $24 = 8\lambda$ $\therefore$ $\lambda = 3$.

$\therefore$ $y = 2x + 3$ is the required tangent.

(c) **Refer Rule (a).**

$$\tan(\pm 45^o) = \frac{M - 3}{1 + 3M} \Rightarrow M = -2, \frac{1}{2}$$

or $m = 3, t = \tan\alpha = \tan 45^o = 1$

$\therefore$ $M = \frac{m - t}{1 + mt}$ and $\frac{m + t}{1 - mt}$ or $\frac{1}{2}, -2$

Ans. $x - 2y + 12 = 0, 4x + 2y + 3 = 0$

7. Any tangent to $y^2 = 4a(x + a)$ is

$$y = m(x + a) + \frac{a}{m} \quad \textbf{(Note } x + a\textbf{)}$$

Similarly $y = m'(x + b) + b/m'$ is a tangent to the other parabola. Since the tangents are perpendicular $mm' = -1$. In order to find the locus of their point of intersection we have to eliminate the two variables m, m' between the above these relations.

Substracting, we have

$$x(m - m') + a\left(m + \frac{1}{m}\right) - b\left(m' + \frac{1}{m'}\right) = 0$$

Now put $m' = -\frac{1}{m}$ and cancel $m + \frac{1}{m}$.

$$\therefore \quad x\left(m + \frac{1}{m}\right) + a\left(m + \frac{1}{m}\right) + b\left(m + \frac{1}{m}\right) = 0$$

$\therefore$ $x + a + b = 0$ is the required locus.

8. (a) Any tangent to the parabola $y^2 = 4ax$ is

$$y = mx + \frac{a}{m} \quad \text{...(1)}$$

If it is a tangent to the parabola $x^2 = 4by$, then it will cut it in two coincident points. Eliminating y, we get

$$x^2 = 4b\left(mx + \frac{a}{m}\right)$$

or $x^2 - 4bmx - 4b\frac{a}{m} = 0$ ...(2)

The roots of (2) will be equal if $B^2 - 4AC = 0$

or $16b^2m^2 + \frac{16ab}{m} = 0$

or $m^3 = -\frac{a}{b}$ $\therefore$ $m = -\frac{a^{1/3}}{b^{1/3}}$

On putting the value of m in (1), the equation of the common tangent is

$$y = -\frac{a^{1/3}}{b^{1/3}}x - a.\frac{b^{1/3}}{a^{1/3}}$$

or $yb^{1/3} + xa^{1/3} + a^{2/3}b^{2/3} = 0$.

(b) Any tangent to $y^2 = 2x$ is $y = mx + \frac{1}{2m}$.

[Here $a = 1/2$]

If it is tangent to $x^2 = 16y$, then

$$x^2 = 16\left(mx + \frac{1}{2m}\right)$$

will have equal roots as in Q. 3. This gives $m = -1/2$

$\therefore$ $x + 2y + 2 = 0$ is the equation of common tangent.

(c) Circle is with centre $C(0, 3)$ and $r = \sqrt{5}$.

Parabola is $y^2 = x$ and any point on it can be taken as (t^2, t) tangent at which is

$$yy_1 = \frac{1}{2}(x + x_1) \text{ or } ty = \frac{1}{2}(x + t^2)$$

or $x - 2ty + t^2 = 0$ ...(1)

If it is a tangent to the circle, then applying the condition of tangency *i.e.* $p = r$, we get

$$\frac{t^2 - 6t}{\sqrt{(1 + 4t^2)}} = \sqrt{5}$$

or $(t^4 - 12t^3 + 36t^2) = 5 + 20t^2$

or $t^4 - 12t^3 + 16t^2 - 5 = 0$

Clearly $t = 1$ satisfies it

$\therefore$ $(t - 1)(t^3 - 11t^2 + 5t + 5) = 0$

$\therefore$ $(t - 1)(t - 1)(t^2 - 10t - 5) = 0$

$\therefore$ $t = 1, 5 \pm \sqrt{30}$

Putting the values of t in (1), we get the equations of common tangents one of which is

$$x - 2y + 1 = 0.$$

(d) Ans. (c).

Any tangent to the parabola $y^2 = 4x$ is

$$y = mx + \frac{1}{m} \quad (a = 1)$$

or $m^2x - my + 1 = 0$ ...(i)

Apply $p = r$ the condition of tangency with given circle $(3, 0), 3$

$$\frac{3m^2 + 1}{\sqrt{m^4 + m^2}} = 3 \text{ or } (3m^2 + 1)^2 = 9(m^4 + m^2)$$

or $3m^2 = 1$ $\therefore$ $m = \pm\frac{1}{\sqrt{3}}$

Since the tangent touches the parabola above x-axis it will make an acute angle with x-axis so that $\tan\theta = m = +$ive.

Hence we choose $m = \frac{1}{\sqrt{3}}$. Put in (i)

$\therefore \quad x - \sqrt{3}y + 3 = 0 \Rightarrow$ (c)

(e) Ans. (a), (c).

Any point on the parabola $x^2 = y$ is (t, t^2).

Tangent at (t, t^2) is $xx_1 = \frac{1}{2}(y + y_1)$

or $\quad 2x.t = y + t^2$.

If it is a tangent to $y = -x^2 + 4x - 4$ then they will intersect in two coincident points.

$\therefore \quad 2xt + t^2 = -x^2 + 4x - 4$

(Equating the values of y)

or $\quad x^2 + 2x(t-2) + (4 - t^2) = 0$

should have equal roots.

$\therefore \quad D = 0$, i.e., $4(t-2)^2 - 4(4 - t^2) = 0$

or $\quad 2t^2 - 4t = 0 \quad \therefore \quad t = 0, 2$

Putting for t in $2xt = y + t^2$, the equation of common tangents are $y = 0$ and $y = 4x - 4$.

9. (a) $y^2 = 16x \quad \therefore \quad 4a = 16$ or $a = 4$.

Any tangent to parabola is

$$y = mx + \frac{a}{m} \quad \text{or} \quad mx - y + \frac{4}{m} = 0.$$

Apply $p = r$ with the circle $(0,0)$, $\sqrt{8}$ for tangency.

$$\therefore \quad \frac{4/m}{\sqrt{(m^2+1)}} = \sqrt{8}$$

or $\quad 2 = m^4 + m^2 \quad$ or $\quad (m^4 + m^2 - 2) = 0$

or $\quad (m^2 + 2)(m^2 - 1) = 0 \quad \therefore \quad m = \pm 1$

Hence the common tangents are $y = \pm(x + 4)$.

(b) $A(0,0)$, S is $(a, 0)$ then mid-point is $(a/2, 0)$.

Hence right bisector of AS is the line $x = a/2$.

Parabola is $\quad y^2 - 4ax = 0$

Circle is $\quad x^2 + y^2 - \left(\frac{3}{2}a\right)^2 = 0$

If they intersect at P and Q, then solving them we get

or $\quad x^2 + 4ax - \frac{9}{4}a^2 = 0$

or $\quad 4x^2 + 16ax - 9a^2 = 0$

$(2x + 9a)(2x - a) = 0 \quad \therefore \quad x = a/2$

Note: x cannot be –ive because otherwise y will be imaginary from parabola.

Putting $x = \frac{a}{2}$, we get $y^2 = 2a^2 \quad \therefore \quad y = \pm a\sqrt{2}$

$\therefore \quad P$ is $\left(\frac{a}{2}, a\sqrt{2}\right)$ and Q is $\left(\frac{a}{2}, -a\sqrt{2}\right)$

Equation of PQ is $x = \frac{a}{2}$ which is right bisector of AS.

(c) Ans. (d). Any tangent to $y^2 = 8x\,(a = 2)$ is $y = mx + \frac{a}{m}$ or $y = mx + \frac{2}{m}$. If it is a tangent to $xy = -1$, then it will cut the hyperbola in two coincident points

$\therefore \quad x\left(mx + \frac{2}{m}\right) + 1 = 0$ or $m^2x^2 + 2x + m = 0$

$\Delta = 0$ i.e., $4 - 4m^3 = 0 \quad \therefore \quad m = 1$

Hence $y = x + 2$ is the common tangent.

(d) Ans. (d).

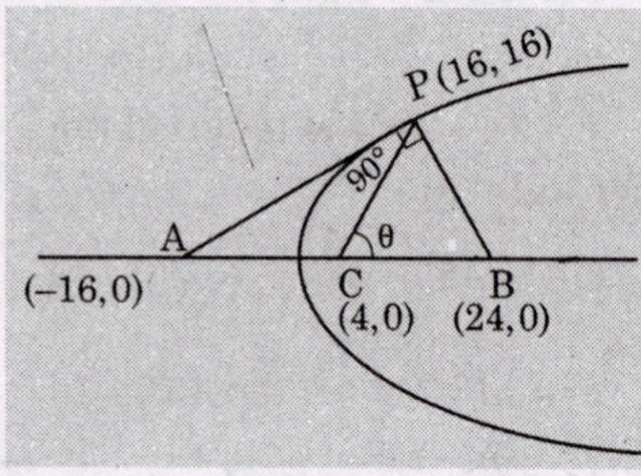

Fig. 11

$a = 4$, the point (16, 16) corresponds to $(at^2, 2at)$ for $t = 2$.

$$ty = x + at^2$$

is tangent and $y = -tx + 2at + at^3$ is normal.

Putting $y = 0$, we get $A(-at^2, 0) = (-16, 0)$

$B(2a + at^2, 0) = (24, 0)$

The circle through A, B, P will be on AB as diameter as $\angle APB = 90^\circ$. Hence centre C is mid-point of AB is $(4, 0)$.

$\therefore \quad$ Slope of $PC = \frac{16 - 0}{16 - 4} = \frac{16}{12} = \frac{4}{3} = \tan\theta$

$\therefore \quad \theta = \tan^{-1}\frac{4}{3} \Rightarrow$ (d)

10. Angle between two curves is equal to the angle between the tangents at their common point.

Solving the two, we get $y = \frac{x^2}{4b}$ from $x^2 = 4by$

Putting the value of y in $y^2 = 4ax$, we get

$\left(\frac{x^2}{4b}\right)^2 = 4ax \quad$ or $\quad x(x^3 - 64ab^2) = 0$

$x = 0 \quad$ or $\quad 4a^{1/3}b^{2/3}$

and hence $y = 0 \quad$ or $\quad 4a^{2/3}b^{1/3}$.

Therefore the points of intersection are $(0, 0)$, $(4a^{1/3}b^{2/3}, 4a^{2/3}b^{1/3})$.

But tangents at the vertex (0, 0) to the two parabolas are axes of x and y respectively and angle between them is $\pi/2$. If the other point be taken as (x_1, y_1) then tangents to the parabolas are

$$yy_1 = 2a(x + x_1) \quad \text{...(1)}$$

$\therefore \quad m_1 = \frac{2a}{y_1} = \frac{2a}{4a^{2/3}\, b^{1/3}} = \frac{1}{2}\frac{a^{1/3}}{b^{1/3}}$

$xx_1 = 2b\,(y + y_1)$ ...(2)

$\therefore \quad m_2 = \frac{x_1}{2b} = \frac{4a^{1/3} b^{2/3}}{2b} = 2\frac{a^{1/3}}{b^{1/3}}$

If θ be the angle between the tangents, then

$$\tan\theta = \frac{m_1 \sim m_2}{1 + m_1 m_2} = \frac{\frac{a^{1/3}}{b^{1/3}}\left(\frac{1}{2} \sim 2\right)}{1 + \frac{a^{2/3}}{b^{2/3}}} = \frac{3a^{1/3}\, b^{1/3}}{2\,(a^{2/3} + b^{2/3})}$$

11. (a) Proceed as in **Q. 10.** 90° at (0, 0), $\tan^{-1}(3/4)$ at $(4a, 4a)$.

(b) Let the circle be $x^2 + y^2 + 2gx + 2fy + c = 0$

Solving with $y^2 = 4ax$, we have

$$\frac{y^4}{16a^2} + y^2 + 2g\cdot\frac{y^2}{4a} + 2fy + c = 0$$

$$\therefore \quad y^4 + 0y^3 + y^2(16a^2 + 8ag) + 32a^2 fy + 16a^2 c = 0$$

If y_1, y_2, y_3, y_4 be the roots of above, then

$y_1 + y_2 + y_3 + y_4 = 0$

Slope of line joining y_1 and $y_2 = \frac{4a}{y_1 + y_2} = m_1$ say.

Slope of line joining y_3 and y_4

$$= \frac{4a}{y_3 + y_4} = -\frac{4a}{y_1 + y_2} = m_2 \text{ say}$$

Clearly $m_1 = -m_2$.

Hence these lines are equally inclined to axes.

12. Equation of the tangent is $y = mx + a/m$, where $m = \tan\alpha$ given. The slope of any normal which is parallel to the tangent will also be m and hence its equation is $y = mx - 2am - am^3$.

In order to find the distance between these two parallel lines we take a point on the tangent and find its distance from the normal. Putting $y = 0$ in the equation of tangent, we get the point $(-a/m^2, 0)$. Its distance from the normal is

$$\frac{m\left(-\frac{a}{m^2}\right) - 2am - am^3}{\sqrt{(1+m^2)}} = \frac{a}{m}\cdot\frac{1 + 2m^2 + m^4}{\sqrt{(1+m^2)}}$$

$$= \frac{a}{m}(1+m^2)^{3/2} = \frac{a}{\tan\alpha}(1 + \tan^2\alpha)^{3/2}$$

$$= a\cot\alpha.\sec^3\alpha = a\frac{\cos\alpha}{\sin\alpha}\cdot\sec^3\alpha$$

$$= a\operatorname{cosec}\alpha\sec^2\alpha$$

13. Suppose any two points on the axis equidistant from the focus $(a, 0)$ be $(a+d, 0)$ and $(a-d, 0)$ where d is constant. Equation of any tangent to the parabola is

$$y = mx + \frac{a}{m} \quad \text{or} \quad m^2 x - my + a = 0.$$

If p_1 and p_2 be the perpendiculars on it, then

$$p_1^2 - p_2^2 = \left[\frac{m^2(a+d) + a}{\sqrt{(m^4 + m^2)}}\right]^2 - \left[\frac{m^2(a-d) + a}{\sqrt{(m^4 + m^2)}}\right]^2$$

$$= \frac{1}{m^2(1+m^2)}[\{a(m^2+1) + dm^2\}^2 - \{a(m^2+1) - dm^2\}^2]$$

$$= \frac{1}{m^2(1+m^2)}[4a(m^2+1).dm^2] = 4ad$$

i.e. constant

$\because \quad (x+y)^2 - (x-y)^2 = 4xy.$

14. Any line through the focus $(a, 0)$ is

$y = m(x - a)$ ...(1)

Any line perpendicular to above through $(a, 0)$ is

$y = -\frac{1}{m}(x - a)$ ...(2)

Solving with directrix $x = -a$, we get the points T and T'

$T(-a, -2am)$ and $T'\left(-a, \frac{2a}{m}\right)$

Mid-point of TT' is $\left[-a, a\left(\frac{1}{m} - m\right)\right]$ ...(3)

Now tangents parallel to lines (1) and (2) are

$y = mx + \frac{a}{m}$, $y = -\frac{1}{m}x - am$.

Substracting we get $0 = x\left(m + \frac{1}{m}\right) + a\left(m + \frac{1}{m}\right)$

$\therefore$ $x = -a$, and hence on putting for x, we get $y = a\left(\frac{1}{m} - m\right)$.

Thus the point of intersection is $\left[-a, a\left(\frac{1}{m} - m\right)\right]$ which is mid-point of TT' by (3).

15. (a) The slope of the chord is $\sqrt{2}$ and the normal whose slope is $\sqrt{2}$ is obtained by putting $m = \sqrt{2}$ in $y = mx - 2am - am^3$ and is therefore given by

$y = x\sqrt{2} - 2a\sqrt{2} - a2\sqrt{2}$

or $y = x\sqrt{2} - 4a\sqrt{2}$.

In order to find the length of the normal we should find its points of intersection with the parabola $y^2 = 4ax$.

Eliminating x between them, we get

$$y^2 = 4a\left(\frac{y + 4a\sqrt{2}}{\sqrt{2}}\right)$$

or $y^2 - 2\sqrt{2}ay - 16a^2 = 0$

or $(y + 2a\sqrt{2})(y - 4a\sqrt{2}) = 0$

$\therefore \quad y = -2a\sqrt{2}$ and $4a\sqrt{2}$

Putting the values of y in the equation of the chord the corresponding values of x are $2a$ and $8a$. Hence their co-ordinates are $(2a, -2a\sqrt{2})$ and $(8a, 4a\sqrt{2})$

Required length

$= \{(8a - 2a)^2 + (4a\sqrt{2} + 2a\sqrt{2})^2\}^{1/2}$

$= \sqrt{(36a^2 + 72a^2)} = 6\sqrt{3a}.$

(b) Proceed as in part (a). (9, – 6), (1, 2), $8\sqrt{2}$

(c) Ans. (b). $y = mx + c$ is a normal to $y^2 = 4ax$ if $c = -2am - am^3$. Here $4a = 12 \quad \therefore \quad a = 3$

$y = -x + k \quad \therefore \quad m = -1, c = k.$

$\therefore \quad k = -6(-1) - 3(-1) = 6 + 3 = 9.$

16. Normal is $y - y_1 = -\dfrac{y_1}{2a}(x - x_1)$. Here $4a = 8$.

$\therefore \quad y - 12 = -\dfrac{12}{4}(x - 18)$

or $\quad y = -3x + 66$

Solving with $y^2 = 8x$, we get $y^2 = 8\dfrac{(y - 66)}{-3}$

or $\quad -3y^2 = 8y - 528$ or $3y^2 + 8y - 528 = 0$

or $\quad 3y^2 + 44y - 36y - 528 = 0$

or $\quad (3y + 44)(y - 12) = 0$

$\therefore \quad y = 12, -\dfrac{44}{3}$ and $x = 18, \dfrac{11 \times 22}{9}$

$\therefore$ Point Q is $\left(\dfrac{11 \times 22}{9}, -\dfrac{44}{3}\right)$ and P is (18, 12).

$\therefore \quad PQ^2 = \left(18 - \dfrac{11 \times 22}{9}\right)^2 + \left(12 + \dfrac{44}{3}\right)^2$

or $\quad 81\,PQ^2 = (162 - 242)^2 + 9(80)^2$

$= 80^2 + 9.80^2 = 80^2.10$

$\therefore \quad 9PQ = 80\sqrt{10}$

17. (a) $y^2 = 6x$ when $y = 6$ then $x = 6$ and hence the point is (6, 6).

Ans. Tangent $x - 2y + 6 = 0$,
Normal $2x + y - 18 = 0$

(b) Ans. (d).

The given parabola is $(x - 3)^2 = (y + 3)$ whose vertex is the point (3, – 3) say A.

Slope of $OA = -1$ and hence slope of normal which is perpendicular to OA is $1 = m$ say. Any normal to $X^2 = 4AY$ is $X = mY - 2Am - Am^3$ **(See g P. 967)**

Now put $X = x - 3, Y = y + 3$,

$4A = 1$, *i.e.*, $A = \dfrac{1}{4}$ and $m = 1$

$\therefore \quad x - 3 = y + 3 - \dfrac{1}{2} - \dfrac{1}{4}$

or $\quad 4x - 12 = 4y + 12 - 2 - 1$

or $\quad 4x - 4y - 21 = 0$

18. (a) $L(a, 2a)$ and $L'(a, -2a)$.

Normals are $x + y = 3a$ and $x - y = 3a$

Tangents are $y = x + a$ and $y = -x - a$ and they are clearly perpendicular and their point of intersection is $(-a, 0)$ which lies on the directrix.

(b) Ans. $(-a, 0)$ *i.e.* $(-1, 0)$ as $4a = 4$ or $a = 1$.

19. As in Q. 16 normal is $y - y_1 = -\dfrac{y_1}{2a}(x - x_1)$

Normal at $(4a, 4a)$; $y - 4a = -\dfrac{4a}{2a}(x - 4a)$

or $\quad 2x + y = 12a$

Normal at $L(a, 2a)$ is $x + y = 3a$

Solving, we get the point $(9a, -6a)$ which clearly satisfies the equation of the parabola.

20. The slope of the given line is $m = \cos\theta$

Also $\quad y^2 = 16x \quad \therefore \quad 4a = 16$ or $a = 4$

Any normal is $y = mx - 2am - am^3$

or $\quad y = x\cos\theta - 8\cos\theta - 4\cos^3\theta$

or $\quad y = x\cos\theta - 11\cos\theta + 3\cos\theta - 4\cos^3\theta$

or $\quad y = (x - 11)\cos\theta - \cos 3\theta$.

$\because \quad \cos 3\theta = 4\cos^3\theta - 3\cos\theta.$

21. $L(a, 2a)$. Tangent is $y = x + a$ and normal is $y = -x + 3a$. Their slopes are 1 and – 1 *i.e.* they make angles of 45° and 135° respectively with the axis. From the figure it is

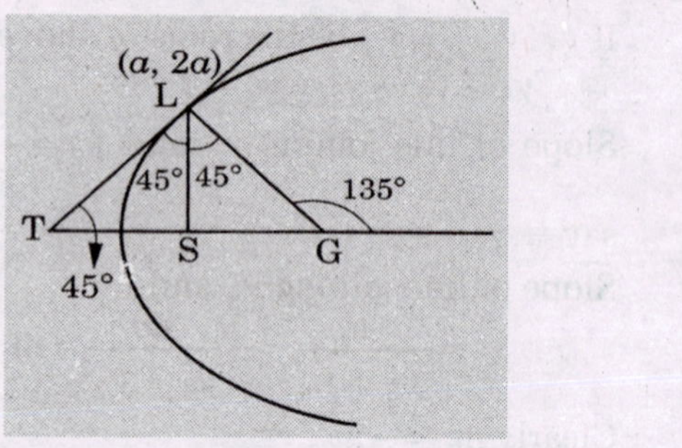

Fig. 12

clear that latus rectum LS is equally inclined at an angle of 45° to both tangent and normal.

22. $y^2 = 4x \quad \therefore \quad 4a = 4$, *i.e.*, $a = 1$.

Any normal to the parabola is

$y = mx - 2am - am^3$. ...(1)

If it passes through the point (15, 12), then

$12 = 15m - 2m - m^3 \quad \because \quad a = 1$

or $\quad m^3 - 13m + 12 = 0$ ...(2)

Above being a cubic in m gives us three values of m showing that there will be three normals to the parabola through the point (15, 12).

Clearly $m = 1$ satisfies (2) and hence it can be written as

$(m - 1)(m^2 + m - 12) = 0$

or $\quad (m - 1)(m + 4)(m - 3) = 0$

$\therefore \quad m = 1, -4, 3,$ and $a = 1$.

Hence from (1) the three normals are

$y = x - 3, y = -4x + 72, y = 3x - 33.$

23. Normal to the parabola $y^2 = 4ax$ at any point $P(at^2, 2at)$ is

$$y = -t\,x + 2at + at^3 \qquad ...(1)$$

It meets the axis $y = 0$ at the point

$G(2a + at^2, 0)$.

If (h, k) be the mid-point of PG, then

$2h = at^2 + 2a + at^2,\ 2k = 2at$

or $\quad h = a + at^2, k = at \quad \therefore \quad t = k/a.$

$\therefore \quad h = a + a\dfrac{k^2}{a^2} \quad$ or $\quad k^2 = a(h - a)$

Hence the locus of the mid-point (h, k) is

$y^2 = a(x - a)$.

Above represents a parabola whose vertex is at $(a, 0)$ and latus rectum is of length a *i.e.* one-fourth of the latus rectum of the original parabola.

24. Any tangent to the parabola is

$$y = mx + a/m \qquad ...(1)$$

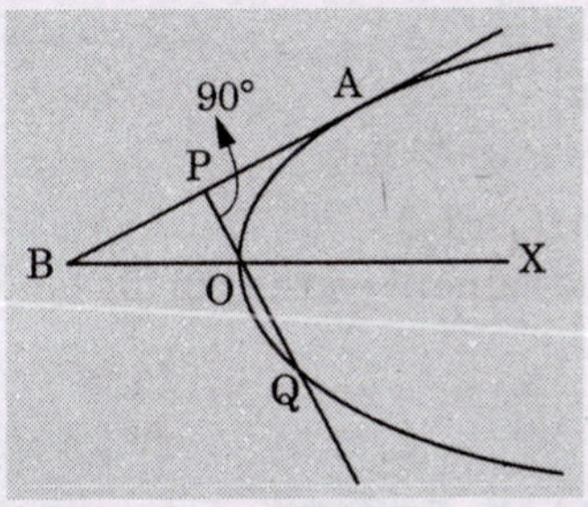

Fig. 13

Any line through vertex O and $\perp$ to tangent is

$$y = -\frac{1}{m}x \qquad ...(2)$$

OP is perpendicular distance of $O(0, 0)$ from (1).

$\therefore \quad OP = \dfrac{a}{\sqrt{(1 + m^2)}} \cdot \dfrac{1}{m}$

The line (2) meets the parabola $y^2 = 4ax$ at Q.

$\therefore \quad \dfrac{1}{m^2}x^2 = 4ax$

$\therefore \quad x = 4am^2, y = -\dfrac{1}{m}x = -4am.$

$\therefore \quad$ Hence $OQ = 4am\sqrt{(m^2 + 1)}$.

$\therefore \quad OP.OQ = \dfrac{a}{\sqrt{(1 + m^2)}} \cdot \dfrac{1}{m} \cdot 4am.\sqrt{(m^2 + 1)}$

$= 4a^2$, *i.e.* constant.

25. The parabola can be written as

$75y^2 = 32(10x - 6)$.

Tangent at (x_1, y_1) is $75yy_1 = 32[5(x + x_1) - 6]$

$75y \cdot \dfrac{8}{5} = 32\left[5\left(x + \dfrac{6}{5}\right) - 6\right]$ at $\left(\dfrac{6}{5}, \dfrac{8}{5}\right)$

or $\quad 4x - 3y = 0$

Above is common tangent to parabola and circle at $(6/5, 8/5)$. The centre of the circle will be on normal at a distance $\pm r$ from the point of contact. Slope of tangent

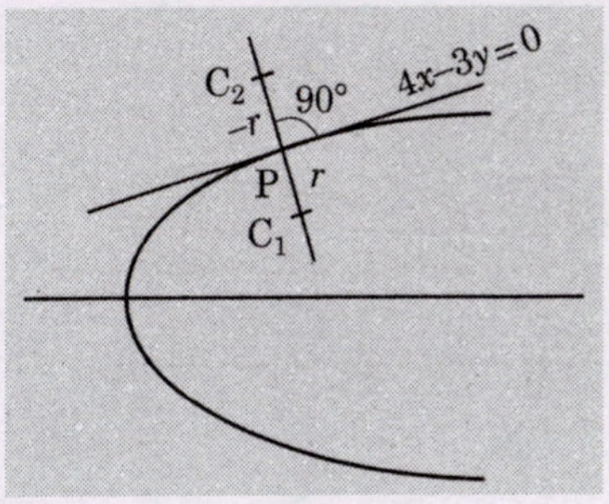

Fig. 14

is 4/3 and hence of normal will be $-3/4 = \tan\theta$

$\therefore \cos\theta = -\dfrac{4}{5}, \sin\theta = \dfrac{3}{5}.$

Hence the co-ordinates of centres are points C_1 and C_2 on the normal through $P(6/5, 8/5)$ and at a distance r or $-r$ from P.

$$\frac{x - 6/5}{-4/5} = \frac{y - 8/5}{3/5} = \underset{C_1}{r}, \underset{C_2}{-r}$$

$\therefore \quad C_1 = \left(\dfrac{-4r + 6}{5}, \dfrac{3r + 8}{5}\right),$

$C_2 = \left(\dfrac{4r + 6}{5}, \dfrac{-3r + 8}{5}\right).$

Since the circle touches x-axis, therefore y co-ordinate of centre is radius

$\therefore \quad \dfrac{3r + 8}{5} = r \quad \therefore \quad r = 4$ for C_1 (Bigger)

or $\quad \dfrac{-3r + 8}{5} = r. \quad \therefore \quad r = 1$ for C_2 (Smaller)

Hence bigger $= (-2, 4), 4$ and smaller $= (2, 1), 1$.

26. Any tangent to parabola $y^2 = 4ax$ is $ty = x + at^2$. It meets axis in T and tangent at vertex A in Y.

$T(-at^2, 0), A(0, 0), Y(0, at)$

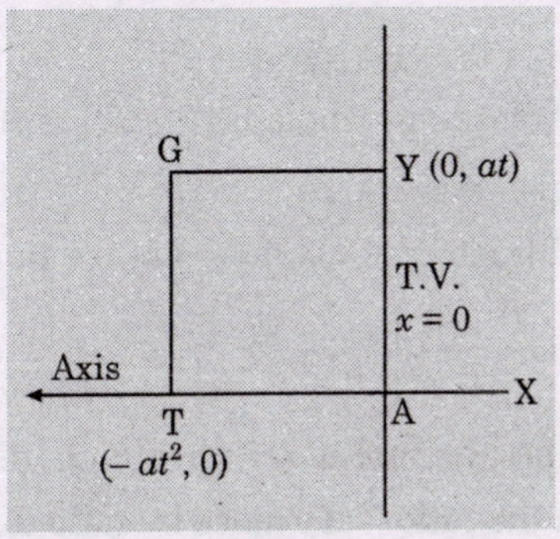

Fig. 15

Now if $G(x, y)$ be the fourth vertex of rectangle $TAYG$ then $x = -at^2, y = at$. Eliminating t, we get

$y^2 = -ax \quad$ or $\quad y^2 + ax = 0$

27. $y = b$ meets the parabola

$y^2 = 4ax$ at $P\left(\dfrac{b^2}{4a}, b\right)$

$\dfrac{dy}{dx} = \dfrac{4a}{2y}$

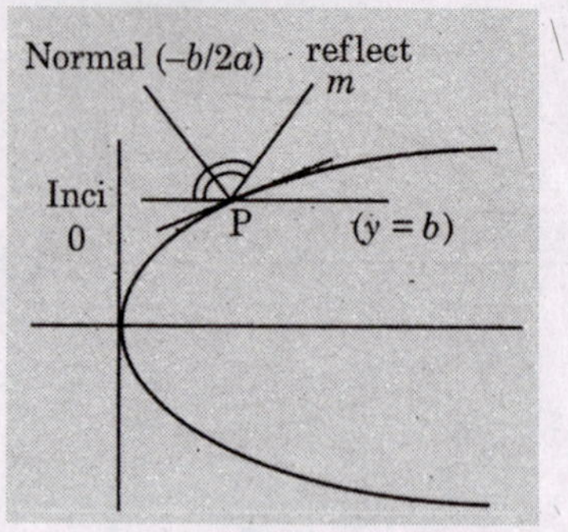

Fig. 16

$\therefore$ Slope of normal $= -\dfrac{2y}{4a} = -\dfrac{y}{2a} = -\dfrac{b}{2a}$

Incident	Normal	Reflected
Slopes 0	$-b/2a$	m

Since the lines are equally inclined to normal, therefore

$$\frac{0-(-b/2a)}{1+0(-b/2a)} = -\frac{m-(-b/2a)}{1+m(-b/2a)}$$

or $\dfrac{b}{2a} = -\dfrac{2am+b}{2a-mb}$

or $2ab - mb^2 = -4a^2m - 2ab$

or $4ab = (b^2 - 4a^2)\,m$ or $m = \dfrac{4ab}{b^2-4a^2}$

Hence equation of reflected ray through P is

$$y - b = \frac{4ab}{b^2-4a^2}\left(x - \frac{b^2}{4a}\right)$$

It is satisfied by the point $(a, 0)$ *i.e.* focus of the parabola.

28. The given parabola is $(y-1)^2 = 4(x-1)$

or $Y^2 = 4X$

where $Y = y-1, X = x-1$ and $A = 1$ ...(1)

Any point P on the parabola is $(T^2, 2T)$ as $A = 1$.

Tangent at P is $TY = X + 1.T^2$

It meets the directrix $X = -A = -1$ at the point Q.

$\therefore$ Q is $\left(-1, \dfrac{T^2-1}{T}\right)$.

Now let R be the point (H, K) which divides QP externally in the ratio $\frac{1}{2} : 1$. Hence by ratio formula

$$H = \frac{\frac{1}{2}.T^2 - 1(-1)}{\frac{1}{2} - 1} = -(T^2+2)$$

$$K = \frac{\frac{1}{2}.2T - 1.\frac{T^2-1}{T}}{\frac{1}{2}-1} = -\frac{2}{T}$$

Hence the locus of the point $R(H, K)$ is obtained by eliminating the variable T.

$\therefore$ $H = -\left(\dfrac{4}{K^2} + 2\right)$ or $(H+2)K^2 + 4 = 0$

or $(X+2)Y^2 + 4 = 0$ is the required locus.

Now replace X by $(x-1)$ and Y by $(y-1)$.

$\therefore$ $(x+1)(y-1)^2 + 4 = 0.$

§3. (a) Point of intersection of two tangents at *P* and *Q*.

$yy_1 = 2a(x+x_1)$ $\qquad t_1 y = x + at_1^2$

$yy_2 = 2a(x+x_2)$ $\qquad t_2 y = x + at_2^2$

Subtracting, we get

$y(y_1 - y_2) = 2a(x_1 - x_2)$

$$y(y_1-y_2) = 2a\left(\frac{y_1^2 - y_2^2}{4a}\right)$$

$\therefore$ $\mathbf{y = \dfrac{y_1+y_2}{2}}$

and $y(t_1 - t_2) = a(t_1^2 - t_2^2)$

$$y = a\left(\frac{t_1^2 - t_2^2}{t_1 - t_2}\right)$$

$\therefore$ $\mathbf{y = a(t_1 + t_2)}$

Putting the value of y in any of the tangent, we get

$$\frac{y_1+y_2}{2}\cdot y_1 = 2ax + 2a\cdot\frac{y_1^2}{4a}$$

$\therefore$ $y_1^2 + y_1y_2 = 4ax + y_1^2$

$\therefore$ $\mathbf{x = \dfrac{y_1y_2}{4a}}$

or $t_1.a(t_1+t_2) = x + at_1^2$

or $at_1^2 + at_1t_2 = x + at_1^2$

or $\mathbf{x = at_1t_2}$.

Hence the point of intersection of two tangents is

* $\left(\dfrac{y_1y_2}{4a}, \dfrac{y_1+y_2}{2}\right)$

or $[at_1t_2, a(t_1+t_2)]$ **(V.Imp.)**

(b) Point of intersection of normals at $(at_1^2, 2at_1)$ and $(at_2^2, 2at_2)$.

The equations of the normals at the points t_1 and t_2 are

$y = -t_1x + 2at_1 + at_1^3$

$y = -t_2x + 2at_2 + at_2^3$

Subtracting,

$0 = -(t_1 - t_2)x + 2a(t_1 - t_2) + a(t_1^3 - t_2^3)$

$\therefore$ $x = 2a + a(t_1^2 + t_1t_2 + t_2^2)$

On putting the value of x in either, we get

$y = -at_1t_2(t_1 + t_2)$

Hence the point of intersection is

* $[2a + a(t_1^2 + t_2^2 + t_1t_2), -at_1t_2(t_1+t_2)]$

(Remember)

(c) Number of tangents and normals through a given point.

(i) We know that $y = mx + a/m$ is always a tangent to the parabola in terms of m, the slope of the tangent. If it passes through the point (h, k), then $k = mh + a/m$ or $^*m^2h - mk + a = 0$.

Above is a quadratic in m and gives two values of m, showing thereby that there will be two tangents passing through the point (h, k) whose slopes m_1, m_2 are given by the equation (1). If they are perpendicular, then

$$m_1 m_2 = -1 \quad \text{or} \quad \frac{a}{h} = -1$$

$\therefore$ Locus is $x = -a$ *i.e.*, directrix.

Hence perpendicular tangents to a parabola intersect on the directrix.

Equation of pair of tangents to a parabola drawn from the given point.

In usual notation it is given by $SS_1 = T^2$.

(ii) We know that the equation of normal at $(am^2, -2am)$ is $y = mx - 2am - am^3$

If it passes through the point (h, k), then

$$k = mh - 2am - am^3 = 0$$

$$^*\text{or} \quad \boldsymbol{am^3 + 0m^2 + m(2a - h) + k = 0.} \quad \text{...(A)}$$

Above is a cubic equation in m and will give us three values of m. If they be denoted by m_1, m_2 and m_3 then we can say that normals at $(am_1^2, -2am_1), (am_2^2, -2am_2), (am_3^2, -2am_3)$ will pass through the point (h, k). Hence from any point (h, k) three normals can be drawn to a parabola whose slopes are given by (A).

$$^*\text{Also} \quad \boldsymbol{m_1 + m_2 + m_3 = \frac{0}{a} = 0.} \quad \text{...(B)}$$

$\because$ coeff. of $m^2 = 0$.

i.e. **Sum of the slopes of these normals is zero.**

Again if y_1, y_2, y_3 be the ordinates of the feet of the normals then

$$y_1 = -2am_1, y_2 = -2am_2, y_3 = -2am_3$$

$$\therefore \quad y_1 + y_2 + y_3 = -2a(m_1 + m_2 + m_3) = 0.$$

Hence sum of the ordinates of the feet of the normals that pass through any point (h, k) is zero.

Again from equation (A) we have

$$^* \quad \boldsymbol{m_1m_2 + m_2m_3 + m_3m_1 = (2a - h)/a} \quad \text{...(C)}$$

$$^* \quad \boldsymbol{m_1m_2m_3 = -k/a} \quad \text{...(D)}$$

Remember result (A), (B), (C) and (D).

Problem Set (3)

Point of intersection of tangents and normals and focal chord.

1. (a) Prove that any two perpendicular tangents to a parabola intersect on the directrix.

(b)* Prove that tangents at the extremities of a focal chord of a parabola are perpendicular and they intersect on the directrix.

2. (a) A circle is described on any focal chord of a parabola as diameter. Prove that locus of its centre is the curve $y^2 = 2a(x - a)$.

(b) PSP' is a focal chord of the parabola $y^2 = 4ax$. From the vertex $A(0, 0)$ and focus $(a, 0)$ perpendiculars p_1, p_2, p_3, p_4 are drawn on the tangents at P and P'. Prove that $p_1\, p_2\, p_3\, p_4 = a^4$.

(c) A triangle ABC of area Δ is inscribed in the parabola $y^2 = 4ax$ such that the vertex A lies at the vertex of the parabola and BC is a focal chord. Prove that the difference of the distances of B and C from the axis of the parabola is $2\Delta/a$.

(d) A circle drawn on any focal chord AB of the parabola $y^2 = 4ax$ as diameter cuts the parabola again at C and D. If the parameters of the points A, B, C, D be t_1, t_2, t_3 and t_4 respectively, then the value of t_3t_4 is :

(a) -1 (b) 2

(c) 3 (d) none

3. (a)* Find the locus of the point of intersection of the tangents to the parabola $y^2 = 4ax$ which (i) include an angle α (ii) an angle of $45°$.

(b)* The angle between a pair of tangents drawn from a point P to the parabola $y^2 = 4ax$ is $45°$. Show that the locus of the point P is a hyperbola. **(I.I.T. 1998)**

(c) Two tangents of the parabola $y^2 = 8x$, meet the tangent at its vertex in the points P and Q. If $PQ = 4$, prove that locus of the point of intersection of the two tangents is $y^2 = 8(x + 2)$.

4. (a)* Prove that the area of triangle inscribed in a parabola is twice the area of the triangle formed by the tangents at the vertices of the triangle. **(I.I.T. 1996)**

(b) Determine the area of the triangle formed by three tangents to a parabola $y^2 = 4ax$, if it is given that their slopes are in H.P.

(c) Tangents to the parabola $y^2 = 4ax$ drawn at the points $A(t_1)$ and $B(t_2)$ meet at the point C, then prove that area of triangle ABC is $\frac{1}{2}a^2(t_2 - t_1)^3$.

5.* Normals are drawn to the parabola $y^2 = 4ax$ at points A, B, C whose parameters are t_1, t_2 and t_3 respectively. If these normals enclose a triangle PQR, then prove that its area is $\frac{a^2}{2}(t_1 - t_2)(t_2 - t_3)(t_3 - t_1)(t_1 + t_2 + t_3)^2$

Also prove that $\Delta PQR = \Delta ABC (t_1 + t_2 + t_3)^2$.

6. (a)* If the point $(at_1^2, 2at_1)$ is one extremity of a focal chord of the parabola $y^2 = 4ax$, find the co-ordinates of the other extremity and show that the length of the chord is $a\left(t_1 + \frac{1}{t_1}\right)^2$.

(b)* If p be the perpendicular distance of a focal chord PQ of length l from the vertex A of the parabola $y^2 = 4ax$, then prove that l varies inversely as p^2.

7. (a) PQ is a variable focal chord of the parabola $y^2 = 4ax$ whose vertex is A. Prove that the locus of the centroid of triangle APQ is a parabola whose latus rectum is $\frac{12}{9}a$.

(b)* Prove that in a parabola semi-latus rectum is the harmonic mean of the segments of a focal chord. **(D.C.E. 1998)**

[Remember above result]

(c) Find the latus rectum of a parabola whose focal chord PSQ is such that $SP = 3$ and $SQ = 2$.

8. Prove that portion of a tangent to a parabola cut off between the directrix and the curve subtends a right angle at the focus.

9. Prove that the tangent and normal at a point P on the parabola $y^2 = 4ax$ are the bisectors of the angle between the focal radius SP and the perpendicular from P on the directrix.

10. Prove that any tangent to a parabola $y^2 = 4ax$ and perpendicular to it from the focus meet on the tangent at the vertex.

11.* From any point P on the parabola $y^2 = 4ax$ perpendicular PN is drawn on the axis meeting it at N. Normal at P meets the axis in G. Prove that the subnormal NG = semi-latus recutm. **(M.N.R. 1994)**

12. The normal to the parabola $y^2 = 4ax$ at a point P on it meets the x-axis in G. Show that P and G are equidistant from the focus S of the parabola.

13. The normal at a point P to the parabola $y^2 = 4ax$ meets its axis at G. Q is another point on the parabola such that QG is perpendicular to the axis of the parabola. Prove that $QG^2 - PG^2$ = constant.

14. Prove that tangent at one extremity of a focal chord of the parabola $y^2 = 4ax$ is parallel to the normal drawn at the other extremity.

15. (a)* A chord of the parabola $y^2 = 4ax$ subtends a right angle at the vertex. Find the locus of the point of intersection of tangents at its extremities.

(b) Tangents are drawn to the parabola $y^2 = 4ax$ from a point P such that its chord of contact subtends an angle of $60°$ at the vertex. Prove that the locus of the point P is $4(y^2 - 4ax) = 3(x + 4a)^2$.

16. (a)* If from the vertex of the parabola $y^2 = 4ax$ a pair of chords be drawn perpendicular to each other and with these chords as adjacent sides a rectangle is completed then prove that the locus of the vertex of the farther angle of the rectangle is the parabola $y^2 = 4a(x - 8a)$.

(b)* Through the vertex O of a parabola $y^2 = 4x$ chords OP and OQ are drawn at right angles to one-another. Show that for all positions of P, PQ cuts the axis of the parabola at a fixed point. Also find the locus of the middle point of PQ. **(I.I.T. 1994)**

(c)* Show that the locus of a point that divides a chord of slope 2 of the parabola $y^2 = 4x$ internally in the ratio 1 : 2 is a parabola. Find the vertex of this parabola. **(I.I.T. 1995)**

17. (a)* Prove that the circle drawn on any focal chord of a parabola as diameter touches the directrix.

(b) Prove that the circle on any focal radius as diameter touches the tangent at the vertex.

18.* Prove that the length of the intercept on the normal at the point $(at^2, 2at)$ of the parabola $y^2 = 4ax$ made by the circle on the line joining the focus and P as diameter is $a\sqrt{(1+t^2)}$.

19. (a)* L, M, N are three points on the parabola $y^2 = 4ax$ whose ordinates are in geometrical progression. Show that the tangents at L and N will meet on the ordinate of M.

(b) The abscissas of any two points on the parabola $y^2 = 4ax$ are in the ratio $\mu : 1$. Prove that the locus of the point of intersection of tangents at these points is $y^2 = (\mu^{1/4} + \mu^{-1/4})\, ax$.

20. (a) If the tangent at the points P and Q on the parabola $y^2 = 4ax$ meet at T and S is the focus, prove that $ST^2 = SP.SQ$.

(b) Tangents PQ, PR are drawn to a parabola $y^2 = 4ax$. If p_1, p_2, p_3 be the perpendiculars from P, Q and R to any tangent to it, then prove that p_1 is the geometric mean of p_2 and p_3.

21.* If tangents to the parabola $y^2 = 4ax$ at the points P and Q intersect at T, prove that TP and TQ subtend equal angles at the focus.

22. (a)* Prove that the orthocentre of the triangle formed by three tangents to a parabola lie on the directrix.

(b)* Tangents to the parabola $y^2 = 4ax$ at any three points enclose a triangle ABC. Prove that the circumcircle of the triangle ABC passes through focus of the parabola.

23. (a)* Find the locus of the point of intersection of two mutually perpendicular normals to the parabola $y^2 = 4ax$ and show that the abscissa of the point can never be smaller than $3a$. What is the ordinate when the abscissa is smallest ?

(b) Find the locus of the point of intersection of normals drawn at the extremities of a focal chord of the parabola $y^2 = 4ax$.

(c)* Prove that the locus of the point of intersection of normals drawn to a parabola $y^2 = 4ax$ at the extremities of a chord which subtends a right angle at the vertex is $y^2 = 16a(x - 6a)$.

24. (a)* If the tangents at two points of a parabola $y^2 = 4ax$ intersect in (h, k), then the corresponding normals intersect in the point $\left(2a - h + \frac{k^2}{a}, -\frac{hk}{a}\right)$.

(b) The point of intersection of normals at points A and B of a parabola $y^2 = 4ax$ lies on the line $y = -a$ then prove that the point of intersection of tangents at A and B will lie on the curve $xy = a^2$.

25. (a)* If the normal at any point $P(at_1^2, 2at_1)$ meets the curve again in $Q(at_2^2, 2at_2)$, then prove that $t_2 = -t_1 - 2/t_1$.
Also prove that minimum value of t_2^2 is 8.

(b) The normal chord of a parabola $y^2 = 4ax$ at the point (p, p) subtends a right angle at the focus.

26. Prove that the normal to $y^2 = 12x$ at (3, 6) meets the parabola again in (27, – 18) and the circle on the normal chord as diameter is $x^2 + y^2 - 30x + 12y - 27 = 0$.

27. In the parabola $y^2 = 4ax$ the tangent at the point P, whose abscissa is equal to the latus rectum meets the axis in T and the normal at P cuts the curve again in Q. Prove that $PT : PQ = 4 : 5$.

28. (a)* A variable chord PQ of the parabola $y^2 = 4x$ is drawn parallel to the line $y = x$. If the parameter of the points P and Q on the parabola be t_1 and t_2 respectively then $t_1 + t_2 = 2$. Also show that the locus of the point of intersection of the normals, at P and Q is $2x - y = 12a$, which is itself a normal to the parabola.

(b) PQ is any chord of the parabola $y^2 = 4ax$ whose right bisector meets the axis in M and the ordinate of the mid-point of PQ meets the axis in L then prove that LM is constant and equal to semi-latus rectum of the parabola.

(c)* Tangents at P and Q to a parabola $y^2 = 4ax$ meet a third tangent in R and S. Prove that the middle point of RS lies on the tangent which is parallel to chord PQ.

(d) Through a fixed point P on the parabola perpendicular chords PQ and PR are drawn. Prove that the chrod QR passes through a fixed point.

29. (a)* PQ is a chord of the parabola drawn in a fixed direction. Prove that the locus of the point of intersection of the normals at P and Q is a straight line which is itself a normal to the parabola.

(b)* The ordinates of points P and Q on the parabola $y^2 = 12x$ are in the ratio 1 : 2. Find the locus of the point of intersection of the normals to the parabola at P and Q. **(Roorkee 1998)**

30. (a)* A is a point on the parabola $y^2 = 4ax$. The normal at A cuts the parabola again at the point B. If AB subtends a right angle at the vertex of the parabola, find the slope of AB.

(b) If a normal chord subtends a right angle at the vertex of the parabola $y^2 = 4ax$, show that it is inclined at an angle $\tan^{-1}\sqrt{2}$ to the axis of the parabola.

31. (a) The length of normal chord which subtends an angle of 90° at the vertex of the parabola $y^2 = 4x$ is :

(a) $6\sqrt{3}$ (b) $7\sqrt{2}$
(c) $8\sqrt{2}$ (d) $9\sqrt{2}$

(b) A focal chord of parabola $y^2 = 4x$ is inclined at an angle of $\pi/4$ with the + ive direction of x-axis, then the slope of normal drawn at the ends of focal chord will satisfy the equation :

(a) $m^2 - 2m - 1 = 0$ (b) $m^2 + 2m - 1 = 0$
(c) $m^2 - 1 = 0$ (d) none

(c) If two different tangents of $y^2 = 4x$ are the normals to the parabola $x^2 = 4ay$, then :

(a) $|a| > \frac{1}{2\sqrt{2}}$ (b) $|a| < \frac{1}{2\sqrt{2}}$
(c) $|a| > \frac{1}{\sqrt{2}}$ (d) $|a| < \frac{1}{\sqrt{2}}$

32. (a) P and Q are the points of contact of the tangents drawn from a point T to the parabola $y^2 = 4ax$. If PQ be a normal to the parabola at P, prove that TP is bisected by the directrix.

(b) The normal at any point P of the parabola $y^2 = 4ax$ cuts the curve again in Q. M is the mid-point of PQ. Prove that the product of the ordinates of the points P and M is constant.

33. (a)* The three normals drawn to the parabola $x^2 = 4y$ are cut by the line $y = 2$ in points whose abscissas are in A.P. Prove that the slopes of the tangents at the co-normal points to the parabola are in G.P.

(b) Tangents are drawn to the parabola $y^2 = 4ax$ at the points P and Q whose inclination to the axes are

θ_1 and θ_2. If A be the vertex of the parabola and the circles on AP and AQ as diameters intersect in R and AR be inclined at an angle ϕ to the axis, then prove that $\cot\theta_1 + \cot\theta_2 + 2\tan\phi = 0$

34. (a)* Find the locus of the point such that two of the normals drawn through it to the parabola $y^2 = 4ax$ are perpendicular to each other.

(b)* Find the locus of the point of intersection of those normals to the parabola $x^2 = 8y$ which are at right angles to each other. **(IIT 1997)**

(c)* If $(x_1, y_1), (x_2, y_2), (x_3, y_3)$ be three points on the parabola $y^2 = 4ax$, the normals at which meet in a point, show that $y_1 + y_2 + y_3 = 0$.

(d) Three normals with slopes m_1, m_2 and m_3 are drawn from a point P not on the axis of the parabola $y^2 = 4x$. If $m_1 m_2 = \alpha$, results in the locus of P being a part of the parabola, find the value of α. **(IIT 2003)**

(e) Prove that only two distinct normals can be drawn to the parabola $y^2 = 4x$ from the point $\left(\frac{11}{4}, \frac{1}{4}\right)$.

35. (a)* Show that the locus of a point such that two of the three normals drawn from it to the parabola $y^2 = 4ax$ coincide is $27ay^2 = 4(x-2a)^3$.

(b)* O is the vertex of the parabola $y^2 = 4ax$ such that normals at three points P, Q and R on it pass through the point $S(h, k)$. These normals cut the axis of the parabola in A, B and C such that OA, OB and OC are in A.P. Prove that the locus of the point S is $27ay^2 = 2(x-2a)^3$.

36. (a)* If P, Q, R be three conormal points of the parabola $y^2 = 4ax$ whose normals pass through the point T, then $SP.SQ.SR = a.ST^2$

(b)* If the three normals drawn at three different points on the parabola $y^2 = 4x$ pass through the point (h, k), then prove that $h > 2$.

37. (a)* Determine the locus of a point $P(h, k)$ such that the slopes of three normals drawn to the parabola $y^2 = 4ax$ from P be connected by the relation $\tan^{-1} m_1^2 + \tan^{-1} m_2^2 + \tan^{-1} m_3^2 = \alpha$.

(b)* Prove that from any point (h, k) three normals can be drawn to a parabola. The tangents drawn at the co-normal points A, B, C enclose a triangle PQR. Prove that the abscissas and ordinates of the vertices of the triangle are the roots of the equations

$$x^3 + (h-2a)x^2 - ak^2 = 0 \quad \text{and}$$

$$y^3 - a(h-2a)y + a^2 k = 0 \text{ respectively.}$$

38. (a) For the semi-cubical parabola $x = 2t^3$, $y = 3t^2$, prove that the locus of the point of intersection of perpendicular tangents is $y = x^2 + 1$.

(b) If a circle passess through the feet of the normals drawn from a point to the parabola $y^2 = 4ax$, then it passes through origin as well.

39. (a)* If the normals at P and Q whose parameters are t_1 and t_2 meet on the parabola, then prove that product of their slopes is 2 and the line joining these points will pass through a fixed point on the axes. Also find the locus of mid-point of PQ.

(b)* If the normals at points P and Q intersect on the parabola itself, then ordinates of P and Q are the roots of $y^2 + ky + 8a^2 = 0$ where k is ordinate of the point of intersection of the normals.

(c)* From a point $(at^2, -2at)$ on the parabola $y^2 = 4ax$ two chords PQ and PR are drawn which are normals to the parabola at Q and R respectively. Prove that the equation to QR is $ty = 2(x+2a)$ and if m_1 and m_2 be the slopes of the normals, then $m_1 m_2 = 2$.

(d) Tangents PT and QT to the parabola $y^2 = 4x$ intersect at T and the normals drawn at the points P and Q intersect at the point $R(9, 6)$ on the parabola. Show that the equation of the circle circumscribing the quadrilateral $PTQR$ is $(x-2)(x-9) + (y+3)(y-6) = 0$.

40.* The tangents at P and Q to $y^2 = 4ax$ meet in T and the corresponding normals meet in R. If the locus of T is a straight line parallel to the axis of the parabola prove that the locus of R is a straight line normal to the parabola.

41. Prove that the circle circumscribing the triangle formed by any three tangents to a parabola passes through its focus.

Solutions to Problem Set (3)

1. (a) Any two tangents to a parabola at the points 't_1' and 't_2' are

$$t_1 y = x + at_1^2, \quad t_2 y = x + at_2^2.$$

Since they are perpendicular

$$\frac{1}{t_1} \cdot \frac{1}{t_2} = -1 \quad \text{or} \quad t_1 t_2 = -1$$

Their point of intersection is

$$\{at_1 t_2, a(t_1 + t_2)\} = \{-a, a(t_1 + t_2)\}.$$

Clearly it lies on the directrix $x = -a$.

(b) For a focal chord $t_1 t_2 = -1$. **(§ 2c, P. 966)**. Rest as in Q.1.

2. (a) PQ being focal chord $\Rightarrow t_1 t_2 = -1$

Centre of circle on PQ as diameter is

$$2x = a(t_1^2 + t_2^2), \; 2y = 2a(t_1 + t_2)$$

Now $t_1^2 + t_2^2 = (t_1 + t_2)^2 - 2at_1 t_2$

Eliminate t_1, t_2 $\quad \therefore \; y^2 = 2a(x-a)$

(b) $P(t_1), P'(t_2) \quad \therefore \; t_1 t_2 = -1$ ...(1)

$T_P \quad t_1 y = x + at_1^2, \quad A(0,0), S(a,0)$

$$p_1 p_2 = \frac{at_1^2}{\sqrt{(1+t_1^2)}} \cdot \frac{a + at_1^2}{\sqrt{(1+t_1^2)}} = a^2 t_1^2$$

$p_3 p_4 = a^2 t_2^2$ as above

$\therefore \quad p_1 p_2 p_3 p_4 = a^4 t_1^2 t_2^2 = a^4$, by (1)

(c) $A(0,0), B(at_1^2, 2at_1), C(at_2^2, 2at_2)$

where $t_1 t_2 = -1$ as BC is a focal chord.

$$\Delta = \frac{1}{2}(x_1 y_2 - x_2 y_1) = \frac{1}{2} \cdot 2a^2 \, t_1 t_2 \, (t_1 - t_2)$$

$$= -a^2 \, (t_1 - t_2) \text{ as } t_1 t_2 = -1$$

or $\Delta = a^2 \, (t_1 - t_2)$ ...(I)

Distance of B and C from axis are $2at_1$ and $2at_2$.

$\therefore \quad D = 2a(t_1 - t_2) = 2a \cdot \dfrac{\Delta}{a^2} = \dfrac{2\Delta}{a}$ by (I)

(d) Ans. (c).

Since AB is a focal chord, $\therefore \; t_1 t_2 = -1$ ...(1)

Circle on AB as diameter is

$$(x - at_1^2)(x - at_2^2) + (y - 2at_1)(y - 2at_2) = 0$$

$$x^2 + y^2 - ax(t_1^2 + t_2^2) - 2ay(t_1 + t_2) + a^2 t_1^2 t_2^2 + 4a^2 t_1 t_2 = 0$$

It meets the parabola $y^2 = 4ax$, *i.e.*, $x = aT^2$, $y = 2aT$ in four points A, B, C, D

$$a^2 T^4 + 4a^2 T^2 - a^2 T^2 (t_1^2 + t_2^2) - 4a^2 T (t_1 + t_2) + a^2 (-1)^2 + 4a^2 (-1) = 0$$

$$a^2 T^4 + 0T^3 + a^2 T^2 (4 - t_1^2 - t_2^2) - 4a^2 T (t_1 + t_2) - 3a^2 = 0$$

It is a fourth degree equation in T whose roots are t_1, t_2, t_3, t_4

$\therefore \quad t_1 t_2 t_3 t_4 = -\dfrac{3a^2}{a^2} = -3$. Put $t_1 t_2 = -1$

$\therefore \quad t_3 t_4 = 3 \Rightarrow$ (c).

3. (a) Let the tangents be drawn at the points 't_1' and 't_2' and (h, k) be their point of intersection.

$\therefore \quad h = at_1 t_2, \; k = a(t_1 + t_2)$ ...(1)

(§ 3 (a), P. 975)

Also their equations are

$$t_1 y = x + at_1^2, \quad t_2 y = x + at_2^2$$

Also their slopes are $1/t_1$ and $1/t_2$ ...(2)

If they include an angle α, then

$$\tan \alpha = \frac{\dfrac{1}{t_1} - \dfrac{1}{t_2}}{1 + \dfrac{1}{t_1 t_2}} = \frac{(t_2 - t_1)}{(t_1 t_2 + 1)}$$

or $\tan^2 \alpha \, (1 + t_1 t_2)^2 = \{(t_1 + t_2)^2 - 4t_1 t_2\}$

or $\tan^2 \alpha \left(1 + \dfrac{h}{a}\right)^2 = \left\{\dfrac{k^2}{a^2} - \dfrac{4h}{a}\right\}$

or $\tan^2 \alpha \, (h + a)^2 = (k^2 - 4ah)$

Hence the required locus is

$$(x + a)^2 \tan^2 \alpha = y^2 - 4ax.$$

In case the tangents include an angle of $45°$ then $\tan 45° = 1$, we get the locus as

$$(x + a)^2 = y^2 - 4ax. \quad \text{...(A)}$$

In case the tangents include a right angle, then $\tan 90° = \infty$, we get the locus as $x + a = 0$ *i.e.* directrix as shown in Q. 1 (a), (b).

(b) Locus is $(x + a)^2 = y^2 - 4ax$ as in (A).

or $x^2 - y^2 + 6ax + a^2 = 0$

or $(x + 3a)^2 - y^2 = 8a^2$

Above represents a hyperbola.

(c) $t_1 y = x + at_1^2, t_2 y = x + at_2^2$.

Here $4a = 8$ or $a = 2$

$h = at_1 t_2, \quad k = a(t_1 + t_2)$

or $h = 2t_1 t_2, \; k = 2(t_1 + t_2)$ ...(1)

Point of intersection of tangents with tangent at the vertex $x = 0$ are $P(0, at_1), Q(0, at_2)$.

$PQ = 4 \quad \therefore \quad a(t_1 - t_2) = 4$

or $(t_1 - t_2) = 2$ as $a = 2$

or $(t_1 + t_2)^2 - 4t_1 t_2 = 4$

or $\dfrac{k^2}{4} - \dfrac{4h}{2} = 4$, by (1)

$\therefore$ Locus is $y^2 = 8(x + 2)$.

4. (a) Let A, B, C be the points $(at_1^2, 2at_1)$ etc. Let P, Q, R be the points of intersection of tangents at B, C; C, A and A, B.

$\therefore \quad P = \{at_2 t_3, a(t_2 + t_3)\}$ etc.

$$\text{Area of } \Delta\, ABC = \frac{1}{2} \begin{vmatrix} at_1^2 & 2at_1 & 1 \\ at_2^2 & 2at_2 & 1 \\ at_3^2 & 2at_3 & 1 \end{vmatrix} \quad \begin{matrix} \text{Apply} \\ R_1 - R_2 \\ R_2 - R_3 \end{matrix}$$

$$= \frac{1}{2} \cdot a \cdot 2a \begin{vmatrix} t_1^2 - t_2^2 & t_1 - t_2 & 0 \\ t_2^2 - t_3^2 & t_2 - t_3 & 0 \\ at_3^2 & 2at_3 & 1 \end{vmatrix}$$

$$= a^2 \cdot (t_1 - t_2)(t_2 - t_3) \begin{vmatrix} t_1 + t_2 & 1 \\ t_2 + t_3 & 1 \end{vmatrix}$$

$$= a^2 \, (t_1 - t_2)(t_2 - t_3)(t_1 - t_3)$$

$$= a^2 \, (t_1 - t_2)(t_2 - t_3)(t_3 - t_1)$$

Area of $\Delta\, PQR$

$$= \frac{1}{2} \begin{vmatrix} at_2 t_3 & a(t_2 + t_3) & 1 \\ at_3 t_1 & a(t_3 + t_1) & 1 \\ at_1 t_2 & a(t_1 + t_2) & 1 \end{vmatrix}$$

Apply $R_1 - R_3$ and $R_2 - R_3$

$$=\frac{1}{2}a.a\begin{vmatrix} t_3(t_2-t_1) & (t_2-t_1) & 0 \\ t_1(t_3-t_2) & (t_3-t_2) & 0 \\ at_1t_2 & a(t_1+t_2) & 1 \end{vmatrix}$$

$$=\frac{1}{2}a^2.(t_2-t_1)(t_3-t_2)\begin{vmatrix} t_3 & 1 \\ t_1 & 1 \end{vmatrix}$$

$$=\frac{1}{2}a^2(t_2-t_1)(t_3-t_2)(t_3-t_1)$$

$$=\frac{1}{2}a^2(t_1-t_2)(t_2-t_3)(t_3-t_1)=\frac{1}{2}\Delta ABC.$$

$\therefore \quad \Delta ABC = 2\Delta PQR$

(b) Area of Δ formed by three tangents at t_1, t_2 and t_3 by part (a) is

$$\frac{1}{2}a^2(t_1-t_2)(t_2-t_3)(t_3-t_1) \qquad ...(1)$$

Slope of the tangent $ty = x + at^2$ is $\frac{1}{t}$

$\therefore \quad \frac{1}{t_1}, \frac{1}{t_2}, \frac{1}{t_3}$ are in H.P. or t_1, t_2, t_3 are in A.P.

If d be the common difference, then from (1)

$$\Delta = \frac{1}{2}a^2(-d)(-d)(2d) = a^2d^3 \text{ i.e. constant.}$$

(c) $A(at_1^2, 2at_1), B(at_2^2, 2at_2), C\{at_1t_2, a(t_1+t_2)\}$

$$\therefore \quad \Delta = \frac{1}{2}.a.a\begin{vmatrix} t_1^2 & 2t_1 & 1 \\ t_2^2 & 2t_2 & 1 \\ t_1t_2 & t_1+t_2 & 1 \end{vmatrix}$$

Make two zeros and expand.

$$\therefore \quad \Delta = \frac{1}{2}a^2(t_2-t_1)^3$$

5. **Refer result § 3 (b) P. 975**. The point of intersection of normals at t_1 and t_2 is

$\{2a + a(t_1^2 + t_2^2 + t_1t_2), -at_1t_2(t_1+t_2)\} = R$, say

Hence the area of the triangle PQR formed by these normals at t_1, t_2 and t_3 is

$$=\frac{1}{2}\begin{vmatrix} 2a+a(t_1^2+t_2^2+t_1t_2) & -at_1t_2(t_1+t_2) & 1 \\ — & — & — \\ — & — & — \end{vmatrix}$$

Apply $C_1 - 2aC_3$, so that $2a$ cancels from C_1. Take a and $-a$ common from C_1 and C_2

$$\therefore \quad \Delta = -\frac{a^2}{2}\begin{vmatrix} t_1^2+t_2^2+t_1t_2 & t_1t_2(t_1+t_2) & 1 \\ — & — & 1 \\ — & — & 1 \end{vmatrix}$$

Apply $R_2 - R_1$ and $R_3 - R_1$ thus making two zeros.

$$\therefore \quad \Delta = -\frac{a^2}{2}\begin{vmatrix} t_1^2+t_2^2+t_1t_2 & t_1t_2(t_1+t_2) & 1 \\ (t_3-t_1)\Sigma t_1 & t_2(t_3-t_1)\Sigma t_1 & 0 \\ (t_3-t_2)\Sigma t_1 & t_1(t_3-t_2)\Sigma t_1 & 0 \end{vmatrix}$$

$$=-\frac{a^2}{2}(t_3-t_1)\Sigma t_1.(t_3-t_2)\Sigma t_1\begin{vmatrix} 1 & t_2 \\ 1 & t_1 \end{vmatrix}$$

$$=\frac{a^2}{2}(\Sigma t_1)^2(t_1-t_2)(t_2-t_3)(t_3-t_1)$$

Also $\Delta' = \frac{a^2}{2}(t_1-t_2)(t_2-t_3)(t_3-t_1)$ by part (a)

$\therefore \quad \Delta = \Delta'(\Sigma t_1)^2$

6. (a) Let PSQ be a focal chord where the points P and Q be t_1 and t_2. Since the chord is focal, we have $t_1t_2 = -1$ **by (c) P. 967** ...(1)

$$PSQ = PS + SQ = (a + x_P) + (a + x_Q) \quad \textbf{(P. 967)}$$

$$= 2a + a(t_1^2 + t_2^2) = a\left[2 + t_1^2 + \frac{1}{t_1^2}\right] \text{ by (1)}$$

$$= a\left[t_1 + \frac{1}{t_1}\right]^2$$

(b) We have to prove that lp^2 = constant, where

$$l = PQ = a\left(t_1 + \frac{1}{t_1}\right)^2 \text{ by part (a).}$$

Also chord PQ is $y(t_1+t_2) - 2x - 2at_1t_2 = 0$

$$p = -\frac{2at_1t_2}{\sqrt{[(t_1+t_2)^2+4]}} \quad \therefore \quad p^2 = \frac{4a^2}{\left(t_1+\frac{1}{t_1}\right)^2}$$

As $t_1t_2 = -1$ for focal chord

Clearly $l.p^2 = 4a^3$ i.e. constant.

7. (a) PQ being focal chord, $t_1t_2 = -1$ or $t_2 = -1/t_1$. If (x, y) be the centroid of ΔAPQ, then

$$3x = a\left(t_1^2 + \frac{1}{t_1^2}\right), 3y = 2a\left(t_1 - \frac{1}{t_1}\right)$$

Eliminating t_1, we get

$$9y^2 = 4a(3x - 2a)$$

or $\quad y^2 = \frac{4a.3}{9}\left(x - \frac{2a}{3}\right)$

It is a parabola whose L.R. is $\frac{12}{9}a = \frac{4}{3}a$.

(b) SP and SQ are segments of a focal chord PSQ.

$\therefore \quad SP = a + at_1^2, SQ = a + t_2^2$

or $\quad SQ = a + a\frac{1}{t_1^2} = \frac{a(1+t_1^2)}{t_1^2}$, as $t_1t_2 = -1$

$$\therefore \quad \frac{1}{SP} + \frac{1}{SQ} = \frac{1}{a(1+t_1^2)} + \frac{t_1^2}{a(1+t_1^2)}$$

$$= \frac{1}{a} = \frac{2}{2a} = \frac{2}{\text{Semi L.R.}}$$

$\therefore \quad \frac{1}{SP}, \frac{1}{\text{Semi L.R.}}, \frac{1}{SQ}$ are in A.P.

or $\quad SP$, Semi L.R., SQ are in H.P.

***i. e.* Semi L.R. is H.M. of segments *SP*, *SQ*.**

(c) We know that l = H.M. of the segments SP and SQ of a focal chord PSQ

$\therefore \quad l = \frac{2.3.2}{2+3} = \frac{12}{5} \quad \therefore$ L.R. $= 2l = \frac{24}{5}$

8. Let P be $(at^2, 2at)$ and tangent at this point is $ty = x + at^2$. It meets the directrix, $x = -a$ in T whose co-ordinates are $\left(-a, \frac{at^2 - a}{t}\right)$ and S is $(a, 0)$.

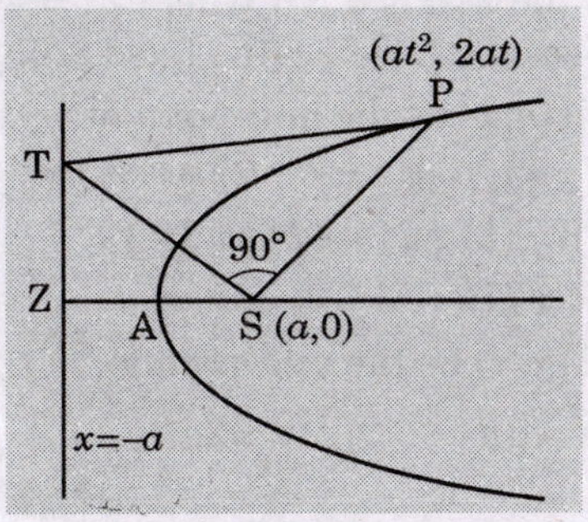

Fig. 17

We have to prove that PT subtends a right angle at the focus $S(a, 0)$ *i.e.* PS is perpendicular to TS.

Slope of $PS = \frac{2at}{a(t^2 - 1)} = m_1$.

Slope of $TS = \frac{(at^2 - a)/t}{(-a - a)}$

$= \frac{a(t^2 - 1)}{-2at} = m_2$

Clearly $m_1 m_2 = \frac{2at}{a(t^2 - 1)} \times \frac{a(t^2 - 1)}{-2at} = -1$.

Hence the two lines are perpendicular.

9. Tangent at $P(at^2, 2at)$ is $ty = x + at^2$

It meets the axis, $y = 0$ at $T(-at^2, 0)$, S is $(a, 0)$

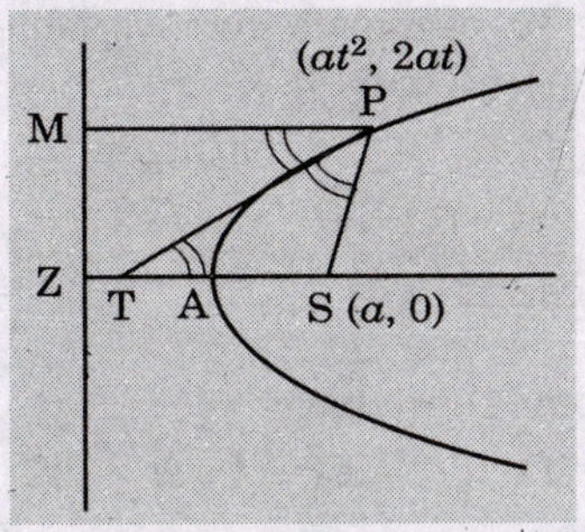

Fig. 18

$\therefore \quad ST = a(1 + t^2)$. Also $SP = a + x = a + at^2$

$\therefore \quad SP = ST$.

$\therefore \quad \angle SPT = \angle PTS$ ...(1)

Also $\angle PTS = \angle MPT$ as ST and PM are parallel

$\therefore \quad \angle SPT = \angle MPT$ showing that tangent at P bisects the angle between SP and PM.

Normal being perpendicular to tangent will also bisect.

10. Tangent is $ty = x + at^2$ ...(1)

slope $= 1/t$.

Any line ⊥ to tangent and passing through the focus is

$y - 0 = -t(x - a)$

or $\quad y = -tx + at$. ...(2)

Solving (1) and (2), we find the co-ordinates of the point of intersection as $(0, at)$ and clearly it lies on the line $x = 0$ *i.e.* tangent at the vertex for all values of t.

11. Normal at $P(at^2, 2at)$ is

$y = -tx + 2at + at^3$.

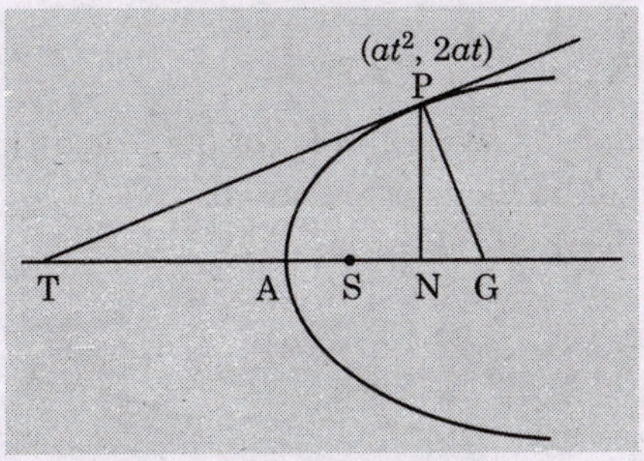

Fig. 19

It meets axis, $y = 0$ at $G(2a + at^2, 0)$

Also N is $(at^2, 0)$

or $\quad NG = 2a + at^2 - at^2 = 2a$

$=$ semi-latus rectum.

12. P is $(at^2, 2at)$, S is $(a, 0)$, G is $(2a + at^2, 0)$

$SP = a + x = a + at^2 = a(1 + t^2)$

$SG = 2a + at^2 - a = a(1 + t^2) = SP$.

Thus P and G are equidistant from the focus.

13. P is $(at^2, 2at)$, G is $(2a + at^2, 0)$

$\therefore \quad PG^2 = 4a^2 + 4a^2t^2$ ...(1)

Q is a point on the parabola such that QG is perpendicular to axis so that its ordinate is QG and abscissa is same as of G.

Hence the point Q is $(2a + at^2, QG)$

But Q lies on the parabola $y^2 = 4ax$

$\therefore \quad QG^2 = 4a(2a + at^2) = 8a^2 + 4a^2t^2$ ...(2)

$\therefore \quad QG^2 - PG^2 = 4a^2$

i.e. constant by (1) and (2).

14. Let $P(at_1^2, 2at_1)$, $Q(at_2^2, 2at_2)$ be a focal chord so that $t_1 t_2 = -1$.

Tangent at P is $t_1 y = x + at_1^2$ and slope $= 1/t_1 = m$.

Normal at Q is $y = -t_2 x + 2at_2 + at_2^3$ and slope $= -t_2 = 1/t_1$ by (1) and (2).

Since the slopes are equal and as such they are parallel.

15. (a) AB subtends a right angle at the vertex

$\therefore \quad t_1 t_2 = -4$ **(by (c_1) P. 967)** ...(1)

If (h, k) be the point of intersection of tangents at A and B, then

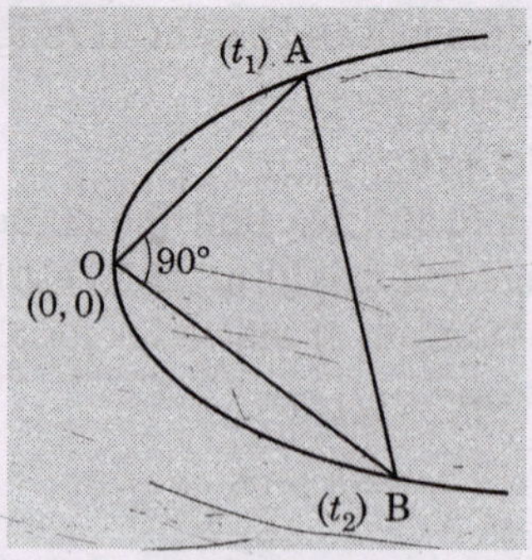

Fig. 20

$h = at_1t_2, \quad k = a(t_1 + t_2)$ or $h = -4a$ by (1)

Hence the locus is $x + 4a = 0$.

(b) $P \quad h = at_1t_2, k = a(t_1 + t_2)$

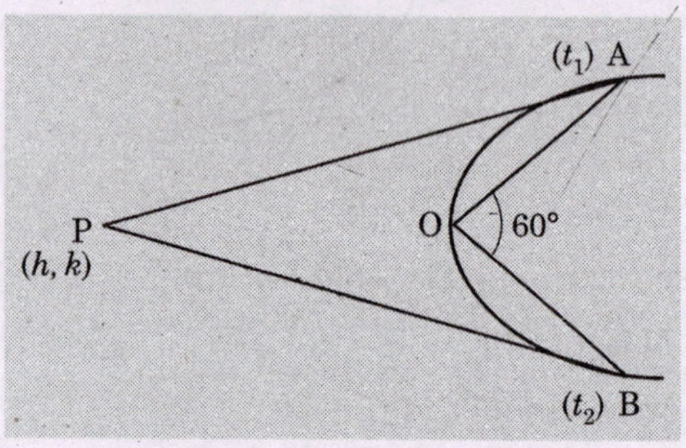

Fig. 21

Also slopes of OA and OB are $\frac{2}{t_1}, \frac{2}{t_2}$

$\therefore \quad \tan 60° = \left(\frac{2}{t_1} - \frac{2}{t_2}\right) \Big/ \left(1 + \frac{2}{t_1} \cdot \frac{2}{t_2}\right)$

$\therefore \quad (t_1t_2 + 4)^2 \cdot 3 = 4(t_1 - t_2)^2$

$= 4\{(t_1 + t_2)^2 - 4t_1t_2\}$

Now put for $t_1 + t_2$ and t_1t_2 and generalise h, k

16. (a) $OA \perp OB \Rightarrow t_1t_2 = -4$ **[(c$_1$) P. 967]** ...(1)

If C is (h, k), then the diagonals of a rectangle bisect each other.

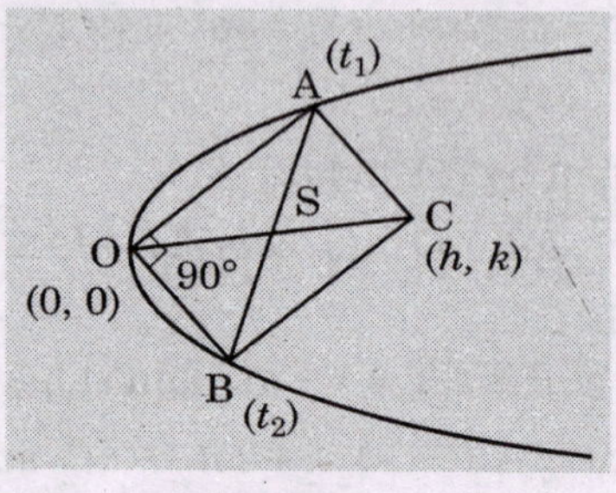

Fig. 22

$h + 0 = a(t_1^2 + t_2^2)$
$k + 0 = 2a(t_1 + t_2)$

$\therefore \quad h = a[(t_1 + t_2)^2 - 2t_1t_2] = a\left[\frac{k^2}{4a^2} + 8\right]$

or $\quad (h - 8a) = \frac{k^2}{4a}$

$\therefore \quad$ Locus is $y^2 = 4a(x - 8a)$.

(b) **By (c$_1$) P. 967**, $t_1t_2 = -4$ as OP and OQ are at right angles. Equation of PQ is

$y(t_1 + t_2) - 2x - 2at_1t_2 = 0.$

It cuts the x-axis $y = 0$ where $2x = -2at_1t_2 = 8a$

$\therefore \; x = 4$ as $a = 1$. Hence the fixed point is $(4, 0)$.

Again if (h, k) be the mid-point of PQ, its equation is $k(y - k) = 2a(x - h)$. It passes through (4, 0)

$\therefore \quad k(0 - k) = 2(4 - h)$ as $a = 1$

or $\quad k^2 = 2(h - 4) \quad \therefore$ Locus is $y^2 = 2(x - 4)$

Alt. : If (x, y) be the mid-point of PQ, then

$2x = a(t_1^2 + t_2^2), 2y = 2a(t_1 + t_2)$

or $\quad 2x = a[(t_1 + t_2)^2 - 2t_1t_2] = a\left[\frac{y^2}{a^2} + 8\right]$, by (1)

or $\quad 2ax = y^2 + 8a^2$ or $y^2 = 2(x - 4)$ as $a = 1$.

(c) $y^2 = 4ax = 4x \quad \therefore \quad a = 1$

$P = (t_1^2, 2t_1)$ and $Q = (t_2^2, 2t_2)$

If $R(x, y)$ be the point R which divides PQ in the ratio 1 : 2, then

$$x = \frac{t_2^2 + 2t_1^2}{3} \qquad ...(1)$$

$$y = \frac{2t_2 + 4t_1}{3} \qquad ...(2)$$

Also slope of chord PQ whose equation is

$y(t_1 + t_2) - 2x - 2t_1t_2 = 0$ (formula $a = 1$)

is $\quad \frac{2}{t_1 + t_2} = 2$ (given) $\quad \therefore \quad t_1 + t_2 = 1 \quad$ ...(3)

We have to eliminate two variables t_1 and t_2 between (1), (2) and (3).

$t_2 = 1 - t_1$ from (3) and putting in (2), we get

$3y = 2(1 - t_1) + 4t_1 = 2(1 + t_1)$

$$\therefore \quad t_1 = \frac{3y - 2}{2} \qquad ...(4)$$

Again from (1), we have

$3x = (1 - t_1)^2 + 2t_1^2 = 1 - 2t_1 + 3t_1^2$

Now put for t_1 from (4) in the above

$3x = 1 - (3y - 2) + 3\left[\frac{9y^2 - 12y + 4}{4}\right]$

or $\quad 3x = 3 - 3y + \frac{3}{4}(9y^2 - 12y + 4)$

or $\quad 4x = 4 - 4y + 9y^2 - 12y + 4$

or $\quad \frac{4x}{9} = y^2 - \frac{16}{9}y + \frac{8}{9} = \left(y - \frac{8}{9}\right)^2 - \frac{64}{81} + \frac{8}{9}$

or $\frac{4x}{9}=\left(y-\frac{8}{9}\right)^2+\frac{8}{81}$

or $\left(y-\frac{8}{9}\right)^2=\frac{4}{9}\left(x-\frac{2}{9}\right)$.

Above represents a parabola with vertex at $\left(\frac{2}{9},\frac{8}{9}\right)$

17. (a) As in **Q. 14** let PQ be the focal chord so that $t_1t_2=-1$.

Circle on PQ as diameter is

$$(x-at_1^2)(x-at_2^2)+(y-2at_1)(y-2at_2)=0.$$

Put $t_2=-\frac{1}{t_1}$

$$(x-at_1^2)\left(x-\frac{a}{t_1^2}\right)+(y-2at_1)\left(y+\frac{2a}{t_1}\right)=0. \quad ...(1)$$

If the above circle touches the directrix then its intersection with the directrix $x=-a$ should give two coincident points. Putting $x=-a$ in (1), we get

$$a^2(1+t_1^2)\times\left(1+\frac{1}{t_1^2}\right)+y^2-2ay\left(t_1-\frac{1}{t_1}\right)-4a^2=0$$

or $y^2-2ay\left(t_1-\frac{1}{t_1}\right)+a^2\left(1+t_1^2+\frac{1}{t_1^2}+1-4\right)=0$

or $y^2-2ay\left(t_1-\frac{1}{t_1}\right)+a^2\left(t_1^2+\frac{1}{t_1^2}-2\right)=0$

or $y^2-2ay\left(t_1-\frac{1}{t_1}\right)+a^2\left(t_1-\frac{1}{t_1}\right)^2=0$

or $\left\{y-a\left(t_1-\frac{1}{t_1}\right)\right\}^2=0$

Above gives us two equal values of y. Thus the directrix $x=-a$ cuts the circle in two coincident points. Hence it touches the circle.

(b) Proceed as above.

18. Normal at $P(at^2, 2at)$ is $y=-tx+2at+at^3$

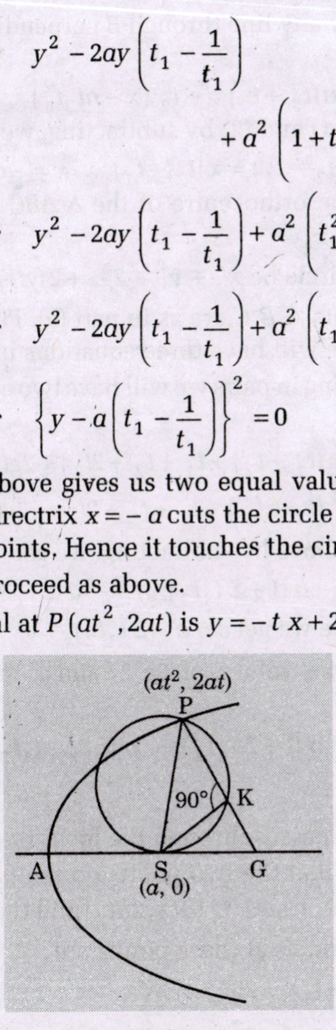

Fig. 23

or $y+tx-2at-at^3=0$ ...(1)

$SP=a+x=a+at^2=a(1+t^2)$ ...(2)

Let the circle cut the normal at K. Since SP is a diameter, therefore

$\angle SKP=90°$.

Hence SK is perpendicular distance of $S(a,0)$ from the normal.

$\therefore \quad SK=\frac{0+at-2at-at^3}{\sqrt{(1+t^2)}}=-at\sqrt{(1+t^2)}$ ...(3)

$\therefore \quad PK^2=SP^2-SK^2$

$=a^2(1+t^2)^2-a^2t^2(1+t^2)$

$=a^2(1+t^2)[1+t^2-t^2]=a^2(1+t^2)$

$\therefore \quad PK=a\sqrt{(1+t^2)}=$ Intercept on normal.

19. (a) Let L, M, N be the points t_1, t_2 and t_3 respectively whose ordinates $2at_1, 2at_2, 2at_3$ are in G.P.

$\therefore \quad t_2^2=t_1t_3$ ...(1)

Also tangents at L and N intersect at (h,k) then

$h=at_1t_3, k=a(t_1+t_3)$

$\therefore \quad h=at_2^2 \quad \therefore$ Locus is $x=at_2^2$.

But this is the equation of the ordinate of the point $M(at_2^2, 2at_2)$

(b) Let P and Q be two points t_1 and t_2 respectively whose abscissas are in the ratio $\mu:1$.

$\therefore \quad \frac{at_1^2}{at_2^2}=\frac{\mu}{1}$ or $t_1=t_2\sqrt{(\mu)}$ ...(1)

If (h,k) be the point of intersection of tangents at P and Q, then

$h=at_1t_2 \qquad k=a(t_1+t_2)$

or $h=a\sqrt{(\mu)}\,t_2^2 \qquad k=a(1+\sqrt{\mu})\,t_2$

Eliminate t_2. $\therefore \quad k^2=a^2(1+\sqrt{\mu})^2t_2^2$

or $k^2=a^2(1+\sqrt{\mu})^2\frac{h}{a\sqrt{\mu}}$

or $k^2=ah\left(\frac{1+\mu+2\sqrt{\mu}}{\sqrt{\mu}}\right)$

or $k^2=ah(\mu^{1/2}+\mu^{-1/2}+2)$.

Generalizing, the locus is

$$y^2=ax(\mu^{1/4}+\mu^{-1/4})^2.$$

20. (a) Let P and Q be the points t_1 and t_2 respectively.

$SP=a+x=a+at_1^2, SQ=a+x=a+at_2^2$

$\therefore \quad SP.SQ=a^2(1+t_1^2)(1+t_2^2).$ ...(1)

We know that tangents at P and Q intersect at T, then T is

$[at_1t_2, a(t_1+t_2)]$ and S is $(a,0)$

$\therefore \quad ST^2=a^2(1-t_1t_2)^2+a^2(t_1+t_2)^2$

$=a^2(1+t_1^2t_2^2-2t_1t_2+t_1^2+t_2^2+2t_1t_2)$

$= a^2 [1 + t_1^2 + t_2^2 + t_1^2 t_2^2]$

$= a^2 (1 + t_1^2)(1 + t_2^2) = SP.SQ$ by (1)

(b) Let Q be $(at_1^2, 2at_1)$ and R be $(at_2^2, 2at_2)$

$\therefore$ P is $\{at_1 t_2, a(t_1 + t_2)\}$ i.e. $T_Q \times T_R$

Let any tangent to the parabola be $y = mx + \frac{a}{m}$

$$p_2 = \frac{mat_1^2 - 2at_1 + a/m}{\sqrt{(1+m^2)}}$$

$$= \frac{a}{m\sqrt{(1+m^2)}} [m^2 t_1^2 - 2mt_1 + 1]$$

$$= \frac{a}{m\sqrt{(1+m^2)}} [mt_1 - 1]^2 \quad ...(1)$$

Similarly $p_3 = \frac{a}{m\sqrt{(1+m^2)}} [mt_2 - 1]^2$ ...(2)

$$p_1 = \frac{mat_1 t_2 - a(t_1 + t_2) + a/m}{\sqrt{(1+m^2)}}$$

$$= \frac{a}{m\sqrt{(1+m^2)}} [m^2 t_1 t_2 - m(t_1 + t_2) + 1]$$

$$= \frac{a}{m\sqrt{(1+m^2)}} [(mt_1 - 1)(mt_2 - 1)] \quad ...(3)$$

Now it is clear that $p_1^2 = p_2 p_3$ by (1), (2) and (3)

p_1 is G.M. of p_2 and p_3.

21. P is $(at_1^2, 2at_1)$, Q is $(at_2^2, 2at_2)$

T is $\{at_1 t_2, a(t_1 + t_2)\}$, S is $(a, 0)$

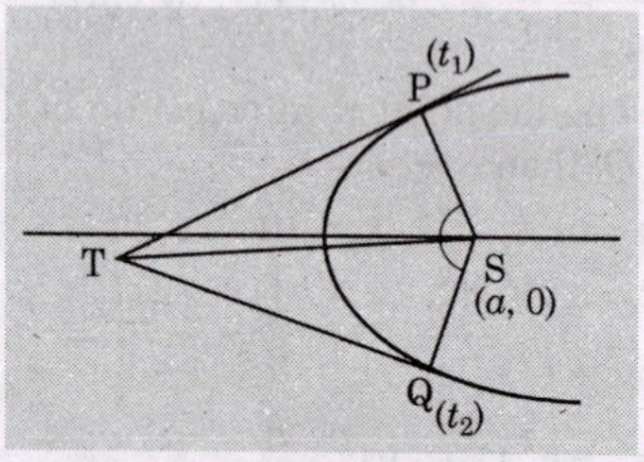

Fig. 24

Slope of $SP = \frac{2at_1 - 0}{at_1^2 - a} = \frac{2t_1}{t_1^2 - 1} = m_1$.

Slope of $SQ = \frac{2t_2}{t_2^2 - 1} = m_2$.

Slope of $ST = \frac{a(t_1 + t_2) - 0}{at_1 t_2 - a} = \frac{t_1 + t_2}{t_1 t_2 - 1} = m_3$.

Put $t_1 = \tan\alpha$ and $t_2 = \tan\beta$

$m_1 = -\tan 2\alpha$, $m_2 = -\tan 2\beta$,

$m_3 = -\tan(\alpha + \beta)$

SP, SQ, ST make angles $-2\alpha, -2\beta, -(\alpha + \beta)$ with x-axis.

$\therefore$ $\angle TSP = -2\alpha + (\alpha + \beta) = \beta - \alpha$

$\angle TSQ = -2\beta + (\alpha + \beta) = \alpha - \beta$

$\therefore$ $\angle TSP = \angle TSQ$ numerically

i.e. equal on opposite sides.

Thus TP and TQ subtend equal angles at the focus S.

22. (a) Let any three tangents to the parabola at t_1, t_2, t_3 be

$BC \equiv t_1 y = x + at_1^2$, $CA \equiv t_2 y = x + at_2^2$,

$AB \equiv t_3 y = x + at_3^2$.

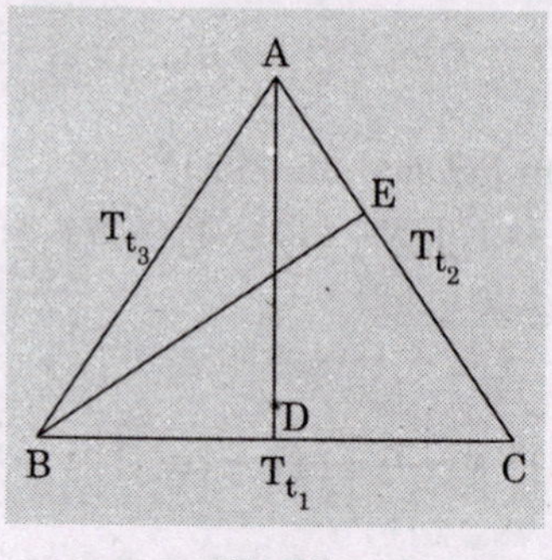

Fig. 25

These tangents form a triangle ABC.

Their points of intersection in pairs are

$A[at_2 t_3, a(t_2 + t_3)], B, \ldots C, \ldots$

Any line through A and perpendicular to side BC is

$$y - a(t_2 + t_3) = -t_1 (x - at_2 t_3) \quad ...(1)$$

Similarly any line through B perpendicular to CA is

$$y - a(t_3 + t_1) = -t_2 (x - at_3 t_1) \quad ...(2)$$

Solving (1) and (2) by subtracting, we get

$-a(t_2 - t_1) = x(t_2 - t_1)$ $\therefore$ $x = -a$.

Hence the orthocentre of the $\Delta\, ABC$ lies on the directrix.

(b) Let the circle be $x^2 + y^2 + 2gx + 2fy + c = 0$.

The points A, B, C are as in part (a). Putting these points we will have three equations in g, f, c. Subtracting in pairs we will have two equations in g and f:

$$a\{t_3^2 (t_1 + t_2) + t_1 + t_2 + 2t_3\} + 2gt_3 + 2f = 0$$

$$a\{t_1^2 (t_2 + t_3) + t_2 + t_3 + 2t_1\} + 2gt_1 + 2f = 0$$

Solving above by subtracting, we get

$2g = -a\{1 + \Sigma t_1 t_2\}$, $2f = -a\{\Sigma t_1 - t_1 t_2 t_3\}$

and hence we get $c = a^2 (\Sigma t_1 t_2)$

Putting the values of $2g, 2f$ and c, the required circle is

$$x^2 + y^2 - a\{1 + \Sigma t_1 t_2\}x - a\{\Sigma t_1 - t_1 t_2 t_3\}y + a^2 (\Sigma t_1 t_2) = 0$$

It clearly passes through the focus $(a, 0)$.

23. (a) Suppose that the two points on the parabola are $P(at_1^2, 2at_1)$ and $Q(at_2^2, 2at_2)$ and the equations of the normals at these points are

$$y = -t_1 x + 2at_1 + at_1^3 \quad ...(1)$$

$$y = -t_2 x + 2at_2 + at_2^3 \quad ...(2)$$

Since the normals are perpendicular.

$\therefore \quad (-t_1)(-t_2) = -1$ or $t_1 t_2 = -1$ ...(3)

If (h, k) be their point of intersection then solving (1) and (2)

$$h = 2a + a(t_1^2 + t_2^2 + t_1 t_2),$$

$$k = -at_1 t_2 (t_1 + t_2).$$

We have to eliminate t_1 and t_2 by the help of (3) to get the locus.

$$k = a(t_1 + t_2) \quad \because \; t_1 t_2 = -1$$

$$h - 2a = a[(t_1 + t_2)^2 - t_1 t_2] = a\left[\frac{k^2}{a^2} + 1\right]$$

or $\quad a(h - 3a) = k^2$

Hence the locus is $y^2 = a(x - 3a)$.

Now for real values of k, h will always be greater than or equal to $3a$.

i.e. abscissa h can never be smaller than $3a$. Its minimum value can be $3a$ and in that case the ordinate k will be zero. The equation $y^2 = a(x - 3a)$ represents a parabola whose vertex is the point $(3a, 0)$ and latus rectum is equal to a. *i.e.* one-fourth of the latus rectum of the original parabola.

(b) Chord being focal, $t_1 t_2 = -1$ **by (c) P. 966**. Rest as in part (a).

Ans. $y^2 = a(x - 3a)$

(c) Here PQ subtends a right angle at the vertex therefore $t_1 t_2 = -4$, **by (c_1) P. 967** Rest as in parts (a) and (b).

24. (a) For tangents $h = at_1 t_2$, $k = a(t_1 + t_2)$

For normals $x = 2a + a(t_1^2 + t_2^2 + t_1 t_2)$,

$$y = -at_1 t_2 (t_1 + t_2)$$

or $\quad x = 2a + a[(t_1 + t_2)^2 - t_1 t_2] = 2a - h + \dfrac{k^2}{a}$

$$y = -\frac{hk}{a}.$$

(b) Point of intersection of normals at t_1, t_2 lies on $y = -a \; \therefore \; -at_1 t_2 (t_1 + t_2) = -a$

or $\quad t_1 t_2 (t_1 + t_2) = 1$ ...(1)

Point of intersection of tangents is

$$x = at_1 t_2, \; y = a(t_1 + t_2)$$

$\therefore \quad xy = a^2 . 1 = a^2$, by (1)

25. (a) Normal at $P(at_1^2, 2at_1)$ is

$$y = -t_1 x + 2at_1 + at_1^3. \qquad ...(1)$$

It meets the curve again at the point $Q(at_2^2, 2at_2)$ and hence its co-ordinates will satisfy (1)

$\therefore \quad 2at_2 = -t_1 . at_2^2 + 2at_1 + at_1^3$

or $\quad 2a(t_2 - t_1) = at_1 (t_1^2 - t_2^2)$

or $\quad -2 = t_1 (t_1 + t_2)$

or $\quad t_2 = -t_1 - \dfrac{2}{t_1}$ **(Remember)** **(V. Imp.)**

From above we have $t_1^2 + t_1 t_2 + 2 = 0$

Above is a quadratic in t_1 and since t_1 is real

$\therefore \quad \Delta \geq 0$

or $\quad t_2^2 - 8 \geq 0 \; \therefore \; t_2^2 \geq 8.$

Hence minimum value of t_2^2 is 8.

(b) Since $x = y$ for (p, p)

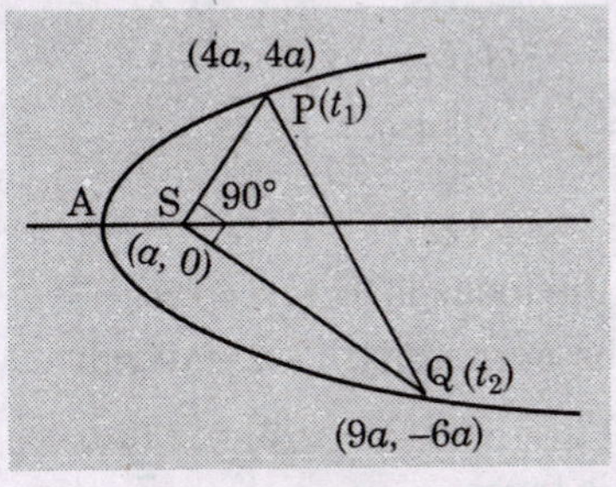

Fig. 26

$\therefore \quad at_1^2 = 2at_1$ or $t_1 = 2$

$\therefore \quad P$ is $(4a, 4a)$. For normal chord

$$t_2 = -t_1 - \frac{2}{t_1} = -3$$

$\therefore \quad Q$ is $(9a, -6a)$

Now you have to prove that $\angle PSQ = 90^\circ$

Apply $m_1 m_2 = -1$ for $PS \perp QS$.

26. Do yourself.

27. Let the points P and Q be $(at_1^2, 2at_1)$ and $(at_2^2, 2at_2)$ respectively.

Abscissa of $P =$ latus retum $= 4a$.

$\therefore \quad at_1^2 = 4a$ or $t_1^2 = 4 \; \therefore \; t_1 = 2$ say.

Again normal at P cuts the curve again at Q, hence as in **Q. 25**,

$$t_2 = -t_1 - \frac{2}{t_1} = -2 - \frac{2}{2} = -3$$

Putting $t_1 = 2$ and $t_2 = -3$ the points P and Q are $(4a, 4a)$, $(9a, -6a)$ respectively.

Again tangent at P is $t_1 y = x + at_1^2$.

It meets the axis, $y = 0$ in $T(at_1^2, 0)$ or $(-4a, 0)$ is the point T.

$\therefore \quad PT^2 = (4a + 4a)^2 + (4a - 0)^2 = 80a^2$

$\therefore \quad PT = 4\sqrt{5}a.$

$\quad PQ^2 = (4a - 9a)^2 + (4a + 6a)^2 = 125a^2$

$\therefore \quad PQ = 5\sqrt{5}a$

$\therefore \quad PT : PQ = 4 : 5.$

28. (a) Equation of the chord; PQ joining the points t_1 and t_2 is $y(t_1 + t_2) - 2x - 2at_1 t_2 = 0$.

Its slope is $\dfrac{2}{t_1 + t_2}$.

Since it is parallel to the line $y = x$ whose slope is 1.

$\therefore \quad \dfrac{2}{t_1 + t_2} = 1$

or $\quad t_1 + t_2 = 2$ ...(1)

If the normals at P and Q intersect at (h, k), then

$$h = 2a + a(t_1^2 + t_2^2 + t_1 t_2),$$

$$k = -at_1 t_2 (t_1 + t_2)$$

$\therefore \quad h - 2a = a[(t_1 + t_2)^2 - t_1 t_2],$

$\quad k = -2at_1 t_2 \quad$ by (1)

or $\quad h - 2a = a\left[4 + \dfrac{k}{2a}\right] = 4a + \dfrac{k}{2}$

or $\quad 2h - k = 12a.$

Hence the locus is $2x - y = 12a.$

It will be normal if $c = -2am - am^3$

or $\quad -12a = -2a(2) - a(8) = -12a,$

which is true.

(b) R is mid-point of PQ

$\therefore \quad R$ is $\left[\dfrac{a}{2}(t_1^2 + t_2^2), \dfrac{2a}{2}(t_1 + t_2)\right]$

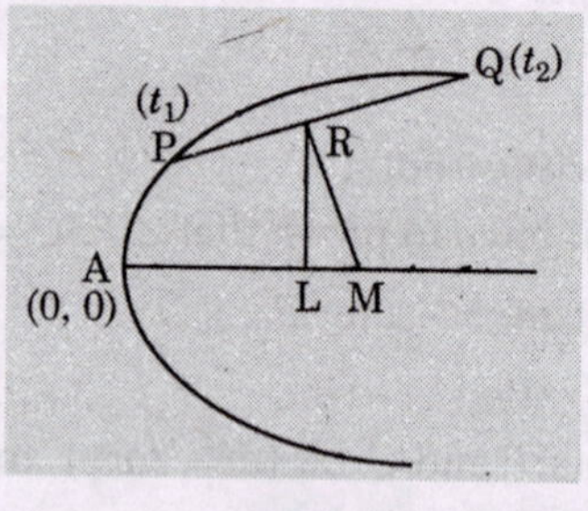

Fig. 27

Also slope of chord PQ is $\dfrac{2}{t_1 + t_2}$.

Hence the right bisector of PQ is

$$y - a(t_1 + t_2) = -\frac{t_1 + t_2}{2}\left[x - \frac{a}{2}(t_1^2 + t_2^2)\right]$$

Putting $y = 0$ in the above, the point M is

$$2a + \frac{a}{2}(t_1^2 + t_2^2) = AM$$

Also $AL = x$ co-ordinate of $R = \dfrac{a}{2}(t_1^2 + t_2^2)$

$\therefore \quad LM = AM - AL = 2a =$ semi-latus rectum.

(c) Let P be t_1 tangent at which is $t_1 y = x + at_1^2$

Similarly tangent at Q, t_2 is $t_2 y = x + at_2^2$

Choose the third tangent as the tangent at the vertex *i.e.* $x = 0$

$\therefore \quad R$ is $(0, at_1)$, $S(0, at_2)$

Mid-point of RS is $\left[0, \dfrac{a}{2}(t_1 + t_2)\right]$ ...(1)

Slope of chord PQ is $\dfrac{2}{t_1 + t_2} = m$, say ...(2)

Hence a tangent parallel to chord is

$$y = mx + \frac{a}{m} \quad ...(3)$$

The point (1) will lie on (3) if $\dfrac{a}{2}(t_1 + t_2) = \dfrac{a}{m}$

or $\quad m = \dfrac{2}{t_1 + t_2}$ which is true by (2).

(d) Let the parameters of P, Q, R be t, t_1, t_2 respectively, $PQ \perp PR$

$\Rightarrow \quad \dfrac{2}{t + t_1} \cdot \dfrac{2}{t + t_2} = -1$

or $\quad t^2 + t(t_1 + t_2) + t_1 t_2 + 4 = 0$ ...(1)

Equation of chord QR is

$$y(t_1 + t_2) - 2x - 2at_1 t_2 = 0$$

Put for $t_1 t_2$ from (1)

or $\quad y(t_1 + t_2) = 2x + 2a\{-t^2 - 4 - t(t_1 + t_2)\}$

or $\quad (t_1 + t_2)\{y + 2at\} = 2\{x - 4a - at^2\}$

or $\quad y + 2at = \dfrac{2}{t_1 + t_2}\{x - 4a - at^2\}$

Above line always passes through a fixed point $(4a + at^2, -2at)$ as t is given.

29. (a) Here $t_1 + t_2 =$ constant $= l$ say. Rest as in Q. 28.

(b) $\dfrac{2at_1}{2at_2} = \dfrac{1}{2} \quad \therefore \; 2t_1 = t_2, \; y^2 = 12x \quad \therefore \; a = 3$

$$h = 2a + a(t_1^2 + t_2^2 + t_1 t_2) = 6 + 3.7t_1^2 \quad \because \; t_2 = 2t_1$$

$$k = -at_1 t_2 (t_1 + t_2) = -6t_1^2 . 3t_1 = 18t_1^3$$

$$\left(\frac{h-6}{21}\right)^3 = t_1^6 = \left(\frac{k}{18}\right)^2$$

$\therefore \quad$ Locus of (h, k) is $y^2 = \dfrac{12}{343}(x - 6)^3$.

30. (a) Let A be $(at_1^2, 2at_1)$ and B be $(at_2^2, 2at_2)$.

The normal at A cuts the curve again at B.

$\therefore \quad t_1 + t_2 = -\dfrac{2}{t_1}$ as in Q. 25. ...(1)

Again AB subtends a right angle at the vertex $O(0, 0)$ of the parabola.

$\therefore \quad t_1 t_2 = -4 \quad$ **Refer (c$_1$) Page 967** ...(2)

Slope of AB is $= \dfrac{2}{t_1 + t_2} = -t_1$ by (1)

In order to find t_1, eliminate t_2 from (1) and (2).

$$t_1 - \frac{4}{t_1} = -\frac{2}{t_1}$$

$\therefore \quad t_1^2 = 2 \quad$ or $\quad t_1 = \pm\sqrt{2}$

$\therefore \quad$ Slope $= \pm\sqrt{2}$.

(b) This is same as part (a).

Alternative : $y = mx - 2am - am^3$

or $\quad \dfrac{mx - y}{2am + am^3} = 1.$

Make the parabola $y^2 = 4ax$ homogeneous.

$\therefore \quad y^2 (2am + am^3) = 4ax(mx - y)$

Since the lines are at right angles, sum of the coefficients of x^2 and y^2 is zero.

$\therefore \quad 2am + am^3 - 4am = 0$

$\therefore \quad m^2 = 2 \quad$ or $\quad m = \sqrt{2} \quad$ or $\quad \tan\theta = \sqrt{2}$

$\therefore \quad \theta = \tan^{-1}\sqrt{2}.$

31. (a) Ans. (a).

By **Q. 25 P. 978** and **Q. 15 P. 977** we have the following :

For normal chord $t_2 = -t_1 - \dfrac{2}{t_1}$ ...(1)

Also chord subtends an angle of 90° at vertex

$\therefore \quad t_1 t_2 = -4$ ...(2)

By (1), $t_1 t_2 = -t_1^2 - 2$ or $-4 = t_1^2 - 2 \quad \therefore \quad t_1^2 = 2$

$\therefore \quad t_2 = -\dfrac{4}{t_1} = -\dfrac{4}{\sqrt{2}} = -2\sqrt{2} \quad$ or $\quad t_2^2 = 8$

$\therefore \quad PQ^2 = a^2 (t_1^2 - t_2^2)^2 + 4a^2 (t_1 - t_2)^2$

$= 1.[(2-8)^2 + 4(\sqrt{2} + 2\sqrt{2})^2] = [36 + 72]$

$PQ^2 = 108 \quad$ or $\quad PQ = 6\sqrt{3}.$

(b) Ans. (b).

Let A, B be the points $(t_1^2, 2t_1)$ and $(t_2^2, 2t_2), (a = 1)$ be two points on the parabola $y^2 = 4x$.

Since AB is a focal chord, $t_1 t_2 = -1$.

Also slope of chord $y(t_1 + t_2) - 2x - 2at_1 t_2 = 0$ is

$\tan\dfrac{\pi}{4} = 1 = \dfrac{2}{t_1 + t_2} \quad \therefore \quad t_1 + t_2 = 2$

Hence t_1, t_2 are the roots of

$m^2 - 2m - 1 = 0$ ...(1)

Slopes of normals at A and B are $-t_1, -t_2$ which are roots of $(-m)^2 - 2(-m) - 1 = 0$

or $\quad m^2 + 2m - 1 = 0$

(c) Ans. (b).

Any tangent to parabola $y^2 = 4x, (a = 1)$:

$y = mx + \dfrac{1}{m}$ ...(1)

Now any normal to parabola $x^2 = 4ay$ is

$x = My - 2aM - aM^3$ ...(2)

or $\quad y = \dfrac{1}{M}x + 2a + aM^2$ ...(3)

If (1) and (3) are same, then

$m = \dfrac{1}{M}$ and $2a + aM^2 = \dfrac{1}{m} = M$

or $\quad aM^2 - M + 2a = 0$

It will have two real roots if $1 - 8a^2 > 0$

or $\quad a^2 < \dfrac{1}{8} \quad \therefore \quad |a| < \dfrac{1}{2\sqrt{2}}.$

32. (a) Let P be t_1 and Q be t_2 so that the point T is $[at_1t_2, a(t_1 + t_2)]$ ...(1)

Again PQ is normal at P

$\therefore \quad t_1 + t_2 = -\dfrac{2}{t_1}$, by **Q. 25 P. 978-987**

If (h, k) be the mid-point of TP, then

$2h = at_1^2 + at_1t_2 = at_1(t_1 + t_2)$ ...(2)

$= at_1\left(-\dfrac{2}{t_1}\right) = -2a$, by (2)

$\therefore \quad h = -a$. It clearly lies on the directrix $x = -a$ whatever be the value of k.

(b) Let P be t_1 and Q be t_2 then point M which is mid-point of PQ is

$\left[\dfrac{a}{2}(t_1^2 + t_2^2), \dfrac{2a}{2}(t_1 + t_2)\right].$ ...(1)

Again PQ is normal at P therefore as in **Q. 25, P. 978-987** we have $t_1 + t_2 = -\dfrac{2}{t_1}$

Product of ordinates of P and M is

$2at_1 \cdot \dfrac{2a}{2}(t_1 + t_2)$

$= 2a^2 t_1\left(-\dfrac{2}{t_1}\right) = -4a^2$ by (1), *i.e.* constant.

33. (a) **Note** that the parabola is $x^2 = 4y$.

and not $y^2 = 4x$

Any point on it $(2t, t^2)$. Tangent is

$x.2t = 2(y + t^2)$

Slope of tangent is t. Hence slope of normal is $-\dfrac{1}{t}$.

$\therefore \quad$ Equation of normal is $y - t^2 = -\dfrac{1}{t}(x - 2t)$

or $\quad ty + x - 2t - t^3 = 0$

or $\quad t^3 - t(y - 2) - x = 0$ ...(1)

It is cut by the line $y = 2$ where $x = t^3$.

Since (1) is a cubic in t there will be three values of t and hence three co-normal points.

It is given that abscissas of the points are in A.P.

$\therefore \quad 2t_2^3 = t_1^3 + t_2^3$

or $\quad t_1^3 + t_2^3 + t_3^3 = 3t_2^3$ ...(2)

Again from (1), $t_1 + t_2 + t_3 = 0$

$\because \quad$ coeff. of t^2 is zero

$\therefore \quad t_1^3 + t_2^3 + t_3^3 = 3t_1t_2t_3$ ...(3)

Hence from (2) and (3),

$3t_1t_2t_3 = 3t_2^3 \quad$ or $\quad t_1t_3 = t_2^2$

Above shows that slopes t_1, t_2, t_3 of the three tangents are in G.P.

(b) Let P and Q be t_1 and t_2 respectively

$\therefore \quad \tan\theta_1 = \dfrac{1}{t_1}$ or $\cot\theta_1 = t_1$

and $\cot\theta_2 = t_2$ ...(1)

Circle on AP as diameter is

$$x(x - at_1^2) + y(y - 2at_1) = 0$$

or $\quad x^2 + y^2 - x.at_1^2 - 2ayt_1 = 0$ ...(2)

Similarly circle on AQ as diameter is

$$x^2 + y^2 - x.at_2^2 - 2ayt_2 = 0 \quad ...(3)$$

These two meet at R whose other common point is A. Hence AR is the common chord of these circles whose equation is given by $S_1 - S_2 = 0$

$$-ax(t_1^2 - t_2^2) - 2ay(t_1 - t_2) = 0$$

or $\quad x(t_1 + t_2) + 2y = 0$

Its slope is $-\dfrac{t_1 + t_2}{2} = \tan\phi$ given.

$\therefore \quad t_1 + t_2 + 2\tan\phi = 0$

$\therefore \quad \cot\theta_1 + \cot\theta_2 + 2\tan\phi = 0$, by (1).

34. Any normal to the parabola is $y = mx - 2am - am^3$. If it passes through the point (h, k), then

$$k = mh - 2am - am^3$$

or $\quad am^3 + 0m^2 + m(2a - h) + k = 0$ ...(1)

Above is a cubic in m showing that there will be three normals passing through the point (h, k). If their slopes be m_1, m_2 and m_3, then

$m_1 + m_2 + m_3 = 0$ ...(2)

$m_1m_2 + m_2m_3 + m_3m_1 = \dfrac{2a - h}{a}$ ...(3)

$m_1m_2m_3 = -k/a$ ...(4)

(a) Since the two normals are perpendicular

$\therefore \quad m_1m_2 = -1.$

Putting in (4), we get $\quad m_3 = \dfrac{k}{a}.$

But m_3 is a root of (1).

$\therefore \quad a.(k/a)^3 + \dfrac{k}{a}(2a - h) + k = 0$

or $\quad y^2 = a(x - 3a)$

(b) Any normal to $y^2 = 4ax$ is $y = mx - 2am - am^3$

$\therefore$ Any normal to $x^2 = 4ay$ is obtained from above by interchanging x and y.

$\therefore$ Normal to $x^2 = 8y, (a = 2)$ is

$$x = my - 4m - 2m^3$$

If it passes through (h, k), then

$$h = mk - 4m - 2m^3$$

or $\quad 2m^3 + 0\,m^2 + m(4 - k) + h = 0$ ...(1)

Above shows that three normals will pass through (h, k). If two of them are perpendicular then $m_2\,m_3 = -1$. But $m_1m_2m_3 = -h/2$

$\therefore \quad -m_1 = -h/2$ or $m_1 = h/2.$

Since m_1 is a root of (1), it will satisfy it.

$\therefore \quad 2\left(\dfrac{h^3}{8}\right) + \dfrac{h}{2}(4 - k) + h = 0$

or $\quad h^2 + 2(4 - k) + 4 = 0$

$\therefore$ Locus of (h, k) is $x^2 - 2y + 12 = 0$

(c) From (1),

$m_1 + m_2 + m_3 = 0$

$\therefore \quad -2am_1 - 2am_2 - 2am_3 = 0$

or $\quad y_1 + y_2 + y_3 = 0$

(d) Let $P(h, k), (k \neq 0)$ through which three normals are drawn to the parabola $y^2 = 4ax\,(a = 1)$ such that product of slopes of two is α, $m_1m_2 = \alpha$.

From eqn. (1) of Q. 34, we have

$$am^3 + 0.m^2 + m(2a - h) + k = 0$$

or $\quad m^3 + 0.m^2 + m(2a - h) + k = 0$, as $a = 1$ ...(1)

$m_1m_2m_3 = -k \quad \therefore \quad m_3 = \dfrac{-k}{m_1m_2} = -\dfrac{k}{\alpha}$, by (1)

But m_3 is a root of (1)

$\therefore \quad k^3 + (2 - h)k\alpha^2 - k\alpha^3 = 0$

Hence locus of P is $y^2 + (2 - x)\alpha^2 - \alpha^3 = 0$ ($k \neq 0$, cancelled).

Above is same as $y^2 - 4x = 0$, as given

Hence on comparing $\alpha^2 = 4$ and $2\alpha^2 - \alpha^3 = 0$ or $\alpha = 2 \quad \therefore \quad \alpha = 2$ which satisfies both.

(e) $4a = 4 \Rightarrow a = 1$

Any normal to the parabola $y^2 = 4ax$ is $y = mx - 2am - am^3$

or $\quad y = mx - 2m - m^3 \qquad \because a = 1$

It passes through $\left(\dfrac{11}{4}, \dfrac{1}{4}\right)$

$\therefore \quad \dfrac{1}{4} = \dfrac{11}{4}m - 2m - m^3$ or $4m^3 - 3m + 1 = 0$

or $\quad (m + 1)(4m^2 - 4m + 1) = 0$

or $\quad (m + 1)(2m - 1)^2 = 0$

$m = -1, 1/2, 1/2$

Hence there will be only two distinct normals that can be drawn from the given point corresponding to $m = -1, m = 1/2$.

35. (a) If two of the normals coincide, then

$m_2 = m_3$ ...(5)

In order to find the locus of the point of intersection (h, k) we have to eliminate the three quantities m_1, m_2 and m_3 between the four equations (2), (3), (4) and (5).

$m_1 + 2m_2 = 0$ from (2) and (5).

$\therefore \quad m_1 = -2m_2$ ...(6)

$m_1(m_2 + m_3) + m_2m_3 = \dfrac{2a - h}{a}$ by (3)

or $m_1(2m_2)+m_2^2=\dfrac{2a-h}{a}$ by (5) as $m_3=m_2$

or $(-2m_2)(2m_2)+m_2^2=\dfrac{2a-h}{a}$ by (6)

$\therefore \quad m_2^2=\dfrac{h-2a}{3a}$ ...(7)

Again $m_1 m_2^2=-\dfrac{k}{a}$, by (4) and (5)

$(-2m_2)\,m_2=-\dfrac{k}{a}$, by (6)

$\therefore \quad m_2^3=\dfrac{k}{2a}$ ...(8)

Now $(m_2^2)^3=(m_2^3)^2$

$\therefore \quad \left(\dfrac{h-2a}{3a}\right)^3=\dfrac{k^2}{4a^2}$ or $27ak^2=4(h-2a)^3$

Hence the required locus of the point (h,k) is

$27ay^2=4(x-2a)^3$.

(b) If the normals at three points $(am_1^2,-2am_1)$ etc. meet in $T(h,k)$ then m_1,m_2,m_3 are the roots of

$am^3+0m^2+m(2a-h)+k=0$

$\therefore \quad \Sigma m_1=0, \Sigma m_1 m_2=\dfrac{2a-h}{a}, m_1 m_2 m_3=-\dfrac{k}{a}$

The normal at m_1 meets the axis $y=0$ in $(2a+m_1^2,0)$ $\therefore$ $OA=2a+m_1^2$

Since OA, OB and OC are in A.P.

$\therefore \quad 2(2a+m_2^2)=2a+m_1^2+2a+m_3^2$

or $2m_2^2=m_1^2+m_3^2$

or $3m_2^2=\Sigma m_1^2$

or $3m_2^2=(\Sigma m_1)^2-2\Sigma m_1 m_2$

$\therefore \quad 3m_2^2=0-2\dfrac{(2a-h)}{a}$

$\therefore \quad m_2^2=2\dfrac{(h-2a)}{3a}$ ...(1)

Again $2m_2^2=m_1^2+m_3^2=(m_1+m_3)^2-2m_1 m_3$

or $2m_2^2=(-m_2)^2-2\left(-\dfrac{k}{am_2}\right)$

or $m_2^2=\dfrac{2k}{am_2}$ or $m_2^3=\dfrac{2k}{a}$ ...(2)

Now $(m_2^3)^2=(m_2^2)^3$

$\therefore \quad \dfrac{4k^2}{a^2}=\dfrac{8(h-2a)^3}{27a^3}$ by (1) and (2)

Hence the locus of (h,k) is

$27ay^2=2(x-2a)^3$

36. (a) Let $P(am_1^2,-2am_1)$ etc., then

$SP=a+x=a+am_1^2$

$\therefore \quad SP.SQ.SR=a^3(1+m_1^2)(1+m_2^2)(1+m_3^2)$

$=a^3[1+\Sigma m_1^2+\Sigma m_1^2 m_2^2+m_1^2 m_2^2 m_3^2]$

$\Sigma m_1^2=(\Sigma m_1)^2-2\Sigma m_1 m_2=0-2\left(\dfrac{2a-h}{a}\right)$

$\Sigma m_1^2 m_2^2=(\Sigma m_1 m_2)^2-2m_1 m_2 m_3\,\Sigma m_1$

$=\left(\dfrac{2a-h}{a}\right)^2-0$

$m_1^2 m_2^2 m_3^2=\dfrac{k^2}{a^2}$

$\therefore \quad SP.SQ.SR$

$=a^3\left[1-2\left(\dfrac{2a-h}{a}\right)+\dfrac{(2a-h)^2}{a^2}+\dfrac{k^2}{a^2}\right]$

$=a[a^2-2ah+h^2+k^2]$

$=a[(h-a)^2+k^2]=a.ST^2$

where S is $(a,0)$ and T is (h,k) through which pass the three normals.

(b) For real values of m_1,m_2,m_3, $\Sigma m_1^2=+$ive

or $(\Sigma m_1)^2-2\Sigma m_1 m_2>0$, $y^2=4x$ $\therefore$ $a=1$

or $0-\dfrac{2(2a-h)}{a}>0$. Put $a=1$

or $(h-2)>0$ $\therefore$ $h>2$

37. (a) We have $\tan^{-1}\dfrac{S_1-S_3}{1-S_2}=\alpha$

or $S_1-S_3=\tan\alpha\,(1-S_2)$ ...(1)

$S_1=\Sigma m_1^2=(\Sigma m_1)^2-2\Sigma m_1 m_2=-\dfrac{2(2a-h)}{a}$

$S_2=\Sigma m_1^2 m_2^2=(\Sigma m_1 m_2)^2-2m_1 m_2 m_3\,\Sigma m_1$

$=\left(\dfrac{2a-h}{a}\right)^2$

$S_3=m_1^2 m_2^2 m_3^2=\left(-\dfrac{k}{a}\right)^2=\dfrac{k^2}{a^2}$

Putting these values in (1) and generalizing, we get

$-\dfrac{2(2a-x)}{a}-\dfrac{y^2}{a^2}=\tan\alpha\left[1-\dfrac{(2a-x)^2}{a^2}\right]$

or $2a(2a-x)+y^2+[a^2-(2a-x)^2]\tan\alpha=0$

or $4a^2-2ax+y^2+\tan\alpha\,[-3a^2+4ax-x^2]=0$

or $-x^2\tan\alpha+y^2-2a(1-2\tan\alpha)\,x$
$+a^2(4-3\tan\alpha)=0$

or $x^2\tan\alpha-y^2+2a(1-2\tan\alpha)\,x$
$+a^2(3\tan\alpha-4)=0$

(b) If A, B, C be the points t_1,t_2,t_3 then P is $\{at_2t_3, a(t_2+t_3)\}$, which is point of intersection of tangents at B and C. Any normal to parabola is

$y=-tx+2at+at^3$.

If it passes through (h, k), then

$$at^3 + 0t^2 + t(2a - h) - k = 0$$

It is a cubic in t and hence gives three values of t say t_1, t_2, t_3.

$$\therefore \quad \Sigma t_1 = 0,\ \Sigma t_1 t_2 = \frac{2a - h}{a},\ t_1 t_2 t_3 = \frac{k}{a} \quad ...(A)$$

The abscissas of P, Q, R are

$$x_1 = at_2 t_3,\ x_2 = at_3 t_1,\ x_3 = at_1 t_2$$

Hence the equation whose roots are x_1, x_2, x_3 is

$$x^3 - x^2 \Sigma x_1 + x \Sigma x_1 x_2 - x_1 x_2 x_3 = 0 \quad ...(1)$$

$$\Sigma x_1 = a \Sigma t_1 t_2 = a \frac{2a - h}{a} = 2a - h$$

$$\Sigma x_1 x_2 = a^2 t_1 t_2 t_3 \Sigma t_1 = 0$$

$$x_1 x_2 x_3 = a^3 t_1^2 t_2^2 t_3^2 = a^3 . \frac{k^2}{a^2} = ak^2, \text{ by (A)}$$

Hence from (1) the required equation is

$$x^3 + x^2 (h - 2a) - ak^2 = 0$$

Similarly the equation giving ordinates of P, Q, R are

$$y^3 - a(h - 2a) y + a^2 k = 0$$

where $y_1 = a(t_2 + t_3) = -at_1$, by (A)

$y_2 = -at_2,\ y_3 = -at_3$

$$\Sigma y_1 = -a \Sigma t_1 = 0, \Sigma y_1 y_2 = a^2 \Sigma t_1 t_2$$

$$= a^2 \frac{(2a - h)}{a} = a(2a - h)$$

$$y_1 y_2 y_3 = -a^3 t_1 t_2 t_3 = -a^2 k$$

Note : We have chosen the normal in t and not in m as we know the point of intersection of tangents at t_1, t_2 and t_3 easily.

38. (a) Any tangent to it is $y - 3t^2 = \frac{1}{t}(x - 2t^3)$

or $\quad x - ty + t^3 = 0$

If it passes through (h, k), then

$$h - tk + t^3 = 0$$

or $\quad t^3 + 0t^2 - tk + h = 0 \quad ...(1)$

Above being a cubic in t shows that there will be three tangents passing through the point (h, k). Let its roots be t_1, t_2, t_3.

Since two tangents are perpendicular, therefore

$$m_1 m_2 = -1 \quad \text{or} \quad \frac{1}{t_1} \cdot \frac{1}{t_2} = -1$$

or $\quad t_1 t_2 = -1$

But $t_1 t_2 t_3 = -h \quad \therefore \quad t_3 = h$

But t_3 is a root of (1)

$\therefore \quad h^3 - hk + h = 0$ or $k = h^2 + 1$

$\therefore \quad$ Locus is $y = x^2 + 1$.

(b) We know that from a point three normals can be drawn to a parabola and sum of the feet of ordinates is zero

i.e. $\quad y_1 + y_2 + y_3 = 0 \quad ...(1)$

Let the circle be $x^2 + y^2 + 2gx + 2fy + c = 0$ and parabola is $y^2 = 4ax \quad \therefore \quad x = \frac{y^2}{4a}$

Eliminating x, we get a biquadratic in y as

$$y^4 + 0 . y^3 + 8y^2 (2a^2 + ag) + 32af^2 y + 16a^2 c = 0$$

Above equation gives the ordinates of the four points of intersection of circle and parabola.

$$\therefore \quad y_1 + y_2 + y_3 + y_4 = 0 \quad \therefore \quad y_4 = 0 \text{ by (1)}$$

$$\therefore \quad x_4 = \frac{y_4^2}{4a} = 0$$

Hence the circle passes through (x_4, y_4) *i.e.* $(0, 0)$.

39. (a) P is $(at_1^2, 2at_1)$ and Q is $(at_2^2, 2at_2)$

$$PQ \text{ is } y(t_1 + t_2) - 2x - 2at_1 t_2 = 0 \quad ...(1)$$

If (h, k) be the point of intersection of normals at P and Q, then

$$h = 2a + a(t_1^2 + t_2^2 + t_1 t_2)$$

$$k = -at_1 t_2 (t_1 + t_2)$$

Also product of their slopes is $(-t_1)(-t_2) = t_1 t_2$

Now (h, k) lies on the parabola $\therefore \ k^2 = 4ah$

or $\ a^2 t_1^2 t_2^2 (t_1 + t_2)^2 = 8a^2 + 4a^2 \{(t_1 + t_2)^2 - t_1 t_2\}$

or $\quad (t_1 - t_2)^2 \{t_1^2 t_2^2 - 4\} + 4\{t_1 t_2 - 2\} = 0$

or $\quad (t_1 t_2 - 2)\{\ \} = 0$

$\therefore \quad t_1 t_2 = 2$

Again if $t_1 t_2 = 2$, then chord PQ becomes

$$y(t_1 + t_2) - 2x - 4a = 0$$

Its intersection with axis $y = 0$ is $(-2a, 0)$ which is a fixed point. If (x, y) be the mid-point of PQ

$$2x = a(t_1^2 + t_2^2) = a[(t_1 + t_2)^2 - 2t_1 t_2],$$

$$2y = 2a(t_1 + t_2)$$

Also $\ t_1 t_2 = 2 \quad \therefore \quad$ Locus of mid-point is obtained by eliminating t_1 and t_2 from the above three and is

$$y^2 = 2a(x + 2a)$$

Alternative easier solution :

(a) Normals at t_1 and t_2 meet on the parabola at (x_1, y_1) or point t_3 say *i.e.*, $y_1 = 2at_3 \quad ...(I)$

Any normal to parabola is $y = -tx + 2at + at^3$

It passes through the point (x_1, y_1) or t_3

$$\therefore \quad y_1 = -t x_1 + 2at + at^3$$

or $\quad at^3 + 0t^2 + (2a - x_1)t - y_1 = 0$

$$\therefore \quad t_1 t_2 t_3 = -\left(-\frac{y_1}{a}\right) = \frac{2at_3}{a} = 2t_3 \text{ by (I)}$$

$\therefore \quad t_1 t_2 = 2$

Also $t_1 + t_2 + t_3 = 0 \quad \therefore \ t_3 = -t_1 - t_2$

(b) From part (a) $t_1 t_2 = 2$. Ordinates are $2at_1$ and $2at_2$. If $S =$ sum and $P =$ product then $S = 2a(t_1 + t_2)$, $P = 2at_1 . 2at_2$

But it is given that $k =$ ordinate of point of intersection of normals $= -at_1 t_2 (t_1 + t_2)$

or $k = -2a(t_1 + t_2) \quad \because \quad t_1 t_2 = 2$

$\therefore \quad S = -k, P = 4a^2 . 2 = 8a^2$

$\therefore \quad y^2 - Sy + P = 0$

or $y^2 + ky + 8a^2 = 0$

(c) Let points Q and R on the parabola be t_1 and t_2

$\therefore \quad QR = y(t_1 + t_2) - 2x - 2at_1 t_2 = 0 \quad ...(1)$

Since the normals at Q and R intersect at the point $(at^2, -2at)$

$\therefore \quad at^2 = 2a + a(t_1^2 + t_2^2 + t_1 t_2)$

$-2at = -at_1 t_2 (t_1 + t_2)$

Eliminating t, we get $(-2at)^2 = 4a(at^2)$

$\therefore \quad a^2 t_1^2 t_2^2 (t_1 + t_2)^2 = 4a\{2a + a(t_1^2 + t_2^2 + t_1 t_2)\}$

$\therefore \quad t_1^2 t_2^2 (t_1 + t_2)^2 = 8 + 4\{(t_1 + t_2)^2 - t_1 t_2\}$

$\therefore \quad (t_1 + t_2)^2 \{t_1^2 t_2^2 - 4\} = -4(t_1 t_2 - 2)$

$(t_1 t_2 - 2)\{ \quad \} = 0 \quad \therefore \quad t_1 t_2 = 2 \quad ...(2)$

and hence $\quad -2at = -2a(t_1 + t_2)$

$\therefore \quad t_1 + t_2 = t \quad ...(3)$

Hence from (1), (2) and (3), the chord is $y . t - 2x - 4a = 0$

or $\quad ty = 2(x + 2a)$

Slope of tangent at $Q = -t_1 = m_1$

$\therefore \quad m_1 m_2 = (-t_1)(-t_2) = t_1 t_2 = 2$

(d) Parabola is $y^2 = 4x \rightarrow a = 1$

$P(t_1^2, 2t_1), Q(t_2^2, 2t_2) \quad \therefore \quad T = \{t_1 t_2, (t_1 + t_2)\} \quad ...(1)$

If normals at P and Q intersect on the parabola then $t_1 t_2 = 2$. Here normals at P and Q meet at $(9, 6)$ which lies on the parabola $y^2 = 4x$

Normals intersect at R, $\{2a + a(t_1^2 + t_2^2 + t_1 t_2),$
$\qquad -at_1 t_2 (t_1 + t_2)\} = (9, 6)$

$\therefore \quad -t_1 t_2 (t_1 + t_2) = 6$ as $a = 1$

$\therefore \quad t_1 + t_2 = -3$ as $t_1 t_2 = 2$

$\therefore \quad t_1, t_2$ are the roots of $t^2 + 3t + 2 = 0$

$\therefore \quad t = -1, -2$

$\therefore$ P is $(1, -2)$, $Q(4, -4)$, R is $(9, 6)$ and T is $(2, -3)$ by (1) and (2).

Now TP is tangent at P and PR is normal at P so that angle at P is 90°. Similarly angle at Q is also 90°. Hence TR will be diameter of the circle circumscribing $PTQR$. Hence its equation is as given.

40. Let P and Q be the points t_1 and t_2 so that T is $[at_1 t_2, a(t_1 + t_2)]$ which lies on a line parallel to the axis say $y = \lambda$

$\therefore \quad a(t_1 + t_2) = \lambda \quad$ or $\quad t_1 + t_2 = \lambda / a = m$

say. Point R is (h, k)

$\therefore \quad h = 2a + a(t_1^2 + t_2^2 + t_1 t_2)$

$k = -at_1 t_2 (t_1 + t_2) = -amt_1 t_2$

$\therefore \quad h = 2a + a[(t_1 + t_2)^2 - t_1 t_2]$

$= 2a + a\left[m^2 + \dfrac{k}{am}\right]$

$\therefore \quad hm = 2am + am^3 + k$

$\therefore$ Locus of (h, k) is $y = mx - 2am - am^3$ which we know is a normal to the parabola.

41. Let $(a, 0)$ be the focus of the parabola $y^2 = 4ax$. Tangents are drawn to the parabola at points A, B, C where parameters are t_1, t_2, t_3. These tangents form an other triangle PQR where P is $\{at_1 t_2, a(t_1 + t_2)\}$ etc.

Let the circle PQR be $x^2 + y^2 + 2gx + 2fy + c = 0$.

It passes through the points P, Q and R

$\therefore \quad a^2 t_1^2 t_2^2 + a^2 (t_1 + t_2)^2 + 2gat_1 t_2$
$\qquad + 2fa(t_1 + t_2) + c = 0 \quad ...(1)$

$a^2 t_2^2 t_3^2 + a^2 (t_2 + t_3)^2 + 2gat_2 t_3 + 2fa(t_2 + t_3)$
$\qquad + c = 0 \quad ...(2)$

$a^2 t_3^2 t_1^2 + a^2 (t_3 + t_1)^2 + 2gat_3 t_1 + 2fa(t_3 + t_1)$
$\qquad + c = 0 \quad ...(3)$

Subtracting (1), (2) and (2), (3), we have

$a^2 t_2^2 (t_1 + t_3) + a^2 (t_1 + t_3 + 2t_2) + 2gat_2 + 2fa = 0 \quad ...(4)$

and $a^2 t_3^2 (t_1 + t_2) + a^2 (t_1 + t_2 + 2t_3) + 2gat_3$
$\qquad + 2fa = 0 \quad ...(5)$

Subtracting (4) and (5), we get after cancelling $(t_2 - t_3)$

$2g = -a(1 + t_1 t_2 + t_2 t_3 + t_3 t_1) \quad ...(6)$

Again eliminating $2g$ between (6) and (7), we have

$2f = -a(t_1 + t_2 + t_3 - t_1 t_2 t_3) \quad ...(7)$

Now putting the values of g, f and c in (1) or (2), we get

$c = a^2 (t_1 t_2 + t_2 t_3 + t_3 t_1)$

Hence the equation of required circle is

$x^2 + y^2 - a(1 + \Sigma t_1 t_2)x - a(\Sigma t_1 - t_1 t_2 t_3)y$
$\qquad + a^2 \Sigma t_1 t_2 = 0$

It clearly passes through focus $(a, 0)$.

$\because \quad a^2 - a^2 (1 + \Sigma t_1 t_2) + a^2 \Sigma t_1 t_2 = 0$

§4. Chord of Contact, Polar, Chord with a give mid-point

(a) Chord of Contact of the point (x_1, y_1).

Proceeding as in the case of circle § 3 Page 898 the equation of the chord of contact is $yy_1 = 2a(x + x_1)$.

Above is of the same form as the tangent at the point (x_1, y_1).

(b) Equation of the polar of the point (x_1, y_1).

Proceeding as in the case of circle § 3 (e), P. 898 the equation of the polar is $yy_1 = 2a(x + x_1)$. It is of the same form as the tangent at the point (x_1, y_1).

(c) Chord of parabola whose mid-point is (h, k).

Any line through the point (h, k) is

$$y - k = m(x - h) \quad \text{...(A)}$$

We have to determine the value of m its slope.

If it meets the parabola in $P(at_1^2, 2at_1)$ and $Q(at_2^2, 2at_2)$, its equation is

$$y(t_1 + t_2) - 2x - 2at_1t_2 = 0 \quad \text{...(B)}$$

Its slope $= \dfrac{2}{t_1 + t_2} = m.$

Since (h, k) is mid-point of PQ.

$\therefore \quad 2k = 2at_1 + 2at_2$

$\therefore \quad t_1 + t_2 = \dfrac{k}{a} \quad \therefore \quad m = \dfrac{2}{t_1 + t_2} = \dfrac{2a}{k}.$

Putting the value of m in (A), the required equation is

$$y - k = \frac{2a}{k}(x - h).$$

or $\quad \boldsymbol{k(y - k) = 2a(x - h)}$ **(V. Imp.)** ...(15)

$$\boldsymbol{ky - 2a(x + h) = k^2 - 4ah}$$

or $\quad \boldsymbol{T = S_1}$ **in usual notation.**

Above is equation of the chord whose mid-point is (h, k) and its slope is $\dfrac{2a}{k}$.

Also the equation of the polar of the point (h, k) is $ky = 2a(x + h)$ whose slope is also $\dfrac{2a}{k}$.

Hence we conclude that the chord whose mid-point is (*h*, *k*) is parallel to the polar of the point (*h*, *k*).

Problem Set (4)

Chord of Contact, Polar, Chord with a given Mid-point.

1. Prove that the locus of the mid-point of a system of parallel chords of a parabola is a line parallel to the axis of the parabola.

2.* Find the locus of the mid-points of the chords of the parabola $y^2 = 4ax$ which pass through a given point (α, β).

3. (a) Find the locus of the mid-points of the chords of the parabola $y^2 = 4ax$ which subtend a right angle at the vertex.

(b) Prove that the locus of the mid-points of the chords of the parabola $y^2 = 4ax$ which pass through the vertex is the parabola $y^2 = 2ax$.

4. (a)* If the perpendicular drawn from P on the polar of P with respect to the parabola $y^2 = 4ax$ touches the parabola $x^2 = 4by$, prove that the locus of P is the straight line $2ax + by + 4a^2 = 0$.

(b) Prove that the locus of the poles of the chords of the parabola which are at a constant distance b from the vertex, is $y^2 + 4a^2(1 - x^2/b^2) = 0$.

5.* Prove that the locus of mid-points of the normal chords of the parabola $y^2 = 4ax$ is $y^2/2a + 4a^3/y^2 = x - 2a$.

6. (a)* Show that the locus of the poles of the normal chords of the parabola $y^2 = 4ax$ is $y^2(x + 2a) + 4a^3 = 0$.

(b)* Prove that the locus of the point of intersection of tangents drawn at the extremities of a normal chord to the parabola $y^2 = 4ax$ is the curve $y^2(x + 2a) + 4a^3 = 0$

(c) Find the locus of points of intersection of tangents drawn at the ends of all normal chords to the parabola $y^2 = 8(x - 1)$. **(Roorkee 2001)**

7.* Tangents are drawn from any point on the line $x + 4a = 0$. Prove that their chord of contact will subtend a right angle at the vertex.

8. Prove that the locus of the poles of tangents to the parabola $y^2 = 4ax$ w.r.t. the circle $x^2 + y^2 = 2ax$ is

$$x^2 + y^2 = ax.$$

9. Prove that the locus of the poles of focal chord of the parabola $y^2 = 4ax$ is the directrix.

10. Prove that the locus of the poles of the tangents to the parabola $y^2 = 4ax$ w.r.t. the parabola $y^2 = 4bx$ is the parabola $y^2 = 4\dfrac{b^2}{a}x$.

11.* From the point $(-1, 2)$ tangent lines are drawn to the parabola $y^2 = 4x$. Find the equation of chord of contact. Also find the area of the triangle formed by chord of contact and the tangents. **(Roorkee 1994)**

12.* From a point A common tangents are drawn to the circle $x^2 + y^2 = \dfrac{a^2}{2}$ and parabola $y^2 = 4ax$. Find the area of the quadrilateral formed by the common tangents, the chord of contact of the circle and the chord of contact of the parabola. **(I.I.T. 1996)**

13. PNP' is a double ordinate of the parabola $y^2 = 4ax$, prove that the locus of the point of intersection of the normal at P and parallel to the axis through P' is the equal parabola $y^2 = 4a(x - 4a)$.

14.* Prove that the length of the chord of contact of the tangents drawn from the point (x_1, y_1) to the parabola $y^2 = 4ax$ is $\dfrac{1}{a}\sqrt{\{(y_1^2 + 4a^2)(y_1^2 - 4ax_1)\}}$.

Hence show that the area of the triangle formed by these tangents and their chord of contact is $\frac{1}{2a}(y_1^2 - 4ax_1)^{3/2}$.

15.* Prove that the locus of the middle points of tangents drawn from points on the directrix to the parabola $y^2 = 4ax$ is $y^2(2x+a) = a(3x+a)^2$.

16. From a point A, common tangents are drawn to the circle $x^2 + y^2 = \frac{a^2}{2}$ and the parabola $y^2 = 4ax$. Find the area of quadrilateral formed by the common tangents and the chords of contacts of the circle and the parabola.

Solutions to Problem Set (4)

1. We know that the equation of the chord whose mid-point is (h, k) is

$$k(y-k) = 2a(x-h) \qquad ...(1)$$

Since the chords are parallel their slope

$$\frac{2a}{k} = \text{constant} = m, \text{say}$$

Hence the locus of mid-point is $\frac{2a}{y} = m$, or $y = \frac{2a}{m}$ which is a line parallel to the axis of the parabola.

2. If the chord (1) passes through (α, β), then

$$k(\beta - k) = 2a(\alpha - h).$$

Hence locus of mid-point (h, k) is

$$y(\beta - y) = 2a(\alpha - x)$$

or $y(y-\beta) = 2a(x-\alpha)$.

3. (a) Let P be t_1 and Q be t_2 and since PQ subtends a right angle at the vertex $O(0, 0)$ therefore as in **(c₁) P. 967** $t_1 t_2 = -4$. If (h, k) be the mid-point, then

$$2h = a(t_1^2 + t_2^2) \quad \text{and} \quad 2k = 2a(t_1 + t_2)$$

or $2h = a[(t_1+t_2)^2 - 2t_1 t_2]$

or $2h = a\left[\frac{k^2}{a^2} + 8\right]$ or $2a(h-4a) = k^2$

$\therefore$ Locus is $y^2 = 2a(x-4a)$

(b) Let OP be the chord through the vertex. If (h, k) be its mid-point, then

$$2h = 0 + at^2,\ 2k = 0 + 2at \quad \therefore \quad k = at$$

$$\therefore \quad 2h = a\frac{k^2}{a^2} \quad \text{or} \quad k^2 = 2ah$$

Hence the locus is $y^2 = 2ax$.

4. (a) Polar of (h, k) w.r.t. $y^2 = 4ax$ is

$$ky = 2a(x+h) \quad \text{or} \quad m = 2a/k$$

Any line through $P(h, k)$ perpendicular to above is

$$y - k = -\frac{k}{2a}(x-h)$$

The above line touches the parabola $x^2 = 4by$. It will cut it in two coincident points. Eliminating y, we get

$$x^2 = 4b\left\{k - \frac{k}{2a}(x-h)\right\}$$

or $2ax^2 + 4bkx - 4bk(2a+h) = 0$

$\therefore$ $\Delta = B^2 - 4AC = 0$

$$16k^2b^2 + 32abk(2a+h) = 0$$

or $bk + 2a(2a+h) = 0$

$\therefore$ Locus is $2ax + by + 4a^2 = 0$

(b) Polar of (h, k) is $ky = 2a(x+h)$

or $2ax - ky + 2ah = 0$

Its distance from the vertex $(0, 0)$ is b.

$$\therefore \quad \frac{2ah}{\sqrt{(4a^2+k^2)}} = b$$

or $4a^2h^2 = b^2(4a^2 + k^2)$

$\therefore$ Locus is $y^2 + 4a^2\left(1 - \frac{x^2}{b^2}\right) = 0$

5. Let the equation of the normal be

$$y = mx - 2am - am^3 \qquad ...(1)$$

If its mid-point be (h, k), then it is same as

$$k(y-k) = 2a(x-h)$$

or $y = \frac{2a}{k}x + \left(k - \frac{2ah}{k}\right) \qquad ...(2)$

Comparing (1) and (2), we get

$$m = \frac{2a}{k} \text{ and } k - \frac{2ah}{k} = -2am - am^3$$

Eliminating the variable m between the above two relations, we get

$$k - \frac{2ah}{k} = -2a\left(\frac{2a}{k}\right) - a\left(\frac{8a^3}{k^3}\right)$$

or $k + \frac{8a^4}{k^3} = \frac{2a}{k}(h-2a)$

or $\frac{k^2}{2a} + \frac{4a^3}{k^2} = h - 2a$

Hence the locus of the mid-point (h, k) is

$$\frac{y^2}{2a} + \frac{4a^3}{y^2} = x - 2a.$$

6. (a) Let the equation of the normal be

$$y = mx - 2am - am^3 \qquad ...(1)$$

If (h, k) be its pole, then its equation is

$$ky = 2a(x+h)$$

or $y = \frac{2a}{k}x + 2a\frac{h}{k} \qquad ...(2)$

Comparing (1) and (2), we get

$$m = \frac{2a}{k}, -2am - am^3 = 2a \cdot \frac{h}{k}.$$

Eliminating the variable m between the above two relations, we get

$$-2a\cdot\left(\frac{2a}{k}\right)-a\cdot\frac{8a^3}{k^3}=2a\cdot\frac{h}{k}$$

or $h+2a+\dfrac{4a^3}{k^2}=0$

or $k^2(h+2a)+4a^3=0$

Hence the required locus is

$$y^2(x+2a)+4a^3=0.$$

(b) If (h,k) be the point of intersection of tangents then C.C. $ky=2a(x+h)$ is same as normal $y=mx-2am-am^3$. Compare and eliminate m as in part (a).

(c) Consider the parabola $y^2=4ax$. Let PQ be any normal chord whose equation is

$$y=mx-2am-am^3 \quad ...(3)$$

If the tangents at P and Q intersect at (h,k) then PQ is chord of contact whose equation is

$$ky=2a(x+h) \quad ...(2)$$

Comparing (1) and (2), we get

$$\frac{k}{1}=\frac{2a}{m}=\frac{2ah}{-a(2m+m^3)}$$

$\therefore$ $m=\dfrac{2a}{k}$ and $k(2m+m^3)=-2h$

Putting for m, we get $k\left(\dfrac{4a}{k}+\dfrac{8a^3}{k^3}\right)=-2h$

or $2a+\dfrac{4a^3}{k^2}=-h$

$\therefore$ $k^2(h+2a)+4a^3=0$

Hence the required locus is $y^2(x+2a)+4a^3=0$.

Here parabola is $y^2=8(x-1)$.

$\therefore$ $a=2$ and replace x by $x-1$.

Hence the locus is $y^2(x-1+2.2)=4.(2)^3$

or $y^2(x+5)=32$.

7. Let the extremities of the chord of contact PQ be t_1 and t_2. The point of intersection of tangents is $[at_1t_2, a(t_1+t_2)]$.

It lies on $x+4a=0$ $\therefore$ $t_1t_2=-4$ ...(1)

Now PQ will subtend a right angle at vertex if $t_1t_2=-4$ [**by (c$_1$) P. 967**]. This is true by (1).

8. Do yourself.

9. If (h,k) be the pole, then the equation of the chord is

$$ky=2a(x+h).$$

Since it is a focal chord it passes through the focus $(a,0)$.

$\therefore$ $2a(a+h)=0$

or $a+h=0$.

Hence the locus of pole (h,k) is $x+a=0$ which is directrix.

10. Any tangent to the parabola $y^2=4ax$ is

$$y=mx+\frac{a}{m}$$

or $my=m^2x+a$ ...(1)

If its pole w.r.t. the parabola $y^2=4bx$ be (h,k), then its equation is

$$ky=2b(x+h).$$

Comparing (1) and (2), we get

$$\frac{m}{k}=\frac{m^2}{2b}=\frac{a}{2bh}$$

$\therefore$ $m=\dfrac{2b}{k}$ and $m=\dfrac{ak}{2bh}$

$\therefore$ $\dfrac{2b}{k}=\dfrac{ak}{2bh}$ or $k^2=\dfrac{4b^2}{a}h$

Hence the locus is $y^2=\dfrac{4b^2}{a}x$ which is a parabola.

11. Chord of contact of $O(-1,2)$ is $yy_1=2a(x+x_1)$,

or $y=x-1$.

Solving with parabola $y^2=4x$, we get the points

$P(3+2\sqrt{2}, 2+2\sqrt{2})$,

$Q(3-2\sqrt{2}, 2-2\sqrt{2})$

$\therefore$ $PQ^2=32+32=64$

$\therefore$ $PQ=8$. Also if p be perpendicular from $O(-1,2)$ on PQ, then area of triangle is

$$\frac{1}{2}PQ\cdot p=\frac{1}{2}8\cdot\left(\frac{4}{\sqrt{2}}\right)=8\sqrt{2}.$$

12. Any tangent to parabola $y^2=4ax$ is

$$y=mx+\frac{a}{m}$$

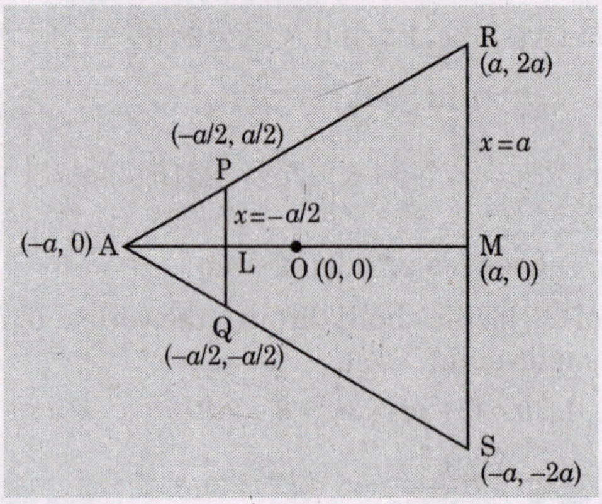

Fig. 28

If it is a tangent to circle $x^2+y^2=\dfrac{a^2}{2}$ then $p=r$ gives

$$2=m^2(m^2+1)=0$$

or $(m^2-1)(m^2+2)=0$

$\therefore$ $m=1,-1.$

Hence common tangents are

$$y = x + a \text{ and } y = -x - a$$

which meet at $A(-a, 0)$

Equation of chord of contact of $A(-a, 0)$ are $x = -\frac{a}{2}$ w.r.t. circle and $x = a$ w.r.t. parabola. We have to find the area enclosed by these four lines. Thus we have to find the area of trapezium $PQRS$

$$A = \frac{1}{2}(PQ + RS)\, LM$$

$$= \frac{1}{2}(4a + a)\frac{3a}{2} = \frac{15a^2}{4}$$

13. Equation of the normal at P

$$y = -t\,x + 2at + at^3$$

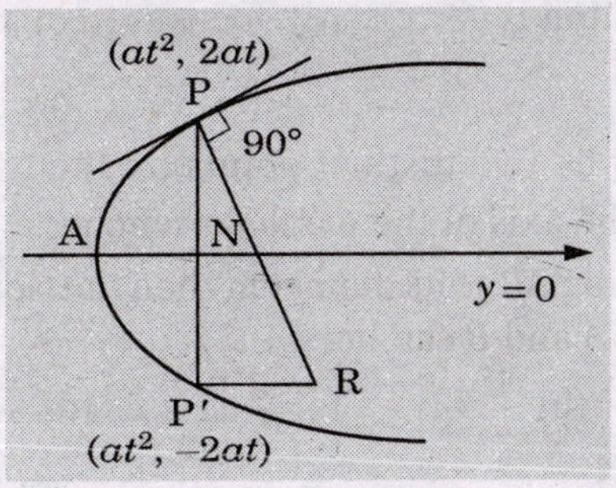

Fig. 29

Equation of $P'R$ is $y = -2at$

They intersect at R whose locus is obtained by eliminating t.

$$y^2 = 4a(x - 4a)$$

14. If A and B be t_1 and t_2, then

$$x_1 = at_1t_2,\ y_1 = a(t_1 + t_2) \quad \text{...(1)}$$

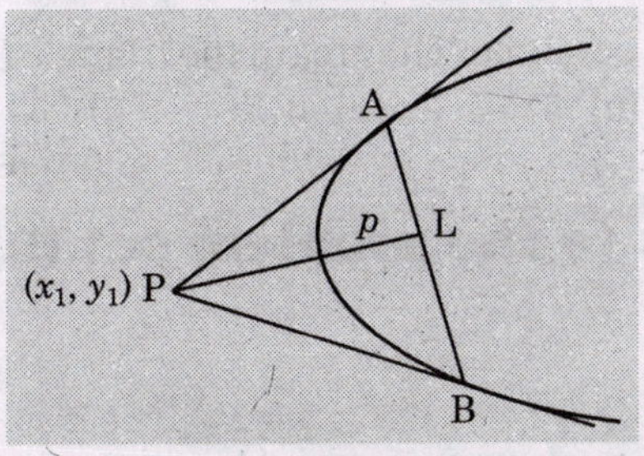

Fig. 30

$$\therefore \quad AB^2 = a^2(t_1^2 - t_2^2)^2 + 4a^2(t_1 - t_2)^2$$

$$= a^2(t_1 - t_2)^2\{(t_1 + t_2)^2 + 4a^2\}$$

$$= a^2\{(t_1 + t_2)^2 - 4t_1t_2\}\{(t_1 + t_2)^2 + 4a^2\}$$

$$= \frac{1}{a^2}(y_1^2 - 4ax_1)(y_1^2 + 4a^2)$$

$\therefore$ AB is as given.

Again if p be perpendicular from (x_1, y_1) on AB whose equation is $yy_1 = 2a(x + x_1)$

or $yy_1 - 2ax - 2ax_1 = 0$

then $$p = \frac{y_1^2 - 4ax_1}{\sqrt{y_1^2 + 4a^2}}$$

$$\therefore \quad \Delta = \frac{1}{2}AB \cdot p = \frac{1}{2a}(y_1^2 - 4ax_1)^{3/2}.$$

15. Any tangent to parabola at $P(at^2, 2at)$ is $ty = x + at^2$

It meets the directrix $x = -a$ at

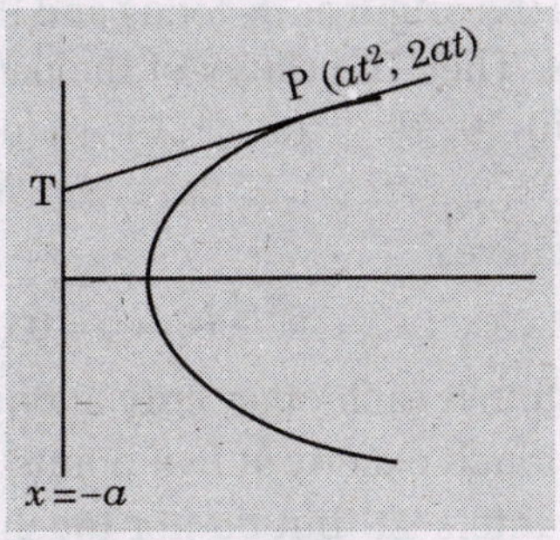

Fig. 31

$$T = \left\{-a, \frac{a(t^2 - 1)}{t}\right\}$$

If (x, y) be the mid-point of PT, then

$$2x = a(t^2 - 1),\ 2y = 2at + \frac{a(t^2 - 1)}{t}$$

or $$2x + a = at^2,\ 2y = \frac{a(3t^2 - 1)}{t}$$

Eliminating t, we get

$$y^2(2x + a) = a(3x + a)^2$$

16. Any tangent to the parabola is $y = mx + \frac{a}{m}$

If it is a tangent to circle then by $p = r$, we have

$$\frac{a/m}{\sqrt{1 + m^2}} = \frac{a}{\sqrt{2}} \quad \text{or} \quad m^4 + m^2 - 2 = 0$$

or $(m^2 - 1)(m^2 + 2) = 0$

$\therefore$ $m^2 = 1$ or $m = \pm 1$

$\therefore$ Common tangents are $y = x + a$ and $y = -x - a$ which meet at $A(-a, 0)$. The chords of contact of the

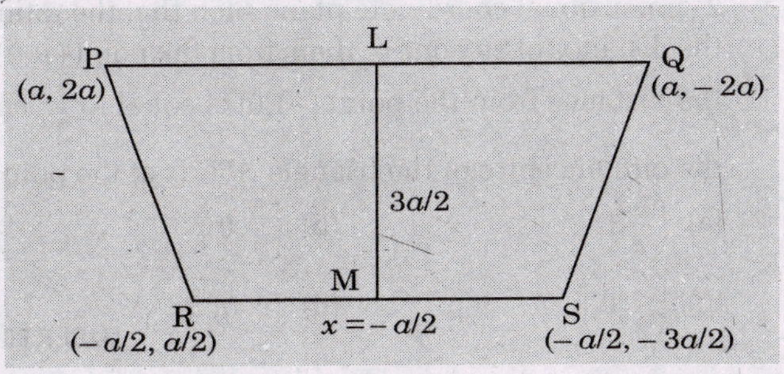

Fig. 32

point $A(-a, 0)$ w.r.t. circle and parabola are $x = -\frac{a}{2}$ and $x = a$ which are parallel and distance between them is $\frac{3a}{2}$. Thus the quadrilateral is a trapezium.

$$\therefore \quad \text{Area} = \frac{1}{2}(PQ + RS)\, LM$$

$$= \frac{1}{2}(4a + a) \cdot \frac{3a}{2} = \frac{15a^2}{4}$$

Problem Set (5)

Multiple Choice Questions

1. A parabola has the origin as its focus and the line $x = 2$ as the directrix. Then the vertex of the parabola at
(a) (2, 0) (b) (0, 2) (c) (1, 0) (d) (0, 1)
(AIEEE 2008)

2. Consider two curves
$$C_1 : y^2 = 4x;\ C_2 : x^2 + y^2 - 6x + 1 = 0 \text{ then}$$
(a) C_1 and C_2 touch each other only at one point
(b) C_1 and C_2 touch exactly at two points
(c) C_1 and C_2 intersect (but do not touch) at exactly two points.
(d) C_1 and C_2 neither intersect nor touch each other
(IIT JEE 2008)

3. If two tangents drawn from a point P on the parabola $y^2 = 4x$ are at right angles, then the locus of P is
(a) $2x - 1 = 0$ (b) $x = 1$
(c) $2x + 1 = 0$ (d) $x = -1$ **(AIEEE 2010)**

4. If P and Q are the points of intersection of the circles
$$x^2 + y^2 + 3x + 7y + 2p - 5 = 0;$$
$$x^2 + y^2 + 2x + 2y - p^2 = 0,$$
then there is a circle passing through P, Q and (1, 1) for
(a) all except one value of p
(b) all except two values of p
(c) exactly one value of p
(d) all values of p **(AIEEE 2009)**

5. The shortest distance between the line $y - x = 1$ and the curve $y = x^2$ is
(a) $\frac{2\sqrt{3}}{8}$ (b) $\frac{3\sqrt{2}}{5}$
(c) $\frac{\sqrt{3}}{4}$ (d) $\frac{3\sqrt{2}}{8}$ **(AIEEE 2009)**

6. Three distinct points A, B and C are given in the 2-dimensional coordinate plane such that the ratio of the distance of any one of them from the point (1, 0) to the distance from the point (−1, 0) is equal to $\frac{1}{3}$. Then the circumcentre of the triangle ABC is at the point
(a) $\left(\frac{5}{4}, 0\right)$ (b) $\left(\frac{5}{2}, 0\right)$
(c) $\left(\frac{5}{3}, 0\right)$ (d) (0, 0)
(AIEEE 2009)

7. The tangent PT and the normal PN to the parabola $y^2 = 4ax$ at a point on it meet its axis at points T and N respectively. The locus of the centroid of the triangle PTN is a parabola whose
(a) vertex is $\left(\frac{2a}{3}, 0\right)$ (b) directrix is $x = 0$
(c) latusrectum is $\frac{2a}{3}$ (d) focus is $(a, 0)$
(IIT-JEE 2009)

8. Let A and B be two distinct points on the hyperbola $y^2 = 4x$. If the axis of the parabola touches a circle of radius r having AB as its diameter, then the slope of the line joining A and B can be
(a) $\frac{-1}{r}$ (b) $\frac{1}{r}$ (c) $\frac{2}{r}$ (d) $\frac{-2}{r}$
(IIT-JEE 2010)

9. Let (x, y) be any point on the parabola $y^2 = 4x$. Let P be the point that divides the line segment from (0, 0) to (x, y) in the ratio 1 : 3. Then locus of P is
(a) $x^2 = y$ (b) $y^2 = 2x$ (c) $y^2 = x$ (d) $x^2 = 2y$
(IIT-JEE 2011)

10. Let S be the focus of the parabola $y^2 = 8x$ and let PQ be the common chord of the circle $x^2 + y^2 - 2x - 4y = 0$ and the given parabola. The area of the triangle PQS is
(a) 4 (b) 5 (c) 6 (d) 8
(IIT-JEE 2012)

Solution to the problem set (5)

1. Ans. (c).

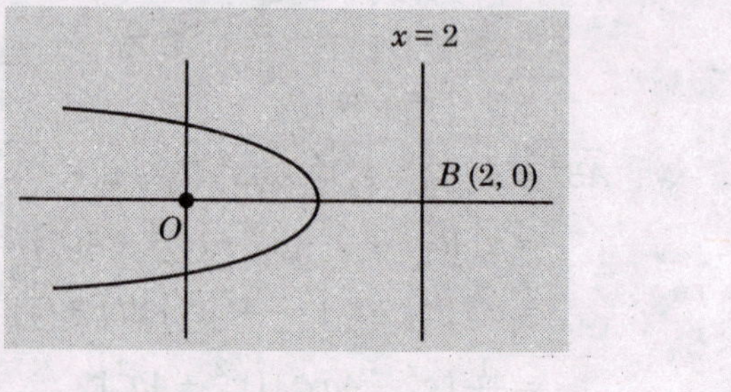

Fig. 33

Vertex = mid point of $OB = (1, 0)$

2. Ans. (b).

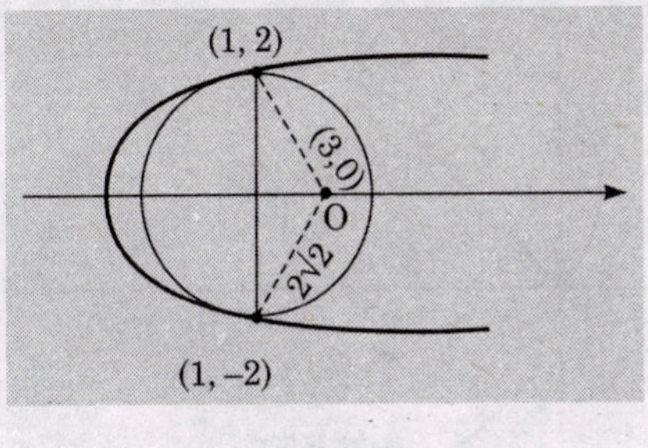

Fig. 34

The circle and the parabola touch each other at $x = 1$ *i.e.*, at the points (1, 2) and (1, – 2)

3. Ans. (d).

Two perpendicular tangents to a parabola intersect at directrix. Thus locus of P is the directrix of the parabola $y^2 = 4x$ *i.e.*, $x = -1$

4. Ans. (a).

$$S + \lambda (S - S') = 0$$

$$\Rightarrow (x^2 + y^2 + 3x + 7y + 2p - 5) + \lambda (x + 5y + 2p - 5 + p^2) = 0$$

This circle satisfy (1, 1).

Therefore $(7 + 2p) + \lambda (p + 1)^2 = 0$

$\lambda = 0$ gives the circle $\left(p = -\frac{7}{2}\right)$

$x^2 + y^2 + 3x + 7y - 12 = 0$ which passes through (1, 1)

5. Ans. (d)

As shortest distance is along the common normal so tangent at P must be parallel to the line $y - x = 1$ and $x = y^2 \Rightarrow 1 = 2yy' \Rightarrow y' = \frac{1}{2y} = 1$

$\therefore$ $P\left(\frac{1}{4}, \frac{1}{2}\right)$. Thus, distance from P to the line $y = x + 1$ is $\frac{3\sqrt{2}}{8}$.

6. Ans. (a). $\frac{PA'}{PB'} = \frac{3}{1}$

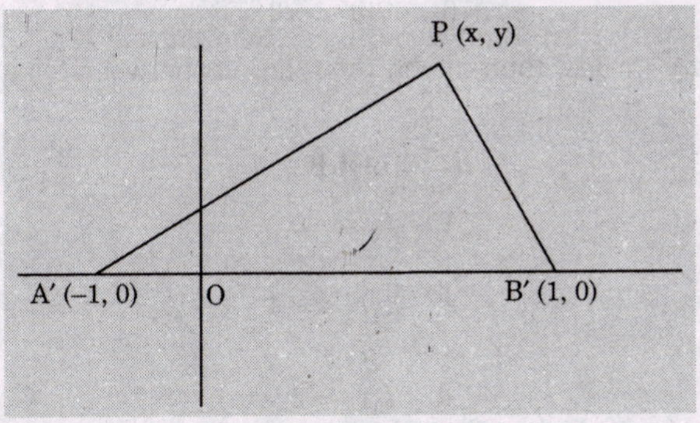

Fig. 35

$$\Rightarrow (x + 1)^2 + y^2 = 9(x - 1)^2 + y^2$$

$$\Rightarrow x^2 + 2x + 1 + y^2 = 9x^2 + 9y^2 - 18x + 9$$

$$\Rightarrow 8x^2 + 8y^2 - 20x + 8 = 0$$

$$\Rightarrow x^2 + y^2 - \frac{10}{4}x + 1 = 0 \quad \therefore \quad \text{Circumcentre}\left(\frac{5}{4}, 0\right)$$

7. Ans. (a) and (b).

Tangent at P is $yt = x + at^2$

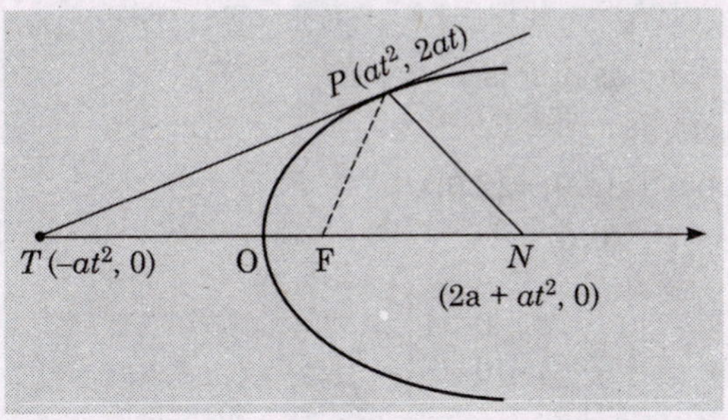

Fig. 36

Let $G = (h, k)$ and normal is $y = -tx + 2at + at^2$

$$\Rightarrow h = \frac{2a + at^2}{3}, k = \frac{2at}{3} \quad \Rightarrow \quad \frac{3h - 2a}{a} = \frac{9k^2}{4a^2}$$

$$\therefore \quad \text{Required parabola } \frac{9y^2}{4a^2} = \frac{3x - 2a}{a} = \frac{3}{2}\left(x - \frac{2a}{3}\right)$$

$$\Rightarrow y^2 = \frac{4a}{3}\left(x - \frac{2a}{3}\right)$$

$$\therefore \quad \text{vertex} = \left(\frac{2a}{3}, 0\right) : \text{focus} = (a, 0)$$

8. Ans. (c) and (d).

Let $A = (t_1^2, 2t_1)$; $B = (t_2^2, 2t_2)$

Centre of circle on AB as diameter $= \left(\frac{t_1^2 + t_2^2}{2}, t_1 + t_2\right)$

Since this circle is of radius r and touches axis of the parabola *i.e.*, x-axis

$\therefore$ $|t_1 + t_2| = r$ and slope of $AB = \frac{2}{t_1 + t_2} = \pm\frac{2}{r}$

9. Ans. (c).

Given $\frac{OP}{PR} = \frac{1}{3}$

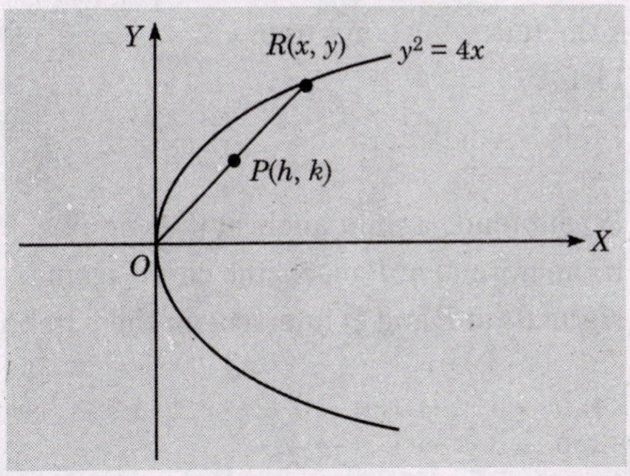

Fig. 37

$\Rightarrow \quad h = \dfrac{1.x + 3.0}{1+3} \Rightarrow x = 4h$

and $k = \dfrac{1.y + 3.0}{1+3} \Rightarrow y = 4k$

Since $R(x, y)$ lies on $y^2 = 4x$

$\therefore \quad (4k)^2 = 4(4h) \Rightarrow k^2 = h$

$\therefore \quad$ locus of P is $y^2 = x$

10. Ans. (a).

Focus is $(a, 0) = (2, 0)$

$P = (0, 0)$

$$A = \frac{1}{2}\begin{vmatrix} 2 & 0 & 1 \\ 2 & 0 & 1 \\ \frac{\alpha^2}{8} & \alpha & 1 \end{vmatrix} = \frac{1}{2}(2\alpha) = \alpha$$

We need y coordinate of $Q(2t^2, 4t)$ satisfies circle, therefore,

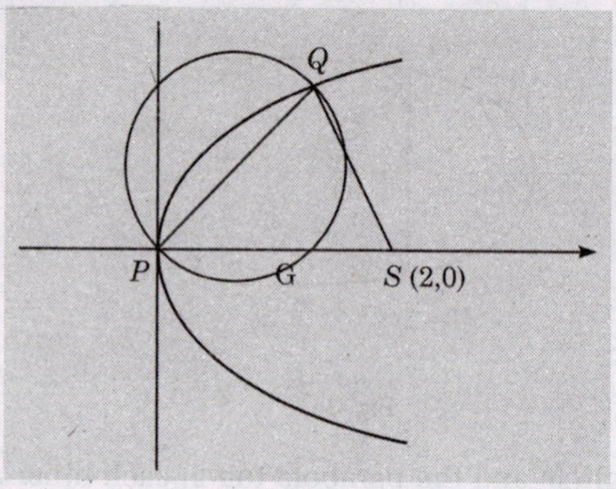

Fig. 38

$4t^4 + 16t^2 - 4t^2 - 16t = 0$

$\Rightarrow \quad t^3 + 3t - 4 = 0 \quad \Rightarrow \quad t = 1$

$\therefore \quad$ Area $= 4t = 4 \times 1 = 4$

MISCELLANEOUS EXERCISE

Matching Entries

Match the entries of List-A and List-B.

1.

List-A	List-B
(a) Focus of parabola $x^2 - 4x - 8y - 4 = 0$ is ...	1. G.P.
(b) Directrix of parabola $y^2 + 4y + 4x + 2 = 0$ is ...	2. $(32, 32)$
(c) Tangent at points P and Q on the parabola $y^2 = 4ax$ meet at T then SP, ST, SQ are in which series where S is focus ?	3. $x = 3/2$
(d) PQ is a focal chord of the parabola $y^2 = 32x$ and if P be $(2, -8)$, then the point Q is ...	4. $(2, 1)$
(e) PQ is a normal chord of the parabola $y^2 = 4ax$ which subtends a right angle at the vertex. PQ is inclined to axis of x at an angle ...	5. $y^2 = 2a(x - 4a)$
(f) The locus of mid-point of the chords of the parabola which subtend a right angle at the vertex is ...	6. $\tan^{-1}\sqrt{2}$

2. Let $P(at_1^2, 2at_1), Q(at_2^2, 2at_2)$ be two points on the parabola $y^2 = 4ax$, then match the relations between t_1 and t_2 under the following conditions :

List-A	List-B
(a) PQ is a focal chord	1. $t_2 = -t_1 - \dfrac{2}{t_1}$
(b) PQ subtends a right angle at the vertex	2. $t_1 t_2 = -1$
(c) If the normal at P meets the curve again at Q	3. $t_1 t_2 = -4$
(d) Normals at P and Q intersect on the parabola	4. $t_1 t_2 = 2$

Answers

1. a → 4, b → 3, c → 1, d → 2 e → 6, f → 5

2. a → 2, b → 3, c → 1, d → 4

Hints/Solutions

1. (a) $(x-2)^2 = 8(y+1)$ or $X^2 = 4AY$

Focus $X = 0, Y = A$

or $x-2=0, y+1=2$ $\therefore$ (2, 1)

(b) **See Q. 1 (c) P. 960-961**

(c) **See Q. 20 (a) P. 977-984**

(d) If the given point be $(at_1^2, 2at_1)$, where $4a = 32$, then $2at_1 = -8$ $\therefore$ $t_1 = -1/2$.

Also $t_1 t_2 = -1$ $\therefore$ $t_2 = -1/t_1 = 2$.

$\therefore$ Other extremity $= (at_2^2, 2at_2) = (32, 32)$ as $a = 8, t_2 = 2$.

(e) **See Q. 31 P. 977-984**

(f) **See Q. 3 (a) P. 995-996**

2. (a) **See § 2 (c) P. 966**

(b) **See Q. 2 (c_1) P. 967**

(c) **See Q. 25 (a) P. 977-986**

(d) **See Q. 39 (a) P. 979-992**

Assertion / Reason

1. **STATEMENT-1 :** The curve $y = \frac{-x^2}{2} + x + 1$ is symmetric with respect to the line $x = 1$.

because

STATEMENT-2 : A parabola is symmetric about its axis. **(I.I.T. 2007)**

Sol. Ans. (a).

The given equation can be written as

$$-2y = x^2 - 2x - 2 = (x-1)^2 - 3$$

$$\therefore \quad (x-1)^2 = -2(y - 3/2) \text{ or } X^2 = -4AY$$

It is symmetrical about the line $X = 0$ *i.e.* $x = 1$ which is axis of the parabola.

Fascinating Facts

- We can see that $\frac{x^2}{a^2} + \frac{y^2}{b^2} = 1$, $b^2 = a^2(1-e^2)$ is also the equation of the ellipse with focus $(-ae, 0)$ directrix $x + \frac{a}{e} = 0$ and eccentricity e. It follows that an ellipse has atleast two focus-directrix pairs.
- If $e = 0$, we get $b^2 = a^2$, and the equation of the ellipse reduces to $\frac{x^2}{a^2} + \frac{y^2}{a^2} = 1 \Rightarrow x^2 + y^2 = a^2$, which is the equation of the circle, thus we can regard a circle as a limiting case of an ellipse or an ellipse with $e = 0$. In this case focus is (0, 0) and the directrix becomes $x = \frac{a}{0}$, a line that does not exist in the system.
- If x increases then y decreases and if x decreases then y increases. When $x = 0$, we get the largest ordinate b and when $x = a$ we get $y = 0$.
- If P be any point on the ellipse with foci F_1 and F_2 then $|PF_1| + |PF_2| =$ constant, which is greater than $|F_1F_2|$ and conversly *i.e.*, if F_1, F_2 be two distinct points and a be a constant such that $a > \frac{1}{2}|F_1F_2|$ then the locus of point P so that $|PF_1| + |PF_2| = 2a$ is an ellipse with foci F_1 and F_2.
- If F_1 and F_2 are fixed points and P is a variable points such that $|PF_1| + |PF_2| = k$ a constant, then locus of P is
  (i) the empty set if $k < |F_1F_2|$
  (ii) the segment (F_1F_2) if $k = |F_1F_2|$

❑

CHAPTER **21** **Co-ordinates Geometry**

The Ellipse

§ 1. Ellipse and its equation in standard form

Definition : Ellipse is the locus of a point which moves so that its distance from a fixed point called focus bears a constant ratio to its distance from a fixed straight line called directrix. This ratio is called eccentricity and is denoted by e. **It is always less than unity.**

Equation of the ellipse in standard form

$$\frac{x^2}{a^2}+\frac{y^2}{b^2}=1.$$

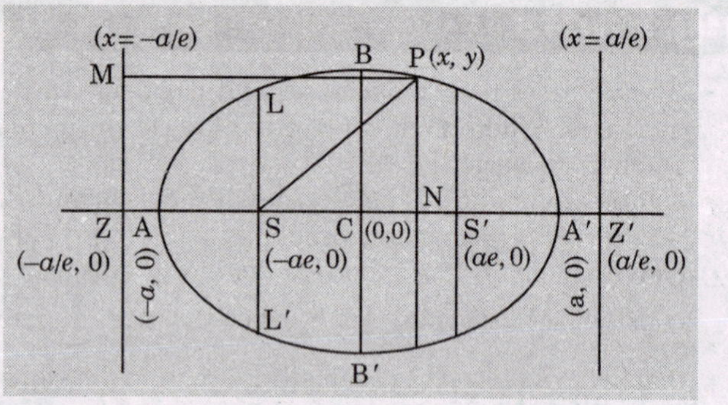

Fig. 1

Let ZM be the directrix of the ellipse and S be the focus. Draw SZ perpendicular on the directrix from the focus. Since the eccentricity e is less than unity, we can always divide ZS both internally and externally in the ratio $1:e$ at the points A and A' respectively so that

$$SA=e\,.\,AZ \qquad ...(1)$$

$$SA'=e\,.\,ZA' \qquad ...(2)$$

Now A and A' are such points that their distances from the focus bear constant ratio to their respective distances from the directrix and hence by definition they lie on the ellipse. Let AA' be of length $2a$ and C be its middle point so that

$$CA=CA'=a \qquad ...(3)$$

Rewriting the relations (1) and (2), we get

$$CA-CS=e\,(CZ-CA)$$

$$CA'+CS=e\,(CZ+CA')$$

Adding, we get $CA+CA'=e\,(2CZ)$

or $\quad 2a=2e.CZ, \qquad$ by (3)

$\therefore \quad \boldsymbol{CZ=a/e.} \qquad ...(4)$

Subtracting, we get

$$2CS=e\,(CA'+CA)=e\,.\,2a$$

$\therefore \quad \boldsymbol{CS=ae.} \qquad ...(5)$

Now choose the point C as origin of co-ordinates and the line CA' as x-axis and a line through C perpendicular to CA' be chosen as y-axis. Hence the co-ordinates of focus S with respect to C as origin are $(-ae, 0)$ and the directrix ZM being parallel to y-axis at a distance $CZ=a/e$ from the origin will have its equation as $x=-a/e$.

From P any point on the ellipse draw perpendicular PM on the directrix. Then by definition

$$SP=e\,.\,PM \qquad \text{or} \qquad SP^2=e^2\,PM^2$$

or $\quad (x+ae)^2+y^2=e^2\,(ZN)^2=e^2\,(CZ+CN)^2$

$$=e^2\left(\frac{a}{e}+x\right)^2, \qquad \text{by (4)}$$

or $\quad x^2+2aex+a^2e^2+y^2=a^2+2aex+e^2x^2.$

or $\quad x^2\,(1-e^2)+y^2=a^2\,(1-e^2)$

or $\quad \dfrac{x^2}{a^2}+\dfrac{y^2}{a^2\,(1-e^2)}=1.$

Let us put $\boldsymbol{b^2=a^2\,(1-e^2)}$ then the above equation takes the form $\boldsymbol{\dfrac{x^2}{a^2}+\dfrac{y^2}{b^2}=1}$ which is the standard form of the equation of the ellipse.

Various results and properties connected with the equation

$$\frac{x^2}{a^2}+\frac{y^2}{b^2}=1.$$

(a) The points $\boldsymbol{A}$ and $\boldsymbol{A'}$ are called the vertices of the ellipse and the line joining them is called the **major axis** whose length $AA'=\boldsymbol{2a}$ where $\boldsymbol{A}$ is $\boldsymbol{(-a, 0)}$ and $\boldsymbol{A'}$ is $\boldsymbol{(a, 0)}$.

(b) The axis of y *i.e.*, $x=0$ cuts the ellipse $x^2/a^2+y^2/b^2=1$ in points B and B' whose co-ordinates are $\boldsymbol{B(0, b), B'(0, -b)}$ and line joining them, *i.e.* $\boldsymbol{BB'}$ is called **minor axis of the ellipse** whose length is $\boldsymbol{2b}$.

(c) We have taken $\boldsymbol{b^2=a^2\,(1-e^2)}$ and since $e<1$ hence $\boldsymbol{a>b}$ or $AA'>BB'$.

(d) **Eccentricity :** From the relation $b^2 = a^2(1 - e^2)$, we get

$$\frac{b^2}{a^2} = 1 - e^2 \quad \text{or} \quad \mathbf{e} = \sqrt{\left(1 - \frac{b^2}{a^2}\right)}.$$

(e) **Latus rectum :** The chord of the ellipse which passes through the focus and is perpendicular to major axis is called latus rectum and its equation is clearly $x = -ae$. If its length be $2l$ then the co-ordinates of the point L i.e. $(-ae, l)$ satisfy the equation of the ellipse

$$\therefore \quad \frac{a^2e^2}{a^2} + \frac{l^2}{b^2} = 1 \qquad l^2 = b^2(1 - e^2)$$

But $b^2 = a^2(1 - e^2)$ or $\frac{b^2}{a^2} = 1 - e^2$

$$\therefore \quad l^2 = b^2 \frac{b^2}{a^2} \quad \text{or} \quad l = \frac{b^2}{a}$$

$$\therefore \quad 2l = \frac{2b^2}{a} = \textbf{length of latus rectum}$$

and $\mathbf{L} = \left(-ae, \frac{b^2}{a}\right)$ and $\mathbf{L'} = \left(-ae, -\frac{b^2}{a}\right)$.

(f) As shown in the figure there is always a second focus $S'(ae, 0)$ and a second directrix $Z'M', x = a/e$.

(g) **Focal distance :** The distance of any point on the ellipse from the focus is called the focal distance of that point.

(h)* **The sum of the focal distances of a point on the ellipse is constant and is equal to the length of the major axis.**

Let the co-ordinates of point P be (x, y) then

$$SP = e \cdot PM = e(CZ + CN)$$
$$= e(a/e + x) = a + ex$$
$$S'P = e \cdot PM' = e(CZ' - CN)$$
$$= e(a/e - x) = a - ex$$
$$\therefore \quad SP + S'P = (a + ex) + (a - ex)$$
$$= 2a = \textbf{major axis.}$$

Another definition of an ellipse :

An ellipse is the locus of a point which moves so that sum of its distances from two fixed points (foci) is constant.

We have already deduced the equation of the ellipse from the above definition.

Another form :

In the equation of the ellipse

$$* \quad \frac{x^2}{a^2} + \frac{y^2}{b^2} = 1 \qquad a^2 > b^2$$

i.e. Denominator of x^2 is greater than denominator of y^2.

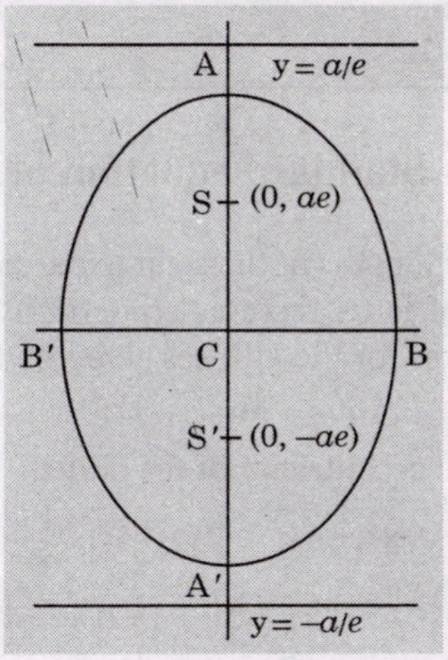

Fig. 2

But if the equation of the ellipse be

$$\frac{x^2}{b^2} + \frac{y^2}{a^2} = 1 \qquad a^2 > b^2$$

i.e. Denominator of y^2 is greater than denominator of x^2 then its shape will be as shown in the adjoining figure. Then the major axis lies along y-axis and is of length $2a$ and minor axis lies along x-axis and is of length $2b$. Foci are $(0, \pm ae)$ on y-axis and directrices are lines parallel to x-axis

i.e. $y = \pm\frac{a}{e}$ and latus rectum $= \frac{2b^2}{a}$

and $e = \sqrt{\left(1 - \frac{b^2}{a^2}\right)}$.

FACTS ABOUT THE ELLIPSE

	$\frac{x^2}{a^2} + \frac{y^2}{b^2} = 1$ $a > 0, b > 0$	$\frac{x^2}{b^2} + \frac{y^2}{a^2} = 1$ $a > 0, b > 0$
Equation of major axis	$y = 0$	$x = 0$
Length of major axis	$2a$	$2a$
Eqn. of minor axis	$x = 0$	$y = 0$
Length of minor axis	$2b$	$2b$
Vertices	$(\pm a, 0)$	$(0, \pm a)$
Foci	$(\pm ae, 0)$	$(0, \pm ae)$
Directrices	$x = \pm\frac{a}{e}$	$x = \pm\frac{a}{e}$
Equations of latera-recta	$x = \pm ae$	$y = \pm ae$
Length of latus rectum	$\frac{2b^2}{a}$	$\frac{2b^2}{a}$
Centre	$(0, 0)$	$(0, 0)$
Focal distances of (x, y)	$a - ex, a + ex$	$a - ey, a + ey$

Problem Set (1)

Standard equation of ellipse $\frac{x^2}{a^2}+\frac{y^2}{b^2}=1$, Points on an ellipse, Eccentricity.

1. Find the lengths of the semi-axes, co-ordinates of foci, length of latus rectum, eccentricity and equation of directrices for the ellipses given by the equations

(i) $25x^2-150x+16y^2=175$

(ii)* The eccentricity of the ellipse

$9x^2+4y^2-30y=0$ is $\frac{1}{3}\sqrt{5}$. (T or F)

(iii) $2x^2+y^2-8x-2y+1=0$

(iv) $4x^2+y^2-8x+2y+1=0$

(v) $25x^2+16y^2=400$.

(vi)* The foci of the ellipse, $25(x+1)^2+9(y+2)^2=225$, are at $(-1,2)$ and $(-1,-6)$. **(M.N.R. 1991)**

2. (a) Find the equation of the ellipse whose focus is the point (6, 7), directrix $x+y+2=0$ and eccentricity $1/\sqrt{3}$.

(b)* An ellipse has eccentricity $\frac{1}{2}$ and one focus at the point $P\left(\frac{1}{2},1\right)$. Its one directrix is the common tangent, nearer to the point P, to the circle $x^2+y^2=1$ and the hyperbola $x^2-y^2=1$. The equation of the ellipse, in the standard form, is .... **(I.I.T. 1996)**

3. Find the eccentricity of the ellipse if

(a) Length of latus rectum = half of major axis.

(b) Length of latus rectum = half of minor axis.

(c)* The angle between the straight lines joining the foci to an extremity of minor axis be 90°.

(d)* An ellipse has OB as a semi-minor axis. F, F' are its foci, and the angle FBF' is a right angle. Then the eccentricity of the ellipse is .... **(I.I.T. 1997)**

(e) In an ellipse, the distance between its foci is 6 and minor axis 8. The eccentricity of the ellipse is :

(a) $\frac{1}{2}$ (b) $\frac{4}{5}$

(c) $\frac{1}{\sqrt{5}}$ (d) $\frac{3}{5}$ **(AIEEE 2006)**

4. Find the equations of the ellipse under given conditions

(a) L.R. = 10, distance between foci = length of minor axis.

(b) foci are (3, 2) and (1, –2) and major axis is of length 10.

(c) centre at (2, –3), focus (3, – 3) and vertex at (4, – 3).

(d)* foci (0, 1), (0, – 1) and minor axis of length 1.

(e)* Find the lengths and the equations of the focal radii drawn to the point $(4\sqrt{3},5)$ on the ellipse $25x^2+16y^2=1600$

(f)* Find the equation of the ellipse which passes through the origin and has its foci at the points (1, 0) and (3, 0).

(g) Find the equation of the ellipse passing through (2, 1) and having $e=1/2$.

(h) The eccentricity of the ellipse with its centre at the origin is 1/2. If one of the directrices is $x=4$, then the equation of the ellipse is :

(a) $3x^2+4y^2=1$ (b) $3x^2+4y^2=12$

(c) $4x^2+3y^2=12$ (d) $4x^2+3y^2=1$ **(AIEEE 2004)**

5. A bar of given length moves with its extremities on two fixed straight lines at right angles. Prove that any point of the rod describes an ellipse.

6. (a)* An ellipse is described by using an endless string which is passed over two pins. If the axes are 6 cm and 4 cm, find necessary length and the distance between the pins.

(b)* A man running round a racecourse notes that the sum of the distances of two flag-posts from him is always 10 metres and the distance between the flag-posts is 8 metres. Prove that the area of the path he encloses in square metres is 15 π.

7.* (a) The distance of a point on the ellipse

$$\frac{x^2}{6}+\frac{y^2}{2}=1$$

from the centre is 2. Find the eccentric angle of the point. **(M.N.R. 1990)**

(b) The eccentric angle of a point P lying in the first quadrant on the ellipse $\frac{x^2}{a^2}+\frac{y^2}{b^2}=1$ is θ. If OP makes an angle φ with x-axis, then $\theta-\phi$ will be maximum when θ =

(a) $\tan^{-1}\sqrt{\frac{a}{b}}$ (b) $\tan^{-1}\sqrt{\frac{b}{a}}$

(c) $\frac{\pi}{4}$ (d) none

8. (a)* Let P be a variable point on the ellipse $\frac{x^2}{a^2}+\frac{y^2}{b^2}=1$ with foci S_1 and S_2. If A be the area of the triangle PS_1S_2, then the maximum value of A is ..... **(I.I.T. 1994)**

(b) If e_1, e_2 be respectively the eccentricities of ellipse $9x^2+4y^2=36$ and hyperbola $9x^2-4y^2=36$, then

(a) $e_1^2 + e_2^2 > 3$ (b) $e_1^2 + e_2^2 = 2$

(c) $e_1^2 + e_2^2 > 4$ (d) $e_1^2 + e_2^2 < 4$

9. If the portion of the line $x\cos\alpha + y\sin\alpha = p$ intercepted by the ellipse $\frac{x^2}{a^2} + \frac{y^2}{b^2} = 1$, subtends a right angle at the centre of the ellipse, prove that the line touches a circle of radius $ab/\sqrt{(a^2+b^2)}$ concentric with the ellipse.

10. (a)* The following equation represents an ellipse, $25(x^2 - 6x + 9) + 16y^2 = 400$, find the centre and the foci of the ellipse. How should the axes be transformed so that the ellipse is represented by the equation $x^2/25 + y^2/16 = 1$.

(b)* Determine the length of latus rectum, eccentricity and co-ordinates of centre of the ellipse $4(x - 2y + 1)^2 + 9(2x + y + 2)^2 = 25$.

11. If $P = (x, y)$, $F_1 = (3, 0)$, $F_2 = (-3, 0)$ and $16x^2 + 25y^2 = 400$, then $PF_1 + PF_2$ equals

(a) 8 (b) 6 (c) 10 (d) 12

(I.I.T. 1998)

12. P is a variable point on the ellipse $\frac{x^2}{a^2} + \frac{y^2}{b^2} = 1$ whose foci are the points S_1 and S_2. Prove that locus of the incentre of ΔPS_1S_2 is an ellipse whose eccentricity is $\sqrt{\frac{2e}{1+e}}$.

13. If the line $x + 2y + 4 = 0$ cutting the ellipse in points whose eccentric angles are 30° and 60° subtends a right angle at the origin, then its equation is :

(a) $\frac{x^2}{4} + \frac{y^2}{16} = 1$ (b) $\frac{x^2}{16} + \frac{y^2}{4} = 1$

(c) $\frac{x^2}{8} + \frac{y^2}{4} = 1$ (d) $\frac{x^2}{4} + \frac{y^2}{8} = 1$

14. Let $P(x_1, y_1)$ and $Q(x_2, y_2)$, $y_1 < 0$, $y_2 < 0$, be the end points of the latus rectum of the ellipse $x^2 + 4y^2 = 4$. The equations of parabolas with latus rectum PQ are

(a) $x^2 + 2\sqrt{3}\,y = 3 + \sqrt{3}$ (b) $x^2 - 2\sqrt{3}\,y = 3 + \sqrt{3}$

(c) $x^2 + 2\sqrt{3}\,y = 3 - \sqrt{3}$ (d) $x^2 - 2\sqrt{3}\,y = 3 - \sqrt{3}$

(IIT 2008)

15. The ellipse $x^2 + 4y^2 = 4$ is inscribed in a rectangle aligned with the coordinate axes, which in turn is inscribed in another ellipse that passes through the point (4, 0). Then the equation of the ellipse is

(a) $4x^2 + 64y^2 = 48$ (b) $x^2 + 16y^2 = 16$

(c) $x^2 + 12y^2 = 16$ (d) $4x^2 + 48y^2 = 48$

(AIEEE 2009)

Solutions to Problem Set (1)

1. (i) $25(x^2 - 6x) + 16y^2 = 175$

$25(x^2 - 6x + 9) + 16y^2 = 175 + 225 = 400$

or $25(x-3)^2 + 16y^2 = 400$

or $\frac{(x-3)^2}{16} + \frac{y^2}{25} = 1$

or $\frac{X^2}{b^2} + \frac{Y^2}{a^2} = 1,\ a^2 > b^2$

where $X = x - 3, Y = y, b^2 = 16, a^2 = 25$

Here major axis lies along y-axis as the denominator of y^2 is greater than that of x^2. Centre is $X = 0, Y = 0$ or $x - 3 = 0,\ y = 0$ *i.e.* (3, 0)

$$e = \sqrt{\left(1 - \frac{b^2}{a^2}\right)} = \sqrt{\left(1 - \frac{16}{25}\right)} = \frac{3}{5}$$

Foci on y-axis $X = 0$, $Y = \pm ae$

$x - 3 = 0,\ y = \pm 5 \cdot 3/5$ *i.e.* $(3, \pm 3)$.

Directrices $Y = \pm\frac{a}{e}$ or $y = \pm\frac{5}{3/5}$ or $y = \pm\frac{25}{3}$

$$L.R. = \frac{2b^2}{a} = 2 \cdot \frac{16}{5} = \frac{32}{5}.$$

(ii) Ans. True.

$$9x^2 + 4\left(y^2 - \frac{15}{2}y + \frac{225}{16}\right) = \frac{225}{4}$$

or $\frac{x^2}{225/36} + \frac{(y - 15/4)^2}{225/16} = 1$

$\therefore\ a^2 = \frac{225}{16}, b^2 = \frac{225}{36}$

$\therefore\ e^2 = 1 - \frac{b^2}{a^2} = 1 - \frac{16}{36} = 1 - \frac{4}{9} = \frac{5}{9}$

$\therefore\ e = \frac{1}{3}\sqrt{5}.$

(iii) $2x^2 + y^2 - 8x - 2y + 1 = 0.$

or $2(x^2 - 4x) + (y^2 - 2y + 1) = 0$

or $2(x^2 - 4x + 4) + (y^2 - 2y + 1) = 8.$

or $2(x-2)^2 + (y-1)^2 = 8$

or $\frac{(x-2)^2}{4} + \frac{(y-1)^2}{8} = 1$ or $\frac{X^2}{4} + \frac{Y^2}{8} = 1.$

where $X = x - 2, Y = y - 1, a^2 = 8, b^2 = 4$

and major axis lies along y-axis as in part (a).

$$e = \sqrt{\left(1 - \frac{b^2}{a^2}\right)} = \sqrt{\left(1 - \frac{4}{8}\right)} = \frac{1}{\sqrt{2}}$$

Centre $X = 0, Y = 0$, *i.e.* (2, 1). Foci lie on y-axis $X = 0, Y = \pm ae$

or $x - 2 = 0,\ y - 1 = \pm 2\sqrt{2}.\frac{1}{\sqrt{2}}$

or $(2, -1)$ and $(2, 3)$

$$L.R. = \frac{2b^2}{a} = 2 \cdot \frac{4}{2\sqrt{2}} = 2\sqrt{2}.$$

Directrices $y = \pm \frac{a}{e}$ or $y - 1 = \pm \frac{2\sqrt{2}}{1/\sqrt{2}} = \pm 4$

$\therefore$ $y = -3, y = 5$

(iv) $\frac{(x-1)^2}{1} + \frac{(y+1)^2}{4} = 1; e = \frac{\sqrt{3}}{2},$

Foci $(1, -1 \pm \sqrt{3})$, Directrices $y = -1 \pm \frac{4}{\sqrt{3}}$.

(v) $e = 3/5$, foci $(0, \pm 3)$,
Directrices $y = \pm (25/3)$.

(vi) The equation can be written as

$$\frac{(x+1)^2}{9} + \frac{(y+2)^2}{25} = 1 \qquad ...(1)$$

$a^2 = 25, b^2 = 9$

Major axis along y-axis; $e = 4/5$.
Foci are $X = 0, Y = \pm ae$
$x + 1 = 0, y + 2 = \pm ae = \pm 4$ as in (iii) etc.

2. (a) By definition $SP = e.PM$

$$\sqrt{\{(x-6)^2 + (y-7)^2\}} = \frac{1}{\sqrt{3}} \frac{x+y+2}{\sqrt{(1+1)}}.$$

Square $6(x^2 + y^2 - 12x - 14y + 85) = x^2 + y^2 + 4 + 2xy + 4y + 4x$

or $5x^2 + 5y^2 - 76x - 88y - 2xy + 506 = 0.$

(b) On solving, the circle and hyperbola intersect where $x^2 = 1$ and $y^2 = 0$

$\therefore$ $A(1, 0)$, $B(-1, 0)$

Out of these two points the point $A(1, 0)$ is nearer to focus $P\left(\frac{1}{2}, 1\right)$. Hence directrix is common tangent at A which is $x.1 + y.0 = 1$ or $x - 1 = 0$. By definition $SP = e.PM$ where S is focus $\left(\frac{1}{2}, 0\right)$ and P any point (x, y) on the ellipse and directrix is the line $x - 1 = 0$ and $e = 1/2$

$$\left(x - \frac{1}{2}\right)^2 + (y-1)^2 = \left(\frac{1}{2}\right)^2 \{x - 1\}^2$$

or $3x^2 - 2x + 4y^2 - 8y + 4 = 0$

or $3\left(x - \frac{1}{3}\right)^2 + 4(y-1)^2 = \frac{1}{3}$

or $9\left(x - \frac{1}{3}\right)^2 + 12(y-1)^2 = 1$

3. (a) $\frac{2b^2}{a} = \frac{1}{2} 2a$ $\therefore$ $2b^2 = a^2$

$$e = \sqrt{\left(1 - \frac{b^2}{a^2}\right)} = \sqrt{\left(1 - \frac{1}{2}\right)} = \frac{1}{\sqrt{2}}.$$

(b) $\frac{2b^2}{a} = \frac{1}{2}.2b$ $\therefore$ $b^2 = \frac{1}{4}a^2$.

$$e = \sqrt{\left(1 - \frac{b^2}{a^2}\right)} = \sqrt{\left(1 - \frac{1}{4}\right)} = \frac{1}{2}\sqrt{3}.$$

(c) $A(ae, 0)$, $B(0, b)$, $A'(-ae, 0)$ s.t. $AB \perp A'B$

$m_1 = \frac{b}{-ae}$ = slope of AB,

$m_2 = \frac{b}{ae}$ = slope of $A'B$

$\therefore$ $m_1 m_2 = -1$ or $\frac{b^2}{-a^2e^2} = -1$ or $b^2 = a^2e^2$

$\therefore$ $e^2 = 1 - \frac{b^2}{a^2} = 1 - e^2$ or $2e^2 = 1$ $\therefore$ $e = \frac{1}{\sqrt{2}}$

(d) Ans. $\frac{1}{\sqrt{2}}$. Use $m_1 m_2 = -1$

$-\frac{b}{ae} \cdot \frac{b}{ae} = -1$ or $b^2 = a^2e^2$

or $a^2(1 - e^2) = a^2e^2$ $\therefore$ $2e^2 = 1$

or $e = 1/\sqrt{2}$.

(e) Ans. (d).

$2ae = 6$, $2b = 8$ $\therefore$ $\frac{ae}{b} = \frac{3}{4}$

or $16a^2e^2 = 9b^2 = 9a^2(1 - e^2)$

or $25e^2 = 9$ or $e = \frac{3}{5}$.

4. (a) $(2b^2/a) = 10$ and $2ae = 2b$ or $b = ae$

but $b^2 = a^2 - a^2e^2$

or $a^2e^2 = a^2 - a^2e^2$ or $2e^2 = 1$

$\therefore$ $e = \frac{1}{\sqrt{2}}$

$\frac{2b^2}{a} = 10$ or $\frac{2a^2(1 - e^2)}{a} = 10$

or $a\left(1 - \frac{1}{2}\right) = 5$ $\therefore$ $a = 10$

and $b = ae = 10 \cdot \frac{1}{\sqrt{2}} = 5\sqrt{2}$.

Hence $a^2 > b^2$ and the equation of the ellipse is

$$\frac{x^2}{a^2} + \frac{y^2}{b^2} = 1 \text{ or } \frac{x^2}{100} + \frac{y^2}{50} = 1$$

or $x^2 + 2y^2 = 100$

(b) We know that in the case of an ellipse the sum of the focal distances of any point on the ellipse is equal to length of major axis.

$$\therefore \sqrt{\{(x-3)^2 + (y-2)^2\}} + \sqrt{\{(x-1)^2 + (y+2)^2\}} = 10 \quad ...(1)$$

But on simplification we find that

$$\{(x-3)^2 + (y-2)^2\} - \{(x-1)^2 + (y+2)^2\} = -4x - 8y + 8 \quad ...(2)$$

Dividing (2) by (1) and noting that $\frac{a^2 - b^2}{a + b} = a - b$, we get

$$\sqrt{\{(x-3)^2 + (y-2)^2\}} - \sqrt{\{(x-1)^2 + (y+2)^2\}} = -\frac{4(x + 2y - 2)}{10} \quad ...(3)$$

Adding (1) and (3), we get

$$2\sqrt{\{(x-3)^2+(y-2)^2\}}=10-\frac{2}{5}.(x+2y-2)$$

$$25(x^2+y^2-6x-4y+13)=(27-x-2y)^2$$

or $24x^2-4xy+21y^2-96x+8y-404=0.$

(c) C is centre, A is vertex and S is focus so that $CA=a$, $CS=ae$.

$$CA=\sqrt{\{(4-2)^2+0^2\}}=2=a$$

$$CS=\sqrt{\{(3-2)^2+0^2\}}=1=ae.$$

$\therefore \quad e=\frac{1}{2}$ or $e^2=\frac{1}{4}=1-\frac{b^2}{a^2}$

or $\frac{1}{4}=1-\frac{b^2}{4}$ $\therefore$ $\frac{b^2}{4}=1-\frac{1}{4}=\frac{3}{4}$

or $b^2=3.$

Hence $a^2=4, b^2=3$ and centre is $(2,-3)$.

$\therefore \quad X=x-2, Y=y+3.$

Hence the equation of the ellipse is $\frac{X^2}{4}+\frac{Y^2}{3}=1$

or $\frac{(x-2)^2}{4}+\frac{(y+3)^2}{3}=1$

or $3x^2+4y^2-12x+24y+36=0.$

(d) Foci lie on y-axis so that the equation of the ellipse is of the form $\frac{x^2}{b^2}+\frac{y^2}{a^2}=1$ where $a^2>b^2$.

Again distance between foci $=2ae=2$ given

$\therefore \quad ae=1.$ Also $2b=1$ given $\therefore$ $b=\frac{1}{2}.$

But $b^2=a^2-a^2e^2$ or $1/4=a^2-1$

or $a^2=5/4.$

Hence the equation of the ellipse is

$$\frac{x^2}{1/4}+\frac{y^2}{5/4}=1 \quad \text{or} \quad 4x^2+\frac{4}{5}y^2=1$$

(e) $\frac{x^2}{64}+\frac{y^2}{100}=1, a^2=100, b^2=64$

Given point on it is $(4\sqrt{3},5)$. Major axis is along y-axis $\therefore$ foci $(0,\pm ae)$ where

$$e^2=1-\frac{b^2}{a^2}=1-\frac{64}{100}=\frac{36}{100}=\frac{9}{25}$$

$\therefore \quad e=\frac{3}{5},$ $\therefore$ foci are $(0,\pm 6)$

Focal distances of P are

$$a\pm ey=10\pm\frac{3}{5}(5)=7 \text{ and } 13$$

Also equation of SP and $S'P$ can be found by two point formula to be $x+4\sqrt{3}y-24\sqrt{3}=0$ and $4\sqrt{3}y-11x+24\sqrt{3}=0$

(f) Centre being mid-point of foci is (2, 0)

Distance between foci $2=2ae$

$\therefore \quad a^2e^2=1$ or $a^2-b^2=1$ ...(1)

If the ellipse be $\frac{(x-2)^2}{a^2}+\frac{y^2}{b^2}=1$ then as it passes through (0, 0)

$\therefore \quad \frac{4}{a^2}=1$ or $a^2=4$ $\therefore$ $b^2=3$ by (1)

Hence $\frac{(x-2)^2}{4}+\frac{y^2}{3}=1$

or $3x^2+4y^2-12x=0$

(g) Let the ellipse be $\frac{x^2}{a^2}+\frac{y^2}{b^2}=1.$

It passes through (2, 1)

$\therefore \quad \frac{4}{a^2}+\frac{1}{b^2}=1$ ...(1)

or $\frac{4}{a^2}+\frac{1}{a^2(1-1/4)}=1$ $\left(\because e=\frac{1}{2}\right)$

or $4+\frac{4}{3}=a^2$ or $a^2=\frac{16}{3}$

$\therefore \quad \frac{1}{b^2}=1-\frac{4}{a^2}=1-\frac{3}{4}=\frac{1}{4}$ from (1)

$\therefore \quad \frac{3x^2}{16}+\frac{y^2}{4}=1$ or $3x^2+4y^2=16$

(h) Ans. (b).

$$e=\frac{1}{2}, x=\frac{a}{e}=4 \Rightarrow 2a=4 \quad \therefore \quad a=2$$

$$b^2=a^2(1-e^2)=4\left(1-\frac{1}{4}\right)=3$$

$\therefore \quad \frac{x^2}{4}+\frac{y^2}{3}=1$ or $3x^2+4y^2=12 \Rightarrow$ (b)

5. Let $P(x,y)$ be any point on the bar such that $PA=a$ and $PB=b$.

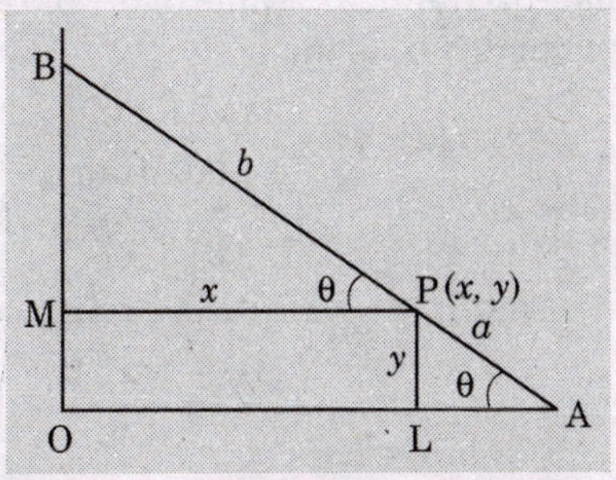

Fig. 3

Clearly from the figure

$$x=OL=PL=PM=b\cos\theta$$

$$y=PL=a\sin\theta$$

$\therefore \quad (x^2/b^2)+(y^2/a^2)=1$

and it represents an ellipse.

6. (a) By **Prop. (h) P. 1003**, $2a=6$ and $2b=4$. We know that $b^2=a^2(1-e^2)$.

$\therefore \quad 4=9(1-e^2)$ or $e=\frac{1}{3}\sqrt{5}.$

Hence the distance between the pegs is

$$2ae = 2.3\frac{1}{3}\sqrt{5} = 2\sqrt{5}\,cm.$$

Now length of the endless string is

$$SPS'S = SP + S'P + SS'$$
$$= 2a + 2ae = 6 + 2\sqrt{5}$$

(b) Clearly, the racecourse will be an ellipse with the flag-posts as its foci. If a and b are the semi-major and minor axes of the ellipse, then Sum of focal distances $= 2a = 10$ and $2ae = 8$.

Also $b = a\sqrt{[(1-e^2)]}$. Solving these equations, we get

$$a = 5, e = \frac{8}{2a} = \frac{8}{10} = \frac{4}{5}$$

and $b = 5\sqrt{\left(1 - \frac{16}{25}\right)} = 3$

∴ Area of the ellipse $= \pi ab = \pi.5.3 = 15\pi$.

7. (a) Any point on the ellipse is $(\sqrt{6}\cos\phi, \sqrt{2}\sin\phi)$. Its distance from the centre is given 2.

$$6\cos^2\phi + 2\sin^2\phi = 4$$

or $3\cos^2\phi + \sin^2\phi = 2$ or $2\cos^2\phi + 1 = 2$

or $2\cos^2\phi = 1$ or $\cos\phi = \pm 1/\sqrt{2}$,

∴ $\phi = \frac{\pi}{4}$ and $\left(2\pi - \frac{\pi}{4}\right) = \frac{7\pi}{4}$

or $\frac{3\pi}{4}$ and $\left(2\pi - \frac{3\pi}{4}\right) = \frac{5\pi}{4}$

(b) Ans. (a).

$$\tan\phi = \text{slope of } OP = \frac{b\sin\theta - 0}{a\cos\theta - 0}$$

∴ $\tan\phi = \frac{b}{a}\tan\theta$ ...(1)

We have to find max. value of $\theta - \phi$. It will be max. when $\tan(\theta - \phi)$ is max.

∴ $$y = \tan(\theta - \phi) = \frac{\tan\theta - \tan\phi}{1 + \tan\theta\tan\phi}$$

$$= \frac{\tan\theta\left(1 - \frac{b}{a}\right)}{1 + \frac{b}{a}\tan^2\theta}$$

or $$y = \frac{a - b}{a\cot\theta + b\tan\theta}$$

y will be maximum if

$Z = a\cot\theta + b\tan\theta$ is min.

$$\frac{dZ}{d\theta} = -a\,\text{cosec}^2\theta + b\sec^2\theta = 0$$

$$\tan^2\theta = \frac{a}{b} \text{ or } \tan\theta = \sqrt{\frac{a}{b}}$$

Clearly $\frac{d^2Z}{d\theta^2} = +\text{ive}$, hence Z is min. so that y is max.

8. (a) Ans. abe. $P(a\cos\theta, b\sin\theta)$, $S_1(ae, 0)$, $S_2(-ae, 0)$. Using $\frac{1}{2}$ base × height rule for area

$$\Delta = \frac{1}{2}(2ae)\,b\sin\theta = abe\sin\theta.$$

It is maximum when $\sin\theta = 1$

∴ $\Delta = abe$.

(b) Ans. (a), (d).

$$\frac{x^2}{4} + \frac{y^2}{9} = 1, \frac{x^2}{4} - \frac{y^2}{9} = 1$$

Major axis along y-axis, $a^2 = 9, b^2 = 4$

Trans. axes along x-axis $a^2 = 4, b^2 = 9$

$$e_1^2 = 1 - \frac{b^2}{a^2},\quad e_2^2 = 1 + \frac{b^2}{a^2}$$

or $e_1^2 = 1 - \frac{4}{9} = \frac{5}{9}$ and $e_2^2 = 1 + \frac{9}{4} = \frac{13}{4}$

$$e_1^2 + e_2^2 = \frac{5}{9} + \frac{13}{4} = \frac{137}{36} > 3 \text{ but } < 4.$$

9. The line $x\cos\alpha + y\sin\alpha = p$ is a tangent to the circle $x^2 + y^2 = p^2$

If it subtends a right angle at the centre of the ellipse then making homogeneous, we get

$$\frac{x^2}{a^2} + \frac{y^2}{b^2} = \left[\frac{x\cos\alpha + y\sin\alpha}{p}\right]^2$$

$A + B = 0$ § 1. (b)

or $$\left(\frac{1}{a^2} - \frac{\cos^2\alpha}{p^2}\right) + \left(\frac{1}{b^2} - \frac{\sin^2\alpha}{p^2}\right) = 0$$

∴ $\frac{1}{p^2} = \frac{1}{a^2} + \frac{1}{b^2}$ ∴ $p = \frac{ab}{\sqrt{(a^2 + b^2)}}$

10. (a) $$\frac{(x-3)^2}{4^2} + \frac{y^2}{5^2} = 1$$

$$\frac{X^2}{b^2} + \frac{Y^2}{a^2} = 1$$

$a^2 > b^2$ *i.e.* major axis is along y-axis. Centre is (3, 0),

$$e^2 = 1 - \left(\frac{b^2}{a^2}\right) = 1 - \frac{16}{25} \quad \therefore e = \frac{3}{5}$$

∴ foci are $X = 0, Y = \pm ae$

or $x - 3 = 0, y = \pm 5.3/5$ ∴ $(3, \pm 3)$

In order to transform the given equation to the form $\frac{x^2}{25} + \frac{y^2}{16} = 1$, the origin should be shifted to the point (3, 0) and then the axes be turned through a right angle.

(b) Put $x - 2y + 1 = X$, $2x + y + 2 = Y$

$$4X^2 + 9Y^2 = 25$$

$$\frac{X^2}{(52/2)^2} + \frac{Y^2}{(5/3)^2} = 1$$

$a = 5/2$, $b = 5/3$

Centre is $X=0, Y=0 \quad \therefore \quad C$ is $(-1, 0)$

$$e^2 = 1 - \frac{b^2}{a^2} = 1 - \frac{4}{9} \quad \therefore \quad e = \frac{\sqrt{5}}{3}$$

$$L.R. = \frac{2b^2}{a} = 2 . \frac{25}{9} . \frac{2}{5} = \frac{20}{9}$$

11. Ans. (b). Refer **Prop. (h), P. 1003.**

$a=5, \ b=4, \ e=3/5,$ foci are F_1, F_2.

12. The points and distances are marked in the figure. If (x, y) be the incentre, then

$$x = \frac{\Sigma\, ax_1}{\Sigma\, a}, \qquad y = \frac{\Sigma\, ay_1}{\Sigma\, a}$$

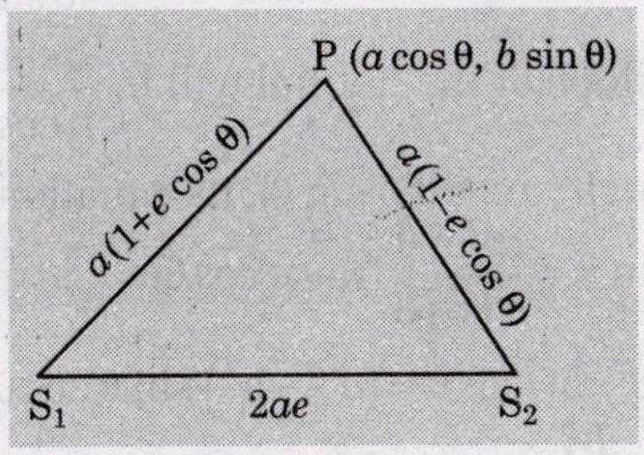

Fig. 4

$$\frac{2ae\,(a\cos\theta) + a\,(1 - e\cos\theta)\,(-ae) + (1 + e\cos\theta)\,(ae)}{2a\,(1+e)}$$

or $\quad x = ae\cos\theta$

$$y = \frac{2ae\,(b\sin\theta) + 0 + 0}{2a\,(1+e)} = b\sin\theta \cdot \frac{e}{1+e}$$

Eliminating θ by $\cos^2\theta + \sin^2\theta = 1$, the required locus is $\dfrac{x^2}{a^2e^2} + \dfrac{y^2}{b^2e^2/(1+e)^2} = 1$

or $\quad \dfrac{x^2}{A^2} + \dfrac{y^2}{B^2} = 1$

Above represents an ellipse whose $E^2 = 1 - \dfrac{B^2}{A^2}$

or $\quad E^2 = 1 - \dfrac{b^2e^2}{(1+e)^2} \dfrac{1}{a^2e^2} = 1 - \dfrac{(1-e)^2}{(1+e)^2} = 1 - \dfrac{1-e}{1+e}$

or $\quad E^2 = \dfrac{2e}{1+e} \quad$ or $\quad E = \sqrt{\dfrac{2e}{1+e}}$

13. Ans. (b).

Let $P\,(a\cos 30^\circ, b\sin 30^\circ)$ and Q be $(a\cos 60^\circ, b\sin 60^\circ)$.

$$\text{Its slope} = \frac{b\,(\sin 60^\circ - \sin 30^\circ)}{a\,(\cos 60^\circ - \cos 30^\circ)} = -\frac{b}{a}$$

But slope of $x + 2y + 4 = 0$ is $-\dfrac{1}{2}$

$\therefore \quad -\dfrac{b}{a} = -\dfrac{1}{2} \quad$ or $\quad a = 2b \qquad$ ...(1)

The chord subtends an angle of 90° at the origin. Making equation of the ellipse homogeneous with the equation of line, we have $\dfrac{x^2}{a^2} + \dfrac{y^2}{b^2} = \left(\dfrac{x+2y}{-4}\right)^2$

or $\quad x^2\left(\dfrac{1}{a^2} - \dfrac{1}{16}\right) - \dfrac{xy}{4} + y^2\left(\dfrac{1}{b^2} - \dfrac{1}{4}\right) = 0$

Since the line subtends an angle of 90° at origin

$\therefore \quad A + B = 0 \quad$ or $\quad \dfrac{1}{a^2} - \dfrac{1}{16} + \dfrac{1}{b^2} - \dfrac{1}{4} = 0$

or $\quad \dfrac{1}{4b^2} - \dfrac{1}{16} + \dfrac{1}{b^2} - \dfrac{1}{4} = 0 \quad \because \ a = 2b$, by (1)

$\therefore \quad \dfrac{5}{4b^2} = \dfrac{5}{16} \quad \therefore \ b^2 = 4 \quad \therefore \ a^2 = 4b^2 = 16$

Hence the equation is $\quad \dfrac{x^2}{16} + \dfrac{y^2}{4} = 1.$

14. Ans. (b), (c).

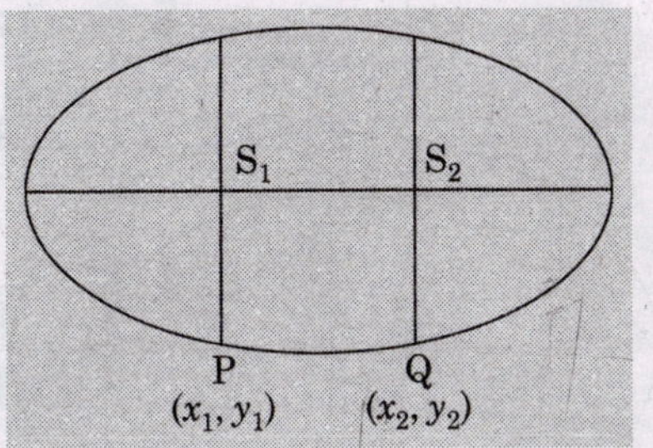

Fig. 5

$\dfrac{x^2}{4} + \dfrac{y^2}{1} = 1 \quad \therefore \quad a^2 = 4, \ b^2 = 1$

$\therefore \quad b^2 = a^2\,(1 - e^2) \Rightarrow ae = \sqrt{3}$

Also $\dfrac{b^2}{a} = \dfrac{1}{2}$. We are given that both y_1 and y_2 are $-$ ive.

The extremities of the latus rectum of the ellipse are given by $(\pm\, ae, \pm\, b^2/a)$ $\quad$ or $\quad (\pm\sqrt{3}, \pm 1/2)$.

Since both y_1 and y_2 are less than zero,

$\therefore \quad P = \left(-\sqrt{3}, -\dfrac{1}{2}\right)$ and $Q = \left(\sqrt{3}, -\dfrac{1}{2}\right)$

Now PQ is the latus rectum of the parabola whose mid-point $\left(0, -\dfrac{1}{2}\right)$ is focus S and $PQ = 2\sqrt{3}$ = length of latus rectum $= 4a \quad \therefore \quad a = \dfrac{1}{2}\sqrt{3}.$

The vertices V_1 and V_2 of the parabola are points at a distance $\pm\, a = \pm\dfrac{\sqrt{3}}{2}$ from S on the line $V_1 V_2$.

$\therefore \quad \dfrac{x - 0}{\cos 90^\circ} = \dfrac{y + 1/2}{\sin 90^\circ} = \dfrac{\sqrt{3}/2,}{V_1} \dfrac{-\sqrt{3}/2}{V_2}$

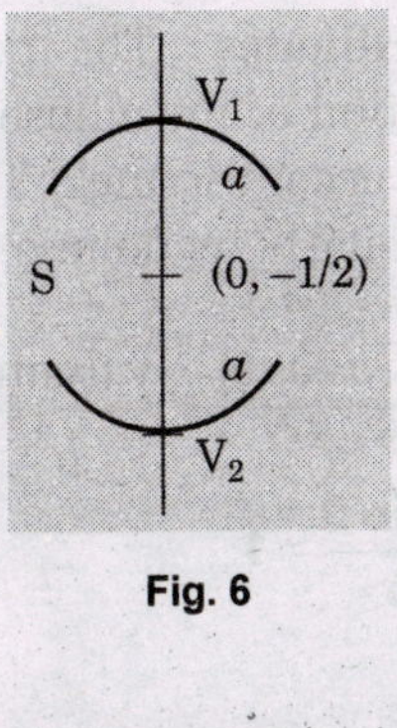

Fig. 6

$V_1 = \left(0, \frac{\sqrt{3}-1}{2}\right)$ and $V_2 = \left(0, -\frac{\sqrt{3}+1}{2}\right)$

Hence the parabola with vertex V_1 is $X^2 = -4AY$ and with vertex V_2 is $X^2 = 4AY$

$$(x-0)^2 = -2\sqrt{3}\left(y - \frac{\sqrt{3}-1}{2}\right)$$

or $x^2 + 2\sqrt{3}y = 3 - \sqrt{3} \Rightarrow$ (c)

and $(x-0)^2 = 2\sqrt{3}\left(y + \frac{\sqrt{3}+1}{2}\right)$

or $x^2 - 2\sqrt{3}\,y = 3 + \sqrt{3} \Rightarrow$ (b)

15. Ans. (c).

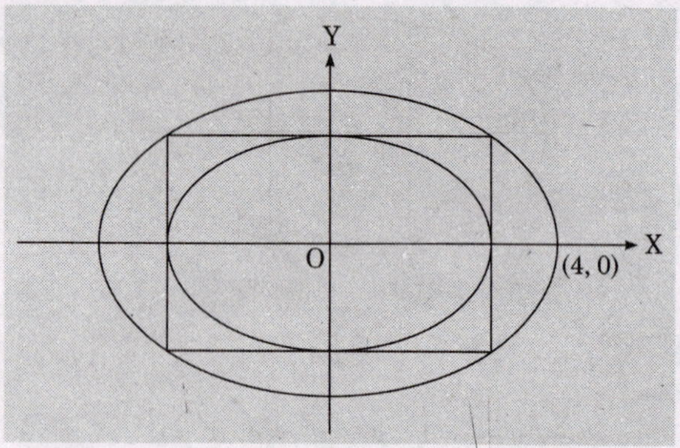

Fig. 7

$E_1 = \frac{x^2}{4} + \frac{y^2}{1} = 1$, where $a = 2, b = 1$

$E_2 = \frac{x^2}{4^2} + \frac{y^2}{b^2} = 1$, where $a = 4$

E_2 passes through (2, 1).

$\frac{4}{4^2} + \frac{1}{b^2} = 1$ or $\frac{1}{b^2} = 1 - \frac{1}{4} = \frac{3}{4}$

or $b^2 = \frac{4}{3}$ $\therefore$ E_2 is $\frac{x^2}{4^2} + \frac{y^2}{4/3} = 1$

or $x^2 + 12y^2 = 16$

§ 2. Tangent and normal to ellipse $\frac{x^2}{a^2} + \frac{y^2}{b^2} = 1$

Tangent at (x_1, y_1) is $\frac{xx_1}{a^2} + \frac{yy_1}{b^2} = 1.$ ...(1)

Normal $\frac{x - x_1}{x_1/a^2} = \frac{y - y_1}{y_1/b^2}.$

Parametric Co-ordinates : The point $(a\cos\theta, b\sin\theta)$ satisfies the equation of the ellipse for all values of θ. This θ is termed as eccentric angle. The point is referred to as point 'θ'. Similarly by point ϕ we mean the point $(a\cos\phi, b\sin\phi)$.

Tangent at 'θ' : $\frac{x(a\cos\theta)}{a^2} + \frac{y(b\sin\theta)}{b^2} = 1,$ by (1)

*or $\frac{x\cos\theta}{a} + \frac{y\sin\theta}{b} = 1.$ ...(2)

Point of intersection of tangents to ellipse at points whose eccentric angles are θ and ϕ is

* $h = a\frac{\cos\left(\frac{\theta+\phi}{2}\right)}{\cos\left(\frac{\theta-\phi}{2}\right)}, k = b\frac{\sin\frac{\theta+\phi}{2}}{\cos\frac{\theta-\phi}{2}}$

$\therefore$ $\frac{h^2}{a^2} + \frac{k^2}{b^2} = \frac{1}{\cos^2\left(\frac{\theta-\phi}{2}\right)}$

Normal at θ : Slope of the tangent is $-\frac{b\cos\theta}{a\sin\theta}$ and hence slope of the normal will be $\frac{a\sin\theta}{b\cos\theta}$ and as it passes through $(a\cos\theta, b\sin\theta)$, its equation is

$$y - b\sin\theta = \frac{a\sin\theta}{b\cos\theta}(x - a\cos\theta)$$

or $ax\sin\theta - by\cos\theta = (a^2 - b^2)\sin\theta\cos\theta$

*or $\frac{ax}{\cos\theta} - \frac{by}{\sin\theta} = a^2 - b^2$ ...(3)

Chord joining two points θ and φ is

* $\frac{x}{a}\cos\frac{\theta+\phi}{2} + \frac{y}{b}\sin\frac{\theta+\phi}{2} = \cos\left(\frac{\theta-\phi}{2}\right)$ ...(4)

Tangent in terms of slope *m*. **(M.N.R. 1995)**

Let the line whose slope be m be $y = mx + c$.

Its points of intersection with the ellipse

$\frac{x^2}{a^2} + \frac{y^2}{b^2} = 1$ are given by $\frac{x^2}{a^2} + \frac{(mx+c)^2}{b^2} = 1$

or $x^2(b^2 + a^2m^2) + 2mca^2x + a^2(c^2 - b^2) = 0$

Above is a quadratic in x which will give us the abscissas of the points of intersection of the line and ellipse. If the line be a tangent to the ellipse then both the values of x should be equal, the condition for which is that the discriminant of the quadratic

i.e. $B^2 - 4AC = 0$

$\therefore$ $4m^2c^2a^4 - 4a^2(b^2 + a^2m^2)(c^2 - b^2) = 0$

or $m^2c^2a^2 = b^2c^2 + a^2m^2c^2 - b^4 - a^2b^2m^2$

or $c^2 = a^2m^2 + b^2$ or $c = \pm\sqrt{(a^2m^2 + b^2)}$.

Hence the equation of tangent to the ellipse in terms of slope m is

* $y = mx \pm \sqrt{(a^2m^2 + b^2)}$. ...(5)

The point of contact of the tangent is

$\left[-\frac{a^2m}{\sqrt{(a^2m^2+b^2)}}, \frac{b^2}{\sqrt{(a^2m^2+b^2)}}\right]$ or $\left(-\frac{a^2m}{c}, \frac{b^2}{c}\right)$

where $c^2 = a^2m^2 + b^2$

In numerical examples if a given line is a tangent then solve with ellipse and it will give two equal roots showing thereby that it is tangent and also the point of contact is determined.

If the ellipse be $\frac{x^2}{b^2}+\frac{y^2}{a^2}=1$ $(a^2>b^2)$ then interchanging x and y i.e. the axes are rotated through a right angle the equation of any tangent is

* $\quad x = my \pm \sqrt{a^2m^2+b^2}$ ...[5 (a)]

Number of tangents through a given point (h, k). **(M.N.R. 1995)**

Equation of any tangent to the ellipse is

$$y = mx + \sqrt{(a^2m^2+b^2)} \text{ depending on } m.$$

If it passes through the point (h, k), then

$$k = mh + \sqrt{(a^2m^2+b^2)}$$

or $\quad (k-mh)^2 = a^2m^2+b^2$

*or $\quad m^2(h^2-a^2)-2hkm+(k^2-b^2)=0$ ...(6)

Above is a quadratic in m and will give us two values of m and hence there will be two tangents that pass through the point (h, k).

Equation of pair of tangents to an ellipse drawn from a given point.

In usual notation it is given by $S.S_1 = T^2$

Director Circle. The locus of the point of intersection of two perpendicular tangents to an ellipse is called director circle.

Let (h, k) be the point of intersection of two tangents whose slopes are given by (6). In case the tangents are perpendicular, then

$$m_1m_2 = -1$$

or $\quad \frac{k^2-b^2}{h^2-a^2}=-1$ or $k^2-b^2=-h^2+a^2$

or $\quad h^2+k^2=a^2+b^2$ ...(7)

Hence the locus of the point of intersection (h, k) is

* $\quad \mathbf{x^2+y^2=a^2+b^2}.$

Above represents a circle called the director circle.

Auxiliary circle. The circle described on the major axis of an ellipse as diameter is called the auxiliary circle and clearly its centre is (0, 0) and radius a so that its equation is

$$\mathbf{x^2+y^2=a^2}. \quad ...(8)$$

Any point on this is $(a\cos\theta, a\sin\theta)$.

Problem Set (2)

(Tangent and Normal)

1. (a)* Find the condition that the line $lx+my=n$ be a (i) tangent (ii) normal (iii) a chord in which eccentric angles of the end points differ by a right angle, to the ellipse $x^2/a^2+y^2/b^2=1$.

(b) Find the conditions that the line $px+qy=r$ intersects the ellipse $\frac{x^2}{a^2}+\frac{y^2}{b^2}=1$ in points whose eccentric angles differ by $\pi/4$. **(Roorkee 2001)**

(c) Prove that the line $x\cos\alpha+y\sin\alpha=p$ passes through the ends of the conjugate diameters of the ellipse $\frac{x^2}{a^2}+\frac{y^2}{b^2}=1$ if $a^2\cos^2\alpha+b^2\sin^2\alpha=2p^2$.

(d) If the straight line $y=4x+c$ is a tangent to the ellipse $x^2/8+y^2/4=1$, then c will be equal to ......

(e)* The number of values of c such that the straight line $y=4x+c$ touches the curve $\frac{x^2}{4}+y^2=1$ is

(a) 0 (b) 1
(c) 2 (d) infinite. **(I.I.T. 1998)**

(f) Tangents are drawn to the ellipse $3x^2+5y^2=32$ and $25x^2+9y^2=450$ passing through the point (3, 5). The number of such tangents are

(a) 2 (b) 3
(c) 4 (d) 0

(g) Tangents are drawn to $x^2+2y^2=2$. The locus of mid-point of intercept made by tangents between the axes is

(a) $\frac{1}{x^2}+\frac{1}{2y^2}=1$ (b) $\frac{1}{4x^2}+\frac{1}{2y^2}=1$
(c) $\frac{1}{2x^2}+\frac{1}{4y^2}=1$ (d) $\frac{1}{2x^2}+\frac{1}{y^2}=1$

(Screening 2004)

2. (a) Let ABC be an equilateral triangle inscribed in the auxiliary circle of the ellipse $\frac{x^2}{a^2}+\frac{y^2}{b^2}=1, (a>b)$. $A'B'C'$ be corresponding triangle inscribed within the ellipse then centroid of the triangle $A'B'C'$ lies at

(a) focus of ellipse
(b) any vertex of the ellipse
(c) centre of the ellipse
(d) none

(b) An ellipse passes through the point (4, – 1) and its axes are along the axes of co-ordinates. If the line $x+4y-10=0$ is a tangent to it then its equation is

(a) $\frac{x^2}{100}+\frac{y^2}{5}=1$ (b) $\frac{x^2}{80}+\frac{y^2}{5/4}=1$
(c) $\frac{x^2}{20}+\frac{y^2}{5}=1$ (d) None of these

3. (a) Find the equation of tangents to the ellipse $\frac{x^2}{a^2}+\frac{y^2}{b^2}=1$ which are (i) inclined to the axis of x at an angle of 60° (ii) which cut off equal intercepts on the axes.

(b) Find the slope of the common tangent of $x^2+y^2=16$ and $\frac{x^2}{25}+\frac{y^2}{4}=1$ in the first quadrant, also find the length of the intercept made by tangent between the co-ordiante axes. **(I.I.T. 2005)**

4. (a) Find the equation of tangent and normal to the ellipse $4x^2+9y^2=36$ at the point $(3,-2)$.

(b) Tangents are drawn to the ellipse $\frac{x^2}{9}+\frac{y^2}{5}=1$ at ends of latus rectum. The area of quadrilateral so formed is

(a) 27 (b) 27/2
(c) 27/4 (d) 27/55 **(IIT-Sc. 2003)**

5. Find the equation of tangent to the ellipse $3x^2+4y^2=12$ which are (i) parallel (ii) perpendicular to the line $y+2x=4$.

6.* Find the points where the line $2x+y=3$ cuts the ellipse $4x^2+y^2=5$. Obtain the equation of the normals at these points and show that these normals include an angle $\tan^{-1}(3/5)$.

7. (a) The tangent at the point $\left(4\cos\phi, \frac{16}{\sqrt{11}}\sin\phi\right)$ to the ellipse $16x^2+11y^2=256$ is also a tangent to the circle $x^2+y^2-2x=15$; find the value of ϕ.

(b)* A circle of radius r is concentric with the ellipse; prove that the common tangent is inclined to the major axis at an angle $\tan^{-1}\sqrt{\left\{\frac{(r^2-b^2)}{(a^2-r^2)}\right\}}$, where a and b are the semi-axes.

8. An ellipse passes through the point $(4,-1)$ and touches the line $x+4y-10=0$. Find its equation given that its axes coincide with co-ordinate axes.

9.* If the normal at the end of latus rectum of the ellipse $\frac{x^2}{a^2}+\frac{y^2}{b^2}=1$ passes through an extremity of minor axis, then prove that $e^4+e^2-1=0$ or $e^2=\frac{\sqrt{5}-1}{2}$. Also find the ratio of the major and minor axes.

10. (a) Find the equations of tangents to the ellipse $9x^2+16y^2=144$ which pass through the point (2, 3).

(b)* The angle between pair of tangents drawn to the ellipse $3x^2+2y^2=5$ from the point (1, 2) is $\tan^{-1}(12/\sqrt{5})$.

(c) The length of a common tangent to $x^2+y^2=16$ and $9x^2+25y^2=225$ is

(a) $\frac{9}{4}$ (b) $\frac{\sqrt{3}}{4}$
(c) $\frac{3}{4}\sqrt{7}$ (d) $\frac{5}{4}\sqrt{7}$

11. Prove that the locus of the mid-points of the portion of the tangents to the ellipse $x^2/a^2+y^2/b^2=1$ intercepted between the axes is $a^2y^2+b^2x^2=4x^2y^2$.

12. (a) Prove that the line $2x+3y=12$ touches the ellipse $\frac{x^2}{9}+\frac{y^2}{4}=2$.

Find the co-ordinates of the point of contact.

(b) From a point on the axis of x common tangents are drawn to the parabola $y^2=4x$ and the ellipse $\frac{x^2}{a^2}+\frac{y^2}{b^2}=1$ $(a>b>0)$. If these tangents form an equilateral triangle with their chord of contact w.r.t. parabola, then set of exhaustive values of a is

(a) (0, 3) (b) $\left(\frac{3}{2},3\right)$
(c) $\left(1,\frac{3}{2}\right)$ (d) $\left(0,\frac{3}{2}\right)$

13. Prove that tangents at the extremities of latus rectum of an ellipse intersect on the corresponding directrix.

14. (a) Prove that sum of the squares of the perpendiculars on any tangent to the ellipse $x^2/a^2+y^2/b^2=1$ from two points on the minor axis each distance $\sqrt{(a^2-b^2)}$ from the centre is $2a^2$.

(b) Prove that the product of the perpendiculars drawn from two foci of an ellipse to the tangent at any point of the ellipse is b^2.

15. (a)* The tangent and normal at any point P of an ellipse $\frac{x^2}{a^2}+\frac{y^2}{b^2}=1$ cut its major axis in points T and T' respectively, so that $TT'=a$. Prove that the eccentric angle of the point P is given by $e^2\cos^2\phi+\cos\phi-1=0$.

(b) The tangent and normal at a point P on the ellipse $\frac{x^2}{a^2}+\frac{y^2}{b^2}=1$ meet the y-axis at A and B respectively. Obtain the equation of the circle on AB as diameter and show that it passes through P as well as the two foci of the ellipse.

16. The tangent and normal to the ellipse $x^2+4y^2=4$ at a point $P(\theta)$ on it meet the major axes in Q and R respectively. If $QR=2$, show that the eccentric angle θ of P is given by $\cos\theta=2/3$.

17.* P and Q are two points on the ellipse $\frac{x^2}{25}+\frac{y^2}{9}=1$ such that sum of their ordinates is 3.
Prove that the locus of the point of intersection of tangents at P and Q is $9x^2+25y^2=150y$.

(b) Prove that the locus of the point of intersection of tangents to an ellipse at two points sum of whose eccentric angles is constant is a straight line.

18. (a) Prove that the portion of the tangent to the ellipse intercepted between the curve and the directrix subtends a right angle at the corresponding focus.

(b) Prove that, in an ellipse, the perpendicular from a focus upon any tangent and the line joining the centre of the ellipse to the point of contact meet on the corresponding directrix. **(I.I.T. 2002)**

19.* If the normal at any point P on the ellipse cuts the major and minor axes in G and g respectively and C be the centre of the ellipse, then prove that $a^2 CG^2 + b^2 Cg^2 = (a^2 - b^2)^2$. **(Bihar C.C.E. 1999)**

20. A tangent having slope of $-4/3$ to the ellipse $\frac{x^2}{18}+\frac{y^2}{32}=1$ intersects the major and minor axes in points A and B respectively. If O is the origin, find the area of $\Delta\, OAB$.

21. A normal inclined at 45° to the x-axis of the ellipse $\frac{x^2}{a^2}+\frac{y^2}{b^2}=1$ is drawn. It meets the major and minor axes in P and Q respectively. If C is the centre of the ellipse, show that the area of $\Delta\, CPQ$ is $\frac{(a^2-b^2)^2}{2(a^2+b^2)}$ sq. units.

22. (a)* If the normal at any point P of the ellipse $x^2/a^2 + y^2/b^2 = 1$ with centre C meets the major and minor axes in G and g respectively, and if CF be perpendicular to the normal, prove that

(i) $PF.PG = b^2$ (ii) $PF.Pg = a^2$.

(b) Find the co-ordinates of all the points P on the ellipse $\frac{x^2}{a^2}+\frac{y^2}{b^2}=1$, for which the area of the triangle PON is maximum, where O denotes the origin and N, the foot of the perpendicular from O to tangent at P. **(I.I.T. 1999)**

(c) With reference to the notation of part (a), find the equations of the loci of the mid-points of PG and Gg.

23. (a)* Prove that the portion of the normal at any point of the ellipse $\frac{x^2}{a^2}+\frac{y^2}{b^2}=1$ intercepted between the curve and major axis is $\frac{b}{a}\sqrt{(rr')}$ where r and r' are the focal distances of the point at which the normal is drawn.

(b) $\frac{x^2}{a^2}+\frac{y^2}{b^2}=1, a>b$ is the equation of an ellipse of eccentricity e. Normal at a variable point P meets the axes at Q and R. The locus of mid-point of QR is an ellipse of eccentricity e' say, then :

(a) $e' = 1$ (b) $e' = 1/e$
(c) $e' = e$ (d) none

24. Prove that the tangent and normal at any point on the ellipse bisects the angle between the focal radii of that point.

25. If the normal at any point P on the ellipse $\frac{x^2}{a^2}+\frac{y^2}{b^2}=1$, meets the axes in G and g respectively, then prove that $PG : Pg = b^2 : a^2$.

26. (a)* A tangent to the ellipse $\frac{x^2}{a^2}+\frac{y^2}{b^2}=1$ cuts the axes in A and B respectively and touches the ellipse at any point P in the first quadrant, so that P divides AB into two equal parts. Find the equation of the tangent. In case P divides AB in the ratio $3:1$ what will be the equation of tangent ?

(b) Consider the family of circles $x^2+y^2=r^2$, $2<r<5$. If in the first quadrant, the common tangent to a circle of this family and the ellipse $4x^2+25y^2=100$ meets the co-ordinate axes at A and B, then find the equation of the locus of the mid-point of AB. **(I.I.T. 1999)**

(c) Find the equation of the largest circle with centre (1, 0) that can be inscribed in the ellipse $x^2+4y^2=16$. **(Roorkee 1999)**

27. (a)* If the normal at the point $P(\theta)$ to the ellipse $\frac{x^2}{14}+\frac{y^2}{5}=1$ intersects it again at the point $Q(2\theta)$, show that $\cos\theta = -2/3$.

(b)* If tangent drawn at a point $(t^2, 2t)$ on the parabola $y^2=4x$ is same as the normal drawn at a point $(\sqrt{5}\cos\phi, 2\sin\phi)$ on the ellipse $4x^2+5y^2=20$, find the values of t and ϕ. **(Roorkee 1996)**

28.* P and Q are corresponding points on an ellipse and the auxiliary circle respectively. The normal at P to the ellipse meets CQ in R where C is the centre of the ellipse. Prove that $CR = a+b$.

29. Any tangent at a point P of ellipse is cut by tangents at the extremities A and A' of major axis in points Q and R respectively. Prove that $AQ \,.\, A'R = b^2$. Also prove that circle on QR as diameter will pass through foci.

30.* Find the co-ordinates of those points on the ellipse $\frac{x^2}{a^2}+\frac{y^2}{b^2}=1$ tangents at which make equal angles with the axes. Also prove that the length of the perpendicular from the centre on either of these is $\sqrt{\left\{\frac{1}{2}(a^2+b^2)\right\}}$.

31. (a)* If p is the length of perpendicular from the focus S of the ellipse $\frac{x^2}{a^2}+\frac{y^2}{b^2}=1$ on the tangent at P, then show that $\frac{b^2}{p^2}=\frac{2a}{SP}-1$.

(b)* Let d be the perpendicular distance from the centre of the ellipse $\frac{x^2}{a^2}+\frac{y^2}{b^2}=1$ to the tangent drawn at a point P on the ellipse. If F_1 and F_2 are two foci of the ellipse, then show that $(PF_1-PF_2)^2=4a^2\left(1-\frac{b^2}{d^2}\right)$. **(I.I.T. 1995)**

32.* Show that there are always two tangents to an ellipse $\frac{x^2}{a^2}+\frac{y^2}{b^2}=1$ from a point (x', y') outside the ellipse and the slopes of the two tangents are given by $a^2m^2+b^2=(y'-mx')^2$. Hence obtain the locus of a point from which the two tangents to the ellipse are inclined at an angle α. **(M.N.R. 1995)**

33.* If S and S_1 are the foci of an ellipse and P a point on it, if e is the eccentricity of the ellipse, prove that

$$\tan\frac{1}{2}PSS_1\,\tan\frac{1}{2}PS_1S=\frac{(1-e)}{(1+e)}.$$

34. Find where the line $2x+y=3$ cuts the curve $4x^2+y^2=5$. Obtain the equations of the normals at the points of intersection and determine the co-ordinates of the point where these normals cut each other.

35. Find the co-ordinates of all the points of intersection of the ellipse $\frac{x^2}{4}+\frac{y^2}{9}=1$ and the circle $x^2+y^2=6$. Write down the equation of the tangents to the ellipse and circle at one of the points of intersection and find the angle between them.

36.* Prove that the sum of the squares of the reciprocals of two perpendicular diameters of an ellipse is constant.

37. The tangent at a point P on an ellipse intersects the major axis in T, and N is the foot of the perpendicular from P to same axis. Show that the circle drawn on NT as diameter intersects the auxiliary circle orthogonally.

38.* Any ordinate NP of an ellipse meets the auxiliary circle in Q, prove that the locus of the intersection of the normals at P and Q is the circle $x^2+y^2=(a+b)^2$.

39.* If P is any point on the ellipse $\frac{x^2}{a^2}+\frac{y^2}{b^2}=1$ whose ordinate is y', prove that the angle between the tangent at P and the focal distance of P is $\tan^{-1}(b^2/aey')$.

40.* If the normals to the ellipse $\frac{x^2}{a^2}+\frac{y^2}{b^2}=1$ at (x_r, y_r) $r=1,2,3$ be concurrent, then prove that

$$\begin{vmatrix} x_1 & y_1 & x_1y_1 \\ x_2 & y_2 & x_2y_2 \\ x_3 & y_3 & x_3y_3 \end{vmatrix}=0$$

41. (a)* Two sides of a triangle inscribed in the ellipse $\frac{x^2}{a^2}+\frac{y^2}{b^2}=1$ are parallel to two given straight lines. Prove that its third side touches a certain ellipse.

(b) Three of the sides of a quadrilateral inscribed in an ellipse are parallel respectively to three given straight lines. Prove that the fourth side will also be parallel to a fixed straight line.

42. (a) Prove that in general four normals can be drawn to an ellipse from any point and the sum of the eccentric angles of the feet of these normals is equal to an odd multiple of two right angles.

(b)* If $\theta_1, \theta_2, \theta_3$ be the eccentric angles of three points on the ellipse normals at which are concurrent, then prove that

$$\sin(\theta_1+\theta_2)+\sin(\theta_2+\theta_3)+\sin(\theta_3+\theta_1)=0$$

Solutions to Problem Set (2)

1. (a) (i) Given line is $lx+my=n$. ...(1)

Any tangent to the ellipse is

$$\frac{x\cos\theta}{a}+\frac{y\sin\theta}{b}=1 \quad ...(2)$$

Comparing (1) and (2), we get

$$\frac{\cos\theta}{al}=\frac{\sin\theta}{bm}=\frac{1}{n}.$$

Eliminating θ, we get by $\cos^2\theta+\sin^2\theta=1$

$$\frac{a^2l^2}{n^2}+\frac{b^2m^2}{n^2}=1,$$

or $a^2l^2+b^2m^2=n^2$.

(ii) Any normal to the ellipse is

$$\frac{ax}{\cos\theta}-\frac{by}{\sin\theta}=a^2-b^2. \quad ...(3)$$

Comparing (1) and (3), we get

$$\frac{l\cos\theta}{a}=-\frac{m\sin\theta}{b}=\frac{n}{a^2-b^2}.$$

Eliminating θ, we get by $\cos^2\theta+\sin^2\theta=1$

$$\frac{n^2}{(a^2-b^2)^2}\left[\frac{a^2}{l^2}+\frac{b^2}{m^2}\right]=1$$

or $\frac{a^2}{l^2}+\frac{b^2}{m^2}=\frac{(a^2-b^2)^2}{n^2}$

(iii) The equation of the chord joining the points θ and ϕ is

$$\frac{x}{a}\cos\frac{\theta+\phi}{2}+\frac{y}{b}\sin\frac{\theta+\phi}{2}=\cos\frac{\theta-\phi}{2}$$

But $\theta-\phi=\frac{\pi}{2}$ given $\therefore\ \theta=\frac{\pi}{2}+\phi$

Hence the equation of the chord becomes

$$\frac{x}{a}\cos\left(\frac{\pi}{4}+\phi\right)+\frac{y}{b}\sin\left(\frac{\pi}{4}+\phi\right)$$

$$=\cos 45^\circ=\frac{1}{\sqrt{2}} \quad ...(4)$$

Comparing (1) and (4), we get

$$\frac{\cos\left(\frac{\pi}{4}+\phi\right)}{al}=\frac{\sin\left(\frac{\pi}{4}+\phi\right)}{bm}=\frac{1}{n\sqrt{2}}$$

Eliminating ϕ, we get by

$$\cos^2\left(\frac{\pi}{4}+\phi\right)+\sin^2\left(\frac{\pi}{4}+\phi\right)=1$$

$$\frac{1}{2n^2}(a^2l^2+b^2m^2)=1 \quad \text{or} \quad a^2l^2+b^2m^2=2n^2.$$

(b) Refer **part (a)** above.
Proceeding exactly as above

$$\frac{\theta-\phi}{2}=\frac{45^\circ}{2}=22\frac{1^\circ}{2}$$

$$\cos^2 22\frac{1^\circ}{2}\left[\frac{a^2l^2+b^2m^2}{n^2}\right]=1$$

or $(1+\cos 45^\circ)(a^2l^2+b^2m^2)=2n^2$

is the required condition.

(c) Already done in (iii) of part (a).
Replace l, m, n by $\cos\alpha, \sin\alpha$ and p respectively.

(d) $c^2=a^2m^2+b^2=132 \quad \therefore \quad c=\pm\sqrt{(132)}$

(e) Ans. (c). $c^2=a^2m^2+b^2=4.16+1=65$

$\therefore \quad c=\pm\sqrt{65}$

(f) Ans. (b).
Putting (3, 5) in the equation of the ellipse, we get $S_1=+$ ive and $S_2=0$ so that the point (3, 5) lies outside $S_1=0$ and hence two tangents can be drawn through the point (3, 5). The point (3, 5) lies on $S_2=0$ and only one tangent can be drawn. Thus the total no. of tangents passing through (3, 5) to the two ellipses is $2+1=3 \Rightarrow$ (b).

(g) Ans. (c).

Any point on the ellipse $\frac{x^2}{2}+\frac{y^2}{1}=1$ is $(\sqrt{2}\cos\theta, \sin\theta)$ tangent at which is $\frac{x\cos\theta}{\sqrt{2}}+\frac{y\sin\theta}{1}=1$. If (h, k) be the mid-point of the portion of tangent intercepted between the axes then $2h=\frac{\sqrt{2}}{\cos\theta}, 2k=\frac{1}{\sin\theta}$. Eliminate θ by $\sin^2\theta+\cos^2\theta=1$ and generalise.

2. (a) Ans. (c).
Any point A on circle is $(a\cos\theta, a\sin\theta)$ and corresponding point on the ellipse is $(a\cos\theta, b\sin\theta)$. Since the triangle inscribed in the circle is equilateral hence the points A, B, C are $\theta, \theta+\frac{2\pi}{3}, \theta+\frac{4\pi}{3}$.

$\therefore$ Centroid of $A'B'C'$ is (x, y) where

$$3x=\cos\theta+\cos(\theta+120^\circ)+\cos(\theta+240^\circ)$$

$$3y=\sin\theta+\sin(\theta+120^\circ)+\sin(\theta+240^\circ)$$

$\therefore \quad 3x=0, 3y=0 \quad \therefore \quad (x, y)=(0, 0)$

$\because \quad 2\cos(\theta+120^\circ)\cos 120^\circ+\cos(\theta+120^\circ)$

$$=-\cos(\theta+120^\circ)+\cos(\theta+120^\circ)=0$$

as $\cos 120^\circ=-\sin 30^\circ=-\frac{1}{2}$

Similarly $y=0$.

(b) Ans. (b) and (c).

Let the ellipse be $\frac{x^2}{a^2}+\frac{y^2}{b^2}=1$

It passes through (4, – 1) $\therefore \quad \frac{16}{a^2}+\frac{1}{b^2}=1 \quad ...(1)$

$y=-\frac{1}{4}x+\frac{5}{2}$ is a tangent, then

$$c^2=a^2m^2+b^2 \quad \text{or} \quad \frac{25}{4}=a^2.\frac{1}{16}+b^2 \quad ...(2)$$

Eliminating b^2, we get $a^4-100a^2+1600=0$

or $(a^2-80)(a^2-20)=0 \quad \therefore \quad a^2=80, 20$

and corresponding values of b^2 are $\frac{5}{4}$ and 5. Hence the ellipses are as given in (b) and (c).

3. (a) Any tangent to ellipse is

$$y=mx+\sqrt{(a^2m^2+b^2)} \quad ...(1)$$

(i) Here $m=\tan 60^\circ=\sqrt{3}$.

$\therefore \quad y=x\sqrt{3}+\sqrt{(3a^2+b^2)}$

(ii) In case the tangent makes equal intercepts on the axes then it is inclined at an angle of $\pm 45^\circ$ to x-axis and hence its slope is

$$m=\tan(\pm 45^\circ)=\pm 1.$$

$\therefore$ Tangents are $y=\pm x+\sqrt{(a^2+b^2)}$.

(b) Any tangent to ellipse is

$$y=mx+\sqrt{a^2m^2+b^2}$$

$a^2=25, b^2=4$ or $mx-y+\sqrt{25m^2+4}=0$

If it is a tangent to circle, then condition of tangency $p=r$ gives $\frac{\sqrt{25m^2+4}}{\sqrt{1+m^2}}=4$

or $25m^2+4=16+16m^2$ or $9m^2=12$

$\therefore \quad m=\pm\frac{2}{\sqrt{3}}$.

Since **tangent lies in 1st quadrant**, it will make an obtuse angle with x-axis and hence its slope $=-$ ive

$\therefore \quad m = -\dfrac{2}{\sqrt{3}}$.

Hence its equation is $2x + \sqrt{3}y = 4\sqrt{7}$.

It meets the co-ordinate axes in points $(2\sqrt{7}, 0)$ and $\left(0, \dfrac{4\sqrt{7}}{\sqrt{3}}\right)$.

$\therefore$ Length of tangent intercepted between axes is

$$\sqrt{a^2 + b^2} = 2\sqrt{7}\sqrt{1 + (4/3)} = 2\sqrt{7} \cdot \frac{\sqrt{7}}{\sqrt{3}} = \frac{14}{\sqrt{3}}.$$

4. (a) Ellipse $\dfrac{x^2}{9} + \dfrac{y^2}{4} = 1$

Tangent at $(3, -2)$ is $\dfrac{x(3)}{9} + \dfrac{y(-2)}{4} = 1$

or $\dfrac{x}{3} - \dfrac{y}{2} = 1$.

$\therefore$ Normal is $\dfrac{x}{2} + \dfrac{y}{3} = k$ and it passes through $(3, -2)$.

$\therefore \quad \dfrac{3}{2} - \dfrac{2}{3} = k \quad \therefore \quad k = \dfrac{5}{6}$

$\therefore$ Normal is $\dfrac{x}{2} + \dfrac{y}{3} = \dfrac{5}{6}$.

(b) Ans. (a)

$$e^2 = 1 - \frac{b^2}{a^2} = 1 - \frac{5}{9} = \frac{4}{9} \quad \therefore \quad e = \frac{2}{3}$$

$$L \text{ is } \left(ae, \frac{b^2}{a}\right) = \left(3 \cdot \frac{2}{3}, \frac{5}{3}\right) = \left(2, \frac{5}{3}\right)$$

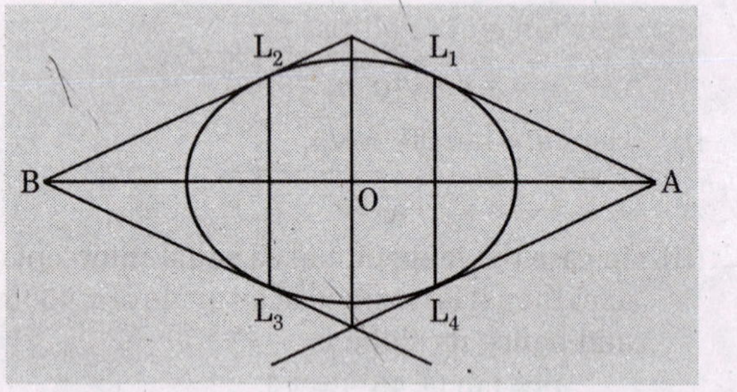

Fig. 8

Tangent at $L = \dfrac{x \cdot 2}{9} + \dfrac{y \cdot 5/3}{5} = 1$

or $\dfrac{2x}{9} + \dfrac{y}{3} = 1$ or $\dfrac{x}{A} + \dfrac{y}{B} = 1$

There will be four tangents at the four extremities of L.R. which will be parallel in pairs. Area of the parallelogram is four times the area of triangle

$$OAB = 4\left(\frac{1}{2} AB\right) = 4\left(\frac{1}{2} \cdot \frac{9}{2} \cdot 3\right) = 27 \text{ sq. units.}$$

5. The ellipse is $\dfrac{x^2}{4} + \dfrac{y^2}{3} = 1 \quad \therefore \quad a^2 = 4, b^2 = 3$.

Slope of the line $y + 2x = 4$ is -2.

Any tangent to the ellipse is

$$y = mx \pm \sqrt{(a^2 m^2 + b^2)}$$

If it is parallel to given line, then $m = -2$ and if it is perpendicular to given line then $m = 1/2$.

Ans. $y = -2x \pm \sqrt{19}, y = \dfrac{1}{2}x \pm 2$.

6. Solving $4x^2 - y^2 = 5$ with the line $y = 3 - 2x$, we get

$$4x^2 + (3 - 2x)^2 = 5$$

or $8x^2 - 12x + 4 = 0$ or $2x^2 - 3x + 1 = 0$

or $(2x - 1)(x - 1) = 0 \quad \therefore \quad x = \dfrac{1}{2}, 1$.

Putting in the equation of the line, we get $y = 2, 1$.

Hence the points of intersection are $\left(\dfrac{1}{2}, 2\right)$ and $(1, 1)$.

Tangent at $\left(\dfrac{1}{2}, 2\right)$ is $4x \cdot \dfrac{1}{2} + y \cdot 2 = 5$.

Slope $= -1$.

Normal at $\left(\dfrac{1}{2}, 2\right)$ is $y - 2 = +1\left(x - \dfrac{1}{2}\right)$

or $2x - 2y + 3 = 0, m_1 = 1$.

Tangent at $(1, 1)$ is $4x \cdot (1) + y \cdot 1 = 5$,

Slope $= -4$.

Normal at $(1, 1)$ is $(y - 1) = \dfrac{1}{4}(x - 1)$

or $x - 4y + 3 = 0$

$m_2 = 1/4$.

Solving the two normals, we find their point of intersection as $\left(-1, \dfrac{1}{2}\right)$.

If θ be the angle between the normals, then

$$\tan\theta = \frac{m_1 - m_2}{1 + m_1 m_2} = \frac{1 - \frac{1}{4}}{1 + \frac{1}{4}} = \frac{3}{5} \quad \therefore \quad \theta = \tan^{-1}\frac{3}{5}$$

7. (a) The equation of the ellipse is $\dfrac{x^2}{16} + \dfrac{11y^2}{256} = 1$.

Tangent at $\left(4\cos\phi, \dfrac{16}{\sqrt{11}}\sin\phi\right)$ is

$$\frac{x}{16} \cdot 4\cos\phi + \frac{11}{256} y \cdot \frac{16}{\sqrt{11}} \sin\phi = 1.$$

i.e. $\dfrac{xx_1}{a^2} + \dfrac{yy_1}{b^2} = 1$

or $4\cos\phi\, x + \sqrt{11}\sin\phi\, y = 16$ ...(1)

If it is a tangent to the circle

$$x^2 + y^2 - 2x - 15 = 0,$$

then perpendicular from the centre $(1, 0)$ is equal to radius $\sqrt{(1 + 15)} = 4$

or $\dfrac{4\cos\phi - 16}{\sqrt{(16\cos^2\phi + 11\sin^2\phi)}} = 4$

or $(\cos\phi - 4)^2 = 16\cos^2\phi + 11(1 - \cos^2\phi)$

or $\cos^2\phi - 8\cos\phi + 16 = 5\cos^2\phi + 11$

or $4\cos^2\phi + 8\cos\phi - 5 = 0$

or $(2\cos\phi + 5)(2\cos\phi - 1) = 0$

$\therefore\quad \cos\phi = \frac{1}{2}$ as $\cos\phi \neq -\frac{5}{2}$

$\therefore\quad \phi = \pm 60°$.

(b) $y = mx + \sqrt{(a^2m^2 + b^2)}$ is any tangent to ellipse. If it is tangent to circle $x^2 + y^2 = r^2$ then the condition of tangency $p = r$ gives

$$\frac{\sqrt{(a^2m^2+b^2)}}{\sqrt{(1+m^2)}} = r$$

or $\quad a^2m^2 + b^2 = r^2(1+m^2)$

$\therefore\quad m^2 = \tan^2\theta = \frac{r^2 - b^2}{a^2 - r^2}$ etc.

8. Let the ellipse be $\frac{x^2}{a^2} + \frac{y^2}{b^2} = 1$.

It passes through (4, −1) $\quad\therefore\quad \frac{16}{a^2} + \frac{1}{b^2} = 1$

or $\quad a^2 + 16b^2 = a^2b^2 \quad$ ...(1)

The given line $x + 4y - 10 = 0$ is $y = -\frac{1}{4}x + \frac{5}{2}$

$\therefore\quad m = -\frac{1}{4}, c = \frac{5}{2}$. The condition of tangency is

$c^2 = a^2m^2 + b^2$

or $\quad \frac{25}{4} = \frac{a^2}{16} + b^2 = \frac{a^2 + 16b^2}{16} = \frac{a^2b^2}{16}$, $\quad$ by (1)

$\therefore\quad a^2b^2 = 100$ or $ab = 10$

or $\quad b = 10/a$.

Putting in (1), we get

$\frac{16}{a^2} + \frac{1}{b^2} = 1$ or $\frac{16}{a^2} + \frac{a^2}{100} = 1$

or $\quad a^4 - 100a^2 + 1600 = 0$

or $\quad (a^2 - 80)(a^2 - 20) = 0 \quad\therefore\quad a^2 = 80, 20$

Hence $\quad b^2 = \frac{100}{a^2} = \frac{100}{80}$ or $\frac{100}{20}$

$= \frac{5}{4}$ or 5

Hence the equations of the ellipse are

$$\frac{x^2}{80} + \frac{y^2}{5/4} = 1 \quad\text{and}\quad \frac{x^2}{20} + \frac{y^2}{5} = 1.$$

9. We know that the extremity of latus rectum in the first quadrant is $(ae, b^2/a)$ normal at which is

$$\frac{x - ae}{ae/a^2} = \frac{y - b^2/a}{b^2/ab^2}$$ **§ 2, Page 1010.**

or $\quad \frac{a}{e}(x - ae) = a\left(y - \frac{b^2}{a}\right)$

It passes through the extremity of minor axis in the 2nd quadrant *i.e.* (0, −b).

$\therefore\quad \frac{a}{e}(0 - ae) = a\left(-b - \frac{b^2}{a}\right)$

or $\quad -a^2 = -ab - b^2 \quad$ ...(1)

or $\quad a^2 - b^2 = ab$ or $a^2e^2 = ab$.

$\therefore\quad e^2 = \frac{b}{a} \quad$ ...(2)

$e^4 = \frac{b^2}{a^2} = 1 - e^2$ or $e^4 + e^2 - 1 = 0$

$\therefore\quad e^2 = \frac{1}{2}(-1 \pm \sqrt{5}) = \frac{\sqrt{5} - 1}{2}$

only as e^2 cannot be – ive

Again by (2),

$$\frac{a}{b} = \frac{1}{e^2} = \frac{2}{\sqrt{5} - 1} = \frac{2(\sqrt{5}+1)}{4} = \frac{\sqrt{5}+1}{2}$$

10. (a) The ellipse is $\frac{x^2}{16} + \frac{y^2}{9} = 1$.

Any tangent is $y = mx + \sqrt{(16m^2 + 9)}$. **§ 2, Eq. (5).**

It passes through the point (2, 3).

$\therefore\quad (3 - 2m)^2 = 16m^2 + 9$.

or $\quad 12m^2 + 12m = 0 \quad\therefore\quad m = 0, -1$.

Hence the tangents are $y = 3$, $x + y = 5$.

(b) As above in part (a) the slopes of the tangents are given by the equation $4m^2 + 24m - 9 = 0$

$\therefore\quad \tan\theta = \frac{m_1 \sim m_2}{1 + m_1m_2} = \frac{4\sqrt{36+9}}{-5} = -\frac{12}{\sqrt{5}}$

$= \frac{12}{\sqrt{5}}$ numerically

(c) Ans. (c).

Ellipse is $\frac{x^2}{25} + \frac{y^2}{9} = 1$

Any point on the ellipse is $(5\cos\theta, 3\sin\theta)$ at which the tangent is

$$\frac{x}{5}\cos\theta + \frac{y}{3}\sin\theta = 1$$

If it is a tangent to circle $x^2 + y^2 = 16$ then $p = r$ gives

$$\frac{1}{\sqrt{\left(\frac{\cos^2\theta}{25} + \frac{\sin^2\theta}{9}\right)}} = 4$$

$\therefore\quad \frac{\cos^2\theta}{25} + \frac{1 - \cos^2\theta}{9} = \frac{1}{16}$

$\therefore\quad \cos\theta = \frac{5\sqrt{7}}{16}$

If l be the length of tangent then $l^2 = S'$

or $\quad l^2 = 25\cos^2\theta + 9\sin^2\theta - 16 = 16\cos^2\theta - 7$

$$= 16 . \frac{25.7}{(16)^2} - 7 = \frac{175 - 112}{16} = \frac{63}{16}$$

$\therefore \quad l = \frac{3}{4}\sqrt{7} \Rightarrow$ (c).

11. Any tangent to the ellipse is $\frac{x\cos\theta}{a} + \frac{y\sin\theta}{b} = 1.$

Putting $y = 0$ and then $x = 0$, we get the points A and B where it meets the axes as

$$A\left(\frac{a}{\cos\theta}, 0\right), B = \left(0, \frac{b}{\sin\theta}\right)$$

If (h, k) be mid-point of AB, then

$$2h = \frac{a}{\cos\theta}, 2k = \frac{b}{\sin\theta},$$

$$\therefore \quad \cos\theta = \frac{a}{2h}, \sin\theta = \frac{b}{2k}$$

Since $\cos^2\theta + \sin^2\theta = 1$

$$\therefore \quad \frac{a^2}{4h^2} + \frac{b^2}{4k^2} = 1$$

or $\quad a^2y^2 + b^2x^2 = 4x^2y^2.$

12. (a) Apply the condition $c^2 = a^2m^2 + b^2$ and the point of contact is

$$\left(-\frac{a^2m}{c}, \frac{b^2}{c}\right) \quad i.e., \quad (3, 2).$$

Alternative method : Eliminating y between the equations of the ellipse and the line, we get

$$\frac{x^2}{9} + \frac{(12 - 2x)^2}{36} = 2$$

or $\quad x^2 + (6 - x)^2 = 18$

or $\quad 2x^2 - 12x + 18 = 0, x^2 - 6x + 9 = 0$

or $\quad (x - 3)^2 = 0 \quad \therefore \quad x = 3.$

Putting $x = 3$ in the equation of the line, we get $y = 2.$

Above shows that the line cuts the ellipse in two coincident points and hence it is a tangent to the ellipse at the point (3, 2).

(b) Ans. (b).

P is a point on axis of x and PA, PB are tangents drawn from P to parabola $y^2 = 4x$, $a = 1$ so that ΔPAB is equilateral. Any tangent to parabola $y = mx + \frac{1}{m}$ where $m = \tan(\pm 30^\circ) = \pm\frac{1}{\sqrt{3}}$

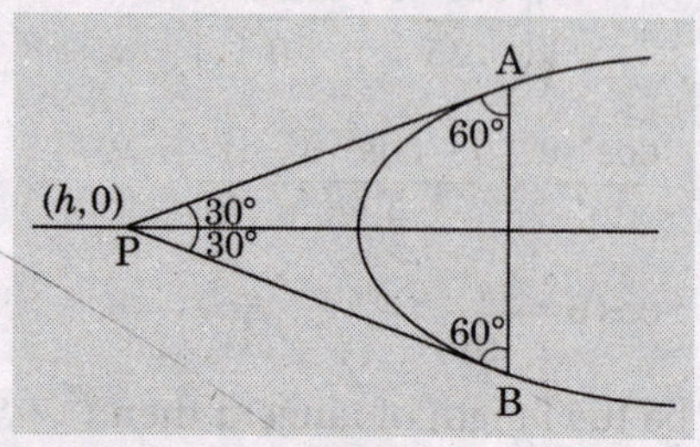

Fig. 9

But these tangents are also tangents to the ellipse. Hence condition of tangency $c^2 = a^2m^2 + b^2$ gives

$$\frac{1}{m^2} = a^2m^2 + b^2 \quad \text{or} \quad 3 = \frac{a^2}{3} + b^2$$

or $\quad 9 = a^2 + 3a^2(1 - e^2)$

$$\therefore \quad \frac{9 - a^2}{3a^2} = 1 - e^2 \quad \text{or} \quad e^2 = 1 - \frac{9 - a^2}{3a^2}$$

or $\quad e^2 = \frac{4a^2 - 9}{3a^2}$ but $0 < e^2 < 1$

$$0 < \frac{4a^2 - 9}{3a^2} < 1 \quad \text{or} \quad 0 < 4a^2 - 9 < 3a^2$$

or $\quad 9 < 4a^2$ and $a^2 < 9$

or $\quad \frac{9}{4} < a^2 < 9 \quad \therefore \quad \frac{3}{2} < a < 3$

$\because \quad a^2 < x^2 < b^2 \Rightarrow a < x < b$ and $-b < x < -a$

13. Let us consider the extremities of L.R. in the 1st and 4th quadrants as $L\,(ae, b^2/a)$, $L'\,(ae, -b^2/a)$ and the corresponding directrix is $x = ae$

Tangent at L is $\frac{x.ae}{a^2} + \frac{y.b^2/a}{b^2}$

or $\quad ex + y = a \qquad$ ...(2)

Solving the two, we get the point $(a/e, 0)$ which lies on $x = a/e.$

Similarly we may consider the tangents at $(-ae, b^2/a)$ and $(-ae, -b^2/a)$ and the corresponding directrix as $x = -a/e.$

14. (a) Any tangent to the ellipse is

$$mx - y + \sqrt{(a^2m^2 + b^2)} = 0 \qquad \text{...(1)}$$

Any two points on the minor axis at a distance of $\sqrt{(a^2 - b^2)}$ from the centre are $(0, k)$ and $(0, -k)$ where $k = \sqrt{(a^2 - b^2)}.$

If p_1 and p_2 be the perpendicular distances of these points, then

$$p_1^2 + p_2^2 = \left[\frac{\sqrt{(a^2m^2 + b^2)} - k}{\sqrt{(1 + m^2)}}\right]^2 + \left[\frac{\sqrt{(a^2m^2 + b^2)} + k}{\sqrt{(1 + m^2)}}\right]^2$$

$$= 2\left[\frac{a^2m^2 + b^2 + a^2 - b^2}{1 + m^2}\right] = 2a^2 \because \quad k^2 = a^2 - b^2.$$

(b) Proceed as in part (a).

15. (a) Let the eccentric angle of the point P be ϕ so that

Tangent is $\frac{x\cos\phi}{a} + \frac{y\sin\phi}{b} = 1 \qquad$ ...(1)

Normal is $\frac{ax}{\cos\phi} - \frac{by}{\sin\phi} = a^2 - b^2 \qquad$ ...(2)

These lines meet the major axis $y=0$ in points T and T' such that $TT'=a$

T is $\left(\frac{a}{\cos\phi}, 0\right)$, T' is $\left(\frac{(a^2-b^2)\cos\phi}{a}, 0\right)$

$\therefore$ TT' is $\frac{a}{\cos\phi} - \frac{(a^2-b^2)\cos\phi}{a} = a$ given

or $a^2 - a^2e^2 . \cos^2\phi = a^2\cos\phi$

or $1 - e^2\cos^2\phi = \cos\phi$

or $e^2\cos^2\phi + \cos\phi - 1 = 0.$

(b) The points P, A and B are $P(a\cos\phi, b\sin\phi)$

$A\left(0, \frac{b}{\sin\phi}\right)$, $B\left(0, -\frac{a^2-b^2}{b}\sin\phi\right)$ by (1), (2) of (a)

Now do yourself.

16. Do it yourself.

17. (a) If (h, k) be point of intersection of tangents at θ and ϕ, then $\frac{h}{a} = \cos\left(\frac{\theta+\phi}{2}\right)\Big/\cos\left(\frac{\theta-\phi}{2}\right)$

$$\frac{k}{b} = \sin\left(\frac{\theta+\phi}{2}\right)\Big/\cos\left(\frac{\theta-\phi}{2}\right)$$

$$\therefore \quad \frac{h^2}{a^2} + \frac{k^2}{b^2} = \frac{1}{\cos^2\left(\frac{\theta-\phi}{2}\right)} \quad \ldots(1)$$

(See P. 1010)

We are given that sum of ordinates is 3.

$\therefore$ $b(\sin\theta + \sin\phi) = 3$

or $2\sin\frac{\theta+\phi}{2}\cos\frac{\theta-\phi}{2} = 1$ ...(2)

as $b = 3$

$$\text{Now } \frac{k}{b} = \frac{\sin\left(\frac{\theta+\phi}{2}\right)}{\cos\left(\frac{\theta-\phi}{2}\right)} \cdot \frac{\cos\left(\frac{\theta-\phi}{2}\right)}{\cos\left(\frac{\theta-\phi}{2}\right)}$$

$$= \frac{1}{2\cos^2\left(\frac{\theta-\phi}{2}\right)} \quad \text{by (2)}$$

$$\therefore \quad \frac{2k}{b} = \frac{1}{\cos^2\left(\frac{\theta-\phi}{2}\right)} \quad \ldots(3)$$

Hence from (1) and (3), we get

$\frac{h^2}{a^2} + \frac{k^2}{b^2} = \frac{2k}{b}$. Now put $a^2 = 25$, $b^2 = 9$

(b) Given $\theta_1 + \theta_2 = 2\alpha$

$$\therefore \quad x = \frac{a\cos\alpha}{\cos\frac{\theta_1-\theta_2}{2}}, \; y = \frac{b\sin\alpha}{\cos\frac{\theta_1-\theta_2}{2}}$$

$$\therefore \quad \frac{y}{x} = \frac{b\sin\alpha}{a\cos\alpha} \text{ or } bx\sin\alpha - ay\cos\alpha = 0$$

Above represents the equation of a line.

18. (a) Tangent at $P(a\cos\theta, b\sin\theta)$ is

$$\frac{x}{a}\cos\theta + \frac{y}{b}\sin\theta = 1.$$

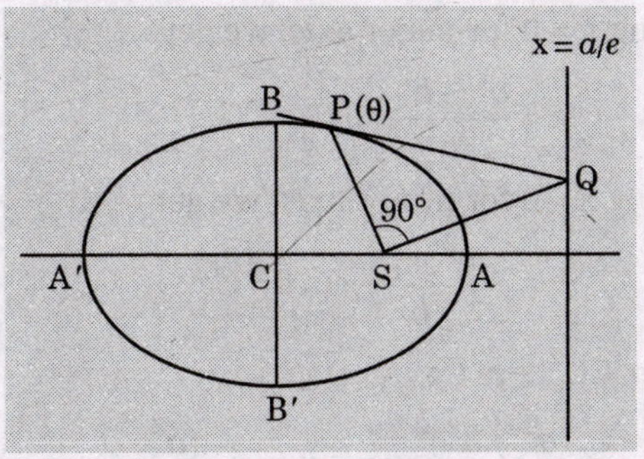

Fig. 10

It meets the directrix $x = (a/e)$ in the point Q $\left(\frac{a}{e}, \frac{b(e-\cos\theta)}{e\sin\theta}\right)$.

$$\text{Slope of } SP = \frac{b\sin\theta}{a(\cos\theta - e)} = m_1$$

$$\text{Slope of } SQ = \frac{b(e-\cos\theta)}{e\sin\theta}\Big/\left(\frac{a}{e} - ae\right)$$

$$= \frac{b(e-\cos\theta)}{a(1-e^2)\sin\theta} = m_2$$

$$\therefore \quad m_1 m_2 = -\frac{b^2}{a^2(1-e^2)} = -\frac{b^2}{b^2} = -1.$$

$\because$ $b^2 = a^2(1-e^2)$.

Hence the line SP and SQ are perpendicular, *i.e.* $\angle PSQ = \pi/2$.

(b) Any tangent to the ellipse is

$$\frac{x}{a}\cos\theta + \frac{y}{b}\sin\theta = 1 \quad \ldots(1)$$

Its point of contact is $P(a\cos\theta, b\sin\theta)$ and its slope is $-\frac{b}{a}\cot\theta$.

Also S the focus is $(ae, 0)$. Any line through focus S and perpendicular to tangent (1) is

$$y - 0 = \frac{a}{b}\tan\theta\,(x - ae) \quad \ldots(2)$$

Also equation of PC where C is centre (0, 0) is

$$y - 0 = \frac{b}{a}\tan\theta\,(x - 0) \quad \ldots(3)$$

In order to find the locus of point of intersection of the lines (2) and (3), we have to eliminate the variable θ between their equations.

Dividing, we get

$$1 = \frac{a^2}{b^2}\frac{x-ae}{x} \text{ or } \frac{a^2-a^2e^2}{a^2} = 1 - \frac{ae}{x}$$

$$\therefore \quad -e^2 = -\frac{ae}{x} \text{ or } x = \frac{a}{e}$$

which is the equation of directrix of the ellipse.

19. Normal at any point $P(a\cos\theta, b\sin\theta)$ is

$$\frac{ax}{\cos\theta} - \frac{by}{\sin\theta} = a^2 - b^2.$$

Putting $y = 0$ for major axis, we get

$$x = \frac{a^2 - b^2}{a}\cos\theta = CG.$$

Putting $x = 0$ for minor axis, we get

$$y = -\frac{a^2 - b^2}{b}\sin\theta = Cg.$$

$$\therefore \quad a^2 CG^2 + b^2 Cg^2$$

$$= \frac{a^2 (a^2 - b^2)^2}{a^2}\cos^2\theta + b^2 \cdot \frac{(a^2 - b^2)^2}{b^2}\sin^2\theta$$

$$= (a^2 - b^2)^2 . (\cos^2\theta + \sin^2\theta) = (a^2 - b^2)^2$$

20. The ellipse is $\frac{x^2}{18} + \frac{y^2}{32} = 1$

$a^2 = 32, b^2 = 18,$ **major axis is along y-axis.**

Any tangent to the ellipse is

$x = my + \sqrt{(a^2 m^2 + b^2)}$ **See 5 (a) P. 1011.**

Slope of tangent is $\frac{1}{m} = -\frac{4}{3}$ $\therefore$ $m = -\frac{3}{4}$.

Hence the equation of tangent is

$$x = -\frac{3}{4}y + \sqrt{32 \cdot \frac{9}{16} + 18}$$

or $4x + 3y = 24$ or $\frac{x}{6} + \frac{y}{8} = 1$

Its intercepts on axes are 6 and 8.

Area of $\Delta OAB = \frac{1}{2}.6.8 = 24$ sq. units.

21. As in Q. 19, $CP = \frac{a^2 - b^2}{a}\cos\theta$, $CQ = -\frac{a^2 - b^2}{b}\sin\theta$

$$\Delta CPQ = \frac{1}{2}CP.CQ$$

$$= -\frac{1}{2}\frac{(a^2 - b^2)^2}{ab}\sin\theta\cos\theta. \qquad ...(1)$$

Also slope of the normal is $\frac{a}{\cos\theta} \cdot \frac{\sin\theta}{b} = \tan 45° = 1,$

given $\therefore$ $\tan\theta = \frac{b}{a}$

$$\therefore \quad \sin\theta = \frac{b}{\sqrt{(a^2 + b^2)}}, \cos\theta = \frac{a}{\sqrt{(a^2 + b^2)}}$$

Putting the values of $\sin\theta$ and $\cos\theta$ in (1), we get

$$\Delta CPQ = -\frac{1}{2}\frac{(a^2 - b^2)^2}{ab} \cdot \frac{b}{\sqrt{(a^2 + b^2)}} \cdot \frac{a}{\sqrt{(a^2 + b^2)}}$$

$$= \frac{1}{2}\frac{(a^2 - b^2)^2}{(a^2 + b^2)} \text{ sq. units.}$$

22. (a) Let P be $(a\cos\theta, b\sin\theta)$. As in Q. 19, the points G and g are

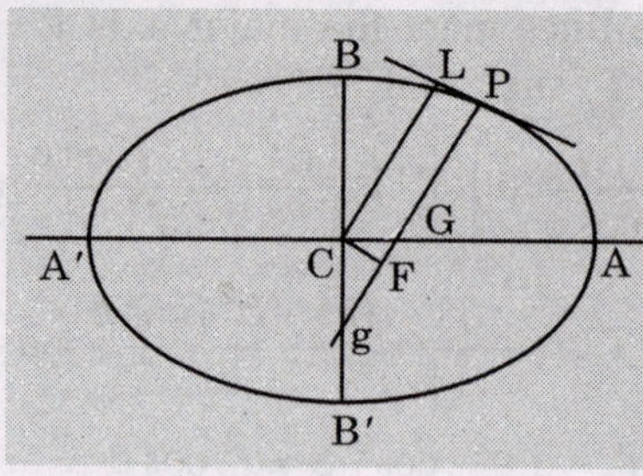

Fig. 11

$$G = \left(\frac{a^2 - b^2}{a}\cos\theta, 0\right),$$

$$g = \left(0, -\frac{a^2 - b^2}{a}\sin\theta\right).$$

$$\therefore \quad PG^2 = \left(a\cos\theta - \frac{a^2 - b^2}{a}\cos\theta\right)^2 + b^2\sin^2\theta$$

$$= \frac{b^4\cos^2\theta}{a^2} + b^2\sin^2\theta \qquad ...(1)$$

$$= \frac{b^2}{a^2}(b^2\cos^2\theta + a^2\sin^2\theta).$$

$$Pg^2 = \frac{a^2}{b^2}(b^2\cos^2\theta + a^2\sin^2\theta) \qquad ...(2)$$

Again CF is perpendicular from C on the normal and CL is perpendicular from C on the tangent

$$\frac{x}{a}\cos\theta + \frac{y}{b}\sin\theta = 1.$$

Clearly,

$$PF = CL = \frac{1}{\sqrt{\left(\frac{\cos^2\theta}{a^2} + \frac{\sin^2\theta}{b^2}\right)}}$$

$$= \frac{ab}{\sqrt{(b^2\cos^2\theta + a^2\sin^2\theta)}} \qquad ...(3)$$

$$\text{Now } PF^2 . PG^2 = \frac{b^2}{a^2}(b^2\cos^2\theta + a^2\sin^2\theta) . \frac{a^2 b^2}{(b^2\cos^2\theta + a^2\sin^2\theta)} = b^4.$$

$$PF^2 . Pg^2 = \frac{a^2}{b^2}(b^2\cos^2\theta + a^2\sin^2\theta) . \frac{a^2 b^2}{(b^2\cos^2\theta + a^2\sin^2\theta)} = a^4.$$

$\therefore$ $PF . PG = b^2$ and $PF . Pg = a^2$.

(b) Let P be the point $(a\cos t, b\sin t)$.

Tangent and normal at P are

$$\frac{x\cos t}{a} + \frac{y\sin t}{b} = 1$$

$$\frac{ax}{\cos t} - \frac{by}{\sin t} = a^2 - b^2.$$

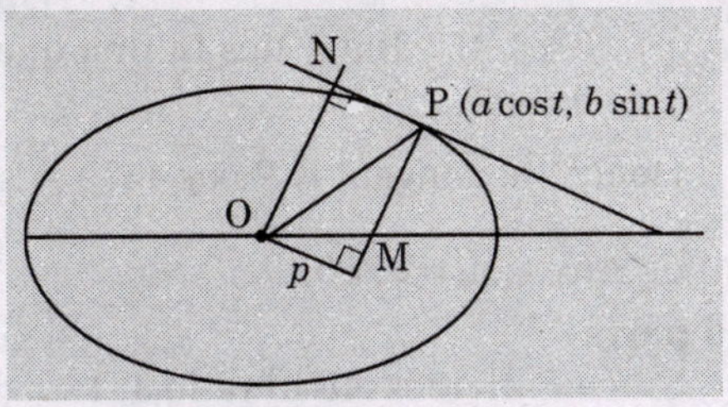

Fig. 12

$$\Delta OPN = \frac{1}{2} ON \,.\, NP = \frac{1}{2} p_1 p_2$$

where p_1 and p_2 are perpendicular distances of $O(0,0)$ from T and N. Δ is max. when $p_1 p_2$ is max.

$$p_1 = \frac{1}{\sqrt{\left(\frac{\cos^2 t}{a^2} + \frac{\sin^2 t}{b^2}\right)}},$$

$$p_2 = \frac{a^2 - b^2}{\sqrt{\left(\frac{a^2}{\cos^2 t} + \frac{b^2}{\sin^2 t}\right)}}$$

$$\therefore \quad p_1 p_2 = \frac{a^2 - b^2}{1 + 1 + \frac{a^2}{b^2}\tan^2 t + \frac{b^2}{a^2}\cot^2 t}$$

Add and subtract 2 in denominator

$$= \frac{a^2 - b^2}{4 + \left(\frac{a}{b}\tan t - \frac{b}{a}\cot t\right)^2}$$

It will be max. when denominator is minimum *i.e.*

$$\frac{a}{b}\tan t - \frac{b}{a}\cot t = 0 \quad \text{or} \quad \tan^2 t = \frac{b^2}{a^2}$$

$$\therefore \quad \tan t = \pm \frac{b}{a} \Rightarrow \sin t = \pm \frac{b}{\sqrt{(a^2 + b^2)}},$$

$$\cos t = \pm \frac{a}{\sqrt{(a^2 + b^2)}}$$

Hence the point P is $\left(\pm \frac{a^2}{\sqrt{(a^2 + b^2)}}, \pm \frac{b^2}{\sqrt{(a^2 + b^2)}}\right)$

(c) If (h, k) be the mid-point of PG, then

$$2h = a\cos\theta + \frac{a^2 - b^2}{a}\cos\theta$$

$$2k = b\sin\theta$$

$$\therefore \quad 2ha = (a^2 + a^2e^2)\cos\theta$$

or $\quad 2h = a(1 + e^2)\cos\theta$

and $2k = b\sin\theta$

Eliminating θ the required locus of (h, k) is

$$\frac{4x^2}{a^2(1 + e^2)^2} + \frac{4y^2}{b^2} = 1$$

Again if (h, k) be mid-point of Gg, then

$$2h = \frac{a^2 - b^2}{a}\cos\theta = ae^2\cos\theta$$

$$2k = -\frac{a^2 - b^2}{b}\sin\theta = -\frac{a^2e^2}{b}\sin\theta$$

Eliminate θ.

$$\frac{4x^2}{a^2e^4} + \frac{4b^2}{a^4e^4}y^2 = 1$$

or $\quad a^2x^2 + b^2y^2 = \frac{1}{4}a^4e^4 = \frac{1}{4}(a^2 - b^2)^2$

23. (a) From Q. 22 the portion of the normal intercepted between the curve and major axis is

$$PG = \frac{b}{a}\sqrt{(b^2\cos^2\theta + a^2\sin^2\theta)}. \qquad ...(1)$$

If S and S' be the foci and P be any point (x, y), then

$$rr' = SP \,.\, S'P = (a - ex)(a + ex) = a^2 - e^2x^2$$

$$= a^2 - e^2(a^2\cos^2\theta) \quad \therefore \; x = a\cos\theta \text{ for point } P$$

$$= a^2 + (b^2 - a^2)\cos^2\theta \quad \because \quad b^2 = a^2 - a^2e^2$$

$$= a^2(1 - \cos^2\theta) + b^2\cos^2\theta$$

$$= a^2\sin^2\theta + b^2\cos^2\theta.$$

$$\therefore \quad \sqrt{(rr')} = \sqrt{(a^2\sin^2\theta + b^2\cos^2\theta)}$$

Hence from (1), we get $PG = \frac{b}{a}\sqrt{(rr')}$.

(b) Ans. (c).

$$ax\sec\theta - by\,\mathrm{cosec}\,\theta = a^2 - b^2$$

$$\therefore \quad Q\left(\frac{a^2 - b^2}{a\sec\theta}, 0\right), R\left(0, -\frac{a^2 - b^2}{b\,\mathrm{cosec}\,\theta}\right)$$

If (h, k) be the mid-point of QR

$$h = \frac{a^2 - b^2}{2a}\cos\theta, \; k = -\frac{a^2 - b^2}{2b}\sin\theta.$$

Eliminating θ, the locus of (h, k) is

$$\frac{x^2}{\left(\frac{a^2 - b^2}{2a}\right)^2} + \frac{y^2}{\left(\frac{a^2 - b^2}{2b}\right)^2} = 1$$

Above represents an ellipse $\frac{x^2}{A^2} + \frac{y^2}{B^2} = 1$

$$a > b \Rightarrow b < a \Rightarrow \frac{1}{b} > \frac{1}{a}$$

$$\therefore \quad B^2 > A^2 \quad \text{or} \quad A^2 < B^2$$

$$\therefore \quad e'^2 = \left(1 - \frac{A^2}{B^2}\right) = \left(1 - \frac{b^2}{a^2}\right) = e^2 \quad \therefore \; e' = e$$

24. Let P be the point (x_1, y_1) the normal at which is

$$\frac{x - x_1}{x_1/a^2} = \frac{y - y_1}{y_1/b^2}.$$

It meets the major axis $y = 0$ in point

$$G\left[x_1\left(1 - \frac{b^2}{a^2}\right), 0\right]$$

or $\quad (e^2x_1, 0) \qquad \because \quad e^2 = 1 - b^2/a^2$

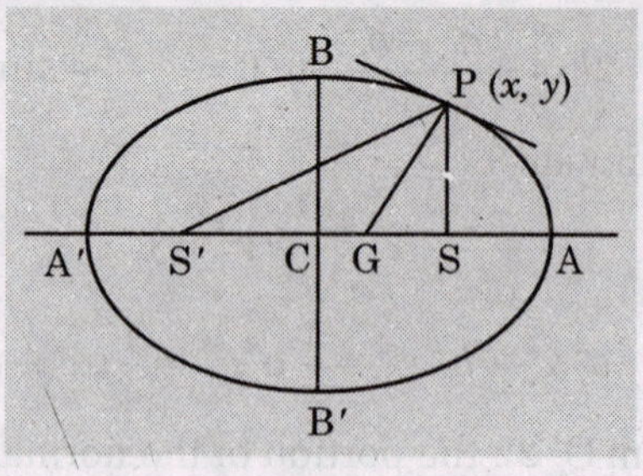

Fig. 13

$\therefore \quad CG = e^2 x_1$.

$\therefore \quad S'G = S'C + CG = ae + e^2 x_1$

$= e(a + ex_1) = e . S'P$

$GS = CS - CG = ae - e^2 x_1$

$= e(a - ex_1) = e . SP$

$\therefore \quad \dfrac{S'G}{GS} = \dfrac{e . S'P}{e . SP} = \dfrac{S'P}{SP}.$

Above relation shows that the normal PG divides the opposite side SS' in the ratio of the arms SP and $S'P$ of angle $S'PS$. Hence the normal PG bisects the angle $S'PS$ and tangent being perpendicular to the normal is the other bisector of $\angle S'PS$.

25. If follows from Q. 22 where we have shown that

$$\frac{PG^2}{Pg^2} = \frac{b^2}{a^2} \div \frac{a^2}{b^2} = \frac{b^4}{a^4}$$

$\therefore \quad PG : Pg :: b^2 : a^2$.

26. (a) Any tangent to the ellipse is $\dfrac{x\cos\theta}{a} + \dfrac{y\sin\theta}{b} = 1$ at the point $P(a\cos\theta, b\sin\theta)$.

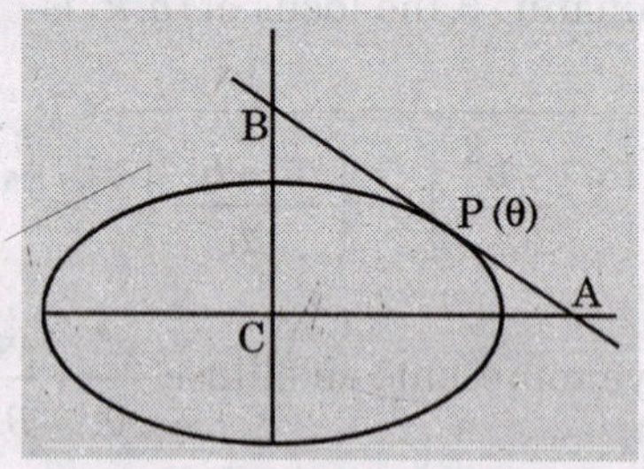

Fig. 14

The points A and B where it meets the axes $y = 0$ and $x = 0$ are

$$A\left(\frac{a}{\cos\theta}, 0\right), B\left(0, \frac{b}{\sin\theta}\right).$$

Now P is mid-point of AB

$$2a\cos\theta = \frac{a}{\cos\theta} + 0,$$

$$2b\sin\theta = 0 + \frac{b}{\sin\theta}$$

$2\cos^2\theta = 1$ and $2\sin^2\theta = 1$

or $\tan^2\theta = 1 \qquad \tan\theta = \pm 1.$

$\therefore \quad \theta = \pm 45°$. But P lies in first quadrant

$\therefore \quad \theta = 45°$.

Hence the tangent is $\dfrac{x}{a}\cos 45° + \dfrac{y}{b}\sin 45° = 1$

or $\quad bx + ay = \sqrt{2ab}$.

2nd part :

Since P divides AB in ratio $3:1$

$$\therefore \quad a\cos\theta = \frac{3.0 + 1.\dfrac{a}{\cos\theta}}{4} = \frac{a}{4\cos\theta}$$

$\therefore \cos^2\theta = 1/4$

$$\text{and } b\sin\theta = \frac{3.\dfrac{b}{\sin\theta} + 1.0}{4} = \frac{3b}{4\sin\theta}$$

$\therefore \quad \sin^2\theta = 3/4$

Both imply $\tan^2\theta = 3$ or $\tan\theta = \pm\sqrt{3} \quad \therefore \quad \theta = 60°$

In this case $\theta = 60°$ and the tangent will be

$$bx + a\sqrt{3}y = 2ab.$$

(b) For ellipse $a^2 = 25, b^2 = 4$

Any tangent to ellipse is

$$y = mx + \sqrt{25m^2 + 4} \qquad \text{...(1)}$$

It meets the axes in A and B whose mid-point is (h, k) say

$$2h = \frac{-\sqrt{25m^2 + 4}}{m}, 2k = \sqrt{25m^2 + 4}$$

$$\therefore \quad \frac{h}{k} = -\frac{1}{m} \qquad \text{...(2)}$$

Again (1) is a tangent to circle $x^2 + y^2 = r^2$. Hence the condition of tangency $p = r$

$$\Rightarrow \quad \frac{\sqrt{25m^2 + 4}}{\sqrt{(1 + m^2)}} = r$$

or $\quad (25m^2 + 4) = r^2 (1 + m^2)$

or $\quad m^2 (25 - r^2) = r^2 - 4$

or $\quad \dfrac{k^2}{h^2}(25 - r^2) = r^2 - 4$

$\therefore \quad$ Locus of (h, k) is $y = \pm x\sqrt{\dfrac{r^2 - 4}{25 - r^2}}$

where r is given.

(c) Ellipse is $\dfrac{x^2}{16} + \dfrac{y^2}{4} = 1$; $a^2 = 16, b^2 = 4$

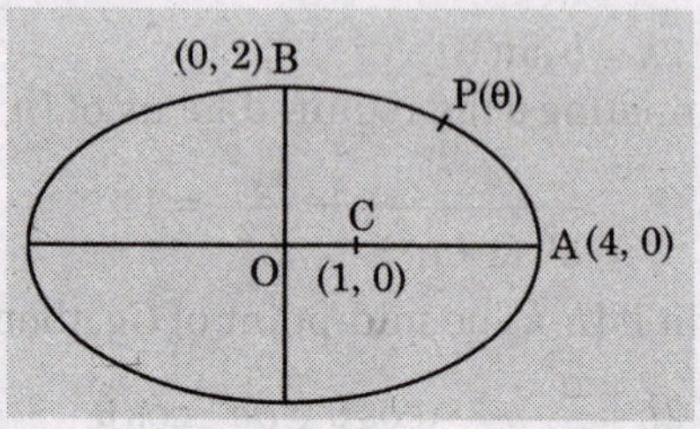

Fig. 15

Let the equation of the circle with centre $C(1,0)$ be $(x-1)^2+y^2=r^2$

Since the circle is to be largest so it will touch the ellipse at some point $P(a\cos\theta, b\sin\theta)$

where tangent is $\frac{x\cos\theta}{a}+\frac{y\sin\theta}{b}=1$ whose

slope is $m_1=-\frac{b\cos\theta}{a\sin\theta}=-\frac{1}{2}\frac{\cos\theta}{\sin\theta}$ ...(1)

Also m_2 = slope of CP

$$=\frac{b\sin\theta}{(a\cos\theta-1)}=\frac{2\sin\theta}{4\cos\theta-1} \quad ...(2)$$

But $m_1m_2=-1$

$\therefore\ -\frac{1}{2}\frac{\cos\theta}{\sin\theta}\times\frac{2\sin\theta}{4\cos\theta-1}=-1$

$\therefore\ \cos\theta=4\cos\theta-1$ or $\cos\theta=1/3$

$\therefore$ Radius of circle is

$\{(a\cos\theta-1)^2+b^2\sin^2\theta\}^{1/2}$

or $\left\{\left(\frac{4}{3}-1\right)^2+4\left(1-\frac{1}{9}\right)\right\}^{1/2}=\sqrt{\frac{33}{9}}=\sqrt{\frac{11}{3}}$

$\therefore$ Circle is $(x-1)^2+y^2=\frac{11}{3}$.

27. (a) Normal at $P(a\cos\theta, b\sin\theta)$ is

$$\frac{ax}{\cos\theta}-\frac{by}{\sin\theta}=a^2-b^2$$

where $a^2=14, b^2=5$.

It meets the curve again at $Q(2\theta)$ *i.e.*

$(a\cos 2\theta, b\sin 2\theta)$

$\therefore\ \frac{a}{\cos\theta}\cdot a\cos 2\theta-\frac{b}{\sin\theta}(b\sin 2\theta)=a^2-b^2.$

or $\frac{14}{\cos\theta}(2\cos^2\theta-1)-\frac{5}{\sin\theta}\cdot(2\sin\theta\cos\theta)=14-5$

or $28\cos^2\theta-14-10\cos^2\theta=9\cos\theta.$

or $18\cos^2\theta-9\cos\theta-14=0,$

Now $14\times18=7\times2\times6\times3=21\times12.$

$\therefore\ 18\cos^2\theta-21\cos\theta+12\cos\theta-14=0$

or $(6\cos\theta-7)(3\cos\theta+2)=0$

$\therefore\ \cos\theta=-2/3.$

The other factor gives $\cos\theta=7/6\ (>1)$ which is not possible.

(b) Tangent to parabola $yy_1=2a(x+x_1),\ a=1$

Normal to ellipse $\frac{ax}{\cos\phi}-\frac{by}{\sin\phi}=a^2-b^2,$

$a^2=5, b^2=4$

or $x-ty=-t^2$ Tangent. ...(1)

$\frac{\sqrt{5}x}{\cos\phi}-\frac{2y}{\sin\phi}=1$ Normal.

or $\sqrt{5}\sin\phi\, x-2\cos\phi\, y=\sin\phi\cos\phi$ ...(2)

Comparing (1) and (2), we get

$$\frac{\sqrt{5}\sin\phi}{1}=\frac{2\cos\phi}{t}=\frac{\sin\phi\cos\phi}{-t^2} \quad ...(3)$$

$\therefore\ (2\cos\phi)^2=-(\sqrt{5}\sin\phi)(\sin\phi\cos\phi)$

or $4\cos^2\phi=-\sqrt{5}\cos\phi\,(1-\cos^2\phi)$

or $\cos\phi\,(\sqrt{5}\cos^2\phi-4\cos\phi-\sqrt{5})=0$

Above gives

$\cos\phi=0, -\frac{1}{\sqrt{5}}, \sqrt{5}$ (rejected)

or $\cos\phi=0, -\cos\alpha,$ where $\cos\alpha=\frac{1}{\sqrt{5}}$

or $\tan\alpha=2$ or $\alpha=\tan^{-1}2$

$\therefore\ \phi=\pm\pi/2, \pi-\alpha, \pi+\alpha$ ...(4)

$\tan\phi=\pm\infty, -2, 2$

Again from (3), $t=\frac{2}{\sqrt{5}}\cdot\frac{1}{\tan\phi}$

$\therefore\ t=0, -\frac{1}{\sqrt{5}}, \frac{1}{\sqrt{5}}$ ...(5)

28. Let P be $(a\cos\theta, b\sin\theta)$ so that Q is $(a\cos\theta, a\sin\theta)$ which lies on the auxiliary circle, C is $(0,0)$.

Equation of CQ is $y-0=\frac{a\sin\theta}{a\cos\theta}(x-0)$

or $y=x\tan\theta.$ ...(1)

Equation of normal at P is

$$\frac{ax}{\cos\theta}-\frac{by}{\sin\theta}=a^2-b^2 \quad ...(2)$$

Both (1) and (2) intersect at R. Solving (1) and (2), we get

$\frac{ax}{\cos\theta}-\frac{b}{\sin\theta}\cdot x\frac{\sin\theta}{\cos\theta}=a^2-b^2$

or $\frac{x}{\cos\theta}(a-b)=a^2-b^2$

$\therefore\ x=(a+b)\cos\theta$

and $y=x\tan\theta=(a+b)\sin\theta$

R is $[(a+b)\cos\theta, (a+b)\sin\theta]$ and C is $(0,0)$

$\therefore\ CR^2=(a+b)^2(\cos^2\theta+\sin^2\theta)=(a+b)^2$

or $CR=a+b$

29. $\frac{x\cos\theta}{a}+\frac{y\sin\theta}{b}=1$ is any tangent

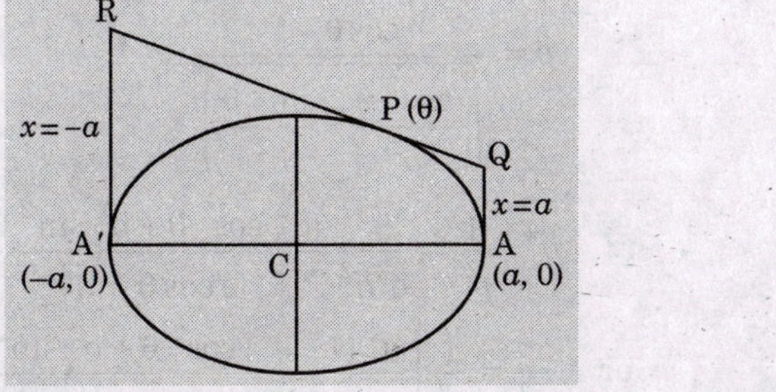

Fig. 16

Tangent at $A(a, 0)$ is $x = a$

Solving, we get Q as $\left(a, \frac{b(1-\cos\theta)}{\sin\theta}\right)$ or $\left(a, b\tan\frac{\theta}{2}\right)$

Similarly R is $\left(-a, \frac{b(1+\cos\theta)}{\sin\theta}\right)$ or $\left(-a, b\cot\frac{\theta}{2}\right)$

$$AQ.A'R = b^2\frac{(1-\cos^2\theta)}{\sin^2\theta} = b^2$$

Circle on QR as diameter is

$$(x-a)(x+a) + (y - b\tan\theta/2).(y - b\cot\theta/2) = 0$$

It will pass through foci $(\pm ae, 0)$ if

$$a^2e^2 - a^2 + b^2 = 0 \quad \text{or} \quad a^2e^2 = a^2 - b^2$$

Above is true.

30. Any point P on the ellipse is $(a\cos\theta, b\sin\theta)$ and the tangent is

$$\frac{x}{a}\cos\theta + \frac{y}{b}\sin\theta = 1$$

Its slope is $-\frac{b\cos\theta}{a\sin\theta} = \pm 1$ ...(1)

[Because the tangent makes equal angles with the axes and hence its slope can be tan 45° or tan 135° *i.e.* ± 1].

From (1) on squaring

$$\frac{\cos^2\theta}{a^2} = \frac{\sin^2\theta}{b^2} = \frac{\cos^2\theta + \sin^2\theta}{a^2+b^2} = \frac{1}{a^2+b^2}$$

$$\therefore \quad \cos\theta = \pm\frac{a}{\sqrt{(a^2+b^2)}}, \sin\theta = \pm\frac{b}{\sqrt{(a^2+b^2)}}$$

Hence the point P is

$$\left(\pm\frac{a^2}{\sqrt{(a^2+b^2)}}, \pm\frac{b^2}{\sqrt{(a^2+b^2)}}\right).$$

Again perpendicular from centre on the tangent is

$$\frac{1}{\sqrt{\left(\frac{\cos^2\theta}{a^2} + \frac{\sin^2\theta}{b^2}\right)}} = \frac{1}{\sqrt{\left(\frac{1}{a^2+b^2} + \frac{1}{a^2+b^2}\right)}} = \sqrt{\left(\frac{a^2+b^2}{2}\right)}$$

31. (a) Tangent at $P(a\cos\theta, b\sin\theta)$ is

$$\frac{x}{a}\cos\theta + \frac{y}{b}\sin\theta = 1$$

Also $\quad SP = a - ex = a(1 - e\cos\theta)$

p is length of perpendicular from focus $S(ae, 0)$

$$p = \frac{e\cos\theta - 1}{\sqrt{\left(\frac{\cos^2\theta}{a^2} + \frac{\sin^2\theta}{b^2}\right)}}$$

$$\therefore \quad b^2 \cdot \frac{1}{p^2} = \frac{b^2}{a^2b^2}\frac{(b^2\cos^2\theta + a^2\sin^2\theta)}{(e\cos\theta - 1)^2}$$

$$\text{or} \quad \frac{b^2}{p^2} = \frac{1}{a^2}\left[\frac{a^2(1-e^2)\cos^2\theta + a^2\sin^2\theta}{(1-e\cos\theta)^2}\right]$$

$$= \frac{(1-e^2\cos^2\theta)}{(1-e\cos\theta)^2}$$

$$\text{or} \quad \frac{b^2}{p^2} = \frac{1+e\cos\theta}{1-e\cos\theta}$$

Again $\frac{2a}{SP} - 1 = \frac{2a}{a(1-e\cos\theta)} - 1 = \frac{1+e\cos\theta}{1-e\cos\theta}$

Hence $\frac{b^2}{p^2} = \frac{2a}{SP} - 1.$

(b) $PF_1 = a + ex, PF_2 = a - ex$

$PF_1 - PF_2 = 2ex = 2e.a\cos\theta$

$\therefore \quad (PF_1 - PF_2)^2 = 4a^2e^2\cos^2\theta$ ...(1)

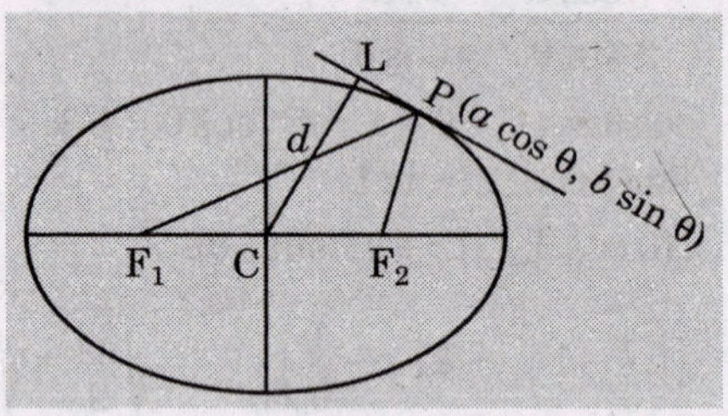

Fig. 17

Tangent at $P(\theta)$ is $\frac{x}{a}\cos\theta + \frac{y}{b}\sin\theta = 1$

$$\therefore \quad d = \frac{1}{\sqrt{\left(\frac{\cos^2\theta}{a^2} + \frac{\sin^2\theta}{b^2}\right)}}$$

$$\therefore \quad \frac{1}{d^2} = \frac{\cos^2\theta}{a^2} + \frac{\sin^2\theta}{b^2}$$

$$\text{or} \quad \frac{b^2}{d^2} = \frac{b^2}{a^2}\cos^2\theta + \sin^2\theta$$

$$\therefore \quad 1 - \frac{b^2}{d^2} = 1 - \frac{b^2}{a^2}\cos^2\theta - \sin^2\theta$$

$$= \cos^2\theta\left(1 - \frac{b^2}{a^2}\right) = \cos^2\theta . e^2$$

$$4a^2\left(1 - \frac{b^2}{d^2}\right) = 4a^2\cos^2\theta . e^2 \quad \text{...(2)}$$

Hence from (1) and (2) we get the required result.

32. Let (x', y') be taken as (h, k).

See P. 1011 eqn. (6)

$$\tan\alpha = \frac{m_1 - m_2}{1 + m_1m_2}$$

$$\therefore \quad \tan^2\alpha(1 + m_1m_2)^2 = (m_1 + m_2)^2 - 4m_1m_2$$

$$\text{or} \quad \tan^2\alpha\left(1 + \frac{k^2 - b^2}{h^2 - a^2}\right)^2 = \frac{4h^2k^2}{(h^2-a^2)^2} - \frac{4(k^2-b^2)}{(h^2-a^2)}$$

$$\therefore \quad \tan^2\alpha(x^2 + y^2 - a^2 - b^2)^2$$

$$= 4[x^2b^2 + a^2y^2 - a^2b^2]$$

33. From ΔPSS_1 by sine rule we have

$$\frac{SP}{\sin\phi}=\frac{S_1P}{\sin\theta}=\frac{SS_1}{\sin[\pi-(\theta+\phi)]}$$

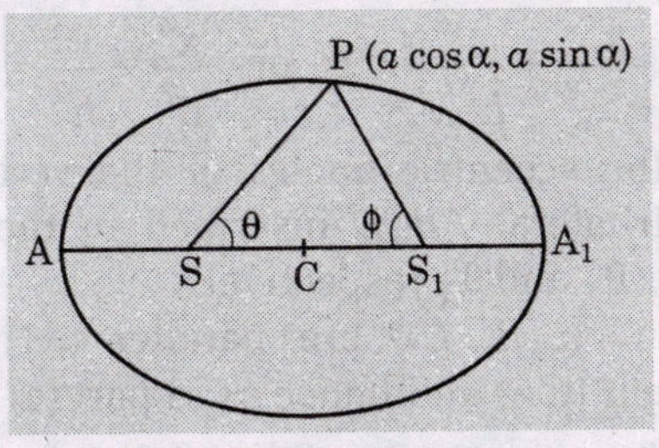

Fig. 18

or $\dfrac{SP+S_1P}{\sin\phi+\sin\theta}=\dfrac{2ae}{\sin(\theta+\phi)}$

$\therefore$ $\dfrac{\sin(\theta+\phi)}{\sin\theta+\sin\phi}=\dfrac{e}{1}$

or $\dfrac{2\sin\dfrac{\theta+\phi}{2}\cos\dfrac{\theta+\phi}{2}}{2\sin\dfrac{\theta+\phi}{2}\cos\dfrac{\theta-\phi}{2}}=\dfrac{e}{1}$

or $\dfrac{e}{1}=\dfrac{\cos\left\{\frac{1}{2}(\theta+\phi)\right\}}{\cos\left\{\frac{1}{2}(\theta-\phi)\right\}}$

Apply componendo and dividendo.

$$\frac{1-e}{1+e}=\frac{2\sin(\theta/2)\sin(\phi/2)}{2\cos(\theta/2)\cos(\phi/2)}$$

$$=\tan\frac{\theta}{2}\tan\frac{\phi}{2}$$

34. Ans. $P\left(\frac{1}{2},2\right),Q(1,1)$

Tangents at P and Q are

$4x.\frac{1}{2}+y.2=5$ and $4x.1+y.1=5$

or $2x+2y=5$ and $4x+y=5$

Hence normals are $2x-2y+3=0$, $x-4y+3=0$

They intersect at $\left(-1,\frac{1}{2}\right)$.

35. $[\pm\sqrt{(12/5)},\pm\sqrt{(18/5)}]$

$$\frac{1}{2}\sqrt{\left(\frac{3}{5}\right)}x+\frac{1}{3}\sqrt{\left(\frac{2}{5}\right)}y=1$$

$$2\sqrt{\left(\frac{3}{5}\right)}x+3\sqrt{\left(\frac{3}{5}\right)}y=6;\ \tan^{-1}\frac{1}{\sqrt{6}}$$

36. Let $PP'=2r$ be inclined at an angle θ to major axis

$\therefore$ P is $(r\cos\theta, r\sin\theta)$. It lies on ellipse

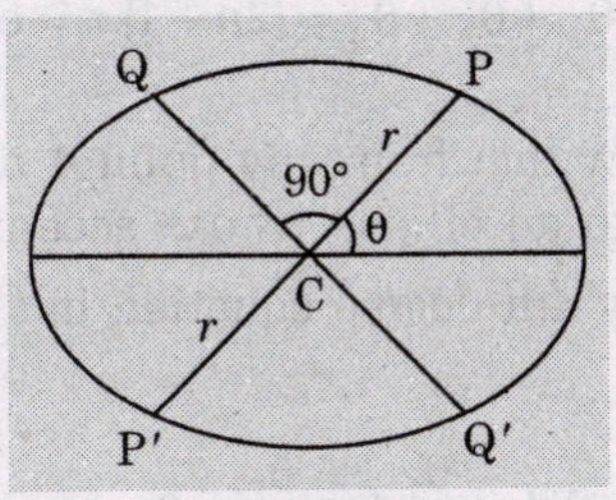

Fig. 19

$\therefore$ $r^2\left(\dfrac{\cos^2\theta}{a^2}+\dfrac{\sin^2\theta}{b^2}\right)=1$

or $\dfrac{1}{(PP')^2}=\dfrac{1}{4r^2}=\dfrac{1}{4}\left[\dfrac{\cos^2\theta}{a^2}+\dfrac{\sin^2\theta}{b^2}\right]$

Replace θ by $90°+\theta$

$\therefore$ $\dfrac{1}{(QQ')^2}=\dfrac{1}{4r_1^2}=\dfrac{1}{4}\left[\dfrac{\sin^2\theta}{a^2}+\dfrac{\cos^2\theta}{b^2}\right]$

$\therefore$ $\dfrac{1}{(PP')^2}+\dfrac{1}{(QQ')^2}=\dfrac{1}{4}\left(\dfrac{1}{a^2}+\dfrac{1}{b^2}\right)=\text{constant.}$

37. If P be $(a\cos\theta, b\sin\theta)$, then

$$N(a\cos\theta,0),T\left(\frac{a}{\cos\theta},0\right)$$

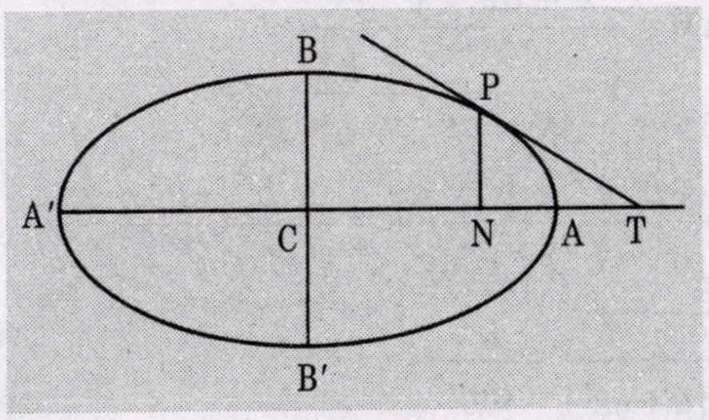

Fig. 20

Circle on NT as diameter

$$(x-a\cos\theta)\left(x-\frac{a}{\cos\theta}\right)+y^2=0$$

$$x^2+y^2-x\left(a\cos\theta+\frac{a}{\cos\theta}\right)+a^2=0$$

Auxiliary circle is $x^2+y^2-a^2=0$

Clearly, $2g_1g_2+2f_1f_2=c_1+c_2$

i.e., $0=a^2-a^2=0$

38. P is $(a\cos\theta, b\sin\theta)$

$\therefore$ Q is $(a\cos\theta, a\sin\theta)$

Normal at P is $\dfrac{ax}{\cos\theta}-\dfrac{by}{\sin\theta}=a^2-b^2$ ...(1)

Normal at Q to circle will pass through centre $C(0,0)$. [or put $b=a$ in (1)]

$\therefore$ Its equation $y=x\dfrac{\sin\theta}{\cos\theta}$ ...(2)

Solving (1) and (2), we get

$$\frac{ax}{\cos\theta}-\frac{b}{\sin\theta}.x.\frac{\sin\theta}{\cos\theta}=a^2-b^2$$

$\therefore$ $\dfrac{(a-b)}{\cos\theta}x=a^2-b^2$ or $x=(a+b)\cos\theta$

$\therefore$ $y=(a+b)\sin\theta$

$\therefore$ Locus of point of intersection is

$$x^2+y^2=(a+b)^2$$

39. Tangent at $P(x',y')$ is $\dfrac{xx'}{a^2}+\dfrac{yy'}{b^2}=1$

where $\dfrac{x'^2}{a^2}+\dfrac{y'^2}{b^2}=1$ ...(1)

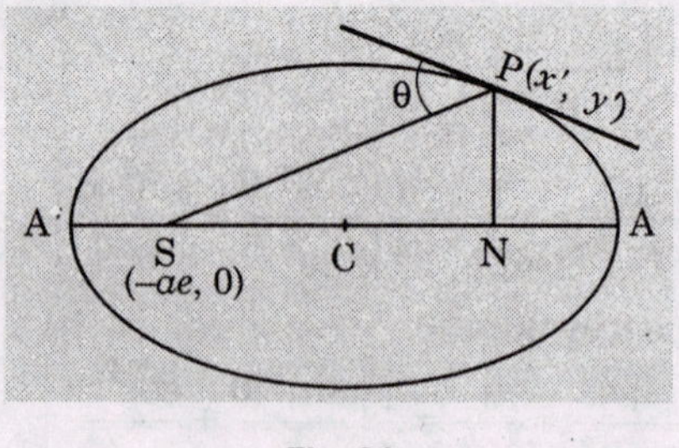

Fig. 21

Slope of tangent is $-\frac{x'}{y'}\frac{b^2}{a^2}$

Slope of SP is $\frac{y'}{x'+ae}$ where S is $(-ae, 0)$

$$\therefore \quad \tan\theta = \frac{\frac{y'}{x'+ae} + \frac{x'}{y'}\frac{b^2}{a^2}}{1 - \frac{y'}{x'+ae}\cdot\frac{x'}{y'}\frac{b^2}{a^2}}$$

$$= \frac{a^2y'^2 + b^2x'^2 + b^2x'ae}{x'y'(a^2-b^2) + a^3ey'} = \frac{a^2b^2 + b^2x'ae}{x'y'a^2e^2 + a^3ey'} \quad \text{by (1)}$$

$$= \frac{b^2a(a+ex')}{a^2ey'(a+ex')} = \frac{b^2}{aey'}$$

40. Normal at (x_1, y_1)

$$\frac{a^2(x-x_1)}{x_1} = \frac{b^2(y-y_1)}{y_1}$$

$$a^2y_1x - b^2x_1y - x_1y_1(a^2-b^2) = 0$$

Similarly normals at $(x_2, y_2), (x_3, y_3)$ be written as and these three lines are concurrent if determinant of the coefficients is zero.

$$\therefore \quad \begin{vmatrix} a^2y_1 & -b^2x_1 & -(a^2-b^2)x_1y_1 \\ - & - & - \\ - & - & - \end{vmatrix} = 0$$

Take out $a^2, -b^2$ and a^2-b^2 common from C_1, C_2 and C_3 and you get the result as given.

41. (a) Let the vertices of the triangle A, B, C be the points on the ellipse whose eccentric angles are $\theta_1, \theta_2, \theta_3$ respectively.

Chord AB is

$$\frac{x}{a}\cos\frac{(\theta_1+\theta_2)}{2} + \frac{y}{b}\sin\frac{(\theta_1+\theta_2)}{2} = \cos\frac{(\theta-\theta_2)}{2}$$

It is parallel to given line and hence its slope is constant $\therefore\ -\frac{b}{a}\cot\frac{\theta_1+\theta_2}{2} = \text{constant}$

or $\theta_1 + \theta_2 = 2\alpha$ (say)

Similarly $\theta_2 + \theta_3 = 2\beta \ \therefore\ \theta_1 - \theta_3 = 2(\alpha - \beta)$

Now chord CA is

$$\frac{x}{a}\cos\frac{\theta_1+\theta_3}{2} + \frac{y}{b}\sin\frac{\theta_1+\theta_3}{2} = \cos\frac{\theta_1-\theta_3}{2}$$

or $\frac{x}{a}\cos\theta + \frac{y}{b}\sin\theta = \cos(\alpha-\beta) = \lambda$, say

or $\frac{x}{a\lambda}\cos\theta + \frac{y}{b\lambda}\sin\theta = 1$

Above is clearly the equation of tangent to ellipse

$$\frac{x^2}{a^2\lambda^2} + \frac{y^2}{b^2\lambda^2} = 1 \quad \text{or} \quad \frac{x^2}{a^2} + \frac{y^2}{b^2} = \lambda^2$$

(b) Let the eccentric angles of the vertices of the quadrilateral $ABCD$ inscribed in the ellipse be $\theta_1, \theta_2, \theta_3$ and θ_4 respectively.

Given AB, BC, CD are parallel to three given straight lines and hence as in part (a)

$$\theta_1 + \theta_2 = 2\alpha, \theta_2 + \theta_3 = 2\beta, \theta_3 + \theta_4 = 2\gamma$$

we have to prove that the fourth side DA will also be parallel to a fixed direction.

Now $\theta_1 + \theta_4 = (\theta_1+\theta_2) - (\theta_2+\theta_3) + (\theta_3+\theta_4)$
$= 2\alpha - 2\beta + 2\gamma = \text{constant}$

Hence slope of $DA = -\frac{b}{a}\cot\frac{\theta_1+\theta_4}{2} = \text{constant}$

Therefore it is parallel to a fixed direction.

42. (a) Normal at any point whose eccentric angle is θ, is

$$\frac{ax}{\cos\theta} - \frac{by}{\sin\theta} = a^2 - b^2$$

If it passes through (h, k), then

$$\frac{ah}{\cos\theta} - \frac{bk}{\sin\theta} = a^2 - b^2$$

Replace $\cos\theta$ by $\frac{1-t^2}{1+t^2}$ and $\sin\theta$ by $\frac{2t}{1+t^2}$, where $t = \tan\frac{\theta}{2}$

$$ah.\frac{1+t^2}{1-t^2} - bk.\frac{1+t^2}{2t} = a^2 - b^2$$

or $\quad 2ah(t+t^3) - bk(1-t^4) = (a^2-b^2)(2t-2t^3)$

or $\quad bkt^4 + 2(ak + a^2 - b^2)t^3 + 0t^2 + 2(ah - a^2 + b^2) - bk = 0$

Its roots are $\tan\frac{\theta_r}{2}, r = 1, 2, 3, 4.$

$$\tan\left(\frac{\theta_1}{2} + \frac{\theta_2}{2} + \frac{\theta_3}{2} + \frac{\theta_4}{2}\right) = \frac{S_1 - S_3}{1 - S_2 + S_4} = \infty = \tan\frac{\pi}{2}$$

Because $S_2 = 0, S_4 = -\frac{bk}{bk} = -1$

$$\therefore \quad \frac{\theta_1+\theta_2+\theta_3+\theta_4}{2} = n\pi + \frac{\pi}{2}$$

$\therefore\ \theta_1 + \theta_2 + \theta_3 + \theta_4 = (2n+1)\pi$ = odd multiple of π.

(b) We know that from any point 4 normals can be drawn to an ellipse whose eccentric angles are given by 4th degree equation in $t = \tan\frac{\theta}{2}$ of part (a).

$$\Sigma\tan\frac{\theta_1}{2}\tan\frac{\theta_2}{2} = 0,$$

$$\tan\frac{\theta_1}{2}\tan\frac{\theta_2}{2}\tan\frac{\theta_3}{2}\tan\frac{\theta_4}{2} = -1$$

There will be six terms in Ist sigma. Eliminating $\tan\frac{\theta_4}{2}$, we have

$$\Sigma\left(\tan\frac{\theta_1}{2}\tan\frac{\theta_2}{2} + \tan\frac{\theta_3}{2}\tan\frac{\theta_4}{2}\right) = 0$$

$$\Sigma\left(\tan\frac{\theta_1}{2}\tan\frac{\theta_2}{2} - \frac{\tan\frac{\theta_3}{2}}{\tan\frac{\theta_1}{2}\tan\frac{\theta_2}{2}\tan\frac{\theta_3}{2}}\right) = 0$$

or $$\Sigma\left(\tan\frac{\theta_1}{2}\tan\frac{\theta_2}{2} - \cot\frac{\theta_1}{2}\cot\frac{\theta_2}{2}\right) = 0$$

or $$\Sigma\frac{\left(\cos^2\frac{\theta_1}{2}\cos^2\frac{\theta_2}{2} - \sin^2\frac{\theta_1}{2}\sin^2\frac{\theta_2}{2}\right)}{\sin\frac{\theta_1}{2}\sin\frac{\theta_2}{2}\cos\frac{\theta_1}{2}\cos\frac{\theta_2}{2}} = 0$$

or $$\Sigma\, 4\frac{\cos\frac{\theta_1+\theta_2}{2}\cos\frac{\theta_1-\theta_2}{2}}{\sin\theta_1\sin\theta_2} = 0$$

or $2\Sigma(\cos\theta_1 + \cos\theta_2)\sin\theta_3 = 0$ ... six terms

or $\sin(\theta_1+\theta_2) + \sin(\theta_2+\theta_3)$
$+\sin(\theta_3+\theta_1) = 0$

§3 Diameter

Any line passing through the centre (0, 0) of an ellipse is called a diameter hence its equation is of the form $y = mx$.

Conjugate diameter : Two diameters $y = m_1 x$ and $y = m_2 x$ of an ellipse are said to be conjugate if each bisects chords parallel to the other.

Let $y = m_2 x$ bisect all chords of the ellipse which are parallel to the diameter $y = m_1 x$. If (h, k) be the mid-point of the chords parallel to $y = m_1 x$ then it will lie on $y = m_2 x$.

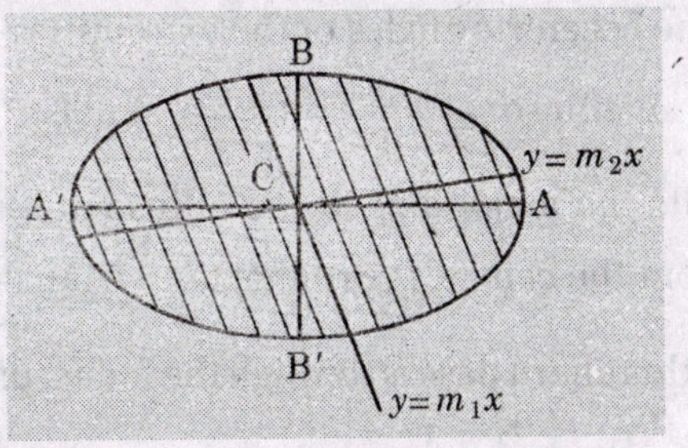

Fig. 22

$\therefore \quad k = m_2 h$. ...(A)

But if (h, k) be the mid-point of the chord, then its equation is

$$\frac{hx}{a^2} + \frac{ky}{b^2} = \frac{h^2}{a^2} + \frac{k^2}{b^2}.$$

Its slope is $-\frac{hb^2}{ka^2}$.

But this chord is parallel to $y = m_1 x$.

$\therefore \quad -\frac{hb^2}{ka^2} = m_1$. ...(B)

But from (A) $\frac{h}{k} = \frac{1}{m_2}$

$\therefore \quad -\frac{1}{m_2}\frac{b^2}{a^2} = m_1$ from (B)

$\therefore \quad m_1 m_2 = -b^2/a^2$ is the required condition for any two diameters to be conjugate.

Eccentric angles of extremities of two conjugate semi-diameters.

Let θ and ϕ be the eccentric angles of the extremities P and D of two conjugate semi-diameters CP and CD.

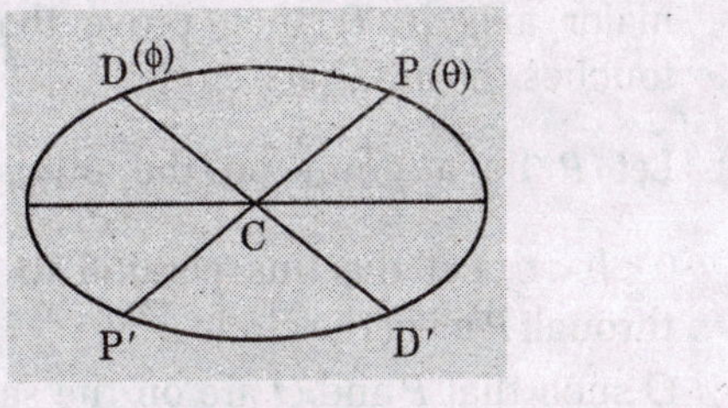

Fig. 23

Hence P is $(a\cos\theta, b\sin\theta)$,

D is $(a\cos\phi, b\sin\phi)$

$$m_1 = \text{slope of } CP = \frac{b\sin\theta}{a\cos\theta}$$

$$m_2 = \text{slope of } CD = \frac{b\sin\phi}{a\cos\phi}$$

Since CP and CD are conjugate semi-diameters

$\therefore \quad m_1 m_2 = -b^2/a^2$

or $\frac{b^2\sin\theta\sin\phi}{a^2\cos\theta\cos\phi} = -\frac{b^2}{a^2}$

or $\cos\theta\cos\phi + \sin\theta\sin\phi = 0$

or $\cos(\phi - \theta) = 0$

$\therefore \quad \phi - \theta = \pi/2.$ or $\phi = \pi/2 + \theta$.

Hence if P is $(a\cos\theta, b\sin\theta)$

then D is $\{a\cos(\pi/2+\theta), b\sin(\pi/2+\theta)\}$

i.e. $(-a\sin\theta, b\cos\theta)$.

Sum of the Squares of two semi-conjugate diameters is constant.

$\therefore \quad CP^2 = a^2\cos^2\theta + b^2\sin^2\theta$

$CD^2 = a^2\sin^2\theta + b^2\cos^2\theta$

$\therefore \quad CP^2 + CD^2 = a^2(\cos^2\theta + \sin^2\theta)$
$+ b^2(\sin^2\theta + \cos^2\theta)$
$= a^2 + b^2$, *i.e.* constant.

Problem Set (3)

Auxiliary circle, Chord of contact, Polar and Conjugate diameters.

1. Prove that the product of the perpendiculars drawn from the foci of an ellipse on any tangent to it is constant and equal to the square of semi minor axis. Prove also that the locus of the feet of the perpendiculars is the auxiliary circle of the ellipse.

2.* Show that the locus of the feet of perpendiculars drawn from the centre of the ellipse $\frac{x^2}{a^2}+\frac{y^2}{b^2}=1$ on any tangent to it is $(x^2+y^2)^2=a^2x^2+b^2y^2$.

3. (a) P is any point on the ellipse $x^2/a^2+y^2/b^2=1$ and Q the corresponding point on the auxiliary circle. If the tangent at P to the ellipse cuts the major axis in T, then prove that the line QT touches the auxiliary circle.

(b) Let P be a point on the ellipse $\frac{x^2}{a^2}+\frac{y^2}{b^2}=1$, $0<b<a$. Let the line parallel to y-axis passing through P meet the circle $x^2+y^2=a^2$ at the point Q such that P and Q are on the same side of the x-axis. For two positive real numbers r and s, find the locus of the point R on PQ such that $PR:RQ=r:s$ as P varies over the ellipse. **(I.I.T. 2001)**

4. (a) Find the locus of the point the chord of contact of tangents from which to the ellipse $\frac{x^2}{a^2}+\frac{y^2}{b^2}=1$.

(i) subtends a right angle at the centre of the ellipse.

(ii) touches the circle $x^2+y^2=c^2$.

(b)* The tangent to the ellipse $\frac{x^2}{a^2}+\frac{y^2}{b^2}=1$ at a point whose eccentric angle is θ cuts the auxiliary circle in points L and M. If LM subtends a right angle at the centre of the ellipse, then prove that its eccentricity is $(1+\sin^2\theta)^{-1/2}$. If θ be $\pi/4$ then find e.

5. (a)* Prove that the locus of the poles of the normal chords of the ellipse $\frac{x^2}{a^2}+\frac{y^2}{b^2}=1$ is

$$\frac{a^6}{x^2}+\frac{b^6}{y^2}=(a^2-b^2)^2.$$

(b)* Prove that the locus of the pole with respect to the ellipse $\frac{x^2}{a^2}+\frac{y^2}{b^2}=1$ of any tangent to the auxiliary circle is the curve $\frac{x^2}{a^4}+\frac{y^2}{b^4}=\frac{1}{a^2}$. **(M.N.R. 1997)**

(c) If the product of the perpendiculars from the foci of an ellipse $x^2/a^2+y^2/b^2=1$ upon the polar of P be always c^2, prove that the locus of P is the ellipse $(c^2+a^2-b^2)b^4x^2+c^2a^4y^2=a^4b^4$.

6. (a)* Find the locus of the mid-points of the normal chords of the ellipse $\frac{x^2}{a^2}+\frac{y^2}{b^2}=1$.

(b)* Find the locus of the mid-points of chords of ellipse, the tangents at the extremities of which intersect at right angles.

Another form : Perpendicular tangents are drawn to the ellipse $\frac{x^2}{a^2}+\frac{y^2}{b^2}=1$. Find the locus of the mid-points of the chords of contact.

(c) A tangent to the ellipse $x^2+4y^2=4$ meets the ellipse $x^2+2y^2=6$ at P and Q. Prove that the tangents at P and Q of the ellipse $x^2+2y^2=6$ are at right angles. **(I.I.T. Re-ex. 1997)**

(d)* Find the locus of the mid-points of the chords of the ellipse whose poles are on the auxiliary circle or tangents at the extremities of which intersect on the auxiliary circle.

(e) Tangents are drawn from any point on the circle $x^2+y^2=c^2$ to the ellipse $\frac{x^2}{a^2}+\frac{y^2}{b^2}=1$. Find the locus of the mid-points of the chords of contact.

7. Find the locus of the mid-points of the chords of the ellipse which

(a) touch the auxiliary circle

(b)* subtend a right angle at the centre of the ellipse

(c)* If $(1/2, 2/5)$ be the middle-point of the chord of the ellipse $\frac{x^2}{25}+\frac{y^2}{16}=1$, then prove that its length is $7/5\sqrt{41}$.

8. (a)* The eccentric angles of the extremities of a chord of an ellipse $\frac{x^2}{a^2}+\frac{y^2}{b^2}=1$ are θ_1 and θ_2. The chord cuts the major axis of the ellipse at a distance d from the centre. Prove that $\tan\frac{\theta_1}{2}\tan\frac{\theta_2}{2}=\frac{d-a}{d+a}$

If this chord passes through the focus, prove that

(i) $\tan\frac{\theta_1}{2}\tan\frac{\theta_2}{2}+\frac{1-e}{1+e}=0$

(ii) $\cos\frac{\theta_1-\theta_2}{2}=e\cos\frac{\theta_1+\theta_2}{2}$

(iii) $e=\frac{\sin\theta_1+\sin\theta_2}{\sin(\theta_1+\theta_2)}$

(iv) The chord joining the points θ_1,θ_2 where $\theta_1+\theta_2=2\alpha$ is parallel to the tangent to the ellipse at the point α.

(b)* If the chord through the points P and Q whose eccentric angles are θ and ϕ on the ellipse $x^2/a^2 + y^2/b^2 = 1$ passes through a focus S, and S' is the other focus, prove that

(i) $SP \cdot S'P = a^2 \sin^2 \theta + b^2 \cos^2 \theta$

(ii) the perimeter of $\Delta S'PQ = 4a$

(iii) $(a^2 - b^2)\cos^2 \frac{1}{2}(\theta + \phi) = a^2 \cos^2 \frac{1}{2}(\theta - \phi)$

(iv) $\tan \frac{1}{2}\theta \tan \frac{1}{2}\phi + \frac{(1-e)}{(1+e)} = 0$

9.* Find the locus of the mid-points of the lines joining the extremities of two semi-conjugate diameters.

10.* Find the locus of the point of intersection of tangents at the ends of semi-conjugate diameters of an ellipse. **(D.C.E. 1997)**

Another form :
The eccentric angles of two points P and Q on the ellipse differ by $\pi/2$. Find the locus of
(a) mid-point of PQ, (b) point of intersection of tangents at P and Q.

11. If the points of intersection of the ellipses $\frac{x^2}{a^2} + \frac{y^2}{b^2} = 1$ and $\frac{x^2}{p^2} + \frac{y^2}{q^2} = 1$ be the extremities of the conjugate diameters of first ellipse, then prove that $\frac{a^2}{p^2} + \frac{b^2}{q^2} = 2$.

12. (a)* Prove that the tangents drawn to the ellipse $\frac{x^2}{a} + \frac{y^2}{b} = (a+b)$ at the points where it is cut by any tangent to the ellipse $\frac{x^2}{a^2} + \frac{y^2}{b^2} = 1$ intersect at right angles.

(b) From any point on the ellipse $\frac{x^2}{a^2} + \frac{y^2}{b^2} = 1$ tangents are drawn to the circle $x^2 + y^2 = r^2$. Show that the chord of contact touches the ellipse $a^2x^2 + b^2y^2 = r^4$.

(c) If the chord of contact of the tangents drawn from the point (α, β) to the ellipse $\frac{x^2}{a^2} + \frac{y^2}{b^2} = 1$ touches the circle $x^2 + y^2 = c^2$, prove that the point (α, β) lies on the ellipse $x^2/a^2 + y^2/b^2 = 1/c^2$.

(d) PA and PB are tangents drawn from a point P to the ellipse $\frac{x^2}{a^2} + \frac{y^2}{b^2} = 1$. The area of the triangle formed by the chord of contact AB and axes of co-ordinates is constant. Prove that locus of P is a hyperbola.

13. Two perpendicular tangents are drawn to an ellipse $\frac{x^2}{a^2} + \frac{y^2}{b^2} = 1$. These tangents intercept chords of length l_1 and l_2 on the auxiliary circle, prove that $l_1^2 + l_2^2 = (S_1S_2)^2$ where S_1 and S_2 are the foci of the ellipse.

14.* If the eccentric angles of points P and Q on the ellipse be θ and $\pi/2 + \theta$ and α be the angle between the normals at P and Q then prove that the eccentricity e is given by $2\sqrt{1-e^2} = e^2 \sin^2 2\theta \tan \alpha$.

15.* Prove that the ellipse $\frac{x^2}{a^2} + \frac{y^2}{b^2} = 1$ and the circle $x^2 + y^2 = ab$ intersect at an angle $\tan^{-1} \frac{a-b}{\sqrt{ab}}$.

16. The line passing through the extremity A of the major axis and extremity B of the minor axis of the ellipse $x^2 + 9y^2 = 9$ meets its auxiliary circle at the point M. Then the area of the triangle with vertices at A, M and the origin O is

(a) $\frac{31}{10}$ (b) $\frac{29}{10}$ (c) $\frac{21}{10}$ (d) $\frac{27}{10}$

(IIT 2009)

Solutions to Problem Set (3)

1. Any tangent to the ellipse is
$y = mx + \sqrt{(a^2m^2 + b^2)}$; Foci are $(ae, 0), (-ae, 0)$.
If p_1 and p_2 be the perpendiculars from the foci on the tangent, then

$$p_1p_2 = \frac{aem + \sqrt{(a^2m^2 + b^2)}}{\sqrt{(m^2+1)}} \cdot \frac{-aem + \sqrt{(a^2m^2 + b^2)}}{\sqrt{(m^2+1)}}$$

$$= \frac{(a^2m^2 + b^2) - a^2e^2m^2}{m^2+1} = \frac{a^2m^2(1-e^2) + b^2}{m^2+1}$$

$$= \frac{b^2(m^2+1)}{m^2+1} = b^2 \qquad \because \ a^2(1-e^2) = b^2.$$

Any line through focus $(\pm ae, 0)$ and perpendicular to tangent is

$$y - 0 = \frac{-1}{m}(x \pm ae) \quad \text{or} \quad my + x = \pm ae.$$

These lines meet the tangent at feet of perpendiculars and in order to find the locus we have to eliminate the variable m.

$\therefore \quad (y - mx)^2 + (my + x)^2 = a^2m^2 + b^2 + a^2e^2$

or $\quad y^2(1+m^2) + x^2(1+m^2) = a^2m^2 + a^2 - a^2e^2 + a^2e^2$

or $\quad (x^2 + y^2)(1 + m^2) = a^2(1 + m^2)$

or $\quad x^2 + y^2 = a^2$ which is auxiliary circle.

Hence the feet lie on auxiliary circle.

2. Any tangent is $y = mx + \sqrt{(a^2m^2 + b^2)}$ ...(1)

Any line through $C(0,0)$ and perpendicular to tangent is

$$y = -\frac{1}{m}x \quad \text{...(2)}$$

In order to find the locus of the foot of perpendicular we have to eliminate the variable m between (1) and (2).

From (1), $(y - mx)^2 = a^2m^2 + b^2$

or $\left(y + \frac{x}{y}\cdot x\right)^2 = a^2\frac{x^2}{y^2} + b^2$, by (2)

or $(x^2 + y^2)^2 = a^2x^2 + b^2y^2$

is the required locus.

3. (a) Tangent at $P(a\cos\theta, b\sin\theta)$ is

$$\frac{x}{a}\cos\theta + \frac{y}{b}\sin\theta = 1$$

and it cuts the major axis $y = 0$ at $T\left(\frac{a}{\cos\theta}, 0\right)$

Q is a point on the auxiliary circle

$\therefore$ Q is $(a\cos\theta, a\sin\theta)$

Slope of line QT

$$= \frac{a\sin\theta - 0}{a\cos\theta - \frac{a}{\cos\theta}} = \frac{\sin\theta\cos\theta}{(\cos^2\theta - 1)}$$

$$= \frac{\sin\theta\cos\theta}{-\sin^2\theta} = \frac{\cos\theta}{\sin\theta}$$

Hence the line QT is

$$y - 0 = -\frac{\cos\theta}{\sin\theta}\left(x - \frac{a}{\cos\theta}\right)$$

or $x\cos\theta + y\sin\theta = a$.

Above is clearly a tangent to the auxiliary circle $x^2 + y^2 = a^2$ at the point $(a\cos\theta, a\sin\theta)$, *i.e.* the point Q.

(b) P is a point on the ellipse and Q the corresponding point on the auxiliary circle where PQ is parallel to y-axis and both P and Q are on same side of x-axis. R is a point which divides PQ in the ratio $r:s$. If its co-ordinates be (x, y), then

$$x = \frac{ra\cos\theta + sa\cos\theta}{r+s},$$

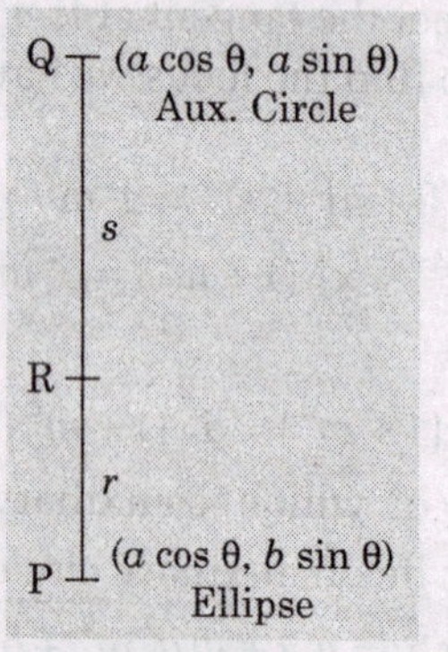

Fig. 24

$$y = \frac{ra\sin\theta + sb\sin\theta}{r+s}$$

$$x = a\cos\theta,\ y = \frac{ra + sb}{r+s}\sin\theta$$

In order to find the locus of R, we have to eliminate the variable θ from the above two relations. We know that $\cos^2\theta + \sin^2\theta = 1$.

$\therefore$ $\frac{x^2}{a^2} + \frac{y^2(r+s)^2}{(ra+sb)^2} = 1$ is the required locus.

4. (a) (i) Let the point from which tangents are drawn be (x_1, y_1) so that the equation of chord of contact is

$$\frac{xx_1}{a^2} + \frac{yy_1}{b^2} = 1 \quad \text{...(1)}$$

It subtends a right angle at the centre (0, 0) of ellipse

$$\frac{x^2}{a^2} + \frac{y^2}{b^2} = 1.$$

Making the equation of the ellipse homogeneous by the help of equation of chord of contact we get the equation of the lines joining the origin to the points of intersection of the chord of contact and the ellipse as

$$\frac{x^2}{a^2} + \frac{y^2}{b^2} = \left(\frac{xx_1}{a^2} + \frac{yy_1}{b^2}\right)^2$$

or $x^2\left(\frac{1}{a^2} - \frac{x_1^2}{a^4}\right) - \frac{2xy\,x_1y_1}{a^2b^2} + y^2\left(\frac{1}{b^2} - \frac{y_1^2}{b^4}\right) = 0$ ...(2)

Since these lines are at right angles, therefore sum of the coefficients of x^2 and y^2 in (2) should be zero

$$\therefore \quad \frac{1}{a^2} - \frac{x_1^2}{a^4} + \frac{1}{b^2} - \frac{y_1^2}{b^4} = 0.$$

Hence the locus of the point (x_1, y_1) is

$$\frac{x^2}{a^4} + \frac{y^2}{b^4} = \frac{1}{a^2} + \frac{1}{b^2}$$

(ii) The line (1) touches the circle $x^2 + y^2 = c^2$

Therefore perpendicular from centre (0, 0) is equal to radius c.

$$\therefore \quad \frac{1}{\sqrt{\left(\frac{x_1^2}{a^4} + \frac{y_1^2}{b^4}\right)}} = c \quad \text{or} \quad \frac{x_1^2}{a^4} + \frac{y_1^2}{b^4} = \frac{1}{c^2}$$

Hence the locus is $\frac{x^2}{a^4} + \frac{y^2}{b^4} = \frac{1}{c^2}$.

(b) Tangent at 'θ' is $\frac{x\cos\theta}{a} + \frac{y\sin\theta}{b} = 1$

Auxiliary circle is $x^2 + y^2 = a^2$

Make homogeneous and put $A+B=0$ as the lines joining origin to points of intersection are perpendicular.

$$\therefore \quad x^2+y^2=a^2\left(x\frac{\cos\theta}{a}+y\frac{\sin\theta}{b}\right)^2$$

$$\therefore \quad (1-\cos^2\theta)+\left(1-\sin^2\theta.\frac{a^2}{b^2}\right)=0$$

$$\text{or} \quad \sin^2\theta\left[1-\frac{a^2}{a^2(1-e^2)}\right]=-1$$

$$\text{or} \quad -e^2\sin^2\theta=-(1-e^2)$$

$$\therefore \quad e^2(1+\sin^2\theta)=1$$

$$\therefore \quad e=(1+\sin^2\theta)^{-1/2}$$

Put $\theta=45°$ $\therefore$ $e=\sqrt{\frac{2}{3}}$

5. (a) Any normal to the ellipse is

$$\frac{ax}{\cos\theta}-\frac{by}{\sin\theta}=a^2-b^2 \quad \text{...(1)}$$

If its pole be (h,k) then (1) is same as polar of (h,k) *i.e.*

$$\frac{hx}{a^2}+\frac{ky}{b^2}=1 \quad \text{...(2)}$$

Comparing (1) and (2), we get

$$\frac{a}{\cos\theta}\cdot\frac{a^2}{h}=\frac{-b}{\sin\theta}\cdot\frac{b^2}{k}=\frac{a^2-b^2}{1}$$

$$\therefore \quad \frac{a^3}{h}=(a^2-b^2)\cos\theta, \frac{b^3}{k}=-(a^2-b^2)\sin\theta.$$

Square and add

$$\frac{a^6}{h^2}+\frac{b^6}{k^2}=(a^2-b^2)^2(\cos^2\theta+\sin^2\theta)=(a^2-b^2)^2$$

$$\therefore \quad \text{Locus is } \frac{a^6}{x^2}+\frac{b^6}{y^2}=(a^2-b^2)^2.$$

(b) Any tangent to auxiliary circle $x^2+y^2=a^2$ is $x\cos\theta+y\sin\theta=a$.

Rest as in part (a).

(c) If P be (h,k), its polar is $\frac{hx}{a^2}+\frac{ky}{b^2}-1=0$

$$p_1p_2=\frac{\left(\frac{aeh}{a^2}-1\right)\left(-\frac{aeh}{a^2}-1\right)}{\frac{h^2}{a^4}+\frac{k^2}{b^4}}=c^2, \text{given}$$

$$\text{or} \quad \left(1-\frac{e^2h^2}{a^2}\right)=\frac{c^2}{a^4b^4}(b^4h^2+a^4k^2)$$

$$\text{or} \quad a^4b^4-a^2e^2b^4h^2=c^2b^4h^2+c^2a^4k^2$$

$$\text{or} \quad a^4b^4=b^4h^2[c^2+a^2-b^2]+c^2a^4k^2$$

$\therefore$ Locus of (h,k) is as given.

6. (a) Any normal to the ellipse is

$$\frac{ax}{\cos\theta}-\frac{by}{\sin\theta}=a^2-b^2 \quad \text{...(1)}$$

If its middle point be (h,k), then its equation is

$$\frac{hx}{a^2}+\frac{ky}{b^2}=\frac{h^2}{a^2}+\frac{k^2}{b^2}, \text{ by } T=S_1 \quad \text{...(2)}$$

Comparing (1) and (2), we get

$$\frac{a^3}{h\cos\theta}=\frac{-b^3}{k\sin\theta}=\frac{a^2-b^2}{(h^2/a^2)+(k^2/b^2)}=L, \text{ say}$$

$$\frac{a^3}{h}=L\cos\theta, \frac{b^3}{k}=-L\sin\theta$$

$$\therefore \quad \frac{a^6}{h^2}+\frac{b^6}{k^2}=L^2.1 \quad \text{Now generalize}$$

$$\left(\frac{a^6}{x^2}+\frac{b^6}{y^2}\right)\left(\frac{x^2}{a^2}+\frac{y^2}{b^2}\right)^2=(a^2-b^2)^2$$

(b) Let (x_1,y_1) be the point of intersection of perpendicular tangents so that (x_1,y_1) lies on director circle

$$\therefore \quad x_1^2+y_1^2=a^2+b^2 \quad \text{...(1)}$$

Then the chord will be chord of contact of (x_1,y_1)

$$\therefore \quad \frac{xx_1}{a^2}+\frac{yy_1}{b^2}=1 \quad \text{...(2)}$$

If its mid-point is (h,k), then its equation is

$$\frac{hx}{a^2}+\frac{ky}{b^2}=\frac{h^2}{a^2}+\frac{k^2}{b^2} \quad \text{...(3)}$$

Compare (2) and (3) and find x_1, y_1 and put in (1)

$\therefore$ Locus of (h,k) is

$$\left(\frac{x^2}{a^2}+\frac{y^2}{b^2}\right)^2(a^2+b^2)=x^2+y^2$$

Another form : Equation of polar is same as the equation of chord of contact. Hence the same answer.

(c)
$$\frac{x^2}{4}+\frac{y^2}{1}=1 \quad \text{...(1)}$$

$$\frac{x^2}{6}+\frac{y^2}{3}=1 \quad \text{...(2)}$$

Any tangent to (1) is $\frac{x\cos\theta}{2}+\frac{y\sin\theta}{1}=1$ ...(3)

It cuts (2) in P and Q tangents at which meet at (h,k) say, then it is chord of contact of (h,k) w.r.t. ellipse (2).

Hence the equation is $\frac{hx}{6}+\frac{ky}{3}=1$ ...(4)

Comparing (3) and (4) as they represent the same line PQ,

$$\frac{\cos\theta}{h/3}=\frac{\sin\theta}{k/3}=1$$

Eliminating θ, we get $\frac{h^2}{9}+\frac{k^2}{9}=1$

$\therefore$ locus of (h, k) is $x^2 + y^2 = 9 = 6 + 3 = a^2 + b^2$

i.e. director circle of 2nd ellipse.

Hence the tangents are at right angles.

(d) It is same as part (b). Here (x_1, y_1) will lie on auxiliary circle $x^2 + y^2 = a^2$.

Ans. $\left(\frac{x^2}{a^2} + \frac{y^2}{b^2}\right)^2 a^2 = x^2 + y^2$

(e) This is another form of part (b) or (d).

Ans. Replace a^2 by c^2 in part (d).

7. (a) The chord whose mid-point is (h, k) is given by (2) of part (a). If it touches the auxiliary circle $x^2 + y^2 = a^2$ then apply $p = r$

$$\therefore \quad \frac{\frac{h^2}{a^2} + \frac{k^2}{b^2}}{\sqrt{\left(\frac{h^2}{a^4} + \frac{k^2}{b^4}\right)}} = a$$

$\therefore$ Locus of mid-point is

$$\left(\frac{x^2}{a^2} + \frac{y^2}{b^2}\right)^2 = a^2\left(\frac{x^2}{a^4} + \frac{y^2}{b^4}\right)$$

(b) If it subtends a right angle at the centre, then make it homogeneous with the ellipse

$$\frac{hx}{a^2} + \frac{ky}{b^2} = \frac{h^2}{a^2} + \frac{k^2}{b^2} = L, \text{ say}$$

or $\frac{1}{L}\left(\frac{hx}{a^2} + \frac{ky}{b^2}\right) = 1$

$\therefore$ Ellipse $\frac{x^2}{a^2} + \frac{y^2}{b^2} = 1$ is

$$\frac{x^2}{a^2} + \frac{y^2}{b^2} = 1 . \frac{1}{L^2}\left(\frac{hx}{a^2} + \frac{ky}{b^2}\right)^2$$

$\therefore$ $A + B = 0$

$$\frac{h^2}{a^4 L^2} - \frac{1}{a^2} + \frac{k^2}{b^4 L^2} - \frac{1}{b^2} = 0$$

or $\frac{h^2}{a^4} + \frac{k^2}{b^4} = L^2\left(\frac{1}{a^2} + \frac{1}{b^2}\right)$

$\therefore$ Locus of (h, k) is

$$\frac{x^2}{a^4} + \frac{y^2}{b^4} = \left(\frac{x^2}{a^2} + \frac{y^2}{b^2}\right)^2\left(\frac{1}{a^2} + \frac{1}{b^2}\right)$$

(c) $T = S_1$ or $\frac{hx}{a^2} + \frac{ky}{b^2} = \frac{h^2}{a^2} + \frac{k^2}{b^2}$ is the equation of the chord whose mid-point is $(h, k) = \left(\frac{1}{2}, \frac{2}{5}\right)$.

$\therefore$ Chord is $4x + 5y = 4$

Solving with ellipse by eliminating y, we get

$x^2 - x - 12 = 0$

$\therefore$ $x = 4, -3$ $\therefore$ $y = -\frac{12}{5}$ and $\frac{16}{5}$

$\therefore$ Points are $\left(4, -\frac{12}{5}\right)$ and $\left(-3, \frac{16}{5}\right)$

$\therefore$ Length $= \sqrt{7^2\left(1 + \frac{16}{25}\right)} = \frac{7}{5}\sqrt{(41)}$

8. (a) (i) The equation of the chord joining θ_1 and θ_2 is

$$\frac{x}{a}\cos\left(\frac{\theta_1 + \theta_2}{2}\right) + \frac{y}{b}\sin\left(\frac{\theta_1 + \theta_2}{2}\right) = \cos\left(\frac{\theta_1 - \theta_2}{2}\right). \quad \text{...(1)}$$

It cuts the major axis at a point distant d from centre *i.e.*, at $(d, 0)$.

$$\therefore \quad \frac{d}{a}\cos\frac{\theta_1 + \theta_2}{2} = \cos\left(\frac{\theta_1 - \theta_2}{2}\right)$$

$$\text{or} \quad \frac{d}{a} = \frac{\cos\frac{\theta_1 - \theta_2}{2}}{\cos\frac{\theta_1 + \theta_2}{2}}. \quad \text{...(2)}$$

Apply componendo and dividendo

$$\frac{d - a}{d + a} = \frac{\cos\frac{\theta_1 - \theta_2}{2} - \cos\frac{\theta_1 + \theta_2}{2}}{\cos\frac{\theta_1 - \theta_2}{2} + \cos\frac{\theta_1 + \theta_2}{2}}$$

$$= \frac{2\sin\frac{\theta_1}{2}\sin\frac{\theta_2}{2}}{2\cos\frac{\theta_1}{2}\cos\frac{\theta_2}{2}}$$

$$\text{or} \quad \frac{d - a}{d + a} = \tan\frac{\theta_1}{2}\tan\frac{\theta_2}{2} \quad \text{...(3)}$$

If the chord (1) passes through focus $(ae, 0)$, then putting $d = ae$ in (3) we get

$$\frac{ae - a}{ae + a} = \tan\frac{\theta_1}{2}\tan\frac{\theta_2}{2}$$

$$\text{or} \quad \tan\frac{\theta_1}{2}\tan\frac{\theta_2}{2} + \frac{1 - e}{1 + e} = 0$$

(ii) It follows by putting $(ae, 0)$ in (1).

(iii) From (2), $e = \dfrac{\cos\frac{\theta_1 - \theta_2}{2}}{\cos\frac{\theta_1 + \theta_2}{2}}$

Multiply above and below by $2\sin\frac{\theta_1 + \theta_2}{2}$

$$\therefore \quad e = \frac{2\sin\frac{\theta_1 + \theta_2}{2}\cos\frac{\theta_1 - \theta_2}{2}}{2\sin\frac{\theta_1 + \theta_2}{2}\cos\frac{\theta_1 + \theta_2}{2}}$$

$$= \frac{\sin\theta_1 + \sin\theta_2}{\sin(\theta_1 + \theta_2)}$$

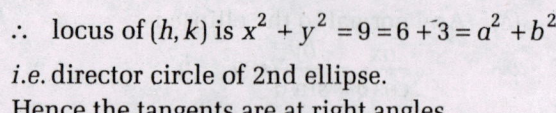

(iv) $T_\alpha = \dfrac{x\cos\alpha}{a} + \dfrac{y\sin\alpha}{b} = 1$ ...(1)

Chord joining θ_1 and θ_2 is

$$\frac{x}{a}\cos\frac{\theta_1+\theta_2}{2} + \frac{y}{b}\sin\frac{\theta_1+\theta_2}{2} = \cos\frac{\theta_1-\theta_2}{2}$$

Put $\theta_1 + \theta_2 = 2\alpha$ and it becomes

$$\frac{x\cos\alpha}{a} + \frac{y\sin\alpha}{b} = \frac{\cos(\theta_1-\theta_2)}{2} \quad ...(2)$$

Clearly (1) and (2) are parallel.

(b) (i) $(a+ex)(a-ex) = a^2 - e^2x^2$

$= a^2 - e^2a^2\cos^2\theta = a^2 - (a^2-b^2)\cos^2\theta$

$= a^2\sin^2\theta + b^2\cos^2\theta$

(ii) Perimeter of $\Delta S'PQ$ where PQ is a focal chord

$= S'P + S'Q + PQ$

$= S'P + S'Q + PS + SQ$

$= (S'P + SP) + (S'Q + SQ)$

$= 2a + 2a = 4a$

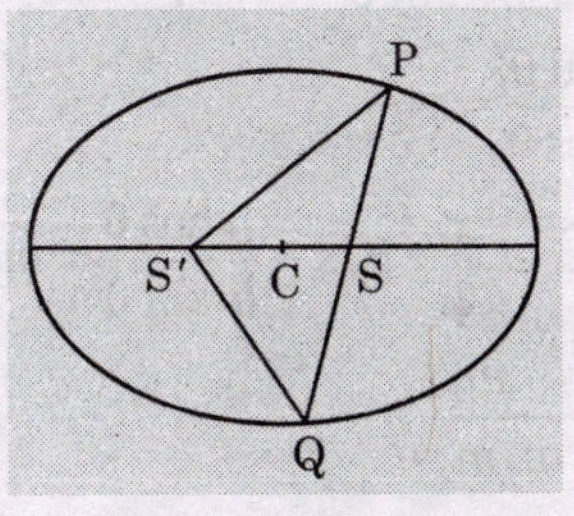

Fig. 25

(iii) Replace $a^2 - b^2$ by a^2e^2 and it becomes Q. 8 (ii).

(iv) See result (3) **Q. 8 (a) above**, replace d by ae.

9. Let P be $(a\cos\theta, b\sin\theta)$ then D is $(-a\sin\theta, b\cos\theta)$.

If (h, k) be the mid-point of PD, then

$2h = a(\cos\theta - \sin\theta)$,

$2k = b(\sin\theta + \cos\theta)$

$\therefore \quad \dfrac{4h^2}{a^2} + \dfrac{4k^2}{b^2} = (\cos\theta - \sin\theta)^2 + (\sin\theta + \cos\theta)^2 = 2.$

Hence the locus of mid-point (h, k) is

$$\frac{x^2}{a^2} + \frac{y^2}{b^2} = \frac{1}{2}.$$

10. Tangent at P is $\dfrac{x\cos\theta}{a} + \dfrac{y\sin\theta}{b} = 1$

Tangent at D is $-\dfrac{x\sin\theta}{a} + \dfrac{y\cos\theta}{b} = 1$

In order to find the locus of the point of intersection of these tangents we have to eliminate θ for which we square and add.

$\therefore \quad \dfrac{x^2}{a^2}\cdot 1 + \dfrac{y^2}{b^2}\cdot 1 + 0 = 2$ or $\dfrac{x^2}{a^2} + \dfrac{y^2}{b^2} = 2.$

11. Subtracting in order to find their points of intersection, we get

$$x^2\left(\frac{1}{a^2} - \frac{1}{p^2}\right) + y^2\left(\frac{1}{b^2} - \frac{1}{q^2}\right) = 0$$

Above equation will represent a pair of conjugate diameters of first ellipse if

$$m_1m_2 = -\frac{b^2}{a^2}$$

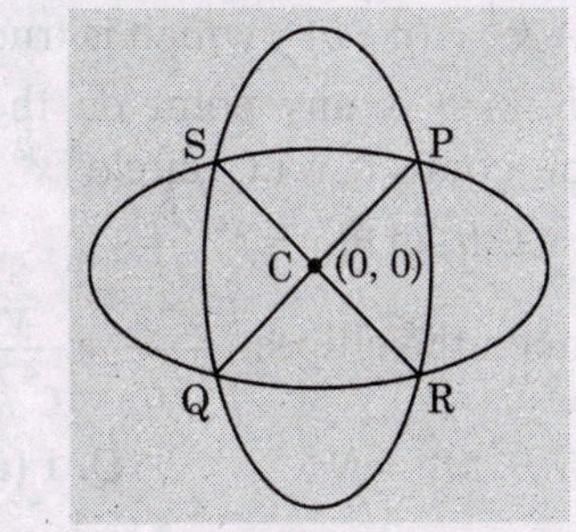

Fig. 26

But $m_1m_2 = A/B = -b^2/a^2$

$\therefore \quad \left(\dfrac{1}{a^2} - \dfrac{1}{p^2}\right) \div \left(\dfrac{1}{b^2} - \dfrac{1}{q^2}\right) = -\dfrac{b^2}{a^2}$

or $\quad a^2\left(\dfrac{1}{a^2} - \dfrac{1}{p^2}\right) + b^2\left(\dfrac{1}{b^2} - \dfrac{1}{q^2}\right) = 0$

or $\quad \dfrac{a^2}{p^2} + \dfrac{b^2}{q^2} = 2$

12. (a) Let PQ be any tangent to ellipse

$$\frac{x^2}{a^2} + \frac{y^2}{b^2} = 1$$

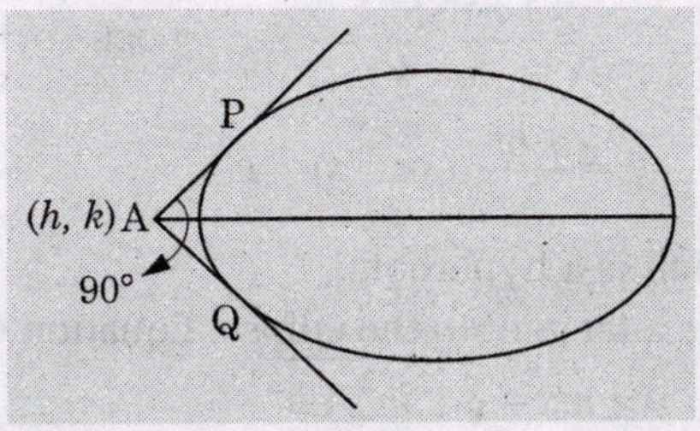

Fig. 27

which cuts the ellipse

$$\frac{x^2}{a(a+b)} + \frac{y^2}{b(a+b)} = 1 \quad ...(1)$$

at P and Q. The tangents at P and Q are at right angles and hence the point $A(h, k)$ will lie on the director circle of 2nd ellipse.

$\therefore \quad (h, k)$ lies on $x^2 + y^2 = A^2 + B^2$

$x^2 + y^2 = a(a+b) + b(a+b) = (a+b)^2$

Since (h, k) lies on it

$\therefore \quad h^2 + k^2 = (a+b)^2$ ...(2)

Again PQ is chord of contact of (h, k) w.r.t. (1)

$\therefore \quad \dfrac{hx}{a(a+b)} + \dfrac{ky}{b(a+b)} = 1$

It will be a tangent to

$$\frac{x^2}{a^2}+\frac{y^2}{b^2}=1 \text{ if } a^2l^2+b^2m^2=n^2$$

Q. 1 (a) P. 1011-14.

$$a^2\cdot\frac{h^2}{a^2(a+b)^2}+b^2\cdot\frac{k^2}{b^2(a+b)^2}=1$$

or $h^2+k^2=(a+b)^2$, which is true by (2).

(b) $(a\cos\theta, b\sin\theta)$ is any point on the ellipse. Its chord of contact w.r.t. circle $x^2+y^2=r^2$ is $(a\cos\theta)\,x+(b\sin\theta)\,y=r^2$

It will touch the ellipse $\frac{x^2}{r^4/a^2}+\frac{y^2}{r^4/b^2}=1$

if $A^2L^2+B^2M^2=N^2$ **Q. 1 (a) P. 1011-14**

or $a^2\cos^2\theta.\frac{r^4}{a^2}+b^2\sin^2\theta.\frac{r^4}{b^2}=(r^2)^2$

or $r^4.1=r^4$, which is true.

(c) Apply $p=r$ with chord of contact $\frac{\alpha x}{a^2}+\frac{\beta y}{b^2}=1$ and generalize (α,β) to get the locus.

(d) Let P be (h,k) then its chord of contact w.r.t. ellipse

$$\frac{x^2}{a^2}+\frac{y^2}{b^2}=1 \text{ is } \frac{hx}{a^2}+\frac{ky}{b^2}=1$$

It meets the axes in $A\left(\frac{a^2}{h},0\right)$ and $B\left(0,\frac{b^2}{k}\right)$

∴ Area of rt. angled triangle OAB is $\frac{1}{2}OA.OB$

$$=\frac{1}{2}\frac{a^2}{h}.\frac{b^2}{k}=\frac{\lambda}{2} \quad \therefore \text{ Locus of } (h,k)$$

is $xy=\frac{a^2b^2}{\lambda}$ or $xy=c^2$,

which is a hyperbola.

13. $AB=l_1$ is a tangent to the ellipse. Equation of AB is

$$y=mx+\sqrt{a^2m^2+b^2}. \quad ...(1)$$

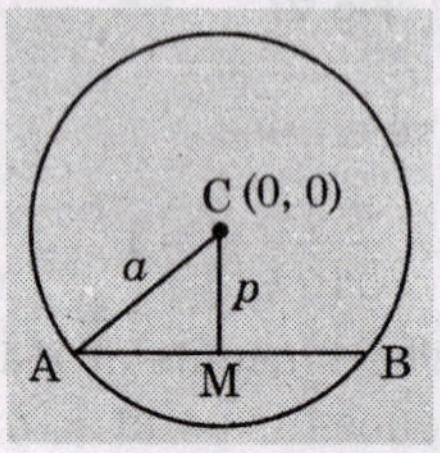

Fig. 28

It intercepts a length l_1 on auxiliary circle

$$x^2+y^2=a^2$$

$$\therefore \quad a^2-p^2=AM^2=\left(\frac{l_1}{2}\right)^2$$

If p be length of perpendicular from centre $(0,0)$ to chord AB given by (1), then

$$p=\frac{\sqrt{(a^2m^2+b^2)}}{\sqrt{(m^2+1)}}$$

$$\therefore \quad a^2-p^2=a^2-\frac{a^2m^2+b^2}{m^2+1}=\frac{a^2-b^2}{(m^2+1)}$$

$$\therefore \quad \frac{l_1^2}{4}=\frac{a^2-b^2}{(m^2+1)}$$

For perpendicular tangent replace m by $-1/m$ and l_1 by l_2

$$\therefore \quad \frac{l_2^2}{4}=\frac{(a^2-b^2)}{\frac{1}{m^2}+1}=\frac{(a^2-b^2)\,m^2}{m^2+1}$$

$$\therefore \quad \frac{l_1^2+l_2^2}{4}=(a^2-b^2)\frac{(m^2+1)}{m^2+1}=a^2e^2$$

$$\therefore \quad l_1^2+l_2^2=4a^2e^2=(2ae)^2=(S_1S_2)^2$$

14. Normal at θ, $\frac{ax}{\cos\theta}-\frac{by}{\sin\theta}=a^2-b^2$

Its slope is $\frac{a\sin\theta}{b\cos\theta}=m_1$

Slope of normal at $\frac{\pi}{2}+\theta$ is $-\frac{a\cos\theta}{b\sin\theta}=m_2$

$$\therefore \quad \tan\alpha=\frac{m_1-m_2}{1+m_1m_2}$$

$$=\left[\frac{a}{b}.\frac{\sin^2\theta+\cos^2\theta}{\sin\theta\cos\theta}\right]\div\frac{a^2-b^2}{b^2}=\frac{2ab}{a^2e^2}.\frac{1}{\sin 2\theta}$$

$$\therefore \quad e^2\sin 2\theta\tan\alpha=\frac{2a.a\sqrt{1-e^2}}{a^2}=2\sqrt{1-e^2}$$

15. $b^2x^2+a^2y^2=a^2b^2$ Ellipse ...(1)

and $x^2+y^2=ab$ Circle

or $a^2x^2+a^2y^2=a^3b$ ...(2)

Solving (1) and (2) by subtracting,

$$(b^2-a^2)\,x^2=a^2b\,(b-a)$$

$$\therefore \quad x^2=\frac{a^2b}{b+a},$$

Similarly, $y^2=\frac{ab^2}{a+b}$ ...(3)

Above gives the point of intersection say (x_1,y_1). Tangent at (x_1,y_1) to circle $x^2+y^2=ab$ is

$xx_1+yy_1=ab$, $m_1=-\frac{x_1}{y_1}=-\sqrt{\frac{a}{b}}$ by (3)

Slope of tangent to ellipse is

$$-\frac{x_1}{y_1}\frac{b^2}{a^2}=-\sqrt{\frac{a}{b}}.\frac{b^2}{a^2}=m_2, \text{ by (3)}$$

$$\tan\theta = \frac{m_1 - m_2}{1 + m_1 m_2} = \frac{\sqrt{\frac{a}{b}}\left[1 - \frac{b^2}{a^2}\right]}{1 + \frac{a}{b}\cdot\frac{b^2}{a^2}}$$

$$= \frac{a^2 - b^2}{a(a+b)}\cdot\sqrt{\frac{a}{b}}$$

or $\tan\theta = \frac{a-b}{\sqrt{ab}}$.

16. Ans. (d).

Ellipse is $\frac{x^2}{9} + \frac{y^2}{1} = 1$

Auxiliary circle is $\frac{x^2}{9} + \frac{y^2}{9} = 1$

Area of $\Delta OAM = \frac{1}{2} OA \cdot OM \sin(\pi - 2\theta)$

$= \frac{1}{2}.3.3.\sin 2\theta$

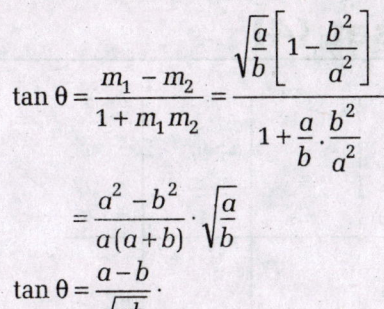

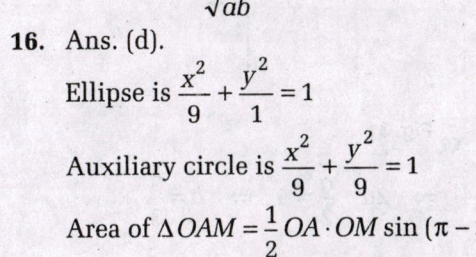

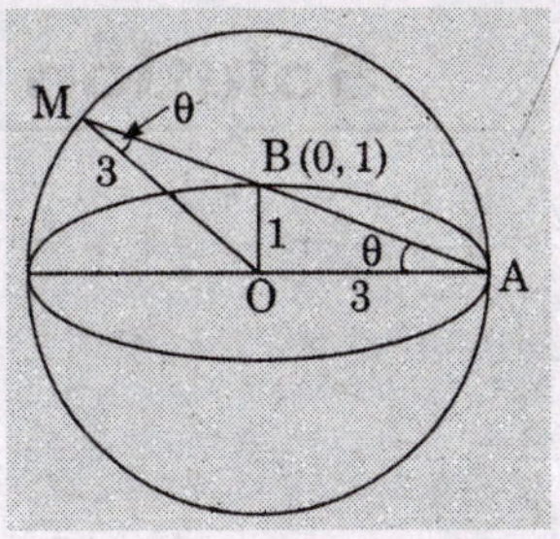

Fig. 29

where $\tan\theta = \frac{1}{3}$ from ΔAOB.

$\therefore \quad \sin 2\theta = \frac{2t}{1+t^2} = \frac{2\cdot\frac{1}{3}}{1+\frac{1}{9}} = 2\times\frac{3}{10} = \frac{3}{5}$

$\therefore \quad$ Area $= \frac{9}{2}\cdot\frac{3}{5} = \frac{27}{10}$

Problem Set (4)

Multiple Choice Questions

1. The ellipse $x^2 + 4y^2 = 4$ is inscribed in a rectangle alingent with the coordinate axes, which in turn is inscribed in another ellipse that passes through the point (4, 0) then the equation of the ellipse is

(a) $x^2 + 12y^2 = 16$ (b) $4x^2 + 48y^2 = 48$

(c) $4x^2 + 64y^2 = 48$ (c) $x^2 + 16y^2 = 16$

(AIEEE 2009)

2. The normal at a point P on the ellipse $x^2 + 4y^2 = 16$ meets the x-axis at Q. If M is the mid point of the line segment PQ, then the locus of M intersects the latusrectum of the given ellipse at the points

(a) $\left(\pm\frac{3\sqrt{5}}{2}, \pm\frac{2}{7}\right)$ (b) $\left(\pm\frac{3\sqrt{5}}{2}, \pm\frac{\sqrt{19}}{4}\right)$

(c) $\left(\pm 2\sqrt{3}, \pm\frac{1}{7}\right)$ (d) $\left(\pm 2\sqrt{3}, \pm\frac{4\sqrt{3}}{7}\right)$

(IIT-JEE 2009)

3. A focus of an ellipse is at the origin. The directrix is the line $x = 4$ and the eccentricity is $\frac{1}{2}$. Then the length of the semi major axis is

(a) $\frac{5}{3}$ (b) $\frac{8}{3}$ (c) $\frac{2}{3}$ (d) $\frac{4}{3}$

(AIEEE 2008)

4. An ellipse has OB as semi minor axis, F and F' are its foci and the angle FBF' is a right angle. The eccentricity of the ellipse is

(a) $\frac{1}{2}$ (b) $\frac{1}{4}$

(c) $\frac{1}{\sqrt{2}}$ (d) none of these

(IIT 1997; AIEEE 2005)

5. If tangents are drawn to the ellipses $x^2 + 2y^2 = 2$ then the locus of the mid point of the intercept made by the tangents between the coordinate axes is

(a) $x^2 + 2y^2 = 4x^2y^2$ (b) $2x^2 + y^2 = 4x^2y^2$

(c) $2x^2 + y^2 = 4$ (d) $x^2 + 2y^2 = 4$

(IIT 2004)

6. Tangents are drawn to the ellipse $\frac{x^2}{9} + \frac{y^2}{5} = 1$ at the end of the latus rectum. The area of the quadrilateral so formed is

(a) 27 (b) $\frac{27}{2}$ (c) $\frac{27}{4}$ (d) $\frac{27}{55}$

(IIT 2003)

7. The radius of the circle passing through the foci of the ellipse $\frac{x^2}{16} + \frac{y^2}{9} = 1$ having its centre at (0, 3) is

(a) 4 (b) 3 (c) $\sqrt{12}$ (d) $\frac{7}{2}$

(IIT 1995; AIEEE 2002)

8. The eccentricity of an ellipse, with its centre at the origin is $\frac{1}{2}$. If one of the directrix is $x = 4$, then equation of the ellipse is

(a) $3x^2 + 4y^2 = 1$ (b) $3x^2 + 4y^2 = 12$

(c) $4x^2 + 3y^2 = 12$ (d) $4x^2 + 3y^2 = 1$

(AIEEE 2004)

Solution to the Problem set (4)

1. Ans. (a). $x^2+4y^2=4 \Rightarrow \frac{x^2}{4}+\frac{y^2}{1}=1$

$\Rightarrow \quad a=2, b=1 \quad \therefore \quad P \equiv P(2,1)$

Required ellipse $\frac{x^2}{a^2}+\frac{y^2}{b^2}=1 \Rightarrow \frac{x^2}{4^2}+\frac{y^2}{b^2}=1$

(2, 1) lies on it

$\therefore \quad \frac{4}{16}+\frac{1}{b^2}=1 \Rightarrow \frac{1}{b^2}=1-\frac{1}{4}=\frac{3}{4} \Rightarrow b^2=\frac{4}{3}$

$\therefore \quad \frac{x^2}{16}+\frac{y^2}{4/3}=1 \Rightarrow x^2+12y^2=16$

2. Ans. (c). Normal is $4x\sec\phi-2y\,\text{cosec}\,\phi=12$

$\phi=Q(3\cos\phi, 0)$

$M=(\alpha,\beta)$

$\alpha=\frac{3\cos\phi+4\cos\phi}{2}=\frac{7}{2}\cos\phi$

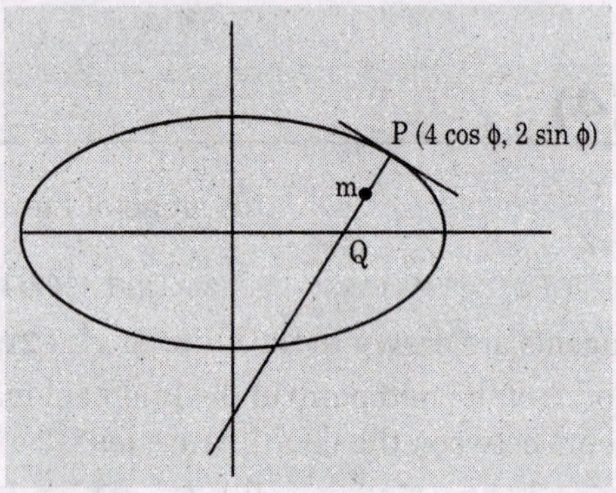

Fig. 30

$\Rightarrow \quad \cos\phi=\frac{2}{7}\alpha, \beta=\sin\phi$

Using $\cos^2\phi+\sin^2\phi=1 \Rightarrow \frac{4}{49}\alpha^2+\beta^2=1$

$\Rightarrow \quad \frac{4}{49}x^2+y^2=1$

$\therefore \quad$ latus rectum $x=\pm 2\sqrt{3}$

$\frac{48}{49}+y^2=1 \Rightarrow y=\pm\frac{1}{7}$

$\therefore \quad$ Required coordinates $=\left(\pm 2\sqrt{3}, \pm\frac{1}{7}\right)$

3. Ans. (b).

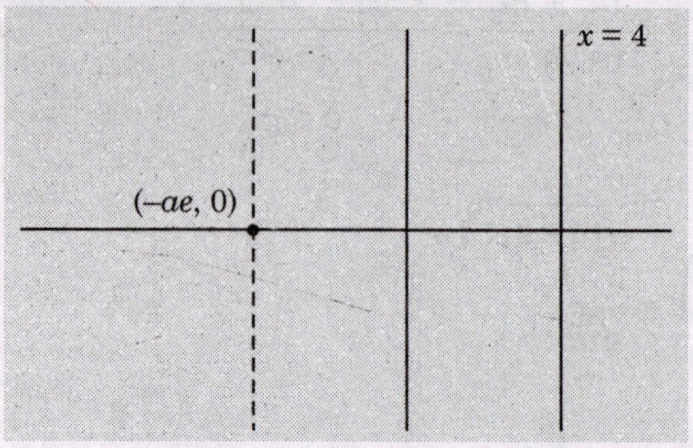

Fig. 31

$\frac{a}{e}-ae=4 \Rightarrow 2a-\frac{a}{2}=4 \Rightarrow a=\frac{8}{3}$

4. Ans. (c).

5. Equation of the tangent at (x_1, y_1) is $xx_1+2yy_1=2$

Let it meet x-axis at A and y axis at B. Then

$A=\left(\frac{2}{x_1}, 0\right), B=\left(0, \frac{1}{y_1}\right)$

Let $P(h,k)$ be the mid point of AB. Then

$h=\frac{1}{x_1}, k=\frac{1}{2y_1}$

$\Rightarrow \quad x_1=\frac{1}{h}, y_1=\frac{1}{2k} \quad \therefore \quad x_1^2+2y_1^2=2$

$\Rightarrow \quad \frac{1}{h^2}+\frac{1}{2k^2}=2 \quad \Rightarrow \quad h^2+2k^2=4h^2k^2$

$\therefore \quad$ locus $= x^2+2y^2=4x^2y^2$

6. Ans. (a).

Area of quadrilateral formed by tangents at the ends of latus rectum $=\frac{2a^2}{e}$. Here $a^2=9, b^2=5, e=\frac{2}{3}$

$\therefore \quad$ Area $=2\times 9\times\frac{3}{2}=27$

7. Ans. (a).

$e^2=\frac{16-9}{16}=\frac{7}{16} \quad \Rightarrow \quad e=\frac{\sqrt{7}}{4}$

$\therefore \quad$ Foci are $F_1(\sqrt{7},0), F_2(-\sqrt{7},0)$

$B(0,3)$ is one end of minor axes therefore, radius of required circle $=BF_1=\sqrt{7+9}=4$

8. Ans. (b).

MISCELLANEOUS EXERCISE

Matching Entries

Match the entries of List-A and List-B.

1. **List-A** | **List-B**

(a) S and S' are foci and B is end of minor axis of an ellipse. If $\Delta SS'B$ is equilateral, then eccentricity of ellipse is ... | 1. 10

(b) If $P(x, y)$ be a point on the ellipse $16x^2 + 25y^2 = 400$ and $F_1 = (3, 0), F_2 = (-3, 0)$ then $PF_1 + PF_2 = ...$	2. $\frac{(x-2)^2}{4} + \frac{(y+3)^2}{3} = 1$
(c) A circle with centre at (0, 3) passes through the foci of ellipse $\frac{x^2}{16} + \frac{y^2}{9} = 1$. Its radius is of length	3. $\frac{1}{2}$
(d) In an ellipse $C = (2, -3), S = (3, -3)$ and A is $(4, -3)$, then the equation of ellipse is	4. 4

2.

List-A	List-B
(a) If p_1, p_2 be the lengths of perpendiculars drawn from the two foci of an ellipse to any tangent to it then $p_1 p_2 =$	1. $-\frac{2}{3}$
(b) The angle between a pair of tangents drawn to the ellipse $3x^2 + 2y^2 = 5$ from the point (1, 2) is	2. $x - ey - e^3 a = 0$
(c) The equation of normal to the ellipse $\frac{x^2}{a^2} + \frac{y^2}{b^2} = 1$ at the positive end of latus rectum is	3. b^2
(d) If the normal at the point $P(\theta)$ to the ellipse $\frac{x^2}{14} + \frac{y^2}{5} = 1$ meets it again at the point 2θ, then $\cos\theta =$	4. $\tan^{-1}\left(\frac{12}{\sqrt{5}}\right)$

3. Locus of the point of intersection of two perpendicular tangents to

List-A	List-B
(a) Circle $x^2 + y^2 = a^2$	1. $x = -a$
(b) Ellipse $\frac{x^2}{a^2} + \frac{y^2}{b^2} = 1$	2. $x^2 + y^2 = a^2 + a^2$
(c) Hyperbola $\frac{x^2}{a^2} - \frac{y^2}{b^2} = 1$	3. $x^2 + y^2 = a^2 + b^2$
(d) Parabola $y^2 = 4ax$	4. $x^2 + y^2 = a^2 - b^2$

Answers

1. a → 3, b → 1, c → 4, d → 2 **2.** a → 3, b → 4, c → 2, d → 1 **3.** a → 2, b → 3, c → 4, d → 1

Hints/Solutions

1. (a) $SS' = 2ae, S$ is $(ae, 0)$ and B is $(0, b)$.

$\therefore \quad SB = \sqrt{b^2 + a^2e^2} = a$

Now Δ is equilateral

$\therefore \quad SS' = SB$ or $2ae = a$

$\therefore \quad e = 1/2.$

(b) **See Q. h P. 1003**

(c) **See Q. 3 (c) P. 1004-1007**

(d) **See Q. 4 (c) P. 1004-1007**

2. (a) **See Q. 14 (b) P. 1012-1018**

(b) **See Q. 10 (b) P. 1012-1017**

(c) L is $\left(ae, \frac{b^2}{a}\right)$

Normal is $\frac{x - ae}{ae/a^2} = \frac{y^2 - b^2/a}{b^2/ab^2}$

$(x - ae) = e[y - a(1 - e^2)]$

or $x - ae = ey - ae + ae^3$

or $x - ey - e^3 a = 0$

(d) **See Q. 27 (a) P. 1013-1023**

3. (a) **See Director Circle**

(b) **See Director Circle 1011**

(c) **See § 2.6**

(d) **See Q. 1 (a)**

❑

CHAPTER 22

Co-ordinates Geometry

The Hyperbola

§ 1. Hyperbola

Definition : Hyperbola is the locus of a point which moves so that its distance from a fixed point called focus bears a constant ratio to its distance from a fixed straight line called directrix. This ratio is called eccentricity and is denoted by e. It is always greater than unity.

Equation of the Hyperbola in Standard form

$$\frac{x^2}{a^2}-\frac{y^2}{b^2}=1.$$

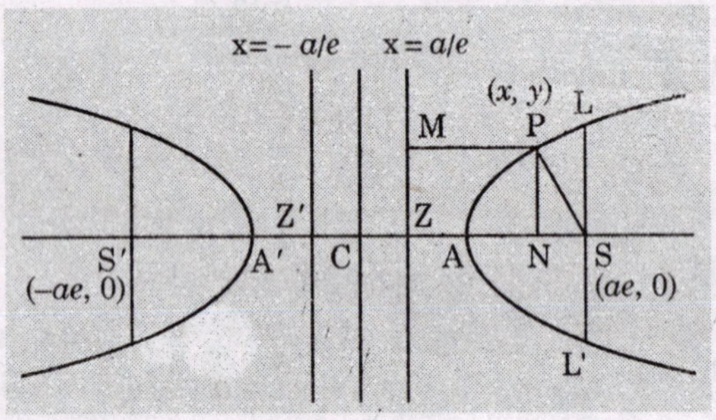

Fig. 1

Let ZM be the directrix of the hyperbola and S be the focus. Draw SZ perpendicular to the directrix from the focus.

Now since eccentricity e is greater than one, we can always divide SZ internally and externally in the ratio $e:1$, at the points A and A' respectively so that

$$SA = e\,.\,AZ \qquad ...(1)$$
$$SA' = e\,.\,ZA' \qquad ...(2)$$

Now A and A' are points such that their distances from the focus bear a constant ratio from their distances from the directrix; hence by definition they lie on the hyperbola.

Let AA' be of length $2a$ and C be its middle point, so that

$$CA = CA' = a \qquad ...(3)$$

Rewriting the relations (1) and (2), we get

$$(CS - CA) = e\,(CA - CZ)$$

and $(CS + CA') = e\,(CZ + CA')$

Adding, we get $2CS = e\,(CA + CA') = e2a$ by (3)

$$\therefore \quad \boldsymbol{CS = ae} \qquad ...(4)$$

Subtracting, we get

$$(CA' + CA) = e\,(2CZ)$$

or $2a = 2e\,CZ \quad \therefore \quad \boldsymbol{CZ = a/e}. \qquad ...(5)$

Now choose the point C as the origin of co-ordinates and lines $A'CA$ as x-axis and a line through C perpendicular to AA' as y-axis. Hence the co-ordinates of focus, w.r.t. C as origin are $(ae, 0)$ and directrix ZM being parallel to y-axis at a distance $CZ = a/e$ from the origin will have its equation as $x = a/e$.

If $P(x, y)$ be any point on the hyperbola, draw PM perpendicular on the directrix, then by definition,

$$SP = e\,.\,PM \quad \text{or} \quad SP^2 = e^2\,.\,PM^2$$

or $(x - ae)^2 + y^2 = e^2\,(ZN)^2 = e^2\,(CN - CZ)^2$

$$= e^2\,(x - a/e)^2 \qquad \text{by (5)}$$

$\therefore \quad x^2 - 2aex + a^2e^2 + y^2 = e^2x^2 - 2aex + a^2$

or $x^2\,(1 - e^2) + y^2 = a^2\,(1 - e^2)$

or $\dfrac{x^2}{a^2} - \dfrac{y^2}{a^2\,(e^2 - 1)} = 1$

Now since $e > 1 \;\therefore\; a^2\,(e^2 - 1)$ is certainly + ive and so we put $b^2 = a^2\,(e^2 - 1)$ and the above equation takes the form

$$\frac{x^2}{a^2}-\frac{y^2}{b^2}=1$$

which is the standard form of the equation of the hyperbola.

Various results and properties connected with the equation

$$\frac{x^2}{a^2}-\frac{y^2}{b^2}=1.$$

(a) The points A and A' are called vertices of the hyperbola and the line joining them is called the **transverse axis** whose length $AA' = 2a$ when A is $(a, 0)$ and A' is $(-a, 0)$.

(b) The axis of y i.e. $x = 0$ does not cut the hyperbola in real points as $y^2 = -b^2$ (on putting $x = 0$). But if

B and B' be two points on y-axis such that $CB = CB' = b$ then the line BB' is called its **conjugate axis.**

(c) **Latus rectum :** The chord of the hyperbola which passes through the focus and is perpendicular to its transverse axis is called latus rectum and its equation is clearly $x = ae$.
If its length be $2l$ then the co-ordinates of the point L are (ae, l) which will satisfy the equation of the hyperbola

$$\therefore \quad \frac{a^2e^2}{a^2} - \frac{l^2}{b^2} = 1$$

or $l^2 = b^2(e^2 - 1) = b^2 . b^2/a^2 \quad \therefore \quad l = b^2/a.$

$$2l = 2b^2/a = \text{ length of latus rectum}$$

and **L is $(ae, b^2/a)$ and L' is $(ae, -b^2/a)$.**

(d) As shown in the figure there is always a second focus $S'(-ae, 0)$ and a second directrix $Z'M, x = -a/e$.

(e) **Eccentricity :** We know that
$b^2 = a^2(e^2 - 1)$

$$\therefore \quad e^2 = 1 + \frac{b^2}{a^2} = \frac{a^2 + b^2}{a^2} = 1 + \left(\frac{\text{Conj. axis}}{\text{Tran. axis}}\right)^2$$

(f) **Focal distance :** The distance of any point on the hyperbola from the focus is called the focal distance of the point.

(g) **The difference of the focal distances of a point on the hyperbola is constant and is equal to the length of the transverse axis.**
Let the co-ordinates of point P be (x, y) then from the figure
* $SP = e . PM = e . ZN = e(CN - CZ)$
$= e(x - a/e) = ex - a$
*$S'P = e . PM' = e . NZ'$
$= e(CN + CZ') = e(x + a/e) = ex + a$
*∴ $S'P - SP = 2a$ (constant)

§ 2. Important Results

Most of the results proved for the ellipse $x^2/a^2 + y^2/b^2 = 1$ are true for the hyperbola $x^2/a^2 - y^2/b^2 = 1$ if we replace b^2 by $-b^2$.

We give below the list of corresponding results applicable in the case of hyperbola.

1. **Tangent at (x_1, y_1) is** $\dfrac{xx_1}{a^2} - \dfrac{yy_1}{b^2} = 1.$

2. **Normal at (x_1, y_1) is** $\dfrac{x - x_1}{x_1/a^2} = \dfrac{y - y_1}{-y_1/b^2}$

3. The line $y = mx + c$ is a tangent to the hyperbola if $c^2 = a^2m^2 - b^2$ and the point of contact in this case becomes

$$\left(-\frac{a^2m}{c}, -\frac{b^2}{c}\right)$$

The line $lx + my = n$ will be a tangent to the hyperbola if

$$a^2l^2 - b^2m^2 = n^2.$$

4. The line $y = mx + \sqrt{(a^2m^2 - b^2)}$ is always a tangent to the hyperbola.

5. From any point (h, k) outside the hyperbola two tangents (real) can be drawn whose slopes are given by

$$m^2(h^2 - a^2) - 2mhk + (k^2 + b^2) = 0$$

Their combined equation is given by $SS_1 = T^2$.

6. **Director circle :** The locus of the point of intersection of two prependicular tangents to a hyperbola is called its director circle and its equation is

$$x^2 + y^2 = a^2 - b^2.$$

7. Equation of the chord of contact of tangents drawn from (h, k) is

$$\frac{hx}{a^2} - \frac{ky}{b^2} = 1.$$

8. Polar of any point (h, k) is

$$\frac{hx}{a^2} - \frac{ky}{b^2} = 1.$$

9. Equation of the chord of the hyperbola whose middle point is (h, k) is

$$\frac{hx}{a^2} - \frac{ky}{b^2} = \frac{h^2}{a^2} - \frac{k^2}{b^2} \quad \text{or} \quad T = S_1.$$

10. **Auxiliary Circle :** The circle described on transverse axis of the hyperbola as diameter is called auxiliary circle and its equation is

$$x^2 + y^2 = a^2$$

11. **Diameter :** The locus of the middle points of a system of parallel chords is called a diameter and its equation is

$$y = \frac{b^2}{a^2m}x.$$

It is a line passing through the centre.

12. **Conjugate diameters :** Two diameters $y = mx$ and $y = m'x$ are said to be conjugate if each bisects chords parallel to the other and the condition for two diameters to be conjugate is

$$mm' = b^2/a^2$$

13. **Parametric equation of the hyperbola** $\dfrac{x^2}{a^2} - \dfrac{y^2}{b^2} = 1$ **:**

*$x = a \sec\theta$, $y = b \tan\theta$, are the parametric equations of the hyperbola as

$$\sec^2\theta - \tan^2\theta = 1.$$

The point $(a \sec\theta, b \tan\theta)$ is referred to as the point θ.

14. **Tangent at the point $(a \sec\theta, b \tan\theta)$ is**

$$* \quad \frac{x \sec\theta}{a} - \frac{y \tan\theta}{b} = 1.$$

15. Normal at the point $(a\sec\theta, b\tan\theta)$ is

* $$\frac{ax}{\sec\theta}+\frac{by}{\tan\theta}=a^2+b^2.$$

16. Asymptotes of the hyperbola $x^2/a^2-y^2/b^2=1$ are

$$\frac{x^2}{a^2}-\frac{y^2}{b^2}=0 \quad \text{or} \quad y=\pm\frac{b}{a}x.$$

*Angle between the asymptotes is $2\tan^{-1}(b/a)$.

17. Rectangular Hyperbola :

A hyperbola is said to be rectangular if the angle between its asymptotes is 90°

$\therefore \quad 2\tan^{-1}(b/a)=90^o$ or $\tan^{-1}(b/a)=45^o$

or $b/a=\tan 45^o=1$

$\therefore \quad b=a.$

Hence the equation of rectangular hyperbola is

* $$x^2-y^2=a^2.$$

18. Eccentricity of rectangular hyperbola : We know that

* $e^2=1+\dfrac{b^2}{a^2}=1+\dfrac{a^2}{a^2}=2 \quad \therefore \quad e=\sqrt{2}.$

FACTS ABOUT THE HYPERBOLA

S.No.	Properties	$\frac{x^2}{a^2}-\frac{y^2}{b^2}=1$ $a>0, b>0$	$\frac{y^2}{a^2}-\frac{x^2}{b^2}=1$ $a>0, b>0$
1.	Equation of transverse axis	$y=0$	$x=0$
2.	Length of transverse axis	$2a$	$2b$
3.	Equation of cojugate axis	$x=0$	$y=0$
4.	Length of cojugate axis	$2b$	$2b$
5.	Vertices	$(\pm a, 0)$	$(0 \pm a)$
6.	Foci	$x=\pm\frac{a}{e}$	$(0, \pm ae)$
7.	Directrix	$(0, 0)$	$y=\pm\frac{a}{e}$
8.	Centre	$x=\pm ae$	$(0, 0)$
9.	Equation of latra-recta	$\frac{2b^2}{a}$	$y=+-ae$
10.	Length of latus rectum	$\lvert ex-a\rvert$	$\frac{2b^2}{a}$
11.	Focal distance of any point (x, y)	$\lvert ex+a\rvert$	$\lvert ey-a\rvert$ $\lvert ey+a\rvert$

Problem Set (1)

Standard equation of hyperbola $\frac{x^2}{a^2}-\frac{y^2}{b^2}=1$, Standard points on it. Eccentricity.

1. (a) Find the equation of the hyperbola whose focus is the point (1, 1), directrix is $2x+y=1$, eccentricity is $\sqrt{3}$.

   (b) Let PQ be a double ordinate of the hyperbola $\frac{x^2}{a^2}-\frac{y^2}{b^2}=1$ such that OPQ is an equilateral triangle, O being the centre of hyperbola. Prove that the eccentricity of the hyperbola is greater than $2/\sqrt{3}$.

2. (a) Find the equation of the hyperbola whose focus is the point (2, 1) and the directrix is the straight line $2x+3y-1=0$ and whose eccentricity is $\sqrt{2}$. **(D.C.E. 1997)**

   (b) A hyperbola, having the transverse axis of length $2\sin\theta$, is confocal with the ellipse $3x^2+4y^2=12$. Then its equation is

   (a) $x^2\operatorname{cosec}^2\theta-y^2\sec^2\theta=1$

   (b) $x^2\sec^2\theta-y^2\operatorname{cosec}^2\theta=1$

   (c) $x^2\sin^2\theta-y^2\cos^2\theta=1$

   (d) $x^2\cos^2\theta-y^2\sin^2\theta=1$ **(I.I.T. 2007)**

3. Find the co-ordinates of foci, the eccentricity and latus rectum. Determine also the equation of its directrices for the following hyperbolas :

   (a) $4x^2-9y^2=36$

   (b) $9y^2-4x^2=36$

   (c) $9x^2-16y^2+18x+32y-151=0$

   (d) $x^2+2x-y^2+5=0$

   (e) $9x^2-16y^2-72x+96y-144=0$

4. Prove that the difference of the focal distances of a point P on the hyperbola $x^2/a^2-y^2/b^2=1$ is equal to the length of its transverse axis.

5. Find the locus of a point which moves so that the difference of its distances from the points (5, 0) and (– 5, 0) is 2.

6. Two straight lines pass through the fixed points $(\pm a, 0)$ and have gradients whose product is $k>0$. Show that the locus of the points of intersection of the lines is a hyperbola.

7.* The distance between the foci of a hyperbola is 16 and its eccentricity is $\sqrt{2}$. Prove that its equation is $x^2-y^2=32$.

8. (a)* Define conjugate hyperbola. If e and e' be the eccentricities of a hyperbola and its conjugate then prove that $\frac{1}{e^2}+\frac{1}{e'^2}=1$.

   (b) If e and e' be the eccentricities of two conics S and S' such that $e^2+e'^2=3$, then both S and S' are

(a) ellipses (b) parabolas
(c) hyperbolas (d) none of these

9. (a) Prove that the locus of the point of intersection of the lines $\sqrt{3}x - y - 4\sqrt{3}k = 0$ and $\sqrt{3}kx + ky - 4\sqrt{3} = 0$ for different values of k is a hyperbola whose eccentricity is 2.

(b) The eccentricity of the hyperbola $3x^2 - y^2 = 4$ is :
(a) 1 (b) 2
(c) -2 (d) 5 **(AIEEE 2002)**

10. (a)* If the foci of the ellipse $\frac{x^2}{16} + \frac{y^2}{b^2} = 1$ and the hyperbola $\frac{x^2}{144} - \frac{y^2}{81} = \frac{1}{25}$ conincide, then the value of b^2 is
(a) 1 (b) 5
(c) 7 (d) 9 **(M.N.R. 1992)**

(b)* The foci of ellipse $\frac{x^2}{25} + \frac{y^2}{9} = 1$ coincide with the foci of the hyperbola $\frac{x^2}{4} - \frac{y^2}{12} = 1$.
Is this statement true ?

(c)* The vertices and the foci of a hyperbola are the points $(\pm 5, 0)$ and $(\pm, 7, 0)$. Then the hyperbola is rectangular. Is this statement true?

(d) Which one of the following is independent of α in the hyperbola $(0 < \alpha < \pi/2)$

$$\frac{x^2}{\cos^2 \alpha} - \frac{y^2}{\sin^2 \alpha} = 1$$

(a) ecentricity (b) abscissa of foci
(c) directrix (d) vertex **(Screening 2003)**

11. Let a hyperbola has its transverse and conjugate axis coinciding with the major and minor axis of the ellipse $\frac{x^2}{25} + \frac{y^2}{16} = 1$ respectively, if the hyperbola passes through one of the foci of the ellipse and the product of the eccentricities of hyperbola and ellipse is one, then
(a) equation of hyperbola is $\frac{x^2}{9} - \frac{y^2}{16} = 1$
(b) focus of hyperbola is $(5, 0)$
(c) vertex of hyperbola is $(5\sqrt{2}, 0)$
(d) equation of hyperbola is $\frac{x^2}{16} - \frac{y^2}{25} = 1$ **(I.I.T. 2006)**

12. Consider a branch of the hyperbola $x^2 - 2y^2 - 2\sqrt{2}x - 4\sqrt{2}y - 6 = 0$ with vertex at the point A. Let B be one of the end points of its latus rectum. If C is the focus of the hyperbola nearest to the point A, then the area of the triangle ABC is
(a) $1 - \sqrt{\frac{2}{3}}$ (b) $\sqrt{\frac{3}{2}} - 1$ (c) $1 + \sqrt{\frac{2}{3}}$ (d) $\sqrt{\frac{3}{2}} + 1$ **(IIT 2008)**

Solutions to Problem Set (1)

1. (a) Apply $SP = e \, . \, PM$

$$7x^2 + 12xy - 2y^2 - 2x + 4y - 7 = 0.$$

(b) Let the vertex P be (α, β) so that Q is $(\alpha, -\beta)$ such that $\Delta\, OPQ$ be equilateral

$\therefore \quad OP = OQ = PQ = 2\beta$

$\therefore \quad \sqrt{\alpha^2 + \beta^2} = 2\beta$ or $\alpha^2 = 3\beta^2$ ...(1)

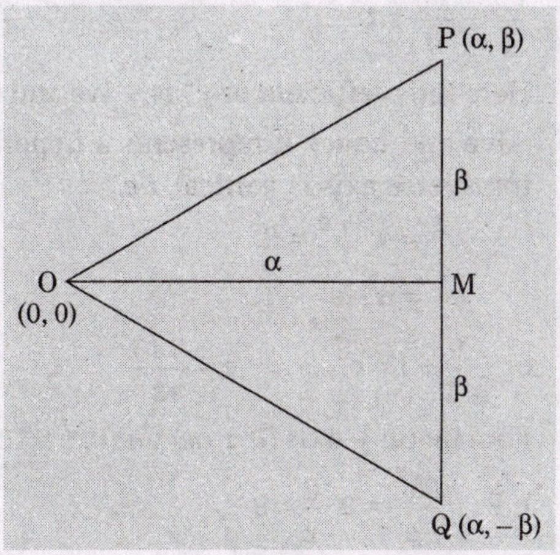

Fig. 2

Now (α, β) lies on hyperbola $\therefore \frac{\alpha^2}{a^2} - \frac{\beta^2}{b^2} = 1$

$\therefore \quad \frac{3\beta^2}{a^2} - \frac{\beta^2}{b^2} = 1 \therefore \frac{3b^2}{a^2} - 1 = \frac{b^2}{\beta^2} = +\text{ive} \geq 0$ by (1)

$\therefore \quad \frac{b^2}{a^2} > \frac{1}{3}$ or $e^2 - 1 > \frac{1}{3} \Rightarrow e^2 > \frac{4}{3} \quad \therefore \quad e > \frac{2}{\sqrt{3}}$

2. (a) $5x^2 - 5y^2 - 24xy - 44x - 14y + 63 = 0$

(b) Ans (a).

Ellipse is $\frac{x^2}{4} + \frac{y^2}{3} = 1, a^2 = 4, b^2 = 3$

$\therefore \quad e^2 = 1 - \frac{b^2}{a^2} = 1 - \frac{3}{4} = \frac{1}{4}$

or $\quad e = \frac{1}{2} \quad \therefore \quad ae = 2 \, . \, \frac{1}{2} = 1$

Since hyperbola is confocal with ellipse

$\therefore \quad ae = AE$, where $2A = 2\sin\theta$ or $A = \sin\theta$

or $\quad 1 = \sin\theta\, E \quad \therefore \quad E^2 = \operatorname{cosec}^2\theta = 1 + \frac{B^2}{A^2}$

$B^2 = A^2 (\operatorname{cosec}^2\theta - 1) = \sin^2\theta (\operatorname{cosec}^2\theta - 1)$

$= 1 - \sin^2\theta = \cos^2\theta$

$\therefore \quad$ Hyperbola is $\frac{x^2}{A^2} - \frac{y^2}{B^2} = 1$

or $\quad \frac{x^2}{\sin^2\theta} - \frac{y^2}{\cos^2\theta} = 1 \Rightarrow$ (a)

3. (a) $\frac{x^2}{9}-\frac{y^2}{4}=1 \quad \therefore \quad a^2=9, b^2=4$

$$b^2=a^2(e^2-1) \quad \therefore \quad e=\frac{\sqrt{(13)}}{3}$$

Foci $(\pm ae, 0)$, i.e. $(\pm\sqrt{13}, 0)$

L.R. $=\frac{2b^2}{a}=\frac{8}{3}$, Directrices $x=\pm\frac{a}{e}=\pm\frac{9}{\sqrt{13}}$.

(b) $\frac{y^2}{4}-\frac{x^2}{9}=1$.

Here the coefficient of y^2 is + ive and that of x^2 is – ive and hence it represents a hyperbola whose transverse axis is vertical, *i.e.*

$$a^2=4, \ b^2=9.$$

$$b^2=a^2(e^2-1)$$

or $\frac{9}{4}+1=e^2 \quad \therefore \quad e=\frac{\sqrt{13}}{2}$

Foci lie on y-axis $(0, \pm ae)$ *i.e.* $(0, \pm\sqrt{13})$

L.R. $=\frac{2b^2}{a}=2\cdot\frac{9}{2}=9$

(c) The given equation can be written as

$$9(x^2+2x)-16(y^2-2y)=151$$

or $9(x^2+2x+1)-16(y^2-2y+1)$

$$=151+9-16=144$$

or $\frac{(x+1)^2}{16}-\frac{(y-1)^2}{9}=1$

or $\frac{X^2}{16}-\frac{Y^2}{9}=1$

where $X=x+1, Y=y-1, a^2=16, b^2=9$

Centre is $X=0, Y=0$, *i.e.* $(-1, 1)$,

$$b^2=a^2(e^2-1) \quad \therefore \quad e=5/4$$

Foci are $X=\pm ae, Y=0$ or $x+1=\pm 4.5/4, y-1=0$

or (4, 1) and (– 6, 1).

Directrices $X=\pm a/e$ or $x+1=\pm 16/5$

or $5x-11=0, 5x+21=0$

(d) Directrices $y=\pm\sqrt{2}$, foci $(-1, \pm 2\sqrt{2}), e=\sqrt{2}$.

(e) Centre (4, 3), $e=5/4$, foci (9, 3), (– 1, 3).

Directrices $5x-36=0, 5x-4=0$

4. **See (g) P. 1039.**

5. **Proceed as in (h), Ellipse P. 1006.**

6. $y=m_1(x-a), y=m_2(x+a)$ where $m_1m_2=k$, given. In order to find the locus of their point of intersection we have to eliminate the unknown m_1 and m_2. Multiplying, we get

$$y^2=m_1m_2(x^2-a^2) \quad \text{or} \quad y^2=k(x^2-a^2)$$

or $\frac{x^2}{l}-\frac{y^2}{k}=a^2$ which represents a hyperbola.

7. $2ae=16 \quad \therefore \quad ae=8, e=\sqrt{2}$

$\therefore \quad a=4\sqrt{2}$ or $a^2=32$

$\therefore \quad b^2=a^2(e^2-1)=32(2-1)=32.$

Hence the hyperbola is $x^2-y^2=32$.

8. (a) $\frac{x^2}{a^2}-\frac{y^2}{b^2}=1, b^2=a^2(e^2-1)$

or $e^2=1+\frac{b^2}{a^2}=\frac{a^2+b^2}{a^2}$

Conj. Hyp. $\frac{x^2}{a^2}-\frac{y^2}{b^2}=-1$ or $\frac{y^2}{b^2}-\frac{x^2}{a^2}=1$

Trans. axis is along y-axis and conj. along x-axis.

$$a^2=b^2(e'^2-1)$$

or $e'^2=1+\frac{a^2}{b^2}=\frac{a^2+b^2}{b^2}$

$\therefore \quad \frac{1}{e^2}+\frac{1}{e'^2}=\frac{a^2+b^2}{a^2+b^2}=1.$

(b) Ans. (c).

$e^2+e'^2=3 \Rightarrow$ Both e and e' must be greater than 1 and hence both must be hyperbolas.

9. (a) $\sqrt{3}x-y=4\sqrt{3}k, \ k(\sqrt{3}x+y)=4\sqrt{3}$

In order to find the locus of their point of intersection we have to eliminate the variable k between their equations.

From 1st $\frac{\sqrt{3}x-y}{4\sqrt{3}}=k$ and putting in (2), we get

$$(\sqrt{3}x-y)(\sqrt{3}x+y)=(4\sqrt{3})^2$$

or $3x^2-y^2=48$

or $\frac{x^2}{16}-\frac{y^2}{48}=1 \quad \therefore \quad a^2=16, b^2=48$

$b^2=a^2(e^2-1)$ or $48=16(e^2-1)$

$\therefore \quad e^2=4$ or $e=2$

Hence the locus is hyperbola whose eccentricity is 2.

(b) Ans. (b).

$$e^2=1+\frac{b^2}{a^2}=1+3=4 \quad \therefore \quad e=2$$

$\because \quad a^2=\frac{4}{3}, b^2=\frac{4}{1}$

10. (a) Ans. (c).

For hyperbola $e^2=1+\frac{b^2}{a^2}=1+\frac{81}{144}=\frac{225}{144}$

$\therefore \quad e=\frac{15}{12}=\frac{5}{4}$, i.e., $e>1$. Also $a^2=\frac{144}{25}$

Hence the foci are $(\pm ae, 0)$, i.e.

$$\left(\pm\frac{12}{5}\cdot\frac{5}{4}, 0\right)=(\pm 3, 0)$$

Now the foci coincide therefore for ellipse

$$ae=3 \quad \text{or} \quad a^2e^2=9$$

or $a^2\left(1-\dfrac{b^2}{a^2}\right)=9$

or $a^2-b^2=9$ or $16-9=b^2$ $\therefore$ $b^2=7.$

(b) Yes, true. Foci are $(\pm 4,0)$.

(c) No, $a=5, ae=7$ $\Rightarrow$ $a^2e^2=49$

or $a^2\left(1+\dfrac{b^2}{a^2}\right)=49$ or $a^2+b^2=49$

or $b^2=24$

Since $a^2\neq b^2$, hence hyperbola is not rectangular.

(d) Ans. (b).

$$e^2=1+\frac{b^2}{a^2}=1+\frac{\sin^2\alpha}{\cos^2\alpha}=\frac{1}{\cos^2\alpha}, a^2=\cos^2\alpha$$

$\therefore$ $a^2e^2=1$

$\therefore$ Foci $(\pm ae,0)=(\pm 1,0)$, which is independent of α.

11. Ans. (a), (b).

$$e^2=1-\frac{b^2}{a^2}=1-\frac{16}{25}=\frac{9}{25} \quad \therefore \quad e=\frac{3}{5}$$

Hence e' for hyperbola $=\dfrac{5}{3}$ as $ee'=1$

Also foci of ellipse are $(\pm ae,0)=(\pm 3,0)$. The equation of hyperbola is $\dfrac{x^2}{A^2}-\dfrac{y^2}{B^2}=1$ and it passes through $(\pm 3,0)$.

$\therefore$ $A^2=9.$

$e'^2=1+\dfrac{B^2}{A^2}$ for hyperbola

$\therefore$ $\dfrac{25}{9}=1+\dfrac{B^2}{9}$ $\therefore$ $B^2=16$

Hence equation of hyperbola is $\dfrac{x^2}{9}-\dfrac{y^2}{16}=1$

Its foci are at $(\pm Ae',0)=\left(\pm 3.\dfrac{5}{3},0\right)=(\pm 5,0)$

12. Ans. (b).

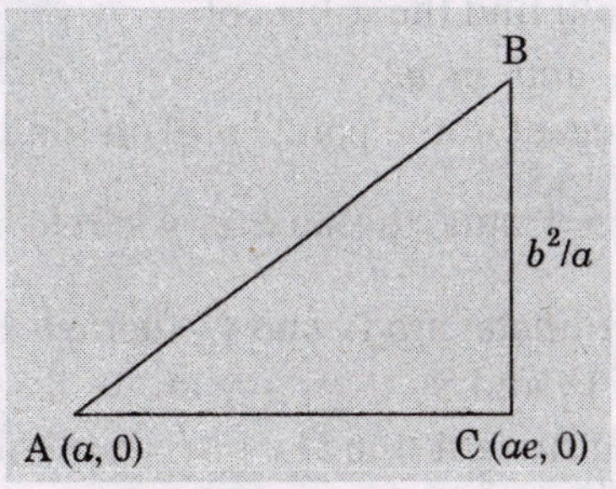

Fig. 3

The given equation can be written as $(x-\sqrt{2})^2-2(y+\sqrt{2})^2=6+2-4=4$

or $\dfrac{(x-\sqrt{2})^2}{2^2}-\dfrac{(y+\sqrt{2})^2}{(\sqrt{2})^2}=1$

Above represents a hyperbola $\dfrac{X^2}{a^2}-\dfrac{Y^2}{b^2}=1$

where $a^2=4, b^2=2$ and $e^2=1+\dfrac{b^2}{a^2}=1+\dfrac{1}{2}=\dfrac{3}{2}$

Vertex $A=(a,0), C=(ae,0)$

and $BC=$ semi L.R. $=\dfrac{b^2}{a}$

$\therefore$ Area $=\dfrac{1}{2}AC\,.\,BC=\dfrac{1}{2}a(e-1)\cdot\dfrac{b^2}{a}$

$=\dfrac{1}{2}2\left(\sqrt{\dfrac{3}{2}}-1\right).\dfrac{2}{2}=\left(\sqrt{\dfrac{3}{2}}-1\right)$

Problem Set (2)

(Tangents and Normals)

1. Find the equations of tangents to the hyperbola $x^2-4y^2=36$ which are perpendicular to the line $x-y+4=0$.

2. (a) Find the equations of the tangents to the hyperbola $x^2-3y^2=9$ which are parallel to the line $y=3x+5$.

(b)* Equation of tangent to the hyperbola $2x^2-3y^2=6$ which is parallel to the line $y=3x+4$ is

(i) $y=3x+5$
(ii) $y=3x-5$
(iii) $y=3x+5$ and $y=3x-5$
(iv) None **(M.N.R. 1993)**

(c) If the point of contact of tangent $y=mx+\sqrt{a^2m^2-b^2}$ to the hyperbola $\dfrac{x^2}{a^2}-\dfrac{y^2}{b^2}=1$ be $(a\sec\theta, b\tan\theta)$ then prove that $\theta=\sin^{-1}(b/am)$.

3. (a) Prove that the line $y=x+2$ touches the hyperbola $5x^2-9y^2=45$, find also its point of contact.

(b) $2x+\sqrt{6}y=2$ touches the hyperbola $x^2-2y^2=4$, then the point of contact is

(a) $\left(\dfrac{1}{2},\dfrac{1}{\sqrt{6}}\right)$ (b) $(4,-\sqrt{6})$
(c) $(4,\sqrt{6})$ (d) $(-2,\sqrt{6})$

(Screening 2004)

4. Find the equation of the tangents drawn from the point $(-2, -1)$ to the hyperbola $2x^2 - 3y^2 = 6$.

5. (a) If m_1 and m_2 are the slopes of the tangents to the hyperbola $\frac{x^2}{25} - \frac{y^2}{16} = 1$ which pass through the point (6, 2) find the values of $m_1 + m_2$ and $m_1 m_2$.

(b)* If the tangent at the point (p, q) on the hyperbola $\frac{x^2}{a^2} - \frac{y^2}{b^2} = 1$ cuts the auxiliary circle in points whose ordinates are y_1 and y_2 then q is Harmonic mean of y_1 and y_2.

6. Prove that the straight line $21x + 5y = 116$ touches the hyperbola $7x^2 - 5y^2 = 232$ and find its point of contact.

7. (a)* Prove that the locus of the point of intersection of two perpendicular tangents to the hyperbola $\frac{x^2}{a^2} - \frac{y^2}{b^2} = 1$ is the circle $x^2 + y^2 = a^2 - b^2$.

(b) Find the locus of the points of intersection of two tangents to a hyperbola $\frac{x^2}{a^2} - \frac{y^2}{b^2} = 1$, if sum of their slopes is constant λ.

8.* Find the condition that the line $lx + my + n = 0$ be a

(i) Tangent

(ii) Normal to the hyperbola $\frac{x^2}{a^2} - \frac{y^2}{b^2} = 1$.

9. (a) Find the equation of the common tangents to the parabola $y^2 = 8x$ and the hyperbola $3x^2 - y^2 = 3$.

(b) Determine the equations of common tangents to the hyperbolas

$$\frac{x^2}{a^2} - \frac{y^2}{b^2} = 1 \text{ and } \frac{y^2}{a^2} - \frac{x^2}{b^2} = 1.$$

10.* Show that the product of the lengths of the perpendiculars drawn from foci on any tangent to the hyperbola $\frac{x^2}{a^2} - \frac{y^2}{b^2} = 1$ is b^2.

Prove further that the feet of the perpendiculars lie on the auxiliary circle $x^2 + y^2 = a^2$.

11. Show that the locus of the middle points of the portions of the tangents to the hyperbola $\frac{x^2}{a^2} - \frac{y^2}{b^2} = 1$ intercepted between the axes is $4x^2y^2 = a^2y^2 - b^2x^2$.

12.* Show that the locus of the foot of the perpendiculars drawn from the centre C of the hyperbola $x^2/a^2 - y^2/b^2 = 1$ on any tangent is $(x^2 + y^2)^2 = a^2x^2 - b^2y^2$ and on any normal is $(a^2y^2 - b^2x^2)(x^2 + y^2)^2 = (a^2 + b^2)^2 x^2y^2$

13.* A normal to the hyperbola $\frac{x^2}{a^2} - \frac{y^2}{b^2} = 1$ meets the axes in Q and R, and lines QL and RL are drawn at right angles to the axes and meet at L. [In other words the rectangle $QORL$ is completed].

Prove that locus of the point L is the hyperbola $a^2x^2 - b^2y^2 = (a^2 + b^2)^2$

Prove further that the locus of the middle point of QR is $4(a^2x^2 - b^2y^2) = (a^2 + b^2)^2$.

14. If two points P and Q on the hyperbola $\frac{x^2}{a^2} - \frac{y^2}{b^2} = 1$, whose centre is C be such that CP is perpendicular to CQ, $a < b$ then prove that $\frac{1}{CP^2} + \frac{1}{CQ^2} = \frac{1}{a^2} - \frac{1}{b^2}$

15. The tangent at a point P on the hyperbola $\frac{x^2}{a^2} - \frac{y^2}{b^2} = 1$ meets one of its directrices in F. Show that PF subtends a right angle at the corresponding focus.

16. (a) If the normal at P to the hyperbola $\frac{x^2}{a^2} - \frac{y^2}{b^2} = 1$ meets the transverse axis in G and conjugate axis in g and CF be perpendicular to the normal from the centre, then prove that

$PF.PG = CB^2 = b^2$, $PF.Pg = CA^2 = a^2$

Also prove that $SG = e.SP$ where S is the focus.

(b) Let $P(a\sec\theta, b\tan\theta)$ and $Q(a\sec\phi, b\tan\phi)$, where $\theta + \phi = \pi/2$, be two points on the hyperbola $\frac{x^2}{a^2} - \frac{y^2}{b^2} = 1$. If (h, k) is the point of intersection of the normals at P and Q, then k is equal to

(a) $\frac{a^2 + b^2}{a}$ (b) $-\left(\frac{a^2 + b^2}{a}\right)$

(c) $\frac{a^2 + b^2}{b}$ (d) $-\left(\frac{a^2 + b^2}{b}\right)$

(I.I.T. 1999)

17. Prove that the area of the traingle formed by the lines $x - y = 0$, $x + y = 0$ and any tangent to the hyperbola $x^2 - y^2 = a^2$ is a^2.

18. (a)* Show that the locus of the middle points of the normal chords of the rectangular hyperbola $x^2 - y^2 = a^2$ is $(y^2 - x^2)^3 = 4a^2x^2y^2$.

(b)* Find the locus of the poles of the normal chords of the hyperbola $\frac{x^2}{a^2} - \frac{y^2}{b^2} = 1$

or

Find the locus of the point of intersection of tangents drawn at the extremities of a normal chord of the hyperbola $\frac{x^2}{a^2} - \frac{y^2}{b^2} = 1$. Deduce the corresponding result if the hyperbola be rectangular *i.e.* $x^2 - y^2 = a^2$.

19. Let two perpendicular chords of the ellipse $\frac{x^2}{a^2} + \frac{y^2}{b^2} = 1, a > b$ each passing through exactly one of the foci meet at a point P. If from P two tangetns are drawn to the hyperbola $\frac{x^2}{a^2} - \frac{y^2}{b^2} = 1$, then $\angle QPR =$

(a) $\frac{\pi}{4}$ (b) $\frac{\pi}{3}$

(c) $\frac{\pi}{2}$ (d) $2\tan^{-1}\frac{b}{a}$

20. (i) Chords of the hyperbola $x^2 - y^2 = a^2$ touch the parabola $y^2 = 4ax$. Prove that locus of their middle point is the curve $y^2(a - x) = x^3$.

(ii) Show that the locus of poles with respect to the parabola $y^2 = 4ax$ of tangents to the hyperbola $x^2 - y^2 = a^2$ is the ellipse $4x^2 + y^2 = 4a^2$.

(iii) If $x = 9$ is the chord of contact of the hyperbola $x^2 - y^2 = 9$, then the equation of the corresponding pair of tangents is

(a) $9x^2 - 8y^2 + 18x - 9 = 0$

(b) $9x^2 - 8y^2 - 18x + 9 = 0$

(c) $9x^2 - 8y^2 - 18x - 9 = 0$

(d) $9x^2 - 8y^2 + 18x + 9 = 0$. **(I.I.T. 1999)**

(iv) A straight line touches the rectangular hyperbola $9x^2 - 9y^2 = 8$ and the parabola $y^2 = 32x$. Determine the equations of the lines.

21. (a)* Chords of the circle $x^2 + y^2 = a^2$ touch the hyperbola $x^2/a^2 - y^2/b^2 = 1$. Prove that locus of their middle point is the curve $(x^2 + y^2)^2 = a^2x^2 - b^2y^2$.

(b)* Find the locus of the mid-points of the chords of the circle $x^2 + y^2 = 16$, which are tangent to the hyperbola $9x^2 - 16y^2 = 144$. **(Roorkee 1997)**

22. (a) Prove that the locus of the middle points of the chords of the hyperbola $\frac{x^2}{a^2} - \frac{y^2}{b^2} = 1$ which pass through a fixed point (α, β) is a hyperbola whose centre is $(\alpha/2, \beta/2)$.

(b)* Find the equation of the chord of the hyperbola $25x^2 - 16y^2 = 400$ which is bisected at the point (6, 2).

23. (a)* From points on the circle $x^2 + y^2 = a^2$ tangents are drawn to the hyperbola $x^2 - y^2 = a^2$. Prove that the locus of the middle points of the chords of contact is the curve $(x^2 - y^2)^2 = a^2(x^2 + y^2)$.

(b) Prove that the chord of the hyperbola which touches the conjugate hyperbola is bisected at the point of contact.

24. (a)* A series of chords of the hyperbola $\frac{x^2}{a^2} - \frac{y^2}{b^2} = 1$ touch the circle on the line joining the foci as diameter. Show that the locus of the poles of these chords with respect to the hyperbola is $\frac{x^2}{a^4} + \frac{y^2}{b^4} = \frac{1}{a^2 + b^2}$.

(b)* Prove that the locus of the point the chord of contact of tangents from which to the hyperbola touches the circle on the line joining the foci as diameter is $\frac{x^2}{a^4} + \frac{y^2}{b^4} = \frac{1}{a^2 - b^2}$.

25. The point P on the hyperbola with focus S is such that the tangent at P, the latus rectum through S and one asymptote are concurrent. Prove that SP is parallel to the other asymptote.

26. A variable tangent to the hyperbola $\frac{x^2}{a^2} - \frac{y^2}{b^2} = 1$ meets the transverse axis and the tangent at the vertex $(a, 0)$ at Q and R. Show that the locus of the mid-point of QR is $x(4y^2 + b^2) = ab^2$.

27. Prove that the co-ordinates of any point on the hyperbola $x^2/a^2 - y^2/b^2 = 1$ can be expressed as $x = \frac{1}{2}a\left(t + \frac{1}{t}\right), y = \frac{1}{2}b\left(t - \frac{1}{t}\right)$ and that the equation of the tangent at the above point 't' is $\frac{x}{a}(t^2 + 1) - \frac{y}{b}(t^2 + 1) = 2t$.

28.* For any real t

$$x = \frac{e^t + e^{-t}}{2}, y = \frac{e^t - e^{-t}}{2}$$

is a point on the hyperbola $x^2 - y^2 = 1$. Show that the area bounded by the hyperbola and the lines joining its centre to the points corresponding to t_1 and $-t_1$ is t_1.

29. C is the centre of the hyperbola $\frac{x^2}{a^2} - \frac{y^2}{b^2} = 1$. The tangent at any point P on this hyperbola meets the straight lines $bx - ay = 0$ and $bx + ay = 0$ in the points Q and R respectively. Show that $CQ \cdot CR = a^2 + b^2$.

30. A circle of variable radius cuts the rectangular hyperbola $x^2 - y^2 = 9a^2$ in points P, Q, R and S. Determine the equation of the locus of the centroid of triangle PQR.

31.* A series of hyperbolas are such that the length of their transverse axis is $2a$. Show that locus of a point P on each such that its distance from the transverse axis is equal to its distance from an asymptote is the curve $(x^2-y^2)^2=4x^2(x^2-a^2)$.

32.* A variable chord of the hyperbola $\frac{x^2}{a^2}-\frac{y^2}{b^2}=1$ touches the circle $x^2+y^2=c^2$. Show that locus of its mid-point is $\left(\frac{x^2}{a^2}-\frac{y^2}{b^2}\right)^2=c^2\left(\frac{x^2}{a^4}+\frac{y^2}{b^4}\right)$

33.* A tangent to the hyperbola $\frac{x^2}{a^2}-\frac{y^2}{b^2}=1$ cuts the ellipse $\frac{x^2}{a^2}+\frac{y^2}{b^2}=1$ in P and Q. Prove that the locus of the mid-point of PQ is $\left(\frac{x^2}{a^2}+\frac{y^2}{b^2}\right)^2=\frac{x^2}{a^2}-\frac{y^2}{b^2}$.

(I.S.M. 1990)

34. Tangents are drawn from any point on the hyperbola $\frac{x^2}{9}-\frac{y^2}{4}=1$ to the circle $x^2+y^2=9$. Find the locus of the mid-point of the chords of contact. **(I.I.T. 2005)**

Solutions to Problem Set (2)

1. Slope of the given line $x-y+4=0$ is 1 and hence slope of tangent perpendicular to it is $-1=m$. Also $a^2=36, b^2=9$. Hence the tangent is $y=mx\pm\sqrt{(a^2m^2-b^2)}$ or $y=-x\pm 3\sqrt{3}$.

2. (a) Proceed as above $3x-y\pm 2\sqrt{6}=0$.

(b) Ans. (iii). $a^2=3, b^2=2, m=3$ and the equation of tangent to hyperbola is
$$y=mx\pm\sqrt{(a^2m^2-b^2)}.$$

(c) Tangent at $(a\sec\theta, b\tan\theta)$ is
$$\frac{x\sec\theta}{a}-\frac{y\tan\theta}{b}=1$$
$$\therefore\quad m=\frac{\sec\theta}{a}\cdot\frac{b}{\tan\theta}=\frac{b}{a\sin\theta}$$
$$\therefore\quad \sin\theta=\frac{b}{am}\quad\text{or}\quad \theta=\sin^{-1}\left(\frac{b}{am}\right)$$

3. (a) Solving the line with the hyperbola you will find two coincident points and hence it is a tangent and point of contact is $(-9/2, -5/2)$.

(b) And. (b).
Compare $xx_1-2yy_1=4$ with $2x+\sqrt{6}y=2$

Alt : Eliminate y, we get $x^2-8x+16=0$
or $(x-4)^2=0$
$\therefore\quad x=4$ and hence $y=-\sqrt{6}$

4. Hyperbola is $x^2/3-y^2/2=1$, *i.e.* $a^2=3, b^2=2$

Any tangent is $y=mx+\sqrt{(a^2m^2-b^2)}$. It passes through $(-2,-1)$
$$\therefore\quad (2m-1)^2=3m^2-2\quad\text{or}\quad m^2-4m+3=0$$
$$\therefore\quad m=3 \text{ or } 1.$$
Hence the tangents on putting for m are
$$3x-y+7=0,\ x-y+1=0.$$

5. (a) Proceed as above $m_1+m_2=24/11$, $m_1m_2=20/11$.

(b) Here we choose the tangent as
$$\frac{xp}{a^2}-\frac{yq}{b^2}=1 \text{ where } \frac{p^2}{a^2}-\frac{q^2}{b^2}=1 \quad ...(1)$$
Its intersection with $x^2+y^2=a^2$ is given by eliminating x as we are concerned with ordinates
$$\left(1+\frac{yq}{b^2}\right)^2\frac{a^4}{p^2}+y^2=a^2$$
or $(b^2+yq)^2a^4+b^4y^2p^2=a^2p^2b^4$
or $y^2(a^4q^2+b^4p^2)+2yqb^2a^4+a^4b^4-a^2p^2b^4=0$ ...(2)

Above is a quadratic in y. We have to prove that q is H.M. 'H' of y_1 and y_2
$$\text{Now } H=\frac{2y_1y_2}{y_1+y_2}=\frac{(a^4b^4-a^2p^2b^4)}{-2qb^2a^4} \text{ by (2)}$$
$$=\frac{a^4b^4(1-p^2/a^2)}{-2qb^2.a^4}=\frac{b^2}{-q}\left[-\frac{q^2}{b^2}\right]=q, \text{ by (1)}.$$
$\therefore\quad q$ is H.M. 'H' of y_1 and y_2.

6. Ans. $(6,-2)$.

7. (a) Any tangent to hyperbola is
$$y=mx+\sqrt{(a^2m^2-b^2)}.$$
If it passes through the point (h,k), then
$$(k-mh)^2=(a^2m^2-b^2)$$
or $m^2(h^2-a^2)-2mhk+(k^2+b^2)=0$ ...(1)

Above is a quadratic in m showing that there will be two tangents that pass through the point (h,k). Since the tangents are perpendicular
$$\therefore\quad m_1m_2=-1\quad\text{or}\quad \frac{k^2+b^2}{h^2-a^2}=-1$$
or $k^2+b^2=-h^2+a^2$.

Hence the locus is $x^2+y^2=a^2-b^2$ which is called director circle.

(b) Any tangent to hyperbola is
$$y=mx+\sqrt{a^2m^2-b^2}$$
If it passes through the point (h,k), then
$$(k-mh)^2=a^2m^2-b^2$$
or $m^2(h^2-a^2)-2mhk+k^2+b^2=0$ ...(1)

Then there will be two tangents passing through (h,k) whose slopes are given by (1)
$$\text{Now } m_1+m_2=\lambda\quad\therefore\quad \frac{2hk}{h^2-a^2}=\lambda$$
$\therefore\quad$ Locus is $\lambda(x^2-a^2)=2xy$.

8. $lx+my+n=0$ ...(1)

Any tangent is $\dfrac{x\sec\theta}{a}-\dfrac{y\tan\theta}{b}=1.$ ...(2)

Comparing (1) and (2), we get

$$\frac{\sec\theta}{al}=\frac{\tan\theta}{-bm}=\frac{1}{-n}$$

$\therefore\quad \sec\theta=-\dfrac{al}{n},\ \tan\theta=\dfrac{bm}{n}.$

But $\sec^2\theta-\tan^2\theta=1$

$\therefore\quad a^2l^2-b^2m^2=n^2$ is the required condition.

Any normal to the hyperbola is

$$\frac{ax}{\sec\theta}-\frac{by}{\tan\theta}=a^2+b^2. \quad ...(3)$$

Comparing (1) and (3), we get

$$\frac{l\sec\theta}{a}=\frac{m\tan\theta}{b}=\frac{-n}{(a^2+b^2)}$$

$$\therefore\quad \sec\theta=\frac{a}{l}\left(\frac{-n}{a^2+b^2}\right),\ \tan\theta=\frac{b}{m}\left(\frac{-n}{a^2+b^2}\right).$$

But $\sec^2\theta-\tan^2\theta=1$

$$\therefore\quad \left(\frac{n}{a^2+b^2}\right)^2\left[\frac{a^2}{l^2}-\frac{b^2}{m^2}\right]=1$$

or $\dfrac{a^2}{l^2}-\dfrac{b^2}{m^2}=\dfrac{(a^2+b^2)^2}{n^2}.$

9. (a) $y^2=8x\quad\therefore\quad 4a=8$ or $a=2$

Any tangent to the parabola is

$y=mx+2/m$ ...(1)

If it is also a tangent to the hyperbola

$x^2/1-y^2/3=1$ *i.e.* $a^2=1,\ b^2=3$, then

$c^2=a^2m^2-b^2$ or $4/m^2=1.m^2-3.$

or $m^4-3m^2-4=0$ or $(m^2-4)(m^2+1)=0$

$\therefore\ m=\pm 2.$ Putting for m in (1), we get the tangents as

$2x-y+1=0$ and $2x+y+1=0.$

(b) Tangent to $\dfrac{x^2}{a^2}-\dfrac{y^2}{b^2}=1$ is

$y=m_1x\pm\sqrt{(a^2m_1^2-b^2)}$ ...(1)

The other hyperbola is $\dfrac{x^2}{(-b^2)}-\dfrac{y^2}{(-a^2)}=1$

Any tangent to it is

$y=m_2x\pm\sqrt{(-b^2)\,m_2^2-(-a^2)}$ ...(2)

If (1) and (2) are same, then

$m_1=m_2$ and $a^2m_1^2-b^2=-b^2m_2^2+a^2$

or $a^2m_1^2-b^2=a^2-b^2m_1^2$

or $(a^2+b^2)\,m_1^2=a^2+b^2$

$\therefore\quad m_1^2=1\quad\therefore\quad m_1=\pm 1$

Hence the common tangents are

$y=\pm x\pm\sqrt{a^2-b^2}$

10. Proceed exactly as in **Q. 1 P. 1029-1030** and change b^2 into $-b^2$.

11. Any tangent to the hyperbola is $\dfrac{x}{a}\sec\theta-\dfrac{y}{b}\tan\theta=1$

Putting $y=0$ and then $x=0$, we get the points where it meets the axes

$$A=\left(\frac{a}{\sec\theta},0\right),B=\left(0,-\frac{b}{\tan\theta}\right).$$

If (h,k) be the mid-point of AB, then

$$2h=\frac{a}{\sec\theta},2k=\frac{-b}{\tan\theta}$$

But $\sec^2\theta-\tan^2\theta=1\quad\therefore\quad \dfrac{a^2}{4h^2}-\dfrac{b^2}{4k^2}=1.$

$\therefore$ Locus of mid-point (h,k) is $a^2y^2-b^2x^2=4x^2y^2.$

12. Any tangent to the hyperbola is

$\dfrac{x}{a}\sec\theta-\dfrac{y}{b}\tan\theta=1$ ...(1)

Any line through (0, 0) and perpendicular to (1) is

$\dfrac{x\tan\theta}{b}+\dfrac{y}{a}\sec\theta=0$ ...(2)

Both the lines (1) and (2) meet at foot of perpendicular and in order to find its locus we have to eliminate the variable θ between (1) and (2). From (2) we get $\sin\theta=-by/ax$

$$\therefore\quad \cos\theta=\frac{\sqrt{(a^2x^2-b^2y^2)}}{ax}$$

and $\tan\theta=\dfrac{-by}{\sqrt{(a^2x^2-b^2y^2)}}$ ...(3)

Putting for $\sec\theta$ and $\tan\theta$ from (3) in (1), we get

$$\frac{x}{a}\frac{ax}{\sqrt{(a^2x^2-b^2y^2)}}-\frac{y}{b}\frac{-by}{\sqrt{(a^2x^2-b^2y^2)}}=1$$

or $(x^2+y^2)^2=(a^2x^2-b^2y^2)$

2nd part : Any normal at the point θ is

$ax\cos\theta+by\cot\theta=(a^2+b^2)$ ...(4)

Any line through centre (0, 0) and perpendicular to (4) is

$xb\cot\theta-ya\cos\theta=0$

$\therefore\quad \sin\theta=bx/ay$

$$\therefore\quad \cos\theta=\frac{\sqrt{(a^2y^2-b^2x^2)}}{ay},$$

$$\cot\theta=\frac{\sqrt{(a^2y^2-b^2x^2)}}{bx}.$$

Substituting the values of $\cos\theta$ and $\cot\theta$ in (4), we get the locus of the foot of perpendicular from centre on any normal as

$$\sqrt{(a^2y^2-b^2x^2)}\left[ax\cdot\frac{1}{ay}+by\cdot\frac{1}{bx}\right]=a^2+b^2.$$

Squaring

$$(a^2y^2-b^2x^2)(x^2+y^2)^2=(a^2+b^2)^2\,x^2y^2.$$

13. Any normal to the hyperbola is

$ax\cos\theta + by\cot\theta = a^2 + b^2$. ...(1)

Putting $y = 0$ and then $x = 0$, we get the points Q and R where it meets the axes as

$$Q\left(\frac{a^2+b^2}{a}\sec\theta, 0\right) \text{ and } R\left(0, \frac{a^2+b^2}{b}\tan\theta\right)$$

Line through Q perp. to x-axis is $x = \frac{a^2+b^2}{a}\sec\theta$.

Line through R perp. to y-axis is $y = \frac{a^2+b^2}{b}\tan\theta$.

Both these lines meet at the point L and in order to find its locus, we have to eliminate θ between their equations by the help of relation $\sec^2\theta - \tan^2\theta = 1$.

or $$\frac{a^2x^2}{(a^2+b^2)^2} - \frac{b^2y^2}{(a^2+b^2)^2} = 1$$

or $a^2x^2 - b^2y^2 = (a^2+b^2)^2$

2nd part : If (h, k) be the mid-point of QR, then

$$2h = \frac{a^2+b^2}{a}\sec\theta,\ 2k = \frac{a^2+b^2}{b}\tan\theta$$

$$4(a^2h^2 - b^2k^2) = (a^2+b^2)^2(\sec^2\theta - \tan^2\theta)$$

or $4(a^2x^2 - b^2y^2) = (a^2+b^2)^2$ is the required locus.

14. Let the equation to CP be $y = mx$. Its intersection with $\frac{x^2}{a^2} - \frac{y^2}{b^2} = 1$ is given by

$$x^2(b^2 - a^2m^2) = a^2b^2 \quad ...(1)$$

$$\therefore \quad CP^2 = x^2 + y^2 = x^2 + m^2x^2$$

$$= (1+m^2)\frac{a^2b^2}{b^2 - a^2m^2} \text{ by (1)}$$

Replacing m by $-1/m$, we get

$$CQ^2 = \frac{1+m^2}{m^2}\cdot\frac{a^2b^2 \cdot m^2}{b^2m^2 - a^2} = \frac{(1+m^2)a^2b^2}{b^2m^2 - a^2}$$

$$\therefore \quad \frac{1}{CP^2} + \frac{1}{CQ^2}$$

$$= \frac{1}{(1+m^2)}\cdot\frac{b^2(1+m^2) - a^2(1+m^2)}{a^2b^2} = \frac{1}{a^2} - \frac{1}{b^2}$$

Alt. Method : Let $CP = r_1$ be inclined to transverse axis at an angle θ so that P is $(r_1\cos\theta, r_1\sin\theta)$ and P lies on the hyperbola

$$\therefore \quad r_1^2\left(\frac{\cos^2\theta}{a^2} - \frac{\sin^2\theta}{b^2}\right) = 1$$

Replacing θ by $90^o + \theta$

$$r_2^2\left(\frac{\sin^2\theta}{a^2} - \frac{\cos^2\theta}{b^2}\right) = 1$$

$$\therefore \quad \frac{1}{r_1^2} + \frac{1}{r_2^2} = \cos^2\theta\left(\frac{1}{a^2} - \frac{1}{b^2}\right) + \sin^2\theta\left(\frac{1}{a^2} - \frac{1}{b^2}\right)$$

$$\therefore \quad \frac{1}{CP^2} + \frac{1}{CQ^2} = \frac{1}{a^2} - \frac{1}{b^2} \quad \because \cos^2\theta + \sin^2\theta = 1.$$

15. Refer figure **Q. 18 P. 1014-1020 Ellipse.** Let P be $(a\sec\theta, b\tan\theta)$.

Tangent at P is $\frac{x}{a}\sec\theta - \frac{y}{b}\tan\theta = 1$.

It meets the directrix $x = a/e$ at the point F given as $\left[\frac{a}{e}, \frac{b(\sec\theta - e)}{e\tan\theta}\right]$ and focus S is $(ae, 0)$

Slope of SP is $\frac{b\tan\theta}{a(\sec\theta - e)} = m_1$

Slope of SF is $\frac{b(\sec\theta - e)}{e\tan\theta}\Big/\left(\frac{a}{e} - ae\right)$

$$\frac{b}{a}\frac{(\sec\theta - e)}{(1-e^2)\tan\theta} = m_2$$

$$\therefore \quad m_1m_2 = \frac{b^2}{a^2}\cdot\frac{1}{(1-e^2)} = -1 \quad \because \quad b^2 = a^2(e^2 - 1)$$

Hence the lines SP and SF are perpendicular *i.e.* $\angle FSP = \pi/2$.

16. (a) Proceed as in **Q. 25 P. 1014-1023 of Ellipse.**

$$PG^2 = \frac{b^2}{a^2}(b^2\sec^2\theta + a^2\tan^2\theta),$$

$$Pg^2 = \frac{a^2}{b^2}(b^2\sec^2\theta + a^2\tan^2\theta)$$

$PF = CL$ = perpendicular from centre C on the tangent $= \frac{ab}{\sqrt{(b^2\sec^2\theta + a^2\tan^2\theta)}}$

$$PG \cdot PF = b^2 = CB^2$$

and $Pg \cdot PF = a^2 = CA^2$

(b) Ans. (d).

Normals at θ, ϕ where $\phi = \frac{\pi}{2} - \theta$ pass through (h, k).

$$\therefore \quad ah\cos\theta + bk\cot\theta = a^2 + b^2$$

$$ah\sin\theta + bk\tan\theta = a^2 + b^2$$

Eliminate h,

$$bk(\cot\theta\sin\theta - \tan\theta\cos\theta) = (a^2+b^2)(\sin\theta - \cos\theta)$$

or $k = -(a^2+b^2)/b$.

17. Any tangent to the hyperbola $x^2 - y^2 = a^2$ at P $(a\sec\theta, a\tan\theta)$ is

$$x\sec\theta - y\tan\theta = a \quad ...(1)$$

Also $$x - y = 0 \quad ...(2)$$

$$x + y = 0 \quad ...(3)$$

Solving the above three lines in pairs, we get the points A, B, C as

$$\left(\frac{a}{\sec\theta - \tan\theta}, \frac{a}{\sec\theta - \tan\theta}\right),$$

$$\left(\frac{a}{\sec\theta + \tan\theta}, \frac{-a}{\sec\theta + \tan\theta}\right) \text{ and } (0, 0).$$

Since one vertex is the origin therefore the area of triangle ABC is $\frac{1}{2}(x_1y_2 - x_2y_1)$

$$= \frac{a^2}{2}\left[\frac{-1}{(\sec^2\theta - \tan^2\theta)} - \frac{1}{(\sec^2\theta - \tan^2\theta)}\right]$$

$$= \frac{a^2}{2}(-2) = -a^2 = a^2$$

18. (a) If (h, k) be the mid-point of the chord of the hyperbola $x^2 - y^2 = a^2$ then its equation by $T = S_1$ is

$$hx - ky = h^2 - k^2 \quad ...(1)$$

But since (1) is normal to the hyperbola its equation is

$$x\cos\theta + y\cot\theta = 2a \quad ...(2)$$

Putting $b = a$ in **Result 15 Page 1041.**

Comparing (1) and (2), we get

$$\frac{h}{\cos\theta} = -\frac{k}{\cot\theta} = \frac{h^2 - k^2}{2a}$$

$$\therefore \quad \sec\theta = \frac{h^2 - k^2}{2ah} \text{ and } \tan\theta = \frac{h^2 - k^2}{-2ak}$$

Put in $\sec^2\theta - \tan^2\theta = 1$

$$\therefore \quad \frac{(h^2 - k^2)^2}{4a^2}\left(\frac{1}{h^2} - \frac{1}{k^2}\right) = 1$$

Hence the locus of the mid-point (h, k) is

$$(x^2 - y^2)^2(y^2 - x^2) = 4a^2x^2y^2$$

or $\quad (y^2 - x^2)^3 = 4a^2x^2y^2$

(b) Let (h, k) be the pole of the normal chord or point of intersection of tangents at its extremities so that its equation is

$$\frac{hx}{a^2} - \frac{ky}{b^2} = 1 \quad ...(1)$$

i.e. polar of (h, k) or chord of contact of the point (h, k).

Since (1) is a normal chord its equation is of the form

$$ax\cos\theta + by\cot\theta = a^2 + b^2 \quad ...(2)$$

Comparing (1) and (2), we get

$$\frac{h}{a^3\cos\theta} = \frac{-k}{b^3\cot\theta} = \frac{1}{a^2 + b^2}$$

$$\therefore \quad (a^2 + b^2)\sec\theta = \frac{a^3}{h}$$

and $(a^2 + b^2)\tan\theta = -\frac{b^3}{k}$

Squaring and subtracting thereby eliminating θ, we get

$$(a^2 + b^2)^2 \cdot 1 = \frac{a^6}{h^2} - \frac{b^6}{k^2}$$

Generalising, the locus of the point (h, k) is

$$\frac{a^6}{x^2} - \frac{b^6}{y^2} = (a^2 + b^2)^2$$

Note : In case the hyperbola is $x^2 - y^2 = a^2$ *i.e.* rectangular then putting $b = a$ in (3), we get

$$a^6\frac{(y^2 - x^2)}{x^2y^2} = 4a^4$$

$$\therefore \quad a^2(y^2 - x^2) = 4x^2y^2$$

or $\quad \frac{1}{x^2} - \frac{1}{y^2} = \frac{4}{a^2}$

19. Ans. (c).

The equation of two perpendicular chords drawn through each of the foci be $y = m(x - ae)$ and $y = -\frac{1}{m}(x + ae)$. Locus of their point of intersection P is obtained by eliminating the variable m.

Multiplying the equations of chords, we have

$$y^2 = -(x^2 - a^2e^2) \quad \text{or} \quad x^2 + y^2 = a^2 - b^2$$

Above represents the director circle of hyperbola $\frac{x^2}{a^2} - \frac{y^2}{b^2} = 1$ which we know is the locus of the point of intersection of perpendicular tangents QP and QR. Hence $\angle QPR = \pi/2$.

20. (i) If (h, k) be the mid-point of the chord, then its equation by $T = S_1$ is $hx - ky = (h^2 - k^2)$

or $\quad y = \frac{h}{k}x + \frac{k^2 - h^2}{k}$

If it touches the parabola $y^2 = 4ax$, then by $c = a/m$, we get

$$\frac{k^2 - h^2}{k} = a\frac{k}{h} \quad \text{or} \quad ak^2 = hk^2 - h^3$$

or $\quad y^2(x - a) = x^3$ is the required locus.

(ii) Any tangent to the hyperbola $x^2 - y^2 = a^2$ is

$$x\sec\theta - y\tan\theta = a$$

$$x - y\sin\theta = a\cos\theta \quad ...(1)$$

If its pole w.r.t. parabola $y^2 = 4ax$ be (h, k) then it is same as $ky = 2a(x + h)$

or $\quad 2ax - ky = -2ah \quad ...(2)$

Compare (1) and (2), $\quad \frac{1}{2a} = \frac{\sin\theta}{k} = \frac{\cos\theta}{-2h}$

Eliminate θ by $\cos^2\theta + \sin^2\theta = 1$

$k^2 + 4h^2 = 4a^2 \quad \therefore$ Locus is $4x^2 + y^2 = 4a^2$.

(iii) Ans. (b). Comparing chord of contact of point (h, k) *i.e.* $hx - ky = 9$ with $x = 9$, we get $h = 1$, $k = 0$

$\therefore \quad$ Pair of tangents is $SS_1 = T^2$ etc.

(iv) Ans. $9x - 3y + 8 = 0$, $9x + 3y + 8 = 0$.

Any tangent to the parabola $y^2 = 32x$ is

$$y = mx + \frac{8}{m} \quad (\because \; a = 8)$$

If it touches the hyperbola $x^2 - y^2 = \frac{8}{9}$, then condition of tangency $c^2 = a^2 m^2 - b^2$ gives

$$\left(\frac{8}{m}\right)^2 = \frac{8}{9}(m^2 - 1) \quad \therefore \quad m^2(m^2 - 1) - 72 = 0$$

or $\quad m^4 - m^2 - 72 = 0 \quad$ or $\quad (m^2 - 9)(m^2 + 8) = 0$

$\therefore \quad m^2 = 9 \quad$ or $\quad m = 3, -3$

Equation of common tangents is

$$y = mx + \frac{8}{m} \text{ or } y = 3x + \frac{8}{3} \text{ and } y = -3x + \frac{8}{-3}$$

or $\quad 9x - 3y + 8 = 0$ and $9x + 3y + 8 = 0$

21. (a) Let (h, k) be the mid-point of the chord of the circle $x^2 + y^2 = a^2$, so that its equation by $T = S_1$ is

$$hx + ky = h^2 + k^2$$

or $\quad y = -\frac{h}{k}x + \frac{h^2 + k^2}{k}$ *i.e.* of the form

$$y = mx + c$$

It will touch the hyperbola if $c^2 = a^2 m^2 - b^2$

$$\therefore \quad \left(\frac{h^2 + k^2}{k}\right)^2 = a^2\left(-\frac{h}{k}\right)^2 - b^2$$

or $\quad (h^2 + k^2)^2 = a^2 h^2 - b^2 k^2$

Generalising, the locus of mid-point (h, k) is

$$(x^2 + y^2)^2 = a^2 x^2 - b^2 y^2$$

(b) Proceed as in (a).

$$(x^2 + y^2)^2 = 16x^2 - 9y^2.$$

22. (a) Equation of the chord of the hyperbola whose mid-point is (h, k) by $T = S_1$ is

$$\frac{hx}{a^2} - \frac{ky}{b^2} = \frac{h^2}{a^2} - \frac{k^2}{b^2}.$$

It passes through the point (α, β)

$$\therefore \quad \frac{h\alpha}{a^2} - \frac{k\beta}{b^2} = \frac{h^2}{a^2} - \frac{k^2}{b^2}$$

$\therefore$ Locus of (h, k) is $\dfrac{x^2 - \alpha x}{a^2} - \dfrac{y^2 - \beta y}{b^2} = 0$

or $\quad \dfrac{(x - \alpha/2)^2}{a^2} - \dfrac{(y - \beta/2)^2}{b^2} = \dfrac{1}{4}\left(\dfrac{\alpha^2}{a^2} - \dfrac{\beta^2}{b^2}\right) = k^2$, say.

Above equation represents a hyperbola whose centre is $(\alpha/2, \beta/2)$.

(b) $T = S_1$

Ans. $\quad 75x - 16y = 418.$

23. (a) Any point on the circle $x^2 + y^2 = a^2$ is $(a\cos\theta, a\sin\theta)$. Chord of contact of this point w.r.t. the hyperbola $x^2 - y^2 = a^2$ is

$$x(a\cos\theta) - y(a\sin\theta) = a^2$$

or $\quad x\cos\theta - y\sin\theta = a \quad$ ...(1)

If its mid-point be (h, k), then it is same as $T = S_1$.

or $\quad hx - ky = h^2 - k^2 \quad$ ...(2)

Comparing (1) and (2), we get

$$\frac{\cos\theta}{h} = \frac{\sin\theta}{k} = \frac{a}{h^2 - k^2}$$

But $\cos^2\theta + \sin^2\theta = 1$

$$\therefore \quad \left(\frac{ah}{h^2 - k^2}\right)^2 + \left(\frac{ak}{h^2 - k^2}\right)^2 = 1$$

Hence the locus of the mid-point (h, k) is

$$a^2(x^2 + y^2) = (x^2 - y^2)^2.$$

(b) Hyp. $\frac{x^2}{a^2} - \frac{y^2}{b^2} = 1$, Conj. $\frac{x^2}{a^2} - \frac{y^2}{b^2} = -1$

Any tangent say AB at (p, q) to conj. hyp. be

$$\frac{xp}{a^2} - \frac{yq}{b^2} = -1 \quad \text{...(1)}$$

where $\quad \dfrac{p^2}{a^2} - \dfrac{q^2}{b^2} + 1 = 0$

or $\quad b^2 p^2 - a^2 q^2 + a^2 b^2 = 0 \quad$ ...(2)

We have to show that point of contact (p, q) is mid point of AB. A and B are obtained by solving the hyperbola with tangent (1). Eliminating y we get

$$\frac{x^2}{a^2} - \frac{1}{b^2}\left[1 + \frac{xp}{a^2}\right]^2\left(\frac{b^2}{q}\right)^2 = 1$$

or $\quad x^2\left\{\dfrac{1}{a^2} - \dfrac{p^2}{a^4}\dfrac{b^2}{q^2}\right\} - x\left\{\dfrac{2p}{a^2}\dfrac{b^2}{q^2}\right\} - \left\{\dfrac{b^2}{q^2} + 1\right\} = 0$

or $\quad x^2\left\{\dfrac{a^2q^2 - b^2p^2}{a^4 q^2}\right\} - x\left\{\dfrac{2p\,b^2}{q^2\,a^2}\right\} - \left\{\dfrac{b^2}{q^2} + 1\right\} = 0$

or $\quad x^2\dfrac{a^2b^2}{a^4q^2} - x\left\{\dfrac{2p\,b^2}{q^2\,a^2}\right\} - \left\{\dfrac{b^2}{q^2} + 1\right\} = 0 \quad$ [by (2)]

$$x_1 + x_2 = \frac{2p}{q^2}\cdot\frac{b^2}{a^2} \div \frac{a^2b^2}{a^4q^2} = 2p$$

$$\therefore \quad \frac{x_1 + x_2}{2} = p, \text{ similarly } \frac{y_2 + y_2}{2} = q$$

Hence point of contact is mid-point of chord AB.

24. (a) The foci of the hyperbola are the points $S(ae, 0)$ and $S'(-ae, 0)$. Circle on SS' as diameter is

$$(x - ae)(x + ae) + y^2 = 0$$

or $\quad x^2 + y^2 = a^2 e^2 \quad$ ...(1)

If (h, k) be the pole of the chord which touches (1), then its equation is the polar of (h, k) w.r.t. hyperbola

i.e. $\quad \dfrac{hx}{a^2} - \dfrac{ky}{b^2} = 1 \quad$ ...(2)

Since the line (2) touches the circle (1) therefore perpendicular from centre (0, 0) should be equal to radius ae.

$$\therefore \quad \frac{1}{\sqrt{\left(\frac{h^2}{a^4}+\frac{k^2}{b^4}\right)}} = ae$$

or $\quad \dfrac{h^2}{a^4}+\dfrac{k^2}{b^4}=\dfrac{1}{a^2e^2}=\dfrac{1}{a^2+b^2} \quad \because \; b^2=a^2(e^2-1)$

Generalising, the locus of the pole (h, k) is the ellipse

$$\frac{x^2}{a^4}+\frac{y^2}{b^4}=\frac{1}{a^2+b^2}$$

(b) If (h, k) be the point, then chord of contact is $\dfrac{hx}{a^2}-\dfrac{ky}{b^2}=1$. It touches the circle on the join of $(ae, 0)$ and $(-ae, 0)$ as diameter

or $\quad x^2+y^2=a^2e^2=a^2-b^2$

Apply $p = r$

$$\therefore \quad \frac{1}{\sqrt{\left(\frac{h^2}{a^4}+\frac{k^2}{b^4}\right)}}=\sqrt{a^2-b^2}$$

$\therefore \quad$ Locus is $\dfrac{x^2}{a^4}+\dfrac{y^2}{b^4}=\dfrac{1}{a^2-b^2}$

25. Let $P(a\sec\theta, b\tan\theta)$ be a point on the hyperbola tangent at which is

$$\frac{x}{a}\sec\theta-\frac{y}{b}\tan\theta=1 \qquad \text{...(1)}$$

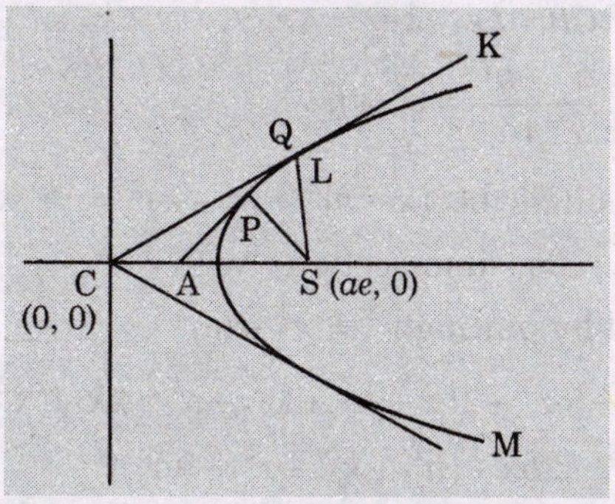

Fig. 4

The equation of L.R. ; SL through $S(ae, 0)$ is

$$x = ae \qquad \text{...(2)}$$

The asymptotes are

$$y=\frac{b}{a}x \quad \text{and} \quad y=-\frac{b}{a}x \qquad \text{...(3)}$$

Lines (1), (2) and (3) are concurrent. Clearly (2) and (3) intersect at (ae, be) and this point will lie on (1)

$$\therefore \quad \sec\theta-\tan\theta=\frac{1}{e} \qquad \text{...(4)}$$

Hence $\quad \sec\theta+\tan\theta=e \qquad$ ...(5)

Adding and subtracting (4) and (5), we get

$$\sec\theta=\frac{e^2+1}{2e}, \tan\theta=\frac{e^2-1}{2e}$$

$\therefore \quad P$ is $\left[\dfrac{a(e^2+1)}{2e}, \dfrac{a(e^2-1)}{2e}\right]$, S is $(ae, 0)$

Now show that slope of SP is $-b/a$ so that it is parallel to other asymptote $y=-\dfrac{b}{a}x$.

26. The equation of the tangent at the point θ is

$$\frac{x}{a}\sec\theta-\frac{y}{b}\tan\theta=1$$

It meets the transverse axis $y = 0$ and tangent at vertex $x = a$ in the point $Q(a\cos\theta, 0)$ and $R\left[a, \dfrac{b(1-\cos\theta)}{\sin\theta}\right]$.

If (h, k) be the mid-point of QR, then

$$2h=a+a\cos\theta=a(1+\cos\theta)$$

$$\therefore \quad \cos\theta=\frac{2h-a}{a}$$

$$2k=\frac{b(1-\cos\theta)}{\sin\theta}$$

Also $\quad 4hk=ab\dfrac{(1-\cos^2\theta)}{\sin\theta}=ab\sin\theta$

$$\therefore \quad 16h^2k^2=a^2b^2[1-\cos^2\theta]$$

$$=a^2b^2\left[1-\left(\frac{2h-a}{a}\right)^2\right]$$

$$=b^2[a^2-(2h-a)^2]=b^2[4ha-4h^2]$$

$\therefore \quad 4hk^2=b^2(a-h) \quad$ or $\quad 4hk^2+b^2h=b^2a$.

Hence the locus of the point (h, k) is

$$x(4y^2+b^2)=ab^2.$$

27. $x=\dfrac{a}{2}\left(t+\dfrac{1}{t}\right), y=\dfrac{b}{2}\left(t-\dfrac{1}{t}\right)$

$$\frac{x^2}{a^2}-\frac{y^2}{b^2}=\frac{1}{4}\left[\left(t+\frac{1}{t}\right)^2-\left(t-\frac{1}{t}\right)^2\right]=\frac{1}{4}\cdot 4\left(t\cdot\frac{1}{t}\right)=1$$

Hence the point t lies on the hyperbola $\dfrac{x^2}{a^2}-\dfrac{y^2}{b^2}=1$

Tangent at any point (x_1, y_1) is $\dfrac{xx_1}{a^2}-\dfrac{yy_1}{b^2}=1$

Putting for (x_1, y_1) in terms of t, we get the result as given.

28. Substituting the point in the equation of hyperbola, we get

$$\frac{1}{4}[(e^t+e^{-t})^2-(e^t-e^{-t})^2]=\frac{1}{4}4e^te^{-t}=1.$$

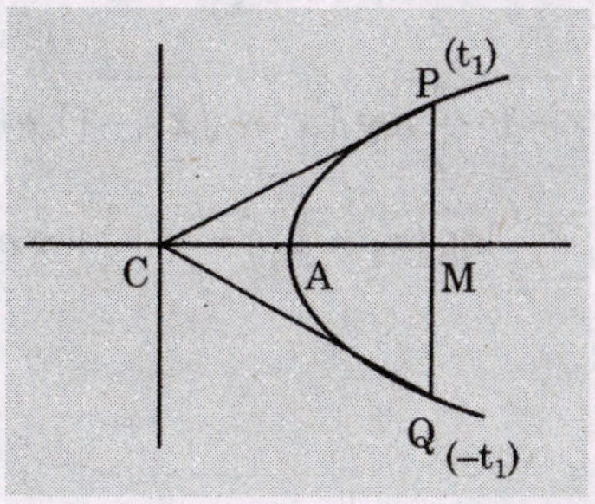

Fig. 5

Above is true for all values of t. Hence the point lies on the hyperbola $x^2 - y^2 = 1$.

Let $P(x_1, y_1)$ be the point corresponding to t_1 then

$$x_1 = \frac{1}{2}(e^t + e^{-t}), y_1 = \frac{1}{2}(e^t - e^{-t})$$

If $Q(x_2, y_2)$ be the point corresponding to $-t_1$ then

$$x_2 = \frac{1}{2}(e^{-t} + e^t) = x_1,$$

$$y_2 = \frac{1}{2}(e^{-t} - e^t) = -y_1$$

$\therefore$ The point Q is $(x_1, -y_1)$. Hence PQ is a double ordinate.

The vertex $A(1,0)$ corresponds to $t = 0$

$$\Delta CPQ = \frac{1}{2}(x_1 y_2 - x_2 y_1) = \frac{1}{2}(-x_1 y_1 - x_1 y_1)$$

$$= -x_1 y_1 = x_1 y_1.$$

$$\text{Area } APMQA = 2 \text{ area } APMA = 2\int_0^{t_1} y \frac{dx}{dt} dt$$

$$= 2\int_0^{t_1} \frac{1}{2}(e^t - e^{-t}) . \frac{1}{2}(e^t - e^{-t}) \, dt$$

$$= \frac{1}{2}\int_0^{t_1} (e^{2t} + e^{-2t} - 2) \, dt$$

$$= \frac{1}{2}\left[\frac{e^{2t}}{2} - \frac{e^{-2t}}{2} - 2t\right]_0^{t_1}$$

$$= \frac{1}{2}\left[\frac{e^{2t_1} - e^{-2t_1}}{2} - 2t_1\right]$$

$$= \frac{1}{2}(e^{t_1} + e^{-t_1}) \cdot \frac{1}{2}(e^{t_2} - e^{-t_1}) - t_1$$

$$= x_1 y_1 - t_1.$$

Hence the required shaded area is

$$(x_1 y_1) - (x_1 y_1 - t_1) = t_1$$

Alternative : Required area $= 2\left[\Delta - \int_1^{x_1} y \, dx\right]$ ...(1)

$$\Delta = \frac{1}{2} x_1 y_1 \quad \text{and} \quad \int_1^{x_1} y \, dx = \int_1^{x_1} \sqrt{(x^2 - 1)} \, dx$$

$$= \left[\frac{x}{2}\sqrt{x^2 - 1} - \frac{1}{2}\log\{x + \sqrt{x^2 - 1}\}\right]_1^{x_1}$$

$$= \frac{x_1}{2}\sqrt{x_1^2 - 1} - \frac{1}{2}\log\{x_1 + \sqrt{x_1^2 - 1}\} - 0$$

$$= \frac{1}{2} x_1 y_1 - \frac{1}{2}\log(x_1 + y_1) = \Delta - \frac{1}{2}\log e^{t_1}$$

$$= \Delta - \frac{1}{2} t_1$$

Putting in (1), we get

$$\text{Area} = 2\Delta - 2\Delta + 2.\frac{1}{2} t_1 = t_1$$

29. P is $(a \sec\theta, b \tan\theta)$

Tangent at P is $\frac{x \sec\theta}{a} - \frac{y \tan\theta}{b} = 1$

It meets $bx - ay = 0$, *i.e.* $\frac{x}{a} = \frac{y}{b}$ in Q.

$$\therefore \quad Q \text{ is } \left(\frac{a}{\sec\theta - \tan\theta}, \frac{b}{\sec\theta - \tan\theta}\right)$$

It meets $bx + ay = 0$, *i.e.* $\frac{x}{a} = -\frac{y}{b}$ in R.

$$\therefore \quad R \text{ is } \left(\frac{a}{\sec\theta + \tan\theta}, \frac{-b}{\sec\theta + \tan\theta}\right)$$

$$\therefore \quad CQ.CR = \frac{\sqrt{(a^2 + b^2)}}{\sec\theta - \tan\theta} \cdot \frac{\sqrt{(a^2 + b^2)}}{\sec\theta + \tan\theta}$$

$$= a^2 + b^2 \quad \because \sec^2\theta - \tan^2\theta = 1$$

Note : See also Q. 17.

Alternative : The given lines are $\frac{x}{a} = \pm\frac{y}{b}$ which are asymptotes. The equation of the hyperbola can be written as $xy = c^2$ where $c^2 = \frac{a^2 + b^2}{4}$ with reference to asymptotes as axes. If $P(x_1, y_1)$ be any point on it, then $x_1 y_1 = c^2$ and tangent is $\frac{x}{x_1} + \frac{y}{y_1} = 2$. It meets the asymptotes, *i.e.*, axes in Q and R.

$\therefore$ Q *is* $(2x_1, 0)$ and R is $(0, 2y_1)$

$$\therefore \quad CQ.CR = 2x_1 . 2y_1 = 4x_1 y_1$$

$$= 4.\frac{a^2 + b^2}{4} = a^2 + b^2$$

30. Let the circle be $(x - h)^2 + (y - k)^2 = r^2$ where r is variable. Its intersection with $x^2 - y^2 = 9a^2$ is obtained by putting $y^2 = x^2 - 9a^2$.

$$x^2 + x^2 - 9a^2 - 2hx + h^2 + k^2 - r^2 = 2k\sqrt{(x^2 - 9a^2)}$$

or $\quad [2x^2 - 2hx + (h^2 + k^2 - r^2 - 9a^2)]^2$

$$= 4k^2 (x^2 - 9a^2)$$

or $\quad 4x^4 - 8hx^3 + ... = 0$

$\therefore$ Above gives the abscissas of the four points of intersection.

$$\therefore \quad \Sigma x_1 = \frac{8h}{4} = 2h.$$

$$x_1 + x_2 + x_3 + x_4 = 2h$$

Similiarly $y_1 + y_2 + y_3 + y_4 = 2k$.

Now if (α, β) be the centroid of ΔPQR, then $3\alpha = x_1 + x_2 + x_3$, $3\beta = y_1 + y_2 + y_3$

$$\therefore \quad x_4 = 2h - 3\alpha, \; y_4 = 2k - 3\beta$$

But (x_4, y_4) lies on $x^2 - y^2 = 9a^2$

$$\therefore \quad (2h - 3\alpha)^2 + (2k - 3\beta)^2 = 9a^2$$

Hence the locus of centroid (α, β) is

$$(2h - 3x)^2 + (2k - 3y)^2 = 9a^2$$

or $\left(x-\frac{2h}{3}\right)^2+\left(y-\frac{2k}{3}\right)^2=a^2$

31. Let the hyperbola be $\frac{x^2}{a^2}-\frac{y^2}{b^2}=1$ and one of its asymptotes is $\frac{x}{a}-\frac{y}{b}=0$.

Here a is given but b is not known. Choose any point (h,k) on the hyperbola.

$$\therefore \quad \frac{h^2}{a^2}-\frac{k^2}{b^2}=1 \quad ...(1)$$

By given condition, $k=\dfrac{\frac{h}{a}-\frac{k}{b}}{\sqrt{\left(\frac{1}{a^2}+\frac{1}{b^2}\right)}}$

$$\text{or} \quad k^2\left(\frac{1}{a^2}+\frac{1}{b^2}\right)=\left(\frac{h}{a}-\frac{k}{b}\right)^2 \quad ...(2)$$

In order to find the locus of (h,k) we have to eliminate the unknown b^2. Now from (2),

$$\frac{k^2}{a^2}-\frac{h^2}{a^2}=-\frac{2hk}{ab}$$

$$(k^2-h^2)^2=\frac{4a^2h^2k^2}{b^2}$$

$$\text{or} \quad (k^2-h^2)^2=4a^2h^2\left(\frac{h^2}{a^2}-1\right), \text{by (1)}$$

$$\text{or} \quad (x^2-y^2)^2=4x^2(x^2-a^2)$$

is the required locus.

32. See similar Q. 7 (a). in Ellipse, **P. 1029-1033.**

33. See similar Q. 6. in Ellipse, **P. 1029-1032.**

34. Any point on the given hyperbola is $(3\sec\theta, 2\tan\theta)$. Its chord of contact w.r.t. circle $x^2+y^2=9$ is

$$x(3\sec\theta)+y(2\tan\theta)-9=0 \quad ...(1)$$

If (h,k) be the mid-point of the chord of the circle, then by $T=S_1$ its equation is

$$xh+yk=h^2+k^2 \quad ...(2)$$

Comparing (1) and (2), we get

$$\frac{3\sec\theta}{h}=\frac{2\tan\theta}{k}=\frac{9}{h^2+k^2}$$

$$\therefore \quad \sec\theta=\frac{9h}{3(h^2+k^2)}, \tan\theta=\frac{9k}{2(h^2+k^2)}$$

Eliminating θ by $\sec^2\theta-\tan^2\theta=1$, we have

$$\frac{81}{(h^2+k^2)^2}\left[\frac{h^2}{9}-\frac{k^2}{4}\right]=1$$

$$\therefore \quad \text{Locus of } (h,k) \text{ is} \quad 9(4x^2-9y^2)=4(x^2+y^2)^2.$$

§3. Some More Important Results

1. Equation of the hyperbola referred to asymptotes as axes :

$xy=c^2$ where $c^2=\frac{a^2+b^2}{4}$ for $\frac{x^2}{a^2}-\frac{y^2}{b^2}=1$

$c^2=\frac{a^2}{2}$ for $x^2-y^2=a^2$, *i.e.* rectangular.

2. Parametric equation of hyperbola $xy=c^2$:

$x=ct$, $y=c/t$ satisfy the equation of the hyperbola $xy=c^2$.

and the point $(ct, c/t)$ is referred as the point 't'

3. Chord joining points t_1 and t_2 on the hyperbola $xy=c^2$

Let P be $(ct_1, c/t_1)$ and Q be $(ct_2, c/t_2)$ then the chord PQ is

$$y-\frac{c}{t_1}=\frac{(c/t_2-c/t_1)}{(ct_2-ct_1)}(x-ct_1)$$

$$\text{or} \quad y-\frac{c}{t_1}=-\frac{1}{t_1t_2}(x-ct_1)$$

$$\text{or} \quad \boldsymbol{x+yt_1t_2-c(t_1+t_2)=0} \quad ...(a)$$

4. Tangent at the point t_1 to the hyperbola $xy=c^2$.

Putting $t_2=t_1$ in the equation of the chord (a) we get the equation of the tangent at the point t_1 as

$$\boldsymbol{x+yt_1^2-2ct_1=0.} \quad ...(b)$$

Another form : Multiplying (b) by c/t_1 we get

$$x(c/t_1)+y(ct_1)=2c^2$$

If we call the point t_1 *i.e.* $(ct_1, c/t_1)$ as (x_1, y_1) then it being on the hyperbola we have $x_1y_1=c^2$.

$$\therefore \quad \text{Tangent is } xy_1+yx_1=2x_1y_1$$

$$\text{or} \quad \boldsymbol{\frac{x}{x_1}+\frac{y}{y_1}=2} \quad ...(c)$$

5. Normal to the hyperbola $xy=c^2$ at the point 't_1' when the hyperbola is rectangular.

Slope of the tangent at t_1 from (b) is $-1/t_1^2$ and hence slope of the normal will be t_1^2 and as it passes through $(ct_1, c/t_1)$, its equation is

$$y-c/t_1=t_1^2(x-ct_1)$$

$$\text{or} \quad \boldsymbol{xt_1^3-yt_1-ct_1^4+c=0.} \quad ...(d)$$

Another form :

From (c), the equation of normal will be $\frac{x}{y_1}-\frac{y}{x_1}=\lambda$. It passes through (x_1, y_1)

$$\therefore \quad \lambda=\frac{x_1}{y_1}-\frac{y_1}{x_1} \quad \therefore \quad \boldsymbol{xx_1-yy_1=x_1^2-y_1^2}$$

Problem Set (3)

Hyperbola $xy = c^2$ referred to asymptotes as axes.

1. (a) If tangent and normal to a rectangular hyperbola cut off intercepts a_1 and a_2 on one axis and b_1 and b_2 on the other show that $a_1 a_2 + b_1 b_2 = 0$.

(b)* If a triangle is inscribed in a rectangular hyperbola, prove that its orthocentre lies on the curve.

(c)* Prove that the locus of the poles of the normal chords of the rectangular hyperbola $xy = c^2$ is the curve $(x^2 - y^2)^2 + 4c^2 \cdot xy = 0$.

2. (a)* Prove that the portion of the tangent to the hyperbola intercepted between the asymptotes is bisected at the point of contact and the area of the triangle formed by the tangent and the two asymptotes is constant.

(b) AB is a diameter of the rectangular hyperbola $xy = c^2$. Tangent at A intersects the line through B parallel to either asymptote in the point P. Prove that P lies on $xy + 3c^2 = 0$

3. (a)* Show that the normal to the hyperbola (reactangular) $xy = c^2$ at the point t_1 meets the curve again at the point t_2 such that $t_1^3 t_2 = -1$.

(b)* If the normal at P to the rectangular hyperbola $xy = c^2$ meets the curve again in Q, show that circle on PQ as diameter cuts the curve at the other end of the diameter through P. **(J.E.E. W.B. 1998)**

4.* If the hyperbola be rectangular and its equation be $xy = c^2$, prove that the locus of the middle points of chords of constant length $2d$ is $(x^2 + y^2)(xy - c^2) = d^2 xy$.

5.* A rectangular hyperbola whose centre is C is cut by any circle of radius r in four points P, Q, R and S. Prove that $CP^2 + CQ^2 + CR^2 + CS^2 = 4r^2$.

6.* If a circle cuts a rectangular hyperbola $xy = c^2$ in A, B, C, D and the parameters of these four points be t_1, t_2, t_3 and t_4 respectively, then prove that

(a) $t_1 t_2 t_3 t_4 = 1$

(b) The centre of mean position of the four points bisects the distance between the centres of the two curves.

7.* Prove that from any point (α, β) four normals can be drawn to the rectangular hyperbola $xy = c^2$ and that if the co-ordinates of the four feet of the normals P, Q, R, S be (x_i, y_i) $i = 1, 2, 3, 4$. Then

(a) $\alpha = x_1 + x_2 + x_3 + x_4$ and $\beta = y_1 + y_2 + y_3 + y_4$

(b) $x_1 x_2 x_3 x_4 = y_1 y_2 y_3 y_4 = -c^4$

8. (a)* A circle cuts the rectangular hyperbola $xy = 1$ in the points (x_r, y_r), $r = 1, 2, 3, 4$.
Prove that $x_1\ x_2\ x_3\ x_4 = y_1\ y_2\ y_3\ y_4 = 1$.

(b)* If the circle $x^2 + y^2 = a^2$ intersects the hyperbola $xy = c^2$ in four points $P(x_1, y_1), Q(x_2, y_2), R(x_3, y_3), S(x_4, y_4)$, then

(A) $x_1 + x_2 + x_3 + x_4 = 0$

(B) $y_1 + y_2 + y_3 + y_4 = 0$

(C) $x_1\ x_2\ x_3\ x_4 = c^4$

(D) $y_1\ y_2\ y_3\ y_4 = c^4$. **(I.I.T. 1998)**

9. If four points be taken on a rectangular hyperbola such that the chords joining any two points is perpendicular to the chord joining the other two, and if $\alpha, \beta, \gamma, \delta$ be the inclinations to either asymptote of the straight lines joining these points to the centre, prove that $\tan\alpha \tan\beta \tan\gamma \tan\delta = 1$.

10. Prove that the locus of mid-points of the focal radius vectors drawn from the right hand focus to all points of the hyperbola $x^2/9 - y^2/16 = 1$ is another hyperbola whose centre is $(2 \cdot 5, 0)$.

11. The asymptote of the hyperbola $\frac{x^2}{a^2} - \frac{y^2}{b^2} = 1$ makes an angle of 60° with x-axis. Write down the equation of diameter conjugate to the diameter $y = 2x$.

12. Find the distances from $A(4, 2)$ to the points in which the line $3x - 5y = 2$ meets the hyperbola $xy = 24$. Are these points on the same side of A?

13.* The normal at the three points P, Q, R on a rectangular hyperbola, intersect at a point S on the curve; prove that the centre of the hyperbola is the centroid of the triangle PQR.

14.* If a rectangular hyperbola circumscribes a triangle, prove that it also passes through the orthocentre of the triangle.

Or

If a triangle is inscribed in a rectangular hyperbola, prove that the orthocentre of the triangle lies on the curve.

Or

If t_4 be the parameter of the orthocentre, then prove that $t_1 t_2 t_3 t_4 = -1$ where t_1, t_2, t_3 are the parameters of the vertices of the triangle.

15.* If a circle cuts a rectangular hyperbola $xy = c^2$ in A, B, C and D and the parameters of these four points be t_1, t_2, t_3 and t_4 respectively, prove the following :

(a) $t_1 t_2 t_3 t_4 = 1$, find the value of $\Sigma \frac{1}{t_1}$.

(b) If H be the orthocentre of the triangle ABC, then H and D are extremities of a diameter of the rectangular hyperbola.

(c) The centre of mean position of the four points bisects the distance between the centres of the two curves.

(d) The centre of the circle through A, B and C is

$$\left[\frac{c}{2}\left(t_1+t_2+t_3+\frac{1}{t_1t_2t_3}\right), \frac{c}{2}\left(\frac{1}{t_1}+\frac{1}{t_2}+\frac{1}{t_3}+t_1t_2t_3\right)\right].$$

16.* A variable straight line of slope 4 intersects the hyperbola $xy=1$ at two points. Find the locus of the point which divides the line segment between these two points in the ratio $1:2$. **(I.I.T. 1997)**

Solutions to Problem Set (3)

1. (a) Let the hyperbola be $xy = c^2$.

Tangent at any point t is $x + yt^2 - 2ct = 0$.

Putting $y=0$ and then $x=0$ intercepts on the axes are

$$a_1 = 2ct \quad \text{and} \quad b_1 = 2c/t \qquad \text{...(1)}$$

Normal is $xt^3 - yt - ct^4 + c = 0$

Intercepts as above are

$$a_2 = \frac{c(t^4-1)}{t^3}, b_2 = -\frac{c(t^4-1)}{t} \qquad \text{...(2)}$$

$$\therefore \quad a_1a_2 + b_1b_2 = 2ct\,\frac{c(t^4-1)}{t^3} - \frac{2c}{t}\,c\,\frac{(t^4-1)}{t} = 0,$$

by (1) and (2).

(b) Let the parameters of the vertices A, B, C of the points on the hyperbola $xy = c^2$ be t_1, t_2, t_3 respectively. Equation of the side BC is

$x + yt_2t_3 - c(t_2+t_3) = 0$ **[§3 eq. (a), P. 1053]**

Its slope is $-1/t_2t_3$

Any line through A perpendicular to BC is

$$y - \frac{c}{t_1} = t_2t_3(x - ct_1)$$

or $\quad y - xt_2t_3 = \dfrac{c}{t_1} - ct_1t_2t_3 \qquad$ ...(1)

Similarly any line through B perpendicular to CA is

$$y - xt_3t_1 = \frac{c}{t_2} - ct_1t_2t_3 \qquad \text{...(2)}$$

Solving (3) and (2), we get the orthocentre as $\left(\dfrac{-c}{t_1t_2t_3}, -ct_1t_2t_3\right)$. This point clearly satisfies the equation $xy = c^2$ of the rectangular hyperbola.

(c) Equation of the normal is

$$xt^3 - yt = c(t^4-1) \qquad \text{...(1)}$$

If its pole be (x_1, y_1) then it should be same as the polar of (x_1, y_1) *i.e.*, $xy_1 + yx_1 = 2c^2$.

Comparing (1) and (2), we get

$$\frac{t^3}{y_1} = -\frac{t}{x_1} = \frac{t^4-1}{2c}$$

$$\therefore \quad t^2 = -\frac{y_1}{x_1}, \text{ and } \frac{t^2}{x^2} = \frac{(t^4-1)^2}{4c^2}$$

$$\therefore \quad 4c^2t^2 = (t^4-1)^2\,x_1^2$$

or $\quad 4c^2\left(-\dfrac{y_1}{x_1}\right) = \left(\dfrac{y_1^2}{x_1^2} - 1\right)^2 x_1^2$

Locus of pole (x_1, y_1) is $(x^2-y^2)^2 + 4c^2xy = 0$.

2. (a) Any tangent is $\dfrac{x}{x_1} + \dfrac{y}{y_1} = 2$.

Q is $(2x_1, 0)$, R is $(0, 2y_1)$.

Clearly mid-point of QR is (x_1, y_1) which is point of contact P.

Area of $\Delta\, CQR = \dfrac{1}{2}CQ\,.\,CR \sin 2\alpha$

$$= \frac{1}{2}(2x_1)(2y_1)\sin 2\alpha$$

where 2α is the angle between the asymptotes such that $\tan\alpha = \dfrac{b}{a}$

$$= \frac{4}{2}.c^2.\frac{2\tan\alpha}{1+\tan^2\alpha}$$

where $c^2 = \dfrac{1}{4}(a^2+b^2)$

$$= (a^2+b^2).\frac{ab}{(a^2+b^2)} = ab.$$

(b) $A\left(ct, \dfrac{c}{t}\right) \qquad \therefore \qquad B = \left(-ct, \dfrac{-c}{t}\right)$

Tangent at A, $x + yt^2 - 2ct = 0$

Line through B parrallel to asymptote say $x=0$ is $x = -ct$. Eliminate t and we get $xy + 3c^2 = 0$

3. (a) Normal at $P(ct_1, c/t_1)$ is $xt_1^3 - yt_1 - ct_1^4 + c = 0$.

If it passes through $Q(ct_2, c/t_2)$, then

$$ct_2t_1^3 - c\frac{t_1}{t_2} - ct_1^4 + c = 0$$

or $\quad (t_2t_1^3 + 1) - \dfrac{t_1}{t_2}(t_2t_1^3 + 1) = 0$

or $\quad (t_2t_1^3 + 1)\left(1 - \dfrac{t_1}{t_2}\right) = 0$

$$\therefore \quad t_1^3t_2 = -1 \text{ as } t_1 \neq t_2$$

(b) Since normal at P, t_1 passes through Q, t_2, we have as in part (a).

$$t_1^3t_2 = -1. \qquad \text{...(1)}$$

In the examination students should prove this relation. Circle on PQ as diameter is

$$(x-ct_1)(x-ct_2)+\left(y-\frac{c}{t_1}\right)\left(y-\frac{c}{t_2}\right)=0.$$

It will pass through the other end of the diameter through P, *i.e.* $(-ct_1, -c/t_1)$, if

$$(-ct_1-ct_1)(-ct_1-ct_2)+\left(-\frac{c}{t_1}-\frac{c}{t_1}\right)\left(-\frac{c}{t_1}-\frac{c}{t_2}\right)=0$$

or $\quad 2t_1(t_1+t_2)+\frac{2}{t_1}\left(\frac{t_1+t_2}{t_1t_2}\right)=0$

or $\quad t_1+\frac{1}{t_1^2t_2}=0$ or $t_1^3t_2=-1$

which is true by (1).

t_1+t_2 cannot be zero as in that case $t_2=-t_1$, *i.e.* Q becomes the extremity of the diameter through P whereas PQ is a normal at P.

4. If (h, k) be the middle point of the chord of length $2d$ inclined at an angle θ to the x-axis, then its extremities are $(h+d\cos\theta, k+d\sin\theta)$ and $(h-d\cos\theta, k-d\sin\theta)$

These extremities lie on the hyperbola $xy=c^2$

$\therefore \quad (h+d\cos\theta)(k+d\sin\theta)=c^2$ ...(1)

$(h-d\cos\theta)(k-d\sin\theta)=c^2$ ...(2)

Adding and subtracting (1) and (2), we get

$hk+d^2\sin\theta\cos\theta=c^2$ ...(3)

and $h\sin\theta+k\cos\theta=0$

$\therefore \quad \tan\theta=-\frac{k}{h}.$ ...(4)

Dividing (3) by $\cos^2\theta$ and putting

$\sec^2\theta=1+\tan^2\theta$, we get

$(hk-c^2)(1+\tan^2\theta)+d^2\tan\theta=0.$

Putting for $\tan\theta$ from (4), we get

$$(hk-c^2)\left(\frac{h^2+k^2}{h^2}\right)-d^2\cdot\frac{k}{h}=0$$

Generalising the locus of (h, k) is

$(xy-c^2)(x^2+y^2)=d^2xy$

5. Taking the rectangular asymptotes as the axes of reference the equation of the hyperbola and the circle are

$xy=k^2$ ...(1)

and $x^2+y^2+2gx+2fy+c=0$ ...(2)

where $g^2+f^2-c=r^2$ (given) ...(3)

Eliminating y between (1) and (2), we get a biquadratic in x giving us the abscissas of the four points of intersection as

$x^4+2gx^3+cx^2+2fk^2x+k^4=0$

Its roots are x_1, x_2, x_3 and x_4 then

$\Sigma x_1=-2g, \Sigma x_1x_2=c$

$\therefore \quad x_1^2+x_2^2+x_3^2+x_4^2=(\Sigma x_1)^2-2\Sigma x_1x_2=4g^2-2c$

Similarly $y_1^2+y_2^2+y_3^2+y_4^2=4f^2-2c$

$\therefore \quad CP^2+CQ^2+CR^2+CS^2$

$=(x_1^2+y_1^2)+(\quad)+(\quad)+(\quad)$

$=\Sigma x_1^2+\Sigma y_1^2=4g^2-2c+4f^2-2c$

$=4(g^2+f^2-c)=4r^2$

6. (a) Let the equation of the hyperbola referred to rectangular asymptotes as axes be $xy=c^2$ or its parametric equation be

$x=ct, y=c/t$ ...(1)

and that of the circle be

$x^2+y^2+2gx+2fy+k=0$ ...(2)

Solving (1) and (2), we get

$$c^2t^2+\frac{c^2}{t^2}+2gct+2f\frac{c}{t}+k=0$$

or $\quad c^2t^4+2gct^3+kt^2+2fct+c^2=0$ ...(3)

Above equation being of fourth degree in t gives us the four parameters t_1, t_2, t_3, t_4 of the points of intersection.

$\therefore \quad t_1+t_2+t_3+t_4=-\frac{2gc}{c^2}=-\frac{2g}{c}$ ...(4)

$t_1t_2t_3+t_1t_2t_4+t_3t_4t_1+t_3t_4t_2$

$=-\frac{2fc}{c^2}=-\frac{2f}{c}$ ...(5)

$t_1t_2t_3t_4=\frac{c^2}{c^2}=1.$ It proves (a). ...(6)

Dividing (5) by (6), we get

$\frac{1}{t_1}+\frac{1}{t_2}+\frac{1}{t_3}+\frac{1}{t_4}=-\frac{2f}{c}$ ...(7)

(b) The centre of mean position of the four points of intersection is

$$\left[\frac{c}{4}(t_1+t_2+t_3+t_4), \frac{c}{4}\left(\frac{1}{t_1}+\frac{1}{t_2}+\frac{1}{t_3}+\frac{1}{t_4}\right)\right]$$

$$=\left[\frac{c}{4}\left(-\frac{2g}{c}\right), \frac{c}{4}\left(-\frac{2f}{c}\right)\right], \text{ by (4) and (7)}$$

$=(-g/2, -f/2)$

Above is clearly the mid-point of (0, 0) and $(-g, -f)$ *i.e.* the join of the centres of the two curves.

7. Equation of the normal to the hyperbola $xy=c^2$ at any point whose parameter is t is

$xt^3-yt-ct^4+c=0$ ...(1)

If it passes through (α, β), then

$ct^4-\alpha t^3+0t^2+\beta t-c=0$ ...(2)

Above equation being of fourth degree in t, gives us four values of t showing that there will be four points the normals at all of which will pass through (α, β). Hence the proposition.

(a) If t_1, t_2, t_3 and t_4 be the four values of t, then these are the roots of (2)

$\therefore \quad t_1 + t_2 + t_3 + t_4 = \dfrac{\alpha}{c}$ ...(3)

or $\quad ct_1 + ct_2 + ct_3 + ct_4 = \alpha$

or $\quad x_1 + x_2 + x_3 + x_4 = \alpha$

Also $\quad t_1\, t_2\, t_3\, t_4 = -\dfrac{c}{c} = -1$ ...(4)

and $t_1\, t_2\, t_3 + t_1\, t_2\, t_4 + t_3\, t_4\, t_1 + t_3\, t_4\, t_2 = -\beta/c$ ....(5)

or $\quad c\left[\dfrac{1}{t_1} + \dfrac{1}{t_2} + \dfrac{1}{t_3} + \dfrac{1}{t_4}\right] = \beta$,

on dividing (5) by (4)

or $\quad y_1 + y_2 + y_3 + y_4 = \beta$.

(b) Again $x_1 x_2 x_3 x_4 = c^4\, t_1 t_2 t_3 t_4 = -c^4$, from (4)

or $\quad y_1\, y_2\, y_3\, y_4 = \dfrac{c^4}{t_1\, t_2\, t_3\, t_4} = -c^4$, from (4).

8. (a) $x^2 + y^2 + 2gx + 2fy + c = 0$ cuts $xy = 1$

Eliminating y, we get

$$x^2 + \frac{1}{x^2} + 2gx + \frac{2f}{x} + c = 0$$

or $\quad x^4 + 2gx^3 + cx^2 + 2fx + 1 = 0$

$\therefore \quad x_1 x_2 x_3 x_4 = 1$,

$\quad y_1 y_2 y_3 y_4 = \dfrac{1}{x_1 x_2 x_3 x_4} = 1$

(b) Ans. (A), (B), (C), (D).

9. Let the parameters of four points be t_1, t_2, t_3, t_4

Slopes of chords are $-\dfrac{1}{t_1 t_2}$ and $-\dfrac{1}{t_3 t_4}$

Since they are perpendicular

$\therefore \quad t_1 t_2 t_3 t_4 = -1$ ...(1)

Now if P be $(ct_1, c/t_1)$, then inclination of CP to asymptote say $y = 0$ *i.e.* x-axis is α.

$\therefore \quad \tan\alpha = \text{slope of } CP = c/t_1 \div ct_1 = \dfrac{1}{t_1^2}$

$\therefore \quad \tan\alpha \tan\beta \tan\gamma \tan\delta = \dfrac{1}{t_1^2 t_2^2 t_3^2 t_4^2} = 1$, by (1)

10. $e = 5/3$, Foci are $(\pm 5, 0)$. Right hand focus is $(5, 0)$.

Let P be $(3\sec\theta, 4\tan\theta)$ and S is $(5, 0)$

If (h, k) be the mid-point of focal radius, then

$$2h = 3\sec\theta + 5, \quad 2k = 4\tan\theta$$

Now $\quad \sec^2\theta - \tan^2\theta = 1$

$\therefore \quad \left(\dfrac{2h-5}{3}\right)^2 - \left(\dfrac{k}{2}\right)^2 = 1$ or $\dfrac{4}{9}\left(x - \dfrac{5}{2}\right)^2 - \dfrac{1}{4}y^2 = 1$

Above is a hyperbola with centre at $(2\cdot 5, 0)$.

11. Slope of $\dfrac{x}{a} - \dfrac{y}{b} = 1$ is $\dfrac{b}{a} = \tan 60^o = \sqrt{3}$

Also slope of one diameter is $m_1 = 2$.

Two diameters are conjugate if $m_1 m_2 = b^2/a^2$

$\therefore \quad 2m_2 = 3 \quad \therefore \quad m_2 = 3/2$.

Hence the other diameter is $y = \dfrac{3}{2}x$ or $2y - 3x = 0$

12. The point $A(4, 2)$ lies on $3x - 5y - 2 = 0$

It meets the hyperbola in $B\left(\dfrac{20}{3}, \dfrac{18}{5}\right)$ and $C(-6, -4)$.

If we put these points in the line the results are of opposite signs and hence the points are on opposite sides of line and hence on opposite sides of point A which lies on the line. It is easy to find that $AB = \dfrac{8}{15}\sqrt{34}$ and $AC = 2\sqrt{34}$.

13. Let t be the parameter of any of the points P, Q, R so that normal is

$$xt^3 - yt - ct^4 + c = 0. \quad ...(1)$$

It passes through a point S on the curve say $(ct', c/t')$, then as in **Q. 3, P. 1053-1055**, we have

$$t^3 t' + 1 = 0 \quad ...(2)$$

Above being a cubic in t gives us the parameters of the three points P, Q, R say t_1, t_2, t_3.

$\therefore \quad t_1 + t_2 + t_3 = 0; \quad \because$ Coeff. of $t^2 = 0$ ...(3)

$\quad \dfrac{1}{t_1} + \dfrac{1}{t_2} + \dfrac{1}{t_3} = \dfrac{\Sigma\, t_1 t_2}{t_1 t_2 t_3} = 0$;

$\because \quad$ Coeff. of $t = 0$ ...(4)

If (h, k) be the centroid of $\Delta\, PQR$, then

$$h = \frac{\Sigma\, x_1}{3} = \frac{c}{3}(t_1 + t_2 + t_3) = 0, \text{ by (3)}$$

$$k = \frac{\Sigma\, y_1}{3} = \frac{c}{3}\left(\frac{1}{t_1} + \frac{1}{t_2} + \frac{1}{t_3}\right) = 0, \text{ by (4)}$$

Hence centroid (h, k) is $(0, 0)$ which is centre of hyperbola.

14. Let the parameters of the vertices A, B and C of the triangle ABC be t_1, t_2 and t_3 respectively.

Equation of BC is $x + yt_2 t_3 = c(t_2 + t_3)$

Its slope is $-1/t_2 t_3$.

The equation of the line through A and perpendicular to BC is $(y - c/t_1) = t_2 t_3\,(x - ct_1)$

or $\quad y + ct_1 t_2 t_3 = t_2 t_3\left(x + \dfrac{c}{t_1 t_2 t_3}\right)$. ...(1)

Similarly, the equation of the line through B and perpendicular to CA is

$$y + ct_1 t_2 t_3 = t_3 t_1\left(x + \frac{c}{t_1 t_2 t_3}\right). \quad ...(2)$$

Orthocentre is the point of intersection of (1) and (2).

Subtracting (1) and (2), we get

$$0 = t_3 x(t_2 - t_1) + \frac{ct_3}{t_1 t_2 t_3}(t_2 - t_1)$$

or $x = -\frac{c}{t_1 t_2 t_3}$ and hence $y = -ct_1 t_2 t_3$

$\therefore$ orthocentre is $\left(\frac{-c}{t_1 t_2 t_3}, -ct_1 t_2 t_3\right)$ ...(3)

This point clearly lies on the hyperbola $xy = c^2$ and if its parameter be t_4 *i.e.*, it is $\left(ct_4, \frac{c}{t_4}\right)$, then comparing with (3), we get $\frac{-1}{t_1 t_2 t_3} = t_4$

or $t_1 t_2 t_3 t_4 = -1$.

15. (a) Let the equation of the rectangular hyperbola referred to rectangular asymptotes as axes be $xy = c^2$ or its parametric equations be $x = ct$ and $y = \frac{c}{t}$ ...(1)

and that of the circle be

$$x^2 + y^2 + 2gx + 2fy + k = 0. \quad ...(2)$$

Solving (1) and (2), we get

$$c^2 t^2 + \frac{c^2}{t^2} + 2gct + 2f.\frac{c}{t} + k = 0$$

or $c^2 t^4 + 2gct^3 + kt^2 + 2fct + c^2 = 0.$ ...(3)

Above equation being of fourth degree in t gives us the four parameters t_1, t_2, t_3 and t_4 of the points of intersection.

$\therefore$ $t_1 + t_2 + t_3 + t_4 = -\frac{2gc}{c^2} = -\frac{2g}{c}$. ...(4)

$t_1 t_2 t_3 + t_1 t_2 t_4 + t_3 t_4 t_1 + t_3 t_4 t_2 = -\frac{2fc}{c^2} = -\frac{2f}{c}$ ...(5)

$t_1 t_2 t_3 t_4 = \frac{c^2}{c^2} = 1$, which proves (a). ...(6)

Dividing (5) by (6), we get

$\frac{1}{t_4} + \frac{1}{t_3} + \frac{1}{t_2} + \frac{1}{t_1} = -\frac{2f}{c}$. ...(7)

(b) Orthocentre of the triangle ABC is $\left(\frac{-c}{t_1 t_2 t_3}, -ct_1 t_2 t_3\right)$ from result (3) Q.14.

or H is the point $\left(-ct_4, \frac{-c}{t_4}\right)$,

$\because$ $t_1 t_2 t_3 t_4 = 1$, by (6)

and D is the point $\left(ct_4, \frac{c}{t_4}\right)$ and clearly H and D are extremities of a diameter.

(c) The centre of mean position of the four points is

$$\left[\frac{c}{4}(t_1 + t_2 + t_3 + t_4), \frac{c}{4}\left(\frac{1}{t_1} + \frac{1}{t_2} + \frac{1}{t_3} + \frac{1}{t_4}\right)\right]$$

$$= \left[\frac{c}{4}\left(\frac{-2g}{c}\right), \frac{c}{4}\left(\frac{-2f}{c}\right)\right], \quad \text{from (4) and (7)}$$

or $\left(\frac{-g}{2}, \frac{-f}{2}\right)$ which is clearly the mid-point of $(0, 0)$ and $(-g, -f)$ *i.e.*, of the join of the centres of the two curves.

(d) Let the circle through ABC meet the hyperbola in fourth point D; then from (4) and (7), the centre $(-g, -f)$ is

$$\left[\frac{c}{2}(t_1 + t_2 + t_3 + t_4), \frac{c}{2}\left(\frac{1}{t_1} + \frac{1}{t_2} + \frac{1}{t_3} + \frac{1}{t_4}\right)\right] \quad ...(8)$$

Also $t_1 t_2 t_3 t_4 = 1$, from (6)

$\therefore$ $t_4 = \frac{1}{t_1 t_2 t_3}$ ...(9)

Putting the value of t_4 in (8), we get the required centre in terms of the parameters of the given points A, B, C in the form as given.

16. Let the line be $y = 4x + c$ (c variable)

Its intersection with $xy = 1$ is given by

$x(4x + c) = 1$

or $4x^2 + cx - 1 = 0$ ...(1)

or $y(y - c) = 4$

or $y^2 - cy - 4 = 0$ ...(2)

Above gives the abscissas of points of intersection P and Q say x_1, x_2. If (h, k) divides PQ in the ratio 1 : 2 then

$$h = \frac{x_2 + 2x_1}{3}, k = \frac{y_2 + 2y_1}{3}$$

Now from (1) and (2),

$$x_1 = \frac{-c + \sqrt{c^2 + 16}}{8}, x_2 = \frac{-c - \sqrt{c^2 + 16}}{8}$$

and $y_1 = \frac{c + \sqrt{c^2 + 16}}{2}, y_2 = \frac{c - \sqrt{c^2 + 16}}{2}$

$\therefore$ $3h = x_2 + 2x_1 = x_2 + x_1 + x_1$

$3k = y_2 + 2y_1 = y_2 + y_1 + y_1$

$3h = -\frac{2c}{8} + \frac{-c + \sqrt{c^2 + 16}}{8}$

or $24h = -3c + \sqrt{c^2 + 16}$ ...(3)

$3k = \frac{2c}{2} + \frac{c + \sqrt{c^2 + 16}}{2}$

or $6k = 3c + \sqrt{c^2 + 16}$ ...(4)

We have to eliminate the variable c

$\therefore$ Subtracting (4) from (3),

$24h - 6k = -6c$ or $c = k - 4h$

Putting the value of c in (4), we get

$6k - 3(k - 4h) = \sqrt{c^2 + 16}$

or $(3k + 12h)^2 = c^2 + 16 = (k - 4h)^2 + 16$

or $16h^2 + k^2 + 10hk - 2 = 0$

$\therefore$ Locus of (h, k) is $16x^2 + y^2 + 10xy - 2 = 0$.

Problem Set (4)

Multiple Choice Questions

1. The line $y+2x=1$ is tangent to the hyperbola $\frac{x^2}{a^2}-\frac{y^2}{b^2}=1$. If this line passes through the point of intersection of the nearest directrix and x-axis, then the eccentricity of the hyperbola is

(a) $\frac{3}{2}$ (b) 2 (c) $\frac{5}{2}$ (d) 3

(IIT-JEE 2010)

2. Tangents are drawn to the hyperbola $\frac{x^2}{9}-\frac{y^2}{4}=1$ parallel to the straight line $2x-y=1$. The points of contact of the tangent on the hyperbola are

(a) $\left(\frac{a}{2\sqrt{2}},\frac{1}{\sqrt{2}}\right)$ (b) $\left(-\frac{9}{2\sqrt{2}},-\frac{1}{\sqrt{2}}\right)$

(c) $(3\sqrt{3},-2\sqrt{2})$ (d) $(-3\sqrt{3},2\sqrt{2})$

(IIT-JEE 2012)

3. Let the eccentricity of the hyperbola $\frac{x^2}{a^2}-\frac{y^2}{b^2}=1$ be reciprocal to that of the ellipse $x^2+4y^2=4$. If the hyperbola passes through a focus of the ellipse then

(a) the equation of the hyperbola is $\frac{x^2}{3}-\frac{y^2}{2}=2$

(b) a focus of the hyperbola is (2, 0)

(c) the eccentricity of the hyperbola is $\sqrt{\frac{5}{3}}$

(d) the equation of the hyperbola is $x^2-3y^2=3$

(IIT-JEE 2011)

4. Let $P(6,3)$ be a point on the hyperbola $\frac{x^2}{a^2}-\frac{y^2}{b^2}=1$. If the normal at the point P intersect the x-axis at $(9,0)$ then the eccentricity of the hyperbola is

(a) $\sqrt{\frac{5}{2}}$ (b) $\sqrt{\frac{3}{2}}$ (c) $\sqrt{2}$ (d) $\sqrt{3}$

(IIT JEE 2011)

Solution to the Problem set (4)

1. Ans. (b).

$y=-2x+1$ passes through $\left(\frac{a}{e},0\right)$ so, $\frac{a}{e}=\frac{1}{2}e$

$y=-2x+1$ touches the hyperbola $\frac{x^2}{a^2}-\frac{y^2}{b^2}=1$

$\Rightarrow\ 1=4a^2-b^2=4a^2-a^2(1-e^2)$

$\Rightarrow\ 1=\frac{e^2}{4}(\sqrt{-e^2})\Rightarrow e^4-5e^2+4=0$

$\Rightarrow\ e^2=4, \quad \Rightarrow\ c=2 \qquad (\because e^2\neq 1)$

2. Ans. (a) and (b).

Slope of tangent = 2

Equation of tangents $y=2\pm\sqrt{9\times 4-4}$

$\Rightarrow\ y=2x\pm\sqrt{32} \quad \Rightarrow\ 2x-y\pm 4\sqrt{2}=0 \qquad \ldots(1)$

If point of contact is (x_1,y_1), then (1) will be identical to the equation

$$\frac{xx_1}{9}-\frac{yy_1}{4}=1$$

$\Rightarrow\ \frac{x_1/9}{2}=\frac{y_1/4}{1}=\frac{-1}{\pm 4\sqrt{2}}$

$\therefore\ (x_1,y_1)=\left(\frac{-9}{2\sqrt{2}},\frac{-1}{\sqrt{2}}\right)$ and $\left(\frac{9}{2\sqrt{2}},\frac{1}{\sqrt{2}}\right)$

3. Ans. (b), (d).

Given ellipse is $\frac{x^2}{4}+\frac{y^2}{1}=1\Rightarrow a^2=4, b^2=1$

$\therefore\ e=\sqrt{1-\frac{b^2}{a^2}}=\sqrt{1-\frac{1}{4}}=\frac{\sqrt{3}}{2}=$ eccentricity of the hyperbola

Now, foci of an ellipse $=(\pm ae,0)=(\pm\sqrt{3},0)$

$\frac{x^2}{a^2}-\frac{y^2}{b^2}=1$ passes through $(\pm\sqrt{3},0)$

$\Rightarrow\ a^2=3 \quad \Rightarrow\ b^2-a^2(e^2-1)=1$

$\Rightarrow$ Equation of the hyperbola is $\frac{x^2}{3}-\frac{y^2}{1}=1$

$\Rightarrow\ x^2-3y^2=3$

$\therefore$ Focus of the hyperbola $=(\pm ae,0)\equiv(\pm 2,0)$

4. Ans. (b).

Equation of normal $\frac{a^2x}{x_1}+\frac{b^2y}{y_1}=a^2+b^2$

$\Rightarrow\ \frac{a^2x}{6}+\frac{b^2y}{3}=a^2+b^2$

It passes through the point (9, 0) so, $\frac{9a^2}{6}+0=a^2+b^2$

$\Rightarrow\ \frac{b^2}{a^2}=\frac{1}{2}$

$\therefore$ eccentricity of the hyperbola is

$e^2=1+\frac{b^2}{a^2}=1+\frac{1}{2}=\frac{3}{2} \quad \Rightarrow\ e=\sqrt{\frac{3}{2}}$

MISCELLANEOUS EXERCISE

Matching Entries

Match the entries of List-A and List-B.

1. **List-A** | **List-B**

(a) If e and e' be the eccentricities of a hyperbola and its conjugate, then $\frac{1}{e^2}+\frac{1}{e'^2}=$ | 1. $y^2+b^2=c^2(x^2-a^2)$

(b) The vertices of the hyperbola $9x^2-16y^2-36x+96y-252=0$ are | 2. 0

(c) Locus of the point of intersection of two tangents to the hyperbola $\frac{x^2}{a^2}-\frac{y^2}{b^2}=1$ product of whose slopes is c^2 is | 3. 1

(d) If the tangent and normal to a rectangular hyperbola cut off intercepts a_1, a_2 on one axis and b_1, b_2 on the other axis, then $a_1a_2+b_1b_2=$ | 4. (6, 3), (– 2, 3)

Answers

1. a → 3, b → 4, c → 1, d → 2

Hints/Solutions

1. (a) **Q. 8 (a) P. 1040**

(b) The equation can be rewritten as

$$9(x^2-4x+4-4)-16(y^2-6y+9-9)=252$$

$$9(x-2)^2-16(y-3)^2=252+36-144=144$$

or $\frac{(x-2)^2}{16}-\frac{(y-3)^2}{9}=1$

or $\frac{X^2}{A^2}-\frac{Y^2}{B^2}=1$

∴ vertices are $X=\pm A, Y=0$

or $(x-2)=\pm 4, y-3=0$

or $x=6,-2$ and $y=3$

∴ vertices are (6, 3), (– 2, 3)

(c) Any tangent to the hyperbola is $y=mx+\sqrt{a^2m^2-b^2}$, if it passes through the point (h,k), then $(k-mh)^2=a^2m^2-b^2$

or $m^2(h^2-a^2)-2mhk+(k^2+b^2)=0$

$$m_1m_2=\frac{k^2+b^2}{h^2-a^2}=c^2 \text{ (given)}$$

∴ Locus of (h,k) is

$$y^2+b^2=c^2(x^2-a^2) \Rightarrow \text{(d)}.$$

(d) **Q. 1 (a) P. 1054**

Fascinating Facts

- We can see that $\frac{x^2}{a^2}-\frac{y^2}{b^2}=1$ where $b^2=a^2(e^2-1)$ is also the equation of the hyperbola with focus $(-ae,0)$ directrix $x+\frac{a}{e}=0$ and eccentricity e. Therefore, a hyperbole has atleast two focus directrix pairs.
- If P be any point on the hyperbola with foci F_1 and F_2 then $|PF_1|-|PF_2|=\pm 2a$ and conversly if F_1, F_2 be two distinct points and a be a constant such that $0<a<\frac{1}{2}|F_1F_2|$ then the locus of the points P so that $|PF_1|-|PF_2|=\pm 2a$ is a hyperbola with foci F_1 & F_2.
- If F_1, F_2 are fixed points and P is a variable point such that $||PF_1|-|PF_2||=$ constant say k then locus of P is
  (i) the empty set if $k>|F_1F_2|$
  (ii) the set of all points in the line F_1F_2 except those which lie between F_1 and F_2 if $k=|F_1F_2|$
- The distance of any point on the hyperbola from the two foci are called focal distance of point.

❑

CHAPTER **23**

Co-ordinate Geometry of Three Dimensions

§1. Point in Space :

1. Distance between two given points is
$$[(x_2 - x_1)^2 + (y_2 - y_1)^2 + (z_2 - z_1)^2]^{1/2}$$

2. Division of the join of two points
$$x = \frac{m_1 x_2 + m_2 x_1}{m_1 + m_2},\ y = \frac{m_1 y_2 + m_2 y_1}{m_1 + m_2},$$
$$z = \frac{m_1 z_2 + m_2 z_1}{m_1 + m_2}$$

3. General co-ordinates of a point on a line joining two given points
$$\left(\frac{x_1 + \lambda x_2}{\lambda + 1}, \frac{y_1 + \lambda y_2}{\lambda + 1}, \frac{z_1 + \lambda z_2}{\lambda + 1}\right)$$

Mid-point of a line $\left(\frac{S_1}{2}, \frac{S_2}{2}, \frac{S_3}{2}\right)$

Centroid of a triangle $\left(\frac{S_1}{3}, \frac{S_2}{3}, \frac{S_3}{3}\right)$

Centroid of a tetrahedron $\left(\frac{S_1}{4}, \frac{S_2}{4}, \frac{S_3}{4}\right)$

Co-ordinates of points on axes and co-ordinate planes are indicated in the adjoining figure.

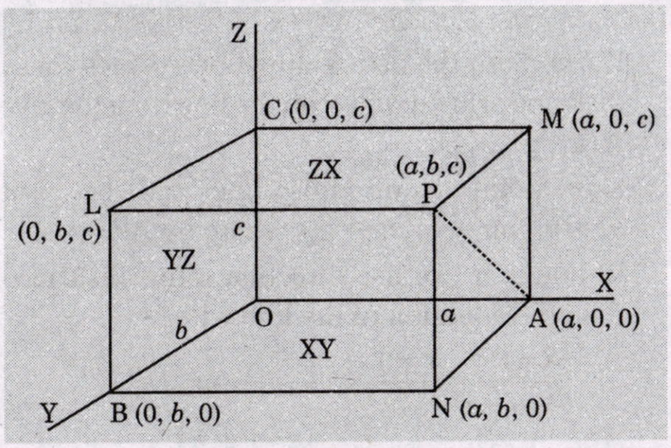

Fig. 1

Any point on x-axis will have both y and z zero and any point in yz-plane will have its x as zero.

Also $\quad PA = \sqrt{(y^2 + z^2)}$

$\quad = $ distance of P from x-axis.

§2. Direction-Cosines and Projections :

1. If a line makes angles α, β, γ with co-ordinate axes then $\cos\alpha, \cos\beta, \cos\gamma$ or l, m, n are called direction cosines of the given line and are denoted by l, m, n.
D.C.'s of axes are 1, 0, 0; 0, 1, 0; 0, 0, 1

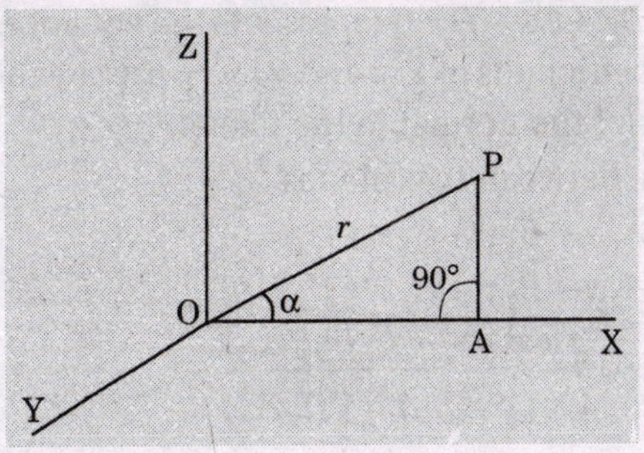

Fig. 2

2. If OP be a line with direction cosines l, m, n and $OP = r$ then the co-ordinates of point P are (lr, mr, nr).

3. If l, m, n be the direction-cosines of a line, then
$$l^2 + m^2 + n^2 = 1$$

4. If a, b, c be the direction-ratios, then the direction-cosines are
$$\left\{\frac{a}{\sqrt{(\Sigma a^2)}}, \frac{b}{\sqrt{(\Sigma a^2)}}, \frac{c}{\sqrt{(\Sigma a^2)}}\right\}$$

5. Direction-ratios of a line joining two given points are
$$x_2 - x_1, y_2 - y_1, z_2 - z_1$$

6. Projection of line joining two given points on another line whose direction-cosines are given is
$$(x_2 - x_1)\, l + (y_2 - y_1)\, m + (z_2 - z_1)\, n$$

7. Angle between two given lines is given by
$$\cos\theta = l_1 l_2 + m_1 m_2 + n_1 n_2$$
$$= \frac{\Sigma a_1 a_2}{(\Sigma a_1^2 . \Sigma a_2^2)^{1/2}}$$
$$\sin\theta = [(l_1 m_2 - l_2 m_1)^2 + (m_1 n_2 - m_2 n_1)^2 + (n_1 l_2 - n_2 l_1)^2]^{1/2}$$

8. Lagrange's identity :

$$(l_1^2 + m_1^2 + n_1^2)(l_2^2 + m_2^2 + n_2^2) - (l_1 l_2 + m_1 m_2 + n_1 n_2)^2$$
$$= (l_1 m_2 - l_2 m_1)^2 + (m_1 n_2 - m_2 n_1)^2 + (n_1 l_2 - n_2 l_1)^2$$
$$= \begin{vmatrix} l_1 & m_1 \\ l_2 & m_2 \end{vmatrix}^2 + \begin{vmatrix} m_1 & n_1 \\ m_2 & n_2 \end{vmatrix}^2 + \begin{vmatrix} n_1 & l_1 \\ n_2 & l_2 \end{vmatrix}^2$$

9. Conditions for two lines to be (a) Perpendicular (b) Parallel.

(a) $l_1 l_2 + m_1 m_2 + n_1 n_2 = 0$

or $a_1 a_2 + b_1 b_2 + c_1 c_2 = 0$

(b) $l_1 = l_2, m_1 = m_2, n_1 = n_2$ D.C. equal

or $\frac{a_1}{a_2} = \frac{b_1}{b_2} = \frac{c_1}{c_2}$ D.R. proportional

§3. The Plane :

1. Every equation of first degree of the form $Ax + By + Cz + D = 0$ represents the equation of a plane the coefficients of x, y and z *i.e.* A, B, C are the direction ratios of the normal to the plane.

2. Angle between two planes

$$A_1 x + B_1 y + C_1 z + D_1 = 0,$$
$$A_2 x + B_2 y + C_2 z + D_2 = 0$$

is $\cos\theta = \dfrac{A_1 A_2 + B_1 B_2 + C_1 C_2}{\sqrt{(\Sigma A_1^2)}\sqrt{(\Sigma A_2^2)}}$

3. The above planes are parallel or perpendicular according as their normals are parallel or perpendicular

i.e. $\frac{A_1}{A_2} = \frac{B_1}{B_2} = \frac{C_1}{C_2}$ **Parallel**

or $A_1 A_2 + B_1 B_2 + C_1 C_2 = 0$ **Perpendicular**

4. Equation of a plane through the intersection of two planes $P = 0, Q = 0$ is $P + \lambda Q = 0$ and through a given point is $A(x - x_1) + B(y - y_1) + C(z - z_1) = 0$

5. Equation of planes in particular cases :

Equation of co-ordinate planes

yoz, zox and *xoy* are $x = 0, y = 0, z = 0$ respectively and of planes parallel to co-ordinate planes, are $x = \lambda, y = \mu, z = \nu$ respectively. The direction ratios of normal to the planes are 1, 0, 0; 0, 1, 0; 0, 0, 1 *i.e.*, coefficents of x, y and z in their equations.

Planes parallel to co-ordinate planes are perpendicular to co-ordinate axes.

6. **Perpendicular to co-ordinate planes** $x = 0, y = 0, z = 0$ or parallel to axes are $by + cz + d = 0$ (x missing), $ax + cz + d = 0$ (y missing), $ax + by + d = 0$ (z missing). $ax + by + cz + d = 0$ is perpendicular to co-ordinate plane $x = 0$ if their normals a, b, c and $1, 0, 0$ are perpendicular.

$\therefore$ $a.1 + b.0 + c.0 = 0$

$\therefore$ $a = 0$ and hence its equation is $by + cz + d = 0$ (**the terms of x missing**)

7. **Intercepts form** of the equation of a plane

$$\frac{x}{a} + \frac{y}{b} + \frac{z}{c} = 1$$

Normal form of the equation of a plane

$$lx + my + nz = p$$

where l, m, n are the d.c.'s of the normal to the plane.

Plane parallel to a given plane

$ax + by + cz + d = 0$ is $ax + by + cz + d' = 0$ Constant term is changed only.

Angle between a line and a plane.

$$\frac{x - x_1}{l} = \frac{y - y_1}{m} = \frac{z - z_1}{n}, \; ax + by + cz + d = 0$$

It is complement of the angle between the line and normal to the plane. If l, m, n be d.r.'s of line and a, b, c be d.r.'s of normal and θ be the angle between the line and plane, then

$$\cos(90° - \theta) = \frac{al + bm + cn}{\sqrt{(\Sigma a^2)}\sqrt{(\Sigma l^2)}}$$

8. Distance of a point (x', y', z') from

$$Ax + By + Cz + D = 0$$

is $\dfrac{Ax' + By' + Cz' + D}{\sqrt{(A^2 + B^2 + C^2)}}$

9. Equations of planes bisecting angles between two given planes are

$$\frac{a_1 x + b_1 y + c_1 z + d_1}{\sqrt{(a_1^2 + b_1^2 + c_1^2)}} = \pm \frac{a_2 x + b_2 y + c_2 z + d_2}{\sqrt{(a_2^2 + b_2^2 + c_2^2)}}$$

10. If A_x, A_y, A_z be the projections of an area A on the co-ordinate planes, then $A^2 = A_x^2 + A_y^2 + A_z^2$.

§ 4. The Straight Line :

1. **Equation of a line passing through a given point**

$$\frac{x - x_1}{l} = \frac{y - y_1}{m} = \frac{z - z_1}{n} = r \text{ say.}$$

If l, m, n are the actual direction cosines then r is the distance of any point P on the line from the given point $A(x_1, y_1, z_1)$.

Any point P on this line can be written as $(lr + x_1, mr + y_1, nr + z_1)$ where $r = AP$.

If, however, we use direction ratios instead of d.c.'s, then the equation of the line will be

$$\frac{x - x_1}{a} = \frac{y - y_1}{b} = \frac{z - z_1}{c} = r$$

Here $r \neq AP$ as $a^2 + b^2 + c^2 \neq 1$.

Line parallel to plane $ax + by + cz + d = 0$

In this case it will be perpendicular to normal

$\therefore$ $al + bm + cn = 0$

Line perpendicular to a plane

In this case it will be parallel to the normal

$\therefore$ $\frac{a}{l} = \frac{b}{m} = \frac{c}{n}$

Line to lie in the plane

In this case, the normal to the plane will be perpendicular to the line

$\therefore \quad al + bm + cn = 0$

Also the point (x_1, y_1, z_1) through which the line passes will also lie on the plane.

$\therefore \quad ax_1 + by_1 + cz_1 + d = 0$

2. **Line through two given points is**

$$\frac{x - x_1}{x_2 - x_1} = \frac{y - y_1}{y_2 - y_1} = \frac{z - z_1}{z_2 - z_1}$$

Line of intersection of two planes.

$$P \equiv a_1 x + b_1 y + c_1 z + d_1 = 0,$$
$$Q \equiv a_2 x + b_2 y + c_2 z + d_2 = 0.$$

D.R.'s of line l, m, n are given by

$$a_1 l + b_1 m + c_1 n = 0,$$
$$a_2 l + b_2 m + c_2 n = 0$$

and any point on it is obtained by putting $z = 0$ and solving for x and y.

Just as in two dimension geometry the two lines $P = 0$ and $Q = 0$ taken together represent a point (*i.e.*, point of intersection of the two lines) and any line through their point of intersection is given by $P + \lambda Q = 0$. Similarly in 3D geometry two planes $P = 0$ and $Q = 0$ taken together represent a line (*i.e.*, line of intersection of the two planes)

$\therefore$ x-axis is intersection of co-ordinate planes $y = 0,\ z = 0$

$y =$ axis is intersection of co-ordinate planes $z = 0,\ x = 0$

z-axis is intersection of co-ordinate planes $x = 0,\ y = 0$

Similarly any plane through the line of intersection of two planes $P = 0$ and $Q = 0$ is given by $P + \lambda Q = 0$.

3. **Square of perpendicular distance of a given point (x_1, y_1, z_1)**

from the line $\dfrac{x - \alpha}{l} = \dfrac{y - \beta}{m} = \dfrac{z - \gamma}{n}$ is

$$\begin{vmatrix} x_1 - \alpha & y_1 - \beta \\ l & m \end{vmatrix}^2 + \begin{vmatrix} y_1 - \beta & z_1 - \gamma \\ m & n \end{vmatrix}^2 + \begin{vmatrix} z_1 - \gamma & x_1 - \alpha \\ n & l \end{vmatrix}^2$$

l, m, n are actual d.c.'s. In case we use D.R.'s a, b, c then divide by $(a^2 + b^2 + c^2)$.

4. **Intersection of a line and a plane** : Take the general co-ordinates of a point on the line $(lr + x_1,\ mr + y_1,\ nr + z_1)$ and put it in the equation of the plane and you will find the value of parameter and hence the point of intersection.

5. **Plane through a given line**

$$\frac{x - x_1}{l_1} = \frac{y - y_1}{m_1} = \frac{z - z_1}{n_1} \qquad \text{...(A)}$$

is $\quad a(x - x_1) + b(y - y_1) + c(z - z_1) = 0 \qquad$ ...(1)

where $al_1 + bm_1 + cn_1 = 0 \qquad$ ...(2)

The condition (1) implies that the plane will pass through the point (x_1, y_1, z_1) through which the line passes. The second condition implies that the normal a, b, c will be perpendicular to line l_1, m_1, n_1.

6. **Plane through a given line (A) and parallel to another line $\dfrac{x - x_2}{l_2} = \dfrac{y - y_2}{m_2} = \dfrac{z - z_2}{n_2}$:**

Since the plane is parallel to line its normal is perpendicular to line l_2, m_2, n_2.

$\therefore \quad al_2 + bm_2 + cn_2 = 0 \qquad$ ...(3)

Hence the plane from (1), (2) and (3) is

$$\begin{vmatrix} x - x_1 & y - y_1 & z - z_1 \\ l_1 & m_1 & n_1 \\ l_2 & m_2 & n_2 \end{vmatrix} = 0 \qquad \text{...(4)}$$

We have eliminated a, b, c.

7. **The condition for two given lines to intersect *i.e.* coplanar is**

$$\begin{vmatrix} x_2 - x_1 & y_2 - y_1 & z_2 - z_1 \\ l_1 & m_1 & n_1 \\ l_2 & m_2 & n_2 \end{vmatrix} = 0$$

If the given lines intersect *i.e.*, coplanar then the point (x_2, y_2, z_2) through which the second line passes will lie on plane (4). Hence putting the point in (4) we get the required condition as given.

8. **Foot of perpendicular from a point $A(\alpha, \beta, \gamma)$ to the line $\dfrac{x - x_1}{l} = \dfrac{y - y_1}{m} = \dfrac{z - z_1}{n}$ and length and equation of perpendicular** : If P be the foot of perpendicular, then P is $(lr + x_1,\ mr + y_1,\ nr + z_1)$. Find the direction ratios of AP and apply the condition of

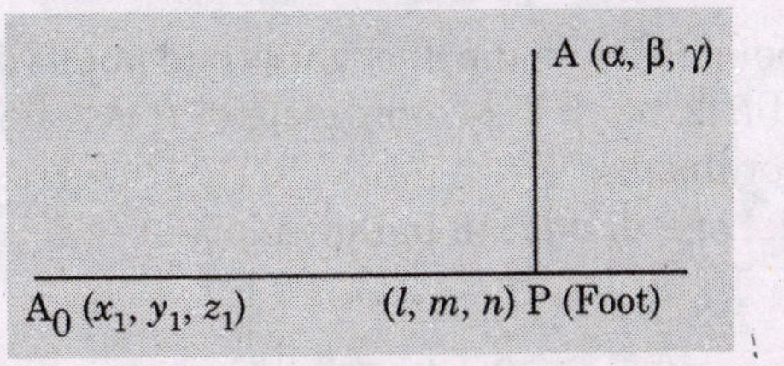

Fig. 3

perpendicularity of AP and the given line. This will give the value of r and hence the point P which is foot of perpendicular. Its length is the distance AP and its equation is the line joining two known points A and P.

9. **Foot of perpendicular from a point $A(\alpha, \beta, \gamma)$ to a given plane $ax + by + cz + d = 0$** : If AP be the perpendicular from A to given plane then it is parallel to normal so that its equation is

$$\frac{x - \alpha}{a} = \frac{y - \beta}{b} = \frac{z - \gamma}{c} = r \text{ (say)}$$

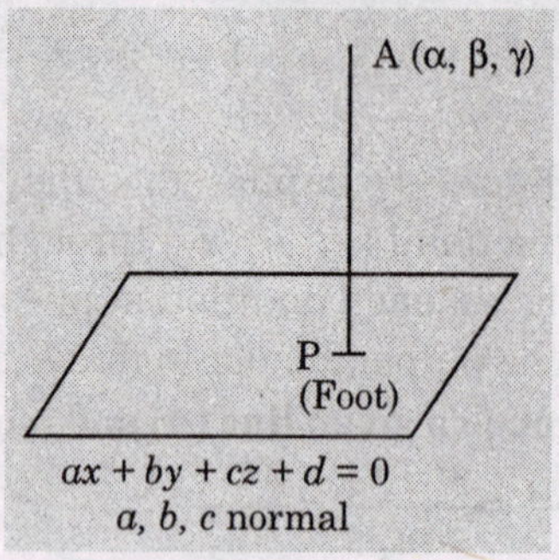

Fig. 4

Any point P on it is $(ar+\alpha, br+\beta, cr+\gamma)$. It lies on the given plane and we find the value of r and hence the point P.

Image (reflection) of a point A in the line or plane. Find the foot of perpendicular P from A to the line or plane then point B such that P is mid-point of AB is the image or reflection of point A.

Problem Set (1)

Points

1. Prove that the three points P, Q, R whose co-ordinates are respectively $(3, 2, -4)$, $(5, 4, -6)$ and $(9, 8, -10)$ are collinear, and find the ratio in which the point Q divides PR.

Ans. 1 : 2.

Sol. For collinearity it is easy to see that

$$PQ + QR = PR.$$

Let Q divide PR in the ratio $\lambda : 1$ then the point $Q(5, 4, -6)$ is

$$\left(\frac{9\lambda+3}{\lambda+1}, \frac{8\lambda+2}{\lambda+1}, \frac{-10\lambda-4}{\lambda+1}\right).$$

Comparing the x-co-ordinate of Q,

$$\frac{9\lambda+3}{\lambda+1} = 5; \quad \therefore \quad 9\lambda+3 = 5\lambda+5;$$

$$\therefore \quad 4\lambda = 2 \quad \text{or} \quad \lambda = \frac{1}{2}$$

and this value of λ makes the y and z-co-ordinates of Q to be $4, -6$ respectively. Also the required ratio is

$$\lambda : 1 \quad \text{or} \quad \frac{1}{2} : 1 \quad \text{or} \quad 1 : 2.$$

2. A point P lies on the line whose end points are $A(1, 2, 3)$ and $B(2, 10, 1)$. If z-co-ordinate of P is 7, find its other co-ordinates.

Sol. Let P divide AB in the ratio $\lambda : 1$

$$\therefore \quad P\left(\frac{2\lambda+1}{\lambda+1}, \frac{10\lambda+2}{\lambda+1}, \frac{\lambda+3}{\lambda+1}\right).$$

But z-co-ordinate of P is 7

$$\therefore \quad \frac{\lambda+3}{\lambda+1} = 7 \quad \text{or} \quad \lambda = -\frac{2}{3}$$

Putting for λ we get the point P as $(-1, -14, 7)$

3. Find the distance of the point $(1, 2, 0)$ from the point where the line joining $A(2, -3, 1)$ and $B(3, -4, -5)$ cuts the plane $2x + y + z = 7$.

Sol. Let the line AB cut the plane in P whose co-ordinates can be taken as

$$\left(\frac{3\lambda+2}{\lambda+1}, \frac{-4\lambda-3}{\lambda+1}, \frac{-5\lambda+1}{\lambda+1}\right).$$

Since it lies on the plane $2x + y + z = 7$, we get $\lambda = \frac{1}{2}$.

Hence the point P is $(7/3, -10/3, -3/3)$ and its distance from $(1, 2, 0)$ is

$$\sqrt{\left(\frac{16}{9} + \frac{256}{9} + 1\right)} = \frac{1}{3}\sqrt{(281)}$$

4. Prove that the plane $ax + by + cz + d = 0$ divides the line joining the points (x_1, y_1, z_1) and (x_2, y_2, z_2) in the ratio

$$-\frac{(ax_1 + by_1 + cz_1 + d_1)}{ax_2 + by_2 + cz_2 + d_2}$$

Hint. Proceed exactly as above taking the ratio as $\lambda : 1$ and the value of λ is found to be as given.

5. Find the ratio in which the yz-plane divides the join of the points $(-2, 4, 7)$ and $(3, -5, 8)$ and also find the co-ordinates of the point of intersection of this line with the yz-plane.

Sol. The co-ordinates of any point on the line joining the two points are

$$\left(\frac{3\lambda-2}{\lambda+1}, \frac{-5\lambda+4}{\lambda+1}, \frac{8\lambda+7}{\lambda+1}\right)$$

If the point is in the yz-plane, then its x-co-ordinate should be zero.

$$\frac{3\lambda-2}{\lambda+1} = 0 \quad \text{or} \quad 3\lambda - 2 = 0 \quad \therefore \quad \lambda = \frac{2}{3}.$$

Hence the required ratio is 2 : 3, and putting $\lambda = \frac{2}{3}$ the required point is $\left(0, \frac{2}{5}, \frac{37}{5}\right)$.

6. A, B, C are three points on the axes of x, y and z respectively at distances a, b, c from the origin O; then the co-ordinates of the point which is equidistant from A, B, C and O is

(a) (a, b, c)
(b) $\left(\frac{a}{2}, \frac{b}{2}, \frac{c}{2}\right)$
(c) $\left(\frac{a}{3}, \frac{b}{3}, \frac{c}{3}\right)$
(d) None

Ans. (b).

Sol. Let P be the required point (x, y, z) and the point A, B, C and O are $(a, 0, 0)$, $(0, b, 0)$, $(0, 0, c)$ and $(0, 0, 0)$; we are given that $PO = PA = PB = PC$.

Taking $PO = PA$

or $PO^2 = PA^2$, we get

$$x^2 + y^2 + z^2 = (x - a)^2 + y^2 + z^2$$

or $0 = a^2 - 2ax$ *i.e.* $x = a/2$

Similarly taking $PO^2 = PB^2$ and $PO^2 = PC^2$,

we get $y = b/2$ and $z = c/2$.

7. The ratio in which the sphere $x^2 + y^2 + z^2 = 504$ divides the line joining the points $(12, -4, 8)$ and $(27, -9, 18)$ is

(a) $-2:3$ (b) $2:3$ (c) $3:4$ (d) $1:2$

Ans. (a), (b).

Sol. Find the general co-ordinates of a point on the line joining given points and it must satisfy the equation of the given sphere, thus giving you $9\lambda^2 - 4 = 0$ or $\lambda = \pm\frac{2}{3}$ etc.

Problem Set (2)

Direction Cosines and Line

1. Find the direction-cosines of the line which is equally inclined to the axis.

Sol. If the line makes angle α, β, γ with the axes, then $\cos\alpha = \cos\beta = \cos\gamma$. $\because$ $\alpha = \beta = \gamma$ given

or $\frac{l}{1} = \frac{m}{1} = \frac{n}{1} = \pm\frac{\sqrt{(l^2 + m^2 + n^2)}}{\sqrt{(1+1+1)}} = \pm\frac{1}{\sqrt{3}}$

$\therefore$ d.c.'s are $\pm\frac{1}{\sqrt{3}}$, $\pm\frac{1}{\sqrt{3}}$, $\pm\frac{1}{\sqrt{3}}$.

Either all signs are + or all −.

2. If α, β, γ be the angles which a line makes with the positive directions of the axes, the prove that

$$\sin^2\alpha + \sin^2\beta + \sin^2\gamma = 2.$$

Sol. We know that $\cos^2\alpha + \cos^2\beta + \cos^2\gamma = 1$.

$\therefore$ $1 - \sin^2\alpha + 1 - \sin^2\beta + 1 - \sin^2\gamma = 1$

or $\sin^2\alpha + \sin^2\beta + \sin^2\gamma = 2.$

3. (a) If a line makes angles α, β, γ with axes of co-ordinates then $\cos 2\alpha + \cos 2\beta + \cos 2\gamma =$

(a) -2 (b) -1

(c) 1 (d) 2

Ans. (b).

Sol. $(2\cos^2\alpha - 1) + (2\cos^2\beta - 1) + (2\cos^2\gamma - 1)$

$$= 2(l^2 + m^2 + n^2) - 3 = 2 - 3 = -1 \Rightarrow \text{(b)}$$

(b) A line makes the same angle θ with each of the x and z axes. If the angle β which it makes with y-axis is such that $\sin^2\beta = 3\sin^2\theta$, then $\cos^2\theta =$

(a) $\frac{2}{3}$ (b) $\frac{1}{5}$

(c) $\frac{3}{5}$ (d) $\frac{2}{5}$ **(AIEEE 2004)**

Sol. Ans. (c).

$l = n = \cos\theta$ given, $m = \cos\beta$

$l^2 + m^2 + n^2 = 1 \Rightarrow 2\cos^2\theta + \cos^2\beta = 1$

$\therefore$ $2\cos^2\theta = 1 - \cos^2\beta = \sin^2\beta = 3\sin^2\theta$

$$= 3(1 - \cos^2\theta)$$

$\therefore$ $5\cos^2\theta = 3 \Rightarrow \cos^2\theta = \frac{3}{5} \Rightarrow$ (c).

4. Which of the following triplets give the direction cosines of a line ?

(a) 1, 1, 1 (b) 1, −1, 1

(c) 1, 1, −1 (d) $\frac{1}{\sqrt{3}}, \frac{1}{\sqrt{3}}, \frac{1}{\sqrt{3}}$

Ans. (d).

Sol. $\because$ $l^2 + m^2 + n^2 = 1$.

5. A st. line which makes angle of 60° with each of y- and z-axes, is inclined with x-axis at an angle

(a) 45° (b) 30° (c) 75° (d) 60°

Ans. (a). $m = \cos 60^o, n = \cos 60^o$

Sol. $\therefore$ $l^2 + \cos^2 60^o + \cos^2 60^o = 1$

$\therefore$ $l^2 = 1 - \frac{1}{2} = \frac{1}{2}$ $\therefore$ $l = \frac{1}{\sqrt{2}} = \cos\alpha$ $\therefore$ $\alpha = 45^o$

6. (a) The projections of a line segment on x, y, z axes are 12, 4, 3. The length and the direction cosines of the line segments are

(a) 13, < 12/13, 4/13, 3/13 >

(b) 19, < 12/19, 4/19, 19 >

(c) 11, < 12/11, 4/11, 3/11 >

(d) None of these

Ans. (a).

Sol. $OA = 12$ = Projection of $OP = r$ on x-axis

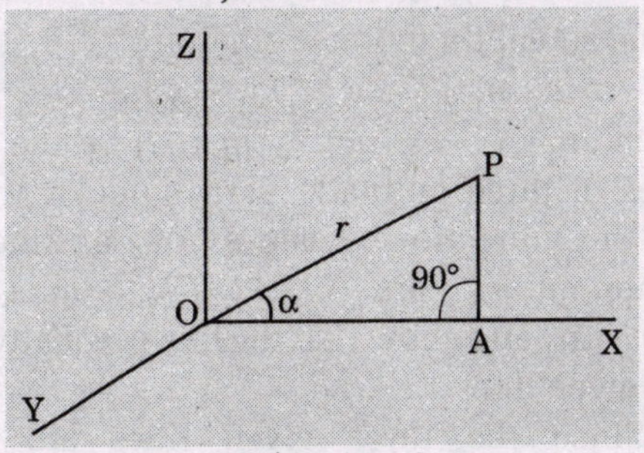

Fig. 5

$\therefore$ $12 = r\cos\alpha = rl,$

$4 = rm, 3 = rn,$

$\therefore$ Squaring and adding, $r = 13$

$\therefore$ l, m, n are as given.

(b) The projections of a vector on the three co-ordinate axes are 6, – 3, 2 respectively. The direction cosines of the vector are

(a) $\frac{-6}{7}, \frac{-3}{7}, \frac{2}{7}$ (b) 6, – 3, 2

(c) $\frac{6}{5}, \frac{-3}{5}, \frac{2}{5}$ (d) $\frac{6}{7}, \frac{-3}{7}, \frac{2}{7}$ **(AIEEE 2009)**

Sol. Ans. (d).

Given that direction ratios are 6, – 3, 2

∴ Direction cosines are

$\frac{6}{7}, -\frac{3}{7}, \frac{2}{7}$ as $\sqrt{a^2+b^2+c^2} = \sqrt{49} = 7.$

7. If (l_1, m_1, n_1) and (l_2, m_2, n_2) are the direction-cosines of two lines, then the direction-ratios of another line which is perpendicular to both the given lines are $(m_1 n_2 - m_2 n_1), (n_1 l_2 - n_2 l_1), (l_1 m_2 - l_2 m_1)$.

Prove further that if the given lines be perpendicular to each other, then these direction-ratios are the actual direction cosines.

Sol. Let (l, m, n) be the direction-cosines of the required line; then since it is perpendicular to both given lines, we have

$$l l_1 + m m_1 + n n_1 = 0.$$
$$l l_2 + m m_2 + n n_2 = 0.$$

$$\therefore \quad \frac{l}{m_1 n_2 - m_2 n_1} = \frac{m}{n_1 l_2 - n_2 l_1} = \frac{n}{l_1 m_2 - l_2 m_1}.$$

Thus we get the direction-ratios. The actual direction-cosines are

$$\frac{m_1 n_2 - m_2 n_1}{\sqrt{[\Sigma (m_1 n_2 - m_2 n_1)^2]}}, \frac{n_1 l_2 - n_2 l_1}{\sqrt{[\Sigma (m_1 n_2 - m_2 n_1)^2]}}, \frac{l_1 m_2 - l_2 m_1}{\sqrt{[\Sigma (m_1 n_2 - m_2 n_1)^2]}}.$$

Now $\sqrt{[\Sigma (m_1 n_2 - m_2 n_1)^2]} = \sin\theta$, where θ is the angle between the lines whose direction cosines are l_1, m_1, n_1 and l_2, m_2, n_2. In case these lines be perpendicular, *i.e.*, $\theta = 90^o$ then $\sin\theta = 1$,

i.e., $\sqrt{[\Sigma (m_1 n_2 - m_2 n_1)^2]} = 1.$

∴ the actual direction cosines are

$m_1 n_2 - m_2 n_1, n_1 l_2 - n_2 l_1, l_1 m_2 - l_2 m_1$

8. If (l_1, m_1, n_1), (l_2, m_2, n_2), (l_3, m_3, n_3) be the direction cosines of three mutually perpendicular lines, then find the direction cosines of a line whose direction-ratios are $l_1 + l_2 + l_3$, $m_1 + m_2 + m_3$, $n_1 + n_2 + n_3$ and show that the line is equally inclined to the given lines.

Sol. Since the three given lines are mutually perpendicular, we have

$$l_1 l_2 + m_1 m_2 + n_1 n_2 = 0, \quad l_2 l_3 + m_2 m_3 + n_2 n_3 = 0$$
$$l_3 l_1 + m_3 m_1 + n_3 n_1 = 0. \quad ...(1)$$

Also $l_1^2 + m_1^2 + n_1^2 = l_2^2 + m_2^2 + n_2^2$
$$= l_3^2 + m_3^2 + n_3^2 = 1 \quad ...(2)$$

Now $\sqrt{[(l_1 + l_2 + l_3)^2 + (m_1 + m_2 + m_3)^2 + (n_1 + n_2 + n_3)^2]}$
$$= \sqrt{[\Sigma l_1^2 + \Sigma l_2^2 + \Sigma l_3^2 + 2\Sigma l_1 l_2 + 2\Sigma l_2 l_3 + 2\Sigma l_3 l_1]} = \sqrt{3} \text{ from (1), (2)}$$

Hence the direction cosines are

$$\left(\frac{l_1 + l_2 + l_3}{\sqrt{3}}, \frac{m_1 + m_2 + m_3}{\sqrt{3}}, \frac{n_1 + n_2 + n_3}{\sqrt{3}}\right) \quad ...(3)$$

If θ be the angle between the lines whose direction-cosines are (l_1, m_1, n_1) and those given by (3), then

$$\cos\theta = \frac{l_1(l_1 + l_2 + l_3)}{\sqrt{3}} + \frac{m_1(m_1 + m_2 + m_3)}{\sqrt{3}} + \frac{n_1(n_1 + n_2 + n_3)}{\sqrt{3}}$$

$$= \frac{\Sigma l_1^2 + \Sigma l_1 l_2 + \Sigma l_1 l_3}{\sqrt{3}} = \frac{1}{\sqrt{3}} \text{ by (1);}$$

$$\theta = \cos^{-1}\frac{1}{\sqrt{3}}.$$

Similarly we can show that the angle between each of the other two lines and the line with d.c.'s given by (3) is also $\cos^{-1}\frac{1}{\sqrt{3}}$.

9. If the edges of a rectangular parallelopiped be a, b, c show that the angles between the four diagonals are given by

$$\cos^{-1}\frac{\pm a^2 \pm b^2 \pm c^2}{a^2 + b^2 + c^2}.$$

Sol. The four diagonals are *AL*, *BM*, *CN* and *OP* where the co-ordinates of *O* are (0,0,0), *P* (*a,b,c*), *A* (*a*,0,0), *B* (0,*b*,0), *C* (0,0,*c*), *L* (0,*b*,*c*), *M* (*a*,0,*c*) and *N* (*a*,*b*,0).

Direction ratios of *OP* are $a-0, b-0, c-0$. *i.e.* a, b, c.

∴ d.c.'s are $\frac{a}{\sqrt{(\Sigma a^2)}}, \frac{b}{\sqrt{(\Sigma a^2)}}, \frac{c}{\sqrt{(\Sigma a^2)}}$

and D.R.'s of *AL* are

$0 - a, b - 0, c - 0$, *i.e.* $-a, b, c$.

∴ d.c.'s are $\frac{-a}{\sqrt{(\Sigma a^2)}}, \frac{b}{\sqrt{(\Sigma a^2)}}, \frac{c}{\sqrt{(\Sigma a^2)}}$

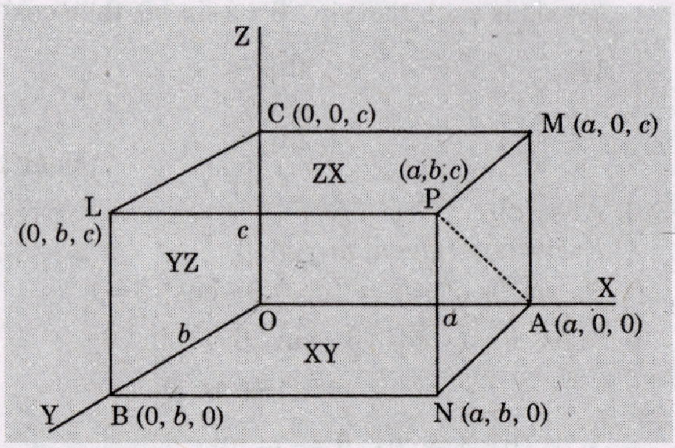

Fig. 6

Similarly the direction-cosines of BM and CN are

$$\frac{a}{\sqrt{(\Sigma a^2)}}, \frac{-b}{\sqrt{(\Sigma a^2)}}, \frac{c}{\sqrt{(\Sigma a^2)}}$$

and $\frac{a}{\sqrt{(\Sigma a^2)}}, \frac{b}{\sqrt{(\Sigma a^2)}}, \frac{-c}{\sqrt{(\Sigma a^2)}}$ respectively.

If θ be the angle between OP and AL, we get

$$\cos\theta = \frac{a(-a)+b(b)+c(c)}{\sqrt{(a^2+b^2+c^2)}\sqrt{(a^2+b^2+c^2)}}$$

$$= \frac{-a^2+b^2+c^2}{a^2+b^2+c^2} \qquad \text{...(1)}$$

Similarly we can find the angle between other pairs and hence the angles in general between the six pairs are given by

$$\cos^{-1}\frac{\pm a^2 \pm b^2 \pm c^2}{a^2+b^2+c^2}.$$

Note. The ambiguous signs cannot be either all + ive or all –ive for in that case $\theta = \cos^{-1} 1$ or $\cos^{-1}(-1)$, *i.e.*, $\theta = 0$ or $180°$ which is impossible as the diagonals are not parallel.

10. Prove that the angle between two diagonals of a cube is $\cos^{-1}\frac{1}{3}$.

Sol. Cube is a rectangular parallelopiped whose edges a, b, c are all equal. If θ be the angle between diagonals OP and AL then putting $a = b = c$ in (1) of Q. 9.

$$\cos\theta = \frac{-1+1+1}{1+1+1} = \frac{1}{3}; \quad \therefore \quad \theta = \cos^{-1}\left(\frac{1}{3}\right).$$

11. A line makes angles $\alpha, \beta, \gamma, \delta$ with the four diagonals of a cube; show that

$$\cos^2\alpha + \cos^2\beta + \cos^2\gamma + \cos^2\delta = \frac{4}{3},$$

Sol. From Q. 9, d.c.'s of the four diagonals of a cube on putting $a = b = c$ are

$$OP\left(\frac{1}{\sqrt{3}}, \frac{1}{\sqrt{3}}, \frac{1}{\sqrt{3}}\right), AL\left(\frac{-1}{\sqrt{3}}, \frac{1}{\sqrt{3}}, \frac{1}{\sqrt{3}}\right)$$

$$BM\left(\frac{1}{\sqrt{3}}, \frac{-1}{\sqrt{3}}, \frac{1}{\sqrt{3}}\right), CN\left(\frac{1}{\sqrt{3}}, \frac{1}{\sqrt{3}}, \frac{-1}{\sqrt{3}}\right)$$

Let l, m, n be d.c.'s of a line which is inclined at angles $\alpha, \beta, \gamma, \delta$ respectively to the four diagonals; then

$$\cos\alpha = l.\frac{1}{\sqrt{3}} + m.\frac{1}{\sqrt{3}} + n.\frac{1}{\sqrt{3}} = \frac{l+m+n}{\sqrt{3}}.$$

Similarly $\cos\beta = \frac{-l+m+n}{\sqrt{3}}, \cos\gamma = \frac{l-m+n}{\sqrt{3}},$

$$\cos\delta = \frac{l+m-n}{\sqrt{3}}.$$

$$\therefore \quad \cos^2\alpha + \cos^2\beta + \cos^2\gamma + \cos^2\delta$$

$$= \frac{1}{3}[(l+m+n)^2 + (-l+m+n)^2 + (l-m+n)^2 + (l+m-n)^2]$$

$$= \frac{1}{3}.4(l^2+m^2+n^2) = \frac{4}{3}.$$

12. (a) The direction-cosines of a moving line in two adjacent positions are l, m, n and $l+\delta l, m+\delta m, n+\delta n$. Show that the small angle $\delta\theta$ between the positions is given by $(\delta\theta)^2 = (\delta l)^2 + (\delta m)^2 + (\delta n)^2$.

Sol. $\Sigma l^2 = l^2 + m^2 + n^2 = 1 \qquad \text{...(1)}$

$$\Sigma(l+\delta l)^2 = (l+\delta l)^2 + (m+\delta m)^2 + (n+\delta n)^2 = 1 \qquad \text{...(2)}$$

Also $\cos\delta\theta = \Sigma l(l+\delta l)$

$$= l(l+\delta l) + m(m+\delta m) + n(n+\delta n) \qquad \text{...(3)}$$

Now $\quad \delta l = l + \delta l - l;$

$$\therefore \quad (\delta l)^2 = (l+\delta l)^2 + l^2 - 2l(l+\delta l)$$

$$\therefore \quad \delta l^2 + \delta m^2 + n^2 = \Sigma(l+\delta l)^2 + \Sigma l^2 + 2\Sigma l(l+\delta l)$$

$= 1 + 1 - 2\cos\delta\theta$ by (1), (2) and (3)

$$= 2(1-\cos\delta\theta) = 2.2\sin^2\frac{\delta\theta}{2}$$

$$= 4\left(\frac{\delta\theta}{2}\right)^2 = \delta\theta^2;$$

$\because \quad$ when α is small then $\sin\alpha = \alpha$.

(b) Show that the points $A(1,-6,10)$, $B(-1,-3,4)$, $C(5,-1,1)$ and $D(7,-4,7)$ are the vertices of a rhombus.

Sol. $AB = \sqrt{4+9+36} = 7 = BC = CD = AD$

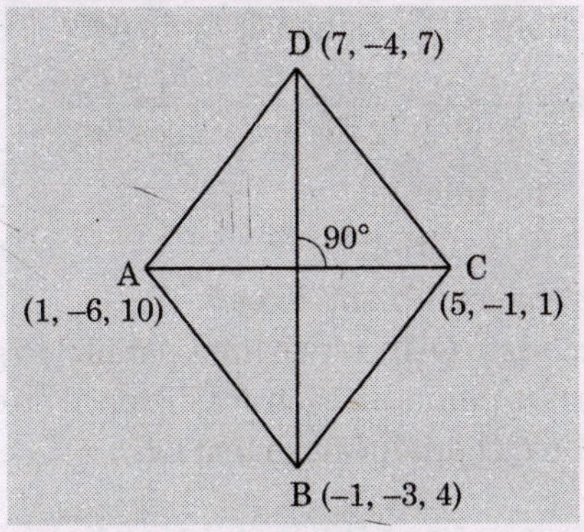

Fig. 7

Hence it will be a square or rhombus.

D.R.'s of AD are 6, 2, – 3

D.R.'s of AB are 2, – 3, 6

$$a_1a_2 + b_1b_2 + c_1c_2 = 12 - 6 - 18 = -12 \neq 0.$$

$\therefore \quad \angle A$ is not a right angle.

Hence $ABCD$ is not a square but a rhombus. You may verify that AC is $\perp$ to BD *i.e.*, diagonals are $\perp$ and hence a rhombus.

13. (a) The vertices of a triangle ABC are $A(-1,-2,-3)$, $B(-1,2,3)$ and $C(0,0,0)$. Then the direction ratios of internal bisector of $\angle C$ are :

(a) 0, 0, 1 (b) 1, – 1, 1

(c) – 1, 0, 0 (d) none

Sol. Ans. (c).

$CA = CB = \sqrt{14}$. Internal bisector divides the opposite side AB in the ratio of $CA:CB$, *i.e.*, $\sqrt{14}:\sqrt{14}$. Hence it will meet AB at its mid-point $D(-1, 0, 0)$.

$\therefore$ Direction ratios of CD are $-1, 0, 0 \Rightarrow$ (c).

(b) The vertices of a triangle ABC are $A(-1, 2, -3)$, $B(5, 0, -6)$, $C(0, 4, -1)$. Then the direction ratios of the external bisector of $\angle BAC$ are :

(a) 11, 20, 21 (b) −11, 20, 20
(c) −11, 20, 23 (d) none

Sol. Ans. (c).

The external bisector of $\angle A$ will divide the opposite side BC externally in the ratio $AB:AC$ where $AB = 7$ and $AC = 3$. If it meets BC at E, then by ratio formula E is $\left(-\frac{15}{4}, 7, \frac{11}{4}\right)$ and A is $(-1, 2, -3)$ $\therefore$ D.R.'s of AE by

$x_2 - x_1, y_2 - y_1, z_2 - z_1$ are $-11, 20, 23$.

(c) If l_1, m_1, n_1 and l_2, m_2, n_2 are D.C.'s of the two lines inclined to each other at an angle θ, then the D.C.'s of the internal and external bisectors of the angle between these lines are

(a) $\frac{l_1 + l_2}{2\sin(\theta/2)}, \frac{m_1 + m_2}{2\sin(\theta/2)}, \frac{n_1 + n_2}{2\sin(\theta/2)}$

(b) $\frac{l_1 + l_2}{2\cos(\theta/2)}, \frac{m_1 + m_2}{2\cos(\theta/2)}, \frac{n_1 + n_2}{2\cos(\theta/2)}$

(c) $\frac{l_1 - l_2}{2\sin(\theta/2)}, \frac{m_1 - m_2}{2\sin(\theta/2)}, \frac{n_1 - n_2}{2\sin(\theta/2)}$

(d) $\frac{l_1 - l_2}{2\cos(\theta/2)}, \frac{m_1 - m_2}{2\cos(\theta/2)}, \frac{n_1 - n_2}{2\cos(\theta/2)}$

Ans. (b) for internal
(c) for external

Sol. $l_1 l_2 + m_1 m_2 + n_1 n_2 = \cos\theta$

Through origin O draw two lines parallel to given lines and take two points on each at a distance r from O and a point R on QO produced so that $OR = r$.

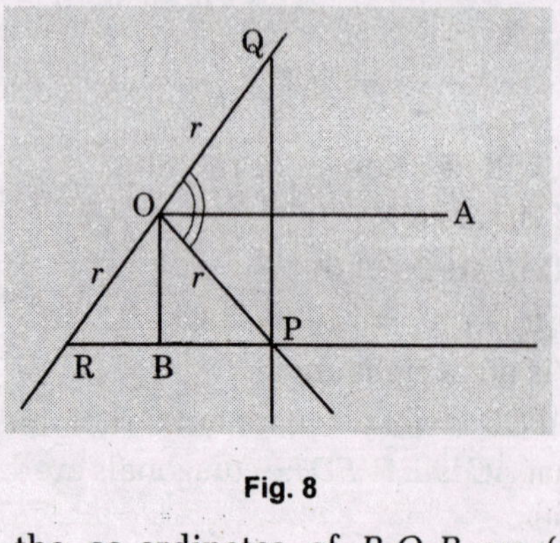

Fig. 8

Then the co-ordinates of P, Q, R are $(l_1 r, m_1 r, n_1 r)$, $(l_2 r, m_2 r, n_2 r)$ and $(-l_2 r, -m_2 r, -n_2 r)$ respectively.

If A, B be the mid-points of PQ and PR then OA and OB are along the bisectors of the lines

D.R.'s of OA are $l_1 + l_2, m_1 + m_2, n_1 + n_2$

D.R.'s of OB are $l_1 - l_2, m_1 - m_2, n_1 - n_2$

Now $\Sigma(l_1 + l_2)^2 = 1 + 1 + 2\cos\theta$

$$= 2(1 + \cos\theta) = 4\cos^2(\theta/2)$$

and $\Sigma(l_1 - l_2)^2 = 1 + 1 - 2\cos\theta = 2(1 - \cos\theta)$

$$= 4\sin^2(\theta/2)$$

$\therefore$ D.C. of internal and external bisectors are as given in (b) and (c) respectively.

14. (a) Prove that the acute angle between the lines whose direction-cosines are given by the relations $l + m + n = 0$ and $l^2 + m^2 - n^2 = 0$ is $\pi/3$.

Sol. Eliminating n, we get

$l^2 + m^2 - (l + m)^2 = 0;$ $\therefore$ $2lm = 0,$

When $l = 0$ then $m + n = 0$ or $m = -n$;

$$\therefore \quad \frac{l}{0} = \frac{m}{1} = \frac{n}{-1}. \qquad ...(1)$$

When $m = 0$ then $l + n = 0$ or $l = -n$;

$$\therefore \quad \frac{l}{1} = \frac{m}{0} = \frac{n}{-1}. \qquad ...(2)$$

Hence the D.R.'s of the lines are 0, 1, −1; 1, 0, −1,

$$\therefore \quad \cos\theta = \frac{0.1 + 1.0 + (-1)(-1)}{\sqrt{(0+1+1)}.\sqrt{(0+1+1)}} = \frac{1}{2};$$

$\therefore$ $\theta = \pi/3$

(b) If the angle θ between the line $\frac{x+1}{1} = \frac{y-1}{2} = \frac{z-2}{2}$ and the plane $2x - y + \sqrt{\lambda}z + 4 = 0$ is such that $\sin\theta = \frac{1}{3}$, then the value of λ is :

(a) $\frac{3}{4}$ (b) $-\frac{4}{3}$
(c) $\frac{5}{3}$ (d) $-\frac{3}{5}$

Sol. Ans. (c).

If θ be the angle between line and plane, then $90^\circ - \theta$ is the angle between line and normal to the plane whose D.R.'s are line 1, 2, 2 and plane, 2, −1, $\sqrt{\lambda}$

$$\therefore \quad \cos(90^\circ - \theta) = \frac{1.2 + 2(-1) + 2\sqrt{\lambda}}{3.\sqrt{5+\lambda}} = \frac{1}{3} \quad \text{given}$$

$\therefore$ $2\sqrt{\lambda} = \sqrt{5+\lambda}$ or $4\lambda = 5 + \lambda$

$\therefore$ $\lambda = 5/3$.

(c) A line with direction cosines proportional to 2, 1, 2 meets each of the lines $x = y + a = z$ and $x + a = 2y = 2z$. The co-ordinates of each of the points of intersection are given by

(a) $(3a, 3a, 3a), (a, a, a)$
(b) $(3a, 2a, 3a), (a, a, a)$
(c) $(3a, 2a, 3a), (a, a, 2a)$
(d) $(2a, 3a, 3a), (2a, a, a)$ **(AIEEE 2004)**

Sol. Ans. (b).

The given lines are $\frac{x}{1} = \frac{y+a}{1} = \frac{z}{1} = r$ say,

and $\frac{x+a}{2} = \frac{y}{1} = \frac{z}{1} = r'$ say

P and Q are points on these lines.

$\therefore \quad P = (r, r-a, r), Q = (2r'-a, r', r')$

D.R.'s of $PQ = 2r' - r - a, r' - r + a, r' - r$

They are proportional to 2, 1, 2 as given

$\therefore \quad 2r' - r - a = 2\lambda$

$r' - r + a = \lambda$

$r' - r = 2\lambda$

$\therefore \quad \frac{r'-r+a}{r'-r} = \frac{1}{2}$ and $\frac{2r'-r-a}{r'-r} = 1$

$\therefore \quad 2r' - 2r + 2a = r' - r$

and $2r' - r - a = r' - r$

$\Rightarrow \quad r' = a$ and hence $r = 3a$

Hence, the points P and Q are $(3a, 2a, 3a)$ and (a, a, a).

15. Prove that the angle between the lines whose direction cosines are connected by the relations $l + m + n = 0$ and $2lm + 2nl - mn = 0$ is $2\pi/3$.

Sol. Eliminating n as above, we have

$$(2l + m)(l - m) = 0$$

When $2l + m = 0$ then $\frac{l}{1} = \frac{m}{-2} = \frac{n}{1}$

When $l - m = 0$ then $\frac{l}{1} = \frac{m}{1} = \frac{n}{-2}$.

$\therefore$ D.R.'s are 1, – 2, 1 and 1, 1, – 2

If θ be the angle between the lines, then

$$\cos\theta = \frac{\Sigma a_1 a_2}{\sqrt{\Sigma a_1^2} \cdot \sqrt{\Sigma a_2^2}}$$

or $\cos\theta = \frac{1.1 - 2.1 + 1(-2)}{\sqrt{6}.\sqrt{6}} = \frac{-3}{6} = \frac{-1}{2}$

$$= -\cos(\pi/3) = \cos(\pi - \pi/3)$$

Hence $\theta = \frac{2\pi}{3} = 120^o$

16. Prove that the straight lines whose direction-cosines are given by the relations

$al + bm + cn = 0$ and $fmn + gnl + hlm = 0$

are perpendicular if $\frac{f}{a} + \frac{g}{b} + \frac{h}{c} = 0$ and parallel if

$\sqrt{(af)} \pm \sqrt{(bg)} \pm \sqrt{(ch)} = 0$

or $a^2 f^2 + b^2 g^2 + c^2 h^2 - 2bcgh - 2cahf - 2abfg = 0$

Sol. Eliminating l between the given relations, we get

$$fmn + (gn + hm)\left(\frac{bm + cn}{-a}\right) = 0$$

$\because \quad l = \left(\frac{bm + cn}{-a}\right)$

or $bhm^2 + mn(ch + bg - af) + cgn^2 = 0$

or $bh\left(\frac{m}{n}\right)^2 + (ch + bg - af)\frac{m}{n} + cg = 0$ ...(1)

Let $\frac{m_1}{n_1}$ and $\frac{m_2}{n_2}$ be the roots of the above equation, then in case the lines be parallel, their direction-cosines are equal and hence, both the roots of (1) should be equal the condition for which is $B^2 - 4AC = 0$.

i.e. $(ch + bg - af)^2 = 4bcgh$ ...(A)

or $ch + bg - af = \pm 2\sqrt{(bcgh)}$

or $ch + bg \pm 2\sqrt{(bcgh)} = af$

or $[\sqrt{(ch)} \pm \sqrt{(bg)}]^2 = [\sqrt{(af)}]^2$

or $\pm[\sqrt{(ch)} \pm \sqrt{(bg)}] = \sqrt{(af)}$

or $\sqrt{(af)} \pm \sqrt{(bg)} \pm \sqrt{(ch)} = 0$

is the required condition.

The second form of condition is obtained by simplifying result (A).

Again from (1) we have $\frac{m_1}{n_1} \cdot \frac{m_2}{n_2}$ = product of the roots of (1).

or $\frac{m_1 m_2}{n_1 n_2} = \frac{cg}{bh}$; $\therefore \frac{m_1 m_2}{cg} = \frac{n_1 n_2}{bh}$

or $\frac{m_1 m_2}{g/b} = \frac{n_1 n_2}{h/c}$ ...(1)

Similarly if we eliminate n between the given relations, we shall have

$$\frac{l_1 l_2}{f/a} = \frac{m_1 m_2}{g/b} \quad ...(2)$$

$\therefore \quad \frac{l_1 l_2}{f/a} = \frac{m_1 m_2}{g/b} = \frac{n_1 n_2}{h/c}$ from (2) and (3)

Now if the lines are perpendicular, then

$$l_1 l_2 + m_1 m_2 + n_1 n_2 = 0$$

$\therefore \quad \frac{f}{a} + \frac{g}{b} + \frac{h}{c} = 0$ is the required condition.

17. Prove that the two lines whose direction cosines are connected by the two relations

$al + bm + cn = 0$ and $ul^2 + vm^2 + wn^2 = 0$

are perpendicular if

$a^2(v + w) + b^2(w + u) + c^2(u + v) = 0$

and parallel if $\frac{a^2}{u} + \frac{b^2}{v} + \frac{c^2}{w} = 0$.

Sol. Eliminating n between the given relations, we get

$$ul^2 + vm^2 + w\left(\frac{al + bm}{-c}\right)^2 = 0$$

or $(c^2 u + a^2 w)\frac{l^2}{m^2} + 2abw.\frac{l}{m} + (b^2 w + c^2 v) = 0$ ...(1)

$\therefore \quad \frac{l_1}{m_1} \cdot \frac{l_2}{m_2}$ = product of roots $= \frac{b^2 w + c^2 v}{c^2 u + a^2 w}$

or $\frac{l_1 l_2}{b^2 w + c^2 v} = \frac{m_1 m_2}{c^2 u + a^2 w} = \frac{n_1 n_2}{a^2 v + b^2 u}$ by symmetry.

If the lines be perpendicular, then

$$l_1 l_2 + m_1 m_2 + n_1 n_2 = 0$$

or $a^2(v+w)+b^2(w+u)+c^2(u+v)=0$. **Proved.**

Again if the lines be parallel, then their d.c.'s are equal so that the roots of (1) should be equal, *i.e.*, $B^2-4AC=0$

or $4a^2b^2w^2-4(c^2u+a^2w)(b^2w+c^2v)=0$

or $a^2c^2vw+b^2c^2uw+c^4uv=0$

or $\frac{a^2}{u}+\frac{b^2}{v}+\frac{c^2}{w}=0$ on dividing by c^2uvw.

18. Prove that the equation of the line of shortest distance between the lines

$$\frac{x}{2}=\frac{y}{-3}=\frac{z}{1} \text{ and } \frac{x-2}{3}=\frac{y-1}{-5}=\frac{z+2}{2} \text{ is}$$

$$3(x-21)=3y+92=3z-32$$

Sol. Let $P(2r_1,-3r_1,r_1)$ and $Q(3r_2+2,-5r_2+1,2r_2-2)$ be two points on the given lines along the line of shortest distance. D.R.'s of PQ are

$$2r_1-3r_2-2,-3r_1+5r_2-1,r_1-2r_2+2 \quad \text{...(1)}$$

PQ is perpendicular to both the given lines.

Applying $a_1a_2+b_1b_2+c_1c_2=0$, we have

$$14r_1-23r_2+1=0 \text{ and } 23r_1-38r_2+3=0$$

Solving, we get $r_1=\frac{31}{3}$ and $r_2=\frac{19}{3}$ ...(2)

$\therefore$ P is $\left(\frac{62}{3},-31,\frac{31}{3}\right)$, Q is $\left(21,-\frac{92}{3},\frac{32}{3}\right)$

D.R.'s of PQ are $\frac{1}{3},\frac{1}{3},\frac{1}{3}$ from (1) and (2)

$\therefore$ Eq. of S.D. is $\frac{x-21}{1/3}=\frac{y+(92/3)}{1/3}=\frac{z-(32/3)}{1/3}$

or $3(x-21)=3y+92=3z-32$

Problem Set (3)

Plane

1. (a) A plane meets the co-ordinate axes in A, B, C such that the centroid of the triangle ABC is the point (p,q,r) show that the equation of the plane is $\frac{x}{p}+\frac{y}{q}+\frac{z}{r}=3$.

Sol. Let the equation of the plane be

$$\frac{x}{a}+\frac{y}{b}+\frac{z}{c}=1. \quad \text{...(1)}$$

$\therefore$ A is $(a,0,0)$, B is $(0,b,0)$ and C is $(0,0,c)$.

Centroid of the triangle ABC is

$$\frac{a+0+0}{3},\frac{0+b+0}{3},\frac{0+0+c}{3} \quad i.e. \quad \left(\frac{a}{3},\frac{b}{3},\frac{c}{3}\right)$$

But we are given that the centroid is the point (p,q,r) $\therefore$ $\frac{a}{3}=p$, $\frac{b}{3}=q$, $\frac{c}{3}=r$.

or $a=3p$, $b=3q$ and $c=3r$.

Putting the values of a, b and c in (1), we get the required equation of the plane as

$$\frac{x}{3p}+\frac{y}{3q}+\frac{z}{3r}=1 \quad \text{or} \quad \frac{x}{p}+\frac{y}{q}+\frac{z}{r}=3.$$

(b) A plane is parallel to two lines whose direction ratios are $(1,0,-1)$ and $(-1,1,0)$ and it contains the point $(1,1,1)$. If it cuts co-ordinate axes at A, B, C, then find the volume of the tetrahedron $OABC$.

(I.I.T. 2004)

Sol. The equation of the plane through the point $(1,1,1)$ is

$$a(x-1)+b(y-1)+c(z-1)=0 \quad \text{...(1)}$$

It is parallel to the lines with direction ratios $1,0,-1$ and $-1,1,0$.

$\therefore$ $a+0\cdot b-c=0$ $\therefore$ $a=c$.

and $-a+b+0\cdot c=0$ $\therefore$ $a=b$.

Hence $a=b=c$. Thus the equation of the plane is

$$x+y+z=3 \quad \text{or} \quad \frac{x}{3}+\frac{y}{3}+\frac{z}{3}=1.$$

It meets the co-ordinate axes at the points A, B, C *i.e.*, $(3,0,0)$, $(0,3,0)$ and $(0,0,3)$.

Hence the volume of tetrahedron $OABC$ is $\frac{1}{6}abc=\frac{1}{6}.3.3.3=\frac{9}{2}$ cubic units.

2. (a) Show that the four points $(0,4,3)$, $(-1,-5,-3)$, $(-2,-2,1)$ and $(1,1,-1)$ are coplanar, and find the common plane.

Sol. Here we shall find the equation of the plane passing through any three points say $(0,4,3)$, $(-2,-2,1)$ and $(1,1,-1)$ and then show that the fourth point $(-1,-5,-3)$, satisfies it.

General equation of a plane through the point $(0,4,3)$ is

$$A(x-0)+B(y-4)+C(z-3)=0 \quad \text{...(1)}$$

It will pass through $(-2,-2,1)$ and $(1,1,-1)$ if

$$-2A-6B-2C=0 \text{ or } A+3B+C=0 \quad \text{...(2)}$$

and $A-3B-4C=0$ or $A-3B-4C=0$. ...(3)

Solving (2) and (3) by the method of cross-multiplication, we get

$$\frac{A}{-12+3}=\frac{B}{1+4}=\frac{C}{-3-3}$$

or $\frac{A}{-9}=\frac{B}{5}=\frac{C}{-6}=k$, say

$\therefore$ $A=-9k$, $B=5k$ and $C=-6k$.

Putting the values of A, B and C in (1) and cancelling k, we get the equation of the plane as

$$-9(x-0)+5(y-4)-6(z-3)=0$$

or $9x-5y+6z+2=0$

and clearly the co-ordinates of the point $(-1,-5,-3)$ satisfy it and hence the given four points are coplanar and equation of the common plane is $9x-5y+6z+2=0$.

(b) Prove that the plane through the points $A(1,1,1)$, $B(1,-1,1)$ and $C(-1,-3,-5)$ passes through the point $(2,\lambda,4)$ for all values of λ.

Sol. As in part (a), the equation of the plane through $A(1,1,1)$ is

$$a(x-1)+b(y-1)+c(z-1)=0$$

It passes through $B(1,-1,1)$. $\therefore -2b=0 \Rightarrow b=0$

Again it passes through $C(-1,-3,-5)$.

$\therefore \quad a(-2)+0+c(-5-1)=0$

$\therefore \quad a+3c=0$ or $a=-3c,\ b=0,\ c=c$

Hence, the equation of the plane is

$-3c(x-1)+c(z-1)=0$ or $3x-z-2=0$

It passes through the point $(2,\lambda,4)$ for all values of λ as the term of y is missing in its equation.

3. If from a point $P(a,b,c)$ perpendiculars PA, PB are drawn to yz and zx planes, then the equation of the plane OAB is

(a) $bcx+cay+abz=0$ (b) $bcx+cay-abz=0$

(c) $bcx-cay+abz=0$ (d) $-bcx+cay+abz=0$

Sol. Ans. (b).

$A(0,b,c)$ in yz-plane $B(a,0,c)$ in zx-plane. Plane through O is $px+qy+rz=0$. It passes through A and B

$\therefore \quad 0p+qb+rc=0$ and $pa+0b+rc=0$

$\therefore \quad \dfrac{p}{bc}=\dfrac{q}{ca}=\dfrac{r}{-ab}$. Hence the plane is as in (b).

4. O is the origin and A is the point (a,b,c). Find the direction cosines of the join of OA and deduce the equation of the plane through A at right angles to OA.

Sol. D.R.'s of OA are $a-0, b-0, c-0$ or a,b,c.

$\therefore$ D.C.'s of OA are

$$\frac{a}{\sqrt{(a^2+b^2+c^2)}}, \frac{b}{\sqrt{(\Sigma a^2)}}, \frac{c}{\sqrt{(\Sigma a^2)}}$$

Equation of any plane through A, *i.e.* (a,b,c) is

$$A(x-a)+B(y-b)+C(z-c)=0.$$

But plane is at right angles to OA which therefore is normal and whose D.R.'s are a,b,c.

Hence the plane is

$$a(x-a)+b(y-b)+c(z-c)=0$$

or $\quad ax+by+cz=a^2+b^2+c^2$

5. (a) Find the equation of the plane through the intersection of the planes $x+2y+3z-4=0$ and $2x+y-z+5=0$ and perpendicular to the plane $5x+3y+6z+8=0$.

Sol. Any plane through the intersection of the given planes is

$$(x+2y+3z-4)+\lambda(2x+y-z+5)=0$$

or $\quad x(1+2\lambda)+y(2+\lambda)+z(3-\lambda)-(4-5\lambda)=0 \quad ...(1)$

Since the plane (1) is perpendicular to the plane

$$5x+3y+6z+8=0$$

$\therefore \quad 5(1+2\lambda)+3(2+\lambda)+6(3-\lambda)=0$

or $\quad 29+7\lambda=0;\ \lambda=-29/7.$

Putting the value of λ in (1), we get the equation of the required plane as

$$-51x-15y+50z-173=0$$

or $\quad 51x+15y-50z+173=0$

(b) The plane $2x-y+3z+5=0$ is rotated through $90°$ about its line of intersection with the plane $5x-4y-2z+1=0$. Determine the equation of the plane in the new position.

Sol. Plane through the intersection of given planes is

$$(2x-y+3z+5)+\lambda(5x-4y-2z+1)=0$$

or $\quad (2+5\lambda)x-(1+4\lambda)y+(3-2\lambda)z+(5+\lambda)=0 \quad ...(1)$

This plane makes an angle of $90°$ with the plane

$$2x-y+3z+5=0$$

Applying the condition of perpendicularity

$\Sigma a_1 a_2=0,$

$2(2+5\lambda)+1(1+4\lambda)+3(3-2\lambda)=0$

or $\quad 8\lambda+14=0 \quad \therefore \quad \lambda=-7/4$

$\therefore$ Required equation of plane from (1) on putting $\lambda=-7/4$ is

$$27x-24y-26z-13=0.$$

6. Determine the three planes through the intersection of the planes $x+y+z=1$ and $2x+3y-z+4=0$ which are parallel to the three co-ordinate axes. Also find the equation of the plane perpendicular to the yz-plane and passing through the point $(2,3,1)$ and $(4,-5,3)$.

Sol. Any plane through the intersection of the given planes is

$$(x+y+z-1)+\lambda(2x+3y-z+4)=0$$

or $\quad x(1+2\lambda)+y(1+3\lambda)+z(1-\lambda)-(1-4\lambda)=0 \quad ...(1)$

If it is parallel to x-axis, *i.e.* perpendicular to yz-plane, then by **R. 6 P. 1062** the coefficient of x should be zero.

i.e. $\quad 1+2\lambda=0$ or $\lambda=-\dfrac{1}{2}$.

Putting the value of λ in (1), we get the equation of the required plane as $y-3z+6=0$.

Similarly the equation of planes parallel to the other two axes or perpendicular to other two co-ordinate planes are $x+4z=7$ and $3x+4y+3=0$

Again general equation of the plane perpendicular to yz-plane or parallel to the axis of x is $by+cz+d=0$ $\quad (\because a=0)$.

Since it passes through the given points, we have

$3b+c+d=0$ and $-5b+3c+d=0$

$\therefore \quad \dfrac{b}{1-3}=\dfrac{c}{-5-3}=\dfrac{d}{9+5}$ or $\dfrac{b}{1}=\dfrac{c}{4}=\dfrac{d}{-7}$.

$\therefore$ the required equation of the plane is $y+4z-7=0$.

7. Find the equation of the plane through the points $(-1,1,1)$ and $(1,-1,1)$ and perpendicular to the plane $x+2y+2z=7$.

Sol. Any plane through $(-1, 1, 1)$ is

$$A(x+1)+B(y-1)+C(z-1)=0 \quad \text{...(1)}$$

It passes through $(1, -1, 1)$

$$\therefore \quad 2A-2B+0C=0. \quad \text{...(2)}$$

It is perpendicular to the plane

$$x+2y+2z=7 \quad \therefore \quad A+2B+2C=0. \quad \text{...(3)}$$

Solving (2) and (3), we get

$$\frac{A}{4}=\frac{B}{-4}=\frac{C}{6} \text{ or } \frac{A}{2}=\frac{B}{2}=\frac{C}{-3}=k, \text{ say}$$

and hence A, B, C are proportional to 2, 2, -3 and putting in (1) the equation of the plane is

$$2(x+1)+2(y-1)-3(z-1)=0$$

or $\quad 2x+2y-3z+3=0$

8. Find the equation of the plane through the intersection of the planes $x+3y+6=0$ and $3x-y-4z=0$, whose perpendicular distance from the origin is unity.

Sol. Any plane through the intersection of given planes is

$$(x+3y+6)+\lambda(3x-y-4z)=0$$

or $\quad (1+3\lambda)x+(3-\lambda)y-4\lambda z+6=0. \quad$ ...(1)

Its perpendicular distance from (0, 0, 0) is 1.

$$\therefore \quad \frac{6}{[(1+3\lambda)^2+(3-\lambda)^2+16\lambda^2]^{1/2}}=1.$$

or $\quad 1+6\lambda+9\lambda^2+9+\lambda^2-6\lambda+16\lambda^2=36$

$\therefore \quad 26\lambda^2=26$ or $\lambda=\pm 1$.

Putting the value of λ in (1), the required equations are

$2x+y-2z+3=0$

and $x-2y-2z-3=0$.

9. A variable plane passes through a fixed point (a, b, c) and meets the axes of reference in A, B and C. Show that the locus of the point of intersection of the planes through A, B and C parallel to the co-ordinate planes is

$$ax^{-1}+by^{-1}+cz^{-1}=1.$$

Sol. Let the plane be $\frac{x}{\alpha}+\frac{y}{\beta}+\frac{z}{\gamma}=1$.

It passes through (a, b, c);

$$\therefore \quad \frac{a}{\alpha}+\frac{b}{\beta}+\frac{c}{\gamma}=1. \quad \text{...(1)}$$

It meets the axes in $A(\alpha, 0, 0), B(0, \beta, 0), C(0, 0, \gamma)$.

Also planes through A, B and C and parallel respectively to the co-ordinate planes are

$x=\alpha, y=\beta, z=\gamma$ respectively. ...(2)

The locus of the point of intersection of the planes is obtained by eliminating the variables α, β, γ.

Putting for α, β, γ from (2) in (1), we get the required locus as $\frac{a}{x}+\frac{b}{y}+\frac{c}{z}=1$

or $\quad ax^{-1}+by^{-1}+cz^{-1}=1$.

10. A variable plane at a constant distance p from the origin meets the axes in A, B and C. Through A, B, C planes are drawn parallel to the co-ordinate planes; show that locus of their point of intersection is $x^{-2}+y^{-2}+z^{-2}=p^{-2}$.

Sol. Let the equation of the plane be

$$\frac{x}{a}+\frac{y}{b}+\frac{z}{c}=1.$$

It meets the axes in $A(a, 0, 0), B(0, b, 0), C(0, 0, c)$. Its distance from origin is given.

$$\therefore \quad \frac{1}{\sqrt{\left(\frac{1}{a^2}+\frac{1}{b^2}+\frac{1}{c^2}\right)}}=p$$

or $\quad \frac{1}{p^2}=\frac{1}{a^2}+\frac{1}{b^2}+\frac{1}{c^2} \quad$ ...(1)

Planes through A, B, C and parallel to co-ordinate planes are $x=a$, $y=b$ and $z=c$ respectively. ...(2)

Locus of their point of intersection is obtained by eliminating the variables a, b, c between (1) and (2). Putting for a, b and c from (2) in (1), we get the required locus as $\frac{1}{p^2}=\frac{1}{x^2}+\frac{1}{y^2}+\frac{1}{z^2}$

or $\quad x^{-2}+y^{-2}+z^{-2}=p^{-2}$.

11. (a) A variable plane is at a constant distance p from the origin and meets the axes in A, B and C. Show that the locus of the centroid of the tetrahedron $OABC$ is

$$x^{-2}+y^{-2}+z^{-2}=16p^{-2}$$

Sol. Let the plane be $\frac{x}{a}+\frac{y}{b}+\frac{z}{c}=1$.

Its distance from origin is p given.

$$\frac{1}{\sqrt{\left(\frac{1}{a^2}+\frac{1}{b^2}+\frac{1}{c^2}\right)}}=p$$

or $\quad \frac{1}{p^2}=\frac{1}{a^2}+\frac{1}{b^2}+\frac{1}{c^2} \quad$ ...(1)

Also the points O, A, B, C are respectively.

$(0, 0, 0), (a, 0, 0), (0, b, 0)$ and $(0, 0, c)$.

$$x=\frac{0+a+0+0}{4} \quad \text{or} \quad x=\frac{a}{4}, y=\frac{b}{4}, z=\frac{c}{4}.$$

$\therefore \quad a=4x, b=4y, c=4z.$

Putting for a, b, c in (1), we get the locus of centroid as

$$\frac{1}{p^2}=\frac{1}{16x^2}+\frac{1}{16y^2}+\frac{1}{16z^2}$$

or $\quad x^{-2}+y^{-2}+z^{-2}=16p^{-2}$

(b) If the planes $x=cy+bz, y=az+cx$ and $z=bx+ay$ pass through a line, then

$$a^2+b^2+c^2+2abc-1=0$$

Sol. Let l, m, n be the d.c.'s of the line through which the given planes pass. This line will be perpendicular to normals of the given planes

$$-l+cm+bn=0$$
$$cl-m+an=0$$
$$bl+am-n=0$$

Eliminating l, m, n, we have

$$\begin{vmatrix} -1 & c & b \\ c & -1 & a \\ b & a & -1 \end{vmatrix}=0$$

or $\quad -1(1-a^2)-c(-c-ba)+b(ac+b)=0$

or $\quad a^2+b^2+c^2+2abc-1=0$

12. (a) A variable plane is at a constant distance $3p$ from the origin and meets the axes in A, B, C. Show that the locus of the centroid of the triangle ABC is $x^{-2}+y^{-2}+z^{-2}=p^{-2}$

Sol. As above we have $\dfrac{1}{\sqrt{\left(\dfrac{1}{a^2}+\dfrac{1}{b^2}+\dfrac{1}{c^2}\right)}}=3p$

$\therefore \quad \dfrac{1}{9p^2}=\dfrac{1}{a^2}+\dfrac{1}{b^2}+\dfrac{1}{c^2}$ ...(1)

If (x, y, z) be the centroid of $\Delta\, ABC$, then

$x=\dfrac{a+0+0}{3}=\dfrac{a}{3}, y=\dfrac{b}{3}, z=\dfrac{c}{3}$;

$\therefore \quad a=3x, b=3y$ and $c=3z$.

Putting for a, b, c in (1), we get the locus as given.

13. A point P moves on the plane $\dfrac{x}{a}+\dfrac{y}{b}+\dfrac{z}{c}=1$ which is fixed. The plane through P perpendicular to OP meets the axes in A, B and C. The planes through A, B, C parallel to yz, zx, xy planes intersect in Q. Prove that if the axes be rectangular, the locus of Q is

$$\frac{1}{x^2}+\frac{1}{y^2}+\frac{1}{z^2}=\frac{1}{ax}+\frac{1}{by}+\frac{1}{cz}.$$

Sol. If the co-ordinates of the point P be (α, β, γ), then

$\dfrac{\alpha}{a}+\dfrac{\beta}{b}+\dfrac{\gamma}{c}=1.$ ...(1)

Again direction cosines of OP are proportional to α, β, γ and hence these are also the direction-ratios of the normal to the plane which is perpendicular to OP and since it passes through P, its equation is

$$\alpha(x-\alpha)+\beta(y-\beta)+\gamma(z-\gamma)=0$$

or $\quad \alpha x+\beta y+\gamma z=\alpha^2+\beta^2+\gamma^2.$ ...(2)

It meets the axes in A, B, C and hence the co-ordinates of these points are $\left(\dfrac{\alpha^2+\beta^2+\gamma^2}{\alpha}, 0, 0\right)$ etc. The equation of the plane through A and parallel to the yz-plane is $x=\dfrac{\alpha^2+\beta^2+\gamma^2}{\alpha}$. Similarly the equations of other planes are $y=\dfrac{\alpha^2+\beta^2+\gamma^2}{\beta}$ and $z=\dfrac{\alpha^2+\beta^2+\gamma^2}{\gamma}$.

The locus of their point of intersection is obtained by eliminating α, β, γ between the three equations of the planes and relation (1).

$$\frac{1}{x^2}+\frac{1}{y^2}+\frac{1}{z^2}=\frac{\alpha^2+\beta^2+\gamma^2}{(\alpha^2+\beta^2+\gamma^2)^2}=\frac{1}{\alpha^2+\beta^2+\gamma^2}.$$

Again $\dfrac{1}{ax}+\dfrac{1}{by}+\dfrac{1}{cz}=\dfrac{\alpha/a+\beta/b+\gamma/c}{(\alpha^2+\beta^2+\gamma^2)}=\dfrac{1}{\alpha^2+\beta^2+\gamma^2}$ from (1)

$\therefore \quad \dfrac{1}{x^2}+\dfrac{1}{y^2}+\dfrac{1}{z^2}=\dfrac{1}{ax}+\dfrac{1}{by}+\dfrac{1}{cz}$

is the required locus.

14. Two systems of rectangular axes have the same origin. If a plane cuts them at distances a, b and c and a', b', c' respectively from the origin, prove that

$$\frac{1}{a^2}+\frac{1}{b^2}+\frac{1}{c^2}=\frac{1}{a'^2}+\frac{1}{b'^2}+\frac{1}{c'^2}$$

Sol. Let the equation of the plane with respect to the first system be $x/a+y/b+z/c=1$, the axes being OX, OY and OZ.

Similarly the equation of the same plane with respect to the second system $\xi/a'+\eta/b'+\zeta/c'=1$; the axes being $(O\xi, O\eta, O\zeta)$.

Now from a point outside a plane only one perpendicular can be drawn and hence the length of the perpendicular from origin to the plane written w.r.t. two different systems of rectangular axes must be the same.

$$\therefore \quad \frac{1}{\sqrt{\left(\dfrac{1}{a^2}+\dfrac{1}{b^2}+\dfrac{1}{c^2}\right)}}=\frac{1}{\sqrt{\left(\dfrac{1}{a'^2}+\dfrac{1}{b'^2}+\dfrac{1}{c'^2}\right)}}$$

or $\quad \dfrac{1}{a^2}+\dfrac{1}{b^2}+\dfrac{1}{c^2}=\dfrac{1}{a'^2}+\dfrac{1}{b'^2}+\dfrac{1}{c'^2}.$

15. From any point P are drawn PM and PN perpendiculars to zx and xy-planes. O is the origin and α, β, γ and θ are the angles which OP makes with the co-ordinate planes and with the plane OMN. Prove that if the co-ordinates of the plane P are (a, b, c), then

(a) The plane OMN is $\dfrac{x}{a}-\dfrac{y}{b}-\dfrac{z}{c}=0.$

(b) $\theta=\sin^{-1}\dfrac{abc}{\sqrt{(a^2+b^2+c^2)(b^2c^2+c^2a^2+a^2b^2)}}$

(c) $\operatorname{cosec}^2\theta=\operatorname{cosec}^2\alpha+\operatorname{cosec}^2\beta+\operatorname{cosec}^2\gamma.$

Sol. M is the foot of the perpendicular from (a, b, c) on the zx-plane and hence this point is $(a, 0, c)$. Similarly N in the xy-plane is $(a, b, 0)$ and $O\,(0, 0, 0)$.

Any plane through (0, 0, 0) is

$Ax+By+Cz=0$ ...(1)

It passes through M and N; we have

$Aa+Bb+C.0=0$ and $Aa+0.b+Cc=0.$

$\therefore \quad \dfrac{A}{bc}=\dfrac{B}{-ac}=\dfrac{C}{-ab}.$

Hence from (1) the equation of the plane OMN is $bcx-acy-abz=0$ or $\dfrac{x}{a}-\dfrac{y}{b}-\dfrac{z}{c}=0.$

Again direction cosines of OP are proportional to $a-0, b-0, c-0$, *i.e.* a, b, c and the direction cosines of the normal to plane OMN are proportional to $\frac{1}{a}, -\frac{1}{b}, -\frac{1}{c}$. Now if θ is the angle between the line OP and the plane OMN, then $90^o - \theta$ is the angle between the line OP and the normal to the plane OMN whose direction-ratios are written above.

$\therefore \quad \cos(90° - \theta)$

$$= \frac{a\left(\frac{1}{a}\right) + b\left(-\frac{1}{b}\right) + c\left(-\frac{1}{c}\right)}{\sqrt{(a^2+b^2+c^2)}\sqrt{\left(\frac{1}{a^2}+\frac{1}{b^2}+\frac{1}{c^2}\right)}}$$

or $\quad \sin\theta = \dfrac{-abc}{\sqrt{(a^2+b^2+c^2)}\sqrt{(b^2c^2+c^2a^2+a^2b^2)}}$

Neglecting –ive sign, we have

$$\theta = \sin^{-1}\frac{abc}{\sqrt{(a^2+b^2+c^2)}\sqrt{(b^2c^2+c^2a^2+a^2b^2)}}. \quad ...(2)$$

Again α is the angle between the line OP and the yz-plane, *i.e.* $x=0$ and hence $90^o - \alpha$ is the angle between line OP and the normal to the plane $x=0$ whose direction ratios are (1, 0, 0).

$\therefore \quad \cos(90^o - \alpha) = \dfrac{a.1 + b.0 + c.0}{\sqrt{(a^2+b^2+c^2)}\sqrt{(1^2+0^2+0^2)}}$

or $\quad \sin\alpha = \dfrac{a}{\sqrt{(a^2+b^2+c^2)}}$

or $\quad \operatorname{cosec}^2\alpha = \dfrac{a^2+b^2+c^2}{a^2}$.

Similarly, $\operatorname{cosec}^2\beta = \dfrac{a^2+b^2+c^2}{b^2}$

and $\operatorname{cosec}^2\gamma = \dfrac{a^2+b^2+c^2}{c^2}$

$\therefore \quad \operatorname{cosec}^2\alpha + \operatorname{cosec}^2\beta + \operatorname{cosec}^2\gamma$

$$= (a^2+b^2+c^2)\left(\frac{1}{a^2}+\frac{1}{b^2}+\frac{1}{c^2}\right)$$

$$= \frac{(a^2+b^2+c^2)(b^2c^2+c^2a^2+a^2b^2)}{a^2b^2c^2}$$

$= \operatorname{cosec}^2\theta$ from (2)

16. T is a parallelopiped in which A, B, C and D are vertices of one face. And the face just above it has corresponding vertices A', B', C', D'. T is now compressed to S with face $ABCD$ remaining same and A', B', C', D' shifted to A'', B'', C'', D'' in S. The volume of parallelopiped S is reduced to 90% of T. Prove that locus of A'' is a plane. **(I.I.T. 2004)**

Sol. Let the equation of the plane $ABCD$ be $ax+by+cz+d=0$ and the height of the parallelopiped be h *i.e.* the upper face $A'B'C'D'$ be at a height h. Now base remains the same but A', B', C', D' is shifted to A'', B'', C'', D'' and now the volume is compressed to 90 percent of what it was. If the vertex A'' be (α, β, γ) then by given condition,

$$\frac{a\alpha + b\beta + c\gamma + d}{\sqrt{a^2+b^2+c^2}} = H = \frac{90}{100}h = 0 \cdot 9\, h$$

$\therefore \quad a\alpha + b\beta + c\gamma + d = (0 \cdot 9)\sqrt{\Sigma a^2} \cdot h = k$ say

Hence the locus of A'' is $ax+by+cz+(d-k)=0$ which represents a plane parallel to plane $ABCD$.

Problem Set (4)

Line and Plane

1. Find the co-ordinates of the point where the line joining the points $(2, -3, 1), (3, -4, -5)$ cuts the plane $2x+y+z=7$.

Sol. D.R.'s of the line are $x_2 - x_1, y_2 - y_1, z_2 - z_1$ or $1, -1, 6$. It passes through $(2, -3, 1)$.

Hence the equations are $\dfrac{x-2}{1} = \dfrac{y+3}{-1} = \dfrac{z-1}{-6} = r$, say.

The co-ordinates of any point on this line are $(r+2, -r-3, -6r+1)$.

If the point lies on the plane $2x+y+z=7$, we have $2r+4-r-3-6r+1=7; \therefore r=-1$.

Putting the value of r we get the co-ordinates of the required point as $(1, -2, 7)$.

2. (a) Prove that the distance of the point of intersection of the line $\dfrac{x-2}{3} = \dfrac{y+1}{4} = \dfrac{z-2}{12}$ and the plane $x-y+z=5$ from the point $(-1, -5, -10)$ is 13.

Sol. Any point on the line is $3r+2, 4r-1, 12r+2$. If it lies on the plane $x-y+z=5$, then

$(3r+2)-(4r-1)+(12r+2)=5. \quad \therefore r=0.$

Hence the point of intersection is $(2, -1, 2)$.

Its distance from $(-1, -5, -10)$ is

$\sqrt{[(2+1)^2+(-1+5)^2+(2+10)^2]} = \sqrt{(9+16+144)} = 13.$

(b) If the line $x=y=z$ intersects the line

$$x\sin A + y\sin B + z\sin C = 2d^2$$

$$x\sin 2A + y\sin 2B + z\sin 2C = d^2,$$

where $A+B+C=\pi$, then

$$\sin\frac{A}{2}\sin\frac{B}{2}\sin\frac{C}{2} =$$

(a) $\frac{1}{8}$ (b) $\frac{1}{12}$

(c) $\frac{1}{16}$ (d) $\frac{1}{32}$

Sol. Ans. (c).

Any point on given line $\frac{x}{1}=\frac{y}{1}=\frac{z}{1}=\lambda$ is $(\lambda,\lambda,\lambda)$.

If it intersects the given line, it must lie on both the planes representing the line.

$$\lambda(\sin A+\sin B+\sin C)=2d^2$$

and $\lambda(\sin 2A+\sin 2B+\sin 2C)=d^2$

Dividing, $\frac{\sin 2A+\sin 2B+\sin 2C}{\sin A+\sin B+\sin C}=\frac{1}{2}$

$$\frac{4\sin A\sin B\sin C}{4\cos\frac{A}{2}\cos\frac{B}{2}\cos\frac{C}{2}}=\frac{1}{2}$$

$$8\sin\frac{A}{2}\sin\frac{B}{2}\sin\frac{C}{2}=\frac{1}{2}\text{ etc.}$$

See Trigonometrical identities **Q. 8, Page 1134.**

3. (a) Find the distance of point $(1,-2,3)$ from the plane $x-y+z=5$ measured parallel to the line whose direction cosines are proportional to $2,3,-6$.

Sol. Here we are not required to find the perpendicular distance of the point $(1,-2,3)$ from the plane, but the distance measured parallel to line whose D.R.'s are 2, 3, – 6. Any line through $(1,-2,3)$ parallel to the line whose D.R.'s are 2, 3, – 6 is

$$\frac{x-1}{2}=\frac{y+2}{3}=\frac{z-3}{-6}=r\text{, say.}$$

Any point on it is $(2r+1,3r-2,-6r+3)$

If it lies on the plane $x-y+z=5$, then

$(2r+1)-(3r-2)+(-6r+3)=5.\quad\therefore\quad r=\frac{1}{7}$

$\therefore$ point is $\left(\frac{9}{7},\frac{-11}{7},\frac{15}{7}\right)$ and its distance from $(1,-2,3)$ is $\frac{1}{7}\sqrt{(4+9+36)}=\frac{7}{7}=1.$

(b) Prove that the equations of the line through (x_1,y_1,z_1) perpendicular to the lines

$$\frac{x}{l_1}=\frac{y}{m_1}=\frac{z}{n_1}\text{ and }\frac{x}{l_2}=\frac{y}{m_2}=\frac{z}{n_2}$$

and $\frac{x-x_1}{m_1n_2-m_2n_1}=\frac{y-y_1}{n_1l_2-n_2l_1}=\frac{z-z_1}{l_1m_2-l_2m_1}$

Sol. Let the line though (x_1,y_1,z_1) be

$$\frac{x-x_1}{l}=\frac{y-y_1}{m}=\frac{z-z_1}{n}.$$

Since it is perpendicular to the given lines,

$\therefore\quad ll_1+mm_1+nn_1=0,\quad ll_2+mm_2+nn_2=0.$

$$\frac{l}{m_1n_2-m_2n_1}=\frac{m}{n_1l_2-n_2l_1}=\frac{n}{l_1m_2-l_2m_1}$$

Putting the proportionate values of l,m,n in (1), we get the required equation is as given.

4. (a) The plane $2x+y+2z=9$ intersects the co-ordinate axes at A,B,C. The orthocentre of the triangle ABC is

(a) $(2,1,2)$ (b) $\left(\frac{3}{2},3,\frac{3}{2}\right)$ (c) $\left(\frac{3}{13},\frac{1}{13},\frac{3}{13}\right)$ (d) $\left(\frac{9}{7},\frac{27}{7},\frac{9}{7}\right)$

Sol. Ans. (a).

The points A,B,C are

$$A\left(\frac{9}{2},0,0\right),\ B(0,9,0),\ C\left(0,0,\frac{9}{2}\right)$$

Let (p,q,r) be the co-ordinates of orthocentre O, then $OA\perp BC, OB\perp CA, OC\perp AB$ by

$$\Sigma a_1a_2=0\Rightarrow p=r=2q$$

$\therefore\quad \frac{p}{1}=\frac{q}{1/2}=\frac{r}{1}=\lambda$ say ...(1)

Also orthocentre lies on $2x+y+2z=9$

$\therefore\quad 2p+q+2r=9$ ...(2)

or $\lambda\left(2+\frac{1}{2}+2\right)=9\ \therefore\ \lambda=2$ ...(3)

Hence from (1) and (2), $p=2,q=1,r=2$

$\therefore$ Orthocentre is $(2,1,2)$.

(b) Two systems of rectangular axes have the same origin. If a plane cuts them at distances a,b,c and a',b',c' from the origin, then

(a) $\Sigma\frac{1}{a^2}+\Sigma\frac{1}{a'^2}=0$

(b) $\Sigma\frac{1}{a^2}-\Sigma\frac{1}{a'^2}=0$

(c) $\frac{1}{a^2}+\frac{1}{b^2}-\frac{1}{c^2}+\frac{1}{a'^2}+\frac{1}{b'^2}-\frac{1}{c'^2}=0$

(d) $\frac{1}{a^2}-\frac{1}{b^2}-\frac{1}{c^2}+\frac{1}{a'^2}-\frac{1}{b'^2}-\frac{1}{c'^2}=0$ **(AIEEE 2003)**

Sol. Ans. (b).

The equations of the planes w.r.t. two different systems of axes having the same origin by intercepts form are

$$\frac{x}{a}+\frac{y}{b}+\frac{z}{c}=1\text{ and }\frac{x}{a'}+\frac{y}{b'}+\frac{z}{c'}=1$$

The distance of origin (same) from above two forms of the same plane is equal.

$\therefore\quad p=p'\Rightarrow$ (b)

5. Find the equations of the plane through the point (x,y,z) and

(i) parallel to the lines

$$\frac{x}{l_1}=\frac{y}{m_1}=\frac{z}{n_1}\text{ and }\frac{x}{l_2}=\frac{y}{m_2}=\frac{z}{n_2};$$

(ii) perpendicular to the straight line

$$\frac{x-\alpha}{l}=\frac{y-\beta}{m}=\frac{z-\gamma}{n}$$

Sol. (i) Any plane through (x_1,y_1,z_1) is

$$A(x-x_1)+B(y-y_1)+C(z-z_1)=0$$

Since the plane is parallel to the lines, hence the normal whose D.C.'s are proportional to A,B,C is perpendicular to the given lines

$\therefore\quad Al_1+Bm_1+Cn_1=0$

and $Al_2+Bm_2+Cn_2=0$

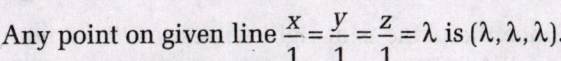

$$\therefore \quad \frac{A}{m_1 n_2 - m_2 n_1} = \frac{B}{n_1 l_2 - n_2 l_1} = \frac{C}{l_1 m_2 - l_2 m_1}$$

Putting for A, B, C in (1), we get the plane as

$$\Sigma (x - x_1)(m_1 n_2 - m_2 n_1) = 0$$

(ii) Since the plane is perpendicular to the line therefore normal is parallel to the line and hence d.c.'s are same *i.e.* l, m, n.

$\therefore$ Plane is

$$l(x - x_1) + m(y - y_1) + n(z - z_1) = 0.$$

6. A plane makes intercepts $OA = a, OB = b, OC = c$ on the co-ordinate axes (rectangular). Prove that the area of the triangle ABC is $\frac{1}{2}\sqrt{b^2c^2 + c^2a^2 + a^2b^2}$.

Sol. The equation of the plane is $\frac{x}{a} + \frac{y}{b} + \frac{z}{c} = 1$

where A is $(a, 0, 0)$, $B(0, b, 0)$ and $C(0, 0, c)$. The projection of these points in yz plane $x = 0$ is obtained by puting $x = 0$.

$A'(0,0,0)$, $B'(0,b,0)$, $C'(0,0,c)$.

If A_x be the area of $\Delta A'B'C'$ in the yz-plane which is right angled at A' then $A_x = \frac{1}{2}bc$. Similarly $A_y = \frac{1}{2}ca$ and $A_z = \frac{1}{2}ab$. If A be the area of ΔABC, then

$$A^2 = A_x^2 + A_y^2 + A_z^2$$

$$\therefore \quad A = \frac{1}{2}\sqrt{b^2c^2 + c^2a^2 + a^2b^2}$$

(b) The plane $\frac{x}{2} + \frac{y}{3} + \frac{z}{1} = 1$ meets the co-ordinate axes in the points A, B, C respectively. The area of triangle ABC in square units is :

(a) 5/2 (b) 7/2

(c) 9/2 (d) none

Sol. Proceed as in part (a). $a = 2, b = 3, c = 1$

7. From a point $P(x', y', z')$, a plane is drawn at right angles to OP to meet co-ordinate axes at A, B and C. Prove that area of the triangle ABC is $r^5 / 2x'y'z'$ where $r = OP$.

Sol. D.R.'s of OP are $x' - 0, y' - 0, z' - 0$ *i.e.*, x', y', z'

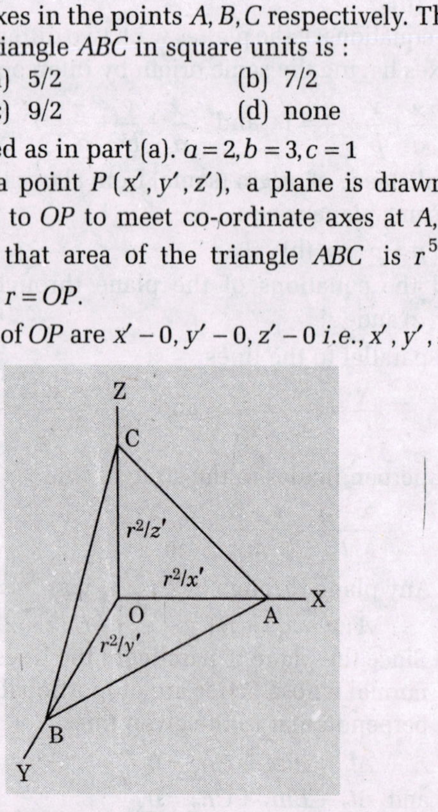

Fig. 8

Since the plane is at right anlges to OP, its normal is parallel to OP.

Hence the equation of the plane through P at right angles to OP is

$$x'(x - x') + y'(y - y') + z'(z - z') = 0$$

or $\quad xx' + yy' + zz' = x'^2 + y'^2 + z'^2 = r^2 \quad \because \ OP = r$

The points A, B, C where the plane meets the axes of co-ordinates are

$$\left(\frac{r^2}{x'}, 0, 0\right), \left(0, \frac{r^2}{y'}, 0\right), \left(0, 0, \frac{r^2}{z'}\right)$$

Now the projection of ΔABC on the yz-plane is clearly right angled $\Delta OB'C'$ whose area is

$$A_x = \frac{1}{2} OB' \cdot OC' = \frac{1}{2} \cdot \frac{r^2}{y'} \cdot \frac{r^2}{z'} = \frac{1}{2} \cdot \frac{r^4}{y'z'} \qquad ...(1)$$

Similarly as in above $A_y = \frac{1}{2}\frac{r^4}{z'x'}$, $A_z = \frac{1}{2}\frac{r^4}{x'y'}$

$$\therefore \quad A = \frac{1}{2}\sqrt{(A_x^2 + A_y^2 + A_z^2)}$$

$$= \frac{1}{2}\frac{r^4}{x'y'z'}\sqrt{[x'^2 + y'^2 + z'^2]} = \frac{1}{2}\frac{r^5}{x'y'z'}$$

8. Determine the equation of the plane on which the co-ordinates of the foot of perpendicular drawn from origin O is the point $P(\alpha, \beta, \gamma)$.

Sol. Clearly OP whose $D.R.$'s are $\alpha - 0, \beta - 0, \gamma - 0$ will be normal of the plane which passes through the point $P(\alpha, \beta, \gamma)$. Hence its equation is

$$\alpha(x - \alpha) + \beta(y - \beta) + \gamma(z - \gamma) = 0$$

or $\quad \alpha x + \beta y + \gamma z = \alpha^2 + \beta^2 + \gamma^2$

Foot of perpendicular from a point to a plane.

[Image]

9. (a) Show that if the axes are rectangular, the equation to the perpendicular from the point (α, β, γ) to the plane $ax + by + cz + d = 0$ are $\frac{x - \alpha}{a} = \frac{y - \beta}{b} = \frac{z - \gamma}{c}$ and deduce the perpendicular distance of the point (α, β, γ) from the plane. Find also the co-ordinates of the foot of the perpendicular.

Sol. The line being perpendicular to plane, *i.e.* parallel to normal so that its d.c.'s are proportional to a, b, c the D.R.'s of the normal to the plane. Also it passes through (α, β, γ) hence its equations are

$$\frac{x - \alpha}{a} = \frac{y - \beta}{b} = \frac{z - \gamma}{c} = r \text{ (say)}.$$

Any point on this line is

$$(ar + \alpha, br + \beta, cr + \gamma) \qquad ...(1)$$

If it lies on the plane $ax + by + cz + d = 0$, then

$$a(ar + \alpha) + b(br + \beta) + c(cr + \gamma) + d = 0$$

or $\quad r = -\frac{a\alpha + b\beta + c\gamma + d}{a^2 + b^2 + c^2} \qquad ...(2)$

Putting the value of r in (1), we shall find the co-ordinates of the foot of the perpendicular. This is called the image of the given point in the given plane.

Now perp. distance of plane from (α,β,γ) is the distance between points (α,β,γ) and $(ar+\alpha, br+\beta, cr+\gamma)$ for value of r given by (2) and is

$$\sqrt{(a^2r^2+b^2r^2+c^2r^2)} = r.\sqrt{(a^2+b^2+c^2)}$$

$$= -\frac{a\alpha+b\beta+c\gamma+d}{\sqrt{(a^2+b^2+c^2)}} \text{ by (2)}$$

$$= \frac{a\alpha+b\beta+c\gamma+d}{\sqrt{(a^2+b^2+c^2)}} \text{ in magnitude}$$

(b) Let the line $\frac{x-2}{3}=\frac{y-1}{-5}=\frac{z+2}{2}$ lie in the plane $x+3y-\alpha z+\beta=0$. Then (α,β) equals

(a) $(-5, 5)$ (b) $(6, -17)$

(c) $(-6, 7)$ (d) $(5, -15)$ **(AIEEE 2009)**

Sol. Ans. (c).

Line lies in the plane implies the point $(2, 1, -2)$ lies on the plane $\Rightarrow 2\alpha+\beta=-5$. Also, normal 1, 3, $-\alpha$ of the plane is perpendicular to the line $3-15-2\alpha=0$

$\therefore$ $\alpha=-6$ and hence $\beta=7$ by (1).

$\therefore$ $(\alpha,\beta)=(-6,7)\Rightarrow$ (c).

10. (a) Find the image of the point $(2,-1,3)$ in the plane $3x-2y+z=9$

Sol. The line through $P(2,-1,3)$ perpendicular to given plane or parallel to its normal $3, -2, 1$ is

$$\frac{x-2}{3}=\frac{y+1}{-2}=\frac{z-3}{1}=r \text{ say}$$

Its intersection with the plane is found as usual to be $\left(\frac{11}{7},-\frac{5}{7},\frac{20}{7}\right)$ which is the foot of perpendicular Q. The image of P in the plane will be the point R say (x_1,y_1,z_1) such that Q is mid-point of PR

$$\therefore \quad \frac{2+x_1}{2}=\frac{11}{7}, \frac{-1+y_1}{2}=\frac{-5}{7}, \frac{3+z_1}{2}=\frac{20}{7}$$

$$\therefore \quad R \text{ is } (x_1,y_1,z_1) \text{ or } \left(\frac{8}{7},\frac{-3}{7},\frac{19}{7}\right)$$

(b) The image of the point $(-1,3,4)$ in the plane $x-2y=0$ is :

(a) $(15,11,4)$ (b) $\left(-\frac{17}{3},-\frac{19}{3},1\right)$

(c) $(8,4,4)$ (d) $\left(-\frac{17}{3},-\frac{19}{3},4\right)$

(AIEEE 2006)

Sol. Ans. (d).

First find the foot of perpendicular from $(-1,3,4)$ to the plane $x-2y=0$ as in last question to be $\left(-\frac{10}{3},-\frac{5}{3},4\right)$.

It will be mid-point of $(-1,3,4)$ and image say (p,q,r).

$$\therefore \quad \frac{p-1}{2}=-\frac{10}{3}, \frac{q+3}{2}=-\frac{5}{3}, \frac{r+4}{2}=4$$

$$\therefore \quad (p,q,r)=\left(-\frac{17}{3},-\frac{19}{3},4\right)$$

11. (a) Find the image of the point $P(1,0,0)$ in the line $\frac{x-1}{2}=\frac{y+1}{-3}=\frac{z+10}{8}$

Sol. Any point Q on the given line is $(2r+1,-3r-1,8r-10)$.

Direction ratios of PQ are

$2r+1-1, -3r-1-0, 8r-10-0$

i.e., $2r, -3r-1, 8r-10$

If Q be the foot of perpendicular then Q is perpendicular to the line whose *D.R.*'s are $2, -3, 8$

$\therefore$ $2(2r)-3(-3r-1)+8(8r-10)=0$

or $77r-77=0$ $\therefore$ $r=1$

Putting $r=1$ the point Q is $(3,-4,-2)$ and P is $(1,0,0)$.

If $R(x,y,z)$ be the reflection (image) of P in the line then Q is mid-point of PR.

$$\therefore \quad (3,-4,-2)=\left(\frac{x+1}{2},\frac{y}{2},\frac{z}{2}\right)$$

Above gives $x=5, y=-8, z=-4$

$\therefore$ R is $(5,-8,-4)$.

(b) Find the equation of the plane passing through $(2,1,0)$; $(4,1,1)$; $(5,0,1)$. Find the point Q such that its distance from the plane is equal to the distance of point $P(2,1,6)$ from the plane and the line joining P and Q is perpendicular to the plane.

(IIT 2003)

Sol. Proceeding as in **Q. 2, P. 1070** the equation of the plane is $x+y-2z-3=0$.

Now if P is the point $(2, 1, 6)$, then by definition the required point Q is its image in the plane. By last Q. 10 the point Q is $(6,5,-2)$. Clearly the mid-point of PQ *i.e.*, $(4,3,2)$ lies on the plane and PQ is perpendicular to the plane.

12. A variable plane makes intercepts on the co-ordinate axes the sum of whose squares is constant and equal to k^2. Show that the locus of the foot of the perpendicular from origin to the plane is

$$(x^{-2}+y^{-2}+z^{-2})(x^2+y^2+z^2)^2=k^2$$

Sol. Let the plane be $\frac{x}{a}+\frac{y}{b}+\frac{z}{c}=1$ ...(1)

where by given condition $a^2+b^2+c^2=k^2$ ...(2)

Any line through origin and perpendicular to plane *i.e.* parallel to normal to the plane whose D.R.'s are

$\frac{1}{a},\frac{1}{b},\frac{1}{c}$ is $\frac{x-0}{1/a}=\frac{y-0}{1/b}=\frac{z-0}{1/c}=r.$ ...(3)

Any point on it is $\left(\frac{r}{a},\frac{r}{b},\frac{r}{c}\right)$. ...(4)

It will lie on the plane (1) if

$$r\left(\frac{1}{a^2}+\frac{1}{b^2}+\frac{1}{c^2}\right)=1; \quad \therefore \quad r=\frac{1}{a^{-2}+b^{-2}+c^{-2}}.$$

Putting the values of r in (4), the co-ordinates of foot of perpendicular

$$x = \frac{a^{-1}}{a^{-2}+b^{-2}+c^{-2}},\ y = \frac{b^{-1}}{\Sigma a^{-2}},\ z = \frac{c^{-1}}{\Sigma a^{-2}}$$

$$\therefore \quad x^2+y^2+z^2 = \frac{a^{-2}+b^{-2}+c^{-2}}{(a^{-2}+b^{-2}+c^{-2})^2}$$

$$= \frac{1}{(a^{-2}+b^{-2}+c^{-2})} \quad ...(5)$$

Also

$$x^{-2}+y^{-2}+z^{-2} = (a^{-2}+b^{-2}+c^{-2})^2\,(a^2+b^2+c^2)$$

$$= \frac{1}{(x^2+y^2+z^2)^2}\cdot k^2 \quad \text{by (2) and (5)}$$

$\therefore$ Locus is $(x^{-2}+y^{-2}+z^{-2})(x^2+y^2+z^2)^2 = k^2$.

13. Prove that two lines in which the planes $3x-7y-5z=1$ and $5x-13y+3z+2=0$ cut the plane $8x-11y+2z=0$ include a right angle.

Sol. If l, m, n be the d.c.'s of the line given by

$3x-7y-5z=1$ and $8x-11y+2z=0$

then it is perpendicular to normals of both the planes

$\therefore \quad 3l-7m-5n=0$

$8l-11m+2n=0. \quad \therefore \quad \frac{l}{-69} = \frac{m}{-46} = \frac{n}{23}$

$\therefore$ D.R.'s are $3, 2, -1$. ...(1)

The D.R.'s of the line given by

$5x-13y+3z+2=0$ and $8x-11y+2z=0$ are given by

$5l-13m+3n=0, \quad 8l-11m+2n=0$

$\therefore \quad \frac{l}{7} = \frac{m}{14} = \frac{n}{49}$ ...(2)

$\therefore$ D.R.'s are 1, 2, 7.

Again $a_1a_2+b_1b_2+c_1c_2 = 3.1+2.2+(-1).7=0$.

Hence the lines are perpendicular.

14. (a) Find the equation of plane passing through line $x+2y+z-2=0=2x+y-z-3$, whose perpendicular distance from $(2, 1, -1)$ is $\frac{1}{\sqrt{6}}$. **(I.I.T. 2005)**

Sol. $P+\lambda Q=0$

$\therefore \quad (1+2\lambda)\,x+(2+\lambda)\,y+(1-\lambda)\,z-(2+3\lambda)=0$

Its distance from $(2, 1, -1)$ is $\frac{1}{\sqrt{6}}$.

$$\therefore \quad \frac{2(1+2\lambda)+1(2+\lambda)+(1-\lambda)(-1)-(2+3\lambda)}{\{(1+2\lambda)^2+(2+\lambda)^2+(1-\lambda)^2\}^{1/2}} = \frac{1}{\sqrt{6}}, \text{ given}$$

$$\therefore \quad \frac{1+3\lambda}{\sqrt{6}\,(1+\lambda+\lambda^2)} = \frac{1}{\sqrt{6}}$$

or $\quad (1+3\lambda)^2 = \lambda^2+\lambda+1$

or $\quad 8\lambda^2+5\lambda=0$

$\therefore \quad \lambda = 0, -5/8; \lambda=0$ is rejected.

Putting $\lambda=-5/8$, the required plane is $2x-11y-13z+1=0$.

(b) Find the equation of the plane through the line

$P \equiv ax+by+cz+d=0,$

$Q = a'x+b'y+c'z+d'=0$

and parallel to the line $\frac{x}{l} = \frac{y}{m} = \frac{z}{n}$.

Sol. Equation of a plane through the line, *i.e.* the intersection of the given planes is $P+\lambda Q=0$ and d.c.'s of the normal are $a+\lambda a', b+\lambda b', c+\lambda c'$ and since it is parallel to the given line, the normal is perpendicular to it and hence; we have

$$l(a+\lambda a')+m(b+\lambda b')+n(c+\lambda c')=0.$$

$\therefore \quad \lambda = -\frac{al+bm+cn}{a'l+b'm+c'n}$ and hence the required equation of the plane is

$$P(a'l+b'm+c'n) = Q(al+bm+cn)=0.$$

15. The plane $ax+by=0$ is rotated about its line of intersection with the plane $z=0$ through an angle α. Prove that the equation of the plane in its new position is $ax+by \pm z\sqrt{a^2+b^2}\tan\alpha=0$.

Sol. The plane through the intersection of given planes is $ax+by+\lambda z=0$

Since the rotation is α, the angle between the planes or between their normals $a, b, 0$ and $a, b\ \lambda$ is α

$$\therefore \quad \cos\alpha = \frac{a^2+b^2+0}{\sqrt{a^2+b^2}\sqrt{a^2+b^2+\lambda^2}}$$

$$= \sqrt{\frac{a^2+b^2}{a^2+b^2+\lambda^2}}$$

$$\therefore \quad \sec^2\alpha = \frac{a^2+b^2+\lambda^2}{a^2+b^2} = 1+\frac{\lambda^2}{a^2+b^2}$$

$$\therefore \quad \sec^2\alpha-1 = \tan^2\alpha = \frac{\lambda^2}{a^2+b^2}$$

$\therefore \quad \lambda = \pm\sqrt{a^2+b^2}\tan\alpha$ etc.

16. Prove that the equation to the two planes inclined at an angle α to xy-plane and containing the line $y=0, \quad z\cos\beta = x\sin\beta$ is

$$(x^2+y^2)\tan^2\beta+z^2-2zx\tan\beta = y^2\tan^2\alpha.$$

Sol. Equation of a plane containing the given line by $P+\lambda Q=0$ is $(x\sin\beta-z\cos\beta)+\lambda y=0$ and the other plane is xy-plane *i.e.*, $z=0$, *i.e.*, $0.x+0.y+1.z=0$

The *D.R.'s* of the normals of two planes are $\sin\beta, \lambda, -\cos\beta$ and $0, 0, 1$ and they include an angle α.

$$\therefore \quad \cos\alpha = \frac{-\cos\beta}{\sqrt{\sin^2\beta+\lambda^2+\cos^2\beta}}$$

or $\quad (\lambda^2+1)\cos^2\alpha = \cos^2\beta$

$$\therefore \quad \lambda = \pm\frac{\sqrt{(\cos^2\beta-\cos^2\alpha)}}{\cos\alpha} \quad ...(1)$$

The two values of λ are equal and opposite.

Hence, the combined equation of the two planes is $[(x\sin\beta - z\cos\beta) + \lambda y][(x\sin\beta - z\cos\beta) - \lambda y] = 0$

or $(x\sin\beta - z\cos\beta)^2 - \dfrac{\cos^2\beta - \cos^2\alpha}{\cos^2\alpha} y^2 = 0$ from (1)

$$x^2\sin^2\beta + z^2\cos^2\beta - 2zx\sin\beta\cos\beta + y^2 = y^2\cos^2\beta\, sec^2\alpha$$

Dividing throughout by $\cos^2\beta$, we get

$$x^2\tan^2\beta + z^2 - 2zx\tan\beta + y^2 sec^2\beta = y^2 sec^2\alpha$$

or $(x^2 + y^2)\tan^2\beta + z^2 - 2zx\tan\beta + y^2(sec^2\beta - \tan^2\beta) = y^2 sec^2\alpha$

or $(x^2 + y^2)\tan^2\beta + z^2 - 2zx\tan\beta = y^2(sec^2\alpha - 1) = y^2\tan^2\alpha$

$\because \quad \sec^2\beta - \tan^2\beta = 1$ and $sec^2\alpha - 1 = \tan^2\alpha$

17. Find the equation of the plane which contains the line $x = \dfrac{y-3}{2} = \dfrac{z-5}{3}$, and which is perpendicular to the plane $2x + 7y + 3z = 1$.

Sol. Plane through given line is

$Ax + B(y-3) + C(z-5) = 0.$ ...(1)

where $A.1 + B.2 + C.3 = 0.$ ...(2)

Also the plane is perpendicular to $2x + 7y - 3z = 1$.

$\therefore \quad A.2 + B.7 + C.(-3) = 0.$ ...(3)

Solving (2) and (3), we get

$$\frac{A}{-27} = \frac{B}{9} = \frac{C}{3} \text{ or } \frac{A}{9} = \frac{B}{-3} = \frac{C}{-1}.$$

Hence the required plane is

$9x - 3(y-3) - 1(z-5) = 0$

or $9x - 3y - z + 14 = 0.$

18. Find the equation of the plane through the line $\dfrac{x-1}{2} = \dfrac{y-2}{3} = \dfrac{z-3}{4}$ and parallel to the co-ordinate axes.

Sol. Equation of a plane through the given line is $A(x-1) + B(y-2) + C(z-3) = 0$

where $2A + 3B + 4C = 0.$

If the plane is parallel to x-axis, *i.e.* ⊥ to yz-plane, *i.e.* $x = 0$;

$A.1 + B.0 + C.0 = 0. \quad \therefore \quad A = 0$

and hence $3B + 4C = 0$ or $\dfrac{B}{4} = \dfrac{C}{-3}.$

Thus the equation of the plane is $4(y-2) - 3(z-3) = 0$ or $4y - 3z + 1 = 0$. Similarly the equation of planes parallel to y-axis and z-axis are $2x - z + 1 = 0$ and $3x - 2y + 1 = 0$ respectively.

19. (a) Show that the equation of the plane through the line $\dfrac{x-1}{3} = \dfrac{y+6}{4} = \dfrac{z+1}{2}$ and parallel to $\dfrac{x-2}{2} = \dfrac{y-1}{-3} = \dfrac{z+4}{5}$ is $26x - 11y - 17z - 109 = 0$ and show that the point $(2, 1, -4)$ lies on it.

What is the conclusion you draw about the nature of two lines ?

Sol. Plane through first line is

$A(x-1) + B(y+6) + C(z+1) = 0$ ...(1)

where $3A + 4B + 2C = 0$ ...(2)

It is parallel to 2nd line and hence normal is perpendicular to it

$\therefore \quad 2A - 3B + 5C = 0$ ...(3)

Solving (2) and (3), we get

$$\frac{A}{26} = \frac{B}{-11} = \frac{C}{-17}$$

Putting for A, B and C in (1) the required plane is $26(x-1) - 11(y+6) - 17(z+1) = 0$

or $26x - 11y - 17z - 109 = 0$

The point $(2, 1, -4)$ clearly satisfies this plane. But it is a point which lies on the 2nd line and hence we conclude that this plane contains the 2nd line also and hence the two given lines are coplanar, *i.e.*, they lie in the same plane.

(b) The line $\dfrac{x-4}{1} = \dfrac{y-2}{1} = \dfrac{z-k}{2}$ lies exactly on the plane $2x - 4y + z = 7$ then value of k is

(a) 7 (b) −7

(c) 1 (d) no real value

(Screening 2003)

Ans. (a). Normal $2, -4, 1$ is perpendicular to line $1, 1, 2$ as $2.1 - 4.1 + 1.2 = 0$. The point $(4, 2, k)$ through which the line passes must lie on the plane $2x - 4y + z - 7 = 0$

$\therefore \quad 8 - 8 + k - 7 = 0 \quad \therefore \quad k = 7.$

(c) How is the line $\dfrac{x-4}{4} = \dfrac{y-12}{12} = \dfrac{z-8}{8}$ related to the planes

(a) $x - y + z = 0$ (b) $x - y + z - 6 = 0$

Sol. Normal to both the planes is $1, -1, 1$ and D.R.'s of the line are 4, 12, 8. Since $4.1 + 12(-1) + 8(1) = 0$, hence the line is either parallel to plane or lies in the plane. The point (4, 12, 8) through which the line passes also satisfies the plane (a) but not (b). Hence the line lies in plane (a) but is parallel to (b).

20. Show that the lines

$$\frac{x-5}{4} = \frac{y-7}{4} = \frac{z+3}{-5}, \frac{x-8}{7} = \frac{y-4}{1} = \frac{z-5}{3}$$

are coplanar; find their common point and the equation of the plane in which they lie.

Sol. General co-ordinates of the points on the two lines are $(4r_1 + 5, 4r_1 + 7, -5r_1 - 3)$ and $(7r_2 + 8, r_2 + 4, 3r_2 + 5)$.

If the two lines intersect, then these points should coincide for some values of r_1 and r_2 and hence we have $4r_1 + 5 = 7r_2 + 8$ *or* $4r_1 - 7r_2 = 3$.

Similarly, $4r_1 - r_2 = -3$ and $-5r_1 - 3r_2 = 8$.

Solving the first two equations, we get $r_2 = -1$ and $r_1 = -1$, and these values of r_1 and r_2 satisfy the third equation as well and hence the two lines intersect, and putting the values of r_1 and r_2 in the general co-ordinates the common point of intersection is (1, 3, 2).

Again, the equation of the plane in which they lie is the plane containing one of them and parallel to the other and its equation is

$$\begin{vmatrix} x-5 & y-7 & z+3 \\ 4 & 4 & -5 \\ 7 & 1 & 3 \end{vmatrix} = 0$$

or $(x-5)\,17-(y-7)\,47+(z+3)\,(-24)=0$

or $17x-47y-24z+172=0.$

Clearly the point (8, 4, 5) through which the second line passes also satisfies this plane. Hence the second line also lies in this plane so that the two lines are coplanar.

21. Show that the lines $\dfrac{x+4}{3}=\dfrac{y+6}{5}=\dfrac{z-1}{-2}$

and $3x-2y+z+5=0=2x+3y+4z-4$

are coplanar. Find also the co-ordinates of their point of intersection and the equation of the plane in which they lie.

Sol. Equation of any plane through the line

$3x-2y+z+5=0, 2x+3y+4z-4=0$

is $(3x-2y+z+5)+\lambda\,(2x+3y+4z-4)=0$

or $(3+2\lambda)\,x+(-2+3\lambda)\,y+(1+4\lambda)\,z+(5-4\lambda)=0$

If it is parallel to $\dfrac{x+4}{3}=\dfrac{y+6}{5}=\dfrac{z-1}{-2}$, then

$3\,(3+2\lambda)+5\,(-2+3\lambda)-2\,(1+4\lambda)=0.$

$\therefore\quad 13\lambda=3$ or $\lambda=\dfrac{3}{13}$

Hence the plane is $45x-17y+25z+53=0.$

The point $(-4,-6,1)$ on the other line clearly satisfies it.

$\because\quad 45\,(-4)-17\,(-6)+25\,(1)+53=0$

and hence the other line also lies in this plane, so that the two lines are coplanar.

Point of intersection

Any point on the line is $(3r-4, 5r-6, -2r+1)$.

As the two lines meet, this point should satisfy both the equations of the other line.

$\therefore\quad 3\,(3r-4)-2\,(5r-6)+(-2r+1)+5=0$

or $-3r+6=0;\ \therefore\ r=2.$

and $2\,(3r-4)+3\,(5r-6)+4\,(-2r+1)-4=0$

$13r-26=0;\quad \therefore\ r=2.$

Since the two values of r are equal, therefore the two lines intersect and putting $r=2$, the point of intersection is $(2, 4, -3)$.

22. (a) Prove that the lines

$$\frac{x-a+d}{\alpha-\delta}=\frac{y-a}{\alpha}=\frac{z-a-d}{\alpha+\delta},$$

$$\frac{x-b+c}{\beta-\gamma}=\frac{y-b}{\beta}=\frac{z-b-c}{\beta+\gamma}$$

are coplanar and find the equation to the plane in which they lie.

Sol. The lines will be coplanar if by § 4 (7), P. 1063

$$\begin{vmatrix} a-d-b+c & a-b & a+d-b-c \\ \alpha-\delta & \alpha & \alpha+\delta \\ \beta-\gamma & \beta & \beta+\gamma \end{vmatrix}=0$$

Add 3rd column to first and it becomes twice the second and hence the determinant is zero as the two columns are identical.

Again the equation of the plane in which they lie is

$$\begin{vmatrix} x-a+d & y-a & z-a-d \\ \alpha-\delta & \alpha & \alpha+\delta \\ \beta-\gamma & \beta & \beta+\gamma \end{vmatrix}=0$$

Adding 1st and 3rd columns and subtracting twice the 2nd, we get

$$\begin{vmatrix} x+z-2y & y-a & z-a-d \\ 0 & \alpha & \alpha+\delta \\ 0 & \beta & \beta+\gamma \end{vmatrix}=0$$

or $\{\alpha\,(\beta+\gamma)-\beta\,(\alpha+\delta)\}\,(x+z-2y)=0$

or $x+z-2y=0.$

(b) Lines $\dfrac{x-1}{2}=\dfrac{y+1}{3}=\dfrac{z-1}{4}, \dfrac{x-3}{1}=\dfrac{y-k}{2}=\dfrac{z}{1}$ intersect for k equal to

(a) 2/9 (b) 9/2

(c) 0 (d) 1 **(IIT-Sc. 2004)**

Sol. Ans. (b). Condition of coplanarity gives

$$\begin{vmatrix} 2 & k+1 & -1 \\ 2 & 3 & 4 \\ 1 & 2 & 1 \end{vmatrix}=0$$

or $-10+2k+2-1=0\quad \therefore\ k=9/2$

(c) If the straight lines $x=1+s, y=-3-\lambda s, z=1+\lambda s$ and $x=\dfrac{t}{2}, y=1+t, z=2-t$ with parameters s and t respectively are coplanar, then $\lambda =$

(a) -2 (b) -1

(c) $-1/2$ (d) 0 **(AIEEE 2004)**

Sol. Ans. (a).

The equation of the lines can be written as

$$\frac{x-1}{1}=\frac{y+3}{-\lambda}=\frac{z-1}{\lambda}=s$$

and $\dfrac{x}{1/2}=\dfrac{y-1}{1}=\dfrac{z-2}{-1}=t$

The condition of coplanarity gives

$$\begin{vmatrix} 1-0 & -3-1 & 1-2 \\ 1 & -\lambda & \lambda \\ 1/2 & 1 & -1 \end{vmatrix}=0. \text{ Apply } C_3+C_2$$

or $\Delta=\begin{vmatrix} 1 & -4 & -5 \\ 1 & -\lambda & 0 \\ 1/2 & 1 & 0 \end{vmatrix}=0$

or $-5\left(1+\dfrac{\lambda}{2}\right)=0\quad \therefore\ \lambda=-2$

23. Prove that the plane through the point (α, β, γ) and the line $x = py + q = rz + s$ is given by

$$\begin{vmatrix} x & py+q & rz+s \\ \alpha & p\beta+q & r\gamma+s \\ 1 & 1 & 1 \end{vmatrix} = 0$$

Sol. The given line can be written in symmetrical form as

$$\frac{x}{1} = \frac{(y+q/p)}{1/p} = \frac{z+s/r}{1/r}.$$

Any plane through this line is

$$Ax + B(y+q/p) + C(z+s/r) = 0$$

where $A.1 + B.1/p + C.1/r = 0$

Also it passes through (α, β, γ),

$\therefore$ $A.\alpha + B(\beta + q/p) + C(\gamma + s/r) = 0.$

Eliminating A, B, C we get the plane as

$$\begin{vmatrix} x & y+q/p & z+s/r \\ \alpha & \beta+q/p & \gamma+s/r \\ 1 & 1/p & 1/r \end{vmatrix} = 0$$

or $$\begin{vmatrix} x & py+q & rz+s \\ \alpha & p\beta+q & r\gamma+s \\ 1 & 1 & 1 \end{vmatrix} = 0$$

We have multiplied C_2 and C_3 by p and r respectively.

24. Prove that the planes

$$2x + y + z + 4 = 0, \quad y - z + 4 = 0,$$
$$3x + 2y + z + 8 = 0$$

intersect in a line.

Sol. The symmetrcial form of the line given by first two planes is given by

$$2l + m + n = 0, \quad 0l + m - n = 0$$

$\therefore$ $m = n$ and $2l + 2m = 0$

$$\frac{l}{1} = \frac{m}{-1} = \frac{n}{-1}$$

Putting $x = 0$ and solving $y + z + 4 = 0$ and $y - z + 4 = 0$ we get $y = -4, z = 0$.

$\because$ Hence, any point is $(0, -4, 0)$

$\therefore$ Line is $\frac{x}{1} = \frac{y+4}{-1} = \frac{z}{-1}$

It will lie on the 3rd plane if normal is perpendicular to it and the point $(0, -4, 0)$ lies on it. This point clearly satisfies the equation of the 3rd plane and also

$$3(1) + 2(-1) + 1(-1) = 0.$$

Hence the line lies in the 3rd plane. Thus the three planes intersect in a line.

25. Find the nature of intersection of the three planes

$$2x + y - 4z - 17 = 0,$$
$$3x + 2y - 2z - 25 = 0$$
and $$2x - 4y + 3z + 25 = 0$$

Sol. As in last question the equation of the line of intersection of first two planes is

$$\frac{x-9}{6} = \frac{y+1}{-8} = \frac{z-0}{1} = r$$

It is neither parallel or lies in the 3rd plane as the point $(9, -1, 0)$ does not lie on it and also it is not perpendicular to normal $2, -4, 3$ as $2(6) - 4(-8) + 3(1) = 47 \neq 0$

The co-ordinates of any point on this line are

$$6r + 9, -8r - 1, r$$

It will lie on the 3rd plane if

$$2(6r+9) - 4(-8r-1) + 3r + 25 = 0$$

or $47r + 47 = 0$ $\therefore$ $r = -1$

Hence, the point becomes $(3, 7, -1)$. Thus the three planes meet at a point $(3, 7, -1)$.

Paragraph for Question No. 26 :

Consider the line $L_1 : \frac{x+1}{3} = \frac{y+2}{1} = \frac{z+1}{2}$,

$$L_2 : \frac{x-2}{1} = \frac{y+2}{2} = \frac{z-3}{3}$$

26. (a) The unit vector perpendicular to both L_1 and L_2 is

(a) $\frac{-\hat{i}+7\hat{j}+7\hat{k}}{\sqrt{99}}$ (b) $\frac{-\hat{i}-7\hat{j}+5\hat{k}}{5\sqrt{3}}$

(c) $\frac{-\hat{i}+7\hat{j}+5\hat{k}}{5\sqrt{3}}$ (d) $\frac{7\hat{i}-7\hat{j}-\hat{k}}{\sqrt{99}}$

Sol. Ans. (b). If $l\mathbf{i} + m\mathbf{j} + n\mathbf{k}$ be the vector perpendicular to both then

$$3l + m + 2n = 0$$
$$l + 2m + 3n = 0$$

Eliminating l, m, n, we get

$$\begin{vmatrix} \mathbf{i} & \mathbf{j} & \mathbf{k} \\ 3 & 1 & 2 \\ 1 & 2 & 3 \end{vmatrix} = -\mathbf{i} - 7\mathbf{j} + 5\mathbf{k}$$

Hence a unit vector is $\frac{-\mathbf{i}-7\mathbf{j}+5\mathbf{k}}{\sqrt{1+49+25}} = \frac{-\mathbf{i}-7\mathbf{j}+5\mathbf{k}}{5\sqrt{3}}$

(b) The shortest distance between L_1 and L_2 is

(a) 0 (b) $\frac{17}{\sqrt{3}}$

(c) $\frac{41}{5\sqrt{3}}$ (d) $\frac{17}{5\sqrt{3}}$

Sol. Ans. (d). $P(-1, -2, -1)$ and $Q(2, -2, 3)$ are two points on the lines L_1 and L_2. D.R. of the line perpendicular to both are $-1, -7, 5$.

$$\therefore \quad \text{S.D.} = l(x_2 - x_1) + m(y_2 - y_1) + n(z_2 - z_1)$$
$$= \frac{-1(2+1) - 7(2-2) + 5(3+1)}{\sqrt{1+49+25}} = \frac{17}{5\sqrt{3}}$$

(c) The distance of the point $(1, 1, 1)$ from the plane passing through the point $(-1, -2, -1)$ and whose normal is perpendicular to both the lines L_1 and L_2 is

(a) $\frac{2}{\sqrt{75}}$ (b) $\frac{7}{\sqrt{75}}$

(c) $\frac{13}{\sqrt{75}}$ (d) $\frac{23}{\sqrt{75}}$

Sol. Ans. (c). The required plane is

$$-1(x+1)-7(y+2)+5(z+1)=0$$

or $\quad x+7y-5z+10=0$

or $\quad p=\dfrac{1+7-5+10}{\sqrt{1+49+25}}=\dfrac{13}{\sqrt{75}}$

§5. The Sphere

1. The centre and radius of the sphere
$$x^2+y^2+z^2+2ux+2vy+2wz+d=0$$
are $(-u,-v,-w)$ and $\sqrt{(u^2+v^2+w^2-d)}$

2. Sphere on the join of **two given points as diameter.**
$$(x-x_1)(x-x_2)+(y-y_1)(y-y_2)+(z-z_1)(z-z_2)=0$$

3. The equation of sphere $OABC$ is
$$x^2+y^2+z^2-ax-by-cz=0$$
where A, B, C are $(a,0,0,)$, $(0,b,0)$ and $(0,0,c)$.

4. The equation of the **tangent plane** at (x_1, y_1, z_1) is
$$xx_1+yy_1+zz_1+u(x+x_1)+v(y+y_1)+w(z+z_1)+d=0$$
and it is perpendicular to the radius through the point of contact.

5. Condition for **orthogonal intersection** of two spheres is
$$2u_1u_2+2v_1v_2+2w_1w_2=d_1+d_2$$

6. The square of the **length of the tangent from** a given point to a given sphere in whose equation, the coefficients of x^2, y^2 and z^2 are each unity is obtained by substituting the co-ordinates of the point in its equation.

7. The **radical plane** of two given spheres is
$$2x(u_1-u_2)+2y(v_1-v_2)+2z(w_1-w_2)+d_1-d_2=0$$
i.e., $\quad S_1-S_2=0$

8. **Coaxial spheres** $x^2+y^2+z^2+2ux+d=0$, where d is constant and u variable.

§ 6 Plane section of a sphere

To prove that the section of a sphere by a plane is a circle and to find its radius and centre.

The dotted line denotes the section of the sphere by a plane and let P be any point on it. From O draw ON perpendicular to the plane and the foot of the

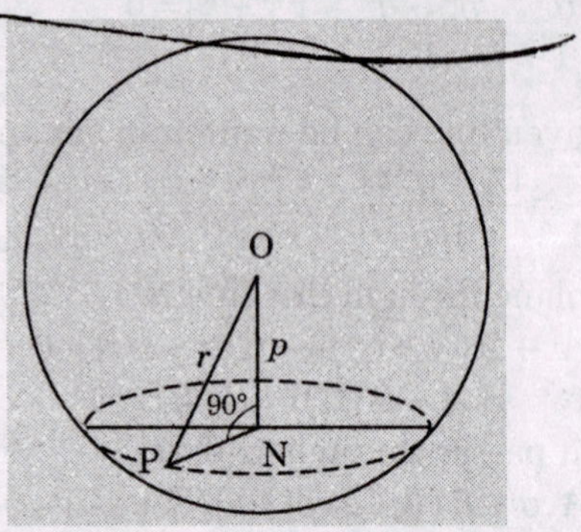

Fig. 9

perpendicular be N. Now NP is any line in the plane and ON is perpendicular to the plane; thus ON is perpendicular to every line lying in the plane.

$\therefore \quad ON$ is $\perp$ to NP and as such $OP^2=ON^2+NP^2$

or $\quad NP=\sqrt{OP^2-ON^2}=$ constant

as OP is equal to the radius of the sphere and ON is the perpendicular from the centre on the given plane. Thus for all positions of P; NP is constant hence the locus of this point P is a circle whose centre is the point N and radius NP.

Centre. The foot of the perpendicular from the centre of the sphere to the plane is the centre of the circle.

$(\text{radius})^2=(\text{radius of sphere})^2-(\perp \text{ from centre on the plane})^2$.

Great Circle. The section of a sphere by a plane through the centre of the sphere is a great circle. Its centre and radius are the same as those the given sphere.

Problem Set (5)

Ex. 1. Find the equation of a sphere which passes through origin and intercepts lengths a, b and c on the axes respectively.

Or

Find the equation of a sphere passing through origin and the points, $(a,0,0)$, $(0,b,0)$ and $(0,0,c)$.

Or

If the plane $x/a+y/b+z/c=1$ meets the co-ordinate axes in points A, B, C and O be the origin. Find the sphere $OABC$.

Sol. Let the equation of sphere $OABC$ be
$$x^2+y^2+z^2+2ux+2vy+2wz+d=0.$$

It passes through origin

$\therefore \quad d=0.$

Hence its equation is
$$x^2+y^2+z^2+2ux+2vy+2wz=0.$$

Since the sphere passes through the point $A(a,0,0)$ and similarly through $B(0,b,0)$ and $C(0,0,c)$.

It passes through $A(a,0,0)$;

$\therefore \quad a^2+2ua=0$ or $2u=-a.$

Similarly $2v=-b$ and $2w=-c$.

Hence the equation of sphere $OABC$ is

$x^2+y^2+z^2-ax-by-cz=0.$ **[Remember]**

Ex. 2. Find the equation of the sphere circumscribing the tetrahedron whose faces are

$$x=0, y=0, z=0, \frac{x}{a}+\frac{y}{b}+\frac{z}{c}=1.$$

Sol. Solving and taking three planes at a time, we get the four vertices as $O(0,0,0), A(a,0,0)$ and $B(0,b,0)$ and $C(0,0,c)$, so that the sphere $OABC$ as in Ex. 1. is

$$x^2+y^2+z^2-ax-by-cz=0.$$

Ex. 3. A sphere of radius k passes through the origin and meets the axes in A, B, C. Prove that the centroid of the triangle ABC lies on the sphere, $9(x^2+y^2+z^2)=4k^2$.

Sol. Let the co-ordinates of A, B and C be $(a,0,0), (0,b,0)$ and $(0,0,c)$ and the fourth point be $(0,0,0)$. The equation of the sphere through these points is $x^2+y^2+z^2-ax-by-cz=0$

It radius is $\sqrt{\left(\frac{a^2}{4}+\frac{b^2}{4}+\frac{c^2}{4}\right)}=k.$

$\therefore \quad a^2+b^2+c^2=4k^2$ ...(1)

If (f,g,h) be the co-ordinates of the centroid of $\Delta\, ABC$ then $f=a/3, g=b/3$ and $h=c/3$. Putting in (1) for a,b,c we get $9(f^2+g^2+h^2)=4k^2$. Generalising, we get the required locus as given.

Ex. 4. A plane passes through a fixed point (p,q,r) and cuts the axes in A, B, C. Show that the locus of the centre of the sphere $OABC$ is $\frac{p}{x}+\frac{q}{y}+\frac{r}{z}=2.$

Sol. Let the equation of the plane be

$$\frac{x}{a}+\frac{y}{b}+\frac{z}{c}=1 \qquad ...(1)$$

and hence the points A, B, C are $(a,0,0), (0,b,0)$ and $(0,0,c)$ and the equation of the sphere $OABC$ is $x^2+y^2+z^2-ax-by-cz=0$. If (f,g,h) be the centre, then

$$f=\frac{a}{2}, g=\frac{b}{2} \text{ and } h=\frac{c}{2}. \qquad ...(2)$$

Now the plane (1) passes through (p,q,r).

$\therefore \quad p/a+q/b+r/c=1.$ ...(3)

Putting the values of a, b and c from (2) in (3), we get $p/2f+q/2g+r/2h=1$. Generalizing, (f,g,h) we get the locus as $p/x+q/y+r/z=2$.

Ex. 5. A sphere of constant radius r passes through the origin O and cuts the axes in A, B and C. Prove that the locus of the foot of the perpendicular from O to the plane ABC is given by

$$(x^2+y^2+z^2)^2(x^{-2}+y^{-2}+z^{-2})=4r^2$$

Sol. Plane is $x/a+y/b+z/c=1$. ...(1)

Sphere is $x^2+y^2+z^2-ax-by-cz=0$, ...(2)

where $a^2+b^2+c^2=4r^2$. ...(3)

Any line through origin perpendicular to plane (1) is

$$\frac{x}{1/a}=\frac{y}{1/b}=\frac{z}{1/c}=\lambda.$$

Any point on it is $(\lambda/a, \lambda/b, \lambda/c)$.

If it is foot of perpendicular (x,y,z), then

$$x=\frac{\lambda}{a}, y=\frac{\lambda}{b}, z=\frac{\lambda}{c};$$

$$\therefore \quad a=\frac{\lambda}{x},\ b=\frac{\lambda}{y} \text{ and } c=\frac{\lambda}{z}.$$

Putting in (3), we get

$$\lambda^2(x^{-2}+y^{-2}+z^{-2})=4r^2. \qquad ...(4)$$

Putting in (1), we get $\frac{1}{\lambda}(x^2+y^2+z^2)=1.$ ...(5)

Eliminating λ between (4) and (5), we get the required locus as

$$(x^2+y^2+z^2)^2(x^{-2}+y^{-2}+z^{-2})=4r^2.$$

Ex. 6. Find the equation of a sphere through the four points $(0,0,0), (-a,b,c), (a,-b,c), (a,b,-c)$ and determine its radius.

Sol. Since the sphere passes through origin, its equation is of the form

$$x^2+y^2+z^2+2ux+2vy+2wz=0. \qquad ...(1)$$

Substituting the co-ordinates of the other given points, we get

$$a^2+b^2+c^2-2ua+2vb+2wc=0. \qquad ...(2)$$

$$a^2+b^2+c^2+2ua-2vb+2wc=0. \qquad ...(3)$$

$$a^2+b^2+c^2+2ua+2vb-2wc=0. \qquad ...(4)$$

Adding (2) and (3), $2(a^2+b^2+c^2)=-4wc$

or $\quad 2w=\dfrac{a^2+b^2+c^2}{-b}.$

Similarly, $2v=\dfrac{a^2+b^2+c^2}{-c}$ and $2u=\dfrac{a^2+b^2+c^2}{-a}$

Putting the values of u, v, w in (1), we get

$$x^2+y^2+z^2-(a^2+b^2+c^2)\left(\frac{x}{a}+\frac{y}{b}+\frac{z}{c}\right)=0.$$

The radius of the sphere is $\sqrt{(u^2+v^2+w^2)}, d$ being zero

or $\quad R=\sqrt{\left\{\dfrac{(a^2+b^2+c^2)^2}{4}\left(\dfrac{1}{a^2}+\dfrac{1}{b^2}+\dfrac{1}{c^2}\right)\right\}}$

$$=\frac{a^2+b^2+c^2}{2}\sqrt{(a^{-2}+b^{-2}+c^{-2})}.$$

Another form. Prove that the equation to a sphere circumscribing the tetrahedron whose faces are

$\frac{y}{b}+\frac{z}{c}=0, \frac{z}{c}+\frac{x}{a}=0, \frac{x}{a}+\frac{y}{b}=0, \frac{x}{a}+\frac{y}{b}+\frac{z}{c}=1$ is

$$\frac{x^2+y^2+z^2}{a^2+b^2+c^2}-\frac{x}{a}-\frac{y}{b}-\frac{z}{c}=0.$$

If we solve the four equations taking three at a time, we get the points $(0,0,0), (-a,b,c), (a,-b,c), (a,b,-c)$.

(b) Find the equation of the sphere passing through the points (0, 0, 0), (– 1, 1, 1), (1, – 1, 1) and (1, 1, – 1).

Sol. Proceed as in part (a).

$$x^2+y^2+z^2=3(x+y+z)$$

Ex. 7. (a). Find the co-ordinates of the centre and the radius of the circle

$$x+2y+2z=15, x^2+y^2+z^2-2y-4z=11.$$

Length of the perpendicular from the centre (0, 1, 2) on given plane is

$$\frac{0+2+4-15}{\sqrt{(1+4+4)}}=\frac{-9}{3}=\frac{9}{3}=3.$$

$\therefore$ (radius of circle)^2 = (radius of sphere)^2

– (perp. from centre on the plane)^2

i.e., $r^2=R^2=p^2=16-9=7;\quad \therefore\quad r=\sqrt{7}.$

Centre of the circle is the foot of the perpendicular from the centre of the sphere (0, 1, 2) to the plane $x+2y+2z=15.$ Any line through (0, 1, 2) perpendicular to plane, *i.e.* parallel to its normal whose D.R.'s are 1, 2, 2 is

$$\frac{x-0}{1}=\frac{y-1}{2}=\frac{z-2}{2}=r \text{ say.}$$

Any point on it is $r, 2r+1, 2r+2.$ For foot of perpendicular this must lie on the given plane;

$\therefore\quad r+2(2r+1)+2(2r+2)=15$

or $\quad 9r=9;\quad \therefore\quad r=1.$

Hence the centre of circle is (1, 3, 4).

(b) The centre of the circle

$$x^2+y^2+z^2-3x+4y-2z-5=0$$

and $5x-2y+4z+7=0$ is

(a) $\left(\frac{3}{2},-2,1\right)$ (b) (1, 1, 1)

(c) (– 1, – 1, – 1) (d) (0, 0, 0)

Sol. Ans. (c).

Find the foot of perp. from centre $\left(\frac{3}{2},-2,1\right)$ to the plane. Any line through centre, perpendicular to plane *i.e.*, parallel to normal is

$$\frac{x-3/2}{5}=\frac{y+2}{-2}=\frac{z-1}{4}=r$$

Any point on the line is $(5r+3/2,-2r-2,4r+1)$. It lies on given plane.

$$\therefore\quad 5\left(5r+\frac{3}{2}\right)-2(-2r-2)+4(4r+1)+7=0$$

$$r(25+4+16)+\left(\frac{15}{2}+4+4+7\right)=0$$

$$\therefore\quad 45r+\frac{45}{2}=0\qquad \therefore\quad r=-\frac{1}{2}$$

$\therefore$ Foot of perpendicular or centre of circle is (– 1, – 1, – 1) $\Rightarrow$ (c).

Ex. 8. (a). Find the equation of the sphere through the circle $x^2+y^2+z^2=9, 2x+3y+4z=5$ and the point (1, 2, 3).

Sol. Sphere through the given circle is given by

$$S+\lambda P=0.$$

or $\quad (x^2+y^2+z^2-9)+\lambda(2x+3y+4z-5)=0.$

It passes through (1, 2, 3); $\quad\therefore\quad \lambda=-\frac{1}{3}.$

$\therefore$ Required sphere is

$$3(x^2+y^2+z^2)-2x-3y-4z-22=0.$$

(b) Find the equation of the sphere through the circle $x^2+y^2=a^2, z=0$ and through the point (α,β,γ).

Since $z=0$ the equation of the circle can be written as $S=x^2+y^2+z^2=a^2$ and $P=z=0.$ **(Note z^2)**

The sphere through the given circle is $S+\lambda P=0$

Pass through (α,β,γ) find the value of λ.

Ans. $(x^2+y^2+z^2-a^2)\gamma+(a^2-\alpha^2-\beta^2-\gamma^2)z=0.$

(c) A circle with centre (2, 3, 0) and radius 1 is drawn in the plane $z=0$. Find the equation of the sphere which passes through this circle and the point (1, 1, 1).

Circle is $(x-2)^2+(y-3)^2=1, z=0$

Write it as $S\equiv(x-2)^2+(y-3)^2+z^2-1=0,$

Required sphere is $S+\lambda P=0$ and pass through (1, 1, 1) so that $\lambda=-5.$

Ans. $x^2+y^2+z^2-4x-6y-5z+12=0.$

Ex. 9. (a). Find the equation of a sphere for which the circle $x^2+y^2+7y-2z+2=0,\ 2x+3y+4z=8$ is a great circle.

Sol. Equation of a sphere through given circle is

$$(x^2+y^2+z^2+7y-2z+2)+\lambda(2x+3y+4z-8)=0.$$

Its centre is $\left(-\lambda,-\frac{7+3\lambda}{2},-\frac{4\lambda-2}{2}\right).$

If the given circle is a great circle, then the plane $2x+3y+4z-8=0$ passes through centre.

$$\therefore\quad -2\lambda-\frac{3}{2}(7+3\lambda)-2(4\lambda-2)-8=0.$$

$$\therefore\quad \left(-2-\frac{9}{2}-8\right)\lambda-\frac{21}{2}+4-8=0,$$

$$\frac{29\lambda}{2}+\frac{29}{2}=0;$$

$\therefore\quad \lambda=-1.$

Putting $\lambda=-1$, we get the equation of sphere as

$$x^2+y^2+z^2-2x+4y-6z+10=0.$$

(b) Obtain the equation of the sphere having the circle $x^2+y^2+z^2+10y-4z=18,$ $x-2y+z=3$ as a great circle.

Ans. $x^2+y^2+z^2+3x+4y-z-17=0.$

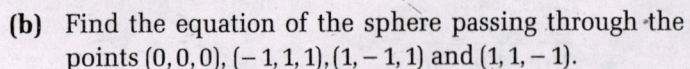

Ex. 10. A variable plane is parallel to the given plane $\frac{x}{a}+\frac{y}{b}+\frac{z}{c}=0$ and meets the axis in A, B, C respectively. Prove that the circle ABC lies on the cone $yz\,(b/c+c/b)+zx\,(a/c+c/a)+xy\,(a/b+b/a)=0$.

The equation of the plane parallel to the given plane is

$$\frac{x}{a}+\frac{y}{b}+\frac{z}{c}=k. \quad ...(1)$$

The co-ordinates of the points A, B and C are $(ak, 0, 0), (0, bk, 0)$ and $(0, 0, ck)$.

As in **Ex. 1, P. 1082** the equation of the sphere $OABC$ is

$$x^2+y^2+z^2-akx-bky-ckz=0$$

or $$x^2+y^2+z^2=k\,(ax+by+cz). \quad ...(2)$$

Equations (1) and (2) together represent the circle ABC whose locus can be obtained by eliminating k between (1) and (2), and is therefore

$$(x^2+y^2+z^2)=\left(\frac{x}{a}+\frac{y}{b}+\frac{z}{c}\right)(ax+by+cz)$$

or $$yz\left(\frac{b}{c}+\frac{c}{b}\right)+zx\left(\frac{c}{a}+\frac{a}{c}\right)+xy\left(\frac{a}{b}+\frac{b}{a}\right)=0.$$

Ex. 11. Find the equation of the two tangent planes to the sphere $x^2+y^2+z^2-2y-6z+5=0$ which are parallel to the plane $2x+2y-z=0$.

Sol. Any plane parallel to the given plane is

$$2x+2y-z+\lambda=0 \quad ...(1)$$

If it is a tangent plane then perpendicular from centre $(0, 1, 3)$ should be equal to radius $\sqrt{(0+1+9-5)}=\sqrt{5}$.

$$\therefore \quad \frac{0+2.1-3+\lambda}{\sqrt{(4+4+1)}}=\pm\sqrt{5}; \quad \therefore \lambda=1\pm 3\sqrt{5}.$$

Hence the required tangent planes are

$$2x+2y-z+(1\pm 3\sqrt{5})=0.$$

Ex. 12. Show that the plane $2x-2y+z+12=0$ touches the sphere $x^2+y^2+z^2-2x-4y+2z-3=0$ and find the point of contact.

Sol. If the given plane touches the sphere then perpendicular from centre $(1, 2, -1)$ to the given plane should be equal to the radius $\sqrt{(1+4+1+3)}$, *i.e.* 3.

$$\therefore \quad p=\frac{2(1)-2(2)+1(-1+12)}{\sqrt{(4+4+1)}}=\frac{9}{3}=3=\text{radius}.$$

Hence the given plane touches the sphere.

Again the point of contact is the foot of perpendicular from the centre of sphere $(1, 2, -1)$ to the tangent plane. Any line perpendicular to tangent plane will be parallel to its normal whose direction ratio are $2, -2, 1$ and hence its equations are

$$\frac{x-1}{2}=\frac{y-2}{-2}=\frac{z+1}{1}=r \text{ (say).}$$

Any point on the line is $(2r+1, -2r+2, r-1)$.

If it is foot of perpendicular from centre then it will lie on the plane $2x-2y+z+12=0$.

$$\therefore \quad 2(2r+1)-2(-2r+2)+(r-1)+12=0$$

$$\therefore \quad r=-1.$$

Putting $r=-1$ the point of contact is $(-1, 4, -2)$.

Ex. 13. Find the equation of a sphere touching the three co-ordinate planes. How many such spheres can be drawn ?

Sol. Let the radius of the sphere be a; then the distance of its centre from co-ordinate planes which it is touching should be equal to radius a. Hence its centre is (a, a, a). But since the centre can be in any octant we say that its centre is $(\pm a, \pm a, \pm a)$ and radius a, so that its equation is $(x\pm a)^2+(y\pm a)^2+(z\pm a)^2=a^2$.

or $$x^2+y^2+z^2\pm 2ax\pm 2ay\pm 2az+2a^2=0.$$

There can be an infinite number of such spheres depending on the value of a. In case the radius *i.e.* a be given; then only eight such spheres can be drawn.

Ex. 14. Prove that the equation of a sphere which lies in the octant $OXYZ$ and touches the co-ordinate planes is of the form $x^2+y^2+z^2-2\lambda\,(x+y+z)+2\lambda^2=0$.

Sol. The centre of the sphere being in octant $OXYZ$ will be $(\lambda, \lambda, \lambda)$ from Q. 13 etc.

Ex. 15. A sphere is inscribed in the tetrahedron whose faces are $x=0, y=0, z=0$ and $2x+6y+3z-14=0$. Find its centre, radius and equation.

Sol. The equation of the sphere touching co-ordinate planes is $x^2+y^2+z^2-2\lambda\,(x+y+z)+2\lambda^2=0$, (by Q. 12). Its centre is $(\lambda, \lambda, \lambda)$ and radius λ.

If it touches $2x+6y+3z-14=0$; then perpendicular from centre should be equal to radius.

$$\therefore \quad \frac{2\lambda+6\lambda+3\lambda-14}{\sqrt{(4+36+9)}}=\lambda$$

or $$11\lambda-14=\pm 7\lambda \quad \therefore \lambda=\frac{7}{9} \text{ or } \frac{7}{2} \text{ etc.}$$

$$\left(\frac{7}{9}, \frac{7}{9}, \frac{7}{9}\right), \frac{7}{9}, 81\,(x^2+y^2+z^2)-126\,(x+y+z)+98=0.$$

Ex. 16. Prove that the equation of the sphere which cuts orthogonally each of spheres

$x^2+y^2+z^2=a^2+b^2+c^2$, $x^2+y^2+z^2+2ax=a^2$, $x^2+y^2+z^2+2by=b^2$, $x^2+y^2+z^2+cz=c^2$ is

$$x^2+y^2+z^2+\frac{b^2+c^2}{a}x+\frac{c^2+a^2}{b}y+\frac{a^2+b^2}{c}z+a^2+b^2+c^2=0.$$

Sol. Let the equation of the sphere be

$$x^2+y^2+z^2+2ux+2vy+2wz+d=0.$$

It cuts 1st sphere orthogonally,

$$\therefore \quad 2u.0+2v.0+2w.0=-(a^2+b^2+c^2)+d=0.$$

$$\therefore \quad d=a^2+b^2+c^2.$$

It cuts 2nd sphere orthogonally,

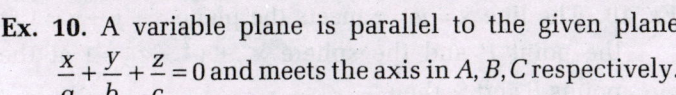

$\therefore \quad 2u.a + 2v.0 + 2w.0 = -a^2 + d$

or $\quad 2ua = -a^2 + (a^2 + b^2 + c^2)$ by (1).

$\therefore \quad 2u = \dfrac{b^2 + c^2}{a}$. ...(1)

Similarly, $\quad 2v = \dfrac{c^2 + a^2}{b}$ and $2w = \dfrac{a^2 + b^2}{c}$

Ex. 17. Two spheres of radii r_1 and r_2 cut orthogonally. Prove that the radius of the common circle is $\dfrac{r_1 r_2}{\sqrt{(r_1^2 + r_2^2)}}$

Sol. Let the equations to the common circle be

$$x^2 + y^2 = a^2, z = 0. \quad ...(1)$$

The equations of given spheres through the circle are

$$x^2 + y^2 + z^2 + 2\lambda z - a^2 = 0. \textbf{ (Note } z^2\textbf{)} \quad ...(2)$$

$$x^2 + y^2 + z^2 + 2\mu z - a^2 = 0 \quad ...(3)$$

where $\quad r_1^2 = \lambda^2 + a^2$ and $r_2^2 = \mu^2 + a^2$.

Again (2) and (3) cut orthogonally if

$2\lambda\mu = a^2 + a^2 \quad$ or $\quad \lambda^2\mu^2 = a^4$

or $\quad (r_1^2 - a^2)(r_2^2 - a^2) = a^4$

or $\quad r_1^2 r_2^2 = a^2 (r_1^2 + r_2^2)$.

$\therefore \quad a = \dfrac{r_1 r_2}{\sqrt{(r_1^2 + r_2^2)}}$ = radius of circle.

Ex. 18. The line $x = y = z$ meets the plane $x + y + z = 1$ at the point P and the sphere $x^2 + y^2 + z^2 = 1$ at the points R and S, then

(a) $PR + PS = 2$ (b) $PR \times PS = 2/3$
(c) $PR = PS$ (d) $PR + PS = RS$

Sol. Ans. (a), (b), (d).

Clearly the given line $x = y = z$ meets the plane where $3x = 1$ or $x = \dfrac{1}{3} = y = z$, *i.e.*, P is $\left(\dfrac{1}{3}, \dfrac{1}{3}, \dfrac{1}{3}\right)$. It meets the sphere $x^2 + y^2 + z^2 = 1$ where $3x^2 = 1 = 3y^2 = 3z^2$

$\therefore \quad x = y = z = \dfrac{1}{\sqrt{3}}$ or $-\dfrac{1}{\sqrt{3}}$

$\therefore \quad R$ is $\left(\dfrac{1}{\sqrt{3}}, \dfrac{1}{\sqrt{3}}, \dfrac{1}{\sqrt{3}}\right)$ and S is $\left(-\dfrac{1}{\sqrt{3}}, -\dfrac{1}{\sqrt{3}}, -\dfrac{1}{\sqrt{3}}\right)$.

$\therefore \quad PR^2 = \left(\dfrac{1}{\sqrt{3}} - \dfrac{1}{3}\right)^2 (1 + 1 + 1)$

$\therefore \quad PR = \left(\dfrac{1}{\sqrt{3}} - \dfrac{1}{3}\right)\sqrt{3} = \left(1 - \dfrac{1}{\sqrt{3}}\right)$

Similarly, $\quad PS = 1 + \dfrac{1}{\sqrt{3}}$ and $RS = \dfrac{2}{\sqrt{3}} \cdot \sqrt{3} = 2$

$\therefore \quad PR + PS = 2 \Rightarrow$ (a)

$PR \cdot PS = 1 - \dfrac{1}{3} = \dfrac{2}{3} \Rightarrow$ (b)

$\therefore \quad PR + PS = RS \Rightarrow$ (d)

Problem Set (6)

1. If the line $2x + y = k$ passes through the point which divides the line segment joining the point (1, 1) and (2, 4) in the ratio (3 : 2), then k equals

(a) $\dfrac{29}{5}$ (b) 5 (c) 6 (d) $\dfrac{11}{5}$

(AIEEE 2012)

2. A line is drawn through the point (1, 2) to meet the coordinate axes at P and Q such that it forms a triangle OPQ, where O is the origin. If the area of a triangle OPQ is least, then the slope of the line PQ is

(a) $-\dfrac{1}{4}$ (b) -4 (c) -2 (d) $-\dfrac{1}{2}$

(AIEEE 2012)

3. If the distance of the point $P(1, -2, 1)$ from the plane $x + 2y - 2z = \alpha$, $\alpha > 0$, is 5 then the foot of the perpendicular from P to the plane is

(a) $\left(\dfrac{8}{4}, \dfrac{4}{3}, \dfrac{-7}{3}\right)$ (b) $\left(\dfrac{4}{3}, \dfrac{-4}{3}, \dfrac{1}{3}\right)$

(c) $\left(\dfrac{1}{3}, \dfrac{2}{3}, \dfrac{10}{3}\right)$ (d) $\left(\dfrac{2}{3}, \dfrac{-1}{3}, \dfrac{5}{2}\right)$ **(IIT-JEE 2010)**

4. A line with positive direction cosines passes through the point $P(2, -1, 2)$ and makes equal angles with the coordinate axes. The line meets the plane $2x + y + z = 9$ at point Q. The length of the line segment PQ equals

(a) 1 (b) $\sqrt{2}$ (c) $\sqrt{3}$ (d) 2

(IIT JEE 2009)

5. A equation of a plane parallel to the plane $x - 2y + 2z = 5$ and at a unit distance from the origin is

(a) $x - 2y + 2z - 3 = 0$ (b) $x - 2y + 2z + 1 = 0$
(c) $x - 2y + 2z - 1 = 0$ (d) $x - 2y + 2z + 5 = 0$

(AIEEE 2012)

6. The equation of a plane passing through the line of intersection of the planes $x + 2y + 3z = 2$ and $x - y + z = 3$ and at a distance $\dfrac{2}{\sqrt{3}}$ from the point $(3, 1, -1)$ is

(a) $5x - 11y + z = 17$ (b) $\sqrt{2}x + y = 3\sqrt{2} - 1$
(c) $x + y + z = \sqrt{3}$ (d) $x - \sqrt{2}y = 1 - \sqrt{2}$

(IIT-JEE 2012)

7. Equation of the plane containing the straight line $\dfrac{x}{2} = \dfrac{y}{3} = \dfrac{z}{4}$ and perpendicular to the plane containing the straight line $\dfrac{x}{3} = \dfrac{y}{4} = \dfrac{z}{2}$ and $\dfrac{x}{4} = \dfrac{y}{2} = \dfrac{z}{3}$ is

(a) $x + 2y - 2z = 0$ (b) $3x + 2y - 2z = 0$
(c) $x - 2y + z = 0$ (d) $5x + 2y - 4z = 0$

(IIT-JEE 2010)

8. If the lines $\frac{x-1}{2}=\frac{y+1}{3}=\frac{z-1}{4}$ and $\frac{x-3}{1}=\frac{y-k}{2}=\frac{z}{1}$, intersect, then

(a) $\frac{2}{a}$ (b) $\frac{9}{2}$
(c) 0 (d) none of these

(AIEEE 2012; IIT-Sc. 2004)

9. If the distance between the planes $Ax-2y+z=d$ and the plane containing the lines $\frac{x-1}{2}=\frac{y-2}{3}=\frac{z-3}{4}$ and $\frac{x-2}{3}=\frac{y-3}{4}=\frac{z-4}{5}$ is $\sqrt{6}$ then value of $|d|$ is

(a) 6 (b) –6
(c) 1/6 (d) none of these

(IIT-JEE 2010)

Hints / Solution to Problem set (6)

1. Ans. (c).

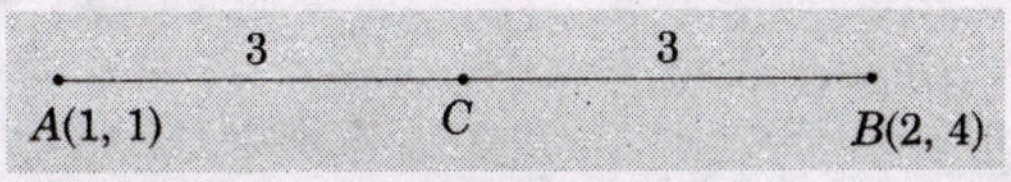

Fig. 10(a)

Coordinates of $C=\left(\frac{8}{5},\frac{14}{5}\right)$

Line $2x+y=k$ passes through c

$\therefore \quad \frac{2\times 8}{5}+\frac{14}{5}=k \Rightarrow k=6$

2. Ans. (c).

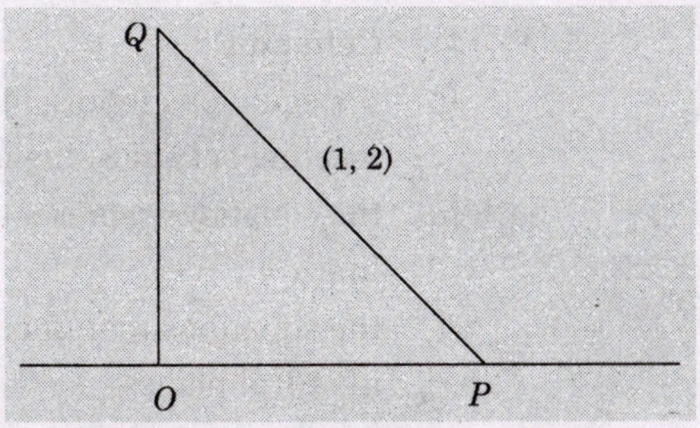

Fig. 10(b)

$(y-2)=m(x-1)$

$OP=1-\frac{2}{m}$

$OQ=2-m$

Area of $\Delta POQ=\frac{1}{2}OP\times OQ=\frac{1}{2}\left(1-\frac{2}{m}\right)(2-m)$

$=\frac{1}{2}\left[2-m-\frac{4}{m}+2\right]=\frac{1}{2}\left[4-\left(m+\frac{4}{m}\right)\right]$

$\Rightarrow \quad m=-2$

3. Ans. (a).

$D=\left|\frac{1-4-2-\alpha}{3}\right|=5 \Rightarrow \alpha+5=15 \quad [\because \alpha>0]$

$\Rightarrow \quad \alpha=10$

$\Rightarrow$ Plane is $x+2y-2z=10$ for positive (α,β,γ)

$\therefore \quad \frac{\alpha-1}{1}=\frac{\beta+2}{2}=\frac{\gamma-1}{-2}=-\frac{(1-4-2-10)}{9}=\frac{5}{3}$

$\Rightarrow \quad \alpha=\frac{8}{3},\beta=\frac{4}{3},\gamma=-\frac{7}{3}$

4. Ans. (c).

$a=b=c=1$

$2x+y+z=9$

$\therefore$ Equation of lines are $\frac{x-2}{1}=\frac{y+1}{1}=\frac{z-2}{1}$

$x-2=y+1=z-2=r$

$\Rightarrow \quad Q\equiv(r+2,r-1,r+2)$

$\because$ Q lies on the plane $2x+y+z=9$

$\Rightarrow \quad 2(r+2)+(r-1)+(r+2)=9 \Rightarrow r=1$

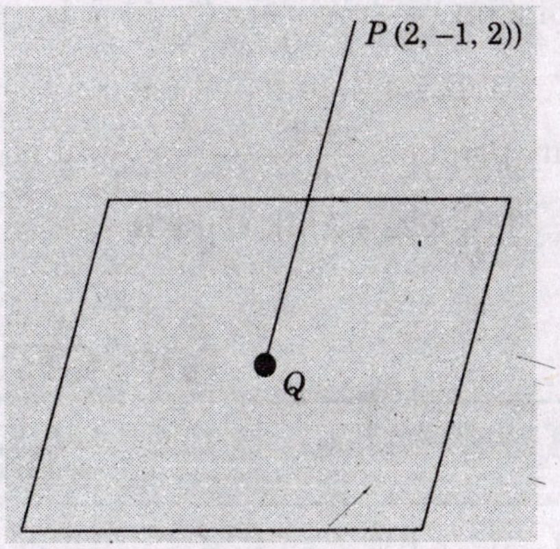

Fig. 11)

$\therefore \quad Q(3,0,3)$

$\Rightarrow \quad PQ=\sqrt{1+1+1}=\sqrt{3}$

5. Ans. (a).

Equation of the parallel plane $x-2y+2z+d=0$

$\therefore \quad \left|\frac{d}{\sqrt{1^2+2^2+2^2}}\right|=1 \Rightarrow d=\pm 3$

Thus, equation of the required plane is $x-2y+2z\pm 3=0$

6. Ans. (a). Equation of the required plane

$(x+2y+3z-2)+\lambda(x-y+z-3)=0$

$\Rightarrow \quad (1+\lambda)x+(2-\lambda)y+(3+\lambda)z-(2+3\lambda)=0$

Distance from point $(3,1,-1)$

$=\left|\frac{3+3\lambda+2-\lambda-3-\lambda-2-3\lambda}{\sqrt{(1+\lambda)^2+(2-\lambda)^2+(3+\lambda)^2}}\right|=\frac{2}{\sqrt{3}}$

$\Rightarrow \quad \left|\frac{-2\lambda}{\sqrt{3\lambda^2+4\lambda+14}}\right|=\frac{2}{\sqrt{3}}$

$\Rightarrow \quad 3\lambda^2=3\lambda^2+4\lambda+14$

$\Rightarrow \quad \lambda=-\frac{7}{2}$

Hence required equation of the plane $5x-11y+z-17=0$

7. Ans. (c).

Direction ratio of normal to the plane containing the straight line

$$\begin{vmatrix} \hat{i} & \hat{j} & \hat{k} \\ 3 & 4 & 2 \\ 4 & 2 & 3 \end{vmatrix} = 8\hat{i} - \hat{j} - 10\hat{k}$$

$$\therefore \quad \text{Required plane} = \begin{vmatrix} x-0 & y-0 & z-0 \\ 2 & 3 & 4 \\ 8 & -1 & -10 \end{vmatrix} = 0$$

$\Rightarrow \quad -26x + 52y - 26z = 0$

$\Rightarrow \quad x - 2y + z = 0$

8. Ans. (b).

Any point on $\frac{x-1}{2} = \frac{y+1}{3} = \frac{z-1}{4} = \lambda$ is

$(2\lambda + 1, 3\lambda - 1, 4\lambda + 1)$; $\lambda \in \mathbf{R}$

Any point on $\frac{x-3}{1} = \frac{y-k}{2} = \frac{z}{1} = \mu$ is

$(\mu + 3, 2\mu + k, \mu)$, $\mu \in \mathbf{R}$

The given lines intersects if and only if the system of equations

$$2\lambda + 1 = \mu + 3$$
$$3\lambda - 1 = 2\mu + k$$
$$4\lambda + 1 = \mu$$

On solving we get $\lambda = \frac{-3}{2}, \mu = -5$

$\Rightarrow \quad k = \frac{9}{2}$

9. Ans. (a).

Equation of plane $\begin{vmatrix} x-1 & y-2 & z-3 \\ 2 & 3 & 4 \\ 3 & 4 & 5 \end{vmatrix} = 0$

$x - 2y + z = 0$ ...(1)

$Ax - 2y + z = d$ ...(2)

from (1) and (2) $\frac{A}{1} = \frac{-2}{-2} = \frac{1}{1} \Rightarrow A = 1$

Hence, distance between planes is $\left|\frac{d}{\sqrt{1+1+4}}\right| = \sqrt{6}$

$\Rightarrow \quad |d| = 6$

MISCELLANEOUS EXERCISE

Matching Entries

1. Consider the following linear equations :

$$ax + by + cz = 0$$
$$bx + cy + az = 0$$
$$cx + ay + bz = 0$$

Column-I	Column-II
(a) $a+b+c \neq 0$ and $a^2+b^2+c^2 = ab+bc+ca$	(p) the equations represent planes meeting only at a single point
(b) $a+b+c = 0$ and $a^2+b^2+c^2 \neq ab+bc+ca$	(q) the equations represent the line $x = y = z$
(c) $a+b+c \neq 0$ and $a^2+b^2+c^2 \neq ab+bc+ca$	(r) the equations represent identical planes
(d) $a+b+c = 0$ and $a^2+b^2+c^2 = ab+bc+ca$	(s) the equations represent the whole of the three dimensional space **(I.I.T. 2007)**

2.

Column-I	Column-II
(a) A plane parallel to plane $3x - 7y + z = 5$.	(p) $2x - 2y + 4z = 8$
(b) A plane perpendicular to the plane $3x + 7y + 2z = 5$	(q) $3x - 7y + z + 6 = 0$
(c) A plane passing through the point (2, 2, 2) is	(r) $14x + 6y + 21z = 42$
(d) A plane making intercepts 3, 7, 2 on the co-ordinate axes.	(s) $4x - 2y + z = 6$

3.

Column-I	Column-II
(a) $\frac{x-2}{3} = \frac{y-7}{4} = \frac{z+5}{2}$	(p) perp. to plane $3x + 4y + 2z = 1$
(b) $\frac{x+1}{3} = \frac{y-3}{4} = \frac{z+7}{2}$	(q) passes through (2, 7, − 5)

(c) $\frac{x-5}{1}=\frac{y+2}{3}=\frac{z-2}{4}$

(d) $\frac{x}{2}=\frac{y-2}{5}=\frac{z+6}{1}$

(r) d.c.'s are $\frac{2}{\sqrt{30}},\frac{5}{\sqrt{30}},\frac{1}{\sqrt{30}}$

(s) lies in the plane $7x-y-z=35$

4. Consider the line $\frac{x-2}{3}=\frac{y-3}{4}=\frac{z-4}{5}$

Column-I	Column-II
(a) Point on the line at a distance $10\sqrt{2}$ from (2, 3, 4)	(p) (– 1, – 1, – 1)
(b) Point on the line common to plane $x+y+z+3=0$	(q) (2, 3, 4)
(c) Point on the line at a distance $\sqrt{29}$ from origin	(r) (8, 11, 14)
(d) Point on the line common to the plane $x+y-z+3=0$	(s) (– 4, – 5, – 6)

Hints / Solutions

1. Ans. (a) → (r), (b) → (q), (c) → (p), (d) → (s)

Refer Q. 11 P. 1105.

$$\Delta=\begin{vmatrix} a & b & c \\ b & c & a \\ c & a & b \end{vmatrix}=-(a^3+b^3+c^3-3abc)$$

$$\Delta=-(a+b+c)\,[a^2+b^2+c^2-ab-bc-cc]$$

$$=-(a+b+c).\frac{1}{2}[(a-b)^2+(b-c)^2+(c-a)^2]$$

$$a \Rightarrow \frac{1}{2}[(a-b)^2+(b-c)^2+(c-a)^2]=0$$

$$\Rightarrow \quad a-b=0, b-c=0, c-a=0$$

$$\Rightarrow \quad a=b=c$$

Hence the equations represent identical planes

$\therefore$ (a) → (r)

$b \Rightarrow \Delta=0$ as $a+b+c=0$ and hence the equations have infinitely many solutions.

$\therefore \quad ax+by=-cz=(a+b)\,z$ ...(1)

$bx+cy=-az=(b+c)\,z$ ...(2)

Multiply 1 by (b) and (2) by (a) and subtract

$\therefore \quad (b^2-c^2)\,y=(b^2-c^2)\,z \quad \therefore y=z$

Similarly $x=z \quad \therefore x=y=z$ which represents the equation of a line.

(c) $\Rightarrow$ (p) $\quad \because \quad \Delta \neq 0$

(d) $\Rightarrow$ (s) $\quad \therefore$ Here $a=0, b=0, c=0$.

Hence the equations represent the whole of three dimensional space.

2. (a)→ (q), (b)→ (p, s), $\quad \because \sum a_1\, a_2=0$

(c)→ (p, q, s), (d)→ (r)

$\frac{x}{3}+\frac{y}{7}+\frac{z}{2}=1 \quad \Rightarrow$ (r)

3. Ans. (a)→ (p, q), (b)→ (p, q), (c)→ (s), (d)→ (q, r)

(a) Parallel to normal 3, 4, 2 $\quad \therefore$ (a)→ (p)

It passes through the point (2, 7, – 5) $\therefore$ (a)→ (q)

(b) Parallel to normal 3, 4, 2 $\therefore$ (b)→ (p)

The point (2, 7, – 5) satisfies its equation $\therefore$ (b) → (q)

(c) The plane passes through the point (5, – 2, 2) and normal 7, – 1, 1 is perpendicular to 1, 3, 4 as $\sum a_1\, a_2=0 \quad \therefore$ (c)→ (s)

(d) The point (2, 7, – 5) satisfies its equation

$\therefore$ (d)→ (q). Also its d.c.'s are $\frac{2}{\sqrt{30}},\frac{5}{\sqrt{30}},\frac{1}{\sqrt{30}}$

$\therefore$ (d) → (r)

4. Ans. (a)→ (r), (b)→ (p), (c)→ (r), (d)→ (s)

(a) Any point on the given line is

$(3r+2, 4r+3, 5r+4)$

Its distance from (2, 3, 4) is

$r^2\,(9+16+25)=(10\sqrt{2})^2$

$\therefore \quad r^2=4$ or $r=\pm 2$

$\therefore$ (a) → (r), (s) for $r=2,-2$

(b) $\because \quad (3r+2)+(4r+3)+(5r+4)+3=0$

$12r+12=0 \Rightarrow r=-1 \;\therefore$ Point is (– 1, – 1, – 1)

$\therefore$ (b)→ (p)

(c) $(3r+2)^2+(4r+3)^2+(5r+4)^2=29$

$\Rightarrow \quad 50r^2+76r=0 \quad \therefore \quad r=0,\frac{-76}{50}$

For $r=0$, the point is (2, 3, 4). $\quad \therefore$ (c)→ (q)

(d) Putting the point in the equation of plane, $r=-2$. $\quad \therefore$ Point is (– 4, – 5. – 6)

$\therefore$ (d)→ (s)

Assertion / Reason

1. Consider the planes $3x-6y-2z=15$ and $2x+y-2z=5$. **(IIT 2007)**

STATEMENT-1 : The parametric equations of the line of intersection of the given planes are $x=3+14t$, $y=1+2t, z=15t$.

because

STATEMENT-2 : The vectors $14\mathbf{i}+2\mathbf{j}+15\mathbf{k}$ is parallel to the line of intersection of the given planes. **(I.I.T. 2007)**

Sol. Ans. (d).

Putting $z = 0$ and solving for x, y, we get the point on the line of intersection as $(3, -1, 0)$

Also the direction ratios of the line of intersection are given by

$$3l - 6m - 2n = 0 \text{ and } 2l + m - 2n = 0$$

$$\therefore \quad \frac{l}{14} = \frac{m}{2} = \frac{n}{15}$$

$$\therefore \quad \frac{x-3}{14} = \frac{y+1}{2} = \frac{z-0}{15} = \lambda$$

$$\therefore \quad x = 14\lambda + 3, y = 2\lambda - 1, z = 15\lambda$$

Hence statement-1 is false. (use value of y)

Above line is parallel to $14\mathbf{i} + 2\mathbf{j} + 15\mathbf{k}$

$\therefore$ Statement-2 is true.

2. **Statement 1.** The point $A(1, 0, 7)$ is the mirror image of the point $B(1, 6, 3)$ in the line $\frac{x}{1} = \frac{y-1}{2} = \frac{z-2}{3}$

Statement 2. The line $\frac{x}{1} = \frac{y-1}{2} = \frac{z-2}{3}$ bisects the line segment joining $A(1, 0, 7)$ and $B(1, 6, 3)$ **(AIEEE 2011)**

Sol. Ans. (b).

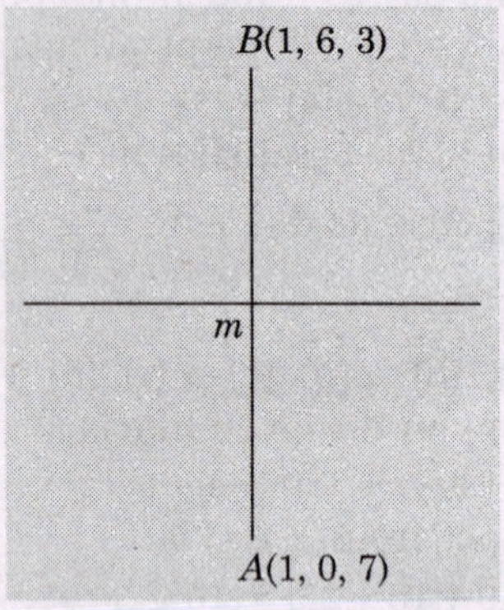

Fig. 12

Mid point of $AB = M(1, 3, 5)$

M lies on line

Direction ratios of AB is $(0, 6, -4)$

Direction ratios of given line is $(1, 2, 3)$

$\therefore$ AB is perpendicular to line

Hence $0.1 + 6.2 - 4.3 = 0$

3. **Statement 1.** The point $A(3, 1, 6)$ is the mirror image of the point $B(1, 3, 4)$ in the plane $x - y + z = 5$.

Statement-2. The plane $x - y + z = 5$ bisects the line segment joining $A(3, 1, 6)$ and $B(1, 3, 4)$. **(AIEEE 2010)**

Sol. Ans.(b).

Mirror image of $B(1, 3, 4)$ in plane $x - y + z = 5$ is

$$\frac{x-1}{1} = \frac{y-3}{-1} = \frac{z-4}{1} = -2\frac{(1-3+4-5)}{1+1+1} = 2$$

$\Rightarrow$ $x = 3, y = 1, z = 6$

$\therefore$ Mirror image of $B(1, 3, 4)$ is $A(3, 1, 6)$

Statement 1 is true. Statement 2 is true but it is not the correct explanation.

4. Consider three planes $P_1 : x - y + z = 1$; $P_2 : x + y - z = 1$; $P_3 : x - 3y + 3z = 2$. Let L_1, L_2, L_3 be the lines of intersection of the planes P_2 and P_3, P_3 and P_1, P_1 and P_2 respectively. **(IIT 2008)**

Statement 1. At least two of lines L_1, L_2 and L_3 are non-parallel.

Statement 2. The three planes do not have a common point.

Sol. Ans. (d).

For plane P_1 and P_2; d.r.'s $(0, 2, 2)$

For plane P_2 and P_3; $(0, -2, -2) \Rightarrow (0, 2, 2)$

For plane P_1 and P_3; $(0, -2, -2) \Rightarrow (0, 2, 2)$

All the three lines are parallel, therefore (2) is true, (1) is false.

Comprehension

1. **(a)** The shortest distance from the plane $12x + 4y + 3z = 327$ to the sphere $x^2 + y^2 + z^2 + 4x - 2y - 6z = 155$ is

(a) 26 (b) $11\frac{4}{13}$

(c) 13 (d) 39 **(AIEEE 2003)**

Sol. Ans. (c).

Sphere is $(-2, 1, 3)$, $r = 13$

If p be perpendicular distance of plane from the centre of the sphere, then

$$p = \left|\frac{-24 + 4 + 9 - 327}{\sqrt{(144 + 16 + 9)}}\right| = \frac{338}{13} = 26$$

$\therefore$ Shortest distance of the plane from the sphere is $p - r = 26 - 13 = 13$.

(b) A line $x + y = 3$ meets the circle $x^2 + y^2 - 4x + 6y - 3 = 0$ at A and B. A variable line meets the axes at L and M respectively so that AM and BL meet at right angles at the point N. Prove that the locus of the point N is $x^2 + y^2 - 8x + 2y + 9 = 0$

Sol. The given line meets the given circle in points A and B. Solving their equations we get the points as $A(2, 1)$, $B(6, -3)$. A variable line LM is such that AM and BL meet at N at right angles. In other words AB subtends a right angle at variable point N. Hence locus of N will be a circle on AB as diameter.

Hence its equation is

$$(x-2)(x-6) + (y-1)(y+3) = 0$$

or $\quad x^2 + y^2 - 8x + 2y + 9 = 0$

(c) Circles of constant radius r are drawn to pass through the ends of a variable diameter of the ellipse $\frac{x^2}{a^2}+\frac{y^2}{b^2}=1$. Prove that locus of their centres is the curve

$$(x^2+y^2)(a^2x^2+b^2y^2+a^2b^2)=r^2(a^2x^2+b^2y^2)$$

Sol. Let the circle be $(x-h)^2+(y-k)^2=r^2$

It passes through $(a\cos\theta, b\sin\theta)$ and $(-a\cos\theta, -b\sin\theta)$

$\therefore\ (a\cos\theta-h)^2+(b\sin\theta-k)^2=r^2$ ...(1)

and $(a\cos\theta+h)^2+(b\sin\theta+k)^2=r^2$ ...(2)

Subtracting (1) and (2), $4ah\cos\theta+4bk\sin\theta=0$

$\therefore\ \tan\theta=-\frac{ah}{bk}$ ...(3)

Adding (1) and (2),

$2(a^2\cos^2\theta+h^2)+2(b^2\sin^2\theta+k^2)=2r^2$ ...(4)

Eliminate θ between (3) and (4) and generalize (h,k).

2. Let a, b and c be three real numbers satisfying

$$[a\,b\,c]\begin{bmatrix}1&9&7\\8&2&7\\7&3&7\end{bmatrix}=[0\ 0\ 0] \quad ...(1)$$

(IIT-JEE 2011)

(i) If the point $P(a,b,c)$ which reference to (1) lies on the plane $2x+y+z=1$ then the value of $7a+b+c$ is

(a) 0 (b) 12
(c) 7 (d) 6

(ii) Let ω be a solution of $x^3-1=0$ with Im $(\omega)>0$, if $a=2$ with b and c satisfy (1), then the value of $\frac{3}{\omega^a}+\frac{1}{\omega^b}+\frac{3}{\omega^c}$ is equal to

(a) −2 (b) 2
(c) 3 (d) −3

(iii) Let $b=6$ with a and c satisfying (1). If α and β are the roots of the quadratic equation $ax^2+bx+c=0$, then $\sum_{n=0}^{\infty}\left(\frac{1}{\alpha}+\frac{1}{\beta}\right)^n$ is

(a) 6 (b) 7
(c) $\frac{6}{7}$ (d) ∞

Sol. $a+8b+7c=0$ ...(i)

$9a+2b+3c=0$ ...(ii)

$a+b+c=0$ ...(iii)

$$\Delta=\begin{vmatrix}1&8&7\\9&2&3\\1&1&1\end{vmatrix}=1(-1)-8(6)+7(7)=0$$

Let $c=\lambda \Rightarrow a+8b=-7\lambda$

and $a+b=-\lambda \Rightarrow b=\frac{-6}{7}\lambda$ and $a=-\frac{\lambda}{7}$

$\therefore\ (a,b,c)=\left(\frac{-\lambda}{7},\frac{-6\lambda}{7},\lambda\right), \lambda\in\mathbf{R}$

(i) Ans. (d).

Point $P(a,b,c)$ lies on the plane $2x+y+z=1$

$\therefore\ \frac{-2\lambda}{7}-\frac{6\lambda}{7}+\lambda=1\Rightarrow\lambda=-7$

so, $7a+b+c=7+6-7=6$

(ii) Ans. (a).

$a=2\Rightarrow\lambda=-14$

$\therefore\ b=12, c=-14$

Now $\frac{3}{\omega^a}+\frac{1}{\omega^b}+\frac{3}{\omega^c}=\frac{3}{\omega^2}+\frac{1}{\omega^{12}}+3\omega^{14}$

$=3\omega+1+3\omega^2=3(\omega+\omega^2)+1=-2$

(iii) Ans. (b).

$b=6, \Rightarrow \lambda=-7$

$\Rightarrow\ a=1$ and $c=-7$

so, $ax^2+bx+c=0\Rightarrow x^2+6x-7=0\Rightarrow x=-7,1$

$\therefore\ \sum_{n=0}^{\infty}\left(\frac{1}{\alpha}+\frac{1}{\beta}\right)^n=\sum_{n=0}^{\infty}\left(\frac{6}{7}\right)^n$

$=1+\frac{6}{7}+\left(\frac{6}{7}\right)^2+...\infty=\frac{1}{1-\frac{6}{7}}$ (Infinite G.P.)

$=7$

Fascinating Facts

- Skew lines are non-coplanar lines.
- Parallel lines are not skew lines.
- If two lines intersect, the shortest distance between them is zero.
- Shortest distance between two skew lines is perpendicular to both the lines.
- The number of lines which are equally inclined to the co-ordinate axes is 4. If l, m, n, are the d.c.'s of a line then the maximum value of $lmn=\frac{1}{3\sqrt{3}}$.
- The angle between two diagonals of a cube is $\cos^{-1}\left(\frac{1}{3}\right)$.
- The ratio in which the line segment PQ joining $P(x_1, y_1, z_1)$ and $Q(x_2, y_2, z_2)$ is divided by coordinate planes are as follows :

(i) by yz-plane $=-\frac{x_1}{x_2}$

(ii) by zx-plane $=-\frac{y_1}{y_2}$

(iii) by xy-plane $=-\frac{z_1}{z_2}$

- Signs of three coordinates in eight octants.

Coordinate	I	II	III	IV	V	VI	VII	VIII
x	+	−	−	+	+	−	−	+
y	+	+	−	−	+	+	−	−
z	+	+	+	+	−	−	−	−

CHAPTER 24

Vectors

Addition of Vectors

§1. Introduction.

(i) Scalars and Vectors. Those quantities which have **only magnitude** and are not related to any direction in space are called **scalars** whereas those which have **both magnitude and direction** are called **vector quantities.** The speed of a train is a scalar quantity as it is not associated with any direction, it simply gives the rate of motion but its velocity or acceleration is a vector quantity as it gives both the magnitude and direction.

(ii) Representation and notation of vectors.
Symbolically a vector is often denoted by two letters with an arrow over them *i.e.* $\vec{AB}$. A is called the origin (initial point) and B the terminus. Its magnitude is given by the length AB and direction is from A to B as indicated by the arrow. We write vector quantities also in single letter notation like **a**, **b**, **c** and the corresponding letters a, b, c denote their magnitudes. Thus if $\vec{AB} = \mathbf{a}$ then $|\vec{AB}| = a$, where $|\vec{AB}|$ means the magnitude of vector **a**.

The magnitude $|\mathbf{a}|$ of vector **a** is called its **modulus** or **module.**

Since it is difficult to write bold type letters **a, b, c,**... we may use $\bar{a}, \bar{b}, \bar{c}, \ldots$ *i.e.* place a bar over ordinary letters $a, b, c, \ldots$ or else we may take $\alpha, \beta, \gamma, \ldots$ to represent the vectors and $a, b, c, \ldots$ to represent their magnitudes. Another alternative is to use $A, B, C, \ldots$ letters for vectors and small letters $a, b, c, \ldots$ to represent their magnitudes.

(iii) Like and unlike vectors. Vectors are said to be like when they have the same sense of direction and unlike when they have opposite directions.

(iv) Collinear or parallel vectors. Two or more vectors are said to be collinear when they act along the same line or along parallel lines.

(v) Coplanar Vectors. Three or more vectors are said to be coplanar when they are parallel to the same plane or lie in the same plane whatever their magnitudes be.
Note that two vectors are always coplanar.

(vi) Equal Vectors. Two vectors are said to be equal when they have the same length (magnitude) and are parallel (having the same sense of direction). $\vec{AB} = \vec{CD}$ see fig. 1.

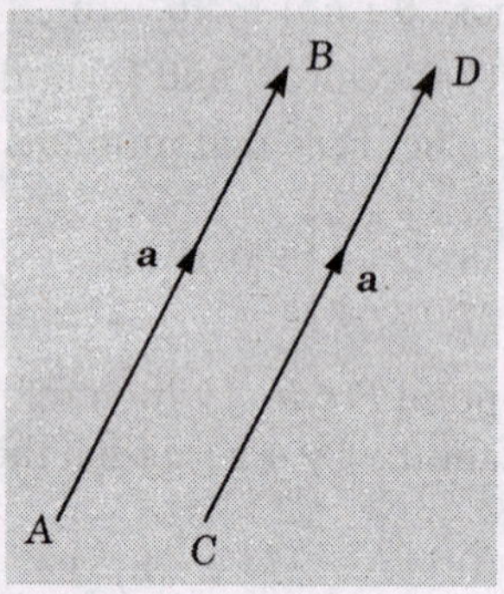

Fig. 1

(vii) Zero Vector. If the origin and terminal points of a vector coincide, then it is said to be a zero vector. It is denoted by **0**, its magnitude is zero and its direction indeterminate. Geometrically it is just a point.

(viii) Unit Vector. A vector whose magnitude is of unit length is called a unit vector. If **a** is a vector whose magnitude is a, then unit vector in the direction of **a** is denoted by $\hat{\mathbf{a}}$ and is obtained by dividing the vector **a** by its magnitude a. Thus $\hat{\mathbf{a}} = \dfrac{\mathbf{a}}{a}$.

Any two unit vectors $\hat{\mathbf{a}}$ and $\hat{\mathbf{b}}$ should not be taken to be equal because although both of them have their magnitude unity but their directions may be different.

(ix) Position Vector. If O be a fixed origin and P any point then the vector $\vec{OP}$ is called the position vector of the point P w.r.t. the origin O.

(x) Scalar multiple of a vector. If **a** be a given vector, then k**a** is a vector whose magnitude is $|k|$ times the magnitude of vector **a** and whose direction is the same as that of **a** or **opposite** of **a** according as k is positive or negative.

Negative of a Vector. If **a** be a given vector then $-$**a** is a vector whose magnitude is same as that of **a** but direction opposite to that of **a**.

(xi) Co-initial Vectors. The vectors having the same initial point are called co-initial vectors.

(xii) Localized and free Vectors. A vector drawn parallel to a given vector through a specified point in space is called a localized vector. But if the origin of vectors is not specified, the vectors are called free vectors.

(xiii) Displacement Vector : When a particle is displaced from a point A to other point B, then the displacement AB is a vector *i.e.* $\overrightarrow{AB}$ is called displacement vector of the particle.

(xiv) Addition of Vectors. Let **a** and **b** be any two vectors. Choose any point O as origin and draw the vectors **a** and **b** so that the **terminus** of **a** coincides with the **origin** of **b** *i.e.,* $\overrightarrow{OA} = \mathbf{a}$ and $\overrightarrow{AB} = \mathbf{b}$. Then the vector given by $\overrightarrow{OB}$ is defined as the sum of vectors **a** and **b**.

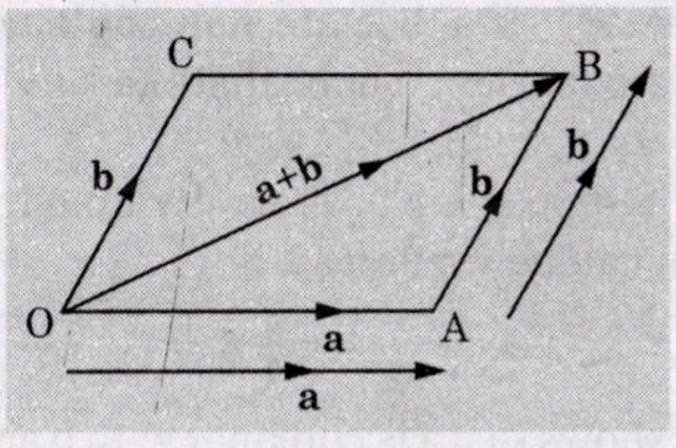

Fig. 2

The above law is called **triangle law of addition.** Since $\overrightarrow{OC} = \overrightarrow{AB} = \mathbf{b}$, we can also say $\overrightarrow{OA} + \overrightarrow{OC} = \overrightarrow{OB}$, which is known as **parallelogram law of addition.**

Note. It should be noted that the magnitude of $\mathbf{a} + \mathbf{b}$ is not equal to the sum of the magnitudes of **a** and **b**.

(xv) Geometrical Interpretation

We know that in a triangle any side is less than the sum of the other two sides or it is greater than the difference of the two sides. Both these results can be expressed in vector form as under with reference to above figure.

$$|\mathbf{a} + \mathbf{b}| \le |\mathbf{a}| + |\mathbf{b}|$$

The equality will hold when both **a** and **b** have the same direction and $|\mathbf{a} + \mathbf{b}| \ge ||\mathbf{a}| - |\mathbf{b}||$

The equality will hold when **a** and **b** are in opposite directions.

(xvi) Properties.

(i) $\mathbf{a} + \mathbf{b} = \mathbf{b} + \mathbf{a}$ **(Commutative law)**

(ii) $(\mathbf{a} + \mathbf{b}) + \mathbf{c} = \mathbf{a} + (\mathbf{b} + \mathbf{c})$ **(Associative law)**

(xvii) Sum of any number of Vectors.

If we are to find the sum of any number of vectors **a, b, c, d, e,...**, say, then form a broken line whose segments in length and direction represent these vectors. Then the vector joining the origin of the first vector to the terminal point of the last vector will represent the vector sum.

$$\mathbf{a} + \mathbf{b} + \mathbf{c} + \mathbf{d} + \mathbf{e} = \overrightarrow{OA} + \overrightarrow{AB} + \overrightarrow{BC} + \overrightarrow{CD} + \overrightarrow{DE} = \overrightarrow{OE}$$

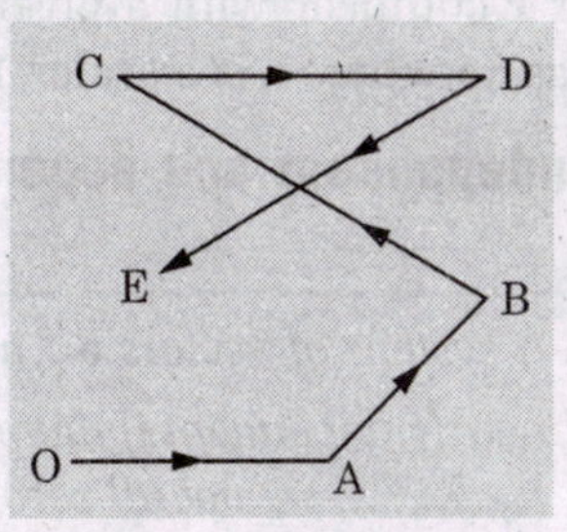

Fig. 3

In particular if the **terminal point of last vector** coincides with the origin of the first vector, then the sum will be the zero vector.

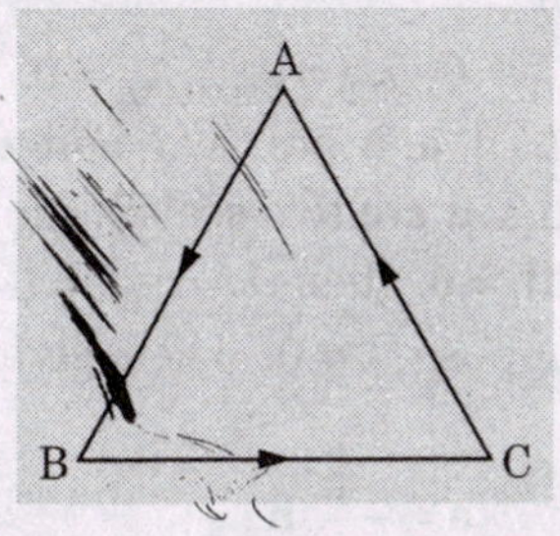

Fig. 4

Thus $\overrightarrow{OA} + \overrightarrow{AB} + \overrightarrow{BC} + \overrightarrow{CD} + \overrightarrow{DO} = \overrightarrow{OO} = \mathbf{0}$

Similarly, $\overrightarrow{AB} + \overrightarrow{BC} + \overrightarrow{CA} = \overrightarrow{AA} = \mathbf{0}$.

(xviii) Expression of a vector in terms of position vectors of its end points.

The position vectors of the points A and B w.r.t. O as origin are **a** and **b** respectively *i.e.* $\overrightarrow{OA} = \mathbf{a}$.

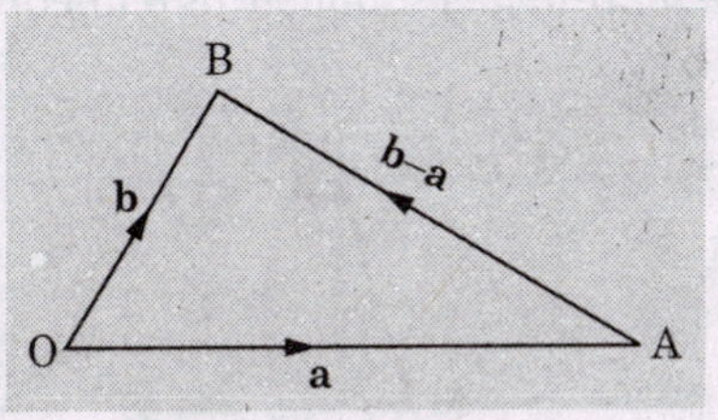

Fig. 5

$\overrightarrow{OB} = \mathbf{b}$, then we know that

$$\overrightarrow{OA} + \overrightarrow{AB} = \overrightarrow{OB}$$

$$\therefore \quad \overrightarrow{AB} = \overrightarrow{OB} - \overrightarrow{OA} = \mathbf{b} - \mathbf{a}.$$

Thus $\overrightarrow{AB} = $ (P. V. of B) – (P. V. of A). **(V. Imp.)**

Similarly, $\overrightarrow{BA} = \mathbf{a} - \mathbf{b} = $ (P. V. of A) – (P. V. of B)

(xix) Linear Combination of Vectors.

If a vector **r** is expressible as $\mathbf{r} = x\mathbf{a} + y\mathbf{b} + z\mathbf{c} + \ldots$ where x, y, z are scalars, then **r** is said to be a linear combination of vectors **a, b, c**.

(xx) Relation between two collinear vectors.

Any vector **r** collinear with a given vector **a** can be expressed as x**a** where x is a scalar, *i.e.* $\mathbf{r} = x\mathbf{a}$.

§2. Linearly independent and dependent system of vectors.

(i) Definition. *A system of vectors* $\mathbf{a}_1, \mathbf{a}_2, \mathbf{a}_3, \mathbf{a}_4, \ldots, \mathbf{a}_n$ *is said to be linearly dependent if there exists a system of scalars* $\lambda_1, \lambda_2, \lambda_3 \ldots, \lambda_n$ *not all zero such that*

$$\lambda_1 \mathbf{a}_1 + \lambda_2 \mathbf{a}_2 + \ldots.. \lambda_n \mathbf{a}_n = \mathbf{0}.$$

A system of vectors which is not linearly dependent is called linearly independent. Thus a set of vectors $\mathbf{a}_1, \mathbf{a}_2, \ldots, \ldots \mathbf{a}_n$ *is said to be linearly independent if every relation of the type* $\lambda_1 \mathbf{a}_1 + \lambda_2 \mathbf{a}_2 + \ldots.. \lambda_n \mathbf{a}_n = 0$ *implies that*

$$\lambda_1 = 0,\ \lambda_2 = 0, \ldots, \lambda_n = 0.$$

Theorem I. If **a**, **b** are two **non-zero non-collinear** vectors and λ, μ are two scalars such that

$$\lambda\,\mathbf{a} + \mu\mathbf{b} = \mathbf{0}, \text{ then } \lambda = 0,\ \mu = 0$$

Proof. Suppose $\lambda \neq 0$. Then given relation can be written as

$$\mathbf{a} = -\frac{\mu}{\lambda}\mathbf{b};$$

which shows that **a** and **b** are collinear. But this is contrary to the hypothesis. Hence $\lambda = 0$. Similarly, we can show that $\mu = 0$.

§3. Resolution of Vectors.

(i) Coplanar Vectors.

Theorem I. *Let* **a**, **b** *be two* **non-zero non-collinear** *vectors and* **r** *any vector coplanar with* **a** *and* **b**. *Then* **r** *can be represented uniquely as a linear combination of* **a** and **b**.

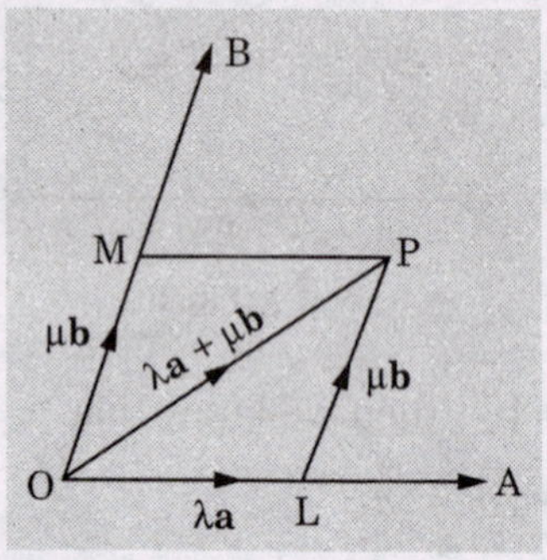

Fig. 6

Proof : Let $\vec{OA} = \mathbf{a}$, $\vec{OB} = \mathbf{b}$, and $\vec{OP} = \mathbf{r}$.

The lines OA, OB and OP are coplanar.

Through the point P draw lines parallel to OA and OB to meet OB and OA in M and L respectively. Then we have $\mathbf{r} = \vec{OP} = \vec{OL} + \vec{LP} = \vec{OL} + \vec{OM} = \lambda\mathbf{a} + \mu\mathbf{b}$

[$\because$ $\vec{OL}, \vec{OM}$ are collinear with **a** and **b**, we can find scalars λ and μ such that $\vec{OL} = \lambda\mathbf{a}$ and $\vec{OM} = \mu\mathbf{b}$].

Uniqueness. Suppose, if possible, there is another representation of **r** as $\mathbf{r} = \lambda'\mathbf{a} + \mu'\mathbf{b}$.

Then $\quad \lambda\mathbf{a} + \mu\mathbf{b} = \lambda'\mathbf{a} + \mu'\mathbf{b}$ ...(1)

or $\quad (\lambda - \lambda')\,\mathbf{a} + (\mu - \mu')\,\mathbf{b} = \mathbf{0}.$

Since **a** and **b** are non-collinear vectors, we have $\lambda - \lambda' = 0$ and $\mu - \mu' = 0$ *i.e.* $\lambda = \lambda'$ and $\mu = \mu'$. Thus the resolution of **r** as a linear combination of **a** and **b** is unique.

Another form. (Compare the coefficients)

If **a** and **b** be non-collinear and we have a relation of the form (1), then we say compare the coefficients of non-collinear vectors on both sides.

$\therefore \quad \lambda = \lambda'$ and $\mu = \mu'$

(ii) Non-Coplanar Vectors.

Theorem II. If **a**, **b**, **c** are **non-coplanar** vectors and λ, μ, ν are scalars such that $\lambda\mathbf{a} + \mu\mathbf{b} + \nu\mathbf{c} = 0$, then $\lambda = \mu = \nu = 0$.

Proof : Suppose $\lambda \neq 0$. Then dividing by λ, the given relation can be written as

$$\mathbf{a} = -\frac{\mu}{\lambda}\mathbf{b} - \frac{\nu}{\lambda}\mathbf{c},$$

which shows that **a** is coplanar with **b** and **c**. But this is contrary to the hypothesis. Hence we must have $\lambda = 0$. Similarly we can prove that $\mu = 0$ and $\nu = 0$.

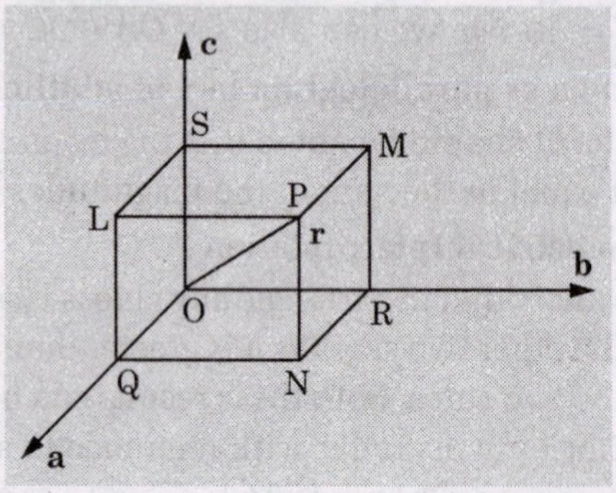

Fig. 7

Theorem III. If **a**, **b**, **c** are three **non-coplanar vectors**, then any vector **r** can be expressed uniquely as a linear combination of vectors **a**, **b** and **c**.

Another form (Compare the coefficients) :

If **a**, **b**, **c** are non-coplanar vectors and we have a relation of the form (1), then we say compare the coefficents of non-coplanar vectors on both sides.

$\therefore \quad \lambda = \lambda', \mu = \mu'$ and $\nu = \nu'$

§ 4. The unit vectors i, j, k (Orthonormal system of unit vectors)

Let OX, OY and OZ be three mutually perpendicular straight lines in the right-handed orientation. This statement means that when one rotates from OX to OY, then OZ lies in the direction in which a right handed

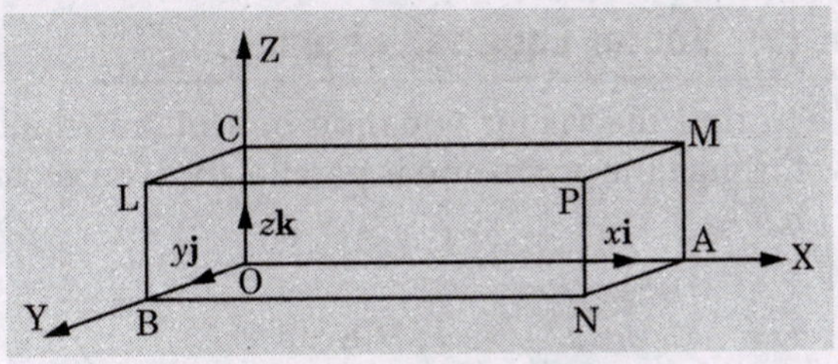

Fig. 8

screw will advance. These three mutually perpendicular lines can uniquely determine the position of a point. Hence these lines can be taken as the co-ordinate axes with O as origin. The planes XOY, YOZ and ZOX, are called co-ordinate planes.

Let **i, j, k** denote unit vectors along OX, OY, OZ respectively.

Let $\vec{OP}$ represent a vector **r**. With OP as diagonal, construct a rectangular parallelopiped whose three coterminous edges OA, OB, OC lie along OX, OY and OZ respectively. Let $OA = x$, $OB = y$ and $OC = z$. Then $\vec{OA} = x\mathbf{i}$, $\vec{OB} = y\mathbf{j}$ and $\vec{OC} = z\mathbf{k}$. Now we have

$$\mathbf{r} = \vec{OP} = \vec{ON} + \vec{NP} = \vec{OA} + \vec{AN} + \vec{NP}$$

$$= \vec{OA} + \vec{OB} + \vec{OC} = x\mathbf{i} + y\mathbf{j} + z\mathbf{k}.$$

Thus $\mathbf{r} = x\mathbf{i} + y\mathbf{j} + z\mathbf{k}$.

Here x, y, z are called the co-ordinates of the point P referred to the axes OX, OY and OZ. Also $x\mathbf{i}$, $y\mathbf{j}$ and $z\mathbf{k}$ are called the **resolved parts** of the vector **r** in the directions of **i, j** and **k** respectively.

Direction cosines. If α, β, γ are the angles which OP makes with the co-ordinate axes OX, OY and OZ respectively, then $\cos\alpha, \cos\beta$ and $\cos\gamma$ are called the direction cosines (d.c.'s) of the line OP. These d.c.'s are usually denoted by l, m, n.

If $OP = r$, then clearly $x = r\cos\alpha = lr$,

$y = r\cos\beta = mr$ and $z = r\cos\gamma = nr$.

Substituting these values in the relation

$$\mathbf{r} = x\mathbf{i} + y\mathbf{j} + z\mathbf{k},$$

we get

$$\mathbf{r} = lr\mathbf{i} + mr\mathbf{j} + nr\mathbf{k}.$$

$$\therefore \quad \hat{\mathbf{r}} = \frac{\mathbf{r}}{r} = l\mathbf{i} + m\mathbf{j} + n\mathbf{k}.$$

Hence the direction cosines of vector **r** *are the coefficients of* **i, j, k** *in the rectangular resolution of the unit vector* $\hat{\mathbf{r}}$.

Also $\quad OP^2 = ON^2 + NP^2 = OA^2 + AN^2 + NP^2$

$$= OA^2 + OB^2 + OC^2$$

or $\quad r^2 = x^2 + y^2 + z^2$, *i.e.* $|\mathbf{r}|^2 = x^2 + y^2 + z^2$.

Hence *magnitude of the* **vector** $x\mathbf{i} + y\mathbf{j} + z\mathbf{k}$ is $\sqrt{x^2 + y^2 + z^2}$.

Now dividing $r^2 = x^2 + y^2 + z^2$ by r^2, we get

$$1 = \frac{x^2}{r^2} + \frac{y^2}{r^2} + \frac{z^2}{r^2} = l^2 + m^2 + n^2.$$

Thus the sum of the squares of direction cosines is equal to unity.

Note : We often write the vector $\mathbf{r} = x\mathbf{i} + y\mathbf{j} + z\mathbf{k}$ as $\mathbf{r} = x, y, z$. For example, if $\mathbf{a} = 1, 2, -7$, then $\mathbf{a} = \mathbf{i} + 2\mathbf{j} - 7\mathbf{k}$. In fact, any vector in three dimensional space may be defined as an ordered triad of real numbers.

However, if $\mathbf{i} + 2\mathbf{j} - 7\mathbf{k}$ or $x\mathbf{i} + y\mathbf{j} + z\mathbf{k}$ represents the position vectors of certain points A and P w.r.t. an origin O then we shall write it as point $A(1, 2, -7)$ and $P(x, y, z)$.

§5. Collinearity and Coplanarity.

(i) Collinearity of three points.

(a) First method : To prove that three points A, B, C are collinear, find the vectors $\vec{AB}$ and $\vec{BC}$ and show that one of them is a scalar multiple of the other.

(b) Second method : To prove the collinearity of three points A, B, C with position vectors **a, b, c** respectively, we may use the following theorem.

Three points with position vectors **a, b, c** *are collinear if and only if there exist scalars* x, y, z *not all zero such that*

(i) $x\mathbf{a} + y\mathbf{b} + z\mathbf{c} = \mathbf{0}$

(ii) $x + y + z = 0$.

For proof of this theorem **see Q. 28, P. 1097-1107.**

(ii) Method to prove three vectors to be coplanar.

Three vectors **a, b, c** will be coplanar if one of them can be expressed as a linear combination of the remaining two vectors. Thus **a, b, c** will be coplanar if we can find two scalars λ and μ such that

$$\mathbf{a} = \lambda\mathbf{b} + \mu\mathbf{c}$$

(iii) Method to prove four points to be coplanar.

(a) First Method : To prove that the four points A, B, C, D are coplanar find the vectors $\vec{AB}, \vec{AC}$ and $\vec{AD}$ and then prove them to be coplanar by the method given in (ii).

(b) Second Method : To prove that the four points A, B, C, D with position vectors **a, b, c, d** are coplanar, use the following theorem.

Four points with position vectors **a, b, c, d** *are coplanar if and only if there exist scalars x, y, z, u not all zero such that*

(i) $x\mathbf{a} + y\mathbf{b} + z\mathbf{c} + u\mathbf{d} = \mathbf{0}$ and

(ii) $x + y + z + u = 0$.

For proof of this theorem see **Q. 31, P. 1097-1108.**

(iv) Ratio Formula. If A, B are points **a** and **b**, *i.e.* $\vec{OA} = \mathbf{a}$, $\vec{OB} = \mathbf{b}$ then the point P which divides AB in the ratio $m:n$ is given by

$$\mathbf{r} = \frac{m\mathbf{b} + n\mathbf{a}}{m+n}.$$

Mid-point of AB is $\dfrac{\mathbf{a}+\mathbf{b}}{2}$.

Centroid of triangle ABC is $\dfrac{\mathbf{a}+\mathbf{b}+\mathbf{c}}{3}$

where **a, b, c** are the position vectors of the vertices w.r.t. to an origin O.

§ 6. (a) Vector Equation of a Line.

(i) Equation of a straight line passing through a given point whose position vector is **a** and which is parallel to given vector **b**.

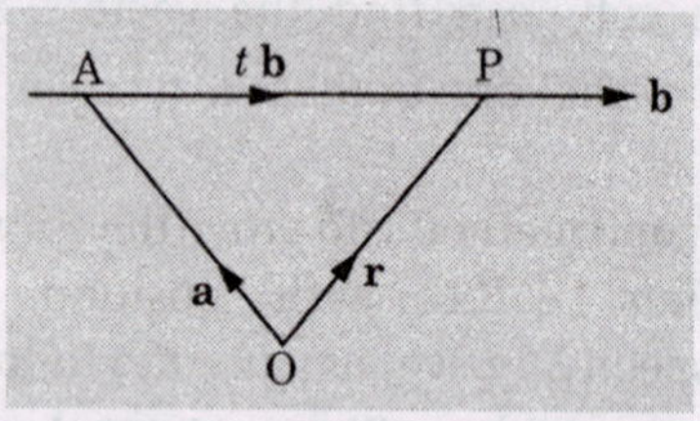

Fig. 9

The line through $A(\mathbf{a})$ is parallel to **b**. If $P(\mathbf{r})$ be any point on the line, then

$$\vec{OP} = \vec{OA} + \vec{AP}$$

or $\quad \mathbf{r} = \mathbf{a} + t\,\mathbf{b}$ ...(1)

(ii) Equation of a line through two points $A(\mathbf{a})$ and $B(\mathbf{b})$:

$\vec{AB} = \mathbf{b} - \mathbf{a}$. Hence the required line is one through **a** and parallel to $\mathbf{b} - \mathbf{a}$. Therefore from (1), the equation is $\mathbf{r} = \mathbf{a} + t\,(\mathbf{b} - \mathbf{a})$,

or $\quad \mathbf{r} = (1-t)\,\mathbf{a} + t\,\mathbf{b}$

or $\quad (1-t)\,\mathbf{a} + t\,\mathbf{b} - \mathbf{r} = 0$ ...(2)

Above is of the form $x\,\mathbf{a} + y\,\mathbf{b} + z\,\mathbf{r} = 0$

where $x + y + z = (1-t) + t - 1 = 0$

because **a, b** and **r** *i.e.* points A, B and P being points on AB are collinear.

§ 6. (b) Vector Equation of plane.

To find the vector equation of a plane which passes through the origin and is parallel to given vectors **a** and **b**.

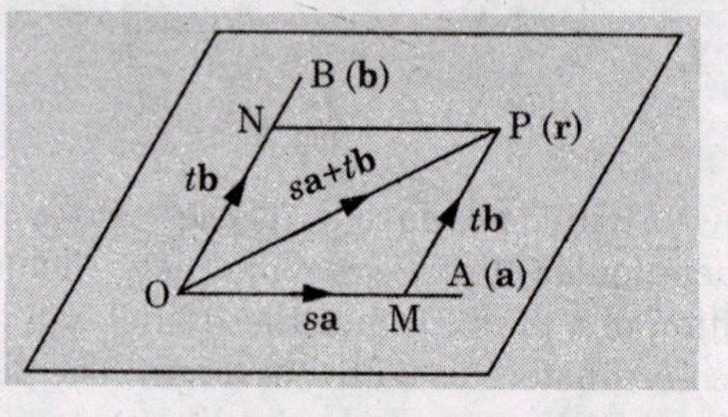

Fig. 10

Choosing O as origin, let the vectors OA and OB be **a** and **b**. Let P be any point on the plane. From P draw PM and PN parallel to OB and OA respectively meeting OA and OB in M and N respectively.

$\vec{OM}$ being collinear with $OA = s\mathbf{a}$.

$\vec{ON}$ being collinear with $OB = t\mathbf{b}$.

If **r** be the position vector of P, any point on the plane, then

$$\mathbf{r} = \vec{OP} = \vec{OM} + \vec{MP} = \vec{OM} + \vec{ON} = s\mathbf{a} + t\,\mathbf{b}.$$

Hence the vector equation of the required plane is given by

$$\mathbf{r} = s\mathbf{a} + t\,\mathbf{b} \qquad \text{...(1)}$$

or $\quad \rho = s\alpha + t\,\beta$,

where s and t are scalars which vary as the point P moves on the plane.

Cor. 1. To find the vector equation of a plane through a given point c and parallel to a and b.

Let **c** be the position vector of any point C on the plane and P be any point on it.

Now the vector $\vec{CP}$ is coplanar with **a** and **b** and as such

$$\vec{CP} = s\mathbf{a} + t\,\mathbf{b}.$$

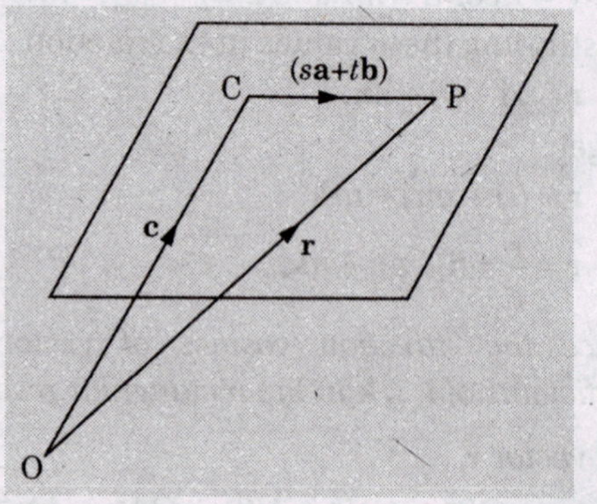

Fig. 11

If **r** be the position vector of P, then

$$\mathbf{r} = \vec{OP} = \vec{OC} + \vec{CP} = \mathbf{c} + s\mathbf{a} + t\,\mathbf{b}.$$

Hence the required vector equation of the plane is $\mathbf{r} = \mathbf{c} + s\mathbf{a} + t\,\mathbf{b}$ or $\rho = \gamma + s\alpha + t\,\beta$ where s and t are scalars which vary as the point P moves on the plane.

Cor. 2. To find the vector equation of a plane that passes through three points whose position vectors are a, b and c.

Let **a**, **b**, **c** be position vectors of the points A, B and C respectively on the plane, so that $\vec{AB} = \mathbf{b} - \mathbf{a}$ and $\vec{AC} = \mathbf{c} - \mathbf{a}$.

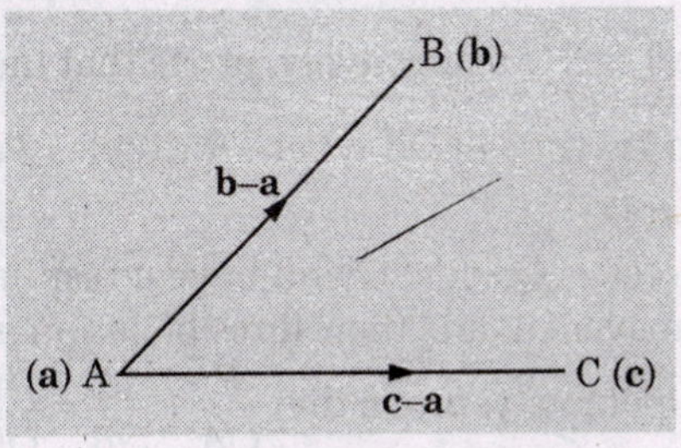

Fig. 12

Now the required plane is one through the point **a** and parallel to $\vec{AB}$ and $\vec{AC}$, *i.e.* through **a** and parallel to **b** – **a** and **c** – **a** and hence by Cor. 1, its equation is

$$\mathbf{r} = \mathbf{a} + s\,(\mathbf{b} - \mathbf{a}) + t\,(\mathbf{c} - \mathbf{a})$$

or $\mathbf{r} = (1 - s - t)\,\mathbf{a} + s\mathbf{b} + t\mathbf{c}$ ...(3)

or $0 = (1 - s - t)\,\alpha + s\beta + t\,\gamma - \rho$

Above is of the form $x\mathbf{a} + y\mathbf{b} + r\mathbf{c} - \mathbf{r} = 0$

where $x + y + z + w = (1 - s - t) + s + t - 1 = 0$

Hence the equation $\mathbf{r} = a\alpha + b\beta + c\gamma$ will represent the equation of a plane if $a + b + c = 1 - s - t + s + t = 1$

§7. Bisectors of the angles between two straight lines

Let the two lines pass through a point $A\,(\mathbf{a})$ and be parallel to vectors **b** and **c** so that their equations are $\mathbf{r} = \mathbf{a} + t\,\mathbf{b}$ and $\mathbf{r} = \mathbf{a} + k\,\mathbf{c}$. Choose P any point on the internal bisector AP. Draw PN parallel to AM, therefore

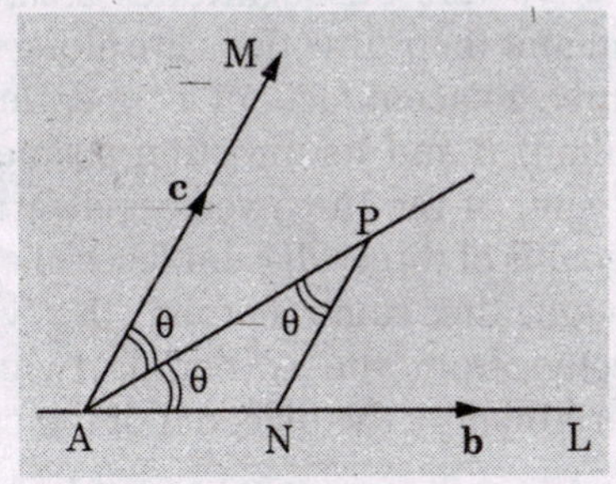

Fig. 13

$$\angle APN = \angle PAM = \angle PAN$$

Hence $AN = NP$ and therefore each is the same scalar multiple of unit vector $\hat{\mathbf{b}}$ and $\hat{\mathbf{c}}$ along these directions.

$\therefore \quad \vec{AN} = t\,\hat{\mathbf{b}}, \quad \vec{NP} = t\,\hat{\mathbf{c}}$

$\therefore \quad \vec{AP} = \vec{AN} + \vec{NP} = t\,(\hat{\mathbf{b}} + \hat{\mathbf{c}})$

If **r** be the position vector of P on the internal bisector, then

$$\mathbf{r} = \vec{OP} = \vec{OA} + \vec{AP} = \mathbf{a} + t\,(\hat{\mathbf{b}} + \hat{\mathbf{c}}) \quad ...(1)$$

Similarly the equation of external bisector is the same as the internal bisector of – **b** and **c**.

$$\therefore \quad \mathbf{r} = \mathbf{a} + t\,(\hat{\mathbf{c}} - \hat{\mathbf{b}}) \quad ...(2)$$

Particular Case : In case the point A be origin then the equations (1) and (2) on putting $\mathbf{a} = 0$ reduce to $\mathbf{r} = t\,(\hat{\mathbf{b}} + \hat{\mathbf{c}})$ and $\mathbf{r} = t\,(\hat{\mathbf{c}} - \hat{\mathbf{b}})$.

Problem Set (1)

Addition of vectors, Collinear and Coplanar points and vectors. Ratio formula, Vector equation of a line, Bisectors of the angle between two lines.

1. If **a**, **b** are the vectors forming consecutive sides of a regular hexagon $ABCDEF$, express the vectors $\vec{CD}, \vec{DE}, \vec{EF}, \vec{FA}, \vec{AC}, \vec{AD}, \vec{AE}$, and $\vec{CE}$ in terms of **a** and **b**.

2. Five forces $\vec{AB}, \vec{AC}, \vec{AD}, \vec{AE}, \vec{AF}$ act at the vertex A of a regular hexagon $ABCDEF$. Prove that their resultant is a force $6\,\vec{AO}$ where O is the centroid of the hexagon.

3. (a) $ABCDE$ is pentagon, prove that the resultant of forces $\vec{AB}, \vec{AE}, \vec{BC}, \vec{DC}, \vec{ED}$ and $\vec{AC}$ is $3\,\vec{AC}$.

(b) The points D, E, F divide the respective sides of $\Delta\,ABC$ in the ratios as shown in the figure V-15 on **Page 1102**. P is a point in AB which divides AB in the ratio 1 : 3. Prove that $5\,(\vec{AD} + \vec{BE} + \vec{CF}) = 2\vec{CP}$.

4. (i) Prove that the resultant of two forces acting at point O and represented by $\vec{OB}$ and $\vec{OC}$ is given by $2\,\vec{OD}$ where D is the mid-point of BC.

(ii) If C is the middle point of AB and P is any point outside AB, then

(a) $\vec{PA} + \vec{PB} = \vec{PC}$ (b) $\vec{PA} + \vec{PB} = 2\,\vec{PC}$

(c) $\vec{PA} + \vec{PB} + \vec{PC} = \vec{0}$ (d) $\vec{PA} + \vec{PB} + 2\,\vec{PC} = \vec{0}$.

(M.N.R. 1991)

5. (a)* Prove that sum of three vectors determined by the medians of a triangle directed from the vertices is zero.

(b) The vectors $\vec{AB} = 3\mathbf{i} + 4\mathbf{k}$ and $\vec{AC} = 5\mathbf{i} - 2\mathbf{j} + 4\mathbf{k}$ are the sides of a triangle ABC. The length of the median through A is :

(a) $\sqrt{18}$ (b) $\sqrt{72}$

(c) $\sqrt{33}$ (d) $\sqrt{288}$ **(AIEEE 2003)**

6. (a) Three vectors of magnitudes $a, 2a, 3a$ meet in a point and their directions are along the diagonals of three adjacent faces of a cube. Determine their resultant R and its direction cosines. Prove also that sum of the three vectors determined by the diagonals of three adjacent faces of a cube passing through the same corner, the vectors being directed from the corner, is twice the vector determined by the diagonal of the cube.

(b) Three force vectors $\vec{P}, \vec{Q}, \vec{R}$ of 15 kg. each act along AB, BC and CA respectively. The position vectors of A, B and C are given by

$$\vec{OA} = 2\mathbf{i} - 4\mathbf{j} + 3\mathbf{k},\ \vec{OB} = 5\mathbf{i} + 3\mathbf{j} - 2\mathbf{k},$$
$$\vec{OC} = -2\mathbf{i} + 2\mathbf{j} + 3\mathbf{k}.$$

Find the resultant force vector $\vec{S}$ of the vectors $\vec{P}, \vec{Q}$ and $\vec{R}$.

(c) What is the unit vector parallel to $\mathbf{a} = 3\mathbf{i} + 4\mathbf{j} - 2\mathbf{k}$? What vector should be added to $\mathbf{a}$ so that resultant is the unit vector $\mathbf{i}$?

7. The vertices of a quadrilateral are $A(1, 2, -1)$, $B(-4, 2, -2)$, $C(4, 1, -5)$ and $D(2, -1, 3)$. At the point A forces of magnitudes 2, 3, 2 kg act along AB, AC and AD respectively. Find their resultant.

8. Prove that the system of concurrent forces at a point and represented by $\vec{OA}, \vec{OB}, \vec{OC}$ is equivalent to the system of forces represented by $\vec{OD}, \vec{OE}, \vec{OF}$ acting at the same point where D, E, F are the middle points of the sides BC, CA and AB respectively of triangle ABC. Also prove that

$$\vec{AD} + \frac{2}{3}\vec{BE} + \frac{1}{3}\vec{CF} = \frac{1}{2}\vec{AC}$$

and $\vec{OE} + \vec{OF} + \vec{DO} = \vec{OA}$.

9.* Two forces act at the vertex A of a quadrilateral $ABCD$ represented by $\vec{AB}, \vec{AD}$ and two at C represented by $\vec{CB}$ and $\vec{CD}$. Prove that their resultant is represented by $4\,\vec{EF}$ where E and F are the middle points of AC and BD respectively.

10. $ABCD$ is a quadrilateral and E the point of intersection of the lines joining the middle points of opposite sides. Show that the resultant of $\vec{OA}, \vec{OB}, \vec{OC}$ and $\vec{OD}$ is equal to $4\,\vec{OE}$ where O is any point.

11.* If O is the circumcentre and O' the orthocentre of a triangle ABC, then prove that

(i) $\vec{OA} + \vec{OB} + \vec{OC} = \vec{OO'}$

(ii) $\vec{O'A} + \vec{O'B} + \vec{O'C} = 2\vec{O'O}$

(iii) $\vec{AO'} + \vec{O'B} + \vec{O'C} = 2\,\vec{AO} = \vec{AP}$

where AP is the diameter through A of circum-circle.

12. ABC is a triangle and P any point in BC. If $\vec{PQ}$ is the resultant of $\vec{AP}, \vec{PB}$ and $\vec{PC}$, show that $ABQC$ is a parallelogram and Q therefore a fixed point.

13. If two concurrent forces be represented by $n\,\vec{OP}$ and $m\,\vec{OQ}$ respectively, prove that their resultant is given by $(m+n)\,\vec{OR}$ where R divides PQ such that $n\,PR = m\,RQ$. **(M.N.R. 1991)**

14. (a) Forces P, Q act at O and have a resultant R. If any transversal cuts their lines of action at A, B and C respectively, prove that $\dfrac{P}{OA} + \dfrac{Q}{OB} = \dfrac{R}{OC}$.

(b) A transversal cuts the sides OL, OM and diagonal ON of a parallelogram at A, B and C respectively, prove that $\dfrac{OL}{OA} + \dfrac{OM}{OB} = \dfrac{ON}{OC}$.

15. (a) If G is the centroid of the triangle ABC, show that $\vec{GA} + \vec{GB} + \vec{GC} = \mathbf{0}$ and conversely if $\vec{GA} + \vec{GB} + \vec{GC} = \mathbf{0}$, then G is the centroid of triangle ABC.

(b) If A, B, C and P, Q, R be two triangles whose centroids are respectively G and G' then prove that $\vec{AP} + \vec{BQ} + \vec{CR} = 3\,\vec{GG'}$.

16.* Prove that the medians of a triangle are concurrent and find the point of concurrency. **(M.N.R. 1991)**

17. (a) The lines joining the vertices of a tetrahedron to the centroids of opposite faces are concurrent. **(M.N.R. 1995)**

(b) The joins of the mid-points of the opposite edges of a tetrahedron intersect and bisect each other.

18. The four diagonals of a parallelopiped and the joins of the mid-points of opposite edges are concurrent at a common point of bisection.

19.* (a) Prove that the diagonals of a parallelogram bisect each other and conversely if the diagonals of a quadrilateral bisect each other, it is a parallelogram.

(b) The sides of a parallelogram are $2\mathbf{i} + 4\mathbf{j} - 5\mathbf{k}$ and $\mathbf{i} + 2\mathbf{j} + 3\mathbf{k}$. Find the unit vectors parallel to the diagonals.

20. $ABCD$ is a parallelogram and O the point of intersection of diagonals. Show that for any origin the sum of the position vectors of the vertices is equal to four times that of O.

21. If M, N are the mid-points of the sides AB, CD of a parallelogram $ABCD$, prove that DM and BN cut the diagonal AC in its points of trisection which are also the points of trisection of DM and BC respectively.

22. $ABCD$ is a paralleogram, P and Q are the mid-points of the sides AB and BC respectively. Prove that DP and AC meet in a common point of trisection and similarly DQ and AC.

23. Prove that the figure formed by joining the mid-points of the sides of a quadrilateral taken in order is a parallelogram.

24.* Prove that in any triangle the line joining the mid-points of any two sides is parallel to the third side and half of its length.

25. (a)* Prove that the straight line joining the mid-points of two non-parallel sides of a trapezium is parallel to the parallel sides and half of their sum.

(b)* Prove, by vector methods or otherwise, that the point of intersection of the diagonals of a trapezium lies on the line passing through the mid-points of the parallel sides. (You may assume that the trapezium is not a parallelogram.) **(I.I.T. 1998)**

26.* Prove that the straight line joining the mid-points of the diagonals of a trapezium is parallel to the parallel sides and half of their difference.

27.* (a) Prove that internal bisectors of the angles of a triangle are concurrent. Also find the position vector of the point of concurrency. **(I.I.T. 2001)**

(b) Prove that the altitudes of a triangle are concurrent and hence find the position vector of the orthocentre of the triangle in terms of position vectors of its vertices.

28. Prove that three points with position vectors **a**, **b**, **c** are collinear if and only if there exist scalars x, y, z not all zero such that

(i) $x\mathbf{a} + y\mathbf{b} + z\mathbf{c} = 0$ and

(ii) $x + y + z = 0$.

29. Prove that the following points are collinear :

(a) $\mathbf{a} - 2\mathbf{b} + 3\mathbf{c}$, $2\mathbf{a} + 3\mathbf{b} - 4\mathbf{c}$, $-7\mathbf{b} + 10\mathbf{c}$.

(b) $\mathbf{a}$, $\mathbf{b}$, $3\mathbf{a} - 2\mathbf{b}$.

(c) $-2\mathbf{a} + 3\mathbf{b} + 5\mathbf{c}$, $\mathbf{a} + 2\mathbf{b} + 3\mathbf{c}$, $7\mathbf{a} - \mathbf{c}$.

(d) $\mathbf{a} + \mathbf{b} + \mathbf{c}$, $4\mathbf{a} + 3\mathbf{b}$, $10\mathbf{a} + 7\mathbf{b} - 2\mathbf{c}$.

(e) Find the condition that the three points whose position vectors are $\mathbf{A} = a\mathbf{i} + b\mathbf{j} + c\mathbf{k}$, $\mathbf{B} = \mathbf{i} + c\mathbf{j}$, $\mathbf{C} = -\mathbf{i} - \mathbf{j}$ are collinear.

30. (a) $A(1, 2, 3)$, $B(3, 4, 7)$, $C(-3, -2, -5)$. and find the ratio in which point B divides AC.

(b) If $\vec{AO} + \vec{OB} = \vec{BO} + \vec{OC}$, prove that A, B, C are collinear.

31.* If **a**, **b** are two non-collinear vectors, show that points $l_1\mathbf{a} + m_1\mathbf{b}$, $l_2\mathbf{a} + m_2\mathbf{b}$, $l_3\mathbf{a} + m_3\mathbf{b}$ are colinear if

$$\begin{vmatrix} l_1 & l_2 & l_3 \\ m_1 & m_2 & m_3 \\ 1 & 1 & 1 \end{vmatrix} = 0.$$

32. (a) The vectors **a** and **b** are non-collinear. Find for what value of x, the vectors $\mathbf{c} = (x-2)\mathbf{a} + \mathbf{b}$ and $\mathbf{d} = (2x+1)\mathbf{a} - \mathbf{b}$ are collinear ?

(b) If **a** and **b** are non-collinear vectors and

$\mathbf{A} = (p + 4q)\mathbf{a} + (2p + q + 1)\mathbf{b}$

$\mathbf{B} = (-2p + q + 2)\mathbf{a} + (2p - 3q - 1)\mathbf{b}$

then determine p and q so that $3\mathbf{A} = 2\mathbf{B}$.

33. (a) **a**, **b**, **c** are three non-zero vectors such that any two of them are non-collinear. If $\mathbf{a} + 2\mathbf{b}$ is collinear with **c** and $\mathbf{b} + 3\mathbf{c}$ is collinear with **a** then prove that $\mathbf{a} + 2\mathbf{b} + 6\mathbf{c}$ is a null vector.

(b) **a**, **b**, **c** are three non-zero vectors such that any two of them are non-collinear. If $\mathbf{a} + \mathbf{b}$ is collinear with **c** and $\mathbf{b} + \mathbf{c}$ is collinear with **a**, then what is their sum ?

34. (a) The points with position vectors $10\mathbf{i} + 3\mathbf{j}$, $12\mathbf{i} - 5\mathbf{j}$ and $a\mathbf{i} + 11\mathbf{j}$ are collinear if a equals 8. **(M.N.R. 1992)**

(b) The vectors $x\mathbf{i} - 3\mathbf{j} + 7\mathbf{k}$ and $\mathbf{i} + y\mathbf{j} - z\mathbf{k}$ are collinear then the value of $\frac{xy^2}{z} =$

(a) 9/7 (b) $-9/7$
(c) 6/7 (d) $-6/7$

(c) The points with position vectors $60\mathbf{i} + 3\mathbf{j}$, $40\mathbf{i} - 8\mathbf{j}$, $a\mathbf{i} - 52\mathbf{j}$ are collinear if $a = -40$.

(d) Prove that the points with position vectors $\mathbf{a} + \mathbf{b}$, $\mathbf{a} - \mathbf{b}$ and $\mathbf{a} + k\mathbf{b}$ are collinear for all real values of k.

(e) Does there exist scalars a, b, c such that
$$a(\mathbf{k}) + b(\mathbf{j} + \mathbf{k}) + c(-\mathbf{j} + 2\mathbf{k}) = \mathbf{i}\ ?$$

(f) Prove that the vectors $\mathbf{i} - 3\mathbf{j} + 2\mathbf{k}$, $2\mathbf{i} - 4\mathbf{j} - 4\mathbf{k}$ and $3\mathbf{i} + 2\mathbf{j} - \mathbf{k} = 0$ are linearly independent.

35. Prove that the necessary and sufficient condition for any four points in three dimensional space to be coplanar is that there exists a linear relation connecting their position vectors such that the algebraic sum of the coefficients (not all zero) in it is zero.

36.* If **a**, **b**, **c** are non-coplanar vectors, prove that the following vectors are coplanar.

(a) $3\mathbf{a} - 7\mathbf{b} - 4\mathbf{c}, 3\mathbf{a} - 2\mathbf{b} + \mathbf{c}, \mathbf{a} + \mathbf{b} + 2\mathbf{c}$.

(b) $5\mathbf{a} + 6\mathbf{b} + 7\mathbf{c}, 7\mathbf{a} - 8\mathbf{b} + 9\mathbf{c}, 3\mathbf{a} + 20\mathbf{b} + 5\mathbf{c}$.

(c) $\mathbf{a} - 2\mathbf{b} + 3\mathbf{c}, -2\mathbf{a} + 3\mathbf{b} - 4\mathbf{c}, \mathbf{a} - 3\mathbf{b} + 5\mathbf{c}$.

(d) $5\mathbf{a} + 6\mathbf{b} + 7\mathbf{c}, 7\mathbf{a} - 8\mathbf{b} + 9\mathbf{c}, \mathbf{a} - 20\mathbf{b} + 5\mathbf{c}$.

37. If the vectors $2, -1, 1$; $1, 2, -3$ and $3, a, 5$ are coplanar then prove that $a = -4$.

38.* If **a**, **b**, **c** are non-coplanar vectors, prove that the four points as given below are coplanar.

(a) $2\mathbf{a} + 3\mathbf{b} - \mathbf{c}, \mathbf{a} - 2\mathbf{b} + 3\mathbf{c}, 3\mathbf{a} + 4\mathbf{b} - 2\mathbf{c}, \mathbf{a} - 6\mathbf{b} + 6\mathbf{c}$.

(b) $6\mathbf{a}+2\mathbf{b}-\mathbf{c}, 2\mathbf{a}-\mathbf{b}+3\mathbf{c}, -\mathbf{a}+2\mathbf{b}-4\mathbf{c}, -12\mathbf{a}-\mathbf{b}-3\mathbf{c}$.

(c) $6\mathbf{a}-4\mathbf{b}+10\mathbf{c}, -5\mathbf{a}+3\mathbf{b}-10\mathbf{c}$,
$4\mathbf{a}-6\mathbf{b}-10\mathbf{c}, \ 2\mathbf{b}+10\mathbf{c}$.

39. If $\mathbf{a}, \mathbf{b}, \mathbf{c}$ be any three non-zero, non-coplanar vectors, then find the linear relation between the following four vectors :

$$\mathbf{a}-2\mathbf{b}+3\mathbf{c}, 2\mathbf{a}-3\mathbf{b}+4\mathbf{c}, 3\mathbf{a}-4\mathbf{b}+5\mathbf{c}, 7\mathbf{a}-11\mathbf{b}+15\mathbf{c}.$$

40. If $\mathbf{a}, \mathbf{b}, \mathbf{c}$ be any three non-coplanar vectors, then prove that the points

$$l_1\mathbf{a}+m_1\mathbf{b}+n_1\mathbf{c}, \ l_2\mathbf{a}+m_2\mathbf{b}+n_2\mathbf{c},$$
$$l_3\mathbf{a}+m_3\mathbf{b}+n_3\mathbf{c}, \ l_4\mathbf{a}+m_4\mathbf{b}+n_4\mathbf{c}$$

are coplanar if

$$\begin{vmatrix} l_1 & l_2 & l_3 & l_4 \\ m_1 & m_2 & m_3 & m_4 \\ n_1 & n_2 & n_3 & n_4 \\ 1 & 1 & 1 & 1 \end{vmatrix} = 0$$

41.* (a) Find all the values of λ such that $(x, y, z) \neq (0,0,0)$ and $(\mathbf{i}+\mathbf{j}+3\mathbf{k})\,x+(3\mathbf{i}-3\mathbf{j}+\mathbf{k})\,y+(-4\mathbf{i}+5\mathbf{j})\,z = \lambda\,(x\mathbf{i}+y\mathbf{j}+z\mathbf{k})$.

(Roorkee 2001)

(b) If $\mathbf{a}, \mathbf{b}, \mathbf{c}$ form a system of linearly independent vectors then the system of vectors $\mathbf{a}-2\mathbf{b}+\mathbf{c}, 2\mathbf{a}-\mathbf{b}+\mathbf{c}$ and $3\mathbf{a}+\mathbf{b}+2\mathbf{c}$ is also linearly independent.

(c) Prove that the vectors $-\mathbf{i}-2\mathbf{j}+2\mathbf{k}, \ \mathbf{i}+\mathbf{j}+\mathbf{k}$ and $2\mathbf{i}+3\mathbf{j}-\mathbf{k}$ are linearly dependent.

42.* (a) If $\mathbf{a}=2\mathbf{p}+3\mathbf{q}-\mathbf{r}$,
$\mathbf{b}=\mathbf{p}-2\mathbf{q}+2\mathbf{r}$
and $\mathbf{c}=-2\mathbf{p}+\mathbf{q}-2\mathbf{r}$
and $\mathbf{R}=3\mathbf{p}-\mathbf{q}+2\mathbf{r}$, express $\mathbf{R}$ in terms of $\mathbf{a}, \mathbf{b}, \mathbf{c}$, when $\mathbf{p}, \mathbf{q}, \mathbf{r}$ are non-coplanar vectors.

(b) In terms of unit vectors $\mathbf{i}, \mathbf{j}$ and $\mathbf{k}$
$\mathbf{a}=2,-1,1;\ \mathbf{b}=1,3,-2;\ \mathbf{c}=-2,1,-3$ and $\mathbf{d}=3,2,5$.
Determine the scalars x, y, z such that $\mathbf{d}=x\mathbf{a}+y\mathbf{b}+z\mathbf{c}$.

43. (a) A vector A has components A_1, A_2, A_3 in a right handed rectangular Cartesian co-ordinate system Ox, Oy, Oz. The co-ordinate system is rotated about the z-axis through an angle $\pi/2$. Find the components of A in new co-ordinate system in terms of A_1, A_2, A_3.

(b) The axes of co-ordinates are rotated about z-axis through an angle of $\pi/4$ in anti-clockwise direction and the components of a vector are $2\sqrt{2}$, $3\sqrt{2}$, 4. Then the components of the same vector in the original system are $-1, 5, 4$.

44. Let $\mathbf{r_1}, \mathbf{r_2}, \mathbf{r_3}, \ldots \mathbf{r_n}$ be the position vectors of points $P_1, P_2, P_3, \ldots P_n$ relative to an origin O. Show that if the vector equation $\mathbf{a_1 r_1}+\mathbf{a_2 r_2}+\ldots\ldots \mathbf{a}_n\mathbf{r}_n=\mathbf{0}$ holds, then a similar equation will also hold good with respect to any other origin P if $a_1+a_2+\ldots a_n=0$.

45. A particle, in equilibrium, is subjected to four forces

$$\mathbf{F}_1=-10\mathbf{k}, \ \mathbf{F}_2=U\left[\frac{4}{13}\mathbf{i}-\frac{12}{13}\mathbf{j}+\frac{3}{13}\mathbf{k}\right],$$
$$\mathbf{F}_3=V\left[-\frac{4}{13}\mathbf{i}-\frac{12}{13}\mathbf{j}+\frac{3}{13}\mathbf{k}\right],$$
$$\mathbf{F}_4=W\,[\cos\theta\,\mathbf{i}+\sin\theta\,\mathbf{j}]$$

Solve for U, V and W as functions of θ.

46. (a) If the resultant of two forces is equal in magnitude to one of the components and perpendicular to it in direction, find the other component using vector method.

(b) Find the horizontal force and a force inclined at an angle of 60° to the vertical whose resultant is a vertical force P kg wt.

(c) A man travelling east at 8 km per hour finds that the wind seems to blow directly from the north. On doubling the speed, he finds that it appears to come from N-E. Find the velocity of the wind.

47. (a) Unit vectors $\mathbf{i}$ and $\mathbf{j}$ are parallel to adjacent edges of a large square table. The directions of $\mathbf{i}$ and $\mathbf{j}$ are referred to as east and north. An ant walking on the table makes the following movement successively.

(i) 4 cm. 30° east of north,
(ii) 12 cm. south-west,
(iii) 6 cm. east, and
(iv) 9 cm. west-north. Find the magnitude and direction of ant's resultant displacement.

(b) A ship is sailing towards north at a speed of $1\cdot25$ m/sec. The current is taking it towards east at the rate of 1 m/sec. and a sailor is climbing a vertical pole on the ship at the rate of $0\cdot5$ m/sec. Find the velocity of the sailor in space.

48. (a) In a triangle OAB, E is the mid-point of OB and D is a point on AB such that $AD:DB=2:1$. If OD and AE intersect at P, determine the ratio $OP:PD$ using vector methods.

(b)* In a triangle ABC, D and E are points on BC and AC respectively, such that $BD=2DC$ and $AE=3EC$. Let P be the point of intersection of AD and BE. Find BP/PE using vector methods.

(I.I.T. 1993)

49. (a) In a triangle ABC, D divides BC in the ratio $3:2$ and E divides CA in the ratio $1:3$. The lines AD and BE meet at H and CH meets AB in F. Find the ratio in which F divides AB.

(b)* Points D, E, F divide the sides BC, CA and AB of a triangle respectively in the ratio $2:3, 1:2$ and $3:1$. Prove that the lines AD, BE and CF are concurrent and find the P. V. of the point of concurrency.

50. P, Q, R divide the sides BC, CA and AB of a triangle ABC in the ratio $1:2$. The three lines AP, BQ and CR enclose a triangle XYZ. Prove that the triangles ABC and XYZ have the same centroid.

51. The median AD of a triangle ABC is bisected at E and BE is produced to meet AC in F. Prove by vector method that $EF = \frac{1}{4} BF$.

52. In a quadrilateral $PQRS$, $\vec{PQ} = \mathbf{a}$, $\vec{QR} = \mathbf{b}$ and $\vec{SP} = \mathbf{a} - \mathbf{b}$, M is the mid-point of QR and X is a point of SM such that $SX = \frac{4}{5} SM$. Examine whether P, X and R are collinear. **(M.N.R. 1996)**

53.* (a) Prove that the internal bisectors of the angles of a triangle are concurrent. **(I.I.T. 2001)**

(b) If I be the centre of a circle inscribed in a triangle ABC, then the vector sum
$|\vec{BC}|\vec{IA} + |\vec{CA}|\vec{IB} + |\vec{AB}|\vec{IC} = \ldots\ldots$

(c) The vector $\mathbf{a} + \mathbf{b}$ bisects the angle between the vectors $\mathbf{a}$ and $\mathbf{b}$ if either $|\mathbf{a}| = |\mathbf{b}|$ or angle between $\mathbf{a}$ and $\mathbf{b}$ is 0.

54.* The vector $-\mathbf{i} + \mathbf{j} - \mathbf{k}$, bisects the angle between the vectors $\mathbf{c}$ and $3\mathbf{i} + 4\mathbf{j}$. Determine the unit vector along $\mathbf{c}$. **(Roorkee 1991)**

55. (a) If $\mathbf{a} = 7\mathbf{i} - 4\mathbf{j} - 4\mathbf{k}$ and $\mathbf{b} = -2\mathbf{i} - \mathbf{j} + 2\mathbf{k}$, determine the vector $\mathbf{c}$ of modulus $5\sqrt{6}$ which is along the internal bisector of the angle between the vectors $\mathbf{a}$ and $\mathbf{b}$.

(b) The position vectors of the points A and B w.r.t. an origin are $\mathbf{a} = \mathbf{i} + 3\mathbf{j} - 2\mathbf{k}$ and $\mathbf{b} = 3\mathbf{i} + \mathbf{j} - 2\mathbf{k}$ respectively. Determine the vector $\vec{OP}$ which bisects the angle AOB, where P is a point on AB.

(c) If the vector $-\mathbf{i} + \mathbf{j} - \mathbf{k}$ bisects the angle between the vectors $\mathbf{c}$ and the vector $3\mathbf{i} + 4\mathbf{j}$ then find the unit vector along $\mathbf{c}$.

56. Using vector method, find the ratio in which the bisector of an angle in a triangle divides the opposite side. **(M.N.R. 1994)**

57.* The position vectors of the points P and Q are $5\mathbf{i} + 7\mathbf{j} - 2\mathbf{k}$ and $-3\mathbf{i} + 3\mathbf{j} + 6\mathbf{k}$ respectively. The vector $\mathbf{A} = 3\mathbf{i} - \mathbf{j} + \mathbf{k}$ passes through the point P and the vector $\mathbf{B} = -3\mathbf{i} + 2\mathbf{j} + 4\mathbf{k}$ passes through the point Q. A third vector $2\mathbf{i} + 7\mathbf{j} - 5\mathbf{k}$ intersects vectors $\mathbf{A}$ and $\mathbf{B}$. Find the position vectors of the points of intersection. **(Roorkee 1997)**

58.* If $\mathbf{a}, \mathbf{b}, \mathbf{c}$ are the position vectors of the vertices of an equilateral triangle whose orthocentre is at the origin, then prove that $\mathbf{a} + \mathbf{b} + \mathbf{c} = 0$.

59. Let two non-collinear unit vectors $\hat{\mathbf{a}}$ and $\hat{\mathbf{b}}$ form an acute angle. A point P moves so that at any time t the position vector $\vec{\mathbf{OP}}$ (where O is the origin) is given by $\hat{\mathbf{a}} \cos t + \hat{\mathbf{b}} \sin t$. When P is farthest from origin O, let M be the length of $\vec{\mathbf{OP}}$ and $\hat{\mathbf{u}}$ be the unit vector along $\vec{\mathbf{OP}}$. Then,

(a) $\hat{\mathbf{u}} = \dfrac{\hat{\mathbf{a}} + \hat{\mathbf{b}}}{|\hat{\mathbf{a}} + \hat{\mathbf{b}}|}$ and $M = (1 + \hat{\mathbf{a}} \cdot \hat{\mathbf{b}})^{1/2}$

(b) $\hat{\mathbf{u}} = \dfrac{\hat{\mathbf{a}} - \hat{\mathbf{b}}}{|\hat{\mathbf{a}} - \hat{\mathbf{b}}|}$ and $M = (1 + \hat{\mathbf{a}} \cdot \hat{\mathbf{b}})^{1/2}$

(c) $\hat{\mathbf{u}} = \dfrac{\hat{\mathbf{a}} + \hat{\mathbf{b}}}{|\hat{\mathbf{a}} + \hat{\mathbf{b}}|}$ and $M = (1 + 2\hat{\mathbf{a}} \cdot \hat{\mathbf{b}})^{1/2}$

(d) $\hat{\mathbf{u}} = \dfrac{\hat{\mathbf{a}} - \hat{\mathbf{b}}}{|\hat{\mathbf{a}} - \hat{\mathbf{b}}|}$ and $M = (1 + 2\hat{\mathbf{a}} \cdot \hat{\mathbf{b}})^{1/2}$ **(I.I.T. 2008)**

Solutions to Problem Set (1)

1. $\vec{AB} = \mathbf{a}$, $\vec{BC} = \mathbf{b}$

$\therefore \quad \vec{AC} = \vec{AB} + \vec{BC} = \mathbf{a} + \mathbf{b}$ ...(1)

$\vec{AD} = 2\vec{BC} = 2\mathbf{b}$ ...(2)

($\because$ AD is parallel to BC and twice its length).

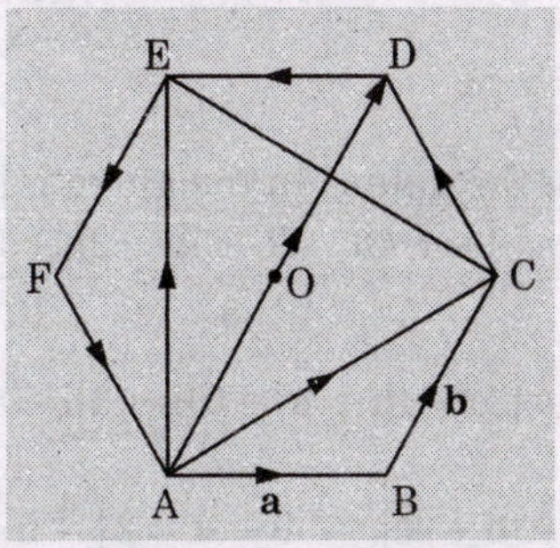

Fig. 14

$\vec{CD} = \vec{AD} - \vec{AC} = 2\mathbf{b} - (\mathbf{a} + \mathbf{b}) = \mathbf{b} - \mathbf{a}$. ...(3)

$\vec{FA} = -\vec{CD} = \mathbf{a} - \mathbf{b}$ ...(4)

$\vec{DE} = -\vec{AB} = -\mathbf{a}$ ...(5)

$\vec{EF} = -\vec{BC} = -\mathbf{b}$ ...(6)

$\vec{AE} = \vec{AD} + \vec{DE} = 2\mathbf{b} - \mathbf{a}$ by (2) and (5) ...(7)

$\vec{CE} = \vec{CD} + \vec{DE} = \mathbf{b} - \mathbf{a} - \mathbf{a} = \mathbf{b} - 2\mathbf{a}$, by (3) and (5)

or $\vec{CE} = \vec{AE} - \vec{AC} = 2\mathbf{b} - \mathbf{a} - (\mathbf{a} + \mathbf{b}) = \mathbf{b} - 2\mathbf{a}$ by (1) and (7).

2. Refer fig. Ex. 1. If $\mathbf{R}$ be the resultant, then

$\mathbf{R} = \vec{AB} + \vec{AC} + \vec{AD} + \vec{AE} + \vec{AF}$

$= \vec{ED} + \vec{AC} + \vec{AD} + \vec{AE} + \vec{CD}$

[$\because$ $\vec{AB} = \vec{ED}$ and $\vec{AF} = \vec{CD}$]

$= (\vec{AC} + \vec{CD}) + (\vec{AE} + \vec{ED}) + \vec{AD}$

$= \vec{AD} + \vec{AD} + \vec{AD} = 3\vec{AD} = 6\vec{AO}$

3. (a) $\mathbf{R} = \overrightarrow{AB} + \overrightarrow{AE} + \overrightarrow{BC} + \overrightarrow{DC} + \overrightarrow{ED} + \overrightarrow{AC}$

$= (\overrightarrow{AB} + \overrightarrow{BC}) + (\overrightarrow{AE} + \overrightarrow{ED} + \overrightarrow{DC}) + \overrightarrow{AC}$

$= \overrightarrow{AC} + \overrightarrow{AC} + \overrightarrow{AC} = 3\overrightarrow{AC}.$

(b) For convenience sake, choose A as origin and the P.Vs. of B and C be taken $\mathbf{b}$ and $\mathbf{c}$ respectively. P.Vs of various other points, by ratio formula, are :

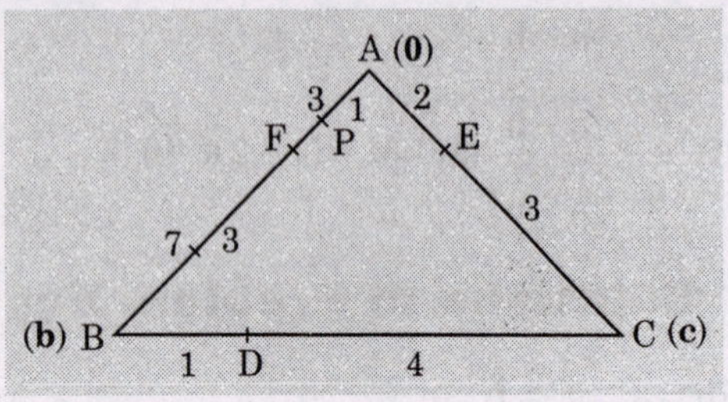

Fig. 15

$D = \dfrac{\mathbf{c} + 4\mathbf{b}}{5}, E = \dfrac{2}{5}\mathbf{c}, F = \dfrac{3}{10}\mathbf{b}, P = \dfrac{1}{4}\mathbf{b}$

$\overrightarrow{AD} = \dfrac{\mathbf{c} + 4\mathbf{b}}{5}, \overrightarrow{BE} = \dfrac{2}{5}\mathbf{c} - \mathbf{b}, \overrightarrow{CF} = \dfrac{3}{10}\mathbf{b} - \mathbf{c},$

$\overrightarrow{CP} = \dfrac{1}{4}\mathbf{b} - \mathbf{c}$

Putting the values in the given relation

$$\text{L.H.S.} = 5\left[\frac{\mathbf{c} + 4\mathbf{b}}{5} + \frac{2\mathbf{c} - 5\mathbf{b}}{5} + \frac{3\mathbf{b} - 10\mathbf{c}}{10}\right]$$

$$= \frac{1}{2}[2\mathbf{c} + 8\mathbf{b} + 4\mathbf{c} - 10\mathbf{b} + 3\mathbf{b} - 10\mathbf{c}]$$

$$= \frac{1}{2}[\mathbf{b} - 4\mathbf{c}] = \frac{1}{2}\mathbf{b} - 2\mathbf{c} = 2\left(\frac{1}{4}\mathbf{b} - \mathbf{c}\right) = 2\overrightarrow{CP}.$$

4. (i) $\mathbf{R} = \overrightarrow{OB} + \overrightarrow{OC}$

$= (\overrightarrow{OD} + \overrightarrow{DB}) + (\overrightarrow{OD} + \overrightarrow{DC})$

$= 2\overrightarrow{OD} + (\overrightarrow{DB} + \overrightarrow{DC}) = 2\overrightarrow{OD} + \mathbf{0} = 2\overrightarrow{OD}$

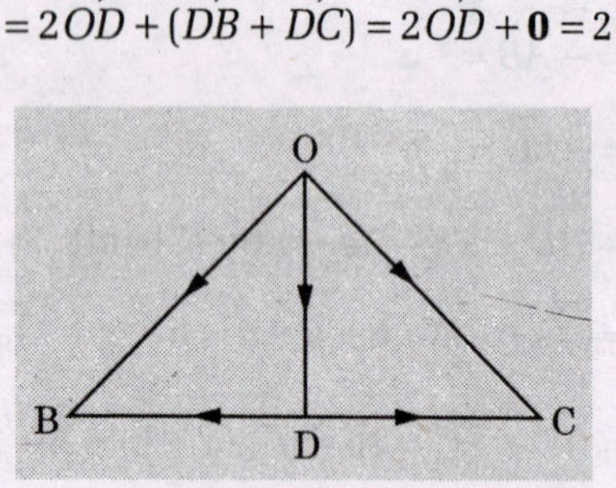

Fig. 16

[D being mid-point of BC, we have $\overrightarrow{DB} = -\overrightarrow{DC}$].

(ii) Ans. (b), by part (i).

$\overrightarrow{PA} + \overrightarrow{PB} = 2\overrightarrow{PC}$ where C is mid-point of AB.

5. (a) **1st Method :** $\overrightarrow{AB} + \overrightarrow{AC} = 2\overrightarrow{AD}$ by Q. 4

$\overrightarrow{BC} + \overrightarrow{BA} = 2\overrightarrow{BE}, \quad \overrightarrow{CA} + \overrightarrow{CB} = 2\overrightarrow{CF}.$

Adding, we get

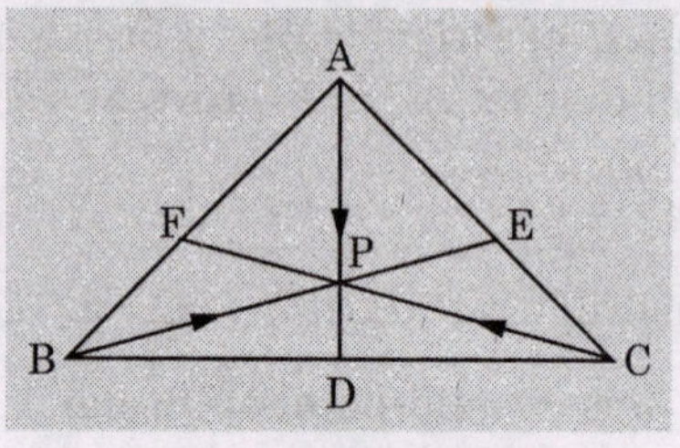

Fig. 17

$(\overrightarrow{AB} + \overrightarrow{BA}) + (\overrightarrow{AC} + \overrightarrow{CA}) + (\overrightarrow{BC} + \overrightarrow{CB})$

$= 2(\overrightarrow{AD} + \overrightarrow{BE} + \overrightarrow{CF})$

or $\mathbf{0} + \mathbf{0} + \mathbf{0} = 2(\overrightarrow{AD} + \overrightarrow{BE} + \overrightarrow{CF})$

or $\overrightarrow{AD} + \overrightarrow{BE} + \overrightarrow{CF} = \mathbf{0}$.

2nd Method :

Let the position vectors of A, B, C w.r.t. an origin O be $\mathbf{a}, \mathbf{b}, \mathbf{c}$ respectively so that those of mid-points D, E and F are respectively

$\dfrac{\mathbf{b} + \mathbf{c}}{2}, \dfrac{\mathbf{c} + \mathbf{a}}{2}, \dfrac{\mathbf{a} + \mathbf{b}}{2}$

$\overrightarrow{AD} = \overrightarrow{OD} - \overrightarrow{OA} = \dfrac{\mathbf{b} + \mathbf{c}}{2} - \mathbf{a} = \dfrac{\mathbf{b} + \mathbf{c} - 2\mathbf{a}}{2},$

$\overrightarrow{BE} = \overrightarrow{OE} - \overrightarrow{OB} = \dfrac{\mathbf{c} + \mathbf{a}}{2} - \mathbf{b} = \dfrac{\mathbf{c} + \mathbf{a} - 2\mathbf{b}}{2},$

and $\overrightarrow{CF} = \overrightarrow{OF} - \overrightarrow{OC} = \dfrac{\mathbf{a} + \mathbf{b}}{2} - \mathbf{c} = \dfrac{\mathbf{a} + \mathbf{b} - 2\mathbf{c}}{2}.$

$\therefore \quad \overrightarrow{AD} + \overrightarrow{BE} + \overrightarrow{CF} = \mathbf{0}$, on adding R.H.S.

(b) Ans. (c).

With respect to A as origin the point B is $(3, 0, 4)$ and C is $(5, -2, 4)$ $\therefore$ Mid-point D of BC is $(4, -1, 4)$.

$\therefore \quad AD^2 = 16 + 1 + 16 = 33 \quad \therefore \quad AD = \sqrt{33}$

6. (a) Let the length of an edge of the cube be taken as unity and the vectors represented by OA, OB, OC (the three coterminous edges of unit length be $\mathbf{i}, \mathbf{j}$ and $\mathbf{k}$ respectively. OR, OS and OT are the three diagonals of the three adjacent faces of the cube along which act the forces of magnitudes $a, 2a$ and $3a$ respectively. In order to find the vectors representing these forces, we shall first find unit vectors in these directions and then multiply them by the corresponding given magnitudes of these forces.

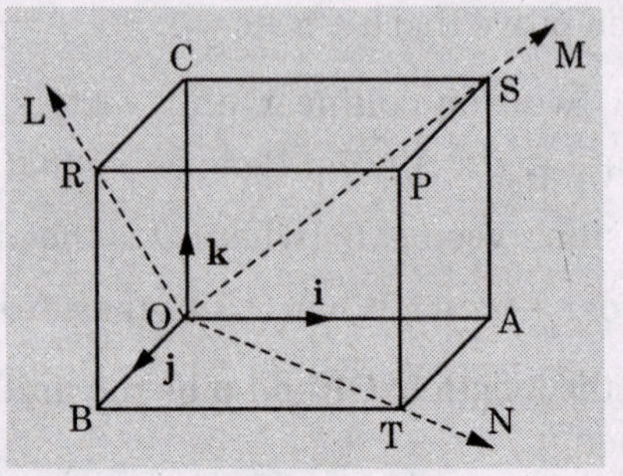

Fig. 18

Since $\vec{OR} = \mathbf{j} + \mathbf{k}$, the unit vectors along OR is

$$\frac{1}{\sqrt{(2)}}(\mathbf{j}+\mathbf{k}).$$

Hence the force $\mathbf{F}_1$ of magnitude a along OR is given by

$$\mathbf{F}_1 = \frac{a}{\sqrt{(2)}}(\mathbf{j}+\mathbf{k}).$$

Exactly in a similar manner the force $\mathbf{F}_2$ of magnitude $2a$ along OS is $\frac{2a}{\sqrt{(2)}}(\mathbf{k}+\mathbf{i})$ and a force $\mathbf{F}_3$ of magnitude $3a$ along OT is $\frac{3a}{\sqrt{(2)}}(\mathbf{i}+\mathbf{j})$.

If $\mathbf{R}$ be their resultant, then $\mathbf{R} = \mathbf{F}_1 + \mathbf{F}_2 + \mathbf{F}_3$

$$= \frac{a}{\sqrt{(2)}}(\mathbf{j}+\mathbf{k}) + \frac{2a}{\sqrt{(2)}}(\mathbf{k}+\mathbf{i}) + \frac{3a}{\sqrt{(2)}}(\mathbf{i}+\mathbf{j})$$

$$= \frac{5a}{\sqrt{(2)}}\mathbf{i} + \frac{4a}{\sqrt{(2)}}\mathbf{j} + \frac{3a}{\sqrt{(2)}}\mathbf{k}$$

$$\therefore \quad |\mathbf{R}| = \sqrt{\left(\frac{25a^2}{2} + \frac{16a^2}{2} + \frac{9a^2}{2}\right)} = 5a.$$

Thus $R = 5a$.

$\therefore$ Direction cosines are $\frac{5a}{R\sqrt{(2)}}, \frac{4a}{R\sqrt{(2)}}, \frac{3a}{R\sqrt{(2)}}$

or $\frac{1}{\sqrt{(2)}}, \frac{4}{5\sqrt{(2)}}, \frac{3}{5\sqrt{(2)}} \quad \because R = 5a.$

Again $\vec{OR} + \vec{OS} + \vec{OT} = \mathbf{j}+\mathbf{k}+\mathbf{i}+\mathbf{k}+\mathbf{i}+\mathbf{j}$

$$= 2(\mathbf{i}+\mathbf{j}+\mathbf{k}).$$

Also $\quad \vec{OP} = \vec{OT} + \vec{TP} = (\mathbf{i}+\mathbf{j}+\mathbf{k})$

$$[\because \vec{OT} = \mathbf{i}+\mathbf{j} \text{ and } \vec{TP} = \vec{OC} = \mathbf{k}]$$

$$\vec{OR} + \vec{OS} + \vec{OT} = 2\vec{OP}.$$

(b) $\vec{AB} = \vec{OB} - \vec{OA} = (5\mathbf{i}+3\mathbf{j}-2\mathbf{k}) - (2\mathbf{i}-4\mathbf{j}+3\mathbf{k})$

$$= 3\mathbf{i}+7\mathbf{j}-5\mathbf{k}$$

$\vec{BC} = \vec{OC} - \vec{OB} = (-2\mathbf{i}+2\mathbf{j}+3\mathbf{k}) - (5\mathbf{i}+3\mathbf{j}-2\mathbf{k})$

$$= -7\mathbf{i}-\mathbf{j}+5\mathbf{k}$$

and $\vec{CA} = \vec{OA} - \vec{OC} = (2\mathbf{i}-4\mathbf{j}+3\mathbf{k}) - (-2\mathbf{i}+2\mathbf{j}+3\mathbf{k})$

$$= 4\mathbf{i}-6\mathbf{j}$$

$$\therefore \quad \vec{S} = \vec{P} + \vec{Q} + \vec{R} = 15\left[\frac{\vec{AB}}{|\vec{AB}|} + \frac{\vec{BC}}{|\vec{BC}|} + \frac{\vec{CA}}{|\vec{CA}|}\right]$$

$$= 15\left[\frac{3\mathbf{i}+7\mathbf{j}-5\mathbf{k}}{\sqrt{(83)}} + \frac{-7\mathbf{i}-\mathbf{j}+5\mathbf{k}}{5\sqrt{(3)}} + \frac{4\mathbf{i}-6\mathbf{j}}{2\sqrt{(13)}}\right].$$

(c) We have $\mathbf{a} = 3\mathbf{i}+4\mathbf{j}-2\mathbf{k}$

$\therefore \quad |\mathbf{a}| = \sqrt{9+16+4} = \sqrt{29}$

$\therefore$ Therefore the unit vector parallel to $\mathbf{a}$

$$= \frac{\mathbf{a}}{|\mathbf{a}|} = \frac{1}{\sqrt{(29)}}(3\mathbf{i}+4\mathbf{j}-2\mathbf{k}).$$

Now suppose $\mathbf{b}$ is the vector which when added to $\mathbf{a}$ gives the resultant $\mathbf{i}$.

Then $\quad \mathbf{a}+\mathbf{b} = \mathbf{i}$

or $\quad \mathbf{b} = \mathbf{i} - \mathbf{a} = \mathbf{i} - (3\mathbf{i}+4\mathbf{j}-2\mathbf{k})$

$\therefore \quad \mathbf{b} = -2\mathbf{i}-4\mathbf{j}+2\mathbf{k}.$

7. In terms of unit vectors $A(1, 2, -1)$ is $\mathbf{i}+2\mathbf{j}-\mathbf{k}$ and similarly we can write down the other points with respect to O as origin.

$\therefore \quad \vec{AB} = \vec{OB} - \vec{OA} = (-4\mathbf{i}+2\mathbf{j}-2\mathbf{k}) - (\mathbf{i}+2\mathbf{j}-\mathbf{k})$

or $\quad \vec{AB} = -5\mathbf{i}+0\mathbf{j}-\mathbf{k} \quad \therefore \quad |\vec{AB}| = \sqrt{25+1} = \sqrt{26}.$

$\therefore$ Unit vector along $AB = \frac{1}{\sqrt{(26)}}(-5\mathbf{i}-\mathbf{k}).$

$\therefore$ A force of magnitude 2 kg along AB is

$$2 \cdot \frac{1}{\sqrt{(26)}}(-5\mathbf{i}-\mathbf{k}) = \frac{1}{\sqrt{(26)}}(-10\mathbf{i}-2\mathbf{k}) \quad \text{...(1)}$$

Similarly forces of magnitudes 3 and 2 kg along AC and AD are respectively

$$3 \cdot \frac{1}{\sqrt{(26)}}(3\mathbf{i}-\mathbf{j}-4\mathbf{k}) = \frac{1}{\sqrt{(26)}}(9\mathbf{i}-3\mathbf{j}-12\mathbf{k}) \quad \text{...(2)}$$

and $2 \cdot \frac{1}{\sqrt{(26)}}(\mathbf{i}-3\mathbf{j}+4\mathbf{k}) = \frac{1}{\sqrt{(26)}}(2\mathbf{i}-6\mathbf{j}+8\mathbf{k}) \quad$ ...(3)

Adding (1), (2) and (3), the resultant $\mathbf{R}$ is

$$\mathbf{R} = \frac{1}{\sqrt{(26)}}(\mathbf{i}-9\mathbf{j}-6\mathbf{k}).$$

Its magnitude is

$$\sqrt{\left(\frac{1+81+36}{26}\right)} = \sqrt{\left(\frac{118}{26}\right)} \text{ kg.}$$

Also d.c.'s of the resultant are

$$\frac{1}{\sqrt{(118)}}, \frac{-9}{\sqrt{(118)}}, \frac{-6}{\sqrt{(118)}}.$$

8. Refer Q. 4, $\vec{OB} + \vec{OC} = 2\vec{OD}$,

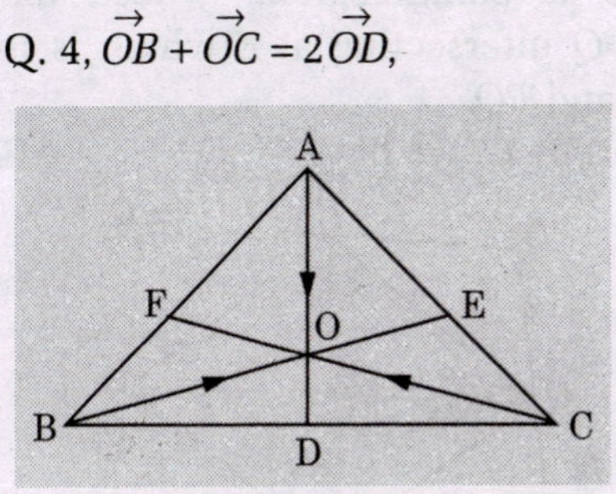

Fig. 19

$$\vec{OC} + \vec{OA} = 2\vec{OE} \text{ and } \vec{OA} + \vec{OB} = 2\vec{OF}.$$

Adding, we get

$$2(\vec{OA} + \vec{OB} + \vec{OC}) = 2(\vec{OD} + \vec{OE} + \vec{OF}).$$

or $\quad \vec{OA} + \vec{OB} + \vec{OC} = \vec{OD} + \vec{OE} + \vec{OF}.$

2nd part : $\quad \frac{2}{3}BE = BO, \; \frac{1}{3}CF = OF$

$$\therefore \quad \vec{AD} + \frac{2}{3}\vec{BE} + \frac{1}{3}\vec{CF} = \vec{AD} + \vec{BO} + \vec{OF}$$

$= \vec{AD} + \vec{BF}$. But $BF = FA$ ∴ $\vec{BF} = \vec{FA}$

$= \vec{FA} + \vec{AD} = \vec{FD} = \frac{1}{2}\vec{AC}$.

∵ FD is the line joining the mid-points of the sides of a triangle and hence parallel to AC and half its length.

Finally,

$$\vec{OE} + \vec{OF} + \vec{DO} = \frac{1}{2}\left[2\vec{OE} + 2\vec{OF} - 2\vec{OD}\right]$$

$$= \frac{1}{2}\left[(\vec{OA} + \vec{OC}) + (\vec{OA} + \vec{OB}) - (\vec{OB} + \vec{OC})\right]$$

$$= \frac{1}{2}\cdot 2.\vec{OA} = \vec{OA}.$$

9. $\vec{AB} + \vec{AD} = 2\vec{AF}$, where F is mid-point of BD by Q. 4.

$\vec{CB} + \vec{CD} = 2\vec{CF}$;

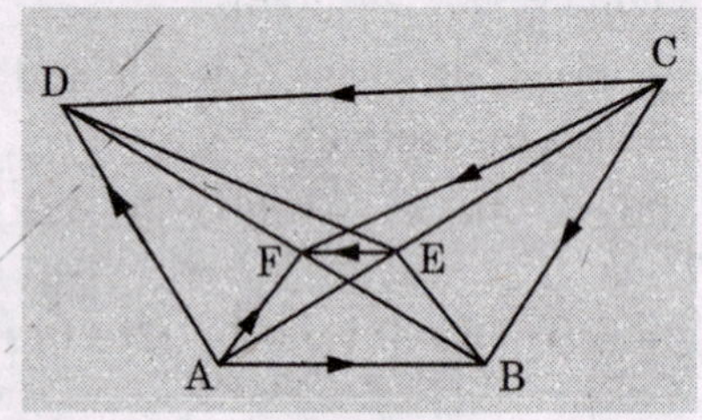

Fig. 20

∴ $\vec{AB} + \vec{AD} + \vec{CB} + \vec{CD} = 2(\vec{AF} + \vec{CF})$

$= -2(\vec{FA} + \vec{FC}) = -2[2\vec{FE}]$,

where E is the mid-point of AC

$= -4\vec{FE} = 4\vec{EF}$.

10. We know that the figure formed by the lines joining the mid-points of the sides of quadrilateral is $||^m$. Hence $MPNQ$ is a parallelogram, whose diagonals are MN and PQ intersecting at E which is mid-point of both MN and PQ.

For any origin O, we have

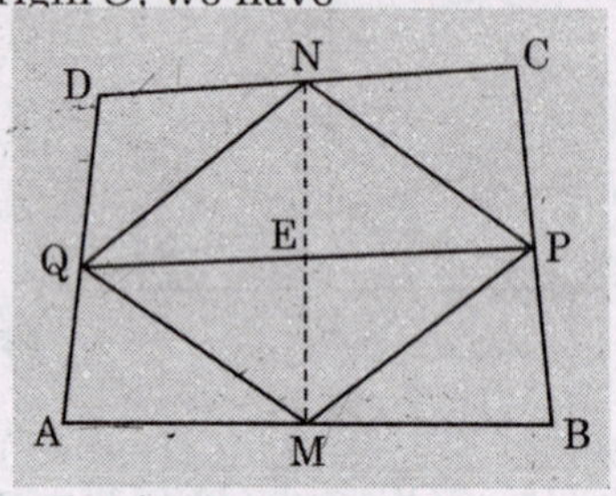

Fig. 21

∴ $\vec{OA} + \vec{OB} = 2(\vec{OM})$,

M is the mid-point of AB

$\vec{OC} + \vec{OD} = 2(\vec{ON})$, N is mid-point of CD

∴ $\vec{OA} + \vec{OB} + \vec{OC} + \vec{OD} = 2(\vec{OM} + \vec{ON})$

$= 2[2\vec{OE}] = 4\vec{OE}$

where E is mid-point of MN as it is the intersection of diagonals of a $||^m$.

11. O is the circumcentre which is the intersection of right bisectors of sides of the triangle and O' is orthocentre which is the point of intersection of altitudes drawn from the vertices. Also from geometry we know that

$$2OD = AO' \quad \therefore \quad 2\vec{OD} = \vec{AO'} \qquad ...(1)$$

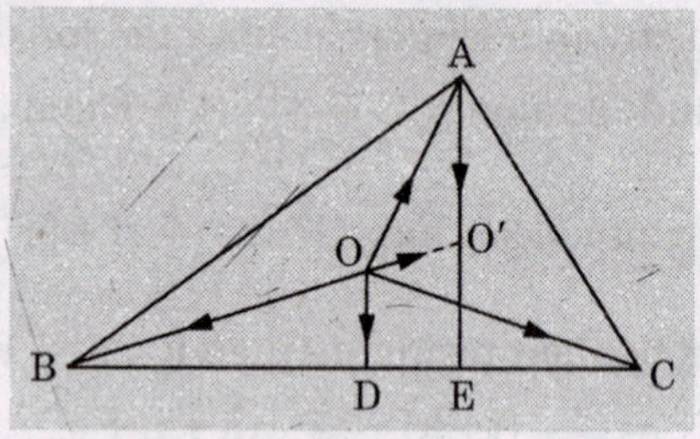

Fig. 22

(i) $\vec{OA} + \vec{OB} + \vec{OC} = \vec{OO'}$.

Now $\vec{OB} + \vec{OC} = 2\vec{OD} = \vec{AO'}$.

∴ $\vec{OA} + \vec{OB} + \vec{OC} = \vec{OA} + \vec{AO'} = \vec{OO'}$ by (1)

(ii) To prove $\vec{O'A} + \vec{O'B} + \vec{O'C} = 2\vec{O'O}$

L.H.S. $= 2\vec{DO} + 2\vec{O'D}$ by (1)

$= 2(\vec{O'D} + \vec{DO}) = 2\vec{O'O}$

(iii) We have to prove

$\vec{AO'} + \vec{O'B} + \vec{O'C} = 2\vec{AO} = \vec{AP}$.

L.H.S. $= 2\vec{AO'} - \vec{AO'} + \vec{O'B} + \vec{O'C}$.

But $-\vec{AO'} = +\vec{O'A} = 2\vec{AO'} + (\vec{O'A} + \vec{O'B} + \vec{O'C})$

$= 2\vec{AO'} + 2\vec{O'O}$, by part (ii)

$= 2(\vec{AO'} + \vec{O'O}) = 2\vec{AO}$

$= 2$ (The vector represented by the radius through A of the circumcircle)

$= \vec{AP}$ (where AP is a diameter through A of the circumcircle).

12. We are given that

$(\vec{AP} + \vec{PB}) + \vec{PC} = \vec{PQ}$ or $\vec{AB} + \vec{PC} = \vec{PQ}$

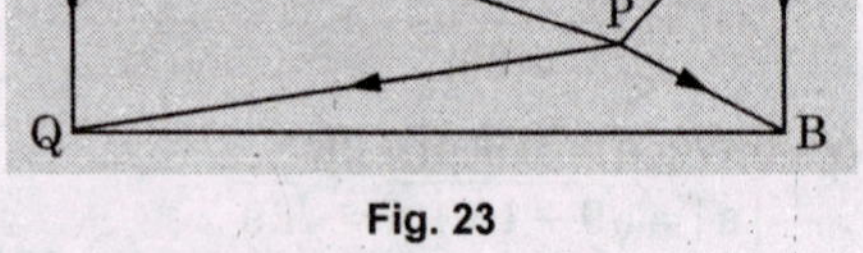

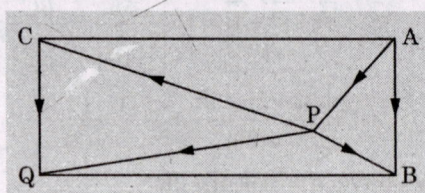

Fig. 23

∴ $\vec{AB} = \vec{PQ} - \vec{PC} = \vec{CQ}$

∴ AB is parallel and equal to CQ.

Again writing the given relation as

$$(\vec{AP}+\vec{PC})+\vec{PB}=\vec{PQ}$$

we get $\quad \vec{AC}=\vec{PQ}-\vec{PB}=\vec{BQ}.$

$\therefore \quad AC$ is parallel and equal to BQ. ...(2)

Hence from (1) and (2) the figure $ABQC$ is a prallelogram.

Again $\vec{AQ}=\vec{AB}+\vec{BQ}=\vec{AB}+\vec{AC}, \quad \because \ \vec{BQ}=\vec{AC}$ by (2).

Above relation shows that with the change in the position of P in BC the position vector of Q does not change and hence Q is a fixed point.

13. $\vec{OP}=\vec{OR}+\vec{RP} \quad \therefore \quad n\vec{OP}=n.\vec{OR}+n.\vec{RP}$ ...(1)

and $\vec{OQ}=\vec{OR}+\vec{RQ} \ \therefore \ \ m\vec{OQ}=m\vec{OR}+m\vec{RQ}$ ...(2)

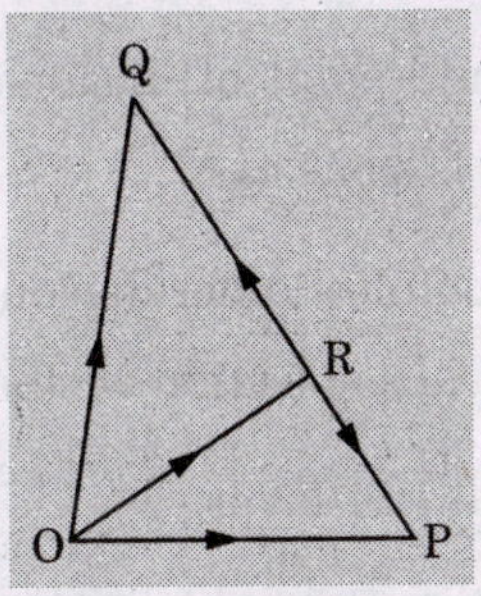

Fig. 24

Adding (1) and (2), we get

$$n\vec{OP}+m\vec{OQ}=(m+n)\,\vec{OR}+(n\vec{RP}+m\vec{RQ})=(m+n)\,\vec{OR}$$

$\because \quad$ We are given that $n.\vec{PR}=m\vec{RQ}$.

$\therefore \quad n(-\vec{RP})=m\vec{RQ} \quad$ or $\quad n\vec{RP}+m\vec{RQ}=\mathbf{0}$

i.e. The point R divides PQ in the ratio $m:n$.

Cor. In case the forces be $1.\vec{OP}$ and $1.\vec{OQ}$ then their resultant will be $(1+1)\,\vec{OR}$ *i.e.* $2\vec{OR}$ where R divides PQ in the ratio 1 : 1 *i.e.*, R is the middle point of PQ.

14. (a) Let the forces **P** and **Q** be represented by $\vec{OL}$ and $\vec{OM}$ so that the diagonal $\vec{ON}$ represents the resultant R.

$\therefore \quad \mathbf{P}+\mathbf{Q}=\mathbf{R}.$ ...(1)

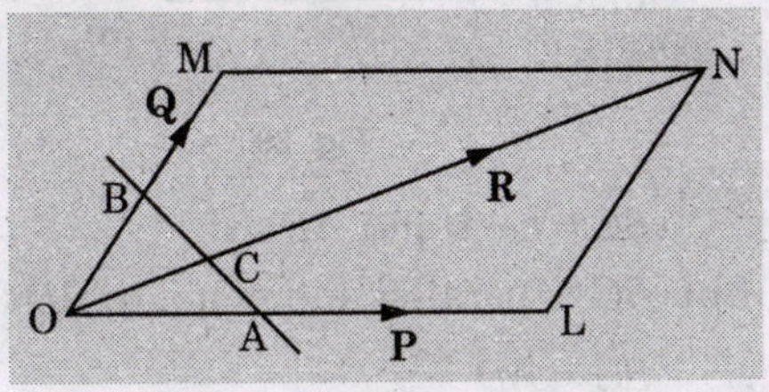

Fig. 25

Again let $\mathbf{P}=\vec{OL}=m\vec{OA}, \ \mathbf{Q}=\vec{OM}=n\vec{OB}$

and $\mathbf{R}=\vec{ON}=t.\vec{OC}$.

$\therefore \quad m=\dfrac{P}{OA};\ n=\dfrac{Q}{OB};\ t=\dfrac{R}{OC}$ ...(2)

Hence from (1), we get

$$m.\vec{OA}+n.\vec{OB}=t.\vec{OC}$$

or $\quad m.\vec{OA}+n.\vec{OB}-t.\vec{OC}=0.$ ...(3)

But A, B, C are collinear and we know that if there exists a relation of the form $x\mathbf{a}+y\mathbf{b}+z\mathbf{c}=0$ between the P.V.'s of three collinear points then $x+y+z=0$. **(See Q. 28 P. 968-78)**

Hence from (3) we must have

$$m+n-t=0 \ \therefore \ m+n=t.$$

Now putting the values of m, n and t from (2) in $m+n=t$ we get

$$\frac{P}{OA}+\frac{Q}{QB}=\frac{R}{OC}.$$

(b) From the fig. part (a), we have

$$\vec{ON}=\vec{OL}+\vec{LN} \qquad ...(1)$$

Let $\vec{OL}=\lambda\,\vec{OA}, \quad \vec{OM}=\mu\,\vec{OB}$ and $\vec{ON}=\nu\vec{OC}$, then

$$\lambda=\frac{OL}{OA},\ \mu=\frac{OM}{OB} \text{ and } \nu=\frac{ON}{OC}$$

From (1) $\ \nu\vec{OC}=\lambda\,\vec{OA}+\mu\,\vec{OB}.$

Since A, B, C are collinear, we have

$$\nu=\lambda+\mu \ \ i.e., \ \frac{ON}{OC}=\frac{OL}{OA}+\frac{OM}{OB}.$$

15. (a) Let the position vectors of the vertices be **a**, **b** and **c** respectively so that the position vector of G, the centroid, is $\dfrac{\mathbf{a}+\mathbf{b}+\mathbf{c}}{3}$.

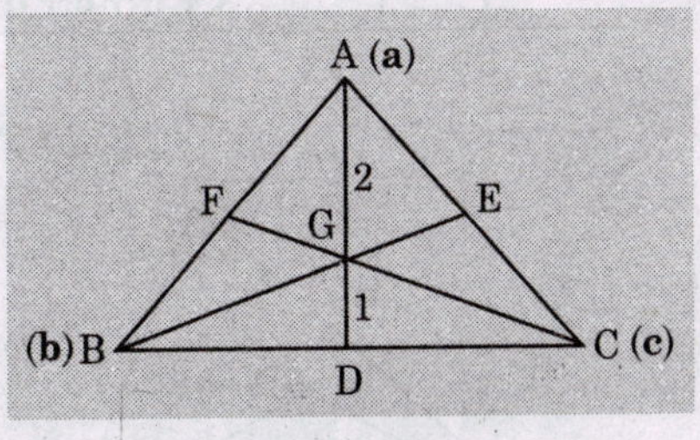

Fig. 26

$\vec{GA}=$ P. V. of $A-$ P. V. of G

$$=\mathbf{a}-\frac{\mathbf{a}+\mathbf{b}+\mathbf{c}}{3}=\frac{2\mathbf{a}-\mathbf{b}-\mathbf{c}}{3}.$$

Similarly $\vec{GB}=\dfrac{2\mathbf{b}-\mathbf{c}-\mathbf{a}}{3}, \quad \vec{GC}=\dfrac{2\mathbf{c}-\mathbf{a}-\mathbf{b}}{3}.$

$$\therefore \quad \vec{GA}+\vec{GB}+\vec{GC}=\frac{1}{3}(2\Sigma\ \mathbf{a}-2\Sigma\ \mathbf{a})=\mathbf{0}.$$

Conversely, let $\vec{GA}+\vec{GB}+\vec{GC}=\mathbf{0}$.

Then $(\vec{OA}-\vec{OG})+(\vec{OB}-\vec{OG})+(\vec{OC}-\vec{OG})=\mathbf{0}.$

$$\therefore \quad \vec{OA}+\vec{OB}+\vec{OC}=3\vec{OG}$$

or $\quad \vec{OG}=\dfrac{\vec{OA}+\vec{OB}+\vec{OC}}{3}$

Hence G is the centroid of the points A, B and C.

(b) W.r.t. any origin let **a** and **p** be position vectors of A and P respectively etc. so that P.V. of G and G' are

$$\vec{OG} = \frac{\mathbf{a}+\mathbf{b}+\mathbf{c}}{3} \text{ and } \vec{OG'} = \frac{\mathbf{p}+\mathbf{q}+\mathbf{r}}{3}$$

Now $\vec{AP} + \vec{BQ} + \vec{CR} = (\mathbf{p}-\mathbf{a}) + (\mathbf{q}-\mathbf{b}) + (\mathbf{r}-\mathbf{c})$

$= \Sigma\,\mathbf{p} - \Sigma\,\mathbf{a} = 3(\vec{OG'} - \vec{OG}) = 3\vec{GG'}$

16. Refer fig. Q. 15.

The mid-points D, E and F are $\frac{\mathbf{b}+\mathbf{c}}{2}, \frac{\mathbf{c}+\mathbf{a}}{2}, \frac{\mathbf{a}+\mathbf{b}}{2}$.

We know that centroid divides a median AD in the ratio 2 : 1.

Hence the point G is $\frac{2.\frac{\mathbf{b}+\mathbf{c}}{2} + 1.\mathbf{a}}{2+1} = \frac{\mathbf{a}+\mathbf{b}+\mathbf{c}}{3}$.

The symmetry of the result shows that the point G lies on the median BE and CF as well and divides them in the ratio 2 : 1. Therefore the three medians are concurrent at the point $\frac{\mathbf{a}+\mathbf{b}+\mathbf{c}}{3}$ which is also the centroid of the triangle ABC.

17. (a) G_1 the centroid of $\Delta\, BCD$ is $\frac{\mathbf{b}+\mathbf{c}+\mathbf{d}}{3}$ and A is **a**.

The position vector of a point G which divides AG_1 in the ratio 3 : 1 is

$$\frac{3.\frac{\mathbf{b}+\mathbf{c}+\mathbf{d}}{3} + 1.\mathbf{a}}{3+1} = \frac{\mathbf{a}+\mathbf{b}+\mathbf{c}+\mathbf{d}}{4}$$

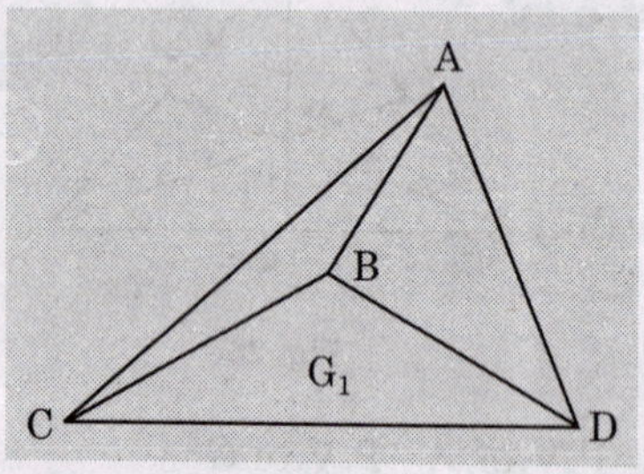

Fig. 27

The symmetry of the result shows that this point will also lie on BG_2, CG_3 and DG_4. Hence these four lines concur at the point $\frac{\mathbf{a}+\mathbf{b}+\mathbf{c}+\mathbf{d}}{4}$ which is called the centroid of the tetrahedron.

(b) The mid-point of DA is $\frac{\mathbf{a}+\mathbf{d}}{2}$ and that of BC is $\frac{\mathbf{b}+\mathbf{c}}{2}$ and the mid-point of these mid-points is $\frac{\mathbf{a}+\mathbf{b}+\mathbf{c}+\mathbf{d}}{4}$ and symmetry of the result proves the theorem.

18. Taking O as origin let the position vectors of A, B and C be **a**, **b** and **c** respectively, so that those of L, M and N are $\mathbf{b}+\mathbf{c}$, $\mathbf{c}+\mathbf{a}$, $\mathbf{a}+\mathbf{b}$ respectively and that of P is $\mathbf{a}+\mathbf{b}+\mathbf{c}$.

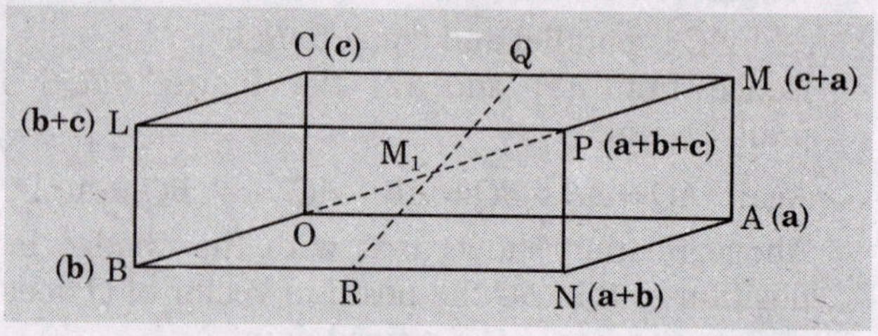

Fig. 28

If M_1 be the mid-point of diagonal OP, then M_1 is $\frac{\mathbf{a}+\mathbf{b}+\mathbf{c}}{2}$.

If M_2 be the mid-point of diagonal AL, then M_2 is $\frac{\mathbf{a}+\mathbf{b}+\mathbf{c}}{2}$ which is same as M_1.

Similarly mid-point of other diagonals CN and BM is also the point whose position vector is $\frac{\mathbf{a}+\mathbf{b}+\mathbf{c}}{2}$.

Again mid-point R of BN is

$\frac{1}{2}(\mathbf{b}+\mathbf{a}+\mathbf{b}) = \frac{\mathbf{a}+2\mathbf{b}}{2}$

and mid-point Q of CM is $\frac{1}{2}(\mathbf{c}+\mathbf{c}+\mathbf{a}) = \frac{2\mathbf{c}+\mathbf{a}}{2}$.

∴ Mid-point of QR is

$$\frac{\mathbf{a}+2\mathbf{b}+2\mathbf{c}+\mathbf{a}}{4} = \frac{\mathbf{a}+\mathbf{b}+\mathbf{c}}{2}.$$

In a similar manner we can show that the mid-points of the join of other opposite edges are also the same.

19. (a) Let A be taken as origin and the position vectors of B, C and D be taken as **b**, **c** and **d** respectively.

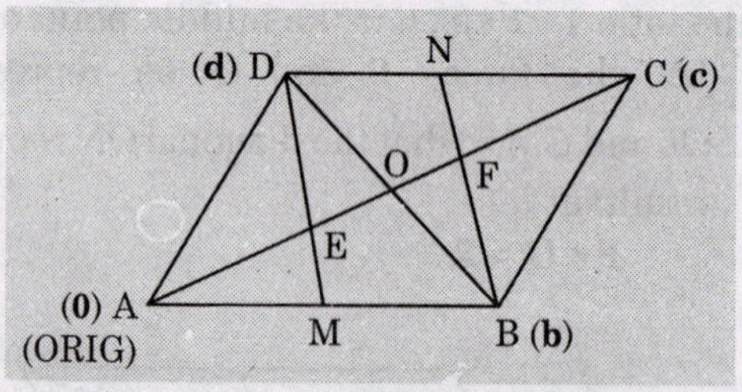

Fig. 29

∴ $\vec{BC} = \mathbf{c} - \mathbf{b}$ and $\vec{AD} = \mathbf{d}$

But BC is parallel and equal to AD

∴ $\vec{BC} = \vec{AD}$

or $\mathbf{c}-\mathbf{b} = \mathbf{d}$ or $\mathbf{c} = \mathbf{b}+\mathbf{d}$ or $\frac{\mathbf{c}}{2} = \frac{\mathbf{b}+\mathbf{d}}{2}$

i.e. mid-point of diagonal AC is same as mid- point of diagonal BD. Hence the diagonals bisect each other.

Converse : We are given that diagonals bisect each other.

i.e. $\frac{\mathbf{c}}{2} = \frac{\mathbf{b}+\mathbf{d}}{2}$ or $\mathbf{c} = \mathbf{b}+\mathbf{d}$ ...(1)

$\vec{AB} = \mathbf{b}$, $\vec{DC} = \mathbf{c} - \mathbf{d} = \mathbf{b}$, by (1)

∴ AB is parallel and equal to DC.

$\vec{AD} = \mathbf{d}$ and $\vec{BC} = \mathbf{c} - \mathbf{b} = \mathbf{d}$, by (1)

∴ AD is parallel and equal to BC.

Hence the figure is a parallelogram.

(b) $\vec{AB} = 2\mathbf{i} + 4\mathbf{j} - 5\mathbf{k} = 2, 4, -5$

$\vec{AD} = \mathbf{i} + 2\mathbf{j} + 3\mathbf{k} = 1, 2, 3$

∴ $\vec{AC} = \vec{AB} + \vec{BC} = 3, 6, -2$

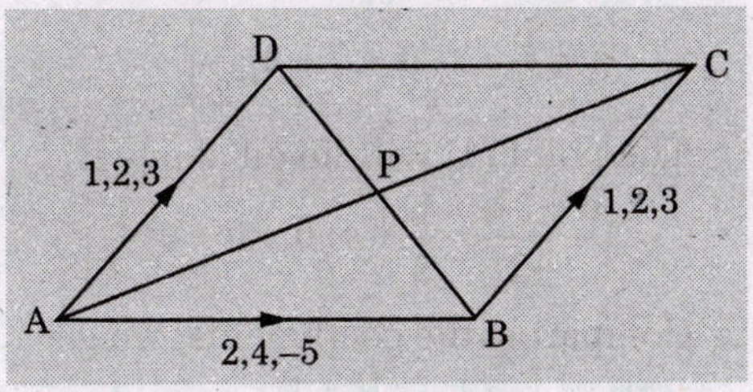

Fig. 30

∴ Unit vector along AC

$$= \frac{\vec{AC}}{|\vec{AC}|} = \frac{3, 6, -2}{\sqrt{(9+36+4)}} = \frac{3\mathbf{i}+6\mathbf{j}-2\mathbf{k}}{7}$$

Similarly $\vec{BD} = \vec{AD} - \vec{AB} = -1, -2, 8$.

∴ Unit vector along BD

$$= \frac{\vec{BD}}{|\vec{BD}|} = \frac{-1, -2, 8}{\sqrt{(1+4+64)}} = \frac{-\mathbf{i}-2\mathbf{j}+8\mathbf{k}}{\sqrt{69}}.$$

20. Let O' be any origin. Then

$\vec{O'A} + \vec{O'C} = 2\vec{O'O}$ [∵ O is the mid-point of AC]

and $\vec{O'B} + \vec{O'D} = 2\vec{O'O}$

[∵ O is also the mid-pt. of BD].

Hence $\vec{O'A} + \vec{O'B} + \vec{O'C} + \vec{O'D} = 4\vec{O'O}$ as required.

21. Refer figure Q. 19.

The figure being a parallelogram.

$\mathbf{c} = \mathbf{b} + \mathbf{d}$. ...(1)

The P.V. of a point E which divides AC in the ratio 1 : 2 is $\frac{1.\mathbf{c}+2.\mathbf{0}}{1+2} = \frac{\mathbf{c}}{3}$ and the point which divides DM in the ratio 2 : 1 is

$$\frac{2.\frac{\mathbf{b}}{2}+1.\mathbf{d}}{2+1} = \frac{\mathbf{b}+\mathbf{d}}{3} = \frac{\mathbf{c}}{3},$$

by (1) and this is same as E.

Similarly the point F which divides AC in the ratio 2 : 1 is $\frac{2\mathbf{c}+1.\mathbf{0}}{3} = \frac{2\mathbf{c}}{3}$ and the point which divides NB in the ratio 1 : 2 is

$$\frac{1.\mathbf{b}+2.\frac{\mathbf{c}+\mathbf{d}}{2}}{3} = \frac{\mathbf{b}+(\mathbf{c}+\mathbf{d})}{3} = \frac{2\mathbf{c}}{3}$$

by (1), which is same as the point F.

Thus E and F are the points of trisection of diagonal AC and also the points of trisection of DM and BN respectively.

22. Do yourself.

23. Let the position vectors of B, C, D w.r.t. A as origin be **b, c** and **d** and hence those of L, M, N, P are $\frac{\mathbf{b}}{2}$, $\frac{\mathbf{b}+\mathbf{c}}{2}$, $\frac{\mathbf{c}+\mathbf{d}}{2}$, $\frac{\mathbf{d}}{2}$ respectively.

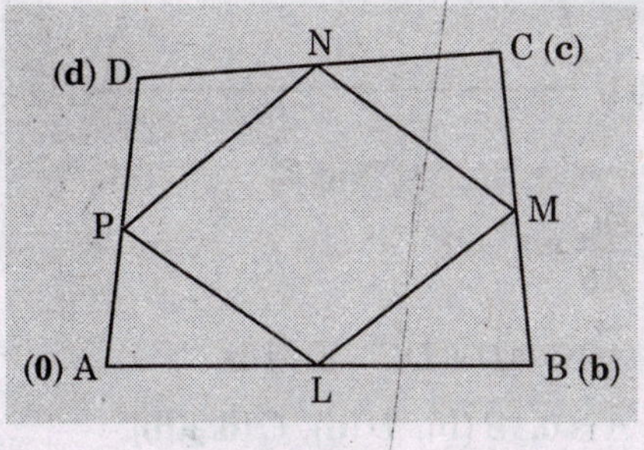

Fig. 31

$\vec{LM}$ = P.V. of M − P.V. of L

$$= \frac{\mathbf{b}+\mathbf{c}}{2} - \frac{\mathbf{b}}{2} = \frac{\mathbf{c}}{2}.$$

$\vec{PN}$ = P.V. of N − P.V. of P

$$= \frac{\mathbf{c}+\mathbf{d}}{2} - \frac{\mathbf{d}}{2} = \frac{\mathbf{c}}{2}.$$

Above shows that LM is parallel and equal to PN.

Similarly we can show MN is parallel and equal to LP.

Hence $PLMN$ is a parallelogram.

24. Let **a, b, c** be the position vectors of the vertices A, B and C respectively so that the P. V's. of mid-points D, E and F are

$$\frac{\mathbf{b}+\mathbf{c}}{2}, \frac{\mathbf{c}+\mathbf{a}}{2}, \frac{\mathbf{a}+\mathbf{b}}{2}$$

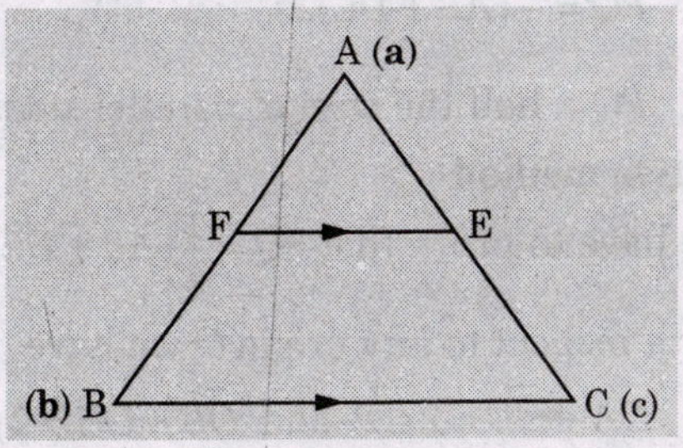

Fig. 32

∴ $\vec{BC}$ = P.V. of C − P.V. of B

$= \mathbf{c} - \mathbf{b}$

$\vec{FE}$ = P.V. of E − P.V. of F

$$= \frac{\mathbf{c}+\mathbf{a}}{2} - \frac{\mathbf{a}+\mathbf{b}}{2} = \frac{1}{2}(\mathbf{c}-\mathbf{b})$$

$\therefore \quad \vec{FE} = \frac{1}{2}\vec{BC}.$

Above shows that FE is parallel to BC and half its length.

25. (a) Take A as origin and the position vectors of B and D as **b** and **d** respectively.

Now DC is parallel to AB

$\therefore \quad \vec{DC} = t\,\vec{AB} = t\mathbf{b}.$

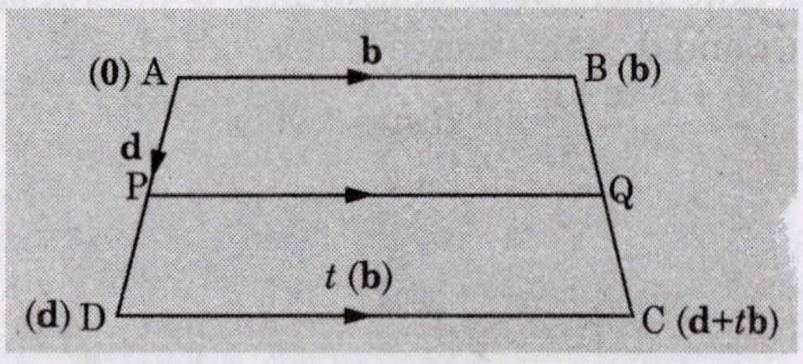

Fig. 33

$\therefore \quad \frac{DC}{AB} = t \qquad$ ...(1)

$\therefore \quad \vec{AC} = \vec{AD} + \vec{DC} = \mathbf{d} + t\,\mathbf{b}$

$\therefore \quad A$ is $\mathbf{0}$, $B(\mathbf{b})$, $D(\mathbf{d})$, $C(\mathbf{d} + t\mathbf{b})$.

$\therefore$ P, the mid-point of AD, is $\mathbf{d}/2$ and Q, the mid-point of BC, is $\frac{\mathbf{b} + \mathbf{d} + t\,\mathbf{b}}{2}$

$\therefore \quad \vec{PQ} =$ P.V. of Q − P.V. of P

$$= \frac{\mathbf{b} + \mathbf{d} + t\,\mathbf{b}}{2} - \frac{\mathbf{d}}{2} = \frac{1}{2}(1+t)\,.\,\mathbf{b}$$

or $\quad \vec{PQ} = \frac{1}{2}(1+t)\,\vec{AB}$

$\therefore$ $\vec{PQ}$ is scalar multiple of $\vec{AB}$ and hence PQ is parallel to AB.

Also $\quad \frac{PQ}{AB} = \frac{1}{2}(1+t) = \frac{1}{2}\left(1 + \frac{DC}{AB}\right)$

$$= \frac{1}{2}\,\frac{AB + DC}{AB}, \quad \text{by (1)}.$$

$\therefore \quad PQ = \frac{1}{2}(AB + DC).$

i.e., PQ = half the sum of parallel sides.

Alternative method :

We have to prove that $PQ = \frac{1}{2}(AB + DC)$

With respect to any origin O we have

$\vec{OA} + \vec{OD} = 2\,\vec{OP}$ and $\vec{OB} + \vec{OC} = 2\,\vec{OQ}$

$\therefore \quad (\vec{OB} - \vec{OA}) + (\vec{OC} - \vec{OD}) = 2\,(\vec{OQ} - \vec{OP})$

or $\quad \vec{AB} + \vec{DC} = 2\,\vec{PQ}$

i.e. $\quad \vec{PQ} = \frac{1}{2}(\vec{AB} + \vec{DC})$

Now AB and DC are parallel so that PQ is also parallel to them and in magnitude equal to half their sum.

(b) The P.Vs. of the points A, B, C, D are written in (1) of part (a).

Equations of AC and BD are

$$\mathbf{r} = \lambda\,(\mathbf{d} + t\,\mathbf{b}) \text{ and } \mathbf{r} = (1 - \mu)\,\mathbf{b} + \mu\,\mathbf{d}$$

For point of intersection say T compare the coefficients

$\lambda = \mu,\ t\,\lambda = 1 - \mu = 1 - \lambda$ or $(t+1)\,\lambda = 1$

$\therefore \quad \lambda = \frac{1}{t+1} = \mu \quad \therefore \quad T$ is $\frac{\mathbf{d} + t\,\mathbf{b}}{t+1} \qquad$ ...(1)

Let R and S be mid-points of parallel sides AB and DC, then R is $\frac{\mathbf{b}}{2}$ and S is $\mathbf{d} + t\,\frac{\mathbf{b}}{2}$

Equation of RS by $\mathbf{r} = \mathbf{a} + s\,(\mathbf{b} - \mathbf{a})$ by **§ 6. P. 965** is

$$\mathbf{r} = \frac{\mathbf{b}}{2} + s\left[\mathbf{d} + (t-1)\,\frac{\mathbf{b}}{2}\right].$$

The point (1) will lie on above if

$$\frac{\mathbf{d} + t\,\mathbf{b}}{1+t} = \frac{\mathbf{b}}{2} + s\left[\mathbf{d} + (t-1)\,\frac{\mathbf{b}}{2}\right]$$

Comparing the coefficients, we get

$$\frac{t}{1+t} = \frac{1}{2} + s\,\frac{(t-1)}{2} \text{ and } \frac{1}{1+t} = s$$

$$\therefore \quad \frac{t}{1+t} = \frac{1}{2} + \frac{1}{1+t}\cdot\frac{t-1}{2} = \frac{2t}{2(1+t)} = \frac{t}{1+t}$$

which is true. **Hence proved.**

26. Proceeding as in Q. 25, the position vector of C is $\mathbf{d} + t\,\mathbf{b}$ where

$t = \frac{DC}{AB} \qquad$ ...(1)

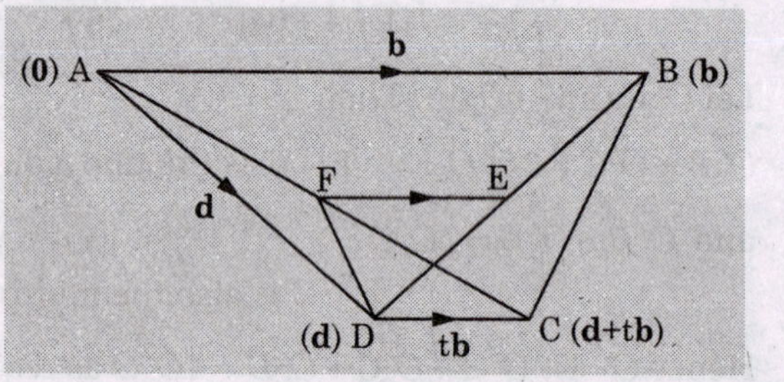

Fig. 34

$\therefore \quad$ P.V. of F, the mid-point of diagonal AC is $\frac{0 + \mathbf{d} + t\,\mathbf{b}}{2}$ E is the mid-point of DB.

$\therefore \quad$ P.V. of E is $\frac{\mathbf{d} + \mathbf{b}}{2}$.

$\therefore \quad \vec{FE} =$ P.V. of E − P.V. of F

$$= \frac{\mathbf{d} + \mathbf{b}}{2} - \frac{\mathbf{d} + t\,\mathbf{b}}{2} = \frac{(1-t)}{2}\,\mathbf{b}$$

or $\quad \vec{FE} = \frac{1-t}{2}\,\vec{AB}$

$\therefore$ $\vec{FE}$ is scalar multiple of $\vec{AB}$ and hence FE is parallel to AB.

Also $\quad \frac{FE}{AB} = \frac{1-t}{2} = \frac{1}{2}\left(1 - \frac{DC}{AB}\right) = \frac{1}{2}\,\frac{(AB - DC)}{AB}$

$\therefore \quad FE = \frac{1}{2}(AB - DC).$

or $\quad FE =$ half the difference of parallel sides.

Aternative method.

As in last question $\vec{OA} + \vec{OC} = 2\,\vec{OF}$

and $\vec{OB} + \vec{OD} = 2\,\vec{OE}$

$\therefore \quad (\vec{OB} - \vec{OA}) + (\vec{OD} - \vec{OC}) = 2\,(\vec{OE} - \vec{OF})$

or $\quad \vec{AB} + \vec{CD} = 2\,\vec{FE}$

$\therefore \quad \vec{FE} = \frac{1}{2}(\vec{AB} + \vec{CD})$

or $\quad \vec{FE} = \frac{1}{2}(\vec{AB} - \vec{DC})$ etc. as in Q. 25.

27. (a) We know from geometry that the internal bisector of an angle of a triangle divides the opposite side in the ratio of the sides containing the angle. If **a, b, c** be the position vectors of the vertices A, B, C respectively and the opposite sides be of lengths x, y, z then if the internal bisector of angle A meets BC in D, then by the given condition

$$D = \frac{z\mathbf{c} + y\mathbf{b}}{y+z} \text{ and } A \text{ is } \mathbf{a}.$$

Therefore the position vector of a point I on AD which divides it in the ratio $y+z : x$ is

$$\frac{x\mathbf{a} + (y+z).(z\mathbf{c} + y\mathbf{b})/(y+z)}{x+y+z} = \frac{x\mathbf{a} + y\mathbf{b} + z\mathbf{c}}{x+y+z}.$$

The symmetry of the result shows that this point also lies on the internal bisectors of angles B and C. Hence the three bisectors are concurrent.

(b) Let **a, b, c** be the P.V.s of the vertices and AD is the altitude then D divides BC in the ratio

$$\frac{BD}{DC} = \frac{AD \cot B}{AD \cot C} = \frac{\tan C}{\tan B}$$

$\therefore \quad$ P.V. of D is $\dfrac{\mathbf{b}\tan B + \mathbf{c}\tan C}{\tan B + \tan C}$

Now we should find a point on AD so that this point also lies on other altitudes BE and CF also.

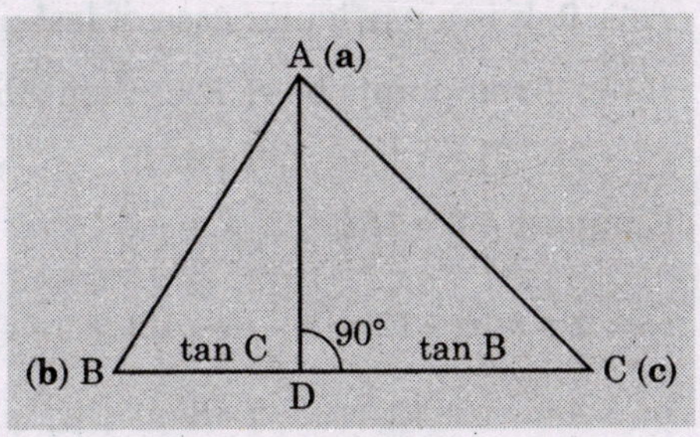

Fig. 35

Hence as in Q. 27 we divide AD in the ratio $\tan B + \tan C : \tan A$ to get the P. V. of a point H on AD as

$$\frac{(\tan B + \tan C)\dfrac{[\mathbf{b}\tan B + \mathbf{c}\tan C]}{\tan B + \tan C} + \mathbf{a}\tan A}{\tan B + \tan C + \tan A} = \frac{\Sigma\, \mathbf{a}\tan A}{\Sigma \tan A} \quad ...(1)$$

Symmetry of the result shows that this point will also lie on other altitudes. Hence the altitudes are concurrent and the P.V. of orthocentre is given by (1).

Note. See for alternative method, **Q. 31 (b) Page 1123-1137.**

28. Let us suppose that the points A, B, C are collinear and their position vectors are **a**, **b** and **c** respectively. Let C divide the join of **a** and **b** in the ratio $y : x$

$\therefore \quad \mathbf{c} = \dfrac{x\mathbf{a} + y\mathbf{b}}{x+y}$

or $\quad x\mathbf{a} + y\mathbf{b} - (x+y)\,\mathbf{c} = \mathbf{0}$

or $\quad x\mathbf{a} + y\mathbf{b} + z\mathbf{c} = \mathbf{0}$, where $z = -(x+y)$

Also $\quad x + y + z = x + y - (x+y) = 0.$

Conversely, let $x\mathbf{a} + y\mathbf{b} + z\mathbf{c} = \mathbf{0}$, where $x + y + z = 0.$

$\therefore \quad x\mathbf{a} + y\mathbf{b} = -z\mathbf{c} = (x+y)\,\mathbf{c}, \quad \because x + y = -z$

or $\quad \mathbf{c} = \dfrac{x\mathbf{a} + y\mathbf{b}}{x+y}.$

Above relation shows that **b** divides the join of **a** and **b** in the ratio $y : x$. Hence the three points A, B, C are collinear.

29. (a) Let the given points be A, B and C

$\therefore \quad \vec{AB} =$ P.V. of $B -$ P.V. of A

$= (2\mathbf{a} + 3\mathbf{b} - 4\mathbf{c}) - (\mathbf{a} - 2\mathbf{b} + 3\mathbf{c}) = \mathbf{a} + 5\mathbf{b} - 7\mathbf{c}$

$\vec{AC} =$ P.V. of $C -$ P.V. of A

$= (-7\mathbf{b} + 10\mathbf{c}) - (\mathbf{a} - 2\mathbf{b} + 3\mathbf{c}) = -\mathbf{a} - 5\mathbf{b} + 7\mathbf{c} = -\vec{AB}$

Since $\vec{AC} = -\vec{AB}$, it follows that the points A, B and C are collinear.

2nd Method :

Let $\mathbf{l} = \mathbf{a} - 2\mathbf{b} + 3\mathbf{c}$, $\mathbf{m} = 2\mathbf{a} + 3\mathbf{b} - 4\mathbf{c}$, $\mathbf{n} = -7\mathbf{b} + 10\mathbf{c}$.

Now if we are able to choose three scalars x, y, z such that

$x\mathbf{l} + y\mathbf{m} + z\mathbf{n} = \mathbf{0}$

and also $x + y + z = 0$.

then the three points will be collinear. Choosing (by trial)

$x = 2,\ y = -1,\ z = -1,$ we get

$x + y + z = 2 - 1 - 1 = 0$ and also

$x\mathbf{l} + y\mathbf{m} + z\mathbf{n} = 2(\mathbf{a} - 2\mathbf{b} + 3\mathbf{c})$
$\qquad - 1(2\mathbf{a} + 3\mathbf{b} - 4\mathbf{c}) - 1(-7\mathbf{b} + 10\mathbf{c}) = \mathbf{0}.$

Hence the three points are collinear.

3rd Method : Equation of line through first two points is $\mathbf{r} = (1-t)\,\mathbf{a} + t\mathbf{b}.$

$\mathbf{r} = (1-t)(\alpha - 2\beta + 3\gamma) + t(2\alpha + 3\beta - 4\gamma)$

If the three points are collinear, then 3rd point $-7\beta + 10\gamma$ lies on it.

$\therefore \quad -7\beta + 10\gamma = (1-t)(\alpha - 2\beta + 3\gamma) + t(2\alpha + 3\beta - 4\gamma)$

Comparing the coefficients,

$1 - t + 2t = 0, \quad -2(1-t) + 3t = -7,$

$3(1-t) - 4t = 10$

$\therefore \quad t = -1$ and this value satisfies the other two also.

(b), (c), (d). Do yourself.

(e) The points A, B, C will be collinear if $\vec{AB} = \lambda \vec{BC}$

$(1-a)\mathbf{i} + (c-b)\mathbf{j} - c\mathbf{k} = \lambda\{-2\mathbf{i} - (c+1)\mathbf{j}\}$

Comparing, $1 - a = -2\lambda$,

$c - b = -\lambda(c+1), -c = 0$

Putting $c = 0$, we have $1 - a = -2\lambda$ and $-b = -\lambda$

$\therefore \quad \frac{1-a}{-2} = b$ or $a - 2b = 1$

30. (a) In terms of unit vectors

$\mathbf{a} = \mathbf{i} + 2\mathbf{j} + 3\mathbf{k}$ etc.

$\vec{AB} =$ P.V. of $B -$ P.V. of $A = 2\mathbf{i} + 2\mathbf{j} + 4\mathbf{k}$

$\vec{BC} =$ P.V. of $C -$ P.V. of $B = -6\mathbf{i} + 6\mathbf{j} - 12\mathbf{k}$

$= -3(2\mathbf{i} + 2\mathbf{j} + 4\mathbf{k}) = -3\vec{AB}$

$\therefore \quad 3\vec{BA} = \vec{BC}$ and hence the three points are collinear.

From the relation $3\vec{BA} = \vec{BC}$ we conclude that $\frac{BC}{BA} = \frac{3}{1}$.

(b) L.H.S. $= \vec{AB}$ R.H.S. $= \vec{BC}$

$\therefore \quad \vec{AB} = \vec{BC}$, hence collinear.

31. We know that three points whose P.V's. are α, β, γ are collinear if there exists a relation of the form $x\alpha + y\beta + z\gamma = \mathbf{0}$ where $x + y + z = 0$.

(See Q. 28 P. 1099-1109)

Now $x\alpha + y\beta + z\gamma = \mathbf{0}$ gives

$x(l_1\mathbf{a} + m_1\mathbf{b}) + y(l_2\mathbf{a} + m_2\mathbf{b}) + z(l_3\mathbf{a} + m_3\mathbf{b}) = \mathbf{0}$

or $(xl_1 + yl_2 + zl_3)\mathbf{a} + (xm_1 + ym_2 + zm_3)\mathbf{b} = \mathbf{0}$

Since **a** and **b** are two non-collinear vectors it follows that

$xl_1 + yl_2 + zl_3 = 0$ ...(1)

$xm_1 + ym_2 + zm_3 = 0$ ...(2)

Because otherwise one is expressible as a scalar multiple of the other which would mean that **a** and **b** are collinear.

Also $x + y + z = 0$. ...(3)

Eliminating x, y, z from (1), (2) and (3), we get

$$\begin{vmatrix} l_1 & l_2 & l_3 \\ m_1 & m_2 & m_3 \\ 1 & 1 & 1 \end{vmatrix} = 0$$

32. (a) Both the vectors **c** and **d** are non-zero as the coefficients of **b** in both are non-zero.

Two vectors **c** and **d** are collinear if one of them is a linear multiple of the other.

$\therefore \quad \mathbf{d} = \lambda\mathbf{c}$

or $(2x+1)\mathbf{a} - \mathbf{b} = \lambda\{(x-2)\mathbf{a} + \mathbf{b}\}$ ...(1)

or $\{(2x+1) - \lambda(x-2)\}\mathbf{a} - (1+\lambda)\mathbf{b} = 0$

Above is of the form $p\mathbf{a} + q\mathbf{b} = 0$ where **a** and **b** are non-collinear and hence we must have $p = 0, q = 0$.

$\therefore \quad 2x + 1 - \lambda(x-2) = 0$ ...(2)

$1 + \lambda = 0$ ...(3)

From (2), $\lambda = -1$ and putting in (1) we get $x = \frac{1}{3}$.

Note : We could also say compare the coefficients of **a** and **b** (non-collinear) in (1) and we get the results (2) and (3).

(b) Putting the values of **A** and **B** and then equating the coefficients of **a** and **b** on both sides, we get

$3(p + 4q) = 2(-2p + q + 2)$

$3(2p + q + 1) = 2(2p - 3q - 1)$

or $7p + 10q = 4$ and $2p + 9q = -5$.

Solving them, we get $p = 2$ and $q = -1$.

33. (a) $\mathbf{a} + 2\mathbf{b} = x\mathbf{c}$ ...(1)

$\mathbf{b} + 3\mathbf{c} = y\mathbf{a}$ ...(2)

Now $\mathbf{a} + 2\mathbf{b} + 6\mathbf{c} = x\mathbf{c} + 6\mathbf{c} = (x+6)\mathbf{c}$ ...(3) by (1)

or $= \mathbf{a} + 2(\mathbf{b} + 3\mathbf{c}) = \mathbf{a} + 2y\mathbf{a}$ by (2)

$= (1 + 2y)\mathbf{a}$ ...(4)

From above we conclude that

$(1 + 2y)\mathbf{a} = (x + 6)\mathbf{c}$

or $p\mathbf{a} - q\mathbf{c} = 0$ where **a** and **c** are non-collinear.

Hence we must have $p = 0, q = 0$ or $x = -6$ and $y = -1/2$. Hence in either case

$\mathbf{a} + 2\mathbf{b} + 6\mathbf{c} = \mathbf{0}$, by (3) or (4).

(b) Ans. **0**. It is a particular case of last part.

34. (a) If the given points be A, B, C, then $\vec{AB} = k(\vec{BC})$

or $2\mathbf{i} - 8\mathbf{j} = k[(a-12)\mathbf{i} + 16\mathbf{j}]$

Compare $-8 = 16k \quad \therefore k = -\frac{1}{2}$

$\therefore \quad 2 = k(a - 12) = -\frac{1}{2}(a - 12)$

or $4 = -a + 12 \quad \therefore a = 8$

(b) Ans. (b).

Since the vectors are collinear $\therefore \mathbf{a} = k\mathbf{b}$. In other words coefficients of **i**, **j** and **k** are proportional

$\therefore \quad \dfrac{x}{1} = -\dfrac{3}{y} = \dfrac{7}{-z} \quad \therefore \quad xy = -3, xz = -7$

$\therefore \quad \dfrac{xy^2}{z} = \dfrac{x^2y^2}{xz} = \dfrac{(-3)^2}{-7} = -\dfrac{9}{7}$

(c) Do yourself as in (1).

(d) $\vec{AB} = \lambda\, \vec{BC}$ for all real k.

(e) From above we have

$(-1)\,\mathbf{i} + (b-c)\,\mathbf{j} + (a+b+2c)\,\mathbf{k} = 0.$

Above is a linear relation between three non-coplanar vectors **i, j, k** and hence each scalar must be zero. $\therefore \; -1 = 0, b - c = 0, a + b + 2c = 0.$

Th. II P. 1094

Above is not possible. Hence scalars a, b, c shall not exist to satisfy the given condition.

(f) $a\alpha + b\beta + c\gamma = 0$

$\Rightarrow \quad (a + 2b + 3c)\,\mathbf{i} + (-3a - 4b + 2c)\,\mathbf{j} + (2a - 4b - c)\,\mathbf{k} = 0$

$\therefore \quad a + 2b + 3c = 0, -3a - 4b + 2c = 0,$

and $2a - 4b - c = 0$ for L.I.

$$\Delta = \begin{vmatrix} 1 & 2 & 3 \\ -3 & -4 & 2 \\ 2 & -4 & -1 \end{vmatrix} = 1.12 - 2(-1) + 3(20) = 74 \neq 0.$$

Hence the system of equations has a **trivial** solution given by $a = 0, b = 0, c = 0$.

Therefore the given vectors are linearly independent. **(§ 2. P. 1094)**

35. Let us suppose that the points A, B, C and D whose position vectors are **a, b, c** and **d** respectively are coplanar. In that case the lines AB and CD will intersect at some point P (it being assumed that AB and CD are not parallel and if they are, then we will choose any other pair of non-parallel lines formed by given points). If P divides AB in the ratio $q : p$ and CD in the ratio $n : m$ then the position vector of P written from AB and CD are

$$\frac{p\mathbf{a} + q\mathbf{b}}{p+q} = \frac{m\mathbf{c} + n\mathbf{d}}{m+n}$$

or $\dfrac{p}{p+q}\mathbf{a} + \dfrac{q}{p+q}\mathbf{b} - \dfrac{m}{m+n}\mathbf{c} - \dfrac{n}{m+n}\mathbf{d} = \mathbf{0}$

or $L\mathbf{a} + M\mathbf{b} + N\mathbf{c} + P\mathbf{d} = \mathbf{0}$

where $L + M + N + P = \dfrac{p}{p+q} + \dfrac{q}{p+q} - \dfrac{m}{m+n} - \dfrac{n}{m+n} = 1 - 1 = 0$

Hence the condition is necessary.

Converse : Let $l\mathbf{a} + m\mathbf{b} + n\mathbf{c} + p\mathbf{d} = \mathbf{0}$ where

$l + m + n + p = 0$ ...(1)

and we will show that the points A, B, C, D are coplanar. Now of the three scalars $l + m,\ l + n,\ l + p$ one at least is not zero for if all of them are zero, then

$l + m = 0,\ l + n = 0,\ l + p = 0$

$\therefore \quad m = n = p = -l$

Hence $l + m + n + p = 0 \Rightarrow l - 3l = 0 \Rightarrow l = 0$

Hence $m = n = p = -l = 0$

Thus $l = 0,\ m = 0,\ n = 0,\ p = 0$ which is against the hypothesis.

Let us suppose that $l + m$ is not zero and therefore

$l + m = -(n + p) \neq 0$, by (1). ...(2)

Also from the given relation, we have

$l\,\mathbf{a} + m\,\mathbf{b} = -(n\,\mathbf{c} + p\,\mathbf{d})$

or $\dfrac{l\,\mathbf{a} + m\,\mathbf{b}}{l+m} = \dfrac{n\,\mathbf{c} + p\,\mathbf{d}}{n+p}$, by (2) ...(3)

L.H.S. represents a point which divides AB in the ratio $m : l$ and R.H.S. represents a point which divides CD in the ratio $p : n$. These points being the same, it follows that a point on AB is the same as a point on CD, showing that the lines AB and CD intersect. Hence the four points A, B, C and D are coplanar.

36. (a) If the given vectors are coplanar, then we should be able to express one of them as a linear combination of the other two.

Let us assume that

$3\mathbf{a} - 7\mathbf{b} - 4\mathbf{c} = x(3\mathbf{a} - 2\mathbf{b} + \mathbf{c}) + y(\mathbf{a} + \mathbf{b} + 2\mathbf{c})$

where x and y are scalars. Since **a, b, c** are non-coplanar, equating the coefficients of **a, b** and **c**, we get

$3x + y = 3,\ -2x + y = -7,\ x + 2y = -4$

Solving the first two, we find that $x = 2$ and $y = -3$. These values of x and y satisfy the third equation as well.

Hence the given vectors are coplanar.

(b) Here $\quad 5\mathbf{a} + 6\mathbf{b} + 7\mathbf{c} = \dfrac{1}{2}(7\mathbf{a} - 8\mathbf{b} + 9\mathbf{c}) + \dfrac{1}{2}(3\mathbf{a} + 20\mathbf{b} + 5\mathbf{c}).$

(c) $\mathbf{a} - 2\mathbf{b} + 3\mathbf{c} = \dfrac{1}{3}(\mathbf{a} - 3\mathbf{b} + 5\mathbf{c}) - \dfrac{1}{3}(-2\mathbf{a} + 3\mathbf{b} - 4\mathbf{c}).$

(d) Proceed as above.

37. Since the three vectors are coplanar, so one of them is expressible as a linear combination of the other two.

$\therefore \quad 3, a, 5 = x(2, -1, 1) + y(1, 2, -3)$

Comparing the coefficients of **i, j, k**

$2x + y = 3, -x + 2y = a, x - 3y = 5$

Solving, we get $x = 2, y = -1$ and hence

$-2 - 2 = a$ or $a = -4.$

38. (a) Let the given points be A, B, C and D. If they are coplanar, then the three coterminous vectors $\vec{AB},\ \vec{AC},\ \vec{AD}$ should be coplanar

$\vec{AB} = \vec{OB} - \vec{OA} = -\mathbf{a} - 5\mathbf{b} + 4\mathbf{c}$

$\vec{AC} = \vec{OC} - \vec{OA} = \mathbf{a} + \mathbf{b} - \mathbf{c}.$

and $\vec{AD} = \vec{OD} - \vec{OA} = -\mathbf{a} - 9\mathbf{b} + 7\mathbf{c}.$

If they are coplanar, then as in Q. 32 one of them is expressible as a linear combination of the other two.

Let $\vec{AD} = x\,\vec{AB} + y\,\vec{AC}$

$\therefore \quad -\mathbf{a} - 9\mathbf{b} + 7\mathbf{c} = x(-\mathbf{a} - 5\mathbf{b} + 4\mathbf{c}) + y(\mathbf{a} + \mathbf{b} - \mathbf{c})$

Since **a, b, c** are non-coplanar, equating the coefficients, we get

$$-x + y = -1,\ -5x + y = -9,\ 4x - y = 7.$$

Solving first two, we get $x = 2$, $y = 1$ and these values satisfy the third also. Hence $\vec{AB}, \vec{AC}$ and $\vec{AD}$ are coplanar which in turn means that the four points A, B, C, D are coplanar.

2nd Method :

We know from Q. 31 that the four points are coplanar if we can choose four scalars l, m, n, p such that

$$l(2\mathbf{a} + 3\mathbf{b} - \mathbf{c}) + m(\mathbf{a} - 2\mathbf{b} + 3\mathbf{c}) + n(3\mathbf{a} + 4\mathbf{b} - 2\mathbf{c}) + p(\mathbf{a} - 6\mathbf{b} + 6\mathbf{c}) = \mathbf{0} \quad \text{...(1)}$$

where $l + m + n + p = 0$ ...(2)

The relation (1) can be put in the form

$$2\mathbf{a} + 3\mathbf{b} - \mathbf{c} = (1 - s - t)(\mathbf{a} - 2\mathbf{b} + 3\mathbf{c}) + s(3\mathbf{a} + 4\mathbf{b} - 2\mathbf{c}) + t(\mathbf{a} - 6\mathbf{b} + 6\mathbf{c}) \quad \text{...(3)}$$

which satisfies the condition (2).

For taking L.H.S. to R.H.S. the sum of the coefficients is $(1 - s - t) + s + t - 1$. *i.e.* 0.

Since **a, b, c** are non-coplanar, equating the coefficients of **a, b, c** in (3), we get

$$1 - s - t + 3s + t = 2 \text{ or } 2s = 1,\ \therefore\ s = \frac{1}{2}$$

$$(1 - s - t)(-2) + 4s - 6t = 3 \text{ or } 6s - 4t = 5$$

$$\therefore\ -4t = 5 - 6s = 5 - 3 = 2,\ \therefore\ t = -\frac{1}{2}.$$

and $(1 - s - t)(3) - 2s + 6t = -1$

or $-5s + 3t = -4$

The last one is satisfied for $s = \frac{1}{2}$ and $t = -\frac{1}{2}$.

Thus the four points can be put in the form $l\alpha + m\beta + n\gamma + p\delta = 0$ where $l + m + n + p = 0$

Therefore the four points are coplanar.

(b) $A, 6\mathbf{a} + 2\mathbf{b} - \mathbf{c},\quad B,\ 2\mathbf{a} - \mathbf{b} + 3\mathbf{c},$

$C,\ -\mathbf{a} + 2\mathbf{b} - 4\mathbf{c},\ D,\ -12\mathbf{a} - \mathbf{b} - 3\mathbf{c}$

$\vec{AB} = \vec{OB} - \vec{OA} = -4\mathbf{a} - 3\mathbf{b} + 4\mathbf{c}$

$\vec{BC} = \vec{OC} - \vec{OB} = -3\mathbf{a} + 3\mathbf{b} - 7\mathbf{c}$

$\vec{CD} = \vec{OD} - \vec{OC} = -11\mathbf{a} - 3\mathbf{b} + \mathbf{c}$

If the given four points are coplanar, then the three vectors written above are coplanar and as such one of them is expresssible as a linear combination of the other two.

Let $-4\mathbf{a} - 3\mathbf{b} + 4\mathbf{c} = x(-3\mathbf{a} + 3\mathbf{b} - 7\mathbf{c}) + y(-11\mathbf{a} - 3\mathbf{b} + \mathbf{c})$

Comparing the coefficients of **a, b, c,** we get

$$-3x - 11y = -4,\ 3x - 3y = -3,\ -7x + y = 4.$$

Solving the first two, we get $y = \frac{1}{2}$, $x = -\frac{1}{2}$ and these values satisfy the third also. Hence the given vectors are coplanar or the given four points are coplanar.

2nd Method :

The equation of the plane through the last three points is $\mathbf{r} = (1 - s - t)\,\alpha + s\beta + t\gamma$

If the four points are coplanar, then the point S will also satisfy it. Hence we have

$$6\mathbf{a} + 2\mathbf{b} - \mathbf{c} = (1 - s - t)(2\mathbf{a} - \mathbf{b} + 3\mathbf{c}) + s(-\mathbf{a} + 2\mathbf{b} - 4\mathbf{c}) + t(-12\mathbf{a} - \mathbf{b} - 3\mathbf{c}).$$

Equating the coefficients of **a**, **b** and **c** on both sides, we get

$$6 = (1 - s - t)(2) + s(-1) + t(-12)$$

or $\quad -3s - 14t = 4,$

$$2 = (1 - s - t)(-1) + s(2) + t(-1) \quad \text{or} \quad 3s = 3.$$

$\therefore \quad s = 1$ and $t = -\frac{1}{2}$.

$$-1 = (1 - s - t)(3) + s(-4) + t(-3)$$

or $\quad -7s - 6t = -4.$

The last one is also satisfied by $s = 1$ and $t = -\frac{1}{2}$.

Hence the four points are coplanar.

(c) Proceed as in part (a) or (b).

39. Refer **Theorem III Page 1094** Any vector **r** can be uniquely expressed as a linear combination of three non-coplanar vectors. Let us choose that

$$7\mathbf{a} - 11\mathbf{b} + 15\mathbf{c} = x(\mathbf{a} - 2\mathbf{b} + 3\mathbf{c}) + y(2\mathbf{a} - 3\mathbf{b} + 4\mathbf{c}) + z(3\mathbf{a} - 4\mathbf{b} + 5\mathbf{c})$$

Comparing the coefficients of **a, b** and **c** on both sides we get, $x + 2y + 3z = 7,$

$$-2x - 3y - 4z = -11, 3x + 4y + 5z = 15.$$

Eliminate x and then solve for y and z etc.

$\therefore \quad x = 1, y = 3, z = 0.$

40. We know that the four points $\alpha, \beta, \gamma, \delta$ are coplanar if there exists a relation of the form

$x\alpha + y\beta + z\gamma + w\delta = \mathbf{0}$ such that

$x + y + z + w = 0$

$$\therefore \quad x(l_1\,\mathbf{a} + m_1\,\mathbf{b} + n_1\,\mathbf{c}) + y(l_2\,\mathbf{a} + m_2\,\mathbf{b} + n_2\,\mathbf{c}) + z(l_3\,\mathbf{a} + m_3\,\mathbf{b} + n_3\,\mathbf{c}) + w(l_4\,\mathbf{a} + m_4\mathbf{b} + n_4\,\mathbf{c}) = \mathbf{0}$$

or $\quad (\Sigma\, xl_1)\,\mathbf{a} + (\Sigma\, xm_1)\,\mathbf{b} + (\Sigma\, xn_1)\,\mathbf{c} = \mathbf{0}$

Now **a, b, c** are three **non-coplanar** vectors and hence if there exists a relation of the form $l\mathbf{a} + m\mathbf{b} + n\mathbf{c} = \mathbf{0}$ between them, then $l = 0, m = 0, n = 0$ (for otherwise one would be expressible as a linear combination of the other two which would mean that **a, b, c** are coplanar). **[Th. II P. 1094]**

$$\therefore \quad xl_1 + yl_2 + zl_3 + wl_4 = 0 \quad \text{...(1)}$$

$$xm_1 + ym_2 + zm_3 + wm_4 = 0 \quad \text{...(2)}$$

$$xn_1 + yn_2 + zn_3 + wn_4 = 0 \quad \text{...(3)}$$

Also $x+y+z+w=0$ ...(4)

Eliminating x, y, z and w, we get

$$\begin{vmatrix} l_1 & l_2 & l_3 & l_4 \\ m_1 & m_2 & m_3 & m_4 \\ n_1 & n_2 & n_3 & n_4 \\ 1 & 1 & 1 & 1 \end{vmatrix} = 0.$$

41. (a) $(\mathbf{i}+\mathbf{j}+3\mathbf{k})\,x+(3\mathbf{i}-3\mathbf{j}+\mathbf{k})\,y+(-4\mathbf{i}+5\mathbf{j})\,z = \lambda\,(x\mathbf{i}+y\mathbf{j}+z\mathbf{k})$

$(x+3y-4z-\lambda x)\,\mathbf{i}+(x-3y+5z-\lambda y)\,\mathbf{j} + (3x+y+0z-\lambda z)\,\mathbf{k}=\mathbf{0}.$

Above is a relation of the form $l\,\mathbf{i}+m\,\mathbf{j}+n\,\mathbf{k}=\mathbf{0}$ where $\mathbf{i}, \mathbf{j}$ and $\mathbf{k}$ are non-coplanar and hence each of the coefficients l, m, n is zero.

$\therefore$ $(1-\lambda)\,x+3y-4z=0$

$x-(3+\lambda)\,y+5z=0$

$3x+y-\lambda z=0$

Eliminating x, y, z, we get

$$\begin{vmatrix} 1-\lambda & 3 & -4 \\ 1 & -3-\lambda & 5 \\ 3 & 1 & -\lambda \end{vmatrix} = 0$$

or $(1-\lambda)(3\lambda+\lambda^2-5)-3(-\lambda-15) - 4(1+9+3\lambda)=0$

$-\lambda^3+\lambda^2(1-3)+\lambda(5+3+3-12) + (-5+45-40)=0$

$-\lambda^3-2\lambda^2-\lambda=0$ or $\lambda(\lambda^2+2\lambda+1)=0$

$\therefore$ $\lambda(\lambda+1)^2=0$ which gives $\lambda=0,-1,-1.$

(b) Given $\mathbf{a}, \mathbf{b}, \mathbf{c}$ are L.I.

$\therefore$ $p\mathbf{a}+q\mathbf{b}+r\mathbf{c}=0 \Rightarrow p=0, q=0, r=0$ ...(1)

Now consider

$x(\mathbf{a}-2\mathbf{b}+\mathbf{c})+y(2\mathbf{a}-\mathbf{b}+\mathbf{c}) + z(3\mathbf{a}+\mathbf{b}+2\mathbf{c})=0$

or $(x+2y+3z)\,\mathbf{a}+(-2x-y+z)\,\mathbf{b} + (x+y+2z)\,\mathbf{c}=0$

Hence by (1) we have

$x+2y+3z=0, -2x-y+z=0, x+y+2z=0$

Above is a set of homogeneous equations.

$$\Delta=\begin{vmatrix} 1 & 2 & 3 \\ -2 & -1 & 1 \\ 1 & 1 & 2 \end{vmatrix} = -3+10-3=4\neq 0$$

Since $\Delta\neq 0$, the system of equations has only a trivial solution *i.e.*, $x=0, y=0, z=0$

Hence L.I. **(§ 2. P. 1094)**

(c) Proceeding as in part (c), we have $L\mathbf{a}+M\mathbf{b}+N\mathbf{c}=0$ implies

$(-x+2y+z)\,\mathbf{i}+(-2x+3y+z)\,\mathbf{j} + (2x-y+z)\,\mathbf{k}=0$

Above implies

$-x+2y+z=0, -2x+3y+z=0, 2x-y+z=0$

because $\mathbf{i}, \mathbf{j}, \mathbf{k}$ are three non-coplanar vectors and hence they form a linearly independent set.

Now we have three homogeneous equations and

$$\Delta=\begin{vmatrix} -1 & 2 & 1 \\ -2 & 3 & 1 \\ 2 & -1 & 1 \end{vmatrix}$$ C_1+C_2 makes two columns identical $\therefore$ $\Delta=0.$

Hence the system of equations have **non-trivial** solution.

$\therefore$ L, M, N are not all zero.

Hence the given system is linearly dependent.

42. (a) Let us suppose that $\mathbf{R}=x\mathbf{a}+y\mathbf{b}+z\mathbf{c}$ ...(1)

$=x(2,3,-1)+y(1,-2,2)+z(-2,1,-2)$

$=(2x+y-2z)\,\mathbf{p}+(3x-2y+z)\,\mathbf{q} + (-x+2y-2z)\,\mathbf{r}$

$=3\mathbf{p}-\mathbf{q}+2\mathbf{r}$ (given)

Comparing, we get

$2x+y-2z=3, 3x-2y+z=-1, -x+2y-2z=2$

Eliminate z and solve for x and y and then find z.

$\therefore$ $x=2, y=5, z=3$ $\therefore$ $\mathbf{R}=2\mathbf{a}+5\mathbf{b}+3\mathbf{c}.$

(b) Put the values and equate the coefficients $\mathbf{i}, \mathbf{j}, \mathbf{k}$ on both sides. Thus we have the following equations :

$2x+y-2z=3, -x+3y+z=2, x-2y-3z=5.$

Solving these, we get $x=-2, y=1, z=-3.$

43. (a) When rotated through $\pi/2$, the new x-axis is along old y-axis and new y-axis is along the old negative x-axis ; z-axis remains same as before.

Hence the components of A in the new system are $A_2, -A_1, A_3$.

(b) If $\mathbf{i}', \mathbf{j}', \mathbf{k}'$ be new unit vectors along the co-ordinate axes, then

$\mathbf{a}=2\sqrt{2}\mathbf{i}'+3\sqrt{2}\mathbf{j}'+4\mathbf{k}'$ ...(1)

$\mathbf{i}', \mathbf{j}', \mathbf{k}'$ are obtained by rotating by 45° about z-axis.

$\mathbf{i}'=\mathbf{i}\cos 45^\circ+\mathbf{j}\sin 45^\circ=\dfrac{\mathbf{i}+\mathbf{j}}{\sqrt{2}}$

$\mathbf{j}'=-\mathbf{i}\cos 45^\circ+\mathbf{j}\sin 45^\circ=\dfrac{-\mathbf{i}+\mathbf{j}}{\sqrt{2}}$

$\mathbf{k}'=\mathbf{k}$, Putting in (1)

$\mathbf{a}=2\sqrt{2}\left[\dfrac{\mathbf{i}+\mathbf{j}}{\sqrt{2}}\right]+3\sqrt{2}\left[\dfrac{-\mathbf{i}+\mathbf{j}}{\sqrt{2}}\right]+4\mathbf{k}$

$\mathbf{a}=(2-3)\,\mathbf{i}+(2+3)\,\mathbf{j}+4\mathbf{k}$

$\mathbf{a}=-\mathbf{i}+5\mathbf{j}+4\mathbf{k}$

44. $\mathbf{r}_1$ is the position vector of P_1 w.r.t. origin O and let the position vector of P be α so that $OP_1=\mathbf{r}_1, OP=\alpha.$

Now if we choose P as origin, then position vector of P_1 will be

$$\vec{PP_1}=\vec{OP_1}-\vec{OP}=\mathbf{r}_1-\alpha$$

The given relation when written w.r.t. P as origin becomes

$\Sigma\,a_1(\mathbf{r}_1-\alpha)=\mathbf{0}$ or $\Sigma\,a_1\,\mathbf{r}_1-\alpha\Sigma\,a_1=\mathbf{0}.$

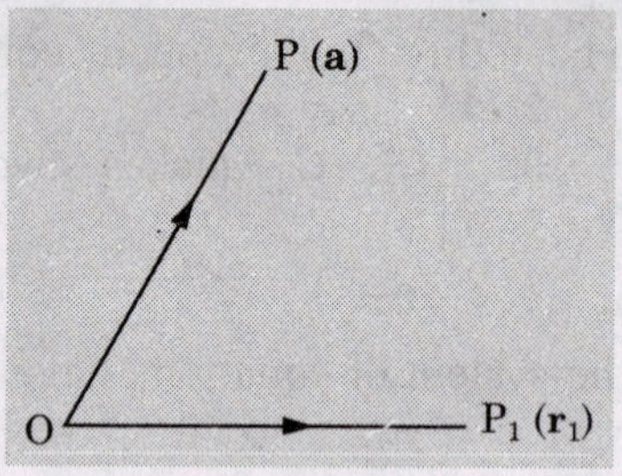

Fig. 36

It will reduce to

$$\sum a_1 \mathbf{r}_1 = \mathbf{0} \text{ if } \sum a_1 = 0$$

i.e. $a_1 + a_2 + a_3 + \ldots a_n = 0$

45. The resultant of the forces is given by

$$\mathbf{F_1} + \mathbf{F_2} + \mathbf{F_3} + \mathbf{F_4} = \left(\frac{4}{13}U - \frac{4}{13}V + W\cos\theta\right)\mathbf{i}$$
$$+\left(-\frac{12}{13}U - \frac{12}{13}V + W\sin\theta\right)\mathbf{j} + \left(\frac{3}{13}U + \frac{3}{13}V - 10\right)\mathbf{k}.$$

Since the forces are in equilibrium, we have

L.H.S. = 0 $\Rightarrow$ R.H.S. = 0

But **i, j, k** are non-coplanar, we must have each of the coefficient in R.H.S. equal to zero.

$$\frac{4}{13}U - \frac{4}{13}V + W\cos\theta = 0.$$
$$-\frac{12}{13}U - \frac{12}{13}V + W\sin\theta = 0.$$
and $\frac{3}{13}U + \frac{3}{13}V - 10 = 0.$

The above equations can be re-written as

$$U - V = -\frac{13}{4}W\cos\theta \quad \ldots(1)$$
$$U + V = \frac{13}{12}W\sin\theta \quad \ldots(2)$$
$$U + V = \frac{130}{3} \quad \ldots(3)$$

Equating (2) and (3), we get

$$W = 40\,\text{cosec}\,\theta$$

From (1) and (2) on putting for W and adding and subtracting, we get

$$U = \frac{65}{3}(1 - 3\cot\theta), \qquad V = \frac{65}{3}(1 + 3\cot\theta).$$

46. (a) Let P be horizontal in the direction of unit vector **i**. The resultant is also P but perpendicular to it in the direction of unit vector **j**. If Q be the other force making an angle θ (obtuse) as resultant is perpendicular to P, then the two forces are $P\mathbf{i}$ and $Q\cos\theta\mathbf{i} + Q\sin\theta\mathbf{j}$. Their resultant is $P\mathbf{j}$.

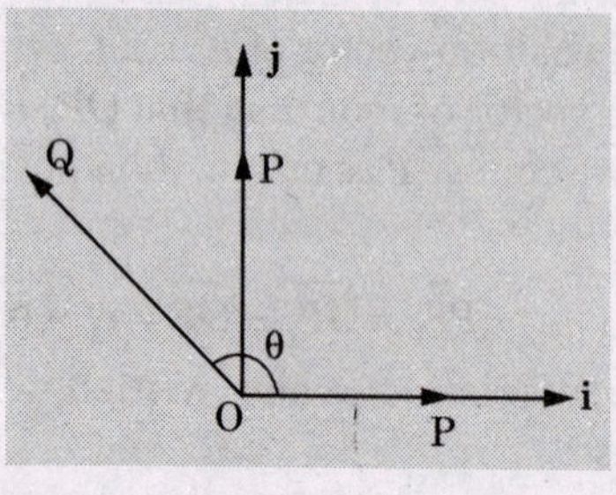

Fig. 37

$\therefore \quad P\mathbf{j} = P\mathbf{i} + (Q\cos\theta\mathbf{i} + Q\sin\theta\mathbf{j})$

Equating the coefficients of **i** and **j**, we get

$$P + Q\cos\theta = 0 \quad \text{and} \quad Q\sin\theta = P.$$

or $\quad Q\cos\theta = -P \quad$ and $\quad Q\sin\theta = P$

Squaring and adding $Q = P\sqrt{2}$ and dividing

$$\tan\theta = -1 \quad \therefore \quad \theta = 135°.$$

(b) $P\mathbf{j} = F_1\mathbf{i} + (-F_2\cos 30°\,\mathbf{i} + F_2\sin 30°\,\mathbf{j})$

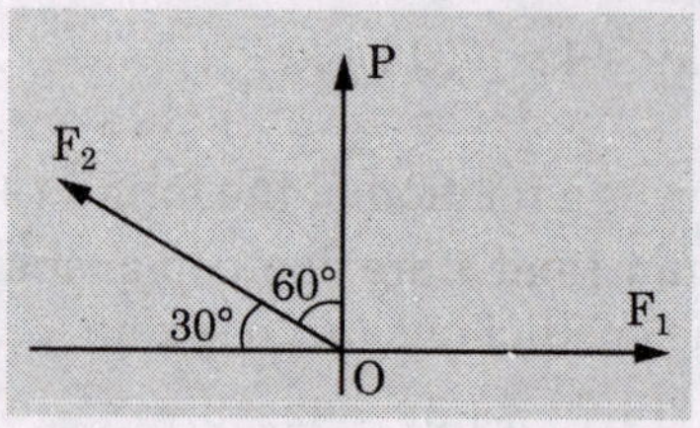

Fig. 38

Equating the coefficients of **i** and **j**, we get

$$F_1 - F_2 \cdot \frac{\sqrt{3}}{2} = 0 \quad \text{and} \quad F_2 \cdot \frac{1}{2} = P.$$

$\therefore \quad F_2 = 2P \quad$ and $\quad F_1 = \sqrt{3}\,P.$

(c) The velocity of wind relative to man

= Actual of wind − Actual of man ...(1)

Let **i** and **j** represent unit vectors along East and North. Let the actual velocity of wind be given by $x\mathbf{i} + y\mathbf{j}$.

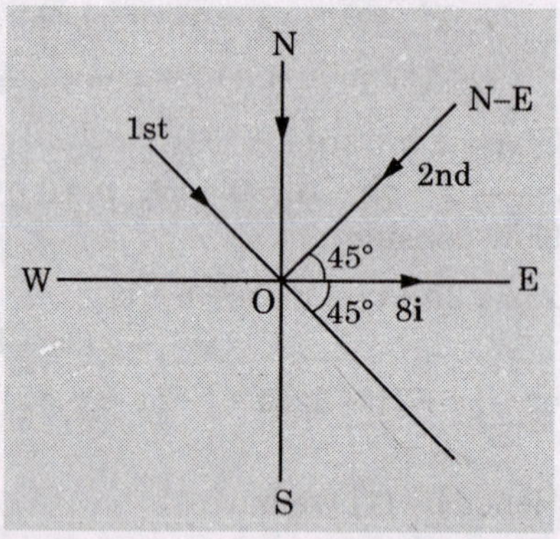

Fig. 39

In the 1st case the man's velocity is $8\mathbf{i}$ and that of the wind relative to man being **from** north is $-p\mathbf{j}$.

$\therefore \quad -p\mathbf{j} = (x\mathbf{i} + y\mathbf{j}) - 8\mathbf{i}$ by (1)

Comparing coefficients $x - 8 = 0, y = -p$ ...(2)

In the 2nd case when the man doubles his speed, it seems to come from N-E.

$$-q(\mathbf{i} + \mathbf{j}) = (x\mathbf{i} + y\mathbf{j}) - 16\mathbf{i}$$

$\therefore \quad x - 16 = -q, y = -q$ ...(3)

Putting $x = 8$, we get $q = 8 \quad \therefore \quad y = -8$

Hence the velocity of wind is $x\mathbf{i} + y\mathbf{j} = 8(\mathbf{i} - \mathbf{j})$

Its magnitude is $\sqrt{(8^2 + 8^2)} = 8\sqrt{2}$ and $\tan 0 = -1$

$\therefore \quad \theta = -45°$. Hence its direction is from N-W.

47. (a) Let **i** and **j** be parallel to two adjacent edges OA (east) and OB (north) of a large square table and let P, Q, R, S represent the position of the ant after the four successive displacements. Then according to the question, we have

30° east of north $= 60^\circ$ with east

$\vec{OP} = 4\cos 60^\circ\ \mathbf{i} + 4\sin 60^\circ\ \mathbf{j} = 2\mathbf{i} + 2\sqrt{3}\,\mathbf{j}$

$\vec{PQ} = -12\cos 45^\circ\ \mathbf{i} - 12\sin 45^\circ\ \mathbf{j} = -6\sqrt{2}\mathbf{i} - 6\sqrt{2}\mathbf{j}$

$\vec{QR} = 6\mathbf{i}$

$\vec{RS} = -9\cos 45^\circ\ \mathbf{i} + 9\sin 45^\circ\ \mathbf{j} = -\dfrac{9}{\sqrt{2}}\mathbf{i} + \dfrac{9}{\sqrt{2}}\mathbf{j}$

$$\therefore\quad \vec{OS} = \vec{OP} + \vec{PQ} + \vec{QR} + \vec{RS}$$

$$= \frac{1}{\sqrt{2}}\left[(8\sqrt{2} - 21)\,\mathbf{i} + (2\sqrt{6} - 3)\,\mathbf{j}\right]$$

$$\therefore\quad OS = \frac{1}{\sqrt{(2)}}\sqrt{[(8\sqrt{2} - 21)^2 + (2\sqrt{6} - 3)^2]}$$

$$= \frac{1}{\sqrt{(2)}}\cdot\sqrt{602 - 336\sqrt{(2)} - 12\sqrt{(6)}}$$

$$= \sqrt{301 - 168\sqrt{(2)} - 6\sqrt{(6)}}$$

which is the magnitude of the resultant displacement and if OS makes an angle θ with OA, then

$\tan\theta = \dfrac{2\sqrt{6} - 3}{8\sqrt{(2)} - 21}$, which gives the direction.

(b) We take the unit vectors $\mathbf{i}, \mathbf{j}, \mathbf{k}$ parallel to east, north and vertical upwards in the direction of pole. Then the velocity vectors of the current, ship and the sailor are respectively $\mathbf{i}$, $1\cdot 25\,\mathbf{j}$ and $0\cdot 5\,\mathbf{k}$. The velocity $\mathbf{v}$ of the sailor in space is the resultant of these vectors.

Hence $\quad \mathbf{v} = \mathbf{i} + 1\cdot 25\,\mathbf{j} + 0\cdot 5\,\mathbf{k}$.

Then $\quad |\mathbf{v}| = \sqrt{1 + (1\cdot 25)^2 + (0\cdot 5)^2}$

$$= \sqrt{1 + 1\cdot 5625 + \cdot 25}$$

$$= \sqrt{2\cdot 8125} = 1\cdot 677 \text{ m/sec.}$$

If α, β, γ are the angles made by the direction of $\mathbf{v}$ with east, north and upward vertical, we have

$$\cos\alpha = \frac{1}{1\cdot 677} = 0\cdot 59, \cos\beta = \frac{1\cdot 25}{1\cdot 677} = 0\cdot 75$$

and $\cos\gamma = \dfrac{0\cdot 5}{1\cdot 677} = 0\cdot 3.$

48. (a) With O as origin let $\mathbf{a}$ and $\mathbf{b}$ be the position vectors of A and B respectively.

Then the position vector of E, the mid-point of OB, is $\mathbf{b}/2$. Again, since $AD : DB = 2 : 1$, the position vector of D is

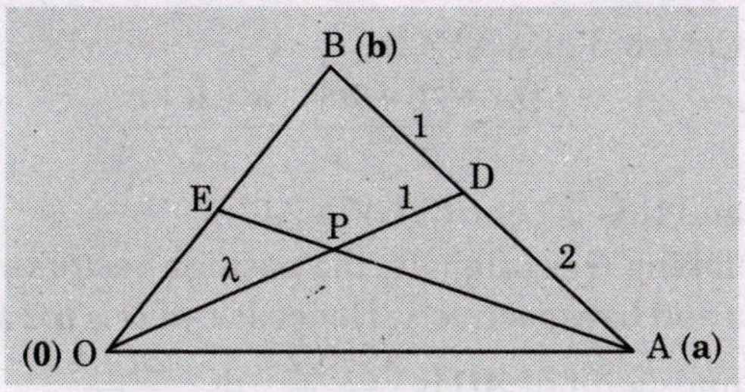

Fig. 40

$$\frac{1.\mathbf{a} + 2\mathbf{b}}{1 + 2},\ \textit{i.e.}\ \frac{\mathbf{a} + 2\mathbf{b}}{3}$$

Equations of OD and AE are

$$\mathbf{r} = t\,\frac{\mathbf{a} + 2\mathbf{b}}{3} \qquad ...(1)$$

and $\mathbf{r} = \mathbf{a} + s\left(\dfrac{\mathbf{b}}{2} - \mathbf{a}\right)$ or $\mathbf{r} = (1 - s)\,\mathbf{a} + s\,\dfrac{\mathbf{b}}{2}$ ...(2)

If they intersect at P, then we will have identical values of $\mathbf{r}$. Hence comparing the coefficients of $\mathbf{a}$ and $\mathbf{b}$, we get $\dfrac{t}{3} = 1 - s, \dfrac{2t}{3} = \dfrac{s}{2}\quad \therefore\quad t = \dfrac{3}{5}$ or $s = \dfrac{4}{5}$.

Putting for t in (1) or for s in (2), we get the position vector of point of intersection P as

$$\frac{\mathbf{a} + 2\mathbf{b}}{5} \qquad ...(3)$$

Now let P divide OD in the ratio $\lambda : 1$. Hence by ratio formula the P.V. of P is

$$\frac{\dfrac{\lambda\,(\mathbf{a} + 2\mathbf{b})}{3} + 1.0}{\lambda + 1} = \frac{\lambda}{3(\lambda + 1)}(\mathbf{a} + 2\mathbf{b}) \qquad ...(4)$$

Comparing (3) and (4), we get

$$\frac{\lambda}{3\,(\lambda + 1)} = \frac{1}{5}$$

or $\quad 5\lambda = 3\lambda + 3\quad \therefore\quad 2\lambda = 3\quad$ or $\quad \lambda = \dfrac{3}{2}$

$\therefore\quad OP : PD = 3 : 2$

(b) Let the position vectors of A and B be $\mathbf{a}$ and $\mathbf{b}$ respectively. Equations of AD and BE are

$$\mathbf{r} = \mathbf{a} + t\,(\mathbf{b}/3 - \mathbf{a}) \qquad ...(1)$$

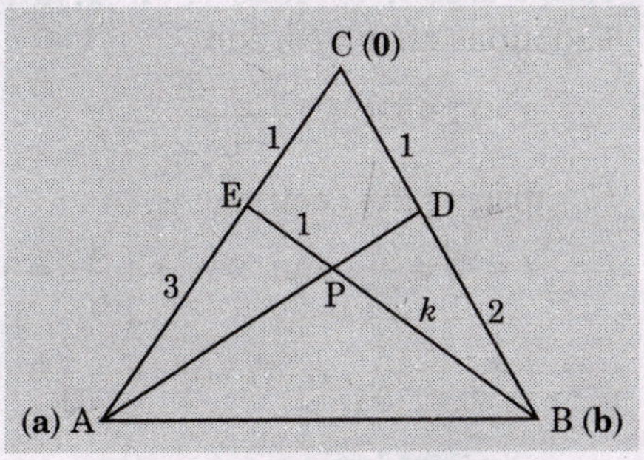

Fig. 41

$$\mathbf{r} = \mathbf{b} + s\,(\mathbf{a}/4 - \mathbf{b}) \qquad ...(2)$$

If they intersect at P we must have identical values of $\mathbf{r}$. Comparing the coefficients of $\mathbf{a}$ and $\mathbf{b}$ in (1) and (2), we get $1 - t = \dfrac{s}{4}, \dfrac{t}{3} = 1 - s$, solving we get

$t = \dfrac{9}{11}, s = \dfrac{8}{11}$. Putting for t or s in (1) or (2), we get

the point P as $\dfrac{2\mathbf{a} + 3\mathbf{b}}{11}$.

Let P divide BE in the ratio $k : 1$, then P is

$$\frac{k\cdot\dfrac{\mathbf{a}}{4} + \mathbf{b}}{k + 1} = \frac{2\mathbf{a} + 3\mathbf{b}}{11}.$$

Comparing **a** and **b**, we get $11k = 8(k+1)$ and $11 = 3(k+1)$ $\therefore$ $k = 8/3$ and this satisfies the 2nd relation also. Hence the required ratio is 8 : 3.

49. (a) Take A as origin and the position vectors of B and C be **b** and **c**. Hence the position vectors of other points under given conditions are

$$D \ \frac{3\mathbf{c}+2\mathbf{b}}{5}, \quad E \ \frac{1.0+3\mathbf{c}}{4} = \frac{3}{4}\mathbf{c}.$$

Equations of AD and BE are

$$AD \text{ is } \mathbf{r} = t\,\frac{3\mathbf{c}+2\mathbf{b}}{5}$$

$$BE \text{ is } \mathbf{r} = (1-s)\,\mathbf{b} + s\,.\frac{3}{4}\mathbf{c}.$$

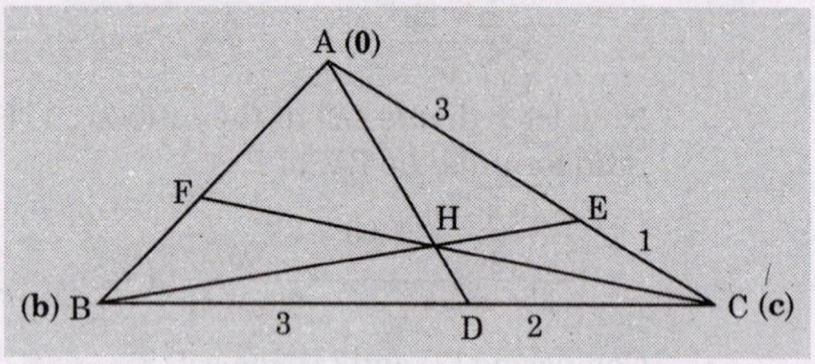

Fig. 42

They intersect at H. Comparing coefficients of **b** and **c**, we get $\frac{2}{5}t = 1-s$, $\frac{3}{5}t = \frac{3}{4}s$.

$$\therefore \quad s = \frac{4}{5}t. \quad \therefore \quad \frac{2}{5}t + \frac{4}{5}t = 1 \quad \therefore \quad t = \frac{5}{6}, s = \frac{4}{6}$$

Point H is $\frac{3\mathbf{c}+2\mathbf{b}}{6}$

Now F is point of intersection of AB and CH whose equations are $\mathbf{r} = t\,\mathbf{b}$ and

$$\mathbf{r} = (1-s)\,\mathbf{c} + s\,\frac{3\mathbf{c}+2\mathbf{b}}{6}$$

Comparing the coefficients,

$$t = \frac{2s}{6} = \frac{s}{3} \quad \text{and} \quad 1 - s + \frac{3}{6}s = 0 \quad \therefore \ s = 2$$

$$\therefore \quad t = \frac{1}{3}s = \frac{2}{3} \quad \therefore \text{ P.V. of } F = \frac{2}{3}\mathbf{b}$$

or $\quad \vec{AF} = \frac{2}{3}\mathbf{b}, \vec{FB} = \mathbf{b} - \frac{2}{3}\mathbf{b} = \frac{1}{3}\mathbf{b}$

$\therefore \quad AF : FB = 2 : 1.$

(b) Taking A as origin, let the P.V.s of B and C be **b** and **c** respectively. By ratio formula the points D, E, F are

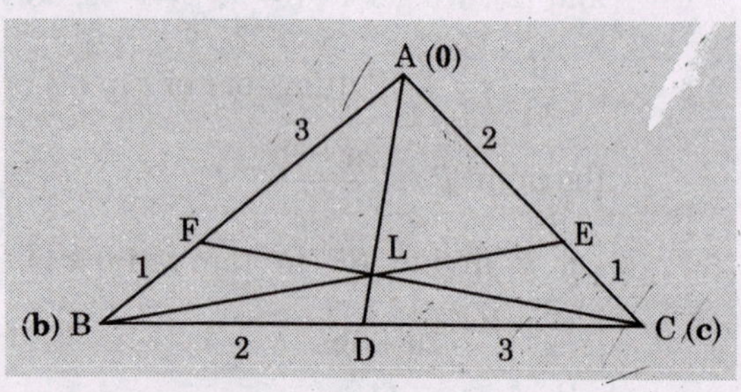

Fig. 43

$$D = \frac{3\mathbf{b}+2\mathbf{c}}{5}, E = \frac{2\mathbf{c}}{3}, F = \frac{3\mathbf{b}}{4}$$

$A, \mathbf{0} \quad B, \mathbf{b} \quad C, \mathbf{c}$

Equations of AD, BE and CF are

$$AD \quad \mathbf{r} = \frac{t\,(3\mathbf{b}+2\mathbf{c})}{5}$$

$$BE \quad \mathbf{r} = (1-s)\,\mathbf{b} + s\left(\frac{2\mathbf{c}}{3}\right)$$

$$CF \quad \mathbf{r} = (1-p)\,\mathbf{c} + p\left(\frac{3\mathbf{b}}{4}\right)$$

Let AD and BE intersect at L, then comparing the coefficients of **b** and **c**, we get

$\left(\frac{3t}{5}\right) = 1 - s$, $\left(\frac{2t}{5}\right) = \frac{2}{3}s$. Solving, we get $t = 5/6, s = 1/2$.

$\therefore$ Point L is $\frac{3\mathbf{b}+2\mathbf{c}}{6}$. The line CF will pass through this point L if

$$\frac{3\mathbf{b}+2\mathbf{c}}{6} = (1-p)\,\mathbf{c} + p\left(\frac{3\mathbf{b}}{4}\right)$$

Comparing, $\frac{3}{6} = \frac{3}{4}p$, $\frac{2}{6} = 1 - p$

$\therefore \ p = \frac{2}{3}$ and this value satisfies the other relation.

Hence the three lines are concurrent at L.

50. Let **a**, **b**, **c** be the position vectors of the points A, B, C respectively. Hence by ratio formula, the position vectors of P, Q, R are $P \ \frac{2\mathbf{b}+\mathbf{c}}{3}, Q \ \frac{2\mathbf{c}+\mathbf{a}}{3}, R \ \frac{2\mathbf{a}+\mathbf{b}}{3}$.

$$\text{Line } AP \text{ is} \quad \mathbf{r} = (1-t)\,\mathbf{a} + t\,\frac{2\mathbf{b}+\mathbf{c}}{3}$$

$$BQ \text{ is} \quad \mathbf{r} = (1-s)\,\mathbf{b} + s\,\frac{2\mathbf{c}+\mathbf{a}}{3}$$

$$CR \text{ is} \quad \mathbf{r} = (1-q)\,\mathbf{c} + q\,\frac{2\mathbf{a}+\mathbf{b}}{3}$$

Solving the last two by comparing the coefficients after equating the values of **r**, we get the point X.

$$1 - s = \frac{q}{3}, \ \frac{2s}{3} = 1 - q, \quad \frac{s}{3} = \frac{2q}{3}$$

$$\therefore \quad s = 2q, \ q = 3/7, \quad s = 6/7$$

$\therefore \quad X$ is $\frac{2\mathbf{a}+\mathbf{b}+4\mathbf{c}}{7}$ and similarly

$$Y = \frac{4\mathbf{a}+2\mathbf{b}+\mathbf{c}}{7}, \ Z = \frac{\mathbf{a}+4\mathbf{b}+2\mathbf{c}}{7}$$

Centroid of $\Delta\, XYZ$ is

$$\frac{1}{7}\frac{(7\mathbf{a}+7\mathbf{b}+7\mathbf{c})}{3} = \frac{\mathbf{a}+\mathbf{b}+\mathbf{c}}{3}$$

and this is centroid of $\Delta\, ABC$.

51. Taking C as origin let the position vectors of A and B be **a** and **b** respectively. Hence P.V. of D is $\mathbf{b}/2$ and of E, the mid-point of AD is $\frac{\mathbf{a}+\mathbf{b}/2}{2}$ or $\frac{2\mathbf{a}+\mathbf{b}}{4}$.

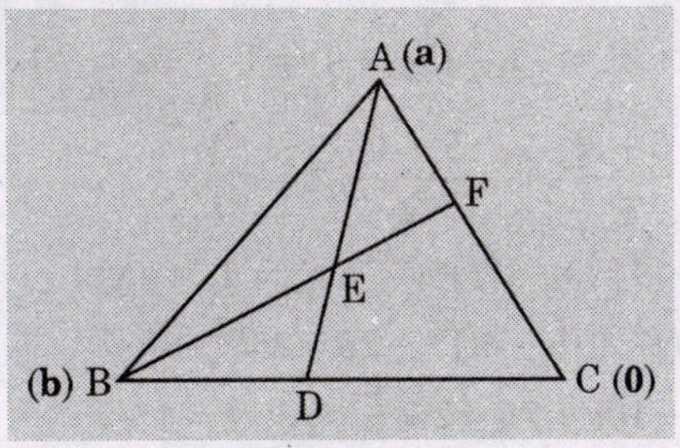

Fig. 44

Now F is the point of intersection of $\vec{CA}$ and $\vec{BE}$ whose equations are

$$\mathbf{r} = t\,\mathbf{a} \qquad \text{...(1)}$$

and $\mathbf{r} = (1-s)\,\mathbf{b} + s\,\dfrac{(2\mathbf{a}+\mathbf{b})}{4}$ ...(2)

(1) and (2) intersect at F. For identical values of $\mathbf{r}$ compare the coefficients of $\mathbf{a}$ and $\mathbf{b}$ in (1) and (2)

$\therefore \quad t = \dfrac{s}{2}, -1 - s + \dfrac{s}{4} = 0 \qquad \therefore \quad s = \dfrac{4}{3}$ and $t = \dfrac{2}{3}$

$\therefore \quad$ P.V. of F is $\dfrac{2}{3}\mathbf{a}$

$\vec{EF} =$ P.V. of $F -$ P.V. of E

$= \dfrac{2}{3}\mathbf{a} - \dfrac{2\mathbf{a}+\mathbf{b}}{4} = \dfrac{2\mathbf{a}-3\mathbf{b}}{12}$

$\vec{BF} =$ P.V. of $F -$ P.V. of B

$= \dfrac{2}{3}\mathbf{a} - \mathbf{b} = \dfrac{2\mathbf{a}-3\mathbf{b}}{3}$

$\therefore \quad \dfrac{1}{4}\vec{BF} = \dfrac{2\mathbf{a}-3\mathbf{b}}{12} = \vec{EF} \quad \therefore \quad EF = \dfrac{1}{4}BF.$ **Proved.**

52. Take P as origin, then $\vec{PQ} = \mathbf{a} \Rightarrow Q$ is $\mathbf{a}$.

$\vec{PR} = \vec{PQ} + \vec{QR} = \mathbf{a} + \mathbf{b} \quad \therefore \quad R$ is $\mathbf{a}+\mathbf{b}$.

$\vec{PS} = -\vec{SP} = -(\mathbf{a}-\mathbf{b}) = \mathbf{b}-\mathbf{a}. \quad \therefore \quad S$ is $\mathbf{b}-\mathbf{a}$.

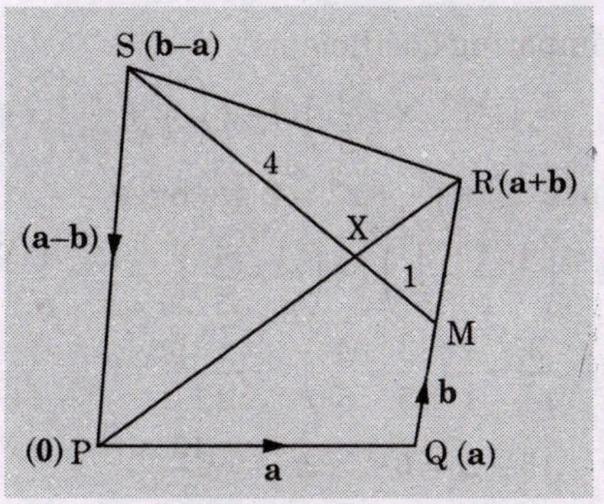

Fig. 45

M is mid-point of QR.

$\therefore \quad M$ is $\dfrac{\mathbf{a}+\mathbf{a}+\mathbf{b}}{2} = \dfrac{2\mathbf{a}+\mathbf{b}}{2}$

Now $5\,SX = 4\,SM = 4\,(SX + XM)$

$\therefore \quad SX = 4\,XM$

$\therefore \quad X$ divides SM in the ratio $4:1$.

$$\therefore \quad X = \frac{4\cdot\dfrac{(2\mathbf{a}+\mathbf{b})}{2} + 1\,(\mathbf{b}-\mathbf{a})}{4+1} = \frac{3\mathbf{a}+3\mathbf{b}}{5} = \frac{3}{5}(\mathbf{a}+\mathbf{b})$$

Now P is $\mathbf{0}$, X is $\dfrac{3}{5}(\mathbf{a}+\mathbf{b})$, R is $\mathbf{a}+\mathbf{b}$.

$\therefore \quad PX = \dfrac{3}{5}(\vec{PR})$

Hence points P, X and R are collinear.

53. (a) We have already proved this question in **Q. 27, P. 1097-1109.** Here below we give another method.

Let the position vectors of the vertices be $\mathbf{a}, \mathbf{b}, \mathbf{c}$ and lengths of sides be x, y, z respectively as shown in the figure.

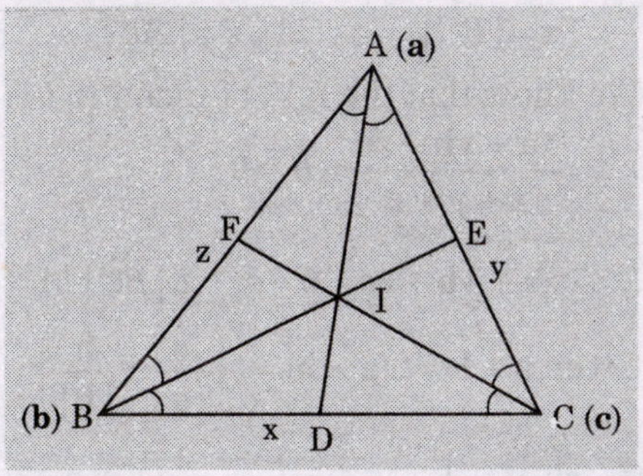

Fig. 46

$\vec{BC} = \mathbf{c}-\mathbf{b} \quad \therefore \quad$ Unit vector $\widehat{BC}$ is $\dfrac{\mathbf{c}-\mathbf{b}}{x}$ etc.

Bisector of $\angle A$ is $\mathbf{r} = \mathbf{a} + p\,(\widehat{AB} + \widehat{AC})$ ...(1)

Bisector of $\angle B$ is $\mathbf{r} = \mathbf{b} + q\,(\widehat{BA} + \widehat{BC})$ ...(2)

or $\quad \mathbf{r} = \mathbf{a} + p\left(\dfrac{\mathbf{b}-\mathbf{a}}{z} + \dfrac{\mathbf{c}-\mathbf{a}}{y}\right)$

and $\mathbf{r} = \mathbf{b} + q\left(\dfrac{\mathbf{a}-\mathbf{b}}{z} + \dfrac{\mathbf{c}-\mathbf{b}}{x}\right)$

We re-write them as under

or $\quad \mathbf{r} = \left(1 - \dfrac{p}{z} - \dfrac{p}{y}\right)\mathbf{a} + \dfrac{p}{z}\mathbf{b} + \dfrac{p}{y}\mathbf{c}$ ...(1)

$\mathbf{r} = \dfrac{q}{z}\mathbf{a} + \left(1 - \dfrac{q}{z} - \dfrac{q}{x}\right)\mathbf{b} + \dfrac{q}{x}\mathbf{c}$ ...(2)

If they intersect at (1), then we must have identical values of $\mathbf{r}$. Comparing the coefficients of $\mathbf{a}$, $\mathbf{b}$ and $\mathbf{c}$, we get

$1 - \dfrac{p}{z} - \dfrac{p}{y} = \dfrac{q}{z}$ ...(1)

$\dfrac{p}{z} = 1 - \dfrac{q}{z} - \dfrac{q}{x}$ ...(2)

$\dfrac{p}{y} = \dfrac{q}{x}$ ...(3)

or $\quad 1 - \dfrac{p\,(y+z)}{yz} = \dfrac{1}{z}\left(\dfrac{px}{y}\right)$, by (1) and (3)

$\therefore \quad 1 = \dfrac{p(x+y+z)}{yz}$ or $p = \dfrac{yz}{x+y+z}$

and $q = \dfrac{x}{y}\, p = \dfrac{zx}{x+y+z}$.

Putting the value of p in (1) or of q in (2), we get the point of intersection as

$$\mathbf{r} = \frac{x\mathbf{a} + y\mathbf{b} + z\mathbf{c}}{x+y+z}.$$

The symmetry of the result shows that this is also the point of intersection of other pairs of bisectors. Hence the three internal bisectors are concurrent.

(b) With respect to any origin say I the P.Vs. of A, B, C be **a**, **b** and **c** and the lengths of opposite sides be

$$x = |\vec{BC}|, y = |\vec{CA}|, z = |\vec{AB}|$$

We know that the P.V. of incentre I is

$$\frac{x\mathbf{a} + y\mathbf{b} + z\mathbf{c}}{x+y+z} = \vec{II} = \mathbf{0}$$

$\therefore \quad x\mathbf{a} + y\mathbf{b} + z\mathbf{c} = \mathbf{0}$ or $\Sigma |\vec{BC}| \vec{IA} = \mathbf{0}$

(c) Given $\mathbf{a} + \mathbf{b} = t(\hat{\mathbf{a}} + \hat{\mathbf{b}}) = t\left(\dfrac{\mathbf{a}}{|\mathbf{a}|} + \dfrac{\mathbf{b}}{|\mathbf{b}|}\right)$

$\therefore \quad \left(1 - \dfrac{t}{|\mathbf{a}|}\right)\mathbf{a} = \left(\dfrac{t}{|\mathbf{b}|} - 1\right)\mathbf{b}$

Above is of the form $L\,\mathbf{a} = M\,\mathbf{b}$

If **a** and **b** are **non-collinear**, then above relation implies that $L = 0, M = 0 \quad \therefore \quad t = |\mathbf{a}| = |\mathbf{b}|$.

In case **a** and **b are collinear** then angle between them is zero.

54. Let $\hat{\mathbf{c}} = x\,\mathbf{i} + y\,\mathbf{j} + z\,\mathbf{k}$ where $x^2 + y^2 + z^2 = 1$ ...(1)

and unit vector along $3\mathbf{i} + 4\mathbf{j}$ is $\dfrac{3\mathbf{i} + 4\mathbf{j}}{5}$.

The bisectors of these two is given by $\mathbf{r} = t(\hat{\mathbf{a}} + \hat{\mathbf{b}})$

(§ 7, P. 1097)

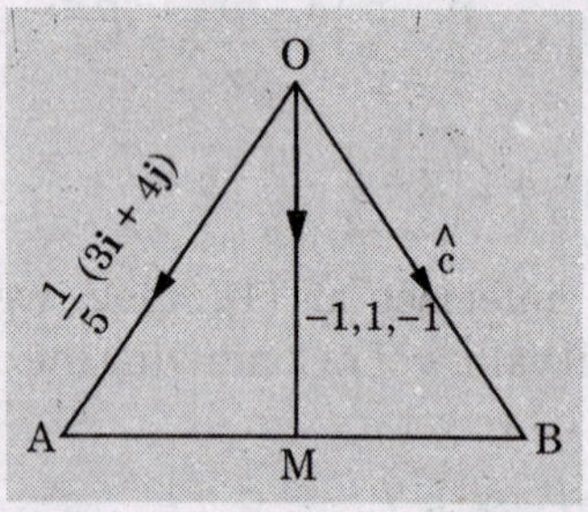

Fig. 47

or $\quad \mathbf{r} = t\left(x\,\mathbf{i} + y\,\mathbf{j} + z\,\mathbf{k} + \dfrac{3\mathbf{i} + 4\mathbf{j}}{5}\right)$

or $\quad \mathbf{r} = \dfrac{1}{5} t\,[(5x+3)\,\mathbf{i} + (5y+4)\,\mathbf{j} + 5z\,\mathbf{k}]$ ...(2)

But the bisector is given by $-\mathbf{i} + \mathbf{j} - \mathbf{k}$ ...(3)

Comparing (2) and (3), we get

$$\frac{t}{5}(5x+3) = -1, \frac{t}{5}(5y+4) = 1, \frac{t}{5}.5z = -1$$

$\therefore \quad x = -\dfrac{5+3t}{5t}, y = \dfrac{5-4t}{5t}, z = -\dfrac{1}{t}$

Putting in (1) i.e. $x^2 + y^2 + z^2 = 1$, we get

$$(5+3t)^2 + (5-4t)^2 + 25 = 25t^2$$

or $\quad 25t^2 - 10t + 75 = 25t^2 \quad \therefore \quad t = 15/2$

$\therefore \quad x = -\dfrac{55}{2} \cdot \dfrac{2}{75} = -\dfrac{11}{15}, y = \dfrac{10}{15}, z = -\dfrac{2}{15}$

$\therefore \quad \hat{\mathbf{c}} = \dfrac{1}{15}(-11\mathbf{i} + 10\mathbf{j} - 2\mathbf{k})$

55. (a) $\hat{\mathbf{a}} = \dfrac{1}{9}(7\mathbf{i} - 4\mathbf{j} - 4\mathbf{k})$

$\hat{\mathbf{b}} = \dfrac{1}{3}(-2\mathbf{i} - \mathbf{j} + 2\mathbf{k})$

$\mathbf{c} = t\,[\hat{\mathbf{a}} + \hat{\mathbf{b}}] = t \,.\, \dfrac{1}{9}(\mathbf{i} - 7\mathbf{j} + 2\mathbf{k})$ ...(1)

$|\mathbf{c}| = 5\sqrt{6} \Rightarrow \dfrac{t^2}{81}(1 + 49 + 4) = 25 \times 6$

$\therefore \quad t^2 = \dfrac{25 \times 6 \times 81}{54} = 225 \quad \therefore t = \pm 15$

Putting for t in (1), we get

$$\mathbf{c} = \pm\frac{5}{3}(\mathbf{i} - 7\mathbf{j} + 2\mathbf{k}).$$

(b) $|\vec{OA}| = |\vec{OB}| = \sqrt{14}$

$\Delta\, AOB$ is isosceles. Hence the bisector of angle AOB will bisect the base AB. Hence P is mid-point $(2, 2, -2)$ of AB

$\therefore \quad \vec{OP} = 2(\mathbf{i} + \mathbf{j} - \mathbf{k})$

(c) Let the unit vector along **c** be

$x\mathbf{i} + y\mathbf{j} + z\mathbf{k}$, where $\Sigma x^2 = 1$

$\therefore \quad -\mathbf{i} + \mathbf{j} - \mathbf{k} = t\left[x\mathbf{i} + y\mathbf{j} + z\mathbf{k} + \dfrac{3\mathbf{i} + 4\mathbf{j}}{5}\right]$

Comparing coefficients,

$$-1 = t\left(x + \frac{3}{5}\right), 1 = t\left(y + \frac{4}{5}\right), -1 = tz$$

Since $x^2 + y^2 + z^2 = 1$, we have

i.e. $\left(-\dfrac{1}{t} - \dfrac{3}{5}\right)^2 + \left(\dfrac{1}{t} - \dfrac{4}{5}\right)^2 + \left(-\dfrac{1}{t}\right)^2 = 1$

or $\quad \dfrac{3}{t^2} + \dfrac{2}{t}\left(\dfrac{3}{5} - \dfrac{4}{5}\right) + \dfrac{9+16}{25} = 1$

or $\quad 15 - 2t = 0 \quad \therefore \quad t = \dfrac{15}{2}$

$\therefore \quad x = -\dfrac{2}{15} - \dfrac{3}{5} = -\dfrac{11}{15}, y = \dfrac{2}{15} - \dfrac{4}{5} = -\dfrac{10}{15},$

$z = -\dfrac{2}{15}$

$\therefore \quad \mathbf{c} = x\mathbf{i} + y\mathbf{j} + z\mathbf{k} = -\dfrac{1}{15}(11\mathbf{i} + 10\mathbf{j} + 2\mathbf{k})$

56. Taking A as origin, let the position vectors of B and C be **b** and **c** respectively. $\vec{AB} = \mathbf{b}$ and $\vec{AC} = \mathbf{c}$. If

$AB = c$ and $AC = b$ then the unit vector along these is $\hat{AB} = \frac{\mathbf{b}}{c}$ and $\hat{AC} = \frac{\mathbf{c}}{b}$. The equation of the internal bisector of angle A is $\mathbf{r} = t\,(\hat{AB} + \hat{AC})$ § 7, Page 1097.

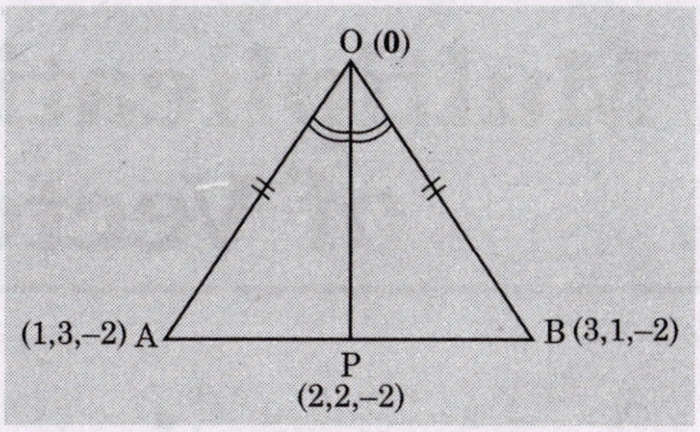

Fig. 48

or $\mathbf{r} = t\left(\frac{\mathbf{b}}{c} + \frac{\mathbf{c}}{b}\right)$ ...(1)

Again the equation of BC joining $\mathbf{b}$ and $\mathbf{c}$ is

$\mathbf{r} = (1 - s)\,\mathbf{b} + s\,\mathbf{c}$ § 6, Page 1096 ...(2)

If they meet at D, then on comparing (1) and (2)

$$\frac{t}{c} = 1 - s \quad \text{and} \quad \frac{t}{b} = s.$$

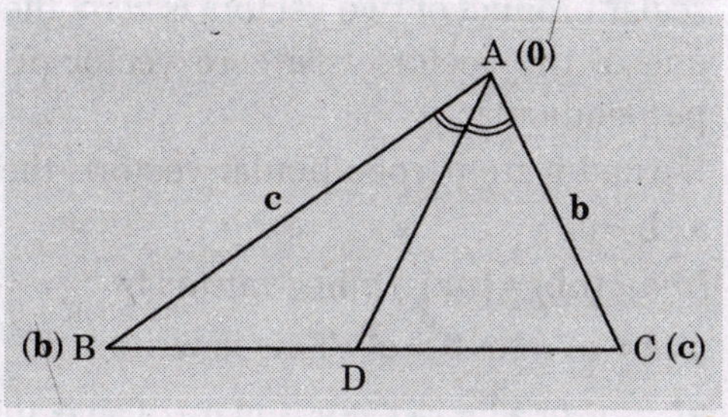

Fig. 49

Adding, we get

$$t\left(\frac{1}{b} + \frac{1}{c}\right) = 1 \quad \therefore \quad t = \frac{bc}{b + c}.$$

Putting in (1), we get

$$\mathbf{r} = \frac{bc}{b + c}\left[\frac{\mathbf{b}}{c} + \frac{\mathbf{c}}{b}\right] = \frac{b\,\mathbf{b} + c\,\mathbf{c}}{b + c}$$

Above shows that D divides BC the join of $\mathbf{b}$ and $\mathbf{c}$ in the ratio $c : b$ *i.e.* $AB : AC$ *i.e.* the sides containing the angle.

57. Let the vector $2\mathbf{i} + 7\mathbf{j} - 5\mathbf{k}$ intersect vectors $\vec{A}$ and $\vec{B}$ in points L and M which we have to determine. Take them to be (x_1, y_1, z_1) and (x_2, y_2, z_2).

PL is collinear with vector $\vec{A}$.

$\therefore \quad \vec{PL} = \lambda\,\vec{A}$

Comparing the coefficient of $\mathbf{i}, \mathbf{j}, \mathbf{k}$, we get

$$\frac{x_1 - 5}{3} = \frac{y_1 - 7}{-1} = \frac{z_1 + 2}{1} = \lambda \text{ say}$$

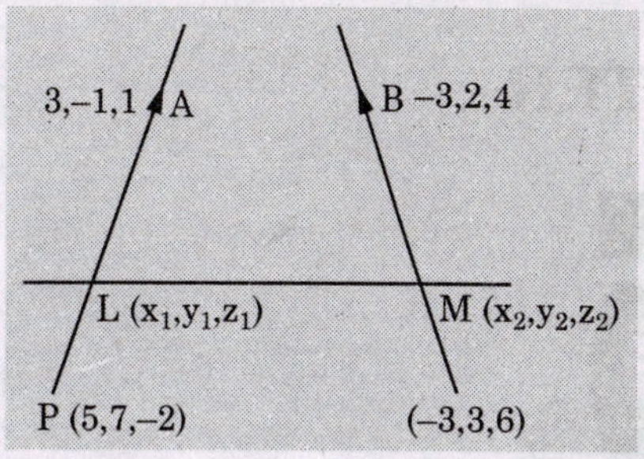

Fig. 50

L is $3\lambda + 5, -\lambda + 7, \lambda - 2.$

Similarly, $\vec{QM} = \mu\,\vec{B}$

$$\therefore \quad \frac{x_2 + 3}{-3} = \frac{y_2 - 3}{2} = \frac{z_2 - 6}{4} = \mu \text{ say}$$

$\therefore \quad M$ is $-3\mu - 3, 2\mu + 3, 4\mu + 6$

Again LM is collinear with vector $2, 7, -5$.

$$\therefore \quad \frac{x_2 - x_1}{2} = \frac{y_2 - y_1}{7} = \frac{z_2 - z_1}{-5} = \nu \text{ say}$$

$$\text{or} \quad \frac{-3\mu - 3\lambda - 8}{2} = \frac{2\mu + \lambda - 4}{7} = \frac{4\mu - \lambda + 8}{-5} = \nu$$

$$\text{or} \quad 3\mu + 3\lambda + 2\nu = -8$$
$$2\mu + \lambda - 7\nu = 4$$
$$4\mu - \lambda + 5\nu = -8$$

Eliminate λ and solve for μ and ν and then putting their values we get λ.

$\therefore \quad \lambda = \mu = \nu = -1$

$\therefore \quad$ Point L is $(2, 8, -3)$ or $2\mathbf{i} + 8\mathbf{j} - 3\mathbf{k}$

and M is $(0, 1, 2)$ or $\mathbf{j} + 2\mathbf{k}$.

58. In an equilateral triangle G and H coincide.

$\therefore \quad \frac{1}{3}(\mathbf{a} + \mathbf{b} + \mathbf{c}) = \mathbf{0}$ or $\mathbf{a} + \mathbf{b} + \mathbf{c} = \mathbf{0}.$

59. Ans. (a).

$\vec{OP} = \mathbf{a}\cos t + \mathbf{b}\sin t$

$M = |\vec{OP}| = |\,\mathbf{a}\cos t + \mathbf{b}\sin t\,|$

$\therefore \quad M^2 = 1.\cos^2 t + 1.\sin^2 t + 2\,\mathbf{a}\,.\,\mathbf{b}\sin t\cos t$

$= 1 + \mathbf{a}\,.\,\mathbf{b}\sin 2t$

$\therefore \quad$ Max. value of $M^2 = (1 + \mathbf{a}\,.\,\mathbf{b})$

when $\sin 2t = 1$ or $t = \pi/4$

$\therefore \quad M = (1 + \mathbf{a}\,.\,\mathbf{b})^{1/2}$

$\therefore \quad \mathbf{u} = (\mathbf{a} + \mathbf{b}) \cdot \frac{1}{\sqrt{2}}$ where $= t = \frac{\pi}{4}$

$$\therefore \quad \hat{\mathbf{u}} = \frac{(\mathbf{a} + \mathbf{b}) \cdot \frac{1}{\sqrt{2}}}{|\mathbf{a} + \mathbf{b}| \cdot \frac{1}{\sqrt{2}}} = \frac{\mathbf{a} + \mathbf{b}}{|\mathbf{a} + \mathbf{b}|}$$

❑

CHAPTER

25

Multiplication of Vectors

§ 1. Scalar Product or dot product.

(i) Definition. *The scalar product of two vectors* **a** *and* **b** *of module a and b respectively is equal to ab* $\cos\theta$ *where* θ *is the angle between the directions of* **a** *and* **b**.

This product is expressed as **a . b** *i.e.*, by putting a dot between the vectors **a** and **b**. $\therefore$ $\mathbf{a}.\mathbf{b} = ab\cos\theta$.

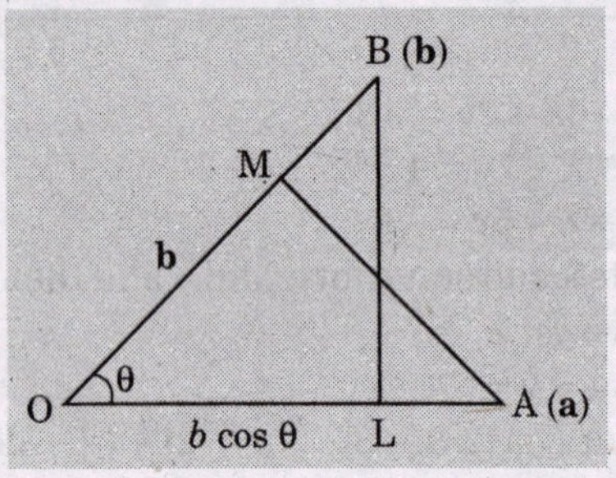

Fig. 1

(ii) Geometrical Interpretation of dot product.

OL is the projection of vector **b** in the direction of [See figure] vector **a** and $OL = b\cos\theta$

$\therefore$ $\mathbf{a}.\mathbf{b} = a(b\cos\theta) = OA.OL = a.p_1$

$= b(a\cos\theta) = OB.OM = b.p_2$.

Area of a rectangle whose sides are a and p_1 or b and p_2 *i.e.*, length of one vector and projection of other on it.

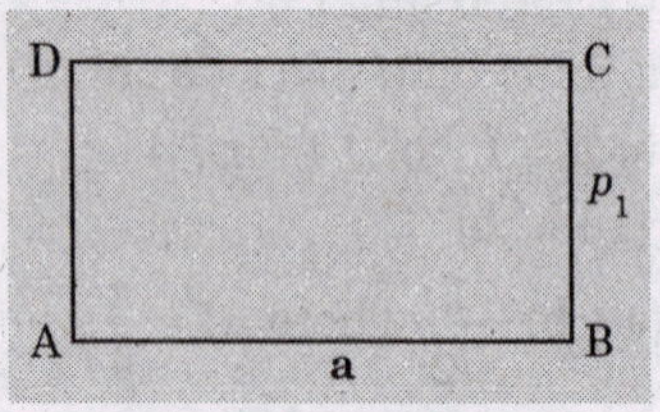

Fig. 2

i.e., **a . b** *is equal to the product of the length of one of them with the resolved part of the other (i.e. projection) in the direction of the other. Thus*

Projection of b in the direction of ***OA***

$$= OL = \frac{\mathbf{a}.\mathbf{b}}{|\mathbf{a}|}$$

$$\vec{OL} = \frac{\mathbf{a}.\mathbf{b}}{|\mathbf{a}|}\hat{\mathbf{a}} = \frac{\mathbf{a}.\mathbf{b}}{|\mathbf{a}|}\frac{\mathbf{a}}{|\mathbf{a}|} = \frac{\mathbf{a}.\mathbf{b}}{|\mathbf{a}|^2}\mathbf{a}$$

and **Projection of a in the direction of** ***OB***

$$= OM = \frac{\mathbf{a}.\mathbf{b}}{|\mathbf{b}|} \quad \text{and} \quad \vec{OM} = \frac{\mathbf{a}.\mathbf{b}}{|\mathbf{b}|^2}\mathbf{b}$$

(iii) Properties :

(a) **Commutative :** $\mathbf{a}.\mathbf{b} = \mathbf{b}.\mathbf{a} = ab\cos\theta$.

(b) If $\mathbf{a}.\mathbf{b} = 0$ then $ab\cos\theta = 0$ which implies either $a = 0$ or $b = 0$ or $\cos\theta = 0$ ($i.e. \theta = \pi/2$). Hence if the scalar product of two vectors is zero, then at least one of the vectors is a zero vector or they are perpendicular.

(c) If **a** and **b** are perpendicular vectors, then $\mathbf{a}.\mathbf{b} = 0$.

(d) $(m\mathbf{a}).(n\mathbf{b}) = (n\mathbf{a}).(m\mathbf{b}) = mn(\mathbf{a}.\mathbf{b})$

(e) $\mathbf{a}.\mathbf{a} = a.a\cos 0 = a^2$. This is written as $\mathbf{a}^2 = a^2$ or $\mathbf{a}^2 = |\mathbf{a}|^2$ *i.e.* square of a vector is equal to square of its module.

(f) **Distributive Law.** $\mathbf{a}.(\mathbf{b}+\mathbf{c}) = \mathbf{a}.\mathbf{b} + \mathbf{a}.\mathbf{c}$.

(g) **Orthonormal Triads. i, j, k unit vectors**

$$\mathbf{i}^2 = \mathbf{j}^2 = \mathbf{k}^2 = \mathbf{1}.$$

Also $\mathbf{i}.\mathbf{j} = 0$, $\mathbf{j}.\mathbf{k} = 0$, $\mathbf{k}.\mathbf{i} = 0$.

(h) **In terms of unit vectors,** let

$$\mathbf{a} = a_1\mathbf{i} + a_2\mathbf{j} + a_3\mathbf{k}, \quad \mathbf{b} = b_1\mathbf{i} + b_2\mathbf{j} + b_3\mathbf{k}.$$

$$\therefore \quad (\mathbf{a}.\mathbf{b}) = (a_1\mathbf{i} + a_2\mathbf{j} + a_3\mathbf{k}).(b_1\mathbf{i} + b_2\mathbf{j} + b_3\mathbf{k}).$$

$$= a_1b_1 + a_2b_2 + a_3b_3 = ab\cos\theta,$$

by relations in (g).

$$\therefore \quad \cos\theta = \frac{a_1b_1 + a_2b_2 + a_3b_3}{ab}$$

$$= \frac{\Sigma\, a_1b_1}{\sqrt{(\Sigma\, a_1^2)}.\sqrt{(\Sigma\, b_1^2)}}$$

(i) $(\mathbf{a}+\mathbf{b}+\mathbf{c}+\ldots\ldots\ldots).(\mathbf{p}+\mathbf{q}+\mathbf{r}+\ldots\ldots\ldots)$

$= (\mathbf{a}.\mathbf{p}+\mathbf{a}.\mathbf{q}+\mathbf{a}.\mathbf{r}+\ldots) + (\mathbf{b}.\mathbf{p}+\mathbf{b}.\mathbf{q}+\mathbf{b}.\mathbf{r}+\ldots)$

$+ (\mathbf{c}.\mathbf{p}+\mathbf{c}.\mathbf{q}+\mathbf{c}.\mathbf{r}+\ldots) + \ldots$

§ 2. The components of a vector r in the direction of a given vector a and perpendicular to a in the plane of r and a.

Let **b** be a vector perpendicular to **a** in the plane of **r** and **a**. We can express **r** uniquely in terms of **a** and **b**.

Let

$$\mathbf{r} = x\mathbf{a} + y\mathbf{b} \quad \text{...(1)}$$

Multiplying (1) scalarly with **a**, we obtain

$$\mathbf{r}\,.\,\mathbf{a} = x\,(\mathbf{a}\,.\,\mathbf{a}) + y\,(\mathbf{b}\,.\,\mathbf{a}) = x\mathbf{a}^2 \quad [\because\ \mathbf{b}\,.\,\mathbf{a} = 0]$$

$$\therefore \quad x = \frac{\mathbf{r}\,.\,\mathbf{a}}{|\mathbf{a}|^2}.$$

Putting this value of x in (1), we get

$$y\mathbf{b} = \mathbf{r} - \frac{\mathbf{r}\,.\,\mathbf{a}}{|\mathbf{a}|^2}\,\mathbf{a}$$

Thus the resolved parts of **r** in the direction of **a** and perpendicular to **a** are

$$\left(\frac{\mathbf{r}\,.\,\mathbf{a}}{|\mathbf{a}|^2}\right)\mathbf{a} \text{ and } \mathbf{r} - \left(\frac{\mathbf{r}\,.\,\mathbf{a}}{|\mathbf{a}|^2}\right)\mathbf{a} \text{ respectively.}$$

§ 3. Vector product or cross product.

(i) Definition. *The vector product of two non-null and non-parallel vectors* **a** and **b** *is a vector whose module is* $ab \sin\theta$, θ *being the angle between the directions of* **a** and **b** *and whose direction is that of a unit vector* $\hat{\mathbf{n}}$ *perpendicular to both* **a** and **b** *such that* **a**, **b**, $\hat{\mathbf{n}}$ *are in the right handed orientation. By the right handed*

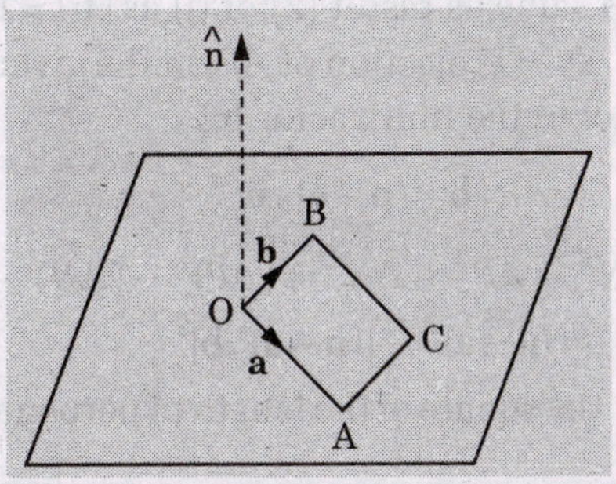

Fig. 3

orientiation we mean that if we turn the vector **a** *into the vector* **b**, *then,* **n** *will point in the direction in which a right-handed screw would move if turned in the same manner.*

Thus $\mathbf{a} \times \mathbf{b} = ab \sin\theta\, \hat{\mathbf{n}}$ where $\hat{\mathbf{n}}$ is a unit vector perpendicular to the plane of **a** and **b** such that **a**, **b**, $\hat{\mathbf{n}}$ form a right-handed orientation.

When **a** or **b** or both are null vectors or **a** is parallel to **b** then $\hat{\mathbf{n}}$ is not defined.

In this case, we agree to write $\mathbf{a} \times \mathbf{b} = \mathbf{0}$.

(ii) Geometrical Interpretation.

The modulus $ab \sin\theta$ of $\mathbf{a} \times \mathbf{b}$ is the area of the parallelogram whose adjacent sides are represented by **a** and **b** or it is twice the area of the triangle *OAB*.

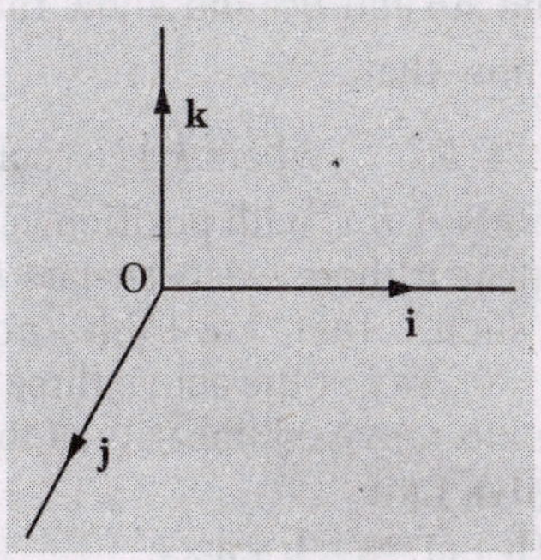

Fig. 4

(iii) Properties :

(a) **Vector Product is not commutative**

i.e. $\mathbf{a} \times \mathbf{b} \neq \mathbf{b} \times \mathbf{a}$ but $\mathbf{a} \times \mathbf{b} = -(\mathbf{b} \times \mathbf{a})$.

(b) $(m\mathbf{a}) \times \mathbf{b} = m\,(\mathbf{a} \times \mathbf{b}) = \mathbf{a} \times (m\mathbf{b})$.

(c) If the vectors are collinear, then

$$\mathbf{a} \times \mathbf{b} = \mathbf{0}, \quad \because\ \theta = 0 \text{ or } \pi.$$

As a consequence of above $\mathbf{a} \times \mathbf{a} = \mathbf{0}$.

(d) **Unit Vectors i, j, k.**

$$\mathbf{i} \times \mathbf{i} = \mathbf{j} \times \mathbf{j} = \mathbf{k} \times \mathbf{k} = \mathbf{0}$$

$$\mathbf{i} \times \mathbf{j} = \mathbf{k} = -\,\mathbf{j} \times \mathbf{i},\ \ \mathbf{j} \times \mathbf{k} = \mathbf{i} = -\,\mathbf{k} \times \mathbf{j},$$

$$\mathbf{k} \times \mathbf{i} = \mathbf{j} = -\,\mathbf{i} \times \mathbf{k}$$

$$\mathbf{i} \times \mathbf{j} \times \mathbf{k} \times \mathbf{i} \qquad \textbf{Representation}$$

$$= \mathbf{k} \quad \mathbf{i} \quad \mathbf{j}$$

(e) $\mathbf{a} \times \mathbf{b}$ in terms of unit vectors.

Let $\mathbf{a} = a_1\mathbf{i} + a_2\mathbf{j} + a_3\mathbf{k}$, $\therefore\ a = \sqrt{\Sigma\ a_1^2}$

$\mathbf{b} = b_1\mathbf{i} + b_2\mathbf{j} + b_3\mathbf{k}$, $\therefore\ b = \sqrt{\Sigma\ b_1^2}$

then $\mathbf{a} \times \mathbf{b} = (a_1\mathbf{i} + a_2\mathbf{j} + a_3\mathbf{k}) \times (b_1\mathbf{i} + b_2\mathbf{j} + b_3\mathbf{k})$

or $ab \sin\theta\, \hat{\mathbf{n}} = a_1b_2\,\mathbf{i} \times \mathbf{j} + a_1b_3\ \mathbf{i} \times \mathbf{k}$

$$+ a_2b_1\ \mathbf{j} \times \mathbf{i} + a_2b_3\ \mathbf{j} \times \mathbf{k} + a_3b_1\ \mathbf{k} \times \mathbf{i} + a_3b_2\ \mathbf{k} \times \mathbf{j}$$

$$= (a_2b_3 - a_3b_2)\,\mathbf{i} + (a_3b_1 - a_1b_3)\,\mathbf{j} + (a_1b_2 - a_2b_1)\,\mathbf{k} \quad \text{...(1)}$$

We have used the relations given in (d) above.

Above can be expressed in determinant form as

$$\mathbf{a} \times \mathbf{b} = \begin{vmatrix} \mathbf{i} & \mathbf{j} & \mathbf{k} \\ a_1 & a_2 & a_3 \\ b_1 & b_2 & b_3 \end{vmatrix}.$$

(f) **Sine of the angle between a and b.**

Squaring both sides of (1) and noting that $\hat{\mathbf{n}}^2 = 1$

$$a^2b^2 \sin^2\theta = \Sigma\ (a_2b_3 - a_3b_2)^2.$$

$$\therefore \quad \sin^2\theta = \frac{\Sigma\ (a_2b_3 - a_3b_2)^2}{\Sigma\ a_1^2\,.\,\Sigma\ b_1^2}.$$

(g) **Condition for vectors to be parallel.**

In this case $\mathbf{a} \times \mathbf{b} = \mathbf{0}$ as $\theta = 0$ or π and hence from (e) the last two rows of the determinant must have their corresponding elements proportional.

$\therefore \quad \dfrac{a_1}{b_1} = \dfrac{a_2}{b_2} = \dfrac{a_3}{b_3}.$

(h) **Condition for three points *A, B, C* to be collinear.**
Determine $\vec{AB}$ and $\vec{BC}$ and show that $\vec{AB} \times \vec{BC}$ is zero or show that

$\vec{AB} = k\,\vec{BC}.$ where k is a scalar.

(i) Three points A, B, C with position vectors as **a, b, c** are collinear if there exists scalars l, m, n (not all zeros) such that $l\mathbf{a} + m\mathbf{b} + n\mathbf{c} = 0$ where $l + m + n = 0$. Any of the above three methods can be chosen to prove collinearity of three points.

(j) **Distributive Law.**

$\mathbf{a} \times (\mathbf{b} + \mathbf{c}) = \mathbf{a} \times \mathbf{b} + \mathbf{a} \times \mathbf{c}.$

(k) **Distance of a point γ from a line $\mathbf{r} = \alpha + t\,\beta$.**
Let CL be the required perpendicular distance of C from the line passing through α and parallel to vector β. From the figure

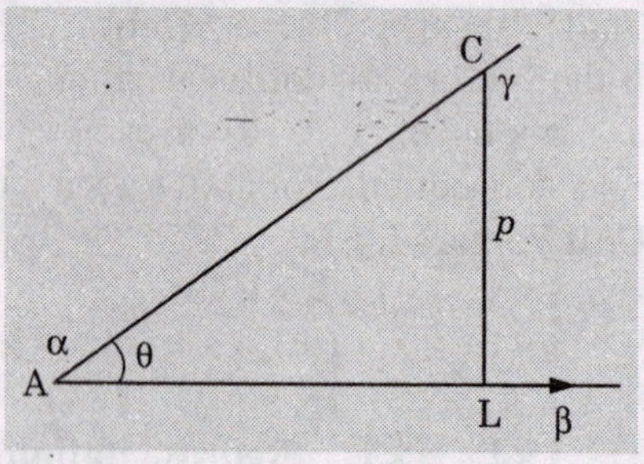

Fig. 5

$CL = AC \sin\theta$

$p = AC \sin\theta$ ...(1)

Now $\beta \times \vec{AC} = |\beta|\,AC \sin\theta\,\hat{\mathbf{n}}$

$\therefore \quad |\beta \times (\gamma - \alpha)| = |\beta|\,AC \sin\theta$

$\therefore \quad p = AC \sin\theta = \dfrac{|\beta \times (\gamma - \alpha)|}{|\beta|}$ ...(2)

(l) **Trigonometrical results by the help of vectors**
Sine rule, cosine rule, projection formulae and formula for $\sin(\alpha \pm \beta)$ and $\cos(\alpha \pm \beta)$ please see **Q. 74, 75 P. 1150-51.**

§ 4. To find the perpendicular distance of a given point from a given line.

Let the given line pass through a given point A (**a**) and be parallel to the **unit vector b** and let P (**p**) be the given point. From P draw PN perpendicular to the given line. Then

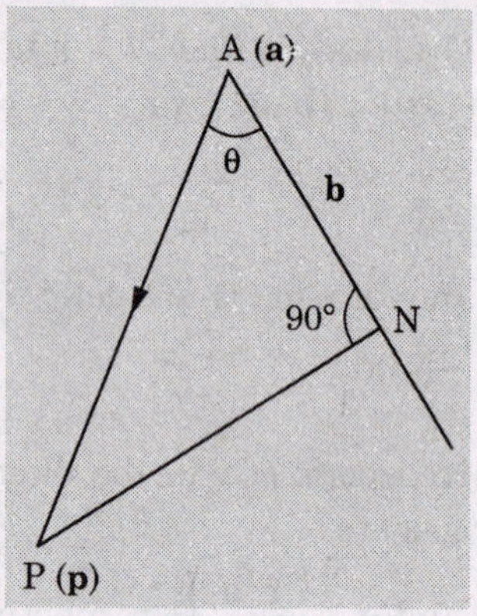

Fig. 6

$\vec{PA} = \mathbf{a} - \mathbf{p}$ or $\vec{AP} = \mathbf{p} - \mathbf{a}$

Now $\vec{AP} \times \mathbf{b} = |\vec{AP}|\,|\mathbf{b}| \sin\theta\,\hat{\mathbf{n}}$, where $\angle PAN = \theta$

or $\quad |\vec{AP} \times \mathbf{b}| = AP \sin\theta, \quad \because |\mathbf{b}| = 1.$

$\therefore \quad |(\mathbf{p} - \mathbf{a}) \times \mathbf{b}| = PN$

since $PN = AP \sin\theta$.

Thus required perpendicular distance

$PN = |(\mathbf{p} - \mathbf{a}) \times \mathbf{b}|$

Above is same as result (2) of (j) as $|\mathbf{b}| = 1$.

Aliter : AN = Projection of AP on the given line which is parallel to the unit vector **b**.

$= \vec{AP} \cdot \mathbf{b} = (\mathbf{p} - \mathbf{a}) \cdot \mathbf{b}$

Then $PN^2 = AP^2 - AN^2 = (\vec{AP})^2 - (\vec{AN})^2$

$= (\mathbf{p} - \mathbf{a})^2 - [(\mathbf{p} - \mathbf{a}) \cdot \mathbf{b}]^2$

which is the square of the length of perpendicular PN.

Problem Set (1)

Scalar and vector product of two vectors. Projection of a vector on another vector. Condition of two vectors being parallel or perpendicular. Area of triangle, parallelogram and quadrilateral.

1. (a) Find the cosine of the angle between the directions of the vectors

$\mathbf{a} = 4\mathbf{i} + 3\mathbf{j} + \mathbf{k}, \quad \mathbf{b} = 2\mathbf{i} - \mathbf{j} + 2\mathbf{k}.$

Also find a unit vector perpendicular to both **a** and **b**.

What is the sine of the angle between **a** and **b** ?

(b) The value of sine of the angle between the vectors $\mathbf{i} - 2\mathbf{j} + 3\mathbf{k}$ and $2\mathbf{i} + \mathbf{j} + \mathbf{k}$ is :

(a) $\dfrac{5}{21}$ (b) $\dfrac{5}{\sqrt{7}}$ (c) $\dfrac{5}{\sqrt{14}}$ (d) $\dfrac{5}{2\sqrt{7}}$

(AIEEE 2002)

(c) Two vectors **a** and **b** are expressed in terms of unit vectors as follows $\mathbf{a} = 3\mathbf{i} + \mathbf{j} + 2\mathbf{k}, \quad \mathbf{b} = 2\mathbf{i} - 2\mathbf{j} + 4\mathbf{k}$. What is the unit vector perpendicular to each of the vectors ? Also determine the sine of the angle between the given vectors.

(d) If $\mathbf{a} = a_1\mathbf{i} + a_2\mathbf{j} + a_3\mathbf{k}$ and $\mathbf{b} = b_1\mathbf{i} + b_2\mathbf{j} + b_3\mathbf{k}$, then prove the Lagrange's identity

$$(a_1^2 + a_2^2 + a_3^2)(b_1^2 + b_2^2 + b_3^2) - (a_1b_1 + a_2b_2 + a_3b_3)^2$$
$$= (a_1b_2 - a_2b_1)^2 + (a_2b_3 - a_3b_2)^2 + (a_3b_1 - a_1b_3)^2$$

2. (a) The vector $x\mathbf{i} + y\mathbf{j} + z\mathbf{k}$ makes with the plane of the two vectors 2, 3, – 1 and 1 – 1, 2 an acute angle $\cot^{-1}\sqrt{2}$ then show that $x(y+z) = yz$.

(b) If $\mathbf{a}, \mathbf{b}, \mathbf{c}$ be unit vectors which satisfy the following conditions $\mathbf{a}.\mathbf{b} = 0$, $\mathbf{a}.\mathbf{c} = 0$ and angle between $\mathbf{b}$ and $\mathbf{c}$ is $\pi/6$, then show that $\mathbf{a} = \pm 2(\mathbf{b} \times \mathbf{c})$.

(c) If the vector sum of **a** and **b** trisects the angle between them, show that the angle between the vectors **a** and **b** is $3\cos^{-1}\left(\frac{a}{2b}\right)$ where $|\mathbf{a}| = a$ and $|\mathbf{b}| = b, a > b$.

3. (a) $\mathbf{a} = \mathbf{i} + \mathbf{j} - \mathbf{k}$, $\mathbf{b} = -\mathbf{i} + 2\mathbf{j} + 2\mathbf{k}$ and $\mathbf{c} = -\mathbf{i} + 2\mathbf{j} - \mathbf{k}$, find a unit vector normal to the vectors $\mathbf{a} + \mathbf{b}$ and $\mathbf{b} - \mathbf{c}$. **(Roorkee 2000)**

(b) A unit vector normal to the plane through the points $\mathbf{i}, 2\mathbf{j}, 3\mathbf{k}$ is :

(a) $6\mathbf{i} + 3\mathbf{j} + 2\mathbf{k}$ (b) $\mathbf{i} + 2\mathbf{j} + 3\mathbf{k}$

(c) $\frac{6\mathbf{i} + 3\mathbf{j} + 2\mathbf{k}}{7}$ (d) $\frac{6\mathbf{i} + 3\mathbf{j} + 2\mathbf{k}}{9}$ **(AIEEE 2002)**

(c) If $\mathbf{a} = 2\mathbf{i} + 3\mathbf{j} + 6\mathbf{k}$, $\mathbf{b} = 3\mathbf{i} - 6\mathbf{j} + 2\mathbf{k}$ and $\mathbf{c} = 6\mathbf{i} + 2\mathbf{j} - 3\mathbf{k}$, show that $\mathbf{a} \times \mathbf{b} = 7\mathbf{c}$ and $\mathbf{b} \times \mathbf{c} = 7\mathbf{a}$.

Also prove that $\mathbf{a} \times (\mathbf{b} \times \mathbf{c}) = (\mathbf{a} \times \mathbf{b}) \times \mathbf{c} = \mathbf{0}$ in this case.

4. (a) Find the vector **r** which is perpendicular to $\mathbf{a} = \mathbf{i} - 2\mathbf{j} + 5\mathbf{k}$ and $\mathbf{b} = 2\mathbf{i} + 3\mathbf{j} - \mathbf{k}$ and $\mathbf{r}.(2\mathbf{i} + \mathbf{j} + \mathbf{k}) + 8 = 0$. **(Roorkee 2001)**

(b) Two vertices of a triangle are at $-\mathbf{i} + 3\mathbf{j}$ and $2\mathbf{i} + 5\mathbf{j}$ and its orthocentre is at $\mathbf{i} + 2\mathbf{j}$. Find the position vector of third vertex. **(Roorkee 2001)**

(c) The values of a for which points A, B, C with position vectors $2\mathbf{i} - \mathbf{j} + \mathbf{k}$, $\mathbf{i} - 3\mathbf{j} - 5\mathbf{k}$ and $a\mathbf{i} - 3\mathbf{j} + \mathbf{k}$ respectively are the vertices of a right angled triangle with $\angle C = \pi/2$ are :

(a) $-2, -1$ (b) $-2, 1$

(c) $2, -1$ (d) $2, 1$ **(AIEEE 2006)**

5. (a) By taking vectors **a** and **b** from either Ex. 3 or Ex. 1 prove that $\mathbf{a} \times \mathbf{b}$ is a vector which is perpendicular to both **a** and **b**.

(b) **a** and **b** are two vectors satisfying the condition $\mathbf{a} \times \mathbf{b} = \mathbf{0}$. Does it imply that one of the vectors **a** or **b** must be a null vector ? Give an example in support of your answer.

6. (a) Prove that a vector of magnitude 9 perpendicular to both the vectors

$\mathbf{a} = 4\mathbf{i} - \mathbf{j} + 3\mathbf{k}$ and $\mathbf{b} = -2\mathbf{i} + \mathbf{j} - 2\mathbf{k}$ is $-3\mathbf{i} + 6\mathbf{j} + 6\mathbf{k}$.

(b) $\mathbf{a}, \mathbf{b}, \mathbf{c}, \mathbf{d}$ are four distinct vectors satisfying the conditions $\mathbf{a} \times \mathbf{b} = \mathbf{c} \times \mathbf{d}$ and $\mathbf{a} \times \mathbf{c} = \mathbf{b} \times \mathbf{d}$, then prove that $\mathbf{a} \cdot \mathbf{b} + \mathbf{c} \cdot \mathbf{d} \neq \mathbf{a} \cdot \mathbf{c} + \mathbf{b} \cdot \mathbf{d}$. **(I.I.T. 2004)**

7. (a) Given $A = (1, 2, 5)$, $B = (5, 7, 9)$ and $C = (3, 2, -1)$. Find a unit vector normal to the plane of the triangle ABC.

(b) The unit vector perpendicular to the plane determined by

$P(1, -1, 2)$, $Q(2, 0, -1)$, $R(0, 2, 1)$ is...... **(I.I.T. 1994)**

(c) Let $\mathbf{u} = \mathbf{i} + \mathbf{j}$, $\mathbf{v} = \mathbf{i} - \mathbf{j}$ and $\mathbf{w} = \mathbf{i} + 2\mathbf{j} + 3\mathbf{k}$. If $\mathbf{n}$ is a unit vector such that $\mathbf{u}.\mathbf{n} = 0$ and $\mathbf{v}.\mathbf{n} = 0$ then $|\mathbf{w}.\mathbf{n}| =$

(a) 0 (b) 1

(c) 2 (d) 3 **(AIEEE 2003)**

8. (a) If **a** and **b** lie on a plane normal to the plane containing **c** and **d** show that $(\mathbf{a} \times \mathbf{b}).(\mathbf{c} \times \mathbf{d}) = 0$.

(b)* If the four vectors $\mathbf{a}, \mathbf{b}, \mathbf{c}, \mathbf{d}$ are coplanar, show that $(\mathbf{a} \times \mathbf{b}) \times (\mathbf{c} \times \mathbf{d}) = 0$

(c) Let the vectors $\mathbf{a}, \mathbf{b}, \mathbf{c}$ and $\mathbf{d}$ be such that $(\mathbf{a} \times \mathbf{b}) \times (\mathbf{c} \times \mathbf{d}) = \mathbf{0}$. Let P_1 and P_2 be planes determined by the pairs of vectors **a**, **b** and **c**, **d** respectively. Then the angle between P_1 and P_2 is

(a) 0 (b) $\frac{\pi}{4}$

(c) $\frac{\pi}{3}$ (d) $\frac{\pi}{2}$ **(I.I.T. Sc. 2000)**

9. (a) If $\mathbf{A} = 2\mathbf{i} + 2\mathbf{j} + 3\mathbf{k}$, $\mathbf{B} = -\mathbf{i} + 2\mathbf{j} + \mathbf{k}$ and $\mathbf{C} = 3\mathbf{i} + \mathbf{j}$, and $\mathbf{A} + t\mathbf{B}$ is perpendicular to $\mathbf{C}$ then determine t.

(b)* Find the value of the constant S such that the scalar product of the vector $\mathbf{i} + \mathbf{j} + \mathbf{k}$ with the unit vector parallel to the sum of the vectors $2\mathbf{i} + 4\mathbf{j} - 5\mathbf{k}$ and $S\mathbf{i} + 2\mathbf{j} + 3\mathbf{k}$ is equal to one. **(M.N.R. 1992)**

(c) Find λ, if the vectors $2\mathbf{i} + \mathbf{j} + \mathbf{k}$ and $\mathbf{i} - 4\mathbf{j} + \lambda\mathbf{k}$ are mutually perpendicular.

10. (a) T_p, T_q and T_r of a G.P. are +ive numbers a, b, c respectively. Prove that the vectors

$$\alpha = \mathbf{i}\log a + \mathbf{j}\log b + \mathbf{k}\log c$$
$$\beta = \mathbf{i}(q - r) + \mathbf{j}(r - p) + \mathbf{k}(p - q)$$

are perpendicular. **(Dhanbad 1992)**

(b)* Let $\mathbf{a} = 2\mathbf{i} + \mathbf{k}$, $\mathbf{b} = \mathbf{i} + \mathbf{j} + \mathbf{k}$ and $\mathbf{c} = 4\mathbf{i} - 3\mathbf{j} + 7\mathbf{k}$. Find vector **r** which satisfies $\mathbf{r} \times \mathbf{b} = \mathbf{c} \times \mathbf{b}$ and $\mathbf{r}.\mathbf{a} = 0$. **(I.I.T. 1990)**

(c) Prove that a vector **r** which satisfies $\mathbf{r} \times \mathbf{b} = \mathbf{c} \times \mathbf{b}$ and $\mathbf{r}.\mathbf{a} = 0$ is $\mathbf{c} - \left(\frac{\mathbf{c}.\mathbf{a}}{\mathbf{b}.\mathbf{a}}\right)\mathbf{b}$.

11.* (a) Determine the values of c so that for all real x, the vectors $cx\mathbf{i} - 6\mathbf{j} + 3\mathbf{k}$ and $x\mathbf{i} + 2\mathbf{j} + 2cx\mathbf{k}$ make an obtuse angle with each other. **(I.I.T. 1991)**

(b) The angle between the vectors $\mathbf{a} = \lambda\mathbf{i} - 3\mathbf{j} - \mathbf{k}$ and $\mathbf{b} = 2\lambda\mathbf{i} + \lambda\mathbf{j} - \mathbf{k}$ is acute, whereas the vector **b** makes with the axes of co-ordinates an obtuse angle. Determine λ.

(c) Find the domain of λ for which the vector $\mathbf{r} = (\lambda^2 - 4)\mathbf{i} + 2\mathbf{j} + (\lambda^2 - 9)\mathbf{k}$ makes acute angles with the co-ordinate axes.

(d) Show that a unit vector making an obtuse angle with x-axis and perpendicular to the plane containing the points $A(1, 2, 3)$, $B(2, 3, 4)$, $C(1, 5, 7)$ also makes an obtuse angle with z-axis.

12.* (a) The vectors $\mathbf{a} = 2\lambda^2\mathbf{i} + 4\lambda\mathbf{j} + \mathbf{k}$ and $\mathbf{b} = 7\mathbf{i} - 2\mathbf{j} + \lambda\mathbf{k}$ make an obtuse angle whereas the angle between $\mathbf{b}$ and $\mathbf{k}$ is acute and less than $\pi/6$, then determine the domain of λ.

(b) Find λ and μ if the vectors $\mathbf{a} = 3\mathbf{i} + \lambda\mathbf{j} - \mathbf{k}$ is perpendicular to the vector $\mathbf{b} = 2\mathbf{i} + \mathbf{j} + \mu\mathbf{k}$ and $|\mathbf{a}| = |\mathbf{b}|$.

(c) If the vectors $\mathbf{a} = \lambda \log_2 x, -6, 3$ and $\mathbf{b} = \log_2 x, 2, 2\lambda \log_2 x$ make an obtuse angle for any $x \in (0, \infty)$ then show that λ belongs to $(-4/3, 0)$.

(d) Find the values of x for which the angle between the vectors $\mathbf{a} = x, -3, -1$ and $\mathbf{b} = 2x, x, -1$ is acute and the angle between the vector $\mathbf{b}$ and y-axis is obtuse.

(e) The unit vectors $\mathbf{a}, \mathbf{b}, \mathbf{c}$ are such that $\mathbf{a}$ and $\mathbf{b}$ are perpendicular and $\mathbf{c}$ is inclined at an angle θ to both $\mathbf{a}$ and $\mathbf{b}$. If $\mathbf{c} = p\mathbf{a} + q\mathbf{b} + r(\mathbf{a} \times \mathbf{b})$ then prove that $p^2 = q^2 = \frac{1 - r^2}{2} = \cos^2 \theta$.

13. (a) If $\mathbf{r} = x\mathbf{i} + y\mathbf{j} + z\mathbf{k}$, then $(\mathbf{r} \times \mathbf{i}) . (\mathbf{r} \times \mathbf{j}) + xy =$

(a) 0 (b) 1
(c) xy (d) $\mathbf{i} \times \mathbf{j}$ **(AIEEE 2002)**

(b) Let the position vectors of the points P, A and B be $\mathbf{r}$, $\mathbf{i} + \mathbf{j} + \mathbf{k}$ and $-\mathbf{i} + \mathbf{k}$. If PA is perpendicular to PB but $\mathbf{r}$ is not perpendicular to $\mathbf{r} - (\mathbf{j} + 2\mathbf{k})$, then $\mathbf{r}$ is :

(a) $\mathbf{i} + 2\mathbf{k}$ (b) $\mathbf{i} + 2\mathbf{j}$
(c) $\mathbf{j} - 2\mathbf{k}$ (d) $\mathbf{j} + 2\mathbf{k}$

(c) Let $\mathbf{r} \times \mathbf{a} = \mathbf{b} \times \mathbf{a}$ and $\mathbf{r} . \mathbf{c} = 0$ where $\mathbf{a} . \mathbf{c} \neq 0$ then $(\mathbf{a} . \mathbf{c})(\mathbf{r} \times \mathbf{b}) + (\mathbf{b} . \mathbf{c})(\mathbf{a} \times \mathbf{r}) =$

(a) $\mathbf{c}$ (b) $(\mathbf{a} . \mathbf{b})\,\mathbf{c}$
(c) $(\mathbf{a} \times \mathbf{b}) \times \mathbf{c}$ (d) 0

14.* (a) The vector $\vec{B} = 3\mathbf{j} + 4\mathbf{k}$ is to be written as the sum of a vector $\vec{B}_1$ parallel to $\vec{A} = \mathbf{i} + \mathbf{j}$ and a vector $\vec{B}_2$ perpendicular to $\vec{A}$. Then $\vec{B}_1 = \frac{3}{2}(\mathbf{i} + \mathbf{j})$. **(M.N.R. 1993)**

(b)* If $\mathbf{a} = \mathbf{i} + \mathbf{j} + \mathbf{k}$, $\mathbf{b} = 4\mathbf{i} + 3\mathbf{j} + 4\mathbf{k}$ and $\mathbf{c} = \mathbf{i} + \alpha\mathbf{j} + \beta\mathbf{k}$ are linearly dependent vectors and $|\mathbf{c}| = \sqrt{3}$, then

(a) $\alpha = 1, \beta = -1$ (b) $\alpha = 1, \beta = \pm 1$
(c) $\alpha = -1, \beta = \pm 1$ (d) $\alpha = \pm 1, \beta = 1$ **(I.I.T. 1998)**

(c) Show that the vectors

$$\mathbf{a} = \frac{1}{7}(2\mathbf{i} + 3\mathbf{j} + 6\mathbf{k}),\quad \mathbf{b} = \frac{1}{7}(3\mathbf{i} - 6\mathbf{j} + 2\mathbf{k}),$$

$\mathbf{c} = \frac{1}{7}(6\mathbf{i} + 2\mathbf{j} - 3\mathbf{k})$ form an orthonormal triad. Also find two vectors of magnitude 3 each being normal to the plane containing the vectors $\mathbf{a}$ and $\mathbf{b}$.

(d) Let α, β, γ be distinct real numbers. Prove that the points with position vectors $\alpha\mathbf{i} + \beta\mathbf{j} + \gamma\mathbf{k}$, $\beta\mathbf{i} + \gamma\mathbf{j} + \alpha\mathbf{k}$, $\gamma\mathbf{i} + \alpha\mathbf{j} + \beta\mathbf{k}$ form an equilatereal triangle. **(Screening 1994)**

15. (a) Prove that the points

$$2\mathbf{i} - \mathbf{j} + \mathbf{k},\quad \mathbf{i} - 3\mathbf{j} - 5\mathbf{k},\quad 3\mathbf{i} - 4\mathbf{j} - 4\mathbf{k}$$

are the vertices of a right angled triangle. Find also the other two angles.

(b)* Find a vector of magnitude $\sqrt{51}$ which makes equal angles with the vectors

$$\mathbf{a} = \frac{1}{3}(\mathbf{i} - 2\mathbf{j} + 2\mathbf{k}),\quad \mathbf{b} = \frac{1}{5}(-4\mathbf{i} - 3\mathbf{k}) \text{ and } \mathbf{c} = \mathbf{j}$$

16. (a)* The vector $\vec{OA} = \mathbf{i} + 2\mathbf{j} + 2\mathbf{k}$ turns through a right angle passing through the +ive x-axis on the way. Determine the vector in its new position.

(b) The vector $OP = 5\mathbf{i} + 12\mathbf{j} + 13\mathbf{k}$ turns through a right angle about O passing through the +ive side of y-axis on its way. Find the vector in its new position.

(c) Three vectors $\mathbf{a}, \mathbf{b}, \mathbf{c}$ are such that they are of equal magnitude and angle between each pair is same. If $\mathbf{a} = \mathbf{i} + \mathbf{j}$ and $\mathbf{b} = \mathbf{j} + \mathbf{k}$, then determine the vector $\mathbf{c}$.

(d) The vectors $\mathbf{a}, \mathbf{b}, \mathbf{c}$ of equal magnitude are such that taken pairwise they make equal angles. If $\mathbf{a} = \mathbf{i} + \mathbf{j}$, $\mathbf{b} = \mathbf{j} + \mathbf{k}$ and $\mathbf{c}$ makes an obtuse angle with x-axis then prove that $\mathbf{c} = \frac{1}{3}(-\mathbf{i} + 4\mathbf{j} - \mathbf{k})$.

17. (a) In parallelogram $ABCD$ the interior bisectors of the consecutive angles B and C intersect in P. Use vector methods to find $\angle BPC$. **(Roorkee 1992)**

(b) If $\mathbf{v}$ is the unit vector along the incident ray, $\mathbf{w}$ is the unit vector along the reflected ray and $\mathbf{a}$ is the unit vector outward normal to the plane at point P, express $\mathbf{w}$ in terms of $\mathbf{a}$ and $\mathbf{v}$. **(I.I.T. 2005)**

(c)* If $\mathbf{a}, \mathbf{b}, \mathbf{c}, \mathbf{d}$ be the position vectors of the vertices of a cyclic quadrilateral $ABCD$, then show that

$$\frac{|\mathbf{a} \times \mathbf{b} + \mathbf{b} \times \mathbf{d} + \mathbf{d} \times \mathbf{a}|}{(\mathbf{b} - \mathbf{a}) . (\mathbf{d} - \mathbf{a})} + \frac{|\mathbf{b} \times \mathbf{c} + \mathbf{c} \times \mathbf{a} + \mathbf{d} \times \mathbf{b}|}{(\mathbf{b} - \mathbf{c}) . (\mathbf{d} - \mathbf{c})} = 0$$

18. (a) The position vector of the points A, B, C, D are $\mathbf{i} + \mathbf{j} + \mathbf{k}$, $2\mathbf{i} + 3\mathbf{j}$, $3\mathbf{i} + 5\mathbf{j} - 2\mathbf{k}$, $\mathbf{k} - \mathbf{j}$ respectively. Show that AB and CD are parallel.

(b) The position vectors of A, B, C, D with respect to the origin are respectively

$$2\mathbf{i} + 3\mathbf{j} + 5\mathbf{k},\ \mathbf{i} + 2\mathbf{j} + 3\mathbf{k},\ -5\mathbf{i} + 4\mathbf{j} - 2\mathbf{k},\ \mathbf{i} + 10\mathbf{j} + 10\mathbf{k}.$$

Show that AB and CD are parallel.

19. (a)* The position vectors $\mathbf{a}, \mathbf{b}, \mathbf{c}$ and $\mathbf{d}$ of four points A, B, C and D on a plane are such that $(\mathbf{a} - \mathbf{d}) . (\mathbf{b} - \mathbf{c}) = (\mathbf{b} - \mathbf{d}) . (\mathbf{c} - \mathbf{a}) = \mathbf{0}$, then the point D is the orthocentre of ΔABC. Is this true ?

(b) The position vectors of four points A, B, C, D lying in a plane are $\mathbf{a}, \mathbf{b}, \mathbf{c}, \mathbf{d}$ respectively. They satisfy the relation $|\mathbf{a} - \mathbf{d}| = |\mathbf{b} - \mathbf{d}| = |\mathbf{c} - \mathbf{d}|$ then the point D is circumcentre of ΔABC. Is this statement true or false ?

20. (a) P, Q, R, S are the points $\mathbf{i}-\mathbf{k}$, $-\mathbf{i}+2\mathbf{j}$, $2\mathbf{i}-3\mathbf{k}$ and $3\mathbf{i}-2\mathbf{j}-\mathbf{k}$ respectively, Show that the projection of PQ on RS is equal to that of RS on PQ each being $-4/3$. Also find the cosine of their inclination.

(b) Let $\mathbf{u}, \mathbf{v}, \mathbf{w}$ be such that $|\mathbf{u}|=1, |\mathbf{v}|=2$ and $|\mathbf{w}|=3$. If the projection of $\mathbf{v}$ along $\mathbf{u}$ is equal to that of $\mathbf{w}$ along $\mathbf{u}$ and $\mathbf{v}, \mathbf{w}$ are perpendicular to each other then $|\mathbf{u}-\mathbf{v}+\mathbf{w}|=$

(a) 2 (b) $\sqrt{7}$
(c) $\sqrt{14}$ (d) 14 **(AIEEE 2004)**

(c) $\mathbf{a}=\hat{\mathbf{i}}+\hat{\mathbf{j}}-\hat{\mathbf{k}}$, $\mathbf{b}=\hat{\mathbf{i}}-2\hat{\mathbf{j}}+\hat{\mathbf{k}}$, $\mathbf{c}=\hat{\mathbf{i}}-\hat{\mathbf{j}}-\hat{\mathbf{k}}$, then a vector in plane of $\mathbf{a}$ and $\mathbf{b}$ whose projection on $\mathbf{c}$ is of magnitude $\left(\frac{1}{\sqrt{3}}\right)$ is given by

(a) $2\hat{\mathbf{i}}-3\hat{\mathbf{j}}+2\hat{\mathbf{k}}$ (b) $4\hat{\mathbf{i}}-7\hat{\mathbf{j}}+4\hat{\mathbf{k}}$
(c) $4\hat{\mathbf{i}}-2\hat{\mathbf{j}}+2\hat{\mathbf{k}}$ (d) $4\hat{\mathbf{i}}+13\hat{\mathbf{j}}-10\hat{\mathbf{k}}$ **(I.I.T. 2006)**

(d)* Find the distance of the point $B(\mathbf{i}+2\mathbf{j}+3\mathbf{k})$ from the line which is passing through $A(4\mathbf{i}+2\mathbf{j}+2\mathbf{k})$ and which is parallel to the vector $\vec{C}=2\mathbf{i}+3\mathbf{j}+6\mathbf{k}$. **(Roorkee 1993)**

21. (a) Find the perpendicular distance of $A(1, 4, -2)$ from the line BC where the co-ordinates of B and C are $(2, 1, -2)$ and $(0, -5, 1)$ respectively.

(b) In ΔABC of part 21 (a) if M be the foot of perpendicular from the vertex A to the base BC, then find the co-ordinates of M.

(c) The vertices A, B, C of a triangle are $(4, 2, 3)$, $(1, 3, 1)$ and $(-5, 5, -2)$. Find the length of perpendicular drawn from A on BC.

22. (a) A line l is passing through the point $\mathbf{b}$ and is parallel to vector $\mathbf{c}$. Determine the distance of the point $A(\mathbf{a})$ from the line l in the form

$$\left[\mathbf{b}+\frac{(\mathbf{a}-\mathbf{b}).\mathbf{c}}{\mathbf{c}^2}\mathbf{c}-\mathbf{a}\right] \text{ or } \left[\frac{(\mathbf{b}-\mathbf{a})\times\mathbf{c}}{|\mathbf{c}|}\right]$$

(b) In the figure **V-64** on **P. 1136** AD is perpendicular to BC. Prove that the foot D of perpendicular is $\left(\frac{2}{3}, -\frac{1}{3}, \frac{5}{3}\right)$ and its length is $\frac{1}{\sqrt{3}}$.

23. Prove that the perpendicular distance of a corner of a unit cube from the diagonal not passing through it is $\frac{1}{3}\sqrt{6}$.

24. (a) Find the projection of $\mathbf{b}=2\mathbf{i}+3\mathbf{j}-2\mathbf{k}$ in the direction of vector $\mathbf{a}=\mathbf{i}+2\mathbf{j}+3\mathbf{k}$. What is the vector determined by the projection ?

(b) The projection of the vector $\mathbf{i}-2\mathbf{j}+\mathbf{k}$ on the vector $4\mathbf{i}-4\mathbf{j}+7\mathbf{k}$ is 19/9.

25. (a) If $\mathbf{a}=4\mathbf{i}+6\mathbf{j}$ and $\mathbf{b}=3\mathbf{j}+4\mathbf{k}$, find the vector form of the component of $\mathbf{a}$ along $\mathbf{b}$.

(b) Let $\beta=4\mathbf{i}+3\mathbf{j}$ and γ be two vectors perpendicular to each other in the x-y plane. All the vectors in the same plane having projections 1 and 2 along β and γ respectively are given by ....

▸ Geometrical Problems

26. (a) Prove by vector method that in a right angled triangle ABC, $AB^2+AC^2=BC^2$, angle A being a right angle. Also prove that mid-point of the hypotenuse is equidistant from the vertices.

(b) If P be the middle point of the side BC of a triangle ABC prove that

$$AB^2+AC^2=2(AP^2+BP^2).$$ **(J.E.E.W.B. 1991)**

(c) Prove that the medians to the base of an isosceles triangle is perpendicular to the base.

(d) The sides a, b, c of a triangle ABC are connected by the relation $a^2+b^2=5c^2$. Prove by vector method that the medians drawn to the sides a and b are perpendicular.

(e) If $A_1, A_2, \ldots, A_n$ be n points on a circle of unit radius then prove that $\sum_{i=1}^{n}\sum_{j=1}^{n} A_i A_j \le n^2$.

27. (a) Show that in a parallelogram the sum of the squares on the diagonals is twice the sum of the squares on two adjacent sides or sum of the squares on all the sides.

(b) The difference of the squares on the diagonals is four times the rectangle contained by either of these sides and the projection of the other upon it.

(c) The difference of the squares on two adjacent sides is equal to the rectangle contained by either diagonal and the projection of the other upon it.

28. (a) Prove that the parallelogram whose diagonals are equal is a rectangle.

(b)* Prove that the diagonals of a rhombus are at right angles.

29. Prove that the angle in a semi-circle is right angle.

30. If two medians of a triangle are equal, the triangle is isosceles.

31.* (a) Prove that in any triangle, the perpendiculars from the vertices upon the opposite sides are concurrent.

(b) Prove that the right bisectors of the sides of a triangle are concurrent.

32. Let ABC and PQR be any two triangles in the same plane. Assume that the perpendiculars from the points A, B, C to the sides QR, RP, PQ respectively are concurrent. Using vector methods or otherwise, prove that the perpendiculars from P, Q, R to BC, CA, AB respectively are also concurrent. **(I.I.T. 2000)**

33. (a) If O be the circumcentre; G, the centroid and H, the orthocentre of triangle ABC, prove that O, G, H are collinear and G divides OH in the ratio $1:2$.

(b) O, G, H are the circumcentre, centroid and orthocentre of a ΔABC whose vertices are the points $\mathbf{a}, \mathbf{b}, \mathbf{c}$ w.r.t. O as origin; then prove that $\mathbf{a} + \mathbf{b} + \mathbf{c} = OH$.

34. (a) In a quadrilateral $ABCD$, prove that $AB^2 + BC^2 + CD^2 + DA^2 = AC^2 + BD^2 + 4PQ^2$ where P and Q are the middle points of the diagonals AC and BD.

(b) Prove that in a parallelopiped the sum of the squares on the diagonals is equal to four times the sum of the squares on three coterminous edges.

35.* (a) Prove that in a tetrahedron if two pairs of opposite edges are perpendicular, the third pair is also perpendicular. Also show that sum of the squares on two opposite edges is the same for each pair for such a tetrahedron.

(b) Prove that any two opposite edges of a regular tetrahedron are perpendicular.

36. (a) Find the equation of the plane passing through the point $A(3, -2, 1)$ and perpendicular to the vector $4\mathbf{i} + 7\mathbf{j} - 4\mathbf{k}$. If PM be the perpendicular from the point $P(1, 2, -1)$ to this plane, find its length.

(b) Find the distance of $P(\mathbf{i} + \mathbf{j} + \mathbf{k})$ from the plane L which passes through the three points $A(2\mathbf{i} + \mathbf{j} + \mathbf{k})$, $B(\mathbf{i} + 2\mathbf{j} + \mathbf{k})$, $C(\mathbf{i} + \mathbf{j} + 2\mathbf{k})$. Also find the position vector of the foot of perpendicular from P on the plane L. **(Roorkee 1992)**

37. (a) If the perpendicular drawn from $P(1, 2, 0)$ to the plane $\mathbf{r} \cdot (3\mathbf{i} - \mathbf{j} + \mathbf{k}) = 2$ meets it at M then find the point M and distance MP.

(b)* The co-ordinates of three points A, B, C are respectively $(2, 1, 3), (-1, 2, 4)$ and $(0, 2, 1)$. Determine the equation of plane ABC and its point of intersection with line $\mathbf{r} = (\mathbf{i} - \mathbf{j} + \mathbf{k}) + \lambda (2\mathbf{i} + \mathbf{k})$.

38.* (a) Let points P, Q and R have position vectors $\mathbf{r}_1 = 3\mathbf{i} - 2\mathbf{j} - \mathbf{k}$, $\mathbf{r}_2 = \mathbf{i} + 3\mathbf{j} + 4\mathbf{k}$ and $\mathbf{r}_3 = 2\mathbf{i} + \mathbf{j} - 2\mathbf{k}$ relative to an origin O. Find the distance of P from the plane OQR. **(Roorkee 1990)**

(b) The vertices of a triangle ABC are $(4, 2, 3)$; $(1, 3, 1)$ and $(-5, 5, -2)$ respectively. Find the length of the perpendicular drawn from origin O to plane of ΔABC.

39.* Determine the equation of plane through the point $\mathbf{a} = (\mathbf{i} + 2\mathbf{j} - \mathbf{k})$ and perpendicular to the line of intersection of planes $\mathbf{r} \cdot (3\mathbf{i} - \mathbf{j} + \mathbf{k}) = 1$ and $\mathbf{r} \cdot (\mathbf{i} + 4\mathbf{j} - 2\mathbf{k}) = 2$.

40. (a) The equations of the lines l_1, l_2, l_3 are

$l_1 : \mathbf{r} = (4\mathbf{i} - \mathbf{j} + 2\mathbf{k}) + \lambda (6\mathbf{i} - 4\mathbf{j} + 2\mathbf{k})$

$l_2 : \mathbf{r} = (9\mathbf{i} - 3\mathbf{j} + 5\mathbf{k}) + \mu (2\mathbf{i} - \mathbf{j} + \mathbf{k})$

$l_3 : \mathbf{r} = (\mathbf{i} + \mathbf{j} - \mathbf{k}) + \nu (\mathbf{j} - \mathbf{k})$

then prove the following :

(i) The lines l_1 and l_2 intersect at $\mathbf{i} + \mathbf{j} + \mathbf{k}$.

(ii) The lines l_1 and l_3 do not intersect.

(iii) The equation of the plane containing the lines l_1 and l_2 is $\mathbf{r} \cdot (\mathbf{i} + \mathbf{j} - \mathbf{k}) = 1$

(b) Let $P(3, 2, 6)$ be a point in space and Q be a point on the line $\mathbf{r} = (\hat{\mathbf{i}} - \hat{\mathbf{j}} + 2\hat{\mathbf{k}}) + \mu(-3\hat{\mathbf{i}} + \hat{\mathbf{j}} + 5\hat{\mathbf{k}})$. Then the value of μ for which the vector $\overline{PQ}$ is parallel to the plane $x - 4y + 3z = 1$ is

(a) $\frac{1}{4}$ (b) $-\frac{1}{4}$

(c) $\frac{1}{8}$ (d) $-\frac{1}{8}$ **(I.I.T. 2009)**

41. (a)* If $|\mathbf{a} + \mathbf{b}| = |\mathbf{a} - \mathbf{b}|$, then show that $\mathbf{a}$ and $\mathbf{b}$ are perpendicular. **(Karnatak C.E.E. 1999)**

(b)* If the sum of two unit vectors be a unit vector then angle between them is $\frac{2\pi}{3}$. Also prove that the modulus of their difference is $\sqrt{3}$. **(M.P.C.E.E. 1999)**

(c) If $|\mathbf{a} + \mathbf{b}| = |\mathbf{a}|$, then prove that $2\mathbf{a} + \mathbf{b}$ is perpendicular to $\mathbf{b}$.

42.* (a) Prove that $|\mathbf{i} \times \mathbf{a}|^2 + |\mathbf{j} \times \mathbf{a}|^2 + |\mathbf{k} \times \mathbf{a}|^2 = 2\mathbf{a}^2$.

(b) If $\mathbf{a}$, $\mathbf{b}$ and $\mathbf{c}$ are unit vectors, then $|\mathbf{a} - \mathbf{b}|^2 + |\mathbf{b} - \mathbf{c}|^2 + |\mathbf{c} - \mathbf{a}|^2$ does not exceed

(a) 4 (b) 9

(c) 8 (d) 6 **(I.I.T. Sc. 2001)**

43. (a) Prove that $\left(\frac{\mathbf{a}}{a^2} - \frac{\mathbf{b}}{b^2}\right)^2 = \left(\frac{\mathbf{a} - \mathbf{b}}{ab}\right)^2$.

(b)* If $\mathbf{a}$ and $\mathbf{b}$ are unit vectors and θ is the angle between them, show that

$$\sin \frac{\theta}{2} = \frac{1}{2} |\mathbf{a} - \mathbf{b}|.$$

44. (a) If $\mathbf{a}, \mathbf{b}, \mathbf{c}$ are unit vectors such that $\mathbf{a} + \mathbf{b} + \mathbf{c} = \mathbf{0}$, then, $\mathbf{a} \cdot \mathbf{b} + \mathbf{b} \cdot \mathbf{c} + \mathbf{c} \cdot \mathbf{a} = ...$

(b) $\cos 2A + \cos 2B + \cos 2C \geq -3/2$.

45. (a) Show that if $\mathbf{a} + 2\mathbf{b} + 3\mathbf{c} = 0$, then $\mathbf{a} \times \mathbf{b} + \mathbf{b} \times \mathbf{c} + \mathbf{c} \times \mathbf{a}$ is equal to $6(\mathbf{b} \times \mathbf{c})$ or $2(\mathbf{a} \times \mathbf{b})$ or $3(\mathbf{c} \times \mathbf{a})$.

(b) If $|\mathbf{a}| = |\mathbf{b}|$, then $(\mathbf{a} + \mathbf{b}) \cdot (\mathbf{a} - \mathbf{b})$ is zero.

46. (a) If $\mathbf{a}$ and $\mathbf{b}$ are two unit vectors inclined at an angle 2θ to each other, then $|\mathbf{a} + \mathbf{b}| < 1$ if $\frac{\pi}{3} < \theta < \frac{2\pi}{3}$.

(b) If the unit vectors $\mathbf{a}$ and $\mathbf{b}$ are inclined at an angle 2θ such that $|\mathbf{a} - \mathbf{b}| < 1$ and $0 \leq \theta \leq \pi$, then show that θ lies in the interval $[0, \pi/6)$ and $(5\pi/6, \pi]$.

47. (a) If $\mathbf{a}, \mathbf{b}, \mathbf{c}$ are non-coplanar vectors and $\mathbf{n} \cdot \mathbf{a} = \mathbf{n} \cdot \mathbf{b} = \mathbf{n} \cdot \mathbf{c} = 0$, show that $\mathbf{n}$ is a null vector.

(b)* If $\mathbf{X} \cdot \mathbf{A} = 0$, $\mathbf{X} \cdot \mathbf{B} = 0$, $\mathbf{X} \cdot \mathbf{C} = 0$ for some non-zero vector $\mathbf{X}$, then prove that $[\mathbf{A}\,\mathbf{B}\,\mathbf{C}] = 0$.

(c) If a straight line is equally inclined to three coplanar straight lines, prove that it is perpendicular to their plane.

48. (a) If $\mathbf{a}, \mathbf{b}, \mathbf{c}$ are mutually perpendicular vectors of equal magnitude, show that $\mathbf{a} + \mathbf{b} + \mathbf{c}$ is equally inclined to $\mathbf{a}$, $\mathbf{b}$ and $\mathbf{c}$.

(b)* If $|\mathbf{a}|=3, |\mathbf{b}|=5, |\mathbf{c}|=7$ and $\mathbf{a}+\mathbf{b}+\mathbf{c}=0$. Prove that the angle between **a** and **b** is $\pi/3$.

(c)* Let $\vec{u}, \vec{v}, \vec{w}$ be vectors such that $\vec{u}+\vec{v}+\vec{w}=0$. If $|\vec{u}|=3, |\vec{v}|=4, |\vec{w}|=5$ then the value of the $\vec{u}\cdot\vec{v}+\vec{v}\cdot\vec{w}+\vec{w}\cdot\vec{u}$ is -25. **(I.I.T. 1995)**

49. (a) Let **a**, **b**, **c** be the vectors of lengths 3, 4, 5 respectively. If each one is perpendicular to the sum of other two, then find the magnitude of vector $\mathbf{a}+\mathbf{b}+\mathbf{c}$.

(b)* If $\mathbf{e}_1$ and $\mathbf{e}_2$ are non-collinear unit vectors, compute $(2\mathbf{e}_1-5\mathbf{e}_2)\cdot(3\mathbf{e}_1+\mathbf{e}_2)$ if $|\mathbf{e}_1+\mathbf{e}_2|=\sqrt{3}$.

(c) If **a** and **b** are two unit vectors such that $\mathbf{a}+2\mathbf{b}$ and $5\mathbf{a}-4\mathbf{b}$ are perpendicular to each other then the angle between **a** and **b** is

(a) 45° (b) 60°

(c) $\cos^{-1}\left(\frac{1}{3}\right)$ (d) $\cos^{-1}\left(\frac{2}{7}\right)$

(I.I.T. Sc. 2002)

50.* A line makes angles $\alpha, \beta, \gamma, \delta$ with the diagonals of a cube, prove that

$$\cos^2\alpha+\cos^2\beta+\cos^2\gamma+\cos^2\delta=4/3.$$

Also prove that the angle between two diagonals of a cube is $\cos^{-1}(1/3)$.

51.* If **a**, **b**, **c** are coplanar vectors, prove that

$$\begin{vmatrix} \mathbf{a} & \mathbf{b} & \mathbf{c} \\ \mathbf{a}\cdot\mathbf{a} & \mathbf{a}\cdot\mathbf{b} & \mathbf{a}\cdot\mathbf{c} \\ \mathbf{b}\cdot\mathbf{a} & \mathbf{b}\cdot\mathbf{b} & \mathbf{b}\cdot\mathbf{c} \end{vmatrix}=0$$

Another form :

If the vectors **a**, **b**, **c** are coplanar and **a**, **b** are non-collinear, then show that

$$\begin{vmatrix} \mathbf{a}\cdot\mathbf{a} & \mathbf{a}\cdot\mathbf{b} \\ \mathbf{a}\cdot\mathbf{b} & \mathbf{b}\cdot\mathbf{b} \end{vmatrix}\mathbf{c}=\begin{vmatrix} \mathbf{c}\cdot\mathbf{a} & \mathbf{a}\cdot\mathbf{b} \\ \mathbf{c}\cdot\mathbf{b} & \mathbf{b}\cdot\mathbf{b} \end{vmatrix}\mathbf{a}+\begin{vmatrix} \mathbf{a}\cdot\mathbf{a} & \mathbf{c}\cdot\mathbf{a} \\ \mathbf{a}\cdot\mathbf{b} & \mathbf{c}\cdot\mathbf{b} \end{vmatrix}\mathbf{b}.$$

52.* Prove that $(\mathbf{a}\times\mathbf{b})^2=\mathbf{a}^2\mathbf{b}^2-(\mathbf{a}\cdot\mathbf{b})^2=a^2b^2-(\mathbf{a}\cdot\mathbf{b})^2$

or $(\mathbf{a}\times\mathbf{b})^2=\begin{vmatrix} \mathbf{a}\cdot\mathbf{a} & \mathbf{a}\cdot\mathbf{b} \\ \mathbf{b}\cdot\mathbf{a} & \mathbf{b}\cdot\mathbf{b} \end{vmatrix}$

and deduce the identity

$$({m_1}^2+{n_1}^2+{p_1}^2)({m_2}^2+{n_2}^2+{p_2}^2)-(m_1m_2+n_1n_2+p_1p_2)^2$$
$$=(m_1n_2-m_2n_1)^2+(n_1p_2-n_2p_1)^2+(p_1m_2-p_2m_1)^2$$

53.* For any two vectors **u** and **v**, prove that

$$(1+|\mathbf{u}|^2)(1+|\mathbf{v}|^2)=(1-\mathbf{u}\cdot\mathbf{v})^2+|\mathbf{u}+\mathbf{v}+(\mathbf{u}\times\mathbf{v})^2|.$$ **(I.I.T. 1998)**

54. (a) Prove that $(\mathbf{a}-\mathbf{b})\times(\mathbf{a}+\mathbf{b})=2\mathbf{a}\times\mathbf{b}$ and interpret it.

(b) Prove that $\mathbf{a}\times(\mathbf{b}+\mathbf{c})+\mathbf{b}\times(\mathbf{c}+\mathbf{a})+\mathbf{c}\times(\mathbf{a}+\mathbf{b})=0$.

55. (a) If $\mathbf{a}\times\mathbf{b}=\mathbf{c}\times\mathbf{d}$ and $\mathbf{a}\times\mathbf{c}=\mathbf{b}\times\mathbf{d}$, show that $\mathbf{a}-\mathbf{d}$ is parallel to $\mathbf{b}-\mathbf{c}$.

(b) If $\mathbf{a}\times\mathbf{b}=\mathbf{a}\times\mathbf{c}$, then prove that **b** differs from **c** by a vector which is parallel to **a**.

(c) If $\mathbf{a}\times\mathbf{b}=\mathbf{c}\times\mathbf{b}=\mathbf{0}$, then show that $\mathbf{a}-\mathbf{c}=k\,\mathbf{b}$, where k is a scalar.

56. Let $\mathbf{a}=\mathbf{i}+\mathbf{j}$ and $\mathbf{b}=2\mathbf{i}-\mathbf{k}$. Show that the points of intersection of the lines $\mathbf{r}\times\mathbf{a}=\mathbf{b}\times\mathbf{a}$ and $\mathbf{r}\times\mathbf{b}=\mathbf{a}\times\mathbf{b}$ is $3\mathbf{i}+\mathbf{j}-\mathbf{k}$. **(I.I.T. 1992)**

57.* Interpret the equations :

(i) $\mathbf{a}\cdot\mathbf{b}=\mathbf{a}\cdot\mathbf{c}$ (ii) $\mathbf{a}\times\mathbf{b}=\mathbf{a}\times\mathbf{c}$

and prove that if both the equations hold simultaneously, then $\mathbf{b}=\mathbf{c}$ if $\mathbf{a}\neq\mathbf{0}$.

58.* (a) Find the vector area of a triangle OAB where $\vec{OA}=\mathbf{a}$, $\vec{OB}=\mathbf{b}$ and they are inclined at an angle θ and, hence find the vector area of a triangle whose vertices are the points **a**, **b** and **c**.

(b) If **a**, **b**, **c** are vectors from the origin to the points A, B, C show that $\mathbf{a}\times\mathbf{b}+\mathbf{b}\times\mathbf{c}+\mathbf{c}\times\mathbf{a}$ is perpendicular to the plane ABC.

59. (a) Find the perpendicular distance of the vertex A from the base of a $\Delta\,ABC$ with **a**, **b**, **c** as position vectors of A, B, C respectively.

(b)* If A, B, C, D are any four points in space, prove that

$$|\vec{AB}\times\vec{CD}+\vec{BC}\times\vec{AD}+\vec{CA}\times\vec{BD}|=4\,(\text{area of }\Delta\,ABC)$$

60.* Given that vectors **A**, **B**, **C** form a triangle such that $\mathbf{A}=\mathbf{B}+\mathbf{C}$. Find a, b, c, d such that the area of the triangle is $5\sqrt{6}$ where $\mathbf{A}=a\mathbf{i}+b\mathbf{j}+c\mathbf{k}$, $\mathbf{B}=d\mathbf{i}+3\mathbf{j}+4\mathbf{k}$, $\mathbf{C}=3\mathbf{i}+\mathbf{j}-2\mathbf{k}$. **(Roorkee 1990)**

61.* (a) ABC is a triangle, E and F are mid-points of AC and AB respectively. CP is drawn parallel to AB to meet BE produced in P. Show that $\Delta\,FEP=\Delta\,FCE=\frac{1}{4}\Delta\,ABC$.

(b)* The points D, E, F divide sides BC, CA, AB of triangle ABC in the ratio $1:2$. The pair of lines AD, BE; BE, CF; CF, AD meet at P, Q and R respectively. Prove that area of $\Delta\,PQR=\frac{1}{7}\Delta\,ABC$.

(c) In a triangle the points D, E, F divide the sides BC, CA and AB respectively in the ratio $n:1$. If Δ be the area of $\Delta\,ABC$, then prove that area of $\Delta\,DEF=\frac{n^2-n+1}{(n+1)^2}\Delta$.

(d) The internal bisectors of the angles of a triangle meet the opposite sides at the points D, E and F. Prove that area of $\Delta\,DEF$ is always less than one-fourth the area of $\Delta\,ABC$.

62.* A, B, C and D are four points such that

$$\vec{AB}=m(2\mathbf{i}-6\mathbf{j}+2\mathbf{k}),\ \vec{BC}=(\mathbf{i}-2\mathbf{j})$$

and $$\vec{CD}=n(-6\mathbf{i}+15\mathbf{j}-3\mathbf{k}).$$

Find the conditions on the scalars m and n so that CD intersects AB at some point E. Also find the area of the triangle BCE. **(Roorkee 1995)**

63. (a) Find the area of the parallelogram whose adjacent sides are $\mathbf{a} = \mathbf{i} + 2\mathbf{j} + 3\mathbf{k}, \mathbf{b} = 3\mathbf{i} - 2\mathbf{j} + \mathbf{k}$.

(b) Show that the area of a triangle whose two adjacent sides are determined by the vectors $\mathbf{a} = 3\mathbf{i} + 4\mathbf{j},\ \mathbf{b} = -5\mathbf{i} + 7\mathbf{j}$ is $20\frac{1}{2}$ square units.

(c) The area of a triangle whose vertices are $A(1, -1, 2),\ B(2, 1, -1),\ C(3, -1, 2)$ is $\sqrt{13}$.

64.* (a) Let $\vec{OA} = \mathbf{a}, \vec{OB} = 10\mathbf{a} + 2\mathbf{b}$ and $\vec{OC} = \mathbf{b}$ where O, A and C are non-collinear points. Let p denote the area of the quadrilateral $OABC$, and let q denote the area of the parallelogram with OA and OC as adjacent sides. If $p = kq$, then $k =$ .... **(I.I.T. Re-ex. 1997)**

(b) If a quadrilateral $ABCD$ is such that $\vec{AB} = \mathbf{b}, \vec{AD} = \mathbf{d}$ and $\vec{AC} = p\mathbf{b} + q\mathbf{d}\ (p + q \geq 1)$, then the area of the quadrilateral is $\frac{1}{2}(p + q)\,|\mathbf{b} \times \mathbf{d}|$. Is this statement true or false ?

65. (a) Find the area of the parallelogram having diagonals $3\mathbf{i} + \mathbf{j} - 2\mathbf{k}$ and $\mathbf{i} - 3\mathbf{j} + 4\mathbf{k}$.

(b) If $\mathbf{a} = 2\mathbf{i} - 3\mathbf{j} + \mathbf{k}, \mathbf{b} = -\mathbf{i} + \mathbf{k},\ \mathbf{c} = 2\mathbf{j} - \mathbf{k}$, find the area of the parallelogram having diagonals $\mathbf{a} + \mathbf{b}$ and $\mathbf{b} + \mathbf{c}$.

66. (a) The vectors $\mathbf{A} = 3\mathbf{i} - \mathbf{k},\ \mathbf{B} = \mathbf{i} + 2\mathbf{j}$ are adjacent sides of a parallelogram. Its area is $\sqrt{41}$.

(b) The area of a parallelogram is $5\sqrt{3}$ then its diagonals are given by vectors

(a) $3, 2, -1; 3, -1, 4$ (b) $\frac{3}{2}, \frac{1}{2}, -1; 2, -6, 8$

(c) $3, 1, -2; 1, 3, 4$ (d) none

where vector x, y, z is $x\mathbf{i} + y\mathbf{j} + z\mathbf{k}$.

67. (a) Find two unit vectors parallel to the diagonals of a parallelogram whose sides are $2\mathbf{i} + 4\mathbf{j} - 5\mathbf{k}$ and $\mathbf{i} + 2\mathbf{j} + 3\mathbf{k}$. Find the vector product of the two vectors given above. Can this product be of use in finding the area of the $||^m$. If so find this area.

(b) The diagonals of a parallelogram are given by vectors $2\mathbf{i} + 3\mathbf{j} - 6\mathbf{k}$ and $3\mathbf{i} - 4\mathbf{j} - \mathbf{k}$. Determine its sides and also the area. **(Roorkee 2001)**

68.* Given $\mathbf{a} = \mathbf{i} + 2\mathbf{j} + 3\mathbf{k},\ \ \mathbf{b} = -\mathbf{i} + 2\mathbf{j} + \mathbf{k}$, and $\mathbf{c} = 3\mathbf{i} + \mathbf{j}$, find a unit vector in the direction of the resultant of these vectors. Also find a vector $\mathbf{r}$ which is normal to both $\mathbf{a}$ and $\mathbf{b}$. What is the inclination of $\mathbf{r}$ and $\mathbf{c}$?

69.* Find all possible vectors $\mathbf{a}$ and $\mathbf{b}$ such that

$\mathbf{a} \times \mathbf{b} = 2\mathbf{i} + 2\mathbf{j} - \mathbf{k},\quad \mathbf{a} + \mathbf{b} = \mathbf{i} - 3\mathbf{j} - 4\mathbf{k}$. **(M.N.R. 1997)**

70.* Vectors $\vec{AB} = 3\mathbf{i} - \mathbf{j} + \mathbf{k}$ and $\vec{CD} = -3\mathbf{i} + 2\mathbf{j} + 4\mathbf{k}$ are not coplanar. The position vectors of points A and C are $6\mathbf{i} + 7\mathbf{j} + 4\mathbf{k}$ and $-9\mathbf{j} + 2\mathbf{k}$ respectively. Find the position vectors of a point P on the line AB and a point Q on the line CD such that $\vec{PQ}$ is perpendicular to $\vec{AB}$ and $\vec{CD}$ both. **(Roorkee 1998)**

71. (a)* AC and BD are two diagonals of a quadrilateral, prove that its area is $\frac{1}{2}\vec{AC} \times \vec{BD}$.

(b)* The position vectors of the vertices of a quadrilateral with A as orgin are $B(\mathbf{b}),\ D(\mathbf{d})$ and $C(l\mathbf{b} + m\mathbf{d})$. Prove that the area of the quadrilateral is $\frac{1}{2}(l + m)\ |\mathbf{b} \times \mathbf{d}|$.

72. (a) If one diagonal of a quadrilateral bisects the other, then prove by vectors that it bisects the quadrilateral as well.

(b) Determine the lengths of the diagonals of a parallelogram constructed on the vectors $\mathbf{a} = 2\mathbf{m} + \mathbf{n}$ and $\mathbf{b} = \mathbf{m} - 2\mathbf{n}$, where $\mathbf{m}$ and $\mathbf{n}$ are unit-vectors forming an angle of 60°.

(c) If $\mathbf{a}, \mathbf{b}, \mathbf{c}, \mathbf{d}$ be the vertices of a cyclic quadrilateral $ABCD$, then prove that

$$\frac{|\mathbf{a} \times \mathbf{b} + \mathbf{b} \times \mathbf{d} + \mathbf{d} \times \mathbf{a}|}{(\mathbf{b} - \mathbf{a}) . (\mathbf{d} - \mathbf{a})} + \frac{|(\mathbf{b} \times \mathbf{c} + \mathbf{c} \times \mathbf{d} + \mathbf{d} \times \mathbf{b})|}{(\mathbf{b} - \mathbf{c}) . (\mathbf{d} - \mathbf{c})} = 0$$

73. (a) Find 3-dimensional vectors $\mathbf{v}_1, \mathbf{v}_2, \mathbf{v}_3$ satisfying $\mathbf{v}_1 . \mathbf{v}_1 = 4, \mathbf{v}_1 . \mathbf{v}_2 = -2, \mathbf{v}_1 . \mathbf{v}_3 = 6,$ $\mathbf{v}_2 . \mathbf{v}_2 = 2, \mathbf{v}_2 . \mathbf{v}_3 = -5, \mathbf{v}_3 . \mathbf{v}_3 = 29.$ **(I.I.T. 2001)**

(b) Let $\vec{A}(t) = f_1(t)\,\mathbf{i} + f_2(t)\,\mathbf{j}$ and

$\vec{B}(t) = g_1(t)\,\mathbf{i} + g_2(t)\,\mathbf{j},\quad t \in [0, 1]$

where f_1, f_2, g_1, g_2 are continuous functions. If $\vec{A}(t)$ and $\vec{B}(t)$ are non-zero vectors for all t and $\vec{A}(0) = 2\mathbf{i} + 3\mathbf{j},\ \vec{A}(1) = 6\mathbf{i} + 2\mathbf{j},\ \vec{B}(0) = 3\mathbf{i} + 2\mathbf{j}$ and $\vec{B}(1) = 2\mathbf{i} + 6\mathbf{j}$, then show that $\vec{A}(t)$ and $\vec{B}(t)$ are parallel for some t. **(I.I.T. 2001)**

74.* Prove by vectors that in any triangle ABC

(i) $a^2 = b^2 + c^2 - 2bc\cos A$.

(ii) $a = b\cos C + c\cos B$.

(iii) $a\cos B - b\cos A = \dfrac{a^2 - b^2}{c}$.

(iv) $2(bc\cos A + ca\cos B + ab\cos C) = a^2 + b^2 + c^2$.

(v) $(a + b + c)(\cos A + \cos B + \cos C)$
$= a(1 + \cos A) + b(1 + \cos B) + c(1 + \cos C)$.

(vi) $\dfrac{\sin A}{a} = \dfrac{\sin B}{b} = \dfrac{\sin C}{c}$.

Another form of (vi) :

If $\mathbf{a} + \mathbf{b} + \mathbf{c} = \mathbf{0}$, show that $\mathbf{a} \times \mathbf{b} = \mathbf{b} \times \mathbf{c} = \mathbf{c} \times \mathbf{a}$.

(vii) If the vectors $\mathbf{a}, \mathbf{b}$ and $\mathbf{c}$ form the sides BC, CA and AB respectively, of a triangle ABC, then

(a) $\mathbf{a} . \mathbf{b} + \mathbf{b} . \mathbf{c} + \mathbf{c} . \mathbf{a} = 0$

(b) $\mathbf{a} \times \mathbf{b} = \mathbf{b} \times \mathbf{c} = \mathbf{c} \times \mathbf{a}$

(c) $\mathbf{a} . \mathbf{b} = \mathbf{b} . \mathbf{c} = \mathbf{c} . \mathbf{a}$

(d) $\mathbf{a} \times \mathbf{b} + \mathbf{b} \times \mathbf{c} + \mathbf{c} \times \mathbf{a} = \mathbf{0}$ **(I.I.T. Sc. 2000)**

75.* Prove by vector methods the following :

(i) $\cos(\alpha \pm \beta) = \cos\alpha\cos\beta \mp \sin\alpha\sin\beta$.

(ii) $\sin(\alpha \pm \beta) = \sin\alpha\cos\beta \pm \cos\alpha\sin\beta$.

Solutions to Problem Set (1)

1. (a) $\mathbf{a}\,.\,\mathbf{b} = ab\cos\theta = a_1 a_2 + b_1 b_2 + c_1 c_2$

where $a = \sqrt{\Sigma\ a_1^{\,2}},\ b = \sqrt{\Sigma\ b_1^{\,2}}$

$\therefore\quad \sqrt{16+9+1}\,\sqrt{4+1+4}\cos\theta$

$= 4.2 + 3(-1) + 1.2.$

or $\sqrt{26}\,.\,3\cos\theta = 7$ or $\cos\theta = \dfrac{7}{3\sqrt{(26)}}$.

We know that $\mathbf{a}\times\mathbf{b}$ represents a vector which is perpendicular to both $\mathbf{a}$ and $\mathbf{b}$.

Now $\mathbf{a}\times\mathbf{b} = \begin{vmatrix} \mathbf{i} & \mathbf{j} & \mathbf{k} \\ 4 & 3 & 1 \\ 2 & -1 & 2 \end{vmatrix} = 7\mathbf{i} - 6\mathbf{j} - 10\mathbf{k}.$

Hence a unit vector will be obtained by dividing $7\mathbf{i} - 6\mathbf{j} - 10\mathbf{k}$ by its module

$\sqrt{49+36+100} = \sqrt{185}.$

The required unit vector is $\dfrac{1}{\sqrt{(185)}}\,[7\mathbf{i} - 6\mathbf{j} - 10\mathbf{k}]$.

Again, $\mathbf{a}\times\mathbf{b} = ab\sin\theta\,\hat{\mathbf{n}}$

$7\mathbf{i} - 6\mathbf{j} - 10\mathbf{k} = \sqrt{26}\,\sqrt{9}\sin\theta\,\hat{\mathbf{n}}.$

Square both sides and we know that square of a vector is equal to square of its module

i.e. $\mathbf{a}^2 = a^2$ and $\hat{\mathbf{n}}^2 = 1$

$\therefore\quad 49 + 36 + 100 = 26\times 9\sin^2\theta\,.\,1$

$\therefore\quad \sin\theta = \sqrt{\left(\dfrac{185}{26\times 9}\right)} = \dfrac{1}{3}\sqrt{\left(\dfrac{185}{26}\right)}.$

(b) Ans. (d).

$\mathbf{a}\times\mathbf{b} = |\mathbf{a}|\,|\mathbf{b}|\sin\theta\,\hat{\mathbf{n}}$

$\mathbf{a}\times\mathbf{b} = \begin{vmatrix} \mathbf{i} & \mathbf{j} & \mathbf{k} \\ 1 & -2 & 3 \\ 2 & 1 & 1 \end{vmatrix} = \sqrt{14}\,\sqrt{6}\sin\theta\,\hat{\mathbf{n}}$

$\therefore\quad -5\mathbf{i} + 5\mathbf{j} + 5\mathbf{k} = \sqrt{14}\,\sqrt{6}\sin\theta\,\hat{\mathbf{n}}$

Take modulus of both sides

$5\sqrt{1+1+1} = \sqrt{14}\,\sqrt{6}\sin\theta$

$\therefore\quad \sin\theta = \dfrac{5\sqrt{3}}{\sqrt{2}\,\sqrt{7}\,.\,\sqrt{2}\,\sqrt{3}} = \dfrac{5}{2\sqrt{7}}$

Alt. Find $\cos\theta$ by dot product.

$\cos\theta = \dfrac{2-2+3}{\sqrt{4}\,\sqrt{6}} = \dfrac{3}{\sqrt{84}}$

$\therefore\quad \sin^2\theta = 1 - \dfrac{9}{84} = \dfrac{75}{84} = \dfrac{25}{28}\quad \therefore\ \sin\theta = \dfrac{5}{2\sqrt{7}}.$

(c) Ans. $\dfrac{1}{\sqrt{(3)}}[\mathbf{i} - \mathbf{j} - \mathbf{k}]$, $\sin\theta = \dfrac{2}{\sqrt{(7)}}$.

(d) $\mathbf{a}\,.\,\mathbf{b} = ab\cos\theta = \Sigma a_1 b_1$

$\mathbf{a}\times\mathbf{b} = ab\sin\theta\,\hat{\mathbf{n}}$

$(\mathbf{a}\times\mathbf{b})^2 = a^2 b^2\sin^2\theta\,.\,1 = a^2b^2 - a^2b^2\cos^2\theta$

or $\begin{vmatrix} \mathbf{i} & \mathbf{j} & \mathbf{k} \\ a_1 & a_2 & a_3 \\ b_1 & b_2 & b_3 \end{vmatrix}^2 = a^2b^2 - (\mathbf{a}\,.\,\mathbf{b})^2$

$\therefore\quad \Sigma(a_2b_3 - a_3b_2)^2 = \Sigma a_1^{\,2}\,\Sigma b_1^{\,2} - (\Sigma a_1 b_1)^2$

Hence the proof of Lagrange's identity.

2. (a) $\mathbf{n}$ = normal to the plane of given vectors is

$\begin{vmatrix} \mathbf{i} & \mathbf{j} & \mathbf{k} \\ 2 & 3 & -1 \\ 1 & -1 & 2 \end{vmatrix} = 5(\mathbf{i} - \mathbf{j} - \mathbf{k})$

If θ be the angle between the vector x, y, z and the plane then $(90° - \theta)$ is the angle between x, y, z and normal to the plane.

$\therefore\quad \cos(90° - \theta) = \dfrac{5(1, -1, -1)\,.\,(x, y, z)}{5\sqrt{3}\,\sqrt{x^2+y^2+z^2}}$

or $\sin^2\theta\,.\,3(x^2+y^2+z^2) = (x-y-z)^2$

But $\cot\theta = \sqrt{2}\quad \therefore\quad \operatorname{cosec}\theta = \sqrt{3}$

$\therefore\quad \dfrac{1}{3}\,.\,3(x^2+y^2+z^2) = (x-y-z)^2$

or $-2xy + 2yz - 2zx = 0\ \therefore\ yz = x(y+z)\ \Rightarrow$ (b)

(b) $\mathbf{a}$ is perpendicular to both $\mathbf{b}$ and $\mathbf{c}$ and hence it is parallel to $\mathbf{b}\times\mathbf{c}\quad \therefore\quad \mathbf{a} = t\,(\mathbf{b}\times\mathbf{c})$

Square both sides. All are unit vectors

$1 = t^2\,(1.1\sin 30^{\circ})^2\,.\,1 = t^2\,.\,\dfrac{1}{4}$

$\therefore\quad t = \pm 2$ etc.

(c) Let the angle between $\mathbf{a}$ and $\mathbf{b}$ be 3θ and the modulus of $\mathbf{a}+\mathbf{b} = \lambda$ (say)

By given condition of trisection of angle,

$(\mathbf{a}+\mathbf{b})\,.\,\mathbf{a} = \lambda a\cos\theta$

$(\mathbf{a}+\mathbf{b})\,.\,\mathbf{b} = \lambda b\cos 2\theta$

$\therefore\quad \dfrac{a^2 + ab\cos 3\theta}{ab\cos 3\theta + b^2} = \dfrac{a\cos\theta}{b\cos 2\theta}$

or $\cos 2\theta\,(a + b\cos 3\theta) = \cos\theta\,(a\cos 3\theta + b)$

$\therefore\quad a(\cos 2\theta - \cos 3\theta\cos\theta)$

$= b(\cos\theta - \cos 2\theta\cos 3\theta)$

$\therefore\quad \dfrac{a}{b} = \dfrac{2\cos\theta - 2\cos 2\theta\cos 3\theta}{2\cos 2\theta - 2\cos 3\theta\cos\theta}$

$\dfrac{a}{b} = \dfrac{2\cos\theta - (\cos 5\theta + \cos\theta)}{2\cos 2\theta - (\cos 4\theta + \cos 2\theta)}$

or $\dfrac{a}{b} = \dfrac{\cos\theta - \cos 5\theta}{\cos 2\theta - \cos 4\theta} = \dfrac{2\sin 3\theta\sin 2\theta}{2\sin 3\theta\sin\theta}$

or $\dfrac{a}{b} = \dfrac{2\sin\theta\cos\theta}{\sin\theta} = 2\cos\theta$

$\therefore\quad \theta = \cos^{-1}\left(\dfrac{a}{2b}\right)$ or $3\theta = 3\cos^{-1}\left(\dfrac{a}{2b}\right)$

3. (a) $\mathbf{a}+\mathbf{b} = 0\,\mathbf{i} + 3\mathbf{j} + \mathbf{k},\ \mathbf{b} - \mathbf{c} = 3\mathbf{k}$

$(\mathbf{a}+\mathbf{b})\times(\mathbf{b}-\mathbf{c}) = (3\mathbf{j}+\mathbf{k})\times 3\mathbf{k} = 9\mathbf{i}$

$\therefore$ Unit vector is $\mathbf{i}$.

(b) Ans. (c).

If the given points be A, B, C then $\vec{AB} \times \vec{AC}$ is normal to plane through A, B, C

or $(2\mathbf{j}-\mathbf{i}) \times (3\mathbf{k}-\mathbf{i}) = 6\mathbf{j}\times\mathbf{k} - 3\mathbf{i}\times\mathbf{k} - 2\mathbf{j}\times\mathbf{i} + 0$

$= 6\mathbf{i} - 3(-\mathbf{j}) - 2(-\mathbf{k}) = 6\mathbf{i} + 3\mathbf{j} + 2\mathbf{k}$

Hence a unit vector normal to the plane is

$$\frac{6\mathbf{i}+3\mathbf{j}+2\mathbf{k}}{\sqrt{36+9+4}} = \frac{6\mathbf{i}+3\mathbf{j}+2\mathbf{k}}{7} \Rightarrow \text{(c)}$$

(c) Calculate $\mathbf{a}\times\mathbf{b}$ as in Ex. 1 and it comes out to be $42\mathbf{i}+14\mathbf{j}-21\mathbf{k}$

so that $\mathbf{a}\times\mathbf{b} = 7(6\mathbf{i}+2\mathbf{j}-3\mathbf{k}) = 7\mathbf{c}$.

Now $(\mathbf{a}\times\mathbf{b})\times\mathbf{c} = 7\mathbf{c}\times\mathbf{c} = \mathbf{0}$ as cross product of two like vectors is zero.

$$\text{Again } \mathbf{b}\times\mathbf{c} = \begin{vmatrix} \mathbf{i} & \mathbf{j} & \mathbf{k} \\ 3 & -6 & 2 \\ 6 & 2 & -3 \end{vmatrix} = 14\mathbf{i}+21\mathbf{j}+42\mathbf{k}. = 7(2\mathbf{i}+3\mathbf{j}+6\mathbf{k}) = 7\mathbf{a}$$

$\therefore$ $\mathbf{a}\times(\mathbf{b}\times\mathbf{c}) = \mathbf{a}\times 7\mathbf{a} = 7(\mathbf{a}\times\mathbf{a}) = \mathbf{0}$.

Hence $(\mathbf{a}\times\mathbf{b})\times\mathbf{c} = \mathbf{a}\times(\mathbf{b}\times\mathbf{c}) = \mathbf{0}$.

4. (a) It is parallel to $\mathbf{a}\times\mathbf{b}$ or $-13\mathbf{i}+11\mathbf{j}+7\mathbf{k}$

$\therefore$ $\mathbf{r} = t(\mathbf{a}\times\mathbf{b})$

In order to find t, it lies in the plane

$\mathbf{r}.(2\mathbf{i}+\mathbf{j}+\mathbf{k}) + 8 = 0$

or $t(-26+11+7)+8=0$ $\therefore t=1$.

(b) Apply the vectors $\vec{AH}$ and $\vec{BC}$ are perpendicular and $\vec{BH}$ and $\vec{AC}$ are perpendicular.

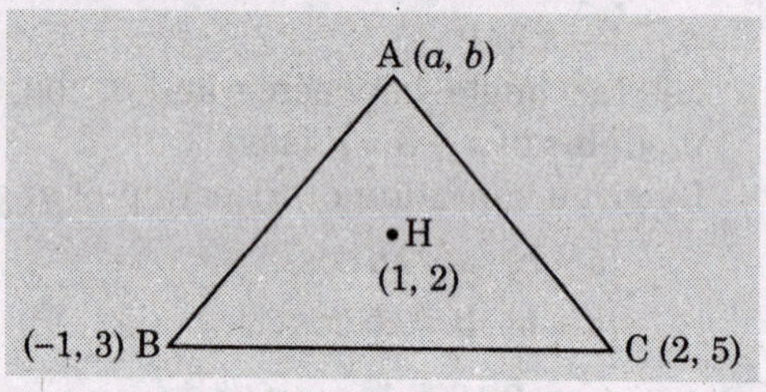

Fig. 7

This will give us two relations in a, b *i.e.* $7-3a-2b=0$ and $-1-2a+b=0$. Solving these we get the values of a, b as 5/7 and 17/7.

(c) Ans. (d).

From the figure $AC \perp BC$

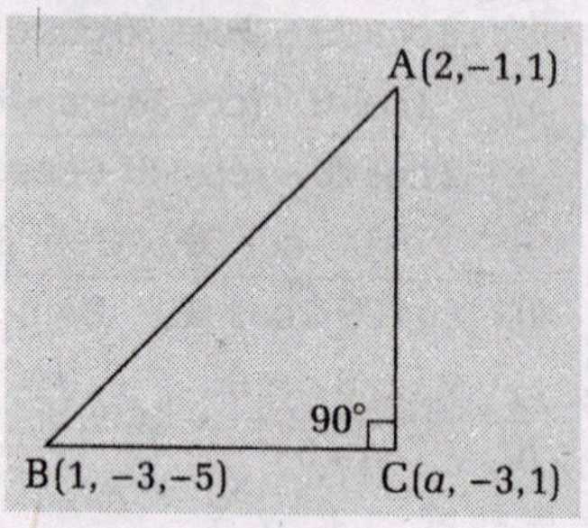

Fig. 8)

$\therefore$ $\vec{AC}.\vec{BC} = 0$

$[(a-2)\,\mathbf{i} - 2\mathbf{j} + 0\mathbf{k}].[(a-1)\,\mathbf{i} + 0\mathbf{j} + 6\mathbf{k}] = 0$

$\therefore$ $(a-2)(a-1).1+0+0=0$

$\therefore$ $a = 2, 1$.

5. (a) $\mathbf{a} = 4\mathbf{i}+3\mathbf{j}+\mathbf{k}$, $\mathbf{b} = 2\mathbf{i}-\mathbf{j}+2\mathbf{k}$

and $\mathbf{a}\times\mathbf{b} = 7\mathbf{i}-6\mathbf{j}-10\mathbf{k}$, by Ex.1.

We have to show that $(\mathbf{a}\times\mathbf{b})$ is perpendicular to both $\mathbf{a}$ and $\mathbf{b}$

$(\mathbf{a}\times\mathbf{b}).\mathbf{a} = 4.7+3(-6)+1(-10)$

$= 28-18-10 = 0$

$(\mathbf{a}\times\mathbf{b}).\mathbf{b} = 2.7-1(-6)+2(-10) = 14+6-20 = 0$

Hence $\mathbf{a}\times\mathbf{b}$ is perpendicular to both $\mathbf{a}$ and $\mathbf{b}$ as its dot product with both is zero.

(b) If $\mathbf{a}\times\mathbf{b} = \mathbf{0}$, then it does not *necessarily* imply that at least one of $\mathbf{a}$ or $\mathbf{b}$ is a null vector for the cross product of two non-zero parallel vectors may be zero. For example, if $\mathbf{a} = \mathbf{i}+\mathbf{j}+2\mathbf{k}$ and $\mathbf{b} = 2\mathbf{i}+2\mathbf{j}+4\mathbf{k}$, then $\mathbf{a}\times\mathbf{b} = \mathbf{0}$ as can be easily verified, where both $\mathbf{a}$ and $\mathbf{b}$ are non-zero.

6. (a) $\mathbf{a}\times\mathbf{b} = -\mathbf{i}+2\mathbf{j}+2\mathbf{k}$.

Hence the required unit vector is

$$\frac{-\mathbf{i}+2\mathbf{j}+2\mathbf{k}}{\sqrt{(1+4+4)}} = \frac{1}{3}(-\mathbf{i}+2\mathbf{j}+2\mathbf{k})$$

Therefore a vector of magnitude 9 is

$$9.\frac{1}{3}(-\mathbf{i}+2\mathbf{j}+2\mathbf{k}) = -3\mathbf{i}+6\mathbf{j}+6\mathbf{k}.$$

(b) Subtracting the given relations, we have

$\mathbf{a}\times(\mathbf{b}-\mathbf{c}) = (\mathbf{c}-\mathbf{b})\times\mathbf{d} = \mathbf{d}\times(\mathbf{b}-\mathbf{c})$

$\therefore$ $(\mathbf{a}-\mathbf{d})\times(\mathbf{b}-\mathbf{c}) = 0$

$\Rightarrow$ $(\mathbf{a}-\mathbf{d})$ is parallel to $\mathbf{b}-\mathbf{c}$

Hence their dot product is not zero.

$\therefore$ $(\mathbf{a}-\mathbf{d})\cdot(\mathbf{b}-\mathbf{c}) \neq 0$

or $\mathbf{a}\cdot\mathbf{b} - \mathbf{a}\cdot\mathbf{c} - \mathbf{d}\cdot\mathbf{b} + \mathbf{d}\cdot\mathbf{c} \neq 0$

or $\mathbf{a}\cdot\mathbf{b} + \mathbf{c}\cdot\mathbf{d} \neq \mathbf{a}\cdot\mathbf{c} + \mathbf{b}\cdot\mathbf{d}$

7. (a) Here P.V. of point $A(1, 2, 5)$ is $\mathbf{i}+2\mathbf{j}+5\mathbf{k}$ etc.

$\therefore$ $\vec{AB}$ = P.V. of B − P.V. of $A = 4\mathbf{i}+5\mathbf{j}+4\mathbf{k}$,

$\vec{AC}$ = P.V. of C − P.V. of $A = 2\mathbf{i}+0\mathbf{j}-6\mathbf{k}$.

$\therefore$ $\vec{AB}\times\vec{AC}$ is a vector perpendicular to the plane determined by $\vec{AB}$ and $\vec{AC}$, *i.e.* plane ABC

$$\therefore \quad \vec{AB}\times\vec{AC} = \begin{vmatrix} \mathbf{i} & \mathbf{j} & \mathbf{k} \\ 4 & 5 & 4 \\ 2 & 0 & -6 \end{vmatrix} = -30\mathbf{i}+32\mathbf{j}-10\mathbf{k}.$$

$\therefore$ Unit vector normal to the plane ABC is

$$\frac{-30\mathbf{i}+32\mathbf{j}-10\mathbf{k}}{\sqrt{(30^2+32^2+10^2)}} = \frac{-30\mathbf{i}+32\mathbf{j}-10\mathbf{k}}{2\sqrt{(506)}} = \frac{-15\mathbf{i}+16\mathbf{j}-5\mathbf{k}}{\sqrt{(506)}}.$$

(b) Ans. $\frac{1}{\sqrt{(6)}}(2\mathbf{i}+\mathbf{j}+\mathbf{k})$

(c) Ans. (d).

$\mathbf{u}.\mathbf{n} = 0$ and $\mathbf{v}.\mathbf{n} = 0$ imply $\mathbf{n}$ is perpendicular to both $\mathbf{u}$ and $\mathbf{v}$ and hence parallel to $\mathbf{u}\times\mathbf{v}$.

$\therefore$ $\mathbf{n} = \lambda(\mathbf{u}\times\mathbf{v}) = \lambda(\mathbf{i}+\mathbf{j})\times(\mathbf{i}-\mathbf{j})$

or $\mathbf{n} = \lambda(\mathbf{j}\times\mathbf{i} - \mathbf{i}\times\mathbf{j}) = \lambda(-\mathbf{k}-\mathbf{k}) = -2\lambda\mathbf{k}$

Hence the unit vector along **n** = **k**.

∴ $\mathbf{w}.\mathbf{n} = (\mathbf{i}+2\mathbf{j}+3\mathbf{k}).\mathbf{k} = 3$

8. (a) Normal of the plane containing **c** and **d** is along $\mathbf{n}_1 = \mathbf{c}\times\mathbf{d}$. Normal of the plane containing **a** and **b** is $\mathbf{n}_2 = \mathbf{a}\times\mathbf{b}$. These two planes are perpendicular therefore

$\mathbf{n}_1.\mathbf{n}_2 = 0$ or $(\mathbf{a}\times\mathbf{b}).(\mathbf{c}\times\mathbf{d}) = 0$.

(b) $\mathbf{n}_1 = \mathbf{a}\times\mathbf{b}$ is normal to plane containing **a**, **b**.

$\mathbf{n}_2 = \mathbf{c}\times\mathbf{d}$ is normal to plane containing **c**, **d**.

But **a**, **b**, **c**, **d** are coplanar therefore $\mathbf{n}_1$ and $\mathbf{n}_2$ are parallel.

∴ $\mathbf{n}_1\times\mathbf{n}_2 = 0$ or $(\mathbf{a}\times\mathbf{b})\times(\mathbf{c}\times\mathbf{d}) = 0$.

(c) Ans. (a). We have $\mathbf{n}_1\times\mathbf{n}_2 = 0$ where $\mathbf{n}_1, \mathbf{n}_2$ are normals to the planes P_1 and P_2.

Since $\mathbf{n}_1\times\mathbf{n}_2 = 0$ ∴ $\mathbf{n}_1$ and $\mathbf{n}_2$ are parallel and hence angle between them is zero.

9. (a) $\mathbf{A} = 2, 2, 3;\ \mathbf{B} = -1, 2, 1;\ \mathbf{C} = 3, 1, 0$

∴ $\mathbf{A}+t\mathbf{B} = 2-t,\ 2+2t,\ 3+t$ ...(1)

$\mathbf{C} = 3,\ 1,\ 0$ ...(2)

Since (1) and (2) are perpendicular, their dot product is zero.

∴ $6-3t+2+2t = 0$ or $8-t = 0$ or $t = 8$.

(b) Ans. $S = 1$.

(c) Ans. $\lambda = 2$

10. (a) $a = AR^{p-1}$

∴ $\log a = \log A + (p-1)\log R$

$\alpha = \log a, \log b, \log c$

$\beta = q-r, r-p, p-q$

$\alpha.\beta = \Sigma(q-r)\log a$

$= \Sigma(q-r)[\log A + (p-1)\log R]$

$= \log A\,\Sigma(q-r) + \log R\,\Sigma(p-1)(q-r)$

$= 0 + 0 = 0$

(b) Let $\mathbf{r} = x\mathbf{i}+y\mathbf{j}+z\mathbf{k}$. Then

$\mathbf{r}\times\mathbf{b} = \mathbf{c}\times\mathbf{b}$ gives $(\mathbf{r}-\mathbf{c})\times\mathbf{b} = 0$

$$\begin{vmatrix} \mathbf{i} & \mathbf{j} & \mathbf{k} \\ x-4 & y+3 & z-7 \\ 1 & 1 & 1 \end{vmatrix} = 0$$

or $(y-z+10)\,\mathbf{i} + (z-x-3)\,\mathbf{j} + (x-y-7)\,\mathbf{k} = 0$

∴ coefficient of **i**, **j** and **k** are each zero.

∴ $y-z = -10,\ z-x = 3,\ x-y = 7$.

Also $\mathbf{r}.\mathbf{a} = 0 \Rightarrow 2x + 0.y + z = 0$

or $z = -2x$.

Then $z-x = 3$ gives $-2x-x = -3$ or $x = -1$

∴ $z = 2$ and $y = z-10 = -8$

Hence $\mathbf{r} = -\mathbf{i}-8\mathbf{j}+2\mathbf{k}$.

(c) $(\mathbf{r}-\mathbf{c})\times\mathbf{b} = 0 \Rightarrow \mathbf{r}-\mathbf{c}$ is parallel to **b**

∴ $\mathbf{r}-\mathbf{c} = \lambda\,\mathbf{b}$ ∴ $\mathbf{r} = \mathbf{c}+\lambda\,\mathbf{b}$

∴ $\mathbf{r}.\mathbf{a} = (\mathbf{c}+\lambda\,\mathbf{b}).\mathbf{a} = 0$ as $\mathbf{r}.\mathbf{a} = 0$

∴ $-\dfrac{\mathbf{c}.\mathbf{a}}{\mathbf{b}.\mathbf{a}} = \lambda$

11. (a) Let θ be the angle between the given vectors. Then

$\mathbf{a}\cdot\mathbf{b} = |\mathbf{a}||\mathbf{b}|\cos\theta = ++-$ ive (θ is obtuse)

or $a_1a_2 + b_1b_2 + c_1c_2 = -$ ive

or $cx\cdot x - 6\cdot 2 + 3\cdot 2cx = -$ ive

or $cx^2 + 6cx - 12$ is – ive for all real x.

Now refer § 6, **Quad. Eq.** It will be so if $\Delta < 0$ and the sign is same as of first term

∴ $36c^2 + 48c < 0$ or $c(3c+4) = -$ ive

$3\{c-(-4/3)(c-0)\} = -$ ive

i.e. c lies between – 4/3 and 0 and as such it will be – ive and so the sign of the quadratic in x is also – ive.

Hence the angle is obtuse.

(b) $\mathbf{a}.\mathbf{b} = +$ ive and $\mathbf{b}.\mathbf{i}$ or $\mathbf{b}.\mathbf{j}$ or $\mathbf{b}.\mathbf{k} = -$ ive

or $2\lambda^2 - 3\lambda + 1 > 0$ and 2λ or λ or $-1 = -$ ive

$(2\lambda-1)(\lambda-1) > 0$ and $\lambda = -$ ive

∴ $\lambda < \frac{1}{2}$ or $\lambda > 1$ and $\lambda = -$ ive.

Now no value of λ which is greater than 1 can be – ive. Hence only those values of λ which are less than $\frac{1}{2}$ and at the same time – ive are the required values.

∴ $\lambda \in]-\infty, 0[$

(c) By definition we have

$\mathbf{r}.\mathbf{i} > 0,\ \mathbf{r}.\mathbf{j} > 0$ and $\mathbf{r}.\mathbf{k} > 0$

∴ $\lambda^2 - 4 > 0,\ 2 > 0,\ \lambda^2 - 9 > 0$

∴ $(\lambda+2)(\lambda-2) > 0$ and $(\lambda+3)(\lambda-3) > 0$

∴ $-2 < \lambda$ or $\lambda > 2$ and $-3 < \lambda$ or $\lambda > 3$

∴ $\lambda \in (-3, -2)$ or $\lambda \in (2, 3)$

∴ $\lambda \in \{(-3, -2) \cup (2, 3)\}$

(d) Any unit vector perpendicular to the plane containing the points A, B and C is

$$\mathbf{r} = \frac{\vec{AB}\times\vec{AC}}{|\vec{AB}\times\vec{AC}|}$$

$\vec{AB} = 1, 1, 1,\ \vec{AC} = 0, 3, 4$

∴ $\vec{AB}\times\vec{AC} = \begin{vmatrix} \mathbf{i} & \mathbf{j} & \mathbf{k} \\ 1 & 1 & 1 \\ 0 & 3 & 4 \end{vmatrix} = \mathbf{i}-4\mathbf{j}+3\mathbf{k}$

∴ $\mathbf{r} = \pm\dfrac{\mathbf{i}-4\mathbf{j}+3\mathbf{k}}{\sqrt{26}}$

Since **r** makes obtuse angle with x-axis

∴ $\mathbf{r}.\mathbf{i}$ must be – ive. Hence

$\mathbf{r} = -\dfrac{(\mathbf{i}-4\mathbf{j}+3\mathbf{k})}{\sqrt{26}} = \dfrac{-\mathbf{i}+4\mathbf{j}-3\mathbf{k}}{\sqrt{26}}$

Since $\mathbf{r}.\mathbf{k} = -3 = -$ ive, therefore it makes an obtuse angle with z-axis also.

12. (a) I. $\mathbf{a}.\mathbf{b} = ab\cos\theta = -$ ive as θ is obtuse

∴ $14\lambda^2 - 8\lambda + \lambda < 0$ or $7\lambda(2\lambda-1) < 0$

∴ $0 < \lambda < \frac{1}{2} = D_1$ ...(1)

II. $\mathbf{b}.\mathbf{k} = |\mathbf{b}|.1.\cos\theta, \quad \lambda = \sqrt{53+\lambda^2}\cos\theta$

$\therefore \quad \cos\theta = \dfrac{\lambda}{\sqrt{53+\lambda^2}}$

Since $\theta < \dfrac{\pi}{6} \quad \therefore \quad \sin\theta < \dfrac{1}{2}$ and $\cos\theta > \dfrac{\sqrt{3}}{2}$

$\therefore \quad \dfrac{\lambda}{\sqrt{53+\lambda^2}} > \dfrac{\sqrt{3}}{2}$ or $4\lambda^2 > 3(53+\lambda^2)$

$\therefore \quad \lambda^2 > 159$ or $\lambda > \sqrt{159} = D_2$ ...(2)

(1) and (2) are separate independent conditions. But if they are to hold simultaneously it can't be possible. Hence the domain of λ *i.e.* intersection $D_1 \cap D_2$ is a null set.

(b) $6 + \lambda - \mu = 0, \; 10 + \lambda^2 = 5 + \mu^2$

or $\mu^2 - \lambda^2 = 5$ or $(\mu+\lambda)(\mu-\lambda) = 5.$

$\lambda = -\dfrac{31}{12}, \mu = \dfrac{41}{12}$

(c) We must have $\mathbf{a}.\mathbf{b} < 0$ as $\cos\theta = -$ ive. If $\log_2 x = y$, then we have $\lambda y^2 - 12 + 6\lambda y < 0 \; \forall \; x \in (0, \infty)$

or $\lambda y^2 + 6\lambda y - 12 < 0$ *i.e.*, $-$ ive

The sign of a quadratic is same as that of the first term provided $\Delta < 0$

Hence we must have $36\lambda^2 + 48\lambda < 0$ and $\lambda < 0$

$3(\lambda + 4/3)(\lambda - 0) < 0$ and $\lambda < 0$

$\therefore \quad \lambda \in (-4/3, 0)$ satisfies both the above conditions.

(d) $\mathbf{a}.\mathbf{b} > 0$ and $\mathbf{b}.\mathbf{j} < 0 \quad \therefore \quad 2x^2 - 3x + 1 > 0$ and $x < 0$

or $(2x-1)(x-1) > 0$ and $x < 0$

$\therefore \quad x < \dfrac{1}{2}$ or $x > 1$ and $x < 0$

Since $x < 0$, the value $x > 1$ is ruled out.

$\therefore \quad x < 1/2$ and $x < 0 \Rightarrow x < 0$

(e) Given $\mathbf{a}^2 = \mathbf{b}^2 = \mathbf{c}^2 = 1$ ...(1)

$\mathbf{c}.\mathbf{a} = \mathbf{c}.\mathbf{b} = \cos\theta$ ...(2)

$\mathbf{a}.\mathbf{b} = 0$ ...(3)

Also $\mathbf{c} = p\mathbf{a} + q\mathbf{b} + r(\mathbf{a}\times\mathbf{b})$ ...(4)

$\therefore \quad \mathbf{a}.\mathbf{c} = p\mathbf{a}.\mathbf{a} + q\mathbf{a}.\mathbf{b} + r\mathbf{a}.(\mathbf{a}\times\mathbf{b})$

$\therefore \quad \cos\theta = p.1 + q.0 + r[\mathbf{a} \;\; \mathbf{a} \;\; \mathbf{b}]$

$\therefore \quad p = \cos\theta \quad \because \quad [\mathbf{a} \;\; \mathbf{a} \;\; \mathbf{b}] = 0$

(§ 5 (d) P. 1152)

Similarly, $q = \cos\theta$

Squaring (4), we have

$1 = p^2.1 + q^2.1 + r^2(a^2b^2\sin^2 90°)$
$+ 2pq\,\mathbf{a}.\mathbf{b} + 2qr\,\mathbf{b}.(\mathbf{a}\times\mathbf{b}) + 2pr\,\mathbf{a}.(\mathbf{a}\times\mathbf{b})$

or $1 = \cos^2\theta + \cos^2\theta + r^2 + 0 + 0 + 0$

$\dfrac{1-r^2}{2} = \cos^2\theta$

$\therefore \quad p^2 = q^2 = \dfrac{1-r^2}{2} = \cos^2\theta$

Note : $\mathbf{a}\times\mathbf{b}$ is a vector perpendicular to both $\mathbf{a}$ and $\mathbf{b}$ and hence its dot product with both $\mathbf{a}$ and $\mathbf{b}$ is zero *i.e.*, $\mathbf{a}.(\mathbf{a}\times\mathbf{b}) = 0$ and $\mathbf{b}.(\mathbf{a}\times\mathbf{b}) = 0$.

This is also expressed as $[\mathbf{a} \;\; \mathbf{a} \;\; \mathbf{b}] = 0, [\mathbf{b} \;\; \mathbf{a} \;\; \mathbf{b}] = 0$ as shown in next exercise. **(§ 5 (d) P. 1152)**

13. (a) Ans. (a). $\mathbf{r}\times\mathbf{i} = y(-\mathbf{k}) + z(\mathbf{j})$

$\mathbf{r}\times\mathbf{j} = x(\mathbf{k}) + z(-\mathbf{i})$

$\therefore \quad (\mathbf{r}\times\mathbf{i}).(\mathbf{r}\times\mathbf{j}) = (-y\mathbf{k} + z\mathbf{j}).(x\mathbf{k} - z\mathbf{i})$
$= -xy.1 + 0$

$\therefore \quad (\mathbf{r}\times\mathbf{i}).(\mathbf{r}\times\mathbf{j}) + xy = 0$

(b) Ans. (d).

$\vec{PA} \perp \vec{PB} \Rightarrow (\mathbf{a}-\mathbf{r})(\mathbf{b}-\mathbf{r}) = 0$

or $\mathbf{r}^2 - \mathbf{r}.(\mathbf{a}+\mathbf{b}) + \mathbf{a}.\mathbf{b} = 0$ ...(1)

But $\mathbf{a}.\mathbf{b} = -1 + 0 + 1 = 0$

and $\mathbf{a}+\mathbf{b} = \mathbf{j} + 2\mathbf{k}$

Hence from (1), we have

$\mathbf{r}^2 - \mathbf{r}.(\mathbf{j}+2\mathbf{k}) + 0 = 0$

$\mathbf{r}.[\mathbf{r} - (\mathbf{j}+2\mathbf{k})] = 0$

Now we know that $\mathbf{a}.\mathbf{b} = 0 \Rightarrow$ either $\mathbf{a} = 0$ or $\mathbf{b} = 0$ or $\mathbf{a}$ and $\mathbf{b}$ are perpendicular.

By virtue of given condition we have $\mathbf{b} = 0$

$\therefore \quad \mathbf{r} - (\mathbf{j}+2\mathbf{k}) = 0 \quad \therefore \quad \mathbf{r} = \mathbf{j} + 2\mathbf{k}.$

(c) Ans. (d).

Given $(\mathbf{r}-\mathbf{b})\times\mathbf{a} = 0$

Above implies that $\mathbf{r}-\mathbf{b}$ and $\mathbf{a}$ are parallel.

$\therefore \quad \mathbf{r} - \mathbf{b} = t\,\mathbf{a}$ or $\mathbf{r} = \mathbf{b} + t\mathbf{a}$ ...(1)

$\therefore \quad \mathbf{r}.\mathbf{c} = (\mathbf{b}.\mathbf{c}) + t(\mathbf{a}.\mathbf{c})$

or $0 = (\mathbf{b}.\mathbf{c}) + t(\mathbf{a}.\mathbf{c}) \quad \therefore \quad t = -\dfrac{(\mathbf{b}.\mathbf{c})}{(\mathbf{a}.\mathbf{c})}$ ...(2)

Hence from (1) and (2), putting for t

$\mathbf{r} = \mathbf{b} - \dfrac{\mathbf{b}.\mathbf{c}}{\mathbf{a}.\mathbf{c}}\mathbf{a}$

$\therefore \quad (\mathbf{r}\times\mathbf{b}) = (\mathbf{b}\times\mathbf{b}) - \dfrac{\mathbf{b}.\mathbf{c}}{\mathbf{a}.\mathbf{c}}(\mathbf{a}\times\mathbf{b})$

$\therefore \quad (\mathbf{a}.\mathbf{c})(\mathbf{r}\times\mathbf{b}) + (\mathbf{b}.\mathbf{c})(\mathbf{a}\times\mathbf{b}) = 0$

14. (a) Any vector perpendicular to $\mathbf{A} = \mathbf{i} + \mathbf{j}$ is $(\mathbf{i} - \mathbf{j} + \lambda\mathbf{k})$ as their dot product is zero for all values of λ.

$\therefore \quad 3\mathbf{j} + 4\mathbf{k} = p(\mathbf{i}+\mathbf{j}) + q(\mathbf{i} - \mathbf{j} + \lambda\mathbf{k})$

parallel to A perp. to A.

Comparing, $p + q = 0, \quad p - q = 3, \quad q\lambda = 4.$

$\therefore \quad p = 3/2, \quad q = -3/2, \quad \lambda = -8/3$

$\therefore \quad \mathbf{B}_1$ which is parallel to $\mathbf{A} = \dfrac{3}{2}(\mathbf{i}+\mathbf{j})$

(b) Ans. (d). $1 + \alpha^2 + \beta^2 = 3, \mathbf{c} = l\mathbf{a} + m\mathbf{b}$

On comparing coefficients, we get

$l + 4m = 1 = \beta \quad \therefore \quad \beta = 1$ and hence

$\alpha^2 = 1$ or $\alpha = \pm 1.$

(c) Clearly each vector is of unit modulus and also $\mathbf{a}.\mathbf{b} = 0, \mathbf{b}.\mathbf{c} = 0, \mathbf{c}.\mathbf{a} = 0.$

Hence they form an orthonormal triad. Also the two vectors of magnitude 3 normal to the plane of **a** and **b** are

$$3 \cdot \frac{\mathbf{a} \times \mathbf{b}}{|\mathbf{a} \times \mathbf{b}|} \text{ and } 3 \cdot \frac{\mathbf{b} \times \mathbf{a}}{|\mathbf{b} \times \mathbf{a}|}.$$

(d) $|\vec{AB}| = |\vec{BC}| = |\vec{CA}| = \sqrt{\Sigma (\alpha - \beta)^2}$

15. (a) Let the given points be A, B and C

$\therefore \quad \vec{AB} = \vec{OB} - \vec{OA} = -\mathbf{i} - 2\mathbf{j} - 6\mathbf{k}$

$\therefore \quad |\vec{AB}| = \sqrt{1 + 4 + 36} = \sqrt{41},$

$\vec{BC} = 2\mathbf{i} - \mathbf{j} + \mathbf{k}, \ |\vec{BC}| = \sqrt{6},$

$\vec{CA} = -\mathbf{i} + 3\mathbf{j} + 5\mathbf{k}, \quad |\vec{CA}| = \sqrt{35}.$

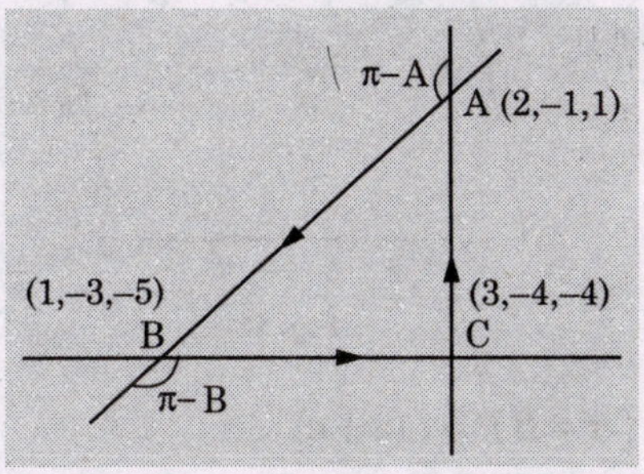

Fig. 9

Clearly $\quad 35 + 6 = 41,$ *i.e.* $\quad BC^2 + CA^2 = AB^2$ and hence the triangle is right angled at C.

Alternately :

$\vec{BC} \cdot \vec{CA} = 2(-1) - 1(3) + 1 \cdot 5 = 0,$

$\therefore \quad \vec{BC}$ is $\perp$ to $\vec{CA}$

Again $\quad \vec{AB} \cdot \vec{BC} = AB \cdot BC \cos(\pi - B)$

or $\quad -2 + 2 - 6 = -\sqrt{41}\sqrt{6} \cos B$

$\therefore \quad \cos B = \sqrt{\left(\frac{6}{41}\right)}$ or $B = \cos^{-1} \sqrt{\left(\frac{6}{41}\right)}.$

B is the angle between $\vec{BA}$ and $\vec{BC}$ and hence $\pi - B$ is the angle between $\vec{AB}$ and $\vec{BC}$.

Similarly $\qquad A = \cos^{-1} \sqrt{\left(\frac{35}{41}\right)}.$

Aliter : $A = \frac{\pi}{2} - B = \frac{\pi}{2} - \cos^{-1} \sqrt{\left(\frac{6}{41}\right)}$

$= \sin^{-1} \sqrt{\left(\frac{6}{41}\right)} = \cos^{-1} \sqrt{\left(\frac{35}{41}\right)}$

(b) Let the required vector be

$\alpha = d_1 \mathbf{i} + d_2 \mathbf{j} + d_3 \mathbf{k}$ where

$d_1^2 + d_2^2 + d_3^2 = 51 \quad$ (given) $\qquad$ ...(1)

Now $\alpha \cdot \beta = |\alpha||\beta| \cos\theta$ or $\cos\theta = \frac{(\alpha \cdot \beta)}{|\alpha||\beta|}$

Each of the given vectors **a, b, c** is a unit vector

$\therefore \quad \cos\theta = \frac{\mathbf{d} \cdot \mathbf{a}}{|\mathbf{d}||\mathbf{a}|} = \frac{\mathbf{d} \cdot \mathbf{b}}{|\mathbf{d}||\mathbf{b}|} = \frac{\mathbf{d} \cdot \mathbf{c}}{|\mathbf{d}||\mathbf{c}|}$

or $\quad \mathbf{d} \cdot \mathbf{a} = \mathbf{d} \cdot \mathbf{b} = \mathbf{d} \cdot \mathbf{c} \quad$ as $\quad |\mathbf{d}| = \sqrt{51}$

cancels out and $|\mathbf{a}| = |\mathbf{b}| = |\mathbf{c}| = 1.$

$\therefore \quad \frac{1}{3}(d_1 - 2d_2 + 2d_3) = \frac{1}{5}(-4d_1 + 0d_2 - 3d_3) = d_2$

$\therefore \quad d_1 - 5d_2 + 2d_3 = 0 \qquad$ from 1st and 3rd.

$4d_1 + 5d_2 + 3d_3 = 0 \qquad$ from 2nd and 3rd.

$\therefore \quad \frac{d_1}{-15 - 10} = \frac{d_2}{8 - 3} = \frac{d_3}{5 + 20}$

or $\quad \frac{d_1}{5} = \frac{d_2}{-1} = \frac{d_3}{-5} = \lambda,$ say.

Putting for d_1, d_2 and d_3 in (1), we get

$(25 + 1 + 25)\lambda^2 = 51 \qquad \therefore \ \lambda = \pm 1$

Hence the required vectors are $\pm(5\mathbf{i} - \mathbf{j} - 5\mathbf{k})$.

16. (a) $\vec{OA} = 1, 2, 2; \quad \vec{OX} = 1, 0, 0$

Suppose $\vec{OA'} = x, y, z$ after turning

$\vec{OA} \perp \vec{OA'} \quad \therefore \quad x + 2y + 2z = 0 \qquad$ ...(1)

$|\vec{OA}| = |\vec{OA'}| \quad \therefore \quad \sqrt{(x^2 + y^2 + z^2)} = 3 \qquad$ ...(2)

$\angle AOX = \theta \quad \therefore \quad \vec{OA} \cdot \vec{OX} = 3 \cdot 1 \cos\theta$

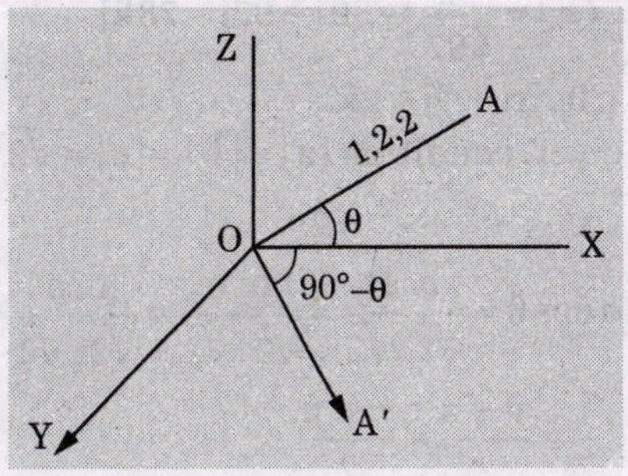

Fig. 10

or $\quad 1 = 3\cos\theta \qquad$ ...(3)

$\angle A'OX = 90^\circ - \theta$

$\therefore \quad \vec{OA'} \cdot \vec{OX} = 3 \cdot 1 \cdot \cos(90^\circ - \theta)$

or $\quad x = 3\sin\theta \qquad$ ...(4)

Squaring and adding (3) and (4), $x^2 + 1 = 9$

$\therefore \quad x = 2\sqrt{2}$ (+ive only)

as θ is acute and $\sin\theta$ is + ive by (4).

Putting for x in (1) and (2), we get

$2(y + z) = -x = -2\sqrt{2} \quad \therefore \quad y + z = -\sqrt{2}$

$8 + y^2 + z^2 = 9 \quad \therefore \quad y^2 + z^2 = 1$

$\therefore \quad (y + z)^2 - 2yz = 1$ or $2 - 2yz = 1$

$\therefore \quad yz = 1/2.$

Since $y + z = -2, yz = 1/2 \quad \therefore \quad y$ and z are the roots of $t^2 + \sqrt{2}t + \frac{1}{2} = 0$ or $\left(t + \frac{1}{\sqrt{2}}\right)^2 = 0$

$\therefore \quad y = z = -\dfrac{1}{\sqrt{2}}$

$\vec{OA'} = x, y, z = 2\sqrt{2}, -\dfrac{1}{\sqrt{2}}, -\dfrac{1}{\sqrt{2}}$

$= \dfrac{1}{\sqrt{2}}[4, -1, -1] = \dfrac{1}{\sqrt{2}}(4\mathbf{i} - \mathbf{j} - \mathbf{k})$

(b) Let $\vec{OQ} = x\mathbf{i} + y\mathbf{j} + z\mathbf{k}$ be new position of $\vec{OP}$.

$\therefore \quad |\vec{OP}| = |\vec{OQ}|$

or $\quad x^2 + y^2 + z^2 = 338 \qquad \ldots(1)$

$OP \perp OQ \quad \Rightarrow \quad 5x + 12y + 13z = 0 \qquad \ldots(2)$

Also $\vec{OP}$, $\mathbf{j}$ and $\vec{OQ}$ are coplanar.

$$\therefore \quad \begin{vmatrix} x & y & z \\ 0 & 1 & 0 \\ 5 & 12 & 13 \end{vmatrix} = 0$$

$\therefore \quad 13x - 5z = 0 \qquad \ldots(3)$

Solving the above equations, we get

$$z = \frac{13x}{5}, y = -\frac{97}{30}x \text{ and } x = \pm 30\sqrt{\frac{2}{97}}$$

Since the vector OQ will be inclined to x-axis at an obtuse angle $(90° + \theta)$

$\therefore \quad x = -30\sqrt{\dfrac{2}{97}} \quad \therefore \quad y = 97\sqrt{\dfrac{2}{97}}, z = -78\sqrt{\dfrac{2}{97}}$

$$\vec{OQ} = \sqrt{\frac{2}{97}}[-30\mathbf{i} + 97\mathbf{j} - 78\mathbf{k}]$$

(c) Let $\mathbf{c}$ be $x\mathbf{i} + y\mathbf{j} + z\mathbf{k}$.

By given condition $|\mathbf{a}| = |\mathbf{b}| = |\mathbf{c}| = \sqrt{2}$

$\therefore \quad x^2 + y^2 + z^2 = 2.$

Also $\cos\theta = \dfrac{\mathbf{a}.\mathbf{b}}{\sqrt{2}.\sqrt{2}} = \dfrac{\mathbf{b}.\mathbf{c}}{\sqrt{2}.\sqrt{2}} = \dfrac{\mathbf{c}.\mathbf{a}}{\sqrt{2}.\sqrt{2}}$

$\therefore \quad \dfrac{1}{2} = \dfrac{y+z}{2} = \dfrac{x+y}{2}$

$\therefore \quad x + y = 1, y + z = 1.$ Subtracting $\quad x - z = 0$

$\therefore \quad x = z = 1 - y.$

Putting for x and z in (1), we get

$(1-y)^2 + y^2 + (1-y)^2 = 2$

or $\quad 3y^2 - 4y = 0 \quad$ or $\quad y(3y - 4) = 0$

$\therefore \quad y = 0$, or $4/3 \qquad$ when $y = 0, x = z = 1$

$\therefore \quad \mathbf{c} = \mathbf{i} + \mathbf{k}. \qquad$ when $y = 4/3, x = z = -1/3$

$\therefore \quad \mathbf{c} = \dfrac{1}{3}(-\mathbf{i} + 4\mathbf{j} - \mathbf{k})$

(d) $|\mathbf{a}| = |\mathbf{b}| = \sqrt{2}$. Choose $\mathbf{c} = x\mathbf{i} + y\mathbf{j} + z\mathbf{k}$

$\therefore \quad x^2 + y^2 + z^2 = 2 \qquad \ldots(1)$

Also $\mathbf{c}$ makes obtuse angle with x-axis

$\therefore \quad \mathbf{c}.\mathbf{i} = x = -$ ive

Again $\cos\theta = \dfrac{\mathbf{a}.\mathbf{b}}{\sqrt{2}\sqrt{2}} = \dfrac{\mathbf{b}.\mathbf{c}}{\sqrt{2}\sqrt{2}} = \dfrac{\mathbf{c}.\mathbf{a}}{\sqrt{2}\sqrt{2}}$

$\dfrac{1}{2} = \dfrac{y+z}{2} = \dfrac{x+y}{2} \quad \therefore \quad y + z = 1$ and $x = z$

$\therefore \quad y = 1 - z = 1 - x \quad \because \quad z = x$

Putting in (1), we get

$\therefore \quad x^2 + (1-x)^2 + x^2 = 2$

or $\quad 3x^2 - 2x - 1 = 0 \quad$ or $\quad (3x+1)(x-1) = 0$

$\therefore \quad x = -1/3 \qquad$ as x is $-$ ive

$\therefore \quad y = \dfrac{4}{3}$ and $z = -\dfrac{1}{3}. \quad \therefore \quad \mathbf{c}$ is as given.

17. (a) Let $\vec{BA} = \vec{CD} = \mathbf{a}$ and $\vec{BC} = \mathbf{c}$ so that $\vec{CB} = -\mathbf{c}$

The internal bisector of $\angle B$ is given by (formula)

(§7 P. ....)

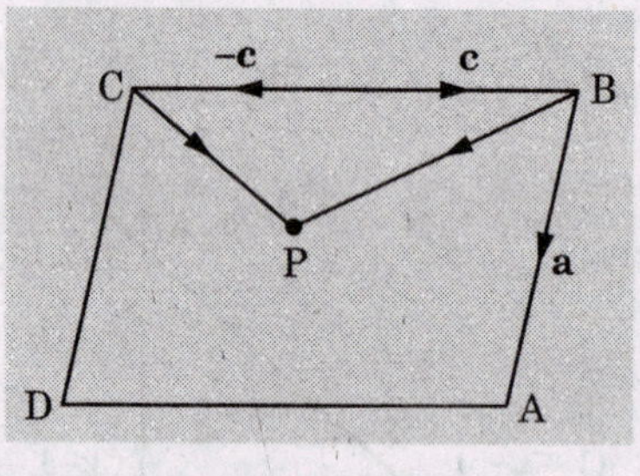

Fig. 11

$\mathbf{r} = \vec{BP} = t(\hat{\mathbf{a}} + \hat{\mathbf{c}}) \qquad \ldots(1)$

Similarly the internal bisector of $\angle C$ where $\vec{CB} = -\mathbf{c}$ and $\vec{CD} = \mathbf{a}$

$\therefore \quad \mathbf{r} = \vec{CP} = s(\hat{\mathbf{a}} - \hat{\mathbf{c}}) \qquad \ldots(2)$

Clearly $\vec{BP}.\vec{CP} = t\,s(\hat{\mathbf{a}}^2 - \hat{\mathbf{c}}^2) = t\,s(1-1) = 0$

$\therefore \quad BP$ is perpendicular to CP

$\therefore \quad \angle BPC = 90^{\circ}$

(b) We know that incident ray and reflected rays are equally inclined to the normal to the surface at P. Hence $\mathbf{a}$ is the unit vector along the bisector of $\mathbf{w}$ and $-\mathbf{v}$.

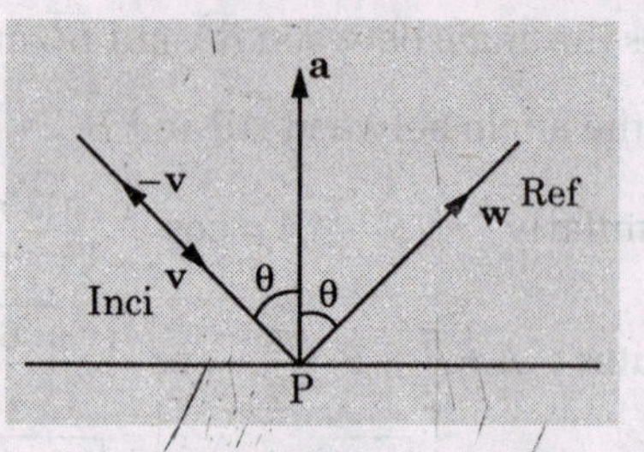

Fig. 12

$\therefore \quad \mathbf{a} = t(\mathbf{w} - \mathbf{v})$. Squaring both sides,

$1 = t^2[1 + 1 + 2\,\mathbf{w}.(-\mathbf{v})]$

$= t^2(2 + 2\cos 2\theta) = 4t^2\cos^2\theta$

$\therefore \quad t = \dfrac{1}{2\cos\theta} \quad \therefore \quad \mathbf{a} = \dfrac{1}{2\cos\theta}(\mathbf{w} - \mathbf{v})$

or $\quad \mathbf{w} = \mathbf{v} + (2\cos\theta)\,\mathbf{a} = \mathbf{v} + 2(\mathbf{a}.(-\mathbf{v}))\,\mathbf{a}$

or $\quad \mathbf{w} = \mathbf{v} - 2(\mathbf{a}.\mathbf{v})\,\mathbf{a}$

(c) $\tan A = \dfrac{\sin A}{\cos A} = \dfrac{\vec{AB} \times \vec{AD}}{\vec{AB} \cdot \vec{AD}} = \dfrac{(\mathbf{b}-\mathbf{a}) \times (\mathbf{d}-\mathbf{a})}{(\mathbf{b}-\mathbf{a}) \cdot (\mathbf{d}-\mathbf{a})} = \dfrac{N^r}{D^r}$

of T_1 as $\mathbf{a} \times \mathbf{a} = 0$

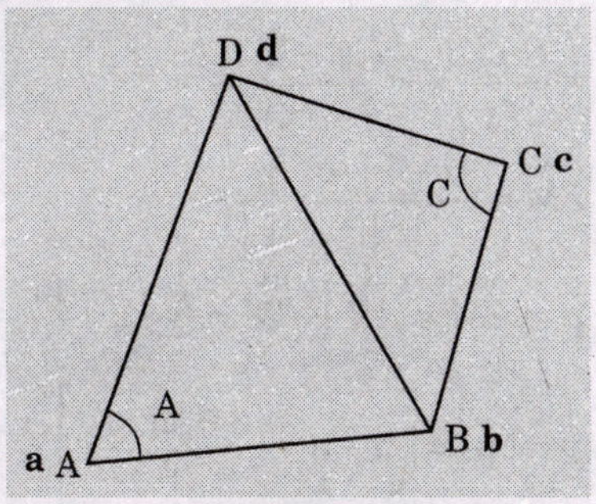

Fig. 13

$\tan C$ = 2nd term as above

We have to prove that $T_1 + T_2 = 0$

or $\tan A + \tan C = 0$ or $\sin(A+C) = 0$

or $A + C = \pi$

which is true as the quadrilateral is cyclic.

18. (a) $\vec{AB}$ = P.V. of B – P.V. of $A = \mathbf{i} + 2\mathbf{j} - \mathbf{k}$.

$\vec{CD}$ = P.V. of D – P.V. of $C = -3(\mathbf{i} + 2\mathbf{j} - \mathbf{k})$.

Clearly $\vec{CD} = -3\vec{AB}$ and hence they are parallel.

(b) Proceed as above.

19. (a) Yes. From the given relations $DA \perp BC, DB \perp CA$

Hence D is orthocentre of ΔABC.

(b) True.

The given relation implies that $DA = DB = DC$, *i.e.*, D is equidistant from the vertices of ΔABC and hence D is the circumcentre of ΔABC.

20. (a) $\vec{PQ} = -2\mathbf{i} + 2\mathbf{j} + \mathbf{k}, \quad \therefore PQ = 3.$

$\vec{RS} = \mathbf{i} - 2\mathbf{j} + 2\mathbf{k}, \quad \therefore RS = 3.$

Now $\mathbf{a} \cdot \mathbf{b} = ab\cos\theta = |\mathbf{a}|$. Projection of $\mathbf{b}$ in the direction of $\mathbf{a} = |\mathbf{b}|$. Projection of $\mathbf{a}$ in the direction of $\mathbf{b}$.

Now $\vec{PQ} \cdot \vec{RS} = -2.1 + 2(-2) + 1.2 = -4$.

Hence $-4 = 3$. (Projection of $\vec{RS}$ in the direction of $\vec{PQ}$) = 3. (Projection of $\vec{PQ}$ in the direction of $\vec{RS}$)

Hence either projection $= -\dfrac{4}{3}$.

Again $\vec{PQ} \cdot \vec{RS} = PQ \cdot RS \cos\theta = 3 \cdot 3\cos\theta$

or $-\dfrac{4}{9} = \cos\theta, \quad \therefore \theta = \cos^{-1}\left(-\dfrac{4}{9}\right)$.

Refer alternative method **§ 4 P. 1122.**

(b) Ans. (c).

By given condition

$$\frac{\mathbf{v} \cdot \mathbf{u}}{|u|} = \frac{\mathbf{w} \cdot \mathbf{u}}{|u|} \quad \therefore \quad (\mathbf{v} - \mathbf{w}) \cdot \mathbf{u} = 0 \qquad \text{...(1)}$$

$\therefore \quad \mathbf{u} - \mathbf{v} + \mathbf{w} = \mathbf{u} - (\mathbf{v} - \mathbf{w})$

$\therefore \quad |\mathbf{u} - \mathbf{v} + \mathbf{w}|^2 = |\mathbf{u} - (\mathbf{v} - \mathbf{w})|^2$

$= \mathbf{u}^2 + (\mathbf{v} - \mathbf{w})^2 - 2\mathbf{u} \cdot (\mathbf{v} - \mathbf{w})$

$= \mathbf{u}^2 + \mathbf{v}^2 + \mathbf{w}^2 - 2\mathbf{v} \cdot \mathbf{w} = 0$ by (1)

$= 1 + 4 + 9 - 2.0 = 14$ as $\mathbf{v} \perp \mathbf{w} \rightarrow \mathbf{v} \cdot \mathbf{w} = 0$

$\therefore \quad |\mathbf{u} - \mathbf{v} + \mathbf{w}| = \sqrt{14}$

(c) Ans. (d).

Any vector in the plane of $\mathbf{a}$ and $\mathbf{b}$ is

$\mathbf{r} = \lambda\mathbf{a} + \mu\mathbf{b} = \lambda(\mathbf{i} + \mathbf{j} - \mathbf{k}) + \mu(\mathbf{i} - 2\mathbf{j} + \mathbf{k})$

or $\mathbf{r} = (\lambda + \mu)\mathbf{i} + (\lambda - 2\mu)\mathbf{j} + (\mu - \lambda)\mathbf{k}$

$\mathbf{c} = \mathbf{i} - \mathbf{j} - \mathbf{k}$.

Projection of $\mathbf{r}$ on $\mathbf{c} = \dfrac{\mathbf{r} \cdot \mathbf{c}}{|\mathbf{c}|} = \dfrac{1}{\sqrt{3}}$

$$\frac{(\lambda + \mu) - (\lambda - 2\mu) - (\mu - \lambda)}{\sqrt{3}} = \frac{1}{\sqrt{3}}$$

or $\lambda + 2\mu = 1 \quad \therefore \quad \lambda = 1 - 2\mu$

$\therefore \quad \mathbf{r} = (1 - \mu)\mathbf{i} + (1 - 4\mu)\mathbf{j} + (3\mu - 1)\mathbf{k}$

For $\mu = -3, \quad \mathbf{r} = 4\mathbf{i} + 13\mathbf{j} - 10\mathbf{k}$

(d) $BM^2 = AB^2 - AM^2 \qquad \text{...(1)}$

$\vec{AB} = -3, 0, 1 = -3\mathbf{i} + 0\mathbf{j} + \mathbf{k}$

$\therefore \quad AB^2 = \vec{AB}^2 = 9 + 1 = 10$

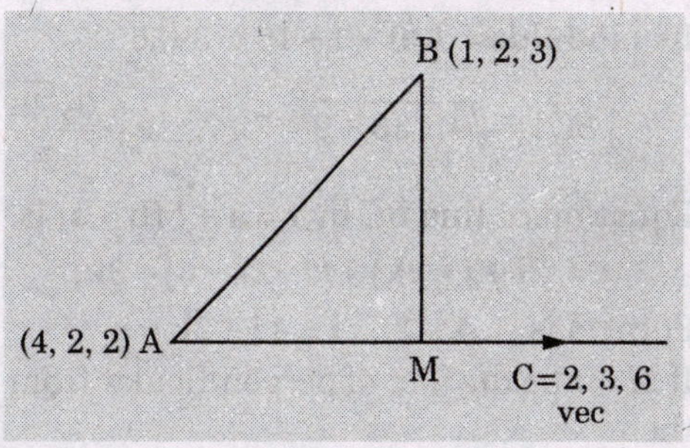

Fig. 14

AM = Projection of $\vec{AB}$ in the direction of $\vec{C}$

$= 2\mathbf{i} + 3\mathbf{j} + 6\mathbf{k}$

$$\therefore \quad AM = \frac{\vec{AB} \cdot \vec{C}}{|\vec{C}|} = \frac{(-3\mathbf{i} + 0\mathbf{j} + \mathbf{k}) \cdot (2\mathbf{i} + 3\mathbf{j} + 6\mathbf{k})}{7} = 0$$

$\therefore \quad BM^2 = 10 - 0 = 10 \quad \therefore \quad BM = \sqrt{(10)}$ by (1)

Note : If the projection of a vector $\mathbf{a}$ on $\mathbf{b}$ is zero, it means that $\mathbf{a}$ and $\mathbf{b}$ are perpendicular. Hence $\vec{AB}$ is $\perp$ to $\mathbf{c}$.

21. (a) Refer Q. 20, the vector $\vec{BC} = 0 - 2, -5 - 1, 1 + 2$ or $-2, -6, 3$. Also $\vec{BA} = 1 - 2, 4 - 1, -2 + 2$ or $-1, 3, 0$.

If $AM = p$ be the perpendicular from A on BC then

$AM = \sqrt{BA^2 - BM^2}$ where $BA = \sqrt{1 + 9 + 0} = \sqrt{10}$

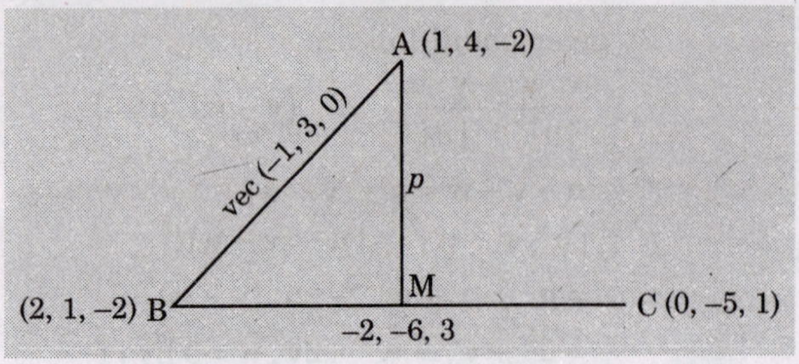

Fig. 15

BM is projection $\vec{BA} = -1, 3, 0$ on $\vec{BC} = -2, -6, -3$.

$$\therefore \quad BM = \frac{\vec{BA}\,.\,\vec{BC}}{|\vec{BC}|} = \frac{(-1,3,0)\,.\,(-2,-6,-3)}{\sqrt{4+36+9}}$$

$$= \frac{2-18+0}{7} = -\frac{16}{7} = \frac{16}{7}$$

$$\therefore \quad p = \sqrt{BA^2 - BM^2} = \sqrt{10 - \frac{256}{49}}$$

$$= \frac{\sqrt{236}}{7} = \frac{3}{7}\sqrt{26}.$$

Alternative Method :

From the figure $p = AB \sin\theta$

or $\quad p = \dfrac{AB\,.\,BC\sin\theta}{BC} = \dfrac{|\vec{BA}\times\vec{BC}|}{|\vec{BC}|}$

$$N^r = \begin{vmatrix} \mathbf{i} & \mathbf{j} & \mathbf{k} \\ -1 & 3 & 0 \\ -2 & -6 & -3 \end{vmatrix} = -9\mathbf{i} - 3\mathbf{j} - 12\mathbf{k}$$

Its modulus $= 3\sqrt{9+1+16} = 3\sqrt{26}$

$$|\vec{BC}| = \sqrt{4+36+9} = 7 \quad \therefore \quad p = \frac{3\sqrt{26}}{7}.$$

(b) Equation of line BC by $\mathbf{r} = \mathbf{a} + t\,(\mathbf{b} - \mathbf{a})$ is

$$\mathbf{r} = (2\mathbf{i} + \mathbf{j} - 2\mathbf{k}) + t\,(-2\mathbf{i} - 6\mathbf{j} + 3\mathbf{k}) \qquad ...(1)$$

Point A is $(1, 4, -2) = \mathbf{i} + 4\,\mathbf{j} - 2\mathbf{k} = \mathbf{a}$

If $M = \mathbf{r}$ be the foot of perpendicular from A on BC then

$$\vec{AM} \cdot \vec{BC} = 0$$

$$(\mathbf{r} - \mathbf{a}) \cdot \vec{BC} = 0$$

or $\quad [(\mathbf{i} - 3\mathbf{j} + 0\mathbf{k}) + t\,(-2\mathbf{i} - 6\mathbf{j} + 3\mathbf{k})] \cdot (-2\mathbf{i} - 6\mathbf{j} + 3\mathbf{k}) = 0$

or $\quad (-2 + 18 + 0) + t\,(4 + 36 + 9) = 0 \quad \therefore \quad t = -\dfrac{16}{49}$

Putting for t in (1), we get the coordinates of foot of perpendicular M as

$$\left(\frac{130}{49}, \frac{145}{49}, -\frac{146}{49}\right)$$

(c) Proceed as in part (a). Ans. $\dfrac{\sqrt{10}}{7}$.

22. (a) This is another form of **§ 4 Page 1122.**

As in **Q. 21 (a)** (alt. method) the required distance is $\quad p = BA\sin\theta$

$$= \frac{BA\,.\,BC\sin\theta}{BC} = \frac{|\vec{BA}\times\vec{BC}|}{|\vec{BC}|} = \frac{|(\mathbf{a}-\mathbf{b})\times\mathbf{c}|}{|\mathbf{c}|} \qquad ...(1)$$

Again BM = Projection of $\vec{BA}$ on $\vec{BC}$

$$= \frac{\vec{BA}\,.\,\vec{BC}}{|\mathbf{c}|} = \frac{(\mathbf{a}-\mathbf{b})\,.\,\mathbf{c}}{|\mathbf{c}|}$$

$$\therefore \quad \vec{BM} = \frac{(\mathbf{a}-\mathbf{b})\,.\,\mathbf{c}}{|\mathbf{c}|}\,\frac{\mathbf{c}}{|\mathbf{c}|}$$

$$\mathbf{p} = \vec{AM} = \vec{AB} + \vec{BM} = \mathbf{b} - \mathbf{a} + \frac{(\mathbf{a}-\mathbf{b})\,.\,\mathbf{c}}{|\mathbf{c}|}\,\frac{\mathbf{c}}{|\mathbf{c}|}$$

$$\therefore \quad p = |\mathbf{p}| = \left|\,\mathbf{b} - \mathbf{a} + \frac{(\mathbf{a}-\mathbf{b})\,.\,\mathbf{c}}{|\mathbf{c}|^2}\,\mathbf{c}\,\right| \qquad ...(2)$$

(1) and (2) give the required results.

(b) Let D be (x, y, z), then $AD \perp BC$.

$$\therefore \quad \vec{AD}\,.\,\vec{BC} = 0$$

$(x-1), y, (z-2)$ is $\perp$ to $4, -2, -2$.

$$\therefore \quad 4\,(x-1) - 2y - 2\,(z-2) = 0$$

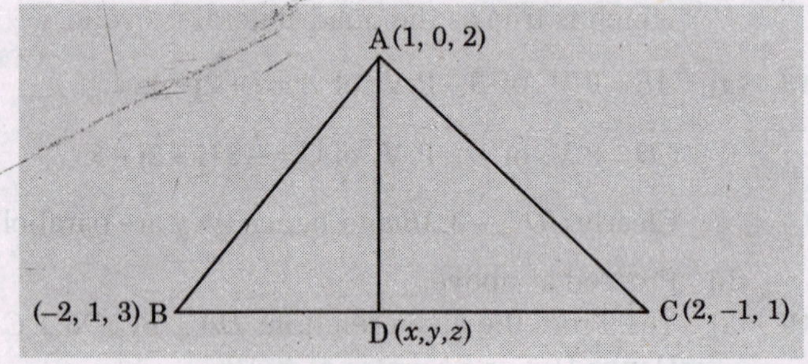

Fig. 16

or $\quad 2x - y - z = 0 \qquad ...(1)$

The point D lies on BC, $\quad \mathbf{r} = (1-t)\,\alpha + t\,\beta$

or $\quad \mathbf{r} = \alpha + t\,(\beta - \alpha)$

$$x\mathbf{i} + y\mathbf{j} + z\mathbf{k} = -2\mathbf{i} + \mathbf{j} + 3\mathbf{k} + t\,(4\mathbf{i} - 2\mathbf{j} - 2\mathbf{k})$$

Comparing $\mathbf{i}, \mathbf{j}, \mathbf{k}$, we find the values of x, y, z in t and putting in (1), we get $t = 2/3$.

$$\therefore \quad x\mathbf{i} + y\mathbf{j} + z\mathbf{k} = \frac{1}{3}\,(2\mathbf{i} - \mathbf{j} + 5\mathbf{k})$$

$$\therefore \quad \text{Point } D\,(x, y, z) \text{ is } \left(\frac{2}{3}, -\frac{1}{3}, \frac{5}{3}\right)$$

$$\vec{AD} = \frac{1}{3}\,(-\mathbf{i} - \mathbf{j} + \mathbf{k}) \quad \therefore \quad AD = \frac{1}{3}\sqrt{3} = \frac{1}{\sqrt{3}}$$

23. Let the unit vectors along the edges be $\mathbf{i}, \mathbf{j}, \mathbf{k}$. Then P.V. of P is $\mathbf{i} + \mathbf{j} + \mathbf{k}$ w.r.t. O as origin. Its four diagonals are AL, BM, CN and OP.

Let CM be perpendicular from $C\,(\mathbf{k})$ on OP, then

$$CM^2 = OC^2 - OM^2 \qquad ...(1)$$

OM = projection of $\vec{OC}$ on $\vec{OP}$

$$= \frac{\vec{OC}\,.\,\vec{OP}}{|\vec{OP}|} = \frac{\mathbf{k}\,.\,(\mathbf{i}+\mathbf{j}+\mathbf{k})}{\sqrt{3}} = \frac{1}{\sqrt{3}} \qquad ...(2)$$

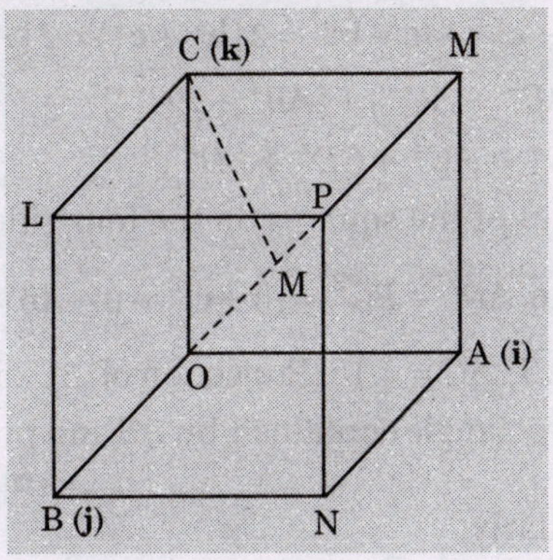

Fig. 17

Hence from (1) and (2),

$$CM = \sqrt{1 - \frac{1}{3}} = \sqrt{\frac{2}{3}} = \frac{1}{3}\sqrt{6}.$$

24. (a) Ans. $\frac{2}{\sqrt{(14)}}$.

$$\frac{2}{\sqrt{(14)}}\left(\frac{\mathbf{i}+2\mathbf{j}+3\mathbf{k}}{\sqrt{(14)}}\right) = \frac{1}{7}(\mathbf{i}+2\mathbf{j}+3\mathbf{k}).$$

(b) Do yourself.

25. (a) Projection of **a** along **b** is $\frac{\mathbf{a}\,.\,\mathbf{b}}{|\mathbf{b}|}$

$$= \frac{4\cdot 0 + 6\cdot 3 + 0\cdot 4}{5} = \frac{18}{5}.$$

Hence the vector determined by this projection is

$$\frac{18}{5}\hat{\mathbf{b}} = \frac{18}{5}\left(\frac{3\mathbf{j}+4\mathbf{k}}{5}\right) = \frac{18}{25}(3\mathbf{j}+4\mathbf{k}).$$

(b) $\beta = 4\mathbf{i} + 3\mathbf{j}$ $\therefore$ $\gamma = 3\lambda\mathbf{i} - 4\lambda\mathbf{j}$ for all values of λ.

We have chosen γ such that $\beta\,.\,\gamma = 0$ as β and γ are perpendicular.

Let the required vector be $\alpha = p\mathbf{i} + q\mathbf{j}$

Projection of α in the direction of $\beta = \frac{\alpha\,.\,\beta}{|\beta|}$.

$$\therefore \quad 1 = \frac{4p+3q}{5} \quad \therefore \quad 4p + 3q = 5 \qquad ...(1)$$

$$2 = \frac{3\lambda p - 4\lambda q}{\pm 5\lambda} \quad \therefore \quad 3p - 4q = 10 \qquad ...(2)$$

$$\text{or} \quad 3p - 4q = -10 \qquad ...(3)$$

Modulus of vector γ is 5λ if $\lambda > 0$ and -5λ if $\lambda < 0$

Solving (1) and (2), we get $p = 2, q = -1$ and solving (1) and (3), we get $p = -\frac{2}{5}$ and $q = \frac{11}{5}$

$$\therefore \quad \alpha = 2\mathbf{i} - \mathbf{j} \quad \text{or} \quad \frac{1}{5}(-2\mathbf{i} + 11\mathbf{j})$$

26. (a) Let the position vectors of points B and C w.r.t. A as origin be **b** and **c** so that $\vec{AB} = \mathbf{b}$, $\vec{AC} = \mathbf{c}$. Since they are at right angles, therefore $\mathbf{b}\,.\,\mathbf{c} = 0 = \mathbf{c}\,.\,\mathbf{b}$.

Now $\vec{BC} = \vec{AC} - \vec{AB} = \mathbf{c} - \mathbf{b}$.

Again square of a vector is square of its module.

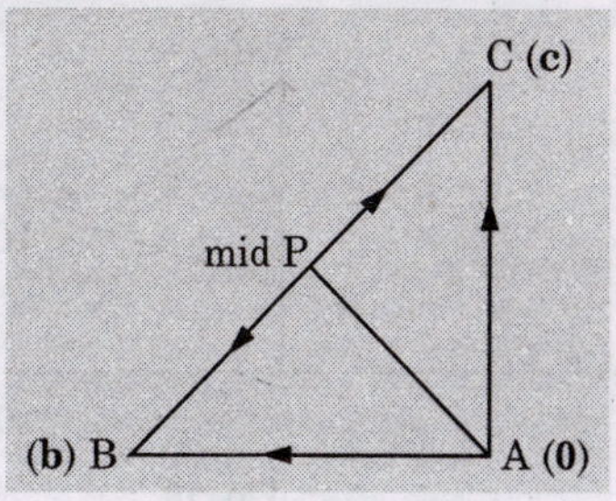

Fig. 18

$$\therefore \quad BC^2 = \vec{BC}^2 = (\mathbf{c}-\mathbf{b})^2 = \mathbf{c}^2 + \mathbf{b}^2 - 2\,\mathbf{c}\,.\,\mathbf{b}$$

$$= \vec{AC}^2 + \vec{AB}^2 - 0 = AC^2 + AB^2.$$

If P be the mid-point of BC so that $PC = PB$.

Also $\quad \vec{PB} = -\vec{PC}. \qquad ...(1)$

Now $\mathbf{b} = \vec{AB} = \vec{AP} + \vec{PB}$,

$$\mathbf{c} = \vec{AC} = \vec{AP} + \vec{PC} = \vec{AP} - \vec{PB}, \text{ by (1)}.$$

$$\therefore \quad \mathbf{b}\,.\,\mathbf{c} = (\vec{AP} + \vec{PB})\,.\,(\vec{AP} - \vec{PB}) = \vec{AP}^2 - \vec{PB}^2$$

$$\text{or} \quad 0 = AP^2 - PB^2, \quad \therefore \quad AP = PB = PC.$$

Hence the mid-point P of BC is equidistant from the three vertices.

(b) Taking A as origin let the position vectors of B and C be **b** and **c** respectively so that P.V. of P the mid-point is $\frac{\mathbf{b}+\mathbf{c}}{2}$.

$$\text{L.H.S.} = AB^2 + AC^2 = \vec{AB}^2 + \vec{AC}^2 = \mathbf{b}^2 + \mathbf{c}^2$$

$$\text{R.H.S.} = 2(AP^2 + PB^2) = 2[\vec{AP}^2 + \vec{PB}^2]$$

$$= 2\left[\left(\frac{\mathbf{b}+\mathbf{c}}{2}\right)^2 + \left(\mathbf{b} - \frac{\mathbf{b}+\mathbf{c}}{2}\right)^2\right]$$

$$= 2\,.\,\frac{1}{4}[(\mathbf{b}+\mathbf{c})^2 + (\mathbf{b}-\mathbf{c})^2] = \mathbf{b}^2 + \mathbf{c}^2 = \text{L.H.S.}$$

(c) Refer fig. Q. 26 (a).

The triangle being isosceles, we have

$$AB = AC. \qquad ...(1)$$

Now $\vec{AP} = \frac{\mathbf{b}+\mathbf{c}}{2}$ where P is mid-point of BC.

Also, $\quad \vec{BC} = \mathbf{c} - \mathbf{b}$.

$$\therefore \quad \vec{AP}\,.\,\vec{BC} = \frac{\mathbf{b}+\mathbf{c}}{2}\,.\,(\mathbf{c}-\mathbf{b}) = \frac{1}{2}(\mathbf{c}^2 - \mathbf{b}^2)$$

$$= \frac{1}{2}(AC^2 - AB^2) = 0, \qquad \text{by (1)}$$

$\therefore$ Median AP is perp. to base BC.

(d) With A as origin let the position vectors of vertices B and C be **b** and **c** respectively.

$$\text{Now } \vec{AD}\,.\,\vec{BE} = \left(\frac{\mathbf{b}+\mathbf{c}}{2} - 0\right)\,.\,\left(\frac{\mathbf{c}}{2} - \mathbf{b}\right)$$

$$= \frac{1}{4}(\mathbf{b}+\mathbf{c})(\mathbf{c} - 2\mathbf{b})$$

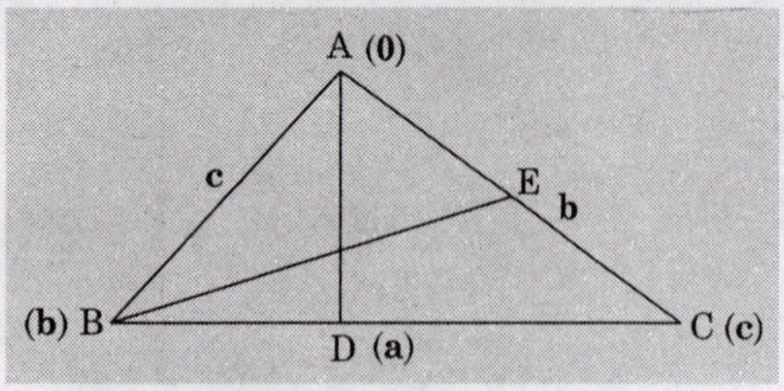

Fig. 19

$$= \frac{1}{4}(-2\mathbf{b}^2 + \mathbf{c}^2 - \mathbf{b}.\mathbf{c}) \quad ...(1)$$

From the given relation $a^2 + b^2 = 5c^2$ we have

$BC^2 + AC^2 = 5AB^2$

or $\quad \vec{BC}^2 + \vec{AC}^2 = 5\vec{AB}^2 \qquad \because \mathbf{a}^2 = |\mathbf{a}|^2$

or $\quad (\mathbf{c} - \mathbf{b})^2 + \mathbf{c}^2 = 5\mathbf{b}^2$ or $2\mathbf{c}^2 - 2\mathbf{c}.\mathbf{b} = 4\mathbf{b}^2$

or $\quad 2(\mathbf{c}^2 - 2\mathbf{b}^2 - \mathbf{b}.\mathbf{c}) = 0 \qquad ...(2)$

Hence from (1) and (2), we have

$\vec{AD}.\vec{BE} = 0 \Rightarrow AD \perp BE$

(e) With centre O of the circle as origin let the position vectors of A_i be $\mathbf{r}_i$ such that $|\mathbf{r}_i| = 1$.

Now $\sum_{i=1}^{n} \sum_{j=1}^{n} (A_i . A_j)^2 = \Sigma\Sigma (\mathbf{r}_i - \mathbf{r}_j)^2$

$= (\mathbf{r}_1 - \mathbf{r}_2)^2 + (\mathbf{r}_1 - \mathbf{r}_3)^2 + ... + (\mathbf{r}_1 - \mathbf{r}_n)^2$
$+ (\mathbf{r}_2 - \mathbf{r}_3)^2 + (\mathbf{r}_2 - \mathbf{r}_4)^2 + ... + (\mathbf{r}_2 - \mathbf{r}_n)^2$
$+ (\mathbf{r}_3 - \mathbf{r}_4)^2 + (\mathbf{r}_3 - \mathbf{r}_5)^2 + ... + (\mathbf{r}_3 - \mathbf{r}_n)^2$
$... + (\mathbf{r}_n - \mathbf{r}_{n-1})^2$

$= (n-1)[\mathbf{r}_1^2 + \mathbf{r}_2^2 + ... \mathbf{r}_n^2] - (2\Sigma_i . \Sigma_j \mathbf{r}_i . \mathbf{r}_j)$

Add $\mathbf{r}_1^2 + \mathbf{r}_2^2 + ... + \mathbf{r}_n^2$ in both the brackets

$= n[\mathbf{r}_1^2 + \mathbf{r}_2^2 + ... + \mathbf{r}_n^2] - (\mathbf{r}_1 + \mathbf{r}_2 + ... \mathbf{r}_n)^2$

$\therefore \quad \sum_{i=1}^{n} \sum_{j=1}^{n} (A_i A_j)^2 = n(1 + 1 + 1 ... n) - L^2,$

$\leq n.n = n^2$, as $L^2 \geq 0$

27. Taking A as origin let the position vectors of B and C be $\mathbf{b}$ and $\mathbf{c}$ so that, that of D is $\mathbf{b} + \mathbf{c}$ by parallelogram law. Let O be the intersection of the diagonals. Also

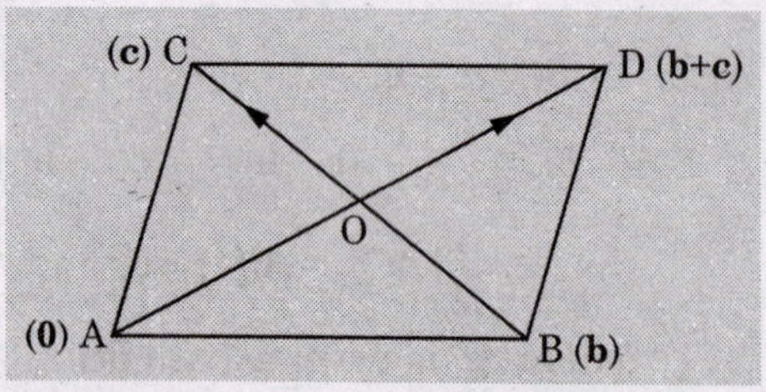

Fig. 20

$\vec{BC} =$ P.V. of $C -$ P.V. of $B = \mathbf{c} - \mathbf{b}$

(a) Now $AD^2 + BC^2 = \vec{AD}^2 + \vec{BC}^2$

$= (\mathbf{b} + \mathbf{c})^2 + (\mathbf{c} - \mathbf{b})^2 = 2(\mathbf{b}^2 + \mathbf{c}^2) = 2(AB^2 + AC^2)$

$= [(AB^2 + AC^2) + (AB^2 + AC^2)]$

$= AB^2 + AC^2 + CD^2 + BD^2$.

= Sum of the squares on the four sides.

(b) Again $\vec{AD}^2 - \vec{BC}^2 = (\mathbf{b} + \mathbf{c})^2 - (\mathbf{c} - \mathbf{b})^2 = 4\mathbf{b}.\mathbf{c}$

$= 4\vec{AB}.\vec{AC} = 4AB$ (Projection of AC on AB)

$= 4$ (rectangle contained by AB and projection of AC on AB).

(c) Similarly,

$\vec{AC}^2 - \vec{AB}^2 = \mathbf{c}^2 - \mathbf{b}^2 = (\mathbf{c} + \mathbf{b}).(\mathbf{c} - \mathbf{b}) = \vec{AD}.\vec{BC}$

$=$ diag. AD (Projection of diag. BC on AD)

28. (a) Here $AD = BC$ since diagonals are equal.

$\therefore \quad \vec{AD}^2 = \vec{BC}^2$ or $(\mathbf{b} + \mathbf{c})^2 - (\mathbf{c} - \mathbf{b})^2 = 0$

or $\quad 4\mathbf{b}.\mathbf{c} = 0$

i.e., $\vec{AB}.\vec{AC} = 0, \quad \therefore AB \perp AC$

and hence the parallelogram is a rectangle.

(b) If the figure **V-68** of **Q. 27 (a) above** is a rhombus, then $\quad AB = AC. \qquad ...(1)$

$\therefore \quad \vec{AD}.\vec{BC} = (\mathbf{b} + \mathbf{c}).(\mathbf{c} - \mathbf{b}) = \mathbf{c}^2 - \mathbf{b}^2$

$= \vec{AC}^2 - \vec{AB}^2 = AC^2 - AB^2 = 0, \qquad$ by (1)

$\therefore \vec{AD} \perp \vec{BC}$ or $AD \perp BC$, *i.e.* diagonals are perpendicular in a rhombus.

29. Take the centre O as origin and AB is the diameter so that $OA = OB$.

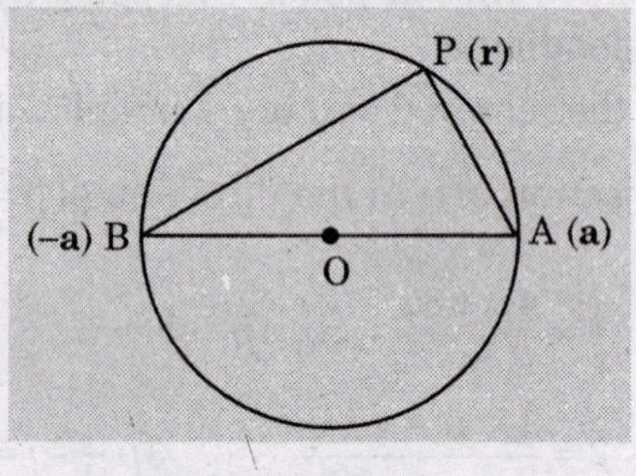

Fig. 21

If the point A be $\mathbf{a}$ then B is $-\mathbf{a}$ and $|\mathbf{a}| = r =$ radius. Let P be any point $\mathbf{r}$ on the circumference, so that $|\mathbf{r}| = OP = r$.

Then $\vec{AP} =$ P.V. of $P -$ P.V. of $A = \mathbf{r} - \mathbf{a}$

and $\vec{BP} =$ P.V. of $P -$ P.V. of $B = \mathbf{r} + \mathbf{a}$.

$\therefore \quad \vec{AP}.\vec{BP} = (\mathbf{r} - \mathbf{a}).(\mathbf{r} + \mathbf{a}) = \mathbf{r}^2 - \mathbf{a}^2 = r^2 - r^2 = 0$

Hence AP is $\perp$ to BP, *i.e.* angle in a semi-circle is a right angle.

30. Taking A as origin, let P.V.s. of B and C be $\mathbf{b}$ and $\mathbf{c}$ respectively and hence those of the mid-points F and E are $\mathbf{b}/2$ and $\mathbf{c}/2$.

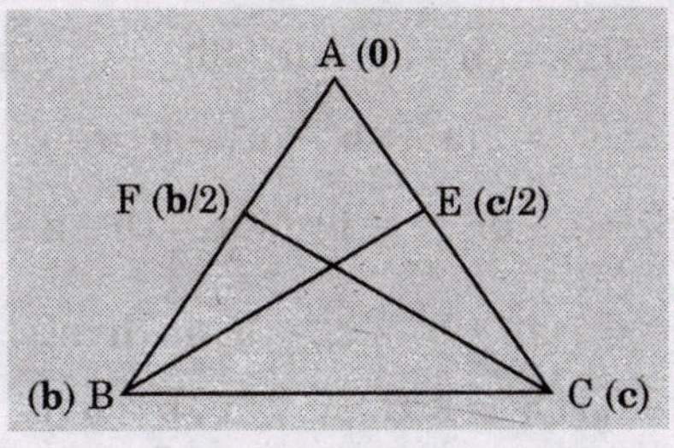

Fig. 22

$\therefore \quad \vec{BE} = \mathbf{c}/2 - \mathbf{b}, \vec{CF} = \mathbf{b}/2 - \mathbf{c}.$

$BE = CF$ (given),

$\therefore \quad BE^2 = CF^2 \quad \text{or} \quad \vec{BE}^2 = \vec{CF}^2$

or $\left(\frac{\mathbf{c}}{2} - \mathbf{b}\right)^2 = \left(\frac{\mathbf{b}}{2} - \mathbf{c}\right)^2$

or $\frac{\mathbf{c}^2}{4} + \mathbf{b}^2 - \mathbf{c}\,.\,\mathbf{b} = \frac{\mathbf{b}^2}{4} + \mathbf{c}^2 - \mathbf{b}\,.\,\mathbf{c}$

or $\frac{3}{4}(\mathbf{b}^2 - \mathbf{c}^2) = 0$ or $\mathbf{b}^2 = \mathbf{c}^2$ or $\vec{AB}^2 = \vec{AC}^2$

or $AB^2 = AC^2, \ \therefore \ AB = AC.$

Hence the triangle is isosceles.

31. (a) Let the point of intersection O of two altitudes BQ and CR be taken as origin and the position vectors of the vertices A, B, C be $\mathbf{a}, \mathbf{b}, \mathbf{c}$ respectively. Let AO produced meet BC at P. We will show that AP is perpendicular to BC, showing thereby that the three altitudes are concurrent,

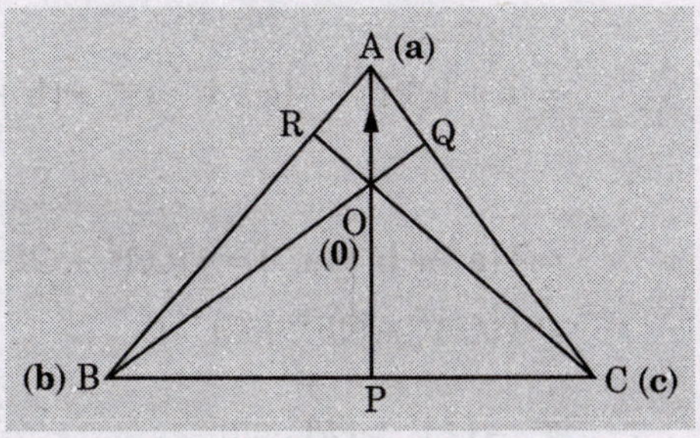

Fig. 23

$\therefore \quad \vec{OB} = \mathbf{b}, \quad \therefore \quad \vec{BQ} = \mu\mathbf{b}$

as it is collinear with $\vec{OB}$.

Similarly since $\vec{OC} = \mathbf{c}$, $\therefore$ $\vec{CR} = \nu\,\mathbf{c}$

Now $\vec{AC} = \mathbf{c} - \mathbf{a}$ and $\vec{AB} = \mathbf{b} - \mathbf{a}$.

Since $BQ \perp AC$, we have $\mu\mathbf{b}\,.\,(\mathbf{c} - \mathbf{a})$ and so $\mathbf{a}\,.\,\mathbf{b} = \mathbf{b}\,.\,\mathbf{c}$

Again since $CR \perp$ to AB,

$\nu\mathbf{c}\,.\,(\mathbf{b} - \mathbf{a}) = 0, \ \therefore \ \mathbf{b}\,.\,\mathbf{c} = \mathbf{c}\,.\,\mathbf{a}$

$\therefore \quad \mathbf{a}\,.\,\mathbf{b} = \mathbf{b}\,.\,\mathbf{c} = \mathbf{c}\,.\,\mathbf{a}$ or $\mathbf{a}\,.\,(\mathbf{c} - \mathbf{b}) = 0$

or $\lambda\mathbf{a}\,.\,(\mathbf{c} - \mathbf{b}) = 0.$

$\therefore \quad \vec{AP}\,.\,\vec{BC} = 0$ or AP is $\perp$ to BC.

(b) Let the right bisectors of sides BC and CA meet at O and taking O as origin let the position vectors of A, B and C be taken as $\mathbf{a}, \mathbf{b}, \mathbf{c}$ respectively. Hence the mid-points D, E, F are

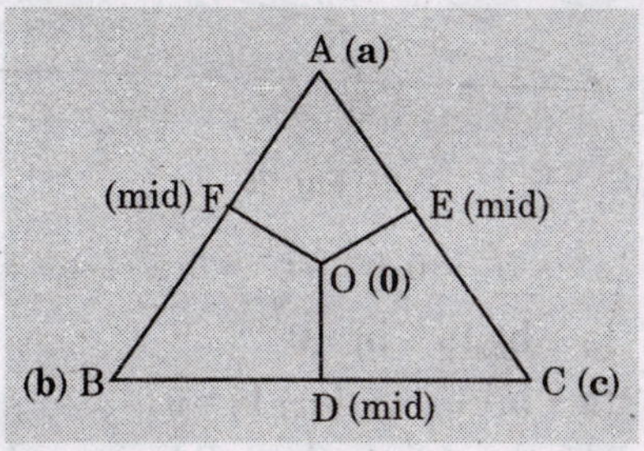

Fig. 24

$\frac{\mathbf{b}+\mathbf{c}}{2}, \ \frac{\mathbf{c}+\mathbf{a}}{2}, \ \frac{\mathbf{a}+\mathbf{b}}{2}.$

$\because \quad OD \perp BC, \ \therefore \ \frac{\mathbf{b}+\mathbf{c}}{2}\,.\,(\mathbf{c} - \mathbf{b}) = 0$ *i.e.* $\mathbf{b}^2 = \mathbf{c}^2$

Again since $OE \perp CA$, $\therefore$ $\frac{\mathbf{c}+\mathbf{a}}{2}\,.\,(\mathbf{a} - \mathbf{c}) = 0,$

or $\mathbf{a}^2 = \mathbf{c}^2 \qquad \therefore \quad \mathbf{a}^2 = \mathbf{b}^2 = \mathbf{c}^2.$ ...(1)

Now we have to prove that OF is also $\perp$ to AB which will be true if

$\frac{\mathbf{a}+\mathbf{b}}{2}\,.\,(\mathbf{b} - \mathbf{a}) = 0$ *i.e.,* $\mathbf{b}^2 = \mathbf{a}^2$

which is true by (1).

32. It is a very simple question. Let the perpendiculars from A, B, C to QR, RP and PQ be concurrent at O. With O as origin, let the position vectors of the six points be $A\,(\mathbf{a}), B\,(\mathbf{b}), C\,(\mathbf{c}), P\,(\mathbf{p}), Q\,(\mathbf{q}), R\,(\mathbf{r})$

$OA \perp QR, \quad OB \perp RP, \quad OC \perp PQ$

$\Rightarrow \quad \mathbf{a}\,.\,(\mathbf{r} - \mathbf{q}) = 0, \quad \mathbf{b}\,(\mathbf{p} - \mathbf{r}) = 0, \quad \mathbf{c}\,(\mathbf{q} - \mathbf{p}) = 0$ ...(1)

Let the perpendiculars from P to BC and Q to CA intersect at any point whose position vector is ρ then

$(\rho - \mathbf{p})\,.\,(\mathbf{c} - \mathbf{b}) = 0, (\rho - \mathbf{q})\,.\,(\mathbf{a} - \mathbf{c}) = 0$ ...(2)

and we shall prove that perpendicular from R to AB also passes through P.

or $(\rho - \mathbf{r})\,.\,(\mathbf{b} - \mathbf{a}) = 0$ ...(3)

From (2) $\rho\,.\,(\mathbf{c} - \mathbf{b}) = \mathbf{p}\,.\,(\mathbf{c} - \mathbf{b})$

$\rho\,.\,(\mathbf{a} - \mathbf{c}) = \mathbf{q}\,.\,(\mathbf{a} - \mathbf{c})$

Adding $\rho\,.\,(\mathbf{a} - \mathbf{b}) = \mathbf{p}\,.\,\mathbf{c} - \mathbf{p}\,.\,\mathbf{b} + \mathbf{q}\,.\,\mathbf{a} - \mathbf{q}\,.\,\mathbf{c}$

$= (\mathbf{p} - \mathbf{q})\,.\,\mathbf{c} - \mathbf{b}\,.\,\mathbf{r} + \mathbf{a}\,.\,\mathbf{r}$ by relations in (1)

$\therefore \quad \rho\,.\,(\mathbf{a} - \mathbf{b}) = 0 + \mathbf{r}\,(\mathbf{a} - \mathbf{b})$

$\therefore \quad (\rho - \mathbf{r})\,.\,(\mathbf{a} - \mathbf{b}) = 0 \Rightarrow (3).$

33. (a) Let O, the circumcentre of the $\Delta\,ABC$ be chosen as origin and P.V. of A, B, C be taken as $\mathbf{a}, \mathbf{b}, \mathbf{c}$. Hence P.V. of G the centroid is

$\vec{OG} = \frac{\mathbf{a}+\mathbf{b}+\mathbf{c}}{3}$ ...(1)

Since O is circumcentre $\therefore$ $OA = OB = OC$

$= \vec{OA}^2 = \vec{OB}^2 = \vec{OC}^2$ or $\mathbf{a}^2 = \mathbf{b}^2 = \mathbf{c}^2$

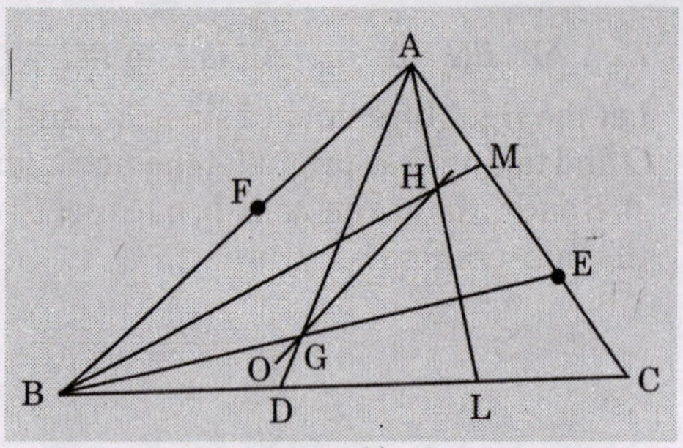

Fig. 25

$$\mathbf{a}^2 - \mathbf{b}^2 = 0, \mathbf{b}^2 - \mathbf{c}^2 = 0, \mathbf{c}^2 - \mathbf{a}^2 = 0$$

or $(\mathbf{a}+\mathbf{b}).(\mathbf{a}-\mathbf{b}) = 0$

or $(\mathbf{a}+\mathbf{b}+\mathbf{c}-\mathbf{c}).(\mathbf{a}-\mathbf{b}) = 0$ ...(2)

Let P be the point whose P.V. is $\mathbf{a}+\mathbf{b}+\mathbf{c}$.

$\therefore$ $(\vec{OP} - \vec{OC}).(\vec{OA} - \vec{OB}) = 0$

or $\vec{CP} \perp$ to $\vec{BA}$ or $CP \perp BA$

In a similar manner we can show that BP is $\perp$ to AC and AP is $\perp$ to CB.

Hence P is the orthocentre which is H.

$\therefore$ $\vec{OP} = \vec{OH} = \mathbf{a}+\mathbf{b}+\mathbf{c} = 3\vec{OG}$ ...(3)

$\therefore$ $OH = 3OG$

or $OG + GH = 3OG$ or $GH = 2.OG$

or $\dfrac{OG}{GH} = \dfrac{1}{2}$

Above shows that O, G, H are collinear and G divides OH in the ratio $1:2$.

(b) $\dfrac{\mathbf{a}+\mathbf{b}+\mathbf{c}}{3}$ is P.V. of G

$\therefore$ $\mathbf{a}+\mathbf{b}+\mathbf{c} = 3\vec{OG} = \vec{OH}$ by (3)

We know that G divides OH in the ratio $1:2$.

34. (a) Choose D as origin and let the position vectors of A, B and C be $\mathbf{a}$, $\mathbf{b}$ and $\mathbf{c}$ respectively.

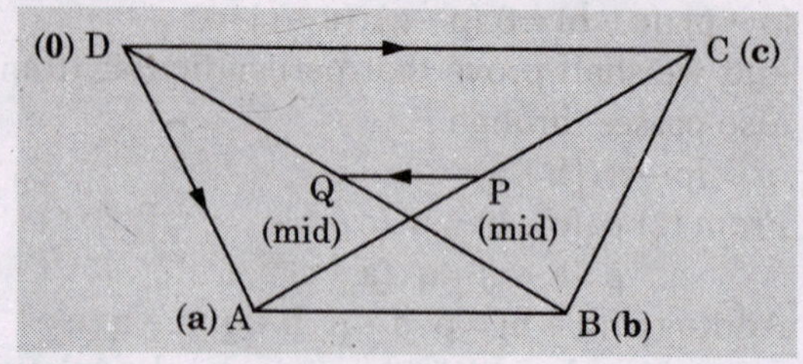

Fig. 26

$\therefore$ $\vec{AB} = \mathbf{b}-\mathbf{a}$, $\vec{BC} = \mathbf{c}-\mathbf{b}$, $\vec{CD} = -\mathbf{c}$, $\vec{DA} = \mathbf{a}$,

$\vec{AC} = \mathbf{c}-\mathbf{a}$, $\vec{BD} = -\mathbf{b}$.

Also points P and Q are mid-points of AC and BD.

$\therefore$ P is $\dfrac{\mathbf{a}+\mathbf{c}}{2}$ and Q is $\dfrac{\mathbf{b}}{2}$. $\therefore$ $\vec{PQ} = \dfrac{1}{2}(\mathbf{b}-\mathbf{a}-\mathbf{c})$.

Again square of a vector is equal to square of its module.

$\therefore$ L.H.S. $= (\mathbf{b}-\mathbf{a})^2 + (\mathbf{c}-\mathbf{b})^2 + \mathbf{c}^2 + \mathbf{a}^2$

$= 2(\mathbf{a}^2 + \mathbf{b}^2 + \mathbf{c}^2 - \mathbf{b}.\mathbf{a} - \mathbf{c}.\mathbf{b})$

R.H.S. $= (\mathbf{c}-\mathbf{a})^2 + (-\mathbf{b})^2 + 4.\dfrac{1}{4}(\mathbf{b}-\mathbf{a}-\mathbf{c})^2$

$= 2[\mathbf{a}^2 + \mathbf{b}^2 + \mathbf{c}^2 - \mathbf{b}.\mathbf{a} - \mathbf{b}.\mathbf{c}]$.

Hence L.H.S. = R.H.S., $\because$ $\mathbf{c}.\mathbf{b} = \mathbf{b}.\mathbf{c}$.

(b) Let the position vectors, of A, B, C be $\mathbf{a}, \mathbf{b}, \mathbf{c}$ relative to O as origin, then those of D, E and F are respectively $\mathbf{a}+\mathbf{b}$, $\mathbf{b}+\mathbf{c}$ and $\mathbf{c}+\mathbf{a}$.

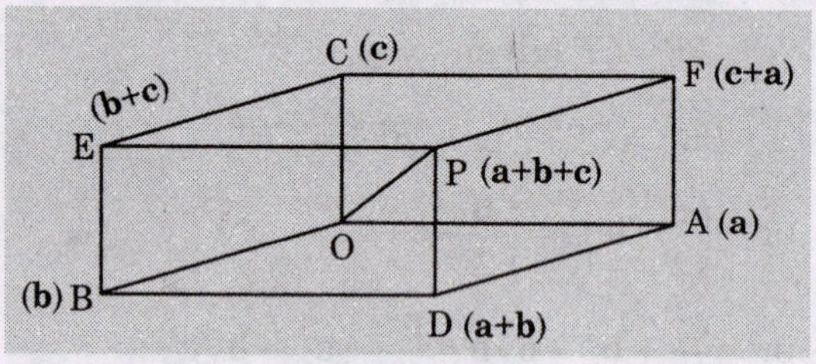

Fig. 27

The four diagonals are OP, CD, AE and BF.

$\therefore$ $\vec{OP} = \vec{OD} + \vec{DP} = \mathbf{a}+\mathbf{b}+\mathbf{c}$,

$\vec{CD} = \vec{OD} - \vec{OC} = \mathbf{a}+\mathbf{b}-\mathbf{c}$,

$\vec{AE} = \vec{OE} - \vec{OA} = \mathbf{b}+\mathbf{c}-\mathbf{a}$,

$\vec{BF} = \vec{OF} - \vec{OB} = \mathbf{c}+\mathbf{a}-\mathbf{b}$.

$\therefore$ $OP^2 + CD^2 + AE^2 + BF^2 = \vec{OP}^2 + \vec{CD}^2 + \vec{AE}^2 + \vec{BF}^2$

$= (\mathbf{a}+\mathbf{b}+\mathbf{c})^2 + (\mathbf{a}+\mathbf{b}-\mathbf{c})^2 + (\mathbf{b}+\mathbf{c}-\mathbf{a})^2 + (\mathbf{c}+\mathbf{a}-\mathbf{b})^2$

$= 4(\mathbf{a}^2 + \mathbf{b}^2 + \mathbf{c}^2) = 4(\vec{OA}^2 + \vec{OB}^2 + \vec{OC}^2)$

$= 4(OA^2 + OB^2 + OC^2)$,

$\because$ $\mathbf{a}^2 = \vec{OA}^2 = OA^2$ etc.

35. (a) Taking D as origin, let the position vectors of A, B, C be $\mathbf{a}$, $\mathbf{b}$ and $\mathbf{c}$ respectively.

$\because$ $AC \perp$ to DB, $\therefore$ $(\mathbf{c}-\mathbf{a}).\mathbf{b} = 0$

or $\mathbf{b}.\mathbf{c} = \mathbf{b}.\mathbf{a}$ ...(1)

Again $AB \perp$ to DC.

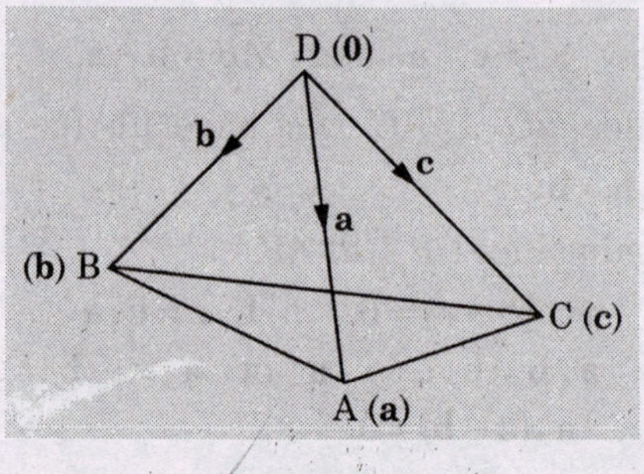

Fig. 28

$\therefore \quad (\mathbf{b}-\mathbf{a}).\mathbf{c}=0$ or $\mathbf{b}.\mathbf{c}=\mathbf{a}.\mathbf{c}$ ...(2)

Hence from (1) and (2), we get

$\mathbf{a}.\mathbf{b}=\mathbf{b}.\mathbf{c}=\mathbf{c}.\mathbf{a}$ ...(3)

$\therefore \quad \mathbf{a}.\mathbf{b}=\mathbf{c}.\mathbf{a}$, it follows that $\mathbf{a}.(\mathbf{b}-\mathbf{c})=0$, which shows that DA is $\perp$ to CB.

Hence if two pairs of opposite edges are perpendicular, then the third pair is also perpendicular.

Again $AB^2+CD^2=\vec{AB}^2+\vec{CD}^2=(\mathbf{b}-\mathbf{a})^2+\mathbf{c}^2$

$=\mathbf{a}^2+\mathbf{b}^2+\mathbf{c}^2-2\,\mathbf{a}.\mathbf{b}=\mathbf{a}^2+\mathbf{b}^2+\mathbf{c}^2-2\,\mathbf{b}.\mathbf{c}$

$=\mathbf{a}^2+\mathbf{b}^2+\mathbf{c}^2-2\,\mathbf{c}.\mathbf{a}$, by (3)

$=BC^2+DA^2=CA^2+DB^2$.

Hence sum of the squares on the two opposite edges is the same for each pair.

(b) Since the tetrahedron is regular, therefore $DA=DB=DC=AB=BC=CA$.

$\therefore \quad \mathbf{a}^2=\mathbf{b}^2=\mathbf{c}^2=(\mathbf{b}-\mathbf{a})^2=(\mathbf{c}-\mathbf{b})^2=(\mathbf{a}-\mathbf{c})^2$ ...(1)

Let us prove that the opposite edges DA and BC are perpendicular

or $\vec{DA}.\vec{BC}=0$ or $\mathbf{a}.(\mathbf{c}-\mathbf{b})=0$. ...(2)

Now from (1), we have $(\mathbf{b}-\mathbf{a})^2=(\mathbf{a}-\mathbf{c})^2$

or $\mathbf{b}^2+\mathbf{a}^2-2\mathbf{b}.\mathbf{a}=\mathbf{a}^2+\mathbf{c}^2-2\mathbf{a}.\mathbf{c}$

or $2\mathbf{a}^2-2\mathbf{b}.\mathbf{a}=2\mathbf{a}^2-2\mathbf{a}.\mathbf{c}$, by (1)

or $\mathbf{a}.(\mathbf{b}-\mathbf{c})=0$, which is (2).

Hence any pair of opposite edges are perpendicular.

36. (a) Let $A=\mathbf{a}=3\mathbf{i}-2\mathbf{j}+\mathbf{k}$ be the point through which the plane passes. Let us choose $L=\mathbf{r}=(x\mathbf{i}+y\mathbf{j}+z\mathbf{k})$ any point (x,y,z) on this plane.

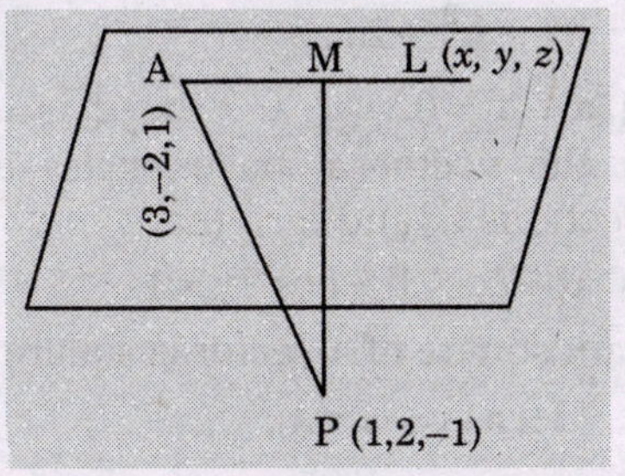

Fig. 29

Therefore, $\vec{AL}=\mathbf{r}-\mathbf{a}$

or $\vec{AL}=(x-3)\,\mathbf{i}+(y+2)\,\mathbf{j}+(z-1)\,\mathbf{k}$.

Since $4\mathbf{i}+7\mathbf{j}-4\mathbf{k}=\mathbf{n}$, say, is normal to the plane, therefore $(\mathbf{r}-\mathbf{a}).\mathbf{n}=0$

or $(x-3).4+(y+2).7+(z-1)(-4)=0$

or $4x+7y-4z+6=0$.

Again PM is perpendicular from $P(1,2,-1)=\mathbf{i}+2\mathbf{j}-\mathbf{k}$ to the plane so that PM is projection of AP along the vector $\mathbf{n}$ which is normal to the plane.

$$\therefore \quad PM=\frac{\vec{PA}.\vec{\mathbf{n}}}{|\vec{\mathbf{n}}|}=\frac{(2\mathbf{i}-4\mathbf{j}+2\mathbf{k}).(4\mathbf{i}+7\mathbf{j}-4\mathbf{k})}{\sqrt{(16+49+16)}}$$

$$=\frac{8-28-8}{9}=-\frac{28}{9}=\frac{28}{9}\text{ units.}$$

(b) A, B, C are (2, 1, 1), (1, 2, 1) and (1, 1, 2) respectively. $\therefore \ \vec{AB}\times\vec{AC}$ is normal $\mathbf{n}$ to the plane.

$$\therefore \quad \mathbf{n}=\begin{vmatrix}\mathbf{i} & \mathbf{j} & \mathbf{k}\\ -1 & 1 & 0\\ -1 & 0 & 1\end{vmatrix}=\mathbf{i}+\mathbf{j}+\mathbf{k}$$

If $Q(x,y,z)$ be any point on the plane, then $\vec{QA}$ is $\perp$ to $\mathbf{n}$.

$\therefore \quad (x-2, y-1, z-1).(1,1,1)=0$

or $x+y+z-4=0$

If p be perpendicular from $P(1, 1, 1)$ on the plane, then $PM=$ Projection of $\vec{PA}$ on $\mathbf{n}$

$$=\frac{\vec{PA}.\mathbf{n}}{|\mathbf{n}|}=\frac{(1,0,0).(1,1,1)}{\sqrt{3}}=\frac{1}{\sqrt{3}}=p$$

If M be the foot of perpendicular say (x,y,z), from $P(1,1,1)$.

$\therefore \quad \vec{PM}$ is along the normal $\mathbf{i}+\mathbf{j}+\mathbf{k}$

$$\frac{x-1}{1}=\frac{y-1}{1}=\frac{z-1}{1}$$

$$=\frac{[(x-1)^2+(y-1)^2+(z-1)^2]^{1/2}}{[1+1+1]^{1/2}}$$

$$=\frac{p}{\sqrt{(3)}}=\frac{1}{\sqrt{(3)}}\cdot\frac{1}{\sqrt{(3)}}=\frac{1}{3}$$

$\therefore \quad x=\frac{1}{3}+1=\frac{4}{3}=y=z.$

$\therefore \quad M$ the foot of perpendicular is $\frac{4}{3}(\mathbf{i}+\mathbf{j}+\mathbf{k})$.

37. (a) As in Q. 36 (b), $MP=\frac{1}{\sqrt{11}}$ by projection and point M is $\left(\frac{14}{11},\frac{21}{11},\frac{1}{11}\right)$.

(b) The equation of plane through given points as in last **Q. 36 (b)** is $\mathbf{r}-(3\mathbf{i}+8\mathbf{j}+\mathbf{k})=17$.

Solving with given line on putting the value of $\mathbf{r}$ from line in the equation of plane, we get $-4+\lambda(7)=17$

$\therefore \quad 7\lambda=21$ or $\lambda=3$.

Hence the point of intersection is

$7\mathbf{i}-\mathbf{j}+4\mathbf{k}$ or $(7,-1,4)$.

38. (a) We have $\mathbf{r}_1=\vec{OP}=3\mathbf{i}-2\mathbf{j}-\mathbf{k}$,

$\mathbf{r}_2 = \vec{OQ} = \mathbf{i} + 3\mathbf{j} + 4\mathbf{k}$

$\mathbf{r}_3 = \vec{OR} = 2\mathbf{i} + \mathbf{j} - 2\mathbf{k}$

Then $\vec{OQ} \times \vec{OR} = \begin{vmatrix} \mathbf{i} & \mathbf{j} & \mathbf{k} \\ 1 & 3 & 4 \\ 2 & 1 & -2 \end{vmatrix}$

$= -10\mathbf{i} + 10\mathbf{j} - 5\mathbf{k} = \mathbf{n}$, say.

Above is in the direction of normal to the plane OQR.

Now the distance of P from the plane OQR

$=$ Projection of $\vec{PO}$ on $\vec{OQ} \times \vec{OR}$, *i.e.* $\mathbf{n}$ (say)

$$\text{Proj.} = \frac{\vec{OP}\,.\,\mathbf{n}}{|\mathbf{n}|} = \frac{|(3\mathbf{i} - 2\mathbf{j} - \mathbf{k})\,.\,(-10\mathbf{i} + 10\mathbf{j} - 5\mathbf{k})|}{\sqrt{[(-10^2) + 10^2 + (-5)^2]}}$$

$$= \frac{45}{15} = 3.$$

(b) Normal to plane ABC is $\mathbf{n} = \vec{AB} \times \vec{AC} = \mathbf{i} + 3\mathbf{j}$

$$\mathbf{p} = \text{projection of } \vec{\mathbf{OA}} \text{ on } \mathbf{n} = \frac{\vec{OA}\,.\,\mathbf{n}}{|\mathbf{n}|} = \sqrt{10}$$

39. $\mathbf{r}\,.\,\mathbf{n}_1 = q_1$, $\mathbf{r}\,\mathbf{n}_2 = q_2$ are two planes. The line of intersection of these planes will be perpendicular to both $\mathbf{n}_1$ and $\mathbf{n}_2$ and hence parallel to $\mathbf{n}_1 \times \mathbf{n}_2$.

$$\mathbf{n}_1 \times \mathbf{n}_2 = \mathbf{N} = \begin{vmatrix} \mathbf{i} & \mathbf{j} & \mathbf{k} \\ 3 & -1 & 1 \\ 1 & 4 & -2 \end{vmatrix} = -2\mathbf{i} + 7\mathbf{j} + 13\mathbf{k}$$

Since the given plane is perpendicular to $\mathbf{N}$ and hence its normal is $\mathbf{N}$ and it passes through $\mathbf{a}$. Hence its equation is $(\mathbf{r} - \mathbf{a})\,.\,\mathbf{N} = 0$

or $\mathbf{r}\,.\,\mathbf{N} = \mathbf{a}\,.\,\mathbf{N}$

or $\mathbf{r}\,.\,(-2\mathbf{i} + 7\mathbf{j} + 13\mathbf{k}) = 1(-2) + 2(7) - 1(13).$

or $\mathbf{r}\,.\,(-2\mathbf{i} + 7\mathbf{j} + 13\mathbf{k}) = -1.$

40. (a) (i) If the lines l_1 and l_2 intersect, they will have identical values of $\mathbf{r}$ and hence compare the coefficients of $\mathbf{i}, \mathbf{j}$ and $\mathbf{k}$ in both.

$4 + 6\lambda = 9 + 2\mu$ or $6\lambda - 2\mu = 5$ ...(1)

$-1 - 4\lambda = -3 - \mu$ or $4\lambda - \mu = 2$ ...(2)

$2 + 2\lambda = 5 + \mu$ or $2\lambda - \mu = 3.$ ...(3)

Solving first two, we get $\lambda = -1/2, \mu = -4.$

These values satisfy the third. Hence l_1, l_2 intersect and putting for λ in (1) or for μ in (2), the point of intersection is $\mathbf{i} + \mathbf{j} + \mathbf{k}$ or $(1, 1, 1)$.

(ii) Find similar three equations by comparing and the values of λ and μ will not satisfy the third and hence they do not intersect.

(iii) l_1 and l_2 intersect at $\mathbf{i} + \mathbf{j} + \mathbf{k} = \mathbf{a}$ say by a l_1 is parallel to $6, -4, 2$ and l_2 is parallel to $2, -1, 1$. If $\mathbf{n}$ be the normal of the plane containing l_1 and l_2 then $\mathbf{n}$ is parallel to their cross product.

$$\therefore \quad \mathbf{n} = \begin{vmatrix} \mathbf{i} & \mathbf{j} & \mathbf{k} \\ 6 & -4 & 2 \\ 2 & -1 & 1 \end{vmatrix} = -2\mathbf{i} - 2\mathbf{j} + 2\mathbf{k}$$

Hence the equation of the plane is

$(\mathbf{r} - \mathbf{a})\,.\,\mathbf{n} = 0$ or $\mathbf{r}\,.\,\mathbf{n} = \mathbf{a}\,.\,\mathbf{n}$

where $\mathbf{a}$ is point of intersection

$\mathbf{i} + \mathbf{j} + \mathbf{k}$ or $(1, 1, 1)$.

$\mathbf{r}\,.(-2\mathbf{i} - 2\mathbf{j} + 2\mathbf{k}) = -2 - 2 + 2$

or $\mathbf{r}\,.(\mathbf{i} + \mathbf{j} - \mathbf{k}) = 1$

Note : The point $\mathbf{a}$ may be chosen as any point $(4, -1, 2)$ on l_1 or any point $(9, -3, 5)$ on l_2 instead of the point of intersection $(1, 1, 1)$ chosen as above. The answer will be same.

(b) Ans. (a).

$P(3, 2, 6)$. Any point Q on the given line is $(1 - 3\mu, -1 + \mu, 2 + 5\mu)$.

D.R.'s of PQ are $x_2 - x_1, y_2 - y_1, z_2 - z_1$

or $-2 - 3\mu, -3 + \mu, -4 + 5\mu$

PQ is parallel to plane $x - 4y + 3z = 1$ and hence it is perpendicular to normal, $1, -4, 3$

$\therefore \quad 1(-2 - 3\mu) - 4(-3 + \mu) + 3(-4 + 5\mu) = 0$

or $(-2 + 12 - 12) - \mu\,(3 + 4 - 15) = 0$

or $-2 + 8\mu = 0 \quad \therefore \quad \mu = \frac{1}{4}$

41. (a) We know that square of a vector is square of its module

$\therefore \quad |\mathbf{a} + \mathbf{b}|^2 = |\mathbf{a} - \mathbf{b}|^2$ or $(\mathbf{a} + \mathbf{b})^2 = (\mathbf{a} - \mathbf{b})^2$

or $4\mathbf{a}\,.\,\mathbf{b} = 0$ which implies that $\mathbf{a}$ and $\mathbf{b}$ are perpendicular.

(b) $|\mathbf{a} + \mathbf{b}| = 1$ (given)

$|\mathbf{a} + \mathbf{b}|^2 = (\mathbf{a} + \mathbf{b})^2 = 1 + 1 + 2.1.1\cos\theta = 1$

$\therefore \quad \cos\theta = -1/2 \quad \therefore \quad \theta = 2\pi/3$

$\therefore \quad |\mathbf{a} - \mathbf{b}|^2 = (\mathbf{a} - \mathbf{b})^2 = 1 + 1 - 2.1.1\cos\theta = 3.$

$\therefore \quad |\mathbf{a} - \mathbf{b}| = \sqrt{3}.$

(c) $|\mathbf{a} + \mathbf{b}| = |\mathbf{a}| \Rightarrow (\mathbf{a} + \mathbf{b})^2 = \mathbf{a}^2$

$\mathbf{a}^2 + \mathbf{b}^2 + 2\mathbf{a}\,.\,\mathbf{b} = \mathbf{a}^2$

or $\mathbf{b}\,.(2\mathbf{a} + \mathbf{b}) = 0. \quad \therefore \quad 2\mathbf{a} + \mathbf{b}$ is $\perp$ to $\mathbf{b}$.

42. (a) Let the vector $\mathbf{a}$ make angles α, β, γ with the directions $\mathbf{i}, \mathbf{j}$ and $\mathbf{k}$ so that

$\cos^2\alpha + \cos^2\beta + \cos^2\gamma = 1$ ...(1)

Again square of a vector is square of its modulus

$\therefore \quad |\mathbf{i} \times \mathbf{a}|^2 = (\mathbf{i} \times \mathbf{a})^2$

$= (1\,.\,a\sin\alpha)^2\,.\,1 = a^2\sin^2\alpha$

$\therefore \quad \Sigma|\mathbf{i} \times \mathbf{a}|^2 = a^2\,\Sigma\sin^2\alpha$

$= a^2\,(1 - \cos^2\alpha + 1 - \cos^2\beta + 1 - \cos^2\gamma)$

$= a^2\,(3 - 1) = 2a^2 = 2\mathbf{a}^2.$

Alternative : Take $\mathbf{a} = a_1\mathbf{i} + a_2\mathbf{j} + a_3\mathbf{k}.$

$\therefore \quad |\mathbf{a}|^2 = a_1^2 + a_2^2 + a_3^2$ ...(1)

$\mathbf{i} \times \mathbf{a} = a_2\,(\mathbf{i} \times \mathbf{j}) + a_3\,(\mathbf{k} \times \mathbf{i})$

$(\mathbf{i} \times \mathbf{a})^2 = (a_2\mathbf{k} - a_3\mathbf{j})^2 = a_2^2 + a_3^2$

$\therefore \quad \Sigma\,(\mathbf{i} \times \mathbf{a})^2 = \Sigma\,(a_2^2 + a_3^2) = 2\Sigma\,a_1^2 = 2|\mathbf{a}|^2 = 2\mathbf{a}^2.$

(b) Ans. (b).

$E = 2(1+1+1) - 2\Sigma\, \mathbf{a}.\mathbf{b} = 6 - 2\Sigma\,(\mathbf{a}.\mathbf{b})$ ...(1)

Again $(\mathbf{a}+\mathbf{b}+\mathbf{c})^2 \geq 0$

$\therefore \quad (1+1+1) + 2\Sigma\,(\mathbf{a}.\mathbf{b}) \geq 0$

$\therefore \quad 3 \geq -2\Sigma\,(\mathbf{a}.\mathbf{b})$

or $3 \geq E - 6$ or $9 \geq E \;\therefore\; E \leq 9$ by (1)

Hence E does not exceed 9.

43. (a) We know that $\frac{\mathbf{a}}{a} = \hat{\mathbf{a}}$ and $\hat{\mathbf{a}}^2 = 1$.

Hence we have to prove that

$$\left(\frac{\hat{\mathbf{a}}}{a} - \frac{\hat{\mathbf{b}}}{b}\right)^2 = \left(\frac{\hat{\mathbf{a}}}{b} - \frac{\hat{\mathbf{b}}}{a}\right)^2$$

or $(b\hat{\mathbf{a}} - a\hat{\mathbf{b}})^2 = (a\hat{\mathbf{a}} - b\hat{\mathbf{b}})^2$

or $b^2.1 + a^2.1 - 2ab\,\hat{\mathbf{a}}.\hat{\mathbf{b}} = a^2.1 + b^2.1 - 2ab\,\hat{\mathbf{a}}.\hat{\mathbf{b}}$

Clearly L.H.S. = R.H.S.

(b) Here **a** and **b** are unit vectors inclined at an angle θ so that $\mathbf{a}^2 = \mathbf{b}^2 = 1$

and $\mathbf{a}.\mathbf{b} = |\mathbf{a}||\mathbf{b}|\cos\theta = \cos\theta$ ...(1)

Now $|\mathbf{a}-\mathbf{b}|^2 = (\mathbf{a}-\mathbf{b})^2$

$= \mathbf{a}^2 + \mathbf{b}^2 - 2\mathbf{a}.\mathbf{b} = 1 + 1 - 2.1.1\cos\theta$ by (1)

$= 2(1-\cos\theta) = 2.2\sin^2(\theta/2) = 4\sin^2(\theta/2)$.

44. (a) Squaring $\mathbf{a}+\mathbf{b}+\mathbf{c} = \mathbf{0}$ and noting that $\mathbf{a}^2 = |\mathbf{a}|^2 = 1$ etc., we get

$\mathbf{a}.\mathbf{b} + \mathbf{b}.\mathbf{c} + \mathbf{c}.\mathbf{a} = -3/2$.

(b) Let O the circumcentre of triangle ABC be taken as origin and $OA = OB = OC = R$ (circumradius)

$\therefore \quad \vec{OA}^2 = \vec{OB}^2 = \vec{OC}^2 = R^2$

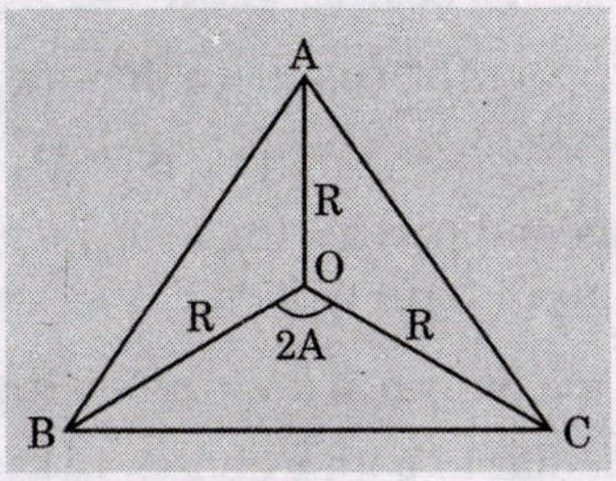

Fig. 30

Also $\vec{OB}.\vec{OC} = R.R\cos 2A$ as angle at the centre is twice the angle at the circumference.

Now $(\vec{OA} + \vec{OB} + \vec{OC})^2 \geq 0$

or $R^2 + R^2 + R^2 + 2R^2(\cos 2A + \cos 2B + \cos 2C) \geq 0$

$\therefore \quad \cos 2A + \cos 2B + \cos 2C \geq -3/2$.

45. (a) Multiplying the given relations vectorially by **a**, **b** and **c** and noting that $\alpha \times \beta = -(\beta \times \alpha)$ and $\alpha \times \alpha = \mathbf{0}$ we have $2(\mathbf{a}\times\mathbf{b}) = 3(\mathbf{c}\times\mathbf{a})$,

$(\mathbf{a}\times\mathbf{b}) = 3(\mathbf{b}\times\mathbf{c}), (\mathbf{c}\times\mathbf{a}) = 2(\mathbf{b}\times\mathbf{c})$

With the help of above relations, the given vector is same as given.

(b) Do yourself.

46. (a) Squaring both sides, we have

$\sqrt{(1+1+2.1.1.\cos 2\theta)} < 1$

or $2|\cos\theta| < 1$ or $|\cos\theta| < 1/2$

$\therefore \quad -\frac{1}{2} < \cos\theta < \frac{1}{2} \;\therefore\; \frac{\pi}{3} < \theta < \frac{2\pi}{3}$

(b) $|\mathbf{a}-\mathbf{b}|^2 = 1 + 1 - 2\cos 2\theta = 2.2\sin^2\theta$

$\therefore \quad |\mathbf{a}-\mathbf{b}| < 1 \Rightarrow 2|\sin\theta| < 1$

or $|\sin\theta| \leq \frac{1}{2}$ but $0 \leq \theta \leq \pi \;\therefore\; |\sin\theta| = \sin\theta < \frac{1}{2}$

$\therefore \quad \theta \in \left[0, \frac{\pi}{6}\right)$ or $\left(\frac{5\pi}{6}, \pi\right]$

47. (a) Let us suppose that **n** is not a null vector. Now $\mathbf{n}.\mathbf{a} = 0$, and $\mathbf{n}.\mathbf{b} = 0$ so that **n** is perpendicular to both **a** and **b** and hence perpendicular to the plane of **a** and **b**. Further $\mathbf{n}.\mathbf{c} = 0$ so that **n** is also perpendicular to **c** also and hence **c** will lie in the plane of **a** and **b**. This would mean that **a**, **b**, **c** are coplanar and this is contrary to the hypothesis. Hence the vector **n** must be a null vector.

(b) Since X is non-zero, the given conditions will be satisfied if X is perp. to all the vectors **A**, **B**, **C** *i.e.* **A**, **B**, **C** are coplanar and so $[\mathbf{A}\,\mathbf{B}\mathbf{C}] = 0$.

See § 5 (e), P. 1152.

(c) Let the vectors representing the three lines be **a**, **b**, **c** and **n** be a unit vector along the given straight line which is equally inclined to above three lines.

$\mathbf{n}.\mathbf{a} = 1.a\cos\theta$ or $\mathbf{n}.\frac{\mathbf{a}}{a} = \cos\theta$.

or $\mathbf{n}.\hat{\mathbf{a}} = \cos\theta$.

Hence by the given condition, we have

$\mathbf{n}.\hat{\mathbf{a}} = \mathbf{n}.\hat{\mathbf{b}} = \mathbf{n}.\hat{\mathbf{c}} = \cos\theta$.

Since the three unit vectors are all different (as their directions are different) and coplanar the above relation will hold good only when $\cos\theta = 0$ *i.e.* $\theta = \pi/2$. Hence **n** is perpendicular to **a**, **b** and **c** as such it is perpendicular to their plane.

48. (a) We have $\mathbf{a}.\mathbf{b} = \mathbf{b}.\mathbf{c} = \mathbf{c}.\mathbf{a} = 0$ ...(1)

as **a**, **b**, **c** are mutually perpendicular.

Again their magnitudes are same *i.e.* $a = b = c$.

Also $(\mathbf{a}+\mathbf{b}+\mathbf{c})^2 = \Sigma\;\mathbf{a}^2 + 2\Sigma\;\mathbf{a}.\mathbf{b}$

$= a^2 + b^2 + c^2 = 3a^2$, by (1) ...(2)

$\therefore \quad |\mathbf{a}+\mathbf{b}+\mathbf{c}| = \sqrt{3}a$.

Now $(\mathbf{a}+\mathbf{b}+\mathbf{c}).\mathbf{a} = a^2 + \mathbf{b}.\mathbf{a} + \mathbf{c}.\mathbf{a} = a^2$, by (1)

or $a\sqrt{3}.a.\cos\theta_1 = a^2$,

$\therefore \quad \cos\theta_1 = 1/\sqrt{3},$ by (2).

Similarly $(\mathbf{a}+\mathbf{b}+\mathbf{c}).\mathbf{b}$ and $(\mathbf{a}+\mathbf{b}+\mathbf{c}).\mathbf{c}$ will give

$$\cos\theta_2 = 1/\sqrt{3} \text{ and } \cos\theta_3 = 1/\sqrt{3}.$$

Hence $\theta_1 = \theta_2 = \theta_3$. In other words $\mathbf{a}+\mathbf{b}+\mathbf{c}$ is equally inclined to **a**, **b** and **c**.

(b) $\mathbf{a}+\mathbf{b}+\mathbf{c}=0 \Rightarrow \mathbf{c} = -(\mathbf{a}+\mathbf{b})$. Squaring,

$$\mathbf{c}^2 = \mathbf{a}^2 + \mathbf{b}^2 + 2\mathbf{a}.\mathbf{b}$$

or $\quad 49 = 9 + 25 + 2(3.5)\cos\theta$

$\therefore \quad 30\cos\theta = 15$ or $\cos\theta = 1/2 \quad \therefore \theta = \pi/3.$

(c) Square etc.

49. (a) $\mathbf{a}.(\mathbf{b}+\mathbf{c}) = 0, \mathbf{b}.(\mathbf{c}+\mathbf{a}) = 0, \quad \mathbf{c}.(\mathbf{a}+\mathbf{b}) = 0$

Adding, $\mathbf{2(a.b+b.c+c.a)=0}$ ...(1)

Also $\quad \mathbf{a}^2 = |\mathbf{a}|^2 = 9, \mathbf{b}^2 = 16, \mathbf{c}^2 = 25$

Now $(\mathbf{a}+\mathbf{b}+\mathbf{c})^2 = \Sigma\,\mathbf{a}^2 + 2\Sigma\,\mathbf{a}.\mathbf{b}$

$$= 9 + 16 + 25 + 0 = 50$$

$\therefore \quad |\mathbf{a}+\mathbf{b}+\mathbf{c}| = 5\sqrt{2}$

(b) $(\mathbf{e}_1 + \mathbf{e}_2)^2 = 3 \Rightarrow 1 + 1 + 2\,\mathbf{e}_1.\mathbf{e}_2 = 3$

$\therefore \quad \mathbf{e}_1.\mathbf{e}_2 = 1/2$

Ans. 11/2

(c) Ans. (b). $(\mathbf{a}+2\mathbf{b}).(5\mathbf{a}-4\mathbf{b}) = 0$

or $\quad 5 - 8 + (10-4)\,\mathbf{a}.\mathbf{b} = 0$

or $\quad 6\cos\theta = 3$ or $\cos\theta = 1/2 \therefore \theta = \pi/3$

50. Let a be the edge of the cube so that

$$\vec{OA} = a\mathbf{i},\ \vec{OB} = a\mathbf{j},\ \vec{OC} = a\mathbf{k}$$

$$\vec{ON} = a(\mathbf{i}+\mathbf{j}),\ \vec{OL} = a(\mathbf{j}+\mathbf{k})$$

$$\vec{OM} = a(\mathbf{k}+\mathbf{i}).$$

The four diagonals are

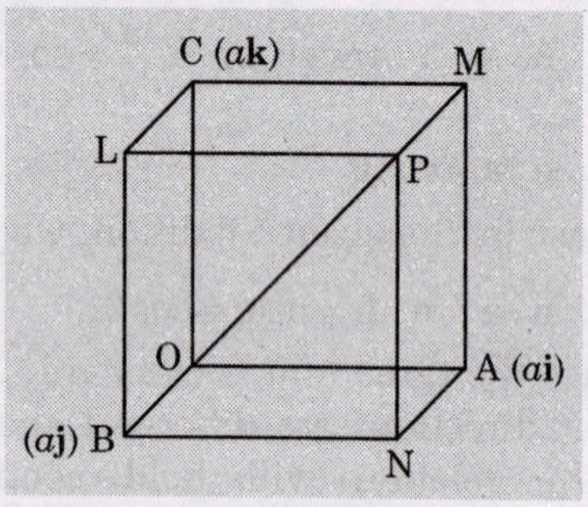

Fig. 31

$$\vec{AL} = a(\mathbf{j}+\mathbf{k}-\mathbf{i}),\quad \vec{BM} = a(\mathbf{k}+\mathbf{i}-\mathbf{j})$$

$$\vec{CN} = a(\mathbf{i}+\mathbf{j}-\mathbf{k}),\quad \vec{OP} = a(\mathbf{i}+\mathbf{j}+\mathbf{k})$$

Let a unit vector along the line be $l\mathbf{i}+m\mathbf{j}+n\mathbf{k}$ where $l^2+m^2+n^2=1$ and it makes angles $\alpha, \beta, \gamma, \delta$ with the four diagonals AL, BM, CN and OP respectively.

$$\cos\alpha = \frac{a(\mathbf{j}+\mathbf{k}-\mathbf{i}).(l\mathbf{i}+m\mathbf{j}+n\mathbf{k})}{a\sqrt{3}.1}$$

or $\quad \cos\alpha = \dfrac{m+n-l}{\sqrt{3}}$

$\therefore \quad \Sigma\cos^2\alpha = \frac{1}{3}[(m+n-l)^2 + (n+l-m)^2 + (l+m-n)^2 + (l+m+n)^2]$

$$= \frac{1}{3}\cdot 4\Sigma\, l^2 = \frac{4}{3}.$$

Again if angle between the diagonals OP and CN be θ, then

$$\vec{OP}.\vec{CN} = |\vec{OP}||\vec{CN}|\cos\theta.$$

$$a(\mathbf{i}+\mathbf{j}+\mathbf{k}).a(\mathbf{i}+\mathbf{j}-\mathbf{k}) = a\sqrt{3}.a\sqrt{3}\cos\theta$$

$$a^2 = 3a^2\cos\theta, \textit{ i.e. } \cos\theta = 1/3.$$

Similarly angles between any other two diagonals is $\cos^{-1}(1/3)$.

51. We know that between any three coplanar vectors **a**, **b** and **c** there exists a relation of the form

$$x\,\mathbf{a} + y\,\mathbf{b} + z\,\mathbf{c} = \mathbf{0} \quad ...(1)$$

where x, y, z are scalars.

Multiplying both sides of (1) scalarly by **a** and **b** respectively

$$x\,\mathbf{a}.\mathbf{a} + y\,\mathbf{a}.\mathbf{b} + z\,\mathbf{a}.\mathbf{c} = 0 \quad ...(2)$$

$$x\,\mathbf{b}.\mathbf{a} + y\,\mathbf{b}.\mathbf{b} + z\,\mathbf{b}.\mathbf{c} = 0 \quad ...(3)$$

Eliminating x, y, z from (1), (2) and (3), we get

$$\begin{vmatrix} \mathbf{a} & \mathbf{b} & \mathbf{c} \\ \mathbf{a}.\mathbf{a} & \mathbf{a}.\mathbf{b} & \mathbf{a}.\mathbf{c} \\ \mathbf{b}.\mathbf{a} & \mathbf{b}.\mathbf{b} & \mathbf{b}.\mathbf{c} \end{vmatrix} = 0$$

Another form :

Expanding the above determinant, we get the value of **c** as given.

52. We know that $\mathbf{a}\times\mathbf{b} = ab\sin\theta\,\hat{\mathbf{n}}$.

Squaring both sides, we get

$$(\mathbf{a}\times\mathbf{b})^2 = a^2b^2\sin^2\theta\,\hat{\mathbf{n}}^2$$

$$= a^2b^2(1-\cos^2\theta), \quad \because \hat{\mathbf{n}}^2 = 1$$

$$= a^2b^2 - a^2b^2\cos^2\theta = \mathbf{a}^2\mathbf{b}^2 - (\mathbf{a}.\mathbf{b})^2$$

$$(\because a^2 = \mathbf{a}^2, \quad \mathbf{a}.\mathbf{b} = ab\cos\theta).$$

For the second part $\mathbf{a} = (m_1\mathbf{i} + n_1\mathbf{j} + p_1\mathbf{k})$ and $\mathbf{b} = \mathrm{m}_2\mathbf{i} + \mathrm{n}_2\mathbf{j} + \mathrm{p}_2\mathbf{k}$

53. Let $|\mathbf{u}| = a, |\mathbf{v}| = b, \mathbf{u}\times\mathbf{v} = ab\sin\theta\,\hat{\mathbf{n}}$, where $\hat{\mathbf{n}}$ is perpendicular to both **u** and **v**, $|\mathbf{a}|^2 = a^2$

L.H.S. $= (1+a^2)(1+b^2)$

R.H.S. $= (1-ab\cos\theta)^2 + (\mathbf{u}+\mathbf{v})^2 + (\mathbf{u}\times\mathbf{v})^2 + 2(\mathbf{u}+\mathbf{v}).ab\sin\theta\,\hat{\mathbf{n}}$

$$= 1 + a^2b^2\cos^2\theta - 2ab\cos\theta + a^2 + b^2 + 2ab\cos\theta + a^2b^2\sin^2\theta.1 + 0$$

as $\hat{\mathbf{n}}$ is $\perp$ to both **u** and **v**

$$= 1 + a^2b^2(\cos^2\theta + \sin^2\theta) + a^2 + b^2$$

$$= 1 + a^2 + b^2 + a^2b^2 = (1+a^2)(1+b^2)$$

54. (a) Let O be the intersection of diagonals and $\vec{AO} = \mathbf{a}$, $\vec{OD} = \mathbf{b}$ so that $\vec{OB} = -\mathbf{b}$.

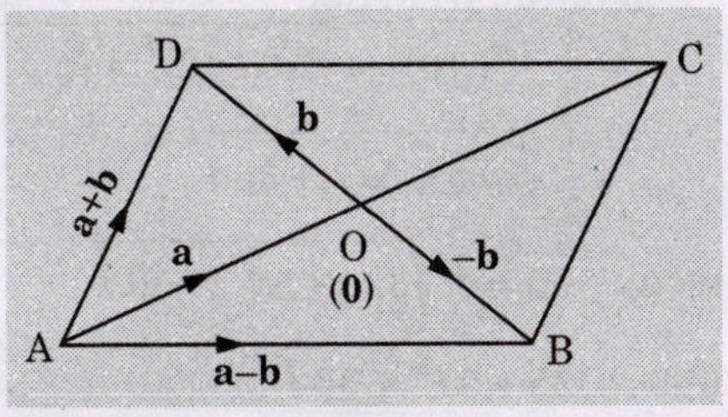

Fig. 32

$\therefore \quad \vec{AD} = \vec{AO} + \vec{OD} = \mathbf{a} + \mathbf{b}$, $\vec{AB} = \vec{AO} + \vec{OB} = \mathbf{a} - \mathbf{b}$

Now $(\mathbf{a}-\mathbf{b}) \times (\mathbf{a}+\mathbf{b}) = \mathbf{a}\times\mathbf{a} - \mathbf{b}\times\mathbf{a} + \mathbf{a}\times\mathbf{b} - \mathbf{b}\times\mathbf{b}$

$= \mathbf{a}\times\mathbf{b} + \mathbf{a}\times\mathbf{b} = 2(\mathbf{a}\times\mathbf{b})$,

$\because \quad \mathbf{b}\times\mathbf{a} = -(\mathbf{a}\times\mathbf{b})$

We know that $\mathbf{a}\times\mathbf{b}$ represents the vector area of $||^m$ whose adjacent sides are **a** and **b**.

$\therefore$ $(\mathbf{a}-\mathbf{b})\times(\mathbf{a}+\mathbf{b})$ represents the vector area of $||^m$ *ABCD* whose adjacent sides are *AB* and *AD* and it is equal to $2(\mathbf{a}\times\mathbf{b})$ *i.e.* twice the vector area of $||^m$ whose adjacent sides are semi-diagonals of the first $||^m$ or $= 4\left(\frac{1}{2}\mathbf{a}\times\mathbf{b}\right)$ = four times the vector area of the triangle whose adjacent sides are semi-diagonals of the $||^m$.

(b) L.H.S. $= (\mathbf{a}\times\mathbf{b}) + (\mathbf{a}\times\mathbf{c}) + (\mathbf{b}\times\mathbf{c}) + (\mathbf{b}\times\mathbf{a}) + (\mathbf{c}\times\mathbf{a}) + (\mathbf{c}\times\mathbf{b})$

$= (\mathbf{a}\times\mathbf{b}) - (\mathbf{c}\times\mathbf{a}) + (\mathbf{b}\times\mathbf{c}) - (\mathbf{a}\times\mathbf{b}) + (\mathbf{c}\times\mathbf{a}) - (\mathbf{b}\times\mathbf{c}) = \mathbf{0}$.

55. (a) We have to prove that $\mathbf{a}-\mathbf{d}$ is parallel to $\mathbf{b}-\mathbf{c}$ and hence their cross product should be shown to be zero.

Now $(\mathbf{a}-\mathbf{d})\times(\mathbf{b}-\mathbf{c}) = (\mathbf{a}\times\mathbf{b} - \mathbf{a}\times\mathbf{c}) - (\mathbf{d}\times\mathbf{b} - \mathbf{d}\times\mathbf{c})$

$= (\mathbf{a}\times\mathbf{b} + \mathbf{d}\times\mathbf{c}) - (\mathbf{a}\times\mathbf{c} + \mathbf{d}\times\mathbf{b})$

$= (\mathbf{a}\times\mathbf{b} - \mathbf{c}\times\mathbf{d}) - (\mathbf{a}\times\mathbf{c} - \mathbf{b}\times\mathbf{d})$

$= \mathbf{0} - \mathbf{0} = \mathbf{0}$, by given relations.

Hence $\mathbf{a}-\mathbf{d}$ is parallel to $\mathbf{b}-\mathbf{c}$.

(b) $\mathbf{a}\times\mathbf{b} = \mathbf{a}\times\mathbf{c}$ *i.e.* $\mathbf{a}\times(\mathbf{b}-\mathbf{c}) = 0$,

$\therefore$ **a** is parallel to $\mathbf{b}-\mathbf{c}$.

$\therefore$ $\mathbf{b}-\mathbf{c} = k\mathbf{a}$, that is **b** differs from **c** by a vector which is parallel to **a**.

(c) Proceed as in part (b).

56. The equation of the two lines are

$(\mathbf{r}-\mathbf{b})\times\mathbf{a} = 0$ and $(\mathbf{r}-\mathbf{a})\times\mathbf{b} = 0$

$\therefore$ $(\mathbf{r}-\mathbf{b})$ is parallel to **a**

and $(\mathbf{r}-\mathbf{a})$ is parallel to **b**

$\therefore \quad \mathbf{r} = \mathbf{b} + p\mathbf{a}, \quad \mathbf{r} = \mathbf{a} + q\mathbf{b}$

For their point of intersection we have identical values of **r**

$\therefore \quad p = q = 1$ and hence $\mathbf{r} = \mathbf{a} + \mathbf{b} = 3\mathbf{i} + \mathbf{j} - \mathbf{k}$

57. We have $\mathbf{a}\,.\,\mathbf{b} = \mathbf{a}\,.\,\mathbf{c} \Rightarrow \mathbf{a}\,.\,(\mathbf{b}-\mathbf{c}) = 0$.

$\therefore$ Either $\mathbf{a} = \mathbf{0}$, or $\mathbf{b}-\mathbf{c} = \mathbf{0}$ or **a** is $\perp$ to $\mathbf{b}-\mathbf{c}$.

Again $\mathbf{a}\times\mathbf{b} - \mathbf{a}\times\mathbf{c} \Rightarrow \mathbf{a}\times(\mathbf{b}-\mathbf{c}) = 0$

$\therefore$ Either $\mathbf{a} = \mathbf{0}$ or $\mathbf{b}-\mathbf{c} = \mathbf{0}$ or **a** is parallel to $\mathbf{b}-\mathbf{c}$ *i.e.*, $\mathbf{b}-\mathbf{c} = k\mathbf{a}$.

Interpretation.

But $\mathbf{a} \neq \mathbf{0}$ and hence if both the equations hold simultaneously, then

$\mathbf{b}-\mathbf{c} = \mathbf{0}$, *i.e.* $\mathbf{b} = \mathbf{c}$.

58. (a) We know that $\quad \mathbf{a}\times\mathbf{b} = ab\sin\theta\,\hat{\mathbf{n}}$.

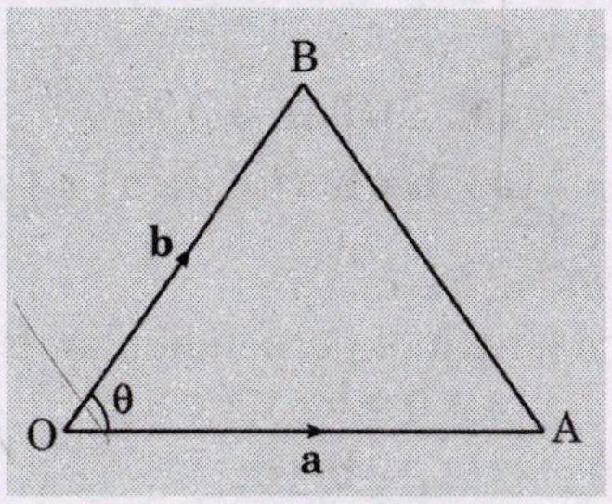

Fig. 33

Area of $\Delta OAB = \frac{1}{2} OA\,.\,OB \sin\theta$.

$= \frac{1}{2} ab\sin\theta$.

$\therefore \quad \mathbf{a}\times\mathbf{b} = 2\Delta\,\hat{\mathbf{n}}$.

Hence vector area of triangle *OAB* is $\frac{1}{2}(\mathbf{a}\times\mathbf{b})$.

$= \frac{1}{2}$ (area of $||^m$ whose adjacent sides are given by **a** and **b**)

Now referred to *O* as origin, let the position vectors of *A*, *B*, *C* be **a**, **b** and **c** respectively.

Then $\vec{BC} = \mathbf{c}-\mathbf{b}$, $\vec{BA} = \mathbf{a}-\mathbf{b}$.

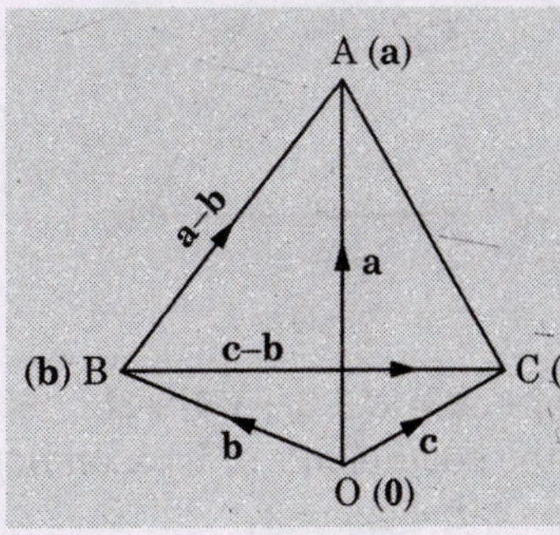

Fig. 34

$\therefore \quad$ Vector area of ΔABC is $\frac{1}{2}\vec{BC}\times\vec{BA}$

$= \frac{1}{2}(\mathbf{c}-\mathbf{b})\times(\mathbf{a}-\mathbf{b})$

$= \frac{1}{2}(\mathbf{c}\times\mathbf{a} - \mathbf{b}\times\mathbf{a} - \mathbf{c}\times\mathbf{b} + \mathbf{b}\times\mathbf{b})$

$= \frac{1}{2}(\mathbf{a}\times\mathbf{b} + \mathbf{b}\times\mathbf{c} + \mathbf{c}\times\mathbf{a})$

$(\because \mathbf{b}\times\mathbf{b} = \mathbf{0}$ and $-\mathbf{c}\times\mathbf{b} = \mathbf{b}\times\mathbf{c})$.

Condition of Collinearity.

If the three points be collinear, then $\Delta = 0$

$\therefore \quad \mathbf{a}\times\mathbf{b}+\mathbf{b}\times\mathbf{c}+\mathbf{c}\times\mathbf{a}=\mathbf{0}.$

(b) As seen in part (a), we have

$$\vec{BC}\times\vec{BA}=\mathbf{a}\times\mathbf{b}+\mathbf{b}\times\mathbf{c}+\mathbf{c}\times\mathbf{a}.$$

and $\vec{BC}\times\vec{BA}$ represents a vector perpendicular to both $\vec{BC}$ and $\vec{BA}$ and hence it is normal to the plane defined by BC and BA.

or $\mathbf{a}\times\mathbf{b}+\mathbf{b}\times\mathbf{c}+\mathbf{c}\times\mathbf{a}$ is perpendicular to the plane ABC.

59. (a) By Q. 58 (a), Area of $\Delta\, ABC$

$$=\frac{1}{2}|\mathbf{a}\times\mathbf{b}+\mathbf{b}\times\mathbf{c}+\mathbf{c}\times\mathbf{a}|=\frac{1}{2}BC\,.\,p$$

and $BC=|\mathbf{b}-\mathbf{c}|$.

Hence length of perpendicular, from A on BC

i.e. $p=\dfrac{|\mathbf{a}\times\mathbf{b}+\mathbf{b}\times\mathbf{c}+\mathbf{c}\times\mathbf{a}|}{|\mathbf{b}-\mathbf{c}|}.$

(b) Without loss of generality we may choose the point D as origin and the position vectors of A, B, C be $\mathbf{a}$, $\mathbf{b}$, $\mathbf{c}$ respectively.

$$\therefore \quad |\vec{AB}\times\vec{CD}+\vec{BC}\times\vec{AD}+\vec{CA}\times\vec{BD}|$$
$$=|(\mathbf{b}-\mathbf{a})\times(-\mathbf{c})+(\mathbf{c}-\mathbf{b})\times(-\mathbf{a})+(\mathbf{a}-\mathbf{c})\times(-\mathbf{b})|$$
$$=2|\mathbf{a}\times\mathbf{b}+\mathbf{b}\times\mathbf{c}+\mathbf{c}\times\mathbf{a}|$$
$$=2\,(2\,\Delta\,ABC)=4\,\Delta,\text{ by part (a).}$$

60. Here $\mathbf{A}=a\mathbf{i}+b\mathbf{j}+c\mathbf{k},\ \mathbf{B}=d\mathbf{i}+3\mathbf{j}+4\mathbf{k},$
$\mathbf{C}=3\mathbf{i}+\mathbf{j}-2\mathbf{k}.$

It is given that $\mathbf{A}=\mathbf{B}+\mathbf{C}$, that is,

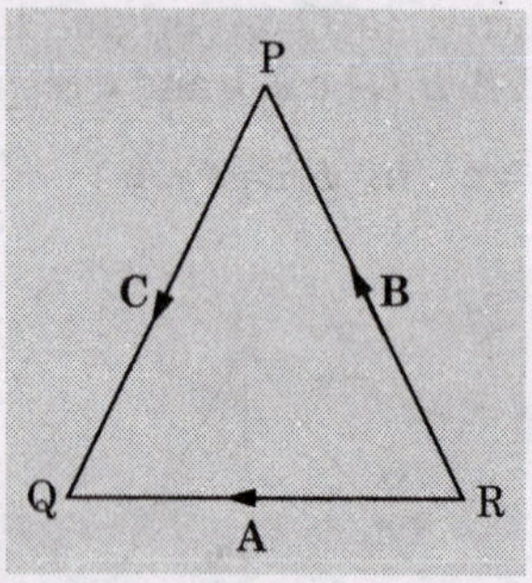

Fig. 35

$$a\mathbf{i}+b\mathbf{j}+c\mathbf{k}=(d+3)\,\mathbf{i}+4\mathbf{j}+2\mathbf{k}. \quad ...(1)$$

Equating the coefficients of $\mathbf{i}, \mathbf{j}, \mathbf{k}$ on both sides of (1),

$a=d+3,\ b=4,\ c=2.$

Also vector area of the triangle

$$=\frac{1}{2}\mathbf{B}\times\mathbf{C}=\frac{1}{2}\begin{vmatrix}\mathbf{i} & \mathbf{j} & \mathbf{k}\\ d & 3 & 4\\ 3 & 1 & -2\end{vmatrix}$$

$$=\frac{1}{2}[-10\mathbf{i}+(2d+12)\,\mathbf{j}+(d-9)\,\mathbf{k}]$$

It should be noted that **A, B, C** are vectors (**not points**) respresenting the sides of a triangle. If they were position vectors of the vertices then area would be given by

$\frac{1}{2}(\mathbf{A}\times\mathbf{B}+\mathbf{B}\times\mathbf{C}+\mathbf{C}\times\mathbf{A})$ **See Q 58, P. 1127-1145**

$\therefore$ Area of the triangle

$$=\frac{1}{2}\sqrt{(-10)^2+(2d+12)^2+(d-9)^2}$$
$$=\frac{1}{2}\sqrt{325+5d^2+30d}.$$

As given, $5\sqrt{6}=\frac{1}{2}\sqrt{325+5d^2+30d}$

or $\quad 600=325+5d^2+30d$

or $\quad 5d^2+30d-275=0$ or $d^2+6d-55=0$

$\therefore \quad d=-11$ or 5. Then $a=-8$ or 8.

$\therefore \quad a=8,\ b=4,\ c=2,\ d=5$

or $\quad a=-8,\ b=4,\ c=2,\ d=-11.$

61. (a) Taking A as origin, let the position vectors of B and C be $\mathbf{b}$ and $\mathbf{c}$ respectively so that points E and F are $\mathbf{c}/2$ and $\mathbf{b}/2$.

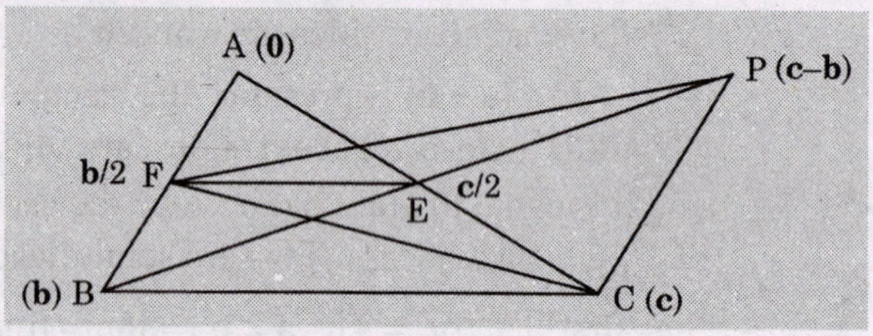

Fig. 36

P is the point of intersection of CP and BE whose equations are $\mathbf{r}=\mathbf{c}+t\,\mathbf{b}$ as CP is || to AB and $\mathbf{r}=\mathbf{b}+s\left(\frac{\mathbf{c}}{2}-\mathbf{b}\right).$ **(§ 6, P. 1152)**

Comparing, we get $t=1-s, 1=s/2$

$\therefore \quad s=2, t=-1$. Hence the point P is $\mathbf{c}-\mathbf{b}$.

$$\Delta\,ABC=\frac{1}{2}\vec{AB}\times\vec{AC}=\frac{1}{2}\mathbf{b}\times\mathbf{c} \quad ...(1)$$

$$\Delta\,FEP=\frac{1}{2}\vec{FE}\times\vec{FP}=\frac{1}{2}\left(\frac{\mathbf{c}}{2}-\frac{\mathbf{b}}{2}\right)\times\left(\mathbf{c}-\frac{3}{2}\mathbf{b}\right)$$
$$=\frac{1}{2}\left[-\frac{3}{4}\mathbf{c}\times\mathbf{b}-\frac{1}{2}\mathbf{b}\times\mathbf{c}\right]=\frac{1}{2}(\mathbf{b}\times\mathbf{c})\left(\frac{3}{4}-\frac{1}{2}\right)$$
$$=\frac{1}{4}\Delta\,ABC, \quad \text{by (1)}$$

$$\Delta\,FCE=\frac{1}{2}\vec{FC}\times\vec{FE}=\frac{1}{2}\left(\mathbf{c}-\frac{\mathbf{b}}{2}\right)\times\left(\frac{\mathbf{c}}{2}-\frac{\mathbf{b}}{2}\right)$$
$$=\frac{1}{2}\left(-\frac{1}{2}\mathbf{c}\times\mathbf{b}-\frac{1}{4}\mathbf{b}\times\mathbf{c}\right)$$
$$=\frac{1}{2}(\mathbf{b}\times\mathbf{c})\left(\frac{1}{2}-\frac{1}{4}\right)=\frac{1}{4}\Delta\,ABC, \quad \text{by (1)}$$

(b) Proceed as above choosing A as origin.

(c) With A as origin let the position vectors of B and C be $\mathbf{b}$ and $\mathbf{c}$ respectively.

$$\therefore \quad \Delta=\frac{1}{2}|(\mathbf{b}\times\mathbf{c})| \quad ...(1)$$

The points D, E and F by ratio formula are

$$D, \frac{n\mathbf{c}+\mathbf{b}}{n+1},\ E, \frac{\mathbf{c}}{n+1},\ F, \frac{n\mathbf{b}}{n+1}$$

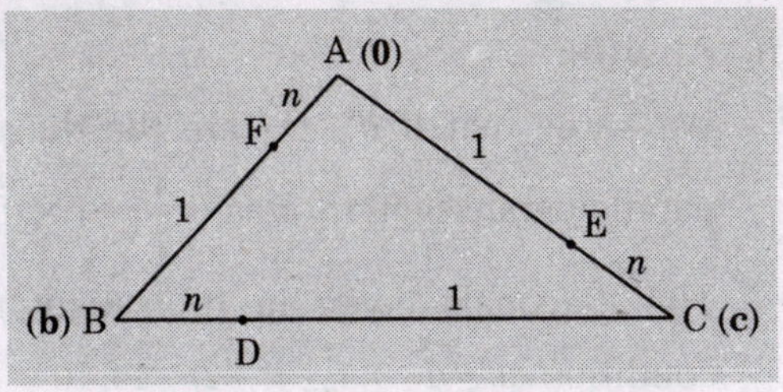

Fig. 37

$\therefore \quad \vec{DE} = \dfrac{1}{n+1}[(1-n)\,\mathbf{c} - \mathbf{b}],$

$\vec{DF} = \dfrac{1}{(n+1)}[(n-1)\,\mathbf{b} - n\mathbf{c}]$

$\Delta\, \vec{DEF} = \dfrac{1}{2}|\,\vec{DE} \times \vec{DF}\,|$

$= \dfrac{1}{2}\cdot\dfrac{1}{(n+1)^2}\,|\,(1-n)\,(n-1)\,\mathbf{c}\times\mathbf{b}$

$+ n\,(\mathbf{b}\times\mathbf{c}) + 0 + 0\,|$

$= \dfrac{1}{2}\cdot\dfrac{1}{(n+1)^2}\,(\mathbf{b}\times\mathbf{c})\,(n + (n-1)^2)$

$= \Delta\,\dfrac{n^2 - n + 1}{(n+1)^2} \qquad \because\ \mathbf{c}\times\mathbf{b} = -\,(\mathbf{b}\times\mathbf{c})$

(d) As in last part (c), $\Delta\, ABC = \dfrac{1}{2}|\,\mathbf{b}\times\mathbf{c}\,|$ ...(1)

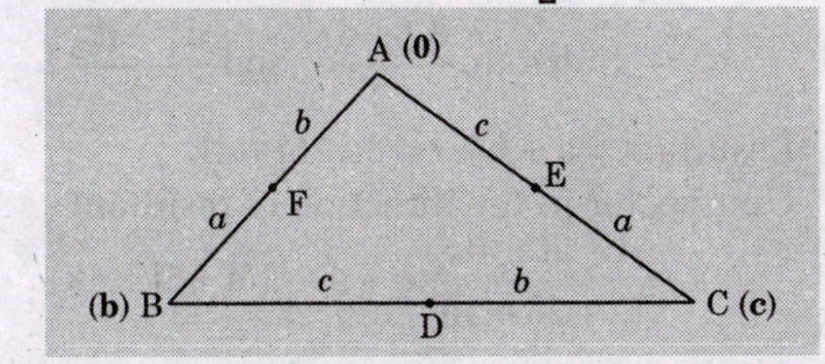

Fig. 38

The internal bisectors divide the opposite sides in the ratio of the arms of the angle. Hence points D, E, F by ratio formula are respectively

$D, \dfrac{b\mathbf{b} + c\mathbf{c}}{b+c},\quad E, \dfrac{c\mathbf{c}}{c+a},\quad F, \dfrac{b\mathbf{b}}{a+b}$

$\therefore \quad \Delta\, DEF = \dfrac{1}{2}|\,\mathbf{L}\times\mathbf{M} + \mathbf{M}\times\mathbf{N} + \mathbf{N}\times\mathbf{L}\,|$

by Q. 58 (a) P. 1127-45

$\therefore \quad \Delta\, DEF = \dfrac{1}{2}\left|\,\dfrac{bc\,(\mathbf{b}\times\mathbf{c})}{(b+c)\,(c+a)} + \dfrac{bc\,(\mathbf{c}\times\mathbf{b})}{(c+a)\,(a+b)}\right.$

$\left. + \dfrac{bc\,(\mathbf{b}\times\mathbf{c})}{(a+b)\,(b+c)}\,\right|$

$= \dfrac{1}{2}\,\dfrac{bc\,(\mathbf{b}\times\mathbf{c})}{(a+b)\,(b+c)\,(c+a)}\;[(a+b) - (b+c) + (c+a)]$

$= \Delta\, ABC\,\dfrac{(bc\,2a)}{(a+b)\,(b+c)\,(c+a)}$ by (1)

$= \Delta\, ABC\,\dfrac{2abc}{(a+b)\,(b+c)\,(c+a)}$ ...(2)

Now $\dfrac{a+b}{2} > \sqrt{ab}, \dfrac{b+c}{2} > \sqrt{bc}, \dfrac{c+a}{2} > \sqrt{ca}$

$\therefore \quad \dfrac{(a+b)\,(b+c)\,(c+a)}{8} > abc$

$\therefore \quad \dfrac{(a+b)\,(b+c)\,(c+a)}{2abc} > 4$

or $\quad \dfrac{2abc}{(a+b)\,(b+c)\,(c+a)} < \dfrac{1}{4}$ ...(3)

$\therefore \quad \Delta\, DEF < \dfrac{1}{4}\,\Delta\, ABC$, by (2) and (3).

62. $\vec{AB} = m\,(2\mathbf{i} - 6\mathbf{j} + 2\mathbf{k}),\ \vec{BC} = (\mathbf{i} - 2\mathbf{j})$

$\vec{CD} = n\,(-6\mathbf{i} + 15\mathbf{j} - 3\mathbf{k}).$

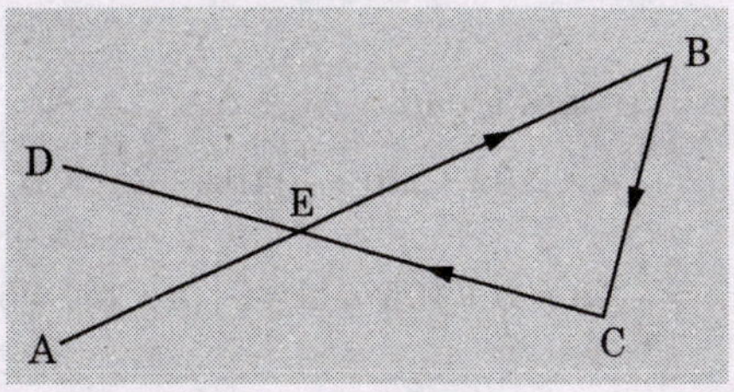

Fig. 39

If AB and CD intersect at E, then

$\vec{EB} = p\,\vec{AB},\ \vec{CE} = q\,\vec{CD}$ ...(1)

where both p and q are + ive quantities less than 1.

Now we know that $\vec{EB} + \vec{BC} + \vec{CE} = \vec{EE} = 0$

$\therefore \quad p\,\vec{AB} + \vec{BC} + q\,\vec{CD} = 0$, by (1)

or $\quad pm\,(2\mathbf{i} - 6\mathbf{j} + 2\mathbf{k}) + (\mathbf{i} - 2\mathbf{j}) + q\,.\,n\,(-6\mathbf{i} + 15\mathbf{j} - 3\mathbf{k}) = 0$

Since $\mathbf{i}, \mathbf{j}, \mathbf{k}$ are non-coplanar, the above relation implies that if $x\mathbf{i} + y\mathbf{j} + z\mathbf{k} = 0$ then $x = 0, y = 0$ and $z = 0$.

$\therefore \quad 2pm + 1 - 6qn = 0,\ -6pm - 2 + 15qn = 0,$

$2pm - 3qn = 0$

Solving these for pm and qn, we get

$pm = \dfrac{1}{2},\ qn = \dfrac{1}{3} \qquad \therefore\ p = \dfrac{1}{2m}, q = \dfrac{1}{3n}$

$\therefore \quad 0 < \dfrac{1}{2m} \le 1,\ 0 \le \dfrac{1}{3n} \le 1$ or $m \ge \dfrac{1}{2}, n \ge \dfrac{1}{3}$

Again Area of $\Delta\, BCE = \dfrac{1}{2}|\,\vec{EC} \times \vec{EB}\,|$

$= \dfrac{1}{2}|-q\,\vec{CD} \times p\,\vec{AB}\,| = \dfrac{1}{2}\,pqnm \begin{vmatrix} \mathbf{i} & \mathbf{j} & \mathbf{k} \\ -6 & 15 & -3 \\ 2 & -6 & 2 \end{vmatrix}$

Put $pm = \dfrac{1}{2}, qn = \dfrac{1}{3}$

$= \dfrac{1}{2}\cdot\dfrac{1}{2}\cdot\dfrac{1}{3}\,|\,12\mathbf{i} - 6\mathbf{j} - 6\mathbf{k}\,| = \dfrac{1}{12}\cdot 6\sqrt{6} = \dfrac{1}{2}\sqrt{6}$

63. (a) Area of $||^m = |\,(\mathbf{a}\times\mathbf{b})\,|$

But $\mathbf{a}\times\mathbf{b} = \begin{vmatrix} \mathbf{i} & \mathbf{j} & \mathbf{k} \\ 1 & 2 & 3 \\ 3 & -2 & 1 \end{vmatrix} = 8\,(\mathbf{i} + \mathbf{j} + \mathbf{k}).$

$\therefore \quad |\,\mathbf{a}\times\mathbf{b}\,| = 8\sqrt{1+1+1} = 8\sqrt{3}$ sq. units.

(b) Area of $\Delta = \dfrac{1}{2}|\,\mathbf{a}\times\mathbf{b}\,| = |20\,\dfrac{1}{2}$ sq. units.

(c) Do yourself.

64. (a) Ans. $k=6$

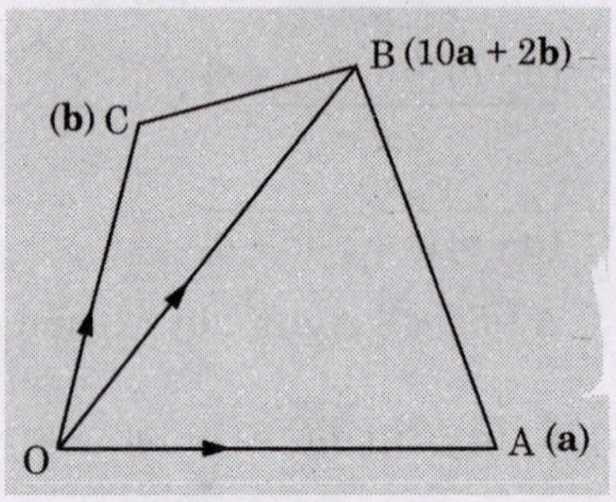

Fig. 40

$p=$ Area of Quad. $=\Delta_1+\Delta_2$

$$=\frac{1}{2}\mathbf{a}\times(10\mathbf{a}+2\mathbf{b})+\frac{1}{2}(10\mathbf{a}+2\mathbf{b})\times\mathbf{b}$$

$$=\frac{1}{2}[2\mathbf{a}\times\mathbf{b}+10\mathbf{a}\times\mathbf{b}]=6\,|(\mathbf{a}\times\mathbf{b})|=6q$$

$p=kq \quad \therefore \quad k=6$

(b) Ans. True.

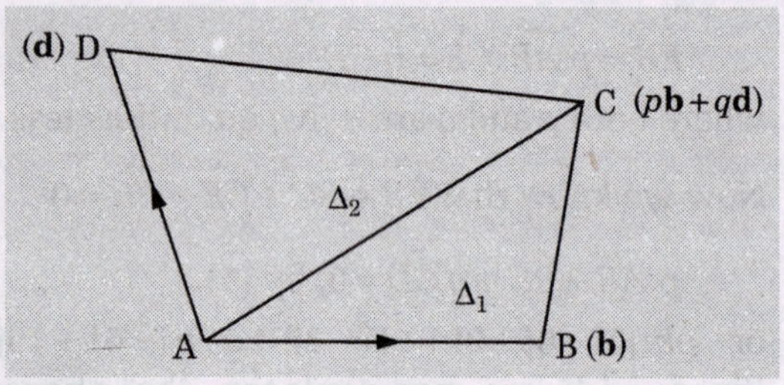

Fig. 41

Area $=\Delta_1+\Delta_2$

$$=\frac{1}{2}|\mathbf{b}\times(p\mathbf{b}+q\mathbf{d})|+\frac{1}{2}|(p\mathbf{b}+q\mathbf{d})\times\mathbf{d}|$$

$$=\frac{1}{2}|q(\mathbf{b}\times\mathbf{d})|+\frac{1}{2}|p(\mathbf{b}\times\mathbf{d})|$$

$$=\frac{1}{2}|(p+q)||(\mathbf{b}\times\mathbf{d})|$$

$$=\frac{1}{2}(p+q)\,|\mathbf{b}\times\mathbf{d}| \text{ as } p+q \text{ is +ive} \geq 1.$$

65. (a) Area of a $||^m$ of sides **a** and **b** is $|\mathbf{a}\times\mathbf{b}|$. If $\mathbf{d}_1$ and $\mathbf{d}_2$ be its diagonals then $\mathbf{d}_1=\mathbf{a}+\mathbf{b}$ and $\mathbf{d}_2=\mathbf{a}-\mathbf{b}$.

Area of a $||^m$ whose sides are $\mathbf{d}_1$ and $\mathbf{d}_2$ is

$$(\mathbf{d}_1\times\mathbf{d}_2)=[(\mathbf{a}+\mathbf{b})\times(\mathbf{a}-\mathbf{b})]=-2(\mathbf{a}\times\mathbf{b})$$

$$=2\times \text{ Area of } ||^m \text{ of sides } \mathbf{a}, \mathbf{b}$$

$\therefore$ Area of $||^m=\frac{1}{2}(\mathbf{d}_1\times\mathbf{d}_2)$

Here $\frac{1}{2}(\mathbf{d}_1\times\mathbf{d}_2)=-\mathbf{i}-7\mathbf{j}-5\mathbf{k}$

$\therefore$ Area $=\sqrt{(1+49+25)}=\sqrt{75}=5\sqrt{3}$.

(b) Proceed as above. First find **a** + **b** and **b** + **c**.

Area $=\frac{1}{2}\sqrt{21}$.

66. (a) (i) $|\mathbf{A}\times\mathbf{B}|=\sqrt{41}$

(ii) $\frac{1}{2}|\mathbf{d}_1\times\mathbf{d}_2|=\frac{1}{2}|\mathbf{a}\times\mathbf{b}|=5\sqrt{3}$

(b) Ans. (b).

We know that if $\vec{d}_1, \vec{d}_2$ are the diagonals of a parallelogram then its area is $\frac{1}{2}|\vec{d}_1\times\vec{d}_2|=5\sqrt{3}$.

The diagonals given in (b) satisfy the above condition as $\vec{d}_1\times\vec{d}_2=-2,-14,10$

$$\therefore \quad \frac{1}{2}|\vec{d}_1\times\vec{d}_2|=\frac{1}{2}\sqrt{300}=5\sqrt{3}$$

67. (a) If **a** and **b** be the adjacent sides of a $||^m$ then the diagonals are $\vec{AC}=\mathbf{a}+\mathbf{b}$, $\vec{BD}=\mathbf{b}-\mathbf{a}$

$\therefore$ Unit vectors are $\frac{\vec{AC}}{|\vec{AC}|}$ and $\frac{\vec{BD}}{|\vec{BD}|}$.

Area of parallelogram $=|\mathbf{a}\times\mathbf{b}|$.

Ans. $\frac{1}{7}(3\mathbf{i}+6\mathbf{j}-2\mathbf{k})$, $\frac{1}{\sqrt{(69)}}(-\mathbf{i}-2\mathbf{j}+8\mathbf{k})$,

$11\sqrt{5}$ sq. units.

(b) If the given diagonals be $\mathbf{d}_1$ and $\mathbf{d}_2$, then

Area $=\frac{1}{2}|\mathbf{d}_1\times\mathbf{d}_2|$

Also if **a** and **b** be the sides, then $\mathbf{d}_1=\mathbf{a}+\mathbf{b}$, $\mathbf{d}_2=\mathbf{a}-\mathbf{b}$

$\therefore$ Sides are $\frac{\mathbf{d}_1+\mathbf{d}_2}{2}$ and $\frac{\mathbf{d}_1-\mathbf{d}_2}{2}$.

68. Resultant $=\mathbf{a}+\mathbf{b}+\mathbf{c}=3\mathbf{i}+5\mathbf{j}+4\mathbf{k}$.

Unit vector in the direction of resultant

$$=\frac{3\mathbf{i}+5\mathbf{j}+4\mathbf{k}}{\sqrt{(9+25+16)}}=\frac{1}{5\sqrt{(2)}}(3\mathbf{i}+5\mathbf{j}+4\mathbf{k}).$$

Also $\quad \mathbf{a}\times\mathbf{b}=-4(\mathbf{i}+\mathbf{j}+\mathbf{k}), \quad \therefore \quad |\mathbf{a}\times\mathbf{b}|=4\sqrt{3}$.

$$(\mathbf{a}\times\mathbf{b}).\mathbf{c}=-4(\mathbf{i}+\mathbf{j}+\mathbf{k}).(3\mathbf{i}+\mathbf{j})=-4(3+1)=-16$$

$$\therefore \quad 4\sqrt{3}.\sqrt{10}\cos\theta=-16 \quad \text{or} \quad \cos\theta=\frac{-4}{\sqrt{(30)}}.$$

69. Let $\mathbf{a}=a_1, a_2, a_3, \quad \mathbf{b}=b_1, b_2, b_3$.

$$\mathbf{a}\times\mathbf{b}=\begin{vmatrix}\mathbf{i} & \mathbf{j} & \mathbf{k}\\ a_1 & a_2 & a_3\\ b_1 & b_2 & b_3\end{vmatrix}=2\mathbf{i}+2\mathbf{j}-\mathbf{k} \quad \text{...(1)}$$

$$\mathbf{a}+\mathbf{b}=(a_1+b_1)\mathbf{i}+(a_2+b_2)\mathbf{j}+(a_3+b_3)\mathbf{k}=\mathbf{i}-3\mathbf{j}-4\mathbf{k} \quad \text{...(2)}$$

Equating the coefficients of **i**, **j**, **k** in both (1) and (2), we have the following six equations :

$a_1+b_1=1, \quad \therefore \quad b_1=1-a_1$

$a_2+b_2=-3, \quad b_2=-3-a_2$

$a_3+b_3=-4. \quad b_3=-4-a_3$

$a_2b_3-a_3b_2=2,$

$a_3b_1-a_1b_3=2,$

$a_1b_2-a_2b_1=-1.$

Eliminating b_1, b_2, b_3 from these, we get

$$a_2(-4-a_3)-a_3(-3-a_2)=2$$

$$a_3(1-a_1)-a_1(-4-a_3)=2$$

$$a_1(-3-a_2)-a_2(1-a_1)=-1$$

or $\quad -4a_2+3a_3=2,\quad a_3+4a_1=2,\quad 3a_1+a_2=1$

Eliminating a_1 from the last two of above equations we get $-4a_2+3a_3=2$ which is same as first of the above equations. Thus we have only one equation in two variables and hence there will be infinite solutions.

Choose $a_3=\lambda$

$\therefore \quad a_2=\dfrac{3\lambda-2}{4}$ and hence $a_1=\dfrac{2-\lambda}{4}$

$$b_1=1-a_1=\frac{2+\lambda}{4},\quad b_2=-3-a_2=\frac{10-3\lambda}{4},$$

$$b_3=-4-a_3=-4-\lambda$$

$$\mathbf{a}=\frac{2-\lambda}{4},\frac{3\lambda-2}{4},\lambda$$

and $\mathbf{b}=\dfrac{2+\lambda}{4},\dfrac{10-3\lambda}{4},-4-\lambda$

In particular, if $\lambda=-2$ then

$\mathbf{a}=1,-2,-2,$ *i.e.* $\mathbf{i}-2\mathbf{j}-2\mathbf{k}$, $\mathbf{b}=0,-1,-2,$ *i.e.* $-\mathbf{j}-2\mathbf{k}$

70. Equation of AB by $\mathbf{r}=\mathbf{a}+t_1\,\mathbf{b}$

is $\quad \mathbf{r}=(6\mathbf{i}+7\mathbf{j}+4\mathbf{k})+t_1\,(3\mathbf{i}-\mathbf{j}+\mathbf{k})$

Any point P on it is

$(6+3t_1, 7-t_1, 4+t_1)$ ...(1)

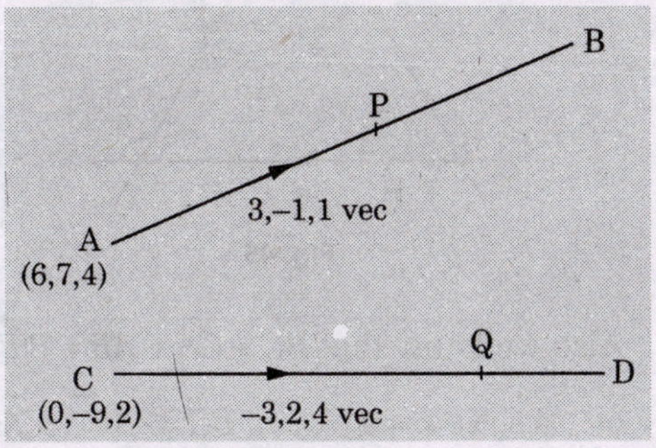

Fig. 42

Similarly any point Q on CD is

$(-3t_2, -9+2t_2, 2+4t_2)$ ...(2)

$\vec{PQ}=$ P.V. of Q – P.V. of P

$$=-3t_2-3t_1-6,-9+2t_2-7+t_1,2+4t_2-4-t_1$$

$$=-3t_2-3t_1-6,-16+t_1+2t_2,-2-t_1+4t_2$$

Now $\vec{PQ}$ is $\perp \vec{AB}$ and $\vec{PQ}\perp\vec{CD}$, where $\vec{AB}$ and $\vec{CD}$ vectors are given as shown in figure. Hence their dot product is zero.

$$\vec{PQ}\cdot\vec{AB}=0 \Rightarrow 11t_1+7t_2+4=0$$

$$\vec{PQ}\cdot\vec{CD}=0 \Rightarrow 7t_1+29t_2-22=0$$

$$\therefore \quad \frac{t_1}{-154-116}=\frac{t_2}{28+242}=\frac{1}{319-49}$$

$\therefore \quad t_1=-1, t_2=1$

Putting the values of t_1 and t_2 in (1), (2), we get the points P and Q as $(3,8,3)$ and $(-3,-7,6)$.

71. (a) Vector area of the quadrilateral $ABCD$

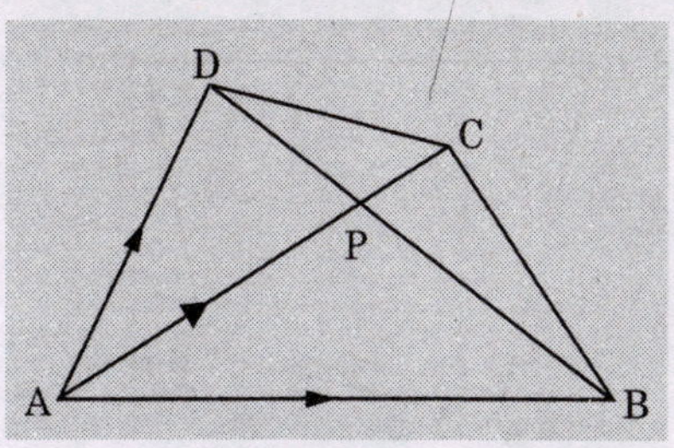

Fig. 43

$=$ Vector area of $\Delta ABC +$ Vector area of ΔACD

$$=\frac{1}{2}\vec{AB}\times\vec{AC}+\frac{1}{2}\vec{AC}\times\vec{AD}$$

$$=\frac{1}{2}\vec{AC}\times\vec{AD}-\frac{1}{2}\vec{AC}\times\vec{AB}$$

$\because \quad \mathbf{a}\times\mathbf{b}=-(\mathbf{b}\times\mathbf{a})$

$$=\frac{1}{2}\vec{AC}\times(\vec{AD}-\vec{AB})=\frac{1}{2}\vec{AC}\times\vec{BD}.$$

(b) Use result of part (a).

72. (a) With A as origin the P.V's of B, C and D be $\mathbf{b},\mathbf{c},\mathbf{d}$ respectively.

By given condition $\quad \dfrac{\mathbf{c}}{2}=\dfrac{\mathbf{b}+\mathbf{d}}{2}$ ...(1)

To prove $\quad \Delta ABC=\Delta ACD$

i.e., $\dfrac{1}{2}\mathbf{b}\times\mathbf{c}=\dfrac{1}{2}\mathbf{c}\times\mathbf{d}$

Multiply both sides of (1) vectorially by $\mathbf{c}$.

$$\therefore \quad 0=\frac{\mathbf{b}\times\mathbf{c}+\mathbf{d}\times\mathbf{c}}{2}$$

or $\quad \dfrac{1}{2}\mathbf{b}\times\mathbf{c}=-\dfrac{1}{2}\mathbf{d}\times\mathbf{c}=\dfrac{1}{2}\mathbf{c}\times\mathbf{d}.$

(b) $ABCD$ is the parallelogram with

$$\mathbf{a}=\vec{AB}=2\mathbf{m}+\mathbf{n} \text{ and } \mathbf{b}=\vec{AD}=\mathbf{m}-2\mathbf{n}.$$

Then $\vec{AC}=\vec{AB}+\vec{BC}=\vec{AB}+\vec{AD}=3\mathbf{m}-\mathbf{n}$

$$\vec{BD}=\vec{AD}-\vec{AB}=-\mathbf{m}-3\mathbf{n}$$

Hence $AC=\sqrt{\vec{AC}^2}=\sqrt{(3\mathbf{m}-\mathbf{n})^2}$

$$=\sqrt{9\mathbf{m}^2+\mathbf{n}^2-6\mathbf{m}\cdot\mathbf{n}}$$

$$=\sqrt{9+1-6\cdot1\cdot1\cos60^\circ}\ [\because\ |\mathbf{m}|=1,|\mathbf{n}|=1]$$

$$=\sqrt{7}.$$

$$BD=\sqrt{BD^2}=\sqrt{(-\mathbf{m}-3\mathbf{n})^2}=\sqrt{\mathbf{m}^2+9\mathbf{n}^2+6\mathbf{m}\cdot\mathbf{n}}$$

$$=\sqrt{1+9+6\cdot1\cdot1\cos60^\circ}=\sqrt{13}.$$

(c) If $ABCD$ be a cyclic quadrilateral, then $A+C=180^\circ=(B+D)$

$\therefore \quad \tan(A+C)=0$ or $\tan A+\tan C=0$

or $\quad \dfrac{\sin A}{\cos A}+\dfrac{\sin C}{\cos C}=0$

Now we know that $\left|\dfrac{\mathbf{a}\times\mathbf{b}}{\mathbf{a}\cdot\mathbf{b}}\right|=\dfrac{ab\sin\theta}{ab\cos\theta}=\tan\theta$

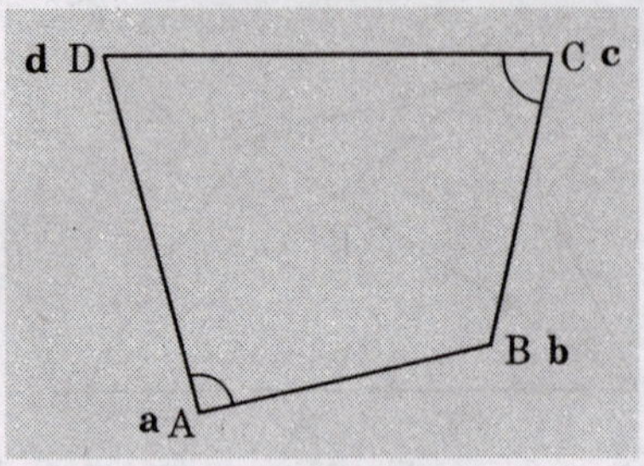

Fig. 44

$$\frac{|\vec{AB} \times \vec{AD}|}{\vec{AB} \cdot \vec{AD}} + \frac{|\vec{CB} \times \vec{CD}|}{\vec{CB} \cdot \vec{CD}} = 0$$

Now put $\vec{AB} = \mathbf{b} - \mathbf{a}$ and $\vec{CB} = \mathbf{b} - \mathbf{c}$ etc.

73. (a) Any three dimensional vector can be expressed as $\mathbf{v} = x\mathbf{i} + y\mathbf{j} + z\mathbf{k}$ involving three unknown x, y, z. Hence if we write $\mathbf{v}_1 = x_1\mathbf{i} + y_1\mathbf{j} + z_1\mathbf{k}$ etc. then we will have nine unknown quantities but we are given only six relations like $\mathbf{v}_1 \cdot \mathbf{v}_1 = 4$. Thus there will be infinite solutions.

$\mathbf{v}_1 \cdot \mathbf{v}_1 = 4, \mathbf{v}_1 \cdot \mathbf{v}_2 = -2, \mathbf{v}_1 \cdot \mathbf{v}_3 = 6$ ...(1)

$\mathbf{v}_2 \cdot \mathbf{v}_2 = 2, \mathbf{v}_2 \cdot \mathbf{v}_3 = -5, \mathbf{v}_3 \cdot \mathbf{v}_3 = 29$ ...(2)

Hence we must assume three quantities. Without loss of generality, let us assume that $y_1 = 0, z_1 = 0$ and $z_2 = 0$.

$\therefore$ $\mathbf{v}_1 = x_1\mathbf{i}, \mathbf{v}_2 = x_2\mathbf{i} + y_2\mathbf{j}$

$\mathbf{v}_3 = x_3\mathbf{i} + y_3\mathbf{j} + z_3\mathbf{k}$ ...(3)

Thus we have to find the values of six unknowns by the help of six relations given in (1) and (2).

$\mathbf{v}_1^2 = 4 \Rightarrow |\mathbf{v}_1| = 2 \Rightarrow x_1 = 2$

$\mathbf{v}_1 \cdot \mathbf{v}_2 = -2 \quad \Rightarrow \quad x_1 x_2 = -2$

or $2x_2 = -2 \quad \therefore \quad x_2 = -1$

$\mathbf{v}_1 \cdot \mathbf{v}_3 = 6 \quad \Rightarrow \quad x_1 x_3 = 6$

or $2x_3 = 6 \quad \therefore \quad x_3 = 3$

$\mathbf{v}_2 \cdot \mathbf{v}_2 = 2 \quad \Rightarrow \quad x_2^2 + y_2^2 = 2$

or $y_2^2 = 2 - x_2^2 = 2 - 1 = 1 \quad \therefore \quad y_2 = 1$ say.

$\mathbf{v}_2 \cdot \mathbf{v}_3 = -5 \quad \Rightarrow \quad x_2 x_3 + y_2 y_3 = -5$

or $-3 + 1 \cdot y_3 = -5 \quad \therefore \quad y_3 = -2.$

Finally $\mathbf{v}_3 \cdot \mathbf{v}_3 = 29$

$\Rightarrow \quad x_3^2 + y_3^2 + z_3^2 = 29 \quad$ or $\quad 9 + 4 + z_3^2 = 29$

$\therefore \quad z_3^2 = 16 \quad$ or $\quad z_3 = 4.$

Putting the values in (3), we get one of the solutions as

$\mathbf{v}_1 = 2\mathbf{i}, \mathbf{v}_2 = -\mathbf{i} + \mathbf{j}, \mathbf{v}_3 = 3\mathbf{i} - 2\mathbf{j} + 4\mathbf{k}.$

(b) From the given data we have the following relations :

If $x, y = x\mathbf{i} + y\mathbf{j}$

$$\left.\begin{aligned} A(0) = 2, 3 &\Rightarrow f_1(0) = 2, f_2(0) = 3 \\ A(1) = 6, 2 &\Rightarrow f_1(1) = 6, f_2(1) = 2 \\ B(0) = 3, 2 &\Rightarrow g_1(0) = 3, g_2(0) = 2 \\ B(1) = 2, 6 &\Rightarrow g_1(1) = 2, g_2(1) = 6 \end{aligned}\right] \quad \text{...(A)}$$

If two vectors are parallel, then their cross-product is zero.

$$\vec{A}(t) \times \vec{B}(t) = 0 \quad \Rightarrow \quad \begin{vmatrix} \mathbf{i} & \mathbf{j} & \mathbf{k} \\ f_1(t) & f_2(t) & 0 \\ g_1(t) & g_2(t) & 0 \end{vmatrix} = 0$$

or $[f_1(t) g_2(t) - f_2(t) g_1(t)]\,\mathbf{k} = 0$

or $f_1(t) g_2(t) - f_2(t) g_1(t) = 0$ for some t.

Let $F(t) = f_1(t) g_2(t) - f_2(t) g_1(t)$

Put $t = 0, 1$

$F(0) = 2.2 - 3.3 = -5$

$F(1) = 6.6 - 2.2 = 32$

Since $F(0)$ and $F(1)$ are of opposite signs we have $F(t) = 0$ for some $t \in [0, 1]$. For such a t, $A(t)$ and $B(t)$ will be parallel.

74. (i) Let the vectors represented by sides BC, CA and AB be denoted by **a, b** and **c** respectively and their modules be denoted by a, b and c.

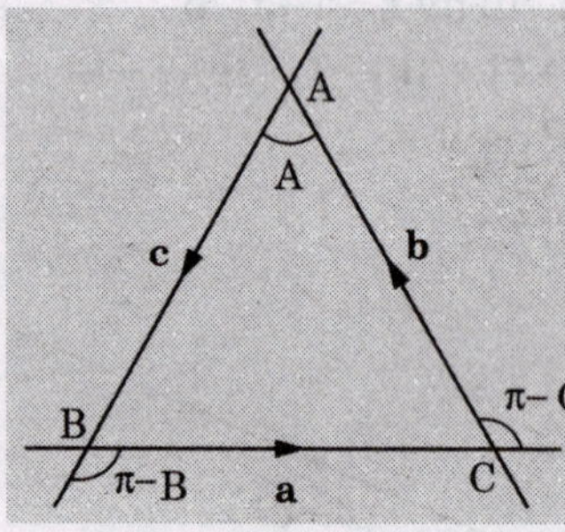

Fig. 45

Also we know that $\vec{BC} + \vec{CA} + \vec{AB} = \vec{BB} = \mathbf{0}$

or $\mathbf{a} + \mathbf{b} + \mathbf{c} = \mathbf{0} \quad \therefore \quad \vec{BC} = -(\vec{CA} + \vec{AB})$ ...(1)

Squaring both sides, we get

$\vec{BC}^2 = \vec{CA}^2 + \vec{AB}^2 + 2\vec{CA} \cdot \vec{AB}$

or $a^2 = b^2 + c^2 + 2bc \cos(\pi - A)$

or $a^2 = b^2 + c^2 - 2bc \cos A.$

$\because$ Angle between AB and AC is A and hence angle between AB and CA is $\pi - A$.

(ii) Multiplying both sides of (1) scalarly by $\vec{BC}$, we get

$\vec{BC} \cdot \vec{BC} = -(\vec{CA} + \vec{AB}) \cdot \vec{BC} = -\vec{CA} \cdot \vec{BC} - \vec{AB} \cdot \vec{BC}$

$a^2 = -ba \cos(\pi - C) - ca \cos(\pi - B)$

or $a^2 = ab \cos C + ca \cos B$

$\therefore \quad a = b \cos C + c \cos B.$

(iii) As in (1) $\mathbf{a} + \mathbf{b} + \mathbf{c} = \mathbf{0}.$ ...(1)

Also $\mathbf{c} \cdot \mathbf{a} = ca \cdot \cos(\pi - B) = -ac \cos B.$

$\mathbf{a} \cdot \mathbf{b} = ab \cos(\pi - C) = -ab \cos C.$ ...(A)

$\mathbf{b} \cdot \mathbf{c} = bc \cos(\pi - A) = -bc \cos A$

$\therefore \quad \mathbf{c} \cdot \mathbf{a} - \mathbf{b} \cdot \mathbf{c} = c(b \cos A - a \cos B)$

[Put $\mathbf{c} = -(\mathbf{a} + \mathbf{b})$]

$\therefore \quad -(\mathbf{a}+\mathbf{b}).(\mathbf{a}-\mathbf{b}) = c\,(b\cos A - a\cos B)$

or $\quad \mathbf{a}^2 - \mathbf{b}^2 = c\,(a\cos B - b\cos A)$

$\therefore \quad \dfrac{a^2 - b^2}{c} = a\cos B - b\cos A.$

(iv) Since $\mathbf{a}+\mathbf{b}+\mathbf{c} = \mathbf{0}$. Square

$\therefore \quad (\mathbf{a}+\mathbf{b}+\mathbf{c})^2 = 0$

or $\quad \Sigma\, \mathbf{a}^2 + 2\Sigma\,(\mathbf{b}.\mathbf{c}) = 0$

or $\quad a^2 + b^2 + c^2 = -2(-bc\cos A - ca\cos B - ab\cos C)$

$= 2(bc\cos A + ca\cos B + ab\cos C)$

by (A) of part (iii).

(v) On simplification it reduces to

$(b\cos C + c\cos B) + (c\cos A + a\cos C) + (a\cos B + b\cos A)$

$= a + b + c$ (by part ii)

(vi) $\mathbf{a}+\mathbf{b}+\mathbf{c} = \mathbf{0} \quad \therefore \quad \mathbf{a}\times(\mathbf{a}+\mathbf{b}+\mathbf{c}) = \mathbf{0}$

or $\quad \mathbf{a}\times\mathbf{a} + \mathbf{a}\times\mathbf{b} + \mathbf{a}\times\mathbf{c} = \mathbf{0}$

or $\quad \mathbf{a}\times\mathbf{b} = -\mathbf{a}\times\mathbf{c}$ or $\mathbf{a}\times\mathbf{b} = \mathbf{c}\times\mathbf{a}$ ...(1)

Again $\mathbf{b}\times(\mathbf{a}+\mathbf{b}+\mathbf{c}) = \mathbf{0}$

$\therefore \quad \mathbf{b}\times\mathbf{a} + \mathbf{b}\times\mathbf{b} + \mathbf{b}\times\mathbf{c} = \mathbf{0}$

$\therefore \quad \mathbf{b}\times\mathbf{c} = -\mathbf{b}\times\mathbf{a}$ or $\mathbf{b}\times\mathbf{c} = \mathbf{a}\times\mathbf{b}$ ...(2)

Hence from (1) and (2), we get

$\mathbf{a}\times\mathbf{b} = \mathbf{b}\times\mathbf{c} = \mathbf{c}\times\mathbf{a}$

$ab\sin(\pi - C)\,\hat{\mathbf{n}} = bc\sin(\pi - A)\,\hat{\mathbf{n}} = ca\sin(\pi - B)\,\hat{\mathbf{n}}$

where $\hat{\mathbf{n}}$ is a unit vector perpendicular to the plane of triangle ABC.

$ab\sin(\pi - C) = bc\sin(\pi - A) = ca\sin(\pi - B)$

or $\quad ab\sin C = bc\sin A = ca\sin B$

Dividing throughout by abc, we get

$\dfrac{\sin A}{a} = \dfrac{\sin B}{b} = \dfrac{\sin C}{c}.$

(vii) Ans. (b). **See Q. 74 (vi) done above.**

75. (i) Let there be two unit vectors **i** and **j** along OX and OY, two perpendicular lines in the plane of the paper. If OP and OQ be any two lines in the same plane making angles α and β with OX respectively then $\angle POQ = \alpha - \beta$. Again let $\vec{OA}$ and $\vec{OB}$ represent unit vectors along OP and OQ respectively.

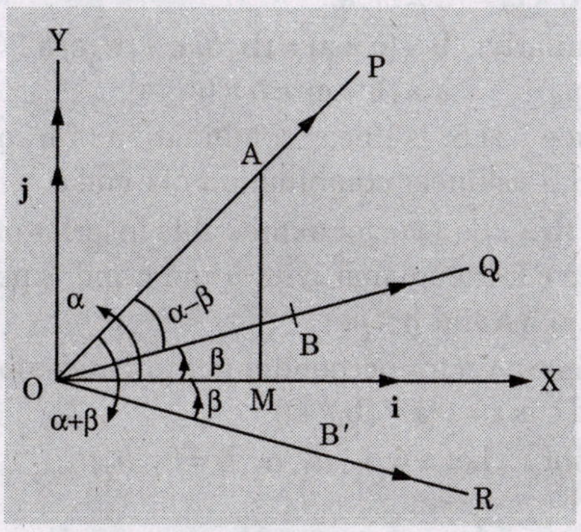

Fig. 46

$\therefore \quad \vec{OA}.\vec{OB} = 1.1\cos(\alpha-\beta) = \cos(\alpha-\beta)$. ...(1)

Again $\vec{OA} = \vec{OM} + \vec{MA} = OA\cos\alpha\mathbf{i} + OA\sin\alpha\mathbf{j}$

$\vec{OA} = \cos\alpha\mathbf{i} + \sin\alpha\mathbf{j}. \quad \because \quad OA = 1$ ...(2)

Similarly, $\vec{OB} = \cos\beta\mathbf{i} + \sin\beta\mathbf{j}.$ ...(3)

$\therefore \quad \vec{OA}.\vec{OB} = (\cos\alpha\mathbf{i} + \sin\alpha\mathbf{j}).(\cos\beta\mathbf{i} + \sin\beta\mathbf{j})$

$= \cos\alpha\cos\beta + \sin\alpha\sin\beta$

$\because \quad \mathbf{i}.\mathbf{i} = \mathbf{j}.\mathbf{j} = 1, \quad \mathbf{i}.\mathbf{j} = 0$

or $\quad \cos(\alpha-\beta) = \cos\alpha\cos\beta + \sin\alpha\sin\beta$, by (1)

In case we are to find the value of $\cos(\alpha+\beta)$, then we shall draw a line OR making an angle β in the clockwise sense so that

$\angle AOB' = \alpha + \beta$, and $\vec{OB'}$ represents a unit vector along OR.

$\therefore \quad \vec{OB'} = \cos(-\beta)\,\mathbf{i} + \sin(-\beta)\,\mathbf{j} = \cos\beta\,\mathbf{i} - \sin\beta\,\mathbf{j}$

$\therefore \quad \vec{OA}.\vec{OB'} = 1.1\cos(\alpha+\beta) = \cos(\alpha+\beta)$

Also $\vec{OA}.\vec{OB'} = (\cos\alpha\mathbf{i} + \sin\alpha\mathbf{j}).(\cos\beta\mathbf{i} - \sin\beta\mathbf{j})$

$= \cos\alpha\cos\beta - \sin\alpha\sin\beta$ as above

$\therefore \quad \cos(\alpha+\beta) = \cos\alpha\cos\beta - \sin\alpha\sin\beta.$

(ii) $\vec{OB}\times\vec{OA} = 1.1\sin(\alpha-\beta)\,\hat{\mathbf{n}}$. Anti-clockwise where $\mathbf{n}$ is a unit vector perpendicular to XY-plane.

Again $\vec{OB}\times\vec{OA} = (\cos\beta\mathbf{i} + \sin\beta\mathbf{j})\times(\cos\alpha\mathbf{i} + \sin\alpha\mathbf{j})$

$= \cos\beta\sin\alpha\,\mathbf{i}\times\mathbf{j} + \sin\beta\cos\alpha\,\mathbf{j}\times\mathbf{i}$

$\because \quad \mathbf{i}\times\mathbf{i} = \mathbf{j}\times\mathbf{j} = 0$

$= \sin\alpha\cos\beta\,.\,\hat{\mathbf{n}} - \cos\alpha\sin\beta\,.\,\hat{\mathbf{n}}$

$= (\sin\alpha\cos\beta - \cos\alpha\sin\beta)\,\hat{\mathbf{n}}$

$\because \quad \mathbf{i}\times\mathbf{j} = \hat{\mathbf{n}}$ and $\mathbf{j}\times\mathbf{i} = -\hat{\mathbf{n}}$

Equating the two values of $\vec{OB}\times\vec{OA}$, we get

$\sin(\alpha-\beta)\,\hat{\mathbf{n}} = (\sin\alpha\cos\beta - \cos\alpha\sin\beta)\,\hat{\mathbf{n}}$

$\therefore \quad \sin(\alpha-\beta) = \sin\alpha\cos\beta - \cos\alpha\sin\beta.$

The other formula for $\sin(\alpha+\beta)$ can be similarly proved if we take the cross product $\vec{OB'}\times\vec{OA}$.

§ 5. Scalar Triple Product

Between two vectors there is either a cross or a dot *i.e.* $\mathbf{a}\times\mathbf{b}$ (a vector) but $\mathbf{a}.\mathbf{b}$ (a scalar). But there is no sign of dot or cross in between a vector and a scalar, *i.e.* $5\,\mathbf{a}$, $a\,\mathbf{a}$, $-2\mathbf{a}$.

Since $\mathbf{a}.\mathbf{b}$ is a scalar, it can occur as a coefficient of a vector *i.e.* $\mathbf{a}.\mathbf{b}\,\mathbf{c} = (\mathbf{a}.\mathbf{b})\,\mathbf{c} = k\,\mathbf{c}$ type. Observe that there is no sign between **b** and **c**.

But $\mathbf{a}\times\mathbf{b}$ = vector, **c** is vector.

∴ We can have both dot and cross product, *i.e.* $(\mathbf{a} \times \mathbf{b}).\mathbf{c}$ is dot product called **scalar triple product.** But $(\mathbf{a} \times \mathbf{b}) \times \mathbf{c}$ is cross product called **vector triple product.**

First we shall consider scalar triple product.

$$(\mathbf{a} \times \mathbf{b}) . \mathbf{c} = \mathbf{c} . (\mathbf{a} \times \mathbf{b})$$

is called the scalar triple product of three vectors **a, b** and **c** and is written as [**a b c**].

Example. Which of the following expressions are meaningful ?

(a) $\mathbf{u} \cdot (\mathbf{v} \times \mathbf{w})$ (b) $(\mathbf{u} \cdot \mathbf{v}) \cdot \mathbf{w}$

(c) $(\mathbf{u} \cdot \mathbf{v})\, \mathbf{w}$ (d) $\mathbf{u} \times (\mathbf{v} \cdot \mathbf{w})$ **(I.I.T. 1998)**

Ans. (a) and (c).

Properties of Scalar triple product.

(a) If **a, b, c** be expressed in terms of unit vectors as

$$\mathbf{a} = a_1 \mathbf{i} + a_2 \mathbf{j} + a_3 \mathbf{k}, \quad \mathbf{b} = b_1 \mathbf{i} + b_2 \mathbf{j} + b_3 \mathbf{k},$$
$$\mathbf{c} = c_1 \mathbf{i} + c_2 \mathbf{j} + c_3 \mathbf{k}.$$

then it is easy to see that

$$[\mathbf{a\ b\ c}] = \begin{vmatrix} a_1 & a_2 & a_3 \\ b_1 & b_2 & b_3 \\ c_1 & c_2 & c_3 \end{vmatrix} = \Delta, \text{ say.}$$

(b) **Geometrical interpretation.**
The scalar triple product [**a b c**] represents the volume of the parallelopiped whose coterminous edges **a, b, c** form a right handed system of vectors.

(c) We know that in a determinant if a line be crossed over two lines the determinant retains its value both in magnitude and sense since it is multiplied by $(-1)^2$ so that it does not change

$$\therefore \quad [\mathbf{a\ b\ c}] = \begin{vmatrix} c_1 & c_2 & c_3 \\ a_1 & a_2 & a_3 \\ b_1 & b_2 & b_3 \end{vmatrix} = [\mathbf{c\ a\ b}]$$

$$= \begin{vmatrix} b_1 & b_2 & b_3 \\ c_1 & c_2 & c_3 \\ a_1 & a_2 & a_3 \end{vmatrix} = [\mathbf{b\ c\ a}]$$

$\therefore \quad [\mathbf{a\ b\ c}] = [\mathbf{b\ c\ a}] = [\mathbf{c\ a\ b}]$

or $\quad \mathbf{a} . (\mathbf{b} \times \mathbf{c}) = (\mathbf{b} \times \mathbf{c}) . \mathbf{a}$ ...(1)

$\quad = \mathbf{b} . (\mathbf{c} \times \mathbf{a}) = (\mathbf{c} \times \mathbf{a}) . \mathbf{b}$ ...(2)

$\quad = \mathbf{c} . (\mathbf{a} \times \mathbf{b}) = (\mathbf{a} \times \mathbf{b}) . \mathbf{c}.$ ...(3)

From (1) and (3) we conclude that

$$\mathbf{a} . (\mathbf{b} \times \mathbf{c}) = (\mathbf{a} \times \mathbf{b}) . \mathbf{c}$$

and similarly from (2) and (1),

$$\mathbf{b} . (\mathbf{c} \times \mathbf{a}) = (\mathbf{b} \times \mathbf{c}) . \mathbf{a} \text{ etc.}$$

From above we observe that in scalar triple product $[\mathbf{a\ b\ c}] = \mathbf{a} . (\mathbf{b} \times \mathbf{c}) = (\mathbf{a} \times \mathbf{b}) . \mathbf{c}$, the position of dot and cross can be interchanged at pleasure provided we maintain the cyclic order of **a, b, c.**

With every change of cyclic order there will be a change of sign *i.e.* $[\mathbf{a\ b\ c}] = -[\mathbf{a\ c\ b}]$ or $= -[\mathbf{b\ a\ c}]$

This follows from the fact that if in a determinant we interchange any two adjacent rows or columns the determinant retains its value but changes its sign.

(d) **Scalar triple product is zero when two vectors are equal**
i.e., $[\mathbf{a\ a\ c}] = 0$ or $[\mathbf{a\ b\ b}] = 0$ etc.
This follows from the fact that a determinant is zero when two rows or columns are identical.

(e) **Condition for Coplanarity.**
In case the three vectors are coplanar, then the volume of the parallelopiped is zero and hence $[\mathbf{a\ b\ c}] = 0$
or $\Delta = 0$.
Four points A, B, C, D with position vectors as **a, b, c, d** will be coplanar if three vectors $\vec{AB}, \vec{AC}, \vec{AD}$ are coplanar
i.e., $[\mathbf{b} - \mathbf{a}, \mathbf{c} - \mathbf{a}, \mathbf{d} - \mathbf{a}] = 0$
Alternative : Any one of the three is expressible as a linear combination of the other two,
i.e., $\vec{AB} = l . \vec{AC} + m . \vec{AD}$

(f) (i) $[\mathbf{a} + \mathbf{b}\ \ \mathbf{c}\ \ \mathbf{d}] = [\mathbf{a\ c\ d}] + [\mathbf{b\ c\ d}]$

(ii) $[\mathbf{a} + \mathbf{b}\ \ \mathbf{a}\ \ \mathbf{b}] = [\mathbf{a\ a\ b}] + [\mathbf{b\ a\ b}] = 0 + 0$
Scalar triple product is zero when two vectors are equal.

(iii) $[\mathbf{a} + \mathbf{b} + \mathbf{c}\ \ \mathbf{a} + \mathbf{b}\ \ \mathbf{d}] = [\mathbf{c}\ \ \mathbf{a} + \mathbf{b}\ \ \mathbf{d}]$
$= [\mathbf{c\ a\ d}] + [\mathbf{c\ b\ d}]$
$\because \quad [\mathbf{a} + \mathbf{b}\ \ \mathbf{a} + \mathbf{b}\ \ \mathbf{d}] = 0$

(iv) $[p\mathbf{a}\ \ q\mathbf{b}\ \ r\mathbf{c}] = pqr\,[\mathbf{a\ b\ c}]$
where p, q, r are all scalars. All the above follow from the simple properties of determinants.

§ 6. Vector Triple Product. (B.I.T.S. 1999)

$$\mathbf{a} \times (\mathbf{b} \times \mathbf{c}) = (\mathbf{a} . \mathbf{c})\, \mathbf{b} - (\mathbf{a} . \mathbf{b})\, \mathbf{c}. \quad ...(1)$$

It is expressible in terms of **b** and **c** as **a . c** and **a . b** both are scalars.

Similarly, $\quad (\mathbf{b} \times \mathbf{c}) \times \mathbf{a} = (\mathbf{a} . \mathbf{b})\, \mathbf{c} - (\mathbf{a} . \mathbf{c})\, \mathbf{b}$

$\therefore \quad \mathbf{a} \times (\mathbf{b} \times \mathbf{c}) = -(\mathbf{b} \times \mathbf{c}) \times \mathbf{a}.$

Even through the cyclic order of the vectors is maintained but the sign is changed. In dot product $\mathbf{a} . (\mathbf{b} \times \mathbf{c}) = (\mathbf{b} \times \mathbf{c}) . \mathbf{a}$.

Similarly, $\mathbf{b} \times (\mathbf{c} \times \mathbf{a}) = (\mathbf{b} . \mathbf{a})\, \mathbf{c} - (\mathbf{b} . \mathbf{c})\, \mathbf{a}$.

Thus $\quad \mathbf{a} \times (\mathbf{b} \times \mathbf{c}) \neq \mathbf{b} \times (\mathbf{c} \times \mathbf{a}),$

Since L.H.S. is linear combination of **b** and **c** whereas R.H.S. is linear combination of **c** and **a.**

$\mathbf{a} \times (\mathbf{b} \times \mathbf{c})$ is a vector expressible in terms of **b** and **c** and hence it is coplanar with **b** and **c** and is perpendicular to both **a** and $\mathbf{b} \times \mathbf{c}$.

Hence a vector perpendicular to **a** and coplanar with **b** and **c** is $\mathbf{r} = t\,[\mathbf{a} \times (\mathbf{b} \times \mathbf{c})]$ **(V. Imp.)**

Proof : Let $\mathbf{a} = a_1, a_2, a_3, \mathbf{b} = b_1, b_2, b_3$
and $\quad \mathbf{c} = c_1, c_2, c_3.$

L.H.S. $= \mathbf{a} \times (\mathbf{b} \times \mathbf{c})$

$$= (a_1\mathbf{i} + a_2\mathbf{j} + a_3\mathbf{k}) \times \begin{vmatrix} \mathbf{i} & \mathbf{j} & \mathbf{k} \\ b_1 & b_2 & b_3 \\ c_1 & c_2 & c_3 \end{vmatrix}$$

$$= (a_1\mathbf{i} + a_2\mathbf{j} + a_3\mathbf{k}) \times \{(b_2c_3 - b_3c_2)\,\mathbf{i} + (b_3c_1 - b_1c_3)\,\mathbf{j} + (b_1c_2 - b_2c_1)\,\mathbf{k}\}$$

$$= \begin{vmatrix} \mathbf{i} & \mathbf{j} & \mathbf{k} \\ a_1 & a_2 & a_3 \\ b_2c_3 - b_3c_2 & b_3c_1 - b_1c_3 & b_1c_2 - b_2c_1 \end{vmatrix} = \text{L.H.S.} \quad \ldots(1)$$

$$\text{R.H.S.} = (\mathbf{a}\,.\,\mathbf{c})\,\mathbf{b} - (\mathbf{a}\,.\,\mathbf{b})\,\mathbf{c} \quad \ldots(2)$$

$$= (a_1c_1 + a_2c_2 + a_3c_3)\,[b_1\mathbf{i} + b_2\mathbf{j} + b_3\mathbf{k}] - (a_1b_1 + a_2b_2 + a_3b_3)\,[c_1\mathbf{i} + c_2\mathbf{j} + c_3\mathbf{k}]$$

The coefficient of **i** in the above is

$$b_1\,(a_1c_1 + a_2c_2 + a_3c_3) - c_1\,(a_1b_1 + a_2b_2 + a_3b_3) = a_2\,(b_1c_2 - b_2c_1) - a_3\,(b_3c_1 - b_1c_3)$$

It is same as coefficient of **i** in (1).

Similarly the coefficients of **j** and **k** in (1) and (2) are same. Hence L.H.S. = R.H.S.

§ 7. Scalar Product of Four Vectors.

$$(\mathbf{a} \times \mathbf{b})\,.\,(\mathbf{c} \times \mathbf{d}) = \begin{vmatrix} \mathbf{a}\,.\,\mathbf{c} & \mathbf{b}\,.\,\mathbf{c} \\ \mathbf{a}\,.\,\mathbf{d} & \mathbf{b}\,.\,\mathbf{d} \end{vmatrix}$$

Let $\mathbf{c} \times \mathbf{d} = \mathbf{n}$,

$\therefore$ L.H.S. $= (\mathbf{a} \times \mathbf{b})\,.\,\mathbf{n} = \mathbf{a}\,.\,(\mathbf{b} \times \mathbf{n})$

[The position of dot and cross can be changed if cyclic order is maintained]

$$= \mathbf{a}\,.\,[\mathbf{b} \times (\mathbf{c} \times \mathbf{d})] = \mathbf{a}\,.\,[(\mathbf{b}\,.\,\mathbf{d})\,\mathbf{c} - (\mathbf{b}\,.\,\mathbf{c})\,\mathbf{d}]$$

$$= (\mathbf{b}\,.\,\mathbf{d})\,(\mathbf{a}\,.\,\mathbf{c}) - (\mathbf{b}\,.\,\mathbf{c})\,(\mathbf{a}\,.\,\mathbf{d})$$

$$= \begin{vmatrix} \mathbf{a}\,.\,\mathbf{c} & \mathbf{b}\,.\,\mathbf{c} \\ \mathbf{a}\,.\,\mathbf{d} & \mathbf{b}\,.\,\mathbf{d} \end{vmatrix} = \begin{vmatrix} \mathbf{a}\,.\,\mathbf{c} & \mathbf{a}\,.\,\mathbf{d} \\ \mathbf{b}\,.\,\mathbf{c} & \mathbf{b}\,.\,\mathbf{d} \end{vmatrix}.$$

§8. To find the shortest distance between two non-intersecting lines passing through the points whose position vectors are a and b and are parallel to the vectors c and d respectively.

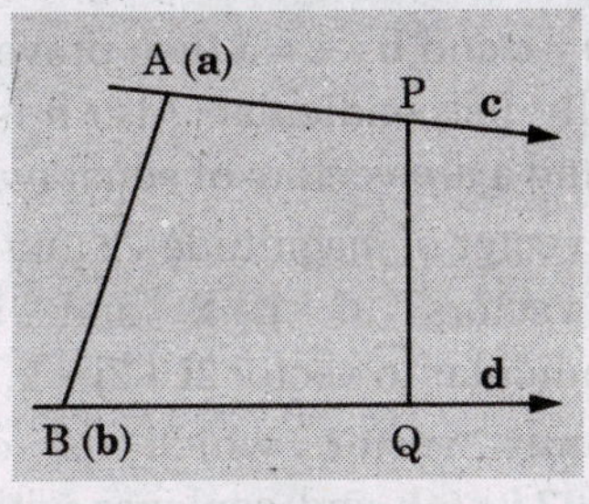

Fig. 47

Let PQ be the shortest distance between the two lines so that PQ is perpendicular to both **c** and **d**. But $\mathbf{c} \times \mathbf{d}$ is a vector perpendicular to both **c** and **d**. Hence PQ is parallel to the vector $\mathbf{c} \times \mathbf{d}$.

Let $\mathbf{c} \times \mathbf{d} = \mathbf{n}$ and let $|\mathbf{n}| = n$. If A, B are the points **a** and **b** respectively, the length p of this common perpendicular PQ is equal to the length of the projection of AB on the vector **n**. Hence

$$(\mathbf{a} - \mathbf{b})\,.\,\mathbf{n} = (\text{modulus of } \mathbf{n})\,.\,(\text{Projection of } (\mathbf{a} - \mathbf{b}) \text{ on } \mathbf{n}) = np$$

$$\therefore \quad p = \frac{1}{n}\,[(\mathbf{a} - \mathbf{b})\,.\,\mathbf{n}] = \frac{1}{n}\,[(\mathbf{a} - \mathbf{b})\,.\,(\mathbf{c} \times \mathbf{d})]$$

$$= \frac{[\mathbf{a} - \mathbf{b}, \mathbf{c}, \mathbf{d}]}{|\mathbf{c} \times \mathbf{d}|} = \frac{(\mathbf{a} - \mathbf{b})\,.\,\mathbf{n}}{|\mathbf{n}|}$$

where $\mathbf{n} = \mathbf{c} \times \mathbf{d}$.

Also the vector determined by S.D. is

$$p\,.\,\hat{\mathbf{n}} = p\,.\,\frac{\mathbf{n}}{|\mathbf{n}|} = \frac{(\mathbf{a} - \mathbf{b})\,.\,\mathbf{n}}{|\mathbf{n}|}\,.\,\frac{\mathbf{n}}{|\mathbf{n}|} = \frac{(\mathbf{a} - \mathbf{b})\,.\,\mathbf{n}}{|\mathbf{n}|^2}\,\mathbf{n}$$

Working Rule : *The shortest distance between two non-intersecting lines parallel respectively to* **c** *and* **d** *will be projection of line joining any two points (one on each line) on the vector* $\mathbf{c} \times \mathbf{d}$ *which is perpendicular to both the lines.*

Ex. 1. A line passes through the point $A\,(6, 2, 2)$ and is parallel to vector $\mathbf{c} = \mathbf{i} - 2\mathbf{j} + 2\mathbf{k}$. Another line passes through $B\,(-4, 0, -1)$ and is parallel to vector $\mathbf{d} = 3\mathbf{i} - 2\mathbf{j} - 2\mathbf{k}$. Find the shortest distance between these two lines.

As stated above in § 8, the shortest distance PQ is the projection of $\overrightarrow{AB}$ on $\mathbf{c} \times \mathbf{d}$.

$$\overrightarrow{AB} = \text{P.V. of } B - \text{P.V. of } A = -10\mathbf{i} - 2\mathbf{j} - 3\mathbf{k} \quad \ldots(1)$$

$$\therefore \quad \text{Projection of } \overrightarrow{AB} \text{ on } \mathbf{c} \times \mathbf{d} \text{ is } \quad \frac{\overrightarrow{AB} \cdot (\mathbf{c} \times \mathbf{d})}{|\mathbf{c} \times \mathbf{d}|} \quad \ldots(2)$$

$$\text{Now } \mathbf{c} \times \mathbf{d} = \begin{vmatrix} \mathbf{i} & \mathbf{j} & \mathbf{k} \\ 1 & -2 & 2 \\ 3 & -2 & -2 \end{vmatrix} = 4(2\mathbf{i} + 2\mathbf{j} + \mathbf{k}) \quad \ldots(3)$$

$$\therefore \quad |\mathbf{c} \times \mathbf{d}| = 4.3 = 12$$

Hence from (1), (2), (3), the required S.D. is

$$\frac{(-10\mathbf{i} - 2\mathbf{j} - 3\mathbf{k})\,.\,4(2\mathbf{i} + 2\mathbf{j} + \mathbf{k})}{12} = \frac{-20 - 4 - 3}{3} = -9 = 9$$

§ 9. Plane

(a) Vector equation of a plane.

Let the unit vector $\hat{\mathbf{n}}$ be normal to the plane. If $\mathbf{r} = \overrightarrow{OP}$ be position vector of any point P on the plane and p the length of perpendicular from O to the plane, then $ON = p$. It is projection of $\overrightarrow{OP}$ on $\hat{\mathbf{n}}$

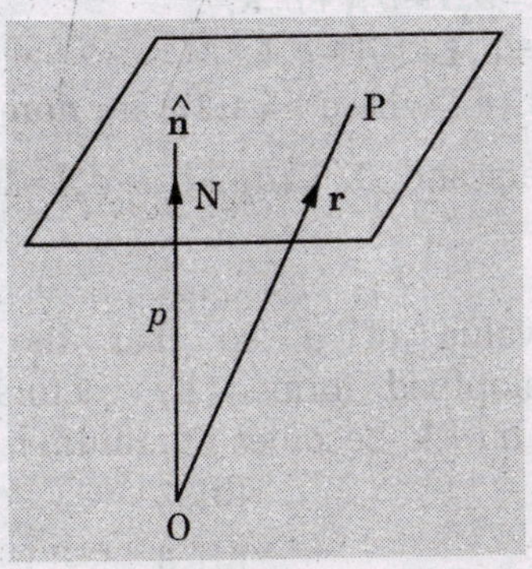

Fig. 48

$\therefore \quad p = \dfrac{\vec{OP} \cdot \hat{\mathbf{n}}}{1} = \mathbf{r} \cdot \hat{\mathbf{n}} = p$ ...(1)

(b) If $\mathbf{n}$ be a vector parallel to unit vector $\hat{\mathbf{n}}$ and of modulus n, then multiplying both sides of (1) by n, we get

$\mathbf{r} \cdot (n\,\hat{\mathbf{n}}) = pn$ or $\mathbf{r} \cdot \mathbf{n} = q$ ...(2)

where $q = pn$ or $p = \dfrac{q}{n} = \dfrac{q}{|\mathbf{n}|}$ ...(3)

Hence when the plane is of the form (2), then length of perpendicular from origin on this plane is $p = \dfrac{q}{|\mathbf{n}|}$.

(c) Plane through a given point A (a).

If $P(\mathbf{r})$ be any point on the plane whose normal is $\mathbf{n}$ then $\vec{AP} = \mathbf{r} - \mathbf{a}$ lies in the plane. Since $\mathbf{n}$ is normal, it is perpendicular to any line lying in the plane.

$\therefore \quad \vec{AP} \cdot \mathbf{n} = 0$ or $(\mathbf{r} - \mathbf{a}) \cdot \mathbf{n} = 0$

or $\mathbf{r} \cdot \mathbf{n} = \mathbf{a} \cdot \mathbf{n} = q$, say

$\therefore \quad p =$ length of perpendicular from origin $= \dfrac{q}{n} = \dfrac{\mathbf{a} \cdot \mathbf{n}}{|\mathbf{n}|}$

(d) Plane through three given points A, B, C whose P.V.s are a, b, c respectively.

The vectors $\vec{AB} = \mathbf{b} - \mathbf{a}$ and $\vec{AC} = \mathbf{c} - \mathbf{a}$ lie in the plane

$\therefore \quad \vec{AB} \times \vec{AC}$ is along the normal

$\therefore \quad \mathbf{n} = (\mathbf{b} - \mathbf{a}) \times (\mathbf{c} - \mathbf{a}) = \mathbf{b} \times \mathbf{c} - \mathbf{a} \times \mathbf{c} - \mathbf{b} \times \mathbf{a} + 0$

or $\quad \mathbf{n} = (\mathbf{b} \times \mathbf{c} + \mathbf{c} \times \mathbf{a} + \mathbf{a} \times \mathbf{b})$

Since the plane passes through $A(\mathbf{a})$, therefore its equation is $\mathbf{r} \cdot \mathbf{n} = \mathbf{a} \cdot \mathbf{n}$ by case (c).

or $\quad \mathbf{r} \cdot (\mathbf{b} \times \mathbf{c} + \mathbf{c} \times \mathbf{a} + \mathbf{a} \times \mathbf{b}) = \mathbf{a} \cdot (\mathbf{b} \times \mathbf{c}) + 0 + 0$

$\quad \mathbf{r} \cdot (\mathbf{b} \times \mathbf{c} + \mathbf{c} \times \mathbf{a} + \mathbf{a} \times \mathbf{b}) = [\mathbf{a}\ \mathbf{b}\ \mathbf{c}]$

$\therefore \quad p =$ length of perpendicular $= \dfrac{q}{n}$

$= \dfrac{[\mathbf{a}\ \mathbf{b}\ \mathbf{c}]}{|\mathbf{b} \times \mathbf{c} + \mathbf{c} \times \mathbf{a} + \mathbf{a} \times \mathbf{b}|}$

Problem Set (2)

Scalar triple product, Vector triple product. Scalar product of four vectors, Reciprocal system of vectors, vector equation of a plane.

1. Find the volume of the parallelopiped whose edges are represented by the vectors

(a) $\mathbf{a} = 2\mathbf{i} - 3\mathbf{j} + 4\mathbf{k},\ \mathbf{b} = \mathbf{i} + 2\mathbf{j} - \mathbf{k}, \mathbf{c} = 3\mathbf{i} - \mathbf{j} + 2\mathbf{k}$

(b) $\mathbf{a} = 2\mathbf{i} - 3\mathbf{j},\ \mathbf{b} = \mathbf{i} + \mathbf{j} - \mathbf{k},\ \mathbf{c} = 3\mathbf{i} - \mathbf{k}$.

(c) $\mathbf{a} = 2\mathbf{i} + \mathbf{j} - \mathbf{k},\ \mathbf{b} = \mathbf{i} + 2\mathbf{j} + 3\mathbf{k}, \mathbf{c} = -3\mathbf{i} - \mathbf{j} + \mathbf{k}$

Also find the area of the face made by **a** and **b**.

(d) If λ be a non-zero scalar, prove that the following vectors $\mathbf{a} = \lambda\mathbf{i} + 2\lambda\mathbf{j} - 3\lambda\mathbf{k}$,

$\mathbf{b} = (2\lambda + 1)\,\mathbf{i} + (2\lambda + 3)\,\mathbf{j} + (\lambda + 1)\,\mathbf{k}$

and $\mathbf{c} = (3\lambda + 5)\,\mathbf{i} + (\lambda + 5)\,\mathbf{j} + (\lambda + 2)\,\mathbf{k}$

are non-coplanar.

2. (a) The volume of the parallelopiped whose edges are represented by $-12\mathbf{i} + \lambda\mathbf{k}$, $3\mathbf{j} - \mathbf{k}$, $2\mathbf{i} + \mathbf{j} - 15\mathbf{k}$ is 546. Find the value of λ.

(b) Let V be the volume of the parallelopiped formed by the vectors

$\mathbf{a} = a_1\mathbf{i} + a_2\mathbf{j} + a_3\mathbf{k}$,
$\mathbf{b} = b_1\mathbf{i} + b_2\mathbf{j} + b_3\mathbf{k}$,
$\mathbf{c} = c_1\mathbf{i} + c_2\mathbf{j} + c_3\mathbf{k}$.

If a_r, b_r, c_r, where $r = 1, 2\ 3$, are non-negative real numbers and $\sum_{r=1}^{3} (a_r + b_r + c_r) = 3L$, show that $V \le L^3$.

(I.I.T. 2002)

(c) The value of a so that the volume of parallelopiped formed by vectors $\mathbf{i} + a\,\mathbf{j} + \mathbf{k}$, $\mathbf{j} + a\,\mathbf{k}, a\,\mathbf{i} + \mathbf{k}$ becomes minimum is

(a) $\sqrt{3}$ (b) 2

(c) $\dfrac{1}{\sqrt{3}}$ (d) 3

(Screening 2003)

(d) The edges of a parallelopiped are of unit length and are parallel to non-coplanar unit vectors **a, b, c** such that $\mathbf{a} \cdot \mathbf{b} = \mathbf{b} \cdot \mathbf{c} = \mathbf{c} \cdot \mathbf{a} = 1/2$. Then the volume of the parallelopiped is

(a) $\dfrac{1}{\sqrt{2}}$ (b) $\dfrac{1}{2\sqrt{2}}$

(c) $\dfrac{\sqrt{3}}{2}$ (d) $\dfrac{1}{\sqrt{3}}$

(I.I.T. 2008)

3.* (a) **a, b, c** are non-zero vectors which are such that $\mathbf{a} \times \mathbf{b} = \mathbf{c}, \mathbf{b} \times \mathbf{c} = \mathbf{a}$ and $\mathbf{c} \times \mathbf{a} = \mathbf{b}$, then prove that the three vectors form a right handed orthonormal triad.

(b) If $\mathbf{a} \times \mathbf{b} = \mathbf{c}$ and $\mathbf{b} \times \mathbf{c} = \mathbf{a}$ then prove that **a, b, c** are mutually perpendicular. Also **b** is a unit vector and **c** and **a** are vectors of equal magnitude.

4. (a) Find a vector of magnitude $\sqrt{2}$ units and coplanar with vectors $3\mathbf{i} - \mathbf{j} - \mathbf{k}$ and $\mathbf{i} + \mathbf{j} - 2\mathbf{k}$ and perpendicular to vector $2\mathbf{i} + 2\mathbf{j} + \mathbf{k}$.

(b) The unit vector which is orthogonal to $\mathbf{a} = 3\,\mathbf{i} + 2\,\mathbf{j} + 6\,\mathbf{k}$ and coplanar with $\mathbf{b} = 2\,\mathbf{i} + \mathbf{j} + \mathbf{k}$ and $\mathbf{c} = \mathbf{i} - \mathbf{j} + \mathbf{k}$ is

(a) $\dfrac{6\mathbf{i} - 5\mathbf{k}}{\sqrt{61}}$ (b) $\dfrac{3\mathbf{j} - \mathbf{k}}{\sqrt{10}}$

(c) $\dfrac{2\mathbf{i} - 5\mathbf{j}}{\sqrt{29}}$ (d) $\dfrac{2\mathbf{i} + \mathbf{j} - 2\mathbf{k}}{3}$

(Screening 2004)

(c) A unit vector coplanar with $\mathbf{i} + \mathbf{j} + 2\mathbf{k}$ and $\mathbf{i} + 2\mathbf{j} + \mathbf{k}$ and perpendicular to $\mathbf{i} + \mathbf{j} + \mathbf{k}$ is ....

(I.I.T. 1992)

(d) Let $\mathbf{a} = 2\mathbf{i} + \mathbf{j} + \mathbf{k}$, $\mathbf{b} = \mathbf{i} + 2\mathbf{j} - \mathbf{k}$ and a unit vector $\mathbf{c}$ be coplanar. If $\mathbf{c}$ is perpendicular to $\mathbf{a}$, then $\mathbf{c} =$

(a) $\frac{1}{\sqrt{2}}(-\mathbf{j}+\mathbf{k})$ (b) $\frac{1}{\sqrt{3}}(-\mathbf{i}-\mathbf{j}-\mathbf{k})$

(c) $\frac{1}{\sqrt{5}}(\mathbf{i}-2\mathbf{j})$ (d) $\frac{1}{\sqrt{3}}(\mathbf{i}-\mathbf{j}-\mathbf{k})$ **(I.I.T. 1999)**

5.* (a) For non-zero vectors $\mathbf{a}, \mathbf{b}, \mathbf{c}$;

$$|(\mathbf{a}\times\mathbf{b}).\mathbf{c}| = |\mathbf{a}||\mathbf{b}||\mathbf{c}|$$

holds if and only if

(i) $\mathbf{a}.\mathbf{b}=0,\ \mathbf{b}.\mathbf{c}=0$ (ii) $\mathbf{b}.\mathbf{c}=0,\ \mathbf{c}.\mathbf{a}=0$

(iii) $\mathbf{c}.\mathbf{a}=0,\ \mathbf{a}.\mathbf{b}=0$ (iv) $\mathbf{a}.\mathbf{b}=\mathbf{b}.\mathbf{c}=\mathbf{c}.\mathbf{a}=0$

(b) Let $\mathbf{a} = 2\mathbf{i} + \mathbf{j} - 2\mathbf{k}$ and $\mathbf{b} = \mathbf{i} + \mathbf{j}$. If $\mathbf{c}$ is a vector such that $\mathbf{a}.\mathbf{c} = |\mathbf{c}|, |\mathbf{c} - \mathbf{a}| = 2\sqrt{2}$ and the angle between $(\mathbf{a}\times\mathbf{b})$ and $\mathbf{c}$ is 30°, then $|(\mathbf{a}\times\mathbf{b})\times\mathbf{c}| =$

(a) $\frac{2}{3}$ (b) $\frac{3}{2}$

(c) 2 (d) 3 **(I.I.T. 1999)**

(c) Let $\vec{V} = 2\mathbf{i} + \mathbf{j} - \mathbf{k}$ and $\vec{W} = \mathbf{i} + 3\mathbf{k}$. If $\vec{U}$ is a unit vector, then the maximum value of the scalar triple product $[\vec{U}\ \vec{V}\ \vec{W}]$ is

(a) -1 (b) $\sqrt{10}+\sqrt{6}$

(c) $\sqrt{59}$ (d) $\sqrt{60}$ **(I.I.T. Sc. 2002)**

(d) Let $\mathbf{a}, \mathbf{b}, \mathbf{c}$ be three non-zero vectors such that $\mathbf{c}$ is a unit vector perpendicular to both $\mathbf{a}$ and $\mathbf{b}$. If the angle between $\mathbf{a}$ and $\mathbf{b}$ be $\frac{\pi}{6}$, prove that

$$[\mathbf{a}\ \mathbf{b}\ \mathbf{c}]^2 = \frac{1}{4}|\mathbf{a}||\mathbf{b}|^2$$

(e) If $\mathbf{a} = \mathbf{i} + \mathbf{j} + \mathbf{k}$, $\mathbf{a}.\mathbf{b} = 1$ and $\mathbf{a}\times\mathbf{b} = \mathbf{j} - \mathbf{k}$, then $\mathbf{b}$ is

(a) $\mathbf{i} - \mathbf{j} + \mathbf{k}$ (b) $2\mathbf{j} - \mathbf{k}$

(c) $\mathbf{i}$ (d) $2\mathbf{i}$ **(Screening 2004)**

6. (a) Let $\mathbf{a}$ and $\mathbf{b}$ be two non-collinear unit vectors. If $\mathbf{u} = \mathbf{a} - (\mathbf{a}.\mathbf{b})\,\mathbf{b}$ and $\mathbf{v} = \mathbf{a}\times\mathbf{b}$, then $|\mathbf{v}|$ is

(a) $|\mathbf{u}|$ (b) $|\mathbf{u}| + |\mathbf{u}.\mathbf{a}|$

(c) $|\mathbf{u}| + |\mathbf{u}.\mathbf{b}|$ (d) $|\mathbf{u}| + \mathbf{u}.(\mathbf{a}+\mathbf{b})$ **(I.I.T. 1999)**

(b) An arc AC of a circle subtends a right-angle at the centre O. The point B divides the arc in the ratio 1 : 2. If $\vec{OA} = \mathbf{a}$ and $\vec{OB} = \mathbf{b}$, then calculate $\vec{OC}$ in terms of $\mathbf{a}$ and $\mathbf{b}$. **(Roorkee 1999)**

7. (a) Prove that $(\mathbf{i}\times\mathbf{a})\cdot(\mathbf{a}\times\mathbf{j}) = (\mathbf{i}\cdot\mathbf{a})(\mathbf{a}\cdot\mathbf{j})$

(b) $\mathbf{a}$ and $\mathbf{b}$ are unit vectors perpendicular to each other. $\mathbf{c}$ is another unit vector inclined at an angle θ to both $\mathbf{a}$ and $\mathbf{b}$.

If $\mathbf{c} = p(\mathbf{a}+\mathbf{b}) + q(\mathbf{a}\times\mathbf{b})$ where $p, q \in R$ then show that $\frac{\pi}{4} \le \theta \le \frac{3\pi}{4}$.

8. Find the constant λ so that the vectors

(a)* $\mathbf{a} = 2\mathbf{i} - \mathbf{j} + \mathbf{k}$, $\mathbf{b} = \mathbf{i} + 2\mathbf{j} - 3\mathbf{k}$, $\mathbf{c} = 3\mathbf{i} + \lambda\mathbf{j} + 5\mathbf{k}$ are coplanar.

(b) If $\mathbf{a} = \mathbf{i} - 3\mathbf{j} + \mathbf{k}$, $\mathbf{b} = 2\mathbf{i} + \lambda\mathbf{j} + \mathbf{k}$, $\mathbf{c} = 3\mathbf{i} + \mathbf{j} - 2\mathbf{k}$ are coplanar, then $\lambda = -4$

(c)* For what values of x and y are the following vectors $x\mathbf{i} + y\mathbf{j}$, $2x\mathbf{i} - y\mathbf{j} + \mathbf{k}$ and $\mathbf{i} - 2\mathbf{j} + \mathbf{k}$ are coplanar ?

9. (a) Prove that $[\mathbf{a}-\mathbf{b}, \mathbf{b}+\mathbf{c}, \mathbf{c}+\mathbf{a}] = 0$, where $\mathbf{a}, \mathbf{b}, \mathbf{c}$ are vectors given in Q. 8 (b).

(b) Let $\mathbf{a} = \mathbf{i} - \mathbf{k}$, $\mathbf{b} = x\,\mathbf{i} + \mathbf{j} + (1-x)\,\mathbf{k}$ and $\mathbf{c} = y\,\mathbf{i} + x\,\mathbf{j} + (1+x-y)\,\mathbf{k}$. Then $[\mathbf{a}\ \mathbf{b}\ \mathbf{c}]$ depends on

(a) only x (b) only y

(c) neither x nor y (d) both x and y **(I.I.T. Sc. 2001)**

(c) If $\mathbf{a}, \mathbf{b}, \mathbf{c}$ are non-coplanar vectors and λ is a real number, then $[\lambda(\mathbf{a}+\mathbf{b})\ \ \lambda^2\mathbf{b}\ \ \lambda\mathbf{c}] = [\mathbf{a}\ \ \mathbf{b}+\mathbf{c}\ \ \mathbf{b}]$ for :

(a) exactly 3 values of λ

(b) exactly 2 values of λ

(c) exactly 1 value of λ

(d) no value of λ **(AIEEE 2005)**

10.* (a) If $\begin{vmatrix} (a-x)^2 & (a-y)^2 & (a-z)^2 \\ (b-x)^2 & (b-y)^2 & (b-z)^2 \\ (c-x)^2 & (c-y)^2 & (c-z)^2 \end{vmatrix} = 0$

and the vectors $\mathbf{A}, \mathbf{B}, \mathbf{C}$, where $\mathbf{A} = a^2\mathbf{i} + a\mathbf{j} + \mathbf{k}$ etc. **are non-coplanar**, then prove that the vectors **X, Y, Z** where $\mathbf{X} = x^2\mathbf{i} + x\mathbf{j} + \mathbf{k}$ **are coplanar**.

(b)* If $\begin{vmatrix} a & a^2 & 1+a^3 \\ b & b^2 & 1+b^3 \\ c & c^2 & 1+c^3 \end{vmatrix} = 0$ and the vectors

$\vec{A} = 1, a, a^2$, $\vec{B} = 1, b, b^2$, $\vec{C} = 1, c, c^2$ are non-coplanar, then the product $abc = -1$

11.* (a) If the vectors $a\mathbf{i} + \mathbf{j} + \mathbf{k}$, $\mathbf{i} + b\mathbf{j} + \mathbf{k}$ and $\mathbf{i} + \mathbf{j} + c\mathbf{k}$ $(a \ne b,\ c \ne 1)$ are coplanar, then prove that the value of $\frac{1}{1-a} + \frac{1}{1-b} + \frac{1}{1-c}$ is 1.

Another form :

$$\frac{1+a}{1-a} + \frac{1+b}{1-b} + \frac{1+c}{1-c} =$$

(a) -2 (b) -1

(c) 1 (d) 2

(b)* Let a, b, c be distinct non-negative numbers. If the vectors $a\mathbf{i} + a\mathbf{j} + c\mathbf{k}$, $\mathbf{i} + \mathbf{k}$ and $c\mathbf{i} + c\mathbf{j} + b\mathbf{k}$ lie in a plane, then c is the Geometric Mean of a and b. **(I.I.T. 1993)**

12.* Let $\mathbf{a} = a_1\mathbf{i} + a_2\mathbf{j} + a_3\mathbf{k}$, $\mathbf{b} = b_1\mathbf{i} + b_2\mathbf{j} + b_3\mathbf{k}$ and $\mathbf{c} = c_1\mathbf{i} + c_2\mathbf{j} + c_3\mathbf{k}$ be three non-zero vectors such that $\mathbf{c}$ is a unit vector perpendicular to both the vectors $\mathbf{a}$ and $\mathbf{b}$. If the angle between $\mathbf{a}$ and $\mathbf{b}$ is $\pi/6$, then

$$\begin{vmatrix} a_1 & a_2 & a_3 \\ b_1 & b_2 & b_3 \\ c_1 & c_2 & c_3 \end{vmatrix}^2 \text{ is equal to}$$

$\frac{1}{4}(a_1^{\ 2}+a_2^{\ 2}+a_3^{\ 2})(b_1^{\ 2}+b_2^{\ 2}+b_3^{\ 2})$

13. (a) x, y, z are distinct scalars such that $[x\mathbf{a}+y\mathbf{b}+z\mathbf{c},\ x\mathbf{b}+y\mathbf{c}+z\mathbf{a},\ x\mathbf{c}+y\mathbf{a}+z\mathbf{b}]=0$ where **a, b, c** are non-coplanar vectors then prove that $x+y+z=0$.

(b) If the vectors $\mathbf{r}_1=\sec^2 A, 1, 1;\ \mathbf{r}_2=1, \sec^2 B, 1;$ $\mathbf{r}_3=1, 1, \sec^2 C$ are coplanar, then

$\cot^2 A+\cot^2 B+\cot^2 C$ is equal to

(a) 0 (b) 1
(c) 2 (d) not defined

(c) If $x \neq 0$ be any real number determine whether the vectors $\mathbf{r}_1, \mathbf{r}_2, \mathbf{r}_3$ are coplanar or not

$\mathbf{r}_1 = x, 2x, -3x$

$\mathbf{r}_2 = 2x+1, 2x+3, x+1$

and $\mathbf{r}_3 = 3x+5, x+5, x+2$

14. If **a, b, c** be three vectors, prove that

(a) $[\mathbf{a}+\mathbf{b},\ \mathbf{b}+\mathbf{c},\ \mathbf{c}+\mathbf{a}]=2[\mathbf{a}\ \mathbf{b}\ \mathbf{c}]$ and hence prove that the vectors $\mathbf{a}+\mathbf{b}$, $\mathbf{b}+\mathbf{c}$, $\mathbf{c}+\mathbf{a}$ are coplanar if and only if **a, b, c** are coplanar.

Another form :

Prove that the volume of the parallelopiped having $\mathbf{a}+\mathbf{b}$, $\mathbf{b}+\mathbf{c}$ and $\mathbf{c}+\mathbf{a}$ as adjacent edges is twice the volume of the parallelopiped having **a, b** and **c** as adjacent edges.

(b) $[\mathbf{a}-\mathbf{b}, \mathbf{b}-\mathbf{c}, \mathbf{c}-\mathbf{a}]=0$

15. (a) $[\mathbf{a}\quad \mathbf{b}+\mathbf{c}\quad \mathbf{a}+\mathbf{b}+\mathbf{c}]=0$

or $\mathbf{a}.\{(\mathbf{b}+\mathbf{c})\times(\mathbf{a}+\mathbf{b}+\mathbf{c})\}=0$

(b) If **a, b, c** are three non-coplanar vectors, then $(\mathbf{a}+\mathbf{b}+\mathbf{c}).(\mathbf{a}+\mathbf{b})\times(\mathbf{a}+\mathbf{c})=-[\mathbf{a}\ \mathbf{b}\ \mathbf{c}]$ **(I.I.T. 1995)**

(c) If **a, b** and **c** are unit coplanar vectors, then the scalar triple product $[2\mathbf{a}-\mathbf{b}\quad 2\mathbf{b}-\mathbf{c}\quad 2\mathbf{c}-\mathbf{a}]=$

(a) 0 (b) 1
(c) $-\sqrt{3}$ (d) $\sqrt{3}$

(I.I.T. Sc. 2000)

16.* (a) $\mathbf{r}=(\mathbf{r}.\mathbf{i})\,\mathbf{i}+(\mathbf{r}.\mathbf{j})\,\mathbf{j}+(\mathbf{r}.\mathbf{k})\,\mathbf{k}$

(b)* $\mathbf{i}\times(\mathbf{a}\times\mathbf{i})+\mathbf{j}\times(\mathbf{a}\times\mathbf{j})+\mathbf{k}\times(\mathbf{a}\times\mathbf{k})=2\mathbf{a}$ **(M.N.R. 1993)**

17.* Let **p, q, r** be three mutually perpendicular vectors of the same magnitude. If a vector **x** satisfies the equation $\mathbf{p}\times[(\mathbf{x}-\mathbf{q})\times\mathbf{p}]+\mathbf{q}\times[(\mathbf{x}-\mathbf{r})\times\mathbf{q}]+\mathbf{r}\times[(\mathbf{x}-\mathbf{p})\times\mathbf{r}]=0$, then **x** is given by

(a) $\frac{1}{2}(\mathbf{p}+\mathbf{q}-2\mathbf{r})$ (b) $\frac{1}{2}(\mathbf{p}+\mathbf{q}+\mathbf{r})$

(c) $\frac{1}{3}(\mathbf{p}+\mathbf{q}+\mathbf{r})$ (d) $\frac{1}{3}(2\mathbf{p}+\mathbf{q}-\mathbf{r})$ **(I.I.T. 1997)**

18.* (a) Prove that $[\mathbf{a}\times\mathbf{b}\quad \mathbf{b}\times\mathbf{c}\quad \mathbf{c}\times\mathbf{a}]=[\mathbf{a}\ \mathbf{b}\ \mathbf{c}]^2$

$$=\begin{vmatrix}\mathbf{a}.\mathbf{a} & \mathbf{a}.\mathbf{b} & \mathbf{a}.\mathbf{c}\\ \mathbf{b}.\mathbf{a} & \mathbf{b}.\mathbf{b} & \mathbf{b}.\mathbf{c}\\ \mathbf{c}.\mathbf{a} & \mathbf{c}.\mathbf{b} & \mathbf{c}.\mathbf{c}\end{vmatrix}.$$

Hence show that the vectors $\mathbf{a}\times\mathbf{b}, \mathbf{b}\times\mathbf{c}, \mathbf{c}\times\mathbf{a}$ are non-coplanar if and only if **a, b, c** are non-coplanar.

(b) If $\mathbf{a}=2\mathbf{i}+3\mathbf{j}+4\mathbf{k}$, $\mathbf{b}=\mathbf{i}+5\mathbf{j}+2\mathbf{k}$ and $\mathbf{c}=3\mathbf{i}+15\mathbf{j}+6\mathbf{k}$, then evaluate

$$\begin{vmatrix}\mathbf{a}.\mathbf{a} & \mathbf{a}.\mathbf{b} & \mathbf{a}.\mathbf{c}\\ \mathbf{b}.\mathbf{a} & \mathbf{b}.\mathbf{b} & \mathbf{b}.\mathbf{c}\\ \mathbf{c}.\mathbf{a} & \mathbf{c}.\mathbf{b} & \mathbf{c}.\mathbf{c}\end{vmatrix}.$$

(c) **a, b, c** are unit vectors such that **a** and **b** are mutually perpendicular and **c** is equally inclined to **a** and **b** at an angle θ. If $\mathbf{c}=x\mathbf{a}+y\mathbf{b}+z(\mathbf{a}\times\mathbf{b})$, then :

(a) $z^2=1-2y^2$ (b) $z^2=1-x^2-y^2$
(c) $z^2=1-2x^2$ (d) $x^2=y^2$

(d) If **u, v, w** be three non-coplanar unit vectors with angles between **u** and **v** is α, between **v** and **w** is β and between **w** and **u** is γ. If **a, b, c** are the unit vectors along bisectors of α, β, γ respectively, then prove that

$$[\mathbf{a}\times\mathbf{b}, \mathbf{b}\times\mathbf{c}, \mathbf{c}\times\mathbf{a}]=\frac{1}{16}[\mathbf{u}\ \mathbf{v}\ \mathbf{w}]^2\times \sec^2\left(\frac{\alpha}{2}\right)\sec^2\left(\frac{\beta}{2}\right)\sec^2\left(\frac{\gamma}{2}\right)$$ **(I.I.T. 2003)**

19.* (a) If the vectors **a, b, c** are non-coplanar, prove that $\mathbf{a}\times\mathbf{b}$, $\mathbf{b}\times\mathbf{c}$ and $\mathbf{c}\times\mathbf{a}$ are also non-coplanar.

(b)* If $\vec{A}, \vec{B}, \vec{C}$ are three non-coplanar vectors, then

$$\frac{\vec{A}.\vec{B}\times\vec{C}}{\vec{C}\times\vec{A}.\vec{B}}+\frac{\vec{B}.\vec{A}\times\vec{C}}{\vec{C}.\vec{A}\times\vec{B}}=0$$

20. **a, b, c** are three non-coplanar unit vectors such that angle between any two is α. If $\mathbf{a}\times\mathbf{b}+\mathbf{b}\times\mathbf{c}=l\,\mathbf{a}+m\,\mathbf{b}+n\,\mathbf{c}$, then determine l, m, n in terms of α. **(I.I.T. 1997)**

21. If **a, b, c** are vectors such that $|\mathbf{b}|=|\mathbf{c}|$, prove that $[(\mathbf{a}+\mathbf{b})\times(\mathbf{a}+\mathbf{c})]\times(\mathbf{b}\times\mathbf{c}).(\mathbf{b}+\mathbf{c})=0$

$=T_1$ say $\quad =T_2$ say

(I.I.T. Re-ex. 1997)

22.* (a) Prove that if **l, m, n** be three non-coplanar vectors then

$$[\mathbf{l}\ \mathbf{m}\ \mathbf{n}](\mathbf{a}\times\mathbf{b})=\begin{vmatrix}\mathbf{l}.\mathbf{a} & \mathbf{l}.\mathbf{b} & \mathbf{l}\\ \mathbf{m}.\mathbf{a} & \mathbf{m}.\mathbf{b} & \mathbf{m}\\ \mathbf{n}.\mathbf{a} & \mathbf{n}.\mathbf{b} & \mathbf{n}\end{vmatrix}$$

(b)* If $\mathbf{A}=p_1\mathbf{a}+q_1\mathbf{b}+r_1\mathbf{c}$, $\mathbf{B}=p_2, q_2, r_2$ and $\mathbf{C}=p_3, q_3, r_3$, then prove that

$$\mathbf{A}.\mathbf{B}\times\mathbf{C}=\begin{vmatrix}p_1 & q_1 & r_1\\ p_2 & q_2 & r_2\\ p_3 & q_3 & r_3\end{vmatrix}(\mathbf{a}.\mathbf{b}\times\mathbf{c})$$

or $[\mathbf{A}\ \mathbf{B}\ \mathbf{C}]=\Delta[\mathbf{a}\ \mathbf{b}\ \mathbf{c}]$

where Δ is determinant of coefficients.

23. (a) If **a, b, c** are three non-coplanar vectors such that volume of parallelopiped formed with **a, b, c** as coterminous edges is equal to volume of parallelopiped formed with $\mathbf{a}\times\mathbf{b}, \mathbf{b}\times\mathbf{c}, \mathbf{c}\times\mathbf{a}$ as coterminous edges, then :

(a) $[\mathbf{a}\ \mathbf{b}\ \mathbf{c}]=0$ (b) $[\mathbf{a}\ \mathbf{b}\ \mathbf{c}]=1$

(c) $[\mathbf{a}\ \mathbf{b}\ \mathbf{c}] = -1$ (d) $[\mathbf{a}\ \mathbf{b}\ \mathbf{c}] \in (-1, 1)$

(b) Let $\mathbf{a} = 3\mathbf{i} + 2\mathbf{k}$ and $\mathbf{b} = 2\mathbf{j} + \mathbf{k}$. If $\mathbf{c}$ is a unit vector, then the maximum value of $[\mathbf{a}\ \mathbf{b}\ \mathbf{c}]$ is :

(a) $\sqrt{59}$ (b) $\sqrt{61}$
(c) $\sqrt{108}$ (d) none

24. (a) Express (a) $\mathbf{a}, \mathbf{b}, \mathbf{c}$ in terms of $\mathbf{b} \times \mathbf{c}, \mathbf{c} \times \mathbf{a}, \mathbf{a} \times \mathbf{b}$ and

(b) $\mathbf{b} \times \mathbf{c}, \mathbf{c} \times \mathbf{a}, \mathbf{a} \times \mathbf{b}$ in terms of $\mathbf{a}, \mathbf{b}, \mathbf{c}$.

(c) If $\mathbf{a}, \mathbf{b}, \mathbf{c}$ are three non-coplanar vectors, then prove that

$$\mathbf{d} = \frac{\mathbf{a}\,.\,\mathbf{d}}{[\mathbf{a}\ \mathbf{b}\ \mathbf{c}]}(\mathbf{b} \times \mathbf{c}) + \frac{\mathbf{b}\,.\,\mathbf{d}}{[\mathbf{a}\ \mathbf{b}\ \mathbf{c}]}(\mathbf{c} \times \mathbf{a}) + \frac{\mathbf{c}\,.\,\mathbf{d}}{[\mathbf{a}\ \mathbf{b}\ \mathbf{c}]}(\mathbf{a} \times \mathbf{b})$$

(d) If $\mathbf{a}, \mathbf{b}, \mathbf{c}$ are three non-coplanar vectors, then show that any vector $\mathbf{r}$ can be written as

$$\mathbf{r} = \frac{1}{[\mathbf{a}\ \mathbf{b}\ \mathbf{c}]}\left[[\mathbf{r}\ \mathbf{b}\ \mathbf{c}]\,\mathbf{a} + [\mathbf{r}\ \mathbf{c}\ \mathbf{a}]\,\mathbf{b} + [\mathbf{r}\ \mathbf{a}\ \mathbf{b}]\,\mathbf{c}\right]$$

25. (a) If $\mathbf{a}, \mathbf{b}, \mathbf{c}$ are non-coplanar vectors and $\mathbf{d}$ is a unit vector, then find the value of

$$|(\mathbf{a}\,.\,\mathbf{d})(\mathbf{b} \times \mathbf{c}) + (\mathbf{b}\,.\,\mathbf{d})(\mathbf{c} \times \mathbf{a}) + (\mathbf{c}\,.\,\mathbf{d})(\mathbf{a} \times \mathbf{b})|$$

and show that it is independent of $\mathbf{d}$. **(Roorkee 1999)**

(b) If $\alpha = p(\mathbf{b} \times \mathbf{c}) + q(\mathbf{c} \times \mathbf{a}) + r(\mathbf{a} \times \mathbf{b})$ and $[\mathbf{a}\ \mathbf{b}\ \mathbf{c}] = \dfrac{1}{p+q+r}$, then find the value of $\alpha\,.\,(\mathbf{a} + \mathbf{b} + \mathbf{c})$.

26.* (a) Prove that $\mathbf{a} \times (\mathbf{b} \times \mathbf{c}) + \mathbf{b} \times (\mathbf{c} \times \mathbf{a}) + \mathbf{c} \times (\mathbf{a} \times \mathbf{b}) = \mathbf{0}$

(b)* For three vectors $\mathbf{u}, \mathbf{v}, \mathbf{w}$ which of the following expressions is not equal to any of the remaining three ?

(a) $\mathbf{u} \cdot (\mathbf{v} \times \mathbf{w})$ (b) $(\mathbf{v} \times \mathbf{w}) \cdot \mathbf{u}$
(c) $\mathbf{v} \cdot (\mathbf{u} \times \mathbf{w})$ (d) $(\mathbf{u} \times \mathbf{v}) \cdot \mathbf{w}$ **(I.I.T. 1998)**

27. (a) If $\mathbf{a}, \mathbf{b}, \mathbf{c}$ and $\mathbf{d}$ be four vectors, then prove that

$$(\mathbf{a} \times \mathbf{b})\,.\,(\mathbf{c} \times \mathbf{d}) + (\mathbf{b} \times \mathbf{c})\,.\,(\mathbf{a} \times \mathbf{d}) + (\mathbf{c} \times \mathbf{a})\,.\,(\mathbf{b} \times \mathbf{d}) = \mathbf{0}.$$

(b) Prove that $\mathbf{d}\,.\,[\mathbf{a} \times \{\mathbf{b} \times (\mathbf{c} \times \mathbf{d})\}] = (\mathbf{b}\,.\,\mathbf{d})\,[\mathbf{a}\ \mathbf{c}\ \mathbf{d}]$

28. (a)* If $(\mathbf{a}, \mathbf{b}, \mathbf{c})$ be three unit vectors such that

$$\mathbf{a} \times (\mathbf{b} \times \mathbf{c}) = \frac{1}{2}\mathbf{b},$$

find the angles which $\mathbf{a}$ makes with $\mathbf{b}$ and $\mathbf{c}$, $\mathbf{b}$ and $\mathbf{c}$ being non-parallel.

(b)* If $\mathbf{a}, \mathbf{b}, \mathbf{c}$ are non-coplanar unit vectors such that $\mathbf{a} \times (\mathbf{b} \times \mathbf{c}) = (\mathbf{b} + \mathbf{c})/\sqrt{2}$, $\mathbf{b}$ and $\mathbf{c}$ are non-parallel, then the angle between $\mathbf{a}$ and $\mathbf{b}$ is $\dfrac{3\pi}{4}$. **(I.I.T. 1995)**

(c) $\mathbf{a}, \mathbf{b}, \mathbf{c}$ are three unit vectors such that $\mathbf{a} \times (\mathbf{b} \times \mathbf{c}) = \dfrac{1}{2}(\mathbf{b} + \mathbf{c})$. Find angle between vectors $\mathbf{a}$ and $\mathbf{b}$ given that vectors $\mathbf{b}$ and $\mathbf{c}$ are non-parallel. **(Roorkee 2000)**

29. (a)* Let $\hat{\mathbf{a}}$ be a unit vector and $\mathbf{b}$ be a non-zero vector not parallel to $\hat{\mathbf{a}}$. Find the angles of the triangle, two sides of which are represented by the vectors $\sqrt{3}\,(\hat{\mathbf{a}} \times \mathbf{b})$ and $\mathbf{b} - (\hat{\mathbf{a}}\,.\,\mathbf{b})\,\hat{\mathbf{a}}$. **(Roorkee 1991)**

(b)* The magnitudes of vectors $\mathbf{a}, \mathbf{b}, \mathbf{c}$ are respectively 1, 1 and 2. If $\mathbf{a} \times (\mathbf{a} \times \mathbf{c}) + \mathbf{b} = \mathbf{0}$, then the acute angle between $\mathbf{a}$ and $\mathbf{c}$ is ...... **(I.I.T. 1997)**

(c) If a vector $\mathbf{a}$ is expressed as the sum of two vectors α and β along and perpendicular to a given vector $\mathbf{b}$, then prove that β is equal to $\dfrac{\mathbf{b} \times (\mathbf{a} \times \mathbf{b})}{|\mathbf{b}|^2}$.

30. (a)* Show that $(\mathbf{a} \times \mathbf{b}) \times \mathbf{c} = \mathbf{a} \times (\mathbf{b} \times \mathbf{c})$ if and only if $\mathbf{a}$ and $\mathbf{c}$ are collinear or $(\mathbf{a} \times \mathbf{c}) \times \mathbf{b} = \mathbf{0}$. **(AIEEE 2006)**

(b)* Prove that the lines $\mathbf{r} = \mathbf{a} + t(\mathbf{b} \times \mathbf{c})$ and $\mathbf{r} = \mathbf{b} + s(\mathbf{c} \times \mathbf{a})$ will intersect if $\mathbf{a}\,.\,\mathbf{c} = \mathbf{b}\,.\,\mathbf{c}$.

31. (a) If c be a given non-zero scalar, and $\mathbf{A}$ and $\mathbf{B}$ be given non-zero vectors such that $\mathbf{A} \perp \mathbf{B}$, find the vector $\mathbf{X}$ which satisfies the equations $\mathbf{A}\,.\,\mathbf{X} = c$ and $\mathbf{A} \times \mathbf{X} = \mathbf{B}$.

(b) Given that vectors $\mathbf{a}$ and $\mathbf{b}$ are perpendicular to each other, find vector $\mathbf{v}$ in terms of $\mathbf{a}$ and $\mathbf{b}$ satisfying the equations $\mathbf{v}\,.\,\mathbf{a} = 0$, $\mathbf{v}\,.\,\mathbf{b} = 1$ and $[\mathbf{v}, \mathbf{a}, \mathbf{b}] = 1$. **(Roorkee 2000)**

32. Given the vectors $\vec{AB} = \mathbf{b}$ and $\vec{AC} = \mathbf{c}$ coincident with two sides of a triangle ABC. Find resolution (w.r.t. the basis $\mathbf{b}, \mathbf{c}$) of the vector drawn from the vertex B of the $\Delta\,ABC$ and coinciding with the altitude BD.

33. (a) If $\mathbf{a}.\,\mathbf{b} \neq \mathbf{0}$, find the vector $\mathbf{r}$ which satisfies the equations $(\mathbf{r} - \mathbf{c}) \times \mathbf{b} = \mathbf{0}$, $\mathbf{r}\,.\,\mathbf{a} = 0$

(b)* It is given that $\mathbf{r} \times \mathbf{b} = \mathbf{c} \times \mathbf{b}$, $\mathbf{r}\,.\,\mathbf{a} = 0$ and $\mathbf{a}\,.\,\mathbf{b} \neq 0$. What is the geometrical meaning of these equations separately ? If the above three statements hold good simultaneously, determine the vector $\mathbf{r}$ in terms of $\mathbf{a}, \mathbf{b}$ and $\mathbf{c}$.

(c) A vector $\mathbf{r}$ satisfies the equations $\mathbf{r} \times \mathbf{a} = \mathbf{b}$ and $\mathbf{r}\,.\,\mathbf{a} = 0$, prove that $\mathbf{r} = \dfrac{\mathbf{a} \times \mathbf{b}}{\mathbf{a}\,.\,\mathbf{a}}$.

34. Let A_r $(r = 1, 2, 3, 4)$ be the area of four faces of a tetrahedron. Let $\mathbf{n}_r$ be the outward drawn normals to the respective faces with magnitudes equal to corresponding areas. Prove that

$$\mathbf{n}_1 + \mathbf{n}_2 + \mathbf{n}_3 + \mathbf{n}_4 = 0.$$

35. (a)* A tetrahedron has vertices at $O(0, 0, 0)$, $A(1, 2, 1)$, $B(2, 1, 3)$ and $C(-1, 1, 2)$. Then the angle between the faces OAB and ABC will be $\cos^{-1}\left(\dfrac{19}{35}\right)$. **(M.N.R. 1994)**

(b) Find the obtuse angle between the medians of an isosceles right angled triangle drawn from the vertices of the acute angles.

36. Prove that the following four points are coplanar :

(a) $(4, 5, 1)$, $(0, -1, -1)$, $(3, 9, 4)$ and $(-4, 4, 4)$.

(b) $4\mathbf{i} + 8\mathbf{j} + 12\mathbf{k}$, $2\mathbf{i} + 4\mathbf{j} + 6\mathbf{k}$, $3\mathbf{i} + 5\mathbf{j} + 4\mathbf{k}$ and $5\mathbf{i} + 8\mathbf{j} + 5\mathbf{k}$.

(c) $\mathbf{i} + 2\mathbf{j} + 3\mathbf{k}$, $3\mathbf{i} - \mathbf{j} + 2\mathbf{k}$, $6\mathbf{i} - 4\mathbf{j} + 2\mathbf{k}$ and $-2\mathbf{i} + 3\mathbf{j} + \mathbf{k}$.

37. (a) The position vectors of the points A, B, C and D are $3\mathbf{i}-2\mathbf{j}-\mathbf{k}$, $2\mathbf{i}+3\mathbf{j}-4\mathbf{k}$, $-\mathbf{i}+\mathbf{j}+2\mathbf{k}$ and $4\mathbf{i}+5\mathbf{j}+\lambda\mathbf{k}$ respectively. If the points A, B, C and D lie on a plane, find the value of λ.

(b) Prove that the vectors

$$\mathbf{a}=x, x+1, x+2,$$
$$\mathbf{b}=x+3, x+4, x+5$$

and $\mathbf{c}=x+6, x+7, x+8$

are coplanar for all values of x.

(c) The number of distinct real values of λ, for which the vectors $-\lambda^2\mathbf{i}+\mathbf{j}+\mathbf{k}$, $\mathbf{i}-\lambda^2\mathbf{j}+\mathbf{k}$ and $\mathbf{i}+\mathbf{j}-\lambda^2\mathbf{k}$ are coplanar, is

(a) zero (b) one
(c) two (d) three **(I.I.T. 2007)**

(d) If $\mathbf{a}, \mathbf{b}, \mathbf{c}$ are non-coplanar vectors and λ is a real number then the vectors $\mathbf{a}+2\mathbf{b}+3\mathbf{c}$, $\lambda\mathbf{b}+4\mathbf{c}$ and $(2\lambda-1)\mathbf{c}$ are non-coplanar for :

(a) all values of λ
(b) all except one value of λ
(c) all except two values of λ
(d) no value of λ **(AIEEE 2004)**

38. (a) Prove that the vectors $x\mathbf{i}+3\mathbf{j}-\mathbf{k}$, $\mathbf{i}+(x-1)\mathbf{j}+2\mathbf{k}$ and $3\mathbf{i}+5\mathbf{j}+2\mathbf{k}$ give rise to two distinct planes for a suitable value of x. Prove that the angle between the two planes is $\cos^{-1}\left(\frac{17}{3\sqrt{239}}\right)$.

(b) Prove that the points $2\mathbf{a}+3\mathbf{b}-\mathbf{c}$, $\mathbf{a}-2\mathbf{b}+3\mathbf{c}$, $3\mathbf{a}+4\mathbf{b}-2\mathbf{c}$ and $\mathbf{a}-6\mathbf{b}+6\mathbf{c}$ are coplanar.

39.* Prove that the vector $\mathbf{r}=\mathbf{a}\times[\mathbf{a}\times\{\mathbf{a}\times\mathbf{a}\times(\mathbf{a}\times\mathbf{b})\}]$ where $|\mathbf{a}|=2, |\mathbf{b}|=5$ and $\mathbf{a}\perp\mathbf{b}$ forms an orthogonal system of vectors with $\mathbf{a}$ and $\mathbf{b}$.

40.* Let $\mathbf{u}$ and $\mathbf{v}$ be unit vectors. If $\mathbf{w}$ is a vector such that $\mathbf{w}+(\mathbf{w}\times\mathbf{u})=\mathbf{v}$, then prove that $|(\mathbf{u}\times\mathbf{v}).\mathbf{w}|\le\frac{1}{2}$ and that the equality holds if and only if $\mathbf{u}$ is perpendicular to $\mathbf{v}$. **(I.I.T. 1999)**

41. If the four points $\mathbf{a}, \mathbf{b}, \mathbf{c}, \mathbf{d}$ are coplanar, prove that

$$[\mathbf{abc}]=[\mathbf{bcd}]+[\mathbf{cad}]+[\mathbf{abd}]$$

42.* If $A_1, A_2, \ldots, A_n$ are the vertices of regular plane polygon with n sides and O is its centre, show that

$$\sum_{i=1}^{n-1}(\vec{OA_i}\times\vec{OA_{i+1}})=(1-n)(\vec{OA_2}\times\vec{OA_1})$$

43. (a) Find out the volume of a prism on triangular base, the three sides of the prism meeting on a vertex are given below :

$\vec{OA}=3\mathbf{i}+4\mathbf{j}+12\mathbf{k}$, $\vec{OB}=12\mathbf{i}+3\mathbf{j}+4\mathbf{k}$,
$\vec{OC}=4\mathbf{i}+12\mathbf{j}+3\mathbf{k}$.

(b) Find the unit vector perpendicular to $\vec{OA}$ and $\vec{OB}$.

(c) Find the angle between $\vec{OA}$ and $\vec{OC}$.

(d) Find the area of triangle OAB.

44. (a)* The points A, B, C, D and E are respectively $A(1,2,1)$, $B(2,1,2)$, $C(0,-4,4)$, $D(2,-2,2)$ and $E(4,1,2)$. The line AB cuts the plane CDE in the point P. Prove by vector method that the point P is $(3,0,3)$.

(b) Find the equation of the plane passing through the points $A(2,1,3)$, $B(-1,2,4)$ and $C(0,2,1)$.

Also determine its point of intersection with the line $\mathbf{r}=\mathbf{i}-\mathbf{j}+\mathbf{k}+t(2\mathbf{i}+\mathbf{k})$.

45.* Three vectors $\mathbf{a}=12, 4, 3$, $\mathbf{b}=8, -12, -9$, $\mathbf{c}=33, -4, -24$ define a parallelopiped. Evaluate the lengths of its edges, area of its faces and its volume.

46.* Find the scalars α and β if

$$\mathbf{a}\times(\mathbf{b}\times\mathbf{c})+(\mathbf{a}.\mathbf{b})\,\mathbf{b}=(4-2\beta-\sin\alpha)\,\mathbf{b}+(\beta^2-1)\,\mathbf{c}$$

and $(\mathbf{c}.\mathbf{c})\,\mathbf{a}=\mathbf{c}$ where $\mathbf{b}$ and $\mathbf{c}$ are non-collinear and α, β are scalars. **(Roorkee 1995)**

47.* Let $\mathbf{a}=\mathbf{i}-\mathbf{j}$, $\mathbf{b}=\mathbf{j}-\mathbf{k}$, $\mathbf{c}=\mathbf{k}-\mathbf{i}$, $\mathbf{d}$ is a unit vector such that $\mathbf{a}.\mathbf{d}=0=[\mathbf{b\,c\,d}]$, then $\mathbf{d}$ equals $\pm(\mathbf{i}+\mathbf{j}-2\mathbf{k})/\sqrt{6}$. **(I.I.T. 1995)**

48. (a)* A non-zero vector $\vec{\mathbf{a}}$ is parallel to the line of intersection of the plane determined by the vectors $\mathbf{i}, \mathbf{i}+\mathbf{j}$ and the plane determined by the vectors $\mathbf{i}-\mathbf{j}, \mathbf{i}+\mathbf{k}$. The angle between $\vec{\mathbf{a}}$ and the vector $\mathbf{i}-2\mathbf{j}+2\mathbf{k}$ is ..... **(I.I.T. 1996)**

(b) A plane p_1 is parallel to two vectors $2\mathbf{j}+3\mathbf{k}$ and $4\mathbf{j}-3\mathbf{k}$. Another plane p_2 is parallel to two other vectors $\mathbf{j}-\mathbf{k}$ and $3\mathbf{i}+3\mathbf{j}$. A vector $\mathbf{a}$ is parallel to the line of intersection of the given planes. The angle between $\mathbf{a}$ and a given vector $2\mathbf{i}+2\mathbf{j}-\mathbf{k}$ is :

(a) $\frac{\pi}{4}$ (b) $\frac{3\pi}{4}$
(c) $\frac{\pi}{2}$ (d) $\frac{\pi}{6}$ **(I.I.T. 2006)**

49.* If $\vec{\mathbf{b}}$ and $\vec{\mathbf{c}}$ are any two non-collinear unit vectors and $\bar{\mathbf{a}}$ is any vector, then

$$(\mathbf{a}.\mathbf{b})\,\mathbf{b}+(\mathbf{a}.\mathbf{c})\,\mathbf{c}+\frac{\mathbf{a}.(\mathbf{b}\times\mathbf{c})}{|\mathbf{b}\times\mathbf{c}|}(\mathbf{b}\times\mathbf{c})=\ldots\ldots$$

(I.I.T. 1996)

50.* The position vectors of two points A and C are $9\mathbf{i}-\mathbf{j}+7\mathbf{k}$ and $7\mathbf{i}-2\mathbf{j}+7\mathbf{k}$ respectively. The point of intersection of vectors $\vec{AB}=4\mathbf{i}-\mathbf{j}+3\mathbf{k}$ and $\vec{CD}=2\mathbf{i}-\mathbf{j}+2\mathbf{k}$ is P. If vector $\vec{PQ}$ is perpendicular to $\vec{AB}$ and $\vec{CD}$ and $PQ=15$ units, find the position vector of Q. **(Roorkee 1996)**

51.* The position vectors of the vertices A, B and C of a tetrahedron $ABCD$ are $\mathbf{i}+\mathbf{j}+\mathbf{k}$, $\mathbf{i}$ and $3\mathbf{i}$ respectively. The altitude from vertex D to the opposite face ABC meets the median line through A of the triangle ABC at a point E. If the length of the side AD is 4 and the volume of the tetrahedron is $\frac{2\sqrt{2}}{3}$, find the position vector of the point E for all its possible positions. **(I.I.T. 1996)**

52.* Let $\hat{x}, \hat{y}$ and $\hat{z}$ be unit vectors such that

$$\hat{x}+\hat{y}+\hat{z}=\mathbf{a},\ \hat{x}\times(\hat{y}\times\hat{z})=\mathbf{b},$$
$$(\hat{x}\times\hat{y})\times\hat{z}=\mathbf{c},\ \mathbf{a}.\hat{x}=3/2,\ \mathbf{a}.\hat{y}=7/4$$

and $|\mathbf{a}|=2$. Find $\hat{x}, \hat{y}$ and $\hat{z}$ in terms of **a**, **b** and **c**. **(Roorkee 1996)**

53. Show that the shortest distance between a diagonal of a rectangular parallelopiped the lengths of whose three coterminous edges are a, b, c and the edges not meeting it are

$$\frac{bc}{\sqrt{(b^2+c^2)}},\ \frac{ca}{\sqrt{(c^2+a^2)}},\ \frac{ab}{\sqrt{(a^2+b^2)}}.$$

54. (a) Explain vector product of four vectors and show that any vector can be expressed as a linear combination of any three non-coplanar vectors.

(b)* If the vectors **b**, **c**, **d** are not coplanar, then prove that

$(\mathbf{a}\times\mathbf{b})\times(\mathbf{c}\times\mathbf{d})+(\mathbf{a}\times\mathbf{c})\times(\mathbf{d}\times\mathbf{b})+(\mathbf{a}\times\mathbf{d})\times(\mathbf{b}\times\mathbf{c})$

is parallel to **a**. **(I.I.T. 1994)**

55. (a) Prove that

$$[\mathbf{a}\times\mathbf{p}, \mathbf{b}\times\mathbf{q}, \mathbf{c}\times\mathbf{r}]+[\mathbf{a}\times\mathbf{q}, \mathbf{b}\times\mathbf{r}, \mathbf{c}\times\mathbf{p}]+[\mathbf{a}\times\mathbf{r}, \mathbf{b}\times\mathbf{p}, \mathbf{c}\times\mathbf{q}]=0$$

(b) Prove that

$$[\mathbf{a}\times\mathbf{b}\ \ \mathbf{c}\times\mathbf{d}\ \ \mathbf{e}\times\mathbf{f}] =[\mathbf{a\,b\,d}][\mathbf{c\,e\,f}]-[\mathbf{a\,b\,c}][\mathbf{d\,e\,f}]$$
$$=[\mathbf{a\,b\,e}][\mathbf{f\,c\,d}]-[\mathbf{a\,b\,f}][\mathbf{e\,c\,d}]$$
$$=[\mathbf{c\,d\,a}][\mathbf{b\,e\,f}]-[\mathbf{c\,d\,b}][\mathbf{a\,e\,f}].$$

56. Prove that $2(\mathbf{c}\times\mathbf{d})\times(\mathbf{a}\times\mathbf{b})=\begin{vmatrix}\mathbf{a} & a_1 & a_2 & a_3\\ \mathbf{b} & b_1 & b_2 & b_3\\ -\mathbf{c} & c_1 & c_2 & c_3\\ -\mathbf{d} & d_1 & d_2 & d_3\end{vmatrix}$

where $\mathbf{a}=a_1\mathbf{i}+a_2\mathbf{j}+a_3\mathbf{k}$ etc.

57. (a)* Solve the following simultaneous equations for vectors **x** and **y**.

$\mathbf{x}+\mathbf{y}=\mathbf{a}$ ...(1)

$\mathbf{x}\times\mathbf{y}=\mathbf{b}$ ...(2)

$\mathbf{x}.\mathbf{a}=1$ ...(3)

(Roorkee 1994)

(b) If $\mathbf{x}\times\mathbf{a}+k\mathbf{x}=\mathbf{b}$ where k is a scalar and **a**, **b** are any two vectors, then determine **x** in terms of **a**, **b** and k.

58.* $\vec{A}=1,1,1,\ \vec{C}=0,1,-1$ are given vectors, then a vector $\vec{B}$ satisfying the equations $\vec{A}\times\vec{B}=\vec{C}$ and $\vec{A}.\vec{B}=3$ is $(5/3, 2/3, 2/3)$. **(I.I.T. 1991)**

59.* Vectors **x**, **y** and **z** each of magnitude $\sqrt{2}$, make angles of 60° with each other. If $\mathbf{x}\times(\mathbf{y}\times\mathbf{z})=\mathbf{a}, \mathbf{y}\times(\mathbf{z}\times\mathbf{x})=\mathbf{b}$ and $\mathbf{x}\times\mathbf{y}=\mathbf{c}$ then find **x**, **y** and **z** in terms of **a**, **b** and **c**. **(Roorkee 1997)**

60.* If $\mathbf{x}\times\mathbf{y}=\mathbf{a}, \mathbf{y}\times\mathbf{z}=\mathbf{b}, \mathbf{x}.\mathbf{b}=\gamma, \mathbf{x}.\mathbf{y}=1$ and $\mathbf{y}.\mathbf{z}=1$ then find **x**, **y** and **z** in terms of **a**, **b**, and γ. **(Roorkee 1998)**

Solutions to Problem Set (2)

1. (a) Volume $=[\mathbf{a\,b\,c}]=\begin{vmatrix}a_1 & a_2 & a_3\\ b_1 & b_2 & b_3\\ c_1 & c_2 & c_3\end{vmatrix}$

$\therefore$ Volume $=\begin{vmatrix}2 & -3 & 4\\ 1 & 2 & -1\\ 3 & -1 & 2\end{vmatrix}$

$=2(4-1)+3(2+3)+4(-1-6)$

$=6+15-28=-7=7$, numerically.

(b) Ans. 4.

(c) Ans. 5, $\sqrt{83}$.

Note : $[\mathbf{a\,b\,c}]=\mathbf{a}.(\mathbf{b}\times\mathbf{c})$.

You could first find $\mathbf{b}\times\mathbf{c}$ and then take the dot product of **a** and $\mathbf{b}\times\mathbf{c}$.

(d) The three vectors are coplanar if $[\mathbf{a\ \ b\ \ c}]=0$

or $\begin{vmatrix}\lambda & 2\lambda & -3\lambda\\ 2\lambda+1 & 2\lambda+3 & \lambda+1\\ 3\lambda+5 & \lambda+5 & \lambda+2\end{vmatrix}=0$

Apply C_2-2C_1, C_3+3C_1 to make two zeros.

$\therefore\ \Delta=\begin{vmatrix}\lambda & 0 & 0\\ 2\lambda+1 & -2\lambda+1 & 7\lambda+4\\ 3\lambda+5 & -5\lambda-5 & 10\lambda+17\end{vmatrix}=0$

or $\lambda\{-(2\lambda-1)(10\lambda+17)+5(\lambda+1)(7\lambda+4)\}=0$

or $\lambda\{15\lambda^2+31\lambda+37\}=0$

Now $\lambda\neq 0$ given and $15\lambda^2+31\lambda+37$ is a quadratic expression where

$D=b^2-4ac=(31)^2-4(15)(37)=-$ ive.

Hence its sign is same as that of the first term *i.e.*, + ive.

Hence $\Delta\neq 0$ so that the given vectors are not coplanar.

2. (a) $546=\begin{vmatrix}-12 & 0 & \lambda\\ 0 & 3 & -1\\ 2 & 1 & -15\end{vmatrix}=12\times 44-6\lambda$

$\therefore\ \lambda=2\times 44-91=-3.$

(b) $V=\begin{vmatrix}a_1 & b_1 & c_1\\ a_2 & b_2 & c_2\\ a_3 & b_3 & c_3\end{vmatrix}=\Sigma\, a_1(b_2c_3-b_3c_2)$ ...(1)

Six terms

Again

$3L=(a_1+b_1+c_1)+(a_2+b_2+c_2)+(a_3+b_3+c_3)$

$\geq 3[(a_1+b_1+c_1)(a_2+b_2+c_2)(a_3+b_3+c_3)]^{1/3}$

by AM $\geq$ GM

or $L^3\geq$ Sum of $3\times3\times3=27$ terms of the type $a_p\,b_q\,c_r\ \ \therefore\ L^3\geq V$.

(c) Ans. (c). $V=\begin{vmatrix}1 & a & 1\\ 0 & 1 & a\\ a & 0 & 1\end{vmatrix}=1-a+a^3$

$\frac{dV}{da} = -1 + 3a^2 = 0 \quad \therefore \quad a = \pm \frac{1}{\sqrt{3}}$.

$\frac{d^2V}{da^2} = 6a = +\text{ive for minimum for } a = \frac{1}{\sqrt{3}}$.

(d) Ans. (a).

Given $\mathbf{a}^2 = \mathbf{b}^2 = \mathbf{c}^2 = 1,\ \mathbf{a}.\mathbf{b} = \mathbf{b}.\mathbf{c} = \mathbf{c}.\mathbf{a} = \frac{1}{2}$

$$V^2 = [\mathbf{a}\,\mathbf{b}\,\mathbf{c}]^2 = \begin{vmatrix} \mathbf{a}.\mathbf{a} & \mathbf{a}.\mathbf{b} & \mathbf{a}.\mathbf{c} \\ \mathbf{b}.\mathbf{a} & \mathbf{b}.\mathbf{b} & \mathbf{b}.\mathbf{c} \\ \mathbf{c}.\mathbf{a} & \mathbf{c}.\mathbf{b} & \mathbf{c}.\mathbf{c} \end{vmatrix}$$

[Q. 18(a) P. 1156-64]

$$= \begin{vmatrix} 1 & 1/2 & 1/2 \\ 1/2 & 1 & 1/2 \\ 1/2 & 1/2 & 1 \end{vmatrix} = \frac{1}{2} \text{ by expansion}$$

$\therefore \quad V = \frac{1}{\sqrt{2}}$

3. (a) **Orthonormal** $\Rightarrow$ mutually perpendicular, *i.e.* orthogonal and each vector is a unit vector.

$\mathbf{a}.(\mathbf{a}\times\mathbf{b}) = \mathbf{a}.\mathbf{c}, \quad \mathbf{b}.(\mathbf{a}\times\mathbf{b}) = \mathbf{b}.\mathbf{c}$

or $\quad 0 = \mathbf{a}.\mathbf{c}$ and $0 = \mathbf{b}.\mathbf{c}$

$\therefore$ **a** and **b** are both $\perp$ to **c**.

Similarly **b** and **c** are $\perp$ to **a** and **c** and **a** are $\perp$ to **b**. Hence all the vectors are mutually perpendicular.

Again $\mathbf{a}\times\mathbf{b} = \mathbf{c} \quad \therefore \quad |\mathbf{a}\times\mathbf{b}| = |\mathbf{c}|$

or $\quad ab \sin 90^\circ .1 = |\mathbf{c}| \quad \therefore \quad ab = c$

Similarly, $\quad bc = a$ and $ca = b$.

Multiplying, we get $a^2b^2c^2 = abc$

$\therefore \quad abc = 1 \qquad ...(1)$

Putting the values of ab, bc and ca in (1), we get $a = b = c = 1$. Hence the vectors are unit vectors. Thus they form an orthonormal triad. Clearly they form a right handed system just as **i**, **j**, **k**.

(b) Here proceed as above to prove that they are mutually perpendicular. Again here we have only two relations (not three as in last part). So we have $ab = c$ and $bc = a$ only. Multiplying $acb^2 = ac$

$\therefore b^2 = 1$ or $b = 1$ and hence $a = c$. Thus **b** is a unit vector and **a** and **c** are of equal magnitude.

Alternate :

$\mathbf{a} = \mathbf{b}\times\mathbf{c}$ and $\mathbf{a}\times\mathbf{b} = \mathbf{c}$

$\therefore \quad \mathbf{a} = \mathbf{b}\times(\mathbf{a}\times\mathbf{b}) = (\mathbf{b}.\mathbf{b})\,\mathbf{a} - (\mathbf{b}.\mathbf{a})\,\mathbf{b}$

or $\quad \mathbf{a} = b^2\mathbf{a} - (\mathbf{b}.\mathbf{a})\,\mathbf{b}$. Comparing coefficients

$1 = b^2$ and $\mathbf{b}.\mathbf{a} = 0 \quad$ *i.e.*, $\quad b = 1$, **a** and **b** are perpendicular.

$\therefore \quad \mathbf{c} = \mathbf{a}\times\mathbf{b} = ab \sin 90^\circ\ \hat{\mathbf{n}}$.

$\therefore \quad c = ab$, but $b = 1 \quad \therefore \quad c = a$.

Also $\mathbf{c} = \mathbf{a}\times\mathbf{b} \Rightarrow \mathbf{c}$ is $\perp$ to both **a** and **b** and **a**, **b** are perpendicular to each other $\therefore$ **a**, **b**, **c** are mutually perpendicular.

4. (a) Refer **§ 6, P. 1152** $\mathbf{r} = t\,\{\mathbf{a}\times(\mathbf{b}\times\mathbf{c})\}$ represents a vector coplanar with **b** and **c** and perpendicular to **a**.

$\therefore \quad \mathbf{r} = t\,[(\mathbf{a}\cdot\mathbf{c})\,\mathbf{b} - (\mathbf{a}\cdot\mathbf{b})\,\mathbf{c}]$

Put the values of **a** . **c** and **a** . **b**

$\mathbf{r} = t\,[2\mathbf{b} - 3\mathbf{c}] = t\,[2\,(3\mathbf{i} - \mathbf{j} - \mathbf{k}) - 3\,(\mathbf{i} + \mathbf{j} - 2\mathbf{k})]$

or $\quad \mathbf{r} = t\,(3\,\mathbf{i} - 5\,\mathbf{j} + 4\,\mathbf{k})$.

Take mod of both sides.

$|\mathbf{r}| = |t|\sqrt{9 + 25 + 16}$

or $\quad \sqrt{2} = |t|.5\sqrt{2} \quad \therefore \quad |t| = \frac{1}{5} \quad \therefore \quad t = \pm\frac{1}{5}$

$\therefore \quad$ Required vector is $\pm\frac{1}{5}(3\mathbf{i} - 5\mathbf{j} + 4\mathbf{k})$.

2nd Method :

Let the vector be $\mathbf{r} = x\mathbf{i} + y\mathbf{j} + z\mathbf{k}$

r is coplanar with **b** and **c**.

$\therefore \quad [\mathbf{r}\,\mathbf{b}\,\mathbf{c}] = 0 \quad$ or $\quad \begin{vmatrix} x & y & z \\ 3 & -1 & -1 \\ 1 & 1 & -2 \end{vmatrix} = 0$

or $\quad 3x + 5y + 4z = 0 \qquad ...(1)$

r is $\perp$ to **a** $\quad \therefore \quad 2x + 2y + z = 0 \qquad ...(2)$

Solving (1) and (2), we get $\frac{x}{-3} = \frac{y}{5} = \frac{z}{-4} = t$, say

x, y, z is $-3t, 5t, -4t$

where $\quad 9t^2 + 25t^2 + 16t^2 = (\sqrt{2})^2$

$50t^2 = 2$ or $t = \pm\frac{1}{5}$

$\mathbf{r} = \pm\frac{1}{5}(3\mathbf{i} - 5\mathbf{j} + 4\mathbf{k})$

(b) Ans. (b). By definition the required vector is $\mathbf{a}\times(\mathbf{b}\times\mathbf{c}) = (\mathbf{a}.\mathbf{c})\,\mathbf{b} - (\mathbf{a}.\mathbf{b})\,\mathbf{c}$

$= 7\,(2\mathbf{i} + \mathbf{j} + \mathbf{k}) - 14\,(\mathbf{i} - \mathbf{j} + \mathbf{k}) = 7\,(0\,\mathbf{i} + 3\,\mathbf{j} - \mathbf{k})$

$\therefore \quad$ unit vector $= \frac{7\,(3\mathbf{j} - \mathbf{k})}{7\sqrt{9+1}} = \frac{3\mathbf{j} - \mathbf{k}}{\sqrt{10}}$

(c) Let the required vector be $x\mathbf{i} + y\mathbf{j} + z\mathbf{k}$

Since it is coplanar with other two given vectors, their scalar triple product is zero or $\Delta = 0$

$\therefore \quad 3x - y - z = 0$

It is perpendicular to $\mathbf{i} + \mathbf{j} + \mathbf{k} \quad \therefore \quad x + y + z = 0$

Solving, we get $x = 0,\ y = -z$. Hence the required vector is $y\mathbf{j} - y\mathbf{k}$ or a unit vector is

$\frac{y\,(\mathbf{j} - \mathbf{k})}{\pm y\sqrt{(2)}} = \pm\frac{\mathbf{j} - \mathbf{k}}{\sqrt{(2)}}$

Note : You can also try by $\mathbf{r} = t\,[\mathbf{a}\times(\mathbf{b}\times\mathbf{c})]$ as in part (a).

(d) Ans. (a). **A similar question is given as in part (a).**

$\mathbf{a} = 2, 1, 1 \quad \mathbf{b} = 1, 2, -1 \quad \mathbf{c} = x, y, z$ with $x^2 + y^2 + z^2 = 1$.

Coplanarity $\Rightarrow \begin{vmatrix} x & y & z \\ 2 & 1 & 1 \\ 1 & 2 & -1 \end{vmatrix} = 0$ Expand.

$\therefore \quad x - y - z = 0 \qquad ...(1)$

Perpendicularity $\Rightarrow 2x+y+z=0$ ...(2)

Adding (1) and (2), we get

$x=0 \quad \therefore \; y+z=0$

or $\dfrac{x}{0}=\dfrac{y}{-1}=\dfrac{z}{1}=\dfrac{\sqrt{x^2+y^2+z^2}}{\sqrt{2}}=\dfrac{1}{\sqrt{2}}$ etc.

5. (a) We have $|(\mathbf{a}\times\mathbf{b}).\mathbf{c}|=|\mathbf{a}||\mathbf{b}||\mathbf{c}|$

$\Leftrightarrow \; ||\mathbf{a}||\mathbf{b}|\sin\theta\,\hat{\mathbf{n}}.\mathbf{c}\,|=|\mathbf{a}||\mathbf{b}||\mathbf{c}|$

$\Leftrightarrow \; ||\mathbf{a}||\mathbf{b}||\mathbf{c}|\sin\theta\cos\alpha\,|=|\mathbf{a}||\mathbf{b}||\mathbf{c}|$

$\Leftrightarrow \; |\sin\theta||\cos\alpha|=1$

$\Leftrightarrow \; \theta=\dfrac{\pi}{2}$ and $\alpha=0$

$\Leftrightarrow$ $\mathbf{a}\perp\mathbf{b}$ and $\mathbf{c}$ is parallel to $\hat{\mathbf{n}}$

$\Leftrightarrow$ $\mathbf{a}\perp\mathbf{b}$ and $\mathbf{c}\perp$ to both $\mathbf{a}$ and $\mathbf{b}$

$\Leftrightarrow$ **a, b, c are mutually perpendicular**

$\Leftrightarrow$ $\mathbf{a}.\mathbf{b}=\mathbf{b}.\mathbf{c}=\mathbf{c}.\mathbf{a}=0.$

Hence (iv) is correct.

(b) Ans. (b).

$|\mathbf{c}-\mathbf{a}|=2\sqrt{2} \Rightarrow |\mathbf{c}-\mathbf{a}|^2=8$

$\Rightarrow \; |\mathbf{c}|^2+|\mathbf{a}|^2-2\mathbf{c}.\mathbf{a}=8$

or $|\mathbf{c}|^2+9-2|\mathbf{c}|=8$

$\Rightarrow \; (|\mathbf{c}|-1)^2=0 \quad \therefore |\mathbf{c}|=1$

Again $\mathbf{a}=2,1,-2, \quad \mathbf{b}=1,1,0$

$\therefore \quad \mathbf{a}\times\mathbf{b}=2,-2,1 \quad \therefore |\mathbf{a}\times\mathbf{b}|=3$

Now $|(\mathbf{a}\times\mathbf{b})\times\mathbf{c}|=|\mathbf{a}\times\mathbf{b}||\mathbf{c}|\sin 30^\circ=3.1.\dfrac{1}{2}=\dfrac{3}{2}.$

(c) $[\mathbf{a}\,\mathbf{b}\,\mathbf{c}]=\mathbf{a}.(\mathbf{b}\times\mathbf{c})=|\mathbf{a}||\mathbf{b}\times\mathbf{c}|\cos\theta$

The maximum value of above will be $|\mathbf{a}||\mathbf{b}\times\mathbf{c}|$ as $\cos\theta\le 1$.

or $1.|3\mathbf{i}-7\mathbf{j}-\mathbf{k}|=\sqrt{9+49+1}=\sqrt{59}$

as **a** is a unit vector.

(d) Since **c** is perpendicular to both **a** and **b** therefore it is parallel to $\mathbf{a}\times\mathbf{b}$.

$\therefore \quad [\mathbf{a}\,\mathbf{b}\,\mathbf{c}]^2=[(\mathbf{a}\times\mathbf{b}).\mathbf{c}]^2=[|\mathbf{a}\times\mathbf{b}||\mathbf{c}|\cos 0]^2$

$=[|\mathbf{a}||\mathbf{b}|\sin 30^\circ\;\hat{\mathbf{n}}]^2\,.1.1=\dfrac{1}{4}|\mathbf{a}|^2\,||\mathbf{b}|^2$

(e) Ans. (c).

$\mathbf{a}=1,1,1, \mathbf{a}\times\mathbf{b}=0,1,-1, \mathbf{a}.\mathbf{b}=1$

Now $\mathbf{a}\times(\mathbf{a}\times\mathbf{b})=(\mathbf{a}.\mathbf{b})\mathbf{a}-(\mathbf{a}.\mathbf{a})\mathbf{b}$

L.H.S. $=\begin{vmatrix}\mathbf{i} & \mathbf{j} & \mathbf{k}\\ 1 & 1 & 1\\ 0 & 1 & -1\end{vmatrix}=-2\,\mathbf{i}+\mathbf{j}+\mathbf{k}$

R.H.S. $=1.(1,1,1)-3\mathbf{b}=\mathbf{i}+\mathbf{j}+\mathbf{k}-3\mathbf{b}$

L.H.S. = R.H.S. $\quad \therefore \; -3\mathbf{b}=-3\mathbf{i} \quad \therefore \; \mathbf{b}=\mathbf{i}$

6. (a) Ans (a), (c).

Here we should evaluate $|\mathbf{u}|, |\mathbf{u}.\mathbf{a}|$ and $|\mathbf{u}.\mathbf{b}|$ to choose the correct answer. Remember

$\mathbf{a}.\mathbf{b}=1.1\cos\theta=\cos\theta, \quad |\mathbf{v}|=|1.1\sin\theta\,\hat{\mathbf{n}}|=\sin\theta,$

$|\mathbf{u}|^2=1+\cos^2\theta.1-2\cos\theta.\cos\theta$

$=1-\cos^2\theta=\sin^2\theta \quad \therefore \; |\mathbf{u}|=\sin\theta$

$\mathbf{u}.\mathbf{a}=1-(\mathbf{a}.\mathbf{b})(\mathbf{a}.\mathbf{b})=1-\cos^2\theta=\sin^2\theta$

$\mathbf{u}.\mathbf{b}=(\mathbf{a}.\mathbf{b})-(\mathbf{a}.\mathbf{b}).1=0$ ...(1)

$\therefore \quad |\mathbf{v}|=\sin\theta=|\mathbf{u}| \;\Rightarrow$ (a) $\Rightarrow$ (c) by (1)

$\because \quad \mathbf{u}.\mathbf{b}=0$

(b) The vector **c** is coplanar with vectors **a** and **b**.

$\therefore \quad \mathbf{c}=x\mathbf{a}+y\mathbf{b}$ ...(1)

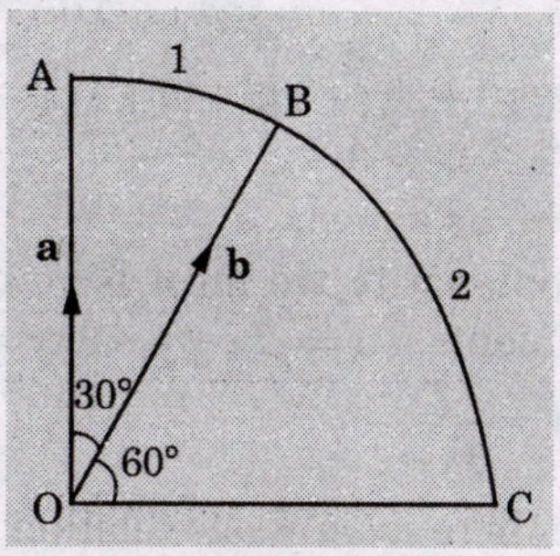

Fig. 49

The point B divides arc AC in the ratio 1 : 2 so that $\angle AOB=30^\circ, \angle BOC=60^\circ$.

We have to find the values of x and y when we are given $|\mathbf{a}|=|\mathbf{b}|=|\mathbf{c}|=r$ say.

$\mathbf{a}.\mathbf{b}=r^2\cos 30^\circ=r^2\dfrac{\sqrt{3}}{2}, \quad \mathbf{a}.\mathbf{c}=0$

$\mathbf{b}.\mathbf{c}=r^2\cos 60^\circ=\dfrac{r^2}{2}$

Multiply both sides of (1) scalarly by **c** and **a**.

$\therefore \quad \mathbf{c}.\mathbf{c}=x\mathbf{a}.\mathbf{c}+y\mathbf{b}.\mathbf{c}$

$\mathbf{c}.\mathbf{a}=x\mathbf{a}.\mathbf{a}+y\mathbf{b}.\mathbf{a}$

or $r^2=0+\dfrac{r^2}{2}y \quad \therefore \; y=2$

$0=xr^2+yr^2\dfrac{\sqrt{3}}{2}.$

Put $y=2 \quad \therefore \; x=-\sqrt{3}.$

$\mathbf{c}=-\sqrt{3}\,\mathbf{a}+2\mathbf{b}$

7. (a) Using the result of § 7, P. 1153

L.H.S. $=\begin{vmatrix}\mathbf{i}\cdot\mathbf{a} & \mathbf{i}\cdot\mathbf{j}\\ \mathbf{a}\cdot\mathbf{a} & \mathbf{a}\cdot\mathbf{j}\end{vmatrix}=\begin{vmatrix}\mathbf{i}\cdot\mathbf{a} & 0\\ \mathbf{a}\cdot\mathbf{a} & \mathbf{a}\cdot\mathbf{j}\end{vmatrix}=(\mathbf{i}.\mathbf{a})(\mathbf{a}.\mathbf{j})$

(b) By given condition $\mathbf{a}^2=\mathbf{b}^2=\mathbf{c}^2=1, \mathbf{a}.\mathbf{b}=0$

and $|\mathbf{a}\times\mathbf{b}|=1.\sin 90^\circ=1$

Now $\mathbf{c}=p(\mathbf{a}+\mathbf{b})+q(\mathbf{a}\times\mathbf{b})$ ...(1)

Multiplying both sides scalarly by **a**, we get

$\mathbf{a}.\mathbf{c}=p(1+0)+q[\mathbf{a}\,\mathbf{a}\,\mathbf{b}]$

$\therefore \quad 1.1\cos\theta=p+q\,0 \quad \therefore \; p=\cos\theta$ ...(2)

Again squaring both sides of (1), we have

$1=p^2[1+1+2(0)]+q^2|\mathbf{a}\times\mathbf{b}|^2$

$+2pq(\mathbf{a}+\mathbf{b}).(\mathbf{a}\times\mathbf{b})$ by (2)

$1=2\cos^2\theta+q^2.1+2pq[[\mathbf{a}\,\mathbf{a}\,\mathbf{b}]+[\mathbf{b}\,\mathbf{a}\,\mathbf{b}]]$

$\therefore \quad q^2=1-2\cos^2\theta=-\cos 2\theta$

Since $q \in R, q^2 \geq 0$.

$\therefore \quad q^2 = -\cos 2\theta \geq 0$ or $\cos 2\theta \leq 0$

$\therefore \quad \frac{\pi}{2} \leq 2\theta \leq \frac{3\pi}{2} \quad \therefore \quad \frac{\pi}{4} \leq \theta \leq \frac{3\pi}{4}$

8. (a) Three vectors, **a, b, c** are coplanar if

$$[\mathbf{a\,b\,c}] = 0 \text{ or } \begin{vmatrix} 2 & -1 & 1 \\ 1 & 2 & -3 \\ 3 & \lambda & 5 \end{vmatrix} = 0$$

or $\quad 2(10 + 3\lambda) + 1(5 + 9) + 1(\lambda - 6) = 0$

or $\quad 7\lambda + 28 = 0 \therefore \lambda = -4$.

(b) Proceed as above.

(c) For coplanarity we must have determinant D of coefficients $= 0 \Rightarrow 2x + y - 3xy = 0$

or $\quad y = \frac{2x}{3x - 1}$

Since there is only one relation in two variables, we will have infinite set of values of x and y. If we choose $x = k$, then $y = \frac{2k}{3k - 1}$.

If $k = 0, x = 0, y = 0$; If $k = 1, x = 1, y = 1$; If $k = 2, x = 2, y = 4/5$ etc.

9. (a) The given scalar triple product is

$$\begin{vmatrix} -1 & -3-\lambda & 0 \\ 5 & \lambda+1 & -1 \\ 4 & -2 & -1 \end{vmatrix} \text{ Apply } R_2 - R_1$$

$\therefore \quad \Delta = 0$.

(b) Ans. (c).

$$[\mathbf{a\,b\,c}] = \begin{vmatrix} 1 & 0 & -1 \\ x & 1 & 1-x \\ y & x & 1+x-y \end{vmatrix}$$

Apply $C_3 + C_1$ to make two zeros in R_1 and expand $\Delta = 1 + x - x = 1$ which is independent of both x and $y \Rightarrow$ (c).

(c) Ans. (d).

Given λ is real. $[\mathbf{a\,b\,c}] \neq 0$. Also we know that scalar triple product is zero when two vectors are equal and $[p\mathbf{a}\; q\mathbf{b}\; r\mathbf{c}] = pqr\,[\mathbf{a\,b\,c}]$. Hence from the given relation we have

$$[\lambda\mathbf{a}\; \lambda^2\mathbf{b}\; \lambda\mathbf{c}] + [\lambda\mathbf{b}\; \lambda^2\mathbf{b}\; \lambda\mathbf{c}] = [\mathbf{a\,b\,b}] + [\mathbf{a\,c\,b}]$$

$$\lambda.\lambda^2.\lambda\,[\mathbf{a\,b\,c}] + \lambda.\lambda^2.\lambda\,[\mathbf{b\,b\,c}] = 0 - [\mathbf{a\,b\,c}]$$

$$\lambda^4\,[\mathbf{a\,b\,c}] = -[\mathbf{a\,b\,c}] \quad \Rightarrow \quad \lambda^4 = -1$$

Above is not possible for any real value of λ.

10. (a) $D = D_1 D_2$ **(See determinants)**

$$= 2\begin{vmatrix} a^2 & a & 1 \\ b^2 & b & 1 \\ c^2 & c & 1 \end{vmatrix}\begin{vmatrix} 1 & x & x^2 \\ 1 & y & y^2 \\ 1 & z & z^2 \end{vmatrix} = 0.$$

Since **A, B, C** are non-coplanar $\therefore D_1 \neq 0$

$$\therefore \quad D_2 = 0 \text{ or } \begin{vmatrix} x^2 & x & 1 \\ y^2 & y & 1 \\ z^2 & z & 1 \end{vmatrix} = 0$$

or **X, Y, Z** are coplanar.

(b) Refer **10 Problem Set 118.** of determinants we have

$$D = D_1 + D_2 = D_1 + abc\,D_1$$

$$D = D_1(1 + abc) = 0 \qquad ...(1)$$

Since the vectors $(1, a, a^2)$, $(1, b, b^2)$, $(1, c, c^2)$ are non-coplanar, we have

$$D_1 = \begin{vmatrix} a & a^2 & 1 \\ b & b^2 & 1 \\ c & c^2 & 1 \end{vmatrix} \neq 0$$

Then (1) gives $abc = -1$.

11. (a) The given vectors are coplanar if

$$\begin{vmatrix} a & 1 & 1 \\ 1 & b & 1 \\ 1 & 1 & c \end{vmatrix} = 0$$

Applying $C_2 - C_1$ and $C_3 - C_1$, we get

$$\Delta = \begin{vmatrix} a & 1-a & 1-a \\ 1 & b-1 & 0 \\ 1 & 0 & c-1 \end{vmatrix} = 0$$

or $\quad a(b-1)(c-1) - (1-a)(c-1) - (1-a)(b-1) = 0$

Dividing by $(1-a)(1-b)(1-c)$, we get

$$\frac{a}{1-a} + \frac{1}{1-b} + \frac{1}{1-c} = 0$$

or $\quad \frac{1}{1-b} + \frac{1}{1-c} = -\frac{a}{1-a}$.

Add $\frac{1}{1-a}$ to both sides.

$$\therefore \quad \frac{1}{1-a} + \frac{1}{1-b} + \frac{1}{1-c} = \frac{1-a}{1-a} = 1$$

Another form :

Ans. (b).

We have proved above that $\Sigma \frac{1}{1-a} = 1$

$$\therefore \quad \frac{2}{1-a} + \frac{2}{1-b} + \frac{2}{1-c} = 2$$

$$\therefore \quad \frac{2}{1-a} - 1 + \frac{2}{1-b} - 1 + \frac{2}{1-c} - 1 = 2 - 3$$

or $\quad \Sigma \frac{1+a}{1-a} = -1 \Rightarrow$ (b)

(b) $\Delta = \begin{vmatrix} a & a & c \\ 1 & 0 & 1 \\ c & c & b \end{vmatrix} = 0 \quad$ Apply $C_2 - C_1$

$$\Delta = \begin{vmatrix} a & 0 & c \\ 1 & -1 & 1 \\ c & 0 & b \end{vmatrix} = 0 \text{ or } ab - c^2 = 0$$

by expanding with C_2. $\therefore c$ is G.M. of a, b.

12. L.H.S. $= [\mathbf{a\,b\,c}]^2 = D^2$, R.H.S. $= \frac{1}{4}|\mathbf{a}|^2\,|\mathbf{b}|^2$

$$\mathbf{a} \times \mathbf{b} = |\mathbf{a}|\,|\mathbf{b}| \sin\frac{\pi}{6}\,\hat{\mathbf{n}}$$

$\therefore \quad (\mathbf{a}\times\mathbf{b}).\mathbf{c}=\frac{1}{2}|\mathbf{a}||\mathbf{b}|\hat{\mathbf{n}}.\mathbf{c}$

$[\mathbf{abc}]=\frac{1}{2}|\mathbf{a}||\mathbf{b}|.1.1.\cos 0^o$ ...(1)

$\because$ $\hat{\mathbf{n}}$ is perpendicular to both **a** and **b** and **c** is also a unit vector perpendicular to both **a** and **b**.

Square both sides of (1)

$D^2=\frac{1}{4}(\Sigma a_1^2)(\Sigma b_1^2)$.

Note : This question has been done in determinants.

13. (a) $\vec{A}\times\vec{B}=(x^2-yz)(\mathbf{a}\times\mathbf{b})+(y^2-zx)(\mathbf{b}\times\mathbf{c})+(z^2-xy)(\mathbf{c}\times\mathbf{a})$

$\therefore \quad [\vec{A}\ \vec{B}\ \vec{C}]=(\vec{A}\times\vec{B}).\vec{C}$

$=[x(x^2-yz)+y(y^2-zx)+z(z^2-xy)][\mathbf{a\ b\ c}]=0$

Since $[\mathbf{a\ b\ c}]\neq 0$

$\therefore \quad x^3+y^3+z^3-3xyz=0$

or $(x+y+z).\frac{1}{2}[(x-y)^2+(y-z)^2+(z-x)^2]=0$

$\therefore \quad (x+y+z)=0 \Rightarrow$ (a)

as x, y, z are distinct.

The second factor is zero only when $x-y=0=y-z=z-x\Rightarrow x=y=z$ which is not possible.

(b) Ans. (d).

Condition of coplanarity gives $D=0$

$$\therefore \begin{vmatrix} \sec^2 A & 1 & 1 \\ 1 & \sec^2 B & 1 \\ 1 & 1 & \sec^2 C \end{vmatrix}=0$$

$\Rightarrow \sec^2 A[\sec^2 B\sec^2 C-1]-1(\sec^2 C-1)+1(1-\sec^2 B)=0$

$\Rightarrow (1+\tan^2 A)(\tan^2 B+\tan^2 C+\tan^2 B\tan^2 C)-\tan^2 C-\tan^2 B=0$

$\Rightarrow \tan^2 B\tan^2 C+\tan^2 A\tan^2 B+\tan^2 C\tan^2 A+\tan^2 A\tan^2 B\tan^2 C=0$

Dividing by $\tan^2 A\tan^2 B\tan^2 C$, we get

$\cot^2 A+\cot^2 B+\cot^2 C+1=0$

or $\Sigma\cot^2 A=-1$

Above is not possible as sum of three positive quantities can not be -1.

(c) $$[\mathbf{r}_1\ \mathbf{r}_2\ \mathbf{r}_3]=\begin{vmatrix} x & 2x & -3x \\ 2x+1 & 2x+3 & x+1 \\ 3x+5 & x+5 & x+2 \end{vmatrix}$$

Expand the above determinant

$\therefore \quad [\mathbf{r}_1\ \mathbf{r}_2\ \mathbf{r}_3]=x(15x^2+31x+37)$

Now quadratic expression $15x^2+31x+37$ is such that its $\Delta=(31)^2-60(37)=-$ ive and hence its sign is same as that of the coefficient of first term *i.e.*, 15 *i.e.*, + ive. Also $x\neq 0$ is a real number.

$\therefore \quad [\mathbf{r}_1.\mathbf{r}_2.\mathbf{r}_3]\neq 0$.

Hence the vectors are non-coplanar.

14. (a) L.H.S. $=(\mathbf{a}+\mathbf{b}).[(\mathbf{b}+\mathbf{c})\times(\mathbf{c}+\mathbf{a})]$

$=(\mathbf{a}+\mathbf{b}).[\mathbf{b}\times\mathbf{c}+\mathbf{b}\times\mathbf{a}+\mathbf{c}\times\mathbf{c}+\mathbf{c}\times\mathbf{a}]$

$=(\mathbf{a}+\mathbf{b}).[\mathbf{b}\times\mathbf{c}+\mathbf{b}\times\mathbf{a}+\mathbf{c}\times\mathbf{a}] \quad \because \mathbf{c}\times\mathbf{c}=\mathbf{0}$

$=\mathbf{a}.(\mathbf{b}\times\mathbf{c})+\mathbf{a}.(\mathbf{b}\times\mathbf{a})+\mathbf{a}.(\mathbf{c}\times\mathbf{a})+\mathbf{b}.(\mathbf{b}\times\mathbf{c})+\mathbf{b}.(\mathbf{b}\times\mathbf{a})+\mathbf{b}.(\mathbf{c}\times\mathbf{a})$

$=[\mathbf{a\ b\ c}]+[\mathbf{a\ b\ a}]+[\mathbf{a\ c\ a}]+[\mathbf{b\ b\ c}]+[\mathbf{b\ b\ a}]+[\mathbf{b\ c\ a}]$

$=[\mathbf{a\ b\ c}]+[\mathbf{a\ b\ c}]=2[\mathbf{a\ b\ c}]$.

Because scalar triple product is zero when two vectors are equal and also $[\mathbf{b\ c\ a}]=[\mathbf{a\ b\ c}]$ as the cyclic order is maintained.

In case **a**, **b**, **c** are coplanar then $[\mathbf{a\ b\ c}]=0$ and hence $[\mathbf{a}+\mathbf{b}\ \ \mathbf{b}+\mathbf{c}\ \ \mathbf{c}+\mathbf{a}]=0$

$\therefore$ **a** + **b**, **b** + **c**, **c** + **a** are also coplanar.

(b) Proceed as above.

15. (a) L.H.S. $=\mathbf{a}.\{(\mathbf{b}+\mathbf{c})\times(\mathbf{a}+\mathbf{b}+\mathbf{c})\}$

$=\mathbf{a}.\{(\mathbf{b}+\mathbf{c})\times\mathbf{a}+0\}=\mathbf{a}.\{\mathbf{b}\times\mathbf{a}+\mathbf{c}\times\mathbf{a}\}$

$=[\mathbf{a\ b\ a}]+[\mathbf{a\ c\ a}]=0$ **§ 5 (d) P. 1152**

(b) L.H.S. $=[\mathbf{a}+\mathbf{b}+\mathbf{c}\ \ \mathbf{a}+\mathbf{b}\ \ \mathbf{a}+\mathbf{c}]=[\mathbf{c}\ \ \mathbf{a}+\mathbf{b}\ \ \mathbf{a}+\mathbf{c}]$

because scalar triple product is zero when two vectors (here **a** + **b**) are equal **§ 5 (d) P 1152**

$=[\mathbf{c}\ \ \mathbf{a}\ \ \mathbf{a}+\mathbf{c}]+[\mathbf{c}\ \ \mathbf{b}\ \ \mathbf{a}+\mathbf{c}]=0+0+[\mathbf{c\ b\ a}]+0$

$=[\mathbf{a\ c\ b}]=-[\mathbf{a\ b\ c}]$ **§ 5 (c) P. 1020**

(c) Ans. (a). Since **a**, **b**, **c** are unit coplanar vectors, therefore $2\mathbf{a}-\mathbf{b}, 2\mathbf{b}-\mathbf{c}, 2\mathbf{c}-\mathbf{a}$ are also coplanar vectors. Hence their scalar triple product is zero.

Note : Alt. $[\mathbf{a\ \ b\ \ c}]=0$ given ...(1)

Now evaluate $(2\mathbf{a}-\mathbf{b}).[(2\mathbf{b}-\mathbf{c})\times(2\mathbf{c}-\mathbf{a})]$

$(2\mathbf{a}-\mathbf{b}).[4\mathbf{b}\times\mathbf{c}-2\mathbf{b}\times\mathbf{a}-0+\mathbf{c}\times\mathbf{a}]$

$=8[\mathbf{a\ b\ c}]-4[\mathbf{a\ b\ a}]+2[\mathbf{a\ c\ a}]-4[\mathbf{b\ b\ c}]+2[\mathbf{b\ b\ a}]-[\mathbf{b\ c\ a}]$

$=(8-1)[\mathbf{a\ b\ c}]=0$, by (1)

16. (a) Let $\mathbf{r}=x\mathbf{i}+y\mathbf{j}+z\mathbf{k}$

Multiply both sides scalarly by **i**

$\therefore \quad \mathbf{r}.\mathbf{i}=x\mathbf{i}.\mathbf{i}+0+0=x.1=x$

Similarly, $\mathbf{r}.\mathbf{j}=y, \quad \mathbf{r}.\mathbf{k}=z$

$\therefore \quad \mathbf{r}=(\mathbf{r}.\mathbf{i}).\mathbf{i}+(\mathbf{r}.\mathbf{j}).\mathbf{j}+(\mathbf{r}.\mathbf{k}).\mathbf{k}$ **(V. Imp.)**

(b) $\mathbf{i}\times(\mathbf{a}\times\mathbf{i})=(\mathbf{i}.\mathbf{i})\mathbf{a}-(\mathbf{i}.\mathbf{a})\mathbf{i}=\mathbf{a}-(\mathbf{a}.\mathbf{i})\mathbf{i}$

$\therefore$ L.H.S. $=(\mathbf{a}+\mathbf{a}+\mathbf{a})-[(\mathbf{a}.\mathbf{i})\mathbf{i}+(\mathbf{a}.\mathbf{j})\mathbf{j}+(\mathbf{a}.\mathbf{k})\mathbf{k}]$

$=3\mathbf{a}-\mathbf{a}=2\mathbf{a}$, by (a)

17. Ans. (b).

$\mathbf{p}^2=\mathbf{q}^2=\mathbf{r}^2=a^2$ ...(1)

$\mathbf{p}.\mathbf{q}=\mathbf{q}.\mathbf{r}=\mathbf{r}.\mathbf{p}=0$ ...(2)

Given $\Sigma(\mathbf{p}.\mathbf{p})(\mathbf{x}-\mathbf{q})-\Sigma\{\mathbf{p}.(\mathbf{x}-\mathbf{q})\}\mathbf{p}=0$

$=\Sigma a^2(\mathbf{x}-\mathbf{q})-\Sigma(\mathbf{p}.\mathbf{x})\mathbf{p}=0$ by (1) and (2)

$=a^2[3\mathbf{x}-(\mathbf{p}+\mathbf{q}+\mathbf{r})]-a^2\mathbf{x}=0$, by (3)

$\therefore \quad 2\mathbf{x} = \mathbf{p} + \mathbf{q} + \mathbf{r}$ or $\mathbf{x} = \frac{1}{2}(\mathbf{p} + \mathbf{q} + \mathbf{r})$.

$\because$ If $\mathbf{x} = \alpha\mathbf{p} + \beta\mathbf{q} + \gamma\mathbf{r}$ where $\mathbf{p}, \mathbf{q}$ and $\mathbf{r}$ are mutually perpendicular then

$\mathbf{x} \cdot \mathbf{p} = \alpha a^2 + 0 + 0$ by (1) and (2)

or $\alpha = \frac{1}{a^2}(\mathbf{x} \cdot \mathbf{p}) \quad \therefore \quad a^2 \mathbf{x} = \Sigma (\mathbf{p} \cdot \mathbf{x})\, \mathbf{p}$ ...(3)

18. (a) $\mathbf{a} = a_1 \mathbf{i} + a_2 \mathbf{j} + a_3 \mathbf{k}$, etc.

$\therefore \quad \mathbf{a} \cdot \mathbf{a} = \Sigma a_1^2, \ \mathbf{a} \cdot \mathbf{b} = \Sigma a_1 b_1$

$$\therefore [\mathbf{a}\,\mathbf{b}\,\mathbf{c}] = \begin{vmatrix} a_1 & a_2 & a_3 \\ b_1 & b_2 & b_3 \\ c_1 & c_2 & c_3 \end{vmatrix} = \Delta$$

$(\mathbf{a} \times \mathbf{b}) \cdot [(\mathbf{b} \times \mathbf{c}) \times (\mathbf{c} \times \mathbf{a})] = (\mathbf{a} \times \mathbf{b}) \cdot [(\mathbf{b} \times \mathbf{c}) \times \mathbf{d}]$

$= (\mathbf{a} \times \mathbf{b}) \cdot [(\mathbf{d} \cdot \mathbf{b})\, \mathbf{c} - (\mathbf{d} \cdot \mathbf{c})\, \mathbf{b}]$

$= (\mathbf{a} \times \mathbf{b}) \cdot [(\mathbf{c} \times \mathbf{a}) \cdot \mathbf{bc} - (\mathbf{c} \times \mathbf{a}) \cdot \mathbf{cb}]$

$= (\mathbf{a} \times \mathbf{b}) \cdot [\{\mathbf{cab}\}\, \mathbf{c} - \{\mathbf{cac}\}\, \mathbf{b}] = (\mathbf{a} \times \mathbf{b}) \cdot [\{\mathbf{abc}\}\, \mathbf{c} - 0]$

$= [\mathbf{abc}]\, [(\mathbf{a} \times \mathbf{b}) \cdot \mathbf{c}] = [\mathbf{abc}]\, [\mathbf{abc}] = [\mathbf{abc}]^2$.

$$\text{Again } \Delta^2 = \begin{vmatrix} a_1 & a_2 & a_3 \\ b_1 & b_2 & b_3 \\ c_1 & c_2 & c_3 \end{vmatrix} \begin{vmatrix} a_1 & a_2 & a_3 \\ b_1 & b_2 & b_3 \\ c_1 & c_2 & c_3 \end{vmatrix}$$

$$= \begin{vmatrix} \Sigma a_1^2 & \Sigma a_1 b_1 & \Sigma a_1 c_1 \\ \Sigma b_1 a_1 & \Sigma b_1^2 & \Sigma b_1 c_1 \\ \Sigma c_1 a_1 & \Sigma c_1 b_1 & \Sigma c_1^2 \end{vmatrix}$$

$$= \begin{vmatrix} \mathbf{a} \cdot \mathbf{a} & \mathbf{a} \cdot \mathbf{b} & \mathbf{a} \cdot \mathbf{c} \\ \mathbf{b} \cdot \mathbf{a} & \mathbf{b} \cdot \mathbf{b} & \mathbf{b} \cdot \mathbf{c} \\ \mathbf{c} \cdot \mathbf{a} & \mathbf{c} \cdot \mathbf{b} & \mathbf{c} \cdot \mathbf{c} \end{vmatrix}$$

(b) By last part given determinant is $[\mathbf{a}\,\mathbf{b}\,\mathbf{c}]^2$ but $\mathbf{c} = 3\mathbf{b}$

$\therefore \quad \Delta = [\mathbf{a}\ \mathbf{b}\ 3\mathbf{b}]^2 = 9\, [\mathbf{a}\ \mathbf{b}\ \mathbf{b}]^2 = 0$.

(c) Ans. (a), (b), (c), (d).

Given $\mathbf{a} \cdot \mathbf{b} = 0$ and $\mathbf{c} \cdot \mathbf{a} = \mathbf{c} \cdot \mathbf{b} = 1.1 \cos\theta$

$\therefore \quad \mathbf{a} \times \mathbf{b} = 1.1 . \sin 90^\circ\ \mathbf{n} \quad \therefore \quad (\mathbf{a} \times \mathbf{b})^2 = 1$

Also we know that $\mathbf{a} \cdot (\mathbf{a} \times \mathbf{b}) = [\mathbf{a}\,\mathbf{a}\,\mathbf{b}] = 0$,

$\mathbf{b} \cdot (\mathbf{a} \times \mathbf{b}) = 0$ and $\mathbf{c} \cdot (\mathbf{a} \times \mathbf{b}) = [\mathbf{c}\,\mathbf{a}\,\mathbf{b}] = [\mathbf{a}\,\mathbf{b}\,\mathbf{c}]$

Now, $\mathbf{c} = x\mathbf{a} + y\mathbf{b} + z(\mathbf{a} \times \mathbf{b})$

Multiplying both sides scalarly by $\mathbf{a}$ and $\mathbf{b}$

$\cos\theta = x.1 + 0 + 0, \cos\theta = y.1$ ...(1)

Again multiplying by $\mathbf{a} \times \mathbf{b}$

$\mathbf{c} \cdot (\mathbf{a} \times \mathbf{b}) = x.0 + y.0 + z(\mathbf{a} \times \mathbf{b})^2 = z.1$

$\therefore \quad [\mathbf{a}\,\mathbf{b}\,\mathbf{c}] = z$

$$\text{Now } [\mathbf{a}\,\mathbf{b}\,\mathbf{c}]^2 = \begin{vmatrix} \mathbf{a} \cdot \mathbf{a} & \mathbf{a} \cdot \mathbf{b} & \mathbf{a} \cdot \mathbf{c} \\ \mathbf{b} \cdot \mathbf{a} & \mathbf{b} \cdot \mathbf{b} & \mathbf{b} \cdot \mathbf{c} \\ \mathbf{c} \cdot \mathbf{a} & \mathbf{c} \cdot \mathbf{b} & \mathbf{c} \cdot \mathbf{c} \end{vmatrix}$$

$$\text{or } \quad z^2 = \begin{vmatrix} 1 & 0 & \cos\theta \\ 0 & 1 & \cos\theta \\ \cos\theta & \cos\theta & 1 \end{vmatrix} = 1 - 2\cos^2\theta$$

$\therefore \quad z^2 = 1 - 2x^2 = 1 - 2y^2$ by (1)

$= 1 - x^2 - x^2 = 1 - x^2 - y^2$.

Also $x^2 = y^2$.

(d) It is a simple question based upon the following standard results.

$[\mathbf{a} \times \mathbf{b}\ \ \mathbf{b} \times \mathbf{c}\ \ \mathbf{c} \times \mathbf{a}] = [\mathbf{a}\ \mathbf{b}\ \mathbf{c}]^2$, by part (a) ...(1)

$[\mathbf{a} + \mathbf{b}\ \ \mathbf{b} + \mathbf{c}\ \ \mathbf{c} + \mathbf{a}] = 2\, [\mathbf{a}\ \mathbf{b}\ \mathbf{c}]$, by Q. 14 (a) ...(2)

Bisector of $\mathbf{a}$ and $\mathbf{b}$ including an angle θ is

$\mathbf{r} = t\, (\mathbf{a} + \mathbf{b})$

$\therefore \quad \mathbf{r}^2 = r^2 = t^2\, (1 + 1 + 2.1.1 \cos\theta)$

$= t^2 . 2\, (1 + \cos\theta) = 4t^2 \cos^2(\theta/2)$

$\therefore \quad r = 2t \cos(\theta/2)$

Hence a unit vector along the bisector is

$$\frac{\mathbf{r}}{|\mathbf{r}|} = \frac{t\,(\mathbf{a} + \mathbf{b})}{2t \cos(\theta/2)} = \frac{\mathbf{a} + \mathbf{b}}{2\cos(\theta/2)} \quad ...(3)$$

Hence using above results, we are given

$$\mathbf{a} = \frac{\mathbf{u} + \mathbf{v}}{2\cos(\alpha/2)}, \mathbf{b} = \frac{\mathbf{v} + \mathbf{w}}{2\cos(\beta/2)},$$

$$\mathbf{c} = \frac{\mathbf{w} + \mathbf{v}}{2\cos(\gamma/2)} \quad ...(4)$$

$\therefore \quad [\mathbf{a} \times \mathbf{b}\ \ \mathbf{b} \times \mathbf{c}\ \ \mathbf{c} \times \mathbf{a}] = [\mathbf{a}\ \mathbf{b}\ \mathbf{c}]^2$, by (1)

$$= \left[\frac{[\mathbf{u} + \mathbf{v}\ \ \mathbf{v} + \mathbf{w}\ \ \mathbf{w} + \mathbf{u}]}{8\cos(\alpha/2)\cos(\beta/2)\cos(\gamma/2)}\right]^2$$

$$= \frac{4\,[\mathbf{u}\ \mathbf{v}\ \mathbf{w}]^2}{64\cos^2(\alpha/2)\cos^2(\beta/2)\cos^2(\gamma/2)}, \text{ by (2)}$$

$$= \frac{1}{16}[\mathbf{u}\ \mathbf{v}\ \mathbf{w}]^2 \sec^2\frac{\alpha}{2} \sec^2\frac{\beta}{2} \sec^2\frac{\gamma}{2}.$$

19. (a) Also from the relation

$[\mathbf{a} \times \mathbf{b}\ \ \mathbf{b} \times \mathbf{c}\ \ \mathbf{c} \times \mathbf{a}] = [\mathbf{a}\,\mathbf{b}\,\mathbf{c}]^2$,

we conclude that

$[\mathbf{a} \times \mathbf{b}\ \ \mathbf{b} \times \mathbf{c}\ \ \mathbf{c} \times \mathbf{a}] \neq 0$ iff $[\mathbf{a}\,\mathbf{b}\,\mathbf{c}] \neq 0$.

Hence $\mathbf{a} \times \mathbf{b}$, $\mathbf{b} \times \mathbf{c}$, $\mathbf{c} \times \mathbf{a}$ are non-coplanar iff $\mathbf{a}, \mathbf{b}, \mathbf{c}$ are non-coplanar.

(b) Since $\vec{A}, \vec{B}, \vec{C}$ are non-coplanar, we have

$[\vec{A}\ \vec{B}\ \vec{C}] \neq 0$

Also $\vec{A} \cdot \vec{B} \times \vec{C} = [\vec{A}\ \vec{B}\ \vec{C}]$,

$\vec{C} \times \vec{A} \cdot \vec{B} = [\vec{C}\ \vec{A}\ \vec{B}] = [\vec{A}\ \vec{B}\ \vec{C}]$

$[\vec{B} \cdot \vec{A} \times \vec{C}] = [\vec{B}\ \vec{A}\ \vec{C}] = -[\vec{A}\ \vec{B}\ \vec{C}]$

and $\vec{C} \cdot \vec{A} \times \vec{B} = [\vec{C}\ \vec{A}\ \vec{B}] = [\vec{A}\ \vec{B}\ \vec{C}]$

Hence L.H.S. $= 1 - 1 = 0$

20. $\mathbf{a}^2 = \mathbf{b}^2 = \mathbf{c}^2 = 1, \ [\mathbf{a}\,\mathbf{b}\,\mathbf{c}] \neq 0$

$\mathbf{a} \cdot \mathbf{b} = \mathbf{b} \cdot \mathbf{c} = \mathbf{c} \cdot \mathbf{a} = \cos\alpha$ ...(1)

Multiply both sides of given relation scalarly by $\mathbf{a}, \mathbf{b}$ and $\mathbf{c}$, we get

$0 + [\mathbf{a}\,\mathbf{b}\,\mathbf{c}] = l.1 + (m + n)\cos\alpha$ ...(2)

$0 = m + (n + l)\cos\alpha$ ...(3)

$[\mathbf{a}\,\mathbf{b}\,\mathbf{c}] + 0 = (l + m)\cos\alpha + n$ ...(4)

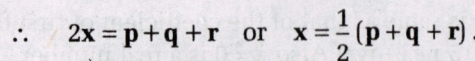

Adding, we get

$$2\,[\mathbf{a\,b\,c}] = (l+m+n) + 2\,(l+m+n)\cos\alpha$$

or $\quad 2\,[\mathbf{a\,b\,c}] = (l+m+n)\,(1+2\cos\alpha)$ ...(5)

From (2), $\quad (m+n) = \dfrac{[\mathbf{a\,b\,c}] - l}{\cos\alpha}$.

Putting in (5), we get

$$2\,[\mathbf{a\,b\,c}] = \left[l + \frac{[\mathbf{a\,b\,c}] - l}{\cos\alpha}\right](1+2\cos\alpha)$$

or $\quad [\mathbf{a\,b\,c}]\left\{2 - \dfrac{1+2\cos\alpha}{\cos\alpha}\right\} = l\left\{1 - \dfrac{1}{\cos\alpha}\right\}(1+2\cos\alpha)$

$\therefore \quad l = \dfrac{[\mathbf{a\,b\,c}]}{(1+2\cos\alpha)\,(1-\cos\alpha)} = n,$ as above

and $m = -(n+l)\cos\alpha$

$$= \frac{-2\,[\mathbf{a\,b\,c}]\cos\alpha}{(1+2\cos\alpha)\,(1-\cos\alpha)}$$

Thus the values of l, m, n depend on $[\mathbf{a\,b\,c}]$.

Hence we now find the value of scalar $[\mathbf{a\,b\,c}]$ in terms of α.

Now $[\mathbf{a\,b\,c}]^2 = \begin{vmatrix} \mathbf{a.a} & \mathbf{a.b} & \mathbf{a.c} \\ \mathbf{b.a} & \mathbf{b.b} & \mathbf{b.c} \\ \mathbf{c.a} & \mathbf{c.b} & \mathbf{c.c} \end{vmatrix}$

$$= \begin{vmatrix} 1 & \cos\alpha & \cos\alpha \\ \cos\alpha & 1 & \cos\alpha \\ \cos\alpha & \cos\alpha & 1 \end{vmatrix}$$

Apply $C_1 + C_2 + C_3$

$$= (1+2\cos\alpha)\begin{vmatrix} 1 & \cos\alpha & \cos\alpha \\ 1 & 1 & \cos\alpha \\ 1 & \cos\alpha & 1 \end{vmatrix}$$

Apply $R_2 - R_1$ and $R_3 - R_1$

$\therefore \quad [\mathbf{a\,b\,c}]^2 = (1+2\cos\alpha)\,(1-\cos\alpha)^2$

$\therefore \quad \dfrac{[\mathbf{a\,b\,c}]}{1-\cos\alpha} = \sqrt{1+2\cos\alpha}$

Putting in the values of l, m, n, we have

$$l = \frac{1}{\sqrt{(1+2\cos\alpha)}} = n,\; m = \frac{-2\cos\alpha}{\sqrt{(1+2\cos\alpha)}}$$

21. **Caution** : T_2 = scalar being dot product and T_1 is a vector and we have $T_1 \times T_2$, *i.e.* Vector × scalar. But there is never a dot or cross between a vector and a scalar.

As a matter of fact, $T_2 = [\mathbf{b\,c\,b}] + [\mathbf{b\,c\,c}] = 0$ (scalar)

We should treat the question as $\mathbf{P}\times\mathbf{Q}\,.\,\mathbf{R} = [\mathbf{P\,Q\,R}]$ where $\mathbf{P} = T_1$

$$\mathbf{Q} = \mathbf{b}\times\mathbf{c} \text{ and } \mathbf{R} = \mathbf{b}+\mathbf{c}$$

$$\mathbf{P} = 0 + \mathbf{a}\times\mathbf{c} + \mathbf{b}\times\mathbf{a} + \mathbf{b}\times\mathbf{c}$$

$\therefore \quad \mathbf{P}\times\mathbf{Q} = (\mathbf{a}\times\mathbf{c} + \mathbf{b}\times\mathbf{a} + \mathbf{b}\times\mathbf{c})\times(\mathbf{b}\times\mathbf{c})$

$= [(\mathbf{b}\times\mathbf{c})\,.\,\mathbf{ac} - (\mathbf{b}\times\mathbf{c})\,.\,\mathbf{ca}] + [(\mathbf{b}\times\mathbf{c})\,.\,\mathbf{ba} - (\mathbf{b}\times\mathbf{c})\,.\,\mathbf{ab}] + 0$

$= [\mathbf{b\,c\,a}]\,\mathbf{c} - [\mathbf{b\,c\,a}]\,\mathbf{b}$

$\because \quad [\mathbf{b\,c\,c}] = [\mathbf{b\,c\,b}] = 0$

$$= [\mathbf{b\,c\,a}]\,[\mathbf{c} - \mathbf{b}]$$

$\therefore \quad \mathbf{P}\times\mathbf{Q}\,.\,\mathbf{R} = [\mathbf{b\,c\,a}]\,[\mathbf{c}-\mathbf{b}]\,.\,[\mathbf{b}+\mathbf{c}] = \lambda\,(\mathbf{c}^2 - \mathbf{b}^2) = 0$

$\because \quad |\mathbf{b}| = |\mathbf{c}|$.

22. (a) Let $\mathbf{l} = l_1\mathbf{i} + l_2\mathbf{j} + l_3\mathbf{k}$ etc.

$$\therefore \quad [\mathbf{l\,m\,n}] = \begin{vmatrix} l_1 & l_2 & l_3 \\ m_1 & m_2 & m_3 \\ n_1 & n_2 & n_3 \end{vmatrix}$$

$$(\mathbf{a}\times\mathbf{b}) = \begin{vmatrix} \mathbf{i} & \mathbf{j} & \mathbf{k} \\ a_1 & a_2 & a_3 \\ b_1 & b_2 & b_3 \end{vmatrix}$$

$$\therefore \quad [\mathbf{l\,m\,n}]\,(\mathbf{a}\times\mathbf{b}) = \begin{vmatrix} l_1 & l_2 & l_3 \\ m_1 & m_2 & m_3 \\ n_1 & n_2 & n_3 \end{vmatrix} \cdot \begin{vmatrix} \mathbf{i} & \mathbf{j} & \mathbf{k} \\ a_1 & a_2 & a_3 \\ b_1 & b_2 & b_3 \end{vmatrix}$$

$$= \begin{vmatrix} l_1\mathbf{i} + l_2\mathbf{j} + l_3\mathbf{k} & \Sigma\, l_1 a_1 & \Sigma\, l_1 b_1 \\ m_1\mathbf{i} + m_2\mathbf{j} + m_3\mathbf{k} & \Sigma\, m_1 a_1 & \Sigma\, m_1 b_1 \\ n_1\mathbf{i} + n_2\mathbf{j} + n_3\mathbf{k} & \Sigma\, n_1 a_1 & \Sigma\, n_1 b_1 \end{vmatrix}$$

$$= \begin{vmatrix} \mathbf{l} & \mathbf{l.a} & \mathbf{l.b} \\ \mathbf{m} & \mathbf{m.a} & \mathbf{m.b} \\ \mathbf{n} & \mathbf{n.a} & \mathbf{n.b} \end{vmatrix} = \begin{vmatrix} \mathbf{l.a} & \mathbf{l.b} & \mathbf{l} \\ \mathbf{m.a} & \mathbf{m.b} & \mathbf{m} \\ \mathbf{n.a} & \mathbf{n.b} & \mathbf{n} \end{vmatrix}.$$

(b) Let $\mathbf{a} = x_1\mathbf{i} + y_1\mathbf{j} + z_1\mathbf{k} = x_1, y_1, z_1$

$$\mathbf{b} = x_2, y_2, z_2,\; \mathbf{c} = x_3, y_3, z_3$$

$$\therefore \quad [\mathbf{a\,b\,c}] = \begin{vmatrix} x_1 & y_1 & z_1 \\ x_2 & y_2 & z_2 \\ x_3 & y_3 & z_3 \end{vmatrix} \quad ...(1)$$

$\mathbf{A} = p_1\mathbf{a} + q_1\mathbf{b} + r_1\mathbf{c}$

$= p_1\,(x_1\mathbf{i} + y_1\mathbf{j} + z_1\mathbf{k}) + q_1\,(x_2\mathbf{i} + y_2\mathbf{j} + z_2\mathbf{k}) + r_1\,(x_3\mathbf{i} + y_3\mathbf{j} + z_3\mathbf{k})$

$= (p_1x_1 + q_1x_2 + r_1x_3)\,\mathbf{i} + (p_1y_1 + q_1y_2 + r_1y_3)\,\mathbf{j} + (p_1z_1 + q_1z_2 + r_1z_3)\,\mathbf{k}$

$= p_1x_1 + q_1x_2 + r_1x_3,\quad p_1y_1 + q_1y_2 + r_1y_3,\quad p_1z_1 + q_1z_2 + r_1z_3$

Similarly we can write down the values of **B** and **C** in terms of p_2, q_2, r_2 and p_3, q_3, r_3.

$\therefore \quad \mathbf{A}\,.\,\mathbf{B}\times\mathbf{C} = [\mathbf{A\,B\,C}]$

$$= \begin{vmatrix} p_1x_1 + q_1x_2 + r_1x_3 & p_1y_1 + q_1y_2 + r_1y_3 & p_1z_1 + q_1z_2 + r_1z_3 \\ \dots\;\dots & \dots\;\dots & \dots\;\dots \\ \dots\;\dots & \dots\;\dots & \dots\;\dots \end{vmatrix}$$

$$= \begin{vmatrix} p_1 & q_1 & r_1 \\ p_2 & q_2 & r_2 \\ p_3 & q_3 & r_3 \end{vmatrix}\begin{vmatrix} x_1 & x_2 & x_3 \\ y_1 & y_2 & y_3 \\ z_1 & z_2 & z_3 \end{vmatrix} = \Delta\,[\mathbf{a\,b\,c}], \quad \text{by (1)}$$

23. (a) Ans. (b), (c).

Given $[\mathbf{a\,b\,c}] \neq 0$

Also $|[\mathbf{a\,b\,c}]| = [\mathbf{b}\times\mathbf{c} \quad \mathbf{c}\times\mathbf{a} \quad \mathbf{a}\times\mathbf{b}]$

or $\quad |[\mathbf{a\,b\,c}]| = [\mathbf{a\,b\,c}]^2$

or $\quad t^2 = |t| \quad \Rightarrow t^2 = \pm t$ or $t\,(t \pm 1) = 0$

But $t = [\mathbf{a\,b\,c}] \neq 0 \quad \therefore \quad t = \pm 1$

(b) Ans. (b).

$$\mathbf{a}\times\mathbf{b}=\begin{vmatrix}\mathbf{i} & \mathbf{j} & \mathbf{k}\\ 3 & 0 & 2\\ 0 & 2 & 1\end{vmatrix}=-4\mathbf{i}-3\mathbf{j}+6\mathbf{k}$$

$\therefore\quad |\mathbf{a}\times\mathbf{b}|=\sqrt{16+9+36}=\sqrt{61}$

Now $[\mathbf{a}\,\mathbf{b}\,\mathbf{c}]=(\mathbf{a}\times\mathbf{b}).\mathbf{c}=|\mathbf{a}\times\mathbf{b}||\mathbf{c}|.\cos\theta$

$\therefore\quad$ Max. value is $\sqrt{61}.1.1=\sqrt{61}$

24. (a) Let $\mathbf{a}=l(\mathbf{b}\times\mathbf{c})+m(\mathbf{c}\times\mathbf{a})+n(\mathbf{a}\times\mathbf{b})$ ...(1)

We have to find the values of l, m and n.

Multiply both sides of (1) scalarly by $\mathbf{a}$.

$\mathbf{a}.\mathbf{a}=l\,\mathbf{a}.(\mathbf{b}\times\mathbf{c})+m\,\mathbf{a}.(\mathbf{c}\times\mathbf{a})+n\,\mathbf{a}.(\mathbf{a}\times\mathbf{b})$

or $\quad \mathbf{a}.\mathbf{a}=l[\mathbf{a}\,\mathbf{b}\,\mathbf{c}]+m[\mathbf{a}\,\mathbf{c}\,\mathbf{a}]+n[\mathbf{a}\,\mathbf{a}\,\mathbf{b}]=l[\mathbf{a}\,\mathbf{b}\,\mathbf{c}]$.

$\because$ Scalar triple product is zero when two vectors are equal

$\therefore\quad l=\dfrac{\mathbf{a}.\mathbf{a}}{[\mathbf{a}\,\mathbf{b}\,\mathbf{c}]}$.

Similarly, multiplying both sides of (1) scalarly by $\mathbf{b}$ and $\mathbf{c}$, we get

$$m=\frac{\mathbf{a}.\mathbf{b}}{[\mathbf{a}\,\mathbf{b}\,\mathbf{c}]},\ n=\frac{\mathbf{a}.\mathbf{c}}{[\mathbf{a}\,\mathbf{b}\,\mathbf{c}]}$$

$$\therefore\quad \mathbf{a}=\frac{\mathbf{a}.\mathbf{a}}{[\mathbf{a}\,\mathbf{b}\,\mathbf{c}]}(\mathbf{b}\times\mathbf{c})+\frac{\mathbf{a}.\mathbf{b}}{[\mathbf{a}\,\mathbf{b}\,\mathbf{c}]}(\mathbf{c}\times\mathbf{a})+\frac{\mathbf{a}.\mathbf{c}}{[\mathbf{a}\,\mathbf{b}\,\mathbf{c}]}(\mathbf{a}\times\mathbf{b})$$

Similarly we can write the values $\mathbf{b}$ and $\mathbf{c}$ as

$$\mathbf{b}=\frac{\mathbf{b}.\mathbf{a}}{[\mathbf{a}\,\mathbf{b}\,\mathbf{c}]}(\mathbf{b}\times\mathbf{c})+\frac{\mathbf{b}.\mathbf{b}}{[\mathbf{a}\,\mathbf{b}\,\mathbf{c}]}(\mathbf{c}\times\mathbf{a})+\frac{\mathbf{b}.\mathbf{c}}{[\mathbf{a}\,\mathbf{b}\,\mathbf{c}]}(\mathbf{a}\times\mathbf{b})$$

$$\text{and } \mathbf{c}=\frac{\mathbf{c}.\mathbf{a}}{[\mathbf{a}\,\mathbf{b}\,\mathbf{c}]}(\mathbf{b}\times\mathbf{c})+\frac{\mathbf{c}.\mathbf{b}}{[\mathbf{a}\,\mathbf{b}\,\mathbf{c}]}(\mathbf{c}\times\mathbf{a})+\frac{\mathbf{c}.\mathbf{c}}{[\mathbf{a}\,\mathbf{b}\,\mathbf{c}]}(\mathbf{a}\times\mathbf{b}).$$

(b) Let $\mathbf{b}\times\mathbf{c}=l\mathbf{a}+m\mathbf{b}+n\mathbf{c}$ ...(2)

Multiply both sides scalarly by $\mathbf{b}\times\mathbf{c}$, we get

$(\mathbf{b}\times\mathbf{c}).(\mathbf{b}\times\mathbf{c})=l\,\mathbf{a}.(\mathbf{b}\times\mathbf{c})+m\,\mathbf{b}.(\mathbf{b}\times\mathbf{c})+n\,\mathbf{c}.(\mathbf{b}\times\mathbf{c})$

$=l[\mathbf{a}\,\mathbf{b}\,\mathbf{c}]+m[\mathbf{b}\,\mathbf{b}\,\mathbf{c}]+n[\mathbf{c}\,\mathbf{b}\,\mathbf{c}]=l[\mathbf{a}\,\mathbf{b}\,\mathbf{c}]$

$\therefore\quad l=\dfrac{(\mathbf{b}\times\mathbf{c}).(\mathbf{b}\times\mathbf{c})}{[\mathbf{a}\,\mathbf{b}\,\mathbf{c}]}$.

Similarly multiplying both sides scalarly by $(\mathbf{c}\times\mathbf{a})$ and $(\mathbf{a}\times\mathbf{b})$, we get

$$m=\frac{(\mathbf{b}\times\mathbf{c}).(\mathbf{c}\times\mathbf{a})}{[\mathbf{a}\,\mathbf{b}\,\mathbf{c}]},\ n=\frac{(\mathbf{b}\times\mathbf{c}).(\mathbf{a}\times\mathbf{b})}{[\mathbf{a}\,\mathbf{b}\,\mathbf{c}]}$$

Substituting the values of l, m, n in (2), we get the required expression for $\mathbf{b}\times\mathbf{c}$ in terms of $\mathbf{a}, \mathbf{b}, \mathbf{c}$.

In a similar manner we can express $(\mathbf{c}\times\mathbf{a})$ and $(\mathbf{a}\times\mathbf{b})$.

(c) Since $\mathbf{a}, \mathbf{b}, \mathbf{c}$ are non-coplanar $\quad\therefore\quad [\mathbf{a}\,\mathbf{b}\,\mathbf{c}]\neq 0$

Let $\mathbf{d}=l(\mathbf{b}\times\mathbf{c})+m(\mathbf{c}\times\mathbf{a})+n(\mathbf{a}\times\mathbf{b})$

Multiply both sides scalarly by $\mathbf{a}$.

$\mathbf{a}.\mathbf{d}=l\,\mathbf{a}.(\mathbf{b}\times\mathbf{c})+m.0+n.0$

$\therefore\quad l=\dfrac{\mathbf{a}.\mathbf{d}}{[\mathbf{a}\,\mathbf{b}\,\mathbf{c}]}$ etc.

(d) Given $[\mathbf{a}\,\mathbf{b}\,\mathbf{c}]\neq 0$

Let $\mathbf{r}=x\,\mathbf{a}+y\,\mathbf{b}+z\,\mathbf{c}$

We have to find x, y, z.

Multiply both sides scalarly by $\mathbf{b}\times\mathbf{c}$

$\therefore\quad \mathbf{r}.(\mathbf{b}\times\mathbf{c})=x\,\mathbf{a}.(\mathbf{b}\times\mathbf{c})+0+0$

$\therefore\quad x=\dfrac{[\mathbf{r}\,\mathbf{b}\,\mathbf{c}]}{[\mathbf{a}\,\mathbf{b}\,\mathbf{c}]}\quad\therefore$ Similarly y and z etc.

25. (a) Given $[\mathbf{a}\,\mathbf{b}\,\mathbf{c}]\neq 0$ as $\mathbf{a}, \mathbf{b}, \mathbf{c}$ are non-coplanar. Also there does not exist any linear relation between them because if any such relation exists, then they would be coplanar.

Also $\quad \mathbf{d}^2=1$

Let $A=x(\mathbf{b}\times\mathbf{c})+y(\mathbf{c}\times\mathbf{a})+z(\mathbf{a}\times\mathbf{b})$

where $x=\mathbf{a}.\mathbf{d}, y=\mathbf{b}.\mathbf{d}, z=\mathbf{c}.\mathbf{d}$.

We have to find the value of modulus of $\mathbf{A}$ *i.e.* $|\mathbf{A}|$ which is independent of $\mathbf{d}$.

Multiplying both sides scalarly by $\mathbf{a}, \mathbf{b}, \mathbf{c}$ and we know that scalar triple product is zero when two vectors are equal.

$$\mathbf{A}.\mathbf{a}=x[\mathbf{a}\,\mathbf{b}\,\mathbf{c}]+0$$

Putting for x, we get

$$(\mathbf{a}.\mathbf{d})[\mathbf{a}\,\mathbf{b}\,\mathbf{c}]=\mathbf{A}.\mathbf{a}$$

Similarly, we have

$$(\mathbf{b}.\mathbf{d})[\mathbf{a}\,\mathbf{b}\,\mathbf{c}]=\mathbf{A}.\mathbf{b}$$

$$(\mathbf{c}.\mathbf{d})[\mathbf{a}\,\mathbf{b}\,\mathbf{c}]=\mathbf{A}.\mathbf{c}$$

Adding the above relations, we get

$$[(\mathbf{a}+\mathbf{b}+\mathbf{c}).\mathbf{d}][\mathbf{a}\,\mathbf{b}\,\mathbf{c}]=\mathbf{A}.(\mathbf{a}+\mathbf{b}+\mathbf{c})$$

or $\quad (\mathbf{a}+\mathbf{b}+\mathbf{c}).[\mathbf{d}[\mathbf{a}\,\mathbf{b}\,\mathbf{c}]-\mathbf{A}]=0$

Since $\mathbf{a}, \mathbf{b}, \mathbf{c}$ are non-coplanar $\mathbf{a}+\mathbf{b}+\mathbf{c}\neq 0$ because otherwise any one is expressible as a linear combination of other two.

Hence $[\mathbf{a}\,\mathbf{b}\,\mathbf{c}]\,\mathbf{d}=\mathbf{A}$

Taking mod of both sides,

$|\mathbf{A}|=|[\mathbf{a}\,\mathbf{b}\,\mathbf{c}]|\cdot 1$ as $\mathbf{d}$ is a unit vector.

It is independent of $\mathbf{d}$.

(b) $\alpha.\mathbf{a}=p[\mathbf{a}\,\mathbf{b}\,\mathbf{c}]+0+0$.

$\therefore\quad \Sigma\alpha.\mathbf{a}=(p+q+r)[\mathbf{a}\,\mathbf{b}\,\mathbf{c}]=1$

by given relation

26. (a) $\mathbf{a}\times(\mathbf{b}\times\mathbf{c})=(\mathbf{a}.\mathbf{c})\,\mathbf{b}-(\mathbf{a}.\mathbf{b})\,\mathbf{c}$

$\therefore\quad$ L.H.S. $=(\mathbf{a}.\mathbf{c})\,\mathbf{b}-(\mathbf{a}.\mathbf{b})\,\mathbf{c}+(\mathbf{b}.\mathbf{a})\,\mathbf{c}-(\mathbf{b}.\mathbf{c})\,\mathbf{a}+(\mathbf{c}.\mathbf{b})\,\mathbf{a}-(\mathbf{c}.\mathbf{a})\,\mathbf{b}=\mathbf{0}$

$\because\quad \mathbf{a}.\mathbf{c}=\mathbf{c}.\mathbf{a},\ \mathbf{a}.\mathbf{b}=\mathbf{b}.\mathbf{a}$ and $\mathbf{b}.\mathbf{c}=\mathbf{c}.\mathbf{b}$

(b) Ans. (c). $[\mathbf{u}\,\mathbf{v}\,\mathbf{w}]=[\mathbf{v}\,\mathbf{w}\,\mathbf{u}]=[\mathbf{w}\,\mathbf{u}\,\mathbf{v}]$

I II IV

Cyclic order maintained.

but $[\mathbf{v}\,\mathbf{u}\,\mathbf{w}]=-[\mathbf{u}\,\mathbf{v}\,\mathbf{w}]$

III

27. (a) Refer **§ 7 Page 1153** the left hand side

$$= \begin{vmatrix} \mathbf{a.c} & \mathbf{a.d} \\ \mathbf{b.c} & \mathbf{b.d} \end{vmatrix} + \begin{vmatrix} \mathbf{b.a} & \mathbf{b.d} \\ \mathbf{c.a} & \mathbf{c.d} \end{vmatrix} + \begin{vmatrix} \mathbf{c.b} & \mathbf{c.d} \\ \mathbf{a.b} & \mathbf{a.d} \end{vmatrix}$$

Keeping in view that $\mathbf{a}\,.\,\mathbf{b} = \mathbf{b}\,.\,\mathbf{a}$ etc. above will be of the form $(x-y)+(y-z)+(z-x)=0$.

(b) L.H.S. $= \mathbf{d}\,.\,[\mathbf{a} \times \{(\mathbf{b}\,.\,\mathbf{d})\,\mathbf{c} - (\mathbf{b}\,.\,\mathbf{c})\,\mathbf{d}\}]$

$= \mathbf{d}\,.\,[(\mathbf{b}\,.\,\mathbf{d})\,(\mathbf{a} \times \mathbf{c}) - (\mathbf{b}\,.\,\mathbf{c})\,(\mathbf{a} \times \mathbf{d})]$

$= (\mathbf{b}\,.\,\mathbf{d})\,[\mathbf{d}\,.\,(\mathbf{a} \times \mathbf{c})] - (\mathbf{b}\,.\,\mathbf{c})\,[\mathbf{d}\,.\,(\mathbf{a} \times \mathbf{d})]$

$= (\mathbf{b}\,.\,\mathbf{d})\,[\mathbf{d\ a\ c}] - (\mathbf{b}\,.\,\mathbf{c})\,[\mathbf{d\ a\ d}]$

$= (\mathbf{b}\,.\,\mathbf{d})\,[\mathbf{a\ c\ d}] - 0 =$ R.H.S.

28. (a) $(\mathbf{a}\,.\,\mathbf{c})\,\mathbf{b} - (\mathbf{a}\,.\,\mathbf{b})\,\mathbf{c} = \frac{1}{2}\mathbf{b}$

or $\left(\mathbf{a}\,.\,\mathbf{c} - \frac{1}{2}\right)\mathbf{b} - (\mathbf{a}\,.\,\mathbf{b})\,\mathbf{c} = \mathbf{0}$

or $x\mathbf{b} - y\mathbf{c} = \mathbf{0}$

Above is a relation between **b** and **c** which are non-parallel

$\therefore \quad x = 0,\ y = 0 \quad \therefore\ \mathbf{a}\,.\,\mathbf{c} = \frac{1}{2}$

or $1.1 \cos\theta = \frac{1}{2}\ \therefore\ \theta = 60^o$

$\mathbf{a}\,.\,\mathbf{b} = 0\ \therefore$ **a** and **b** are at right angles.

$\therefore$ **a** makes with **b** an angle 90° and with **c** an angle of 60°.

(b) We have $(\mathbf{a}\,.\,\mathbf{c})\,\mathbf{b} - (\mathbf{a}\,.\,\mathbf{b})\,\mathbf{c} = \frac{\mathbf{b}+\mathbf{c}}{\sqrt{2}}$

Since **b** and **c** are non-collinear therefore on comparing the coefficients of **b** and **c** on both sides, we get

$\mathbf{a}\,.\,\mathbf{c} = \frac{1}{\sqrt{2}}$ and $\mathbf{a}\,.\,\mathbf{b} = -\frac{1}{\sqrt{2}}$

$\therefore \quad \gamma = \pi/4 \qquad \beta = 3\pi/4$

(c) Refer part (b) above.

We will have $\mathbf{a}\,.\,\mathbf{b} = -\frac{1}{2}$

or $\cos\theta = -\frac{1}{2}\quad \therefore\ \theta = 120^o = \frac{2\pi}{3}$

29. (a) We have $\vec{AB}\,.\,\vec{BC} = \sqrt{3}\,(\hat{\mathbf{a}} \times \mathbf{b})\,.\,[\mathbf{b} - (\hat{\mathbf{a}}\,.\,\mathbf{b})\,\hat{\mathbf{a}}]$

$= \sqrt{3}\,[(\hat{\mathbf{a}} \times \mathbf{b})\,.\,\mathbf{b} - (\hat{\mathbf{a}}\,.\,\mathbf{b})\,\{(\hat{\mathbf{a}} \times \mathbf{b})\,.\,\hat{\mathbf{a}}\}] = \sqrt{3}\,[0 - 0] = 0$

[§ 5 (d), P. 1152]

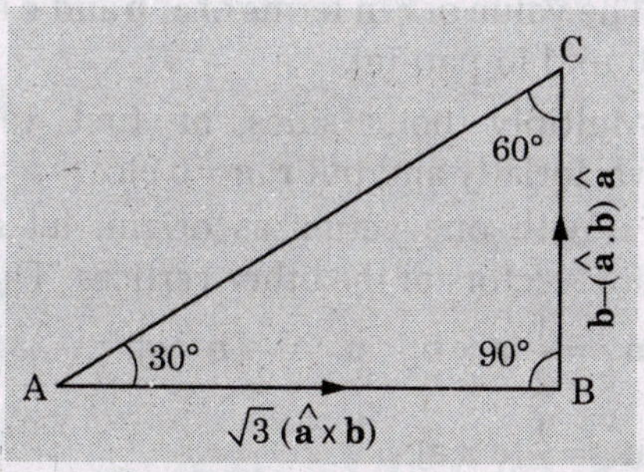

Fig. 50

i.e. Scalar triple product is zero when two vectors are equal.

$\therefore \quad AB \perp BC$ so that $\angle ABC = 90^o$

Now $AB^2 = 3\,(\hat{\mathbf{a}} \times \mathbf{b})^2 = 3\,.\,1 b^2 \sin^2\theta\,.\,1$

$= 3b^2 \sin^2\theta \qquad$ ...(1)

and $BC^2 = (\mathbf{b})^2 + (\hat{\mathbf{a}}\,.\,\mathbf{b})^2\,\hat{\mathbf{a}}^2 - 2\,(\mathbf{b}\,.\,\hat{\mathbf{a}})\,(\hat{\mathbf{a}}\,.\,\mathbf{b})$

$= b^2 + (\hat{\mathbf{a}}\,.\,\mathbf{b})^2 - 2\,(\hat{\mathbf{a}}\,.\,\mathbf{b})^2 \qquad [\because\ \hat{A} = 1]$

$= b^2 - (\hat{\mathbf{a}}\,.\,\mathbf{b})^2 = b^2 - 1\,.\,b^2 \cos^2\theta$

$= b^2\,(1 - \cos^2\theta) = b^2 \sin^2\theta \qquad$ ...(2)

From (1) and (2), we get

$AB^2 = 3BC^2$

$AB = \sqrt{3}\,BC \qquad$ ...(3)

$\therefore \quad \tan A = \frac{BC}{AB} = \frac{1}{\sqrt{(3)}}$, by (3).

Hence $A = 30^o$ and then $C = 60^o$

Thus the angles of $\Delta\,ABC$ are $30^o, 60^o$ and 90°.

(b) Given $\mathbf{a}^2 = \mathbf{b}^2 = 1, \mathbf{c}^2 = 4$. If θ be the angle between **a** and **c**, then

$\mathbf{a}\,.\,\mathbf{c} = 1\,.\,2\,.\cos\theta \qquad$ ...(1)

Now from the given relation, we have

$(\mathbf{a}\,.\,\mathbf{c})\,\mathbf{a} - (\mathbf{a}\,.\,\mathbf{a})\,\mathbf{c} = -\,\mathbf{b}$

or $(2\cos\theta)\,\mathbf{a} - \mathbf{c} = -\,\mathbf{b}$ by (1). Square

$4\cos^2\theta\,.\,1 + 4 - 2\,\{(2\cos\theta)\,(\mathbf{a}\,.\,\mathbf{c})\} = 1$

Put $\mathbf{a}\,.\,\mathbf{c} = 2\cos\theta$ by (1)

$\therefore \quad 4\,(1 - \cos^2\theta) = 1 \quad \therefore\ \sin\theta = \frac{1}{2}$

$\therefore \quad \theta = \pi/6$ (acute)

(c) Given $\mathbf{a} = \alpha + \beta$ or $\beta = \mathbf{a} - \alpha$

Now α is projection of **a** in the direction of **b**

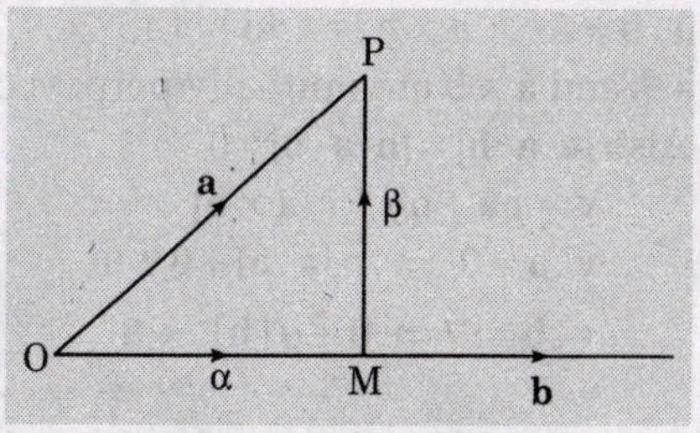

Fig. 51

$$\alpha = \frac{\mathbf{a}\,.\,\mathbf{b}}{|\mathbf{b}|}\,.\,\hat{\mathbf{b}} = \frac{\mathbf{a}\,.\,\mathbf{b}}{|\mathbf{b}|^2}\,.\,\mathbf{b}$$

$$\therefore \quad \beta = \mathbf{a} - \alpha = \mathbf{a} - \frac{\mathbf{a}\,.\,\mathbf{b}}{|\mathbf{b}|^2}\,.\,\mathbf{b}$$

$$= \frac{(\mathbf{b}\,.\,\mathbf{b})\,\mathbf{a} - (\mathbf{a}\,.\,\mathbf{b})\,\mathbf{b}}{|\mathbf{b}|^2} = \frac{\mathbf{b} \times (\mathbf{a} \times \mathbf{b})}{|\mathbf{b}|^2}$$

30. (a) We are given that

$(\mathbf{a}\,.\,\mathbf{c})\,\mathbf{b} - (\mathbf{b}\,.\,\mathbf{c})\,\mathbf{a} = (\mathbf{a}\,.\,\mathbf{c})\,\mathbf{b} - (\mathbf{a}\,.\,\mathbf{b})\,\mathbf{c}.$

$\therefore \quad (\mathbf{a}\,.\,\mathbf{b})\,\mathbf{c} - (\mathbf{b}\,.\,\mathbf{c})\,\mathbf{a} = \mathbf{0}$

or $(\mathbf{a} \times \mathbf{c}) \times \mathbf{b} = \mathbf{0}. \qquad$ ...(1)

From above we conclude that either $\mathbf{b}=\mathbf{0}$ or $\mathbf{a}\times\mathbf{c}=\mathbf{0}$.

But $\mathbf{b}\neq\mathbf{0}$ $\therefore$ $\mathbf{a}\times\mathbf{c}=\mathbf{0}$ and hence $\mathbf{c}=t\,\mathbf{a}$ *i.e.* $\mathbf{a}$ and $\mathbf{c}$ are collinear.

Another form :

Note : In case $\mathbf{a}$ and $\mathbf{c}$ are not collinear, then relation (1) is of the form $x\mathbf{c}-y\mathbf{a}=0$

$\therefore$ $x=0$ and $y=0$

or $\mathbf{a}\,.\,\mathbf{b}=0$ and $\mathbf{b}\,.\,\mathbf{c}=0$

$\therefore$ $\mathbf{b}$ is perpendicular to both $\mathbf{a}$ and $\mathbf{c}$.

or $\mathbf{b}$ is parallel to $\mathbf{a}\times\mathbf{c}$ $\therefore$ $(\mathbf{a}\times\mathbf{c})\times\mathbf{b}=0$

Converse : If $\mathbf{c}=t\mathbf{a}$, then

$(\mathbf{a}\times\mathbf{b})\times\mathbf{c}=(\mathbf{a}\times\mathbf{b})\times t\,\mathbf{a}=t\,[(\mathbf{a}\,.\,\mathbf{a})\,\mathbf{b}-(\mathbf{a}\,.\,\mathbf{b})\,\mathbf{a}]$

and $\mathbf{a}\times(\mathbf{b}\times\mathbf{c})=\mathbf{a}\times(\mathbf{b}\times t\,\mathbf{a})=t\,[(\mathbf{a}\,.\,\mathbf{a})\,\mathbf{b}-(\mathbf{a}\,.\,\mathbf{b})\,\mathbf{a}]$

$\therefore$ $(\mathbf{a}\times\mathbf{b})\times\mathbf{c}=\mathbf{a}\times(\mathbf{b}\times\mathbf{c})$.

(b) If the lines intersect we must have identical values of $\mathbf{r}$ for some values of parameters t and s

$\therefore$ $\mathbf{a}+t\,(\mathbf{b}\times\mathbf{c})=\mathbf{b}+s\,(\mathbf{c}\times\mathbf{a})$

Multiply both sides scalarly by $\mathbf{c}$ and note that scalar triple product is zero when two vectors are equal.

$\therefore$ $\mathbf{a}\,.\,\mathbf{c}+t\,[\mathbf{b}\;\mathbf{c}\;\mathbf{c}]=\mathbf{b}\,.\,\mathbf{c}+s\,[\mathbf{c}\;\mathbf{a}\;\mathbf{c}]$

or $\mathbf{a}\,.\,\mathbf{c}=\mathbf{b}\,.\,\mathbf{c}$ is the required condition.

31. (a) We are given $\mathbf{A}\,.\,\mathbf{X}=c$ ...(1)

$\mathbf{A}\times\mathbf{X}=\mathbf{B}$ ...(2)

Taking cross-product with $\mathbf{A}$ on both sides of (2),

$\mathbf{A}\times(\mathbf{A}\times\mathbf{X})=\mathbf{A}\times\mathbf{B}$.

i.e., $(\mathbf{A}\,.\,\mathbf{X})\,\mathbf{A}-(\mathbf{A}\,.\,\mathbf{A})\,\mathbf{X}=\mathbf{A}\times\mathbf{B}$.

Now using (1), we get $c\mathbf{A}-|\mathbf{A}|^2\,\mathbf{X}=\mathbf{A}\times\mathbf{B}$

or $\mathbf{X}|\mathbf{A}|^2=c\mathbf{A}-\mathbf{A}\times\mathbf{B}$

or $\mathbf{X}=\dfrac{c\mathbf{A}-\mathbf{A}\times\mathbf{B}}{|\mathbf{A}|^2}$.

(b) $\mathbf{a}\,.\,\mathbf{b}=0$ $\mathbf{a}\times\mathbf{b}$ is $\perp$ to both.

$\mathbf{a}$, $\mathbf{b}$ and $\mathbf{a}\times\mathbf{b}$ are mutually perp. vectors.

Also $[\mathbf{a}\;\;\mathbf{a}\;\;\mathbf{b}]=[\mathbf{b}\;\;\mathbf{a}\;\;\mathbf{b}]=0$

$\therefore$ $\mathbf{v}=p\mathbf{a}+q\mathbf{b}+r\,(\mathbf{a}\times\mathbf{b})$ ...(1)

$\mathbf{v}\,.\,\mathbf{a}=0\Rightarrow p\,(\mathbf{a}\,.\,\mathbf{a})+0+0$ $\therefore$ $p=0$

$\mathbf{v}\,.\,\mathbf{b}=1\Rightarrow 0+q\,|\mathbf{b}|^2+0$ $\therefore$ $q=\dfrac{1}{|\mathbf{b}|^2}$

$\mathbf{v}\,.\,(\mathbf{a}\times\mathbf{b})=p\,.\,0+q\,.\,0+r\,.\,|\mathbf{a}\times\mathbf{b}|^2$

or $[\mathbf{v}\;\;\mathbf{a}\;\;\mathbf{b}]=r\,|\mathbf{a}\times\mathbf{b}|^2$

$\therefore$ $r=\dfrac{1}{|\mathbf{a}\times\mathbf{b}|^2}$ $\because$ $[\mathbf{v}\;\mathbf{a}\;\mathbf{b}]=1$

Now put for p, q and r in (1).

32. We are given : $\vec{AB}=\mathbf{b}$, $\vec{AC}=\mathbf{c}$ and $\vec{BD}\perp\vec{AC}$. To find the resolution of $\vec{BD}$ w.r.t. $\mathbf{b}$ and $\mathbf{c}$.

$\vec{BD}=\vec{AD}-\vec{AB}$ ...(1)

But $|\vec{AD}|=$ Projection of $\mathbf{b}$ on $\mathbf{c}=\dfrac{\mathbf{b}\,.\,\mathbf{c}}{|\mathbf{c}|}$.

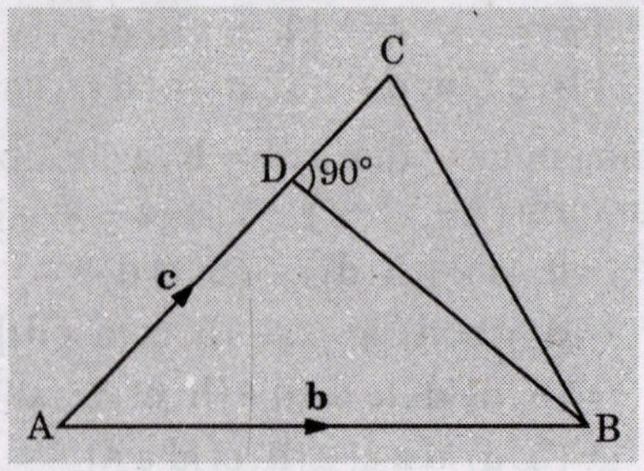

Fig. 52

Also the unit vector in the direction of AC is $\dfrac{\mathbf{c}}{|\mathbf{c}|}$.

Hence $\vec{AD}=\left(\dfrac{\mathbf{b}\,.\,\mathbf{c}}{|\mathbf{c}|}\right)\left(\dfrac{\mathbf{c}}{|\mathbf{c}|}\right)=\dfrac{\mathbf{b}\,.\,\mathbf{c}}{|\mathbf{c}|^2}\,\mathbf{c}$.

Hence from (1), we get $BD=\dfrac{\mathbf{b}\,.\,\mathbf{c}}{|\mathbf{c}|^2}\,\mathbf{c}-\mathbf{b}$.

33. (a) $(\mathbf{r}-\mathbf{c})\times\mathbf{b}=0\Rightarrow\mathbf{r}-\mathbf{c}$ and $\mathbf{b}$ are collinear

$\therefore$ $\mathbf{r}-\mathbf{c}=k\mathbf{b}$ or $\mathbf{r}=\mathbf{c}+k\mathbf{b}$ ...(1)

Again $\mathbf{r}\,.\,\mathbf{a}=0$ $\therefore$ $(\mathbf{c}+k\mathbf{b})\,.\,\mathbf{a}=0$

or $\mathbf{c}\,.\,\mathbf{a}+k\mathbf{b}\,.\,\mathbf{a}=0$ $\therefore$ $k=-\dfrac{\mathbf{a}\,.\,\mathbf{c}}{\mathbf{a}\,.\,\mathbf{b}}$

Putting in (1), we get $\mathbf{r}=\mathbf{c}-\left(\dfrac{\mathbf{a}\,.\,\mathbf{c}}{\mathbf{a}\,.\,\mathbf{b}}\right)\mathbf{b}$

Hence $\mathbf{r}=\dfrac{(\mathbf{a}\,.\,\mathbf{b})\,\mathbf{c}-(\mathbf{a}\,.\,\mathbf{c})\,\mathbf{b}}{\mathbf{a}\,.\,\mathbf{b}}$.

(b) **Geometrical meaning :** Let A, B, C and P be the points whose position vectors are $\mathbf{a}$, $\mathbf{b}$, $\mathbf{c}$ and $\mathbf{r}$ respectively.

First note that $\mathbf{a}\,.\,\mathbf{b}\neq\mathbf{0}\Rightarrow\mathbf{a}\neq\mathbf{0}$, $\mathbf{b}\neq\mathbf{0}$ and $\mathbf{a}$ is not perpendicular to $\mathbf{b}$.

Now $\mathbf{r}\times\mathbf{b}=\mathbf{c}\times\mathbf{b}\Rightarrow(\mathbf{r}-\mathbf{c})\times\mathbf{b}=\mathbf{0}$

$\Rightarrow$ Either $\mathbf{r}-\mathbf{c}=\mathbf{0}$ or $\mathbf{r}-\mathbf{c}$ is parallel to $\mathbf{b}$ $[\because\ \mathbf{b}\neq 0]$

But $\mathbf{r}-\mathbf{c}=\mathbf{0}$ means that points P and C coincide.

And $\mathbf{r}-\mathbf{c}\,||\,\mathbf{b}$ implies that $\vec{CP}$ is parallel to $\vec{OB}$, *i.e.* the figure $OBPC$ is a trapezium.

Again $\mathbf{r}\,.\,\mathbf{a}=\mathbf{0}\Rightarrow$ either $\mathbf{r}=\mathbf{0}$ or $\mathbf{r}\perp\mathbf{a}$ [Note that $\mathbf{a}\neq 0$].

The value of $\mathbf{r}$ in terms of $\mathbf{a}$, $\mathbf{b}$ and $\mathbf{c}$ is the same as found in part (a).

(c) Multiply both sides of first relation by $\mathbf{a}$ vectorially and put $\mathbf{r}\,.\,\mathbf{a}=0$ etc.

34. Hint : With one vertex as origin, let $\mathbf{a}$, $\mathbf{b}$, $\mathbf{c}$ be the position vectors of the other vertices. Then

$\mathbf{n}_1=\frac{1}{2}(\mathbf{a}\times\mathbf{b})$, $\mathbf{n}_2=\frac{1}{2}(\mathbf{b}\times\mathbf{c})$,

$\mathbf{n}_3=\frac{1}{2}(\mathbf{c}\times\mathbf{a})$,

and $\mathbf{n}_4=\frac{1}{2}(\mathbf{b}-\mathbf{c})\times(\mathbf{a}-\mathbf{c})$ etc.

35. (a) Angle between two plane faces is equal to the angle between the normals $\mathbf{n}_1$ and $\mathbf{n}_2$ to the planes. $\mathbf{n}_1$ the normal of face OAB is given by

$$\vec{OA} \times \vec{OB} = \begin{vmatrix} \mathbf{i} & \mathbf{j} & \mathbf{k} \\ 1 & 2 & 1 \\ 2 & 1 & 3 \end{vmatrix} = 5\mathbf{i} - \mathbf{j} - 3\mathbf{k} \qquad ...(1)$$

$\mathbf{n}_2$ the normal of face ABC is given by $\vec{AB} \times \vec{AC}$

$2-1, 1-2, 3-1$ and $-1-1, 1-2, 2-1$, *i.e.* $1, -1, 2$ and $-2, -1, 1$.

$$\therefore \quad \mathbf{n}_2 = \begin{vmatrix} \mathbf{i} & \mathbf{j} & \mathbf{k} \\ 1 & -1 & 2 \\ -2 & -1 & 1 \end{vmatrix} = \mathbf{i} - 5\mathbf{j} - 3\mathbf{k} \qquad ...(2)$$

If θ be the angle between $\mathbf{n}_1$ and $\mathbf{n}_2$, then

$$\cos\theta = \frac{\mathbf{n}_1 \cdot \mathbf{n}_2}{|\mathbf{n}_1||\mathbf{n}_2|} = \frac{5 \cdot 1 + 5 + 9}{\sqrt{35} \cdot \sqrt{35}} = \frac{19}{35}$$

$$\therefore \quad \theta = \cos^{-1}\left(\frac{19}{35}\right)$$

(b) With O as origin and $OA = OB = \lambda$ then A is $\lambda\mathbf{i}$, B is $\lambda\mathbf{j}$ and G is $\frac{\lambda}{3}(\mathbf{i} + \mathbf{j})$.

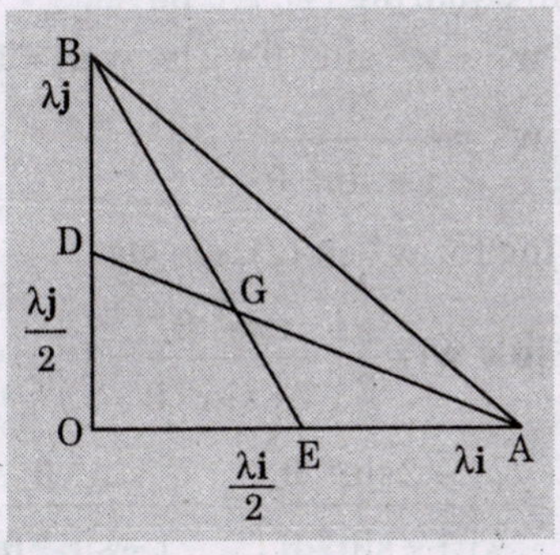

Fig. 53

We have to find angle between medians GA and GB drawn from acute angles A and B.

Median $\vec{GA}$ is $\lambda\mathbf{i} - \frac{\lambda}{3}(\mathbf{i} + \mathbf{j}) = \frac{\lambda}{3}(2\mathbf{i} - \mathbf{j})$

$$\therefore \quad |\vec{GA}| = GA = \frac{\lambda}{3}\sqrt{5}$$

Median $\vec{GB} = \frac{\lambda}{3}(2\mathbf{j} - \mathbf{i}) \quad \therefore \ |\vec{GB}| = GB = \frac{\lambda}{3}\sqrt{5}$

$$\vec{GA} \cdot \vec{GB} = GA \cdot GB \cdot \cos\theta$$

$$\frac{\lambda^2}{9}(2\mathbf{i} - \mathbf{j}) \cdot (2\mathbf{j} - \mathbf{i}) = \frac{\lambda}{3}\sqrt{5} \cdot \frac{\lambda}{3}\sqrt{5}\cos\theta$$

or $-2 - 2 = 5\cos\theta \quad \therefore \ \cos\theta = -4/5$ etc.

36. (a) Let the given points be A, B, C and D.

$\therefore$ A is $(4, 5, 1) = 4\mathbf{i} + 5\mathbf{j} + \mathbf{k}$.

Similarly express B, C, D in terms of unit vectors.

$$\therefore \quad \vec{AB} = \vec{OB} - \vec{OA} = -4\mathbf{i} - 6\mathbf{j} - 2\mathbf{k}$$

$$\vec{BC} = \vec{OC} - \vec{OB} = 3\mathbf{i} + 10\mathbf{j} + 5\mathbf{k}$$

$$\vec{CD} = \vec{OD} - \vec{OC} = -7\mathbf{i} - 5\mathbf{j} + 0\mathbf{k}.$$

If the four points are coplanar, then the vectors $\vec{AB}, \vec{BC}$ and $\vec{CD}$ are coplanar.

$$\therefore \quad [\vec{AB}\ \vec{BC}\ \vec{CD}] = 0.$$

or $\begin{vmatrix} -4 & -6 & -2 \\ 3 & 10 & 5 \\ -7 & -5 & 0 \end{vmatrix} = 0$ or $\begin{vmatrix} 2 & 3 & 1 \\ 3 & 10 & 5 \\ 7 & 5 & 0 \end{vmatrix} = 0$

or $2(0 - 25) - 3(0 - 35) + 1(15 - 70) = 0$

$= -50 + 105 - 55 = 0$

which is true. Hence the four points are coplanar.

(b) Prove that $[\vec{BA}\ \vec{CA}\ \vec{DA}] = 0$

or $\begin{vmatrix} 2 & 4 & 6 \\ 1 & 3 & 8 \\ -1 & 0 & 7 \end{vmatrix} = 0$

or $2(21 - 0) - 4(7 + 8) + 6(0 + 3) = 0$

or $42 - 60 + 18 = 0$

(c) Do yourself.

37. (a) $\vec{AB} = -\mathbf{i} + 5\mathbf{j} - 3\mathbf{k}, \quad \vec{AC} = -4\mathbf{i} + 3\mathbf{j} + 3\mathbf{k}$

and $\vec{AD} = \mathbf{i} + 7\mathbf{j} + (\lambda + 1)\mathbf{k}$

Now A, B, C, D will be coplanar if

$$\begin{vmatrix} -1 & 5 & -3 \\ -4 & 3 & 3 \\ 1 & 7 & \lambda + 1 \end{vmatrix} = 0.$$

This on expansion will give $\lambda = -\frac{146}{17}$.

(b) For vectors to be coplanar $[\mathbf{a}\ \mathbf{b}\ \mathbf{c}] = 0$

$$\therefore \quad \Delta = \begin{vmatrix} x & x+1 & x+2 \\ x+3 & x+4 & x+5 \\ x+6 & x+7 & x+8 \end{vmatrix} = 0$$

Apply $R_3 - R_2, R_2 - R_1$

$$\therefore \quad \Delta = \begin{vmatrix} x & x+1 & x+2 \\ 3 & 3 & 3 \\ 3 & 3 & 3 \end{vmatrix} = 0 \ \forall \ x$$

whether $x > 0$ or $x < 0$.

(c) Ans. (c).

The condition of coplanarity of three vectors $\mathbf{a}, \mathbf{b}, \mathbf{c}$ is $[\mathbf{a}\ \mathbf{b}\ \mathbf{c}] = 0$ or $D = 0$

$$\therefore \quad \begin{vmatrix} -\lambda^2 & 1 & 1 \\ 1 & -\lambda^2 & 1 \\ 1 & 1 & -\lambda^2 \end{vmatrix} = 0 \quad \text{Apply } C_1 + C_2 + C_3$$

$$\therefore \quad \Delta = (2 - \lambda^2)\begin{vmatrix} 1 & 1 & 1 \\ 1 & -\lambda^2 & 1 \\ 1 & 1 & -\lambda^2 \end{vmatrix}$$

Making two zeros and expanding

$$\Delta = (2 - \lambda^2)(1 + \lambda^2) = 0 \quad \therefore \ \lambda = \pm\sqrt{2}$$

Hence only two real values $\Rightarrow$ (c).

(d) Ans. (c)

Since the given vectors are non-coplanar

$$\therefore \quad [\mathbf{A}\ \mathbf{B}\ \mathbf{C}] \neq 0.$$

or $(\mathbf{a}+2\mathbf{b}+3\mathbf{c}).(\lambda\mathbf{b}+4\mathbf{c})\times(2\lambda-1)\mathbf{c}\neq 0$

$=(\mathbf{a}+2\mathbf{b}+3\mathbf{c}).[\lambda(2\lambda-1)\mathbf{b}\times\mathbf{c}+0]\neq 0$

$\because\ \mathbf{c}\times\mathbf{c}=0$

or $\lambda(2\lambda-1)\,\mathbf{a}.(\mathbf{b}\times\mathbf{c})\neq 0$

$\because$ $[\mathbf{b\,b\,c}]=0, [\mathbf{c\,b\,c}]=0$

$\therefore$ $\lambda(2\lambda-1)[\mathbf{a\,b\,c}]\neq 0$

Given $[\mathbf{a\,b\,c}]\neq 0$

Hence above will be zero if $\lambda=0$ or $1/2$.

Hence non-zero for two values of λ.

38. (a) Condition of coplanarity $[\mathbf{a\,b\,c}]=0$ gives

$$\begin{vmatrix} x & 3 & -1 \\ 1 & x-1 & 2 \\ 3 & 5 & 2 \end{vmatrix}=0$$

or $2x^2-9x+4=0$ or $(2x-1)(x-4)=0$

$\therefore$ $x=4,\dfrac{1}{2}$

Hence the given set of vectors are $4,3,-1;\ 1,3,2;\ 3,5,2$ and

$\dfrac{1}{2},3,-1;\ 1,-\dfrac{1}{2},2;\ 3,5,2$

If $\mathbf{n}_1$ be the normal to the plane determined by first set, then

$$\mathbf{n}_1=\mathbf{b}\times\mathbf{c}=\begin{vmatrix} \mathbf{i} & \mathbf{j} & \mathbf{k} \\ 1 & 3 & 2 \\ 3 & 5 & 2 \end{vmatrix}=-4\mathbf{i}+4\mathbf{j}-4\mathbf{k}$$

Similarly, $\mathbf{n}_2=-11\mathbf{i}+4\mathbf{j}+\dfrac{13}{2}\mathbf{k}$

Angle between the planes is equal to angle between the normals $\mathbf{n}_1$ and $\mathbf{n}_2$.

$\therefore$ $\cos\theta=\dfrac{\mathbf{n}_1.\mathbf{n}_2}{|\mathbf{n}_1|.|\mathbf{n}_2|}=\dfrac{17}{3\sqrt{239}}$ etc.

(b) Let the given points be A,B,C,D. If they are coplanar, then $[\vec{AB}\ \vec{AC}\ \vec{AD}]=0$

L.H.S. $=\vec{AB}.\{\vec{AC}\times\vec{AD}\}$

Now $\vec{AC}\times\vec{AD}=(\mathbf{a}+\mathbf{b}-\mathbf{c})\times(-\mathbf{a}-9\mathbf{b}+7\mathbf{c})$

$=(-9+1)(\mathbf{a}\times\mathbf{b})+(7-9)(\mathbf{b}\times\mathbf{c})+(-7+1)(\mathbf{c}\times\mathbf{a})$

$=-8(\mathbf{a}\times\mathbf{b})-2(\mathbf{b}\times\mathbf{c})-6(\mathbf{c}\times\mathbf{a})$

$\therefore$ $\vec{AB}.[\vec{AC}\times\vec{AD}]=[-\mathbf{a}-5\mathbf{b}+4\mathbf{c}]$

$.[-8(\mathbf{a}\times\mathbf{b})-2(\mathbf{b}\times\mathbf{c})-6(\mathbf{c}\times\mathbf{a})]$

But scalar triple product is zero when two vectors are equal.

$\therefore$ L.H.S. $=(2+30-32)[\mathbf{a\,b\,c}]=0[\mathbf{a\,b\,c}]=0$

$\therefore$ Lines AB, AC, AD are coplanar. Hence the four points A,B,C,D are coplanar.

39. Since $\mathbf{a}\perp\mathbf{b}$ $\therefore$ $\mathbf{a}.\mathbf{b}=0$

and $\mathbf{a}\times\mathbf{b}=|\mathbf{a}||\mathbf{b}|\sin 90^\circ\ \mathbf{n}=10\mathbf{n}$

where $\mathbf{n}$ is a unit vector perpendicular to the plane of $\mathbf{a}$ and $\mathbf{b}$. We have to prove that vectors $\mathbf{r},\mathbf{a},\mathbf{b}$ form an orthogonal system.

Now $\mathbf{a}\times(\mathbf{a}\times\mathbf{b})=(\mathbf{a}.\mathbf{b})\,\mathbf{a}-(\mathbf{a}.\mathbf{a})\,\mathbf{b}=0-4\mathbf{b}$ ...(1)

$\{\ \}=\mathbf{a}\times(-4\mathbf{b})=-4\mathbf{a}\times\mathbf{b}$

$\therefore$ $[\ ]=\mathbf{a}\times(-4\mathbf{a}\times\mathbf{b})=-4\{\mathbf{a}\times(\mathbf{a}\times\mathbf{b})\}$

$=-4(-4\mathbf{b})=16\mathbf{b}$, by (1)

$\therefore$ $\mathbf{r}=\mathbf{a}\times[\ ]=\mathbf{a}\times 16\mathbf{b}=16(\mathbf{a}\times\mathbf{b})=16\mathbf{n}$

Now $\mathbf{a}\times\mathbf{b}=\mathbf{n}$ represents a vector which is perpendicular to both $\mathbf{a}$ and $\mathbf{b}$ and $\mathbf{a}$ and $\mathbf{b}$ themselves are perpendicular. Thus $\mathbf{r},\mathbf{a},\mathbf{b}$ are **orthogonal** system of vectors. They are not **orthonormal** as they are not unit vectors.

40. $\mathbf{u}$ and $\mathbf{v}$ are unit vectors $\Rightarrow \mathbf{u}^2=\mathbf{v}^2=1$ and let θ be the angle between $\mathbf{u}$ and $\mathbf{w}$. We have to prove that $|(\mathbf{u}\times\mathbf{v}).\mathbf{w}|\leq\dfrac{1}{2}$

Given $\mathbf{w}+(\mathbf{w}\times\mathbf{u})=\mathbf{v}$ ...(1)

$\therefore$ $\mathbf{w}=\mathbf{v}-(\mathbf{w}\times\mathbf{u})$ Squaring,

$\mathbf{w}^2=1+(\mathbf{w}.1.\sin\theta)^2-2\mathbf{v}.(\mathbf{w}\times\mathbf{u})$

or $\mathbf{w}^2(1-\sin^2\theta)-1=2[\mathbf{v\,w\,u}]=2[\mathbf{u\,v\,w}]$

or $\dfrac{1}{2}(\mathbf{w}^2\cos^2\theta-1)=(\mathbf{u}\times\mathbf{v}).\mathbf{w}$ ...(2)

Again squaring (1), we have

$\mathbf{w}^2+\mathbf{w}^2\sin^2\theta+2[\mathbf{w\,w\,u}]=1$

$\therefore$ $\mathbf{w}^2=\dfrac{1}{1+\sin^2\theta}$.

Putting for $\mathbf{w}^2$ in (2), we get

$[\mathbf{u\,v\,w}]=\dfrac{1}{2}\left(\dfrac{\cos^2\theta}{1+\sin^2\theta}-1\right)$

$=\dfrac{1}{2}\left(\dfrac{-2\sin^2\theta}{1+\sin^2\theta}\right)=-\dfrac{\sin^2\theta}{1+\sin^2\theta}$

$\therefore$ $|[\mathbf{u\,v\,w}]|=\dfrac{\sin^2\theta}{1+\sin^2\theta}=\dfrac{1}{\operatorname{cosec}^2\theta+1}\leq\dfrac{1}{2}$

$\because$ $\operatorname{cosec}^2\theta+1\geq 2$ $\therefore$ $\dfrac{1}{\operatorname{cosec}^2\theta+1}\leq\dfrac{1}{2}$

The equality will hold when $\sin\theta=1$

or $\theta=90^\circ$ $\Rightarrow$ $\mathbf{u}\perp\mathbf{w}$

i.e., $\mathbf{u}.\mathbf{w}=0$ ...(3)

We have to prove that $\mathbf{u}\perp\mathbf{v}$, *i.e.* $\mathbf{u}.\mathbf{v}=0$

Take dot product with $\mathbf{u}$ in both sides of (1).

$\mathbf{u}.\mathbf{w}+[\mathbf{u\,w\,u}]=\mathbf{u}.\mathbf{v}$

$0+0=\mathbf{u}.\mathbf{v}$ $\Rightarrow$ $\mathbf{u}\perp\mathbf{v}$ by (3)

41. If we denote the points by A,B,C,D, then

$\vec{AB}=\mathbf{b}-\mathbf{a},\ \vec{AC}=\mathbf{c}-\mathbf{a},\ \vec{AD}=\mathbf{d}-\mathbf{a}$.

Now A,B,C,D will be coplanar if

$\{(\mathbf{b}-\mathbf{a})\times(\mathbf{c}-\mathbf{a})\}.(\mathbf{d}-\mathbf{a})=0$.

or $\{\mathbf{b}\times\mathbf{c}-\mathbf{b}\times\mathbf{a}-\mathbf{a}\times\mathbf{c}\}.(\mathbf{d}-\mathbf{a})=0$

or $[\mathbf{b\,c\,d}]-[\mathbf{b\,c\,a}]-[\mathbf{b\,a\,d}]+[\mathbf{b\,a\,a}]$

$-[\mathbf{a\,c\,d}]+[\mathbf{a\,c\,a}]=0$ ...(1)

Put $[\mathbf{b\,c\,a}]=[\mathbf{a\,b\,c}]$

$-[\mathbf{b\,a\,d}]=[\mathbf{a\,b\,d}]$

$-[\mathbf{a\,c\,d}]=[\mathbf{c\,a\,d}]$ ...(A)

Also $[\mathbf{b\,a\,a}] = 0, [\mathbf{a\,c\,a}] = 0$

From (1) we get the desired result with the help of relation in (A).

$$[\mathbf{a\,b\,c}] = [\mathbf{b\,c\,d}] + [\mathbf{c\,a\,d}] + [\mathbf{a\,b\,d}].$$

42. If r is the radius of circum-circle, then

$$|\vec{OA_i}| = r \text{ for } i = 1, 2, \ldots.. n.$$

$$\therefore \quad \Sigma\, \vec{OA_i} \times \vec{OA}_{i+1} = \Sigma\, |\vec{OA_i}||\vec{OA}_{i+1}| \sin \frac{2\pi}{n}\, \hat{\mathbf{n}}$$

$$= \Sigma\, r^2 \sin \frac{2\pi}{n} . \hat{\mathbf{n}} = (n-1)\, r^2 \sin \frac{2\pi}{n}\, \hat{\mathbf{n}}$$

and $(1-n)\, \vec{OA_2} \times \vec{OA_1} = (1-n)\, r^2 \sin \dfrac{2\pi}{n} (-\hat{\mathbf{n}})$

$$= (n-1)\, r^2 \sin \frac{2\pi}{n}\, \hat{\mathbf{n}}$$

where $\hat{\mathbf{n}}$ is a unit vector ⊥ to plane of the polygon.

Hence L.H.S. = R.H.S.

43. (a) Volume $= \dfrac{1}{2}\begin{vmatrix} 3 & 4 & 12 \\ 12 & 3 & 4 \\ 4 & 12 & 3 \end{vmatrix}$

$$= \frac{1}{2}[3(9-48) - 4(36-16) + 12(144-12)]$$

$$= \frac{1387}{2} = 693 \cdot 5.$$

(b) $\vec{OA} \times \vec{OB} = \begin{vmatrix} \mathbf{i} & \mathbf{j} & \mathbf{k} \\ 3 & 4 & 12 \\ 12 & 3 & 4 \end{vmatrix} = -20\mathbf{i} + 132\mathbf{j} - 39\mathbf{k}$

∴ Unit vector ⊥ to both $\vec{OA}$ and $\vec{OB}$

$$= \frac{-20\mathbf{i} + 132\mathbf{j} - 39\mathbf{k}}{\sqrt{[(-20)^2 + (132)^2 + (-39)^2]}}$$

$$= \frac{-20\mathbf{i} + 132\mathbf{j} - 39\mathbf{k}}{\sqrt{(19345)}}.$$

(c) $\vec{OA} . \vec{OC} = (3\mathbf{i} + 4\mathbf{j} + 12\mathbf{k}) . (4\mathbf{i} + 12\mathbf{j} + 3\mathbf{k})$

$$\therefore \quad |\vec{OA}||\vec{OC}| \cos\theta = 3.4 + 4.12 + 12.3 = 96.$$

or $\cos\theta = \dfrac{96}{\sqrt{(3^2 + 4^2 + 12^2)}\, \sqrt{(4^2 + 12^2 + 3^2)}}$

$$= \frac{96}{169}$$

$$\therefore \quad \theta = \cos^{-1} \frac{96}{169}.$$

(d) Area of $\Delta\, OAB = \dfrac{1}{2}(OA \times OB) = \dfrac{1}{2}\sqrt{19345}$ from (b).

44. (a) Equation of line AB by $\mathbf{r} = \mathbf{a} + t(\mathbf{b} - \mathbf{a})$ is

$\mathbf{r} = (1, 2, 1) + t(1, -1, 1)$

$\mathbf{r} = (1+t)\,\mathbf{i} + (2-t)\,\mathbf{j} + (1+t)\,\mathbf{k}$ ...(1)

Normal to plane CDE is $\vec{CD} \times \vec{CE}$

$$= 2\begin{vmatrix} \mathbf{i} & \mathbf{j} & \mathbf{k} \\ 1 & 1 & -1 \\ 4 & 5 & -2 \end{vmatrix} = 2(3\mathbf{i} - 2\mathbf{j} + \mathbf{k})$$

Plane through C and normal being $\mathbf{n}$ is

$\mathbf{r} . \mathbf{n} = \mathbf{c} . \mathbf{n}$

$\mathbf{r} . 2(3\mathbf{i} - 2\mathbf{j} + \mathbf{k}) = 24$

or $\mathbf{r} . (3\mathbf{i} - 2\mathbf{j} + \mathbf{k}) = 12$ ...(2)

Line (1) and plane (2) meet at P. Putting for $\mathbf{r}$, we get

$$3(1+t) - 2(2-t) + 1(1+t) = 12$$

$$\therefore \quad 6t = 12 \quad \text{or} \quad t = 2.$$

Hence from (1),

$$\mathbf{r} = 3\mathbf{i} + 0\mathbf{j} + 3\mathbf{k} \quad \therefore \quad P \text{ is } (3, 0, 3)$$

(b) If $\mathbf{n}$ be the normal of the plane ABC, then

$$\mathbf{n} = \vec{AB} \times \vec{AC} = -3\mathbf{i} - 8\mathbf{j} - \mathbf{k}$$

Plane is $(\mathbf{r} - \mathbf{a}) \cdot \mathbf{n} = 0$ or $\mathbf{r} \cdot \mathbf{n} = \mathbf{a} \cdot \mathbf{n}$

or $\mathbf{r} \cdot (3\mathbf{i} + 8\mathbf{j} + \mathbf{k}) = 17$ ...(1)

The given line is $\mathbf{r} = (1+2t)\,\mathbf{i} + (-1)\,\mathbf{j} + (1+t)\,\mathbf{k} = 0$ ...(2)

For point of intersection we have from (1) and (2)

$$3(1+2t) - 8 + (1+t) = 17 \quad \therefore \quad 7t = 21 \quad \text{or} \quad t = 3$$

Putting for t in (2) the point of intersection is given by $\mathbf{r} = 7\mathbf{i} - \mathbf{j} + 4\mathbf{k}$.

∴ Its co-ordinates are $(7, -1, 4)$.

45. Let the three coterminous edges OA, OB, OC be represented by the vectors $\mathbf{a}$, $\mathbf{b}$ and $\mathbf{c}$ respectively. Then

$$\vec{OA} = 12\mathbf{i} + 4\mathbf{j} + 3\mathbf{k}, \quad \vec{OB} = 8\mathbf{i} - 12\mathbf{j} - 9\mathbf{k}$$

and $\vec{OC} = 33\mathbf{i} - 4\mathbf{j} - 24\mathbf{k}$.

$$\therefore \quad OA = \sqrt{12^2 + 4^2 + 3^2} = 13,$$

$$OB = \sqrt{8^2 + (-12)^2 + (-9)^2} = 17$$

and $OC = \sqrt{33^2 + (-4^2) + (-24)^2} = 41.$

Hence lengths of the edges of the parallelopiped are 13, 17 and 41.

Now vector area of the face determined by OA and OB is given by

$$\begin{vmatrix} \mathbf{i} & \mathbf{j} & \mathbf{k} \\ 12 & 4 & 3 \\ 8 & -12 & -9 \end{vmatrix} = 0\mathbf{i} + 132\mathbf{j} - 176\mathbf{k}.$$

Hence area of the face determined by OA and OB.

$$= \sqrt{132^2 + 176^2} = 44\sqrt{3^2 + 4^2} = 220.$$

Similarly areas of other two faces can be found. This is left for the reader.

$$\text{Volume} = \begin{vmatrix} 12 & 4 & 3 \\ 8 & -12 & -9 \\ 33 & -4 & -24 \end{vmatrix} = 12\begin{vmatrix} 12 & 1 & 1 \\ 8 & -3 & -3 \\ 33 & -1 & -8 \end{vmatrix}$$

$$= 12\begin{vmatrix} 12 & 1 & 1 \\ 44 & 0 & 0 \\ 33 & -1 & -8 \end{vmatrix} = -12 \times 44(-8+1)$$

$$= 12 \times 44 \times 7 = 3696.$$

46. From 2nd relation on multiplying both sides by $\mathbf{c}$, we get

$$(\mathbf{c} . \mathbf{c})\, \mathbf{a} . \mathbf{c} = \mathbf{c} . \mathbf{c} \quad \therefore \quad \mathbf{a} . \mathbf{c} = 1 \qquad \ldots(1)$$

Now from first relation, we have

$(\mathbf{a}.\mathbf{c})\,\mathbf{b}-(\mathbf{a}.\mathbf{b})\,\mathbf{c}+(\mathbf{a}.\mathbf{b})\,\mathbf{b}$

$=(4-2\beta-\sin\alpha)\,\mathbf{b}+(\beta^2-1)\,\mathbf{c}$

$\therefore\quad (1+\mathbf{a}.\mathbf{b})\,\mathbf{b}-(\mathbf{a}.\mathbf{b})\,\mathbf{c}$

$=(4-2\beta-\sin\alpha)\,\mathbf{b}+(\beta^2-1)\,\mathbf{c}$, by (1)

Now **b** and **c** are non-collinear and hence equating the coefficients of **b** and **c**, we get

$(1+\mathbf{a}.\mathbf{b})=(4-2\beta-\sin\alpha)$ ...(2)

and $-(\mathbf{a}.\mathbf{b})=(\beta^2-1)$ ...(3)

Eliminating **a . b** by adding (2) and (3), we get

$1=(\beta^2-1)+4-2\beta-\sin\alpha$

$\therefore\quad \sin\alpha=1+(1-2\beta+\beta^2)=1+(1-\beta)^2$

Since $\sin\alpha\le 1\quad\therefore\quad (1-\beta)^2=0$

$\therefore\quad \beta=1$ and hence $\sin\alpha=1$

$\therefore\quad \alpha=2n\pi+\dfrac{\pi}{2}$.

47. Now $\mathbf{a}=\mathbf{i}-\mathbf{j}$ and let $\mathbf{d}=\lambda\,(\mathbf{i}+\mathbf{j}+p\mathbf{k})$.

d is chosen such because $\mathbf{a}.\mathbf{d}=0$

i.e., they are perpendicular.

Also $\lambda^2\,(2+p^2)=1$ as **d** is a unit vector

Also $[\mathbf{bcd}]=0\ \Rightarrow\ \text{Det}=0$

$\Rightarrow\quad p+2=0\quad\therefore\ p=-2\qquad\therefore\quad \lambda=\pm\dfrac{1}{\sqrt6}$.

Alternative Method :

You may choose $\mathbf{d}=x\mathbf{i}+y\mathbf{j}+z\mathbf{k}$

where $\quad x^2+y^2+z^2=1$ ...(1)

and $\quad \mathbf{a}.\mathbf{d}=0\ \Rightarrow\ x-y=0$ ...(2)

and $\quad [\mathbf{b\,c\,d}]=0\qquad (\mathbf{b}\times\mathbf{c}).\mathbf{d}=0$

$(\mathbf{i}+\mathbf{j}+\mathbf{k}).(x\mathbf{i}+y\mathbf{j}+z\mathbf{k})=x+y+z=0$ ...(3)

But $x=y\quad\therefore\ 2y+z=0$

$$\frac{x}{1}=\frac{y}{1}=\frac{z}{-2}=\left(\frac{x^2+y^2+z^2}{1+1+4}\right)^{1/2}=\pm\frac{1}{\sqrt6}$$

by (1), (2) and (3).

$\therefore\quad \mathbf{d}=\pm\dfrac{1}{\sqrt6}(\mathbf{i}+\mathbf{j}-2\mathbf{k})$

48. (a) Ans. $\pi/4$.

$\mathbf{n}_1=\mathbf{i}\times(\mathbf{i}+\mathbf{j})=0+\mathbf{i}\times\mathbf{j}=\mathbf{k}$

$\mathbf{n}_2=(\mathbf{i}-\mathbf{j})\times(\mathbf{i}+\mathbf{k})$

$=0+\mathbf{i}\times\mathbf{k}-\mathbf{j}\times\mathbf{i}-\mathbf{j}\times\mathbf{k}=-\mathbf{i}-\mathbf{j}+\mathbf{k}$

$\therefore\quad \mathbf{a}=\lambda\,(\mathbf{n}_1\times\mathbf{n}_2)=\lambda\,\mathbf{k}\times(-\mathbf{i}-\mathbf{j}+\mathbf{k})$

$\vec{\mathbf{a}}=\lambda\,(-\mathbf{k}\times\mathbf{i}-\mathbf{k}\times\mathbf{j})=\lambda\,(\mathbf{j}\times\mathbf{k}-\mathbf{k}\times\mathbf{i})$

$\vec{\mathbf{a}}=\lambda\,(\mathbf{i}-\mathbf{j})$

$\therefore\quad \vec{\mathbf{a}}=(\lambda,-\lambda,0)\qquad \mathbf{V}=(1,-2,2)$

Angle between **a** and **V**, $\cos\theta=\dfrac{\vec{\mathbf{a}}.\vec{\mathbf{V}}}{|\vec{\mathbf{a}}||\vec{\mathbf{V}}|}$

or $\quad \cos\theta=\dfrac{\lambda+2\lambda+0}{\lambda\sqrt2 .3}=\dfrac{1}{\sqrt2}\quad\therefore\quad \theta=\dfrac{\pi}{4}$

(b) Ans. (a), (b).

Normal to the two planes are given by $\mathbf{N}_1\times\mathbf{N}_2$

$$\mathbf{N}_1=\begin{vmatrix}\mathbf{i}&\mathbf{j}&\mathbf{k}\\0&2&3\\0&4&-3\end{vmatrix}=-18\mathbf{i}$$

$$\mathbf{N}_2=\begin{vmatrix}\mathbf{i}&\mathbf{j}&\mathbf{k}\\0&1&-1\\3&3&0\end{vmatrix}=3\mathbf{i}+3(-\mathbf{j}-\mathbf{k})=3\,(\mathbf{i}-\mathbf{j}-\mathbf{k})$$

Line of intersection is parallel to

$\mathbf{a}=\mathbf{N}_1\times\mathbf{N}_2=54\,(\mathbf{j}-\mathbf{k})$

Given vector $\mathbf{b}=2\mathbf{i}+2\mathbf{j}-\mathbf{k}$

If θ be the angle between **a** and **b**, then

$\cos\theta=\dfrac{\mathbf{a}.\mathbf{b}}{|\mathbf{a}||\mathbf{b}|}\qquad\therefore\ \cos\theta=\pm\dfrac{1}{\sqrt2}$

$\therefore\quad \theta=\dfrac{\pi}{4},\pi-\dfrac{\pi}{4},\qquad$ *i.e.*, $\dfrac{\pi}{4}$ and $\dfrac{3\pi}{4}$

49. Since **b** and **c** are non-collinear unit vectors, therefore $\mathbf{b}\times\mathbf{c}$ is normal to their plane. Thus **b**, **c** and $\mathbf{b}\times\mathbf{c}$ are three non-coplanar vectors. Now any vector **r** can be expressed in terms of three non-coplanar vectors $\vec{\alpha},\vec{\beta},\vec{\gamma}$ as $\mathbf{r}=x\vec{\alpha}+y\vec{\beta}+z\vec{\gamma}$

where x, y, z are projections of **r** in the directions of $\vec{\alpha},\vec{\beta}$ and $\vec{\gamma}$.

$x=$ projection of **r** in the direction of $\alpha=\dfrac{\mathbf{r}.\alpha}{|\alpha|}=\mathbf{r}.\hat{\alpha}$

$y=\mathbf{r}.\hat{\beta},\ z=\mathbf{r}.\hat{\gamma}$

In our problem $\hat{\alpha}=\mathbf{b},\hat{\beta}=\mathbf{c},\hat{\gamma}=\dfrac{\mathbf{b}\times\mathbf{c}}{|\mathbf{b}\times\mathbf{c}|}$, where $\mathbf{r}=\mathbf{a}$.

Hence the given expression is **a**.

50. Equation of a line passing through the point **a** and parallel to vector **b** is $\mathbf{r}=\mathbf{a}+t\,\mathbf{b}$.

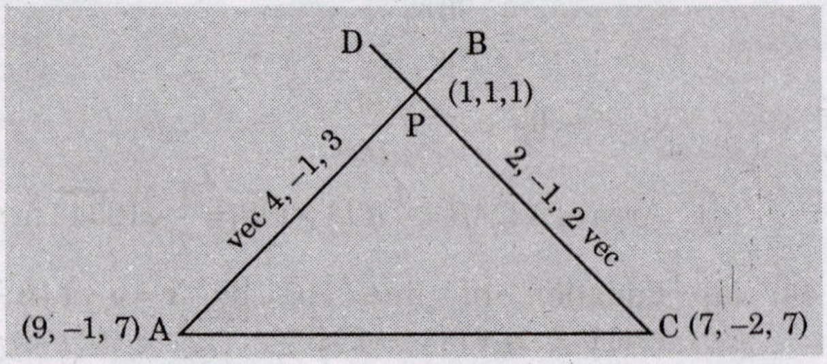

Fig. 54

For *AB* it passes through the point *A* and is along the vector $\vec{AB}$

Equations of *AB* and *CD* are $\mathbf{r}=(9,-1,7)+t\,(4,-1,3)$ and $\mathbf{r}=(7,-2,7)+s\,(2,-1,2)$

where $(9,-1,7)$ means $9\mathbf{i}-\mathbf{j}+7\mathbf{k}$

For point of intersection P, compare the coefficient of $\mathbf{i}, \mathbf{j}$ and $\mathbf{k}$.

$\therefore \quad 9+4t=7+2s, -1-t=-2-s$

and $\quad 7+3t=7+2s.$

or $\quad 2t-s=-1, t-s=1, 3t-2s=0$

Solving them, we get $t=-2, s=-3$

Hence the point P is $(9,-1,7)-2(4,-1,3)=(1,1,1)$

Now let $Q(x,y,z) \quad \therefore \quad \vec{PQ}=x-1, y-1, z-1$

$|\vec{PQ}|=15$

$\therefore \quad (x-1)^2+(y-1)^2+(z-1)^2=225 \quad ...(1)$

$\vec{PQ} \perp \vec{AB}, \quad \vec{PQ} \perp \vec{CD}$

$\therefore \quad \vec{PQ}$ is parallel to $\vec{AB} \times \vec{CD}$

$$\vec{AB} \times \vec{CD} = \begin{vmatrix} \mathbf{i} & \mathbf{j} & \mathbf{k} \\ 4 & -1 & 3 \\ 2 & 1 & 2 \end{vmatrix} = \mathbf{i}-2\mathbf{j}-2\mathbf{k}$$

$\vec{PQ}=x-1, y-1, z-1$ is parallel to $1, -2, -2$.

$$\therefore \quad \frac{x-1}{1}=\frac{y-1}{-2}=\frac{z-1}{-2}=\lambda, \text{ say} \quad ...(2)$$

Putting in (1), $\lambda^2+4\lambda^2+4\lambda^2=225$

$\lambda^2=25$ or $\lambda=5,-5$

Hence from (2),

(x,y,z) is $(6,-9,-9)$ or $(-4,11,11)$.

51. We are given $AD=4$

Volume of tetrahedron $=\dfrac{2\sqrt{2}}{3}=\dfrac{1}{3}\Delta ABC.\, p=\dfrac{2\sqrt{2}}{3}$

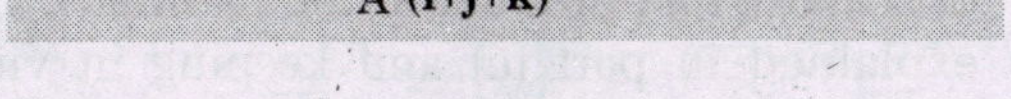

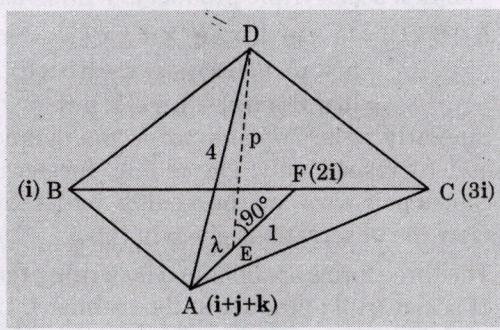

Fig. 55

$$\therefore \quad \frac{1}{2}|\vec{BA} \times \vec{BC}|\, p=2\sqrt{2}$$

or $\quad \dfrac{1}{2}|(\mathbf{j}+\mathbf{k}) \times 2\mathbf{i})|\, p=2\sqrt{2}$

or $\quad |\mathbf{j}-\mathbf{k}|\, p=2\sqrt{2}$ or $\sqrt{2}\, p=2\sqrt{2} \quad \therefore \quad p=2$

We have to find the P.V. of point E. Let it divide median AF in the ratio $\lambda:1$

$$\therefore \quad \text{P.V. of } E \text{ is } \frac{\lambda.2\mathbf{i}+(\mathbf{i}+\mathbf{j}+\mathbf{k})}{\lambda+1} \quad ...(2)$$

$$\therefore \quad \vec{AE}=\text{P.V. of } E-\text{P.V. of } A=\frac{\lambda}{\lambda+1}(\mathbf{i}-\mathbf{j}-\mathbf{k})$$

$$\therefore \quad |\vec{AE}|^2=AE^2=\left(\frac{\lambda}{\lambda+1}\right)^2 \cdot 3 \quad ...(3)$$

Now $\quad p^2+AE^2=AD^2$ or $4+\left(\dfrac{\lambda}{\lambda+1}\right)^2 \cdot 3=16$

$$\therefore \quad 3\left(\frac{\lambda}{\lambda+1}\right)^2=12 \quad \text{or} \quad \frac{\lambda}{\lambda+1}=\pm 2$$

$\lambda=\pm(2\lambda+2)$

$\therefore \quad \lambda=-2,$ or $-2/3$

Putting the values of λ in (2), we get the P.V. of possible positions of E as $(-1,3,3)$ or $(3,-1,-1)$.

52. We are given that $\quad \hat{x}+\hat{y}+\hat{z}=\mathbf{a} \quad ...(1)$

$(\hat{x}.\hat{z})\,\hat{y}-(\hat{x}.\hat{y})\,\hat{z}=\mathbf{b} \quad ...(2)$

$(\hat{x}.\hat{z})\,\hat{y}-(\hat{y}.\hat{z})\,\hat{x}=\mathbf{c} \quad ...(3)$

Also $\quad \mathbf{a}.\hat{x}=3/2, \mathbf{a}.\hat{y}=7/4, |\mathbf{a}|=2$

For convenience sake choose

$\hat{\mathbf{y}}.\hat{\mathbf{z}}=p, \hat{\mathbf{z}}.\hat{\mathbf{x}}=q, \hat{\mathbf{x}}.\hat{\mathbf{y}}=r$

Squaring (1), we get

$1+1+1+2(\hat{x}.\hat{y}+\hat{y}.\hat{z}+\hat{z}.\hat{x})=4$

$$\therefore \quad \hat{x}.\hat{y}+\hat{y}.\hat{z}+\hat{z}.\hat{x}=\frac{1}{2}$$

or $\quad p+q+r=\dfrac{1}{2} \quad ...(4)$

In order to make use of the other given relations *i.e.* $\mathbf{a}.\hat{x}=3/2$ and $\mathbf{a}.\hat{y}=7/4$, multiply both sides of (1) scalarly by $\hat{x}$ and $\hat{y}$.

$1+\hat{x}.\hat{y}+\hat{x}.\hat{z}=3/2$ and $\hat{x}.\hat{y}+1+\hat{y}.\hat{z}=7/4$

$\therefore \quad \hat{x}.\hat{y}+\hat{x}.\hat{z}=\dfrac{1}{2}$ or $q+r=\dfrac{1}{2} \quad ...(5)$

$\hat{x}.\hat{y}+\hat{y}.\hat{z}=\dfrac{3}{4}$ or $p+r=\dfrac{3}{4} \quad ...(6)$

Solving (4), (5) and (6), we get

$$p=0, q=\frac{1}{4}, r=\frac{3}{4}$$

Hence from (2) and (3) on putting for p,q,r, we get

$$-\frac{1}{4}\hat{y}-\frac{3}{4}\hat{z}=\mathbf{b}$$

$$-\frac{1}{4}\hat{y}-0=\mathbf{c} \quad \therefore \quad \hat{y}=-4\mathbf{c}$$

$$\therefore \quad \hat{z}=\frac{4}{3}(\mathbf{c}-\mathbf{b}) \text{ and hence from (1)}$$

$$\hat{x}=\frac{1}{3}(3\mathbf{a}+4\mathbf{b}+8\mathbf{c})$$

53. Let a, b, c be the lengths of the sides OA, OB and OC respectively of the rectangular parallelopiped ($OANB$, $MCLP$).

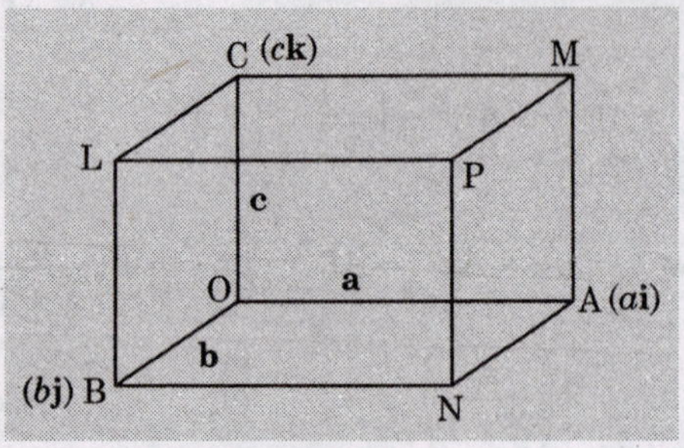

Fig. 56

Take O as the origin of vectors and let **i, j, k** denote unit vectors along OA, OB and OC respectively. Then $\vec{OA} = a\mathbf{i}$, $\vec{OB} = b\mathbf{j}$, $\vec{OC} = c\mathbf{k}$. Also $\vec{OP} = a\mathbf{i} + b\mathbf{j} + c\mathbf{k}$. The edges which do not meet the diagonal OP are BL, BN, AN and their parallels AM, CM and CL.

Suppose we are to find the distance between the diagonal OP and the edge AN.

Now OP is the line passing through O whose position vector is $\mathbf{0}$ and parallel to the vector $a\mathbf{i} + b\mathbf{j} + c\mathbf{k}$. And AN is the line through A whose position vector is $a\mathbf{i}$ and parallel to **j**. Hence by **§ 8 P. 1153**, the shortest distance between OP and AN is given by

$$p = \frac{[0 - a\mathbf{i},\ \mathbf{j},\ a\mathbf{i} + b\mathbf{j} + c\mathbf{k}]}{|\mathbf{j} \times (a\mathbf{i} + b\mathbf{j} + c\mathbf{k})|}.$$

Now $\quad [0 - a\mathbf{i},\ \mathbf{j},\ a\mathbf{i} + b\mathbf{j} + c\mathbf{k}] = \begin{vmatrix} -a & 0 & 0 \\ 0 & 1 & 0 \\ a & b & c \end{vmatrix} = ca$

and $\mathbf{j} \times (a\mathbf{i} + b\mathbf{j} + c\mathbf{k}) = \begin{vmatrix} \mathbf{i} & \mathbf{j} & \mathbf{k} \\ 0 & 1 & 0 \\ a & b & c \end{vmatrix} = c\mathbf{i} - a\mathbf{k}$

so that $\quad |\mathbf{j} \times (a\mathbf{i} + b\mathbf{j} + c\mathbf{k})| = \sqrt{c^2 + a^2}$

$\therefore \quad p = \dfrac{ca}{\sqrt{(c^2 + a^2)}}.$

Similarly, it can be shown that the shortest distance between OP and BN is $\dfrac{bc}{\sqrt{(b^2 + c^2)}}$ and that between OP and BL is $\dfrac{ab}{\sqrt{(a^2 + b^2)}}$.

54. (a) Consider $(\mathbf{a} \times \mathbf{b}) \times (\mathbf{c} \times \mathbf{d}) = \mathbf{P}$

Let us put $\mathbf{c} \times \mathbf{d} = \mathbf{n}$

$\therefore \quad \mathbf{P} = (\mathbf{a} \times \mathbf{b}) \times (\mathbf{c} \times \mathbf{d}) = (\mathbf{a} \times \mathbf{b}) \times \mathbf{n}$

$= (\mathbf{n} \cdot \mathbf{a})\, \mathbf{b} - (\mathbf{n} \cdot \mathbf{b})\, \mathbf{a}$

$\mathbf{P} = [\mathbf{c\,d\,a}]\, \mathbf{b} - [\mathbf{c\,d\,b}]\, \mathbf{a} \qquad \ldots(1)$

Again if we put $\mathbf{a} \times \mathbf{b} = \mathbf{n}$, then proceeding as above

$\mathbf{P} = [\mathbf{a\,b\,d}]\, \mathbf{c} - [\mathbf{a\,b\,c}]\, \mathbf{d} \qquad \ldots(2)$

From (1) and (2) on equating **P**, we get

$[\mathbf{c\,d\,a}]\, \mathbf{b} - [\mathbf{a\,b\,d}]\, \mathbf{c} + [\mathbf{a\,b\,c}]\, \mathbf{d} = [\mathbf{c\,d\,b}]\, \mathbf{a}$

or $\quad [\mathbf{a\,c\,d}]\, \mathbf{b} + [\mathbf{a\,d\,b}]\, \mathbf{c} + [\mathbf{a\,b\,c}]\, \mathbf{d} = [\mathbf{b\,c\,d}]\, \mathbf{a}$

$\because \quad [\mathbf{a\,b\,d}] = -[\mathbf{a\,d\,b}]$ and $[\mathbf{c\,d\,b}] = [\mathbf{b\,c\,d}]$

$$\mathbf{a} = \frac{[\mathbf{a\,c\,d}]\, \mathbf{b} + [\mathbf{a\,d\,b}]\, \mathbf{c} + [\mathbf{a\,b\,c}]\, \mathbf{d}}{[\mathbf{b\,c\,d}]} \qquad \ldots(3)$$

Thus **a** has been expressed as linear combination of three non-coplanar vectors **b, c, d** where $[\mathbf{b\,c\,d}] \neq 0$.

Note : The last three vectors in the above expression (3) are cyclic arrangement of **b c d**, *i.e.* **c d b, d b c, b c d** the first being **a** in each.

(b) We shall expand each term by (1) and (2) of part (a).

$T_1 = [\mathbf{c\,d\,a}]\, \mathbf{b} - [\mathbf{c\,d\,b}]\, \mathbf{a}$, by (1)

$T_2 = [\mathbf{a\,c\,b}]\, \mathbf{d} - [\mathbf{a\,c\,d}]\, \mathbf{b}$, by (2)

$T_3 = [\mathbf{b\,c\,a}]\, \mathbf{d} - [\mathbf{b\,c\,d}]\, \mathbf{a}$, by (1)

Now $[\mathbf{c\,d\,a}] = [\mathbf{a\,c\,d}]$ and $[\mathbf{c\,d\,b}] = [\mathbf{b\,c\,d}]$

because cyclic order is maintained but

$[\mathbf{a\,c\,b}] = [\mathbf{b\,a\,c}] = -[\mathbf{b\,c\,a}]$ order changed

$\therefore \quad T_1 + T_2 + T_3 = -2\,[\mathbf{b\,c\,d}]\, \mathbf{a} = -2k\, \mathbf{a}$, *i.e.*

a vector parallel to **a** as $k = [\mathbf{b\,c\,d}]$ is a non-zero scalar because **b, c, d** are non-coplanar.

55. (a) We know that scalar triple product $[\mathbf{A}, \mathbf{B}, \mathbf{C}]$

$= \mathbf{A} \cdot (\mathbf{B} \times \mathbf{C}) = \mathbf{B} \cdot (\mathbf{C} \times \mathbf{A}) = \mathbf{C} \cdot (\mathbf{A} \times \mathbf{B})$

I $\qquad$ II $\qquad$ III

Expand each of the three given expressions in the forms I, II, III respectively. Remember that scalar product does not change if the cyclic order is kept but with every change of cyclic order there is a change of sign. **...(1)**

The first scalar triple product is written as

$\mathbf{A} \cdot (\mathbf{B} \times \mathbf{C}) = (\mathbf{a} \times \mathbf{p}) \cdot [(\mathbf{b} \times \mathbf{q}) \times (\mathbf{c} \times \mathbf{r})]$

$= (\mathbf{a} \times \mathbf{p}) \cdot [\{(\mathbf{b} \times \mathbf{q}) \cdot \mathbf{r}\}\, \mathbf{c} - \{(\mathbf{b} \times \mathbf{q}) \cdot \mathbf{c}\}\, \mathbf{r}]$

$= [\mathbf{b\,q\,r}]\, [\mathbf{a\,p\,c}] - [\mathbf{b\,q\,c}]\, [\mathbf{a\,p\,r}] \qquad \ldots(2)$

Similarly write 2nd and 3rd in the manner of II and III respectively. On adding, the terms will cancel pair-wise and the result is zero, keeping in view the observations given in (1).

(b) The three forms are obtained by writing the value of scalar triple product in the manner I, II, III as explained in part (c) and keeping in view the observations made in (1).

e.g. $[\mathbf{A\,B\,C}] = \mathbf{A} \cdot (\mathbf{B} \times \mathbf{C})$

$= (\mathbf{a} \times \mathbf{b}) \cdot [(\mathbf{c} \times \mathbf{d}) \times (\mathbf{e} \times \mathbf{f})]$

$= (\mathbf{a} \times \mathbf{b}) \cdot [\{(\mathbf{c} \times \mathbf{d}) \cdot \mathbf{f}\}\, \mathbf{e} - \{(\mathbf{c} \times \mathbf{d}) \cdot \mathbf{e}\}\, \mathbf{f}]$

$= [\mathbf{c\,d\,f}]\, [\mathbf{a\,b\,e}] - [\mathbf{c\,d\,e}]\, [\mathbf{a\,b\,f}]$

$= [\mathbf{a\,b\,e}]\, [\mathbf{f\,c\,d}] - [\mathbf{a\,b\,f}]\, [\mathbf{e\,c\,d}]$

by (1) of part (c)

Above is of the form given in 2nd form of the equations. Similarly we can prove the other two forms by writing the scalar triple product as $\mathbf{B} \cdot (\mathbf{C} \times \mathbf{A})$ and $\mathbf{C} \cdot (\mathbf{A} \times \mathbf{B})$.

56. $(\mathbf{c} \times \mathbf{d}) \times (\mathbf{a} \times \mathbf{b}) = \mathbf{n} \times (\mathbf{a} \times \mathbf{b})$

$= (\mathbf{n} . \mathbf{b})\, \mathbf{a} - (\mathbf{n} . \mathbf{a})\, \mathbf{b}$

$= \{(\mathbf{c} \times \mathbf{d}) . \mathbf{b}\}\, \mathbf{a} - \{(\mathbf{c} \times \mathbf{d}) . \mathbf{a}\}\, \mathbf{b}$

$= [\mathbf{c}\, \mathbf{d}\, \mathbf{b}]\, \mathbf{a} - [\mathbf{c}\, \mathbf{d}\, \mathbf{a}]\, \mathbf{b}$

$= [\mathbf{b}\, \mathbf{c}\, \mathbf{d}]\, \mathbf{a} - [\mathbf{a}\, \mathbf{c}\, \mathbf{d}]\, \mathbf{b}$

$$= \begin{vmatrix} b_1 & b_2 & b_3 \\ c_1 & c_2 & c_3 \\ d_1 & d_2 & d_3 \end{vmatrix} \mathbf{a} - \begin{vmatrix} a_1 & a_2 & a_3 \\ c_1 & c_2 & c_3 \\ d_1 & d_2 & d_3 \end{vmatrix} \mathbf{b} \quad ...(1)$$

Again write $(\mathbf{c} \times \mathbf{d}) \times (\mathbf{a} \times \mathbf{b}) = (\mathbf{c} \times \mathbf{d}) \times \mathbf{m}$

Proceeding as above you will have two more determinants of the form (I) in **c** and **d** and then add. All these four determinants are obtained by expansion of the given determinant in R.H.S. of the question.

57. (a) Multiplying (1) scalarly by **a**, we get

$\mathbf{a} . \mathbf{x} + \mathbf{a} . \mathbf{y} = \mathbf{a}^2$

$\therefore \quad \mathbf{a} . \mathbf{y} = \mathbf{a}^2 - 1$, by (3) of question ...(4)

Again $\quad \mathbf{a} \times (\mathbf{x} \times \mathbf{y}) = \mathbf{a} \times \mathbf{b}$

or $\quad (\mathbf{a} . \mathbf{y})\, \mathbf{x} - (\mathbf{a} . \mathbf{x})\, \mathbf{y} = \mathbf{a} \times \mathbf{b}$

$(\mathbf{a}^2 - 1)\, \mathbf{x} - \mathbf{y} = \mathbf{a} \times \mathbf{b}$, ...(5)

by (3) and (4)

Adding and subtracting (1) and (5), we get

$$\mathbf{x} = \frac{\mathbf{a} + (\mathbf{a} \times \mathbf{b})}{\mathbf{a}^2} \text{ and } \mathbf{y} = \mathbf{a} - \mathbf{x} \text{ etc.}$$

(b) $\mathbf{x} \times \mathbf{a} + k\mathbf{x} = \mathbf{b}$ ...(1)

Pre-multiply the given equation vectorially by **a**

$\mathbf{a} \times (\mathbf{x} \times \mathbf{a}) + k\, (\mathbf{a} \times \mathbf{x}) = \mathbf{a} \times \mathbf{b}$

or $\quad (\mathbf{a} . \mathbf{a})\, \mathbf{x} - (\mathbf{a} . \mathbf{x})\, \mathbf{a} + k\, (\mathbf{a} \times \mathbf{x}) = \mathbf{a} \times \mathbf{b}$ ...(2)

Again pre-multiply the given equation scalarly by **a**

$[\mathbf{a}\ \mathbf{x}\ \mathbf{a}] + k\, (\mathbf{a} . \mathbf{x}) = \mathbf{a} . \mathbf{b}$

or $\quad 0 + k\, (\mathbf{a} . \mathbf{x}) = \mathbf{a} . \mathbf{b}$ ...(3)

In order to eliminate the scalar $(\mathbf{a} . \mathbf{x})$ between (2) and (3), we multiply (2) by k and (3) by **a** and add

$a^2 k\mathbf{x} + k^2\, (\mathbf{a} \times \mathbf{x}) = k\, (\mathbf{a} \times \mathbf{b}) + (\mathbf{a} . \mathbf{b})\, \mathbf{a}$ ...(4)

But from (1), $k\mathbf{x} - \mathbf{b} = -(\mathbf{x} \times \mathbf{a}) = (\mathbf{a} \times \mathbf{x})$

Putting the value of $\mathbf{a} \times \mathbf{x}$ in (4), we get

$a^2 k\mathbf{x} + k^2\, (k\mathbf{x} - \mathbf{b}) = k\, (\mathbf{a} \times \mathbf{b}) + (\mathbf{a} . \mathbf{b})\, \mathbf{a}$

or $\quad k\, (a^2 + k^2)\, \mathbf{x} = k^2 \mathbf{b} + k\, (\mathbf{a} \times \mathbf{b}) + (\mathbf{a} . \mathbf{b})\, \mathbf{a}$

$$\therefore \quad \mathbf{x} = \frac{1}{(a^2 + k^2)} \left[k\mathbf{b} + (\mathbf{a} \times \mathbf{b}) + \frac{(\mathbf{a} . \mathbf{b})}{k} \mathbf{a}\right]$$

58. Let $\vec{B} = (x, y, z) = x\mathbf{i} + y\mathbf{j} + z\mathbf{k}$.

Also $\vec{A} = \mathbf{i} + \mathbf{j} + \mathbf{k}$ and $\vec{C} = \mathbf{j} - \mathbf{k}$.

From $\vec{A} \times \vec{B} = \vec{C}$ on equating the coeff. of **i, j, k** we get

$z - y = 0,\ x - z = 1$ and $y - x = -1$.

These three equations are equivalent to two equations only, *i.e.*

$z - y = 0$ or $y = z$ ...(1)

$x - z = 1$ ...(2)

Also $\vec{A} . \vec{B} = 3$ gives $x + y + z = 3$ ...(3)

Solving (1), (2) and (3), we get

$$x = \frac{5}{3},\ y = z = \frac{2}{3}.$$

Hence $\quad \vec{B} = \left(\frac{5}{3}, \frac{2}{3}, \frac{2}{3}\right)$.

59. $\mathbf{x} . \mathbf{y} = \sqrt{2}\, \sqrt{2} \cos 60^\circ = 1 = \mathbf{y} . \mathbf{z} = \mathbf{z} . \mathbf{x}$ ...(1)

Also $\quad x^2 = y^2 = z^2 = 2$

Again $\quad \mathbf{a} = (\mathbf{x} . \mathbf{z})\, \mathbf{y} - (\mathbf{x} . \mathbf{y})\, \mathbf{z} = \mathbf{y} - \mathbf{z}$, by (1)

$\therefore \quad \mathbf{a} = \mathbf{y} - \mathbf{z},\ \mathbf{b} = \mathbf{z} - \mathbf{x}$ ...(2)

Now $\mathbf{a} \times \mathbf{c} = (\mathbf{y} - \mathbf{z}) \times (\mathbf{x} \times \mathbf{y}) = \mathbf{y} \times (\mathbf{x} \times \mathbf{y}) - \mathbf{z}\, (\mathbf{x} \times \mathbf{y})$

$= [(\mathbf{y} . \mathbf{y})\, \mathbf{x} - (\mathbf{y} . \mathbf{x})\, \mathbf{y}] - [(\mathbf{z} . \mathbf{y})\, \mathbf{x} - (\mathbf{z} . \mathbf{x})\, \mathbf{y}]$

$= (2\mathbf{x} - \mathbf{y}) - (\mathbf{x} - \mathbf{y})$, by (1)

or $\quad \mathbf{a} \times \mathbf{c} = \mathbf{x}$

Similarly, $\quad \mathbf{b} \times \mathbf{c} = \mathbf{y}$

Now $\quad \mathbf{z} = \mathbf{y} - \mathbf{a}$ or $\mathbf{z} = \mathbf{b} + \mathbf{x}$, by (2)

$\therefore \quad \mathbf{z} = (\mathbf{b} \times \mathbf{c} - \mathbf{a})$ or $\mathbf{b} + (\mathbf{a} \times \mathbf{c})$

Note : *This new solution is different from the solution given in 1997 edition. This is by courtesy of Dr. G.S.N. Murti, M.A., Ph.D. of Vishakhapatnam-17.*

60. $\mathbf{x} \times \mathbf{y} = \mathbf{a}$ ...(1)

$\mathbf{y} \times \mathbf{z} = \mathbf{b}$ ...(2)

Also $\mathbf{x} . \mathbf{b} = \gamma,\ \mathbf{x} . \mathbf{y} = 1,\ \mathbf{y} . \mathbf{z} = 1$ ...(A)

We have to make use of the relations given above.

From (1),

$\mathbf{x} . (\mathbf{x} \times \mathbf{y}) = \mathbf{x} . \mathbf{a}$

$\therefore \quad \mathbf{x} . \mathbf{a} = 0 \qquad \because [\mathbf{x}\ \mathbf{x}\ \mathbf{y}] = 0$

Similarly, $\mathbf{y} . \mathbf{a} = 0,\ \mathbf{y} . \mathbf{b} = 0,\ \mathbf{z} . \mathbf{b} = 0$ ...(B)

Multiplying (1) vectorially by **b**,

$\mathbf{b} \times (\mathbf{x} \times \mathbf{y}) = \mathbf{b} \times \mathbf{a}$

or $\quad (\mathbf{b} . \mathbf{y})\, \mathbf{x} - (\mathbf{b} . \mathbf{x})\, \mathbf{y} = \mathbf{b} \times \mathbf{a}$

or $\quad 0 - \gamma \mathbf{y} = -(\mathbf{a} \times \mathbf{b}) \quad \therefore \quad \mathbf{y} = \dfrac{(\mathbf{a} \times \mathbf{b})}{\gamma}$ ...(3)

by using relations in (A) and (B).

Again multiplying (1) vectorially by **y**,

$(\mathbf{x} \times \mathbf{y}) \times \mathbf{y} = \mathbf{a} \times \mathbf{y}$

or $\quad (\mathbf{x} . \mathbf{y})\, \mathbf{y} - (\mathbf{y} . \mathbf{y})\, \mathbf{x} = \mathbf{a} \times \mathbf{y}$

$\mathbf{y} - \mathbf{a} \times \mathbf{y} = |\mathbf{y}|^2\, \mathbf{x}$ by (A)

$$\therefore \quad \mathbf{x} = \frac{1}{|\mathbf{y}|^2} [\mathbf{y} - \mathbf{a} \times \mathbf{y}],$$

where $\mathbf{y} = \dfrac{\mathbf{a} \times \mathbf{b}}{\gamma}$, by (3) ...(4)

Hence **x** is known in terms of **a**, **b** and γ.

Again multiplying (2) vectorially by **y**, we get

$(\mathbf{y} \times \mathbf{z}) \times \mathbf{y} = \mathbf{b} \times \mathbf{y}$

or $\quad |\mathbf{y}|^2\, \mathbf{z} - (\mathbf{y} . \mathbf{z})\, \mathbf{y} = \mathbf{b} \times \mathbf{y}$

or $\quad |\mathbf{y}|^2\, \mathbf{z} = \mathbf{b} \times \mathbf{y} + \mathbf{y}$, by (A)

or $\quad \mathbf{z} = \dfrac{1}{|\mathbf{y}|^2} [\mathbf{b} \times \mathbf{y} + \mathbf{y}]$,

where **y** is given by (3). ...(5)

Results (3), (4) and (5) give the values of **x**, **y** and **z** in terms of **a**, **b** and γ.

§ 10. Reciprocal system of vectors.

The three vectors **a**′, **b**′, **c**′ defined by the equations

$$\mathbf{a}' = \frac{\mathbf{b}\times\mathbf{c}}{[\mathbf{abc}]},\quad \mathbf{b}' = \frac{\mathbf{c}\times\mathbf{a}}{[\mathbf{abc}]},\quad \mathbf{c}' = \frac{\mathbf{a}\times\mathbf{b}}{[\mathbf{abc}]}$$

are called reciprocal system to the vectors **a, b, c** which are non-coplanar, *i.e.* $[\mathbf{a\ b\ c}] \neq 0$.

Property 1. *If* **a, b, c** *and* **a**′, **b**′, **c**′ *be reciprocal system of vectors, then* $\mathbf{a}.\mathbf{a}' = \mathbf{b}.\mathbf{b}' = \mathbf{c}.\mathbf{c}' = 1$

We have $\mathbf{a}.\mathbf{a}' = \mathbf{a}.\dfrac{\mathbf{b}\times\mathbf{c}}{[\mathbf{abc}]} = \dfrac{[\mathbf{abc}]}{[\mathbf{abc}]} = 1.$

Similarly, $\mathbf{b}.\mathbf{b}' = \mathbf{c}.\mathbf{c}' = 1 \quad \therefore \quad \mathbf{a}.\mathbf{a}' + \mathbf{b}.\mathbf{b}' + \mathbf{c}.\mathbf{c}' = 3.$

Note : Because of the property
$\mathbf{a}.\mathbf{a}' = \mathbf{b}.\mathbf{b}' = \mathbf{c}.\mathbf{c}' = 1,$
the two systems of vectors are called reciprocal systems.

Property 2. *The product of any vector of one system with a vector of the other system which does not correspond to it is zero, i.e.*

$$\mathbf{a}.\mathbf{b}' = \mathbf{a}.\mathbf{c}' = \mathbf{b}.\mathbf{c}' = \mathbf{b}.\mathbf{a}' = \mathbf{c}.\mathbf{a}' = \mathbf{c}.\mathbf{b}' = 0$$

We have $\mathbf{a}.\mathbf{b}' = \mathbf{a}.\dfrac{\mathbf{c}\times\mathbf{a}}{[\mathbf{abc}]} = \dfrac{[\mathbf{aca}]}{[\mathbf{abc}]} = 0$

as the numerator is the scalar triple product of three vectors two of which are equal and hence it is zero.

Similarly, $\quad \mathbf{a}.\mathbf{c}' = \mathbf{b}.\mathbf{a}' = \mathbf{b}.\mathbf{c}' = 0,$ etc.

Cor. *Thus we conclude from the two properties that if* **a**′, **b**′, **c**′ *be reciprocal system to* **a, b, c** *then* **a, b, c** *is a reciprocal system to* **a**′, **b**′, **c**′.

Property 3. *The scalar triple product* [**abc**] *of any three non-coplanar vectors is reciprocal to the corresponding scalar triple product formed out of the reciprocal system of vectors* **a**′, **b**′, **c**′.

i.e., $\quad [\mathbf{a'\ b'\ c'}] = \dfrac{1}{[\mathbf{a\ b\ c}]}.$

We have $[\mathbf{a'\ b'\ c'}] = \mathbf{a}'.(\mathbf{b}'\times\mathbf{c}')$ ...(1)

Now substitute the values of **a**′, **b**′ and **c**′ in terms of **a, b** and **c**

$$\therefore \quad [\mathbf{a'\ b'\ c'}] = \frac{(\mathbf{b}\times\mathbf{c}).[(\mathbf{c}\times\mathbf{a})\times(\mathbf{a}\times\mathbf{b})]}{[\mathbf{abc}]^3}, \text{ from (1).} \quad ...(2)$$

Now $(\mathbf{c}\times\mathbf{a})\times(\mathbf{a}\times\mathbf{b}) = (\mathbf{c}\times\mathbf{a})\times\mathbf{m}$ say

$= (\mathbf{m}.\mathbf{c})\,\mathbf{a} - (\mathbf{m}.\mathbf{a})\,\mathbf{c}$

$= (\mathbf{a}\times\mathbf{b}).\mathbf{c}\,\mathbf{a} - (\mathbf{a}\times\mathbf{b}).\mathbf{a}\,\mathbf{c} = [\mathbf{abc}]\,\mathbf{a}$

$\because \quad (\mathbf{a}\times\mathbf{b}).\mathbf{a} = [\mathbf{a\ b\ a}] = 0,$

$$\therefore \quad [\mathbf{a'\ b'\ c'}] = \frac{(\mathbf{b}\times\mathbf{c}).[\mathbf{abc}]\,\mathbf{a}}{[\mathbf{abc}]^3}$$

$$= \frac{[\mathbf{abc}]\,(\mathbf{b}\times\mathbf{c}).\mathbf{a}}{[\mathbf{abc}]^3} \text{ from (2)}$$

$$= \frac{[\mathbf{abc}]\,[\mathbf{bca}]}{[\mathbf{abc}]^3} = \frac{[\mathbf{abc}]\,[\mathbf{abc}]}{[\mathbf{abc}]^3} = \frac{1}{[\mathbf{abc}]}.$$

$\therefore \quad [\mathbf{a\ b\ c}]\,[\mathbf{a'\ b'\ c'}] = 1.$

Note : If $|\mathbf{a\ b\ c}| \neq 0$ then $[\mathbf{a'\ b'\ c'}] \neq 0$ and hence if one system is non-coplanar, then the other is also non-coplanar.

Cor. *From above, we conclude that*

$$[\mathbf{a}\times\mathbf{b},\ \mathbf{b}\times\mathbf{c},\ \mathbf{c}\times\mathbf{a}] = [\mathbf{abc}]^2.$$

Cor. We have seen before that any vector **r** can be expressed in terms of three non-coplanar vectors **a, b, c**

$$\mathbf{r} = x\mathbf{a} + y\mathbf{b} + z\mathbf{c} \quad ...(1)$$

Taking dot product with **b** × **c**, we get

$$\mathbf{r}.(\mathbf{b}\times\mathbf{c}) = x\mathbf{a}.(\mathbf{b}\times\mathbf{c}) + y.0 + z.0$$

$$[\mathbf{rbc}] = x\,[\mathbf{abc}] \quad \therefore \quad x = \frac{[\mathbf{rbc}]}{[\mathbf{abc}]}$$

or $\quad x = \mathbf{r}.\dfrac{(\mathbf{b}\times\mathbf{c})}{[\mathbf{abc}]} = \mathbf{r}.\mathbf{a}'$

Similarly we can find the values of *y* and *z* as **r** . **b**′ and **r** . **c**′ respectively.

where a′, b′, c′ form a reciprocal system of vectors to a, b, c :

$\therefore \quad \mathbf{r} = \mathbf{r}.\mathbf{a}'\,\mathbf{a} + \mathbf{r}.\mathbf{b}'\,\mathbf{b} + \mathbf{r}.\mathbf{c}'\,\mathbf{c}.$

Also in the two systems of vectors [**abc**], [**a**′ **b**′ **c**′] each is reciprocal of the other and as such any vector **r** can also be written as

$\mathbf{r} = \mathbf{r}.\mathbf{a}\mathbf{a}' + \mathbf{r}.\mathbf{b}\mathbf{b}' + \mathbf{r}.\mathbf{c}\mathbf{c}'.$

Again $\mathbf{i}.\mathbf{i} = \mathbf{j}.\mathbf{j} = \mathbf{k}.\mathbf{k} = 1$ and $[\mathbf{i\ j\ k}] = 1.$

∴ The system of vectors **i, j, k** is its own reciprocal.

Hence in terms of unit vectors **i, j, k**, we have

$\mathbf{r} = \mathbf{r}.\mathbf{i}\,\mathbf{i} + \mathbf{r}.\mathbf{j}\,\mathbf{j} + \mathbf{r}.\mathbf{k}\,\mathbf{k}.$

Solved Examples

1. *If* **a, b, c** *are non-coplanar, show that*

$$\mathbf{r} = \frac{(\mathbf{r}.\mathbf{a})\,\mathbf{b}\times\mathbf{c}}{[\mathbf{abc}]} + \frac{(\mathbf{r}.\mathbf{b})\,\mathbf{c}\times\mathbf{a}}{[\mathbf{abc}]} + \frac{(\mathbf{r}.\mathbf{c})\,\mathbf{a}\times\mathbf{b}}{[\mathbf{abc}]}.$$

We have proved that

$\mathbf{r} = \mathbf{r}.\mathbf{a}'\,\mathbf{a} + \mathbf{r}.\mathbf{b}'\,\mathbf{b} + \mathbf{r}.\mathbf{c}'\,\mathbf{c}$

$\mathbf{r} = \mathbf{r}.\mathbf{a}\mathbf{a}' + \mathbf{r}.\mathbf{b}\mathbf{b}' + \mathbf{r}.\mathbf{c}\mathbf{c}'.$

Now put $\mathbf{a}' = \dfrac{\mathbf{b}\times\mathbf{c}}{[\mathbf{abc}]}$ etc. and we get the result.

2. *If* $\quad \mathbf{a}' = \dfrac{\mathbf{b}\times\mathbf{c}}{[\mathbf{abc}]},\ \mathbf{b}' = \dfrac{\mathbf{c}\times\mathbf{a}}{[\mathbf{abc}]},\ \mathbf{c}' = \dfrac{\mathbf{a}\times\mathbf{b}}{[\mathbf{abc}]}$, *then prove that*

$$\mathbf{a} = \frac{\mathbf{b}'\times\mathbf{c}'}{[\mathbf{a'\ b'\ c'}]},\ \mathbf{b} = \frac{\mathbf{c}'\times\mathbf{a}'}{[\mathbf{a'\ b'\ c'}]},\ \mathbf{c} = \frac{\mathbf{a}'\times\mathbf{b}'}{[\mathbf{a'\ b'\ c'}]}$$

$$\mathbf{b}'\times\mathbf{c}' = \frac{(\mathbf{c}\times\mathbf{a})\times(\mathbf{a}\times\mathbf{b})}{[\mathbf{abc}]^2} = \frac{(\mathbf{c}\times\mathbf{a}).\mathbf{b}\mathbf{a} - (\mathbf{c}\times\mathbf{a}).\mathbf{a}\mathbf{b}}{[\mathbf{abc}]^2}.$$

Put $(\mathbf{c}\times\mathbf{a}).\mathbf{a} = [\mathbf{caa}] = 0$

$$= \frac{[\mathbf{cab}]\,\mathbf{a}}{[\mathbf{abc}]^2} = \frac{[\mathbf{abc}]\,\mathbf{a}}{[\mathbf{abc}]^2} = \frac{1}{[\mathbf{abc}]}\,\mathbf{a} \quad ...(1)$$

$\therefore \quad [\mathbf{a'\ b'\ c'}] = \mathbf{a}'.(\mathbf{b}'\times\mathbf{c}')$

$$= \frac{\mathbf{b} \times \mathbf{c}}{[\mathbf{abc}]} \cdot \frac{1}{[\mathbf{abc}]} \mathbf{a} = \frac{[\mathbf{bca}]}{[\mathbf{abc}]^2} \text{ by (1)}$$

$$= \frac{[\mathbf{abc}]}{[\mathbf{abc}]^2} = \frac{1}{[\mathbf{abc}]}. \qquad ...(2)$$

and $\dfrac{\mathbf{b}' \times \mathbf{c}'}{[\mathbf{a}'\,\mathbf{b}'\,\mathbf{c}']} = \dfrac{1}{[\mathbf{abc}]} \mathbf{a}\,[\mathbf{abc}] = \mathbf{a},$ by (1) and (2).

Hence proved.

Similarly we can prove other results.

3. *If* **a, b, c** *and* **a′, b′, c′** *are reciprocal system of vectors, prove that*

(i) $\mathbf{a} \times \mathbf{a}' + \mathbf{b} \times \mathbf{b}' + \mathbf{c} \times \mathbf{c}' = \mathbf{0}$.

(ii) $\mathbf{a}' \times \mathbf{b}' + \mathbf{b}' \times \mathbf{c}' + \mathbf{c}' \times \mathbf{a}' = \dfrac{\mathbf{a} + \mathbf{b} + \mathbf{c}}{[\mathbf{abc}]}$

(iii) $\mathbf{a} \cdot \mathbf{a}' + \mathbf{b} \cdot \mathbf{b}' + \mathbf{c} \cdot \mathbf{c}' = 3$.

(iv) $\mathbf{a}' \cdot (\mathbf{a} + \mathbf{b}) + \mathbf{b}' \cdot (\mathbf{b} + \mathbf{c}) + \mathbf{c}' \cdot (\mathbf{c} + \mathbf{a}) = 3$.

(v) $(\mathbf{a} + \mathbf{b} + \mathbf{c}) \cdot (\mathbf{a}' + \mathbf{b}' + \mathbf{c}')$ is

(a) 3 (b) 2

(c) 1 (d) 0 **(M.N.R. 1992)**

(i) $\mathbf{a}' = \dfrac{\mathbf{b} \times \mathbf{c}}{[\mathbf{abc}]}$ because of reciprocal system.

$\therefore \quad \mathbf{a} \times \mathbf{a}' + \mathbf{b} \times \mathbf{b}' + \mathbf{c} \times \mathbf{c}'$

$$= \frac{1}{[\mathbf{abc}]} [\mathbf{a} \times (\mathbf{b} \times \mathbf{c}) + \mathbf{b} \times (\mathbf{c} \times \mathbf{a}) + \mathbf{c} \times (\mathbf{a} \times \mathbf{b})] = \mathbf{0}$$

See Q. 26 (a), P. 1157-66.

(ii) $\mathbf{b}' \times \mathbf{c}' = \dfrac{1}{[\mathbf{abc}]} \mathbf{a}$ as proved in (1) of Ex. 2 above.

$\therefore \quad \mathbf{a}' \times \mathbf{b}' + \mathbf{b}' \times \mathbf{c}' + \mathbf{c}' \times \mathbf{a}' = \dfrac{1}{[\mathbf{abc}]} [\mathbf{a} + \mathbf{b} + \mathbf{c}]$.

(iii) $\mathbf{a} \cdot \mathbf{a}' = \mathbf{a} \cdot \dfrac{\mathbf{b} \times \mathbf{c}}{[\mathbf{abc}]} = \dfrac{[\mathbf{abc}]}{[\mathbf{abc}]} = 1$

$\therefore \quad \mathbf{a} \cdot \mathbf{a}' + \mathbf{b} \cdot \mathbf{b}' + \mathbf{c} \cdot \mathbf{c}' = 3$.

(iv) Using property 1 and 2 of § 17 the required value is 3.

(v) Ans. (a) by Prop. 1 and 2.

4. *Find a set of vectors reciprocal to the set*

(a) $2\mathbf{i} + 3\mathbf{j} - \mathbf{k},\ \mathbf{i} - \mathbf{j} - 2\mathbf{k},\ -\mathbf{i} + 2\mathbf{j} + 2\mathbf{k}$.

(b) $-\mathbf{i} + \mathbf{j} + \mathbf{k},\ \mathbf{i} - \mathbf{j} + \mathbf{k},\ \mathbf{i} + \mathbf{j} - \mathbf{k}$.

(a) Let the given vectors be **a, b, c** so that

$$[\mathbf{abc}] = \begin{vmatrix} 2 & 3 & -1 \\ 1 & -1 & -2 \\ -1 & 2 & 2 \end{vmatrix} = 3,$$

$$\mathbf{b} \times \mathbf{c} = \begin{vmatrix} \mathbf{i} & \mathbf{j} & \mathbf{k} \\ 1 & -1 & -2 \\ -1 & 2 & 2 \end{vmatrix} = 2\mathbf{i} + \mathbf{k}$$

$$\therefore \quad \mathbf{a}' = \frac{\mathbf{b} \times \mathbf{c}}{[\mathbf{abc}]} = \frac{2\mathbf{i} + \mathbf{k}}{3}.$$

Similarly, $\mathbf{b}' = -\dfrac{8\mathbf{i} + 3\mathbf{j} - 7\mathbf{k}}{3}$

and $\mathbf{c}' = \dfrac{-7\mathbf{i} + 3\mathbf{j} - 5\mathbf{k}}{3}$.

(b) Do yourself.

§11. (a) Work. (Physical interpretation of dot product)

A force is said to do work when its point of application moves.

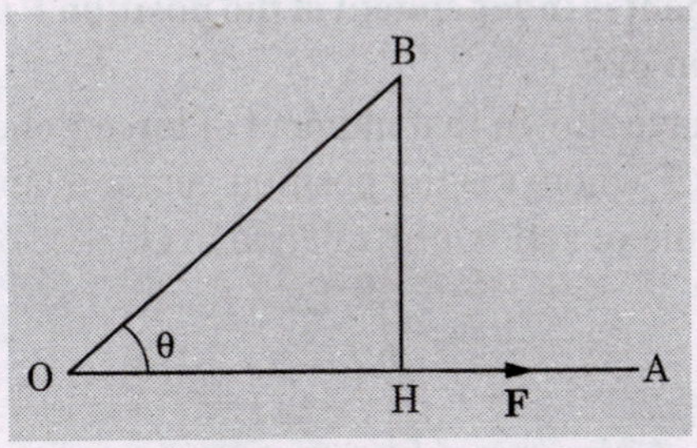

Fig. 57

Suppose there is a force **F** acting at a point O in the direction OA and suppose it displaces the point of application from O to B. Then the displacement in the direction of force

$= OH = OB \cos\theta$. If W be the work done, then W is given by

$$W = |\mathbf{F}|\, OH = |\mathbf{F}|\, OB \cos\theta = \mathbf{F} \cdot \overrightarrow{OB}.$$

Again if **F** be the resultant of two forces $\mathbf{F}_1$ and $\mathbf{F}_2$ acting at the same point O, then $\mathbf{F} = \mathbf{F}_1 + \mathbf{F}_2$ and so the work done by **F** is given by

$$\mathbf{F} \cdot \overrightarrow{OB} = (\mathbf{F}_1 + \mathbf{F}_2) \cdot \overrightarrow{OB} = \mathbf{F}_1 \cdot \overrightarrow{OB} + \mathbf{F}_2 \cdot \overrightarrow{OB}$$

Above shows that the work done by the resultant is equal to the sum of the works done by the forces separately.

Again if the point of application of a force **F** moves first O to B and then from B to C then the work done is

$$\mathbf{F} \cdot \overrightarrow{OB} + \mathbf{F} \cdot \overrightarrow{BC} = \mathbf{F} \cdot (\overrightarrow{OB} + \overrightarrow{BC}) = \mathbf{F} \cdot \overrightarrow{OC}.$$

Above shows that sum of the works done by a force in two consecutive displacements OB and BC is equal to the work done by the force in single displacement OC.

§ 12. Vector moment of a force about a point.

(Physical interpretation of cross product)

The vector moment or torque **M** of a force **F** about any given point O is in magnitude equal to F times the perpendicular distance of O from the line of action of force **F**.

Thus $|\mathbf{M}| = F \cdot ON = F \cdot OP \sin\theta$.

If **r** be the position vector of any point P on the line of action of force **F**, then

$|\mathbf{r} \times \mathbf{F}| = F \cdot OP \sin\theta$.

$|\mathbf{M}| = |\mathbf{r} \times \mathbf{F}|$

The direction of vector moment is to be determined by the right-handed orientation as explained earlier. Thus in the figure the direction of the vector moment is along the normal drawn through O on the plane of the paper and pointing towards the reader.

$\therefore \quad \mathbf{M} = \mathbf{r} \times \mathbf{F}$ and its magnitude is $F.ON$

or $\quad Fr \sin\theta$.

Moment is independent of the position P on the line of action of F.

We have shown that moment of force **F** about a point O is $\mathbf{r} \times \mathbf{F}$ where **r** is the position vector of any point P on the line of action of **F** relative to O.

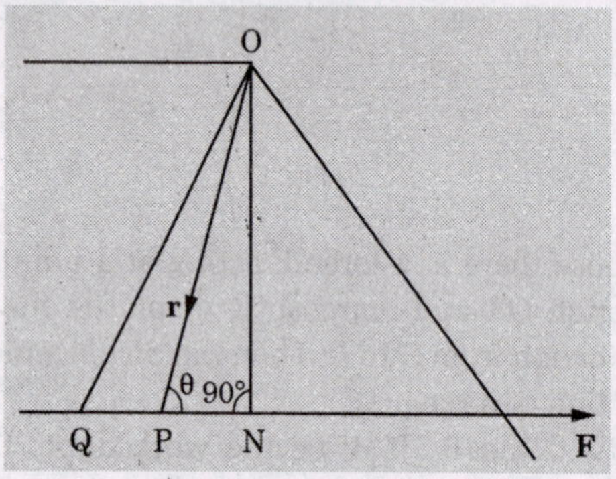

Fig. 48

If in place of P we choose any other point Q on the line of action of **F** whose position vector relative to O be **q**, then moment is $\mathbf{M}' = \mathbf{q} \times \mathbf{F}$.

But $\mathbf{q} = \overrightarrow{OQ} = \overrightarrow{OP} + \overrightarrow{PQ} = \mathbf{r} + \overrightarrow{PQ}$.

$$\mathbf{M}' = \mathbf{q} \times \mathbf{F} = (\mathbf{r} + \overrightarrow{PQ}) \times \mathbf{F} = \mathbf{r} \times \mathbf{F} = \mathbf{M}.$$

since $\overrightarrow{PQ} \times \mathbf{F} = 0$ as both $\overrightarrow{PQ}$ and **F** are in the same line.

Working Rule : In order to get the vector moment of a force **F** about any point O, find the vector product $\mathbf{r} \times \mathbf{F}$ where **r** is the position vector of any point P on the line of action of the force relative to origin O.

Cor. *The algebraic sum of the moments of a system of forces about any point is equal to the moment of their resultant about the same point.*

If **F** be the resultant of a number of forces $\mathbf{F}_1, \mathbf{F}_2, \ldots\ldots\ldots$ acting through a point, then

$$\mathbf{F} = \mathbf{F}_1 + \mathbf{F}_2 + \ldots$$

$$\therefore \quad \mathbf{M} = \mathbf{r} \times \mathbf{F} = \mathbf{r} \times (\mathbf{F}_1 + \mathbf{F}_2 + \ldots)$$
$$= \mathbf{r} \times \mathbf{F}_1 + \mathbf{r} \times \mathbf{F}_2 + \ldots$$

Problem Set (3)

Work, Vector moment of a force.

1. Find the moment about the point $\mathbf{i} + 2\mathbf{j} - \mathbf{k}$ of a force represented by $3\mathbf{i} + \mathbf{k}$ acting through the point $2\mathbf{i} - \mathbf{j} + 3\mathbf{k}$.

2. The force represented by $5\mathbf{i} + \mathbf{k}$ is acting through the point $9\mathbf{i} - \mathbf{j} + 2\mathbf{k}$. Find the moment about the point $3\mathbf{i} - 2\mathbf{j} + \mathbf{k}$.

3. A force $\mathbf{F} = 3\mathbf{i} + 2\mathbf{j} - 4\mathbf{k}$ is acting at the point $(1, -1, 2)$. Find the moment of **F** about the point $(2, -1, 3)$.

(M.N.R. 1990)

4. Find the moment about the point $\mathbf{i} + 2\mathbf{j} + 3\mathbf{k}$ of a force represented by $\mathbf{i} + \mathbf{j} + \mathbf{k}$ acting through the point $-2\mathbf{i} + 3\mathbf{j} + \mathbf{k}$.

5. A force $\mathbf{P} = 4\mathbf{i} - 3\mathbf{k}$ passes through the point A whose position vector is $2\mathbf{i} - 2\mathbf{j} + 5\mathbf{k}$. Find the moment of P about the point B whose position vector is $\mathbf{i} - 3\mathbf{j} + \mathbf{k}$.

6. (a) A force $\mathbf{F} = 3\mathbf{j} - 6\mathbf{k}$ passes through the point A, $4\mathbf{i} - 2\mathbf{j} - 9\mathbf{k}$; find the moment of P about the point B whose position vector is $6\mathbf{i} - 7\mathbf{k}$.

(b) Find the moment of the force $5\mathbf{i} + 10\mathbf{j} + 16\mathbf{k}$ acting at the point $2\mathbf{i} - 7\mathbf{j} + 10\mathbf{k}$ about the point $-5\mathbf{i} + 6\mathbf{j} - 10\mathbf{k}$.

7. (a) Find the vector moment of three forces $\mathbf{i} + 2\mathbf{j} - 3\mathbf{k}$, $2\mathbf{i} + 3\mathbf{j} + 4\mathbf{k}$ and $-\mathbf{i} - \mathbf{j} + \mathbf{k}$ acting on a parcticle at a point $P(0, 1, 2)$ about the point $A(1, -2, 0)$.

(b) A particle is placed at a corner P of a cube of side 1 metre. Forces of magnitudes 2, 3, and 5 kg. wt. act on the particle along the diagonals of the faces passing through the point P. Find the moment of these forces about the corner opposite to P.

(Roorkee 2000)

8. (a) A particle acted on by constant forces $4\mathbf{i} + \mathbf{j} - 3\mathbf{k}$ and $3\mathbf{i} + \mathbf{j} - \mathbf{k}$ is displaced from the point $\mathbf{i} + 2\mathbf{j} + 3\mathbf{k}$ to the point $5\mathbf{i} + 4\mathbf{j} + \mathbf{k}$. Find the total work done by the forces.

(b) A force $\mathbf{F} = 2\mathbf{i} + \mathbf{j} - \mathbf{k}$ acts at a point A whose position vector is $2\mathbf{i} - \mathbf{j}$. Find the moment of **F** about the origin. If the point of application of **F** moves from the point A to the point B (position vector $2\mathbf{i} + \mathbf{j}$), find the work done by **F**.

9. (a) Find the work done in moving an object along a straight line from $(3, 2, -1)$ to $(2, -1, 4)$ in a force field given by $\mathbf{F} = 5\mathbf{i} - 3\mathbf{j} + 2\mathbf{k}$.

(b) Find the work done in moving an object along a vector $\overrightarrow{PQ} = 3\mathbf{i} + 2\mathbf{j} - 5\mathbf{k}$ if the force applied is $\mathbf{F} = 2\mathbf{i} - \mathbf{j} - \mathbf{k}$.

10. Forces acting on a particle have magnitudes 5, 3, 1 kg. wt and act in the directions of the vectors $6\mathbf{i} + 2\mathbf{j} + 3\mathbf{k}$, $3\mathbf{i} - 2\mathbf{j} + 6\mathbf{k}$ and $2\mathbf{i} - 3\mathbf{j} - 6\mathbf{k}$ respectively. These remain constant while the particle is displaced

from the point $A(2\mathbf{i}-\mathbf{j}-3\mathbf{k})$ to $B(5\mathbf{i}-\mathbf{j}+\mathbf{k})$. Find the work done.

11. A particle is displaced from the point whose position vector is $5\mathbf{i}-5\mathbf{j}-7\mathbf{k}$ to the point whose position vector is $6\mathbf{i}+2\mathbf{j}-2\mathbf{k}$ under the action of constant forces $10\mathbf{i}-\mathbf{j}+11\mathbf{k}$, $4\mathbf{i}+5\mathbf{j}+6\mathbf{k}$ and $-2\mathbf{i}+\mathbf{j}-9\mathbf{k}$. Show that the total work done by the forces is 87 units.

12. Constant forces $(2\mathbf{i}-5\mathbf{j}+6\mathbf{k})$, $-\mathbf{i}+2\mathbf{j}-\mathbf{k}$ and $2\mathbf{i}+7\mathbf{j}$ act on a particle. Determine the total work done by the forces in a displacement of the particle from the point $4\mathbf{i}-3\mathbf{j}-2\mathbf{k}$ to the point $6\mathbf{i}+\mathbf{j}-3\mathbf{k}$.

13. Constant forces $\mathbf{P}=2\mathbf{i}-5\mathbf{j}+6\mathbf{k}$ and $\mathbf{Q}=-\mathbf{i}+2\mathbf{j}-\mathbf{k}$ act on a particle. Determine the work done when the particle is displaced from a point A with position vector $4\mathbf{i}-3\mathbf{j}-2\mathbf{k}$ to point B with position vector $6\mathbf{i}+\mathbf{j}-3\mathbf{k}$.

14. Constant forces $P=(2\mathbf{i}-5\mathbf{j}+6\mathbf{k})$ and $Q=-\mathbf{i}+2\mathbf{j}-\mathbf{k}$ act on a particle at the point $A(4,-3,-2)$. Find the moment of the resultant force about the origin $O(0,0,0)$. Also find the work done when the particle is displaced from A to $B(6,1,-3)$.

15. Constant forces $P_1=\mathbf{i}-\mathbf{j}+\mathbf{k}$, $P_2=-\mathbf{i}+2\mathbf{j}-\mathbf{k}$ and $P_3=\mathbf{j}-\mathbf{k}$ act on a particle at a point A. Determine the work done when the particle is displaced from the point A to B where $A=4\mathbf{i}-3\mathbf{j}-2\mathbf{k}$ and $B=6\mathbf{i}+\mathbf{j}-3\mathbf{k}$ are the position vectors of A and B. Also find the moment of the force P_1 about the point $(1,0,1)$.

16. Show that twice the vector area of a closed plane polygon is equal to the sum of the torques about any point in the plane of the polygon of forces represented by the sides of the polygon taken in order.

17. The vertices of a triangle ABC are $A(-1,0,2)$, $B(1,2,0)$ and $C(2,3,4)$. Find
(i) vector area of triangle ABC,
(ii) the moment of a force of magnitude 10 N acting at A along AB, about C.

18. Four forces acting at a point are in equilibrium. Show that the magnitude of each force is proportional to the scalar triple product of the vectors in the direction of the other three. **(M.N.R. 1992)**

19. An odd number of n forces act along the radius vectors of a circle with radius r from the centre to the circumference. The angle between any two adjacent forces is the same. Then the magnitude of the resultant force is

(a) 0 (b) r (c) $\frac{1}{2}nr$ (d) nr.

(M.N.R. 1992)

20. A rigid body is rotating at 5 radians per second about an axis AB where A and B are the points $(2\mathbf{i}+\mathbf{j}+\mathbf{k})$ and $(8\mathbf{i}-2\mathbf{j}+3\mathbf{k})$ respectively. Find the velocity of the particle P of the body at the point $(5\mathbf{i}-\mathbf{j}+\mathbf{k})$.

(Roorkee 1993)

21. A rigid body is rotating about an axis through the point $(3,-1,-2)$. If the particle at the point $(4,1,0)$ has velocity $4\mathbf{i}-4\mathbf{j}+2\mathbf{k}$ and that at the point $(3, 2, 1)$ has velocity $6\mathbf{i}-4\mathbf{j}+4\mathbf{k}$, find the magnitude and direction of the angular velocity of the body. **(Roorkee 1994)**

Solutions to Problem Set (3)

1. $\mathbf{F}=3\mathbf{i}+\mathbf{k}$.

Point O about which moment is to be taken is $\mathbf{i}+2\mathbf{j}-\mathbf{k}$.

$\therefore\quad \mathbf{r}=\vec{OP}=$ P.V. of $P-$ P.V. of O

$=(2\mathbf{i}-\mathbf{j}+3\mathbf{k})-(\mathbf{i}+2\mathbf{j}-\mathbf{k})$

or $\quad \mathbf{r}=\mathbf{i}-3\mathbf{j}+4\mathbf{k}$.

Hence the moment is

$$\mathbf{r}\times\mathbf{F}=(\mathbf{i}-3\mathbf{j}+4\mathbf{k})\times(3\mathbf{i}+\mathbf{k})$$

$$\begin{vmatrix}\mathbf{i} & \mathbf{j} & \mathbf{k}\\ 1 & -3 & 4\\ 3 & 0 & 1\end{vmatrix}=-3\mathbf{i}+11\mathbf{j}+9\mathbf{k}.$$

2. $\mathbf{F}=5\mathbf{i}+\mathbf{k}$, $\mathbf{O}=3\mathbf{i}+2\mathbf{j}+\mathbf{k}$, $\mathbf{P}=9\mathbf{i}-\mathbf{j}+2\mathbf{k}$.

$\mathbf{r}=\vec{OP}=$ P.V. of $P-$ P.V. of O

$=(9\mathbf{i}-\mathbf{j}+2\mathbf{k})-(3\mathbf{i}+2\mathbf{j}+\mathbf{k})=6\mathbf{i}-3\mathbf{j}+\mathbf{k}$.

$\therefore\quad \mathbf{M}=\mathbf{r}\times\mathbf{F}=(6\mathbf{i}-3\mathbf{j}+\mathbf{k})\times(5\mathbf{i}+\mathbf{k})$

$$=\begin{vmatrix}\mathbf{i} & \mathbf{j} & \mathbf{k}\\ 6 & -3 & 1\\ 5 & 0 & 1\end{vmatrix}=-3\mathbf{i}-\mathbf{j}+15\mathbf{k}.$$

3. Here O is $(2,-1,3)$ or $2\mathbf{i}-\mathbf{j}+3\mathbf{k}$.

P is $(1,-1,2)$ or $\mathbf{i}-\mathbf{j}+2\mathbf{k}$.

Ans. $2\mathbf{i}-7\mathbf{j}-2\mathbf{k}$.

4. Ans. $3\mathbf{i}+\mathbf{j}-4\mathbf{k}$.

5. Ans. $\mathbf{M}=\vec{BA}\times\mathbf{P}=-3\mathbf{i}+19\mathbf{j}-4\mathbf{k}$.

6. (a) Ans. $6(2\mathbf{i}+6\mathbf{j}+\mathbf{k})$.

(b) $\mathbf{r}=\vec{OP}=$ P.V. of $P-$ P.V. of O

$=(2\mathbf{i}-7\mathbf{j}+10\mathbf{k})-(-5\mathbf{i}+6\mathbf{j}-10\mathbf{k})=7\mathbf{i}-13\mathbf{j}+20\mathbf{k}$

$\therefore\quad \mathbf{M}=\mathbf{r}\times\mathbf{F}=(7\mathbf{i}-13\mathbf{j}+20\mathbf{k})\times(5\mathbf{i}+10\mathbf{j}+16\mathbf{k})$

$$=\begin{vmatrix}\mathbf{i} & \mathbf{j} & \mathbf{k}\\ 7 & -13 & 20\\ 5 & 10 & 16\end{vmatrix}=-408\mathbf{i}-12\mathbf{j}+135\mathbf{k}.$$

7. (a) Ans. $-(4\mathbf{i}+2\mathbf{j}+5\mathbf{k})$

Use Cor. **§ 12 Page 1177.**

(b) Let O be the origin and unit vectors along OA, OB, OC be $\mathbf{i},\mathbf{j},\mathbf{k}$. Diagonals of the faces through P are $\vec{OL}$ $\mathbf{j}+\mathbf{k}$, $\vec{OM}$ $\mathbf{k}+\mathbf{i}$ and $\vec{ON}$ $\mathbf{i}+\mathbf{j}$ and P is the point $\mathbf{i}+\mathbf{j}+\mathbf{k}$.

Unit vectors along these diagonals are

$$\frac{1}{\sqrt{2}}(\mathbf{j}+\mathbf{k}),\ \frac{1}{\sqrt{2}}(\mathbf{k}+\mathbf{i}),\ \frac{1}{\sqrt{2}}(\mathbf{i}+\mathbf{j})$$

along which act forces of magnitude 2, 3, 5 respectively.

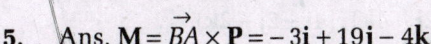

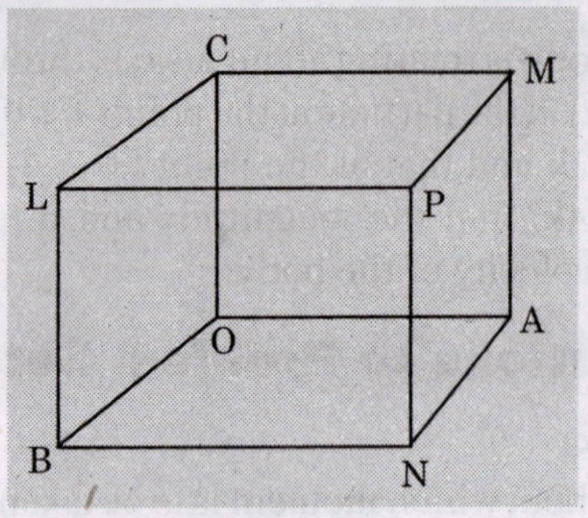

Fig. 59

Hence if **F** be the force, then

$$\mathbf{F}=\frac{1}{\sqrt{2}}[2(\mathbf{j}+\mathbf{k})+3(\mathbf{k}+\mathbf{i})+5(\mathbf{i}+\mathbf{j})]$$

$$=\frac{1}{\sqrt{2}}[8\mathbf{i}+7\mathbf{j}+5\mathbf{k}]$$

Moment of this force F about P is

$$\vec{OP}\times\mathbf{F}=\frac{1}{\sqrt{2}}\begin{vmatrix}\mathbf{i}&\mathbf{j}&\mathbf{k}\\1&1&1\\8&7&5\end{vmatrix}=\frac{1}{\sqrt{2}}(-2\mathbf{i}+3\mathbf{j}-\mathbf{k})$$

$\therefore$ Magnitude $=\frac{1}{\sqrt{2}}.\sqrt{14}=\sqrt{7}$

8. (a) We know that the work done by several forces is equal to the work done by their resultant

$$\mathbf{R}=\mathbf{F}_1+\mathbf{F}_2=(4\mathbf{i}+\mathbf{j}-3\mathbf{k})+(3\mathbf{i}+\mathbf{j}-\mathbf{k})$$
$$=7\mathbf{i}+2\mathbf{j}-4\mathbf{k}.$$

Again if the point is displaced from P to Q, then

$$\vec{PQ}=\text{P.V. of } Q-\text{P.V. of } P$$
$$=(5\mathbf{i}+4\mathbf{j}+\mathbf{k})-(\mathbf{i}+2\mathbf{j}+3\mathbf{k})=4\mathbf{i}+2\mathbf{j}-2\mathbf{k}$$

Hence the work done $=\mathbf{R}.\vec{PQ}$

$$=(7\mathbf{i}+2\mathbf{j}-4\mathbf{k}).(4\mathbf{i}+2\mathbf{j}-2\mathbf{k})$$
$$=28+4+8=40\text{ units.}$$

(b) Proceed as in part (a).

9. (a) Here

$$\vec{PQ}=(2\mathbf{i}-\mathbf{j}+4\mathbf{k})-(3\mathbf{i}+2\mathbf{j}-\mathbf{k})=-\mathbf{i}-3\mathbf{j}+5\mathbf{k}$$

$\therefore$ Work done $=\mathbf{F}.\vec{PQ}$

$$=(4\mathbf{i}-3\mathbf{j}+2\mathbf{k}).(-\mathbf{i}-3\mathbf{j}+5\mathbf{k})$$
$$=-4+9+10=15\text{ units.}$$

(b) Ans. 9 units.

10. Unit vectors in the direction of the forces are

$$\frac{6\mathbf{i}+2\mathbf{j}+3\mathbf{k}}{\sqrt{(36+4+9)}},\ \frac{3\mathbf{i}-2\mathbf{j}+6\mathbf{k}}{7},\ \frac{2\mathbf{i}-3\mathbf{j}-6\mathbf{k}}{7}.$$

Hence if $\mathbf{F}_1,\mathbf{F}_2,\mathbf{F}_3$, be the forces of magnitudes 5, 3, 1, then they are

$$\frac{5}{7}(6\mathbf{i}+2\mathbf{j}+3\mathbf{k}),\quad \frac{3}{7}(3\mathbf{i}-2\mathbf{j}+6\mathbf{k})$$

and $\frac{1}{7}(2\mathbf{i}-3\mathbf{j}-6\mathbf{k})$.

Again if **R** be their resultant, then

$$\mathbf{R}=\mathbf{F}_1+\mathbf{F}_2+\mathbf{F}_3.$$

$$\therefore\quad \mathbf{R}=\frac{1}{7}[(30+9+2)\,\mathbf{i}+(10-6-3)\,\mathbf{j}+(15+18-6)\,\mathbf{k}]$$
$$=\frac{1}{7}(41\,\mathbf{i}+\mathbf{j}+27\mathbf{k}).$$

Again $\vec{AB}=$ P.V. of $B-$ P.V. of A

$$=(5\mathbf{i}-\mathbf{j}+\mathbf{k})-(2\mathbf{i}-\mathbf{j}-3\mathbf{k})=3\mathbf{i}+0\mathbf{j}+4\mathbf{k}$$

The work done by various forces is equal to work done by their resultant.

$\therefore$ Work done $=\mathbf{R}.\vec{AB}$

$$=\frac{1}{7}[41\mathbf{i}+\mathbf{j}+27\mathbf{k}].[3\mathbf{i}+0\mathbf{j}+4\mathbf{k}]$$
$$=\frac{1}{7}[123+0+108]=\frac{231}{7}=33\text{ units.}$$

11. 87 units of work.

12. 17 units of work.

13. If **R** is the resultant of two forces **P** and **Q**, then

$$\mathbf{R}=\mathbf{P}+\mathbf{Q}=\mathbf{i}-3\mathbf{j}+5\mathbf{k}.$$

Also the displacement of the particle.

$$=\vec{AB}=(6\mathbf{i}+\mathbf{j}-3\mathbf{k})-(4\mathbf{i}-3\mathbf{j}-2\mathbf{k})=2\mathbf{i}+4\mathbf{j}-\mathbf{k}.$$

Hence required work done

$$=\mathbf{R}.\vec{AB}=(\mathbf{i}-3\mathbf{j}+5\mathbf{k}).(2\mathbf{i}+4\mathbf{j}-\mathbf{k})$$
$$=2-12-5=-15.$$

14. Resultant force $\mathbf{R}=\mathbf{P}+\mathbf{Q}=\mathbf{i}-3\mathbf{j}+5\mathbf{k}$ and vector $\vec{OA}=4\mathbf{i}-3\mathbf{j}-2\mathbf{k}$.

Hence moment of **R** about $O=\vec{OA}\times\mathbf{R}$

$$=\begin{vmatrix}\mathbf{i}&\mathbf{j}&\mathbf{k}\\4&-3&-2\\1&-3&5\end{vmatrix}=-21\mathbf{i}-22\mathbf{j}-9\mathbf{k}.$$

$\therefore$ Magnitude of moment

$$=\sqrt{(-21)^2+(-22)^2+(-9)^2}=\sqrt{1006}.$$

Also $\vec{AB}=2\mathbf{i}+4\mathbf{j}-\mathbf{k}$.

Hence work done $=1\times2+(-3)(4)+5(-1)=-15$

15. Ans. work done $=9$,

vector moment $=-6\mathbf{i}-6\mathbf{j}$.

16. Let P be any point in the plane of the polygon. Then the vector moment (torque) of the force represented by $\vec{AB}$ about P is

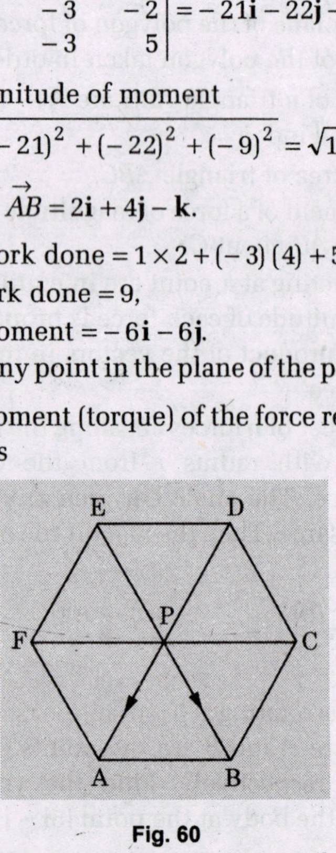

Fig. 60

$\vec{PA} \times \vec{AB}$ = twice the vector area of $\Delta\, PAB$. Similarly moment of force represented by BC about P = twice the vector area of $\Delta\, BPC$.

$\therefore$ Sum of moments

= twice [sum of vector areas of $\Delta\, PAB, \Delta\, PBC, \Delta\, PCD, \dots$]

= twice the vector area of polygon.

17. $\vec{AB} = \vec{OB} - \vec{OA} = 2\mathbf{i} + 2\mathbf{j} - 2\mathbf{k}$

$\vec{AC} = \vec{OC} - \vec{OA} = 3\mathbf{i} + 3\mathbf{j} + 2\mathbf{k}$

Vector area of $\Delta\, ABC$

$$\vec{AB} \times \vec{AC} = \begin{vmatrix} \mathbf{i} & \mathbf{j} & \mathbf{k} \\ 2 & 2 & -2 \\ 3 & 3 & 2 \end{vmatrix} = 10\mathbf{i} + 10\mathbf{j}$$

$$\therefore \quad \Delta = \frac{1}{2} |\vec{AB} \times \vec{AC}| = \frac{1}{2} 10\sqrt{2} = 5\sqrt{2}$$

Now unit vector along $AB = \dfrac{2\mathbf{i} + 2\mathbf{j} - 2\mathbf{k}}{2\sqrt{3}}$

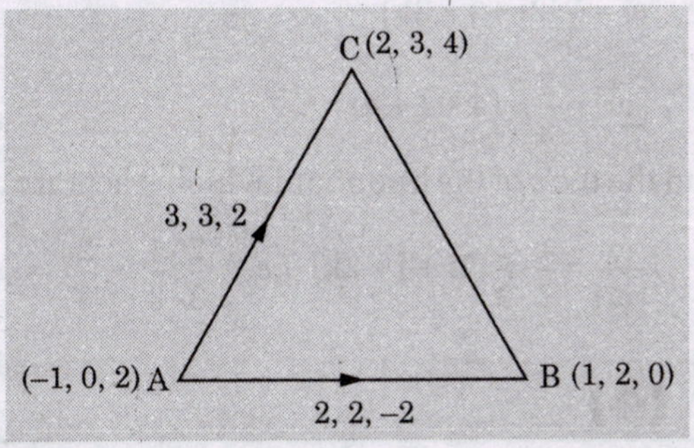

Fig. 61

Hence a force of magnitude 10 N along AB is

$$\mathbf{F} = \frac{10\,(\mathbf{i} + \mathbf{j} - \mathbf{k})}{\sqrt{3}}$$

$\therefore$ Moment = $\mathbf{r} \times \mathbf{F}$

where $\mathbf{r} = \vec{CA} = -3\mathbf{i} - 3\mathbf{j} - 2\mathbf{k}$

$$= \frac{10}{\sqrt{3}} \begin{vmatrix} \mathbf{i} & \mathbf{j} & \mathbf{k} \\ -3 & -3 & -2 \\ 1 & 1 & -1 \end{vmatrix} = \frac{10}{\sqrt{3}} \times 5\,(\mathbf{i} - \mathbf{j})$$

18. Let $\alpha, \beta, \gamma, \delta$ be the unit vectors in the direction of the forces P_1, P_2, P_3, P_4 so that the forces are represented by $P_1\alpha, P_2\beta, P_3\gamma, P_4\delta$ and since they are in equilibrium, we have

$$P_1\alpha + P_2\beta + P_3\gamma + P_4\delta = 0 \qquad \dots(1)$$

Multiply (1) throughout by $\gamma \times \delta$ scalarly and we know that $\alpha \,.\, (\gamma \times \delta) = [\alpha\, \gamma\, \delta]$ and that scalar triple product vanishes when two vectors are equal, *i.e.*, $\gamma \,.\, (\gamma \times \delta) = [\gamma\, \gamma\, \delta] = 0$.

Also we know that for a change of cyclic order in the scalar triple product its sign is changed.

$\therefore \quad P_1\, [\alpha\, \gamma\, \delta] + P_2\, [\beta\, \gamma\, \delta] = 0$

or $\quad -P_1\, [\gamma\, \alpha\, \delta] + P_2\, [\beta\, \gamma\, \delta] = 0$

$$\therefore \quad \frac{P_1}{[\beta\, \gamma\, \delta]} = \frac{P_2}{[\gamma\, \alpha\, \delta]} \qquad \dots(2)$$

Again multiplying (1) scalarly by $\alpha \times \gamma$, we get

$P_2\, [\beta\, \alpha\, \gamma] + P_4\, [\delta\, \alpha\, \gamma] = 0$

or $\quad -P_2\, [\alpha\, \beta\, \gamma] + P_4\, [\gamma\, \delta\, \alpha] = 0$

or $\quad -P_2\, [\alpha\, \beta\, \gamma] - P_4\, [\gamma\, \alpha\, \delta] = 0$

$$\frac{P_2}{[\gamma\, \alpha\, \delta]} = \frac{-P_4}{[\alpha\, \beta\, \gamma]} = \frac{P_1}{[\beta\, \gamma\, \delta]} \quad \text{by (2)} \qquad \dots(3)$$

Again multiplying (1) scalarly by $\alpha \times \beta$,

$P_3\, [\gamma\, \alpha\, \beta] + P_4\, [\delta\, \alpha\, \beta] = 0$

$P_3\, [\alpha\, \beta\, \gamma] + P_4\, [\alpha\, \beta\, \delta] = 0$

$$\therefore \quad \frac{P_3}{[\alpha\, \beta\, \delta]} = \frac{-P_4}{[\alpha\, \beta\, \gamma]} = \frac{P_1}{[\beta\, \gamma\, \delta]} = \frac{P_2}{[\gamma\, \alpha\, \delta]} \quad \text{by (3)}$$

Thus each force is proportional to the scalar triple product of unit vectors in the direction of the other three and therefore to the volume of the parallelopiped determined by these vectors.

19. Let any force be chosen along x-axis *i.e.* in the direction of unit vector **i** and a perpendicular direction *i.e.* y-axis be along the direction of vector **j**. Angle between any two adjacent forces is $2\pi/n$. Hence they will be making an angle, $0, 2\pi/n, 4\pi/n$, ... with the direction of **i**. Resolve each of them along the **i** – **j** direction and R be their resultant, then

$R = r\,(\cos 0\; \mathbf{i} + \sin 0\; \mathbf{j})$

$$+ r\left(\cos \frac{2\pi}{n}\, \mathbf{i} + \sin \frac{2\pi}{n}\, \mathbf{j}\right) + r\,(\quad) + \dots$$

$$= r\left[\cos 0 + \cos \frac{2\pi}{n} + \cos \frac{4\pi}{n} + \dots \cos \frac{2\,(n-1)}{n}\,\pi\right]$$

$$+ \left[\sin 0 + \sin \frac{2\pi}{n} + \sin \frac{4\pi}{n} + \dots \sin \frac{2\,(n-1)}{n}\,\pi\right] = 0$$

Hence (a) is correct answer.

From **R. 38, P. ...... of Trigo.**, we know that sum of n terms of the sines and cosines of angles in A.P. each vanish when the common difference is multiple of $2\pi/n$. Here common difference is $2\pi/n$.

20. Let the vector PM be $\mathbf{r}$ where M is the foot of perpendicular from P on AB,

$$\Delta\, APB = \frac{1}{2}\, AB.PM$$

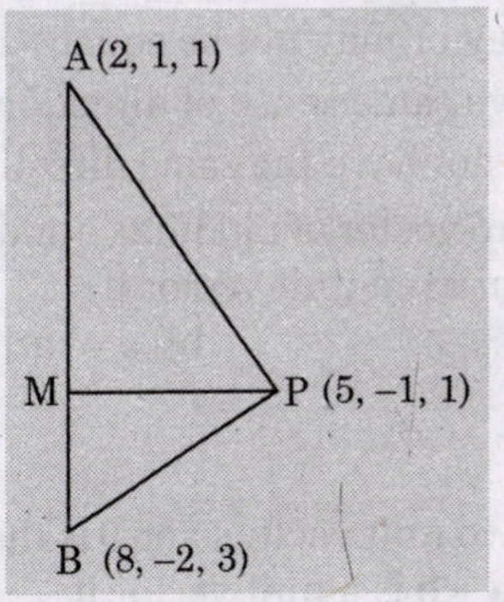

Fig. 62

$\therefore \quad |\vec{PM}| = 2\dfrac{\text{vector area of } \Delta APB}{|\vec{AB}|}$

or $\quad |\mathbf{r}| = 2.\dfrac{1}{2}\dfrac{|\vec{AB} \times \vec{AP}|}{|\beta - \alpha|}$

$\vec{AB} = 6, -3, 2 \quad \therefore \quad |\vec{AB}| = \sqrt{(36 + 9 + 4)} = 7$

$\vec{AP} = 3, -2, 0$

$$\therefore \quad \vec{AB} \times \vec{AP} = \begin{vmatrix} \mathbf{i} & \mathbf{j} & \mathbf{k} \\ 6 & -3 & 2 \\ 3 & -2 & 0 \end{vmatrix} = 4\mathbf{i} + 6\mathbf{j} - 3\mathbf{k}$$

$$\therefore \quad |\mathbf{r}| = \frac{|\mathbf{i} + 6\mathbf{j} - 3\mathbf{k}|}{|6\mathbf{i} - 3\mathbf{j} + 2\mathbf{k}|} = \frac{61}{49}$$

$$\therefore \quad v = |\mathbf{r}| w = \frac{61}{49} \times 5 = \frac{305}{49} = 6 \cdot 2.$$

21. Let A, B, C be the points $(3, -1, -2)$, $(4, 1, 0)$ and $(3, 2, 1)$ respectively so that vectors $\vec{AB}$ and $\vec{AC}$ are

$\vec{AB} = (1, 2, 2) = \mathbf{i} + 2\mathbf{j} + 2\mathbf{k}$

$\vec{AC} = (0, 3, 3) = 3\mathbf{j} + 3\mathbf{k}$

$\vec{v}_1 = 4\mathbf{i} - 4\mathbf{j} + 2\mathbf{k}, \ \vec{v}_2 = 6\mathbf{i} - 4\mathbf{j} + 4\mathbf{k}$

If $\vec{\omega} = \omega_1 \mathbf{i} + \omega_2 \mathbf{j} + \omega_3 \mathbf{k}$ be the angular velocity of the body about the axis through, A then

$$\vec{v_1} = \omega \times \vec{AB}, \quad \vec{v_2} = \omega \times \vec{AC}$$

$$\therefore \quad 4\mathbf{i} - 4\mathbf{j} + 2\mathbf{k} = \begin{vmatrix} \mathbf{i} & \mathbf{j} & \mathbf{k} \\ \omega_1 & \omega_2 & \omega_3 \\ 1 & 2 & 2 \end{vmatrix}$$

Comparing the coefficients of **i**, **j** and **k**, we get

$2(\omega_2 - \omega_3) = 4, \quad 2\omega_1 - \omega_3 = 4, \ 2\omega_1 - \omega_2 = 2$ ...(1)

Similarly,

$$6\mathbf{i} - 4\mathbf{j} + 4\mathbf{k} = \begin{vmatrix} \mathbf{i} & \mathbf{j} & \mathbf{k} \\ \omega_1 & \omega_2 & \omega_3 \\ 0 & 3 & 3 \end{vmatrix}$$

Again comparing **i**, **j**, **k**, we get

$3(\omega_2 - \omega_3) = 6, \quad -3\omega_1 = -4,$

and $3\omega_1 = 4$ ...(2)

From (1) and (2), we easily obtain

$$\omega_1 = \frac{4}{3}, \omega_2 = \frac{2}{3}, \omega_3 = -\frac{4}{3}$$

$$\therefore \quad \vec{\omega} = \frac{2}{3}(2\mathbf{i} + \mathbf{j} - 2\mathbf{k})$$

$$\therefore \quad |\vec{\omega}| = \frac{2}{3}\sqrt{(4 + 1 + 4)} = 2$$

and the d.c's of the line about which it acts are given by

$$\frac{\vec{\omega}}{|\omega|} = \frac{1}{2} \cdot \frac{2}{3}(2\mathbf{i} + \mathbf{j} - 2\mathbf{k}) \ \textit{i.e.,} \ \frac{2}{3}, \frac{1}{3}, -\frac{2}{3}$$

Problem Set (4)

Multiple Choice Questions

1. Two vectors are said to be equal if
(a) their magnitudes are same,
(b) direction is same,
(c) originate from the same point,
(d) they meet at the same point,
(e) they have same magnitude and same sense of direction.

2. Two vectors **a** and **b** are parallel and have equal magnitudes. Then
(a) they are equal,
(b) they are not equal,
(c) they may or may not be equal,
(d) they have same sense of direction,
(e) they do not have the same direction.

3. If **a** is non-zero vector of modulus a and m is a non-zero scalar, then $m\mathbf{a}$ is a unit vector if
(a) $m = \pm 1$ (b) $a = |m|$
(c) $a = \dfrac{1}{|m|}$

4. **a** and **b** are two unit vectors and θ is the angle between them. Then **a** + **b** is a unit vector if
(a) $\theta = \pi/3$ (b) $\theta = \pi/4$
(c) $\theta = \pi/2$ (d) $\theta = 2\pi/3$

5. The position vectors of A and B are **a** and **b** respectively, then the position vector of a point P which divides AB in the ratio 1 : 2 is
(a) $\dfrac{\mathbf{a} + \mathbf{b}}{3}$ (b) $\dfrac{\mathbf{b} + 2\mathbf{a}}{3}$
(c) $\dfrac{\mathbf{a} + 2\mathbf{b}}{3}$ (d) $\dfrac{\mathbf{b} - 2\mathbf{a}}{3}$

6. Point A is **a** + 2**b**, P is **a** and P divides AB in the ratio 2 : 3. The position vector of B is
(a) 2**a** − **b** (b) **b** − 2**a**
(c) **a** − 3**b** (d) **b**

7. θ is the angle between two vectors **a** and **b** then **a** . **b** ≥ 0 only if
(a) $0 \leq \theta \leq \pi$ (b) $\pi/2 \leq \theta \leq \pi$
(c) $0 \leq \theta \leq \pi/2$ (d) $0 < \theta < \pi/2.$

8. If **a** be a non-zero vector, then which of the following is correct ?
(a) **a** . **a** = 0 (b) **a** . **a** > 0
(c) **a** . **a** $\geq$ 0 (d) **a** . **a** $\leq$ 0

9. **a** and **b** are two non-zero vectors, then (**a** + **b**) . (**a** − **b**) is equal to
(a) $a + b$ (b) $(a - b)^2$

(c) $(a+b)^2$ (d) a^2-b^2

(e) $a-b$

10. $\mathbf{a}\,.\,\mathbf{b}=0$ implies only

(a) $\mathbf{a}=\mathbf{0}$ (b) $\mathbf{b}=\mathbf{0}$

(c) $\theta=90^\circ$

(d) either $\mathbf{a}=\mathbf{0}$ or $\mathbf{b}=\mathbf{0}$ or $\theta=90^\circ$,

(e) either $\mathbf{a}=\mathbf{0}$ or $\mathbf{b}=\mathbf{0}$.

11. If **a, b, c** be three non-zero vectors, then the equation $\mathbf{a}\,.\,\mathbf{b}=\mathbf{a}\,.\,\mathbf{c}$ implies

(a) $\mathbf{b}=\mathbf{c}$,

(b) **a** is orthogonal to both **b** and **c**

(c) **a** is orthogonal to $\mathbf{b}-\mathbf{c}$

(d) Either **a** is orthogonal to both **b** and **c** or **a** is orthogonal to $\mathbf{b}-\mathbf{c}$

(e) Either $\mathbf{b}=\mathbf{c}$ or **a** is orthogonal to $\mathbf{b}-\mathbf{c}$

12. If **a** and **b** include an angle of 120° and their magnitudes are 2 and $\sqrt{3}$, then $\mathbf{a}\,.\,\mathbf{b}$ is equal to

(a) 3 (b) $-\sqrt{3}$ (c) $\sqrt{3}$ (d) -3

(e) $-\sqrt{3}/2$.

13. If [**i, j, k**] be a set of orthogonal unit vectors, then fill up the blanks

(a) $\mathbf{i}\,.\,\mathbf{i}+\mathbf{j}\,.\,\mathbf{j}+\mathbf{k}\,.\,\mathbf{k}=$...... (b) $\mathbf{i}\,.\,\mathbf{j}+\mathbf{j}\,.\,\mathbf{k}+\mathbf{k}\,.\,\mathbf{i}=$.......

(c) $\mathbf{i}\,.\,\mathbf{i}=\mathbf{j}\,.\,\mathbf{j}=\mathbf{k}\,.\,\mathbf{k}=$....... (d) $\mathbf{i}\,.\,\mathbf{j}=\mathbf{j}\,.\,\mathbf{k}=\mathbf{k}\,.\,\mathbf{i}=$.......

14. If θ be the angle between the vectors $4(\mathbf{i}-\mathbf{k})$ and $\mathbf{i}+\mathbf{j}+\mathbf{k}$, then θ is

(a) $\pi/4$ (b) $\pi/3$

(c) $\pi/2$ (d) $\cos^{-1}(1/\sqrt{3})$

15. (i) If θ be the angle between the vectors $\mathbf{i}+\mathbf{j}$ and $\mathbf{j}+\mathbf{k}$, then θ is

(a) 0 (b) $\pi/4$

(c) $\pi/2$ (d) $\pi/3$

(e) $\pi/6$

(ii) The angle between the vectors $2\mathbf{i}+3\mathbf{j}+\mathbf{k}$ and $2\mathbf{i}-\mathbf{j}-\mathbf{k}$ is

(a) $\pi/2$ (b) $\pi/4$

(c) $\pi/3$ (d) 0 **(M.N.R. 1990)**

16. If **a** and **b** are two unit vectors, then $\mathbf{a}\times\mathbf{b}$ is a unit vector if ....

17. If [**i, j, k**] be orthonormal set of unit vectors, then fill in the blanks.

(a) $\mathbf{i}\times\mathbf{j}=$......

(b) $\mathbf{j}\times\mathbf{i}=$..........

(c) $\mathbf{i}\times(\mathbf{j}\times\mathbf{k})=$.........

(d) $\mathbf{i}\times(\mathbf{j}\times\mathbf{k})+\mathbf{j}\times(\mathbf{k}\times\mathbf{i})+\mathbf{k}\times(\mathbf{i}\times\mathbf{j})$..........

(e) $\mathbf{i}\,.(\mathbf{j}\times\mathbf{k})+\mathbf{j}\,.(\mathbf{k}\times\mathbf{i})+\mathbf{k}\,.(\mathbf{i}\times\mathbf{j})$.........

18. [**a b c**] is the scalar triple product of three vectors **a, b** and **c**, then [**a b c**] is equal to

(a) [**b a c**] (b) [**c b a**]

(c) [**b c a**] (d) [**a c b**]

19. If θ is the angle between vectors **a** and **b**, then $|\mathbf{a}\times\mathbf{b}|=|\mathbf{a}\,.\,\mathbf{b}|$, then θ is equal to

(a) 0 (b) 180° (c) 135° (d) 45°

20. $\mathbf{a}\times(\mathbf{b}\times\mathbf{c})$ is equal to

(a) $(\mathbf{a}\,.\,\mathbf{b})\,\mathbf{c}-(\mathbf{a}\,.\,\mathbf{c})\,\mathbf{b}$ (b) $(\mathbf{a}\,.\,\mathbf{b})\,\mathbf{a}+(\mathbf{a}\,.\,\mathbf{b})\,\mathbf{c}$

(c) $(\mathbf{b}\,.\,\mathbf{c})\,\mathbf{a}-(\mathbf{b}\,.\,\mathbf{c})\,\mathbf{b}$ (d) $(\mathbf{a}\,.\,\mathbf{c})\,\mathbf{b}-(\mathbf{a}\,.\,\mathbf{b})\,\mathbf{c}$

(e) $(\mathbf{c}\,.\,\mathbf{a})\,\mathbf{a}-(\mathbf{b}\,.\,\mathbf{a})\,\mathbf{c}$.

21. $\mathbf{u}=\mathbf{a}\times(\mathbf{b}\times\mathbf{c})+\mathbf{b}\times(\mathbf{c}\times\mathbf{a})+\mathbf{c}\times(\mathbf{a}\times\mathbf{b})$, then

(a) **u** is a unit vector (b) $\mathbf{u}=\mathbf{a}+\mathbf{b}+\mathbf{c}$

(c) $\mathbf{u}=\mathbf{0}$ (d) $\mathbf{u}\neq\mathbf{0}$

22. If $\mathbf{a}=4\mathbf{i}+2\mathbf{j}-5\mathbf{k}$, $\mathbf{b}=-12\mathbf{i}-6\mathbf{j}+15\mathbf{k}$, then the vectors **a, b** are

(a) perpendicular (b) parallel,

(c) non-coplanar (d) none of these.

23. If the position vectors of three points are $\mathbf{a}-2\mathbf{b}+3\mathbf{c}$, $2\mathbf{a}+3\mathbf{b}-4\mathbf{c}$, $-7\mathbf{b}+10\mathbf{c}$, then the three points are

(a) collinear (b) coplanar

(c) non-collinear (d) neither.

24. (i) If $\mathbf{a}+\mathbf{b}+\mathbf{c}=\mathbf{0}$, $|\mathbf{a}|=3$, $|\mathbf{b}|=5$, $|\mathbf{c}|=7$, then the angle between **a** and **b** is

(a) $\pi/6$ (b) $2\pi/3$

(c) $5\pi/3$ (d) $\pi/3$

(ii) If the vectors **a, b, c** satisfy the condition $\mathbf{a}+\mathbf{b}+\mathbf{c}=0$; the value of $\mathbf{a}\,.\,\mathbf{b}+\mathbf{b}\,.\,\mathbf{c}+\mathbf{c}\,.\,\mathbf{a}$ if $|\mathbf{a}|=1, |\mathbf{b}|=3$ and $|\mathbf{c}|=4$ is

(a) 11 (b) -13

(c) 15 (d) 12

25. If **a, b, c** are any three coplanar unit vectors, then

(a) $\mathbf{a}\,.(\mathbf{b}\times\mathbf{c})=1$ (b) $\mathbf{a}\,.(\mathbf{b}\times\mathbf{c})=3$

(c) $(\mathbf{a}\times\mathbf{b})\,.\,\mathbf{c}=0$ (d) $(\mathbf{c}\times\mathbf{a})\,.\,\mathbf{b}=1$

26. If $\mathbf{a}\,.\,\mathbf{b}=\mathbf{a}\,.\,\mathbf{c}$ and $\mathbf{a}\times\mathbf{b}=\mathbf{a}\times\mathbf{c}$, then

(a) **a** is perpendicular to $\mathbf{b}-\mathbf{c}$

(b) **a** is parallel to $\mathbf{b}-\mathbf{c}$,

(c) either $\mathbf{a}=\mathbf{0}$ or $\mathbf{b}=\mathbf{c}$,

(d) none of these.

27. The vector $2\mathbf{i}+\mathbf{j}-\mathbf{k}$ is perpendicular to $\mathbf{i}-4\mathbf{j}+\lambda\mathbf{k}$ if λ is equal to

(a) 0 (b) -1 (c) -2 (d) -3

28.* The vectors $2\mathbf{i}+3\mathbf{j}-4\mathbf{k}$ and $a\mathbf{i}+b\mathbf{j}+c\mathbf{k}$ are perpendicular when

(a) $a=2,\ b=3,\ c=-4$ (b) $a=4,\ b=4,\ c=5$

(c) $a=4,\ b=4,\ c=-5$ (d) none of these

29. If **a** and **b** are position vectors of A and B respectively the position vector of a point C on AB produced such that $\vec{AC}=3\,\vec{AB}$ is

(a) $3\mathbf{a}-\mathbf{b}$ (b) $3\mathbf{b}-\mathbf{a}$

(c) $3\mathbf{a}-2\mathbf{b}$ (d) $3\mathbf{b}-2\mathbf{a}$

30. **a** and **b** are the position vectors of the points A and B with respect to an origin O. A point C on OA is such that

$2AC = CO$, CD is parallel to OB and $|\vec{CD}| = 3|\vec{OB}|$, then the vector $\vec{AD}$, is ......

31. If $\mathbf{A} = 2\mathbf{i} + 2\mathbf{j} - \mathbf{k}$, $\mathbf{B} = 6\mathbf{i} - 3\mathbf{j} + 2\mathbf{k}$, then $\mathbf{A} \times \mathbf{B}$ will be given by
(a) $2\mathbf{i} - 2\mathbf{j} - \mathbf{k}$ (b) $6\mathbf{i} - 3\mathbf{j} + 2\mathbf{k}$
(c) $\mathbf{i} - 10\mathbf{j} - 18\mathbf{k}$ (d) $\mathbf{i} + \mathbf{j} + \mathbf{k}$.

32.* The number of vectors of unit length perpendicular to vectors $\mathbf{a} = (1, 1, 0)$ and $\mathbf{b} = (0, 1, 1)$ is
(a) one (b) two
(c) three (d) infinite
(e) none

33. A vector $\mathbf{a}$ has components $2p$ and 1 with respect to a rectangular cartesian system. This system is rotated through a certain angle about the origin in the counter-clockwise sense. If, with respect to new system, $\mathbf{a}$ has components $p+1$ and 1, then
(a) $p = 0$, (b) $p = 1$ or $p = -\frac{1}{3}$,
(c) $p = -1$ or $p = \frac{1}{3}$, (d) $p = 1$ or $p = -1$,
(e) none of these.

34. If $|\vec{\alpha} + \vec{\beta}| = |\vec{\alpha} - \vec{\beta}|$, then
(a) $\vec{\alpha}$ is parallel to $\vec{\beta}$
(b) $\vec{\alpha}$ is perpendicular to $\vec{\beta}$
(c) $|\vec{\alpha}| = |\vec{\beta}|$
(d) none of these.

35. If $\vec{a}$ and $\vec{b}$ are two vectors such that $\vec{a} \cdot \vec{b} = 0$ and $\vec{a} \times \vec{b} = \vec{0}$, then
(a) $\vec{a}$ is parallel to $\vec{b}$
(b) $\vec{a}$ is perpendicular to $\vec{b}$
(c) either $\vec{a}$ or $\vec{b}$ is a null vector
(d) none of these

36.* If $\vec{a}, \vec{b}, \vec{c}$ are three non-coplanar vectors and $\vec{p}, \vec{q}, \vec{r}$ are vectors defined by the relations

$$\vec{p} = \frac{\vec{b} \times \vec{c}}{[\vec{a}\ \vec{b}\ \vec{c}]},\quad \vec{q} = \frac{\vec{c} \times \vec{a}}{[\vec{a}\ \vec{b}\ \vec{c}]},\quad \vec{r} = \frac{\vec{a} \times \vec{b}}{[\vec{a}\ \vec{b}\ \vec{c}]}$$

Then the value of the expression

$$(\vec{a} + \vec{b}) \cdot \vec{p} + (\vec{b} + \vec{c}) \cdot \vec{q} + (\vec{c} + \vec{a}) \cdot \vec{r}$$

is equal to
(a) 0 (b) 1 (c) 2 (d) 3

37.* The components of a vector $\vec{a}$ along and perpendicular to a non-zero vector $\vec{b}$ are ..... and ..... respectively.

38.* For any three vectors $\mathbf{a}, \mathbf{b}, \mathbf{c}$

$$(\mathbf{a} - \mathbf{b}) \cdot (\mathbf{b} - \mathbf{c}) \times (\mathbf{c} - \mathbf{a}) = 2\mathbf{a} \cdot \mathbf{b} \times \mathbf{c}.$$

(a) True (b) False.

39. If $\mathbf{a} = 4\mathbf{i} + 6\mathbf{j}$ and $\mathbf{b} = 3\mathbf{j} + 4\mathbf{k}$, then the vector form of component of $\mathbf{a}$ along $\mathbf{b}$ is
(a) $\frac{18}{10\sqrt{(3)}}(3\mathbf{j} + 4\mathbf{k})$, (b) $\frac{18}{25}(3\mathbf{j} + 4\mathbf{k})$
(c) $\frac{18}{\sqrt{(3)}}(3\mathbf{j} + 4\mathbf{k})$, (d) $3\mathbf{j} + 4\mathbf{k}$.

40.* A unit vector perpendicular to the vector

$4\mathbf{i} - \mathbf{j} + 3\mathbf{k}$ and $-2\mathbf{i} + \mathbf{j} - 2\mathbf{k}$ is

(a) $\frac{1}{3}(\mathbf{i} - 2\mathbf{j} + 2\mathbf{k})$ (b) $\frac{1}{3}(-\mathbf{i} + 2\mathbf{j} + 2\mathbf{k})$
(c) $\frac{1}{3}(2\mathbf{i} + \mathbf{j} + 2\mathbf{k})$ (d) $\frac{1}{3}(2\mathbf{i} - 2\mathbf{j} + 2\mathbf{k})$

(M.N.R. 1995)

41. Determine a unit vector which is coplanar with vectors $\mathbf{a} = \mathbf{i} - \mathbf{j}$ and $\mathbf{b} = \mathbf{i} + 2\mathbf{j}$ and is perpendicular to $\mathbf{a}$.

42.* If $\mathbf{u} = \mathbf{i} \times (\mathbf{a} \times \mathbf{i}) + \mathbf{j} \times (\mathbf{a} \times \mathbf{j}) + \mathbf{k} \times (\mathbf{a} \times \mathbf{k})$, then
(a) $\mathbf{u}$ is a unit vector (b) $\mathbf{u} = \mathbf{a} + \mathbf{i} + \mathbf{j} + \mathbf{k}$
(c) $\mathbf{u} = 2\mathbf{a}$ (d) $\mathbf{u} = 8(\mathbf{i} + \mathbf{j} + \mathbf{k})$

43. The volume of a parallelopiped whose sides are given by $\vec{OA} = 2\mathbf{i} - 3\mathbf{j}$, $\vec{OB} = \mathbf{i} + \mathbf{j} - \mathbf{k}$, $\vec{OC} = 3\mathbf{i} - \mathbf{k}$ is
(a) 4/13 (b) 4
(c) 2/7 (d) none of these

44.* If $\alpha = 2\mathbf{i} + 3\mathbf{j} - \mathbf{k}$, $\beta = -\mathbf{i} + 2\mathbf{j} - 4\mathbf{k}$, $\gamma = \mathbf{i} + \mathbf{j} + \mathbf{k}$, then the value of $(\alpha \times \beta) \cdot (\alpha \times \gamma)$ is equal to
(a) 60 (b) 64 (c) 74 (d) -74

45.* Let $\mathbf{a} = 2\mathbf{i} - \mathbf{j} + \mathbf{k}$; $\mathbf{b} = \mathbf{i} + 2\mathbf{j} - \mathbf{k}$ and $\mathbf{c} = \mathbf{i} + \mathbf{j} - 2\mathbf{k}$ be three vectors. A vector in the plane of $\mathbf{b}$ and $\mathbf{c}$ whose projection on $\mathbf{a}$ is of magnitude $\sqrt{(2/3)}$ is
(a) $2\mathbf{i} + 3\mathbf{j} - 3\mathbf{k}$ (b) $2\mathbf{i} + 3\mathbf{j} + 3\mathbf{k}$
(c) $-2\mathbf{i} - \mathbf{j} + 5\mathbf{k}$ (d) $2\mathbf{i} + \mathbf{j} + 5\mathbf{k}$ **(I.I.T. 1993)**

46. If the vectors $\mathbf{c}$, $\mathbf{a} = x\,\mathbf{i} + y\,\mathbf{j} + z\,\mathbf{k}$ and $\mathbf{b} = \mathbf{j}$ are such that $\mathbf{a}, \mathbf{c}, \mathbf{b}$ form a right handed systems, then $\mathbf{c}$ is
(a) $z\,\mathbf{i} - x\,\mathbf{k}$ (b) 0
(c) $y\,\mathbf{j}$ (d) $-z\,\mathbf{i} + x\,\mathbf{k}$

47.* The vector $\mathbf{a}$ lies in the plane of vectors $\mathbf{b}$ and $\mathbf{c}$, then which of the following is correct ?
(a) $\mathbf{a} \cdot (\mathbf{b} \times \mathbf{c}) = 0$ (b) $\mathbf{a} \cdot \mathbf{b} \times \mathbf{c} = 1$
(c) $\mathbf{a} \cdot \mathbf{b} \times \mathbf{c} = -1$ (d) $\mathbf{a} \cdot \mathbf{b} \times \mathbf{c} = 3$

48. If $\mathbf{a} \times \mathbf{b} = \mathbf{c}$, $\mathbf{b} \times \mathbf{c} = \mathbf{a}$ and a, b, c be moduli of the vectors $\mathbf{a}, \mathbf{b}, \mathbf{c}$ respectively, then
(a) $a = 1, b = c$ (b) $c = 1, a = 1$
(c) $b = 2, c = 2a$ (d) $b = 1, c = a$

49. Let $\mathbf{a} = \mathbf{i} + \mathbf{j}$ and $\mathbf{b} = 2\mathbf{i} - \mathbf{k}$, then the point of intersection of the lines $\mathbf{r} \times \mathbf{a} = \mathbf{b} \times \mathbf{a}$ and $\mathbf{r} \times \mathbf{b} = \mathbf{a} \times \mathbf{b}$ is
(a) $(-1, 1, 1)$ (b) $(3, -1, 1)$
(c) $(3, 1, -1)$ (d) $(1, -1, -1)$

50. Let **a**, **b**, **c** be three non-coplanar vectors and **r** be any vector in space such that $\mathbf{r}.\mathbf{a}=1, \mathbf{r}.\mathbf{b}=2$ and $\mathbf{r}.\mathbf{c}=3$. If $[\mathbf{a}\,\mathbf{b}\,\mathbf{c}]=1$, then **r** is equal to :
(a) $(\mathbf{b}.\mathbf{c})\mathbf{a}+2(\mathbf{c}.\mathbf{a})\mathbf{b}+3(\mathbf{a}.\mathbf{b})\mathbf{c}$
(b) $(\mathbf{b}\times\mathbf{c})+2(\mathbf{c}\times\mathbf{a})+3(\mathbf{a}\times\mathbf{b})$
(c) $\mathbf{a}+2\mathbf{b}+3\mathbf{c}$
(d) none

51. Let **a**, **b**, **c** be unit vectors such that $\mathbf{a}+\mathbf{b}+\mathbf{c}=\mathbf{0}$. Which one of the following is correct ?
(a) $\mathbf{a}\times\mathbf{b}=\mathbf{b}\times\mathbf{c}=\mathbf{c}\times\mathbf{a}=\mathbf{0}$
(b) $\mathbf{a}\times\mathbf{b}=\mathbf{b}\times\mathbf{c}=\mathbf{c}\times\mathbf{a}\neq\mathbf{0}$
(c) $\mathbf{a}\times\mathbf{b}=\mathbf{b}\times\mathbf{c}=\mathbf{a}\times\mathbf{c}=\mathbf{0}$
(d) $\mathbf{a}\times\mathbf{b}, \mathbf{b}\times\mathbf{c}, \mathbf{c}\times\mathbf{a}$ are mutually perpendicular
(I.I.T. 2007)

52. Unit vector **c** is inclined at an angle θ to unit vectors **a** and **b** which are perpendicular. For $\mathbf{c}=\lambda(\mathbf{a}+\mathbf{b})+\mu(\mathbf{a}\times\mathbf{b}), \lambda,\mu$ real, θ belongs to :
(a) $\left[0,\frac{\pi}{2}\right]$ (b) $\left[\frac{\pi}{2},\pi\right]$ (c) $\left[\frac{\pi}{4},\frac{3\pi}{4}\right]$ (d) $\left[\frac{\pi}{4},\frac{\pi}{2}\right]$

53. If $\hat{\mathbf{a}}, \hat{\mathbf{b}}, \hat{\mathbf{c}}$ and $\hat{\mathbf{d}}$ are unit vectors such that $(\hat{\mathbf{a}}\times\hat{\mathbf{b}})\cdot(\hat{\mathbf{c}}\times\hat{\mathbf{d}})=1$ and $\hat{\mathbf{a}}\cdot\hat{\mathbf{c}}=\frac{1}{2}$, then
(a) $\hat{\mathbf{a}}, \hat{\mathbf{b}}, \hat{\mathbf{c}}$ are non-coplanar
(b) $\hat{\mathbf{b}}, \hat{\mathbf{c}}, \hat{\mathbf{d}}$ are non-coplanar
(c) $\hat{\mathbf{b}}, \hat{\mathbf{d}}$ are non-parallel
(d) $\hat{\mathbf{a}}, \hat{\mathbf{d}}$ are parallel and $\hat{\mathbf{b}}, \hat{\mathbf{c}}$ are parallel **(I.I.T. 2009)**

54. If **u**, **v**, **w** are non-coplanar vectors and p, q are real numbers, then the equality $[3\mathbf{u}\; p\mathbf{v}\; p\mathbf{w}]-[p\mathbf{v}\;\mathbf{w}\;q\mathbf{u}]-[2\mathbf{w}\;q\mathbf{v}\;q\mathbf{u}]=0$ holds for
(a) all values of (p,q)
(b) exactly one value of (p,q)
(c) exactly two values of (p,q)
(d) more than two but not all values of (p,q)
(AIEEE 2009)

55. Let $ABCD$ be a parallelogram such that $\vec{AB}=\mathbf{q}, \vec{AD}=\mathbf{p}$ and $\angle BAD$ be an acute angle. If **r** is the vector that coincides with the altitudes directed from the vertex B to the side AD, then **r** is given by
(a) $\mathbf{r}=3\mathbf{q}-\frac{3(\mathbf{p}.\mathbf{q})}{(\mathbf{p}.\mathbf{p})}\mathbf{p}$ (b) $\mathbf{r}=-\mathbf{q}+\left(\frac{(\mathbf{p}.\mathbf{q})}{(\mathbf{p}.\mathbf{p})}\right)\mathbf{p}$
(c) $\mathbf{r}=\mathbf{q}-\left(\frac{\mathbf{p}.\mathbf{q}}{(\mathbf{p}.\mathbf{p})}\right)\mathbf{p}$ (d) $\mathbf{r}=-3\mathbf{q}+\frac{3(\mathbf{p}.\mathbf{q})}{(\mathbf{p}.\mathbf{p})}\mathbf{p}$
(AIEEE 2012)

56. Two vectors **a** and **b** are not perpendicular and **c** and **d** are two vectors satisfying $\mathbf{b}\times\mathbf{c}=\mathbf{b}\times\mathbf{d}$ and $\mathbf{a}.\mathbf{d}=0$. Then vector **d** is equal to
(a) $\mathbf{b}-\left(\frac{\mathbf{b}.\mathbf{c}}{\mathbf{a}.\mathbf{b}}\right)\mathbf{c}$ (b) $\mathbf{c}+\left(\frac{\mathbf{a}.\mathbf{c}}{\mathbf{a}.\mathbf{b}}\right)\mathbf{b}$
(c) $\mathbf{b}+\left(\frac{\mathbf{b}.\mathbf{c}}{\mathbf{a}.\mathbf{b}}\right)\mathbf{c}$ (d) $\mathbf{c}-\left(\frac{\mathbf{a}.\mathbf{c}}{\mathbf{a}.\mathbf{b}}\right)\mathbf{b}$
(AIEEE 2011)

57. If **a** and **b** are vectors such that $|\mathbf{a}+\mathbf{b}|=\sqrt{29}$ and $\mathbf{a}\times(2\mathbf{i}+3\mathbf{j}+\mu\mathbf{k})=(2\mathbf{i}+3\mathbf{j}+4\mathbf{k})\times\mathbf{b}$, then a possible value of $(\mathbf{a}+\mathbf{b}).(-7\mathbf{i}+2\mathbf{j}+3\mathbf{k})$ is
(a) 0 (b) 3 (c) 4 (d) 8
(IIT-JEE 2012)

58. If the vectors $\mathbf{a}=\mathbf{i}-\mathbf{j}+2\mathbf{k}$, $\mathbf{b}=2\mathbf{i}+4\mathbf{j}+\mathbf{k}$ and $\mathbf{c}=\lambda\,\mathbf{i}+\mathbf{j}+4\mathbf{k}$ are mutually orthogonal, then $(\lambda,\mu)=$
(a) $(-3,2)$ (b) $(2,-3)$ (c) $(-2,3)$ (d) $(3,-2)$
(AIEEE 2010)

59. Let P, Q, R and S be the points on the plane with position vectors $-2\mathbf{i}-\mathbf{j}$; $4\mathbf{i}$; $3\mathbf{i}+3\mathbf{j}$ and $-3\mathbf{i}+2\mathbf{j}$ respectively. The quadrilateral $PQRS$ must be a
(a) Parallelogram, which is neither a rhombus nor a rectangle
(c) square
(c) rectangle but not a square
(d) rhombus, but not a square **(IIT-JEE 2010)**

60. If $\mathbf{a}=\frac{1}{\sqrt{10}}(3\mathbf{i}+\mathbf{k})$ and $\mathbf{b}=\frac{1}{7}(2\mathbf{i}+3\mathbf{j}-6\mathbf{k})$, then the value of $(2\mathbf{a}-\mathbf{b})\,[(\mathbf{a}\times\mathbf{b})\times(\mathbf{a}+2\mathbf{b})]$ is
(a) −5 (b) −3 (c) 5 (d) 3
(AIEEE 2011)

61. Two adjacent sides of a parallelogram $ABCD$ are given by $\vec{AB}=2\mathbf{i}+10\mathbf{j}+11\mathbf{k}$ and $\vec{AD}=-\mathbf{i}+2\mathbf{j}+2\mathbf{k}$. The side AD is rotated by an acute angle α in the plane of the parallelogram so that AD becomes AD'. If AD' makes a right angle with the side AB, then cosine of the angle α is given by
(a) $\frac{8}{9}$ (b) $\frac{\sqrt{17}}{9}$ (c) $\frac{1}{9}$ (d) $\frac{4\sqrt{5}}{9}$
(IIT-JEE 2010)

62. The vector(s) which is/are coplanar with vectors $\mathbf{i}+\mathbf{j}+2\mathbf{k}$ and $\mathbf{i}+2\mathbf{j}+\mathbf{k}$ are perpendicular to the vector $\mathbf{i}+\mathbf{j}+\mathbf{k}$ is/are
(a) $\mathbf{j}-\mathbf{k}$ (b) $-\mathbf{i}+\mathbf{j}$ (c) $\mathbf{i}-\mathbf{j}$ (d) $-\mathbf{j}+\mathbf{k}$
(IIT-JEE 2011)

63. If the straight line $\frac{x-1}{2}=\frac{y+1}{k}=\frac{z}{2}$ and $\frac{x+1}{5}=\frac{y+1}{2}=\frac{z}{k}$ are coplanar, then the plane(s) containing these two lines is (are)
(a) $y+2z=-1$ (b) $y+z=-1$
(c) $y-z=-1$ (d) $y-2z=-1$
(IIT-JEE 2012)

64. If **a**, **b** and **c** are unit vectors satisfying $|\mathbf{a}-\mathbf{b}|^2+|\mathbf{b}-\mathbf{c}|^2+|\mathbf{c}-\mathbf{a}|^2=9$ then $|2\mathbf{a}+5\mathbf{b}+5\mathbf{c}|$ is
(a) 3 (b) 4 (c) 5 (d) 6

65. Let $\mathbf{a} = -\mathbf{i} - \mathbf{k}$, $\mathbf{b} = -\mathbf{i} - \mathbf{j}$ and $\mathbf{c} = \mathbf{i} + 2\mathbf{j} + 3\mathbf{k}$ be three given vectors. If $\mathbf{r}$ is a vector such that $\mathbf{r} \times \mathbf{b} = \mathbf{c} \times \mathbf{b}$ and $\mathbf{r} . \mathbf{a} = 0$ then the value of $\mathbf{r} . \mathbf{b}$ is

(a) 9 (b) 6 (c) 3 (d) 0

(IIT JEE 2011)

66. If $\mathbf{a}$ and $\mathbf{b}$ are vectors in space given by $\mathbf{a} = \dfrac{\mathbf{i} - 2\mathbf{j}}{\sqrt{5}}$ and $\mathbf{b} = \dfrac{2\mathbf{i} + \mathbf{j} + 3\mathbf{k}}{\sqrt{14}}$ then the value of

$$(2\mathbf{a} + \mathbf{b}) . [(\mathbf{a} \times \mathbf{b}) \times (\mathbf{a} - 2\mathbf{b})] \text{ is}$$

(a) 5 (b) 6 (c) 3 (d) 0

(IIT JEE 2010)

Solutions to Problem Set (4)

1. Ans. (e).

2. Parallel does not imply the same sense of direction. Hence they are equal if the sense of direction is same and not equal if the sense of the direction is opposite. Hence (c) is the correct answer.

3. a is the modulus of vector $\mathbf{a}$. Modulus of $m\mathbf{a}$ is

$$|m|\,a = 1 \text{ if } a = \frac{1}{|m|}.$$

Hence (c) is the correct answer.

4. Ans. (d). $(\mathbf{a} + \mathbf{b})^2 = 1 + 1 + 2(1.1.\cos\theta) = 1$

$\therefore \quad \cos\theta = -1/2 \quad \therefore \; \theta = 2\pi/3.$

5. (b) is the correct answer.

6. $\mathbf{a} = \dfrac{2\mathbf{x} + 3(\mathbf{a} + 2\mathbf{b})}{2 + 3}$; $\therefore$ $5\mathbf{a} - 3\mathbf{a} - 6\mathbf{b} = 2\mathbf{x}$;

$\therefore \quad \mathbf{x} = \mathbf{a} - 3\mathbf{b}$. Hence (c) is the correct answer.

7. $\mathbf{a} . \mathbf{b} = ab\cos\theta \geq 0$ if $\cos\theta \geq 0$; $\therefore$ a and b are +ive. Hence (c) is the correct answer.

i.e. $0 \leq \theta \leq \pi/2$.

8. Square of vector is square of its module;

$\therefore \; \mathbf{a} . \mathbf{a} = a^2 > 0.$

Hence (b) is the correct answer.

9. Clearly (d) is the correct answer.

10. (d) is the correct answer.

11. We have $\mathbf{a} . \mathbf{b} = \mathbf{a} . \mathbf{c} \Rightarrow \mathbf{a} . (\mathbf{b} - \mathbf{c}) = 0$.

It follows that $\mathbf{a}$ is perpendicular to $\mathbf{b} - \mathbf{c}$ or $\mathbf{b} - \mathbf{c} = \mathbf{0}$, *i.e.*, $\mathbf{b} = \mathbf{c}$ or $\mathbf{a} = \mathbf{0}$. But $\mathbf{a}$ is non-zero vector. Hence the correct answer is (e) which includes all the above cases.

12. As $\cos 120^\circ = -\dfrac{1}{2}$.

$$\mathbf{a} . \mathbf{b} = 2\sqrt{3}\left(-\frac{1}{2}\right) = -\sqrt{3}.$$

Hence (b) is correct answer.

13. (a) 3 (b) 0 (c) 1 (d) 0

14. $4(\mathbf{i} - \mathbf{k}) . (\mathbf{i} + \mathbf{j} + \mathbf{k}) = 4(\mathbf{i}^2 - \mathbf{k}^2) + 4(\mathbf{i} . \mathbf{j} - \mathbf{k} . \mathbf{j})$

$= 4(1 - 1) + 4(0 - 0) = 0; \quad \therefore \; \theta = \pi/2.$

Hence (c) is the correct answer.

15. (i) Ans. (d).

(ii) Ans. (a).

16. $\mathbf{a} \times \mathbf{b} = 1.1 \sin\theta\, \hat{\mathbf{n}}$.

It will be a unit vector if $\sin\theta = 1$, *i.e.* $\theta = \pi/2$ *i.e.* if $\mathbf{a}$ and $\mathbf{b}$ are orthogonal.

17. (a) $\mathbf{k}$ (b) $-\mathbf{k}$ (c) $\mathbf{0}$

(d) $\mathbf{0}$ (e) 3

18. Scalar triple product remains unchanged if cyclic order is maintained. Hence (c) is the correct answer.

19. $|ab\sin\theta\,\hat{\mathbf{n}}| = |ab\cos\theta|$

$\therefore \quad ab\sin\theta = ab\cos\theta$ or $\tan\theta = 1$;

$\therefore \quad \theta = 45^\circ$.

Hence (d) is the correct answer.

20. Ans. (d).

21. Ans. (c). **See Q. 26 (a), P. 1157-1166.**

22. Ans. (b).

23. Ans. (a). If A, B, C are the points, then $\vec{BC} = -2\vec{AB}$ and so A, B, C are collinear.

24. (i) Ans. (d). We have $(\mathbf{a} + \mathbf{b})^2 = \mathbf{c}^2$

or $\quad \mathbf{a}^2 + \mathbf{b}^2 + 2\mathbf{a} . \mathbf{b} = \mathbf{c}^2$

or $\quad 9 + 25 + 2.3.5\cos\theta = 49$

$\therefore \quad \cos\theta = 1/2$ so that $\theta = \pi/3$.

(ii) Ans. (b).

25. Ans. (c). **26.** Ans. (c).

27. Ans. (c). **28.** Ans. (b).

29. Ans. (d).

30. The P.V. of point C is

$$\frac{1.0 + 2.\mathbf{a}}{1 + 2} = \frac{2\mathbf{a}}{3} = \vec{OC}$$

$\vec{CD} = 3\mathbf{b}$, by given condition.

$$\vec{OD} = \vec{OC} + \vec{CD} = \frac{2}{3}\mathbf{a} + 3\mathbf{b}$$

$$\vec{AD} = \vec{OD} - \vec{OA} = \left(\frac{2}{3}\mathbf{a} + 3\mathbf{b}\right) - \mathbf{a} = 3\mathbf{b} - \frac{1}{3}\mathbf{a}$$

31. Ans. (c).

32. $\mathbf{a} \times \mathbf{b} = \mathbf{i} - \mathbf{j} + \mathbf{k}$, which is perpendicular to both $\mathbf{a}$ and $\mathbf{b}$. Hence unit vector $= \pm \dfrac{\mathbf{i} - \mathbf{j} + \mathbf{k}}{\sqrt{(3)}}$. (b) is correct.

33. Ans. (b). We have $\mathbf{a} = 2p\mathbf{i} + \mathbf{j}$. On rotation, let $\mathbf{b}$ be the vector with components $p + 1$ and 1 so that $\mathbf{b} = (p + 1)\,\mathbf{i} + \mathbf{j}$. Now under rotation about origin,

$$|\mathbf{a}| = |\mathbf{b}| \Rightarrow |\mathbf{a}|^2 = |\mathbf{b}|^2$$

$\Rightarrow \quad 4p^2 + 1 = (p + 1)^2 + 1$

$\Rightarrow \quad 4p^2 = (p + 1)^2 \Rightarrow 2p = \pm(p + 1)$

Hence $\quad p = 1$ or $-\dfrac{1}{3}$.

34. Ans. (b). **35.** Ans. (c).

36. Ans. (d). **37.** **See § 1, P. 989**

38. Ans. (b). Refer **Q. 14 (b) P. 1156-63**. The given expression is $[\mathbf{a}-\mathbf{b}\ \ \mathbf{b}-\mathbf{c}\ \ \mathbf{c}-\mathbf{a}]=0$.

39. Ans. (b). Note that the component of vector **a** along the vector **b** is $\left(\dfrac{\mathbf{a}\,.\,\mathbf{b}}{|\mathbf{b}|^2}\right)\mathbf{b}$.

(§ 1, P. 1120)

40. Ans. (b).

$$(\mathbf{a}\times\mathbf{b})\div|\mathbf{a}\times\mathbf{b}|=\frac{1}{3}(-\mathbf{i}+2\mathbf{j}+2\mathbf{k})$$

41. Any vector coplanar with vectors **a** and **b** is

$\mathbf{r}=x\mathbf{a}+y\mathbf{b}$. Also $\mathbf{r}\,.\,\mathbf{a}=0$.

$\mathbf{r}=x(\mathbf{i}-\mathbf{j})+y(\mathbf{i}+2\mathbf{j})$

$\mathbf{r}=(x+y)\,\mathbf{i}+(-x+2y)\,\mathbf{j}$

$\mathbf{a}=\mathbf{i}-\mathbf{j}$

$\therefore\ \mathbf{r}\,.\,\mathbf{a}=0$ or $(x+y)+(x-2y)=0\ \therefore\ y=2x$

$\therefore\ \mathbf{r}=3x\mathbf{i}+3x\mathbf{j}=3x(\mathbf{i}+\mathbf{j})$

Hence the unit vector is $\dfrac{3x(\mathbf{i}+\mathbf{j})}{\pm3x\sqrt{2}}=\pm\dfrac{\mathbf{i}+\mathbf{j}}{\sqrt{2}}$

42. Ans. (c).

43. Ans. (b).

44. Ans. (d).

$\alpha\times\beta=-10\mathbf{i}+9\mathbf{j}+7\mathbf{k}$

$\alpha\times\gamma=4\mathbf{i}-3\mathbf{j}-\mathbf{k}$

Dot product $=-40-27-7=-74$

45. Ans. (a) and (c). Any vector **r** in the plane of **b** and **c** is

$\mathbf{r}=\mathbf{b}+t\,\mathbf{c}$

or $\mathbf{r}=(1+t)\,\mathbf{i}+(2+t)\,\mathbf{j}-(1+2t)\,\mathbf{k}$

Projection of **r** on **a** is $\sqrt{\dfrac{2}{3}}\ \ \therefore\ \dfrac{\mathbf{r}\,.\,\mathbf{a}}{|\mathbf{a}|}=\sqrt{\dfrac{2}{3}}$

or $\dfrac{2(1+t)-(2+t)-(1+2t)}{\sqrt{6}}=\pm\sqrt{\dfrac{2}{3}}$

$\therefore\ -t-1=\pm2\ \ \therefore\ t=-3,1$

Putting in (1), we get

$\therefore\ \mathbf{r}=-2\mathbf{i}-\mathbf{j}+5\mathbf{k}$ or $\mathbf{r}=2\mathbf{i}+3\mathbf{j}-3\mathbf{k}$

46. Ans. (a). Since **a**, **c**, **b** form a right handed system

$\therefore\ \mathbf{c}=\mathbf{b}\times\mathbf{a}=\mathbf{j}\times(x\,\mathbf{i}+y\,\mathbf{j}+z\,\mathbf{k})$

$=x(\mathbf{j}\times\mathbf{i})+z(\mathbf{j}\times\mathbf{k})=-x\,\mathbf{k}+z\,\mathbf{i}=z\,\mathbf{i}-x\,\mathbf{k}$

47. Ans. (a). Here (b), (c), (d) are meaningless as there is neither dot nor cross between a scalar $\mathbf{a}\cdot\mathbf{b}$ and a vector **c**.

Since **a**, **b**, **c** are coplanar

$\therefore\ [\mathbf{a}\ \mathbf{b}\ \mathbf{c}]=0$ or $\mathbf{a}\,.(\mathbf{b}\times\mathbf{c})=0$

48. Ans. (d). $\mathbf{a}=\mathbf{b}\times\mathbf{c}$ and $\mathbf{a}\times\mathbf{b}=\mathbf{c}$

$\therefore\ \mathbf{a}=\mathbf{b}\times(\mathbf{a}\times\mathbf{b})=(\mathbf{b}.\mathbf{b})\,\mathbf{a}-(\mathbf{b}.\mathbf{a})\,\mathbf{b}$

or $\mathbf{a}=b^2\mathbf{a}-(\mathbf{b}.\mathbf{a})\,\mathbf{b}$.

Comparing coefficients,

$1=b^2$ and $\mathbf{b}.\mathbf{a}=0$

i.e., $b=1$, **a** and **b** are perpendicular

$\therefore\ \mathbf{c}=\mathbf{a}\times\mathbf{b}=ab\sin90^\circ\,\hat{\mathbf{n}}.\ \ \therefore\ c=ab.$

but $b=1\ \ \therefore\ c=a$

49. Ans. (c). Let $\mathbf{r}=x\,\mathbf{i}+y\,\mathbf{j}+z\,\mathbf{k}$, then

$\mathbf{r}\times\mathbf{a}=\mathbf{b}\times\mathbf{a}\Rightarrow(\mathbf{r}-\mathbf{b})\times\mathbf{a}=0$

$\therefore\ z=-1,\ x-y=2$

$\mathbf{r}\times\mathbf{b}=\mathbf{a}\times\mathbf{b}$

$\Rightarrow\ (\mathbf{r}-\mathbf{a})\times\mathbf{b}=0$

$\therefore\ y=1,\ x+2z=1$

$\therefore\ x=3,\ y=1,\ z=-1$

$\therefore\ \mathbf{r}=3\mathbf{i}+\mathbf{j}-\mathbf{k}$

50. Ans. (b).

Given $[\mathbf{a}\ \mathbf{b}\ \mathbf{c}]\neq0$

Let $\mathbf{r}=x(\mathbf{b}\times\mathbf{c})+y(\mathbf{c}\times\mathbf{a})+z(\mathbf{a}\times\mathbf{b})$

$\therefore\ \mathbf{r}\,.\,\mathbf{a}=x\mathbf{a}\,.\,[\mathbf{b}\times\mathbf{c}]+y\mathbf{a}\,.\,(\mathbf{c}\times\mathbf{a})+z\mathbf{a}\,.\,(\mathbf{a}\times\mathbf{b})$

$1=x\,[\mathbf{a}\ \mathbf{b}\ \mathbf{c}]+y\,[\mathbf{a}\ \mathbf{c}\ \mathbf{a}]+z\,[\mathbf{a}\ \mathbf{a}\ \mathbf{b}]$

$1=x\,.1+y\,.0+z\,.0\ \ \therefore\ x=1$

Similarly multiplying by **b** and **c**, we get $y=2,\ z=3$.

$\therefore\ \mathbf{r}=$ etc. as given in (b).

Note : We could take $\mathbf{r}=x\mathbf{a}+y\mathbf{b}+z\mathbf{c}$.

Multiply the above relation scalarly by **a**, **b**, **c** but we are not given the values of $\mathbf{a}\,.\,\mathbf{a}$, $\mathbf{a}\,.\,\mathbf{b}$ and $\mathbf{a}\,.\,\mathbf{c}$ etc. Hence we chose the above expression for **r**.

51. Ans. (b).

Multiply the given relation vectorially by **a**, **b** and **c** you will have $\mathbf{a}\times\mathbf{b}=\mathbf{c}\times\mathbf{a}=\mathbf{b}\times\mathbf{c}$ etc. $\because\ \mathbf{a}\times\mathbf{a}=0$ and $\mathbf{b}\times\mathbf{a}=-(\mathbf{a}\times\mathbf{b})$

52. Ans. (c).

Given $\mathbf{a}\,.\,\mathbf{b}=0,\ \mathbf{c}\,.\,\mathbf{a}=\mathbf{c}\,.\,\mathbf{b}=1.1\cos\theta$

$\mathbf{c}\,.\,\mathbf{a}=\lambda\,(\mathbf{a}\,.\,\mathbf{a}+\mathbf{a}\,.\,\mathbf{b})+\mu\mathbf{a}\,.\,(\mathbf{a}\times\mathbf{b})$

$1.1\cos\theta=\lambda\,(1+0)+\mu\,.0\qquad\because\ [\mathbf{a}\ \mathbf{a}\ \mathbf{b}]=0$

$\therefore\ \lambda=\cos\theta$

$\mathbf{c}\,.\,\mathbf{c}=\lambda^2\,(\mathbf{a}+\mathbf{b})^2+\mu^2\,(1.1\,.\sin90^\circ\ \mathbf{n})^2+2\lambda\mu\,[(\mathbf{a}+\mathbf{b})\,.\,(\mathbf{a}\times\mathbf{b})]$

$1=\lambda^2\,(1+1+2\,.0)+\mu^2\,.1+2\lambda\mu\,.0$

$1=2\cos^2\theta+\mu^2$

$\therefore\ \mu^2=1-2\cos^2\theta\geq0$ or $\cos^2\theta-\dfrac{1}{2}\leq0$

$$\left(\cos\theta+\frac{1}{\sqrt{2}}\right)\left(\cos\theta-\frac{1}{\sqrt{2}}\right)\leq0$$

$\Rightarrow\ -\dfrac{1}{\sqrt{2}}\leq\cos\theta\leq\dfrac{1}{\sqrt{2}}$

$\cos\dfrac{3\pi}{4}\leq\cos\theta\leq\cos\dfrac{\pi}{4}\ \ \therefore\ \theta\in\left[\dfrac{\pi}{4},\dfrac{3\pi}{4}\right]$

53. Ans. (c). By definition,

$\hat{\mathbf{a}}\times\hat{\mathbf{b}}=1\cdot1\cdot\sin\theta_1\,\hat{\mathbf{n}}_1$

$\therefore\ (\hat{\mathbf{a}}\times\hat{\mathbf{b}})\cdot(\hat{\mathbf{c}}\times\hat{\mathbf{d}})=1$

$\Rightarrow\ \sin\theta_1\sin\theta_2\,\hat{\mathbf{n}}_1\cdot\hat{\mathbf{n}}_2=1$

$\Rightarrow\ \sin\theta_1\sin\theta_2\cos\theta_3=1$

Above is possible when $\theta_1=\theta_2=\dfrac{\pi}{2}$ and $\theta_3=0$ or $\hat{\mathbf{a}}\perp\hat{\mathbf{b}},\ \hat{\mathbf{c}}\perp\hat{\mathbf{d}}$ and $\hat{\mathbf{a}}\times\hat{\mathbf{b}}$ is parallel to $\hat{\mathbf{c}}\times\hat{\mathbf{d}}$.

$\therefore \quad (\hat{\mathbf{a}}\times\hat{\mathbf{b}}) = \lambda\,(\hat{\mathbf{c}}\times\hat{\mathbf{d}})$ ...(1)

$\therefore \quad (\hat{\mathbf{a}}\times\hat{\mathbf{b}})\cdot\hat{\mathbf{c}} = \lambda\,(\hat{\mathbf{c}}\times\hat{\mathbf{d}})\cdot\hat{\mathbf{c}} = \lambda\,[\hat{\mathbf{c}}\,\hat{\mathbf{d}}\,\hat{\mathbf{c}}] = 0$

$\therefore \quad [\hat{\mathbf{a}}\,\hat{\mathbf{b}}\,\hat{\mathbf{c}}] = 0$, *i.e.*, $\hat{\mathbf{a}}, \hat{\mathbf{b}}, \hat{\mathbf{c}}$ are coplanar.

Similarly, $\hat{\mathbf{b}}, \hat{\mathbf{c}}, \hat{\mathbf{d}}$ are also coplanar.

Hence all the four vectors $\hat{\mathbf{a}}, \hat{\mathbf{b}}, \hat{\mathbf{c}}, \hat{\mathbf{d}}$ are coplanar and since $\hat{\mathbf{a}}\cdot\hat{\mathbf{c}} = \dfrac{1}{2}$

$\Rightarrow \quad 1\cdot 1\cdot\cos\theta = \dfrac{1}{2}$

$\Rightarrow \quad \theta = 60°$

So, the angle between $\hat{\mathbf{b}}$ and $\hat{\mathbf{d}}$ is also 60°.

Therefore $\hat{\mathbf{b}}$ and $\hat{\mathbf{d}}$ are non-parallel.

54. Ans. (b).

u, v, w are non-coplanar $\Rightarrow [\mathbf{u}\ \mathbf{v}\ \mathbf{w}] \neq 1$ ...(1)

We are given

$[3\,p\,.\,p - p\,.\,1\,.\,q - 2q\,.\,q]\,[\mathbf{u}\ \mathbf{v}\ \mathbf{w}] = 0$

$\therefore \quad 3p^2 - pq - 2q^2 = 0$ as $[\mathbf{u}\ \mathbf{v}\ \mathbf{w}] \neq 0$ ...(2)

$\therefore$ Above is quadratic in p where p is real.

$\therefore \quad \Delta \geq 0$ or $q^2 - 24q^2 = 0 \Rightarrow -23q^2 = 0 \Rightarrow q = 0$

This in turn implies $p = 0$, by (2).

Hence only one value of (p, q).

55. Ans. (b).

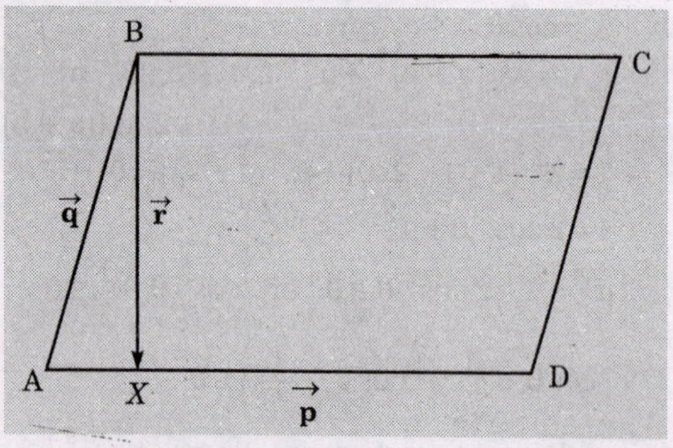

Fig. 63

$$\vec{AX} = \frac{\mathbf{p}\,.\,\mathbf{q}}{|\mathbf{p}|\,.\,|\mathbf{p}|} = \frac{\mathbf{p}\,.\,\mathbf{q}}{|\mathbf{p}|^2}\,.\,\mathbf{p}$$

$$\vec{BX} = \vec{BA} + \vec{AX}$$

$$= -\mathbf{q} + \frac{\mathbf{p}\,.\,\mathbf{q}}{|\mathbf{p}|^2}\,.\,\mathbf{p}$$

56. Ans. (d).

$\mathbf{a}.\mathbf{b} \neq 0, \quad \mathbf{b}\times\mathbf{c} = \mathbf{b}\times\mathbf{d},\ \mathbf{a}\,.\,\mathbf{d} = 0$

$(\mathbf{b}\times\mathbf{c})\times\mathbf{a} = (\mathbf{b}\times\mathbf{d})\times\mathbf{a}$

$(\mathbf{b}\,.\,\mathbf{a})\,\mathbf{c} - (\mathbf{c}\,.\,\mathbf{a})\,\mathbf{b} = (\mathbf{b}\,.\,\mathbf{a})\,\mathbf{d} - (\mathbf{d}\,.\,\mathbf{a})\,\mathbf{b}$

$\Rightarrow \quad \mathbf{d} = \mathbf{c} - \left(\dfrac{\mathbf{a}.\mathbf{c}}{\mathbf{a}.\mathbf{b}}\right).\mathbf{b}$

57. Ans. (c).

Let $\mathbf{c} = 2\mathbf{i} + 3\mathbf{j} + 4\mathbf{k}$

$\mathbf{a}\times\mathbf{c} = \mathbf{c}\times\mathbf{b} \Rightarrow (\mathbf{a}+\mathbf{b})\times\mathbf{c} = 0 \Rightarrow (\mathbf{a}+\mathbf{b})\,||\,\mathbf{c}$

Let $(\mathbf{a}+\mathbf{b}) = \lambda\,\mathbf{c} \Rightarrow |\,\mathbf{a}+\mathbf{b}\,| = |\,\lambda\,|\,|\,\mathbf{c}\,| \Rightarrow \sqrt{29} = |\,\lambda\,|\,.\sqrt{29}$

$\Rightarrow \lambda = \pm 1$

$\therefore \quad \mathbf{a}+\mathbf{b} = \pm(2\mathbf{i} + 3\mathbf{j} + 4\mathbf{k})$

Now $(\mathbf{a}+\mathbf{b})\,.(-7\mathbf{i} + 2\,\mathbf{j} + 3\mathbf{k}) = \pm(-14 + 6 + 12) = \pm 4$

58. Ans. (a).

Given that $\mathbf{a}\perp\mathbf{b}$, $\mathbf{a}\perp\mathbf{b}$ and $\mathbf{c}\perp\mathbf{c}$

Therefore $\mathbf{a}\,.\,\mathbf{c} = 0$ and $\mathbf{b}\,.\,\mathbf{c} = 0$

$\Rightarrow \quad \lambda - 1 + 2\mu = 0$ and $2\lambda + 4 + \mu = 0$

$\Rightarrow \quad \lambda = -3$ and $\mu = 2$

59. Ans. (a).

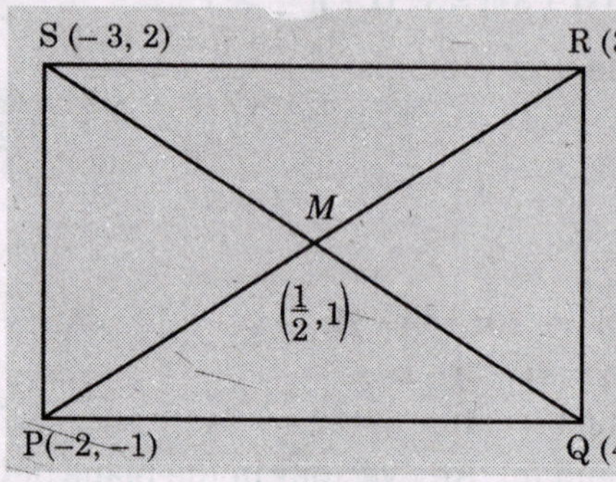

Fig. 64

$PQ = \sqrt{36+1} = \sqrt{37} = RS \Rightarrow PQ \neq PS$

$PS = \sqrt{1+9} = \sqrt{10} = QR$

Slope of $PQ = \dfrac{1}{6}$ and slope of $PS = -3$

$\Rightarrow \quad PQ$ is not perpendicular to PS

Hence, it is a parallelogram, which is neither a rhombus nor a rectangle.

60. Ans. (a).

$(2\mathbf{a}-\mathbf{b})\,.\,[(\mathbf{a}\times\mathbf{b})\times(\mathbf{a}+2\mathbf{b})]$

$= -(2\mathbf{a}-\mathbf{b})\,.\,[(\mathbf{a}+2\mathbf{b})\times(\mathbf{a}\times\mathbf{b})]$

$= -(2\mathbf{a}-\mathbf{b})\,.\,[(\mathbf{a}+2\mathbf{b})\,.\,\mathbf{b})\,\mathbf{a} - [(\mathbf{a}+2\mathbf{b})\,.\,\mathbf{a})\,\mathbf{b}]$

$= -(2\mathbf{a}-\mathbf{b})\,.\,[(\mathbf{a}\,.\,\mathbf{b}) + 2\mathbf{b}.\mathbf{b})\,\mathbf{a} - (\mathbf{a}\,.\,\mathbf{a} + 2\mathbf{b}.\mathbf{a})\,\mathbf{b})]$

$= -(2\mathbf{a}-\mathbf{b})\,[0 + 2\mathbf{a} - (0+\mathbf{b})]$

$= -(2\mathbf{a}-\mathbf{b})^2 = -4\mathbf{a}^2 + 4\mathbf{a}\,.\,\mathbf{b} - \mathbf{b}^2$

$= -4 + 0 - 1 = -5$

61. Ans. (b).

$$\cos\theta = \frac{-2+20+22}{15\times 3} = \frac{8}{9}$$

$\therefore \quad \theta + \alpha = 90° \Rightarrow \alpha = 90° - \theta$

$\Rightarrow \quad \cos\alpha = \sin\theta = \dfrac{\sqrt{17}}{9}$

62. Ans. (a) and (d).

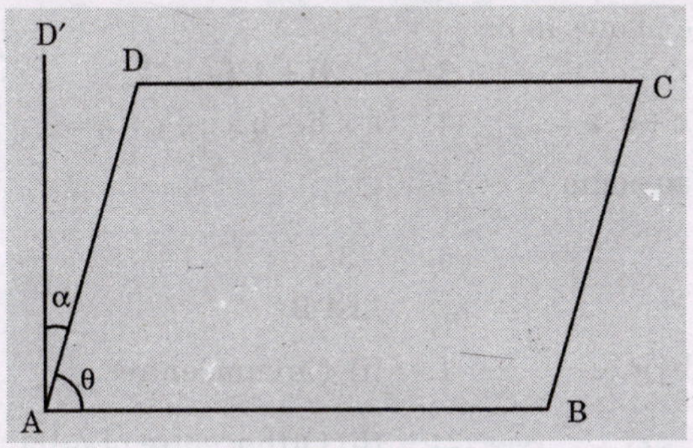

Fig. 65

$\mathbf{a} = \mathbf{i} + \mathbf{j} + 2\mathbf{k},\ \mathbf{b} = \mathbf{i} + 2\mathbf{j} + \mathbf{k},\ \mathbf{c} = \mathbf{i} + \mathbf{j} + \mathbf{k}$

Required vector $\lambda\, \mathbf{c} \times (\mathbf{a} \times \mathbf{b}) = \lambda\, [(\mathbf{c} . \mathbf{b})\, \mathbf{a} - (\mathbf{c} . \mathbf{a})\, \mathbf{b}]$

$= \lambda\, (1 + 2 + 1)\, (\mathbf{i} + \mathbf{j} + 2\mathbf{k}) - (1 + 1 + 2)\, (\mathbf{i} + 2\mathbf{j} + \mathbf{k})]$

$= \lambda\, (-4\mathbf{j} + 4\mathbf{k})$

Hence, our vector is parallel to $-\mathbf{j} + \mathbf{k}$

63. Ans. (b) and (c).

For coplanar lines $[\mathbf{a} - \mathbf{c} \quad \mathbf{b} \quad \mathbf{d}] = 0$

$\mathbf{a} = (1, -1, 0),\ \mathbf{c} = (-1, -1, 0),\ \mathbf{b} = 2\mathbf{i} + k\mathbf{j} + 2\mathbf{k}$

$\mathbf{d} = 5\mathbf{i} + 2\mathbf{j} + k\mathbf{k}$

Now $\begin{vmatrix} 2 & 0 & 0 \\ 2 & k & 2 \\ 5 & 2 & k \end{vmatrix} = 0 \Rightarrow k = \pm 2$

$\mathbf{n}_1 = \mathbf{b}_1 \times \mathbf{d}_1 = 6\mathbf{j} - 6\mathbf{k}$ for $k = 2$,

$\mathbf{n}_2 = \mathbf{b}_2 \times \mathbf{d}_2 = 14\mathbf{j} - 14\mathbf{k}$ for $k = -2$

$\therefore$ equation of the planes are

$(\mathbf{r} - \mathbf{a})\, \mathbf{n}_1 = 0 \Rightarrow y - z = -1$

and $(\mathbf{r} - \mathbf{a})\, \mathbf{n}_2 = 0 \Rightarrow y + z = -1$

64. Ans. (a).

$6 - 2\mathbf{a} . \mathbf{b} - 2\mathbf{b} . \mathbf{c} - 2\mathbf{c} . \mathbf{a} = 0$

$(\mathbf{a} . \mathbf{b} + \mathbf{b} . \mathbf{c} + \mathbf{c} . \mathbf{a}) = \dfrac{-3}{2}$

$|\mathbf{a} + \mathbf{b} + \mathbf{c}|^2 \geq 0$

$3 + 2\, (\mathbf{a} . \mathbf{b} + \mathbf{b} . \mathbf{c} + \mathbf{c} . \mathbf{a}) \geq 0$

$\Rightarrow \mathbf{a} . \mathbf{b} + \mathbf{b} . \mathbf{c} + \mathbf{c} . \mathbf{a} \geq -\dfrac{3}{2}$

since $\mathbf{a} . \mathbf{b} + \mathbf{b} . \mathbf{c} + \mathbf{c} . \mathbf{a} = -\dfrac{3}{2}$

$\Rightarrow |\mathbf{a} + \mathbf{b} + \mathbf{c}| = 0 \quad \Rightarrow \mathbf{a} + \mathbf{b} + \mathbf{c} = 0$

$\Rightarrow |2\mathbf{a} + 5(-\mathbf{a})| = |3\mathbf{a}| = 3$

65. Ans. (a).

$(\mathbf{r} - \mathbf{c}) \times \mathbf{b} = 0$

$\mathbf{r} - \mathbf{c} = \lambda \mathbf{b} \Rightarrow \mathbf{r} = \mathbf{c} + \lambda \mathbf{b},\ \lambda \in \mathbf{R}$

$\therefore \quad \mathbf{r} . \mathbf{a} = 0 \quad \Rightarrow (\mathbf{c} + \lambda \mathbf{b}) . \mathbf{a} = 0$

$\Rightarrow ((1 - \lambda)\, \mathbf{i} + (2 + \lambda)\, \mathbf{j}) + 3\mathbf{k}) . (-\mathbf{i} - \mathbf{k}) = 0$

$\Rightarrow \lambda - 1 - 3 = 0 \quad \Rightarrow \lambda = 4$

$\therefore \quad \mathbf{r} . \mathbf{b} = (-3\mathbf{i} + 6\mathbf{j} + 3\mathbf{k}) . (-\mathbf{i} + \mathbf{j}) = 3 + 6 = 9$

66. Ans. (a).

$\mathbf{a} = \dfrac{\mathbf{i} - 2\mathbf{j}}{\sqrt{5}},\ \mathbf{b} = \dfrac{2\mathbf{i} + \mathbf{j} + 3\mathbf{k}}{\sqrt{14}}$

$|\mathbf{a}| = 1,\ \ |\mathbf{b}| = 1,\ \mathbf{a} . \mathbf{b} = 0$

$\therefore \quad (2\mathbf{a} + \mathbf{b}) . \{(\mathbf{a} \times \mathbf{b}) \times (\mathbf{a} - 2\mathbf{b})\}$

$= (2\mathbf{a} + \mathbf{b})\, \{(\mathbf{a} . (\mathbf{a} - 2\mathbf{b})\, \mathbf{b} - (\mathbf{b} . (\mathbf{a} - 2\mathbf{b})\, \mathbf{a}]$

$= (2\mathbf{a} + \mathbf{b}) . [(1 - 0)\, \mathbf{b} - (0 - 2)\, \mathbf{a}] = (2\mathbf{a} + \mathbf{b}) . (\mathbf{b} + 2\mathbf{a})$

$= 2(\mathbf{a} . \mathbf{b}) + 4(\mathbf{a} . \mathbf{a}) + \mathbf{b} . \mathbf{b} + 2(\mathbf{b} . \mathbf{a})$

$= 0 + 4 + 1 + 0 = 5$

MISCELLANEOUS EXERCISE

Matching Entries

➧ ***Match the entries of List-A and List-B.***

1.

List-A	List-B
(a) D, E, F are mid-points of the sides BC, CA and AB of a triangle ABC, then $\vec{AD} + \vec{BE} + \vec{CF} = \ldots$	1. 90°
(b) The points $2\mathbf{i} - \mathbf{j} + \mathbf{k},\ \mathbf{i} - 3\mathbf{j} - 5\mathbf{k}$ and $3\mathbf{i} - 4\mathbf{j} - 4\mathbf{k}$ are the vertices of a triangle ABC respectively, then $\angle C = \ldots$	2. 8
(c) If the points $10\mathbf{i} + 3\mathbf{j}, 12\mathbf{i} - 5\mathbf{j}$ and $a\mathbf{i} + 11\mathbf{j}$ are collinear, then $\mathbf{a} = \ldots$	3. $\pm (\mathbf{i} - 7\mathbf{j} + 2\mathbf{k})$
(d) The vector $\mathbf{c}$ of moduls $3\sqrt{6}$ directed along the bisectors of angle between the vectors $\mathbf{a} = 7\mathbf{i} - 4\mathbf{j} - 4\mathbf{k}$ and $\mathbf{b} = -2\mathbf{i} - \mathbf{j} + 2\mathbf{k}$ is ...	4. $\vec{0}$

2.

List-A	List-B
(a) If $\mathbf{a} = \mathbf{i} + \mathbf{j} - \mathbf{k}, \mathbf{b} = -\mathbf{i} + 2\mathbf{j} + \mathbf{k}$, and $\mathbf{c} = -\mathbf{i} + 2\mathbf{j} - \mathbf{k}$, then a unit vector $\perp$ to both $\mathbf{a} + \mathbf{b}$ and $\mathbf{b} + \mathbf{c}$ is ...	1. $(\mathbf{a} \times \mathbf{b}) \times (\mathbf{c} \times \mathbf{d}) = 0$ and $(\mathbf{a} \times \mathbf{b}) . (\mathbf{c} \times \mathbf{d}) = 0$
(b) Three points with position vectors $\mathbf{a}, \mathbf{b}, \mathbf{c}$ are collinear if ...	2. $\mathbf{k}$

(c) **a**, **b** and **c**, **d** each determine a plane. The conditions for the planes to be parallel or perpendicular are ... — 3. $-24\mathbf{i}+32\mathbf{j}+30\mathbf{k}$

(d) **a**, **b**, **c** are unit vectors such that $\mathbf{a}+\mathbf{b}+\mathbf{c}=0$, then $\mathbf{a}.\mathbf{b}+\mathbf{b}.\mathbf{c}+\mathbf{c}.\mathbf{a}=...$ — 4. $\mathbf{a}\times\mathbf{b}+\mathbf{b}\times\mathbf{c}+\mathbf{c}\times\mathbf{a}=0$

(e) If $|\mathbf{a}|=50$ and **a** is collinear with $6\mathbf{i}-8\mathbf{j}-\frac{15}{2}\mathbf{k}$ and makes an acute angle with +ive direction of z-axis, then $\mathbf{a}=...$ — 5. $-3/2$

3. **List-A** / **List-B**

(a) If θ be the angle between unit vectors **a** and **b**, then $\frac{1}{2}|\mathbf{a}-\mathbf{b}|=...$ — 1. (i) Circumcentre (ii) Orthocentre of ΔABC

(b) The four points with position vectors $\mathbf{A}=7\mathbf{i}-4\mathbf{j}+7\mathbf{k}$, $\mathbf{B}=\mathbf{i}-6\mathbf{j}+10\mathbf{k}$, $\mathbf{C}=-\mathbf{i}-3\mathbf{j}+4\mathbf{k}$, $\mathbf{D}=5\mathbf{i}-\mathbf{j}+\mathbf{k}$ are the vertices of a square, or rhombus or rectangle or parallelogram. — 2. 3/2

(c) The position vectors of four points A, B, C, D lying in a plane are **a**, **b**, **c**, **d** respectively.
If (i) $|\mathbf{a}-\mathbf{d}|=|\mathbf{b}-\mathbf{d}|=|\mathbf{c}-\mathbf{d}|$ or (ii) $(\mathbf{a}-\mathbf{d}).(\mathbf{b}-\mathbf{c})=(\mathbf{b}-\mathbf{d}).(\mathbf{c}-\mathbf{a})=0$ then determine the position of the point D. — 3. $\left|\sin\frac{\theta}{2}\right|$

(d) If **m** and **n** are unit vectors inclined at 30°, then the area of the parallelogram whose sides are $(\mathbf{m}+2\mathbf{n})$ and $2\mathbf{m}+\mathbf{n}$ is ... — 4. Rhombus

4. **List-A** / **List-B**

(a) $A(1,-1,10), B(-1,-3,7), C(5,-1,\lambda), D(7,-4,7)$ are the vertices of a tetrahedron whose volume is 11 cubic units, then $\lambda=...$ — 1. $3\pi/4$

(b) If **a**, **b**, **c** be three non-coplanar vectors, then $(\mathbf{a}+\mathbf{b}+\mathbf{c}).\{(\mathbf{a}+\mathbf{b})\times(\mathbf{a}+\mathbf{c})\}=...$ — 2. 1 or 7

(c) If the three vectors $\mathbf{i}-\mathbf{j}+\mathbf{k}$, $\mathbf{i}-2\mathbf{j}-\mathbf{k}$ and $3\mathbf{i}+p\mathbf{j}+5\mathbf{k}$ be coplanar, then $p=...$ — 3. $-[\mathbf{a}\ \mathbf{b}\ \mathbf{c}]$

(d) If $\mathbf{a}\times(\mathbf{b}\times\mathbf{c})=\frac{\mathbf{b}+\mathbf{c}}{\sqrt{2}}$ and **b**, **c** be non-collinear and **a**, **b**, **c** non-coplanar, then angle between **a** and **b** is ... — 4. -2

5. **List-A** / **List-B**

(a) If **a** and **b** are perpendicular, then $\mathbf{a}\times[\mathbf{a}\times\{\mathbf{a}\times(\mathbf{a}\times\mathbf{b})\}]=...$ — 1. **0**

(b) $(\mathbf{a}\times\mathbf{b})\times(\mathbf{a}\times\mathbf{c}).\mathbf{d}=...$ — 2. **0**

(c) If **a**, **b**, **c** and **p**, **q**, **r** are reciprocal system of vectors, then $\mathbf{a}\times\mathbf{p}+\mathbf{b}\times\mathbf{q}+\mathbf{c}\times\mathbf{r}$ is equal to — 3. $[\mathbf{a}\ \mathbf{b}\ \mathbf{c}](\mathbf{a}.\mathbf{d})$

(d) $(\mathbf{a}\times\mathbf{b}).(\mathbf{c}\times\mathbf{d})+(\mathbf{b}\times\mathbf{c}).(\mathbf{a}\times\mathbf{d})+(\mathbf{c}\times\mathbf{a}).(\mathbf{b}\times\mathbf{d})=...$ — 4. $|\mathbf{a}|^4\,\mathbf{b}$

Answers

1. (a) → 4, (b) → 1, (c) → 2, (d) → 3
2. (a) → 2, (b) → 4, (c) → 1, (d) → 5, (e) → 3
3. (a) → 3, (b) → 4, (c) → 1, (d) → 2
4. (a) → 2, (b) → 3, (c) → 4, (d) → 1
5. (a) → 4, (b) → 3, (c) → 1, (d) → 2

Hints / Solutions

1. (a) → 4. **Q. 5 P. 967**

(b) → 1.

Find $\vec{AB}, \vec{BC}$ and $\vec{CA}$ and their moduli are $\sqrt{41}, \sqrt{6}, \sqrt{35}$.

$\therefore\quad AB^2=BC^2+CA^2 \quad \therefore \quad \angle C=90^\circ$

(c) → 2. **Q. 34 (a) P. 968**

(d) → 3. **Refer Q. 55 (a) P. 970**

2. (a) → 2. **Refer Q. 3 (a) P. 1123**

(b) → 4.

If A, B, C are collinear, then $\vec{AB}=\mathbf{k}\,\vec{AC}$

$\therefore\quad \vec{AB}\times\vec{AC}=0 \quad$ or $\quad (\mathbf{b}-\mathbf{a})\times(\mathbf{c}-\mathbf{a})=0$

or $\quad \mathbf{b}\times\mathbf{c}-\mathbf{a}\times\mathbf{c}-\mathbf{b}\times\mathbf{a}+0=0$

or $\quad \mathbf{b}\times\mathbf{c}+\mathbf{c}\times\mathbf{a}+\mathbf{a}\times\mathbf{b}=0$

(c) $\rightarrow$ 1.

Normal of the plane containing **c** and **d** is along $\mathbf{n}_1=\mathbf{c}\times\mathbf{d}$. Normal of the plane containing **a** and **b** is $\mathbf{n}_2=\mathbf{a}\times\mathbf{b}$. These two planes are perpendicular, therefore

$$\mathbf{n}_1\,.\,\mathbf{n}_2=0 \quad \text{or} \quad (\mathbf{a}\times\mathbf{b})\,.\,(\mathbf{c}\times\mathbf{d})=0 \Rightarrow \text{(d)}$$

If they are parallel then $\mathbf{n}_1\times\mathbf{n}_2=0 \Rightarrow$ (c)

where $\mathbf{n}_1=\mathbf{a}\times\mathbf{b},\ \mathbf{n}_2=\mathbf{c}\times\mathbf{d}$

(d) $\rightarrow$ 5.

Square and put $a^2=1$

(e) $\rightarrow$ 3.

a is collinear with **b**.

$$\therefore \quad \mathbf{a}=\lambda\mathbf{b} \qquad \text{or} \quad \mathbf{a}=\lambda\left(6,-8,-\frac{15}{2}\right)$$

$$\therefore \quad |\mathbf{a}|=50=\pm\lambda\sqrt{36+64+\frac{225}{4}}=\pm\frac{25}{2}\lambda$$

$$\therefore \quad \lambda=\pm 4.$$

Again $\mathbf{a}\,.\,\mathbf{k}=+$ive as it makes acute angle with z-axis.

$\therefore \quad -\frac{15}{2}\lambda=+$ive. Above is possible when $\lambda=-$ive.

Hence we choose $\lambda=-4$

$\therefore$ **a** = as given in (b) only and not as in (a).

3. (a) $\rightarrow$ 3. **Q. 43 (b) P. 1126**

(b) $\rightarrow$ 4.

$\vec{AB}=$ P.V. of $B-$ P.V. of $A=-6,-2,3$.

$\vec{BC}=-2,3,-6,\quad \vec{CD}=6,2,-3,\quad \vec{DA}=2,-3,6.$

All the vectors have same modulus $=\sqrt{36+4+9}=7$.

Hence the points enclose either a square or a rhombus.

But $\vec{AB}\,.\,\vec{BC}=12-6-18=-12\neq 0$

$\therefore$ AB is not perpendicular to BC.

Therefore it can't be a square and hence a rhombus.

(c) $\rightarrow$ 1. **Q. 19 (a, b) P. 1124**

(d) $\rightarrow$ 2.

$$\mathbf{a}\times\mathbf{b}=(\mathbf{m}+2\mathbf{n})\times(2\mathbf{m}+\mathbf{n})$$
$$=-3\,(\mathbf{m}\times\mathbf{n})$$
$$=-3\,.\,1\,.\,1\,.\sin 30^{\circ}\ \mathbf{n}=-\frac{3}{2}\mathbf{n}$$

$$\therefore \quad \text{Area}=|\mathbf{a}\times\mathbf{b}|=\frac{3}{2}$$

4. (a) $\rightarrow$ 2.

Taking A as origin the vectors

$\vec{AB}=-2,3,-3,\quad \vec{AC}=4,5,\lambda-10,\quad \vec{AD}=6,2,-3.$

$$V=11\Rightarrow\frac{1}{6}\begin{vmatrix}-2 & 3 & -3\\ 4 & 5 & \lambda-10\\ 6 & 2 & -3\end{vmatrix}=\pm 11$$

or $\quad -88+22\lambda=\pm 66 \qquad \therefore \quad \lambda=1$ or 7

(b) $\rightarrow$ 3. **Q. 15 (b) P. 1156**

(c) $\rightarrow$ 4. **Refer Q. 8 P. 1155-62**

(d) $\rightarrow$ 1. **Q. 28 (b) P. 1157-67**

5. (a) $\rightarrow$ 4.

$$\mathbf{a}\perp\mathbf{b} \Rightarrow \mathbf{a}\,.\,\mathbf{b}=0$$

$$\mathbf{a}\times(\mathbf{a}\times\mathbf{b})=(\mathbf{a}\,.\,\mathbf{b})\,\mathbf{a}-(\mathbf{a}\,.\,\mathbf{a})\,\mathbf{b}=-|\mathbf{a}|^2\,\mathbf{b} \qquad \text{...(1)}$$

$$\{\ \}=\mathbf{a}\times-|\mathbf{a}|^2\,\mathbf{b}=-|\mathbf{a}|^2\,(\mathbf{a}\times\mathbf{b})$$

$$\{\ \}=\mathbf{a}\times-|\mathbf{a}|^2\,(\mathbf{a}\times\mathbf{b})=-|\mathbf{a}|^2\,.\,\{\mathbf{a}\times(\mathbf{a}\times\mathbf{b})\}$$

$$=-|\mathbf{a}|^2\,.\,-|\mathbf{a}|^2\,\mathbf{b} \qquad \text{from (1)}$$

$$=|\mathbf{a}|^4\,\mathbf{b}\Rightarrow \text{(c)}$$

(b) $\rightarrow$ 3.

Choose $\mathbf{a}\times\mathbf{c}=\mathbf{n}$, then

$$(\mathbf{a}\times\mathbf{b})\times(\mathbf{a}\times\mathbf{c})=(\mathbf{a}\times\mathbf{b})\times\mathbf{n}=(\mathbf{n}\,.\,\mathbf{a})\,\mathbf{b}-(\mathbf{n}\,.\,\mathbf{b})\,\mathbf{a}$$

Put for $\mathbf{n}$, $[\mathbf{a}\ \mathbf{c}\ \mathbf{a}]\,\mathbf{b}-[\mathbf{a}\ \mathbf{c}\ \mathbf{b}]\,\mathbf{a}=0+[\mathbf{a}\ \mathbf{b}\ \mathbf{c}]\,\mathbf{a}$

$\therefore \quad$ L.H.S. $=[\mathbf{a}\ \mathbf{b}\ \mathbf{c}]\,(\mathbf{a}\,.\,\mathbf{d})$

Note : Remember that $(\mathbf{b}\times\mathbf{c})\times(\mathbf{b}\times\mathbf{a})=[\mathbf{a}\ \mathbf{b}\ \mathbf{c}]\,\mathbf{b}$ etc.

(c) $\rightarrow$ 1. **Q. 3 (i) P. 1176**

(d) $\rightarrow$ 2. **Q. 27 (a) P. 1157-67**

Assertion / Reason

1. Let the vectors $\vec{PQ}, \vec{QR}, \vec{RS}, \vec{ST}, \vec{TU}$ and $\vec{UP}$ represent the sides of a regular hexagon.

Statement-1 : $\vec{PQ}\times(\vec{RS}+\vec{ST})\neq\vec{0}$.

because

Statement-2 : $\vec{PQ}\times\vec{RS}=\vec{0}$ and $\vec{PQ}\times\vec{ST}\neq 0$.

(I.I.T. 2007)

Sol. Ans. (c).

Statement-1 : $\vec{RS}+\vec{ST}=\vec{RT}$

$\therefore$ $\vec{PQ}\times\vec{RT}\neq\mathbf{0}$ as they are not collinear. Hence statement-1 is true.

Statement-2 : $\vec{PQ}\times\vec{RS}=\mathbf{0}$ is false as $\vec{PQ}$ and $\vec{RS}$ are not parallel also $\vec{PQ}\times\vec{ST}=\mathbf{0}$ as they are parallel $\therefore$ $\vec{PQ}\times\vec{ST}\neq\mathbf{0}$ is false. Hence statement-2 is false. Both these facts are contained in (c).

Comprehension

Passage 1

(a) $\mathbf{a}.\mathbf{b}=0 \Rightarrow$ Vectors **a** and **b** are orthogonal.

(b) If $ABCD$ be a cyclic quadrilateral then $A+C=\frac{\pi}{2}$ and $B+D=\frac{\pi}{2}$.

(c) $[\mathbf{a}\,\mathbf{b}\,\mathbf{c}]=\mathbf{a}.(\mathbf{b}\times\mathbf{c})$.

1. If $\mathbf{u}=q-r, r-p, p-q$ and $\mathbf{v}=\frac{1}{a},\frac{1}{b},\frac{1}{c}$ and a,b,c are T_p, T_q, T_r of an HP then the angle between the vectors **u** and **v** is ...

Sol. Ans. $\frac{\pi}{2}$. $\frac{1}{a}=T_p$ of A.P. $=A+(p-1)D=(A-D)+pD$

If θ be the angle between **u** and **v**, then

$$\mathbf{u}.\mathbf{v}=|\mathbf{u}||\mathbf{v}|\cos\theta=\Sigma\,(q-r)\frac{1}{a}$$

$$=\Sigma\,(q-r)\,[(A-D)+pD]$$

$$=(A-D)\,\Sigma\,(q-r)+D\Sigma\,p\,(q-r)$$

$$=0+0=0 \quad \therefore \quad \cos\theta=0 \quad \text{or} \quad \theta=\pi/2$$

2. If $\mathbf{u}=q-r, r-p, p-q$ and $\mathbf{v}=\log a^2, \log b^2, \log c^2$ and a,b,c are T_p, T_q, T_r of a G.P., then angle between vectors **u** and **v** is ...

Sol. Ans. $\frac{\pi}{2}$. $a=AR^{p-1}$

$\therefore \quad \log a=\log A+(p-1)\log R$

If θ be the angle between **u** and **v**, then

$$|\mathbf{u}||\mathbf{v}|\cos\theta=\Sigma\,(q-r)\log a^2=2\Sigma\,(q-r)\log a$$

$$=2\Sigma\,(q-r)\,[\log A+(p-1)\log R]$$

$$=2\,[\log A\,\Sigma\,(q-r)+\log R\,\Sigma\,(p-1)(q-r)]$$

$$=2\,[0+0]=0 \quad \therefore \quad \cos\theta=0 \text{ or } \theta=\pi/2$$

Passage 2

1. If $\mathbf{a},\mathbf{b},\mathbf{c},\mathbf{d}$ be the position vectors of the vertices of a cyclic quadrilateral $ABCD$, then show that

$$\frac{|\mathbf{a}\times\mathbf{b}+\mathbf{b}\times\mathbf{d}+\mathbf{d}\times\mathbf{a}|}{(\mathbf{b}-\mathbf{a}).(\mathbf{d}-\mathbf{a})}+\frac{|\mathbf{b}\times\mathbf{c}+\mathbf{c}\times\mathbf{a}+\mathbf{d}\times\mathbf{b}|}{(\mathbf{b}-\mathbf{c}).(\mathbf{d}-\mathbf{c})}=0$$

Sol. $\tan A=\frac{\sin A}{\cos A}=\frac{\vec{AB}\times\vec{AD}}{\vec{AB}.\vec{AD}}=\frac{(\mathbf{b}-\mathbf{a})\times(\mathbf{d}-\mathbf{a})}{(\mathbf{b}-\mathbf{a}).(\mathbf{d}-\mathbf{a})}=\frac{N^r}{D^r}$ of T_1

as $\mathbf{a}\times\mathbf{a}=0$

$\tan C=$ 2nd term as above

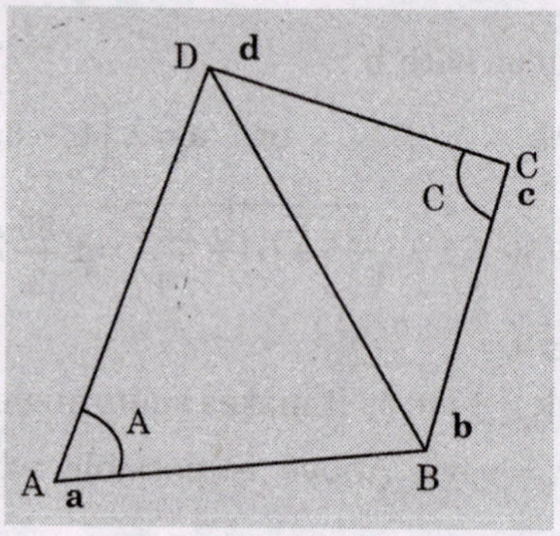

Fig. 66

We have to prove that $T_1+T_2=0$

or $\tan A+\tan C=0$ or $\sin(A+C)=0$

or $A+C=\pi$

which is true as the quadrilateral is cyclic.

❑

Differential Calculus

Integral Calculus

Differential Equations

Probability, Statistics and Reasoning

CHAPTER 26

Differential Calculus

Differentiation

§1. Basic formulae.

(a) Differential coefficient (or Derivative) of a function.

If $y = f(x)$, then we define

$$\frac{dy}{dx} = \lim_{\delta x \to 0} \frac{f(x+\delta x) - f(x)}{\delta x}$$

We may define $\frac{dy}{dx}$ at $x = a$ as

$$\left(\frac{dy}{dx}\right)_{x=a} = \lim_{x \to a} \frac{f(x) - f(a)}{x - a}.$$

Also $$\left(\frac{dy}{dx}\right)_{x=a} = \operatorname*{Lt}_{\delta x \to 0} \frac{f(a+\delta x) - f(a)}{\delta x}.$$

In evaluating the limits the following should be noted :

(i) $\operatorname*{Lt}_{\theta \to 0} \frac{\sin\theta}{\theta} = 1.$

(ii) Limit of sum = Sum of Limits.

(iii) Limit of product = Product of Limits.

(iv) $\operatorname*{Lt}_{h \to 0} (1+h)^{1/h} = e$ and

(v) $\operatorname*{Lt}_{h \to 0} \left(1+\frac{h}{2}\right)^{1/h} = e^{1/2}$ etc.

§2. Fundamental Theorems.

Let $u, v, w, \ldots$ be functions of x whose derivatives exist.

(i) Differential coefficient of constant is zero,

i.e. $\frac{d}{dx}(k) = 0$

(ii) $\frac{d}{dx}(ku) = k\frac{du}{dx}$

(iii) $\frac{d}{dx}(u \pm v) = \frac{du}{dx} \pm \frac{dv}{dx}$ **Sum or difference**

(iv) $\frac{d}{dx}(uv) = u\frac{dv}{dx} + v\frac{du}{dx}$ **Product**

(v) $\frac{d}{dx}\left(\frac{u}{v}\right) = \frac{v\frac{du}{dx} - u\frac{dv}{dx}}{v^2}$ **Quotient**

(vi) If $y = f(t)$ and $t = \phi(x)$ **Function of a function**

then $\frac{dy}{dx} = \frac{dy}{dt} \cdot \frac{dt}{dx}$

(vii) If $u = f(y)$, then $\frac{du}{dx} = \frac{du}{dy} \cdot \frac{dy}{dx} = f'(y)\frac{dy}{dx}$

(viii) $\frac{dy}{dx} \cdot \frac{dx}{dy} = 1$ or $\frac{dy}{dx} = \frac{1}{dx/dy}$

(ix) **Differentiation of one function w.r.t. another function.**

Let $y = f(x)$, $z = \phi(x)$ and we have to differentiate $f(x)$ w.r.t. $\phi(x)$ *i.e.* y w.r.t. z so that we have to find the value of

$$\frac{dy}{dz} = \frac{dy}{dx} \div \frac{dz}{dx} = \frac{dy}{dx} \cdot \frac{dx}{dz}.$$

(x) **Logarithmic Differentiation.**

If $y = [f_1(x)]^{f_2(x)}$

or $y = f_1(x) f_2(x) f_3(x) \ldots$

or $y = \frac{f_1(x) f_2(x) \ldots}{\phi_1(x) \phi_2(x) \ldots}$,

then it will be convenient to take log of both sides before performing differentiation.

Note : For differentiation of $[f_1(x)]^{f_2(x)}$ see **P. 1217** for another easier method.

§ 3. (i) Parametric Equations.

If $x = f(t)$, $y = \phi(t)$, then $\frac{dy}{dx} = \frac{dy}{dt} \div \frac{dx}{dt}$.

(ii) Implicit function. $f(x, y) = c$.

Differentiate each term w.r.t. x and note that

$$\frac{d}{dx}(\phi(y)) = \frac{d}{dy}(\phi(y))\frac{dy}{dx}.$$

For example, $x^3 + y^3 - 3axy = 0$

Differentiating w.r.t. x,

$$3x^2 + 3y^2\frac{dy}{dx} - 3a\left(1 \cdot y + x\frac{dy}{dx}\right) = 0$$

$$(x^2 - ay) + (y^2 - ax)\frac{dy}{dx} = 0$$

$$\therefore \quad \frac{dy}{dx} = -\frac{x^2 - ay}{y^2 - ax}$$

By the help of partial differentiation.

If $f(x, y) = c$, then we can find $\frac{dy}{dx}$ by the help of partial differentiation as under $\frac{dy}{dx} = -\frac{f_x}{f_y}$ where f_x is differential coefficient of $f(x, y)$ w.r.t. x treating y as constant. Similarly f_y is differentiation of $f(x, y)$ w.r.t. y treating x as constant. For example, if $f(x, y) = x^3 + y^3 - 3axy = 0$, then $f_x = 3x^2 - 3ay$, $f_y = 3y^2 - 3ax$

$$\therefore \quad \frac{dy}{dx} = -\frac{f_x}{f_y} = -\frac{x^2 - ay}{y^2 - ax}$$

§ 4. Standard results.

(i) $y = x^n$, $\frac{dy}{dx} = n\,x^{n-1}$,

$y = u^n$, $\frac{dy}{dx} = n\,u^{n-1}\frac{du}{dx}$.

Particular case. $y = \sqrt{x}$, $\frac{dy}{dx} = \frac{1}{2\sqrt{(x)}}$ **(Imp.)**

$y = \frac{1}{x^n}$, $\frac{dy}{dx} = -\frac{n}{x^{n+1}}$.

(ii) $y = e^x$, $\frac{dy}{dx} = e^x$, $y = e^u$, $\frac{dy}{dx} = e^u\frac{du}{dx}$.

(iii) $y = \log x$, $\frac{dy}{dx} = \frac{1}{x}$, $y = \log u$, $\frac{dy}{dx} = \frac{1}{u}\frac{du}{dx}$.

(iv) $y = a^x$, $\frac{dy}{dx} = a^x \log a$,

$y = a^u$, $\frac{dy}{dx} = a^u \log a\frac{du}{dx}$

(v) $y = \sin x$, $\frac{dy}{dx} = \cos x$,

$y = \sin u$, $\frac{dy}{dx} = \cos u \cdot \frac{du}{dx}$.

(vi) $y = \cos x$, $\frac{dy}{dx} = -\sin x$,

$y = \cos u$, $\frac{dy}{dx} = -\sin u \cdot \frac{du}{dx}$.

(vii) $y = \tan x$, $\frac{dy}{dx} = \sec^2 x$,

$y = \tan u$, $\frac{dy}{dx} = \sec^2 u\frac{du}{dx}$.

(viii) $y = \cot x$, $\frac{dy}{dx} = -\operatorname{cosec}^2 x$,

$y = \cot u$, $\frac{dy}{dx} = -\operatorname{cosec}^2 u\frac{du}{dx}$.

(ix) $y = \sec x$, $\frac{dy}{dx} = \sec x \tan x$.

(x) $y = \operatorname{cosec} x$, $\frac{dy}{dx} = -\operatorname{cosec} x \cot x$.

(xi) $y = \sin^{-1} x$, $\frac{dy}{dx} = \frac{1}{\sqrt{(1-x^2)}}$.

(xii) $y = \cos^{-1} x$, $\frac{dy}{dx} = \frac{-1}{\sqrt{(1-x^2)}}$.

(xiii) $y = \tan^{-1} x$, $\frac{dy}{dx} = \frac{1}{1+x^2}$.

(xiv) $y = \cot^{-1} x$, $\frac{dy}{dx} = -\frac{1}{1+x^2}$.

(xv) $y = \sec^{-1} x$, $\frac{dy}{dx} = \frac{1}{|x|\sqrt{x^2-1}}$, $|x| > 0$

(xvi) $y = \operatorname{cosec}^{-1} x$, $\frac{dy}{dx} = \frac{-1}{|x|\sqrt{x^2-1}}$, $|x| > 0$

Problem Set (1)

Differentiate from first principles (or *ab initio*) from Q. 1 to Q. 35.

1.* $\sin x$.
2. $\cos x$
3. $\tan x$.
4. $\cot x$
5. $\sec x$
6. $\operatorname{cosec} x$
7. x^n
8.* e^x
9. $\log x$
10. $(ax+b)^n$
11. $\sqrt{x}$
12. $1/\sqrt{x+a}$
13. $\sin^{-1} x$
14. (a) $\cos^{-1} x$
(b)* $\cos^{-1} x^2$ **(Roorkee 1993)**
15. (a) $\tan^{-1} x$ (b)* $\cot^{-1} x$
16. $\sec^{-1} x$
17. $\operatorname{cosec}^{-1} x$
18.* $\sin^2 x$
19. $\sin x^2$
20. (a) $\sqrt{\sin x}$
(b)* $\sin^{1/3} x$ **(M. N. R. 1997)**
(c) $\sqrt{(\tan\sqrt{x})}$
21. $\sqrt{\tan x}$
22. $\frac{\sin x}{x}$
23.* $\log \cos x$
24. $\sin \log x$
25. $\log \sin^{-1} x$
26. $\cos^2 (\log x)$
27. $\tan (1/x)$.
28.* $e^{\tan x}$.
29. $e^{\sin x}$
30. (a) $x^2 \log x$ (b) xe^x
(c) $x^2 e^{ax}$
31. (a)* $\sin\sqrt{x}$ (b)* $\sin(\sin x)$
32. $\tan^2 ax$.
33. (a) $\cos(ax^2+bx+c)$.

(b) $\cos^{-1}\left[e^{\sqrt{\tan x}}\right]$ **(J.E.E. W.B. 1995)**

34. $\sin(x^2+1)$

35. (a)* $x^2 \cos x$

(b)* Prove that $\underset{h\to 0}{\text{Lt}} \dfrac{(a+h)^2 \sin(a+h) - a^2 \sin a}{h}$

$= 2a \sin a + a^2 \cos a$.

36. $f(x) = \dfrac{x-1}{2x^2-7x+5}$ when $x \neq 1$, $f(x) = -\dfrac{1}{3}$ when $x = 1$, find $f'(1)$.

37. If $f(x) = x \tan^{-1} x$, find $f'(1)$

38. If $y = \dfrac{1}{\sqrt{(x^2+a^2)} + \sqrt{(x^2+b^2)}}$, find $\dfrac{dy}{dx}$.

39. If $y = \sec(x^{\circ} + 30^{\circ})$, find dy/dx.

40. If $y = \cos(2\sin^2 x^3)$, find dy/dx.

41. If $y = \dfrac{5x}{(1-x)^{2/3}} + \cos^2(2x+1)$, find $\dfrac{dy}{dx}$.

42.* If $y = \dfrac{x}{2}\sqrt{a^2+x^2} + \dfrac{a^2}{2}\log[x + \sqrt{x^2+a^2}]$, prove that $\dfrac{dy}{dx} = \sqrt{x^2+a^2}$.

43. If $y = \log_7(\log_7 x)$, prove that $\dfrac{dy}{dx} = \dfrac{\log_7 e}{x \log_e x}$.

44.* If $y = \log_3 \dfrac{\sqrt{x^2+a^2} + \sqrt{x^2+b^2}}{\sqrt{(x^2+a^2)} - \sqrt{(x^2+b^2)}}$, prove that

$\dfrac{dy}{dx} = \dfrac{2x}{[(x^2+a^2)(x^2+b^2)]^{1/2}} \log_3 e$.

45. If $y = \log_{10} x + \log_x 10 + \log_x x + \log_{10} 10$, find dy/dx.

46. If $y = \log x^x$ prove $\dfrac{dy}{dx} = \log(ex)$.

47. Find $\dfrac{dy}{dx}$ if $y = [x + \sqrt{x + \sqrt{x}}]^{1/2}$.

48. (i)* Find $\dfrac{dy}{dx}$ if $y = \log|x|$

(ii) If $y = \log \tan x$, find dy/dx.

Solutions to Problem Set (1)

1. $y = \sin x = f(x)$,

$y + \delta y = \sin(x+\delta x) = f(x+\delta x)$

$\therefore \quad \delta y = \sin(x+\delta x) - \sin x = f(x+\delta x) - f(x)$

$\therefore \quad \dfrac{\delta y}{\delta x} = \dfrac{\sin(x+\delta x) - \sin x}{\delta x} = \dfrac{f(x+\delta x) - f(x)}{\delta x}$

$\therefore \quad \dfrac{dy}{dx} = \lim\limits_{\delta x\to 0} \dfrac{\sin(x+\delta x) - \sin x}{\delta x}$

$= \lim\limits_{\delta x\to 0} \dfrac{f(x+\delta x) - f(x)}{\delta x}$

$= \lim\limits_{\delta x\to 0} \dfrac{2\cos(x+\frac{1}{2}\delta x)\sin\frac{1}{2}\delta x}{\delta x}$

$= \lim\limits_{\delta x\to 0} \cos\left(x + \dfrac{\delta x}{2}\right)\dfrac{\sin(\delta x/2)}{(\delta x/2)}$

$= \cos x \cdot 1 = \cos x \qquad \left(\because \lim\limits_{\theta\to 0}\dfrac{\sin\theta}{\theta} = 1.\right)$

Note : In rest of the questions we will simply write that $\dfrac{dy}{dx} = \lim\limits_{\delta x\to 0}\dfrac{f(x+\delta x) - f(x)}{\delta x}$.

2. Do yourself.

3. $y = \tan x$.

$\therefore \quad \dfrac{dy}{dx} = \lim\limits_{\delta x\to 0}\dfrac{\tan(x+\delta x) - \tan x}{\delta x}$

(Change to sin and cos).

$= \lim\limits_{\delta x\to 0}\dfrac{\sin(x+\delta x - x)}{\delta x . \cos x \cos(x+\delta x)}$

$= \lim\limits_{\delta x\to 0}\dfrac{\sin\delta x}{\delta x} \cdot \dfrac{1}{\cos x\cos(x+\delta x)}$

$= 1 . \sec^2 x = \sec^2 x$.

4. Do yourself.

5. $y = \sec x$

$\therefore \quad \dfrac{dy}{dx} = \lim\limits_{\delta x\to 0}\dfrac{\sec(x+\delta x) - \sec x}{\delta x}$ (Change to cos)

$= \lim\limits_{\delta x\to 0}\dfrac{\cos x - \cos(x+\delta x)}{\delta x . \cos(x+\delta x)\cos x}$

$= \sin x . \dfrac{1}{\cos x \cos x} = \sec x \tan x$

The limit $\sin x$ of $\dfrac{\cos x - \cos(x+\delta x)}{\delta x}$ is to be calculated.

6. Do yourself.

7. $y = x^n$

$\therefore \quad \dfrac{dy}{dx} = \lim\limits_{\delta x\to 0}\dfrac{(x+\delta x)^n - x^n}{\delta x}$

$= \lim\limits_{\delta x\to 0}\dfrac{x^n\left[\left(1+\dfrac{\delta x}{x}\right)^n - 1\right]}{\delta x}$

$= \lim\limits_{\delta x\to 0}\dfrac{x^n\left[1 + n.\dfrac{\delta x}{x} + \dfrac{n(n-1)}{1.2}\left(\dfrac{\delta x}{x}\right)^2 + \cdots\right] - x^n}{\delta x}$

$= \lim\limits_{\delta x\to 0}\dfrac{\delta x}{\delta x}\left[nx^{n-1} + \dfrac{n(n-1)}{1.2}x^{n-2}\,\delta x\right.$

$\left. + \text{higher powers of } \delta x\right]$

$= nx^{n-1}$.

8. Do yourself.

9. We have $y = \log x$.

$\therefore \quad \dfrac{dy}{dx} = \lim\limits_{\delta x\to 0}\dfrac{\log(x+\delta x) - \log x}{\delta x}$

$= \lim\limits_{\delta x\to 0}\dfrac{\log(1+\delta x/x)}{\delta x}$

$= \lim\limits_{\delta x\to 0}\dfrac{(\delta x/x) - \frac{1}{2}(\delta x/x)^2 + \cdots}{\delta x}$

$$= \lim_{\delta x \to 0} \left[\frac{1}{x} - \frac{1}{2} \frac{\delta x}{x^2} + \cdots \right] = \frac{1}{x}.$$

10. Do yourself.

11. $y = \sqrt{x}$

$$\frac{dy}{dx} = \lim_{\delta x \to 0} \frac{\sqrt{x + \delta x} - \sqrt{x}}{\delta x}$$

Multiply above and below by $\sqrt{x + \delta x} + \sqrt{x}$

$$= \lim_{\delta x \to 0} \frac{(x + \delta x) - x}{\delta x \, [\sqrt{(x + \delta x)} + \sqrt{(x)}]}$$

$$= \frac{1}{\sqrt{(x)} + \sqrt{(x)}} = \frac{1}{2\sqrt{(x)}}.$$

12. $y = \dfrac{1}{\sqrt{(x+a)}}$

$$\therefore \quad \frac{dy}{dx} = \lim_{\delta x \to 0} \frac{1}{\delta x} \left[\frac{1}{\sqrt{(x + \delta x + a)}} - \frac{1}{\sqrt{(x+a)}} \right]$$

$$= \lim_{\delta x \to 0} \frac{1}{\delta x} \frac{\sqrt{x+a} - \sqrt{x + a + \delta x}}{\sqrt{(x+a)}\sqrt{(x + a + \delta x)}}$$

$$= \lim_{\delta x \to 0} \frac{1}{\delta x} \cdot \frac{(x+a) - (x + a + \delta x)}{\sqrt{(x+a)}\sqrt{(x+a+\delta x)}.[\sqrt{(x+a)} + \sqrt{(x+a+\delta x)}]}$$

(as in Q.11)

$$= \frac{-1}{\sqrt{(x+a)}\sqrt{(x+a)}\,[2\sqrt{(x+a)}]} = \frac{-1}{2(x+a)^{3/2}}.$$

13. $y = \sin^{-1} x, \qquad \therefore \; x = \sin y$

$$y + \delta y = \sin^{-1}(x + \delta x)$$

$$\therefore \quad (x + \delta x) = \sin(y + \delta y)$$

$$\frac{dy}{dx} = \lim_{\delta x \to 0} \frac{\delta y}{\delta x}$$

$$= \lim_{\delta y \to 0} \frac{\delta y}{\sin(y + \delta y) - \sin y} = \frac{1}{\cos y}$$

$$= \frac{1}{\sqrt{(1 - \sin^2 y)}} = \frac{1}{\sqrt{(1 - x^2)}}$$

The limit is evaluated as in Q.1 for sin x.
Note that when $\delta x \to 0$, δy also tends to zero.

14. (a) Proceed as above

$$y = \cos^{-1} x, \quad \frac{dy}{dx} = \frac{-1}{\sqrt{(1 - x^2)}}$$

(b) $y = \cos^{-1} t \quad$ where $t = x^2$

$$\therefore \quad y + \delta y = \cos^{-1}(t + \delta t)$$

where $(t + \delta t) = (x + \delta x)^2$

$$t = \cos y, \; t + \delta t = \cos(y + \delta y)$$

Also $\dfrac{dy}{dx} = \underset{\delta x \to 0}{\text{Lt}} \dfrac{\delta y}{\delta x} = \text{Lt} \dfrac{\delta y}{\delta t} \cdot \dfrac{\delta t}{\delta x}$

$$= \text{Lt} \frac{\delta y}{\cos(y + \delta y) - \cos y} \cdot \text{Lt} \frac{(x + \delta x)^2 - x^2}{\delta x}$$

$$= \text{Lt} \frac{\delta y}{2 \sin\left(y + \frac{\delta y}{2}\right) \sin\left(-\frac{\delta y}{2}\right)} \text{Lt}\,(2x + \delta x)$$

$$= -\frac{1}{\sin y} . 2x = -2x \frac{1}{\sqrt{(1 - \cos^2 y)}}$$

$$= -\frac{2x}{\sqrt{(1 - t^2)}} = -\frac{2x}{\sqrt{(1 - x^4)}}.$$

15. (a) $y = \tan^{-1} x \; \therefore \; x = \tan y$

$$y + \delta y = \tan^{-1}(x + \delta x)$$

$$\therefore \quad x + \delta x = \tan(y + \delta y)$$

$$\frac{dy}{dx} = \lim_{\delta x \to 0} \frac{\delta y}{\delta x}$$

$$= \lim_{\delta y \to 0} \frac{\delta y}{\tan(y + \delta y) - \tan y} = \frac{1}{\sec^2 y}$$

$$= \frac{1}{1 + \tan^2 y} = \frac{1}{1 + x^2}.$$

The limit is to be calculated as in Q.3 for tan x.

(b) Proceed as above; $y = \cot^{-1} x, \; \dfrac{dy}{dx} = -\dfrac{1}{1 + x^2}.$

16. Do yourself.

$$\frac{dy}{dx} = \frac{1}{\sec y \sqrt{(\sec^2 y - 1)}} = \frac{1}{x\sqrt{(x^2 - 1)}}$$

The limit is to be calculated as in Q.5 for sec x.

17. Do yourself.

18. $y = \sin^2 x$

$$\frac{dy}{dx} = \lim_{\delta x \to 0} \frac{\sin^2(x + \delta x) - \sin^2 x}{\delta x}$$

$$= \lim_{\delta x \to 0} \frac{\sin(x + \delta x + x) \sin(x + \delta x - x)}{\delta x}$$

$$= \lim_{\delta x \to 0} \sin(2x + \delta x) \frac{\sin \delta x}{\delta x} = \sin 2x.$$

We have used

$$\sin^2 A - \sin^2 B = \sin(A + B) \sin(A - B).$$

19. $y = \sin x^2$

$$\therefore \quad \frac{dy}{dx} = \lim_{\delta x \to 0} \frac{\sin(x + \delta x)^2 - \sin x^2}{\delta x}$$

$$= \lim_{\delta x \to 0} \frac{\sin(x^2 + 2x\,\delta x + \delta x^2) - \sin x^2}{\delta x}$$

$$= \lim_{\delta x \to 0} \frac{2\cos\left(x^2 + x\,\delta x + \frac{1}{2}\delta x^2\right) \sin\left(x\,\delta x + \frac{1}{2}\delta x^2\right)}{\delta x}$$

$$= 2\cos x^2 \lim_{\delta x \to 0} \frac{\sin\left(x\,\delta x + \frac{1}{2}\delta x^2\right)}{(x\,\delta x + \frac{1}{2}\delta x^2)} \cdot \frac{x\,\delta x + \frac{1}{2}\delta x^2}{\delta x}$$

$$= 2\cos x^2 . 1 . x = 2x \cos x^2 .$$

20. (a) $y = \sqrt{\sin x}$

$$\frac{dy}{dx} = \lim_{\delta x \to 0} \frac{\sqrt{\sin(x+\delta x)} - \sqrt{\sin x}}{\delta x}$$

$$= \lim_{\delta x \to 0} \frac{\sin(x+\delta x) - \sin x}{\delta x} \cdot \frac{1}{\sqrt{[\sin(x+\delta x)]} + \sqrt{(\sin x)}}$$

$$= \cos x \cdot \frac{1}{2\sqrt{(\sin x)}}$$

(limit is to be calculated as in Q.1 for $\sin x$).

(b) $\dfrac{dy}{dx} = \underset{h \to 0}{\text{Lt}} \dfrac{\sin^{1/3}(x+h) - \sin^{1/3} x}{h}$

If $a = \sin^{1/3}(x+h)$, $b = \sin^{1/3}(x)$ then multiply above and below by $a^2 + b^2 + ab$.

$$\therefore \frac{dy}{dx} = \underset{h \to 0}{\text{Lt}} \frac{\sin(x+h) - \sin x}{h} \cdot \underset{h \to 0}{\text{Lt}} \frac{1}{\sin^{2/3}(x+h) + \sin^{2/3} x + \sin^{1/3}(x+h)\sin^{1/3} x}$$

$$= \cos x \cdot \frac{1}{3\sin^{2/3} x}.$$

(c) $\dfrac{dy}{dx} = \underset{\delta x \to 0}{\text{Lt}} \dfrac{\sqrt{(\tan\sqrt{(x+\delta x)}} - \sqrt{(\tan\sqrt{x})}}{\delta x}$

Rationalize

$$= \underset{\delta x \to 0}{\text{Lt}} \frac{\tan\sqrt{(x+\delta x)} - \tan\sqrt{x}}{\delta x[\sqrt{(\tan\sqrt{(x+\delta x)}} + \sqrt{(\tan\sqrt{x})}]}$$

$$= \frac{1}{2\sqrt{(\tan\sqrt{x})}} \underset{\delta x \to 0}{\text{Lt}} \frac{\sin(\sqrt{x+\delta x} - \sqrt{x})}{\delta x \cos\sqrt{x+\delta x} \cdot \cos\sqrt{x}}$$

by $\tan A - \tan B = \dfrac{\sin(A-B)}{\cos A . \cos B}$

$$= \frac{1}{2\sqrt{(\tan\sqrt{x})}} \cdot \frac{1}{\cos^2\sqrt{x}} \cdot \underset{\delta x \to 0}{\text{Lt}} \left[\frac{\sqrt{x+\delta x} - \sqrt{x}}{\delta x}\right]$$

$$= \frac{1}{2\sqrt{(\tan\sqrt{x})}} \cdot \sec^2\sqrt{x} \cdot \underset{\delta x \to 0}{\text{Lt}} \frac{x + \delta x - x}{\delta x[\sqrt{x+\delta x} + \sqrt{x}]}$$

$$= \frac{1}{2\sqrt{(\tan\sqrt{x})}} \sec^2\sqrt{x} \cdot \frac{1}{2\sqrt{x}}.$$

21. Do yourself.

22. $y = \dfrac{\sin x}{x}$

$$\therefore \frac{dy}{dx} = \lim_{\delta x \to 0} \frac{1}{\delta x}\left[\frac{\sin(x+\delta x)}{x+\delta x} - \frac{\sin x}{x}\right]$$

$$= \lim_{\delta x \to 0} \frac{x\sin(x+\delta x) - (x+\delta x)\sin x}{x(x+\delta x) . \delta x}$$

$$= \lim_{\delta x \to 0}\left[\frac{x[\sin(x+\delta x) - \sin x]}{x(x+\delta x)\delta x} - \frac{\delta x \sin x}{\delta x . x(x+\delta x)}\right]$$

$$= \lim_{\delta x \to 0}\left[\frac{1}{x+\delta x} \cdot \frac{\sin(x+\delta x) - \sin x}{\delta x} - \frac{\sin x}{x(x+\delta x)}\right]$$

$$= \frac{1}{x} . \cos x - \frac{\sin x}{x^2} = \frac{x\cos x - \sin x}{x^2}.$$

The limit $\cos x$ is to be calculated as in Q.1 for $\sin x$.

23. $y = \log\cos x$, $\therefore e^y = \cos x$

$y + \delta y = \log\cos(x+\delta x)$

$\therefore e^{y+\delta y} = \cos(x+\delta x)$

$$\frac{dy}{dx} = \lim_{\delta x \to 0} \frac{\delta y}{\delta x}$$

Now $\dfrac{e^{y+\delta y} - e^y}{\delta x} = \dfrac{\cos(x+\delta x) - \cos x}{\delta x}$, by above

or $\dfrac{e^{y+\delta y} - e^y}{\delta y} \cdot \dfrac{\delta y}{\delta x} = \dfrac{\cos(x+\delta x) - \cos x}{\delta x}$.

Now take limits of both the sides when $\delta x \to 0$ and consequently $\delta y \to 0$, as in Q.2 for $\cos x$ and Q.8 for e^x and $\lim \dfrac{\delta y}{\delta x} = \dfrac{dy}{dx}$.

$$\therefore e^y . \frac{dy}{dx} = -\sin x$$

or $\dfrac{dy}{dx} = -\dfrac{\sin x}{e^y} = -\dfrac{\sin x}{\cos x} = -\tan x$.

Note : $\log\sec x = \log(\cos x)^{-1} = -\log\cos x$.

Hence $\dfrac{d}{dx}\log(\sec x) = \tan x$.

24. $y = \sin\log x$

$$\frac{dy}{dx} = \lim_{\delta x \to 0} \frac{\sin\log(x+\delta x) - \sin\log x}{\delta x}$$

Put $\log x = z$

$\therefore$ $\log(x+\delta x) = z + \delta z$ and as $\delta x \to 0$, δz also tends to zero.

$$\therefore \frac{dy}{dx} = \lim_{\delta z \to 0} \frac{\sin(z+\delta z) - \sin z}{\delta z} \cdot \frac{\delta z}{\delta x}$$

$$= \lim_{\delta z \to 0} \frac{\sin(z+\delta z) - \sin z}{\delta z} \cdot \lim_{\delta x \to 0} \frac{\log(x+\delta x) - \log x}{\delta x}$$

Both the above limits have been calculated in Q.1 and 9.

$$\therefore \frac{dy}{dx} = \cos z . \frac{1}{x} = \frac{1}{x}\cos(\log x).$$

Similarly if $y = \cos(\log x)$, then

$$\frac{dy}{dx} = -\frac{1}{x}\sin(\log x).$$

25. $y = \log\sin^{-1} x$. Put $\sin^{-1} x = t$

$y = \log t$ and $x = \sin t$

$y + \delta y = \log(t + \delta t)$

$x + \delta x = \sin(t + \delta t)$

$$\frac{\delta y}{\delta t} = \frac{\log(t+\delta t) - \log t}{\delta t},$$

$$\frac{\delta x}{\delta t}=\frac{\sin(t+\delta t)-\sin t}{\delta t}$$

Now $\frac{\delta y}{\delta t}=\frac{\delta y}{\delta x}\cdot\frac{\delta x}{\delta t}$

$$\therefore \quad \frac{\log(t+\delta t)-\log t}{\delta t}=\frac{\delta y}{\delta x}\cdot\frac{\sin(t+\delta t)-\sin t}{\delta t}$$

Both the above limits have been calculated in Q.1 and 9.

Hence proceeding to limits, we get

$$\frac{1}{t}=\frac{dy}{dx}\cos t$$

$$\therefore \quad \frac{dy}{dx}=\frac{1}{t\cos t}=\frac{1}{t\sqrt{(1-\sin^2 t)}}$$

$$\text{or} \quad \frac{dy}{dx}=\frac{1}{\sin^{-1}x.\sqrt{(1-x^2)}}$$

26. Use $\cos^2 A-\cos^2 B=\sin(A+B)\sin(B-A)$.

(Note $B-A$)

Ans. $(-1/x)\sin(2\log x)$.

27. $y=\tan(1/x)$

$$\therefore \quad \frac{dy}{dx}=\lim_{\delta x\to 0}\frac{\tan[1/(x+\delta x)]-\tan(1/x)}{\delta x}$$

(change into sin and cos)

$$=\lim\frac{\sin\left(\frac{1}{x+\delta x}-\frac{1}{x}\right)}{\delta x.\cos\left(\frac{1}{x}\right).\cos\left(\frac{1}{x+\delta x}\right)}$$

$$=\lim\frac{\sin\frac{-\delta x}{x(x+\delta x)}}{\delta x}\cdot\frac{1}{\cos\left(\frac{1}{x}\right)\cos\left(\frac{1}{x+\delta x}\right)}$$

Now $\lim\frac{\sin\theta}{\theta}=1$ when $\theta\to 0$,

Here $\frac{\delta x}{x(x+\delta x)}\to 0$

$$\therefore \quad \frac{dy}{dx}=\lim\frac{-\delta x}{\delta x.x(x+\delta x)}\times\frac{1}{\cos\left(\frac{1}{x}\right)\cos\left(\frac{1}{x+\delta x}\right)}$$

$$=-\frac{1}{x^2}\cdot\frac{1}{\cos^2(1/x)}=-\frac{1}{x^2}\sec^2\frac{1}{x}.$$

28. We have $y=e^{\tan x}$ so that $\log y=\tan x$

and $y+\delta y=e^{\tan(x+\delta x)}$,

$$\log(y+\delta y)=\tan(x+\delta x)$$

$$\therefore \quad \frac{\log(y+\delta y)-\log y}{\delta x}=\frac{\tan(x+\delta x)-\tan x}{\delta x}$$

$$\text{or} \quad \frac{\log(y+\delta y)-\log y}{\delta y}\cdot\frac{\delta y}{\delta x}=\frac{\tan(x+\delta x)-\tan x}{\delta x}$$

Both the above limits have been calculated in Q.3 and 9.

When $\delta x\to 0$, δy also $\to 0$,

$$\therefore \quad \frac{1}{y}\cdot\frac{dy}{dx}=\sec^2 x$$

$$\text{or} \quad \frac{dy}{dx}=y\sec^2 x=e^{\tan x}.\sec^2 x.$$

29. Proceed as above : $dy/dx=e^{\sin x}\cos x$

30. (a) $y=x^2\log x$.

$$\frac{dy}{dx}=\lim_{\delta x\to 0}\frac{(x+\delta x)^2\log(x+\delta x)-x^2\log x}{\delta x}$$

$$=\lim_{\delta x\to 0}x^2\left[\frac{\log(x+\delta x)-\log x}{\delta x}\right.$$

$$\left.+\frac{2x\,\delta x\log(x+\delta x)}{\delta x}+\frac{\delta x^2\log(x+\delta x)}{\delta x}\right].$$

$$=x^2\cdot\frac{1}{x}+2x\log x+0=x+2x\log x$$

$$=x(1+2\log x).$$

The limit has been calculated in Q.9.

(b) $y=xe^x$

$$\frac{dy}{dx}=\lim_{\delta x\to 0}\frac{(x+\delta x)e^{x+\delta x}-xe^x}{\delta x}$$

$$=\lim_{\delta x\to 0}\frac{x[e^{x+\delta x}-e^x]}{\delta x}+\frac{\delta x.e^{x+\delta x}}{\delta x}=xe^x+e^x$$

The limit is to be calculated as in Q.8.

(c) $y=x^2e^{ax}$

$$\frac{dy}{dx}=\underset{\delta x\to 0}{\text{Lt}}\frac{(x+\delta x)^2e^{a(x+\delta x)}-x^2e^{ax}}{\delta x}$$

$$=\underset{\delta x\to 0}{\text{Lt}}\frac{x^2[e^{a(x+\delta x)}-e^{ax}]}{\delta x}+\underset{\delta x\to 0}{\text{Lt}}\frac{2x\,\delta x\,e^{a(x+\delta x)}}{\delta x}+\underset{\delta x\to 0}{\text{Lt}}\frac{(\delta x)^2e^{a(x+\delta x)}}{\delta x}$$

$$=\underset{\delta x\to 0}{\text{Lt}}\;x^2\left[\frac{e^{ax}}{\delta x}\left\{1+(a\,\delta x)+\frac{(a\,\delta x)^2}{2!}+\ldots-1\right\}\right]+2xe^{ax}+0$$

$$=x^2e^{ax}.a+2xe^{ax}=e^{ax}(ax^2+2x)$$

31. (a) $y=\sin\sqrt{x}$

$$\frac{dy}{dx}=\lim_{\delta x\to 0}\frac{\sin\sqrt{(x+\delta x)}-\sin\sqrt{x}}{\delta x}$$

$$=\frac{2\cos\frac{\sqrt{(x+\delta x)}+\sqrt{x}}{2}.\sin\frac{\sqrt{(x+\delta x)}-\sqrt{x}}{2}}{(x+\delta x)-x}$$

(Note the D^r)

$$=\frac{2\cos\left[\frac{\sqrt{(x+\delta x)}+\sqrt{x}}{2}\right]}{\sqrt{(x+\delta x)}+\sqrt{(x)}}\cdot\frac{\sin\left[\frac{\sqrt{(x+\delta x)}-\sqrt{x}}{2}\right]}{\sqrt{(x+\delta x)}-\sqrt{(x)}}$$

(Note the D^r)

Now when $\delta x \to 0$, $\frac{\sqrt{(x+\delta x)} - \sqrt{x}}{2} \to 0$

and when $\theta \to 0, \sin\theta \to \theta$

$$= \lim \frac{2\cos\left[\frac{\sqrt{(x+\delta x)}+\sqrt{x}}{2}\right]}{\sqrt{(x+\delta x)}+\sqrt{(x)}} \left\{\frac{[\sqrt{(x+\delta x)}-\sqrt{x}]}{[\sqrt{(x+\delta x)}-\sqrt{(x)}]}\right\} \cdot \frac{1}{2}$$

$$= \frac{2\cos(2\sqrt{x}/2)}{2\sqrt{(x)}} \cdot 1 \cdot \frac{1}{2} = \frac{1}{2\sqrt{(x)}} \cdot \cos\sqrt{x}.$$

(b) $$\frac{dy}{dx} = \underset{\delta x \to 0}{\text{Lt}} \frac{\sin[\sin(x+\delta x)] - \sin[\sin x]}{\delta x}$$

$$= \underset{\delta x \to 0}{\text{Lt}} \frac{1}{\delta x} 2\sin\left[\frac{\sin(x+\delta x) - \sin x}{2}\right] \cos\left[\frac{\sin(x+\delta x)+\sin x}{2}\right]$$

Now as $\delta x \to 0$, $\sin(x+\delta x) - \sin x = \theta \to 0$
and $\sin\theta = \theta$ when $\theta \to 0$

$\therefore$ Limit $= \underset{\delta x \to 0}{\text{Lt}} \frac{1}{\delta x} \cdot 2 \cdot \frac{\sin(x+\delta x) - \sin x}{2} \cdot \cos(\sin x)$

$= \cos x \cdot \cos(\sin x)$ by **Q. 1 P. 1196-97**
$= \cos(\sin x) \cdot \cos x$

32. $y = \tan^2 ax$.

$$\frac{dy}{dx} = \lim_{\delta x \to 0} \frac{\tan^2 a(x+\delta x) - \tan^2 ax}{\delta x}$$

$$= \lim_{\delta x \to 0} \left[\frac{\tan a(x+\delta x) - \tan ax}{\delta x}\right] [\tan a(x+\delta x) + \tan ax]$$

$$= \lim_{\delta x \to 0} \frac{\sin(ax + a\delta x - ax)}{\delta x \cos(ax + a\delta x)\cos ax} \cdot [\tan a(x+\delta x) + \tan ax]$$

$$= \lim_{\delta x \to 0} a \frac{\sin(a\delta x)}{a\delta x} \cdot \left[\frac{\tan a(x+\delta x) + \tan ax}{\cos a(x+\delta x)\cos ax}\right]$$

$$= a \cdot 1 \cdot \frac{2\tan ax}{\cos^2 ax} = 2a\tan ax \sec^2 ax.$$

33. (a) $y = \cos(ax^2 + bx + c)$

$\therefore$ $y = \cos t$ where $t = ax^2 + bx + c$

$y + \delta y = \cos(t + \delta t)$

and $t + \delta t = a(x+\delta x)^2 + b(x+\delta x) + c$

$$\frac{\delta y}{\delta x} = \frac{\delta y}{\delta t} \cdot \frac{\delta t}{\delta x}$$

or $$\frac{\delta y}{\delta x} = \frac{\cos(t+\delta t) - \cos t}{\delta t} \cdot \frac{a[(x+\delta x)^2 - x^2] + b\,\delta x}{\delta x}$$

Also as $\delta x \to 0, \delta t \to 0$

$$\therefore \frac{dy}{dx} = \lim \frac{\delta y}{\delta x}$$

$$= \lim \frac{\cos(t+\delta t) - \cos t}{\delta t} \cdot \frac{a.2x\,\delta x + a\,\delta x^2 + b\,\delta x}{\delta x}$$

$= -\sin t \cdot (2ax + b + 0)$ (Prove yourself)
$= -(2ax+b)\sin(ax^2 + bx + c)$.

(b) Let $y = \cos^{-1}[e^{\sqrt{\tan x}}] = \cos^{-1} u$

$\therefore$ $u = \cos y = e^{\sqrt{\tan x}} = e^v$

where $v = \sqrt{\tan x}$

y is a function of u, u is a function of v and v is a function of x and we have to find $\frac{dy}{dx}$.

or $$\underset{\delta x \to 0}{\text{Lt}} \frac{\delta y}{\delta x} = \underset{\delta x \to 0}{\text{Lt}} \left(\frac{\delta y}{\delta u} \cdot \frac{\delta u}{\delta v} \cdot \frac{\delta v}{\delta x}\right)$$

$$= \underset{\delta x \to 0}{\text{Lt}} \frac{\delta y}{\delta u} \cdot \underset{\delta x \to 0}{\text{Lt}} \frac{\delta u}{\delta v} \cdot \underset{\delta x \to 0}{\text{Lt}} \frac{\delta v}{\delta x} \quad \text{...(1)}$$

It is clear that as $\delta x \to 0$, $\delta v \to 0$, $\delta u \to 0$, $\delta y \to 0$.

Now $v = \sqrt{\tan x}$

$\therefore$ $\delta v = \sqrt{\tan(x+\delta x)} - \sqrt{\tan x}$

$u = \cos y$ $\therefore$ $\delta u = \cos(y + \delta y) - \cos y$

$u = e^v$ $\therefore$ $\delta u = e^{v+\delta v} - e^v$

Hence from (1),

$$\frac{dy}{dx} = \underset{\delta y \to 0}{\text{Lt}} \frac{\delta y}{\cos(y+\delta y) - \cos y} \cdot \underset{\delta u \to 0}{\text{Lt}} \frac{e^{v+\delta v} - e^v}{\delta v} \cdot \underset{\delta x \to 0}{\text{Lt}} \frac{\sqrt{\tan(x+\delta x)} - \sqrt{\tan x}}{\delta x}$$

All the above limits have been calculated in Q. 2, 8, 21 respectively.

$$= -\frac{1}{\sin y} \cdot e^v \cdot \frac{1}{2\sqrt{\tan x}} \cdot \sec^2 x$$

$$= -\frac{1}{\sqrt{1-\cos^2 y}} \cdot e^v \cdot \frac{\sec^2 x}{2\sqrt{\tan x}}$$

$$= -\frac{1}{\sqrt{(1 - e^{2\sqrt{\tan x}})}} \cdot e^{\sqrt{\tan x}} \cdot \frac{\sec^2 x}{2\sqrt{\tan x}}$$

34. Proceed as above $\frac{dy}{dx} = 2x\cos(x^2 + 1)$.

35. (a) $y = x^2 \cos x$.

$$\frac{dy}{dx} = \lim_{\delta x \to 0} \frac{(x+\delta x)^2 \cos(x+\delta x) - x^2 \cos x}{\delta x}$$

$$= \lim_{\delta x \to 0} x^2 \left[\frac{\cos(x+\delta x) - \cos x}{\delta x}\right] + \frac{2x\,\delta x \cos(x+\delta x)}{\delta x} + \frac{(\delta x)^2}{\delta x} \cos(x+\delta x)$$

$$= x^2(-\sin x) + 2x\cos x + 0$$

$$= -x^2 \sin x + 2x\cos x.$$

(b) Above limit is differential coefficient of $x^2 \sin x$ at $x = a$, and it can be shown to be $2a \sin a + a^2 \cos a$ as in part (a).

36. $f(x) = \dfrac{x-1}{2x^2 - 7x + 5} = \dfrac{x-1}{(x-1)(2x-5)} = \dfrac{1}{2x-5}$ as $x \neq 1$.

Also $\quad f(1) = -1/3 \quad$ (given)

$\therefore \quad f'(1) = \lim\limits_{h \to 0} \dfrac{f(1+h) - f(1)}{h}$

$= \lim\limits_{h \to 0} \dfrac{\dfrac{1}{2(1+h)-5} - \left(-\dfrac{1}{3}\right)}{h}$

$= \lim\limits_{h \to 0} \dfrac{\dfrac{1}{2h-3} + \dfrac{1}{3}}{h} = \lim\limits_{h \to 0} \dfrac{2h}{3h(2h-3)}$

$= \lim\limits_{h \to 0} \dfrac{2}{3(2h-3)} = -\dfrac{2}{9}$.

37. $f(x) = x \tan^{-1}(x), \quad f(1) = 1 \tan^{-1} 1$

$f'(1) = \lim\limits_{h \to 0} \dfrac{(1+h)\tan^{-1}(1+h) - \tan^{-1} 1}{h}$

$= \lim\limits_{h \to 0} \dfrac{\tan^{-1}(1+h) - \tan^{-1} 1}{h} + \dfrac{h \tan^{-1}(1+h)}{h}$

$= \lim\limits_{h \to 0} \dfrac{\tan^{-1}\left[\dfrac{(1+h)-1}{1+(1+h).1}\right]}{h} + \tan^{-1}(1+h)$

$= \lim\limits_{h \to 0} \dfrac{\tan^{-1}\{h/(2+h)\}}{(2+h)\{h/(2+h)\}} + \tan^{-1}(1+h)$

Now let $\dfrac{h}{2+h} = x$ and when $h \to 0, x \to 0$,

$\lim\limits_{x \to 0} \dfrac{\tan^{-1} x}{x} = \lim\limits_{\theta \to 0} \dfrac{\theta}{\tan \theta}$ where $x = \tan \theta$.

Also when $x \to 0$, $\theta \to 0$

$= \lim\limits_{\theta \to 0} \dfrac{\theta}{\sin \theta} . \cos \theta = 1.1 = 1.$

$f'(1) = \lim \left[\dfrac{1}{2+h} . 1 + \tan^{-1}(1+h)\right]$

$= \dfrac{1}{2} + \tan^{-1} 1 = \dfrac{1}{2} + \dfrac{\pi}{4}$.

38. $y = \dfrac{1}{\sqrt{(x^2 + a^2)} + \sqrt{(x^2 + b^2)}}$

$\times \dfrac{\sqrt{(x^2 + a^2)} - \sqrt{(x^2 + b^2)}}{\sqrt{(x^2 + a^2)} - \sqrt{(x^2 + b^2)}}$

$= \dfrac{\sqrt{(x^2 + a^2)} - \sqrt{(x^2 + b^2)}}{(x^2 + a^2) - (x^2 + b^2)}$

$= \dfrac{1}{(a^2 - b^2)} [\sqrt{(x^2 + a^2)} - \sqrt{(x^2 + b^2)}]$

Now $\dfrac{d}{dx} \sqrt{u} = \dfrac{1}{2\sqrt{(u)}} \dfrac{du}{dx}$

$\therefore \quad \dfrac{dy}{dx} = \dfrac{1}{(a^2 - b^2)} \left[\dfrac{1}{2\sqrt{(x^2 + a^2)}} . 2x - \dfrac{1}{2\sqrt{(x^2 + b^2)}} . 2x\right]$

$= \dfrac{x}{(a^2 - b^2)} \left[\dfrac{1}{\sqrt{(x^2 + a^2)}} - \dfrac{1}{\sqrt{(x^2 + b^2)}}\right]$.

39. If $y = \sec x$, then $\dfrac{dy}{dx} = \sec x \tan x$ provided x is measured in radians.

Now $180^\circ = \pi$ radians

$\therefore \quad (x^\circ + 30^\circ) = \dfrac{\pi}{180}(x + 30)$ radians

$= \left(\dfrac{\pi x}{180} + \dfrac{\pi}{6}\right)$ radians

$\therefore \quad y = \sec\left(\dfrac{\pi x}{180} + \dfrac{\pi}{6}\right)$

$\therefore \quad \dfrac{dy}{dx} = \sec\left(\dfrac{\pi x}{180} + \dfrac{\pi}{6}\right) \cdot \tan\left(\dfrac{\pi x}{180} + \dfrac{\pi}{6}\right) . \dfrac{\pi}{180}$

$= \dfrac{\pi}{180} \sec(x^\circ + 30^\circ) \tan(x^\circ + 30^\circ)$.

40. Do yourself.

41. $y = 5x(1-x)^{-2/3} + \cos^2(2x+1)$

$\dfrac{dy}{dx} = 5.1(1-x)^{-2/3} + 5x.\left(-\dfrac{2}{3}\right)(1-x)^{-2/3-1}(-1)$

$+ 2\cos(2x+1).\{-\sin(2x+1)\}.2.$

$= \dfrac{5}{(1-x)^{2/3}} \left[1 + \dfrac{2x}{3(1-x)}\right] - 2\sin(4x+2)$

$[\because \sin 2A = 2 \sin A \cos A]$

$= \dfrac{5}{3(1-x)^{5/3}}(3-x) - 2\sin(4x+2).$

42. $y = \dfrac{x}{2}\sqrt{(a^2 + x^2)} + \dfrac{a^2}{2} \log[x + \sqrt{(x^2 + a^2)}]$

$\dfrac{dy}{dx} = \left[\dfrac{1}{2}\sqrt{(a^2 + x^2)} + \dfrac{x}{2} . \dfrac{1}{2\sqrt{(a^2 + x^2)}} . 2x\right]$

$+ \dfrac{a^2}{2} . \left[\left(\dfrac{1}{x + \sqrt{(x^2 + a^2)}}\right) . \left(1 + \dfrac{2x}{2\sqrt{(x^2 + a^2)}}\right)\right]$

$= \dfrac{1}{2\sqrt{(a^2 + x^2)}}(a^2 + 2x^2) + \dfrac{a^2}{2} \dfrac{1}{\sqrt{(a^2 + x^2)}}$

$= \dfrac{1}{2\sqrt{(a^2 + x^2)}}(a^2 + 2x^2 + a^2)$

$= \dfrac{1}{2\sqrt{(a^2 + x^2)}} . 2(a^2 + x^2) = \sqrt{a^2 + x^2}$

43. We know that $\dfrac{d}{dx} \log x = \dfrac{1}{x}$ provided the base is e.

Here in the question the base is 7 which should be changed to e.

$\log_a x = \dfrac{\log_e x}{\log_e a}$.

Now $y = \log_7 (\log_7 x)$

$$\therefore \quad y = \frac{\log\left(\dfrac{\log x}{\log 7}\right)}{\log 7},$$

where $\log 7 = \log_e 7 = k$, say

$$\therefore \quad y = \frac{1}{k}[\log(\log x) - \log k]$$

$$\therefore \quad \frac{dy}{dx} = \frac{1}{k}\cdot\frac{1}{\log x}\cdot\frac{1}{x} = \frac{1}{x\log x}\cdot\log_7 e$$

$$\because \quad k = \log_e 7 \Rightarrow \frac{1}{k} = \log_7 e$$

44. $y = \log_3\left[\dfrac{\sqrt{x^2+a^2}+\sqrt{x^2+b^2}}{\sqrt{(x^2+a^2)}-\sqrt{(x^2+b^2)}}\right]$

$$= \log_e\left[\frac{\sqrt{x^2+a^2}+\sqrt{x^2+b^2}}{\sqrt{(x^2+a^2)}-\sqrt{(x^2+b^2)}}\right].\log_3 e$$

$$= \log_3 e.[\log\{\sqrt{x^2+a^2}+\sqrt{x^2+b^2}\} - \log\{\sqrt{x^2+a^2}-\sqrt{x^2+b^2}\}]$$

$$\therefore \quad \frac{dy}{dx} = \log_3 e\left[\frac{1}{\sqrt{(x^2+a^2)}+\sqrt{(x^2+b^2)}}\cdot\left\{\frac{2x}{2\sqrt{(x^2+a^2)}}+\frac{2x}{2\sqrt{(x^2+b^2)}}\right\}\right]$$

$$-\log_3 e\left[\frac{1}{\sqrt{(x^2+a^2)}-\sqrt{(x^2+b^2)}}\cdot\left\{\frac{2x}{2\sqrt{(x^2+a^2)}}-\frac{2x}{2\sqrt{(x^2+b^2)}}\right\}\right]$$

$$= \log_3 e\left[\frac{x}{\sqrt{(x^2+a^2)}\sqrt{(x^2+b^2)}} - \frac{-x}{\sqrt{(x^2+a^2)}\sqrt{(x^2+b^2)}}\right]$$

$$= \frac{2x}{\sqrt{(x^2+a^2)}\sqrt{(x^2+b^2)}}.\log_3 e.$$

45. $y = \log_{10} x + \log_x 10 + \log_x x + \log_{10} 10.$

Just as in Q.43 we can change the base to e

$$y = \frac{\log x}{\log 10} + \frac{\log 10}{\log x} + 1 + 1$$

$$\therefore \quad \frac{dy}{dx} = \frac{1}{x\log_e 10} - \frac{\log_e 10}{x(\log_e x)^2}.$$

46. $y = x\log x. \therefore \dfrac{dy}{dx} = x.\dfrac{1}{x} + 1.\log x$

$$= \log e + \log x = \log ex$$

47. $\dfrac{dy}{dx} = \dfrac{1}{2\sqrt{[x+\sqrt{(x+\sqrt{x})}]}}$

$$\times\left[1+\frac{1}{2\sqrt{[x+\sqrt{(x)}]}}\left(1+\frac{1}{2\sqrt{(x)}}\right)\right]$$

48. (i) The function $y = \log|x|$ is defined for all real x except $x = 0$ and

$$\log|x| = \begin{cases}\log x \text{ if } x > 0\\ \log(-x) \text{ if } x < 0\end{cases}$$

Hence $\dfrac{d}{dx}\log|x|$

$$= \left\{\frac{1}{x}, x>0; = \left(\frac{1}{-x}\right)(-1) = \frac{1}{x} \text{ if } x<0\right\}$$

thus $\dfrac{d}{dx}\log|x| = \dfrac{1}{x},\ x \neq 0.$

(ii) Ans. $2\operatorname{cosec} 2x$.

§5. Trigonometrical transformations and expansions.

Sometimes by a trigonometrical transformation the derivatives of various functions are calculated in a much simpler way than otherwise. The following trigonometrical expansions and formulae be remembered.

(i) $\sin x = x - \dfrac{x^3}{3!} + \dfrac{x^5}{5!} - \cdots$

$\cos x = 1 - \dfrac{x^2}{2!} + \dfrac{x^4}{4!} - \dfrac{x^6}{6!} + \cdots$

$\tan x = x + \dfrac{1}{3}x^3 + \dfrac{2}{15}x^5 + \cdots$

(ii) (a) $\tan^{-1} x - \tan^{-1} y = \tan^{-1}\dfrac{x-y}{1+xy}$

(b) $\tan^{-1} x + \tan^{-1} y = \tan^{-1}\dfrac{x+y}{1-xy}$

(c) $2\tan^{-1} x = \tan^{-1}\dfrac{2x}{1-x^2}$

(d) $\sin^{-1} x \pm \sin^{-1} y$

$$= \sin^{-1}[x\sqrt{1-y^2} \pm y\sqrt{1-x^2}]$$

(e) $\cos^{-1} x \pm \cos^{-1} y$

$$= \cos^{-1}[xy \mp \sqrt{1-x^2}\sqrt{1-y^2}]$$

(iii) $\sin^{-1} x + \cos^{-1} x = \tan^{-1} x + \cot^{-1} x$

$= \sec^{-1} x + \operatorname{cosec}^{-1} x = \pi/2$

(iv) $\sin^{-1} x = \operatorname{cosec}^{-1}(1/x)$,

$\tan^{-1} x = \cot^{-1}(1/x)$

(v) $\sin^{-1}\cos x = \sin^{-1}\sin\left(\dfrac{1}{2}\pi - x\right) = \dfrac{1}{2}\pi - x.$

(vi) $\tan^{-1}(\tan\theta) = \theta,\ \sin^{-1}(\sin\theta) = \theta,$

$\cos^{-1}(\cos\theta) = \theta.$

(vii)* **Important results of Trigonometry.**

$$\frac{1-\cos x}{1+\cos x} = \frac{2\sin^2(x/2)}{2\cos^2(x/2)} = \tan^2\frac{x}{2},$$

$$\frac{1+\cos x}{1-\cos x}=\cot^2\frac{x}{2}$$

$$\frac{1-\cos x}{\sin x}=\frac{2\sin^2(x/2)}{2\sin(x/2)\cos(x/2)}=\tan(x/2)$$

$$\frac{1+\cos x}{\sin x}=\cot\frac{x}{2}$$

$$\sqrt{1\pm\sin x}=[\cos^2(x/2)+\sin^2(x/2)\pm 2\sin(x/2)\cos(x/2)]^{1/2}$$

$$=[\{\cos(x/2)\pm\sin(x/2)\}^2]^{1/2}$$

$$=\cos(x/2)\pm\sin(x/2)$$

$$\tan A\pm\tan B=\frac{\sin A\cos B\pm\cos A\sin B}{\cos A\cos B}$$

$$=\frac{\sin(A\pm B)}{\cos A\cos B}$$

$$\tan\left(\frac{1}{4}\pi+\theta\right)=\frac{1+\tan\theta}{1-\tan\theta},$$

$$\tan\left(\frac{1}{4}\pi-\theta\right)=\frac{1-\tan\theta}{1+\tan\theta}.$$

(viii) $\cos x=2\cos^2(x/2)-1=1-2\sin^2(x/2)$

$$=\cos^2(x/2)-\sin^2(x/2),$$

(ix) $\sin x=\dfrac{2\tan(x/2)}{1+\tan^2(x/2)}$;

(x) $\cos x=\dfrac{1-\tan^2(x/2)}{1+\tan^2(x/2)}$

(xi) $\tan x=\dfrac{2\tan(x/2)}{1-\tan^2(x/2)}$

(xii) $\sin 3x=3\sin x-4\sin^3 x$

(xiii) $\cos 3x=4\cos^3 x-3\cos x$.

(xiv) **Substitution for differentiation of algebraic functions**

$\sqrt{(a^2-x^2)}$	Put $x=a\sin\theta$
$\sqrt{(a^2+x^2)}$	Put $x=a\tan\theta$
$\sqrt{(x^2-a^2)}$	Put $x=a\sec\theta$
$\sqrt{\left(\dfrac{a+x}{a-x}\right)}$	Put $x=a\cos 2\theta$

Substitutions are so chosen so as to get rid of radicals. Even if the power were 3/2 instead of 1/2, same substitution will work.

Problem Set (2)

Differentiation by the help of trigonometrical transformations. Differentiation of parametric equations.

Differentiate the following :

1. (a) $\tan^{-1}\dfrac{\sqrt{x}-x}{1+x^{3/2}}$.

(b)* If $y=\tan^{-1}\dfrac{1}{x^2+x+1}+\tan^{-1}\dfrac{1}{x^2+3x+3}+\tan^{-1}\dfrac{1}{x^2+5x+7}+\ldots n$ terms,

then prove that $\dfrac{dy}{dx}=\dfrac{1}{(x+n)^2+1}-\dfrac{1}{x^2+1}$

2. (a) $\tan^{-1}\sqrt{\left(\dfrac{1-\cos x}{1+\cos x}\right)}$

(b)* $\tan^{-1}\sqrt{\left(\dfrac{1+\sin x}{1-\sin x}\right)}$.

3. (a) $\tan^{-1}\dfrac{\sin x}{1+\cos x}$ (b) $\tan^{-1}\dfrac{\cos x}{1+\sin x}$

4. (a)* $\tan^{-1}\dfrac{x}{\sqrt{(a^2-x^2)}}$ **(M.P. C.E.E. 1999)**

(b) $\log_e\left(\dfrac{1+x}{1-x}\right)^{1/4}-\dfrac{1}{2}\tan^{-1}x$.

5. (a) $\tan^{-1}\dfrac{\cos x-\sin x}{\cos x+\sin x}$ (b) $\tan^{-1}\dfrac{\sin x+\cos x}{\cos x-\sin x}$

(c) $\tan^{-1}\dfrac{a\cos x-b\sin x}{b\cos x+a\sin x}$

6. (a)* $\tan^{-1}\dfrac{\sqrt{1+x^2}-1}{x}$

(b)* $\tan^{-1}\dfrac{x}{1+\sqrt{(1-x^2)}}+\sin\left\{2\tan^{-1}\sqrt{\left(\dfrac{1-x}{1+x}\right)}\right\}$

(c) If $y=\sin^{-1}\dfrac{1}{\sqrt{(1+x^2)}}+\tan^{-1}\dfrac{\sqrt{1+x^2}-1}{x}$, then show that $\dfrac{dy}{dx}=\dfrac{-1}{2(1+x^2)}$.

7. Differentiate $\tan x^n+\tan^n x-\tan^{-1}\dfrac{a+x^n}{1-ax^n}$.

8. (a) Differentiate $\tan^{-1}\dfrac{5ax}{a^2-6x^2}$

(b) Differentiate $\tan^{-1}\dfrac{3a^2x-x^3}{a(a^2-3x^2)}$

(c) If $y=\tan^{-1}\dfrac{4x}{1+5x^2}+\tan^{-1}\dfrac{2+3x}{3-2x}$ prove that $\dfrac{dy}{dx}=\dfrac{5}{1+25x^2}$.

Differentiate the following :

9. $\cot^{-1} \dfrac{\sqrt{1+\sin x}+\sqrt{1-\sin x}}{\sqrt{(1+\sin x)}-\sqrt{(1-\sin x)}}$

10. (a)* $\tan^{-1} \dfrac{\sqrt{1+x^2}+\sqrt{1-x^2}}{\sqrt{(1+x^2)}-\sqrt{(1-x^2)}}$ **(J.E.E. W.B. 1992)**

(b) $\tan^{-1} \dfrac{\sqrt{1+x}-\sqrt{1-x}}{\sqrt{(1+x)}+\sqrt{(1-x)}}$.

11. (a) $\sin^{-1} \dfrac{2x}{1+x^2}$, (b) $\cos^{-1} \dfrac{1-x^2}{1+x^2}$,

(c) $\tan^{-1} \dfrac{2x}{1-x^2}$

12. If $\tan y = \dfrac{2t}{1-t^2}$ and $\sin x = \dfrac{2t}{1+t^2}$, prove that $\dfrac{dy}{dx} = 1$.

13. (a) If $y = \sin^{-1} \dfrac{2x}{1+x^2} + \sec^{-1} \dfrac{1+x^2}{1-x^2}$, then $\dfrac{dy}{dx} = \dfrac{4}{1+x^2}$.

(b) If $y = \sin^{-1} 2x\sqrt{1-x^2} + \sec^{-1} \dfrac{1}{\sqrt{(1-x^2)}}$, then $\dfrac{dy}{dx} = \dfrac{3}{\sqrt{(1-x^2)}}$.

14. (a)* Differentiate $\cos^{-1} \dfrac{x^{2n}-1}{x^{2n}+1}$.

(b)* Differentiate $\cos^{-1} \dfrac{x-x^{-1}}{x+x^{-1}}$.

15. (a) $\sin^{-1}(3x-4x^3)$, $\cos^{-1}(4x^3-3x)$.

(b) If $u = \sin^{-1}(x-y)$, $x = 3t$, $y = 4t^3$, then $\dfrac{du}{dt} = \dfrac{3}{\sqrt{(1-t^2)}}$.

16. (a) $\sin^{-1} x + \sin^{-1} \sqrt{1-x^2}$,

(b) $\sin^{-1} \sqrt{1-x} + \cos^{-1} \sqrt{x}$.

17. (a)* $\sin^{-1} [x\sqrt{1-x} + \sqrt{x}\sqrt{1-x^2}]$.

(b) If $y = \sin^{-1} (x^2\sqrt{1-x} - \sqrt{x}\sqrt{1-x^4})$, find $\dfrac{dy}{dx}$.

18. Differentiate $\sin^{-1} \dfrac{\sqrt{1+x}+\sqrt{1-x}}{2}$.

19. (a)* Differentiate $\tan^{-1} \dfrac{\sqrt{1+x^2}-1}{x}$ w.r.t. $\tan^{-1} x$.

(b) Differentiate $\tan^{-1} \dfrac{2x}{1-x^2}$ w.r.t. $\sin^{-1} \dfrac{2x}{1+x^2}$.

(M.P. C.E.E. 1999; J.E.E. W.B. 1992)

20. (a)* Differentiate $\sin^{-1} \dfrac{1-x}{1+x}$ w.r.t. to $\sqrt{x}$.

(b)* Differentiate $x^{\sin^{-1} x}$ w.r.t. $\sin^{-1} x$.

21. (a) Differentiate $\tan^{-1} \dfrac{x}{\sqrt{(1-x^2)}}$ w.r.t. $\sec^{-1} \dfrac{1}{2x^2-1}$.

(b) Differentiate $\sin^{-1} x$ w.r.t. $\cos^{-1} \sqrt{1-x^2}$

22. Prove that differential coefficient of $\log_{10} x$ w.r.t. $\log_x 10$ is $-\dfrac{(\log x)^2}{(\log 10)^2}$.

23. (a)* Differentiate $\sec^{-1} \dfrac{1}{2x^2-1}$ w.r.t. $\sqrt{1-x^2}$ at $x = \dfrac{1}{2}$.

(b) Differentiate $\dfrac{\tan^{-1} x}{1+\tan^{-1} x}$ w.r.t. $\tan^{-1} x$.

24. Prove that the derivative of $\tan^{-1}\left(\dfrac{\sqrt{1+x^2}-1}{x}\right)$ with respect to $\tan^{-1}\left(\dfrac{2x\sqrt{1-x^2}}{1-2x^2}\right)$ at $x = 0$, is $\dfrac{1}{4}$.

25. (a) Differentiate $\dfrac{\sqrt{1+x^2}-\sqrt{1-x^2}}{\sqrt{1+x^2}+\sqrt{1-x^2}}$ w.r.t. $\sqrt{1-x^4}$.

(b) Differentiate $\cot^{-1} \dfrac{2\sqrt{1+x^2}-5\sqrt{1-x^2}}{5\sqrt{1+x^2}+2\sqrt{1-x^2}}$ with respect to $\cos^{-1} \sqrt{(1-x^4)}$.

26.* Find the differential coefficient of $\log_{(1-\sqrt{x})} \sin^{-1}(1-\sqrt{x})$ with repect to $2^{2(1-\sqrt{x})}$ and also find its value at $x = \dfrac{1}{4}$. **(Roorkee 1996)**

27. (a)* If $\sqrt{1-x^2} + \sqrt{1-y^2} = a(x-y)$, show that $\dfrac{dy}{dx} = \sqrt{\left(\dfrac{1-y^2}{1-x^2}\right)}$. **(D.C.E. 1997)**

(b)* If $\sqrt{(1-x^6)} + \sqrt{(1-y^6)} = a^3(x^3-y^3)$, prove that $\dfrac{dy}{dx} = \dfrac{x^2}{y^2}\sqrt{\dfrac{(1-y^6)}{(1-x^6)}}$. **(Roorkee 1994)**

(c)* Find $\dfrac{dy}{dx}$ when $\sqrt{1-y^2} + \sqrt{1-t^2} = \alpha(y-t)$ and $x = \sin^{-1} [t \,.\, \sqrt{1-t} + \sqrt{t} \,.\, \sqrt{1-t^2}]$. Express your result as a function of y and t, independent of α. **(Roorkee 1990)**

(d) If $\sqrt{1-x^{2n}}+\sqrt{1-y^{2n}}=a^n(x^n-y^n)$, then prove that $\frac{dy}{dx}=\frac{x^{n-1}}{y^{n-1}}\sqrt{\frac{1-y^{2n}}{1-x^{2n}}}$.

28. (a) If $\sin^{-1}\left(\frac{x^2-y^2}{x^2+y^2}\right)=\log a$, then show that $\frac{dy}{dx}=\frac{y}{x}$.

(b) If $\sqrt{x+y}+\sqrt{y-x}=c$, then show that $\frac{d^2y}{dx^2}=\frac{2}{c^2}$

29. If $y=\tan^{-1}\left(\frac{\log(e/x^2)}{\log(ex^2)}\right)+\tan^{-1}\left(\frac{3+2\log x}{1-6\log x}\right)$, then prove that $\frac{d^2y}{dx^2}=0$.

30. Prove that if

$$y=\tan^{-1}\frac{1}{1+x+x^2}+\tan^{-1}\frac{1}{x^2+3x+3}+\tan^{-1}\frac{1}{x^2+5x+7}+\ldots n \text{ terms},$$

then $y'(0)=\frac{-n^2}{n^2+1}$.

31. (a)* If $y=\sec^{-1}\left(\frac{\sqrt{x}+1}{\sqrt{(x)}-1}\right)+\sin^{-1}\left(\frac{\sqrt{x}-1}{\sqrt{(x)}+1}\right)$, then $\frac{dy}{dx}=0$.

(b) If $y=\sin^{-1}x+\sin^{-1}\sqrt{1-x^2}$, then prove then $dy/dx=0$.

32. (a) If $y=\cos^{-1}\left(\frac{2\cos x+3\sin x}{\sqrt{(13)}}\right)$, then $\frac{dy}{dx}=1$.

(b) If $y=\sin^{-1}\left(\frac{5x+12\sqrt{1-x^2}}{13}\right)$, $\frac{dy}{dx}=\frac{1}{\sqrt{(1-x^2)}}$.

33. (a) If $y=\sin(2\sin^{-1}x)$, $\frac{dy}{dx}=2\sqrt{\left(\frac{1-y^2}{1-x^2}\right)}$.

(b) If $x=a(t-\sin t)$, $y=a(1-\cos t)$, find dy/dx.

34. (a) If $y=\log\tan\frac{x}{2}+\sin^{-1}(\cos x)$, $\frac{dy}{dx}=\operatorname{cosec} x-1$.

(b)* If $x=a\left(\cos t+\log\tan\frac{t}{2}\right)$, $y=a\sin t$, find $\frac{dy}{dx}$.

(M.N.R. 1991)

35. (a) If $x=t+\frac{1}{t}$ and $y=t-\frac{1}{t}$, then prove that $\frac{d^2y}{dx^2}=-\frac{4t^3}{(t^2-1)^3}$.

(b) If $x=\frac{1+t}{t^3}$, $y=\frac{3}{2t^2}+\frac{2}{t}$, then prove that $x\left(\frac{dy}{dx}\right)^3=1+\frac{dy}{dx}$.

36. If $x=\sqrt{\frac{1-t^2}{1+t^2}}$ and $y=\frac{\sqrt{1+t^2}-\sqrt{1-t^2}}{\sqrt{1+t^2}+\sqrt{1-t^2}}$, then the value of $\frac{d^2y}{dx^2}$ at $t=0$ is given by $\frac{1}{2}$.

37. If $f(x)=\prod_{r=1}^{n}[\cos(2r-1)x+i\sin(2r-1)x]$ then show that $[\text{Re } f(x)]''+i[\text{Im } f(x)]''$ is equal to $-n^4 f(x)$.

38. If $f(x)=x^{1/x}$ then prove that $f''(e)$ is equal to $-e^{(1/e)-3}$.

39. If $x=2\cos t-\cos 2t$, $y=2\sin t-\sin 2t$, find the value of dy/dx.

40.* If $x=a\sin 2\theta(1+\cos 2\theta)$, $y=b\cos 2\theta(1-\cos 2\theta)$ prove that $dy/dx=(b\tan\theta)/a$.

41. If $x=\cos^{-1}\frac{1}{\sqrt{(t^2+1)}}$, $y=\sin^{-1}\frac{t}{\sqrt{(1+t^2)}}$, show that dy/dx is independent of t.

42.* If $x=\frac{\sin^3 t}{\sqrt{(\cos 2t)}}$, $y=\frac{\cos^3 t}{\sqrt{(\cos 2t)}}$, find $\frac{dy}{dx}$ at $t=\frac{\pi}{6}$.

43.* If $x=\sin\theta\sqrt{\cos 2\theta}$, $y=\cos\theta\sqrt{\sin 2\theta}$, find dy/dx at $\theta=\pi/4$.

44.* If $y=\sqrt{(a-x)(x-b)}-(a-b)\tan^{-1}\sqrt{\frac{a-x}{x-b}}$ then prove that $\frac{dy}{dx}=\sqrt{\frac{a-x}{x-b}}$.

45. If $x=a(k\sin t+\sin kt)$ $y=a(k\cos t+\cos kt)$, then find $\frac{d^2y}{dx^2}$ in terms of t.

46. If $x^2+xy+y^2=a^2$, prove that $\frac{d^2y}{dx^2}+\frac{6a^2}{(x+2y)^3}=0$

47. If $x=\sin^{-1}2t\sqrt{1-t^2}$ and $y=\frac{\pi}{2}-\cos^{-1}t$, then find the value of $\frac{d^2y}{dx^2}$ at $t=\frac{\pi}{3}$.

Solutions to Problem Set (2)

Before doing these questions please revise the formulae of § 5 P. 1203.

1. (a) $y=\tan^{-1}\frac{\sqrt{x}-x}{1+\sqrt{(x)}\cdot x}=\tan^{-1}\sqrt{x}-\tan^{-1}x$

$$\therefore \quad \frac{dy}{dx}=\frac{1}{1+x}\cdot\frac{1}{2\sqrt{(x)}}-\frac{1}{1+x^2}.$$

(b) $T_1 = \tan^{-1}(x+1) - \tan^{-1} x$,

$T_2 = \tan^{-1}(x+2) - \tan^{-1}(x+1)$ etc.

$\therefore \quad y = \tan^{-1}(x+n) - \tan^{-1} x$ etc.

2. (a) $y = \tan^{-1}[\tan(x/2)] = x/2$

$\therefore \quad \dfrac{dy}{dx} = \dfrac{1}{2}$ **Ref. § 5 (vii), P. 1203**

(b) $y = \tan^{-1} \dfrac{\cos(x/2) + \sin(x/2)}{\cos(x/2) - \sin(x/2)}$

$= \tan^{-1} \dfrac{1 + \tan(x/2)}{1 - \tan(x/2)}$

$= \tan^{-1} \tan(\pi/4 + x/2)$

$= \dfrac{\pi}{4} + \dfrac{x}{2} \quad \therefore \quad \dfrac{dy}{dx} = \dfrac{1}{2}$

3. (a) $y = \tan^{-1} \tan \dfrac{x}{2} = \dfrac{x}{2}, \quad \therefore \quad \dfrac{dy}{dx} = \dfrac{1}{2}$

(b) Put $x = 90^\circ - \theta \quad \therefore \quad y = \theta/2 = 45^\circ - x/2$

$\therefore \quad \dfrac{dy}{dx} = -\dfrac{1}{2}$.

or $\quad y = \tan^{-1} \dfrac{\cos^2(x/2) - \sin^2(x/2)}{[\cos(x/2) + \sin(x/2)]^2}$

$= \tan^{-1} \dfrac{\cos(x/2) - \sin(x/2)}{\cos(x/2) + \sin(x/2)}$

$= \tan^{-1} \tan(\pi/4 - x/2) = \pi/4 - x/2$

$\therefore \quad \dfrac{dy}{dx} = -\dfrac{1}{2}$

4. (a) Put $x = a \sin\theta$

$\therefore \quad y = \tan^{-1} \dfrac{a \sin\theta}{a \cos\theta} = \tan^{-1}(\tan\theta) = \theta$

$= \sin^{-1}(x/a)$.

$\therefore \quad \dfrac{dy}{dx} = \dfrac{1}{\sqrt{(1 - x^2/a^2)}} \cdot \dfrac{1}{a} = \dfrac{1}{\sqrt{(a^2 - x^2)}}$.

(b) Here $y = \dfrac{1}{4}[\log(1+x) - \log(1-x)] - \dfrac{1}{2}\tan^{-1} x$.

then, $\dfrac{dy}{dx} = \dfrac{1}{4}\left[\dfrac{1}{1+x} - \dfrac{1}{1-x}(-1)\right] - \dfrac{1}{2} \cdot \dfrac{1}{1+x^2}$

$= \dfrac{1}{2(1-x^2)} - \dfrac{1}{2(1+x^2)} = \dfrac{x^2}{1-x^4}$.

5. (a) Divide above and below by $\cos x$.

$y = \tan^{-1} \dfrac{1 - \tan x}{1 + \tan x}$

$= \tan^{-1} \tan(\pi/4 - x) = \pi/4 - x$,

$\therefore \quad dy/dx = -1$

(b) Dividing above and below by $\cos x$,

$y = \tan^{-1} \dfrac{1 + \tan x}{1 - \tan x} = \tan^{-1} \tan\left(\dfrac{\pi}{4} + x\right)$

$\therefore \quad y = \dfrac{\pi}{4} + x \quad$ or $\quad \dfrac{dy}{dx} = 1$

(c) Put $a = r\cos\alpha,\ b = r\sin\alpha$

$\therefore \quad r = \sqrt{a^2 + b^2},\ \tan\alpha = b/a$

$\therefore \quad y = \tan^{-1} \dfrac{r\cos(x+\alpha)}{r\sin(x+\alpha)} = \tan^{-1} \cot(x+\alpha)$

$= \tan^{-1} \tan[\pi/2 - (x+\alpha)]$

$\therefore \quad y = \pi/2 - x - \alpha \quad \therefore \quad dy/dx = -1$.

6. (a) Put $x = \tan\theta$.

$\therefore \quad y = \tan^{-1} \dfrac{\sec\theta - 1}{\tan\theta} = \tan^{-1} \dfrac{1 - \cos\theta}{\sin\theta}$

or $\quad y = \tan^{-1} \tan \dfrac{\theta}{2} = \dfrac{\theta}{2} = \dfrac{1}{2}\tan^{-1} x$

$\therefore \quad \dfrac{dy}{dx} = \dfrac{1}{2} \cdot \dfrac{1}{1+x^2}$.

(b) Put $x = \cos\theta$.

$\therefore \quad y = \tan^{-1} \dfrac{\cos\theta}{1 + \sin\theta} + \sin\left[2\tan^{-1} \sqrt{\left(\dfrac{1 - \cos\theta}{1 + \cos\theta}\right)}\right]$.

$= \tan^{-1} \tan\left(\dfrac{\pi}{4} - \dfrac{\theta}{2}\right) + \sin\left[2\tan^{-1} \tan\dfrac{\theta}{2}\right]$

as in Q. 3 (b).

$= \left(\dfrac{\pi}{4} - \dfrac{\theta}{2}\right) + \sin\left(2 \cdot \dfrac{\theta}{2}\right)$

$= \pi/4 - \theta/2 + \sqrt{1 - \cos^2\theta}$

$= \dfrac{\pi}{4} - \dfrac{1}{2}\cos^{-1} x + \sqrt{1 - x^2}$

$\therefore \quad \dfrac{dy}{dx} = \dfrac{1}{2} \dfrac{1}{\sqrt{(1-x^2)}} + \dfrac{1}{2\sqrt{(1-x^2)}}(-2x)$

$= \dfrac{1 - 2x}{2\sqrt{(1-x^2)}}$.

(c) Put $x = \tan\theta$

$\therefore \quad y = \dfrac{\pi}{2} - \theta + \dfrac{\theta}{2} = \dfrac{\pi}{2} - \dfrac{1}{2}\tan^{-1} x$.

$\therefore \quad \dfrac{dy}{dx} = -\dfrac{1}{2} \cdot \dfrac{1}{1+x^2}$, by Q.6 (a).

7. $y = \tan x^n + \tan^n x - (\tan^{-1} a + \tan^{-1} x^n)$

$\therefore \quad dy/dx = (\sec^2 x^n) \cdot n x^{n-1}$

$+ n \tan^{n-1} x \cdot \sec^2 x - 0 - [1/(1 + x^{2n})] \cdot n x^{n-1}$

8. (a) Divide by a^2.

$y = \tan^{-1} \dfrac{\dfrac{3x}{a} + \dfrac{2x}{a}}{1 - \dfrac{3x}{a} \cdot \dfrac{2x}{a}} = \tan^{-1} \dfrac{3x}{a} + \tan^{-1} \dfrac{2x}{a}$

(b) Put $x = a\tan\theta$

$\therefore \quad y = \tan^{-1} \dfrac{3\tan\theta - \tan^3\theta}{1 - 3\tan^2\theta}$

or $\quad y = \tan^{-1}(\tan 3\theta) = 3\theta = 3\tan^{-1} \dfrac{x}{a}$ etc.

(c) $y = \tan^{-1}\dfrac{5x - x}{1 + 5x \cdot x} + \tan^{-1}\dfrac{\frac{2}{3} + x}{1 - \frac{2}{3}x}$

or $y = \tan^{-1} 5x - \tan^{-1} x + \tan^{-1}\dfrac{2}{3} + \tan^{-1} x$

or $y = \tan^{-1} 5x + \tan^{-1}\dfrac{2}{3}$ $\therefore \dfrac{dy}{dx} = \dfrac{5}{1 + 25x^2}$.

9. $y = \cot^{-1}\dfrac{\left(\cos\frac{x}{2} + \sin\frac{x}{2}\right) + \left(\cos\frac{x}{2} - \sin\frac{x}{2}\right)}{\left(\cos\frac{x}{2} + \sin\frac{x}{2}\right) - \left(\cos\frac{x}{2} - \sin\frac{x}{2}\right)}$

$= \cot^{-1}\dfrac{2\cos(x/2)}{2\sin(x/2)}$

or $y = \cot^{-1}\cot\dfrac{x}{2} = \dfrac{x}{2}$, $\therefore \dfrac{dy}{dx} = \dfrac{1}{2}$.

10. (a) Put $x^2 = \cos 2\theta$, $1 + \cos 2\theta = 2\cos^2\theta$,

$1 - \cos 2\theta = 2\sin^2\theta$

$\therefore \quad y = \tan^{-1}\dfrac{\cos\theta + \sin\theta}{\cos\theta - \sin\theta}$

$= \tan^{-1}\tan(\pi/4 + \theta) = \pi/4 + \theta$

$\therefore \quad y = \dfrac{\pi}{4} + \dfrac{1}{2}\cos^{-1} x^2$

$\therefore \quad \dfrac{dy}{dx} = \dfrac{1}{2} \cdot \dfrac{-1}{\sqrt{(1 - x^4)}} \cdot 2x = -\dfrac{x}{\sqrt{(1 - x^4)}}$.

(b) Put $x = \cos\theta$ as in part (a).

$\therefore \quad y = \dfrac{\pi}{4} + \dfrac{1}{2}\theta = \dfrac{\pi}{4} + \dfrac{1}{2}\cos^{-1} x$

$\dfrac{dy}{dx} = -\dfrac{1}{2} \cdot \dfrac{1}{\sqrt{(1 - x^2)}}$

11. (a), (b), (c) each is $2\tan^{-1} x$ if we put $x = \tan\theta$.

$\therefore \dfrac{dy}{dx} = 2 \cdot \dfrac{1}{1 + x^2}$

12. $y = \tan^{-1}[2t/(1 - t^2)] = 2\tan^{-1} t$,

$x = \sin^{-1}[2t/(1 + t^2)] = 2\tan^{-1} t$.

Hence $y = x$, $\quad \therefore dy/dx = 1$.

13. (a) $y = 2\tan^{-1} x + 2\tan^{-1} x = 4\tan^{-1} x$,

$\therefore \quad dy/dx = 4/(1 + x^2)$

(b) Put $x = \sin\theta$, then $y = 2\theta + \theta = 3\theta = 3\sin^{-1} x$ etc.

14. (a) $y = \cos^{-1}\dfrac{x^{2n} - 1}{x^{2n} + 1} = \cos^{-1}\left\{-\left(\dfrac{1 - x^{2n}}{1 + x^{2n}}\right)\right\}$

$= \pi - \cos^{-1}\dfrac{1 - x^{2n}}{1 + x^{2n}}$ **(Formula)**

Put $x^n = \tan\theta$,

$\therefore \quad y = \pi - \cos^{-1}\cos 2\theta = \pi - 2\theta$.

or $y = \pi - 2\tan^{-1} x^n$

$\therefore \quad \dfrac{dy}{dx} = -\dfrac{2}{1 + x^{2n}} \cdot n x^{n-1}$.

(b) As in part (a).

$y = \cos^{-1}\dfrac{x^2 - 1}{x^2 + 1} = \pi - \cos^{-1}\dfrac{1 - x^2}{1 + x^2}$

$= \pi - \cos^{-1}\cos 2\theta$ where $x = \tan\theta$

$= \pi - 2\theta = \pi - 2\tan^{-1} x$

$\therefore \quad \dfrac{dy}{dx} = -\dfrac{2}{1 + x^2}$

15. (a) Put $x = \sin\theta$ in 1st and $x = \cos\theta$ in 2nd

$\therefore \quad y = 3\theta = 3\sin^{-1} x$ or $3\cos^{-1} x$

$\therefore \quad \dfrac{dy}{dx} = \dfrac{3}{\sqrt{(1 - x^2)}}$ or $-\dfrac{3}{\sqrt{(1 - x^2)}}$.

(b) $\sin u = x - y = 3t - 4t^3 = 3\sin\theta - 4\sin^3\theta$

where $t = \sin\theta$, say.

$\therefore \quad \sin u = \sin 3\theta$ or $u = 3\theta = 3\sin^{-1} t$

$\therefore \quad du/dt = 3\big/\sqrt{1 - t^2}$

16. (a) Put $x = \sin\theta$

$\therefore \quad y = \theta + \sin^{-1}\cos\theta$

$= \theta + \sin^{-1}\sin(\pi/2 - \theta) = \theta + \pi/2 - \theta = \pi/2$

$\therefore \quad dy/dx = 0$.

(b) Put $\sqrt{x} = \cos\theta$ $\therefore$ $x = \cos^2\theta$

$\therefore \quad y = \sin^{-1}\sin\theta + \theta = \theta + \theta = 2\theta = 2\cos^{-1}\sqrt{x}$

$\therefore \quad \dfrac{dy}{dx} = -\dfrac{2}{\sqrt{(1 - x)}} \cdot \dfrac{1}{2\sqrt{(x)}} = -\dfrac{1}{\sqrt{(x)}\sqrt{(1 - x)}}$.

17. (a) Put $x = \sin\theta$, and $\sqrt{x} = \sin\phi$

$\therefore \quad y = \sin^{-1}[\sin\theta\sqrt{1 - \sin^2\phi} + \sin\phi\sqrt{1 - \sin^2\theta}]$

or $y = \sin^{-1}(\sin\theta\cos\phi + \cos\theta\sin\phi)$

$= \sin^{-1}\sin(\theta + \phi) = \theta + \phi$

or $y = \sin^{-1} x + \sin^{-1}\sqrt{x}$

$\therefore \quad \dfrac{dy}{dx} = \dfrac{1}{\sqrt{(1 - x^2)}} + \dfrac{1}{\sqrt{(1 - x)}} \cdot \dfrac{1}{2\sqrt{(x)}}$.

(b) Proceed as in part (a).

$y = \sin^{-1} x^2 - \sin^{-1}\sqrt{x}$

$\therefore \quad \dfrac{dy}{dx} = \dfrac{2x}{\sqrt{1 - x^4}} - \dfrac{1}{2\sqrt{x}\sqrt{(1 - x)}}$

18. Put $x = \cos\theta$, $1 + \cos\theta = 2\cos^2(\theta/2)$,

$1 - \cos\theta = 2\sin^2(\theta/2)$

$\therefore \quad y = \sin^{-1}[(1/\sqrt{2})\{\cos(\theta/2) + \sin(\theta/2)\}]$

$= \sin^{-1}\sin(\theta/2 + \pi/4) = \theta/2 + \pi/4$

$\therefore \quad y = \frac{1}{2}\cos^{-1} x + \frac{\pi}{4} \quad \therefore \quad \frac{dy}{dx} = \frac{-1}{2\sqrt{(1-x^2)}}$

19. (a) Let $y = \tan^{-1} \frac{\sqrt{1+x^2}-1}{x}$ and $z = \tan^{-1} x$ and we have to find $\frac{dy}{dz}$.

$\therefore \quad y = \tan^{-1} \frac{\sqrt{1+\tan^2 z}-1}{\tan z} = \tan^{-1} \frac{1-\cos z}{\sin z}$

$\because x = \tan z$.

$= \tan^{-1} \tan\left(\frac{z}{2}\right) = \frac{1}{2} z \quad \therefore y = \frac{1}{2} z.$

$\therefore \quad \frac{dy}{dz} = \frac{1}{2}$

(b) Ans. 1 by Q. 11. Here $y = z = 2\tan^{-1} x$

20. (a) $\sqrt{x} = \tan\theta \;\therefore\; x = \tan^2\theta$

$y = \sin^{-1} \cos 2\theta = \frac{\pi}{2} - 2\theta = \frac{\pi}{2} - 2\tan^{-1}\sqrt{x}$

$y = \frac{\pi}{2} - 2\tan^{-1} z$, where $z = \sqrt{x}$

$\frac{dy}{dz} = -\frac{2}{1+z^2} = -\frac{2}{1+x}$

(b) Put $\sin^{-1} x = t$

$\therefore \quad x = \sin t, \sqrt{(1-x^2)} = \cos t$ ...(1)

$\therefore \quad y = (\sin t)^t$ and $z = t$,

we have to find $\frac{dy}{dz}$ or $\frac{dy}{dt}$.

$\log y = t \log \sin t$. Differentiate w.r.t. t

$\frac{1}{y}\frac{dy}{dt} = \log \sin t + t \cdot \frac{\cos t}{\sin t}$

$\therefore \quad \frac{dy}{dt} = x^{\sin^{-1} x}\left[\log x + \sin^{-1} x \frac{\sqrt{(1-x^2)}}{x}\right]$

21. (a) Let $y = \tan^{-1} \frac{x}{\sqrt{(1-x^2)}}$, $z = \sec^{-1} \frac{1}{2x^2-1}$

Put $x = \cos\theta$

$\therefore \quad y = \tan^{-1} \frac{\cos\theta}{\sin\theta}$

$= \tan^{-1} \tan(\pi/2 - \theta) = \pi/2 - \theta$

$z = \sec^{-1} \frac{1}{2\cos^2\theta - 1}$

$= \sec^{-1}(\sec 2\theta) = 2\theta$

$\therefore \quad y = \frac{\pi}{2} - \frac{1}{2}\cdot z \quad \therefore \quad \frac{dy}{dz} = -\frac{1}{2}$

(b) $z = \cos^{-1}\sqrt{1-x^2} = \sin^{-1} x$

$\therefore \quad y = z$ and $\frac{dy}{dz} = 1$.

22. $yz = \log_{10} x . \log_x 10 = \log_{10} 10 = 1$

$\therefore \quad y = \frac{1}{z} \quad \therefore \quad \frac{dy}{dz} = -\frac{1}{z^2}$

$= -(\log_{10} x)^2 = -\left(\frac{\log x}{\log 10}\right)^2.$

23. (a) $y = \sec^{-1}[1/(2x^2-1)]$, $z = \sqrt{1-x^2}$

$\frac{dy}{dx} = -\frac{2}{\sqrt{(1-x^2)}}$ as in Q. 21,

$\frac{dz}{dx} = \frac{1}{2\sqrt{(1-x^2)}}(-2x) = -\frac{x}{\sqrt{(1-x^2)}}$

$\therefore \quad dy/dx = 2/x.$

At $x = 1/2$, the required value = 4.

(b) $y = \frac{\tan^{-1} x}{1+\tan^{-1} x}$, $z = \tan^{-1} x$

$\therefore \quad y = \frac{z}{1+z} = \frac{z+1-1}{1+z} = 1 - \frac{1}{1+z}.$

$\frac{dy}{dz} = \frac{1}{(1+z)^2} = \frac{1}{(1+\tan^{-1} x)^2}.$

24. Putting $x = \tan\theta$, we have

$y = \tan^{-1} \tan\frac{\theta}{2} = \frac{\theta}{2} = \frac{1}{2}\tan^{-1} x$

$\therefore \quad \frac{dy}{dx} = \frac{1}{2}\cdot\frac{1}{1+x^2} = \frac{1}{2}$ at $x = 0$

Again putting $x = \sin\phi$, we have

$z = \tan^{-1}\left(\frac{2\sin\phi\cos\phi}{1-2\sin^2\phi}\right) = \tan^{-1}\frac{\sin 2\phi}{\cos 2\phi}$

$= \tan^{-1}\tan 2\phi = 2\phi = 2\sin^{-1} x$

$\therefore \quad \frac{dz}{dx} = \frac{2}{\sqrt{1-x^2}} = 2$ at $x = 0$

$\therefore \quad \frac{dy}{dz} = \frac{dy}{dx} \div \frac{dz}{dx} = \frac{1}{2} \div 2 = \frac{1}{4}$

25. (a) Put $x^2 = \cos 2\theta \quad \therefore \sin 2\theta = \sqrt{1-x^4}$

$1+\cos 2\theta = 2\cos^2\theta, 1-\cos 2\theta = 2\sin^2\theta$

$\therefore \quad y = \frac{\cos\theta - \sin\theta}{\cos\theta + \sin\theta} = \frac{1-\tan\theta}{1+\tan\theta} = \tan\left(\frac{\pi}{4} - \theta\right)$

$z = \sin 2\theta$

$\frac{dy}{d\theta} = -\sec^2\left(\frac{\pi}{4} - \theta\right) = \frac{-2}{1+\cos\left(\frac{\pi}{2} - 2\theta\right)} = \frac{-2}{1+\sin 2\theta}$

$\frac{dz}{d\theta} = 2\cos 2\theta$

$\therefore \quad \frac{dy}{dz} = \frac{dy}{d\theta}\cdot\frac{d\theta}{dz} = \frac{-1}{\cos 2\theta(1+\sin 2\theta)}$

$= \frac{-1}{x^2}\cdot\frac{1}{1+\sqrt{1-x^4}} = \frac{-1}{x^2}\cdot\frac{1-\sqrt{1-x^4}}{1-(1-x^4)}$

$= \frac{1}{x^6}[\sqrt{1-x^4} - 1]$

(b) Let $y = \cot^{-1}[\ \ ] = \tan^{-1}\dfrac{5\sqrt{1+x^2}+2\sqrt{1-x^2}}{2\sqrt{1+x^2}-5\sqrt{1-x^2}}$

Divide above and below by $2\sqrt{1+x^2}$

$$\therefore \quad y = \tan^{-1}\frac{\frac{5}{2}+\sqrt{\frac{1-x^2}{1+x^2}}}{1-\frac{5}{2}\sqrt{\frac{1-x^2}{1+x^2}}}$$

or $\quad y = \tan^{-1}\dfrac{5}{2} + \tan^{-1}\sqrt{\dfrac{1-x^2}{1+x^2}}$

Put $x^2 = \cos 2\theta$

$$\therefore \quad y = c + \tan^{-1}\sqrt{\frac{2\sin^2\theta}{2\cos^2\theta}}$$

$$= c + \tan^{-1}(\tan\theta) = c + \theta$$

$$z = \cos^{-1}\sqrt{1-x^4} = \cos^{-1}\sqrt{1-\cos^2 2\theta}$$

$$= \cos^{-1}(\sin 2\theta) = \frac{\pi}{2} - 2\theta = \frac{\pi}{2} - 2(y-c).$$

or $\quad z = \dfrac{\pi}{2} + 2c - 2y$

We have to find the value of $\dfrac{dy}{dz}$.

$$\therefore \quad \frac{dz}{dy} = -2 \quad \text{or} \quad \frac{dy}{dz} = -\frac{1}{2}$$

26. Let us put $t = (1-\sqrt{x})$ ...(1)

$$\therefore \quad y = \log_t \sin^{-1} t,\ z = 2^{2t} = 4^t$$

We have to find the value of $\dfrac{dy}{dz} = \dfrac{dy}{dt} \div \dfrac{dz}{dt}$

$$y = \frac{\log \sin^{-1} t}{\log t} \qquad ...(2)$$

Using formula for **product and not quotient,**

$$\frac{dy}{dt} = \frac{1}{\log t} \cdot \frac{1}{\sin^{-1} t} \cdot \frac{1}{\sqrt{(1-t^2)}} + (\log \sin^{-1} t)\left(-\frac{1}{(\log t)^2}\right) \cdot \frac{1}{t}$$

$$= \frac{1}{\log t} \cdot \frac{1}{\sin^{-1} t} \cdot \frac{1}{\sqrt{(1-t^2)}} - \frac{y \log t}{(\log t)^2} \cdot \frac{1}{t}, \qquad \text{by (2)}$$

$$= \frac{1}{\log t}\left[\frac{1}{\sin^{-1} t \cdot \sqrt{(1-t^2)}} - \frac{y}{t}\right]$$

$$\frac{dz}{dt} = 4^t \log 4$$

Again when $\quad x = \dfrac{1}{4}, t = 1 - \dfrac{1}{2} = \dfrac{1}{2}, \sin^{-1}\dfrac{1}{2} = \dfrac{\pi}{6}$

and $\log t = \log \dfrac{1}{2} = -\log 2$

and $y = \dfrac{\log(\pi/6)}{\log(1/2)} = \dfrac{\log(\pi/6)}{-\log 2}$

$\dfrac{dy}{dz} = \dfrac{dy}{dt} \div \dfrac{dz}{dt}$ where $t = (1-\sqrt{x}) = \dfrac{1}{2}$, at $x = \dfrac{1}{4}$

$$\therefore \quad \frac{dy}{dx} = \frac{1}{\log t}\left[\frac{1}{\sin^{-1} t\sqrt{1-t^2}} - \frac{y}{t}\right] \div (4^t \log 4)$$

$$= \frac{1}{-\log 2}\left[\frac{4\sqrt{3}}{\pi} + \frac{2\log(\pi/6)}{\log 2}\right] \div 2\log 4$$

$$= -\frac{2}{(\log 4)^2}\left[\frac{2\sqrt{3}}{\pi} + \frac{\log(\pi/6)}{\log 2}\right]$$

$\because \quad 2\log 2 = \log 4.$

27. (a) Put $x = \sin\theta$ and $y = \sin\phi$ in the given equation.

$$\therefore \quad \cos\theta + \cos\phi = a(\sin\theta - \sin\phi)$$

or $\quad 2\cos\dfrac{\theta+\phi}{2}\cos\dfrac{\theta-\phi}{2} = 2a\sin\dfrac{\theta-\phi}{2}\cos\dfrac{\theta+\phi}{2}$

or $\quad \cos\dfrac{\theta+\phi}{2}\left[\cos\dfrac{\theta-\phi}{2} - a\sin\dfrac{\theta-\phi}{2}\right] = 0.$

If $\quad \cos\dfrac{\theta+\phi}{2} = 0$, then $\dfrac{\theta+\phi}{2} = \dfrac{\pi}{2}$

$\therefore \quad \theta = \pi - \phi$ or $\sin\theta = \sin\phi$

or $\quad x = y.$

but if we put $x = y$ in the given equation it is not satisfied and hence we must have

$$\cos\frac{\theta-\phi}{2} - a\sin\frac{\theta-\phi}{2} = 0$$

or $\quad \cot\dfrac{\theta-\phi}{2} = a.$

$\therefore \quad \theta - \phi = 2\cot^{-1} a$

or $\quad \sin^{-1} x - \sin^{-1} y = 2\cot^{-1} a.$

Differentiate w.r.t. x,

$$\frac{1}{\sqrt{(1-x^2)}} - \frac{1}{\sqrt{(1-y^2)}}\frac{dy}{dx} = 0.$$

$$\therefore \quad \frac{dy}{dx} = \sqrt{\left(\frac{1-y^2}{1-x^2}\right)}.$$

Alternative Method.

$$\sqrt{1-x^2} + \sqrt{1-y^2} = a(x-y)$$

$$\therefore \quad \frac{1}{2\sqrt{1-x^2}}(-2x) + \frac{1}{2\sqrt{1-y^2}}(-2y)\frac{dy}{dx} = a\left(1 - \frac{dy}{dx}\right)$$

or $\quad \dfrac{a\sqrt{1-x^2}+x}{\sqrt{1-x^2}} = \dfrac{a\sqrt{1-y^2}-y}{\sqrt{1-y^2}}\dfrac{dy}{dx}$

$$\therefore \quad \frac{dy}{dx} = \sqrt{\frac{1-y^2}{1-x^2}} \cdot \frac{a\sqrt{1-x^2}+x}{a\sqrt{1-y^2}-y} \qquad ...(1)$$

Now we have $(1-x^2) - (1-y^2) = -(x^2-y^2)$

Dividing by given relation,

$$\sqrt{1-x^2}-\sqrt{1-y^2}=-\frac{x+y}{a}$$

or $a\sqrt{1-x^2}+x=a\sqrt{1-y^2}-y$ ...(2)

$\therefore$ $\frac{dy}{dx}=\sqrt{\frac{1-y^2}{1-x^2}}$ by (1) and (2)

(b) As in part (a), put $x^3=\sin\theta, y^3=\sin\phi$.

$\therefore$ $\sin^{-1}x^3-\sin^{-1}y^3=2\cot^{-1}a^3$ etc.

(c) $\frac{dy}{dx}=\frac{dy}{dt}\div\frac{dx}{dt}$.

Now see Q. 27 (a) & Q. 17. (a) for the values.

Ans. $\sqrt{1-y^2}\cdot\frac{2\sqrt{t}}{2\sqrt{(t)}+\sqrt{(1+t)}}$.

(d) Differentiating the given relation w.r.t. x,

$$\frac{1}{2\sqrt{1-x^{2n}}}(-2n\,x^{2n-1})+\frac{1}{2\sqrt{1-y^{2n}}}\cdot\left(-2n\,y^{2n-1}\frac{dy}{dx}\right)$$

$$=a^n\left\{n\,x^{n-1}-ny^{n-1}\frac{dy}{dx}\right\}$$

Cancel n from both sides and collect the terms of $\frac{dy}{dx}$.

$$x^{n-1}\left\{\frac{x^n+a^n\sqrt{1-x^{2n}}}{\sqrt{(1-x^{2n})}}\right\}$$

$$=y^{n-1}\left\{\frac{a^n\sqrt{1-y^{2n}}-y^n}{\sqrt{(1-y^{2n})}}\right\}\frac{dy}{dx}$$

$\therefore$ $\frac{dy}{dx}=\frac{x^{n-1}}{y^{n-1}}\sqrt{\frac{1-y^{2n}}{1-x^{2n}}}\cdot\frac{a^n\sqrt{1-x^{2n}}+x^n}{a^n\sqrt{1-y^{2n}}-y^n}$ ...(1)

Now we have to prove the last factor in (1) to be unity to get the answer.

Now $(1-x^{2n})-(1-y^{2n})=-(x^{2n}-y^{2n})$

Dividing by given relation

$$\sqrt{1-x^{2n}}-\sqrt{1-y^{2n}}=-\frac{1}{a^n}(x^n+y^n)$$

or $a^n\sqrt{1-x^{2n}}+x^n=a^n\sqrt{1-y^{2n}}-y^n$ ...(2)

Hence from (1) and (2), we get

$$\frac{dy}{dx}=\frac{x^{n-1}}{y^{n-1}}\sqrt{\frac{1-y^{2n}}{1-x^{2n}}}.$$

28. (a) $\frac{x^2-y^2}{x^2+y^2}=\sin(\log a)=\lambda$, say

$\therefore$ $x^2(1-\lambda)=y^2(1+\lambda)$ ...(1)

$$2x(1-\lambda)=2y\frac{dy}{dx}(1+\lambda) \quad ...(2)$$

Dividing (2) by (1), we have

$$\frac{2}{x}=\frac{2}{y}\frac{dy}{dx} \quad \therefore \quad \frac{dy}{dx}=\frac{y}{x}$$

(b) If the given relation be $l+m=c$, then $l^2-m^2=2x$. Dividing, $l-m=\frac{2x}{c}$

Adding, $2\sqrt{x+y}=c+\frac{2x}{c}$.

Squaring, $4(x+y)=c^2+\frac{4x^2}{c^2}+4x$

Cancel $4x$ and differentiate

$$4\frac{dy}{dx}=\frac{8x}{c^2} \quad \therefore \quad \frac{d^2y}{dx^2}=\frac{2}{c^2}$$

29. $\tan^{-1}\left(\frac{1-2\log x}{1+2\log x}\right)+\tan^{-1}\left(\frac{3+2\log x}{1+3.2\log x}\right)$

$=\tan^{-1}1-\tan^{-1}(2\log x)+\tan^{-1}3+\tan^{-1}(2\log x)$

$=\tan^{-1}1+\tan^{-1}3$

$\therefore$ $y=$ constant $\therefore$ $\frac{dy}{dx}=0$ and $\frac{d^2y}{dx^2}=0$

30. $T_1=\tan^{-1}\frac{(x+1)-x}{1+(x+1)x}=\tan^{-1}(x+1)-\tan^{-1}x$

$T_2=\tan^{-1}\frac{(x+2)-(x+1)}{1+(x+2).(x+1)}$

$=\tan^{-1}(x+2)-\tan^{-1}(x+1)$

... ...

$T_n=\tan^{-1}(x+n)-\tan^{-1}\{x+(n-1)\}$

$\therefore y=\tan^{-1}(x+n)-\tan^{-1}x$ as the terms cancel diagonally

$\therefore$ $\frac{dy}{dx}=y'=\frac{1}{1+(x+n)^2}-\frac{1}{1+x^2}$

$\therefore$ $y'(0)=\frac{1}{1+n^2}-1=\frac{-n^2}{n^2+1}$

31. (a) We know $\sec^{-1}z=\cos^{-1}(1/z)$

and $\cos^{-1}y+\sin^{-1}y=\pi/2$.

$\therefore$ $y=\cos^{-1}\frac{\sqrt{x}-1}{\sqrt{(x)}+1}+\sin^{-1}\frac{\sqrt{x}-1}{\sqrt{(x)}+1}$

$=\frac{\pi}{2}$ $\therefore$ $\frac{dy}{dx}=0$.

(b) $\cos^{-1}x=\sin^{-1}\sqrt{1-x^2}$.

$\therefore$ $y=\sin^{-1}x+\cos^{-1}x=\pi/2$

$\therefore$ $dy/dx=0$.

32. (a) Put $2=r\cos\alpha$, $3=r\sin\alpha$

$\therefore$ $r=\sqrt{13}$, $\tan\alpha=3/2$.

$\therefore \quad y = \cos^{-1} \dfrac{(\cos x \cos \alpha + \sin x \sin \alpha)}{\sqrt{(13)}}$

$= \cos^{-1} \cos(x - \alpha) = x - \alpha$

or $\quad y = x - \tan^{-1} \dfrac{3}{2}, \quad \therefore \quad \dfrac{dy}{dx} = 1.$

(b) Put $x = \sin\theta$ and proceed as above.

33. (a) $y = \sin(2\sin^{-1} x), \quad \therefore \quad \sin^{-1} y = 2\sin^{-1} x.$

Differentiate both sides w.r.t. x,

$$\frac{1}{\sqrt{(1-y^2)}} \frac{dy}{dx} = 2 . \frac{1}{\sqrt{(1-x^2)}},$$

$$\therefore \quad \frac{dy}{dx} = 2\sqrt{\left(\frac{1-y^2}{1-x^2}\right)}$$

(b) $\dfrac{dy}{dx} = \dfrac{\dot{y}}{\dot{x}} = \dfrac{a \sin t}{a(1-\cos t)} = \cot \dfrac{t}{2}$

34. (a) $\dfrac{dy}{dx} = \dfrac{1}{\tan(x/2)} . \sec^2 \dfrac{x}{2} . \dfrac{1}{2} - 1$

$[\because \sin^{-1} \cos x = \sin^{-1} \sin(\pi/2 - x) = \pi/2 - x]$

$$= \frac{1}{2 . \dfrac{\sin(x/2)}{\cos(x/2)} . \cos^2 \dfrac{x}{2}} - 1$$

$$= \frac{1}{2\sin(x/2)\cos(x/2)} - 1 = \operatorname{cosec} x - 1.$$

(b) $\dfrac{dx}{dt} = a\left(-\sin t + \dfrac{1}{\sin t}\right) = \dfrac{a(1-\sin^2 t)}{\sin t} = \dfrac{a\cos^2 t}{\sin t}$

$\dfrac{dy}{dt} = a \cos t$

$\therefore \quad \dfrac{dy}{dx} = a\cos t . \dfrac{\sin t}{a\cos^2 t} = \tan t.$

35. (a) $x^2 - y^2 = 4 \quad \therefore \quad 2x - 2y\dfrac{dy}{dx} = 0$ or $\dfrac{dy}{dx} = \dfrac{x}{y}$

$$\therefore \quad \frac{d^2 y}{dx^2} = \frac{y - x\dfrac{dy}{dx}}{y^2} = \frac{y^2 - x^2}{y^3} = \frac{-4t^3}{(t^2-1)^3}$$

on putting the values of x and y.

(b) $\dfrac{dy}{dx} = \dfrac{\dot{y}}{\dot{x}} = t$ etc.,

Putting $\dfrac{dy}{dx} = t$, L.H.S. = R.H.S. $= 1 + t$

36. Dividing both N^r and D^r by $\sqrt{1+t^2}$, we get

$$y = \frac{1-x}{1+x} = \frac{-1-x+2}{1+x} = -1 + \frac{2}{1+x}$$

$\therefore \quad \dfrac{dy}{dx} = \dfrac{-2}{(1+x)^2}$ and $\dfrac{d^2 y}{dx^2} = \dfrac{4}{(1+x)^3} = \dfrac{4}{8} = \dfrac{1}{2}.$

Because when $t = 0, x = 1.$

37. Ans. (d).

$\sum_{r=1}^{n} (2r-1) = 1 + 3 + 5 + 7 + \ldots n$ terms

$= \dfrac{n}{2}[2 . 1 + (n-1) . 2] = n^2 \qquad \ldots(1)$

$e^{i\theta} = \cos\theta + i\sin\theta$

$\therefore \quad f(x) = e^{ix} . e^{i3x} . e^{i5x} \ldots e^{i(2n-1)x}$

or $\quad f(x) = e^{in^2 x} = \cos n^2 x + i \sin n^2 x \qquad$ by (1)

$\operatorname{Re} f(x) = \cos n^2 x, \operatorname{Im} f(x) = \sin n^2 x \qquad \ldots(2)$

$\therefore \quad [\operatorname{Re} f(x)]'' = -(n^2)^2 \cos n^2 x,$

$i[\operatorname{Im} f(x)]'' = -i(n^2)^2 \sin n^2 x$

Adding we get $-n^4 [\cos n^2 x + i \sin n^2 x]$

$= -n^4 f(x)$ by (2)

38. $\log y = \dfrac{1}{x} \log x \quad \therefore \quad \dfrac{1}{y}\dfrac{dy}{dx} = \dfrac{x . \dfrac{1}{x} - 1 . \log x}{x^2}$

$\therefore \quad f'(x) = f(x) \dfrac{(1 - \log x)}{x^2}$

$\therefore \quad f'(e) = 0$ as $\log e = 1 \qquad \ldots(1)$

Differentiating again by product,

$$f\ (x) = f'(x) \frac{(1-\log x)}{x^2} + f(x) . \frac{x^2 . \left(-\dfrac{1}{x}\right) - (1 - \log x) . 2x}{x^4}$$

$$f''(x) = f'(x) \cdot \frac{1 - \log x}{x^2} + \frac{f(x)}{x^3}[-1 - 2(1 - \log x)]$$

Now put $x = e, f'(e) = 0$ and $(1 - \log x) = 0 \qquad$ by (1)

$\therefore \quad f\ (e) = 0 - \dfrac{f(e)}{e^3} = -\dfrac{e^{1/e}}{e^3} = -e^{(1/e)-3}$

39. $\dfrac{dx}{dt} = 2(\sin 2t - \sin t), \quad \dfrac{dy}{dt} = 2(\cos t - \cos 2t).$

$\therefore \quad \dfrac{dy}{dx} = \dfrac{dy}{dt} \Big/ \dfrac{dx}{dt} = \dfrac{2\sin(3t/2)\sin(t/2)}{2\cos(3t/2)\sin(t/2)} = \tan\dfrac{3t}{2}$

40. $x = a\left(\sin 2\theta + \dfrac{1}{2}\sin 4\theta\right),$

$y = b\left[\cos 2\theta - \dfrac{1}{2}(1 + \cos 4\theta)\right].$

We have used

$2\sin A \cos A = \sin 2A,$

$2\cos^2 A = 1 + \cos 2A.$

$\therefore \quad \dfrac{dx}{d\theta} = 2a(\cos 2\theta + \cos 4\theta)$

$= 2a . 2\cos 3\theta \cos\theta$

$\dfrac{dy}{d\theta} = 2b(\sin 4\theta - \sin 2\theta)$

$= 2b . 2\cos 3\theta \sin\theta.$

$\therefore \quad \dfrac{dy}{dx} = \dfrac{dy}{d\theta} \div \dfrac{dx}{d\theta} = \dfrac{b}{a}\tan\theta.$

41. Put $t = \tan\theta$, then

$x = \theta, \; y = \theta, \; \therefore \; y = x$ or $dy/dx = 1.$

42. From $x = \dfrac{\sin^3 t}{\sqrt{(\cos 2t)}}$, we have

$$\frac{dx}{dt} = \frac{3\sin^2 t \cos t \sqrt{\cos 2t} - [1/2\sqrt{\cos 2t}](-2\sin 2t)\sin^3 t}{\cos 2t}$$

$$= \frac{3\sin^2 t \cos t \cos 2t + \sin 2t \sin^3 t}{(\cos 2t)^{3/2}}$$

And from $y = \dfrac{\cos^3 t}{\sqrt{(\cos 2t)}}$, we have

$$\frac{dy}{dt} = \frac{-3\cos^2 t \sin t \sqrt{\cos 2t} - [1/2\sqrt{\cos 2t}](-2\sin 2t)\cos^3 t}{\cos 2t}$$

$$= \frac{-3\cos^2 t \sin t \cos 2t + \sin 2t \cos^3 t}{(\cos 2t)^{3/2}}$$

$$\therefore \quad \frac{dy}{dx} = \frac{-3\cos^2 t \sin t \cos 2t + \sin 2t \cos^3 t}{3\sin^2 t \cos t \cos 2t + \sin 2t \sin^3 t}.$$

Hence at $t = \pi/6$, we obtain

$$\frac{dy}{dx} = \frac{-3.\frac{3}{4}.\frac{1}{2}.\frac{1}{2} + \frac{\sqrt{3}}{2}.\frac{3\sqrt{3}}{8}}{3.\frac{1}{4}.\frac{\sqrt{3}}{2}.\frac{1}{2} + \frac{\sqrt{3}}{2}.\frac{1}{8}} = \frac{-\frac{9}{16} + \frac{9}{16}}{\frac{3\sqrt{3}}{16} + \frac{\sqrt{3}}{16}} = 0.$$

43. $\dfrac{dx}{d\theta} = \cos\theta\sqrt{(\cos 2\theta)} + \sin\theta . \dfrac{1}{2\sqrt{(\cos 2\theta)}}(-2\sin 2\theta)$

$$= \frac{\cos(\theta + 2\theta)}{\sqrt{(\cos 2\theta)}} = \frac{\cos 3\theta}{\sqrt{(\cos 2\theta)}}$$

$$\frac{dy}{d\theta} = \frac{\cos 3\theta}{\sqrt{(\sin 2\theta)}}$$

$$\therefore \quad \frac{dy}{dx} = \frac{dy}{d\theta} \div \frac{dx}{d\theta} = \sqrt{(\cot 2\theta)} = \sqrt{\left(\cot\frac{\pi}{2}\right)} = 0 \text{ at } \theta = \frac{\pi}{4}.$$

44. It will be convenient to change to parametric form.
Choose $x = a\cos^2 t + b\sin^2 t$ ...(1)

$\therefore \quad a - x = (a-b)\sin^2 t$,

$x - b = (a-b)\cos^2 t$ ...(2)

$\therefore \quad y = (a-b)\sin t\cos t - (a-b).t$ ...(3)

Now (1) and (3) give the parametric equations .

$$\therefore \quad \frac{dy}{dx} = \frac{\dot{y}}{\dot{x}} = \frac{1-\cos 2t}{\sin 2t} = \tan t$$

$$= \sqrt{\tan^2 t} = \sqrt{\frac{a-x}{x-b}}, \text{ by (2)}$$

45. $\dfrac{dy}{dx} = \dfrac{\dot{y}}{\dot{x}} = -\dfrac{\sin t + \sin kt}{\cos t + \cos kt} = -\tan\dfrac{k+1}{2}t$

$$\therefore \quad \frac{d^2y}{dx^2} = \frac{d}{dx}\left(-\tan\frac{k+1}{2}t\right)$$

$$= \frac{d}{dt}\left(-\tan\frac{k+1}{2}t\right)\frac{dt}{dx}$$

$$= -\frac{\frac{k+1}{2}\sec^2\frac{k+1}{2}t}{ak(\cos t + \cos kt)}$$

$$= -\frac{k+1}{4ak} \cdot \frac{1}{\cos^3\frac{k+1}{2}t\cos\frac{k-1}{2}t}.$$

$$\because \quad \cos C + \cos D = 2\cos\frac{C+D}{2}\cos\frac{C-D}{2}$$

46. $\dfrac{dy}{dx} = -\dfrac{f_x}{f_y} = -\dfrac{2x+y}{x+2y}$ ...(1)

Differentiate both sides w.r. to x.

$$\frac{d^2y}{dx^2} = -\frac{1}{(x+2y)^2} \cdot \left[(x+2y)\left(2 + \frac{dy}{dx}\right) - (2x+y)\left(1 + 2\frac{dy}{dx}\right)\right]$$

Now put the value of $\dfrac{dy}{dx}$ from (1) and simplify

$$\frac{d^2y}{dx^2} = -\frac{6(x^2+xy+y^2)}{(x+2y)^3} = \frac{-6a^2}{(x+2y)^3}$$

or $\quad \dfrac{d^2y}{dx^2} + \dfrac{6a^2}{(x+2y)^3} = 0.$ **Hence Proved.**

47. $y = \dfrac{\pi}{2} - \cos^{-1} t = \sin^{-1} t$

$\therefore \quad t = \sin y$

$\therefore \quad x = \sin^{-1}\sin 2y = 2y$

$\therefore \quad \dfrac{dy}{dx} = \dfrac{1}{2}$ and $\dfrac{d^2y}{dx^2} = 0 \quad \forall\, x$ and t.

Problem Set (3)

Differentiation of exponential and logarithmic and implicit functions.

Find dy/dx in Q.1 to 4.

1. (a)* $y = (\sin^{-1} x)^{x^2}$ (b) $y = x^x$

(c) $(\tan x)^{\log x}$ (d) $(x\log x)^{\log\log x}$

2.* $y = (\cot x)^{\sin x} + (\tan x)^{\cos x}$

3. (a) $y = (\cos x)^{\log x} + (\log x)^x$

(b)* $e^{x\sin x^3} + (\tan x)^x$ **(J.E.E.W.B. 1992)**

4. $y = (1 + 1/x)^x + x^{1+1/x}$.

5. If $y^x = x^{\sin y}$, find dy/dx.

6. (a)* If $x^y + y^x = a^b$, find dy/dx.

(b) $\log(x+y) - 2xy = 0$, then $y'(0) =$

(a) 1 (b) –1

(c) 2 (d) 0 **(Screening 2004)**

(c)* If $(\tan^{-1} x)^y + y^{\cot x} = 1$, find dy/dx.

(d) Find dy/dx if $\sqrt{x}+\sqrt{y}=4$.

(e)* Find dy/dx if $x^y+y^x=(x+y)^{x+y}$.

7. (a) If $x^y=y^x$, prove that $\dfrac{dy}{dx}=\dfrac{y(x\log y-y)}{x(y\log x-x)}$.

(b) Find dy/dx if $y^x \cdot x^y=1$.

(c) If $x^4+7x^3y+5x^2y^2-9xy^3+7y^4=0$, then prove that $\dfrac{dy}{dx}=\dfrac{y}{x}$.

8. (a)* If $y=(x^x)^x$, prove that

$dy/dx=x(x^x)^x(1+2\log x)$. **(J.E.E. W.B. 1990)**

(b) Let y be an implicit function of x defined by $x^{2x}-2x^x\cot y-1=0$. Then $y'(1)$ equals

(a) $-\log 2$ (b) -1

(c) 1 (d) $\log 2$ **(A.I.E.E.E. 2009)**

9. (a)* If $y=x^{(x^x)}$, prove that

$dy/dx=x^{x+x^x}[1/x+(1+\log x)\log x]$.

(J.E.E.W.B. 1991)

(b) $y=(\tan x)^{(\tan x)^{\tan x}}$ then prove that $\dfrac{dy}{dx}=2$ at $x=\pi/4$. **(J.E.E. W.B. 1990)**

10. If $y=x^{(\log x)^{\log\log x}}$, prove that

$$\frac{dy}{dx}=\frac{y}{x}(\log x)^{\log\log x}\cdot(2\log\log x+1).$$

11. If $y=e^{x^{e^x}}+x^{e^{e^x}}+e^{x^{x^e}}$, find $\dfrac{dy}{dx}$.

12. If $y=e^{x+e^{x+e^{x\ldots\infty}}}$, prove that $\dfrac{dy}{dx}=\dfrac{y}{1-y}$.

13. (a) If $y=\sqrt{x}^{\sqrt{x}^{\sqrt{x}^{\sqrt{x}\ldots\infty}}}$,

then $x\dfrac{dy}{dx}=\dfrac{y^2}{2-y\log x}$.

(b) If $x^{x^{x\ldots\infty}}$, prove that $\dfrac{dy}{dx}=\dfrac{y^2}{(1-y\log x)\,x}$.

14.* If $y=(\sin x)^{(\sin x)^{(\sin x)\ldots\infty}}$,

then $\dfrac{dy}{dx}=\dfrac{y^2\cot x}{1-y\log\sin x}$.

15. If $y=a^{x^{a^{x\ldots\infty}}}$, then $\dfrac{dy}{dx}=\dfrac{y^2\log y}{x(1-y\log x\log y)}$.

16.* If $x^y=e^{x-y}$, then $\dfrac{dy}{dx}=\dfrac{\log x}{(1+\log x)^2}=\log x(\log ex)^{-2}$

17. (a)* If $x^p\cdot y^q=(x+y)^{p+q}$, prove that $dy/dx=y/x$.

(J.E.E.W.B. 1992)

Also show that $\dfrac{d^2y}{dx^2}=0$.

(b) If $\sqrt{x+y}+\sqrt{y-x}=\lambda$ then show that

$$\frac{d^2y}{dx^2}=\frac{2}{\lambda^2}.$$

18. If $y=\dfrac{x\sin^{-1}x}{\sqrt{(1-x^2)}}+\log\sqrt{1-x^2}$, find $\dfrac{dy}{dx}$.

19. If $e^y=\dfrac{e^{\sin x}(1+\cos x)^n}{(1-\cos x)^m}$, find $\dfrac{dy}{dx}$.

20. If $y=[\log\{\log\sin x^{\circ}\}]^7$, find dy/dx.

21. If $y=x^n\log x+x(\log x)^n$, find dy/dx.

22. (a) If $y=\dfrac{(x+1)^2\sqrt{x-1}}{(x+4)^2e^x}$, find $\dfrac{dy}{dx}$.

(b) $y=\dfrac{2(x-\sin x)^{3/2}}{\sqrt{(x)}}$, find $\dfrac{dy}{dx}$.

(c) $y=\dfrac{\cos^2x\cdot 2^{x^2}(x^3-2x+1)}{\tan x\cosh x\cdot e^{x-2}}$, find $\dfrac{dy}{dx}$.

23. (a)* If $y=x\log\left(\dfrac{x}{a+bx}\right)$, show that

$$x^3\frac{d^2y}{dx^2}=\left(x\frac{dy}{dx}-y\right)^2$$

(J.E.E.W.B. 1991)

Another form :

or $(a+bx)e^{y/x}=x$, then $x^3\dfrac{d^2y}{dx^2}=\left(x\dfrac{dy}{dx}-y\right)^2$.

(b) If $y=\dfrac{1}{1+x+x^2+x^3}$, then find the values of $\dfrac{dy}{dx}$ and $\dfrac{d^2y}{dx^2}$ at $x=0$.

(J.E.E. W.B. 1995)

24. If $y\sqrt{x^2+1}=\log\{\sqrt{(x^2+1)}-x\}$, show that $(x^2+1)\dfrac{dy}{dx}+xy+1=0$.

25. (a)* If $y=\log\left[\dfrac{\sqrt{(1+x)}+\sqrt{(1-x)}}{\sqrt{(1+x)}-\sqrt{(1-x)}}\right]^{1/2}$,

then $\dfrac{dy}{dx}=-\dfrac{1}{2x\sqrt{(1-x^2)}}$.

(b) If $y=\log\dfrac{1+\sqrt{x}}{1-\sqrt{(x)}}$, then $\dfrac{dy}{dx}=\dfrac{1}{\sqrt{(x)}(1-x)}$.

(c)* If $y=\log\left(\dfrac{\sqrt{(x+1)}-1}{\sqrt{(x+1)}+1}\right)+\dfrac{\sqrt{x}}{\sqrt{(x+1)}}$, find $\dfrac{dy}{dx}$.

26. (a) If $y=\{x+\sqrt{(x^2+a^2)}\}^n$, then $\dfrac{dy}{dx}=\dfrac{ny}{\sqrt{(x^2+a^2)}}$.

(b)* $y=a[x+\sqrt{x^2-1}]^n+\dfrac{b}{[x+\sqrt{x^2-1}]^n}$, then prove that $(x^2-1)\dfrac{d^2y}{dx^2}+x\dfrac{dy}{dx}-n^2y=0$

27. If $y=\dfrac{\sqrt{(a^2+x^2)}+\sqrt{(a^2-x^2)}}{\sqrt{(a^2+x^2)}-\sqrt{(a^2-x^2)}}$,

$\dfrac{dy}{dx}=-\dfrac{2a^2}{x^3}\left\{1+\dfrac{a^2}{\sqrt{(a^4-x^4)}}\right\}$.

28.* If $x\sqrt{(1+y)}+y\sqrt{(1+x)}=0$, then $\dfrac{dy}{dx}=-\dfrac{1}{(1+x)^2}$.

29.* If $x^2+y^2=t-\dfrac{1}{t}$, $x^4+y^4=t^2+\dfrac{1}{t^2}$, prove that $x^3y\dfrac{dy}{dx}=1$.

30. If $x=\dfrac{3at}{1+t^3}$, $y=\dfrac{3at^2}{1+t^3}$, then $\dfrac{dy}{dx}=\dfrac{t(2-t^3)}{1-2t^3}$.

31. (a)* If $\sin y=x\sin(a+y)$, then

$\dfrac{dy}{dx}=\dfrac{\sin^2(a+y)}{\sin a}$ or $\dfrac{\sin a}{1+x^2-2x\cos a}$

(b)* If $\sin y=x\cos(a+y)$ show that $\dfrac{dy}{dx}=\dfrac{\cos^2(a+y)}{\cos a}$;

hence show that $\dfrac{dy}{dx}=\cos a$ when $x=0$.

(M.N.R. 1992)

32. (a) If $y=1+\dfrac{c_1}{x-c_1}+\dfrac{c_2x}{(x-c_1)(x-c_2)}+\dfrac{c_3x^2}{(x-c_1)(x-c_2)(x-c_3)}$,

show that $\dfrac{dy}{dx}=\dfrac{y}{x}\left\{\dfrac{c_1}{c_1-x}+\dfrac{c_2}{c_2-x}+\dfrac{c_3}{c_3-x}\right\}$.

(b)* If $y=\dfrac{ax^2}{(x-a)(x-b)(x-c)}+\dfrac{bx}{(x-b)(x-c)}+\dfrac{c}{x-c}+1$,

prove that $\dfrac{y'}{y}=\dfrac{1}{x}\left(\dfrac{a}{a-x}+\dfrac{b}{b-x}+\dfrac{c}{c-x}\right)$.

(I.I.T. 1998)

(c) If $y=\tan^{-1}\dfrac{1}{1+x+x^2}+\tan^{-1}\dfrac{1}{x^2+3x+3}+\tan^{-1}\dfrac{1}{x^2+5x+7}+\ldots n$ terms, then $y'(0)=$

(a) $\dfrac{1}{1+n^2}$ (b) $-\dfrac{n^2}{1+n^2}$

(c) $\dfrac{n}{1+n^2}$ (d) none of these

33.* If $\cos\dfrac{x}{2}\cos\dfrac{x}{2^2}\cdots\cos\dfrac{x}{2^n}=\dfrac{\sin x}{2^n\sin(x/2^n)}$,

prove that $\dfrac{1}{2}\tan\dfrac{x}{2}+\dfrac{1}{2^2}\tan\dfrac{x}{2^2}+\cdots+\dfrac{1}{2^n}\tan\dfrac{x}{2^n}$

$=\dfrac{1}{2^n}\cot\dfrac{x}{2^n}-\cot x$

and $\dfrac{1}{2^2}\sec^2\dfrac{x}{2}+\dfrac{1}{2^4}\sec^2\dfrac{x}{2^2}+\cdots+\dfrac{1}{2^{2n}}\sec^2\dfrac{x}{2^n}$

$=-\dfrac{1}{2^{2n}}\text{cosec}^2\dfrac{x}{2^n}+\text{cosec}^2 x$.

34.* If $y=\sqrt{[\sin x+\sqrt{\{\sin x+\sqrt{(\sin x+\cdots\infty)}\}}]}$, then $\dfrac{dy}{dx}=\dfrac{\cos x}{2y-1}$.

35. If x be less than unity, prove that

(a) $\dfrac{1}{1+x}+\dfrac{2x}{1+x^2}+\dfrac{4x^3}{1+x^4}+\dfrac{8x^7}{1+x^8}+\cdots\infty=\dfrac{1}{1-x}$.

(b) $\dfrac{1-2x}{1-x+x^2}+\dfrac{2x-4x^3}{1-x^2+x^4}+\dfrac{4x^3-8x^7}{1-x^4+x^8}+\cdots\infty=\dfrac{1+2x}{1+x+x^2}$.

(c) Obtain the sum of

$\dfrac{1}{x+1}+\dfrac{2}{x^2+1}+\dfrac{4}{x^4+1}+\ldots\ldots\ldots+\dfrac{2^n}{x^{2n}+1}$.

(Roorkee 1990)

36. (a) If $y=x^2+\dfrac{1}{x^2+}\dfrac{1}{x^2+}\dfrac{1}{x^2+}+\ldots$ad inf.,

prove that $\dfrac{dy}{dx}=\dfrac{2x}{2-}\dfrac{x^2}{x^2+}\dfrac{1}{x^2+}\dfrac{1}{x^2+}\ldots$ad inf.

(b) If $y=x+\dfrac{1}{x+}\dfrac{1}{x+}\dfrac{1}{x+}\ldots$ad inf.,

prove that $\dfrac{dy}{dx}=\dfrac{1}{2-}\dfrac{x}{x+}\dfrac{1}{x+}\ldots$ad inf.

(c) If $y=\dfrac{x}{a+}\dfrac{x}{b+}\dfrac{x}{a+}\dfrac{x}{b+}\ldots+\infty$, then show that $\dfrac{dy}{dx}=\dfrac{b}{a(b+2y)}$.

37. (a) If $y=\cos^{-1}\dfrac{a+b\cos x}{b+a\cos x}$, $b>a$, then $\dfrac{dy}{dx}=\dfrac{\sqrt{b^2-a^2}}{b+a\cos x}$.

(b)* If $y=\dfrac{2}{\sqrt{(a^2-b^2)}}\tan^{-1}\left[\left\{\sqrt{\left(\dfrac{a-b}{a+b}\right)}\right\}\tan\dfrac{x}{2}\right]$

then show that

$\dfrac{dy}{dx}=\dfrac{1}{a+b\cos x}$ and $\dfrac{d^2y}{dx^2}=\dfrac{b\sin x}{(a+b\cos x)^2}$.

(c)* If $x^2+5xy+y^2-2x+y-6=0$, then find the value of d^2y/dx^2 at (1, 1). **(M.N.R. 1996)**

38. (a) If $y=\tan^{-1}\left(\dfrac{\sqrt{a^2-b^2}\sin x}{b+a\cos x}\right)$, $\dfrac{dy}{dx}=\dfrac{\sqrt{a^2-b^2}}{a+b\cos x}$.

(b) If $y = \tan^{-1} \dfrac{x \sin \alpha}{1 - x \cos \alpha}$, find $\dfrac{dy}{dx}$.

39. (a)* If $y = 2 \tan^{-1} \dfrac{x\sqrt{2}}{1 - x^2} + \log \dfrac{1 + x\sqrt{2} + x^2}{1 - x\sqrt{(2)} + x^2}$, then

$\dfrac{dy}{dx} = \dfrac{4\sqrt{2}}{1 + x^4}$. **(J.E.E.W.B. 1990)**

(b)* If $y = \dfrac{1}{3} \log \dfrac{x+1}{\sqrt{(x^2 - x + 1)}} + \dfrac{1}{\sqrt{(3)}} \tan^{-1} \dfrac{2x - 1}{\sqrt{(3)}}$,

then $\dfrac{dy}{dx} = \dfrac{1}{1 + x^3}$.

(c) If $y = \log \sqrt{\dfrac{x^2 + x + 1}{x^2 - x + 1}}$

$+ \dfrac{1}{2\sqrt{3}} \left\{ \tan^{-1} \dfrac{2x+1}{\sqrt{3}} + \tan^{-1} \dfrac{2x-1}{\sqrt{3}} \right\}$,

then prove that $\dfrac{dy}{dx} = \dfrac{1}{x^4 + x^2 + 1}$.

40.* If $x = \tan \dfrac{y}{2} - \log \dfrac{\{1 + \tan (y/2)\}^2}{\tan (y/2)}$, show that

$\dfrac{dy}{dx} = \dfrac{1}{2} \sin y \, (1 + \sin y + \cos y)$.

41. (a)* Find the derivative with respect to x of the function

$(\log_{\cos x} \sin x)(\log_{\sin x} \cos x)^{-1}$

$+ \sin^{-1} \dfrac{2x}{1 + x^2}$ at $x = \dfrac{\pi}{4}$.

(b)* Find the differential of the function :

$f(x) = \log_x \sin x^2 + (\sin x^2)^{\log_e x}$

with respect to $\sqrt{x + 1}$. **(Roorkee 1997)**

(c)* If $y = \log_u |\cos 4x| + |\sin x|$, where $u = \sec 2x$, find dy/dx at $x = -\pi/6$. **(Roorkee 1992)**

42. If $y = e^x (a \cos x + b \sin x)$, where a, b are constants, prove that $\dfrac{d^2 y}{dx^2} - 2\dfrac{dy}{dx} + 2y = 0$.

43. (a)* If $p^2 = a^2 \cos^2 \theta + b^2 \sin^2 \theta$, prove that

$p + \dfrac{d^2 p}{d\theta^2} = \dfrac{a^2 b^2}{p^3}$.

(b) If $y = (\cos t + i \sin t)(\cos 3t + i \sin 3t) \ldots$

$\{\cos (2n - 1) t + i \sin (2n - 1) t\}$

then prove that $\dfrac{d^2 y}{dt^2} = -n^4 y$.

44.* If $x = \sec \theta - \cos \theta$ and $y = \sec^n \theta - \cos^n \theta$,

then show that $(x^2 + 4) \left(\dfrac{dy}{dx} \right)^2 = n^2 (y^2 + 4)$.

45. (a)* If $f(x) = \log_x (\ln x)$, then find $f'(x)$ at $x = e$. Here $\ln x$ means natural logarithm of x, *i.e.* $\log_e x$.

(b)* If $f(x) = \log_{x^2} (\log x)$, then $f'(x)$ at $x = e$ is

(i) 0 (ii) 1

(iii) $1/e$ (iv) $1/2e$ **(M.N.R. 1992)**

(c)* If $xe^{xy} = y + \sin^2 x$, then at $x = 0$, $\dfrac{dy}{dx} = \ldots\ldots$

(I.I.T. 1996)

46. If $y = (ax + b)/(x^2 + c)$, then show that $(2xy' + y) y''' = 3(xy'' + y') y''$, where a, b, c are constants and dash denotes differentiation w.r.t. x.

47. (a)* If $f(x) = \sin (\log x)$ and $y = f\left[\left(\dfrac{2x+3}{3-2x}\right)\right]$, find $\dfrac{dy}{dx}$

(b) $S_n = \dfrac{a(1 - r^n)}{1 - r}$ is the formula for sum of n terms of a geometrical progression, then prove that $(r - 1)\dfrac{d}{dr} S_n = (n - 1) S_n - n S_{n-1}$

(c)* If $\phi(x) = f(x) g(x)$, where $f'(x) g'(x) = c$, then prove that $\dfrac{\phi''}{\phi} = \dfrac{f''}{f} + \dfrac{g''}{g} + \dfrac{2c}{fg}$.

48. (a)* Find $\dfrac{dy}{dx}$ at $x = -1$, when

$(\sin y)^{\sin (\frac{\pi}{2} x)} + \dfrac{\sqrt{3}}{2} \sec^{-1} (2x)$

$+ 2^x \tan \{\log_e (x + 2)\} = 0$.

(I.I.T. 1991)

(b) Suppose $p(x) = a_0 + a_1 x + a_2 x^2 + \ldots + a_n x^n$. If $|p(x)| \le |e^{x-1} - 1|$ for all $x \ge 0$, prove that $|a_1 + 2a_2 + \ldots + na_n| \le 1$. **(I.I.T. 2000)**

49. $y_1 = \dfrac{dy}{dx}$ and $y_2 = \dfrac{d^2 y}{dx^2}$

(a)* If $y = \sin (m \sin^{-1} x)$, then prove that

$(1 - x^2) y_2 - xy_1 + m^2 y = 0$.

(b) If $y = \dfrac{1}{2^{n-1}} \cos (n \cos^{-1} x)$, then prove that

$(1 - x^2)\dfrac{d^2 y}{dx^2} - x\dfrac{dy}{dx} + n^2 y = 0$.

50. (a)* If $y = \{x + \sqrt{(1 + x^2)}\}^m$, then prove that

$(1 + x^2) y_2 + xy_1 - m^2 y = 0$.

(b) If $y^{1/m} + y^{-1/m} = 2x$, prove that

$(x^2 - 1) y_2 + xy_1 - m^2 y = 0$.

(c) If $y = a[x + \sqrt{x^2 + 1}]^n + b[x - \sqrt{x^2 - 1}]^{-n}$ prove that $(x^2 - 1)\dfrac{d^2 y}{dx^2} + x\dfrac{dy}{dx} - n^2 y = 0$.

51.* If $\cos^{-1}\left(\dfrac{y}{b}\right) = \log \left(\dfrac{x}{n}\right)^n$, prove that

$x^2 y_2 + xy_1 + n^2 y = 0$.

52. (a)* If $y = e^{a\sin^{-1} x}$, then prove that

$(1-x^2)\, y_2 - xy_1 - a^2 y = 0.$

(b) If $y = (\sin^{-1} x)^2$, then prove that

$(1-x^2)\, y_2 - xy_1 - 2 = 0.$

53. (a) If $y = a\cos(\log x) + b\sin(\log x)$, then prove that $x^2 y_2 + xy_1 + y = 0.$

(b)* If $y = x^n\, [a\cos(\log x) + b\sin(\log x)]$, then prove that $x^2 y_2 + (1-2n)\, xy_1 + (1+n^2)\, y = 0.$

(c) If $x = a\cos t + b\sin t$ and $y = a\sin t - b\cos t$, prove that $y^2 \dfrac{d^2y}{dx^2} - x\dfrac{dy}{dx} + y = 0.$

54. (a) If $y = (\tan^{-1} x)^2$, then prove that

$(x^2+1)^2\, y_2 + 2x(x^2+1)\, y_1 - 2 = 0.$

(b) If $y = \tan^{-1}\sqrt{x^2-1}$, then show that

$x(x^2-1)\, y_2 + (2x^2-1)\, y_1 = 0.$ **(J.E.E.W.B. 1995)**

(c) If $x^2 + y^2 = 1$, then

(a) $yy'' - 2(y')^2 + 1 = 0$

(b) $yy'' + (y')^2 + 1 = 0$

(c) $yy'' - (y')^2 - 1 = 0$

(d) $yy'' + 2(y')^2 + 1 = 0$ **(I.I.T. Sc. 2000)**

55.* If $y = (\sin^{-1} x)^2 + (\cos^{-1} x)^2$, then prove that

$(1-x^2)\dfrac{d^2y}{dx^2} - x\dfrac{dy}{dx} = 4.$ **(J.E.E.W.B. 1996)**

56. If $y = e^{\sqrt{x}} + e^{-\sqrt{x}}$, then prove that

$x\dfrac{d^2y}{dx^2} + \dfrac{1}{2}\dfrac{dy}{dx} = \dfrac{1}{4}y.$

57. If $y = \cot^{-1}\dfrac{x^x - x^{-x}}{2}$ then $y'(1) =$

(a) −1 (b) 0 (c) log 2 (d) − log 2

Solutions to Problem Set (3)

1. (a) $y = (\sin^{-1} x)^{x^2}.$

Taking log of both sides, we get

$\log y = x^2 \log\sin^{-1} x.$ Differentiate both sides w.r.t. x.

$\therefore\ \dfrac{1}{y}\dfrac{dy}{dx} = 2x\log\sin^{-1} x + x^2 \cdot \dfrac{1}{\sin^{-1} x}\dfrac{1}{\sqrt{(1-x^2)}}$

$\therefore\ \dfrac{dy}{dx} = y\left[2x\log\sin^{-1} x + \dfrac{x^2}{\sqrt{(1-x^2)}\sin^{-1} x}\right]$

$= (\sin^{-1} x)^{x^2}\left[2x\log\sin^{-1} x + \dfrac{x^2}{\sqrt{(1-x^2)}\sin^{-1} x}\right]$

$= 2x(\sin^{-1} x)^{x^2}\log\sin^{-1} x + \dfrac{(\sin^{-1} x)^{x^2-1}\, x^2}{\sqrt{(1-x^2)}}.$

An easier alternative method.

Out of the two functions $\sin^{-1} x$ and x^2 treat $\sin^{-1} x$ as constant and then treat x^2 as constant and differentiate and add the two results. Remember that

$\dfrac{d}{dx}[f_1(x)]^n = n[f_1(x)]^{n-1} \cdot \dfrac{d}{dx} f_1(x)$

$\because$ d.c. of $x^n = nx^{n-1}$

$\dfrac{d}{dx}[a]^{f_2(x)} = a^{f_2(x)} \log a \cdot \dfrac{d}{dx} f_2(x)$

$\because$ d.c. of $a^x = a^x \log a$.

Below we shall do the above example by the method explained above.

Treating x^2 as constant and differentiating $(\sin^{-1} x)^{x^2}$, we get

$x^2 (\sin^{-1} x)^{x^2-1} \times$ d.c. of $\sin^{-1} x$

$= x^2 (\sin^{-1} x)^{x^2-1}\dfrac{1}{\sqrt{(1-x^2)}}$ ...(1)

Now treat $\sin^{-1} x$ as constant and differentiate. Then we get

$(\sin^{-1} x)^{x^2} \log\sin^{-1} x \times$ d.c. of x^2

$= (\sin^{-1} x)^{x^2} \log\sin^{-1} x \cdot (2x).$ ...(2)

$\therefore\ \dfrac{dy}{dx} =$ Sum of the results (1) and (2)

$= 2x\, (\sin^{-1} x)^{x^2} \log\sin^{-1} x + x^2 (\sin^{-1} x)^{x^2-1}\dfrac{1}{\sqrt{(1-x^2)}}$

Rule : $y = [f_1(x)]^{f_2(x)}$

$\dfrac{dy}{dx} =$ Differentiate treating power $f_2(x)$ as constant + Differentiate treating base $f_1(x)$ as constant

d.c. of $x^n = nx^{n-1}$, d.c. of $a^x = a^x \log a$

(b) $\dfrac{dy}{dx} = x \cdot x^{x-1} + x^x \log x = x^x (1 + \log x)$

(c), (d). Try yourself.

2. $y = (\cot x)^{\sin x} + (\tan x)^{\cos x}$

Here students should proceed as follows :

Put $y = u + v$ so that $\dfrac{dy}{dx} = \dfrac{du}{dx} + \dfrac{dv}{dx}$ ...(1)

where $u = (\cot x)^{\sin x}$, $v = (\tan x)^{\cos x}$.

Now $\dfrac{du}{dx}$ and $\dfrac{dv}{dx}$ may be calculated directly as :

$$\frac{du}{dx} = \sin x\,(\cot x)^{\sin x - 1}\,(-\operatorname{cosec}^2 x) + (\cot x)^{\sin x}\,(\log \cot x)\cos x$$

$$\frac{dv}{dx} = \cos x\,(\tan x)^{\cos x - 1}\,\sec^2 x + (\tan x)^{\cos x}\,\log(\tan x)\,(-\sin x).$$

Hence from (1), we get the value of $\frac{dy}{dx}$.

3. (a) Proceed as in Q.2.

$$\frac{dy}{dx} = \left\{\log x\,(\cos x)^{\log x - 1}\,(-\sin x) + (\cos x)^{\log x}.\log(\cos x).\frac{1}{x}\right\} + \left\{x(\log x)^{x-1}.\frac{1}{x} + (\log x)^x.\log(\log x)\right\}$$

$$= (\cos x)^{\log x}\left[\log x(-\tan x) + \frac{1}{x}\log\cos x\right] + (\log x)^x\left[\frac{1}{\log x} + \log(\log x)\right].$$

(b) $\frac{dy}{dx} = e^{x\sin x^3}\,(1.\sin x^3 + 3x^3\cos x^3)$

$+ \{x\tan^{x-1} x\sec^2 x + (\tan x)^x.\log\tan x.1\}.$

4. $\left(1+\frac{1}{x}\right)^x\left[\log\left(1+\frac{1}{x}\right) - \frac{1}{x+1}\right] + x^{1+1/x}\left[\frac{x+1-\log x}{x^2}\right].$

5. $y^x = x^{\sin y}$. Take log of both sides.

$x\log y = \sin y \log x$. Differentiate w.r.t. x.

$$1.\log y + x.\frac{1}{y}\frac{dy}{dx} = \frac{1}{x}\sin y + (\log x)\cos y.\frac{dy}{dx}$$

$$\therefore \left(\log y - \frac{\sin y}{x}\right) = \frac{dy}{dx}\left[\cos y\log x - \frac{x}{y}\right]$$

$$\therefore \frac{dy}{dx} = \frac{y}{x}\left[\frac{x\log y - \sin y}{y\log x\cos y - x}\right].$$

6. (a) $x^y + y^x = a^b$ or $u + v = a^b$,

$$\therefore \frac{du}{dx} + \frac{dv}{dx} = 0.$$

$$yx^{y-1} + x^y\log x.\frac{dy}{dx} + xy^{x-1}\frac{dy}{dx} + y^x\log y = 0,$$

by 2nd Method of Q. 1.

$$\therefore \frac{dy}{dx} = -\frac{yx^{y-1} + y^x\log y}{xy^{x-1} + x^y\log x}.$$

Alternative Method by Partial differentiation

If $f(x, y) = c$ then $\frac{dy}{dx} = -\frac{f_x}{f_y}$

Here $x^y + y^x = a^b$ ...(1)

f_x = differentiation of (1) w. r. t. x, treating y as constant

$$\therefore f_x = y\,x^{y-1} + y^x\log y$$

$$f_y = x^y\log y + xy^{x-1}$$

$\therefore \frac{dy}{dx} = -\frac{f_x}{f_y}$ = As found above.

(b) Ans. (a).

$f(x, y) = \log(x+y) - 2xy = 0.$

When $x = 0, \log y = 0 \therefore y = 1$

$$\therefore \frac{dy}{dx} = -\frac{f_x}{f_y} = -\frac{\frac{1}{x+y} - 2y}{\frac{1}{x+y} - 2x} = -\frac{1-2}{1-0} = 1$$

Alternative : $\frac{1}{(x+y)}\left(1+\frac{dy}{dx}\right) = 2\left(y + x\frac{dy}{dx}\right)$

Now put $x = 0, y = 1 \Rightarrow \frac{dy}{dx} = 1.$

(c) Here $u + v = 1$.

$$\therefore \frac{dy}{dx} = \frac{v\operatorname{cosec}^2 x\log y - \frac{uy}{(1+x^2)\tan^{-1} x}}{u\log\tan^{-1} x + \frac{v\cot x}{y}}$$

(d) Differentiating both sides w.r.t. x, we get

$$\frac{1}{2\sqrt{(x)}} + \frac{1}{2\sqrt{(y)}}.\frac{dy}{dx} = 0,$$

$$\therefore \frac{dy}{dx} = -\sqrt{\left(\frac{y}{x}\right)}.$$

(e) Differentiating both sides w.r.t. x by the alternative method given in **Q. 1, P. 1217**, we get

$$\left[y\,x^{y-1} + x^y\log x.\frac{dy}{dx}\right] + \left[x\,y^{x-1}\frac{dy}{dx} + y^x\log y\right]$$

$$= \left[(x+y)(x+y)^{x+y-1}.\frac{d}{dx}(x+y) + (x+y)^{x+y}\log(x+y).\frac{d}{dx}(x+y)\right]$$

$$= (x+y)^{x+y}\,[1+\log(x+y)]\,[1+(dy/dx)]$$

$$\therefore \frac{dy}{dx}[x^y\log x + xy^{x-1} - (x+y)^{x+y}\{1+\log(x+y)\}$$

$$= (x+y)^{x+y}\{1+\log(x+y)\} - yx^{y-1} - y^x\log y],$$

whence we get $\frac{dy}{dx}$.

Alternative Method :

$$f(x, y) = x^y + y^x - (x+y)^{x+y} = 0$$

$$f_x = y\,x^{y-1} + y^x\log y - \{(x+y)(x+y)^{x+y-1}.1 + (x+y)^{x+y}.\log(x+y)\}$$

$$= y\,x^{y-1} + y^x\log y - (x+y)^{x+y}\,[1+\log(x+y)]$$

Similarly,

$$f_y = x^y\log x + x\,y^{x-1} - (x+y)^{x+y}\,[1+\log(x+y)]$$

$\therefore \quad \dfrac{dy}{dx} = -\dfrac{f_x}{f_y}.$

7. (a) Take log, and differentiate.

(b) Taking logarithm, we get

$$x \log y + y \log x = \log 1 = 0.$$

Differentiating w.r.t. x, we get

$$x.\frac{1}{y}.\frac{dy}{dx} + 1.\log y + y.\frac{1}{x} + \frac{dy}{dx}\log x = 0.$$

$$\therefore \quad \frac{dy}{dx} = -\frac{\log y + y/x}{x/y + \log x}.$$

(c) The L.H.S. is a homogeneous function of degree 4. Hence it represents four straight lines passing through the origin of the form $y - mx = 0$

$\therefore \quad \dfrac{dy}{dx} = m = \dfrac{y}{x}$ for each line. Hence $\dfrac{dy}{dx} = \dfrac{y}{x}$.

8. (a) $y = (x^x)^x \quad \therefore \log y = x \log x^x = x^2 \log x$

$$\therefore \quad \frac{1}{y}\frac{dy}{dx} = 2x \log x + x^2 . \frac{1}{x} = x(1 + 2\log x)$$

$$\therefore \quad \frac{dy}{dx} = x.(x^x)^x\,(1 + 2\log x)$$

(b) Ans. (b).

$u = x^x$ then $\log u = x \log x$

$$\therefore \quad \frac{1}{u}\frac{du}{dx} = x.\frac{1}{x} + 1.\log x$$

$$\therefore \quad \frac{du}{dx} = x^x\,(1 + \log x) = 1$$

$$\therefore \quad \frac{du}{dx} = 1 \text{ at } x = 1 \text{ as } \log 1 = 0 \qquad \ldots(1)$$

$$v = x^{2x}, \frac{dv}{dx} = 2 \text{ at } x = 1 \qquad \ldots(2)$$

Also when $x = 1$, we have

$$1 - 2\cot y - 1 = 0$$

$$\therefore \quad \cot y = 0 \qquad \ldots(3)$$

Now differentiating the given relation,

$$v - 2u\cot y - 1 = 0.$$

Differentiating w.r.t. x and putting $x = 1$,

$$\frac{dv}{dx} - 2\frac{du}{dx}\cot y + 2u\,\text{cosec}^2\, y\frac{dy}{dx} = 0$$

$$2 - 2.1(0) + 2u(1 + \cot^2 y)\frac{dy}{dx} = 0$$

by (1), (2) and (3)

or $\quad 1 + 1(1+0)\dfrac{dy}{dx} = 0 \quad \therefore \quad \dfrac{dy}{dx} = -1.$

9. (a) $y = x^{(x^x)}, \quad \therefore \log y = x^x \log x. \qquad \ldots(1)$

Take log again

$$\log(\log y) = \log[x^x \log x]$$
$$= \log x^x + \log(\log x)$$
$$= x \log x + \log(\log x).$$

Differentiate both sides w.r.t. x

$$\frac{1}{\log y}.\frac{1}{y}.\frac{dy}{dx} = x.\frac{1}{x} + 1.\log x + \frac{1}{\log x}.\frac{1}{x}.$$

$$\therefore \quad \frac{dy}{dx} = y \log y\,[1 + \log x + 1/(x \log x)]$$

$$= x^{(x^x)}.x^x \log x\,[1/ + \log x + 1/(x\log x)]$$

by (1)

$$= x^{(x^x)+x}\left[\log x\,(1 + \log x) + \frac{1}{x}\right].$$

(b) $\log y = (\tan x)^{\tan x} \log \tan x. \qquad \ldots(1)$

Taking log again, we get from (1)

$$\log(\log y) = \tan x \log \tan x + \log(\log \tan x).$$

Differentiate w.r.t. x

$$\frac{1}{\log y}\cdot\frac{1}{y}\frac{dy}{dx} = \sec^2 x \log \tan x$$

$$+ \tan x \cdot \frac{\sec^2 x}{\tan x} + \frac{1}{\log \tan x}\cdot\frac{1}{\tan x}\cdot\sec^2 x$$

$$\therefore \quad \frac{dy}{dx} = y \log y.\sec^2 x$$

$$\cdot\left[\log \tan x + 1 + \frac{1}{(\tan x \log \tan x)}\right]$$

$$= y\,(\tan x)^{\tan x} \log \tan x.\sec^2 x$$

$$\cdot\left[(\log \tan x + 1) + \frac{1}{\tan x \log \tan x}\right]$$

$$= y\,(\tan x)^{\tan x} \sec^2 x\,[\log \tan x$$
$$(\log \tan x + 1) + \cot x]$$

Now at $x = \pi/4$, $y = 1$, $\log \tan(\pi/4) = \log 1 = 0$

$$\therefore \quad \frac{dy}{dx} = 1.1.2\,[0 + 1] = 2$$

10. $y = x^{(\log x)^{\log\log x}}$. Take log of both sides

$$\log y = (\log x)^{\log\log x}.\log x$$

$$\frac{\log y}{\log x} = (\log x)^{\log\log x} \qquad \ldots(1)$$

Taking log again, we get

$$\log(\log y) - \log(\log x) = [\log\log x]\log(\log x)$$

or $\quad \log(\log y) = \log(\log x)\,[\log\log x + 1].$

Differentiate both sides w.r.t. x, we get

$$\frac{1}{\log y}.\frac{1}{y}\frac{dy}{dx} = \frac{1}{\log x}.\frac{1}{x}[\log\log x + 1]$$

$$+ \log(\log x).\frac{1}{\log x}.\frac{1}{x}$$

$$= \frac{1}{x \log x}[2\log\log x + 1]$$

$$\therefore \quad \frac{dy}{dx} = \frac{y}{x}.\frac{\log y}{\log x}[2\log\log x + 1]$$

$$= (y/x)(\log x)^{\log\log x}[2\log\log x + 1], \quad \text{by (1)}.$$

11. $y = e^{x^{e^x}} + x^{e^{e^x}} + e^{x^{x^e}} = u + v + w.$

$$\frac{dy}{dx}=\frac{du}{dx}+\frac{dv}{dx}+\frac{dw}{dx}$$

$u=e^{x^{e^x}}, \log u = x^{e^x} . \log e = x^{e^x}$

$\therefore$ $\log(\log u)=e^x \log x$. Differentiate.

$$\frac{1}{\log u}.\frac{1}{u}\frac{du}{dx}=e^x.\frac{1}{x}+e^x \log x.$$

$$\therefore \quad \frac{du}{dx}=u\log u\left[\frac{e^x}{x}+e^x \log x\right]$$

$$=e^{x^{e^x}}.x^{e^x}\left[\frac{e^x}{x}+e^x \log x\right]$$

Similarly, $\dfrac{dv}{dx}=x^{e^{e^x}}.e^{e^x}\left[\dfrac{1}{x}+e^x \log x\right]$,

and $\dfrac{dw}{dx}=e^{x^{x^e}}.x^{x^e}.x^{e-1}(1+e\log x)$.

Putting the values, we get the value of $\dfrac{dy}{dx}$.

12. $y=e^{x+e^{x+e^{x+\dots}}}=e^{x+y}$.

$\therefore$ $\log y=(x+y)\log e=x+y$.

Hence $\dfrac{1}{y}\dfrac{dy}{dx}=1+\dfrac{dy}{dx}$

or $\dfrac{dy}{dx}\left(\dfrac{1}{y}-1\right)=1$ or $\dfrac{dy}{dx}=\dfrac{y}{1-y}$.

13. (a) $y=(\sqrt{x})^y$ as above.

$\therefore$ $\log y=y\log\sqrt{x}=\dfrac{1}{2}y\log x$.

$$\frac{1}{y}\frac{dy}{dx}=\frac{1}{2}.\left(\frac{dy}{dx}\log x+y.\frac{1}{x}\right).$$

$$\therefore \quad \left(\frac{1}{y}-\frac{1}{2}\log x\right)\frac{dy}{dx}=\frac{1}{2}.\frac{y}{x}$$

$$\therefore \quad x\frac{dy}{dx}=\frac{y^2}{2-y\log x}.$$

(b) Proceed as in (a).

14. Proceed as above.

15. $y=a^{x^y}$.

$\therefore$ $\log y=x^y\log a$

$\therefore$ $\log\log y=y\log x+\log(\log a)$

$$\frac{1}{\log y}.\frac{1}{y}\frac{dy}{dx}=\frac{dy}{dx}.\log x+y.\frac{1}{x}$$

$$\therefore \quad \left(\frac{1}{y\log y}-\log x\right)\frac{dy}{dx}=\frac{y}{x}$$

$$\therefore \quad \frac{dy}{dx}=\frac{y^2\log y}{x(1-y\log x\log y)}.$$

16. $x^y=e^{x-y}$. Taking log, we get

$y\log x=(x-y)\log e=x-y$

$\therefore$ $y(1+\log x)=x$ or $y=x/(1+\log x)$

$$\therefore \quad \frac{dy}{dx}=\frac{(1+\log x).1-x.(1/x)}{(1+\log x)^2}=\frac{\log x}{(1+\log x)^2}$$

$$=\frac{\log x}{(\log e+\log x)^2}=\log x(\log ex)^{-2}$$

17. (a) Taking log, we get

$$p\log x+q\log y=(p+q)\log(x+y)$$

$$p\frac{1}{x}+q\frac{1}{y}\frac{dy}{dx}=(p+q)\frac{1}{x+y}.\left(1+\frac{dy}{dx}\right)$$

$$\frac{p}{x}-\frac{p+q}{x+y}=\left(\frac{p+q}{x+y}-\frac{q}{y}\right)\frac{dy}{dx}$$

or $\dfrac{py-qx}{x(x+y)}=\dfrac{py-qx}{y(x+y)}\dfrac{dy}{dx}$ $\therefore$ $\dfrac{dy}{dx}=\dfrac{y}{x}$.

$x\dfrac{dy}{dx}-y=0$. Differentiate again w.r.t. x

$$x\frac{d^2y}{dx^2}+\frac{dy}{dx}-\frac{dy}{dx}=0$$

$$\therefore \quad \frac{d^2y}{dx^2}=0$$

(b) $\sqrt{x+y}+\sqrt{y-x}=\lambda$

But $(x+y)-(y-x)=2x$

Dividing, $\sqrt{x+y}-\sqrt{y-x}=\dfrac{2x}{\lambda}$

$$\because \quad \frac{a^2-b^2}{a+b}=a-b$$

Adding, $2\sqrt{x+y}=\lambda+\dfrac{2x}{\lambda}$. Square

$$4x+4y=\lambda^2+4x+\frac{4x^2}{\lambda^2}$$

$$\therefore \quad y=\frac{\lambda^2}{4}+\frac{x^2}{\lambda^2} \quad \therefore \quad \frac{dy}{dx}=\frac{2x}{\lambda^2}$$

$$\therefore \quad \frac{d^2y}{dx^2}=\frac{2}{\lambda^2}$$

18. $y=u+v$, $\therefore$ $\dfrac{dy}{dx}=\dfrac{du}{dx}+\dfrac{dv}{dx}$. ...(1)

Now $u=\dfrac{x\sin^{-1}x}{\sqrt{(1-x^2)}}$. Taking log,

$$\log u=\log x+\log\sin^{-1}x-\frac{1}{2}\log(1-x^2)$$

$$\therefore \quad \frac{1}{u}\frac{du}{dx}=\frac{1}{x}+\frac{1}{\sin^{-1}x}.\frac{1}{\sqrt{(1-x^2)}}-\frac{1}{2}\frac{1}{1-x^2}(-2x)$$

$$\therefore \quad \frac{du}{dx}=\frac{x\sin^{-1}x}{\sqrt{(1-x^2)}}.\left[\frac{1}{x}+\frac{1}{\sqrt{(1-x^2)}\sin^{-1}x}+\frac{x}{1-x^2}\right]$$

$$v=\log\sqrt{(1-x^2)}=\frac{1}{2}\log(1-x^2)$$

$$\therefore \quad \frac{dv}{dx}=-\frac{x}{1-x^2}$$

$\therefore \quad \frac{dy}{dx}=\frac{\sin^{-1} x}{\sqrt{(1-x^2)}}+\frac{x}{1-x^2}+\frac{x^2 \sin^{-1} x}{(1-x^2)^{3/2}}-\frac{x}{1-x^2}$, by (1)

$=\frac{\sin^{-1} x}{(1-x^2)^{3/2}}[1-x^2+x^2]=\frac{\sin^{-1} x}{(1-x^2)^{3/2}}$.

19. $e^y=e^{\sin x}\frac{(1+\cos x)^n}{(1-\cos x)^m}$. Take log of both sides

$y \log e=\sin x \log e+n\log(1+\cos x)-m\log(1-\cos x)$

$\frac{dy}{dx}=\cos x-n\frac{\sin x}{1+\cos x}-m\frac{\sin x}{1-\cos x}$

$=\cos x-n\tan(x/2)-m\cot(x/2)$ **[§ 5 P. 1203 (vii)]**

20. Change x^o to $\frac{\pi x}{180}$ radians.

$y=\left[\log\left\{\log \sin\frac{\pi x}{180}\right\}\right]^7$

$\therefore \quad \frac{dy}{dx}=7\left[\log\log\sin\frac{\pi x}{180}\right]^6 \cdot \frac{1}{\log\sin(\pi x/180)}\cdot\frac{1}{\sin(\pi x/180)}\times\cos\frac{\pi x}{180}\cdot\frac{\pi}{180}$

$=\frac{7\pi}{180^o}[\log(\log\sin x^o)]^6\cdot\frac{\cot x^o}{\log\sin x^o}$.

21. $y=x^n\log x+x(\log x)^n$

$dy/dx=nx^{n-1}\log x+x^n.(1/x)+xn(\log x)^{n-1}.(1/x)+1.(\log x)^n$

$=x^{n-1}(1+n\log x)+(\log x)^{n-1}[n+\log x]$

22. (a) Take log etc.

$\frac{dy}{dx}=\frac{(x+1)^2\sqrt{(x-1)}}{(x+4)e^x}\left[\frac{5x-3}{2(x^2-1)}-\frac{x+6}{x+4}\right]$

(b) $\frac{dy}{dx}=y\left\{\frac{3}{2}\cdot\frac{1-\cos x}{x-\sin x}-\frac{1}{2}x\right\}$.

(c) $\frac{dy}{dx}=y\left[-2\tan x+2x\log 2+\frac{3x^2-2}{x^3-2x+1}-\frac{\sec^2 x}{\tan x}-\frac{\sinh x}{\cosh x}-1\right]$.

23. (a) From the given relation $y/x=\log x-\log(a+bx)$.
Differentiate

$\left(x\frac{dy}{dx}-y\right)\Big/x^2=\frac{1}{x}-\frac{1}{a+bx}b=\frac{a}{x(a+bx)}$

$\therefore \quad x\frac{dy}{dx}-y=\frac{ax}{a+bx}$ ...(1)

Differentiate again w.r.t. x

$x\frac{d^2y}{dx^2}+\frac{dy}{dx}-\frac{dy}{dx}=\frac{(a+bx)a-ax.b}{(a+bx)^2}$

or $x\frac{d^2y}{dx^2}=\frac{a^2}{(a+bx)^2}$

$\therefore \quad x^3\frac{d^2y}{dx^2}=\frac{a^2x^2}{(a+bx)^2}=\left(x\frac{dy}{dx}-y\right)^2$, by (1) .

(b) $y=(1+x+x^2+x^3)^{-1}$

$\frac{dy}{dx}=-(1+x+x^2+x^3)^{-2}(1+2x+3x^2)$

$\therefore \quad \frac{dy}{dx}=-1$ at $x=0$

$\frac{d^2y}{dx^2}=2(1+x+x^2+x^3)^{-3}(1+2x+3x^2)^2-(1+x+x^2+x^3)^{-2}.(2+6x)$

$\therefore \quad \left(\frac{d^2y}{dx^2}\right)_{x=0}=2-2=0$

24. $y\sqrt{(x^2+1)}=\log[\sqrt{(x^2+1)}-x]$

Differentiate both sides w.r.t. x

$\frac{dy}{dx}\sqrt{x^2+1}+y.\frac{1}{2\sqrt{(x^2+1)}}.2x$

$=\frac{1}{\sqrt{(x^2+1)}-x}\times\left\{\frac{1}{2}\frac{2x}{\sqrt{(x^2+1)}}-1\right\}$

or $(x^2+1)\frac{dy}{dx}+xy=\sqrt{x^2+1}\cdot\frac{-1}{\sqrt{(x^2+1)}}$

$\therefore \quad (x^2+1)\frac{dy}{dx}+xy+1=0.$

25. (a) Put $x=\sin\theta$

$\therefore \quad \sqrt{1\pm\sin\theta}=\cos(\theta/2)\pm\sin(\theta/2)$

$\therefore \quad y=\frac{1}{2}\log\frac{2\cos(\theta/2)}{2\sin(\theta/2)}=\frac{1}{2}\log\cot\frac{\theta}{2}$

$\therefore \quad \frac{dy}{d\theta}=\frac{1}{2}\cdot\frac{1}{\cot(\theta/2)}\cdot\left(-\frac{1}{2}\text{cosec}^2\frac{\theta}{2}\right)$

$=-\frac{1}{4\cos(\theta/2)\sin(\theta/2)}$

or $\frac{dy}{d\theta}=-\frac{1}{2\sin\theta}$. Also $\frac{dx}{d\theta}=\cos\theta$

$\therefore \quad \frac{dy}{dx}=\frac{dy}{d\theta}\div\frac{dx}{d\theta}=-\frac{1}{2\sin\theta\cos\theta}=\frac{-1}{2x\sqrt{(1-x^2)}}$.

(b) Do yourself.

(c) Put $x=\tan^2\theta$ in the value of y.

$\therefore \quad y=\log\left(\frac{\sec\theta-1}{\sec\theta+1}\right)+\frac{\tan\theta}{\sec\theta}$

$=\log\frac{1-\cos\theta}{1+\cos\theta}+\sin\theta=\log\tan^2\frac{\theta}{2}+\sin\theta$

or $y=2\log\tan(\theta/2)+\sin\theta$

$\therefore \quad \frac{dy}{d\theta}=2.\frac{1}{\tan(\theta/2)}\sec^2\frac{\theta}{2}.\frac{1}{2}+\cos\theta$

or $\frac{dy}{d\theta}=2.\frac{1}{2\sin(\theta/2)\cos(\theta/2)}+\cos\theta$

$=\frac{2}{\sin\theta}+\cos\theta$ ...(1)

$\frac{dx}{d\theta}=2\tan\theta\sec^2\theta=2\frac{\sin\theta}{\cos^3\theta}$

$\therefore\quad \frac{dy}{dx}=\frac{dy}{d\theta}\div\frac{dx}{d\theta}=\left[\frac{2}{\sin\theta}+\cos\theta\right]\frac{\cos^3\theta}{2\sin\theta}$

$=\frac{\cos^3\theta}{\sin^2\theta}+\frac{\cos^4\theta}{2\sin\theta}$

$=\cos\theta.\cot^2\theta+\frac{1}{2}\cos^2\theta.\cot\theta.\cos\theta$

$=\cos\theta\left[\cot^2\theta+\frac{1}{2}\cot\theta\cos^2\theta\right]$

$=\frac{1}{\sqrt{(1+x)}}\left[\frac{1}{x}+\frac{1}{2}\frac{1}{\sqrt{(x)}}.\frac{1}{1+x}\right].$

26. (a) $\frac{dy}{dx}=n[\ ]^{n-1}.\left\{1+\frac{1}{2\sqrt{(x^2+a^2)}}.2x\right\}$

$=n\frac{[\ ]^n}{\sqrt{(x^2+a^2)}}=\frac{ny}{\sqrt{(x^2+a^2)}}$

(b) Since $[x+\sqrt{x^2-1}][x-\sqrt{x^2-1}]$

$=x^2-(x^2-1)=1$ ...(1)

$\therefore\quad y=a(x+\sqrt{x^2-1})^n+b(x-\sqrt{x^2-1})^n$ ...(2)

Differentiating as in part (a),

$y_1=na\frac{(x+\sqrt{x^2-1})^n}{\sqrt{x^2-1}}-nb\frac{(x-\sqrt{x^2-1})^n}{\sqrt{x^2-1}}$

$\therefore\quad (x^2-1)y_1^2=n^2[a(\ )^n-b(\ )^n]^2$

or $(x^2-1)y_1^2=n^2[\{a(\ )^n+b(\ )^n\}^2-4ab.1]$

or $(x^2-1)y_1^2=n^2\{y^2-4ab\}$, by (1) and (2)

Differentiate both sides and cancel $2y_1$ to get the result.

27. $y=\frac{\sqrt{a^2+x^2}+\sqrt{a^2-x^2}}{\sqrt{(a^2+x^2)}-\sqrt{(a^2-x^2)}}$

Multiply above and below by

$\sqrt{a^2+x^2}+\sqrt{a^2-x^2}$.

$\therefore\quad y=\frac{(a^2+x^2)+(a^2-x^2)+2\sqrt{(a^4-x^4)}}{(a^2+x^2)-(a^2-x^2)}$

$=\frac{a^2}{x^2}+\frac{\sqrt{(a^4-x^4)}}{x^2}$

Now differentiate etc., 2nd term by quotient formula.

28. $x\sqrt{(1+y)}+y\sqrt{(1+x)}=0$

$\therefore\quad x\sqrt{(1+y)}=-y\sqrt{(1+x)}$

Square. $x^2(1+y)=y^2(1+x)$

or $(x^2-y^2)+xy(x-y)=0$

or $(x-y)(x+y+xy)=0$

Since $y=x$ does not satisfy the given equation, we have

$x+y+xy=0$,

$y=-x/(1+x)=-[1-1/(1+x)]$

$\therefore\quad \frac{dy}{dx}=-\frac{1}{(1+x)^2}$.

29. $x^2+y^2=t-1/t$, $x^4+y^4=t^2+1/t^2$

$x^4+y^4=(t-1/t)^2+2=(x^2+y^2)^2+2,$

$\therefore 2x^2y^2+2=0$

or $x^2y^2=-1$ or $y^2=-1/x^2$.

Differentiate

$2y\frac{dy}{dx}=\frac{2}{x^3}$ or $x^3y\frac{dy}{dx}=1$

30. $x=\frac{3at}{1+t^3}$, $y=\frac{3at^2}{1+t^3}$.

Clearly $y=t\,x$. Differentiate w.r.t. x

$\therefore\quad \frac{dy}{dx}=t.1+x.\frac{dt}{dx}$. ...(1)

Now $\frac{dx}{dt}=3a.\frac{1+t^3-t.3t^2}{(1+t^3)^2}=\frac{3a.(1-2t^3)}{(1+t^3)^2}$. ...(2)

$\therefore\quad \frac{dy}{dx}=t+\frac{3at}{1+t^3}.\frac{(1+t^3)^2}{3a(1-2t^3)}$ by (1) and (2)

$=t.\frac{1-2t^3+1+t^3}{1-2t^3}=\frac{t(2-t^3)}{1-2t^3}$.

31. (a) $\sin y=x\sin(a+y)$, $\therefore\ x=\frac{\sin y}{\sin(a+y)}$

Differentiate w.r.t. x.

$\therefore\quad 1=\frac{\sin(a+y)\cos y-\sin y\cos(a+y)}{\sin^2(a+y)}.\frac{dy}{dx}$

$\therefore\quad \frac{dy}{dx}=\frac{\sin^2(a+y)}{\sin(a+y-y)}=\frac{\sin^2(a+y)}{\sin a}$.

2nd form :

In this form we want the value of $\frac{dy}{dx}$ in terms of x whereas the value found earlier was in terms of y only.

Hence from given relation, we have

$\tan y=\frac{x\sin a}{1-x\cos a}$

$\therefore\quad y=\tan^{-1}\frac{x\sin a}{1-x\cos a}$

$\therefore\quad \frac{dy}{dx}=$ etc. as given.

(b) Proceed as in part (a). When $x=0$,

$$\sin y = 0 \quad \therefore \quad y = n\pi$$

Hence, $\frac{dy}{dx}$ at $x=0$ is

$$\frac{\cos^2(a+n\pi)}{\cos a} = \frac{\cos^2 a}{\cos a} = \cos a$$

32. (a) Combining first two and the result with 3rd and again the result with 4th term, we get

$$y = \frac{x^3}{(x-c_1)(x-c_2)(x-c_3)} = \frac{x}{x-c_1} \cdot \frac{x}{x-c_2} \cdot \frac{x}{x-c_3}$$

$$\therefore \quad \log y = \log \frac{x}{x-c_1} + \log \frac{x}{x-c_2} + \log \frac{x}{x-c_3}$$

or $\log y = \{\log x - \log(x-c_1)\} + \{\ \} + \{\ \}$.

$$\therefore \quad \frac{1}{y}\frac{dy}{dx} = \left\{\frac{1}{x} - \frac{1}{x-c_1}\right\} + \{\ \} + \{\ \}$$

$$= -\frac{c_1}{x(x-c_1)} - \frac{c_2}{x(x-c_2)} - \frac{c_3}{x(x-c_3)}$$

$$\therefore \quad \frac{dy}{dx} = \frac{y}{x}\left\{\frac{c_1}{c_1-x} + \frac{c_2}{c_2-x} + \frac{c_3}{c_3-x}\right\}.$$

(b) Proceed as in part (a).

(c) Ans. (b).

$$1 + x + x^2 = 1 + x(x+1)$$

$$x^2 + 3x + 3 = 1 + x^2 + 3x + 2 = 1 + (x+1)(x+2)$$

$$x^2 + 5x + 7 = 1 + x^2 + 5x + 6 = 1 + (x+2)(x+3)$$

$$\therefore \quad T_1 = \tan^{-1}(x+1) - \tan^{-1} x$$

$$T_2 = \tan^{-1}(x+2) - \tan^{-1}(x+1)$$

$$T_3 = \tan^{-1}(x+3) - \tan^{-1}(x+2)$$

... ...

$$T_n = \tan^{-1}(x+n) - \tan^{-1}(x+n-1)$$

$$\therefore \quad y = S_n = \tan^{-1}(x+n) - \tan^{-1} x$$

$$\frac{dy}{dx} = \frac{1}{1+(x+n)^2} - \frac{1}{1+x^2}$$

$$\left(\frac{dy}{dx}\right)_{x=0} \frac{1}{1+n^2} - 1 = -\frac{n^2}{1+n^2} \Rightarrow \text{(b)}$$

33. Taking log of both sides, we get

$$\log \cos \frac{x}{2} + \log \cos \frac{x}{2^2} + \log \cos \frac{x}{2^3} + \ldots \log \cos \frac{x}{2^n}$$

$$= \log \sin x - \log 2^n - \log \sin \frac{x}{2^n}$$

Differentiate w.r.t. x

$$-\frac{1}{2}\tan\frac{x}{2} - \frac{1}{2^2}\tan\frac{x}{2^2} - \frac{1}{2^3}\tan\frac{x}{2^3} + \cdots$$

$$= \cot x - \frac{1}{2^n}\cot\frac{x}{2^n}$$

$$\therefore \quad \frac{1}{2}\tan\frac{x}{2} + \frac{1}{2^2}\tan\frac{x}{2^2} + \frac{1}{2^3}\tan\frac{x}{2^3} + \cdots$$

$$= \frac{1}{2^n}\cot\frac{x}{2^n} - \cot x \qquad \ldots(1)$$

Differentiate again w.r.t. x

$$\frac{1}{2^2}\sec^2\frac{x}{2} + \frac{1}{2^4}\sec^2\frac{x}{2^2} + \frac{1}{2^6}\sec^2\frac{x}{2^3} + \cdots$$

$$= \operatorname{cosec}^2 x - \frac{1}{2^{2n}}\operatorname{cosec}^2\frac{x}{2^n}. \qquad \ldots(2)$$

when $n \to \infty$, $2^n \to \infty$, $\therefore \frac{x}{2^n} \to 0$;

$$\therefore \quad \sin\frac{x}{2^n} \Rightarrow \frac{x}{2^n} \quad \text{and} \quad \cos\frac{x}{2^n} \Rightarrow 1.$$

Hence corresponding results, for infinity are

$$= \frac{1}{x/2^n} \cdot \frac{1}{2^n} - \cot x = \frac{1}{x} - \cot x, \qquad \text{by (1)}$$

and $\operatorname{cosec}^2 x - \frac{1}{2^{2n}} \cdot \frac{2^{2n}}{x^2} = \operatorname{cosec}^2 x - \frac{1}{x^2}$, by (2)

34. $y = \sqrt{\sin x + y}$, $\therefore$ $y^2 = \sin x + y$

or $y^2 - y = \sin x$, $\therefore$ $(2y-1)\frac{dy}{dx} = \cos x$

or $\frac{dy}{dx} = \frac{\cos x}{2y-1}$.

35. (a) We know that when $0 < x < 1$, then $\lim_{n\to\infty} x^n = 0$.

Now $(1-x)(1+x) = 1 - x^2$,

$$(1-x)(1+x)(1+x^2) = 1 - x^4.$$

$$(1-x)(1+x)(1+x^2)(1+x^4) = 1 - x^8.$$

$$\therefore \quad (1-x)(1+x)(1+x^2)(1+x^4)(1+x^8)\ldots$$

$$(1+x^{2^{n-1}}) = 1 - x^{2^n}.$$

Making $n \to \infty$, we get

$$(1-x)(1+x)(1+x^2)(1+x^4)(1+x^8)\cdots = 1.$$

Taking log of both sides and differentiating, we get

$$-\frac{1}{1-x} + \frac{1}{1+x} + \frac{2x}{1+x^2} + \frac{4x^3}{1+x^4} + \frac{8x^7}{1+x^8} + \cdots = 0$$

$$\therefore \quad \frac{1}{1+x} + \frac{2x}{1+x^2} + \frac{4x^3}{1+x^4} + \frac{8x^7}{1+x^8} + \cdots$$

$$= \frac{1}{1-x} \qquad \ldots(1)$$

(b) $(1+x+x^2)(1-x+x^2)$

$$= (1+x^2)^2 - x^2 = 1 + x^2 + x^4,$$

$$(1+x+x^2)(1-x+x^2)(1-x^2+x^4)$$

$$= (1+x^2+x^4)(1-x^2+x^4)$$

$= 1 + x^4 + x^8$ etc. as in part (a) (1).

(c) We denote the sum by S, then

$$\frac{1}{x-1} - S = \frac{1}{x-1} - \left\{\frac{1}{x+1} + \frac{2}{x^2+1} + \frac{2^2}{(x^2)^2+1} + \ldots + \frac{2^n}{(x^2)^n+1}\right\}$$

$$= \frac{2}{x^2-1} - \left\{ \frac{2}{x^2+1} + \frac{2^2}{(x^2)^2+1} + \cdots \frac{2^n}{(x^2)^n+1} \right\}$$

$$= \frac{2^2}{(x^2)^2-1} - \left\{ \frac{2^2}{(x^2)^2+1} + \cdots + \frac{2^n}{(x^2)^n+1} \right\}$$

$$= \frac{2^3}{(x^2)^3+1} - \left\{ \cdots\cdots + \frac{2^n}{(x^2)^n+1} \right\}$$

Continuing like this, we get

$$= \frac{2^{n+1}}{(x^2)^{n+1}-1}$$

$$\therefore \quad S = \frac{1}{x-1} - \frac{2^{n+1}}{(x^2)^{n+1}-1}.$$

36. (a) y is given in terms of continued fraction

$$y = x^2 + \cfrac{1}{x^2 + \cfrac{1}{x^2 + \cdots}}$$

$$\therefore \quad y = x^2 + \frac{1}{y} \quad \text{or} \quad y^2 = x^2 y + 1.$$

Differentiate $\quad 2y \dfrac{dy}{dx} = x^2 \dfrac{dy}{dx} + 2xy,$

$$\frac{dy}{dx} = \frac{2xy}{2y-x^2} = \frac{2x}{2-(x^2/y)}$$

$$\therefore \quad \frac{dy}{dx} = \frac{2x}{2 - \cfrac{x^2}{x^2 + \cfrac{1}{x^2 + \cdots}}}$$

(b) Proceed as in part (a).

37. (a) $\cos y = \dfrac{a+b\cos x}{b+a\cos x} \qquad (b > a).$

$$\therefore \quad \log \cos y = \log(a+b\cos x) - \log(b+a\cos x).$$

$$\therefore \quad \frac{1}{\cos y}(-\sin y)\frac{dy}{dx} = \frac{-b\sin x}{a+b\cos x} + \frac{a\sin x}{b+a\cos x}$$

$$= \frac{(a^2-b^2)\sin x}{(a+b\cos x)(b+a\cos x)}$$

$$\text{or} \quad \tan y \frac{dy}{dx} = \frac{(b^2-a^2)\sin x}{(a+b\cos x)(b+a\cos x)} \qquad \ldots(1)$$

We have to put the value of $\tan y$ in (1)

$$\tan y = \frac{\sqrt{1-\cos^2 y}}{\cos y}$$

$$= \frac{\sqrt{(b+a\cos x)^2-(a+b\cos x)^2}}{a+b\cos x}$$

$$= \frac{\sqrt{(b^2-a^2)-(b^2-a^2)\cos^2 x}}{a+b\cos x}$$

$$= \sqrt{b^2-a^2} \cdot \frac{\sin x}{a+b\cos x}.$$

Hence from (1), we get

$$\sqrt{b^2-a^2} \cdot \frac{\sin x}{a+b\cos x} \frac{dy}{dx}$$

$$= \frac{(b^2-a^2)\sin x}{(a+b\cos x)(b+a\cos x)}$$

$$\therefore \quad \frac{dy}{dx} = \frac{\sqrt{b^2-a^2}}{b+a\cos x}.$$

(b) $y = \dfrac{2}{\sqrt{(a^2-b^2)}} \tan^{-1} \left\{ \sqrt{\left(\dfrac{a-b}{a+b}\right)} \tan \dfrac{x}{2} \right\}.$

$$\therefore \quad \frac{dy}{dx} = \frac{2}{\sqrt{(a^2-b^2)}} \cdot \frac{1}{\left(1 + \dfrac{a-b}{a+b} \cdot \dfrac{\sin^2(x/2)}{\cos^2(x/2)} \right)} \cdot$$

$$\sqrt{\left(\frac{a-b}{a+b}\right)} \cdot \sec^2 \frac{x}{2} \cdot \frac{1}{2}.$$

$$= \left(\frac{1}{a+b} \right) \left(\frac{(a+b)\cos^2(x/2)\sec^2(x/2)}{\substack{a\{\cos^2(x/2)+\sin^2(x/2)\} \\ +b\{\cos^2(x/2)-\sin^2(x/2)\}}} \right)$$

$$= \frac{1}{a+b\cos x}$$

Differentiating again, we get

$$\frac{d^2y}{dx^2} = -\frac{1}{(a+b\cos x)^2} \cdot (-b\sin x)$$

$$= \frac{b\sin x}{(a+b\cos x)^2}.$$

(c) $\dfrac{dy}{dx} = -\dfrac{f_x}{f_y} = -\dfrac{2x+5y-2}{5x+2y+1} = -\dfrac{5}{8}$ at (1, 1).

Differentiating again w.r.t. x,

$$\frac{d^2y}{dx^2} = -\frac{(5x+2y+1)\left(2+5\dfrac{dy}{dx}\right) - (2x+5y-2)\left(5+2\dfrac{dy}{dx}\right)}{(5x+2y+1)^2}$$

Now put $x = 1$, $y = 1$, $\dfrac{dy}{dx} = -\dfrac{5}{8}$

$$\therefore \quad \frac{d^2y}{dx^2} = -\frac{1}{64}\left[8\left(2-\frac{25}{8}\right) - (5)\left(5-\frac{10}{8}\right)\right]$$

$$= -\frac{1}{64}\left[16-25-25+\frac{25}{4}\right] = -\frac{1}{256}[89-200] = \frac{111}{256}.$$

38. (a) Proceed as above.

(b) Ans. $\dfrac{\sin \alpha}{1 - 2x\cos\alpha + x^2}.$

39. (a) $y = \log(1+x^2+x\sqrt{2}) - \log(1+x^2-x\sqrt{2})$

$$+ 2\tan^{-1}\frac{x\sqrt{2}}{1-x^2}.$$

$$\therefore \quad \frac{dy}{dx}=\frac{2x+\sqrt{2}}{1+x^2+x\sqrt{(2)}}-\frac{2x-\sqrt{2}}{1+x^2-x\sqrt{(2)}}$$

$$+2.\frac{1}{1+\frac{2x^2}{(1-x^2)^2}}.\text{d.c. of }\frac{x\sqrt{2}}{1-x^2}$$

$$=\frac{2x(-2\sqrt{2x})+\sqrt{2}.2.(1+x^2)}{(1+x^2)^2-2x^2}$$

$$+\frac{2(1-x^2)^2}{1+x^4}.\frac{\sqrt{2}(1+x^2)}{(1-x^2)^2}$$

$$=\frac{2\sqrt{2}(1-x^2)}{1+x^4}+\frac{2\sqrt{2}(1+x^2)}{1+x^4}=\frac{4\sqrt{2}}{1+x^4}.$$

(b) $y=\frac{1}{3}\log(x+1)-\frac{1}{6}\log(x^2-x+1)$

$$+\frac{1}{\sqrt{(3)}}\tan^{-1}\frac{2x-1}{\sqrt{(3)}}.$$

$$\frac{dy}{dx}=\frac{1}{3}.\frac{1}{x+1}-\frac{1}{6}.\frac{2x-1}{x^2-x+1}$$

$$+\frac{1}{\sqrt{(3)}}.\frac{1}{1+\frac{(2x-1)^2}{3}}.\frac{2}{\sqrt{(3)}}$$

$$=\frac{1}{6}.\frac{2(x^2-x+1)-(x+1)(2x-1)}{x^3+1}$$

$$+\frac{2}{3}.\frac{3}{3+4x^2-4x+1}$$

$$=\frac{1}{6}.\frac{-3x+3}{x^3+1}+\frac{1}{2(x^2-x+1)}$$

$$=\frac{1}{2}.\frac{1-x}{x^3+1}+\frac{x+1}{2(x+1)(x^2-x+1)}$$

$$=\frac{1}{2(x^3+1)}.[1-x+x+1]=\frac{1}{x^3+1}$$

(c) $\log\sqrt{\frac{m}{n}}=\frac{1}{2}(\log m-\log n)$

Combine $\log(x^2+x+1)$ with $\tan^{-1}\frac{2x+1}{\sqrt{3}}$ and similarly other two terms etc.

40. Put $\tan\frac{y}{2}=t \quad \therefore \ \sin y=\frac{2t}{1+t^2}, \cos y=\frac{1-t^2}{1+t^2}$

$$\therefore \quad 1+\sin y+\cos y=\frac{2+2t}{1+t^2}$$

and $\quad y=2\tan^{-1}t$ ...(1)

$$\therefore \quad \frac{dy}{dt}=\frac{2}{1+t^2} \quad \text{...(2)}$$

Now $x=t-2\log(1+t)+\log t$

$$\therefore \quad \frac{dx}{dt}=1-\frac{2}{1+t}+\frac{1}{t}=\frac{t^2+1}{t(t+1)} \quad \text{...(3)}$$

$$\therefore \quad \frac{dy}{dx}=\frac{dy}{dt}\div\frac{dx}{dt}=\frac{2}{1+t^2}\cdot\frac{t^2+t}{1+t^2}, \text{ by (2) \& (3)}$$

or $\quad \frac{dy}{dx}=\frac{2t}{1+t^2}\cdot\frac{1}{2}\frac{2t+2}{1+t^2}$

$$=\frac{1}{2}\sin y(1+\sin y+\cos y), \quad \text{by (1)}$$

41. (a) Let $y=(\log_{\cos x}\sin x)(\log_{\sin x}\cos x)^{-1}$

$$+\sin^{-1}\frac{2x}{1+x^2}$$

$$=(\log_{\cos x}\sin x)^2+2\tan^{-1}x\left[\because \log_b a=\frac{1}{\log_a b}\right]$$

$$=\left(\frac{\log_e \sin x}{\log_e \cos x}\right)^2+2\tan^{-1}x.$$

$$\frac{dy}{dx}=2\left(\frac{\log\sin x}{\log\cos x}\right).$$

$$\frac{\cot x.\log\cos x+\tan x\log\sin x}{(\log\cos x)^2}+\frac{2}{1+x^2}$$

Hence at $x=\frac{\pi}{4}$, we have

$$\frac{dy}{dx}=2.\frac{\log(1/\sqrt{2})}{\log(1/\sqrt{2})}$$

$$.\frac{1.\log(1/\sqrt{2})+1.\log(1/\sqrt{2})}{[\log(1/\sqrt{2})]^2}+\frac{2}{1+(\pi^2/16)}$$

$$=\frac{-8}{\log 2}+\frac{32}{\pi^2+16}=8\left(\frac{4}{\pi^2+16}-\frac{1}{\log 2}\right).$$

(b) $y=\frac{\log\sin x^2}{\log x}+(\sin x^2)^{\log x}, z=\sqrt{(x+1)}$

$y=u+v$

$$\therefore \quad \frac{dy}{dx}=\frac{du}{dx}+\frac{dv}{dx}$$

$$\frac{du}{dx}=\frac{(\log x)(2x\cot x^2)-\frac{1}{x}(\log\sin x^2)}{(\log x)^2}$$

quotient ...(1)

$$\frac{dv}{dx}=\log x(\sin x^2)^{\log x-1}.2x\cos x^2$$

$$+(\sin x^2)^{\log x}(\log\sin x^2).\frac{1}{x}$$

(by Rule P. 1217) ...(2)

$$\frac{dz}{dx}=\frac{1}{2\sqrt{(x+1)}} \quad \text{...(3)}$$

$\therefore \quad \frac{dy}{dz}=\frac{dy}{dx}\div\frac{dz}{dx}$ etc. from (1), (2) and (3).

(c) Let us consider a small interval containing the point $x=-\pi/6$ and further $\cos 4x$ retains the same negative sign in this interval. Also $\sin x$ is negative in this interval. So we may write

$$|\cos 4x|=-\cos 4x \text{ and } |\sin x|=-\sin x$$

in this small interval containing the point $x = -\pi/6$

$\therefore \quad y = \log_u(-\cos 4x) + (-\sin x)$

$= \log_{\sec 2x}(-\cos 4x) - \sin x$

$= \dfrac{\log_e(-\cos 4x)}{\log_e \sec 2x} - \sin x$

$\dfrac{4\sin 4x}{-\cos 4x} \cdot \log \sec 2x$

$$\therefore \quad \frac{dy}{dx} = \frac{-\log(-\cos 4x) \cdot \dfrac{\sec 2x \tan 2x}{\sec 2x} \cdot 2}{(\log \sec 2x)^2} - \cos x$$

$$= \frac{-4\tan 4x \log \sec 2x - 2\tan 2x \log(-\cos 4x)}{(\log \sec 2x)^2} - \cos x$$

Hence if $x = -\pi/6$, we have

$$\frac{dy}{dx} = \frac{-4\tan(-2\pi/3)\log\sec(-\pi/3) - 2\tan(-\pi/3)\log[-\cos(-2\pi/3)]}{\log 2^2} - \frac{\sqrt{3}}{2}$$

$$= \frac{4(-\sqrt{3})\log 2 - 2(-\sqrt{3})\log(1/2)}{(\log 2)^2} - \frac{\sqrt{3}}{2}$$

$$= -\frac{\sqrt{3}}{2} - \frac{6\sqrt{3}}{\log 2}.$$

42. $y = e^x(a\cos x + b\sin x)$ ...(1)

$y_1 = e^x(-a\sin x + b\cos x) + e^x(a\cos x + b\sin x)$

$y_1 = e^x(-a\sin x + b\cos x) + y$ ...(2)

$y_2 = e^x(-a\cos x - b\sin x) + e^x(-a\sin x + b\cos x) + y_1$

or $\quad y_2 = -y + (y_1 - y) + y_1$ by (1) and (2)

or $\quad y_2 - 2y_1 + 2y = 0.$

43. (a) We have to prove that $p^4 + p^3 \dfrac{d^2p}{d\theta^2} = a^2b^2$.

$p^2 = a^2\cos^2\theta + b^2\sin^2\theta$.

$\therefore \quad 2p\dfrac{dp}{d\theta} = (b^2 - a^2)\, 2\sin\theta\cos\theta$ ...(1)

Differentiate again w.r.t. θ

$$p\frac{d^2p}{d\theta^2} + \left(\frac{dp}{d\theta}\right)^2 = (b^2 - a^2)(\cos^2\theta - \sin^2\theta)$$

Multiply both sides by p^2

$$p^3\frac{d^2p}{d\theta^2} = p^2(b^2 - a^2)(\cos^2\theta - \sin^2\theta) - \left(p\frac{dp}{d\theta}\right)^2$$

Add p^4 to both sides

$$p^4 + p^3\frac{d^2p}{d\theta^2} = p^2[p^2 + (b^2 - a^2)(\cos^2\theta - \sin^2\theta)] - (b^2 - a^2)^2\sin^2\theta\cos^2\theta \text{ by (1)}$$

Now put the value of p^2

$= (a^2\cos^2\theta + b^2\sin^2\theta)(b^2\cos^2\theta + a^2\sin^2\theta) - (b^2 - a^2)^2\sin^2\theta\cos^2\theta$

$= a^2b^2[\cos^4\theta + \sin^4\theta + 2\sin^2\theta\cos^2\theta]$

$= a^2b^2.(\cos^2\theta + \sin^2\theta)^2 = a^2b^2$

(b) $1 + 3 + 5 + \ldots(2n-1) = \dfrac{n}{2}\{1 + 2n - 1\} = n^2$

or $\quad y = \cos n^2t + i\sin n^2t$ De-Moivre's

$\dfrac{dy}{dt} = n^2\{-\sin n^2t + i\cos n^2t\}$

$\therefore \quad \dfrac{d^2y}{dt^2} = n^2.n^2(-y) = -n^4y.$

44. We have to prove that $\left(\dfrac{dy}{dx}\right)^2 = n^2\dfrac{(y^2+4)}{x^2+4}$.

Using $(a-b)^2 + 4ab = (a+b)^2$,

$$\text{R.H.S.} = \frac{n^2(\sec^n\theta + \cos^n\theta)^2}{(\sec\theta + \cos\theta)^2}. \quad \text{...(1)}$$

Now $\dfrac{dx}{d\theta} = \sec\theta\tan\theta + \sin\theta$

$= \tan\theta(\sec\theta + \cos\theta)$

$\dfrac{dy}{d\theta} = n(\sec^{n-1}\theta\sec\theta\tan\theta + \cos^{n-1}\theta\sin\theta)$

$= n\tan\theta(\sec^n\theta + \cos^n\theta)$

$\therefore \quad \left(\dfrac{dy}{dx}\right)^2 = \left(\dfrac{dy/d\theta}{dx/d\theta}\right)^2 =$ as given by (1) $=$ L.H.S.

45. (a) $f(x) = \log_x(\log x)$

$= \log_x(\log_e x) = \dfrac{\log_e(\log_e x)}{\log_e x}$

[Changing to base e]

$$\therefore \quad f'(x) = \frac{\left[\dfrac{1}{\log x}\cdot\dfrac{1}{x}\right]\log x - \left(\dfrac{1}{x}\right).[\log(\log x)]}{(\log x)^2}$$

$= [1 - \log\log x]/\{x(\log x)^2\}$

$\therefore \quad f'(e) = [1 - \log\log e]/\{e(\log e)^2\}$

$= [1 - \log 1]/e(1)^2 = 1/e.$

(b) Ans. (iv).

$y = \dfrac{1}{2}\log_x(\log x)$

$\therefore \quad \dfrac{dy}{dx} = \dfrac{1}{2}\cdot\dfrac{1}{e},$ by part (a)

(c) Ans. 1.

$$e^{xy}.1 + x.e^{xy}\left(y + x\frac{dy}{dx}\right) = \frac{dy}{dx} + 2\sin x\cos x$$

Put $x = 0$ and $\dfrac{dy}{dx} = 1.$

46. We have $y(x^2 + c) = ax + b$. Differentiating w.r.t. x, we get

$$y'(x^2+c)+y.2x=a \quad ...(1)$$

Differentiating (1) again, we get

$$y''(x^2+c)+y'.2x+y'.2x+y.2=0$$

or $\quad y''(x^2+c)+4xy'+2y=0 \quad ...(2)$

or $\quad x^2+c=-2(2xy'+y)/y'' \quad ...(3)$

Differentiating both sides of (2) w.r.t. x, we get

$$y'''(x^2+c)+y''.2x+4[xy''+y']+2y'=0$$

or $\quad y'''=-\dfrac{6(xy''+y')}{(x^2+c)}=\dfrac{3y''(xy''+y')}{2xy'+y}$, by (3)

or $\quad y'''(2xy'+y)=3y''(xy''+y')$.

47. (a) Since $f(x)=\sin\log x$, we have

$$y=f\left(\frac{2x+3}{3-2x}\right)=\sin\log\left(\frac{2x+3}{3-2x}\right)$$

$$=\sin[\log(2x+3)-\log(3-2x)]$$

$$\therefore \quad \frac{dy}{dx}=\cos[\log(2x+3)-\log(3-2x)]\cdot\left(\frac{2}{2x+3}+\frac{2}{3-2x}\right)$$

$$=\left(\frac{12}{9-4x^2}\right)\cos\log\left(\frac{2x+3}{3-2x}\right).$$

(b) On putting the values of S_n and S_{n-1}, R.H.S. is easily seen to be

$$\frac{a}{1-r}\{-nr^n-1+r^n+nr^{n-1}\}$$

$$\text{L.H.S.}=(r-1).\frac{a}{(1-r)^2}\{(1-r)(-nr^{n-1})-(1-r^n)(-1)\}$$

$$=-\frac{a}{(1-r)}\{-nr^{n-1}+nr^n+1-r^n\}=\text{R.H.S.}$$

(c) $\phi=fg \quad \therefore \quad \phi'=f'g+fg'$

$$\phi''=(f''g+fg'')+2f'g'$$

$$\frac{\phi''}{\phi}=\frac{f''g+fg''+2c}{fg} \quad \text{by given relations}$$

$$=\frac{f''}{f}+\frac{g''}{g}+\frac{2c}{fg}.$$

48. (a) Differentiating the given relation w. r. t. x. The first term is differentiated as explained in easier method **Q. 1, P. 1217.**

$$\sin\left(\frac{\pi}{2}x\right)\left[(\sin y)^{\sin(\frac{\pi}{2}x)-1}\cdot\cos y\frac{dy}{dx}\right]$$

$$+(\sin y)^{\sin(\frac{\pi}{2}x)}\cdot\cos\left(\frac{\pi}{2}x\right)\cdot\frac{\pi}{2}\cdot\log\sin y$$

$$+\frac{\sqrt{3}}{2}\left[\frac{1}{|2x|\sqrt{(4x^2-1)}}\cdot 2\right]+2^x\log 2\tan\log(x+2)$$

$$+2^x\sec^2\log(x+2)\cdot\frac{1}{x+2}=0$$

We have to calculate the value of dy/dx at $x=-1$. We have five terms in the above. The second term vanishes as $\cos(-\pi/2)=0$, the fourth term is zero as $\log 1=0$ and $\tan(0)=0$. The third term is $+\frac{1}{2}$ and the fifth term is $\frac{1}{2}$ as $\sec 0=1$.

The first term at $x=-1$ is

$$(-1)(\sin y)^{-2}\cos y\frac{dy}{dx}$$

$$\therefore \quad -\frac{\cos y}{\sin^2 y}\frac{dy}{dx}+\frac{1}{2}+\frac{1}{2}=0$$

$$\therefore \quad \frac{dy}{dx}=\frac{\sin^2 y}{\cos y} \quad ...(1)$$

Now from the given relation putting $x=-1$, we get

$$(\sin y)^{-1}+\frac{\sqrt{3}}{2}\sec^{-1}(-2)+2^{-1}\tan\log 1=0$$

$$\therefore \quad \frac{1}{\sin y}+\frac{\sqrt{3}}{2}\left(\frac{2\pi}{3}\right)+0=0$$

$$\therefore \quad \sin y=-\frac{\sqrt{3}}{\pi} \quad \text{or} \quad \cos y=\frac{\sqrt{(\pi^2-3)}}{\pi}$$

Hence from (1),

$$\frac{dy}{dx}=\frac{3}{\pi\sqrt{(\pi^2-3)}} \quad \text{at } x=-1$$

(b) $|p(x)|\le|e^{x-1}-1|, x\ge 0$

$$p(x)=a_0+a_1x+a_2x^2+...+a_nx^n$$

$$p'(x)=a_1+2a_2x+3a_3x^2+...+na_nx^{n-1}$$

$$\therefore \quad p'(1)=a_1+2a_2+3a_3+...+na_n$$

We have to to prove that $|p'(1)|\le 1$

Given $|p(x)|\le|e^{x-1}-1|$

$$\therefore \quad |p(1)|\le|e^0-1|\le 0$$

$$\therefore \quad |p(1)|\le 0 \Rightarrow |p(1)|=0$$

Also $-(e^{x-1}-1)\le p(x)\le e^{x-1}-1$

Differentiating,

$$-e^{x-1}\le p'(x)\le e^{x-1} \quad \text{Put } x=1$$

$$-1\le p'(1)\le 1 \Rightarrow |p'(1)|\le 1$$

$$\therefore \quad |a_1+2a_2+3a_3+...+na_n|\le 1.$$

49. (a) $\dfrac{dy}{dx}=y_1=\cos(m\sin^{-1}x)\cdot\dfrac{m}{\sqrt{(1-x^2)}}$.

Squaring, $y_1^2(1-x^2)=m^2(1-y^2)$

$$\because \quad \cos^2\theta=1-\sin^2\theta$$

Differentiate both sides w.r.t. x

$$2y_1y_2(1-x^2)+y_1^2(-2x)=m^2(-2yy_1).$$

Cancel $2y_1$

$$\therefore \quad y_2(1-x^2)-xy_1+m^2y=0$$

(b) $\frac{dy}{dx} = -\frac{1}{2^{n-1}} \sin(n \cos^{-1} x) \times \frac{-n}{\sqrt{(1-x^2)}}$

$\therefore \quad (1-x^2)\left(\frac{dy}{dx}\right)^2 = \frac{n^2}{(2^{n-1})^2}[1-(2^{n-1})^2 y^2]$

or $\quad (1-x^2)\, y_1^2 = \frac{n^2}{(2^{n-1})^2} - n^2 y^2$

Differentiate both sides w.r.t. x

$(1-x^2).2y_1 y_2 - 2xy_1^2 = -n^2.2yy_1$

Cancel $2y_1$

$\therefore \quad (1-x^2)\, y_2 - xy_1 + n^2 y = 0$

50. (a) $y_1 = m\{x + \sqrt{(1+x^2)}\}^{m-1} \cdot \left\{1 + \frac{1.2x}{2\sqrt{(1+x^2)}}\right\}$

$= \frac{my}{\sqrt{(1+x^2)}}$

$\therefore \quad y_1^2 (1+x^2) = m^2 y^2$ etc. as in Q. 49 (a).

(b) Put $y^{1/m} = z \quad \therefore \quad z^2 - 2xz + 1 = 0$

$\therefore \quad z = y^{1/m} = \frac{1}{2}\{2x + \sqrt{(4x^2-4)}\}$

$= x + \sqrt{(x^2-1)}$

$\therefore \quad y = \{x + \sqrt{(x^2-1)}\}^m$ etc. as in Q. 49 (b)

(c) $x - \sqrt{x^2-1} = \frac{x^2-(x^2-1)}{x+\sqrt{x^2-1}} = (x+\sqrt{x^2-1})^{-1}$

$\therefore \quad y = (a+b)[x+\sqrt{x^2+1}]^n$

$\therefore \quad y_1 = \frac{ny}{\sqrt{1+x^2}}$ as in (a), (b)

or $\quad (1+x^2)\, y_1^2 - n^2 y^2 = 0$ etc.

51. $\cos^{-1}\frac{y}{b} = n[\log x - \log n]$. Differentiate

$-\frac{1}{\sqrt{(b^2-y^2)}} \cdot y_1 = n.\frac{1}{x}$. Square

$x^2 y_1^2 = n^2 (b^2 - y^2)$. Differentiate again

$x^2 2y_1 y_2 + 2xy_1^2 = -n^2.2yy_1$.

Cancel $2y_1$

$\therefore \quad x^2 y_2 + xy_1 + n^2 y = 0.$

52. (a) $y_1 = e^{a\sin^{-1} x} . \frac{a}{\sqrt{(1-x^2)}} = \frac{ay}{\sqrt{(1-x^2)}}$

$\therefore \quad y_1^2 (1-x^2) = a^2 y^2$ etc.

(b) Proceed as in (a).

53. (a) $y_1 = -\frac{a\sin(\log x)}{x} + \frac{b\cos(\log x)}{x}$

or $\quad xy_1 = -a\sin(\log x) + b\cos(\log x)$.

Differentiate

$xy_2 + y_1 = -\frac{a\cos(\log x)}{x} - \frac{b\sin(\log x)}{x}$

$\therefore \quad x^2 y_2 + xy_1 + y = 0$

(b) $y_1 = nx^{n-1}\,[a\cos(\log x) + b\sin(\log x)]$

$+ x^n . \frac{1}{x}[-a\sin(\log x) + b\cos(\log x)]$

$\therefore \quad xy_1 = ny + x^n\,[-a\sin(\log x) + b\cos(\log x)]$

Differentiate again etc.

(c) Squaring and adding the given relations, we get

$x^2 + y^2 = a^2.1 + b^2.1$

Differentiating w.r.t. x,

$2yy_1 + 2x = 0 \quad \therefore \quad yy_1 = -x \quad$ ...(1)

Differentiate again w.r.t. x

$\therefore \quad yy_2 + y_1^2 + 1 = 0$

Multiply both sides by y

$y^2 y_2 + y_1 (y_1\, y) + y = 0$

or $\quad y^2 y_2 - xy_1 + y = 0$, by (1)

54. (a) $y_1 = \frac{2\tan^{-1} x}{(1+x^2)}$

$\therefore \quad y_1^2 (1+x^2)^2 = 4y$

Now differentiate again and cancel $2y_1$ etc.

(b) $y_1 = \frac{1}{1+(x^2-1)} . \frac{1}{2\sqrt{x^2-1}} . 2x = \frac{1}{x\sqrt{x^2-1}}$

or $\quad y_1^2 (x^4 - x^2) = 1.$

Differentiate again w.r.t. x

$2y_1 y_2 (x^4 - x^2) + y_1^2 (4x^3 - 2x) = 0$

Cancel $2xy_1$

$\therefore \quad x(x^2-1)\, y_2 + (2x^2-1)\, y_1 = 0$

(c) Ans. (b). $2x + 2yy' = 0$. Differentiate again w.r.t. x.

$1 + y'^2 + yy'' \quad \Rightarrow \quad$ (b).

55. $\frac{dy}{dx} = \frac{2(\sin^{-1} x - \cos^{-1} x)}{\sqrt{1-x^2}}$

or $\quad \sqrt{1-x^2}\frac{dy}{dx} = 2(\sin^{-1} x - \cos^{-1} x)$

Differentiate again w.r.t. x

$\sqrt{1-x^2}\frac{d^2y}{dx^2} + \frac{1}{2\sqrt{1-x^2}}(-2x)\frac{dy}{dx}$

$= 2\left(\frac{1}{\sqrt{1-x^2}} - \frac{(-1)}{\sqrt{1-x^2}}\right)$

$\therefore \quad (1-x^2)\frac{d^2y}{dx^2} - x\frac{dy}{dx} = 4.$

56. $\frac{dy}{dx} = \frac{1}{2\sqrt{x}}(e^{\sqrt{x}} - e^{-\sqrt{x}})$

$\therefore \quad 2\sqrt{x}\, y_1 = e^{\sqrt{x}} - e^{-\sqrt{x}}$

Differentiate w.r.t. x.

$$2\left[\frac{1}{2\sqrt{x}}y_1+\sqrt{x}\,y_2\right]=\frac{1}{2\sqrt{x}}\,[e^{\sqrt{x}}+e^{-\sqrt{x}}]=\frac{1}{2\sqrt{x}}\cdot y$$

or $xy_2+\frac{1}{2}y_1=\frac{1}{4}y$ **Proved.**

57. Ans. (a).

Proceeding as in **Q.8 P. 1214-19**

$z=x^x \quad \therefore \quad \log z = x\log x$

$\therefore \quad \frac{1}{z}\frac{dz}{dx}=x\cdot\frac{1}{x}+1\cdot\log x$ or $\frac{dz}{dx}=z\,(1+\log x)$

or $\frac{dz}{dx}=x^x\,(1+\log x)$

If $t=x^{-x}$, then $\frac{dt}{dx}=-\,x^{-x}\,(1+\log x)$

$$y=\cot^{-1}\frac{x^x-x^{-x}}{2}$$

$$\therefore \quad \frac{dy}{dx}=\frac{-1}{1+\left(\frac{x^x-x^{-x}}{2}\right)^2}\cdot\frac{d}{dx}\left[\frac{x^x-x^{-x}}{2}\right]$$

$$=\frac{-1}{1+\left(\frac{x^x-x^{-x}}{2}\right)^2}\cdot\frac{1}{2}\,[(1+\log x)\,(x^x+x^{-x})]$$

Putting $x=1$.

$$\left(\frac{dy}{dx}\right)_{x=1}=-1\cdot\frac{1}{2}\,(1+\log 1)\,(1+1)$$

$= -1$ as $\log 1=0 \Rightarrow$ (a).

Problem Set (4)

Multiple choice Questions

1. Let $y=\sin^{-1}\frac{2x}{1+x^2}$ where $0<x<1$ and $0<y<\frac{\pi}{2}$, then $\frac{dy}{dx}$ is equal to

(a) $\frac{2}{1+x^2}$ (b) $\frac{2x}{1+x^2}$ (c) $\frac{1}{1+x^2}$ (d) $\frac{-x}{1+x^2}$.

2. If $y=\sin^n x\cos nx$, then $\frac{dy}{dx}=$

(a) $n\sin^{n-1}x\cos(n+1)\,x$

(b) $n\sin^{n-1}x\sin(n+1)\,x$

(c) $n\sin^{n-1}x\cos(n-1)\,x$

(d) $n\sin^{n-1}x\cos nx$.

3. If $x=t+\frac{1}{t}$, $y=t-\frac{1}{t}$ then $\frac{d^2y}{dx^2}$ is equal to

(a) $-4t\,(t^2-1)^{-2}$ (b) $-4t^3\,(t^2-1)^{-3}$

(c) $(t^2+1)\,(t^2-1)^{-1}$ (d) $-4t^2\,(t^2-1)^{-2}$.

4. Given the parametric equations $x=f(t)$, $y=g(t)$, then $\frac{d^2y}{dx^2}$ equals

(a) $\dfrac{\frac{d^2y}{dt^2}\cdot\frac{dx}{dt}-\frac{dy}{dt}\frac{d^2x}{dt^2}}{(dx/dt)^2}$ (b) $\dfrac{\frac{dx}{dt}\frac{d^2y}{dt^2}-\frac{d^2x}{dt^2}\frac{dy}{dt}}{(dx/dt)^3}$

(c) $\frac{d^2y}{dt^2}\Big/\frac{d^2x}{dt^2}$.

5. If $2^x+2^y=2^{x+y}$, then $\frac{dy}{dx}$ is equal to

(a) $(2^x+2^y)/(2^x-2^y)$ (b) $(2^x+2^y)/(1+2^{x+y})$.

(c) $2^{x-y}.\frac{2^y-1}{1-2^x}$ (d) $(2^{x+y}-2^x)/2^y$.

6. The differential coefficient of $\log\tan x$ is :

(a) $2\sec 2x$ (b) $2\operatorname{cosec} 2x$

(c) $2\sec^3 x$ (d) $2\operatorname{cosec}^3 x$

7. The differential coefficient of $f(\log(x))$ where $f(x)=\log x$ is

(a) $x/\log x$ (b) $\log x/x$,

(c) $(x\log x)^{-1}$ (d) None of these

8. If $y^2=P(x)$, a polynomial of degree 3, then $2\frac{d}{dx}\left(y^3\frac{d^2y}{dx^2}\right)$ equals

(a) $P'''(x)+P'(x)$ (b) $P''(x)\,P'''(x)$,

(c) $P(x)\,P'''(x)$ (d) A constant.

9. If $x=3\cos\theta-2\cos^3\theta$, $y=3\sin\theta-2\sin^3\theta$, then $\frac{dy}{dx}=$

(a) $\sin\theta$ (b) $\cos\theta$ (c) $\tan\theta$ (d) $\cot\theta$

(AIEEE 2002)

10. A point on the parabola $y^2=18x$ at which the ordinate increases at twice the rate of abscissa is :

(a) (2, 4) (b) (2, – 4)

(c) $\left(-\frac{9}{8},\frac{9}{2}\right)$ (d) $\left(\frac{9}{8},\frac{9}{2}\right)$

(AIEEE 2004)

11. If $y=\log_y x$, then $\frac{dy}{dx}=$

(a) $\frac{1}{x+\log y}$ (b) $\frac{1}{\log x\,(1+y)}$

(c) $\frac{1}{x\,(1+\log y)}$ (d) $\frac{1}{y+\log x}$

(AIEEE 2002)

12. If $y=x^{e^x}$, then $\frac{dy}{dx}=$

(a) $y\,(\log x+e^x)$ (b) $y\log x\left(\frac{1}{2}+e^x\right)$

(c) $ye^x\,(\log x+x)$ (d) $ye^x\left(\log x+\frac{1}{x}\right)$

(AIEEE 2002)

13. If $x = e^{y + e^{y + e^{y + \ldots \infty}}}$, $x > 0$ then $\frac{dy}{dx} =$

(a) $\frac{x}{1+x}$ (b) $\frac{1}{x}$ (c) $\frac{1-x}{x}$ (d) $\frac{1+x}{x}$

(AIEEE 2004)

14. $\frac{d^2x}{dy^2}$ equals

(a) $\left(\frac{d^2y}{dx^2}\right)^{-1}$ (b) $-\left(\frac{d^2y}{dx^2}\right)^{-1}\left(\frac{dy}{dx}\right)^{-3}$

(c) $\left(\frac{d^2y}{dx^2}\right)\left(\frac{dy}{dx}\right)^{-2}$ (d) $-\left(\frac{d^2y}{dx^2}\right)\left(\frac{dy}{dx}\right)^{-3}$

(AIEEE 2011; I.I.T. 2007)

Fill in the blanks :

15. (i) The derivative of $\tan^{-1}[2x/(1-x^2)]$ w.r.t. $\sin^{-1}[2x/(1+x^2)]$ is ....

(ii) The differential coefficient of x^6 with respect to x^3 is

(a) $6x^6$ (b) $3x^2$

(c) $2x^3$ (d) x^3

(M.N.R. 1990)

16. The derivative of $\sec^{-1}[1/(2x^2-1)]$ with respect to $\sqrt{1-x^2}$ at $x = \frac{1}{2}$ is ....

17. If $f(x) = \log_x(\log x)$, then $f'(x)$ at $x = e$ is ....

18. If $f(x) = \sin(\log x)$ and $y = f\left(\frac{2x+3}{3-2x}\right)$, then $\frac{dy}{dx} =$ ......

Hints/Answers to Problem Set (48)

1. Ans. (a).

Put $x = \tan\theta$. Then $y = \sin^{-1}\frac{2\tan\theta}{1+\tan^2\theta} = \sin^{-1}\sin 2\theta$.

$\therefore \quad y = 2\theta = 2\tan^{-1}x$ and so $\frac{dy}{dx} = \frac{2}{1+x^2}$.

2. Ans. (a).

3. Ans. (b).

We have $\frac{dx}{dt} = 1 - \frac{1}{t^2}$, $\frac{dy}{dt} = 1 + \frac{1}{t^2}$.

$$\therefore \quad \frac{dy}{dx} = \frac{1+(1/t^2)}{1-(1/t^2)} = \frac{t^2+1}{t^2-1} = \left[1 + \frac{2}{t^2-1}\right]$$

and $\frac{d^2y}{dx^2} = \frac{d}{dt}\left(\frac{dy}{dx}\right)\frac{dt}{dx} = 2 \cdot \frac{-1}{(t^2-1)^2} \cdot 2t \times \frac{t^2}{t^2-1}$

$$= -4t^3/(t^2-1)^3.$$

4. Ans. (b).

We have $\frac{dy}{dx} = \frac{dy/dt}{dx/dt}$

$$\therefore \quad \frac{d^2y}{dx^2} = \frac{d}{dt}\left(\frac{dy/dt}{dx/dt}\right)\frac{dt}{dx}$$

$$= \frac{\frac{d^2y}{dt^2}\left(\frac{dx}{dt}\right) - \left(\frac{d^2x}{dt^2}\right)\frac{dy}{dt}}{(dx/dt)^2} \times \frac{1}{dx/dt}$$

$$= \frac{\left(\frac{dx}{dt}\right) \cdot \left(\frac{d^2y}{dt^2}\right) - \left(\frac{d^2x}{dt^2}\right) \cdot \left(\frac{dy}{dt}\right)}{(dx/dt)^3}.$$

5. Ans. (c).

Differentiating both sides w.r.t. x,

$$2^x \log 2 + 2^y \log 2 \frac{dy}{dx} = 2^{x+y} \log 2\left(1 + \frac{dy}{dx}\right)$$

$$\therefore \quad 2^x(1-2^y) = 2^y(2^x-1)\frac{dy}{dx}$$

$$\therefore \quad \frac{dy}{dx} = 2^{x-y} \cdot \frac{2^y-1}{1-2^x} \quad \text{i.e., (c).}$$

6. Ans. (b). **7.** Ans. (c).

8. Ans. (c).

We have

$$P'(x) = 2yy', \; P''(x) = 2yy'' + 2y'^2$$

and $P'''(x) = 2yy''' + 6y'y''$

Also $2\frac{d}{dx}(y^3 y'') = 2[y^3 y''' + 3y^2 y' y'']$

$$= y^2[2yy''' + 6y'y''] = P(x)P'''(x).$$

9. Ans. (d).

$$\frac{dx}{d\theta} = -3\sin\theta + 6\cos^2\theta\sin\theta$$

$$= 3\sin\theta(2\cos^2\theta - 1) = 3\sin\theta\cos 2\theta$$

$$\frac{dy}{d\theta} = 3\cos\theta - 6\sin^2\theta\cos\theta$$

$$= 3\cos\theta(1-2\sin^2\theta) = 3\cos\theta\cos 2\theta$$

$$\therefore \quad \frac{dy}{dx} = \frac{\dot{y}}{\dot{x}} = \frac{\cos\theta}{\sin\theta} = \cot\theta$$

10. Ans. (d).

Given $\frac{dy}{dx} = 2$

$2y\frac{dy}{dx} = 18$ or $2y = 9 \quad \therefore \quad y = \frac{9}{2}$

and $x = \frac{1}{18}y^2 = \frac{1}{18} \cdot \frac{9}{2} \cdot \frac{9}{2} = \frac{9}{8}$

$\therefore$ Required point is $\left(\frac{9}{8}, \frac{9}{2}\right)$.

11. Ans. (c).

$$y = \frac{\log x}{\log y} \quad \therefore \quad y\log y = \log x$$

Differentiating both sides w.r.t. x,

$$\left(y \cdot \frac{1}{y} + \log y\right)\frac{dy}{dx} = \frac{1}{x} \quad \therefore \quad \frac{dy}{dx} = \frac{1}{x(1+\log y)}.$$

12. Ans. (d).

$\log y = e^x \log x$

$\therefore \quad \frac{1}{y}\frac{dy}{dx} = e^x \log x + e^x . \frac{1}{x} = e^x \left(\log x + \frac{1}{x}\right)$

$\therefore \quad \frac{dy}{dx} = ye^x \left(\log x + \frac{1}{x}\right)$

13. Ans. (c).

$x = e^{y+x} \quad \therefore \quad \log x = (y+x)\log e = y + x$

$\therefore \quad \frac{1}{x} - 1 = \frac{dy}{dx}$ or $\frac{dy}{dx} = \frac{1-x}{x} \to$ (c).

14. Ans. (d).

$\frac{dx}{dy} = \frac{1}{dy/dx} = \frac{1}{y'}$

Differentiate both sides w.r.t. y

$\frac{d^2x}{dy^2} = \frac{d}{dy}\left(\frac{1}{y'}\right) = \frac{d}{dx}\left(\frac{1}{y'}\right)\cdot\frac{dx}{dy}$

$= -\frac{1}{(y')^2}\cdot y''\cdot\frac{1}{y'} = -y''(y')^{-3}$

15. (i) Ans. 1.

Put $x = \tan\theta$.

Then $y = \tan^{-1}[2x/(1-x^2)]$

$= \tan^{-1}[2\tan\theta/(1-\tan^2\theta)]$

$= \tan^{-1}\tan 2\theta = 2\theta$

and $z = \sin^{-1}[2x/(1+x^2)]$

$= \sin^{-1}[2\tan\theta/(1+\tan^2\theta)]$

$= \sin^{-1}(\sin 2\theta) = 2\theta$

$\therefore \quad \frac{dy}{dz} = \frac{dy/d\theta}{dz/d\theta} = \frac{2}{2} = 1.$

(ii) Ans. (c).

Let $y = x^6$ and $z = x^3$.

$\therefore \quad \frac{dy}{dz} = \frac{dy/dx}{dz/dx} = \frac{6x^5}{3x^2} = 2x^3$.

16. Ans. 4.

17. Ans. $1/e$. [See Q. 45 P. 1216-26]

18. Ans. $\frac{12}{9-4x^2}\cos\left[\log\left(\frac{2x+3}{3-2x}\right)\right]$.

[See Q. 47 (a) P. 1214-27]

MISCELLANEOUS EXERCISE

Matching Entries

Match the entries of List-A and List-B.

1.

List-A	List-B
(a) If $y = \sin^{-1}\frac{2x}{1+x^2} + \sec^{-1}\frac{1+x^2}{1-x^2}$, then $\frac{dy}{dx} =$	1. $\frac{y}{x}$
(b) If $y = \tan^{-1}\left[\frac{\sqrt{1+x^2}+\sqrt{1-x^2}}{\sqrt{1+x^2}-\sqrt{1-x^2}}\right]$, then $\frac{dy}{dx} = \ldots$	2. $xy(1+2\log x)$
(c) If $x^y = e^{x-y}$, then $\frac{dy}{dx} = \ldots$	3. $\frac{4}{1+x^2}$
(d) If $x^p y^q = (x+y)^{p+q}$, then $\frac{dy}{dx} = \ldots$	4. $\frac{\log x}{(1+\log x)^2}$
(e) If $y = (x^x)^x$ then $\frac{dy}{dx} = \ldots$	5. $-\frac{x}{\sqrt{1-x^4}}$

2.

List-A	List-B
(a) If $x = t - \frac{1}{t}, y = t + \frac{1}{t}$, then $\frac{dy}{dx} =$	1. $\frac{3}{\sqrt{9-x^2}}$
(b) If $y = \left[\cos^2 \tan^{-1}\sqrt{\frac{1+x}{1-x}}\right]$, then $\frac{dy}{dx} =$	2. $\sin 2y(\cot x - 2\sin 2x)$
(c) If $\sqrt{\tan y} = e^{\cos 2x}\sin x$, then $\frac{dy}{dx} =$	3. $\frac{x}{y}$
(d) If $xy = (x+y)^p$ and $\frac{dy}{dx} = \frac{y}{x}$, then $p =$	4. $\frac{1}{2}$
(e) If $y = \sin^{-1}\left(x - \frac{4}{27}x^3\right)$, then $\frac{dy}{dx} =$	5. 2

3. **List-A** **List-B**

(a) If $x = a\cos t, y = a\sin t$ (p) $y_2 = -\frac{4}{a}$ at $t = \frac{\pi}{3}$

(b) $x = a\cos^3 t, y = a\sin^3 t$ (q) $y_2 = 0$ at $t = \frac{\pi}{6}$

(c) $x = \cos^2 t, y = \sin^2 t$ (r) $y_2 = -\frac{1}{a}$ at $t = \frac{\pi}{2}$

(d) $x = a(t - \sin t), y = a(1 - \cos t)$ (s) $y_2 = \frac{4\sqrt{2}}{3a}$ at $t = \frac{\pi}{4}$

Answers

1. (a) $\to$ 3. **Q. 13 (a) P. 1204**
(b) $\to$ 5. **Q. 10 (a) P. 1204**
(c) $\to$ 4. **Q. 16 P. 1214**
(d) $\to$ 1. **Q. 17 (a) P. 1214**
(e) $\to$ 2. **Q. 8 P. 1214**

2. (a) $\to$ 3. $y^2 - x^2 = 4$ $\therefore$ $\frac{dy}{dx} = \frac{x}{y}$

(b) $\to$ 4. Put $x = \cos 2\theta$

$\therefore$ $y = \cos^2 \tan^{-1} \tan\theta = \cos^2\theta$

$= \frac{1}{2}(1 + \cos 2\theta) = \frac{1}{2}(1 + x)$

$\therefore$ $\frac{dy}{dx} = \frac{1}{2}$

(c) $\to$ 2. Take log

$\therefore$ $\frac{1}{2}\log\tan y = \cos 2x + \log \sin x$

$\therefore$ $\frac{1}{2}\frac{\sec^2 y}{\tan y}\cdot\frac{dy}{dx} = -2\sin 2x + \frac{\cos x}{\sin x}$

or $\frac{1}{\sin 2y}\frac{dy}{dx} = \cot x - 2\sin 2x$ etc.

(d) $\to$ 5.

Take log and differentiate and put $\frac{dy}{dx} = \frac{y}{x}$

(e) $\to$ 1.

Put $x = 3\sin\theta$ $\therefore$ $y = \sin^{-1}\sin 3\theta = 3\theta$

or $y = 3\sin^{-1}\frac{x}{3}$ $\therefore$ $\frac{dy}{dx} = \frac{3}{\sqrt{(9 - x^2)}}$

3. Ans. (a)$\to$ (r), (b)$\to$ (s), (c)$\to$ (q), (d)$\to$ (r)

(a) $x^2 + y^2 = a^2$ $\therefore$ $2x + 2y\,y_1 = 0$ or $y_1 = -\frac{x}{y}$

$\therefore$ $y_2 = -\frac{y\cdot 1 - x\,y_1}{y^2} = -\frac{y - x(-x/y)}{y^2} = -\frac{a^2}{y^3}$

$= -\frac{1}{a\sin^3 t}$

$\therefore$ y_2 at $t = \frac{\pi}{2} = -\frac{1}{a}$ $\therefore$ (a)$\to$ (r)

(b) $\dot{x} = 3a\cos^2 t\sin t, \dot{y} = 3a\sin^2 t\cos t$

$\therefore$ $\frac{dy}{dx} = \frac{\dot{y}}{\dot{x}} = -\tan t$

$\therefore$ $\frac{d^2y}{dx^2} = -\sec^2 t\cdot\frac{dt}{dx} = -\frac{1}{\cos^2 t}\cdot\frac{1}{\dot{x}}$

$= -\frac{1}{\cos^2 t}\cdot\frac{1}{-3a\cos^2 t\sin t}$

$= \frac{1}{3a\cos^4 t\sin t}$. Put $t = \frac{\pi}{4}$

$= \frac{1}{3a}(\sqrt{2})^5 = \frac{4\sqrt{2}}{3a}$

(c) $x + y = a$ $\therefore$ $\frac{dy}{dx} = -1$ and $\frac{d^2y}{dx^2} = 0$ $\therefore$ (c)$\to$ (q)

(d) $\frac{dy}{dx} = \frac{\dot{y}}{\dot{x}} = \frac{a\sin t}{a(1 - \cos t)} = \frac{2\sin\frac{t}{2}\cos\frac{t}{2}}{2\sin^2\frac{t}{2}} = \cot\frac{t}{2}$

$\therefore$ $\frac{d^2y}{dx^2} = -\frac{1}{2}\text{cosec}^2\frac{t}{2}\cdot\frac{dt}{dx}$

$= -\frac{1}{2\sin^2\frac{t}{2}}\cdot\frac{1}{\dot{x}} = -\frac{1}{2\sin^2\frac{t}{2}}\cdot\frac{1}{a(1 - \cos t)}$

$= -\frac{1}{4a\sin^4\frac{t}{2}} = -\frac{1}{4a\left(\frac{1}{\sqrt{2}}\right)^4}$

$= -\frac{1}{a}$ at $t = \frac{\pi}{2}$

$\therefore$ (d)$\to$ (r)

❑

CHAPTER 27

Differential Calculus

Functions

§1. Introduction

Defined functions, Dependent and Independent variables. A function $f(x)$ of x is defined for a certain value of x in its domain provided it attains a **unique** and **definite** value for that value of x.

e.g. $y = \frac{4x}{2x-1}$ is not defined for $x = \frac{1}{2}$ (not definite)

$y = \frac{\sin x}{x}$ is not defined for $x = 0$ (Indeterminate)

$y = \sqrt{3x^2}$ is not defined for any $x \in R$ (not unique)

If $y = f(x)$, then x is called independent variable and y the dependent variable. Just as area of a circle is a function of radius r, *i.e.*

$A = \pi r^2 = f(r)$. Area A is dependent on r.

$\therefore$ r is independent variable and A is dependent.

§ 2. Functions.

(A) Definition : *Let X and Y be two non-empty sets. A subset f of X × Y is called a function from X to Y iff to* **each** $x \in X$, *there exists a* **unique** *y in Y such that* $(x, y) \in f$.

The other terms used for functions are "mappings", "transformations" and "operators". We denote this mapping by

$$f : X \to Y \quad \text{or} \quad X \xrightarrow{f} Y$$

It follows from the above definition that a relation from X to Y is a function from X to Y iff

(i) to each $x \in X$ there exists a $y \in Y$ such that $(x, y) \in f$,

(ii) $(x, y_1) \in f$ and $(x, y_2) \in f \Rightarrow y_1 = y_2$.

The condition (i) ensures that to each x in X, f **associates** an element y in Y and condition (ii) guarantees that y is unique.

We call X, the domain of f and Y the co-domain of f. The unique element y in Y assigned to $x \in X$ is called the **image** of x under f or the **value** of f at x and is denoted by $f(x)$. Also x is called a **pre-image** (or **inverse image**) of y. Note that there may be more than one pre-images of y. The **graph** of f is the subset of $X \times Y$ defined by $\{(x, f(x)) : x \in X\}$. The **range** of f is the set of all images under f and is denoted by $f[X]$. Thus

$$f[X] = \{y \in Y : y = f(x) \text{ for some } x \in X\}$$
$$= \{f(x) : x \in X\}.$$

If $A \subset X$, then the set $\{f(x) : x \in A\}$ is called the image of A under f and is denoted by $f[A]$. If $B \subset Y$; then the set $\{x \in X : f(x) \in B\}$ is called the inverse image of B under f and is denoted by $f^{-1}[B]$.

(B) Equal functions : Two functions $f : X \to Y$ and $g : X \to Y$ are said to be equal iff $f(x) = g(x)$ for every $x \in X$ and we write $f = g$.

(C) Constant functions : A function $f : X \to Y$ is called a constant function if, for some $y_0 \in Y$, we have $f(x) = y_0$ for every $x \in X$.

(D) Identity mapping : Let $I_X : X \to X$ defined by

$$I_X(x) = x \quad \forall \ x \in X$$

Then I_X is called the identity mapping on X.

(E) Inclusion function : If $B \subset A$, then the function

$$i : B \to A : i(b) = b \quad \forall \ b \in B$$

is called the inclusion function.

(F) Many-one, one-one onto and into mappings.

Let $f : X \to Y$.

The mapping f is said to be **many-one** iff two or more different elements in X have the same f-image in Y. The mapping f is said to be **one-one** iff different elements in X have different f-images in Y *i.e.* if $x_1 \neq x_2 \Rightarrow f(x_1) \neq f(x_2)$ or equivalently, $f(x_1) = f(x_2) \Rightarrow x_1 = x_2$. One-one mappings are also called **injection.** The mapping f is said to be **into** if there is **at least** one element in Y which is not the f-image of any element in X. Note that in this case the range of f is a proper subset of Y, that is, $f[X] \subset Y$ and $f[X] \neq Y$. The mapping f is said to be **onto** if **every** element in Y is the f-image of at least one element in X. In this case, the range of f is equal to Y, that is, $f[X] = Y$. Onto mappings are also called **surjection.** One-one and onto mappings are called **bijection.**

(G) **Real valued functions :** If A is any set, then a function from A into R (the set of reals) is a real valued function on A.

We denote the collection of all real valued functions on A by $\mathbf{R}^A$. The collection $\mathbf{R}^A$ inherits an algebraic structure from $\mathbf{R}$ in as much as we can define **addition, multiplication** and **scalar multiplication** as follows :

If $a \in A, r \in \mathbf{R}, f, g \in \mathbf{R}^A$,

then $(f+g)(a) = f(a) + g(a)$,

$(fg)(a) = f(a)\, g(a)$,

$(rf)(a) = r[f(a)]$.

(H) **Inverse Mapping :** Let $f : X \to Y$. In general $f^{-1}[\{b\}]$ where $b \in Y$ will consist of more than one element or might even be the empty set ϕ. Now let f be a one-one mapping and let y be any element of $f[X]$. Then there exists a unique element $x \in X$ such that $y = f(x)$. Thus we define a mapping of $f[X]$ onto X which associates to each $y \in f[X]$ a unique element $x \in X$ such that $y = f(x)$. We denote this mapping of $f[X]$ onto X by f^{-1} and call it **the inverse mapping** of f.

Definition. Let $f : X \to Y$ be a one-one mapping. Then the map

$$f^{-1} : f[X] \to X$$

which associates to each element $y \in f[X]$ the element $x \in X$ such that $f(x) = y$ is called the inverse map of f.

If f is one-one and onto, then f^{-1} is a function from Y onto X.

Note that f^{-1} is always a bijective mapping.

(I) **Product or composition of mappings :** Let X, Y, Z be three sets and let

$$f : X \to Y \text{ and } g : Y \to Z.$$

Then under the map f an element $x \in X$ is mapped to an element $y = f(x) \in Y$ which in turn is mapped by g to an element $z \in Z$ such that $z = g(y) = g[f(x)]$.

Thus we have a rule which assigns to each element $x \in X$ a unique element $z = g(f(x)) \in Z$. Hence we have a mapping of X onto Z. This new mapping is called the composition of mappings f and g and is denoted by $g \circ f$. It is defined by

$$(g \circ f)(x) = g(f(x))$$

It can be shown that if X, Y, Z, W are four sets f, g, h three mappings

$$f : X \to Y, \; g : Y \to Z, \; h : Z \to W,$$

then $(h \circ g) \circ f = h \circ (g \circ f)$

In other words, **the composition of mappings is associative.**

Further *if f, g are one-one onto then $g \circ f$ is also one-one onto, and* $(g \circ f)^{-1} = f^{-1} \circ g^{-1}$.

§3. Illustration and introduction of words, 'one-one', 'many one', 'onto and into'.

Ex. 1. Let A be the set of books in a library and B be the set of certain natural numbers. Let $a, b, c, d, \ldots..$ denote different books and let 240, 320, 108, 50 etc. denote some elements of the set B which correspond to the number of pages in the books.

Now choose f to be the correspondence which assigns to each book the number of pages contained in it *i.e.*, $f : A \to B$.

The following points should be clearly understood.

1. Each book $\in A$ is associated to some number $\in B$ (*i.e.*, the number of pages in that book). This number will be the image of the corresponding book.

2. Two or more books may be associated to the same number $\in B$ (*i.e.*, Two or more of books may have the same number of pages).

In this case it will be termed as many one function or mapping as two or more elements $\in A$ will have the same image $\in B$ or an element $\in B$ will have more than one pre-image in A.

3. No book can be associated to different elements of B, *i.e.*, the same book cannot have different number of pages in it *i.e.* each book is associated to a unique number $\in B$ *i.e.* the image of each and every book is **unique.**

4. If all the books $\in A$ are associated to different numbers $\in B$ *i.e.* all the books have different number of pages *i.e.* all the elements of A have different f images in B or an element of B has only one pre-image in A then this mapping is said to be **one-one** mapping.

5. There may be certain numbers in B which do not represent the number of pages of any of the books $\in A$ then the mapping is said to be **into mapping** *i.e.* f is a mapping of A into B. In other words there is at least one element $\in B$ which is not the image of any element $\in A$ then f is a mapping from A into B. In this case the set of images *i.e.*, range of f is a subset of B.

6. Now suppose each number $\in B$ represents the number of pages of at least one book $\in$ to A then the mapping f is said to be **onto mapping** *i.e.* **f : A 'onto' B.** In this case each and every element of set B is the image of at least one element in A. The set B *i.e.*, co-domain is completely covered by the f images of the domain A and consequently $f(A)$ *i.e.*, the set of images $= B$.

7. **Many-one onto mapping.** When two or more books $\in A$ have the same number of pages *i.e.* the same image $\in B$ (*i.e.* many-one) and also each and every number $\in B$ represent the number of pages of at least one book (*i.e.* onto) then $f : A \to B$ is a many-one onto mapping.

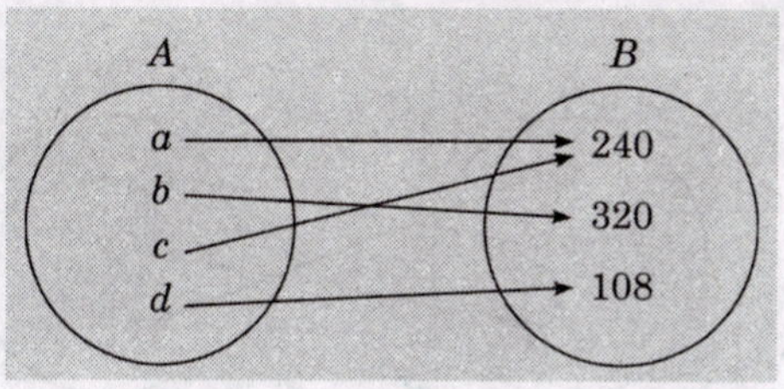

Fig. 1

8. **Many-one into mapping.** When two or more books $\in A$ have the same number of pages *i.e.* the same image $\in B$ (*i.e.* many-one) and there are certain numbers $\in B$ which do not represent the number of pages of any of

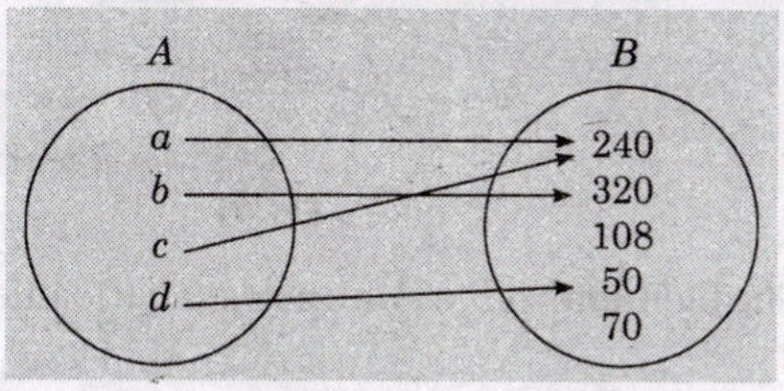

Fig. 2

the books $\in A$ *i.e.* (into) then $f: A \to B$ is a many-one into mapping.

9. **One-one into mapping.** When all the books $\in A$ are having different number of pages *i.e.* they are associated to different numbers $\in B$ (one-one) and there are certain numbers $\in B$ which do not represent the

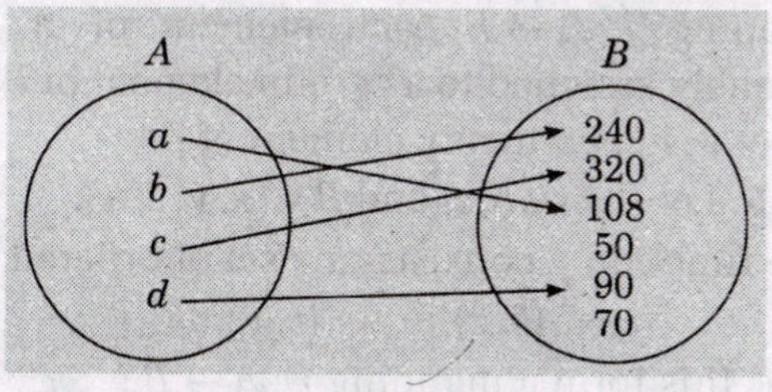

Fig. 3

number of pages of any of the books $\in A$ *i.e.* (into) then $f: A \to B$ is a one-one into mapping.

10. **One-one onto mapping.** When all the books $\in A$ are having different number of pages *i.e.* they are associated to different numbers $\in B$ (one-one) and there is no number $\in B$ which does not represent the number of pages of a book $\in A$ *i.e.* each and every number $\in B$

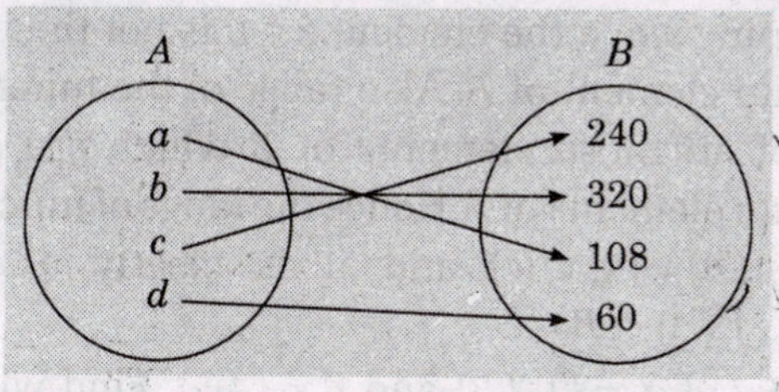

Fig. 4

$\in B$ represents the number of pages of a certain book $\in A$ (onto) then $f: A \to B$ is a one-one onto mapping.

Ex. 2. Let A be the set of students sitting on chairs in a class room and suppose B is the set of chairs in the class

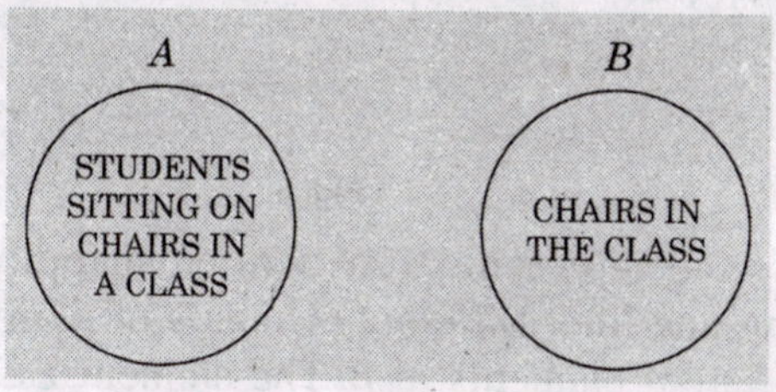

Fig. 5

room. Again let f be the correspondence which associates to each student the chair occupied by him *i.e.*, $f: A \to B$.

1. Each student $\in A$ has a chair $\in B$ to sit on. This chair is the image of the corresponding student $\in A$.
2. Two or more students may occupy the same chair $\in B$. In this case it will be many-one mapping.
3. No student $\in A$ can be associated to two different chairs $\in B$ *i.e.* each student $\in A$ has a unique image in B.
4. If all the students occupy different chairs, it will be one-one mapping.
5. If there be certain chairs which remain unoccupied. In other words there is at least one chair $\in B$ which is not occupied *i.e.* which is not the image of any student $\in A$ it will be into mapping. In this case the range of function f will be the set of all those chairs which are occupied and clearly this set will be a subset of the set B of all the chairs.
6. If all the chairs are occupied *i.e.* some student is sitting on each chair (may be that two students be sitting on the same chair) then it will be an onto mapping.
7. **Many-one onto.** If two or more than two students share a chair (many-one) and no chair is left vacant (onto) then it will be a many-one onto mapping.
8. **Many-one into.** If two or more than two students share a chair (many-one) and some chairs are left vacant (into) then it will be many-one into mapping.
9. **One-one onto.** If all the students occupy different chairs (one-one) and no chair is left vacant (onto) then it will be a one-one onto mapping.
10. **One-one into.** If all the students occupy different chairs (one-one) but some chairs are still left vacant (into), it will be one-one into mapping.

Ex. 3. State whether each of the following diagrams given below define a function or mapping $f: A \to B$ and if so classify it.

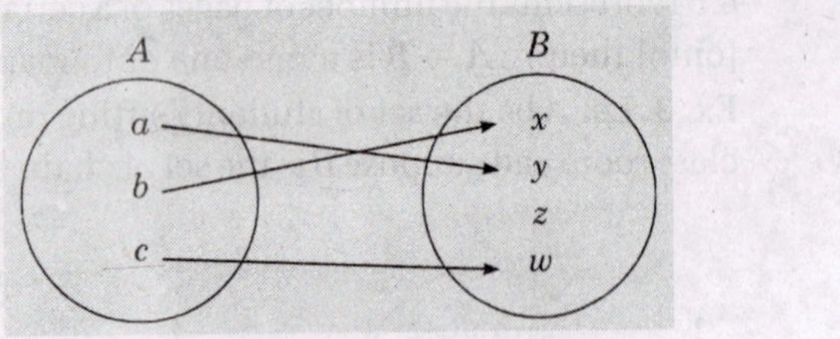

Fig. 6

1. Yes, it represents function or mapping which is **one-one into.** Different elements of A are assigned to different elements of B. The element $z \in B$ is not the image of any element of A.
2. No, it does not represent a mapping as the element $b \in A$ is not assigned to any element of B.

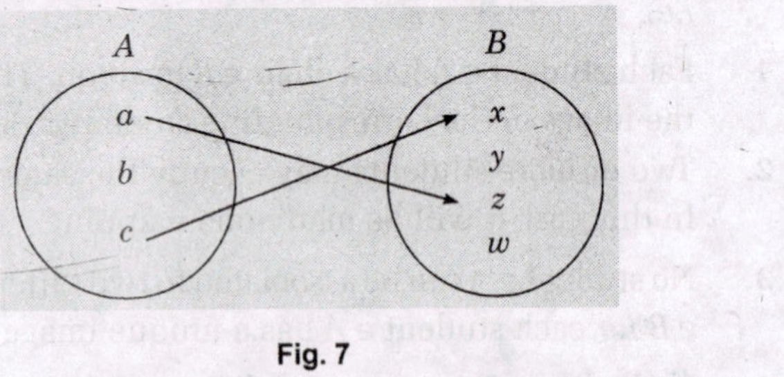

Fig. 7

3. Yes, it represents a mapping which is many-one onto. The elements a and $d \in A$ are assigned to the same element $z \in B$. Also there is no element of B which is not the image of a certain element or elements belonging to A.

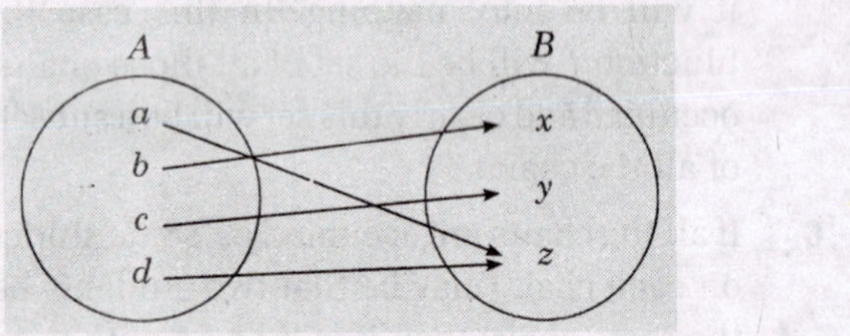

Fig. 8

4. No, it does not represent a mapping because in a mapping $f : A \to B$ each element of A is assigned to a unique element of B. Here $a \in A$ is assigned to both x and $z \in B$ and hence not unique.

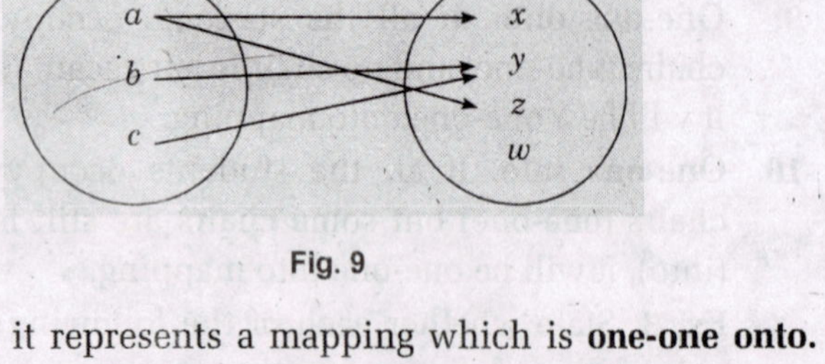

Fig. 9

5. Yes, it represents a mapping which is **one-one onto.** Different elements of A are assigned to different elements of B. Also there is no element of B which is not the image of a certain element of A. **The number of elements in A and B are the same.**

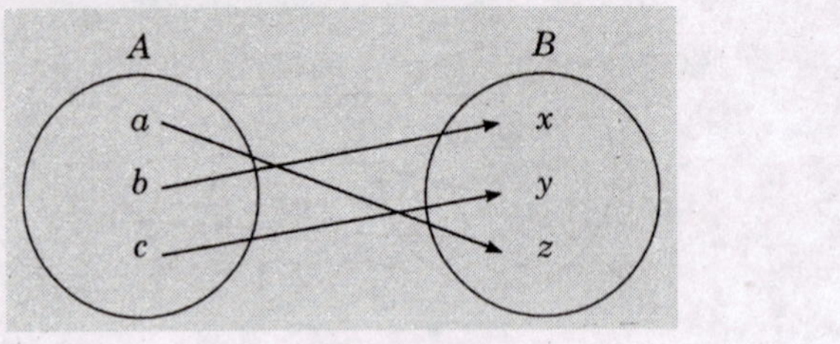

Fig. 10

6. Yes, it represents a mapping which is **many-one into.**

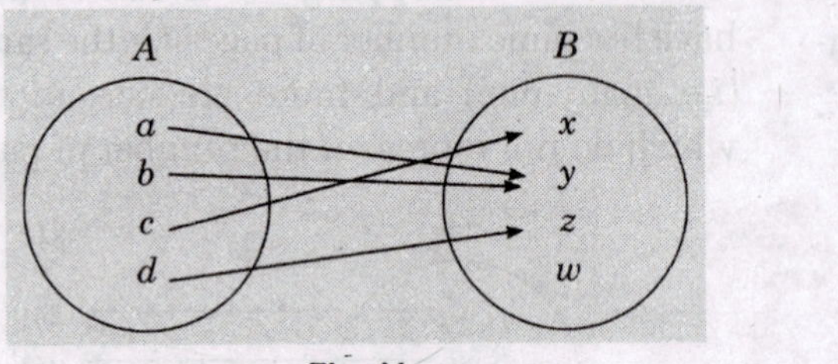

Fig. 11

The elements $a, b \in A$ are asisgned to same element y of B.

Also the element $w \in B$ is not the image of any element $\in A$.

Ex. 4. Let $A = (1, 2, 3)$, $B = (1, 2, 3, 4, 5, 6, 7, 8)$.
If f assigns to each member of A its square then will f be a mapping from A to B.

Sol. $1 \in A$ and $1^2 = 1 \in B$, $2 \in A$ and $2^2 = 4 \in B$.

$3 \in A$ but $3^2 = 9 \notin B$

Hence f is not a mapping from A and B because for a mapping $f : A \to B$ each element of A should be uniquely assigned to a certain element of B. Here $3 \in A$ is not assigned to any element of B.

Ex. 5. Let $A = (a, b, c)$ and $B = (x, y, z, w)$.
The function f consists of a set of ordered pairs

$$(a, x), (b, z), (b, w), (c, y).$$

Does this form a mapping $f : A \to B$?

Sol. No. It is not a mapping because the ordered pairs (b, z) and (b, w) suggest that the element $b \in A$ have two images z and $w \in B$ and for a mapping $f : A \to B$ each element of A should have a unique image $\in B$. If we eliminate the ordered pair (b, z), then $f = [(a, x), (b, w), (c, y)]$

It will be a mapping since each element in A is associated to a unique element $\in B$ *i.e.*, $a \to x, b \to w, c \to y$. Also it is one-one mapping but it is into mapping since the element $z \in B$ is not the image of a certain element of A. Also range of the function is the set of all those elements of B which are images of certain elements of A. Hence the range of function is the set $f(A) = (x, y, w)$ and it is clearly a subset of B *i.e.*, $f(A) \subset B$.

Ex. 6. Let $X = \{1, 2, 3\}$ and $Y = \{4, 5\}$. Find whether the following subsets of $X \times Y$ are functions from X to Y or not.

(i) $f_1 = \{(1, 4), (1, 5), (2, 4), (3, 5)\}$,
(ii) $f_2 = \{(1, 4), (2, 4), (3, 4)\}$,
(iii) $f_3 = \{(1, 4), (2, 5), (3, 5)\}$
(iv) $f_4 = \{(1, 4), (2, 5)\}$.

Sol. (i) No, since (1, 4) and (1, 5) are distinct members of f_1 which have the same first co-ordinate, that is, the element 1 has two distinct images 4 and 5 under f_1.

(ii) Yes, since each member of X has a unique image in Y under f_2. Note that the mapping is **many-one into.** $5 \in Y$ does not have a pre-image.

(iii) Yes. This mapping is **many-one-onto.**

(iv) No, since there is no image of 3 under f_4.

Ex. 7. Let **R** be the set of all real numbers and let $A = \{0, 1\}$. Let

$f : \mathbf{R} \to A$ defined by

$$f(x) = \begin{cases} 0 \text{ when } x \text{ is rational} \\ 1 \text{ when } x \text{ is irrational} \end{cases}$$

Then f is a many-one into function. Here $f[\mathbf{R}] = A$.

Since $\frac{1}{2}$ is rational, we have $f\left(\frac{1}{2}\right) = 0$.

Similarly $f(2) = 0, f\left(\frac{4}{5}\right) = 0$ etc.

Since $\pi, e, \sqrt{2}, \sqrt{5}$ etc. are irrational numbers, we have

$$f(\pi) = f(e) = f(\sqrt{2}) = f\sqrt{(5)} = 1 \text{ etc.}$$

Ex. 8. Let $f : \mathbf{R} \to \mathbf{R}$ be defined by

$$f(x) = x^2 \quad \forall \ x \in \mathbf{R}$$

Then f is a many-one into mapping.

Here $f(a) = a^2, f(-a) = a^2$

where a is a non-zero real number. Also

$$f(0) = 0.$$

Hence $f[\mathbf{R}] = R_+ \cup (0)$

i.e. the range of f consists of all the positive real numbers together with zero

$$f^{-1}[\{1, 2, 3\}] = \{-1, 1, -\sqrt{2}, \sqrt{2}, -\sqrt{3}, \sqrt{3}\}$$

$$f^{-1}[\{-1, -2\}] = \phi \text{ etc.}$$

Ex. 9. Let $f : \mathbf{R} \to \mathbf{R}$ be defined by

$$f(x) = x^3 \quad \forall \ x \in \mathbf{R}.$$

Then f is one-one onto. It is one-one since different real numbers have different images under f, that is

$$x, y \in \mathbf{R} \text{ and } x \neq y \Rightarrow f(x) \neq f(y)$$

It is onto since for each y in **R** there exists some x in **R** such that $x^3 = y$.

Thus $f^{-1}[\{2\}] = 2^{1/3}$ etc.

§ 4. Composite Functions

$$(fog)\,x = f[g(x)], \quad (gof)\,x = g[f(x)]$$

Properties of functions.

(a) Linear property for algebraic function.

If $y = f(x)$ is a linear algebraic function of the form $y = mx + c = f(x)$

then $f(ax + b) = af(x) + f(b)$

In particular $f(x + z) = f(x) + f(z)$

$f(x - z) = f(x) - f(z)$

(b) Logarithmic and Exponential functions.

We know that $\log(pq) = \log p + \log q$

and $a^{p+q} = a^p \cdot a^q$

Hence for logarithmic functions

$f(xy) = f(x) + f(y)$

For exponential functions $f(x + y) = f(x)\,f(y)$

(c) $\log_a x$ is defined if both x and a are +ive and $x \neq 0$ and $a \neq 1$.

Also $\log_a x = y$, then $x = a^y$ exponential form.

***Exponential function is always positive.**

* $\log_a x > \log_a y \Leftrightarrow$ **$x > y$ if $a > 1$**

$\Leftrightarrow$ **$x < y$ if $a < 1$**

Equality of functions.

$f = g$ if $f(x) = g(x) \quad \forall \ x$

Problem Set (1)

Functions, Composite functions.

1. (a) If $f(x) = ax^2 + bx + c$, find $f(0)$, $f(a)$ and $f(b)$.

(b) Let $f(x) = \dfrac{4^x}{4^x + 2}$, prove that $f(x) + f(1 - x) = 1$ and hence show that

$$f\left(\frac{1}{81}\right) + f\left(\frac{2}{81}\right) + \ldots + f\left(\frac{80}{81}\right) = 40.$$

2. (a) If $f(x) = x^2 - 1/x^2$, prove that $f(x) = -f(1/x)$.

(b) If $y = f(x) = (x + 2)/(x - 1)$, then show that $x = f(y)$.

(c) Suppose $f(x) = (x + 1)^2$ for $x \geq -1$. If $g(x)$ is the function whose graph is the reflection of the graph of $f(x)$ with respect to the line $y = x$, then $g(x)$ equals

(a) $-\sqrt{x} - 1, x \geq 0$ (b) $\dfrac{1}{(x+1)^2}, x > -1$

(c) $\sqrt{x + 1}, x \geq -1$ (d) $\sqrt{x} - 1, x \geq 0$

(I.I.T. Sc. 2002)

3. Let $f(x) = \begin{cases} 1, \text{if } x \text{ is a rational number} \\ 0, \text{if } x \text{ is an irrational number} \end{cases}$

be a function from **R** to **R** where **R** is the set of real numbers. Find

(i) $f(1/3)$ (ii) $f(\sqrt{7})$

(iii) $(f \circ f)(1 \cdot 4327)$ (iv) $(f \circ f)(\sqrt{3})$.

4. (a)* If $f(x) = \log_e\left(\frac{1+x}{1-x}\right)$, then show that

$$f(p) + f(q) = f\left(\frac{p+q}{1+pq}\right) \text{ and } f\left(\frac{2x}{1+x^2}\right) = 2f(x)$$

(M.P.C.E.E. 1999)

(b) If $y = f(x) = \frac{px+q}{rx-p}$, then show that $f(y) = x$

5. (a) Given the function $f(x) = (a^x + a^{-x})/2, (a > 0)$. Show that $f(x+y) + f(x-y) = 2f(x)f(y)$.

(b) If $f : (-1, 1) \to B$ be a function defined by $f(x) = \tan^{-1}\frac{2x}{1-x^2}$, then f is both one-one and onto when B is the interval :

(a) $\left[-\frac{\pi}{2}, \frac{\pi}{2}\right]$ (b) $\left]-\frac{\pi}{2}, \frac{\pi}{2}\right[$

(c) $\left]0, \frac{\pi}{2}\right[$ (d) $\left[0, \frac{\pi}{2}\right[$ **(AIEEE 2005)**

6. (a)* If $f(x) = \cos(\log x)$, then evaluate $f(x)f(y) - \frac{1}{2}[f(x/y) + f(xy)]$. **(Karnataka CEE 1999)**

(b) If $f(x) = \cos(\log x)$, then

$$f(x^2)f(y^2) - \frac{1}{2}\left[f\left(\frac{x^2}{2}\right) + f(x^2y^2)\right]$$

has the value

(a) -2 (b) -1

(c) $\frac{1}{2}$ (d) none of these **(MNR 1992)**

(c) If $f(x) = \sin(\log x)$, then

$$f(xy) + f\left(\frac{x}{y}\right) - 2f(x)\cos(\log y) = 0$$

Is this statement true ?

7. (a) Given the function

$$f(x) = \begin{cases} 3^{-x} - 1 & \text{for } -1 \le x < 0, \\ \tan(x/2) & \text{for } 0 \le x < \pi, \\ x/(x^2-2) & \text{for } \pi \le x \le 6. \end{cases}$$

Find $f(-1), f(\pi/6), f(2\pi/3), f(4), f(6)$.

(b) $f : R \to R$ is defined as under :

$$f(x) = \begin{cases} x-4, & x < -9 \\ x^2 - 1, & x \in [-9, 9] \\ 2x+5, & x > 9 \end{cases}$$

Evaluate $f(-15), f(3), f(12)$ and $(f \circ f)5$.

8. (a)* If $f(x) = \cos[\pi^2]x + \cos[-\pi^2]x$, where $[x]$ stands for the greatest integer function, then evaluate $f(\pi/2), f(\pi), f(-\pi)$ and $f(\pi/4)$. **(I.I.T. 1991)**

(b) The graph of the function $\cos x \cos(x+2) - \cos^2(x+1)$ is

(i) a straight line passing through $(0, -\sin^2 1)$ with slope 2.

(ii) a straight line passing through (0, 0)

(iii) a parabola with vertex $(1, -\sin^2 1)$

(iv) a straight line passing through the point $\left(\frac{\pi}{2}, -\sin^2 1\right)$ and parallel to the x-axis.

(I.I.T. Re-ex. 1997)

9. (a) Find $\phi[\psi(x)]$ and $\psi[\phi(x)]$ if $\phi(x) = x^2 + 1$ and $\psi(x) = 3^x$.

(b) If $f(x) = \log_e x$ and $g(x) = e^x$, then show that $(f \circ g)\,x = (g \circ f)\,x = x$

(c) Let $f(x) = [x]$ and $g(x) = |x|$, then evaluate the following :

(i) $(g \circ f)\left(\frac{5}{3}\right) - (f \circ g)\left(-\frac{5}{3}\right)$

(ii) $(g \circ f)\left(\frac{5}{3}\right) - (f \circ g)\left(\frac{5}{3}\right)$

(iii) $(f + 2g)(-1)$

10. (a) If $f(x) = (x-1)/x$ for all real numbers except $x = 0$ and $g(u) = u^2 + 1$ for all real numbers u, find (i) $g[f(1)]$ and (ii) $f[g(-1)]$.

(b)* If $f(x) = (a - x^n)^{1/n}$ where $a > 0$ and n is a +ive integer, then show that $f[f(x)] = x$.

(c) If $f(x) = \sin^2 x + \sin^2\left(x + \frac{\pi}{3}\right) + \cos x \cos\left(x + \frac{\pi}{3}\right)$ and $g(5/4) = 1$ then prove that $(go\,f)\,x = 1$. **(I.I.T. 1996)**

(d) If $f(x) = \cos^2 x + \cos^2\left(\frac{\pi}{3} + x\right) + \cos x \cos\left(\frac{\pi}{3} + x\right)$, then $f(x)$ is :

(a) odd (b) even

(c) periodic (d) $f(0) = f(1)$

11. (a) Let $f(x) = \frac{\alpha x}{x+1}, x \ne -1$. Then, for what value of α is $f\{f(x)\} = x$?

(a) $\sqrt{2}$ (b) $-\sqrt{2}$

(c) 1 (d) -1 **(I.I.T. Sc. 2001)**

(b) Let $g(x) = 1 + x - [x]$ and

$$f(x) = \begin{cases} -1, & x < 0 \\ 0, & x = 0. \\ 1, & x > 0 \end{cases}$$

Then for all x, $f\{g(x)\}$ is equal to

(a) x (b) 1

(c) $f(x)$ (d) $g(x)$ **(I.I.T. Sc. 2001)**

(c) Let $F(x) = \left(f\left(\frac{x}{2}\right)\right)^2 + \left(g\left(\frac{x}{2}\right)\right)^2$. $F(5) = 5$ and $f''(x) = -f(x), g(x) = f'(x)$, then $F(10)$ is equal to :

(a) 5 (b) 10

(c) 0 (d) 3 **(I.I.T. 2006)**

12. (a) If $f(x) = \frac{x^2+2}{x-1}$ when $x < 3$ and $f(x) = \frac{\sin x}{x-3}$

when $x > 3$, for what values of x is the function not defined ?

(b) Rewrite $|x-1| < 3$ in the form $a \le x \le b$.

(c) If $x^2 - 5x + 4 \ge 0$ and $x^2 - 2x - 3 \le 0$ hold simultaneously, then show that $-1 \le x \le 1$.

13. (a)* A cubic expression $f(x)$ satisfies the condition $f(x) + f\left(\frac{1}{x}\right) = f(x)\, f\left(\frac{1}{x}\right)$, then prove that $f(x) = 1 + x^3$ or $1 - x^3$.

If $f(3) = 28$ then prove that $f(2) = 9$.

(b) Let $f(x)$ be a polynomial function satisfying $f(x) f(y) = f(x) + f(y) + f(xy) - 2\ \forall\ x, y \in R$
If $f(2) = 5$ then prove that $f(5) = 26$.

(c) If for non-zero x, $af(x) + bf\left(\frac{1}{x}\right) = \frac{1}{x} - 5$ where $a \ne b$ then find $f(x)$. **(I.I.T. 1995)**

(d) If $2f(x^2) + 3f\left(\frac{1}{x^2}\right) = x^2 - 1$ for all $x \in R - \{0\}$, then $f(x^2)$ is equal to

(a) $\frac{1-x^4}{5x^2}$ (b) $\frac{(1-x^2)(3+2x^2)}{5x^2}$

(c) $\frac{(1-x^2)(3-2x^2)}{3x^2}$ (d) none of these

14. (a) If $f(x) = |x-2|$ and $g(x) = f[f(x)]$, then for $x > 2$, $g'(x) = \ldots\ldots\ldots\ldots$ **(I.I.T. 1990)**

(b) If ϕ is the inverse function of f and

$$f'(x) = \frac{1}{1 + x^n}, \text{ then prove that}$$

$$\phi'(x) = 1 + [\phi(x)]^n$$

(c) If $g(f(x)) = |\sin x|$ and $f(g(x)) = (\sin \sqrt{x})^2$, then

(a) $f(x) = \sin^2 x, g(x) = \sqrt{x}$

(b) $f(x) = \sin x, g(x) = |x|$

(c) $f(x) = x^2, g(x) = \sin \sqrt{x}$

(d) f and g cannot be determined. **(I.I.T. 1998)**

(d) If $f(x) = \frac{ax+b}{cx+d}$ and $(fof)\ x = x$, then so that $d = -a$.

15.* If $f(x) = \begin{cases} x^2 - 4x + 3, & x < 2 \\ x - 4, & x \ge 2 \end{cases}$

$g(x) = \begin{cases} x - 3, & x < 3 \\ x^2 + 2x + 2, & x \ge 3 \end{cases}$

Determine $f + g$ and $\frac{f}{g}$.

16. (a) Prove that the inverse of the function

$$y = \frac{10^x - 10^{-x}}{10^x + 10^{-x}} + 1 \text{ is } y = \frac{1}{2}\log_{10}\frac{x}{2-x}$$

(b) A real valued function is defined as $f(x) = (x+1)^2 - 1, x \ge -1$ then the set $A = \{x : f(x) = f^{-1}(x)\}$ is equal to $\{0, -1\}$.

(c) Prove that the inverse of the function

$$f(x) = \frac{e^x - e^{-x}}{e^x + e^{-x}} + 2 \text{ is given by } \log_e\left(\frac{x-1}{3-x}\right)^{1/2}$$

(Kurukshetra 1996)

(d) Let $f(x) = \frac{e^x - e^{-x}}{2}$ and if $f[g(x)] = x$ then prove that

$$g\left[\frac{e^{1002} - 1}{2e^{501}}\right] \text{ is equal to } 501.$$

(e) Which of the following functions have inverse defined on the ranges :

(a) $f(x) = x^2, x \in \mathbf{R}$ (b) $f(x) = x^3, x \in \mathbf{R}$

(c) $f(x) = e^x, x \in \mathbf{R}$ (d) $f(x) = \sin x,\ 0 < x < 2\pi$

Good question for clarity on composite functions.

17.* Let $f(x) = \tan x, x \in \left]-\frac{\pi}{2}, \frac{\pi}{2}\right[$ and $g(x) = \sqrt{1 - x^2}$.

Determine $f \circ g$ and $g \circ f$.

18. (a) Given $A = \{2, 3, 4\}$, $B = \{2, 5, 6, 7\}$.

Construct an example of each of the following

(i) an injective mapping from A to B.

(ii) a mapping from A to B which is not injective.

(iii) a mapping from B to A.

(b) If $A = \{1, 2, 3, 4\}$, then which of the following are functions from A to itself ?

(a) $f_1 = \{(x, y) : y = x + 1\}$

(b) $f_2 = \{(x, y) : x + y > 4\}$

(c) $f_3 = \{(x, y) : y < x\}$

(d) $f_4 = \{(x, y) : x + y = 5\}$

19. Suppose f is the collection of all ordered pairs of real numbers and $x = 6$ is the first element of some ordered pair in f. Suppose the vertical line through $x = 6$ intersects the graph of f twice. Is f a function ? Why or why not ?

20. (a) Is $g = \{(1, 1), (2, 3), (3, 5), (4, 7)\}$ a function ? If this is described by the formula $g(x) = \alpha x + \beta$, then what values should be assigned to α and β ?

(b) Is the function $f : \mathbf{N} \to \mathbf{N}$ ($\mathbf{N}$ is set of the natural numbers) defined by $f(n) = 2n + 3$ for all $n \in \mathbf{N}$ surjective ?

21. (a) Are the following sets of ordered pairs functions ? If so, examine whether the mapping is surjective or injective :

(i) $\{(x, y) : x$ is a person, y is the mother of $x\}$

(ii) $\{(a, b) : a$ is a person, b is an ancestor of $a\}$

(b) If the mappings f and g are given by

$f = \{(1, 2), (3, 5), (4, 1)\}$,

$g = \{(2, 3), (5, 1), (1, 3)\}$,

then write down pairs in the mappings $f \circ g$ and $g \circ f$.

22. (a) Let $R = \{(1,3), (4,2), (2,4), (2,3), (3,1)\}$ be a relation on the set $A = \{1, 2, 3, 4\}$. The relation R is :

(a) function (b) transitive
(c) not symmetric (d) reflexive **(AIEEE 2004)**

(b) If $f : R \to S$ defined by $f(x) = \sin x - \sqrt{3} \cos x + 1$ is onto, then the interval of S is :

(a) $[0, 3]$ (b) $[-1, 1]$
(c) $[0, 1]$ (d) $[-1, 3]$ **(AIEEE 2004)**

23. (a) If the functions $f : \mathbf{R} \to \mathbf{R}$ and $g : \mathbf{R} \to \mathbf{R}$ be defined by $f(x) = 2x + 1$, $g(x) = x^2 - 2$. Find the formulae for $g \circ f$ and $f \circ g$.

(b) If R is a set of real numbers and $f : R \to R$ is given by the relation $f(x) = \sin x$, $x \in R$ and mapping $g : R \to R$ by the relation $g(x) = x^2$, $x \in R$, then prove that $f \circ g \neq g \circ f$.

24. (a) Let $f : \mathbf{R} \to \mathbf{R}$, $g : \mathbf{R} \to R$ be two functions given by $f(x) = 2x - 3$, $g(x) = x^3 + 5$. Then $(fog)^{-1}(x)$ is equal to

(a) $\left(\dfrac{x+7}{2}\right)^{1/3}$ (b) $\left(x - \dfrac{7}{2}\right)^{1/3}$
(c) $\left(\dfrac{x-2}{7}\right)^{1/3}$ (d) $\left(\dfrac{x-7}{2}\right)^{1/3}$

(b) If $f(x) = \dfrac{3x+2}{5x-3}$, then

(a) $f^{-1}(x) = f(x)$ (b) $f^{-1}(x) = -f(x)$
(c) $(fof)(x) = -x$ (d) $f^{-1}(x) = -\dfrac{1}{19} f(x)$

25. Given $f(x) = \log\left(\dfrac{1+x}{1-x}\right)$ and $g(x) = \dfrac{3x + x^3}{1 + 3x^2}$, then $fog(x)$ equals

(a) $-f(x)$ (b) $3f(x)$
(c) $[f(x)]^3$ (d) none of these

26. (a) Let $f : \mathbf{R} \to \mathbf{R}$ be defined by $f(x) = \cos(5x + 2)$. Is f invertible ?

(b) A mapping is defined as $f : \mathbf{R} \to \mathbf{R}$, $f(x) = \cos x$. Show that it is neither one-one nor surjective.

(c) $f : [0, \infty) \to [0, \infty)$ $f(x) = \dfrac{x}{1+x}$ is

(a) one-one and onto
(b) one-one but not onto
(c) onto but not one-one
(d) neither one-one nor onto **(Screening 2003)**

27. (a) Let $\mathbf{C}$ be the set of complex numbers. Prove that the mapping $f : \mathbf{C} \to \mathbf{R}$ given by $f(z) = |z|, z \in \mathbf{C}$ is neither one-one nor onto.

(b) Let $A = \mathbf{R} - \{3\}$, $B = \mathbf{R} - \{1\}$. Let $f : A \to B$ be defined by $f(x) = (x-2)/(x-3)$. Is f bijective ? Give reasons.

(c) For real x, let $f(x) = x^3 + 5x + 1$, then

(a) f is neither one-one nor onto $\mathbf{R}$
(b) f is one-one but not onto $\mathbf{R}$
(c) f is onto $\mathbf{R}$ but not one-one
(d) f is one-one and onto $\mathbf{R}$ **(AIEEE 2009)**

28. (a) Let $f : \mathbf{R} \to \mathbf{R}$ be defined by $f(x) = 3x + 4, x \in \mathbf{R}$. Is f invertible ? If so, give a formula for f^{-1}.

(M.N.R. 1993)

(b) If $f : \mathbf{R} \to \mathbf{R}$ is defined by $f(x) = x^2 + 1$, then values of $f^{-1}(17)$ and $f^{-1}(-3)$ respectively are

(a) $\phi, \{4, -4\}$ (b) $\{3, -3\}, \phi$
(c) $\phi, \{3, -3\}$ (d) $\{4, -4\}, \phi$

29. (a) The composite mapping $f \circ g$, of the maps $f : R \to R$, $f(x) = \sin x$; $g : R \to R$, $g(x) = x^2$, is

(a) $\sin x + x^2$ (b) $(\sin x)^2$
(c) $\sin x^2$ (d) $\dfrac{\sin x}{x^2}$

(b) Let A and B be two sets with a finite number of elements. Assume that there is injective mapping from A to B and that there is an injective mapping from B to A. Prove that there is a bijective mapping from A to B.

30. Which of the four statements given below, is different from the other ?

(a) $f : A \to B$
(b) $f : x \to f(x)$
(c) f is a mapping of A into B
(d) f is a function of A into B

31. If $A = \{x : -1 \le x \le 1\} = B$. Discuss the following functions w.r.t. one-one onto bijective and write their characteristics.

(a) $f(x) = \dfrac{x}{2}$ (b) $g(x) = |x|$
(c) $h(x) = x|x|$ (d) $k(x) = x^2$
(e) $l(x) = \sin \pi x$

32. (a) Set A has 3 elements and set B has 4 elements. The number of injections that can be defined from A to B is

(a) 144 (b) 12
(c) 24 (d) 64 **(EAMCET 1992)**

(b) The number of surjections from $A = \{1, 2, \dots n\}$, $n \ge 2$, onto $B = \{a, b\}$ is

(a) ${}^nP_2$ (b) $2^n - 2$
(c) $2^n - 1$ (d) none of these

(EAMCET 1992)

(c) Let $E = \{1, 2, 3, 4\}$ and $F\{1, 2\}$. Then the number of onto functions from E to F is

(a) 14 (b) 16
(c) 6 (d) 4 **(I.I.T. Sc. 2001)**

33. (a) Let A and B be two finite sets having m and n elements respectively. Then the total number of mappings from A to B is

(a) mn (b) 2^{mn}

(c) m^n (d) n^m

(b) The total number of injective mappings from a set with m elements to a set with n elements, $m \le n$, is

(a) m^n (b) n^m

(c) $\frac{n!}{(n-m)!}$ (d) $n!$

(c) Let A be a set containing 10 distinct elements, then the total number of distinct functions from A to A is

(a) 101 (b) 10^{10}

(c) 2^{10} (d) $2^{10}-1$ **(M.N.R. 1992)**

34. (a) If the mappings $f: A \to B$ and $g: B \to C$ are both bijective, then the mapping $g\,o\,f: A \to C$ is also bijective.

(a) True (b) False

(b) Let $A = \{0, 1\}$ and N the set of all natural numbers. Then the mapping $f: N \to A$ defined by $f(2n-1) = 0, f(2n) = 1 \;\forall\; n \in N$ is many-one onto.

(a) True (b) False

35. (a) Let f be an injective map with domain $\{x, y, z\}$ and range $\{1, 2, 3\}$ such that exactly one of the following statements is correct and the remaining are false : $f(x) = 1, f(y) \ne 1, f(z) \ne 2$. The value of $f^{-1}(1)$ is

(a) x (b) y

(c) z (d) none of these

(Roorkee 1996)

(b) Given $X = \{1, 2, 3, 4\}$, find all one-one, onto mappings $f: X \to X$ such that $f(1) = 1, f(2) \ne 2$ and $f(4) \ne 4$. **(Roorkee 2000)**

36. (a) Let $E = \{1, 2, 3, 4\}$ and $F = \{1, 2\}$. Then the number of onto functions from E to F is

(a) 14 (b) 16

(c) 6 (d) 4 **(I.I.T. Sc. 2001)**

(b) Let function $f: \mathbf{R} \to \mathbf{R}$ be defined by $f(x) = 2x + \sin x$ for $x \in \mathbf{R}$. Then f is

(a) one-to-one and into

(b) one-to-one but NOT onto

(c) onto but NOT one-to-one

(d) neither one-to-one nor onto **(I.I.T. Sc. 2002)**

37. (a) If the function f and g are defined from the set of real numbers R to R such that $f(x) = e^x, g(x) = 3x - 2$ then find functions fog and gof. Also find the domains of functions $(fog)^{-1}$ and $(gof)^{-1}$. **(Roorkee 1998)**

(b) If $f(x) = \sin x + \cos x, g(x) = x^2 - 1$, then $g(f(x))$ is invertible in domain

(a) $\left[-\frac{\pi}{2}, 0\right]$ (b) $\left[-\frac{\pi}{4}, \frac{\pi}{4}\right]$

(c) $\left[-\frac{\pi}{2}, \pi\right]$ (d) $(0, \pi)$

(Screening 2004)

38. (a) If the function $f: [1, \infty] \to [1, \infty)$ is defined by $f(x) = 2^{x(x-1)}$, then $f^{-1}(x)$ is

(a) $\left(\frac{1}{2}\right)^{x(x-1)}$

(b) $\left(\frac{1}{2}\right)(1 + \sqrt{1 + 4\log_2 x})$

(c) $\left(\frac{1}{2}\right)(1 - \sqrt{1 + 4\log_2 x})$

(d) not defined. **(I.I.T. Sc. 1999)**

(b) If $f: [1, \infty[\to [2, \infty[$ is given by $f(x) = x + \frac{1}{x}$ then $f^{-1}(x)$ equals

(a) $\frac{x + \sqrt{x^2 - 4}}{2}$ (b) $\frac{x}{1 + x^2}$

(c) $\frac{x - \sqrt{x^2 - 4}}{2}$ (d) $1 + \sqrt{x^2 - 4}$

(I.I.T. Sc. 2001)

39. (a)* If $f(x) = \frac{x}{\sqrt{1 + x^2}}$ then show that

$$(f\,o\,f\,o\,f)\,x = \frac{x}{\sqrt{(1 + 3x^2)}}.$$

(b)* A function f satisfies the condition $f\left(x + \frac{1}{x}\right) = x^2 + \frac{1}{x^2}, x \ne 0$. Determine it.

(c) If $f(x) = \begin{cases} 1 + x; & 0 \le x \le 2 \\ 3 - x; & 2 < x \le 3 \end{cases}$

then determine $(f\,o\,f)\,x$.

40. (a) If $f: R \to R$ is given by

$$f(x) = \frac{4^x}{4^x + 2} \;\forall\; x \in R$$

then prove that $f(x) + f(1 - x) = 1$.

Also find the value of

$$f\left(\frac{1}{99}\right) + f\left(\frac{2}{99}\right) + \ldots + f\left(\frac{98}{99}\right)$$

(b) Let $f: N \to R$ be a function satisfying the following conditions.

(a) $f(1) = 1$ and

(b) $f(1) + 2f(2) + \ldots n\,f(n) = n(n+1)\,f(n)$ for $n \ge 2$.

Prove that $f(49) = \frac{1}{98}$.

Solutions to Problem Set (1)

1. (a) $f(0) = a.0 + b.0 + c = c$.

$f(a) = a.a^3 + b.a + c = a^4 + ab + c$.

$f(b) = a.b^2 + b.b + c = ab^2 + b^2 + c$.

(b) $f(x) = \dfrac{4^x}{4^x + 2}$

$\therefore \quad f(1-x) = \dfrac{4^{1-x}}{4^{1-x}+2} = \dfrac{\frac{4}{4^x}}{\frac{4}{4^x}+2}$

or $f(1-x) = \dfrac{2}{4^x+2} \quad \therefore \quad f(x) + f(1-x) = 1$

Combining the 80 terms in 40 pairs equidistant from the beginning and end.

If $x = \dfrac{80}{81}$, then $1 - x = \dfrac{1-80}{81} = \dfrac{1}{81}$

$\therefore \quad f(x) + f(1-x) = 1$

Thus each of 40 pairs will be 1 and hence the sum is 40.

2. (a) $f(1/x) = (1/x)^2 - 1/(1/x)^2$

$= 1/x^2 - x^2 = -f(x)$

(b) Do yourself.

(c) Ans. (d). $y = (x+1)^2 \ (x \geq -1)$.

Its reflection $g(x)$ in the line $y = x$ is given by

$x = (y+1)^2$ or $y + 1 = \pm\sqrt{x}$

or $y = g(x) = \sqrt{x} - 1 \ (x \geq 0)$

3. (i) Since $\frac{1}{3}$ is a rational number by definition of f, we have $f\left(\frac{1}{3}\right) = 1$.

(ii) Since $\sqrt{7}$ is an irrational number, we have by definition of f

$f(\sqrt{7}) = 0$.

(iii) $(f \circ f)(1 \cdot 4327) = f[f(1 \cdot 4327)]$

$= f(1)$ $\quad [\because 1 \cdot 4327$ is rational$]$

$= 1$ since 1 is rational.

(iv) $(f \circ f)(\sqrt{3}) = f[f(\sqrt{3})] = f(0)$ $\quad [\because \sqrt{3}$ is irrational$]$

$= 1$ $\quad [\because 0$ is rational$]$

4. (a) L.H.S. $= \log \dfrac{1+p}{1-p} \cdot \dfrac{1+q}{1-q}$

$\because \quad \log m + \log n = \log mn$

R.H.S. $= \log \left\{\dfrac{1+pq+p+q}{1+pq-p-q}\right\}$

$= \log \dfrac{(1+p)(1+q)}{(1-p)(1-q)} =$ L.H.S.

$f\left(\dfrac{2x}{1+x^2}\right) = \log \left(\dfrac{1+x}{1-x}\right)^2 = 2 \log \dfrac{(1+x)}{(1-x)} = 2f(x)$

(b) $f(y) = \dfrac{py+q}{ry-p}$. Now put for y to get x.

5. (a) We have, $f(x) = (a^x + a^{-x})/2$,

$f(y) = (a^y + a^{-y})/2$

$f(x+y) = \{a^{x+y} + a^{-(x+y)}\}/2$,

$f(x-y) = \{a^{x-y} + a^{-(x-y)}\}/2$.

$\therefore \quad f(x+y) + f(x-y) = \frac{1}{2}[a^{x+y} + a^{-x-y} + a^{x-y} + a^{-x+y}]$

$= \frac{1}{2}[a^x(a^y + a^{-y}) + a^{-x}(a^y + a^{-y})]$

$= \frac{1}{2}(a^x + a^{-x})(a^y + a^{-y}) = 2f(x)f(y)$.

Alternative Method :

We have stated in **§ 4 (b) Page 1237** that for logarithmic functions $f(xy) = f(x) + f(y)$ and for exponential functions $f(x+y) = f(x).f(y)$ and $f(x-y) = f(x).f(-y) = f(x)f(y)$

$\because \quad f(-y) = \dfrac{a^{-y} + a^y}{2} = f(y)$

$\therefore \quad f(x+y) + f(x-y) = 2f(x)f(y)$

(b) Ans. (b).

Put $x = \tan\theta$, then $f(x) = 2\tan^{-1}(\tan\theta) = 2\theta$. The function is one-one onto.

$-1 < \tan\theta < 1 \Rightarrow -\frac{\pi}{4} < \theta < \frac{\pi}{4}$ or $-\frac{\pi}{2} < 2\theta < \frac{\pi}{2}$

$\therefore \quad B$ is interval $\left]-\frac{\pi}{2}, \frac{\pi}{2}\right[$

6. (a) We have $f(x)f(y) = [\cos(\log x)][\cos(\log y)]$ ...(1)

and $f(x/y) + f(xy) = \cos[\log(x/y)] + \cos[\log(xy)]$

$= 2\cos\frac{1}{2}\{\log(x/y) + \log(xy)\}$.

$\cos\frac{1}{2}\{\log(x/y) - \log(xy)\}$

$= 2\cos\frac{1}{2}(\log x^2).\cos\frac{1}{2}\log(1/y^2)$

$= 2\cos\left(2.\frac{1}{2}\log x\right).\cos\left\{\frac{1}{2}(-2)\log y\right\}$

$= 2\cos\log x \cos(-\log y)$

$= 2\cos\log x \cos\log y$ ...(2)

$[\because \cos(-\theta) = \cos\theta]$

$\therefore$ From (1) and (2),

$f(x)f(y) - \frac{1}{2}\{f(x/y) + f(xy)\} = 0$

(b) Ans. (d). The given expression is

$\cos(\log x^2) \cdot \cos(\log y^2)$

$-\frac{1}{2}\left[\cos\log\frac{x^2}{2} + \cos\log(x^2y^2)\right]$

$= \frac{1}{2}[\cos(\log x^2 + \log y^2) + \cos(\log x^2 - \log y^2)]$

$- \frac{1}{2}\left(\cos\log\frac{x^2}{2} + \cos(\log x^2 + \log y^2)\right)$

$= \frac{1}{2}\left[\cos\log\frac{x^2}{y^2} - \cos\log\frac{x^2}{2}\right]$

(c) True. Proceed as in Q. 10 and part (a).

7. (a) $f(-1) = 3^{-(-1)} - 1 = 3 - 1 = 2.$

$f(\pi/6) = \tan(\pi/12) = \tan 15° = 2 - \sqrt{3},$

since $0 < \pi/6 < \pi$,

$f(2\pi/3) = \tan(\pi/3) = \sqrt{3},$

since $0 < 2\pi/3 < \pi$,

$f(4) = \frac{4}{4^2 - 2} = \frac{2}{7}$ and $f(6) = \frac{6}{6^2 - 2} = \frac{3}{17},$

since both the points $x = 4, x = 6$ belong to the closed interval $[\pi, 6]$

(b) $f(-15) = -15 - 4 = -19, f(3) = 3^2 - 1 = 8,$

$f(12) = 2.12 + 5 = 29, (f \circ f) 5 = f[f(5)] = f[25 - 1]$

$= f(24) = 2(24) + 5 = 53$

8. (a) By definition of $[x]$, we have

$[\pi^2] = 9$ and $[-\pi^2] = -10$. Hence

$f(x) = \cos 9x + \cos(-10)x = \cos 9x + \cos 10x$

Now $f(\pi/2) = \cos(9\pi/2) + \cos 5\pi = 0 + (-1) = -1$

and $f(\pi) = \cos 9\pi + \cos 10\pi = -1 + 1 = 0$

$f(-\pi) = \cos(-9\pi) + \cos(-10\pi)$

$= \cos 9\pi + \cos 10\pi = -1 + 1 = 0$

$f(\pi/4) = \cos(9\pi/4) + \cos(10\pi/4)$

$= \frac{1}{\sqrt{(2)}} - 0 = \frac{1}{\sqrt{(2)}}$

(b) Ans. (iv).

$y = \frac{1}{2}[\cos(2x+2) + \cos 2 - \{1 + \cos(2x+2)\}]$

or $y = -\frac{1}{2}(1 - \cos 2) = -\sin^2 1$ *i.e.*, constant

$\therefore$ graph is a line parallel to *x*-axis. Also when $x = \pi/2, y = -\cos^2(\pi/2 + 1) = -\sin^2 1.$

and hence it passes through the point $\left(\frac{\pi}{2}, -\sin^2 1\right).$

9. (a) $\phi(\psi(x)) = \phi(3^x) = (3^x)^2 + 1 = 3^{2x} + 1$

and $\psi(\phi(x)) = \psi(x^2 + 1) = 3^{x^2+1}.$

Note: In $\log_a x$ both x and a are +ive, $a \neq 1, x \neq 0$

(V. Imp.)

(b) Do yourself.

(c) $\left[-\frac{5}{3}\right] = \left[-2 + \frac{1}{3}\right] = -2, \left|-\frac{5}{3}\right| = \frac{5}{3}$

$\left[\frac{5}{3}\right] = \left[1 + \frac{2}{3}\right] = 1, \quad \left|\frac{5}{3}\right| = \frac{5}{3}$

$[-1] = -1, \quad |-1| = 1$

(i) $g f\left(-\frac{5}{3}\right) - f g\left(-\frac{5}{3}\right)$

$= g\left[-\frac{5}{3}\right] - f\left|-\frac{5}{3}\right| = g(-2) - f\left(\frac{5}{3}\right)$

$= |-2| - \left[\frac{5}{3}\right] = 2 - 1 = 1$

(ii) $g f\left(\frac{5}{3}\right) - f g\left(\frac{5}{3}\right)$

$= g\left[\frac{5}{3}\right] - f\left|\frac{5}{3}\right| = g(1) - f\left(\frac{5}{3}\right)$

$= |1| - \left[\frac{5}{3}\right] = 1 - 1 = 0$

(iii) $f(-1) + 2g(-1) = [-1] + 2|-1| = -1 + 2 = 1$

10. (a) (i) $g[f(1)] = g[(1-1)/1] = g(0) = 0 + 1 = 1,$

(ii) $f[g(-1)] = f[(-1)^2 + 1] = f(2) = (2-1)/2 = 1/2$

(b) $f[f(x)] = [a - f(x)^n]^{1/n} = [a - (a - x^n)]^{1/n} = x.$

(c) $f(x) = \frac{1}{2}[1 - \cos 2x + 1 - \cos(2x + 2\pi/3)$

$+ \cos(2x + \pi/3) + \cos(\pi/3)]$

$= \frac{1}{2}\left[2 + \frac{1}{2} - 2\cos\frac{\pi}{3}\cos\left(2x + \frac{\pi}{3}\right) + \cos\left(2x + \frac{\pi}{3}\right)\right]$

or $f(x) = \frac{1}{2}\left[\frac{5}{2} + 0\right] = \frac{5}{4}$

$\therefore \quad (gof)\, x = g[f(x)] = g\left(\frac{5}{4}\right) = 1$

(d) Ans. (b), (c), (d).

Proceeding as in **part (c) above** $f(x) = 5/4 \ \forall\ x$

$\therefore \quad f(-x) = 5/4.$ Also $f(x + \lambda) = 5/4 = f(x)$

Also $f(0) = f(1) = 5/4 \rightarrow$ (b), (c), (d).

11. (a) Ans. (d).

$f[f(x)] = f\left(\frac{\alpha x}{x+1}\right) = f(y) = \frac{\alpha y}{y+1}$

Now put $y = \frac{\alpha x}{x+1}$

$\therefore \quad f[f(x)] = \frac{\alpha^2 x}{(\alpha+1)x + 1} = \frac{x}{1}$ (as given)

By inspection it is clear that $\alpha + 1 = 0$ *i.e.* $\alpha = -1$ makes $f[f(x)] = x.$

(b) Ans. (b).

We know that $x - [x] = \{x\}$ *i.e.* fractional part of x

$\therefore \quad g(x) = 1 + x - [x] = 1 + \{x\} \geq 1 \quad \forall\ x \in R$

or $f[g(x)] = 1$ by definition of $f(x) = 1, x > 0$

(c) Ans. (a).

$F'(x) = 2.\frac{1}{2}[f.f' + g.g']$

$= [f.f' + f'f''] = [f.f' + f'(-f)]$

$\therefore \quad F'(x) = 0$ by given conditions.

$\therefore \quad F(x) =$ constant.

Since $F(5) = 5 \quad \therefore\ F(10) = 5$ as $F(x)$ is constant.

12. (a) Ans.

The function is not defined at $x = 1$ and $x = 3.$

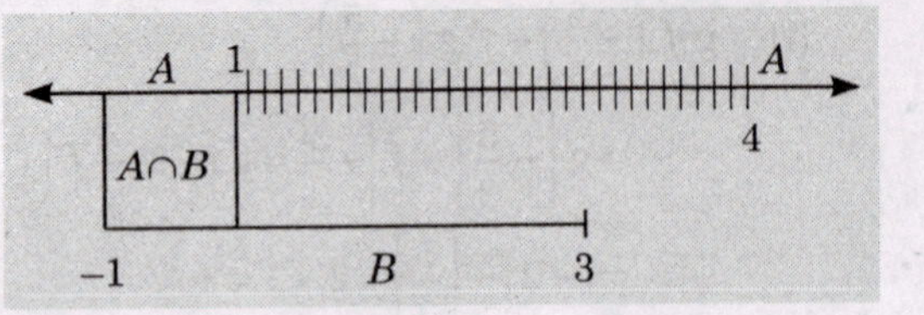

Fig. 12

(b) $\pm(x-1)<3 \Rightarrow x-1<3 \Rightarrow x<4$
and $-(x-1)<3 \quad \Rightarrow \quad -2<x$
$\therefore \quad |x-1|<3 \Rightarrow -2<x<4.$

(c) $(x-1)(x-4)\geq 0 \Rightarrow x\leq 1$ or $x\geq 4$ say A ...(1)
$(x+1)(x-3)\leq 0 \Rightarrow -1\leq x\leq 3$ say B ...(2)
Since both the inequalities hold, the common region of (1) and (2) will be the required. Mark on the real line the regions given by (1) and (2) and then take their intersection.
$\therefore \quad A\cap B = x : -1\leq x\leq 1$

13. (a) $f(x).f\left(\frac{1}{x}\right) = f(x)+f\left(\frac{1}{x}\right)$

$\therefore \quad f(x)\left\{f\left(\frac{1}{x}\right)-1\right\} = f\left(\frac{1}{x}\right)-1+1$ **(Note)**

or $\left\{f\left(\frac{1}{x}\right)-1\right\}\{f(x)-1\}=1$

Above shows that $f(x)-1$ and $f\left(\frac{1}{x}\right)-1$ are reciprocal of each other and so are x and $1/x$. Above is possible when

$f(x)-1=x^n$ or $-x^n$ so that $f\left(\frac{1}{x}\right)-1=\frac{1}{x^n}$

or $-\frac{1}{x^n}$.

Hence $f(x)=1+x^n$ or $1-x^n$, *i.e.*, $1\pm x^n$

Here $f(x)$ is a cubic $\quad\therefore\quad f(x)=1\pm x^3$

Given $f(3)=28 \quad\therefore\quad f(3)=1+3^3=28$

$\therefore \quad f(x)=1+x^3$. Hence $f(2)=1+2^3=9$.

(b) We are given $f(2)=5$, so we put $x=2, y=1$
$f(2)f(1)=f(2)+f(1)+f(2)-2$
or $\quad 5f(1)=5+f(1)+5-2$
or $\quad 4f(1)=8 \quad\therefore\quad f(1)=2$

Now put $y=\frac{1}{x}$ in the given relation

$\therefore \quad f(x)f\left(\frac{1}{x}\right)=f(x)+f\left(\frac{1}{x}\right)+f(1)-2$

or $\quad f(x).f\left(\frac{1}{x}\right)=f(x)+f\left(\frac{1}{x}\right)$

$\because \quad f(1)=2$

$\therefore \quad f(x)=1\pm x^n$ by part (a). Since $f(2)=5$

$\therefore \quad f(x)=x^2+1$

$\therefore \quad f(5)=5^2+1=26$

(c) $af(x)+bf\left(\frac{1}{x}\right)=\frac{1}{x}-5$ ...(1)

Replacing x by $\frac{1}{x}$ we have

$$af\left(\frac{1}{x}\right)+bf(x)=x-5 \qquad ...(2)$$

Multiply (1) by a and (2) by b and subtract to eliminate $f\left(\frac{1}{x}\right)$.

$\therefore \quad (a^2-b^2)f(x)=\frac{a}{x}-bx-5(a-b)$

$\therefore \quad f(x)=\frac{1}{a^2-b^2}\left[\frac{a}{x}-bx\right]-\frac{5}{(a+b)}$

(d) Ans. (b).

$$2f(x^2)+3f\left(\frac{1}{x^2}\right)=x^2-1$$

Replace x^2 by $\frac{1}{x^2}$

$$2f\left(\frac{1}{x^2}\right)+3f(x^2)=\frac{1}{x^2}-1=\frac{1-x^2}{x^2}$$

Eliminating $f\left(\frac{1}{x^2}\right)$ from the above two, we have

$$(9-4)f(x^2)=\frac{(1-x^2)(3+2x^2)}{x^2}$$

$\therefore \quad f(x^2)=\frac{(1-x^2)(3+2x^2)}{5x^2} \Rightarrow$ (b)

14. (a) Ans. 1. We have
$g(x)=f[f(x)]=f[|x-2|]=|x-2|-2.$
Since $x>2$, we have $g(x)=x-2-2=x-4$,
$\therefore \quad g'(x)=1.$

(b) By given condition $\phi(x)=f^{-1}(x)$
$\therefore \quad f[\phi(x)]=x.$ Diff. w. r. t. x
$f'[\phi(x)]\phi'(x)=1$
or $\quad \phi'(x)=\frac{1}{f'(\phi(x))}=1+[\phi(x)]^n$,
by def. of $f'(x)$.

(c) Ans. (a).
The results given in (a) satisfy the given relation.

(d) $(fof)\,x=x \Rightarrow f[f(x)]=x$

or $\quad f\left[\frac{ax+b}{cx+d}\right]=x \quad$ or $\quad \frac{a\left[\frac{ax+b}{cx+d}\right]+b}{c\left[\frac{ax+b}{cx+d}\right]+d}=x$

$\therefore \quad \frac{x(a^2+bc)+b(a+d)}{cx(a+d)+(bc+d^2)}=x$

Clearly if $a+d=0$ or $d=-a$

then in that case L.H.S. $=\frac{x(a^2+bc)+0}{0+(bc+a^2)}=x$

$\because \quad d = -a$

15. The critical points are 2, 3 and so we redefine the functions for $x < 2, 2 \le x < 3, x > 3$.

$$f(x) = \begin{cases} x^2 - 4x + 3, & x < 2 \\ x - 4, & 2 \le x < 3 \\ x - 4, & x \ge 3 \end{cases} \quad \text{from } x \ge 2$$

$$g(x) = \begin{cases} x - 3, & x < 2 \\ x - 3, & 2 \le x < 3 \\ x^2 + 2x + 2, & x > 3 \end{cases} \quad \text{from } x < 3$$

$$\therefore \quad f + g = \begin{cases} x^2 - 3x, & x < 2 \\ 2x - 7, & 2 \le x < 3 \\ x^2 + 2x - 2, & x \ge 3 \end{cases}$$

$$\frac{f}{g} = \begin{cases} \dfrac{x^2 - 4x + 3}{x - 3} = x - 1, & x < 2 \\ \dfrac{x - 4}{x - 3} & 2 \le x < 3 \\ \dfrac{x - 4}{x^2 + 3x + 2}, & x \ge 3 \end{cases}$$

16. (a) From given relations $\dfrac{y - 1}{1} = \dfrac{10^{2x} - 1}{10^{2x} + 1}$

Apply Comp. and Divi.

$$\frac{y}{2 - y} = \frac{2.10^{2x}}{2} = 10^{2x}$$

$$\therefore \quad 2x = \log_{10} \frac{y}{2 - y} \text{ etc.}$$

(b) $y = (x + 1)^2 - 1 \Rightarrow \sqrt{y + 1} - 1 = x$

$\therefore \quad f^{-1}(y) = x = \sqrt{y + 1} - 1$

or $\quad f^{-1}(x) = \sqrt{x + 1} - 1$

Now $\quad f(x) = f^{-1}(x)$

$\Rightarrow \quad (x + 1)^2 - 1 = \sqrt{x + 1} - 1$

or $\quad (x + 1)^4 = (x + 1)$

$\therefore \quad x + 1 = 0$ or $x + 1 = 1^{1/3} = 1, w, w^2$

$\therefore \quad x = -1$, or 0 only as x is real.

(c) $\dfrac{y - 2}{1} = \dfrac{e^x - e^{-x}}{e^x + e^{-x}}$

Apply comp. and divi.

$$\frac{y - 1}{3 - y} = \frac{2e^x}{2e^{-x}} = e^{2x} \quad \therefore x = \frac{1}{2} \log \left(\frac{y - 1}{3 - y} \right) \text{ etc.}$$

(d) $y = \dfrac{e^x - e^{-x}}{2}$ or $2y = t - \dfrac{1}{t}$ or $t^2 - 2ty - 1 = 0$

$$\therefore \quad t = e^x = \frac{2y \pm \sqrt{4y^2 + 4}}{2} = y + \sqrt{y^2 + 1},$$

as t is +ive.

$\therefore \quad x = \log [y + \sqrt{y^2 + 1}]$

$\therefore \quad$ From $f[g(x)] = x$

$$g(x) = f^{-1}(x) = \log [x + \sqrt{x^2 + 1}]$$

$$g\left[\frac{e^{1002} - 1}{2e^{501}}\right] = g\left[\frac{e^z - e^{-z}}{2}\right] \text{ where } z = 501$$

$$= g f(z) = z = 501.$$

(e) Ans. (b), (c).

We know that only one-one onto functions are inversible. In (a), it is not one-one and hence not inversible. In (b) and (c) both are one-one onto and both are inversible. Since

$$f\left(\frac{\pi}{4}\right) = f\left(\frac{3\pi}{4}\right) = \frac{1}{\sqrt{2}} \text{ so it is not one-one.}$$

$\therefore$ (d) is not inversible.

17. From given domain of f, $\left]-\dfrac{\pi}{2}, \dfrac{\pi}{2}\right[$ we conclude that its range $]-\infty, \infty[$ *i.e.*, whole of R

Domain of g is $1 - x^2 \ge 0$ or $x^2 - 1 \le 0$

or $\quad (x + 1)(x - 1) \le 0$ or $-1 \le x \le 1$ or $[-1, 1]$

and for range of g, $y = \sqrt{1 - x^2}$

since $x^2 \le 1 \quad \therefore \quad y \in [0, 1]$

$$(f \circ g)\, x = f(g(x)) = f\{\sqrt{(1 - x^2)}\}$$

$$= f(t), \text{ where } t = \sqrt{1 - x^2} \in [0, 1]$$

$$\text{range of } g \subset \left]-\frac{\pi}{2}, \frac{\pi}{2}\right[\text{ which is domain of } f.$$

$$= \tan t = \tan \sqrt{1 - x^2}$$

$$(g \circ f)\, x = g(f(x)) = g(\tan x)$$

$$= g(t) \text{ where } t = \tan x \in \text{range of } f = R$$

But R is not a subset of domain of $g = [-1, 1]$

Hence $g \circ f$ is not defined.

18. (a) (i) An injective (*i.e.* one-one) mapping A to B may be defined as $f = \{(2, 5), (3, 7), (4, 6)\}$

(ii) A mapping from A to B which is not injective may be defined as $g = \{(2, 2), (3, 5), (4, 2)\}$. It is many-one.

(iii) A mapping from B to A may be def:ned as $h = \{(2, 2), (5, 3), (6, 4), (7, 4)\}$

(b) Ans. (d).

For function **every element** of domain must have a unique image in co-domain ...(A)

Let us redefine each function as a set of ordered pairs and see if they satisfy the above condition (A) of a function.

$f_1 = \{(1, 2), (2, 3), (3, 4)\}$; $(4, 5)$ cannot be an ordered pair as 5 does not belong to co-domain. Thus the element 4 of domain does not have an image.

$f_2 = \{(1, 4), (2, 3), (2, 4), (3, 2), (3, 3), (3, 4), (4, 1), (4, 2), (4, 3), (4, 4)\}$

The uniqueness is violated as the elements have not one but many images.

$f_3 = \{(2, 1), (3, 2), (3, 1), (4, 1), (4, 2), (4, 3)\}$

Not a function as in f_2 uniqueness is violated.

$f_4 = \{(1, 4), (2, 3), (3, 2), (4, 1)\}$

It is a function as each element has a unique image.

19. Ans. No.

First observe that the graph of the function f consists of points represented by the ordered pairs of the form $(x, f(x))$. If the vertical line through $x = 6$ is cut by the graph of f twice, then it means that the element 6 of the domain of f has two images. Hence f is not a function as for f to be a function each element of the domain must have unique image.

20. (a) Ans. $\alpha = 2, \beta = -1$.

Domain $A = \{1, 2, 3, 4\}$

Range $B = \{1, 3, 5, 7\}$

Every element of domain has a unique image in B and hence g is a function. Now $g(x) = \alpha x + \beta$ but $g(2) = 3$, $g(3) = 5$.

$\therefore \quad 2 = 2\alpha + \beta \quad \text{and} \quad 5 = 3\alpha + \beta$

$\therefore \quad \alpha = 2, \beta = -1$

(b) Ans. No. Range will consist of only odd numbers. Thus even numbers will have no pre-image.

21. (a) **(i)** $\neq$ injective (one-one) but surjective (onto)

(ii) It is not a function.

(i) Here the given set of ordered pairs is a function since each person has one and only one mother. This function is surjective but not injective, (why ?). Two persons may have the same mother. It is surjective (onto) as every mother must have a child in A. If in place of mother we had a woman then it may not be onto because every woman need not be a mother.

(ii) Here the given set of ordered pairs is not a function since a person has many ancestors (*e.g.* father, mother, grand father, grand mother, great grand father, great grand mother and so on). So in this case the image $f(a)$ of an element a of the domain is not unique.

(b) Ans. $f \circ g = \{(2, 5), (5, 2), (1, 5)\}$,

$g \circ f = \{(1, 3), (3, 1), (4, 3)\}$

22. (a) Ans. (c).

$(2, 3) \in R$ but $(3, 2) \notin R$ and hence it is not symmetric $\to$ (c).

Again $(4, 2)$ and $(2, 4) \in R$ but $(4, 4) \notin R$. Hence it is not transitive. Also $(1, 1), (2, 2), (3, 3), (4, 4) \notin$ to R and hence it is not reflexive. Also the element 2 does not have a unique image and hence not a function.

(b) Ans. (d).

$$\sin x - \sqrt{3}\cos x = 2\left[\frac{1}{2}\sin x - \frac{\sqrt{3}}{2}\cos x\right]$$

$$= 2\sin(x - \pi/6)$$

$\therefore \quad f(x) = 2\sin(x - \pi/6) + 1$

$\therefore \quad$ Min. value of $f(x) = 2(-1) + 1 = -1$

Max. value of $f(x) = 2(1) + 1 = 3$

Since $f : R \to S$ is onto $\therefore S = [-1, 3]$

23. (a) Ans. The function $g \circ f : \mathbf{R} \to \mathbf{R}$ is defined by

$$(g \circ f)(x) = g(f(x)) = g(2x + 1)$$

$$= (2x+1)^2 - 2 = 4x^2 + 4x - 1$$

and $f \circ g : \mathbf{R} \to \mathbf{R}$ is defined by

$$(f \circ g)(x) = f(g(x)) = f(x^2 - 2)$$

$$= 2(x^2 - 2) + 1 = 2x^2 - 3.$$

(b) Ans. $(f \circ g)(x) = f(g(x)) = f(x^2) = \sin x^2$

and $(g \circ f)(x) = g(f(x)) = g(\sin x) = \sin^2 x$

Since $\sin x^2 \neq \sin^2 x$ for any $x \in \mathbf{R}$, $g \circ f \neq f \circ g$.

24. (a) Ans. (d).

$f(x) = 2x - 3$, $g(x) = x^3 + 5$ are bijections and hence f^{-1} and g^{-1} both exist.

$$y = 2x - 3 \Rightarrow x = \frac{y+3}{2} \quad \therefore \quad f^{-1}(y) = \frac{y+3}{2}$$

$$\therefore \quad f^{-1}(x) = \frac{x+3}{2} \qquad \text{...(1)}$$

$$y = x^3 + 5 \quad \therefore \quad x = (y-5)^{1/3} = g^{-1}(y)$$

$$\therefore \quad g^{-1}(x) = (x-5)^{1/3} \qquad \text{...(2)}$$

$$\therefore \quad (fog)^{-1} x = (g^{-1} of^{-1})\, x$$

$$= g^{-1}[f^{-1}(x)] = g^{-1}\left[\frac{x+3}{2}\right] \text{ by (1)}$$

$$= \left(\frac{x+3}{2} - 5\right)^{1/3} = \left(\frac{x-7}{2}\right)^{1/3}$$

(b) Ans. (a).

$$y = \frac{3x+2}{5x-3} \Rightarrow x = \frac{3y+2}{5y-3} = f^{-1}(y)$$

$$\therefore \quad f^{-1}(x) = \frac{3x+2}{5x-3} = f(x).$$

25. Ans. (b).

$$g(x) = \frac{3x + x^3}{1 + 3x^2} = y, \text{ say} \qquad \text{...(1)}$$

$$\therefore \quad f[g(x)] = f(y) = \log\left(\frac{1+y}{1-y}\right) = \log\left(\frac{1+x}{1-x}\right)^3,$$

on putting for y from (1)

$$= 3\log\left(\frac{1+x}{1-x}\right) = 3f(x)$$

26. (a) Ans. No.

For a function to be invertible it is necessary that it is bijective *i.e.* one-one and onto.

The function given here is neither surjective nor injective as shown below.

Since $-1 \le \cos(5x+2) \le 1$, the range of f

$= \{y : y \text{ is real}, -1 \le y \le 1\}$

which is a proper subset of the co-domain **R**. Hence f is into so that it is not surjective,

f is many-one since $\cos(5x+2)$ has the same value for many values of x. Thus

$$f\left(x+\frac{2}{5}n\pi\right)=\cos\left\{5\left(x+\frac{2}{5}n\pi\right)+2\right\}$$

$$=\cos\{2n\pi+5x+2\}=\cos(5x+2)=f(x),$$

for all $n=0,\pm 1,\pm 2,\pm 3,\ldots$

Since f is not bijective, it is not invertible.

(b) Ans. True. Proceed as above.

(c) Ans. (b). $y=\dfrac{x}{1+x}=\dfrac{1}{1+\dfrac{1}{x}}$ ...(1)

For each value of x there is a unique value of y and hence the mapping is one-one. As x varies in $[0,\infty)$, y varies in $[0, 1]$ which is a subset of $[0,\infty)$. Hence the mapping is not onto.

Alt. From given equation $x=\dfrac{y}{1-y}$. Now for $y=1$, there is no x and hence it is not onto.

27. (a) Ans. True. f is many-one into as shown below.

Let $z=\cos\theta+i\sin\theta$, $0\le\theta\le 2\pi$

Then $f(z)=|z|=+\sqrt{(\cos^2\theta+\sin^2\theta)}=1$.

Thus all complex numbers $z=\cos\theta+i\sin\theta$ where $0\le\theta\le 2\pi$ have the same image 1. It follows that f is many-one. Again since the modulus of a complex number is a non-negative number, we see that no negative real number can be the image of a complex number. For example, there is no complex number z such that $f(z)=|z|=-1$.

Hence f is into. Therefore the function f is neither one-one nor onto.

(b) Ans. Yes. We have

$$x_1, x_2\in A,\ f(x_1)=f(x_2)\Rightarrow\frac{x_1-2}{x_1-3}=\frac{x_2-2}{x_2-3}$$

$\Rightarrow\ (x_1-2)(x_2-3)=(x_1-3)(x_2-2)$

$\Rightarrow\ x_1x_2-2x_2-3x_1+6=x_1x_2-2x_1-3x_2+6$

$\Rightarrow\ x_1=x_2$. Hence one-one

Surjectivity. Let y be any arbitrary element of B and suppose there exists an x such that $f(x)=y$, that is, $(x-2)/(x-3)=y$

or $\quad x-2=xy-3y$.

This gives $x=(3y-2)/(y-1)$. Since $y\ne 1$, x is real. Further $x\ne 3$. For if $x=3$, then $3=(3y-2)/(y-1)$ or $3y-3=3y-2$, which is false. It follows that $x=(3y-2)/(y-1)\in A$ such that $f(x)=y$ and so f is surjective. Thus f has been shown to be bijective.

(c) Ans. (d).

$f'(x)=3x^2+5$ which is always + ive and hence $f(x)$ is strictly increasing. Thus f is one-one.

Also $f(\infty)\to\infty$ and $f(-\infty)\to-\infty$ showing that range of f is whole of R.

$\therefore\quad f$ is one-one, onto.

28. (a) Ans. Yes. $f^{-1}(y)=\frac{1}{3}(y-4)$. $(y\in R)$

(i) f is one-one. For we have

$x_1, x_2\in\mathbf{R}, f(x_1)=f(x_2)$

$\Rightarrow\quad 3x_1+4=3x_2+4\Rightarrow x_1=x_2$

(ii) f is onto :

If $y=f(x)=3x+4$, then $x=\frac{1}{3}(y-4)$, which is also a real number. Thus $f\left\{\frac{1}{3}(y-4)\right\}=y$. It is therefore shown that any arbitrary element y in **R** is the f-image of the element $\frac{1}{3}(y-4)\in\mathbf{R}$. Hence f is onto. Since f is one-one onto (*i.e.* bijective), it is invertible.

The inverse mapping $f^{-1}:\mathbf{R}\to\mathbf{R}$ is defined by

$$f^{-1}(y)=\frac{1}{3}(y-4),\ (y\in\mathbf{R}).$$

(b) Ans. (d).

Let $y=x^2+1$. Then for $y=17$, we have $x=\pm 4$ and for $y=-3$, x becomes imaginary that is, there is no value of x.

Hence $f(17)=\{-4, 4\}$ and $f^{-1}(-3)=\phi$.

29. (a) Ans. (c).

(b) Let f be an injective mapping from A to B. Since f is one-one, number of elements in A is less than or equal to the number of elements in B, that is, $n(A)\le n(B)$. Similarly since there exists an injective mapping $g: B\to A$, we have $n(B)\le n(A)$. Hence $n(A)=n(B)$.

Since the number of elements in A and B is the same, we can define a bijective mapping from A to B.

For if $\quad A=\{a_1, a_2,\ldots a_n\}$

and $\quad B=\{b_1, b_2,\ldots b_n\}$

then one such bijective mapping is

$$h=\{(a_1,b_1),(a_2,b_2),\ldots(a_n,b_n)\}$$

In fact, we can define many such bijective mappings from A to B.

30. Ans. All statements are the same.

31. (i) one-one, $\ne$ onto as $1\in B$ will have no pre-image in A as 1 is the image of 2 by def. and $2\notin A$.

(ii) $\ne$ one-one as both x and $-x\in A$ have the same image. $\ne$ onto. All – ive numbers in B will have no pre-image by definition of $|x|$.

(iii) $h(x)=x^2$ when $x\ge 0$. It is bijection

$=-x^2$ when $x<0$

(iv) $\ne$ one-one, $\ne$ onto

(v) $\ne$ one-one but onto $l(1)=l(-1)=0$

By definition $-1 \le \sin \pi x \le 1$ as x varies from -1 to 1.

32. (a) Ans. (c).

A has 3 elements and B has 4 elements for injective mapping first element of A can go to any of 4 of B, 2nd to 3 of B and 3rd to 2 of B.

$\therefore \quad 4.3.2 = 24.$

In short $^4P_3$.

(b) Ans. (b).

$f : A \to B$ where A has n elements and B has 2 elements.

Each element of A can go to 2 elements of B.

Hence there will be $2.2.2....n$ times $= 2^n$ mappings.

But if each element of A either goes to a only of B or goes to b only of B then in these two cases the mapping will not be surjective.

Hence the number of surjective mappings are $2^n - 2$.

(c) Ans. (a).

Total number of functions form $E \to F$ is $2^4 = 16$.

When all the elements of E go to 1 then it will be into as 2 is left out. Similarly when all elements go to 2 then 1 is left out. Hence in two cases the function will be into. Thus onto functions will be $16 - 2 = 14$.

33. (a) Ans. (d).

Consider an element $a \in A$, it can be assigned to any of the n elements of B *i.e.* it has n images. Similarly each of the m elements of A can have n images in B. Hence the number of mappings is $n \times n \times n \times ... m$ times $= n^m$.

(b) Ans. (c).

$a_1 \in A$ can have n images in B, but the element a_2 will have only $(n-1)$ images as the mappings are to be one-one (injective).

Similarly the elements a_3 will have $(n-2)$ images.

Hence the total number of mappings will be

$$n(n-1)(n-2)...(n-\overline{m-1})$$
$$= n(n-1)(n-2)...(n-m+1)$$

Multiply above and below by

$$(n-m)(n-m-1)...3.2.1$$

$\therefore \quad$ Required number is $\dfrac{n!}{(n-m)!}$

Note : If $m > n$, then for injective mappings n elements of A will have n distinct images and the remaining $m - n\ (m > n)$ elements of A will have no image in B (for injective).

(c) Ans. (b).

Each element can go to itself and the rest as well. Thus it can have 10 images. Similarly we can argue for other elements. Hence the total number of distinct functions from A to A is 10^{10}.

34. (a) Ans. (a). True.

$g \circ f$ is injective (*i.e.* one-one). For we have

$(g \circ f)(x) = (g \circ f)(y)\ (x, y \in A)$

$\Rightarrow \quad g(f(x)) = g(f(y))$

$\Rightarrow \quad f(x) = f(y) \qquad [\because g$ is one-one$]$

$\Rightarrow \quad x = y \qquad [\because f$ is one-one$]$

$g \circ f$ is surjective (*i.e.* onto). For let z be any arbitrary element of C. Then since g is onto there exists an element $y \in B$ such that $g(y) = z$. Again since f is onto there exists an element $x \in A$ such that $f(x) = y$. Thus to each $z \in C$ there exists an element $x \in A$ such that

$$z = g(y) = g(f(x)) = (g \circ f)(x)$$

Hence $g \circ f$ is both injective and surjective and so it is bijective.

(b) Ans. (a).

35. (a) Ans. (b).

Note f is injective.

I. Consider $f(x) = 1$ true, then other two are wrong.

$\therefore \quad f(y) = 1, f(z) = 2$. This is not possible because of injective and in this case it becomes many-one.

II. $f(y) \ne 1$ true, then other two are wrong.

$\therefore \quad f(x) = 2$ or 3, $f(y) = 2$ or 3

$f(z) = 2$

This also violates the definition of injective.

III. Now consider $f(z) \ne 2$ true, then other two are wrong

$\therefore \quad f(x) = 2$ or 3, $f(y) = 1, f(z) = 1$ or 3

$\therefore \quad f(z) = 3$ only as $f(y) = 1$.

Hence $f(x) = 2$ only, keeping in view the definition of injective.

Since $f(y) = 1 \ \therefore \ f^{-1}(1) = y$.

(b) The mapping is to be **one-one onto** with the condition $f(1) = 1, f(2) \ne 2, f(4) \ne 4$ **and nothing about $f(3)$.**

$f(1) = 1, f(2) = 3$ or $4, f(4) = 3, 2$

(not 1 in any because of one-one)

$f(1) = 1 \quad f(2) = 3$ then $f(4) = 2 \ \therefore f(3) = 4$

$f(1) = 1 \quad f(2) = 4$ then $f(4) = 2 \ \therefore f(3) = 3$

$f(1) = 1 \quad f(2) = 4$ or $f(4) = 3 \ \therefore f(3) = 2$

Hence there will be only three one-one onto mappings as shown above and as depicted below in the diagram :

	1	2	3	4
	↓	↓	↓	↓
I	1	3	4	2
II	1	4	3	2
III	1	4	2	3

36. (a) Ans. (a).

Total number of functions from $E \to F$ is $2^4 = 16$. When all the elements of E go to 1 then it will be into as 2 is left out. Similarly when all elements go to 2 then 1 is left out. Hence in two cases the function will be into. Thus onto functions will be $16 - 2 = 14$.

(b) Ans. (a). Clearly Range of $f(x)$ is $(-\infty, \infty)$ and hence onto.
Also $f(x_1) = f(x_2) \Rightarrow x_1 = x_2$ hence one-one.

37. (a) $(f o g)\, x = f\,[3x-2] = e^{3x-2}$

$(g o f)\, x = g\,(e^x) = 3e^x - 2$

$(f o g)\, x = e^{3x-2} = y$, say.

$\therefore \quad 3x - 2 = \log y$

or $\quad x = \dfrac{\log y + 2}{3} = (f o g)^{-1}\, y$

Clearly $y > 0$. Hence domain of $(f o g)^{-1}$ is $(0, \infty)$.

$(g o f)\, x = 3e^x - 2 = y$, say.

$\therefore \quad e^x = \dfrac{y+2}{3}$

or $\quad x = \log\left(\dfrac{y+2}{3}\right) = (g o f)^{-1}\, y$

Clearly $y > -2$. Hence domain of $(g o f)^{-1}$ is $(-2, \infty)$.

(b) Ans. (b). $g\,[f(x)]$

$\therefore \quad g(\sin x + \cos x) = (\sin x + \cos x)^2 - 1$

or $\quad g\,[f(x)] = \sin 2x = y$ is invertible

$\therefore \quad x = \dfrac{1}{2}\sin^{-1} y = \dfrac{1}{2}\left[-\dfrac{\pi}{2}, \dfrac{\pi}{2}\right] = \left[-\dfrac{\pi}{4}, \dfrac{\pi}{4}\right]$

38. (a) Ans. (b). x is + ive by definition.

$y = 2^{x(x-1)} \Rightarrow x^2 - x - \log_2 y = 0$

$x = \dfrac{1}{2}(1 \pm \sqrt{1 + 4\log_2 y})$

Since x is + ive, we choose only + out of ±.

$\therefore \quad x = \dfrac{1}{2}(1 + \sqrt{1 + 4\log_2 y}) \Rightarrow$ (b).

(b) Ans. (a).

$f(x) = y = x + \dfrac{1}{x} \quad \therefore \quad x^2 - xy + 1 = 0$

or $\quad y = \dfrac{x \pm \sqrt{x^2 - 4}}{2} = f^{-1}(x)$

Since $f : [1, \infty[\to [2, \infty[$ we choose + sign

$\therefore \quad f^{-1}(x) = \dfrac{x + \sqrt{x^2 - 4}}{2}$

39. (a) $(f o f)\, x = f\,[f(x)] = f\,[t]$ where $t = \dfrac{x}{\sqrt{1+x^2}}$

$= \dfrac{t}{\sqrt{1+t^2}} = \dfrac{x}{\sqrt{(1+2x^2)}} = z$

$f o [(f o f)\, x] = f(z) = \dfrac{z}{\sqrt{1+z^2}} = \dfrac{x}{\sqrt{(1+3x^2)}}$

(b) $x + \dfrac{1}{x} = t \quad \therefore \quad x^2 + \dfrac{1}{x^2} = t^2 - 2 \quad \therefore \quad f(t) = t^2 - 2$

or $f(x) = x^2 - 2$ is the required function which will satisfy the given condition.

(c) Given $f(x) = \begin{cases} 1 + x; & 0 \le x \le 2 \\ 3 - x; & 2 < x \le 3 \end{cases}$ ...(A) ...(B)

Now $(f o f)\, x = f\,[f(x)]$

$= \begin{cases} f(1+x); & 0 \le x \le 2 \\ f(3-x); & 2 < x \le 3 \end{cases}$

We will redefine above keeping in view the definitions given in (A) and (B).

Now $0 \le x \le 2 \quad \Rightarrow \quad 1 \le 1 + x \le 3$ ...(1)

$\Rightarrow \quad 0 < 1 + x \le 2$ and $2 < 1 + x \le 3$

and $2 < x \le 3 \quad \Rightarrow -3 \le -x < -2$

$\Rightarrow \quad 3 - 3 \le 3 - x < 3 - 2$ or $0 < 3 - x < 1$ ...(2)

$(f o f)\, x = \begin{cases} f(t), & 1 \le t \le 3, \quad t = 1 + x \text{ by (1)} \\ f(z), & 0 < z < 1, \quad z = 3 - x \text{ by (2)} \end{cases}$

Again we write above as

$\begin{cases} f(t); & 0 \le t \le 2 \\ & 2 < t \le 3 \\ f(z); & 0 < z < 1 \end{cases}$

$1 + t = 1 + 1 + x = 2 + x$ by (A)

$3 - t = 3 - (1 + x) = 2 - x$ by (B)

$1 + z = 1 + 3 - x = 4 - x$ by (A)

40. (a) $f(x) + f(1-x) = \dfrac{4^x}{4^x + 2} + \dfrac{4^{1-x}}{4^{1-x} + 2}$

$= \dfrac{4^x}{4^x + 2} + \dfrac{4}{4 + 2.4^x}$

$= \dfrac{4^x}{4^x + 2} + \dfrac{2}{4^x + 2} = \dfrac{4^x + 2}{4^x + 2} = 1$

$f\left(\dfrac{98}{99}\right) = f\left(1 - \dfrac{1}{99}\right), f\left(\dfrac{97}{99}\right) = f\left(1 - \dfrac{2}{99}\right)$

Thus combining terms equidistant from the beginning and end we have terms of the form $[f(x) + f(1-x)] + \ldots$ 49 terms and each of them is equal to 1 as shown above

$\therefore \quad S = f(1) = 49.$

(b) $f(1) + 2f(2) + \ldots nf(n) = n(n+1)\, f(n)$ ...(1)

Replacing n by $(n+1)$ in the above, we have

$f(1) + 2f(2) + \ldots + (n+1)\, f(n+1)$
$= (n+1)(n+2)\, f(n+1)$ ...(2)

Subtracting (1) and (2), we have

$(n+1)\, f(n+1) = (n+1)(n+2)\, f(n+1) - n(n+1)\, f(n)$

Cancel $(n+1)$ and combine

$\therefore \quad nf(n) = (n+1)\, f(n+1)$

Putting $n = 2, 3, \ldots, (n-1)$, we get

$2f(2) = 3f(3) = 4f(4) \ldots = nf(n)$

Using the above result in (1), we have

$f(1) + (n-1)\,[nf(n)] = n(n+1)\, f(n)$

$\therefore \quad f(1) = 2n\, f(n)$ or $f(n) = \frac{1}{2n}$ by (a)

$\therefore \quad f(49) = \frac{1}{2(49)} = \frac{1}{98}$

§ 5. Range and Domain of a Function.

Let $y = f(x)$ and if this function is defined for all values of x which lie between a and b, i.e. $a < x < b$ then the open interval $]a, b[$ will constitute the domain. If, however, $f(x)$ is also defined both for $x = a$ and b, then the domain will consist of the closed interval $[a, b]$.

Range of $f(x) = \{y : y = f(x), x \in \text{domain}\}$.

e.g. $y = \log_x e = f(x)$.

Here we know that x must be +ive and $x \neq 1$. All +ive numbers lie between 0 to ∞ except $x = 1$.

(§ 4 (c) P. 1237)

$\therefore$ Domain is $\{]0, \infty[- 1\}$ or $]0, 1[$ and $]1, \infty[$

or $]0, 1[\cup]1, \infty[$.

or if $f(x) = \log|4 - x^2|$.

We know that $|4 - x^2|$ should be +ive which is so by the definition of mod. Also $|4 - x^2| \neq 0$ *i.e.* $x \neq \pm 2$.

Hence the domain consists of all real values of x except ± 2.

In case $y = \log(4 - x^2)$, then $4 - x^2 \neq 0$

$\therefore \quad x \neq 2$ or -2

Also $4 - x^2$ must be +ive *i.e.,* $x^2 - 4 = -$ ive

or $(x+2)(x-2) = -$ ive $\quad \therefore \quad -2 < x < 2$

Above gives the domain $]-2, 2[$.

Some more examples.

1. $y = \sqrt{(4 - x^2)}$

The function is defined when $4 - x^2 \geq 0$ or $x^2 - 4 \leq 0$ or $(x+2)(x-2) \leq 0 \Rightarrow -2 \leq x \leq 2$ or the closed interval $[-2, 2]$ will represent the domain of y.

Obviously its range will consist of all values of y: $y = f(x), x \in \text{domain}$.

$\therefore$ Range of $y = [0, 2]$

2. (a) $y = \frac{1}{\sqrt{\{(x+3)(4-x)\}}}$

The function is not defined for $x = -3$ and $x = 4$ as it will make $D^r = 0$. Also

$(x+3)(4-x) = +$ ive

or $(x+3)(x-4) = -$ ive

$\therefore \quad -3 < x < 4$ or the interval $]-3, 4[$ constitutes the domain. **Note that −3 and 4 will not be part of domain.**

Range. $y^2\{12 + x - x^2\} = 1$

$x^2y^2 - xy^2 + 1 - 12y^2 = 0$

Since x is real $\therefore \Delta \geq 0$

$y^4 - 4y^2(1 - 12y^2) \geq 0$

or $y^2\{y^2 - 4 + 48y^2\} \geq 0$

or $y^2[49y^2 - 4] \geq 0$

$(7y+2)(7y-2) \geq 0$

$\therefore \quad y \leq \frac{2}{7}$ or $y \geq \frac{2}{7}$

Again y is +ive

$\therefore$ Range is given by $y \geq \frac{2}{7}$ $\therefore$ $R = \left[\frac{2}{7}, \infty\right[$.

(b) $y = \sqrt{(x-1)(x-2)}$

$D =]-\infty, 1] \cup [2, \infty[$

as $x \leq 1$ or as $x \geq 2$

Range $= R$

$y^2 = x^2 - 3x + 2$

$\therefore \quad x^2 - 3x + 2 - y^2 = 0$

Since x is real $\quad \therefore \quad \Delta \geq 0$

$9 - 4(2 - y^2) \geq 0$

or $1 + 4y^2 \geq 0$

$\therefore$ This is true $\forall \; y \in R$

3. $y = \frac{x-2}{x-4}$ ...(1)

Clearly the function is defined for all real values of x except $x = 4$

$\therefore$ Domain is $R - \{4\}$

Again from (1), $xy - 4y = x - 2$

$\therefore \quad x(y-1) = 4y - 2 \quad \therefore \quad x = \frac{4y-2}{y-1}$

Now x is not defined for $y = 1$

$\therefore$ Range $= R - \{1\}$

The following formulae will be useful for finding the domain :

Let $f_1(x)$ and $f_2(x)$ be two functions whose domains are D_1 and D_2 respectively, then

1. dom $[f_1(x) + f_2(x)] = D_1 \cap D_2$
2. dom $[f_1(x) \cdot f_2(x)] = D_1 \cap D_2$
3. dom $\left[\frac{f_1(x)}{f_2(x)}\right] = D_1 \cap D_2 \cap \{x : f_2(x) \neq 0\}$
4. dom $[\sqrt{f_1(x)}] = D_1 \cap \{x : f_1(x) > 0\}$

Domain and Range of Certain Functions :

I. $y = \log_a x, x = +\text{ive}, x \neq 0 = \{x : x > 0\}$

$\therefore \quad D = R^+$ or $]0, \infty[$ or $(0, \infty)$.

Range $= R$ or $]-\infty, \infty[$ or $(-\infty, \infty)$

II. $y = e^x$. It will be reverse of case 1.

$D = R$, Range $= R^+$ as exponential function is always +ive.

III. $y = \sin x, y = \cos x$

$D = R, \quad$ Range $= [-1, 1]$

IV. $y = \sin^{-1} x, y = \cos^{-1} x$.

$D = [-1, 1], R = \left[-\frac{\pi}{2}, \frac{\pi}{2}\right]$ for $\sin^{-1} x$

$R = [0, \pi]$ for $\cos^{-1} x$

V. $y = \tan x$

When $x = \frac{\pi}{2}$ or $(2n+1)\frac{\pi}{2}$, then $y = \infty$.

$\therefore \quad D = R - \left\{(2n+1)\frac{\pi}{2}, n \in I\right\}$

Note : $-\frac{\pi}{2}$ is also included in $(2n+1)\frac{\pi}{2}, n \in I$,

Range = R.

VI. $y = \tan^{-1} x$

$D = R$ and Range $= \left]-\frac{\pi}{2}, \frac{\pi}{2}\right[$

VII. $y = \cot x$ or $\frac{\cos x}{\sin x}$

$D = R - \{x : \sin x = 0\} = R - \{n\pi : n \in I\}$

Range = R.

VIII. $y = \sec x = \frac{1}{\cos x}$

$D = R - \left\{(2n+1)\frac{\pi}{2} : n \in I\right\}$

Range $= y : y \le -1$ or $y \ge 1$

$=]-\infty, -1] \cup [1, \infty[$

IX. $y = \text{cosec } x = \frac{1}{\sin x}$

$D = R - \{n\pi : n \in I\}$

Range = same as in VIII.

Closed and Open Intervals.

If $a \le x \le b$, then we say $x \in [a, b]$ **closed**

If $a < x < b$, then we say $x \in]a, b[$ or (a, b) **open**

Similarly, $x \in [a, b[$ or $[a, b) \Rightarrow a \le x < b$ **Semi-closed or open**

and $x \in]a, b]$ or $(a, b] \Rightarrow a < x \le b$ **Semi-open or closed**

$x > a \Rightarrow x \in (a, \infty)$

$x \ge a \Rightarrow x \in [a, \infty[$ or $[a, \infty)$

$x < b \Rightarrow x \in (-\infty, b)$

$x \le b \Rightarrow x \in]-\infty, b]$ or $(-\infty, b]$

In general, we shall use ( ) or] [when the interval is open *i.e.* $a < x < b$ and [ ] when the interval is closed *i.e.* equality is there *i.e.* $a \le x \le b$.

§ 6. Modulus *x*, *i.e.* | *x* |.

$|x| = x$ if x is + ive *i.e.* $|5| = 5$

$|x| = -x$ if x is – ive *i.e.* $|-5| = -(-5) = 5$

$|x - a| = x - a$ if $x > a$ *i.e.* $x - a$ is +ive

$|x - a| = -(x - a)$ if $x < a$ *i.e.* $x - a$ is – ive.

$|x| = 5 \Rightarrow x = \pm 5$

$|x|^2 = x^2$

$|x| \ge a \,(a + \text{ive}) \Rightarrow x^2 \ge a^2$

or $(x + a)(x - a) \ge 0$

$\Rightarrow x \le -a$ or $x \ge a$

$|x| \le a \,(a + \text{ive}) \Rightarrow x^2 \le a^2$

or $(x + a)(x - a) \le 0$

$\Rightarrow -a \le x \le a.$

Properties of modulus function :

(a) $|x^n| = |x|^n$ (b) $|xy| = |x||y|$

(c) $\left|\frac{x}{y}\right| = \frac{|x|}{|y|}$

(d) $||x| - |y|| \le |x + y| \le |x| + |y|$

Caution : $|f(x)| \ne f(|x|)$
$\ne f(x)$ if $x > 0$
$\ne -f(x)$ if $x < 0$ } **General Mistake**

But $|f(x)| = f(x)$ if $f(x) \ge 0$
$= -f(x)$ if $f(x) < 0$ } **correct Note.**

Illustration.

$f(x) = |x - 1| = x - 1$ if $x - 1 = +$ive or $x \ge 1$

$= -(x - 1)$ if $x - 1 = -$ive or $x < 1$

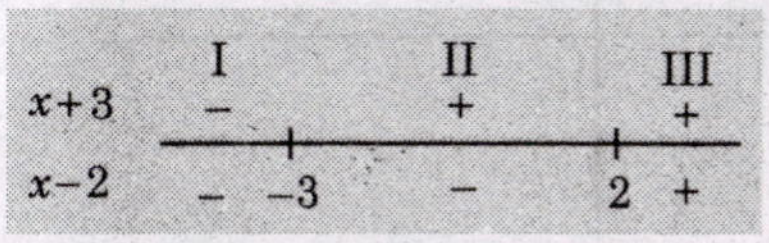

Fig. 13

Again consider $f(x) = |x - 2| + |x + 3|$

The critical points are – 3, 2. Mark them on the real line. We shall re-define the function as under in I, II and III.

I $\quad x < -3$, so that $x - 2 < 0, x + 3 < 0$

$\therefore \quad |x - 2| = -(x - 2), |x + 3| = -(x + 3)$

$\therefore \quad f(x) = -(x - 2) - (x + 3) = -2x - 1$ if $x < -3$

II $\quad -3 \le x < 2, \; x - 2 < 0, \; x + 3 \ge 0$

$\therefore \quad f(x) = -(x - 2) + (x + 3) = 5.$

III $\quad x \ge 0$ then $x - 2 > 0$ and $x + 3 > 0$

$\therefore \quad |x - 2| = x - 2, \; |x + 3| = x + 3$

$\therefore \quad f(x) = (x - 2) + (x + 3) = 2x + 1$ if $x \ge 2$

Hence the given function is re-written as under

$$f(x) = \begin{cases} -2x - 1, & \text{if } x < -3 \quad \text{by I} \\ 5, & \text{if } -3 \le x < 2 \quad \text{by II} \\ 2x + 1, & \text{if } x \ge 2 \quad \text{by III} \end{cases}$$

The graph of modulus function $y = |x|$

If $x > 0, \quad y = x$

If $x < 0, \quad y = -x$

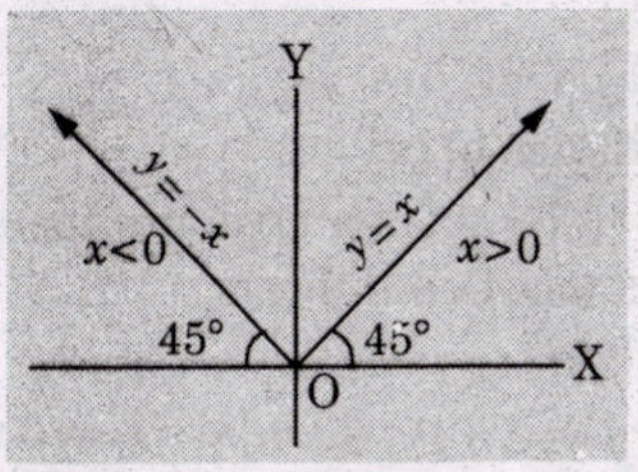

Fig. 14

The graph of $y = |x|$ is continuous as shown in the figure *i.e.*, no break in the curve but has a corner at the origin as shown.

Domain and range of $y = |x|$

Domain $= x \in R$ and Range $= y \in [0, \infty)$

Particular Case : $y = \begin{cases} \frac{|x|}{x}, & \text{if } x \ne 0 \\ 0, & \text{if } x = 0 \end{cases}$

The above function is defined as under

$x<0, |x| = -x$ and $x>0, |x| = x$

$$\therefore \quad y = \begin{cases} -1 & \text{if } x<0 \\ 0 & \text{if } x=0 \\ 1 & \text{if } x>0 \end{cases}$$

Above is called **Singum function.**

The graph of Singum function.

Note : $(0, 1)$ and $(0, -1)$ do not form part of the graph but $(0, 0)$ is a part of the graph.

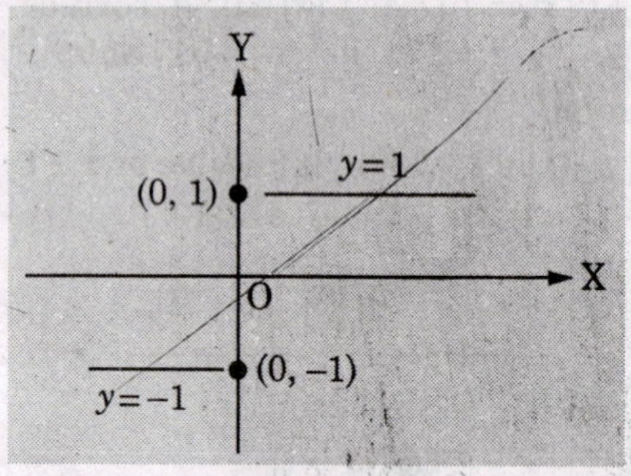

Fig. 15

§ 7. Greatest Integer Function, *i.e.* [x]

$[x]$ means the greatest integer not exceeding x, *i.e.* if

$x = 4\frac{1}{2}, 2\frac{1}{4}, \frac{1}{3}, 5$ then

$[x] = 4, 2, 0, 5$ respectively.

If $\quad x = -4\frac{1}{2}, -2\frac{1}{4}, -\frac{1}{3}, -5$

then $[x] = -5, -3, -1, -5$ respectively.

$\because -4\frac{1}{2} = -5 + \frac{1}{2}$ $\therefore$ greatest integer is -5 which is not exceeding $-4\frac{1}{2}$.

If $x = 6\frac{3}{4}$, then $[x] = 6$ and if $x = -3\frac{1}{2}$, then $[x] = -4$

Rule : Start towards left from the actual value of x and stop at the first integer you arrive at and this will be the value of [x].

In general, $[x] = n$ if $n \le x < n+1$

Domain and Range of [x].

The domain of $[x]$ is set of all real numbers whereas its range $y = [x]$ is set of all integers.

Properties of [x].

(a) $[x] = p \Leftrightarrow p \le x < p+1$ *i.e.* $[x] = 3 \Leftrightarrow 3 \le x < 4$

(b) $[x] > p \Rightarrow [x] = p+1 \Rightarrow x \ge p+1$

(c) $[x] < p \Rightarrow [x] = p-1 \Rightarrow x < p$

(d) $p \le [x] \le q$ then $x \in [p, q+1)$ e.g. $-2 \le [x] \le 3$

$\Rightarrow \quad x \in [-2, 4)$

Ex. 1. If $[x]^2 - 3[x] + 2 \le 0$ then $\{[x]-1\}\{[x]-2\} \le 0$

$1 \le \{x\} \le 2 \Rightarrow x \in [1, 3]$

Ex. 2. $[x]^2 - 10[x] + 16 > 0$

$\{[x]-2\}\{[x]-8\} > 0$

$\Rightarrow \quad [x] < 2$ or $[x] > 8$

$\Rightarrow \quad x < 2$ or $x \ge 9$

$\therefore \quad x \in (-\infty, 2) \cup (9, \infty)$

Graph of [x].

$y = [x] \qquad -3 \le x \le 3.$

Here we shall divide the domain into several intervals between two consecutive integers.

$x = 3,$	$y = [x] = 3$
$2 \le x < 3,$	$y = [x] = 2$
$1 \le x < 2,$	$y = [x] = 1$

Fractional part of x, i.e. $\{x\}$.

$\{x\}$ denotes the fractional part of x.

$\therefore \quad \{x\} = x - [x]$ where $0 \le \{x\} < 1.$

In other words $\{x\}$ is + ive and less than 1.

$\therefore \quad$ If $x = 2\cdot 30$, then $[x] = 2$, $\{x\} = \cdot 30$

If $x = -1\cdot 2$, then $[x] = -2$, $\{x\} = 0\cdot 8$ **(Note)**

$-\cdot 2 = -1 + \cdot 8$, -1 has gone to integral part to make it -2 and fractional part being + ive is $0\cdot 8$ **and not $-\cdot 2$.**

$[nx] = n[x]$ if n is an integer.

$0 \le x < 1,$	$y = [x] = 0$
$-1 \le x < 0,$	$y = [x] = -1$
$-2 \le x < -1,$	$y = [x] = -2$
$-3 \le x < -2,$	$y = [x] = -3$

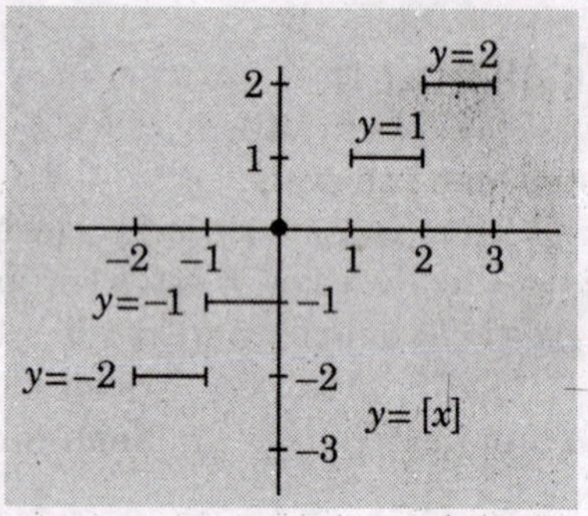

Fig. 16

It may be noted that the graph consists of thick line. The points with small circle like $(3, 2), (2, 1), (1, 0), (0, -1), (-1, -2)$ and $(-2, -3)$ do not form part of the graph.

If we exclude the sign of equality from the domain then we shall proceed as shown below.

If the domain of x be $]-2, 2[$ *i.e.* $-2 < x < 2$ then for evaluating $[x]$, we will have to divide the domain in separate intervals for calculating $[x]$.

i.e. $-2 < x < -1$	$[x] = -2$
$-1 < x < 0$	$[x] = -1$
$0 < x < 1$	$[x] = 0$
$1 < x < 2$	$[x] = 1$

Ex. 3. Solve the equations

(a) $4\{x\} = x + [x]$

(b) $\{x+1\} + 2x = 4[x+1] - 6$

where the symbol $[x]$ and $\{x\}$ have the usual meanings of integral part of x and fractional part of x.

Sol. We know that $[x] + \{x\} = x$

Putting for x in the given part (a),

$4\{x\} = \{x\} + [x] + [x]$

$\therefore \quad 3\{x\} = 2[x]$ ...(1)

Now, $0 \le \{x\} < 1$

$\therefore \quad 0 \le 3\{x\} < 3 \Rightarrow 0 \le 2[x] < 3$ by (1)

or $\quad 0 \le [x] < \frac{3}{2} \quad \therefore \quad [x] = 0$ or 1 ...(2)

Again from (1), $\quad 3\{x - [x]\} = 2[x]$

$\therefore \quad 3x = 5[x]$ or $x = \frac{5}{3}[x] = \frac{5}{3}.0$ or $\frac{5}{3}.1$ by (2)

$\therefore \quad x = 0, \frac{5}{3}$

(b) Using $\{x\} = x - [x]$, we have

$(x+1) - [x+1] + 2x = 4[x+1] - 6$

$\therefore \quad 3x + 1 = 5[x+1] - 6$

or $\quad 3x + 1 = 5([x] + 1) - 6$

or $\quad 3([x] + \{x\}) = 5[x] - 2$

$\therefore \quad 3\{x\} = 2[x] - 2$ ...(1)

Now $0 \le \{x\} < 1 \Rightarrow 0 \le 3\{x\} < 3$

or $\quad 0 \le 2[x] - 2 < 3$ by (1)

or $\quad 2 \le 2[x] < 5$ or $1 \le [x] < 5/2$

$[x]$ is an integer between 1 and 5/2.

$\therefore \quad [x] = 1$ or 2

Hence from (1), $\quad 3\{x\} = 2.1 - 2 = 0$ or $2.2 - 2 = 2$

$\therefore \quad \{x\} = 0$ or $\frac{2}{3}$

$x = [x] + \{x\} = 1 + 0$ or $2 + \frac{2}{3}$ i.e., $1, \frac{8}{3}$

§ 8. Inequalities :

I.* Sign of $(x-a)(x-b)$, $a < b$ **(V. Imp.)**

$(x-a)(x-b)$ is – ive if $a < x < b$ *i.e.* **x lies between a and b.**

$(x-a)(x-b)$ is +ive if either $x < a$ or $x > b$

i.e., **x does not lie between a and b.**

i.e., x is either less than a or greater than b.

(a) $|x| < a \Rightarrow x^2 < a^2 \Rightarrow x^2 - a^2$ is – ive

or $\quad \{x - (-a)\}(x - a) = -$ ive *i.e.* $-a < x < a$

(b) $|x| > a \Rightarrow x^2 \ge a^2 \Rightarrow (x^2 - a^2) \ge 0$

i.e. $\quad \{x - (-a)\}(x - a) \ge 0$

i.e. either $x \le a$ or $x \ge a$.

II. Triangular inequalities.

(c) $|x + y| \le |x| + |y|$

(d) $|x - y| \ge |x| - |y|$

Illustration :

(a) $|x - 3| > 5 \Rightarrow x - 3 < -5$ or $x - 3 > 5$

$\Rightarrow \quad x < -2$ or $x > 8$

$\therefore \quad x \in (-\infty, -2) \cup (8, \infty)$

(b) $|x + 3| \le 2 \Rightarrow -2 \le x + 3 \le 2$

$\Rightarrow \quad -5 \le x \le -1 \quad \therefore x \in (-5, -1)$

(c) $0 < |x - 1| \le 3 \Rightarrow |x - 1| \le 3$

$\Rightarrow \quad -3 \le x - 1 \le 3 \Rightarrow -2 \le x \le 4$

Also $|x - 1| > 0 \Rightarrow x \ne 1$

$\therefore \quad x \in [-2, 4]$ but $x \ne 1$

or $\quad x \in [-2, 1) \cup (1, 4]$

(d) $|x| > x \Rightarrow x < 0$ *i.e.* x is – ive

i.e. if $x = -5$ then $|-5| = 5$ or $5 > -5$

V. Imp. Sign of quadratic $ax^2 + bx + c$ is same as of its first term a provided its $\Delta = b^2 - 4ac$ is – ive.

III. Double Inequality. $a^2 < x^2 < b^2, a < b$.

This is equivalent to two inequalities.

$a < x < b$ and $-b < x < -a$

$4 < x^2 < 9 \Rightarrow 2 < x < 3$ and $-3 < x < -2$

$\because \quad 4 < x^2 \Rightarrow x^2 - 4 = +$ ive

or $\quad \{x - (-2)\}(x - 2) = +$ ive

$\therefore \quad$ either $\quad x < -2$ or $x > 2$ ...(1)

$x^2 < 9 \Rightarrow x^2 - 9 = -$ ive

or $\quad \{x - (-3)\}(x - 3) = -$ ive

$\therefore \quad -3 < x < 3$ ...(2)

Hence from (1) and (2), we get $2 < x < 3$ and $-3 < x < -2$.

Solution of Inequations

$$f(x) = y = \frac{(x-3)(x+4)}{x-2} \ge 0 \text{ i.e. +ive}$$

or $$y = \frac{(x+4)(x-2)(x-3)}{(x-2)^2}$$

The D^r is always + ive and for N^r the change points are $x = -4, 2, 3$ in ascending order. Mark them on the real line in that order.

Start with + sign from extreme right and then in subsequent intervals it will be –, +, –,...

$\therefore \quad y = f(x) = +$ ive $x \ge 3$

$= -$ ive $2 < x \le 3$

$= +$ ive $-4 < x < 2$

$= -$ ive $x \le -4$

The sign of equality will occur for $x = 3$ and $x = -4$. It will not occur for $x = 2$ as the function is not defined for $x = 2$. Hence $y = f(x)$ is +ive when $x \ge 3$, or $-4 < x < 2$.

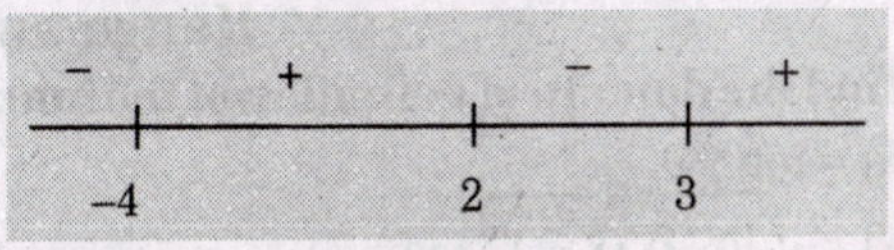

Fig. 17

Note : (1) Consider $\frac{(3-x)(x+4)}{x-2} \ge 0$, *i.e.* + ive .

Write all the factors in the form $x - a$ so that we write $(3 - x)$ as $-(x - 3)$. Then multiplying by – and changing the sign of inequality, we have

$$\frac{(x-3)(x+4)}{x-2} \text{ or } \frac{(x+4)(x-2)(x-3)}{(x-2)^2} < 0 \text{ i.e. – ive}$$

It will be so in $2 < x \le 3$ and $x \le -4$ as shown above

(2) If S is the set for which $\frac{2x+1}{2x^3 + 3x^2 + x} > 0$

or $\dfrac{2x+1}{x(x+1)(2x+1)} > 0$ or $\dfrac{1}{x(x+1)} > 0$

$2x+1 \neq 0$ then $x < -1$ or $x > 0$

$\therefore \quad S =]-\infty, -1[\cup]0, \infty[.$

(3) If S is the set for which $1 - e^{(1/x)-1} > 0$ then determine S.

$1 - e^{(1/x)-1} > 0 \Rightarrow e^{(1/x)-1} < 1$ or $e^{1/x} < e$

Since e is greater than 1 therefore above implies that

$0 < \dfrac{1}{x} < 1$

Now $\dfrac{1}{x} < 1 \Rightarrow x > 1 \therefore x \in]1, \infty[$ or $(1, \infty)$

$0 < \dfrac{1}{x} \Rightarrow \dfrac{1}{x} > 0 \quad \therefore \quad x < 0 \quad \therefore x \in (-\infty, 0)$

$\therefore \quad x \in (-\infty, 0) \cup (1, \infty)$

§ 9. Extension of a function :

Let $f : A \to B$ s.t. $f(x) = y \ \forall x \in A$

If $X \supset A$ *i.e.* X is a super set of A and $Y \supset f(A)$ then another function

$$g : X \to Y \text{ s.t. } g(x) = f(x) \ \forall \ x \in A$$

is called an extension of f from A to X.

Even and Odd Extension

Let $f(x)$ be a function defined on $A = [0, a]$ and $X = [-a, a]$ is a super set of A then an extension of $f(x)$ on $X = [-a, a]$ will be even or odd extension if $f(x)$ becomes an even or odd function on X.

Ex. 1. Let $f(x) = x^2 + 5x - 2$ defined on $A = [0, 2]$.

Let $g(x)$ = Extension of $f(x)$ on $[-2, 2]$

so that $g(x) = f(x) \ \forall \ x \in A$

Let us divide $X = [-2, 2]$ to $[-2, 0[$ and $[0, 2]$

$f(x) = x^2 + 5x - 2, f(-x) = x^2 - 5x - 2$

Let g_e and g_o denote even and odd extensions

$$g_e(x) = \begin{cases} f(x) : x \in [0, 2] \\ f(-x) : x \in [-2, 0[\ \because f(-x) = f(x) \end{cases}$$

for even

$$g_o(x) = \begin{cases} f(x) : x \in [0, 2] \\ -f(-x) : x \in [-2, 0[\quad \because -f(-x) = f(x) \end{cases}$$

for odd.

$$\therefore \quad g_e(x) = \begin{cases} x^2 + 5x - 2 : x \in [0, 2] \\ x^2 - 5x - 2 : x \in [-2, 0[\end{cases}$$

$$g_o(x) = \begin{cases} x^2 + 5x - 2 : x \in [0, 2] \\ -x^2 + 5x + 2 : x \in [-2, 0[\end{cases}$$

Ex. 2. Let $f(x) = x^2 + x + \sin x - \cos x + \log(1 + |x|)$ be defined on $[0, 1]$. Determine its odd extension to interval $[-1, 1]$. **(M.N.R. 1994)**

Let $g_o(x)$ be odd extension of $f(x)$ on $[-1, 1]$

$$\therefore \quad g_o(x) = \begin{cases} f(x) : x \in [0, 1] \\ -f(-x) : x \in [-1, 0[\end{cases}$$

Now $-f(-x) = -[(-x)^2 - x + \sin(-x) - \cos(-x) + \log(1 + |-x|)]$

$= -[x^2 - x - \sin x - \cos x + \log(1 + |x|)]$

$= -x^2 + x + \sin x + \cos x - \log(1 + |x|)$

$$g_o(x) = \begin{cases} x^2 + x + \sin x - \cos x + \log(1 + |x|), x \in [0, 1] \\ -x^2 + x + \sin x + \cos x - \log(1 + |x|), x \in [-1, 0[\end{cases}$$

Ex. 3. Let $f(x) = x^2 + x + \tan x$ be defined on $[0, 2]$. Determine both Even and Odd extension of $f(x)$ on $[-2, 2]$.

Ans. $g_e(x) = \begin{cases} x^2 + x + \tan x, & 0 \le x \le 2 \\ x^2 - x - \tan x, & -2 \le x < 0 \end{cases}$

$= f(-x)$

$g_o(x) = \begin{cases} x^2 + x + \tan x, \ 0 \le x \le 2 \\ -(x^2 - x - \tan x), \ -2 \le x < 0 \end{cases}$

$= -f(-x)$

Problem Set (2)

Range and Domain of a function.

In Q. 1 to 15 find the domain of definition of the functions :

1. (a) $f(x) = \log_x e$

(b)* $f(x) = \sqrt{\log[(5x - x^2)/6]}$

2. (a) $f(x) = \log|4 - x^2|$, (b) $\dfrac{1}{\log_{10}(1-x)} + \sqrt{(x+2)}$

3. (a) $\sqrt{4-x} + \dfrac{1}{\log_{10} x}$ (b)* $\sqrt{1 - \log_3 x}$

4. (a)* $\log_2 \{\log_{1/2}(x^2 + 4x + 4)\}$

(b) $\log_4 \log_5 \log_3 (18x - x^2 - 77)$

(c) $\log[1 - \log_{10}(x^2 - 5x + 16)]$

(d) $\sqrt{\left\{\dfrac{\log_{0.3}|x-2|}{|x|}\right\}}$

5. (a) $\log\{(\log x)^2 - 5\log x + 6\}$

(b) The domain of definition of

$f(x) = \dfrac{\log_2(x+3)}{x^2 + 3x + 2}$ is

(a) $\dfrac{R}{\{-1, -2\}}$ (b) $(-2, \infty)$

(c) $\dfrac{R}{\{-1, -2, -3\}}$ (d) $\dfrac{(-3, \infty)}{\{-1, -2\}}$ **(I.I.T. Sc. 2001)**

(c) $f(x) = \sqrt{\log_{0.4}(x - x^2)}$

(d) The set of all x for which there are **no functions** $f(x) = \log_{\frac{x-2}{x+3}} 2$ and $g(x) = \dfrac{1}{\sqrt{x^2 - 9}}$ is given by $[-3, 2]$. Prove.

6. (a)* $f(x) = 1/(|x| - x)^{1/2}$

(b) $\frac{1}{x+|x|}$

7. (a)* $f(x)=\sqrt{\{\cos(\sin x)\}}+\sin^{-1}\{(1+x^2)/(2x)\}$

(b) The domain of the derivative of the function $f(x)=\begin{cases}\tan^{-1}x & \text{if } |x|\le 1\\ \frac{1}{2}(|x|-1) & \text{if } |x|>1\end{cases}$ is

(a) $\mathbf{R}-\{0\}$ (b) $\mathbf{R}-\{1\}$
(c) $\mathbf{R}-\{-1\}$ (d) $\mathbf{R}-\{-1,1\}$

(I.I.T. Sc. 2002)

8. (a)* $\sin^{-1}\left[\log_2\left(\frac{1}{2}x^2\right)\right]$

(b) $\frac{\sqrt{4-x^2}}{\sin^{-1}(2-x)}$

(c) The natural domain of $\sqrt{\sin^{-1}(2x)+\frac{\pi}{6}}$ for all $x\in R$, is

(a) $\left[-\frac{1}{4},\frac{1}{2}\right]$ (b) $\left[-\frac{1}{4},\frac{1}{4}\right]$
(c) $\left[-\frac{1}{2},\frac{1}{2}\right]$ (d) $\left[-\frac{1}{2},\frac{1}{4}\right]$

(IIT-Sc. 2003)

(d) The domain of the function $f(x)=\sin^{-1}\frac{x-3}{\sqrt{(9-x^2)}}$ is :

(a) [2, 3] (b) [2, 3[
(c) [1, 2] (d) [1, 2[**(AIEEE 2004)**

9. (a) $\log\cos x$

(b) $\cos^{-1}\left(\frac{2-|x|}{4}\right)+[\log(3-x)]^{-1}$

(c) If $y=2^{-x}+\cos^{-1}\left(\frac{x}{2}-1\right)+\log\sqrt{x-[x]}$, then its domain is given by

(a) $(0,4)-\{1\}$ (b) $(0,4)-\{1,2\}$
(c) $(0,4)-\{1,2,3\}$ (d) none

(d) Domain of definition of the function $f(x)=\frac{3}{4-x^2}+\log_{10}(x^3-x)$ is :

(a) $(1,2)$ (b) $(-1,0)\cup(1,2)$
(c) $(1,2)\cup(2,\infty)$ (d) $(-1,0)\cup(1,2)\cup(2,\infty)$

(AIEEE 2003)

(e) If $y=\sin^{-1}\frac{x-1}{x+1}+\log(2-x)$, then its domain is :

(a) $(1,2)$ (b) $(-1,2)$
(c) $[0,2)$ (d) none

10. (a) The domain of definition of the function $y(x)$ given by the equation $2^x+2^y=2$ is

(a) $0<x\le 1$ (b) $0\le x\le 1$
(c) $-\infty<x\le 0$ (d) $-\infty<x<1$

(I.I.T. Sc. 2000)

(b) $f(x)=\sqrt{3-2^x-2^{1-x}}+\sqrt{\sin^{-1}x}$

11. (a) $y=\frac{\sqrt{x-1}}{x^2-4}$, $x\ge 1, x\ne -2, 2$

(b)* If $f_1(x)$ and $f_2(x)$ are defined on domains D_1 and D_2 respectively, then $f_1(x)+f_2(x)$ is defined on $D_1\cup D_2$. True or false ?

12. (a)* $y=\frac{\sqrt{(x^2-4)}}{\cos^{-1}(2-x)}$

(b)* $y=\left\{\frac{4-x^2}{[x]+2}\right\}^{1/2}$

(C.E.T. Punjab 1989)

13. (a)* $y=\frac{\sqrt{\cos x-1/2}}{\sqrt{6+35x-6x^2}}$

(b) $y=\sqrt{16x-x^5}+\log_{1/2}(x^2-1)$

14. $y=\sqrt{\frac{1-|x|}{2-|x|}}=\sqrt{T}$, say

15. If $|2x-1|+|3-x|>5$ or $|a|+|b|>5$

In Q. 16 to 22 find the range of the functions.

16. (a)* $y=\frac{x}{1+x^2}$ (b) $y=\frac{1}{2-\sin 3x}$

17. (a)* $y=\frac{3}{4-x^2}$ (b) $y=3-\frac{4}{x^2-4x+6}$

(c) $y=\frac{x-2}{x^2-2x+3}$

(d) Range of $f(x)=\frac{x^2+x+2}{x^2+x+1}$, $-\infty<x<\infty$, is

(a) $[1,\infty)$ (b) $(-1,\infty)$
(c) $\left[1,\frac{7}{5}\right)$ (d) $\left(1,\frac{7}{3}\right]$

(IIT-Sc. 2003)

18. (a) $y=\log\sqrt{x^2+6x+10}=\log z$

(b)* $y=\sin^{-1}\left[\frac{1}{2}+x^2\right]$

where [ ] denotes the greatest integer function.

19. (a) $y=3\sin x+4\cos(x+\pi/3)+7$

(b) $y=\frac{e^{-x}}{1+[x]}$ (c) $y=4^x-2^x+1$

20.* If $f(x)=1+x^2$ and $f[g(x)]=1+x^2-2x^3+x^4$, then determine the function $g(x)$ along with its domain and range.

21. If $f(x)=\frac{x^2-x}{x^2+2x}$, then find the domain and the range of f. Show that f is one-one. Also find the function $\frac{df^{-1}(x)}{dx}$ and its domain.

(I.I.T. 1999)

22. If $f(x)=\frac{e^x-e^{-|x|}}{e^x+e^{|x|}}$, determine range of $f(x)$.

What are the domain and range of the following functions in Q. 23 to 27 :

23. (a) $y = f(x) = \dfrac{x^2 - 3x + 2}{x^2 + x - 6}$.

Find the limit of $f(x)$ as x approaches 2.

[Range = [$y = f(x) : x \in$ domain of f]

(b)* $y = \dfrac{x + 2}{x^2 - 8x - 4}$ **(Roorkee 1995)**

24. (a) $y = \dfrac{1}{\sqrt{(4 + 3\cos x)}}$ (b)* $y = \dfrac{1}{\sqrt{(x - [x])}}$

25. (a)* $y = \sin\left[\log\left\{\dfrac{\sqrt{4 - x^2}}{1 - x}\right\}\right]$.

(b)* If $f(\sin 2x) = \dfrac{(2\tan x + \sec^2 x)(1 + \cos 2x)}{2}$, then determine the domain and range of $f(t)$.

26. (a) If $f(x) = {}^{7-x}P_{x-3}$, find domain and range of $f(x)$.

(b) The domain and range of the function $f(x) = \sqrt{{}^{x^2+4x}C_{2x^2+3}}$ are ... and ...

(c) Domain of the function $\dfrac{1}{\sqrt{{}^{10}C_{x-1} - 3\,{}^{10}C_x}}$ is given by

(a) 9, 10, 11

(b) 9, 10, 12

(c) all natural numbers

(d) none

27. (a) $y = \log_{10}(3x^2 - 4x + 5)$

(b) $y = \log_2\left[\dfrac{\sin x - \cos x + 3\sqrt{2}}{\sqrt{2}}\right]$

Solutions to Problems Set (2)

1. (a) The function is defined for all positive values of x except unity. This means that the domain of definition of the function consists of the interval $]0, 1[$ and $]1, \infty[$ or $[0, \infty[- 1$.

(b) The function is defined for all values of x for which $\dfrac{5x - x^2}{6} > 0$ ...(1)

and $\log[(5x - x^2)/6] \geq 0 = \log 1$ ...(2)

(1) $\Rightarrow x(5 - x) > 0$ or $x(x - 5) < 0$ ...(3)

(2) $\Rightarrow (5x - x^2)/6 \geq 1$ *i.e.* $x^2 - 5x + 6 \leq 0$ ...(4)

or $x(x - 5) < 0$ and $(x - 2)(x - 3) \leq 0$

$\therefore$ $D_1 =]0, 5[, D_2 = [2, 3]$

Hence the inequalities (1) and (2) will hold for $D_1 \cap D_2$ *i.e.* if $2 \leq x \leq 3$ or $[2, 3]$.

Draw D_1 and D_2 on real line and take the common part of both.

2. (a) Here $f(x)$ is defined for all real values of x except $x = \pm 2$. (Why ?) $4 - x^2 \neq 0$.

(b) $x + 2 \geq 0$ *i.e.* $x \geq -2$ or $-2 \leq x$. $= D_1$

Also $\log_{10}(1 - x) \neq 0$

$\therefore$ $1 - x \neq 1$ $\therefore$ $x \neq 0$. Again $1 - x > 0$

$\therefore$ $1 > x$ or $x < 1, x \neq 0 = D_2$

$D = D_1 \cap D_2$ *i.e.* $-2 \leq x < 1, x \neq 0$

It can be put in the form below :

$(-2 \leq x < 0) \cup (0 < x < 1)$

3. (a) $\sqrt{4 - x}$ is defined if $x \leq 4$ ...(1)

Again $\dfrac{1}{\log_{10} x} = \log_x 10$. This is defined if $x > 0$ and $x \neq 1$.

$\therefore$ $x \in (0, \infty) - 1$ ...(2)

From (1) and (2), we can say that

$x \in (0, 1) \cup (1, 4]$

or $x \in (0, 4] - \{1\}$.

(b) Above is defined if $1 - \log_3 x \geq 0$ and $x > 0$ or $\log_3 x \leq 1 = \log_3 3$ and $x > 0$ or $x \leq 3$ and $x > 0$ $\therefore$ $x \in (0, 3]$.

4. (a) **Before doing this question the following points should be noted carefully :**

$\log_a x$ is defined if $x > 0$ and $x \neq 0$

and $a > 0$ and $a \neq 1$

$\log_a x > \log_a y \Leftrightarrow x > y$, if $a > 1$

$\Leftrightarrow x < y$, if $a < 1$

Hence we must have

$\log_{1/2}(x^2 + 4x + 4) > 0$ or $> \log_{1/2} 1$ ...(1)

and $x^2 + 4x + 4 \neq 0$ ...(2)

(1) $\Rightarrow$ $x^2 + 4x + 4 < 1$ as $a < 1$

$\Rightarrow$ $x^2 + 4x + 3 < 0$

$\Rightarrow$ $(x + 3)(x + 1) < 0$

$\therefore$ $-3 < x < -1$ $\therefore$ $x \in (-3, -1)$

(2) $\Rightarrow$ $(x + 2)^2 \neq 0$ $\therefore$ $x \neq -2$.

Excluding -2 we can say

$x \in (-3, -2) \cup (-2, -1)$.

Above gives the required domain.

(b) $\log_5 \log_3 (18x - x^2 - 77) > 0$

$\Rightarrow$ $\log_3(18x - x^2 - 77) > 5^0 = 1$

$\Rightarrow$ $18x - x^2 - 77 > 3^1$

$\Rightarrow$ $x^2 - 18x + 80 < 0$

$\Rightarrow$ $(x - 8)(x - 10) < 0$ $\therefore$ $x \in (8, 10)$

(c) We must have $x^2 - 5x + 16 > 0$ which is true as $\Delta = -$ive and the sign of first term is $+$ive. Again by definition of $\log x$ we must have $1 - \log_{10}(x^2 - 5x + 16) > 0$

$\therefore \quad \log_{10}(x^2 - 5x + 16) < 1 = \log_{10} 10$

$x^2 - 5x + 16 < 10$ (Base > 1)

or $x^2 - 5x + 6 < 0$ or $(x-2)(x-3) < 0$

or $2 < x < 3 \quad \therefore \quad x \in (2, 3)$

(d) The given function is defined if $x \neq 0, x \neq 2$ and $\log_{0.3} |x - 2| > 0$ as we know that $|x|$ is always + ive

Now $\log_{0.3} |x-2| > 0 = \log_{0.3} 1$

$\Rightarrow \quad |x - 2| < 1$

The base 0·3 being less than 1, the inequality is reversed.

$\therefore \quad -1 \le x - 2 \le 1$ or $1 \le x \le 3$.

Out of above we have to exclude 0 and 2. Hence the domain is $1 \le x \le 3$ but $x \neq 0, x \neq 2$

or $x \in [1, 2) \cup (2, 3]$

5. (a) By definition $(\log x)^2 - 5 \log x + 6 > 0$ and $\log x$ is defined when $x > 0$

$(\log x - 2)(\log x - 3) > 0$

$\therefore \quad \log x < 2$ or $\log x > 3$

or $x < 10^2$ or $x > 10^3$

$\therefore \quad x < 10^2 \Rightarrow x \in (0, 10^2)$ as x cannot be – ive

$x > 10^3 \Rightarrow x \in (10^3, \infty)$

$\therefore \quad x \in (0, 10^2) \cup (10^3, \infty)$

Note : We have Union and not Intersection.

(b) Ans. (d).

$x + 3 > 0 \Rightarrow x > -3 \;\therefore\; x \in (-3, \infty)$

Also $x^2 + 3x + 2 \neq 0$ or $(x+2)(x+1) \neq 0$

i.e. $x \neq -1, \neq -2$

$\therefore \quad$ domain is $\dfrac{(-3, \infty)}{\{-1, -2\}}$

(c) $\log_{0.4}(x - x^2) \ge 0 = \log_{0.4} 1$

Since base is less than 1 above relation implies that $x - x^2 < 1$

or $0 < x^2 - x + 1$ or $x^2 - x + 1 > 0$

or $\left(x - \dfrac{1}{2}\right)^2 + 1 - \dfrac{1}{4} > 0$ or $\left(x - \dfrac{1}{2}\right)^2 + \left(\dfrac{\sqrt{3}}{2}\right)^2 > 0$

Above is true for all $x \in R$

Also $x - x^2 \ge 0$ by definition of $\log_a z$

or $x(1 - x) \ge 0$ or $x(x-1) \le 0$

$\therefore \quad x \in (0, 1) \quad \therefore \quad x \in (0, 1) \cap R = (0, 1)$

(d) $f(x)$ is defined if $\dfrac{x-2}{x+3} > 0$

or $\dfrac{(x+3)(x-2)}{(x+3)^2} > 0 \Rightarrow x < -3$ or $x > 2 = D_1$

and also $x \neq 2, x \neq -3$ by definition of $\log_a b$

$g(x)$ is defined if $x^2 - 9 > 0$

$(x+3)(x-3) > 0$

i.e., $x < -3$ or $x > 3 = D_2$

Fig. 18

Hence both are defined for $D_1 \cap D_2$

i.e., for $x < -3$ and $x > 2$ ...(1)

Therefore both are not defined for

$-3 \le x \le 2$ or $[-3, 2]$

6. (a) The function is defined for all values of x for which $|x| - x > 0$, whence $|x| > x$. If $x > 0$ then $|x| = x$ *i.e.*, not greater than x. Hence all + ive values of x shall not be in the domain of x. But if x is – ive then $|x| = -x > x$ or $0 > 2x$ or $x < 0$ *e.g.* if $x = -5$ then $|-5| = 5$ and $5 > -5$. This inequality will hold for all $x < 0$. Hence the domain of the function is $]-\infty, 0[$.

(b) Above is not defined when $x + |x| = 0$ or $|x| = -x$ *i.e.* x is – ive. $\therefore$ The function is defined when $x > 0$ *i.e.* $x \in (0, \infty)$.

7. (a) The following inequalities must be satisfied simultaneously

$\cos(\sin x) \ge 0, |(1 + x^2)/2x| \le 1.$

For all real x, $-1 \le \sin x \le 1$

$\therefore \quad \cos(\sin x) = \cos(y)$ where $-1 \le y \le 1$

Since $\cos(-\theta) = \cos\theta$

$\therefore \quad \cos(\sin x) = \cos(y)$ where $0 \le y \le 1$ **Ist quad.**

$\therefore \quad \cos(\sin x) \ge 0 \quad \forall \; x \in R$

$\therefore \quad D_1 = R$

Let D_2 be the domain of $\sin^{-1}\left(\dfrac{1+x^2}{2x}\right)$

$\therefore \quad \left|\dfrac{1+x^2}{2x}\right| \le 1$ or $\dfrac{|1+x^2|}{2|x|} \le 1$

But $1 + x^2$ is always +ive $\quad \therefore \quad |1 + x^2| = 1 + x^2$

$\therefore \quad 1 + x^2 \le 2|x|$ or $1 + |x|^2 \le 2|x|$

or $|x|^2 - 2|x| + 1 \le 0$ or $(|x| - 1)^2 \le 0$

$\therefore \quad |x| = 1$ or $x = \pm 1$

$\therefore \quad D_2 = -1, 1$ only

$\therefore \quad D = D_1 \cap D_2 = -1, 1$ *i.e.* only two points $x = -1$ and $x = 1$.

(b) Ans. (c). $|x| < 1 \Rightarrow -1 < x < 1$,

$|x| > 1 \Rightarrow x < -1$ or $x > 1$

$$f(x) = \begin{cases} \tan^{-1} x, & -1 < x < 1 \\ \dfrac{1}{2}(x-1), & x > 1 \\ \dfrac{1}{2}(-x-1), & x < -1 \end{cases}$$

$$\therefore \quad F(x) = f'(x) = \begin{cases} \dfrac{1}{1+x^2}, & -1 < x < 1 \\ \dfrac{1}{2}, & x > 1 \\ -\dfrac{1}{2}, & x < -1 \end{cases}$$

The change points for $f'(x)$ are $x = 1$, $x = -1$

Right hand derivative at $x = 1$ is 1/2 and left hand derivative is also $\dfrac{1}{1+1^2} = \dfrac{1}{2}$.

Hence $f'(x)$ at $x = 1$ is 1/2.

Now consider $x = -1$. Right hand derivative at $x = -1$ is $\dfrac{1}{1+(-1)^2} = \dfrac{1}{2}$ but left hand derivative is $-1/2$.

Hence $f'(x)$ is not defined for $x = -1$.

$\therefore \quad f'(x)$ is defined for all points except -1.

8. (a) We have $-1 \le \log_2 \left(\dfrac{1}{2}x^2\right) \le 1$

$\Rightarrow \quad 2^{-1} \le \dfrac{1}{2}x^2 \le 2 \quad \Rightarrow \quad 1 \le x^2 \le 4$

$\Rightarrow \quad 1 \le x \le 2 \quad$ or $\quad -2 \le x \le -1$.

Thus the required domain is $[-2, -1] \cup [1, 2]$.

(b) $4 - x^2 \ge 0, -1 \le 2 - x \le 1 \qquad x \ne 2,$

$D_1, -2 \le x < 2, \quad D_2, 1 \le x \le 3$

Required domain is intersection of D_1 and D_2 excluding $x = 2$

$\therefore \quad D = [1, 2[\quad$ or $\quad [1, 2)$

(c) Ans. (a).

We must have

$\sin^{-1} 2x + \dfrac{\pi}{6} \ge 0 \quad$ or $\quad \sin^{-1} 2x \ge -\dfrac{\pi}{6}$

$\therefore \quad -\dfrac{\pi}{6} \le \sin^{-1} 2x \qquad$ ...(1)

We know that $-\dfrac{\pi}{2} \le \sin^{-1} 2x \le \dfrac{\pi}{2} \qquad$ ...(2)

$\therefore \quad -\dfrac{\pi}{6} \le \sin^{-1} 2x \le \dfrac{\pi}{2}$

or $\quad \sin\left(-\dfrac{\pi}{6}\right) \le 2x \le \sin\dfrac{\pi}{2}$

or $\quad -\dfrac{1}{2} \le 2x \le 1 \quad$ or $\quad -\dfrac{1}{4} \le x \le \dfrac{1}{2}$

$\therefore \quad$ Required domain is $\left[-\dfrac{1}{4}, \dfrac{1}{2}\right]$.

(d) Ans. (b).

By definition of $\sin^{-1} x$

$-1 \le x - 3 \le 1 \quad \therefore \quad 2 \le x \le 4 \qquad$ ...(1)

Also $\quad 9 - x^2 > 0 \quad \Rightarrow \quad x^2 - 9 < 0$

or $\quad (x+3)(x-3) < 0 \quad \Rightarrow \quad -3 < x < 3 \qquad$ ...(2)

By (1) and (2), $\quad 2 \le x < 3 \quad \therefore \quad x \in [2, 3[$

9. (a) $\cos x$ must be +ive and $\cos x \ne 0$, *i.e.* $x \ne \pi/2$ or $-\pi/2$. Also we know that $\cos x$ is +ive in 1st and 4th quadrants.

$\therefore$ Domain $= \{x : 2n\pi - \pi/2 < x < 2n\pi + \pi/2\}, n \in I$.

(b) We must have $-1 \le \dfrac{2 - |x|}{4} \le 1$

or $\quad -6 \le -|x| \le 2 \quad \Rightarrow \quad -2 \le |x| \le 6$

We have multiplied by minus and reversed the inequality.

$\Rightarrow \quad |x| \le 6 \qquad$ as $|x|$ is + ive.

$\therefore \quad -6 \le x \le 6 \qquad$ ...(1)

Again $\dfrac{1}{\log(3-x)}$ is defined if $3 - x > 0$ and

$3 - x \ne 1 \quad \because \quad \log 1 = 0$

$\therefore \quad x < 3$ and $x \ne 2 \qquad$ ...(2)

$\therefore \quad x \in [-6, 3[$ except 2, by (1) and (2)

$\therefore \quad x \in [-6, 2[\cup]2, 3[$

-6 is included, 2 and 3 are not included.

(c) Ans. (c). $2^{-x} \Rightarrow x \in R$

Also $-1 \le \dfrac{x}{2} - 1 \le 1$

or $\quad -2 \le x - 2 \le 2 \quad$ or $\quad 0 \le x \le 4 \quad \therefore \quad x \in (0, 4)$

$x - [x] > 0 \Rightarrow [x] \ne x \Rightarrow x$ is not an integer.

Hence $x \in (0, 4) - \{1, 2, 3\}$.

(d) Ans. (d).

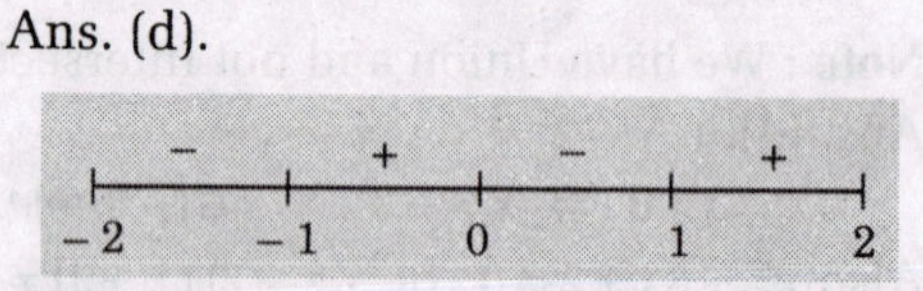

Fig. 19

For the function to be defined we must have

$4 - x^2 \ne 0 \quad \Rightarrow \quad x \ne 2, -2 \qquad$ ...(1)

Also $\quad x^3 - x > 0 \quad \Rightarrow \quad x(x+1)(x-1) > 0$

or $\quad (x+1)(x-0)(x-1) > 0$

From the above chart

$x \in (-1, 0) \cup (1, 2) \cup (2, \infty)$

(e) Ans. (c).

We must have $2 - x > 0 \quad \Rightarrow \quad x < 2 \qquad$ ...(1)

Also $x + 1 \ne 0$, *i.e.*, $x \ne -1 \qquad$ ...(2)

and $\quad -1 \le \dfrac{x-1}{x+1} \le 1$

Above relation leads to two inequalities :

$\dfrac{x-1}{x+1} - 1 \le 0 \quad$ or $\quad -\dfrac{2}{x+1} \le 0 \quad$ or $\quad x + 1 \ge 0$

or $\quad x \ge -1 \qquad$ ...(3)

and $0 \le 1 + \dfrac{x-1}{x+1} \quad$ or $\quad \dfrac{2x}{x+1} \ge 0$

or $\quad 2x(x+1) \ge 0$

or $\quad 2[x - (-1)][x - 0] \ge 0 \quad \Rightarrow \quad x \le -1$ or $x \ge 0$

$\therefore \quad x \ge 0$ by (2) and (3) and $x < 2$ by (1)

$\therefore \quad x \in [0, 2)$

10. (a) Ans. (d).

$2^y = 2 - 2^x > 0$ as exponential function 2^y is always +ive

$\therefore \quad 2^x < 2^1 \Rightarrow x < 1 \Rightarrow x \in (-\infty, 1)$

or $-\infty < x < 1$.

(b) $\sin^{-1} x \geq 0 \Rightarrow 0 \leq x \leq 1$

$3 - y - \dfrac{2}{y} \geq 0$ where $y = 2^x$ is +ive

or $y^2 - 3y + 2 \leq 0$ or $(y-1)(y-2) \leq 0$

$\therefore \quad 1 \leq y \leq 2$ or $2^0 \leq y \leq 2^1$

or $2^0 \leq 2^x \leq 2^1$

$\Rightarrow \quad 0 \leq x \leq 1$ as base 2 is greater than 1

$\therefore \quad x \in [0, 1]$

11. (a) Since $x \geq 1$, but $x \neq 2$

$\therefore \quad x \in [1, 2[\cup]2, \infty[$

We can also say $D = [1, \infty[- 2$

(b) False. Let $x \in D_1 \cup D_2$ such that $x \in D_1$ but $x \notin D_2$. Then $f_1(x)$ is defined but $f_2(x)$ is not defined. Hence $f_1(x) + f_2(x)$ is not defined for $x \in D_1 \cup D_2$.

[Note that $f_1(x) + f_2(x)$ is defined for $x \in D_1 \cap D_2$]

Note : Two functions $f(x)$ and $\phi(x)$ are said to be equal if $f(x) = \phi(x) \quad \forall x$

12. (a) $\cos^{-1}(2-x) \neq 0$

Now $\cos^{-1}(2-x) = 0$ if $2 - x = \cos 0 = 1$

$\therefore \quad x = 1.$ ...(1)

Hence $x = 1$ is excluded from the domain.

Let D_1 = domain of $\sqrt{(x^2-4)}$ then $x^2 - 4 > 0$

$(x+2)(x-2) \geq 0 \quad \therefore \quad x \leq -2$ or $x \geq 2$

D_2 = domain of $\cos^{-1}(2-x)$

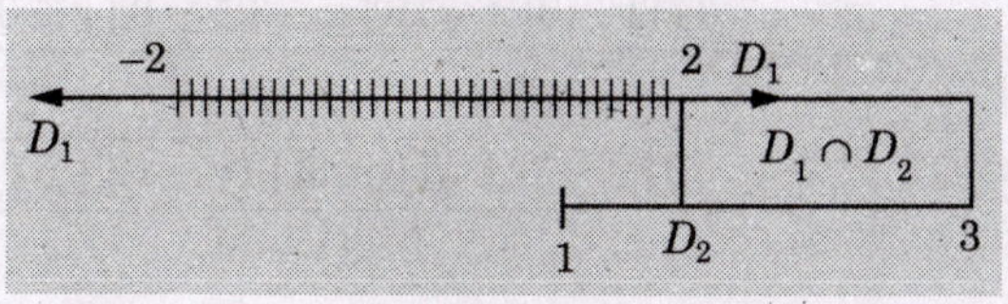

Fig. 20

$\therefore \quad -1 \leq 2 - x \leq 1$ or $x \leq 3, 1 \leq x$

$\therefore \quad 1 \leq x \leq 3.$ Exclude $x = 1$ by (1)

$\therefore \quad D_2 = 1 < x \leq 3.$

The required domain is

$D_1 \cap D_2 = [x : 2 \leq x \leq 3] = [2, 3]$

(b) Domain $= \left\{ x : \dfrac{4 - x^2}{[x] + 2} > 0 \right\}$

Case I. Both N^r and D^r are +ive

i.e. $4 - x^2 \geq 0$ or $x^2 - 4 \leq 0$

or $(x+2)(x-2) \leq 0$

or $D_1 = -2 \leq x \leq 2$ ...(1)

Also $[x] + 2 > 0$ or $[x] > -2$

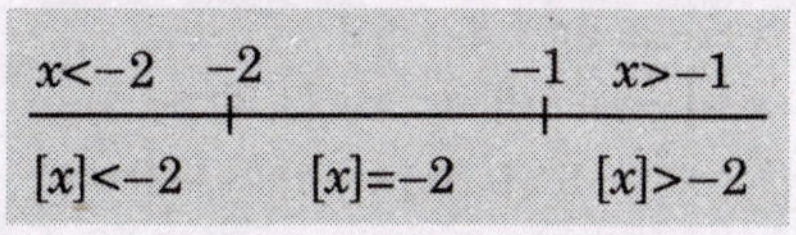

Fig. 21

Now we know $[x] = [-1.7] = -2$

$\therefore \quad [x] > -2 \Rightarrow x \geq -1$

or $D_2 = -1 \leq x$ ...(2)

Combining (1) and (2), *i.e.* taking their intersection

Domain $= D_1 \cap D_2 = -1 \leq x \leq 2$ or $[-1, 2]$

Case II. $4 - x^2 \leq 0$ and $[x] + 2 < 0$

(No sign of equality)

or $x^2 - 4 \geq 0$ and $[x] < -2$

$(x+2)(x-2) \geq 0$ and $[x] < -2$

$D_1 = x \leq -2$ or $x \geq 2$ and $D_2 = x < -2$

$\therefore$ Domain in this case is intersection of above two and hence it is $x < -2$ or $]-\infty, -2[$.

Combining the cases of I and II,

$D =]-\infty, -2[\cup [-1, 2]$

13. (a) D_1 is given by $\cos x \geq \dfrac{1}{2}$

$\therefore \quad 0 \leq x \leq \dfrac{\pi}{3}$ .... 1st quad.

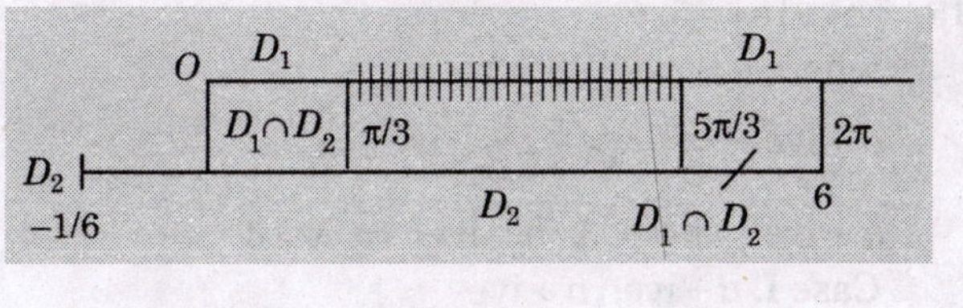

Fig. 22

or $\dfrac{5\pi}{3} \leq x \leq 2\pi$ ... 4th quad., $\pi = 3 \cdot 142$

$D_2 = 6 + 35x - 6x^2 > 0$

or $6x^2 - 35x - 6 < 0$

$(6x+1)(x-6) < 0 \quad \therefore \quad -1/6 < x < 6$

$\therefore \quad D_1 \cap D_2 = [0, \pi/3] \cup [5\pi/3, 6]$

(b) For D_1, $x(16 - x^4) \geq 0$

or $x(4 + x^2)(4 - x^2) \geq 0$

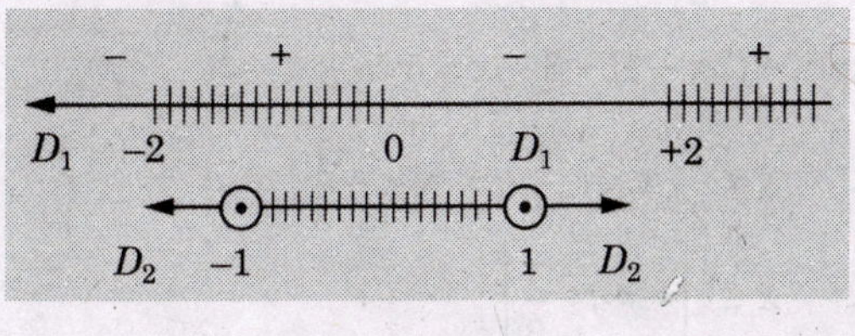

Fig. 22

Since $4 + x^2$ is +ive $\forall \; x \in R$, we must have

$x(x^2 - 4) \leq 0$

or $(x+2)\,x\,(x-2) \leq 0$

Change points are 2, 0, – 2.

$\therefore \quad x \le -2$ or $0 \le x \le 2$

$\therefore \quad x \in]-\infty, -2]$ or $x \in [0, 2]$

For D_2, $x^2 - 1 > 0$ or $(x+1)(x-1) > 0$

$\ne 0$ or $x \ne -1, 1$

$\therefore \quad x < -1$ or $x > 1$, $x \ne -1, x \ne 1$

$\therefore \quad D_1 \cap D_2 =]-\infty, -2] \cup]1, 2]$

14. $|x| \ne 2 \;\therefore\; x \ne 2, -2$ ...(1)

Now T is +ive if

$$T = \frac{[1-|x|]\,[2-|x|]}{[2-|x|]^2} = +\text{ive}$$

$\Rightarrow \quad [|x|-1]\,[|x|-2] > 0$

$\therefore \quad |x| < 1$ or $|x| > 2$

$(x^2 - 1) = -\text{ive}$ or $x^2 - 4 = +\text{ive}$

$(x+1)(x-1) = -\text{ive}$

or $\quad (x+2)(x-2) = +\text{ive}$

$\therefore \quad -1 \le x \le 1$ or $x < -2$ or $x > 2$

No equality by (1)

$\therefore \quad x \in [-1, 1]$

or $\quad x \in (-\infty, -2) \cup (2, \infty)$ ...(2)

Hence from (2)

$D = [-1, 1] \cup (-\infty, -2) \cup (2, \infty)$

Note : Here $D = D_1 \cup D_2$ and not $D_1 \cap D_2$ because of 'or'.

15. $|a| + |b| > 5$

where $a = 2x - 1, b = 3 - x$

$a + \text{ive} \Rightarrow x > \frac{1}{2}$, $a - \text{ive} \Rightarrow x < \frac{1}{2}$

$b + \text{ive} \Rightarrow x < 3$, $b - \text{ive} \Rightarrow x > 3$

Case I. a + ive, b + ive

$\therefore \quad x > \frac{1}{2}, x < 3$ and $2x - 1 + 3 - x > 5$

$\Rightarrow \quad x > 3.$ Contradictory results.

Case II. a + ive, b – ive

$\therefore \quad x > \frac{1}{2}, x > 3 \qquad \therefore \quad x > 3$

$2x - 1 - (3 - x) \ge 5$ or $3x > 9$

$\therefore \quad x > 3 \qquad \therefore \quad x \in]3, \infty[$ ...(1)

Case III. a – ive, b + ive

$x < \frac{1}{2}, x < 3 \qquad \therefore \quad x < \frac{1}{2}$

and $-(2x - 1) + 3 - x > 5 \Rightarrow x < -\frac{1}{3}$

$\therefore \quad x < \frac{1}{2}, x < -\frac{1}{3} \Rightarrow x < -\frac{1}{3}$

$\therefore \quad x \in \left]-\infty, -\frac{1}{3}\right[$ ...(2)

Case IV. a – ive, b – ive.

$x < \frac{1}{2}, x > 3$ and $-(2x-1) - (3-x) > 5$

or $\quad -x > 7$ or $x < -7$. Contradictory results.

$\therefore \quad x \in \left]-\infty, -\frac{1}{3}\right[\cup]3, \infty[$ [from (1) and (2).

16. (a) We have $y = 0$ at $x = 0$ and for $x \ne 0$

$$y = \frac{x}{1 + x^2} \quad \text{or} \quad yx^2 - x + y = 0$$

$\therefore \quad x = \{1 \pm \sqrt{1 - 4y^2}\}/2y$

Since x is real, the range of the function y is determined from the relation $1 - 4y^2 \ge 0$, or

$4\left(y^2 - \frac{1}{4}\right) \le 0$ whence $-\frac{1}{2} \le y \le \frac{1}{2}$.

(b) We have, $2y - y \sin 3x = 1$

or $\quad \sin 3x = (2y - 1)/y$

since $\quad -1 \le \sin 3x \le 1$

we have $\quad -1 \le (2y - 1)/y \le 1$ ...(1)

Since $y > 0$ (Why ?), multiplying the inequality (1) by y, we obtain $-y \le 2y - 1 < y$ whence $1/3 \le y \le 1$.

17. (a) The function is not defined for $x = \pm 2$.

Also $x^2 = \frac{4y - 3}{y}, y \ne 0$ ...(1)

Since x is real $\therefore \; x^2 = \frac{4y-3}{y} \ge 0$

or $\quad \frac{y(4y-3)}{y^2} \ge 0$ or $4y\left(y - \frac{3}{4}\right) = +\text{ive}$

$\therefore \quad y < 0$ or $y \ge 3/4$

$\therefore \quad \text{Range} =]-\infty, 0[\cup [\frac{3}{4}, \infty[$

Note : 0 is not included in the range by (1).

(b) $(y - 3)(x^2 - 4x + 6) + 4 = 0$

or $\quad x^2(y-3) - 4x(y-3) + (6y - 14) = 0$

$$\therefore \quad x = \frac{4(y-3) \pm \sqrt{16(y-3)^2 - 8(y-3)(3y-7)}}{2(y-3)}$$

$$= \frac{2(y-3) \pm \sqrt{(y-3)(4y - 12 - 6y + 14)}}{(y-3)}$$

Now x is defined if $y \ne 3$. ...(1)

Again since x is real, we must have

$(y - 3)(-2y + 2) \ge 0$

or $\quad 2(y-1)(y-3) \le 0$

$\Rightarrow \quad 1 \le y \le 3$ since $y \ne 3$ by (1)

$\therefore \quad 1 \le y < 3$ or $y \in [1, 3[$.

(c) Proceeding as in (b),

$\Delta \ge 0 \Rightarrow -2y^2 + 1 \ge 0$

or $\quad 2y^2 - 1 \le 0$ or $\left(y + \frac{1}{\sqrt{2}}\right)\left(y - \frac{1}{\sqrt{2}}\right) \le 0$

$\therefore \quad -\frac{1}{\sqrt{2}} \le y \le \frac{1}{\sqrt{2}}$

$\therefore \quad$ Range is $\left[-\frac{1}{\sqrt{2}}, \frac{1}{\sqrt{2}}\right]$.

(d) Ans. (d). $y = \dfrac{x^2 + x + 2}{x^2 + x + 1}$

$= x^2 (y-1) + x(y-1) + (y-2) = 0$

Since x is real

$\Delta \geq 0 \Rightarrow (y-1)^2 - 4(y-1)(y-2) \geq 0$

or $(y-1)(7-3y) \geq 0$

or $3(y-1)(y-7/3) \leq 0$

$\therefore \quad y \in [1, 7/3]$

18. (a) $z = (x+3)^2 + 1 \therefore \; z \geq 1 \; \therefore \; z \in [1, \infty)$

$\therefore \quad y = \log z \in [0, \infty) = \text{Range.}$

(b) $\sin y = \left[\dfrac{1}{2} + x^2\right] \leq 1$ as $\dfrac{1}{2} + x^2$ is +ive $\forall x$

$\therefore \left[\dfrac{1}{2} + x^2\right]$ is a + ive integer ≤ 1 *i.e.* 0 and 1 only.

$\therefore$ $\sin y = 0$ or 1 $\therefore$ $y = 0, \pi/2$ only two values.

$\therefore$ Range of $y = \{0, \pi/2\}$ only.

19. (a) $\cos\left(x + \dfrac{\pi}{3}\right) = \dfrac{1}{2}\cos x - \dfrac{\sqrt{3}}{2}\sin x$

$\therefore \quad y = \left(3 - \dfrac{\sqrt{3}}{2}\right)\sin x + \dfrac{1}{2}\cos x + 7$

If $3 - \dfrac{\sqrt{3}}{2} = r\cos\alpha$ and $\dfrac{1}{2} = r\sin\alpha$ then

$y = r\sin(x + \alpha) + 7$

Range of $\sin(x + \alpha)$ is -1 to 1.

$\therefore$ Range of $y = -r + 7, r + 7$

where $r^2 = \left(3 - \dfrac{\sqrt{3}}{2}\right)^2 + \dfrac{1}{4}$

or $r^2 = 9 + \dfrac{3}{4} + \dfrac{1}{4} - 3\sqrt{3} = 10 - 3\sqrt{3}$

or $r = \sqrt{10 - 3\sqrt{3}}$

$\therefore$ Range is $7 - \sqrt{10 - 3\sqrt{3}}, 7 + \sqrt{10 - 3\sqrt{3}}$

(b) The function is defined for

$1 + [x] \neq 0$, *i.e.*, $x \notin (-1, 0)$

$\because \quad 1 + [x] = 0$ if $[x] = -1$ *i.e.*, $x \in (-1, 0)$

$y = \dfrac{e^{-x}}{1 + [x]} \Rightarrow (1 + [x])\, y = e^{-x}$

Now e^{-x} is always + ive.

Hence above is possible if both the factors in L.H.S. are either + ive or both − ive.

$\therefore \quad y > 0$ and $1 + [x] > 0 \Rightarrow x \in [0, \infty)$

or $y < 0$ and $1 + [x] < 0 \Rightarrow x \in (-\infty, -1)$

$\therefore$ Range $y = R - \{0\}$

(c) $y = 4^x - 2^x + 1$

Above is defined for all $x \in R$

$\therefore \quad t^2 - t + 1 - y = 0$ where $t = 2^x$

$\therefore \quad t = 2^x = \dfrac{1}{2}(1 \pm \sqrt{4y - 3})$

$\therefore \quad x = \log_2 \left\{\dfrac{1 \pm \sqrt{4y-3}}{2}\right\}$

Now x is real and hence we must have $4y - 3 \geq 0$ and $1 \pm \sqrt{4y-3} > 0$ by def. of log x.

$\therefore \quad y \geq \dfrac{3}{4}$ and $1 - \sqrt{4y-3} > 0$

as $1 + \sqrt{4y-3}$ is clearly > 0

$\therefore \quad y \geq \dfrac{3}{4}$ and $\sqrt{4y-3} < 1$

or $4y - 3 < 1$ or $y < 1$

$\therefore \quad \dfrac{3}{4} \leq y < 1$

$\therefore$ Range $= \left[\dfrac{3}{4}, 1\right)$

20. $f[g(x)] = 1 + [g(x)]^2 = 1 + x^2 - 2x^3 + x^4$

$\therefore \quad [g(x)]^2 = x^2(x^2 - 2x + 1) = x^2(x-1)^2$

$\therefore \quad g(x) = \pm\{x(x-1)\} = \pm\{x^2 - x\}$

$= \pm\left\{\left(x^2 - x + \dfrac{1}{4}\right) - \dfrac{1}{4}\right\}$

$= \pm\left\{\left(x - \dfrac{1}{2}\right)^2 - \dfrac{1}{4}\right\}$

$\therefore \quad g(x) = \underbrace{\left(x - \dfrac{1}{2}\right)^2}_{+\text{ ive}} - \dfrac{1}{4}$ ...(1)

or $g(x) = \dfrac{1}{4} - \underbrace{\left(x - \dfrac{1}{2}\right)^2}_{+\text{ ive}}$ ...(2)

In either case domain of $g(x)$ is R.

In form (1) of $g(x)$ it is always $\geq -\dfrac{1}{4}$

$\therefore$ Range is $\left[-\dfrac{1}{4}, \infty\right)$.

In the form (2) of $g(x)$ it is always $\leq \dfrac{1}{4}$

$\therefore$ Range is $\left(-\infty, \dfrac{1}{4}\right]$.

21. $f(x)$ is not defined when $x^2 + 2x = 0$ *i.e.* $x = 0, -2$

$\therefore$ Domain is $R - \{0, -2\}$

or $x \in (-\infty, -2) \cup (-2, 0) \cup (0, \infty)$

$y = \dfrac{x^2 - x}{x^2 + 2x}$ $(x \neq 0) \Rightarrow y = \dfrac{x-1}{x+2}$

$\Rightarrow \quad x = \dfrac{1+2y}{1-y}$ $\therefore$ Range is $R - \{1\}$.

or $f^{-1}(y) = \dfrac{1+2y}{1-y}$ or $f^{-1}(x) = \dfrac{1+2x}{1-x}$

In order to find $\dfrac{d}{dx} f^{-1}(x)$ write

$f^{-1}(x) = -2 + \dfrac{3}{1-x}$

$\therefore \quad \dfrac{d}{dx} f^{-1}(x) = \dfrac{3}{(1-x)^2}$

and its domain is given by $R - \{1\}$.

$f(x)$ is one-one.

$$f(x_1) = f(x_2) \Rightarrow \frac{x_1 - 1}{x_1 + 2} = \frac{x_2 - 1}{x_2 + 2}$$

or $\quad x_1 x_2 - x_2 + 2x_1 - 2 = x_1 x_2 + 2x_2 - x_1 - 2$

$\Rightarrow \quad 3x_1 = 3x_2 \Rightarrow x_1 = x_2.$

Hence $f(x)$ is one-one.

22. **Case I** : If $x \geq 0$, then $|x| = x$

$\therefore \quad y = \dfrac{e^x - e^{-x}}{e^x + e^x} = \dfrac{e^{2x} - 1}{2e^{2x}}$

or $\quad e^{2x} = \dfrac{1}{1-2y} \Rightarrow 2x = \log \dfrac{1}{1-2y}$

$\Rightarrow \quad x = \dfrac{1}{2} \log \dfrac{1}{1-2y}$

$\Rightarrow \quad x = -\dfrac{1}{2} \log (1-2y) \geq 0$ as $x \geq 0$

$\therefore \quad \log(1-2y) \leq 0 \quad \therefore \; 1 - 2y \leq 1$

$\Rightarrow \quad -2y \leq 0 \quad$ or $\quad y \geq 0$ ...(1)

Also $1 - 2y > 0$ by definition of $\log_a x$

$\therefore \quad y < \dfrac{1}{2}$ ...(2)

Case II : $x < 0$ then $|x| = -x$

$\therefore \quad y = \dfrac{e^x - e^x}{e^x + e^{-x}} = 0$ ...(3)

Hence from (1), (2) and (3), we have

$$y \in \left[0, \frac{1}{2}\right[\quad \text{or} \quad y \in \left[0, \frac{1}{2}\right)$$

23. (a) We have

$$f(x) = \frac{x^2 - 3x + 2}{x^2 + x - 6} = \frac{(x-1)(x-2)}{(x+3)(x-2)}$$

The function f is not defined at $x = 2$ and $x = -3$.
Hence domain of $f = \{x : x \in R, x \neq -3, x \neq 2\}$.

$$\lim_{x \to 2} \frac{x^2 - 3x + 2}{x^2 + x - 6} = \lim_{x \to 2} \frac{(x-2)(x-1)}{(x-2)(x+3)}$$

$$= \lim_{x \to 2} \frac{x-1}{x+3} = \frac{2-1}{2+3} = \frac{1}{5}.$$

To find the range of f we first observe that it cannot take the value $\frac{1}{5}$ since it is not defined at $x = 2$.

Also for $x \neq 2$, we have $y = f(x) = \dfrac{x-1}{x+3}$

or $\quad xy + 3y = x - 1 \quad$ or $\quad x = -\dfrac{3y+1}{y-1}.$

Hence $y \neq 1$ in the domain of x. Also at $x = -3$, $y = \infty$.

Thus $f(x)$ takes all real values in the domain of x except $y = \frac{1}{5}$ and $y = 1$.

Hence range of $f = \{y : y \in \mathbf{R}, y \neq 1/5, y \neq 1\}$.

(b) $x^2 - 8x - 4 = 0$

$\qquad x = 4 \pm 2\sqrt{5}$

$\therefore \quad$ Domain $= R - \{4 \pm 2\sqrt{5}\}$

Now let $y = \dfrac{x+2}{x^2 - 8x - 4}$

$\therefore \quad x^2 y - (8y + 1)x - (4y + 2) = 0$

Since x is real $\Delta = B^2 - 4AC \geq 0$

$\therefore \quad 80y^2 + 24y + 1 \geq 0$

or $\quad (20y + 1)(4y + 1) = +$ive

$\therefore \quad y \leq -\dfrac{1}{4}$ or $\geq -\dfrac{1}{20}$

Also when $y = 0$, $x = -2 \in R$

$\therefore \quad y = 0$ also belongs to range

$\therefore \quad$ Range $= \left]-\infty, -\dfrac{1}{4}\right[\cup \left[-\dfrac{1}{20}, \infty\right[$

24. (a) Domain $= R$. Since $-1 \leq \cos x \leq 1$

$\therefore \quad y \in \left[\dfrac{1}{\sqrt{7}}, 1\right]$

The function is many-one but not one-one as for so many values of x we will have same image as $\cos(2n\pi + x) = \cos x$.

(b) The function is defined for all $x \in R$ except when $x - [x] = 0 \rightarrow x$ is an integer *i.e.* $x \in I$.

$\therefore \quad$ Domain $= R - I$, where I is the set of integers.

Also $x - [x] > 0$

$\therefore \quad x$ must be positive and $x - [x]$ is a positive fraction < 1.

Again $x - [x] = \dfrac{1}{y^2}$ from given relation

$$0 < x - [x] < 1 \quad \therefore \quad 0 < \frac{1}{y^2} < 1$$

$\therefore \quad y^2 > 1, \quad y^2 - 1 = +$ive or $(y+1)(y-1) > 0$

$\qquad y < -1, y > 1$ but y is +ive.

$\therefore \quad y > 1$. Hence range $=]1, \infty[$

25. (a) $\log_a z$ is defined if $z > 0, z \neq 0$

Hence $\quad \dfrac{\sqrt{4 - x^2}}{1 - x} > 0, \neq 0$

$\qquad 4 - x^2 = +$ive or $x^2 - 4 < 0$, $(x+2)(x-2) < 0$

$\therefore \quad -2 < x < 2$ ...(1)

Now $\sqrt{4 - x^2}$ is certainly +ive so we must have

$\qquad 1 - x > 0 \quad$ or $\quad x < 1$ ...(2)

$\therefore \quad$ Domain $= x : -2 < x < 1$ from (1) and (2)

Range is clearly $[-1, 1]$ as $-1 \leq \sin\theta \leq 1$

(b) R.H.S. $= \left(2\tan x + \dfrac{1}{\cos^2 x}\right)\cos^2 x$

$$= 2\sin x \cos x + 1 = 1 + \sin 2x$$

If $\sin 2x = t$, then we have

$f(t) = 1 + t$, where $t = \sin 2x$

where $-1 \le t \le 1$ $\therefore$ domain is $[-1, 1]$.

Adding 1 throughout,

$0 \le 1 + t \le 2$ or $0 \le f(t) \le 2$

$\therefore$ Range of $f(t)$ is $[0, 2]$.

26. (a) ${}^nP_r$ is defined if both n and r are +ive integers and $r \le n$

$\therefore$ $x \le 7, x \ge 3$ and $x - 3 \le 7 - x$

i.e. $x \le 5$ all the three conditions imply $3 \le x \le 5$

$\therefore$ Domain consists of integers $\{3, 4, 5\}$

Range $= y$ for $x = 3, 4, 5$, ${}^{7-x}P_{x-3}$

i.e. ${}^4P_0$, ${}^3P_1$, ${}^2P_2$

1, 3, 2 or $\{1, 2, 3\}$

(b) Ans. (1, 2, 3) and $1, 2\sqrt{3}$.

Both $x^2 + 4x$ and $2x^2 + 3$ are **+ ive integers.**

Now $2x^2 + 3$ is always +ive for real values of x

$x(x+4) \ge 0$ $\therefore x < -4, x > 0$

Also $x^2 + 4x \ge 2x^2 + 3$ by def. of ${}^nC_r$

or $x^2 - 4x + 3 \le 0, (x-3)(x-1) \le 0$

$\therefore$ $x \in [1, 3]$ $\therefore$ $x = 1, 2, 3$ (x being integer)

Above gives the domain

Range $= f(1), f(2), f(3)$

or $\sqrt{{}^5C_5}, \sqrt{{}^{12}C_{11}}\ \sqrt{{}^{21}C_{21}}$

or $1, \sqrt{12}, 1$ *i.e.* $1, 2\sqrt{3}$

(c) Ans. (d).

By definition of ${}^nC_r$, $r \le n$ $\therefore$ $x \le 10$ ...(1)

Also we know that $\dfrac{{}^nC_r}{{}^nC_{r-1}} = \dfrac{n-r+1}{r}$

Also ${}^{10}C_{x-1} - 3\,{}^{10}C_x \ge 0$

or $\dfrac{1}{3} \ge \dfrac{{}^{10}C_x}{{}^{10}C_{x-1}} = \dfrac{10 - x + 1}{x} = \dfrac{11 - x}{x}$ by (2)

i.e. $x \ge 33 - 3x$ or $x \ge \dfrac{33}{4}$ $\therefore x = 9$ ...(3)

$\therefore$ $x = 9, 10$ by (1) and (3)

27. (a) $3x^2 - 4x + 5$ is always + ive for real values of x as $\Delta = -$ ive and coefficient of first term is +ive. Hence domain is $x \in R$.

For range we have $3x^2 - 4x + 5 = 10^y$

or $3x^2 - 4x + (5 - 10^y) = 0$ where x is real

$\therefore$ $\Delta \ge 0 \Rightarrow 16 - 12(5 - 10^y) \ge 0$

or $10^y \ge \dfrac{11}{3}$ $\therefore$ $y \ge \log_{10}\left(\dfrac{11}{3}\right)$

$\therefore$ Range is $\left[\log_{10}\left(\dfrac{11}{3}\right), \infty\right)$

(b) $y = \log_2\left\{\dfrac{\sqrt{2}\sin\left(x - \frac{\pi}{4}\right) + 3\sqrt{2}}{\sqrt{2}}\right\}$

or $y = \log_2\left\{\sin\left(x - \dfrac{\pi}{4}\right) + 3\right\}$ ...(1)

Now $-1 \le \sin\left(x - \dfrac{\pi}{4}\right) < 1\ \forall\, x \in R$

$\therefore$ $3 - 1 \le 3 + \sin\left(x - \dfrac{\pi}{4}\right) < 4\ \forall\, x \in R$

Hence domain is R.

For range we have

$2^y = \sin\left(x - \dfrac{\pi}{4}\right) + 3$ by (1)

or $2^y - 3 = \sin\left(x - \dfrac{\pi}{4}\right)$

or $-1 \le 2^y - 3 \le 1$ as $-1 \le \sin\theta \le 1$

or $2 \le 2^y \le 4$ or $2^1 \le 2^y \le 2^2$

$\therefore$ $1 \le y \le 2$

Hence range is $[1, 2]$.

§10. Various types of functions

I. Periodic Function. If $f(x + \lambda) = f(x)\ \forall\, x, \lambda > 0$ then $f(x)$ is called a periodic function and λ (least) is called its fundamental period.

Since λ is period of $f(x)$, we have

$f(x) = f(x + \lambda) = f(x + 2\lambda) = f(x + 3\lambda) = \ldots$

We can say $\lambda, 2\lambda, 3\lambda, \ldots$ are all periods of $f(x)$ but only **smallest** of these numbers *i.e.* λ will be called the fundamental period.

We know that

$\sin x = \sin(x + 2\pi) = \sin(x + 4\pi) = \ldots$

$\cos x = \cos(x + 2\pi) = \cos(x + 4\pi) = \ldots$

$\tan x = \tan(x + \pi) = \tan(x + 2\pi) = \ldots$

Hence $\sin x$, $\cos x$ and $\tan x$ are periodic functions and their periods are $2\pi, 2\pi$ and π respectively, *i.e.* least value of λ.

Note : If period of $f(x)$ is λ, then period of $f(ax + b)$ is $\lambda/|a|$. Hence period of $\sin 3x$, $\cos(x/2)$ and $\tan(2x/3)$ will be $2\pi/3, 2\pi/(1/2) = 4\pi$ and $\pi/(2/3) = 3\pi/2$ respectively.

Period of f (x) + g (x).

If period of $f(x)$ and $g(x)$ be p and q respectively then the L.C.M. of p and q will be period of $f(x) + g(x)$.

Note : If there exists a number $r <$ L.C.M. of (p, q) such that $f(x + r) = g(x)$ and $g(x + r) = f(x)$ then r itself will be the period instead of L.C.M. of p, q.

Consider $|\sin x| = \sqrt{\sin^2 x} = \sqrt{\dfrac{1 - \cos 2x}{2}}$

$\therefore$ Period is $\dfrac{2\pi}{2} = \pi$.

Similarly period of $|\cos x| = \pi$

Now if $F(x) = |\cos x| + |\sin x|$

then its period is not π because there exists $\frac{\pi}{2} < \pi$ such that $|\cos(x + \pi/2)| = |\sin x|$

and $|\sin(x + \pi/2)| = |\cos x|$

Hence for $F(x)$ the period will be $\pi/2$ and not π.

Another rule for period of $f(x) + g(x)$

If period of $f(x) = \frac{l}{m}$ and of $g(x) = \frac{p}{q}$ where l, m are coprime and p, q are also coprime then period T of $f(x) + g(x)$ is given by

$$T = \frac{\text{L.C.M. of } (l, p) \text{ of } N^r}{\text{H.C.F. of } (m, q) \text{ of } D^r}$$

II. Bounded Function. The function $f(x)$ is said to be bounded above if there exists M such that $y = f(x) \ngtr M$ (*i.e.* not greater than M) for all x of the domain and M is called upper bound. Similarly $f(x)$ is said to be bounded below if there exists m such that $y = f(x) \nless m$ (*i.e.* never less than m) for all x of the domain and m is called the lower bound.

If, however, there does not exist M and m as stated above, then the function is said to be unbounded.

III. Odd and Even Functions. A function $f(x)$ is said to be odd if it changes sign when the sign of independent variable x is changed.

i.e. if $f(-x) = -f(x)$.

For example, $\sin^3 x \cos x$ is an odd function since

$$\sin^3(-x)\cos(-x) = -\sin^3 x \cos x.$$

A function $f(x)$ is said to be even if its sign does not change when the sign of the independent variable x is changed.

i.e. $f(-x) = f(x)$.

For example $ax^4 + bx^2 + c$ is an even function since its sign is unaltered by changing x into $-x$.

Students must not think that a function is either odd or even. There exist many functions which are neither even nor odd *e.g.*

$$3x^3 + 4x^2 + 5, e^x, \log x \, (x > 0)$$

are such functions.

Problem Set (3)

Even or odd, Identical and Periodic functions

In Q. 1 and 2 are the given functions identical ?

1. (a) $f(x) = x/x$ and $\phi(x) = 1$.
   (b) $f(x) = 1$ and $\phi(x) = \sin^2 x + \cos^2 x$.
2. (a) $f(x) = \log x^2$ and $\phi(x) = 2\log x$.
   (b) $f(x) = \log(x-2) + \log(x-3)$ and $\phi(x) = \log(x-2)(x-3)$.
   (c) $f(x) = x$ and $\phi(x) = (\sqrt{x})^2$.

In Q. 3 to 7 classify the functions for being even or odd :

3. (a) $\log(x + \sqrt{1 + x^2})$ (b) $\sin^5 x + 2\tan^3 x$
   (c) $x^2 - |x|$ **(D.C.E. 1997)**
   (d)* $x\dfrac{a^x + 1}{a^x - 1}$ (e) $\dfrac{\cos x \sin x}{\tan x + \cot x}$
   (f) $\dfrac{\sin^4 x + \cos^4 x}{x + x^2 \tan x}$
4. (a) If $\frac{d}{dx}[f(x)] = e^{-x} f(x) + e^x f(-x)$, then $f(x)$ is {given $f(0) = 0$}
   (a) an even
   (b) odd
   (c) neither even nor odd
   (d) can't say
   (b) If $f: R - R$ such that $f(x+y) + f(x-y) = 2f(x) f(y) \; \forall \; x, y \in R$ and $f(0) \neq 0$, then $f(x)$ is an :
   (a) even function (b) odd function
   (c) periodic function (d) none
5. (a) $\sin x + \cos x$ (b)* $\left[\dfrac{f(x) - f(-x)}{g(x) + g(-x)}\right]^n$
   (c) If $f(x)$ is a function which is both odd and even then $f(3) - f(2)$ is equal to
   (a) 1 (b) −1
   (c) 0 (d) none
6. (a)* If f is an even function defined on the interval $(-5, 5)$, then four real values of x satisfying the equation $f(x) = f\left(\dfrac{x+1}{x+2}\right)$ are ...., ..., ... and .... **(I.I.T. 1996)**
   (b) Show that the function
   $$f(x) = \int_0^x \log_e \left(\frac{1-t}{1+t}\right) dt$$
   is an even function.
   (c) Determine whether $g(x) = \sin \log [x + \sqrt{x^2 + 1}]$ is an even function or odd.
   (d) If f, g be two functions, then prove that
   (i) f odd, g odd $\to (fog)$ is odd.
   (ii) f even, g even $\to (fog)$ is even.
   (iii) f even, g odd $\to (fog)$ is even.
   (iv) f odd, g even $\to (fog)$ is even.
7. A function $f(x)$ can be uniquely expressed as the sum of an even and an odd function.

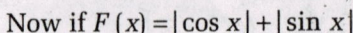

In Q. 8 and 9 find the fundamental period, if any, of the functions :

8. (a) $\sin (x/3)$ (b) $\tan 4x$

(c) $\cos 2\pi x$

9. (a) $|\cos x|$ **(D.C.E. 1997)**

(b)* $\sin^4 x + \cos^4 x$ (c)* $2 \cos \frac{1}{3}(x - \pi)$

10. (a) Does there exist a function which is periodic but has no fundamental period ?

(b)* Show that $x - [x]$, where $[x]$ = greatest integer not exceeding x is periodic.

11. Prove that the following functions are non-periodic :

(a) $\cos x^2$ (b) $x + \sin x$.

(c) $x \cos x$

12.* If the function $f(x) = \sin x + \cos ax$ is periodic, then prove that a is rational number.

13.* Is $\cos \sqrt{t}$ a periodic function ? If yes, then find the period. If not, then give reasons to explain your answer.

14. Find the periods of the following functions :

(a) $\sin \frac{2\pi x}{3} + \cos \frac{\pi x}{2}$ (b) $\tan 3x + \cos \frac{5x}{2}$

(c) $\cos (\cos x) + \cos (\sin x)$

(d) $\frac{1}{2}\left\{\frac{|\sin x|}{\cos x} + \frac{\sin x}{|\cos x|}\right\}$

15. If a function $f(x)$ satisfies the equation

$$f(x+1) + f(x-1) = \sqrt{3} f(x) \quad \forall x \in R$$

Show that $f(x)$ is a periodic function of period 12.

16. A function $f(x)$ is such that

$$f(a+x) = b + [b^3 + 1 - 3b^2 . f(x) + 3b \{f(x)\}^2 - [f(x)]^3]^{1/3}$$

for all $a, b, x \in R$. Prove that $f(x)$ is a periodic function of period $2a$.

Solutions to Problems Set (3)

1. (a) No; $\phi(0) = 1$ and $f(0)$ is not defined.

(b) Yes.

2. (a) No ; $f(x)$ is defined for all $x \neq 0$ and $\phi(x)$ is defined only for $x > 0$.

(b) No ; $f(x)$ is defined only for $x > 3$ but not for $x < 2$ and $\phi(x)$ is defined for $(x-2)(x-3) > 0$ *i.e.* $x > 3$ and for $x < 2$.

(c) No ; $f(x)$ is defined for all x, and $\phi(x)$ only for $x \geq 0$.

3. (a) $f(-x) = \log(-x + \sqrt{1+x^2})$

$= \log [\sqrt{(1+x^2)} - x]$. Rationalize.

$\therefore \quad f(-x) = \log \frac{(1+x^2) - x^2}{\sqrt{(1+x^2)} + x}$

$= -\log [\sqrt{(1+x^2)} + x] = -f(x)$

Since $f(-x) = -f(x)$. $\therefore$ $f(x)$ is odd.

(b) Odd as $f(-x) = -f(x)$

(c) $f(-x) = (-x)^2 - |-x| = x^2 - |x| = f(x)$. Even.

(d) $f(-x) = (-x)\frac{a^{-x} + 1}{a^{-x} - 1} = -x \frac{1 + a^x}{1 - a^x}$

$= x \frac{a^x + 1}{a^x - 1} = f(x)$

Hence $f(x)$ is an even function.

(e) Even as $f(-x) = f(x)$

(f) $f(-x) = \frac{\sin^4 x + \cos^4 x}{-x + x^2 \tan(-x)}$

$= -\frac{\sin^4 x + \cos^4 x}{x + x^2 \tan x} = -f(x)$

Hence $f(x)$ in an odd function.

4. (a) Ans. (b).

$f(x) = \int e^{-x} f(x)\, dx + \int e^x f(-x)\, dx = I_1 + I_2$

$\therefore \; f(-x) = \int e^x f(-x)(-dx) + \int e^{-x} f(x)(-dx)$

$= -[\int e^x f(-x)\, dx + e^{-x} f(x)\, dx]$

$\therefore \quad f(-x) = -f(x)$

Hence $f(x)$ is an odd function of x.

(b) Ans. (a).

Putting both x, y equal to 0 in the given relation

$2f(0) = 2f(0) . f(0)$ or $f(0)[f(0) - 1] = 0$

$\therefore \quad f(0) = 0$ or $f(0) = 1$ but $f(0) \neq 0$

$\therefore \quad f(0) = 1$ ...(1)

Again putting $x = 0$ in the given relation

$f(y) + f(-y) = 2f(0) f(y)$

or $f(y) + f(-y) = 2f(y)$ by (1)

$\therefore \; f(-y) = f(y) \Rightarrow f(x)$ is an even function.

Note : In the above if $f(0) = 0$ then putting $y = 0$ in the given relation

$f(x) + f(x) = 2f(x) . f(0) = 0$ as $f(0) = 0$

$\therefore \quad 2f(x) = 0 \Rightarrow f(x) = 0 \; \forall \; x \in R$

$\therefore \quad f(x)$ is both odd and even.

5. (a) $f(-x) = \sin(-x) + \cos(-x)$

$= -\sin x + \cos x$

Hence $f(-x)$ is neither equal to $f(x)$ nor equal to $-f(x)$. Therefore neither even nor odd.

(b) If the given function be $F(x)$, then

$F(-x) = (-1)^n F(x)$

Hence if n is even, then $F(x)$ is even and if n is odd then $F(-x) = -F(x)$ and hence it is odd.

(c) Ans. (c).

$f(-x) = f(x) \; \forall \; x \in R$

Also $f(-x) = -f(x) \; \forall \; x \in R$

$\therefore \quad f(x) = -f(x) \; \forall \; x \in R$

or $2f(x) = 0 \; \forall \; x \in R$

$\therefore \quad f(3) - f(2) = 0 - 0 = 0$

6. (a) **Ans.** $(-1 \pm \sqrt{5})/2, (-3 \pm \sqrt{5})/2$

$f(x) = f\left(\frac{x+1}{x+2}\right) \quad \therefore \quad x = \frac{x+1}{x+2}$

$\therefore \quad x^2 + x - 1 = 0 \Rightarrow \therefore \quad x = \text{etc.}$

Again $f(-x) = f(x)$ as f is an even function

$\therefore \quad f(-x) = f(x) = f\left(\frac{x+1}{x+2}\right) \quad \therefore -x = \frac{x+1}{x+2}$

or $\quad x^2 + 3x + 1 = 0 \quad \therefore \quad x = \text{etc.}$

(b) By definition $f(-x) = \int_0^{-x} \log\left(\frac{1-t}{1+t}\right) dt \quad$ ...(1)

Now put $-t = z \quad \therefore \; dt = -dz$ and adjust the limits

$\therefore \quad f(-x) = \int_0^{x} \log\left(\frac{1+z}{1-z}\right)(-dz)$

$= \int_0^{x} \log \frac{1-z}{1+z} dz = f(z)$

$\therefore \; f(-x) = f(x)$ and hence $f(x)$ is an even function.

(c) Let $f(x) = \log[x + \sqrt{x^2+1}]$ then as shown in Q. (3) $f(x)$ is an odd function $\therefore \; f(-x) = -f(x)$

Now $g(x) = \sin f(x)$

$\therefore \quad g(-x) = \sin f(-x) = \sin[-f(x)] = -\sin f(x)$

$\therefore \; g(-x) = -g(x)$. Hence the given function is an odd function.

Note : $g(x) = \sin x$ and $f(x) = \log[x + \sqrt{x^2+1}]$ both are odd functions

$\therefore \quad (gof)\, x = g(f(x))$

$\therefore \quad (gof)(-x) = g[f(-x)] = g[-f(x)]$

$= -g[f(x)] = -(gof)\, x$

$\therefore$ gof is also an odd function when both g and f are odd functions.

(d) Part (i) has been proved in last question.

(ii) Given $f(-x) = f(x); g(-x) = g(x)$

$(fog)(-x) = f[g(-x)] = f[g(x)] = (fog)\, x$

Hence fog is an even function. Similarly prove other parts.

7. Consider $F(x) = f(x) + f(-x) \quad$ ...(1)

$F(-x) = f(-x) + f(x) = F(x) \quad \therefore \quad$ Even

$G(x) = f(x) - f(-x) \quad$ ...(2)

$G(-x) = f(-x) - f(x) = -G(x) \quad \therefore \quad$ Odd.

Now $F(x) + G(x) = 2f(x)$ by (1) and (2)

$\therefore \quad f(x) = \frac{1}{2}[F(x) + G(x)] \quad$ ...(3)

where $F(x)$ is even and $G(x)$ is odd function of x.

For uniqueness :

Let, if possible, there exist $F_1(x)$ (even) and $G_1(x)$ (odd) functions of x such that

$f(x) = \frac{1}{2}[F_1(x) + G_1(x)] \quad$ ...(4)

Subtracting (3) and (4), we get

$0 = \frac{1}{2}[\{F(x) - F_1(x)\} + \{G(x) - G_1(x)\}]$

$\therefore \quad F(x) - F_1(x) = 0$ and $G(x) - G_1(x) = 0$

$\therefore \quad F_1(x) = F(x)$ and $G_1(x) = G(x)$

Hence the expression is unique.

8. (a) Since $\sin x$ has period 2π the function $\sin(x/3)$ has the period 6π.

(b) Since $\tan x$ has period π, the function $\tan 4x$ has period $\pi/4$.

(c) Ans. Period is 1.

9. (a) $|\cos x| = \sqrt{\cos^2 x} = \sqrt{(1+\cos 2x)/2}$

Now since the function $\cos 2x$ has period $\frac{2\pi}{2} = \pi$, the given function has also the period π.

(b) $\sin^4 x + \cos^4 x = (\sin^2 x + \cos^2 x)^2 - 2\sin^2 x \cos^2 x$

$= 1 - \frac{1}{2}\sin^2 2x$

$= 1 - \frac{1}{4}(1 - \cos 4x) = \frac{3}{4} + \frac{1}{4}\cos 4x.$

Since the function $\cos 4x$ has period $2\pi/4 = \pi/2$, the given function also has period $\pi/2$.

(c) Ans. Period $= 6\pi$.

(Hint : See Note P. 1260)

10. (a) Yes, for consider the function λ defined by

$\lambda(x) = \begin{cases} 1 \text{ if } x \text{ is rational} \\ 0 \text{ if } x \text{ is irrational} \end{cases}$

For any non-zero rational number r, we have

$\lambda(r+x) = \lambda(x) = \begin{cases} 1 \text{ for rational } x \\ 0 \text{ for irrational } x \end{cases}$

But there is no least number in the set of positive rational numbers.

As another example any constant function $f(x) = c$ (c a constant) is such a function since any real number α is a period but there is no least number in the set of positive real numbers.

(b) Yes, it is periodic, the period being 1.

$f(x+\lambda) = f(x) \Rightarrow x + \lambda - [x+\lambda] = x - [x]$

or $\quad \lambda = [x+\lambda] - [x]$.

This is true for all x and any constant λ. In particular the least integral value of λ *i.e.* 1 is the period. e.g. choose $x = 3\frac{1}{2}, 3, -3\frac{1}{2}$.

$\left[3\frac{1}{2} + 1\right] - \left[3\frac{1}{2}\right] = 4 - 3 = 1,$

$[3+1] - [3] = 4 - 3 = 1.$

$\left[-3\frac{1}{2} + 1\right] - \left[-3\frac{1}{2}\right] = \left[-2\frac{1}{2}\right] - \left[-3\frac{1}{2}\right]$

$= -3 - (-4) = 1.$

11. (a) Suppose, if possible, $\cos x^2$ has a period λ. Then we must have

$\cos(\lambda + x)^2 = \cos x^2$ for all real x.

This gives $(\lambda + x)^2 = 2n\pi \pm x^2$

or $x^2 + 2\lambda x + \lambda^2 \mp x^2 = 2n\pi$. ...(1)

But the relation (1) is impossible, since its right hand side is an integral multiple of 2π, whereas the left hand member contains a quadratic function of a continuous variable x and so (1) cannot hold for real values of x. For example, for $x = 0$ and $x = \lambda$, (1) reduces to

$$\lambda^2 = 2n\pi \text{ and } 4\lambda^2 \mp \lambda^2 = 2n\pi$$

whence dividing, get $4 \mp 1 = 1$ which is false.

(b) Suppose, if possible, $x + \sin x$ has a period λ. Then $\lambda + x + \sin(\lambda + x) = x + \sin x$ for all x.

This gives $\sin(\lambda + x) - \sin x = -\lambda$

or $2\cos(x + \lambda/2)\sin\lambda/2 = -\lambda$

or $\cos(x + \lambda/2) = -\lambda/\{2\sin(\lambda/2)\}$,

which is impossible for any constant λ since the left side is not constant.

(c) Proceeding as above in part (b), we will have

$$\frac{\lambda}{2\sin(\lambda/2)} = \frac{x\sin(x + \lambda/2)}{\cos(x + \lambda)}$$

Hence not periodic as in (b).

12. Let λ be the period of $\sin x + \cos ax$. Then

$$\sin(\lambda + x) + \cos a(\lambda + x) = \sin x + \cos ax$$

for all x.

In this identity, putting $x = 0$ and $x = -\lambda$, we get

$\sin\lambda + \cos a\lambda = 1$,

and $1 = -\sin\lambda + \cos a\lambda$.

Solving these equations, we get

$\sin\lambda = 0$ and $\cos a\lambda = 1$.

Hence $\lambda = n\pi$ and $a\lambda = 2m\pi$, where m, n are non-zero integers

Hence $\dfrac{a\lambda}{\lambda} = \dfrac{2m\pi}{n\pi}$ or $a = \dfrac{2m}{n}$ $(\because \lambda \neq 0)$,

which is a rational number.

13. Suppose $\cos\sqrt{t}$ is periodic with period λ.

Then $\cos\sqrt{(\lambda + t)} = \cos\sqrt{t}$, whence

$$\sqrt{(\lambda + t)} = 2n\pi \pm \sqrt{t}.$$

Squaring both sides, we get

$\lambda + t = 4n^2\pi^2 + t \pm 4n\pi\sqrt{t} \Rightarrow \lambda = 4n^2\pi^2 \pm 4n\pi\sqrt{t}$

Now for any fixed n, λ will not be constant for all t. Hence $\cos\sqrt{t}$ is not periodic.

14. (a) Period of $\sin\dfrac{2\pi x}{3} = \dfrac{2\pi}{\lambda} = \dfrac{2\pi}{2\pi/3} = 3$

Period of $\cos\dfrac{\pi x}{2} = \dfrac{2\pi}{\lambda} = \dfrac{2\pi}{\pi/2} = 4$

$\therefore$ Period of $f + g$ is L.C.M. of 3 and 4 *i.e.*, 12.

(b) Period of $\tan 3x = \dfrac{\pi}{3}$

Period of $\cos\dfrac{5x}{2} = \dfrac{2\pi}{5/2} = \dfrac{4\pi}{5}$

$\therefore$ Period of $f + g = \dfrac{\text{L.C.M. of } \pi, 4\pi}{\text{H.C.F. of } 3, 5} = \dfrac{4\pi}{1}$

(c) $\cos(\cos(\pi + x)) = \cos(-\cos x) = \cos(\cos x)$

$\cos(\sin(\pi + x)) = \cos(-\sin x) = \cos(\sin x)$

Thus both the functions f and g are periodic functions of period π and hence period of $f + g$ is L.C.M. of π and π *i.e.*, π.

But look there exists a number $\dfrac{\pi}{2}$ less than π

such that $\cos\left[\cos\left(\dfrac{\pi}{2} + x\right)\right] + \cos\left[\sin\left(\dfrac{\pi}{2} + x\right)\right]$

$= \cos(-\sin x) + \cos(\cos x)$

$= \cos(\sin x) + \cos(\cos x)$

$= \cos(\cos x) + \cos(\sin x)$

Above shows that period is $\dfrac{\pi}{2}$ but not π as found above.

(d). $\dfrac{\sin x}{|\cos x|}$. Period of $N^r = 2\pi$ and period of $D^r = \pi$

$\therefore$ Period of $\dfrac{N^r}{D^r}$ is L.C.M. of 2π and π *i.e.*, 2π

Similarly period of $\dfrac{|\sin x|}{\cos x}$ is L.C.M. of π and 2π *i.e.*, 2π

Hence the period of $f + g$ is L.C.M. of $2\pi, 2\pi$ *i.e.*, 2π

15. If $f(x + \lambda) = f(x)$ then λ (least) is the period of $f(x)$

$f(x + 1) + f(x - 1) = \sqrt{3}\, f(x)$ ...(1)

Let $x \to x + 1$ and $x \to x - 1$ in (1)

$\therefore$ $f(x + 2) + f(x) = \sqrt{3}\, f(x + 1)$

and $f(x) + f(x - 2) = \sqrt{3}\, f(x - 1)$

Adding the above we have

$f(x + 2) + f(x - 2) + 2f(x)$

$= \sqrt{3}\,[f(x + 1) + f(x - 1)]$

$= \sqrt{3}\,.\sqrt{3}\, f(x) = 3f(x)$ by (1)

$\therefore$ $f(x + 2) + f(x - 2) = f(x)$ ...(2)

Let $x \to x + 2$ in the above

$f(x + 4) + f(x) = f(x + 2)$

$= f(x) - f(x - 2)$ by (2)

$\therefore$ $f(x + 4) + f(x - 2) = 0$ ...(3)

Again let $x \to x + 2$

$\therefore$ $f(x + 6) + f(x) = 0$

$\therefore$ $f(x + 6) = -f(x)$ ...(4)

Now let $x \to x + 6$

$\therefore$ $f(x + 12) = -f(x + 6) = -[-f(x)] = f(x)$ by (4)

$\therefore$ $f(x)$ is a periodic function with period 12.

16. From the given relation on transfer of b and cubing, we have

$\{f(a+x)-b\}^3 = b^3 + 1 - 3b^2 f(x) + 3b\{f(x)\}^2 - \{f(x)\}^3$

$= 1 - \{f(x)-b\}^3$

$\therefore \quad \{f(a+x)-b\}^3 + \{f(x)-b\}^3 = 1 \qquad ...(1)$

Replacing x by $a+x$ in the above, we have

$\{f(2a+x)-b\}^3 + \{f(a+x)-b\}^3 = 1 \qquad ...(2)$

Subtracting (1) and (2), we get

$\{f(2a+x)-b\}^3 - \{f(x)-b\}^3 = 0$

$\therefore \quad f(2a+x) = f(x)$

Hence $f(x)$ is a periodic function of period $2a$.

§11. Increasing and Decreasing Functions.

$y = f(x)$ is an increasing or decreasing function in a certain interval if $\frac{dy}{dx} =$ +ive or – ive respectively in

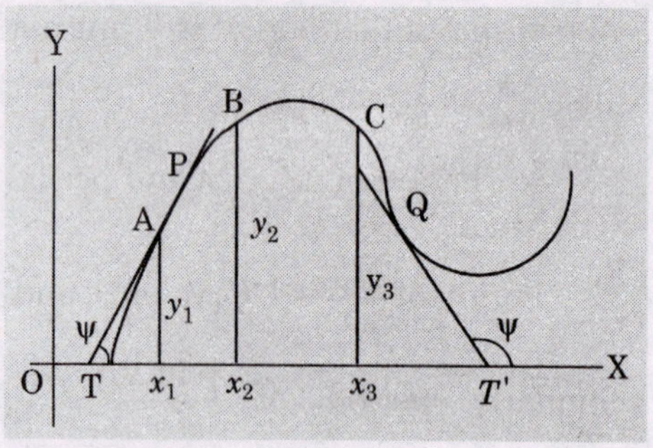

Fig. 24

that interval because the tangent will make an acute angle for increasing function and will make an obtuse angle for decreasing function. Hence,

$\frac{dy}{dx} = \tan \psi$

$= +$ for increasing ; $-$ for decreasing.

Remember $\forall\ x_2 > x_1$

$f(x_2) > f(x_1)$ for increasing function and $f(x_2) < f(x_1)$ for decreasing function *e.g.* $y = \sin x$, $y = \cos x$, $0 \le x \le \pi/2$

$\frac{dy}{dx} = \cos x = +$ ive,

$\frac{dy}{dx} = -\sin x = -$ ive.

$\therefore$ In the given interval $\sin x$ is an increasing function whereas $\cos x$ is a decreasing function.

$x_2 > x_1$ *i.e.* $\pi/3 > \pi/6$

$f(x_2) > f(x_1)$ *i.e.* $\sin(\pi/3) > \sin(\pi/6)$

i.e. $\sqrt{3}/2 > 1/2$

$f(x_2) < f(x_1)$ *i.e.* $\cos(\pi/3) < \cos(\pi/6)$

i.e. $1/2 < \sqrt{3}/2$.

As a matter of fact we should say that $\sin x$ is **strictly increasing** and $\cos x$ is **strictly decreasing**. However if we have the sign of equality also, *i.e.*, $f(x_2) \ge f(x_1)$ or $f(x_2) \le f(x_1)$, then we shall say $f(x)$ is **monotonically increasing or monotonically decreasing.**

Criteria : $y = f(x)$ is increasing (strictly increasing) if $\frac{dy}{dx} > 0$ and non-decreasing if $\frac{dy}{dx} \ge 0$. Similarly $f(x)$ is decreasing (strictly decreasing) if $\frac{dy}{dx} < 0$ and non-increasing if $\frac{dy}{dx} \le 0$.

Ex. 1. Determine the intervals of monotonicity of the function

$f(x) = y = x^4 - 12x^3 + 52x^2 - 96x + 7$

$\frac{dy}{dx} = 4x^3 - 36x^2 + 104x - 96$

$= 4(x^3 - 9x^2 + 26x - 24)$

$= 4(x-2)(x^2 - 7x + 12)$

$= 4(x-2)(x-3)(x-4) = 0$

$\therefore \quad x = 2, 3, 4$

Very important rule :

Mark these points on the real line. Start with +ive sign from $x > 4$ (extreme right) and then with alternately – ive, +ive in successive intervals while moving to the left as shown in the figure :

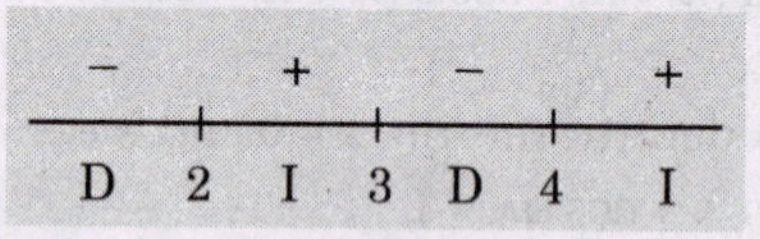

Fig. 45

I stands for increasing and D stands for decreasing.

Hence for $x > 4$, $f(x)$ is increasing

$3 < x < 4$, $f(x)$ decreasing

$2 < x < 3$, $f(x)$ increasing

$x < 2$, $f(x)$ is decreasing

$\therefore \quad f(x)$ is increasing in $]4, \infty[\ \cup\ ]2, 3[$

and $f(x)$ is decreasing in $]-\infty, 2[\ \cup\ ]3, 4[$

Behaviour of a function at $x = a$

$f'(a)$	$f''(a)$	$f''(a)$	Behaviour of f at $x = a$
+			Increasing
–			Decreasing
0	+		Minimum
0	–		Maximum
0	0		?
0	0	±	Inflection
	0	+	?

Problem Set (4)

Increasing and decreasing functions.

1. (a) Separate the intervals in which the polynomial $2x^3 - 15x^2 + 36x + 1$ is increasing or decreasing.

(b) Find the interval of monotonicity of $f(x) = \dfrac{x}{x^2 - 6x - 16}$.

(c) Show that $x^3 - 3x^2 + 3x - 2$ is monotonically increasing in every interval.

2. (a) Determine the interval in which the function $f(x) = 2x + \cot^{-1} x - \log\{x + \sqrt{(1 + x^2)}\}$ is increasing.

(b) Find the intervals of monotonicity of

$$f(x) = \frac{1 - x + x^2}{1 + x + x^2}$$

3. (a) Determine the intervals of monotonicity of $f(x) = \log|x|$.

(b) Determine the intervals of monotonicity of the function $f(x) = (2^x - 1)(2^x - 2)^2$

(c) Determine the intervals of monotonicity of the function

$$f(x) = \begin{vmatrix} x + a^2 & ab & ac \\ ab & x + b^2 & bc \\ ac & bc & x + c^2 \end{vmatrix}$$

(d) Find the intervals of monotonicity of the functions

(i) $x^x, x > 0$ (ii) $\dfrac{x}{\log x}$

4. (a)* Determine the condition so that the function $f(x) = x^3 + px^2 + qx + r$ is an increasing function for all real x.

(b)* Let $h(x) = f(x) - (f(x))^2 + (f(x))^3$ for every real number x. Then

(a) h is increasing whenever f is increasing

(b) h is increasing whenever f is decreasing

(c) h is decreasing whenever f is decreasing

(d) nothing can be said in general. **(I.I.T. 1998)**

(c) If $f(x) = x^3 + bx^2 + cx + d$ and $0 < b^2 < c$, then in $(-\infty, \infty)$, $f(x)$

(a) is increasing (b) has local maxima

(c) is decreasing (d) is bounded

(Screening 2004)

5. (a)* The function $f(x) = \dfrac{\log(\pi + x)}{\log(e + x)}$ is a decreasing function in the interval $]0, \infty[$. Is this statement true or false ?

(b) $f(x) = \begin{cases} x + 7 & \text{if } x < -3 \\ |x + 1| & \text{if } -3 \le x < 1 \\ 5 - 2x & \text{if } x \ge 1 \end{cases}$

Determine the intervals of monotonicity.

(c)* Find the intervals in which the function $f(x) = 3\cos^4 x + 10\cos^3 x + 6\cos^2 x - 3$, $0 \le x \le \pi$; is monotonically increasing or decreasing. **(Roorkee 1995)**

(d) The function $f(x) = \sin^4 x + \cos^4 x$ increases if

(a) $0 < x < \dfrac{\pi}{8}$ (b) $\dfrac{\pi}{4} < x < \dfrac{3\pi}{8}$

(c) $\dfrac{3\pi}{8} < x < \dfrac{5\pi}{8}$ (d) $\dfrac{5\pi}{8} < x < \dfrac{3\pi}{4}$ **(I.I.T. 1999)**

(e) The length of a longest interval in which the function $3\sin x - 4\sin^3 x$ is increasing, is

(a) $\dfrac{\pi}{3}$ (b) $\dfrac{\pi}{2}$

(c) $\dfrac{3\pi}{2}$ (d) π **(I.I.T. Sc. 2002)**

6. (a) Let $f(x) = x^3 + 6x^2 + px + 2$. If the largest possible interval in which $f(x)$ is a decreasing function in $(-3, -1)$ then p is equal to :

(a) 2 (b) 6

(c) 8 (d) 9

(b) If $\dfrac{x^2}{f(4a)} + \dfrac{y^2}{f(a^2 - 5)}$ represents an ellipse with major axis as y-axis and f is a decreasing function, then a belongs to :

(a) (1, 4) (b) (− 1, 1)

(c) (− 1, 5) (d) (5, ∞)

(c) A function is matched below against an interval where it is supposed to be increasing. Which of the following pairs is incorrectly matched :

	Interval	Function $f(x)$
(a)	$\left]-\infty, \frac{1}{3}\right]$	$3x^2 - 2x + 1$
(b)	$]-\infty, -4]$	$x^3 + 6x^2 + 6$
(c)	$]-\infty, \infty[$	$x^3 - 3x^2 + 3x + 3$
(d)	$[2, \infty[$	$2x^3 - 3x^2 - 12x + 6$

(AIEEE 2005)

7. (a)* Determine the intervals of monotonicity of the function $\sin x + \cos x$ in $[0, 2\pi]$.

(b) If $f(x) = \tan^{-1}(\sin x + \cos x), 0 \le x \le \pi$

Determine the intervals of monotonicity.

(c) Find the interval in which the function $f(x) = \sin(\log_e x) + \cos(\log_e x)$ is decreasing.

8. (a)* If $f(x) = \cos(\pi/x)$, then find the intervals in which the function is increasing or decreasing.

(b) If $f(x) = \cos\left(2x + \frac{\pi}{4}\right)$ then find the interval in which the function is increasing.

(c) $y = \sin x - a\sin 2x - \frac{1}{3}\sin 3x + 2ax$, then y increases for all values of x if $a > 1$.

9. (a)* Write the correct entry from column (2) against column (1). Let the function defined in column (1) have domain $(-\pi/2, \pi/2)$

Column 1	Column 2
(i) $x + \sin x$	(A) Increasing
	(B) Decreasing
(ii) $\sec x$	(C) Neither increasing nor decreasing

(I.I.T. 1992)

(b) Show that the function $f(x) = \tan x - x$ never decreases on its domain. **(M.N.R. 1995)**

10. If $f(x) = \frac{x}{\sin x}$ and $g(x) = \frac{x}{\tan x}$, where $0 < x \le 1$, then in this interval

(i) Both $f(x)$ and $g(x)$ are increasing functions.
(ii) Both $f(x)$ and $g(x)$ are decreasing functions.
(iii) $f(x)$ is an increasing function.
(iv) $g(x)$ is an increasing function. **(I.I.T. Re-ex. 1997)**

11.* Show that $x/(1+x) < \log(1+x) < x$ for $x > 0$

12. Prove that $\frac{x}{1+x^2} < \tan^{-1} x < x$ for $x > 0$

13. (a) If $0 < x < 1$ then prove that $\tan^{-1} x < x + \frac{x^3}{6}$

(b)* Prove the inequalities $x - \frac{x^3}{3} < \tan^{-1} x < x - \frac{x^3}{6}$ for $0 < x \le 1$.

14. (a)* If $4x + 8\cos x + \tan x - 2\sec x - 4\log\{\cos x(1+\sin x)\} \ge 6$ for all $x \in [0, \lambda)$ then prove that $\lambda = \pi/6$.

(b) If $0 < x < \pi/2$, then prove that $\tan^2 x + 6\log\sec x + 2\cos x + 4 > 6\sec x$.

15. (a) For all $x \in (0, 1)$

(a) $e^x < 1 + x$ (b) $\log_e(1+x) < x$
(c) $\sin x > x$ (d) $\log_e x > x$

(I.I.T. Sc. 2000)

(b) Let $f(x) = \int e^x (x-1)(x-2)\,dx$. Then f decreases in the interval

(a) $(-\infty, -2)$ (b) $(-2, -1)$
(c) $(1, 2)$ (d) $(2, +\infty)$ **(I.I.T. Sc. 2000)**

(c) $P(x)$ is a polynomial function such that $P(1) = 0$, $P'(x) > P(x), \forall\, x > 1$. Prove that $P(x) > 0, \forall\, x > 1$. **(I.I.T. 2003)**

(d) Using $2(1 - \cos x) \le x, \forall\, x \in [0, \pi/4]$ or otherwise prove that $\sin(\tan x) \ge x, \forall\, x \in [0, \pi/4]$ **(I.I.T. 2003)**

(e) If $f(x) = \int_{x^2}^{x^2+1} e^{-t^2}\,dt$ find the interval in which $f(x)$ is increasing

(a) $(0, \infty)$ (b) $(-\infty, 0)$
(c) $[-2, 2]$ (d) no where

(Screening 2003)

16. (a) If $f(x) = xe^{x(1-x)}$, then $f(x)$ is

(a) increasing on $\left[-\frac{1}{2}, 1\right]$
(b) decreasing on R
(c) increasing on R
(d) decreasing on $\left[-\frac{1}{2}, 1\right]$ **(I.I.T. Sc. 2001)**

(b) Show that

$$f(x) = \int_1^{e^x} [\sin^2(2\log t) - 3\sin(2\log t) + 2]\,dt$$

cannot be decreasing anywhere.

(c) The difference between the greatest and the least values of the function

$$f(x) = \int_0^x (at^2 + 1 + \cos t)\,dt, a > 0, x \in [2, 3] \text{ is :}$$

(a) $\frac{19}{3}a + 1 + \sin 3 - \sin 2$
(b) $\frac{18}{3}a + 1 + 2\sin 3$
(c) $\frac{18}{3}a - 1 + 2\sin 3$
(d) none

17.* Show that

$$1 + x\log\{x + \sqrt{x^2+1}\} \ge \sqrt{1+x^2}$$

for all $x \ge 0$.

18. (a) Show that the function $f : \mathbf{R} \to \mathbf{R}$ defined by $f(x) = x\left[1 + \frac{1}{3}\sin\log x^2\right]$ when $x \ne 0$ and $f(0) = 0$ is everywhere continuous and monotonic but has no differential coefficient at the origin.

(b)* Use the function $f(x) = x^{1/x}$, $x > 0$, to determine the bigger of the two numbers e^π and π^e.

19. (a)* Find the intervals of monotonicity of the function $y = 2x^2 - \log|x|$, $(x \ne 0)$

(b) $y = \frac{|x-1|}{x^2}$

20. (a)* If $y = x^2(x-2)^2$ find for what values of x, y increases.

(b) Show that $f(x) = (x-2)e^x + x + 2$ is +ive for all +ive values of x.

21. (a) Prove that $x - x^3/6 < \sin x < x$ for $0 < x \le \pi/2$.

(b)* Prove that

$2\sin x+\tan x\geq 3x$ where $0\leq x\leq \pi/2$

(I.I.T.1990)

22. (a) If $g(x)=f(x)+f(1-x)$ and $f''(x)<0,\ 0\leq x\leq 1$ then find the intervals of monotonicity of $g(x)$.

(b) If $g(x)=2f\left(\frac{x}{2}\right)+f(2-x)$ and $f''(x)<0$ for all $x\in(0,2)$, then find the intervals of monotonicity of $g(x)$.

23.* If $ax+\frac{b}{x}\geq c$ for all +ive values of x then prove that $4ab\geq c^2$, where a,b,c are +ive constants.

24. If $ax^2+b/x\geq c\ \ \forall\ x>0$ where $a>0, b>0$, then prove that $27ab^2\geq 4c^3$.

25. (a)* Let f and g be increasing and decreasing functions respectively from $[0,\infty)$ to $[0,\infty)$ and let $h(x)=f[g(x)]$. If $h(0)=0$ then $h(x)-h(1)$ is

(i) always zero (ii) always negative

(iii) always positive (iv) Strictly increasing

(v) None of these

(b)* The set of all x for which $\log(1+x)\leq x$ is equal to $(-1,\infty)$.

26.* Let $f(x)=\begin{cases}-x^3+\dfrac{b^3-b^2+b-1}{b^2+3b+2}, & 0\leq x<1\\ 2x-3, & 1\leq x\leq 3\end{cases}$

Find all possible real values of b such that $f(x)$ has the smallest value at $x=1$. **(I.I.T. 1993)**

27. (a)* Let $f(x)=\begin{cases}xe^{ax}, & x\leq 0\\ x+ax^2-x^3, & x>0\end{cases}$ where a is a positive constant. Find the interval in which (i) $f(x)$ is increasing, (ii) $f'(x)$ is increasing.

(I.I.T. 1996)

(b) Let the function $g:(-\infty,\infty)\to\left(-\frac{\pi}{2},\frac{\pi}{2}\right)$ be given by

$g(u)=2\tan^{-1}(e^u)-\frac{\pi}{2}$. Then, g is

(a) even and is strictly increasing in $(0,\infty)$

(b) odd and is strictly decreasing in $(-\infty,\infty)$

(c) odd and is strictly increasing in $(-\infty,\infty)$

(d) neither even nor odd, but is strictly increasing in $(-\infty,\infty)$ **(I.I.T. 2008)**

28. If p and q be +ive quantities and $m\in[0,1]$ then prove that $(p+q)^m\leq p^m+q^m$.

29.* Show that $x^y>y^x\ \ \forall\ x,y$ such that $3\leq x<y$.

30. If $A=\left\{x:\frac{\pi}{6}\leq x\leq\frac{\pi}{3}\right\}$

and $f(x)=\cos x-x(1+x)$ then find $f(A)$.

31. Prove that $|\cos\alpha-\cos\beta|\leq|\alpha-\beta|$.

32. The function $f(x)=1/x$ on its domain is

(a) increasing

(b) decreasing

(c) constant

(d) information insufficient

33. Which of the following functions is periodic :

(a) $f(x)=x-[x]$ where $[x]$ denotes the largest integer less than or equal to the real number x.

(b) $f(x)=\sin(1/x)$ for $x\neq 0, f(0)=0$.

(c) $f(x)=x\cos x$.

(d) None of these.

34. If $y=f(x)=(x+2)/(x-1)$, then

(a) $x=f(y)$

(b) $f(1)=3$

(c) y increases with x for $x<1$

(d) f is a rational function of x.

35. (a) If $g(x)$ be a function defined on $[-1,1]$. If the area of the equilateral triangle with two of its vertices at $(0,0)$ and $[x,g(x)]$ is $\sqrt{3}/4$, then the function is

(a) $g(x)=\pm\sqrt{1-x^2}$ (b) $g(x)=-\sqrt{1-x^2}$

(c) $g(x)=\sqrt{1-x^2}$ (d) $g(x)=\sqrt{1+x^2}$

(b) Let f be a real valued function defined on the interval $]-1,1[$ such that

$e^{-x}f(x)=2+\int_0^x\sqrt{t^4+1}\,.dt\ \forall\ x\in]-1,1[$

and let f^{-1} be the inverse of f. Then $(f^{-1})'(2)$ is equal to

(a) 1 (b) $\frac{1}{3}$

(c) $\frac{1}{2}$ (d) $\frac{1}{e}$ **(IIT-JEE 2010)**

True and False for Q. 36, 37, 38.

36. The derivative of an odd function is always an even function.

37. The inverse of the function $\log_e x$ is 10^x.

38. The inverse of the function

$f(x)=[1-(x-5)^3]^{1/5}$ is $5+(1-x^5)^{1/3}$.

Fill in the Blanks

39. There are exactly two linear functions .... and .... which map $[-1,1]$ to $[0,2]$.

40. Let the function

$f(x)=x^2+x+\sin x-\cos x+\log(1+|x|)$

be defined over the interval $[0,1]$. The odd extensions of $f(x)$ to interval $[-1,1]$ is

(a) $x^2+x+\sin x+\cos x-\log(1+|x|)$

(b) $-x^2+x+\sin x+\cos x-\log(1+|x|)$

(c) $-x^2+x+\sin x-\cos x+\log(1+|x|)$

(d) None of these **(M.N.R. 1994)**

41. Let $f(x) = x^2$ and $g(x) = \sin x \ \forall \ x \in \mathbf{R}$ Then the set of all x satisfying $(fogogof)(x) = (gogof)(x)$ where $fog(x) = fog(x)$ is

(a) $\pm\sqrt{n\pi}, n \in \{0, 1, 2, \ldots\}$

(b) $\pm\sqrt{n\pi}, n \in \{1, 2, \ldots\}$

(c) $\frac{\pi}{2} + 2n\pi, n \in \{\ldots 2, -1, 0, 1, 2, \ldots\}$

(d) $2n\pi, n \in \{\ldots -2, -1, 0, 1, 2, \ldots\}$ **(IIT-JEE 2011)**

42. The function $f : (0, 3) \to [1, 29]$ defined by $f(x) = 2x^3 - 15x^2 + 36x + 1$ is

(a) one-one and onto

(b) onto but not one-one

(c) one-one but not onto

(d) neither one-one nor onto **(IIT-JEE 2012)**

Solutions to Problem Set (4)

1. (a) Let $f(x) = 2x^3 - 15x^2 + 36x + 1$,

Then $f'(x) = 6x^2 - 30x + 36 = 6(x-2)(x-3)$

$f'(x) = +$ive if $x < 2$ or $x > 3$

$\therefore \quad x \in]-\infty, 2[$ or $x \in]3, \infty[$

Hence f is an increasing function when

$x \in]-\infty, 2[\cup]3, \infty[$.

$f'(x)$ is $-$ive if $2 < x < 3$

Hence f is a decreasing function when $x \in]2, 3[$.

(b) $y = \dfrac{x}{x^2 - 6x - 16}$

It is not defined at points given by $x^2 - 6x - 16 = 0$ or $(x+2)(x-8) = 0 \ \therefore \ x = -2, 8$ are to be excluded from the domain.

$$\frac{dy}{dx} = -\frac{x^2 + 16}{(x+2)^2 (x-8)^2}$$

$= -$ive for all real values of x except $-2, 8$. Hence the function is decreasing in $R - \{-2, 8\}$.

(c) $f'(x) = 3(x-1)^2 = +$ive always $\forall \ x$ except $x = 1$

$\therefore$ Increasing.

2. (a) $\dfrac{dy}{dx} = 2 - \dfrac{1}{1+x^2} - \dfrac{1}{\sqrt{(1+x^2)}} = \dfrac{1 + 2x^2 - \sqrt{1+x^2}}{(1+x^2)}$

Since $1 + 2x^2 = 1 + x^2 + x^2 > \sqrt{1+x^2} \quad \forall \ x \in R$

Hence $\dfrac{dy}{dx} = +$ive $\forall \ x \in R$

Therefore $f(x)$ is an increasing function in $]-\infty, \infty[$.

(b) $y = \dfrac{1 + x^2 + x - 2x}{1 + x^2 + x} = 1 - \dfrac{2x}{1 + x + x^2}$

$$\frac{dy}{dx} = -2\frac{(1 + x + x^2).1 - x(1 + 2x)}{(1 + x + x^2)^2}$$

$$\frac{dy}{dx} = \frac{2(x+1)(x-1)}{(1 + x + x^2)^2}$$

$\dfrac{dy}{dx} = +$ive for $x < -1$ or $x > 1$

$= -$ive for $-1 < x < 1$

Increasing in $(-\infty, -1) \cup (1, \infty)$

Decreasing in $(-1, 1)$

3. (a) $x > 0, |x| = x$ and $x < 0, |x| = -x$

$\therefore \quad f'(x) = \dfrac{1}{x}$ for $x > 0 = +$ive

$= \dfrac{1}{(-x)}(-1) = \dfrac{1}{x}$ for $x < 0 = -$ive

Hence $f(x)$ is increasing for $x > 0$ *i.e.* in $]0, \infty[$ and decreasing for $x < 0$ *i.e.* in $]-\infty, 0[$.

(b) $y = f(x) = (t-1)(t-2)^2$

where $t = 2^x = +$ive always

$$\frac{dy}{dx} = \frac{dy}{dt} \cdot \frac{dt}{dx} = (t-2)(3t-4)\{t \log 2\}$$

$\therefore \quad t = 2, 4/3, 0.$

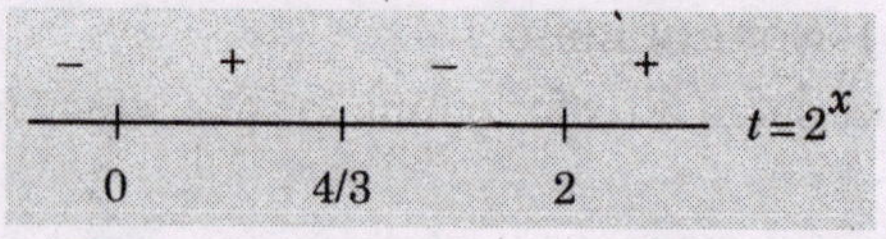

Fig. 26

From above we conclude that

$\dfrac{dy}{dx} = +$ive when $t > 2$ or $0 < t < \dfrac{4}{3}$

or $2^x > 2$ or $0 < 2^x < 4/3$

or $x > \log_2 2 = 1$ or $\log 0 < x < \log_2 (4/3)$

$\therefore \quad x \in]1, \infty[$ or $x \in \left]-\infty, \log_2 \frac{4}{3}\right[$

$\therefore \quad x \in \left]-\infty, \log_2 \frac{4}{3}\right[\cup]1, \infty[$. ...(1)

$\dfrac{dy}{dx} = -$ive when $4/3 < t < 2$ or $t < 0$

But t less than 0 is ruled out as t is always $+$ive

$\therefore \quad \dfrac{4}{3} < 2^x < 2$ or $\log_2 \dfrac{4}{3} < x < \log_2 2$

$\therefore \quad x \in \left]\log_2 \frac{4}{3}, \log_2 2\right[= \left]\log_2 \frac{4}{3}, 1\right[$ ...(2)

Hence (1) gives the intervals during which function increases and (2) gives when the function decreases.

(c) By rule for differentiation of determinants

$$f'(x) = \begin{vmatrix} 1 & 0 & 0 \\ ab & x + b^2 & bc \\ ac & bc & x + c^2 \end{vmatrix}$$

$$+\begin{vmatrix} x+a^2 & ab & ac \\ 0 & 1 & 0 \\ ac & bc & x+c^2 \end{vmatrix} + \begin{vmatrix} x+a^2 & ab & ac \\ ab & x+b^2 & bc \\ 0 & 0 & 1 \end{vmatrix}$$

or $f'(x) = [(x+b^2)(x+c^2) - b^2c^2]$
$+[(x+a^2)(x+c^2) - a^2c^2]$
$+[(x^2+a^2)(x^2+b^2) - a^2b^2]$

or $f'(x) = 3x^2 + 2x(a^2+b^2+c^2)$

or $f'(x) = 3x\left(x + \frac{2}{3}\Sigma a^2\right)$

$= 3\left[x - \left(-\frac{2}{3}\Sigma a^2\right)\right][x-0]$

$= 3[x-l][x-m]$ where $l < m = 0$

$f'(x) = -$ ive when $l < x < m$

∴ $x \in (l, m) = (l, 0)$

Hence decreasing.

$f'(x) = +$ ive when either $x < l$ or $x > m$

∴ $x \in (-\infty, l)$ or $x \in (m, \infty)$ *i.e.*, $(0, \infty)$

∴ $f(x)$ is increasing when

$x \in (-\infty, l) \cup (0, \infty)$, $l = -\frac{2}{3}\Sigma a^2$

(d) (i) $f'(x) = x^x(1 + \log x)$ **Q. 1 (b), P. 1199-1203**

$f'(x) = +$ ive when $1 + \log x > 0$

or $\log x > -1$ or $x > e^{-1} = \frac{1}{e}$

∴ Increasing in $\left(\frac{1}{e}, \infty\right)$.

$f'(x) = -$ ive when $1 + \log x < 0$

or $\log x < -1$ or $x < e^{-1} = \frac{1}{e}$ and $x > 0$

∴ Decreasing in $\left(0, \frac{1}{e}\right)$.

(ii) Proceed as above.

Increasing in (e, ∞) and decreasing in $(0, e)$ as $\log x$ is defined only when $x > 0$.

4. (a) $\frac{dy}{dx} = 3x^2 + 2px + q > 0 \quad \forall\ x \in R$

Now we know that sign of a quadratic expression is same as that of the first term *i.e.* 3 *i.e.* +ive, provided

$\Delta = 4p^2 - 12q < 0$ or $p^2 - 3q < 0$

Alternatively $\frac{dy}{dx} = 3x^2 + 2px + q$

$= 3\left[x^2 + \frac{2p}{3}x + \frac{q}{3}\right]$

$= 3\left[\left(x + \frac{p}{3}\right)^2 + \left(\frac{q}{3} - \frac{p^2}{9}\right)\right]$

$= 3\left[\left(x + \frac{p}{3}\right)^2 + \left(\frac{3q - p^2}{9}\right)\right]$

Now $\frac{dy}{dx} = +$ ive $\forall\ x \in R$ if $3q - p^2 > 0$

or $p^2 - 3q < 0$

(b) Ans. (a) and (c).

$h' = f'(3f^2 - 2f + 1) = f'(+\text{ive})$

∵ $3f^2 - 2f + 1 = 0$ has its $\Delta = -8$

∴ its sign is same as of the first term *i.e.* 3 *i.e.* +ive. Hence h is increasing or decreasing according as f' is +ive or − ive *i.e.* f is increasing or decreasing.

(c) Ans. (a). $\frac{dy}{dx} = 3x^2 + 2bx + c$

Disc $= 4(b^2 - 3c) = 4(b^2 - c) - 8c = -$ ive

as $b^2 < c$ and $c > 0$

Also sign of Ist term *i.e.*, $a = 3$ is +ive. Hence $\frac{dy}{dx}$ is always + ive for all real values of x.

Therefore $f(x)$ is increasing.

5. (a) Ans. True. $x \in]0, \infty[\Rightarrow x +$ ive

$$\frac{dy}{dx} = \frac{\log(e+x)\frac{1}{(\pi+x)} - \log(\pi+x)\cdot\frac{1}{e+x}}{[\log(e+x)]^2}$$

$$= \frac{(e+x)\log(e+x) - (\pi+x)\log(\pi+x)}{(\pi+x)(e+x)[\log(e+x)]^2}$$

Denominator is +ive when $x > 0$ and numerator is − ive as $(e+x) < (\pi+x)$. Since $e < \pi$

Hence decreasing when $x > 0$ *i.e.* in $]0, \infty[$.

(b) Split $y = |x+1|, -3 \le x < 1$ to

$y = -(x+1)$ if $-3 \le x < -1$

$= (x+1)$ if $-1 \le x \le 1$

Increasing in $(-\infty, -3)$ and $(-1, 1)$
Decreasing in $(-3, -1)$ and $(1, \infty)$ } **Ans.**

(c) $\frac{dy}{dx} = -\sin x(12\cos^3 x + 30\cos^2 x + 12\cos x)$

$= -6\sin x\cos x[2\cos^2 x + 5\cos x + 2]$

$= -3\sin 2x(2\cos x + 1)(\cos x + 2)$

Now $\frac{dy}{dx} = 0$ at $\sin 2x = 0$, $\cos x = -\frac{1}{2}$

or $x = 0, \pi/2, 2\pi/3$ and π in $0 \le x \le \pi$

The factor $\cos x + 2$ is always +ive as

$-1 \le \cos x \le 1$

In the interval $0 < x < \pi/2$ all the factors are +ive

∴ $\frac{dy}{dx} = -(+) = -$ ive and hence decreasing

In the interval $\left(\frac{\pi}{2} < x < \frac{2\pi}{3}\right)$

$\sin 2x$ is − ive and $2\cos x + 1$ is +ive

∴ $\frac{dy}{dx} = -(-) = +$ ive and hence increasing.

In the interval $\frac{2\pi}{3} < x < \pi$

$\frac{dy}{dx} = -(+) = -$ ive hence decreasing

Note : You can also say that function increases and decreases alternately.

(d) Ans. (b). $y = f(x) = 1 - \frac{1}{2}(\sin^2 2x)$

$\frac{dy}{dx} = -2\sin 2x \cos 2x = -\sin 4x = +$ ive,

if $f(x)$ is increasing

$\Rightarrow \sin 4x = -$ ive $\therefore \pi < 4x < 2\pi$

or $\frac{\pi}{4} < x < \frac{\pi}{2}$ where $\frac{\pi}{2} = \frac{4\pi}{8} < \frac{3\pi}{8}$

$\therefore$ x satisfies (b).

(e) Ans. (a). $y = \sin 3x$

$\therefore \frac{dy}{dx} = 3\cos 3x \geq 0$ for increasing function.

Above implies $-\frac{\pi}{2} \leq 3x < \frac{\pi}{2}$ or $-\frac{\pi}{6} < x < \frac{\pi}{6}$

Hence the largest interval for x is $\frac{\pi}{6} - \left(-\frac{\pi}{6}\right) = \frac{\pi}{3}$.

6. (a) Ans. (d).

$f'(x) = 3x^2 + 12x + p = -$ ive in $(-3, -1)$

$\therefore f'(x) = \lambda(x+3)(x+1) = \lambda(x^2 - 4x + 3)$

Comparing $\lambda = 3$ and $p = 3\lambda = 9$

(b) Ans. (c).

f is a decreasing function,

$x > y \Rightarrow f(x) < f(y)$ ...(1)

Major axis lies along y-axis $\therefore f(a^2 - 5) > f(4a)$

or $f(4a) < f(a^2 - 5)$ by (1)

$\therefore 4a > a^2 - 5$ by (1) $\therefore a^2 - 4a - 5 < 0$

or $(a+1)(a-5) < 0 \quad \therefore a \in (-1, 5)$

(c) Ans. (a).

For $f(x)$ to be increasing, $f'(x) > 0$

$f'(x) = 6x - 2 = 6\left(x - \frac{1}{3}\right) \neq +$ ive

for $x \in \left]-\infty, \frac{1}{3}\right]$

Hence $f(x)$ is incorrectly matched with the interval.

For (b), $f'(x) = 3x^2 + 12x = 3x(x+4)$

$= 3(x - (-4))(x - 0) = +$ ive

if $x < -4$ or $x > 0 \quad \therefore\ ]-\infty, -4]$

$f'(x)$ is $+$ ive so that $f(x)$ is increasing and hence correctly matched.

Similarly you may verify that $f'(x) = +$ ive for (c) and (d) hence they are correctly matched.

7. (a) $f(x) = \sqrt{2}\sin\left(x + \frac{\pi}{4}\right)$

$f'(x) = \sqrt{2}\cos\left(x + \frac{\pi}{4}\right) > 0$ for $[0, 2\pi]$

Now $\cos\theta$ is $+$ive when θ lies either in 1st or in 4th quadrant.

$\therefore 0 \leq x + \pi/4 < \pi/2 \Rightarrow -\pi/4 \leq x < \pi/4$

...1st quard.

$\Rightarrow 0 \leq x < \frac{\pi}{4} \quad \therefore \quad x \in \left[0, \frac{\pi}{4}\right[$. ...(1)

and $\left[0, \frac{\pi}{4}\right[$ is a subset of $[0, 2\pi]$.

or $\frac{3\pi}{2} < x + \frac{\pi}{4} \leq 2\pi$ ...4th quard.

or $\frac{3\pi}{2} - \frac{\pi}{4} < x \leq 2\pi - \frac{\pi}{4}$

$\therefore x \in \left]\frac{5\pi}{4}, \frac{7\pi}{4}\right] \subset [0, 2\pi]$ ...(2)

$\therefore x \in \left[0, \frac{\pi}{4}\right[\cup \left]\frac{5\pi}{4}, \frac{7\pi}{4}\right]$, by (1) and (2)

It will be decreasing when $f(x)$ is $-$ ive in 2nd and 3rd quadrant.

$\frac{\pi}{2} < x + \frac{\pi}{4} < \frac{3\pi}{2} \quad \therefore \frac{\pi}{4} < x < \frac{5\pi}{4}$

$\therefore x \in \left(\frac{\pi}{4}, \frac{5\pi}{4}\right)$ ...(3)

(b) $\frac{dy}{dx} = \frac{1}{1 + (\sin x + \cos x)^2}(\cos x - \sin x)$

$= \frac{\cos x - \sin x}{2 + \sin 2x} = \frac{\sqrt{2}\cos(x + \pi/4)}{2 + \sin 2x}$

The denominator $2 + \sin 2x$ is always $+$ive.

$\therefore \frac{dy}{dx} > 0$ or < 0 when $\cos x - \sin x > 0$ or < 0

or $\sqrt{2}\cos(x + \pi/4) > 0$ or < 0 in $0 \leq x \leq \pi$.

Hence the same answer as given by (1) and (3) only of part (c), and not by (2) as $0 \leq x \leq \pi$.

(c) $f'(x) < 0 \Rightarrow \frac{\cos(\log_e x) - \sin(\log_e x)}{x} < 0$

or $\cos t - \sin t < 0, t = \log_e x$

or $\sqrt{2}\left[\cos\left(t + \frac{\pi}{4}\right)\right] < 0$

$\therefore t + \frac{\pi}{4}$ lies in 2nd or 3rd quadrant

i.e., $\frac{\pi}{2} < t + \frac{\pi}{4} < \frac{3\pi}{2}$ or $\frac{\pi}{4} < \log_e x < \frac{5\pi}{4}$

or $e^{\pi/4} < x < e^{5\pi/4} \quad \therefore x \in (e^{\pi/4}, e^{5\pi/4})$

In general $x \in (e^{2r\pi + \pi/4}, e^{2r\pi + 5\pi/4})$

8. (a) $\frac{dy}{dx} = \left(-\sin\frac{\pi}{x}\right)\left(-\frac{\pi}{x^2}\right) = \frac{\pi}{x^2}\sin\frac{\pi}{x}$

$\sin\theta$ is $+$ ive when $0 < \theta < \pi$

$\therefore \frac{dy}{dx}$ is $+$ive when $\sin\frac{\pi}{x}$ is $+$ive *i.e.* $0 < \frac{\pi}{x} < \pi$

or $2n\pi < \pi/x < (2n\pi + \pi)$ or $2n < 1/x < (2n+1)$

Taking reciprocal and reversing the inequality, we get

$$\frac{1}{2n+1} < x < \frac{1}{2n} \quad \therefore \quad \left]\frac{1}{2n+1}, \frac{1}{2n}\right[, \; n \in I$$

Similarly it will be decreasing in $\left]\frac{1}{2n+2}, \frac{1}{2n+1}\right[$.

$\sin\theta$ is – ive when $\pi < \theta < 2\pi$ etc.

(b) $\frac{dy}{dx} = -2\sin\left(2x + \frac{\pi}{4}\right) = +$ ive

or $\sin(2x + \pi/4) = -$ ive

$\therefore$ $\pi < 2x + \pi/4 < 2\pi$ (2nd, 3rd quard.)

or $\frac{3\pi}{8} < x < \frac{7\pi}{8}$

(c) Yes. $\frac{dy}{dx} = \cos x - 2a\cos 2x - \cos 3x + 2a$

$= 2\sin 2x \sin x + 2a(1 - \cos 2x)$

$= 4\sin^2 x \cos x + 4a\sin^2 x$

$= 4\sin^2 x(\cos x + a)$

Now $4\sin^2 x$ is + ive and if $\cos x + a > 0$ then $f(x)$ increases for all values of x.

Now the least value of $\cos x$ is – 1.

$\therefore$ $-1 + a > 0 \Rightarrow a > 1$.

9. (a) Ans. (i) → A, (ii) → C

$\frac{dy}{dx} = 1 + \cos x = +$ ive,

$= \sec x \tan x$ can be both ± in $(-\pi/2, \pi/2)$.

(b) $\frac{dy}{dx} = \sec^2 x - 1 \geq 0$ *i.e.* never – ive

The given function is either always increasing or is a constant function $\left(\frac{dy}{dx} = 0\right)$. Thus we can say that it never decreases.

10. Ans. (iii).

$$f'(x) = \frac{\sin x - x\cos x}{\sin^2 x} = \frac{p(x)}{\sin^2 x} \quad \text{...(1)}$$

$p(x) = \sin x - x\cos x$

$\therefore$ $p'(x) = x\sin x = +$ ive in $0 \leq x \leq 1$

$\therefore$ $p(x)$ is an increasing function.

But $p(0) = 0$. $\therefore$ $p(x)$ is > 0 i.e. + ive

Hence from (1), $f'(x) = +$ ive

$\therefore$ $f(x)$ is an increasing function, *i.e.*, (c).

We should find $g'(x)$ and if it is increasing then answer will be (a) also. Now consider

$$g(x) = \frac{x}{\tan x}$$

$$\therefore \quad g'(x) = \frac{\tan x - x\sec^2 x}{\tan^2 x}$$

$$= \frac{\sin x\cos x - x}{\sin^2 x} = \frac{\sin 2x - 2x}{2\sin^2 x}$$

or $$g'(x) = \frac{\phi(x)}{2\sin^2 x} \quad \text{...(2)}$$

where $\phi(x) = \sin 2x - 2x$

$\phi'(x) = 2(\cos 2x - 1) = -$ ive.

$\therefore$ $\phi(x)$ is decreasing but $\phi(0) = 0$

$\therefore$ $\phi(x) < 0$ *i.e.* – ive

Hence from (2), $g'(x) = -$ ive

$\therefore$ $g(x)$ is decreasing.

This is not given in any of the four alternatives.

11. Let $f(x) = \log(1+x) - x/(1+x)$

$$\therefore \quad f'(x) = \frac{1}{1+x} - \frac{1}{1+x} + \frac{x}{(1+x)^2} = \frac{x}{(1+x)^2}$$

Then $f'(x) > 0$ when $x > 0$

and $= 0$ when $x = 0$.

Thus $f(x)$ is monotonically increasing in the interval $]0, \infty[$.

Again $f(0) = 0$

$\therefore$ $f(x) > f(0) = 0$ when $x > 0$.

Hence $f(x)$ is positive for every positive value of x so that

$\log(1+x) > x/(1+x)$ when $x > 0$. ...(1)

Now let $\phi(x) = x - \log(1+x)$

so that $\phi'(x) = 1 - 1/(1+x) = x/(x+1)$

Then $\phi'(x) > 0$, when $x > 0$.

and $= 0$, when $x = 0$.

Therefore ϕ is monotonically increasing in the interval $]0, \infty[$.

Also $\phi(0) = 0$ $\therefore$ $\phi(x) > \phi(0)$ when $x > 0$.

Hence $\phi(x)$ is positive for positive values of x, so that $x > \log(1+x)$ ...(2)

From (1) and (2), we have

$x/(1+x) < \log(1+x) < x$ when $x > 0$.

12. Let $y = f(x) = \frac{x}{1+x^2} - \tan^{-1} x$ ...(1)

$$\therefore \quad \frac{dy}{dx} = 1.\frac{1}{1+x^2} - \frac{2x^2}{(1+x^2)^2} - \frac{1}{1+x^2}$$

$$= -\frac{2x^2}{(1+x^2)^2} < 0 \quad \forall x > 0$$

$\therefore$ y is a decreasing function

$f(0) = 0$, and $x > 0$ therefore $f(x) < 0$

$\therefore$ $\frac{x}{1+x^2} < \tan^{-1} x$ by (1) ...(2)

Choose $\phi(x) = \tan^{-1} x - x$

$$\therefore \quad \phi'(x) = \frac{1}{1+x^2} - 1 = -\frac{x^2}{1+x^2} < 0 \; \forall x > 0$$

∴ ϕ is a decreasing function $\phi(0)=0$

∴ $\phi(x)<0$ or $\tan^{-1}x-x<0$ or $\tan^{-1}x<x$

Another form :

Show that the expression $\tan^{-1}x-\dfrac{x}{1+x^2}$ is always + ive for $x>0$.

This follows from (2) of 1st part of above question.

13. (a) Let $f(x)=\tan^{-1}x-\left(x+\dfrac{x^3}{6}\right)$ ∴ $f(0)=0$

∴ $f'(x)=-\dfrac{x^2(3+x^2)}{2(1+x^2)}<0$

∴ $f(x)$ is decreasing

∴ $f(x)<f(0)=0$ for $0<x<1$

∴ $\tan^{-1}x<x+\dfrac{x^3}{6}$.

(b) Choose $f(x)=x-\dfrac{x^3}{3}-\tan^{-1}x$

∴ $f(0)=0$

∴ $f'(x)=1-x^2-\dfrac{1}{1+x^2}=\dfrac{-x^4}{1+x^2}$

$=-$ ive $\forall\ x\in R$

∴ $f(x)$ is decreasing

∴ $f(x)<f(0)=0,\ x\in]0,1]$

∴ $x-\dfrac{x^3}{3}<\tan^{-1}x$

Again consider $g(x)=\tan^{-1}x-\left(x-\dfrac{x^3}{6}\right)$

$g(0)=0$

$g'(x)=\dfrac{1}{1+x^2}-\left(1-\dfrac{x^2}{2}\right)=\dfrac{x^2(x^2-1)}{2(x^2+1)}=-$ ive.

for all x s.t. $0<x\le 1$

∴ $g(x)<g(0)=0$ for x, s.t. $0<x\le 1$

∴ $g(x)=\tan^{-1}x-\left(x-\dfrac{x^3}{6}\right)<0$

or $\tan^{-1}x<\left(x-\dfrac{x^3}{6}\right)$

14. (a) Let $f(x)=4x+8\cos x+\tan x-2\sec x-4\log\cos x-4\log(1+\sin x)-6$

Clearly $f(0)=8-2-6=0$

$f'(x)=4-8\sin x+\sec^2 x-2\sec x\tan x+4\tan x-\dfrac{4\cos x}{1+\sin x}$

$=4(1-2\sin x)+\sec^2 x(1-2\sin x)+\dfrac{4\sin x}{\cos x}-\dfrac{4\cos x(1-\sin x)}{\cos^2 x}$

$=(4+\sec^2 x)(1-2\sin x)+\dfrac{4}{\cos x}(\sin x-1+\sin x)$

$=(4+\sec^2 x-4\sec x)(1-2\sin x)$

$=(\sec x-2)^2(1-2\sin x)=+$ ive

if $(1-2\sin x)$ is + ive or $\sin x<1/2$

∴ $x\in(0,\pi/6)$

∴ $f(x)$ is an increasing function in $(0,\pi/6)$.

But $f(0)=0$ ∴ $f(x)\ge f(0)$ or ≥ 0

∴ $x\in[0,\pi/6)$ ∴ $\lambda=\pi/6$.

(b) Let

$f(x)=\tan^2 x+6\log\sec x+2\cos x+4-6\sec x$

$f(0)=0$

$f'(x)=\dfrac{2\sin x}{\cos^3 x}(1-\cos x)^3=+$ ive for $0<x<\dfrac{\pi}{2}$

Hence f is an increasing function

∴ $f(x)>f(0)(=0)$

∴ $f(x)$ is >0 etc.

15. (a) Ans. (b).

$y=\log(1+x)-x=f(x),\ f(0)=0$

$\dfrac{dy}{dx}=\dfrac{1}{1+x}-1=-\dfrac{x}{1+x}=-$ ive $\forall\ x\in(0,1)$

∴ $f(x)$ is a decreasing function.

Since $f(0)=0$

∴ $f(x)<0\ \forall\ x\in(0,1)$

∴ $\log(1+x)-x<0$ or $\log(1+x)<x$.

(b) Ans. (c).

$\dfrac{dy}{dx}=e^x(x-1)(x-2)=-$ ive

for decreasing function. Now e^x is + ive always and hence $(x-1)(x-2)=-$ ive

∴ $x\in(1,2)$.

(c) Given $P(1)=0$ and $P'(x)>P(x)\ \forall\ x>1$ ...(a)

We have to prove that $P(x)>0\ \forall\ x>1$

Now $P'(x)-P(x)>0\ \forall\ x>1$, by (a)

Multiplying both sides of inequality by a + ive quantity e^{-x}

∴ $e^{-x}P'(x)-e^{-x}P(x)>0\ \forall\ x>1$

or $\dfrac{d}{dx}[e^{-x}P(x)]>0\ \forall\ x>1$

Above implies that $f(x)=e^{-x}P(x)$ is an increasing function $\forall\ x>1$.

Hence $f(x)>f(1)$

∴ $e^{-x}P(x)>e^{-1}P(1)$ or >0 as $P(1)=0$

⇒ $P(x)>0\ \forall\ x>1$.

(d) We have to prove that

$\sin(\tan x)\ge x\ \forall\ x\in[0,\pi/4]$

Choose $\tan x=t$ ∴ $x=\tan^{-1}t,\ t\in[0,1]$

Let $f(t)=\sin t-\tan^{-1}t$ ∴ $f(0)=0$

$$f'(t) = \cos t - \frac{1}{1+t^2} \qquad ...(1)$$

Now in first quadrant $y = \cos t$ is concave down whereas $y = \frac{1}{1+x^2}$ is concave up which implies that (1) is + ive *i.e.*, $f'(t) > 0$.

Hence $f(t)$ is an increasing fucntion in [0, 1].

$\therefore \quad f(t) > f(0) = 0$

$\therefore \quad \sin t - \tan^{-1} t \geq 0$ or $\sin t \geq \tan^{-1} t$

$\therefore \quad \sin(\tan x) \geq x$

(e) Ans. (b).

Differentiating as explained in Prop. VIII **P. 1522**

$$f'(x) = [e^{-(x^2+1)^2} . 2x - e^{-(x^2)^2} . 2x]$$

$$= 2x . e^{-(x^2+1)^2} [1 - e^{(x^2+1)^2 - x^4}]$$

$$= 2x e^{-(x^2+1)^2} [1 - e^{2x^2+1}]$$

$$= \frac{2}{e^{(x^2+1)^2}} . x [1 - e^{2x^2+1}],$$

where $e^{2x^2+1} = e^{2x^2} . e > e > 1.$

If $f(x)$ is increasing then

$f'(x) = +\text{ive} \Rightarrow +(x)(-) = +\text{ive}$

Hence x must be – ive. $\quad \therefore \quad x \in (-\infty, 0)$.

16. (a) Ans. (a).

$$f'(x) = e^{x(1-x)} . 1 + x . e^{x(1-x)} (1 - 2x)$$

or $\quad f'(x) = e^{x(1-x)} [1 + x - 2x^2]$

$$= -e^{x(1-x)} [2x^2 - x - 1]$$

$$= -e^{x(1-x)} (x-1)(2x+1)$$

$$f'(x) = -2e^{x(1-x)} \left(x + \frac{1}{2}\right)(x-1)$$

or $\quad f'(x) = -2e^{x(1-x)} A$

Now exponential function is always + ive and the sign of $f'(x)$ will be opposite to the sign of A which is – ive in $\left[-\frac{1}{2}, 1\right]$

Hence $f'(x)$ is + ive in $\left[-\frac{1}{2}, 1\right]$ so that $f(x)$ is an increasing function in this interval.

(b) In other words we have to show that $f'(x)$ is always positive.

Differentiating the given function by rule Prop. VIII **P. 1522** definite integral, we have

$$f'(x) = [\sin^2(2\log e^x) - 3\sin(2\log e^x) + 2]\frac{d}{dx}e^x - [\sin^2(2\log 1) - 3\sin(2\log 1)]\frac{d}{dx}(1)$$

or $\quad f'(x) = (\sin^2 2x - 3\sin 2x + 2)e^x - 0$

$$= e^x (\sin 2x - 1)(\sin 2x - 2)$$

$$= (+)(-)(-) = +\text{ive always.}$$

Above shows that $f(x)$ is always increasing.

(c) Ans. (a).

$f'(x) = ax^2 + 1 + \cos x$ is always + ive for $a > 0, \forall x \in R$

Since $\frac{dy}{dx} = +\text{ive}$ always, hence $f(x)$ is an increasing function of x. It will assume greatest value at $x = 3$ and least value at $x = 2$. Hence the difference is :

$$f(3) - f(2) = \int_2^3 (at^2 + 1 + \cos t)\, dt$$

$$= \left[a\frac{t^3}{3} + t + \sin t\right]_2^3 = \frac{19}{3}a + 1 + (\sin 3 - \sin 2)$$

17. (a) Let $f(x) = 1 - \sqrt{1+x^2} + x \log [x + \sqrt{1+x^2}]$

$\therefore \quad f(0) = 0$

Then $\quad f'(x) = -\frac{2x}{2\sqrt{(1+x^2)}} + x\frac{1}{x + \sqrt{(1+x^2)}}\left\{1 + \frac{2x}{2\sqrt{(1+x^2)}}\right\} + \log [x + \sqrt{1+x^2}]$

$$= \frac{-x}{\sqrt{(1+x^2)}} + \frac{x}{\sqrt{(1+x^2)}} + \log [x + \sqrt{1+x^2}]$$

$$= \log [x + \sqrt{1+x^2}] \quad = +\text{ive for } x \geq 0$$

$\therefore \quad f(x)$ is an increasing function of x for all $x \geq 0$.

It follows that

$$f(x) \geq f(0) = 0$$

i.e. $\quad 1 + x\log [x + \sqrt{1+x^2}] \geq \sqrt{1+x^2}$ for all $x \geq 0$.

18. (a) For continuity and differentiability of f **See Q. 44 P. 1311-1328**. We now show that f is monotonic. We have

$$f'(x) = 1 + \frac{1}{3}\sin\log x^2 + \frac{2}{3}\cos\log x^2 \geq 0 \qquad ...(1)$$

for all values of x other than zero.

It follows that f is monotonically increasing.

Note : The least value of $f'(x)$ from (1) could be $1 - \frac{1}{3} = \frac{2}{3}$ when $\sin\log x^2 = -1$ and in that case

$\cos\log x^2 = 0$ or $1 - \frac{2}{3} = \frac{1}{3}$

when $\cos\log x^2 = -1$ and in that case $\sin\log x^2 = 0$. Hence $f'(x)$ is always + ive.

(b) We have $f(x) = x^{1/x}$, $\quad \therefore \quad \log f(x) = \frac{1}{x}\log_e x,$

Differentiating with respect to x, we get

$$\frac{1}{f(x)} . f'(x) = \frac{1}{x} . \frac{1}{x} - \frac{1}{x^2}\log_e x$$

or $\quad f'(x) = \frac{x^{1/x}}{x^2}[1 - \log_e x] \qquad ...(1)$

We have to consider the function for $x = e$, $x = \pi$, $\pi > e \therefore$ for $e < x < \pi$, $\log_e x > 1$ as $x > e$. Then it follows from (1) that $f'(x) < 0$ for $x > e$.

Hence $f(x)$ is a decreasing function of x for $x > e$.

Since $\pi > e$, we conclude

$$f(\pi) < f(e) \Rightarrow \pi^{1/\pi} < e^{1/e}$$

$$\Rightarrow (\pi^{1/\pi})^{e\pi} < (e^{1/e})^{e\pi} \Rightarrow \pi^e < e^\pi$$

Thus e^π is bigger that π^e.

19. (a) We are given $y = 2x^2 - \log|x|$. $(x \neq 0)$.

Then by def. of $|x|$, we have

$$y = 2x^2 - \log(-x) \text{ for } x < 0.$$

and $y = 2x^2 - \log x$ for $x > 0$.

Hence $\frac{dy}{dx} = 4x - \frac{1}{(-x)}(-1)$ for $x < 0$.

and $\frac{dy}{dx} = 4x - \frac{1}{x}$ for $x > 0$.

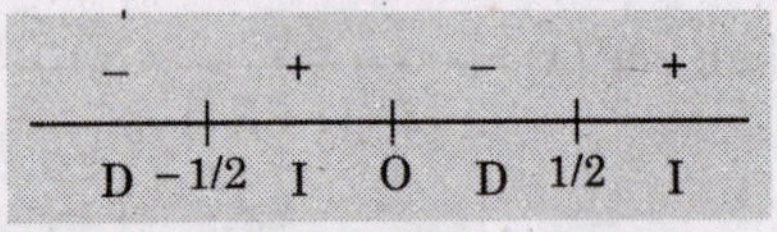

Fig. 27

Hence $\frac{dy}{dx} = 4x - \frac{1}{x} = \frac{(2x-1)(2x+1)}{x}$ for $x \neq 0$.

$$\frac{dy}{dx} = \frac{4}{x^2}\left[x - \left(-\frac{1}{2}\right)\right][x - 0]\left[x - \frac{1}{2}\right]$$

Clearly $\frac{dy}{dx}$ = ...

+ ive	for $x > \frac{1}{2}$	increasing
– ive	for $0 < x < \frac{1}{2}$	decreasing
+ ive	for $-\frac{1}{2} < x < 0$	increasing
– ive	for $x < -\frac{1}{2}$	decreasing

(b) The function can be redefined as under because of $|x - 1|$.

$$y = \frac{x-1}{x^2}, x \geq 1.$$

$$= \frac{-(x-1)}{x^2}, \quad x < 1 \text{ but } x \neq 0$$

Ist Case : $y = \frac{1}{x} - \frac{1}{x^2}, x \geq 1$

$$\therefore \quad \frac{dy}{dx} = -\frac{1}{x^2} + \frac{2}{x^3} = \frac{2-x}{x^3} = -\frac{x(x-2)}{x^4}$$

$\frac{dy}{dx}$ = + ive if $0 < x < 2$ and – ive if $x < 0$ or $x > 2$, but $x \geq 1$. Hence we say

$\therefore \quad \frac{dy}{dx}$ = + ive for (1, 2) and – ive for $x > 2$.

$\therefore \quad$ Increasing in (1, 2) and decreasing in $(2, \infty)$ ...(1)

II Case : $y = -\frac{1}{x} + \frac{1}{x^2}, \; x < 1, x \neq 0$

$$\therefore \quad \frac{dy}{dx} = \frac{1}{x^2} - \frac{2}{x^3} = \frac{x(x-2)}{x^4} \text{ where } x < 1$$

$\frac{dy}{dx}$ = + ive for $x < 0$ or $x > 2$, and – ive if $0 < x < 2$, but $x < 1$. Hence we say

$\therefore \quad \frac{dy}{dx}$ = + ive for $x < 0$ or in $(-\infty, 0)$ and – ive for $x \in (0, 1)$ ...(2)

Combining the results of (1) and (2), we have the following intervals of monotonicity :

$(-\infty, 0) \cup (1, 2)$	for increasing
$(0, 1) \cup (2, \infty)$	for decreasing

20. (a) $y = x^2 (x-2)^2$

$$\frac{dy}{dx} = 2x(x-2)^2 + x^2 \cdot 2(x-2)$$

$$= 2x(x-2)(x-2+x)$$

$$= 4(x-0)(x-1)(x-2)$$

Clearly $\frac{dy}{dx}$ =

= + ive	for $x > 2$
= – ive	for $1 < x < 2$
= + ive	for $0 < x < 1$
= – ive	for $x < 0$

Hence y is an increasing function when

$0 < x < 1$ or $x > 2$.

(b) $f'(x) = (x-1)e^x + 1 = g(x)$, say

where $g(0) = 0$

$g'(x) = x \cdot e^x > 0$ for $x > 0$

$\therefore \quad g$ is increasing function for $x > 0$

But $g(0) = 0 \quad \therefore \quad g(x) > 0$

$\therefore \quad f'(x) > 0$. Hence $f(x)$ is an increasing function of x for $x > 0$. But $f(0) = 0$

$\therefore \quad f(x) > f(0) = 0$

$\therefore \quad f(x) > 0$ *i.e.* always +ive for all +ive values of x.

21. (a) First let $g(x) = \sin x - x$. Then

$g'(x) = \cos x - 1 < 0$ for $0 < x \leq \pi/2$.

Hence $g(x)$ is decreasing for $0 < x \leq \pi/2$.

$\therefore \quad g(x) < g(0)$ for $0 < x < \pi/2$.

or $\quad g(x) < 0$ for $0 < x \leq \pi/2, \quad \because g(0) = 0$

or $\quad \sin x - x < 0 \Rightarrow \sin x < x$ ...(1)

Again, let $f(x) = x - x^3/6 - \sin x$.

Then $f'(x) = 1 - \frac{1}{6} \cdot 3x^2 - \cos x$

$$= 1 - \frac{1}{2}x^2 - \cos x = \phi(x), \text{ say.}$$

Now find the sign of $f'(x)$ in the given interval

Now $\phi'(x) = -x + \sin x < 0$ for $0 < x \leq \pi/2$

[See inequality (1) of **Q. 8 (a), P. 1287-1293**]. We have proved this inequality in (1) above. Hence $\phi(x)$ is decreasing for $0 < x < \pi/2$.

But $\phi(0) = 1 - 0 - 1 = 0$. It follows that
$\phi(x) < 0$ for $0 < x \le \pi/2$, that is,
$f'(x) = 1 - \frac{1}{2}x^2 - \cos x < 0$ for $0 < x \le \pi/2$.

$\therefore$ $f(x)$ is decreasing for $0 < x \le \pi/2$.
Hence $f(x) < f(0)$ for $0 < x < \pi/2$.
or $x - \frac{1}{6}x^3 - \sin x < 0$ for $0 < x \le \pi/2$.

[Note that $f(0) = 0$]

Thus $x - x^3/6 < \sin x$ for $0 < x \le \pi/2$. ...(2)
Finally from (1) and (2), we get
$x - x^3/6 < \sin x < x$ for $0 < x \le \pi/2$.

(b) Let $f(x) = 2\sin x + \tan x - 3x$

$\therefore$ $f'(x) = 2\cos x + \sec^2 x - 3 = g(x)$, say ...(1)

$\therefore$ $g'(x) = -2\sin x + 2\sec^2 x \tan x$
$= 2\sin x(\sec^3 x - 1) \ge 0$ for $0 \le x \le \pi/2$

Hence $g(x)$ is an increasing function.
Since $g(0) = 0$ by (1) we must have $g(x) \ge 0$ or $f'(x) \ge 0$ by (1).
Above shows that $f(x)$ is also an increasing function of x.
But $f(0) = 0$ $\therefore$ $f(x) \ge 0$
or $2\sin x + \tan x - 3x \ge 0$
or $2\sin x + \tan x \ge 3x$

22. (a) $g'(x) = f'(x) - f'(1 - x)$
Now $f''(x) < 0$ when $0 \le x \le 1$
Hence $f'(x)$ is a decreasing function when $0 \le x \le 1$.
Now $g(x)$ is increasing or decreasing according
$g'(x) = f'(x) - f'(1 - x) > 0$ or < 0

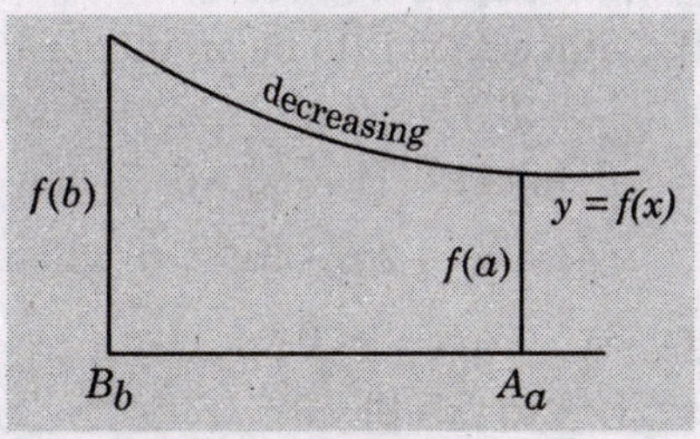

Fig. 28

or $f'(x) > f'(1 - x)$ **for increasing**
i.e. $f'(1 - x) < f'(x)$ ...(1)
Since f' is a decreasing function then by definition later value is less than the earlier value
i.e. $f(a) < f(b)$ when $a > b$.
or $f'(x) < f'(1 - x)$ **for decreasing** ...(2)
Hence (1) $\Rightarrow (1 - x) > x$ or $1 > 2x$ or $x < 1/2$

$\therefore$ $x \in \left[0, \frac{1}{2}\right[$ for $g(x)$ to be increasing and

(2) $\Rightarrow x > (1 - x)$ or $2x > 1$ or $x > \frac{1}{2}$

$\therefore$ $x \in \left]\frac{1}{2}, 1\right]$ for $g(x)$ to be decreasing

(b) Proceed exactly as in part (a).
$g(x)$ is increasing in $\left(0, \frac{4}{3}\right)$ and decreasing in $\left(\frac{4}{3}, 2\right)$.

$\frac{x}{2} > 2 - x$ if $x > \frac{4}{3}$ and $\frac{x}{2} < 2 - x$ if $x < \frac{4}{3}$

23. Let $f(x) = ax + \frac{b}{x} - c$, ...(1)
where $f(x) \ge 0 \ \forall \ x > 0$

$\therefore$ $f'(x) = a - \frac{b}{x^2} > 0$ if $x^2 > \frac{b}{a}$ (both a, b + ive)

$\therefore$ $x < -\sqrt{\frac{b}{a}}$ or $x > \sqrt{\frac{b}{a}}$.

Since x is + ive therefore we choose $x > \sqrt{\frac{b}{a}}$.

Since $f'(x) > 0$, $f(x)$ is an increasing function.

$\therefore$ $x > \sqrt{\frac{b}{a}} \Rightarrow f(x) > f\left(\sqrt{\frac{b}{a}}\right)$ by definition

$ax + \frac{b}{x} - c > a\sqrt{\frac{b}{a}} + b\sqrt{\frac{a}{b}} - c$

or $ax + \frac{b}{x} - c > 2\sqrt{ab} - c$ ...(2)

R.H.S. of (2) being $f\sqrt{\frac{b}{a}}$ is ≥ 0, by (1)

$\therefore$ $2\sqrt{ab} - c \ge 0$ or $4ab \ge c^2$

24. Let $f(x) = ax^2 + b/x - c \ge 0 \ \forall \ x > 0$

$\therefore$ $f'(x) = 2ax - b/x^2$

Now $f'(x) > 0$ if $2ax - \frac{b}{x^2} > 0$ or $x^3 > \frac{b}{2a}$

$\therefore$ $f(x)$ is an increasing function when $x^3 > b/2a$

Now $x^3 > \frac{b}{2a}$ or $x > \left(\frac{b}{2a}\right)^{1/3}$

$\Rightarrow$ $f(x) > f\left(\frac{b}{2a}\right)^{1/3}$

or $ax^2 + \frac{b}{x} - c > a\left(\frac{b}{2a}\right)^{2/3} + \frac{b}{(\ )^{1/3}} - c$

or $f(x) > \frac{a\left(\frac{b}{2a}\right) + b}{(\ )^{1/3}} - c$

$f(x) > \frac{3b/2}{(\ )^{1/3}} - c$. ...(1)

But we are given that
$f(x) \ge 0 \ \forall \ x > 0$ ...(2)

$\therefore$ R.H.S. being $f\left(\frac{b}{2a}\right)^{1/3} \geq 0$ by (1)

$\therefore$ $\frac{3b/2}{(b/2a)^{1/3}} - c \geq 0$

or $\frac{27}{8} b^3 \geq c^3 \cdot \frac{b}{2a}$ or $27ab^2 \geq 4c^3$

25. (a) Ans. (v).

Let $F(x) = h(x) - h(1) = f(g(x)) - h(1)$

$F'(x) = f'(g(x)).g'(x) = (+)(-) = -$ ive.

[As f is increasing function $f'(g(x))$ is + ive and as g is decreasing function $g'(x)$ is – ive.]

Since $F'(x)$ is – ive therefore $F(x)$ *i.e.* $h(x) - h(1)$ is decreasing function.

Now split the interval $I = [0, \infty[$ into two intervals I_1, $0 \leq x < 1$ and I_2, $1 \leq x < \infty$.

Apply the definition of **decreasing function** on $h(x) - h(1)$:

on I_1, $0 \leq x < 1$, $\underset{\text{(Big)}}{h(x)} - \underset{\text{(Less)}}{h(1)} = +$ ive

on I_2, $1 \leq x < \infty$, $\underset{\text{(Less)}}{h(x)} - \underset{\text{(Big)}}{h(1)} = -$ ive

Hence for I, $h(x) - h(1)$ is neither always zero nor always +ive nor always – ive, nor strictly increasing throughout. Hence (v) is the correct answer.

(b) Let $f(x) = \log(1 + x) - x$, $f(0) = 0$

The function is defined for $1 + x > 0$

or $x > -1$ *i.e.* $x \in]-1, \infty[= I$

Now $f'(x) = \frac{1}{1+x} - 1 = \frac{-x}{1+x}$

To determine the sign of $f'(x)$ we split the interval $I =]-1, \infty[$ into two intervals $I_1 =]-1, 0[$ and $I_2 = [0, \infty[$.

on I_1, $x = -$ ive and on I_2, $x = +$ ive

$\therefore$ $f'(x) = +$ ive on I_1

$f'(x) = -$ ive on I_2

$\therefore$ $f(x)$ is increasing on I_1, $-1 < x < 0$

$\underset{\text{(Less)}}{f(x)} - \underset{\text{(Big)}}{f(0)} = -$ ive or $f(x) - 0 < 0$

$\log(1 + x) - x < 0$ or $\log(1 + x) < x$ ...(1)

Again $f(x)$ is decreasing on I_2, $0 < x < \infty$

$\therefore$ $\underset{\text{(Less)}}{f(x)} - \underset{\text{(Big)}}{f(0)} = -$ ive or $f(x) - 0 < 0$

or $\log(1 + x) - x < 0$ or $\log(1 + x) < x$ ...(2)

Hence from (1) and (2),

$\log(1 + x) < x \;\; \forall \;\; x \in]-1, \infty[$

26. $f(x) = \begin{cases} -x^3 + \dfrac{b^3 - b^2 + b - 1}{b^2 + 3b + 2}, & 0 \leq x < 1 \\ 2x - 3, & 1 \leq x < 3 \end{cases}$

We have to find all possible real values of b such that $f(x)$ has the smallest value at $x = 1$. At $x = 1$, $f(x) = 2 - 3 = -1$, so that smallest value of $f(x) = -1$. Hence, the value will be smallest if at all points of the interval $f(x) > -1$.

Now for $x \geq 1$, $f(x) = 2x - 3$ $\therefore$ $f'(x) = 2 = +$ ive so that $f(x)$ is an increasing function and hence $f(x)$ is least at $x = 1$ and its value is -1. Again for $x < 1$, $f'(x) = -3x^2 = -$ ive

Hence $f(x)$ is a decreasing function in the interval $0 \leq x < 1$. Therefore $f(x)$ is smallest at $x = 1$ provided

$$f(1 - 0) = \underset{h \to 0}{\text{Lt}} \; -(1 - h)^3 + \frac{b^3 - b^2 + b - 1}{b^2 + 3b + 2} \geq -1$$

or $-1 + \frac{(b^2 + 1)(b - 1)}{(b + 1)(b + 2)} \geq -1$

or $\frac{(b^2 + 1)(b - 1)}{(b + 1)(b + 2)} \geq 0$ or $\frac{b - 1}{(b + 1)(b + 2)} \geq 0$

as $b^2 + 1$ is + ive always

or $\frac{(b - 1)^2}{(b + 2)(b + 1)(b - 1)}$ is + ive

or $\phi(b) = [(b - (-2))(b - (-1))](b - 1)$ is + ive

$b < -2$, – ive, $-2 < b < -1$, + ive

$-1 < b < 1$, –ive, $b \geq 1$, + ive

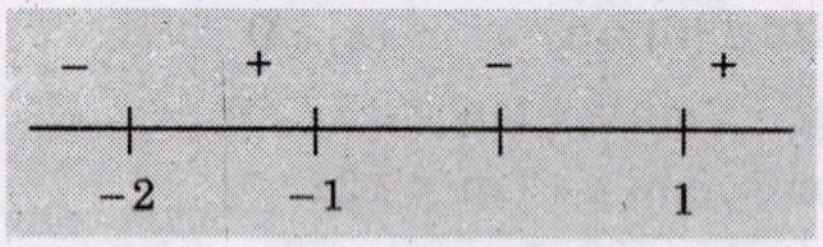

Fig. 29

Hence $-2 < b < -1$ or $b \geq 1$ then $f(x)$ has least value.

The change points are $-2, -1, 1$. Mark them on real line and find the intervals where it is + ive. From the figure it is clear that for $-2 < b < -1$, and $b \geq 1$, $\phi(b)$ is + ive and hence $f(x)$ is smallest in value.

27. (a) (i) Since $f(x)$ is to be an increasing function

$\therefore$ $f'(x) > 0$

$f'(x) = e^{ax}(1 + ax) > 0$ when $x \leq 0$ ...(1)

$f'(x) = 1 + 2ax - 3x^2 > 0$ when $x > 0$

or $3x^2 - 2ax - 1 < 0$ *i.e.* – ive

or $(x - \alpha)(x - \beta) < 0$ ...(2)

Now exponential function is always +ive

$\therefore$ $1 + ax > 0$ or $x > -\frac{1}{a}$, by (1)

From (2), $\alpha < x < \beta$ where

$$\alpha = \frac{a - \sqrt{(a^2 + 3)}}{3}, \beta = \frac{a + \sqrt{(a^2 + 3)}}{3}$$

Since $x > 0$ in this case therefore we choose $x < \beta$.

$\therefore$ x lies in $\left] -\frac{1}{a}, \frac{1}{3}\{a + \sqrt{(a^2 + 3)}\} \right[$

(ii) Choose $F(x) = f'(x) = e^{ax}(1 + ax)$, $x \leq 0$

$= 1 + 2ax - 3x^2$, $x \geq 0$

$F(x)$ will be increasing in $\left(-\frac{2}{a}, 0\right) \cup \left(0, \frac{a}{3}\right)$

(b) Ans. (c).

$$g(u) = 2\tan^{-1} e^u - \frac{\pi}{2}$$

$$g(-u) = 2\tan^{-1}\frac{1}{e^u} - \frac{\pi}{2}$$

$$= 2\cot^{-1} e^u - \frac{\pi}{2} \quad \because \cot^{-1} x = \tan^{-1}\frac{1}{x}$$

$$\therefore \quad g(u) + g(-u) = 2[\tan^{-1} e^u + \cot^{-1} e^u] - \pi$$

$$= 2\cdot\frac{\pi}{2} - \pi = 0$$

$\therefore \quad g(-u) = -g(u)$ and hence $g(u)$ is odd.

Again $g'(u) = 2.\dfrac{e^u}{1+(e^u)^2} > 0$

because $e^u > 0 \ \forall u \in R$

28. Dividing both sides by +ive q^m and putting $\frac{p}{q} = x$ where x is +ive, we have to prove that $(x+1)^m \le x^m + 1$

Consider $f(x) = (x+1)^m - x^m - 1$ where $f(0) = 0$

$$f'(x) = m(x+1)^{m-1} - mx^{m-1}$$

Since $0 \le m \le 1 \quad \therefore \quad -1 \le m-1 \le 0$

$\therefore \quad m-1 \le 0 \ \therefore \quad 1-m > 0$ *i.e.* +ive.

$$\therefore \quad f'(x) = m\left[\frac{1}{(x+1)^{1-m}} - \frac{1}{x^{1-m}}\right] \qquad ...(1)$$

Now $x+1 > x \ \therefore \quad \dfrac{1}{x+1} < \dfrac{1}{x}$

$$\text{or} \quad \frac{1}{(x+1)^{1-m}} < \frac{1}{x^{1-m}} \qquad ...(2)$$

Hence from (1) by the help of (2), $f'(x) = -$ ive

$f(x)$ is decreasing function

$\therefore \quad x \ge 0 \ \Rightarrow f(x) \le f(0)$

$\therefore \quad f(x) \le 0$ as $f(0) = 0$ or $(x+1)^m \le x^{m+1}$.

Now put $x = p/q$.

29. Consider $f(x) = \dfrac{\log x}{x}$

$$f'(x) = \frac{1 - \log x}{x^2} = -\text{ive} \quad \forall \quad x > 3$$

$\because \quad \log_e x \ge \log_e e = 1 \ \forall \ x > e$. Here $x \ge 3$.

$\therefore \quad f(x)$ is a decreasing function of $x \ \forall \ x > e$

i.e. $x \in (e, \infty)$

Hence $x < y \ \Rightarrow f(x) > f(y)$ or $\dfrac{\log x}{x} > \dfrac{\log y}{y}$

or $\quad y\log x > x\log y$ or $\log x^y > \log y^x$

or $\quad x^y > y^x \ \forall \ x < y$, where $x \ge 3$ or $3 \le x$

Hence $x^y > y^x \ \forall \ x, y$ such that $3 \le x < y$.

30. Now $f\left[\frac{\pi}{6}\right] = \cos\frac{\pi}{6} - \frac{\pi}{6}\left[1 + \frac{\pi}{6}\right] = \frac{\sqrt{3}}{2} - \frac{\pi}{6}\left[1 + \frac{\pi}{6}\right] \qquad ...(1)$

$$f\left[\frac{\pi}{3}\right] = \cos\frac{\pi}{3} - \frac{\pi}{3}\left[1 + \frac{\pi}{3}\right] = \frac{1}{2} - \frac{\pi}{3}\left[1 + \frac{\pi}{3}\right] \qquad ...(2)$$

Now $f'(x) = -\sin x - 1 - 2x = -[\sin x + 1 + 2x]$

$= -$ ive in the given interval

Hence $f(x)$ is decreasing function in $\frac{\pi}{6} \le x \le \frac{\pi}{3}$

or $\quad f(\pi/3) < f(\pi/6)$

Hence $\quad f(A) = \{y : f[\pi/3] \le y \le f[\pi/6]\}$

$$f[A] = \left\{y : \frac{1}{2} - \frac{\pi}{3}\left[1 + \frac{\pi}{3}\right] \le y \le \frac{\sqrt{3}}{2} - \frac{\pi}{6}\left[1 + \frac{\pi}{6}\right]\right\}$$

from (1) and (2)

Note : For another method see the chapter of set theory.

31. Consider $f(x) = x + \cos x$

$f'(x) = 1 - \sin x \ge 0 \ \forall \ x$

$\therefore \quad f$ is an increasing function

Hence if $\alpha > \beta$ then $f(\alpha) \ge f(\beta)$

or $\quad \alpha + \cos\alpha \ge \beta + \cos\beta \ \therefore \ \cos\alpha - \cos\beta \ge \beta - \alpha$

Multiplying by minus sign and changing the sign of inequality, we get

$$-(\cos\alpha - \cos\beta) \le \alpha - \beta \qquad ...(1)$$

If $\beta > \alpha$ then $f(\beta) \ge f(\alpha)$

or $\quad \beta + \cos\beta \ge \alpha + \cos\alpha \quad \therefore \ \cos\beta - \cos\alpha \ge \alpha - \beta$

Multiplying by minus sign and changing the sign of inequality

$$+(\cos\alpha - \cos\beta) \le -(\alpha - \beta) \qquad ...(2)$$

From (1) and (2)

$$|(\cos\alpha - \cos\beta)| \le |\alpha - \beta|$$

32. Ans. (b).

The domain of the function $f(x) = 1/x$ consists of all real numbers except 0.

Now $f'(x) = -1/x^2 < 0$ for all $x \ne 0$.

hence $f(x)$ is a decreasing function on its domain.

33. Ans. (a). **See Q. 10 (b) P. 1262-1263.**

34. Ans. (a).

35. (a) Ans. (b) and (c).

The side of the equilateral triangle

$$= \sqrt{(x-0)^2 + [g(x) - 0]^2} = \sqrt{x^2 + g^2(x)}.$$

$\therefore \quad$ Area of the equilateral triangle

$$= \frac{1}{2}bc\sin A = \frac{1}{2}b^2\sin 60°$$

$$= \frac{\sqrt{3}}{4}[x^2 + g^2(x)] = \frac{\sqrt{3}}{4} \text{ (given)}$$

Hence $x^2 + g^2(x) = 1$ or $g^2(x) = 1 - x^2$

$\therefore \quad g(x) = +\sqrt{1-x^2}$ or $g(x) = -\sqrt{1-x^2}$.

Note that a function cannot have two distinct values at a point and so the possibility $g(x) = \pm\sqrt{1-x^2}$ is ruled out.

(b) Ans. (b).

$$f(x) = e^x \left(2 + \int_0^x \sqrt{t^4 + 1}\,.dt\right)$$

Let $g(x) = f^{-1}(x) \Rightarrow g(f(x)) = x$

$\Rightarrow g'(f(x))\, f'(x) \Rightarrow g'(2) = \frac{1}{f'(0)}$ $\quad (\because f(0) = 2)$

Now $f'(x) = e^x \left(2 + \int_0^x \sqrt{t^4 + 1}\, dt\right) + e^x \sqrt{x^4 + 1}$

(By Leibnitz's rule)

$\Rightarrow f'(0) = 2 + 1 = 3 \Rightarrow g'(2) = \frac{1}{3}$

$\Rightarrow (f^{-1})'(2) = \frac{1}{3}$

36. True. Since $f(x)$ is odd, we $f(-x) = -f(x)$.
Also since the derivative $f'(x)$ exists,

we have $f'(x) = \lim_{h \to 0} \frac{f(x+h) - f(x)}{h}$ ...(1)

and also $f'(x) = \lim_{h \to 0} \frac{f(x-h) - f(x)}{-h}$ ...(2)

Hence by (1),

$$f'(-x) = \lim_{h \to 0} \frac{f(-x+h) - f(-x)}{h}$$

$$= \lim_{h \to 0} \frac{-f(x-h) + f(x)}{h},$$

since $f(x)$ is odd

$$= \lim_{h \to 0} \frac{f(x-h) - f(x)}{-h} = f'(x), \text{ by (2).}$$

Thus $f'(-x) = f'(x)$ and so $f'(x)$ is an even function.

37. False. The required inverse is e^x.

38. True. Let $y = [1 - (x-5)^3]^{1/5}$. Then $y^5 = 1 - (x-5)^3$

or $x = 5 + (1 - y^5)^{1/3}$.

Hence the inverse of the function $[1 - (x-5)^3]^{1/5}$ is the function $5 + (1 - x^5)^{1/3}$.

39. Ans. $y = x + 1$ and $y = 1 - x$.
If $y = ax + b$ be a linear function which maps $[-1, 1]$ onto $[0, 2]$, then we have

(i) $y = 0$ when $x = -1$ and $y = 2$ when $x = 1$.
that is, $0 = -a + b$ and $2 = a + b$, giving $a = 1, b = 1$

or (ii) $y = 2$ when $x = -1$ and $y = 0$ when $x = 1$
i.e. $2 = -a + b, 0 = a + b$, which gives $a = -1$ and $b = 1$

Hence either $y = x + 1$ or $y = -x + 1$.

40. Ans. (b).
Odd Extension from [0, 1] to [– 1, 1] means we have to choose the function out of a, b, c, d which satisfies the condition $f(-x) = -f(x)$. Now $|-x| = |x|$

$f(-x) = x^2 - x - \sin x - \cos x + \log(1 + |x|)$

$= -$[function given in b] $\therefore$ (b) is correct.

No other given function satisfies this criteria of $f(-x) = -f(x)$

41. Ans. (a).

$f(x) = x^2, g(x) = \sin x$

$gof(x) = \sin x^2 \Rightarrow gogof(x) = \sin(\sin x^2)$

$\Rightarrow (fogogof)(x) = (\sin(\sin x^2))^2 = \sin^2(\sin x^2)$

Now $\sin^2(\sin x^2) = \sin(\sin x^2)$

$\Rightarrow \sin(\sin x^2) = 0, 1$

$\Rightarrow \sin x^2 = n\pi, (4n+1)\frac{\pi}{2}; n \in \mathbf{I}$

$\Rightarrow \sin x^2 = 0 \Rightarrow x^2 = n\pi$

$\Rightarrow x = \pm\sqrt{n\pi}, \quad n \in \{0, 1, 2, 3, \ldots\}$

42. Ans. (b).

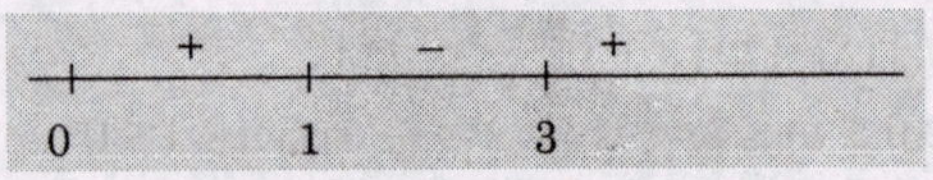

Fig. 30

$f : (0, 3) \to [1, 29]$

$f(x) = 2x^3 - 15x^2 + 36x + 1$

$f'(x) = 6x^3 - 30x + 36$

$= 6(x^2 - 5x + 6)$

$= 6(x-2)(x-3)$

In the given domain function has local maxima, it is many one

Now at $x = 0$, $f(0) = 1$

At $x = 2$, $f(2) = 16 - 60 + 72 + 1 = 29$

at $x = 3$, $f(3) = 54 - 135 + 108 + 1 = 163 - 135 = 28$

It has range $= [1, 29]$

Hence, given function is onto.

MISCELLANEOUS EXERCISE

Matching Entries

Match the entries of column-I with those of column-II under the following conditions :

1.

Column-I	Column-II
(a) $y = \frac{10}{4x^3 - 9x^2 + 6x}$ decreasing	(p) $(-\infty, 0)$

(b) $y = 2x^2 - \log x$ increasing

(c) $y = x - 2\sin x$ decreasing

(d) $y = x^2 e^{-x}$ decreasing

(q) $\left(0, \frac{1}{2}\right)$

(r) $(2, \infty)$

(s) $(0, 2)$

2. Let $f(x) = \log \frac{1+x}{1-x}$ and $g(x) = \frac{3x + x^3}{1 + 3x^2}$ then

Column-I	Column-II
(a) $(fog)\left(\frac{1-e}{1+e}\right)$	(p) 3
(b) $(gof)\left(\frac{e-1}{e+1}\right)$	(q) −3
(c) (fog)	(r) 0
(d) $(fog)\left(\frac{e-1}{e+1}\right)$	(s) 1

3.

Column-I	Column-II
(a) $f(x) = \{x\}$ where $\{x\}$ = fractional part of x	(p) $f^{-1}(x) = \frac{1}{2}(4^x - 4^{-x})$
(b) $f(x) = \frac{16^x - 1}{4^x}$	(q) f is an even function
(c) $f(x) = \log_4 \{x + \sqrt{x^2 + 1}\}$	(r) f is periodic
(d) $f(x) = x \frac{3^x - 1}{3^x + 1}$	(s) f is an odd function

4. Match the following :

Column-I	Column-II
(a) The set $\left[\text{Re}\left(\frac{2iz}{1-z^2}\right) : z \in \mathbf{C}, \lvert z \rvert = 1 \lvert z \neq \pm 1\right]$	(p) $]-\infty, -1[\cup]1, \infty[$
(b) The domain of the function $f(x) = \sin^{-1}\left(\frac{8(3)^{x-2}}{1 - 3^{2(x-1)}}\right)$ is	(q) $]-\infty, 0[\cup]0, \infty[$
(c) If $f(\theta) = \begin{vmatrix} 1 & \tan\theta & 1 \\ -\tan\theta & 1 & \tan\theta \\ -1 & -\tan\theta & 1 \end{vmatrix}$ then the set $\left\{f(\theta) : 0 \le \theta \le \frac{\pi}{2}\right\}$ is	(r) $[2, \infty[$
(d) If $f(x) = x^{3/2}(3x - 10), x \ge 0$ then $f(x)$ is increasing in	(s) $[-\infty, -1] \cup [1, \infty[$
	(t) $]-\infty, 0] \cup [2, \infty[$

(IIT-JEE 2011)

Answers

1. (a)→ (p, q, r), (b)→ (r), (c)→ (q), (d)→ (p, r)
2. (a)→ (q), (b)→ (s), (c)→ (r), (d)→ (p)
3. (a)→ (r), (b)→ (s), (c)→ (p), (d)→ (q)
4. (a)→ (s), (b)→ (t), (c)→ (r), (d)→ (r)

Solutions

1. Ans. (a)→ (p, q, r), (b)→ (r), (c)→ (q), (d)→ (p, r)

(a) Consider $g(x) = 4x^3 - 9x^2 + 6x$

$g'(x) = 12x^2 - 18x + 6 = 6(2x^2 - 3x + 1)$

$= 6(2x - 1)(x - 1)$

$g'(x) = 0$ gives $x = \frac{1}{2}, 1$

∴ $g(x)$ is increasing for $x > 1$ and $x < \frac{1}{2}$

∴ y is decreasing for $x > 1$ and $x < \frac{1}{2}$

i.e., $\left(-\infty, \frac{1}{2}\right) \cup (1, \infty)$

All (p), (q), (r) are subsets of above. ∴ (a)→ (p, q, r)

(b) $\frac{dy}{dx} = 4x - \frac{1}{x} = \frac{(2x+1)(x-0)(2x-1)}{x^2}$

or $\frac{4\left[x-\left(-\frac{1}{2}\right)\right](x-0)\left[x-\frac{1}{2}\right]}{x^2}$

For increasing, $\frac{dy}{dx} = +\text{ive}$

$\therefore \quad x > \frac{1}{2}$ or $x < -\frac{1}{2}$

$\therefore \quad x \in \left(\frac{1}{2}, \infty\right) \cup \left(-\frac{1}{2}, 0\right)$

$\therefore$ (b)→ (r) as $\left(\frac{1}{2}, \infty\right)$ is contained in $(2, \infty)$.

(c) $\frac{dy}{dx} = 1 - 2\cos x = 0$, where $\cos x = \frac{1}{2}$, *i.e.*, $x = \frac{\pi}{3}$

$\therefore \quad \frac{dy}{dx} = -$ ive, where $x \in \left(0, \frac{\pi}{3}\right)$ or $\left(\frac{5\pi}{3}, 2\pi\right)$

$\therefore$ y decreases on $\left(0, \frac{1}{2}\right)$ which is a subset of $\left(0, \frac{\pi}{3}\right)$.

(d) $\frac{dy}{dx} = e^{-x}(2x - x^2)$

$= -e^{-x} \cdot (x-0)(x-2)$

For decreasing,

$\frac{dy}{dx} = -$ ive or $e^{-x}(x-0)(x-2) = +$ ive

$\therefore \quad x < 0$ or $x > 2$

Both are subsets of (p) and (r).

2. Ans. (a)→ (q), (b)→ (s), (c)→ (r), (d)→ (p)

(a) Let $t = \frac{1-e}{1+e}$ $\therefore$ $(fog)\,t = f\,[g\,(t)]$

$= f\left[\frac{3t + t^3}{1 + 3t^2}\right] = f\,(z) = \log\left(\frac{1+z}{1-z}\right)$

$= \log\frac{(1+t)^3}{(1-t)^3} = \frac{3}{3}\log\frac{1+t}{1-t} = 3\log\frac{2}{2e}$

$= 3\log e^{-1} = -3$ $\therefore$ (a)→ (q)

(b) Let $t = \frac{e-1}{e+1}$ $\therefore$ $(gof)\,t = g\,[f\,(t)]$

$= g\left[\frac{1+t}{1-t}\right] = g\,[\log\frac{2e}{2}]$

$= g\,(1) = \frac{3+1}{1+3} = \frac{4}{4} = 1$ $\therefore$ (b)→ (s)

(c) $(fog)\,0 = f\,[g\,(0)] = f(0) = \log\frac{1+0}{1-0} = \log 1 = 0$

$\because$ (c)→ (r)

(d) Let $t = \frac{e-1}{e+1}$

$(fog)\,t = f\,[g\,(t)] = \log\left(\frac{1+g\,(t)}{1-g(t)}\right)$

$= \log\frac{(1+t)^3}{(1-t)^3} = 3\log\frac{1+t}{1-t}$

$= 3\log\frac{2e}{2} = 3\log e = 3$

$\therefore$ (d)→ (p)

3. Ans. (a)→ (r), (b)→ (s), (c)→ (p), (d)→ (q)

(a) (a)→ (r) because $\{x\}$ is a periodic function with period 1. **(See page 1249)**

(b) $f(x) = (4^x - 4^{-x})$

$\therefore \quad f(-x) = (4^{-x} - 4^x) = -f(x)$

$\therefore$ $f(x)$ is an odd function. Hence, (b)→ (s).

(c) $y = \log_4\{x + \sqrt{x^2+1}\}$ $\therefore$ $4^y = x + \sqrt{x^2+1}$

$4^{-y} = \frac{1}{x + \sqrt{x^2+1}} = \frac{x - \sqrt{x^2+1}}{x^2 - (x^2+1)} = -x + \sqrt{x^2+1}$

$\therefore \quad \frac{4^y - 4^{-y}}{2} = x$ or $f^{-1}(x) = \frac{1}{2}(4^x - 4^{-x})$

$\therefore$ (c) → (p).

(d) $f(-x) = -x\frac{3^{-x}-1}{3^{-x}+1} = -x\frac{1-3^x}{1+3^x} = x\frac{3^x-1}{3^x+1}$

$\therefore$ $f(-x) = f(x)$. Hence, f is an even function.

$\therefore$ (d)→ (q).

4. Ans. (a)→ (s), (b)→ (t), (c)→ (r), (d)→ (r)

$\text{Re}\left(\frac{2i\,(x+iy)}{1-(x^2-y^2+2xyi)}\right) = \text{Re}\left(\frac{-2y+2ix}{1-x^2+y^2-2xyi}\right)$

$= \text{Re}\left(\frac{-2y+2ix}{2y(y-ix)}\right) = \text{Re}\left(-\frac{1}{y}\right) = -\frac{1}{y}$

$= -1 \le y \le 1 = \frac{-1}{y} \ge 1$ or $\frac{-1}{y} \le -1$

(b) $-1 \le \frac{8\,.\,3^{x-2}}{1\,.\,3^{2x-2}} \le 1 \Rightarrow -1 \le \frac{8t}{9-t^2} \le 1$

$\Rightarrow \quad -1 \le \frac{8t}{9-t^2} \le 1$

$\Rightarrow \quad 0 \le \frac{9-t^2+8t}{9-t^2} \cap \frac{8t}{9-t^2} - 1 \le 0$

$\Rightarrow \quad 0 \le \frac{(t-9)(t+1)}{(t-3)(t+3)} \cap \frac{(t+9)(t-1)}{(t-3)(t+3)} \ge 0$

$\Rightarrow \quad t \in]-\infty, 9] \cup [-1, 1] \cup [9, \infty[$

$\Rightarrow \quad x \in]-\infty, 0] \cup [2, \infty[$

(c) $f(\theta) = 2\sec^2\theta \Rightarrow f(\theta) \ge 2 \Rightarrow f(\theta) \in [2, \infty[$

(d) $f(x) = x^{3/2}(3x-10)$

$f'(x) = x^{3/2}\,.\,3 + \frac{3}{2}x^{1/2}(3x-10)$

As $f'(x) \ge 0$

$\Rightarrow \quad x^{1/2}\left[3x + \frac{3}{2}(3x-10)\right] \ge 0$

$\Rightarrow \quad 3x + \frac{9x}{2} - 15 \ge 0 \quad \Rightarrow \quad \frac{15x}{2} - 15 \ge 0$

$\Rightarrow \quad x \ge 2 \quad \Rightarrow \quad x \in [2, \infty[$

Assertion / Reason

1. Let $f(x) = \sin^{-1}\dfrac{x-3}{2} - \log_{10}(4-x)$

Statement 1. The domain of $f(x)$ is $[1, 3]$.

Statement 2. $\sin^{-1} x$ is defined for $|x| \le 1$ and $\log_{10} x$ is defined for $x > 0$.

Sol. Refer cover page in the beginning.

Ans. (d).

Statement 1 is false but 2 is true. For $f(x)$ to be defined, we must have

$$-1 < \frac{x-3}{2} < 1 \quad \text{or} \quad -2 < x-3 < 2 \quad \text{or} \quad 1 < x < 5$$

but $\log_{10}(4-x)$ is defined for $4 - x > 0$ or $x < 4$

$D_1 = (-\infty, 4), D_2 = (1, 5)$

Domain of $f(x) = D_1 \cap D_2 = [1, 4)$

$\therefore$ Statement 1 is false but 2 is true.

Comprehension

Passage

1. Let $f(x) = (1-x)^2 \sin^2 x + x^2 \;\forall\, x \in \mathbf{R}$ and let $g(x) = \int_1^x \left(\dfrac{2(t-1)}{t+1} - \log t\right) f(t)\, dt \;\forall\, x \in [1, \infty[$

(IIT-JEE 2012)

(i) Which of the following is true

(a) g is increasing on $]1, \infty[$

(b) g is decreasing on $]1, \infty[$

(c) g is increasing on $]1, 2[$ and decreasing on $]2\, \infty[$

(d) g is decreasing on $]1, 2[$ and increasing on $]2, \infty[$

(ii) Consider the statements :

P: Three exists some $x \in \mathbf{R}$ such that $f(x) + 2x = 2(1 + x^2)$

Q: These exists some $x \in \mathbf{R}$, such that $2f(x) + 1 = 2x(1 + x)$

Then

(a) both P and Q are true

(b) P is true, Q is false

(c) P is false and Q is true

(d) both P and Q are false

Sol. (i) Ans. (b).

$f(x) = (1-x)^2 \sin^2 x + x^2, \quad x \in \mathbf{R}$

$$g(x) = \int_1^x \left(\frac{2(t-1)}{t+1} - \log t\right) f(t)\, dt$$

$$\Rightarrow \quad g'(x) = \left(\frac{2(x-1)}{x+1} - \log x\right) f(x) \cdot 1$$

Let $\phi(x) = \dfrac{2(x-1)}{(x+1)} - \log x$

$$\Rightarrow \quad \phi'(x) = \frac{2[(x+1) - (x-1) \cdot 1]}{(x+1)^2} - \frac{1}{x} = \frac{4}{(1+x)^2} - \frac{1}{x}$$

$$= \frac{-x^2 + 2x - 1}{x(x+1)^2} = \frac{-(x-1)^2}{x(x+1)^2}$$

$\therefore \quad \phi'(x) < 0$

Now for $x \in]1, \infty[$, $\phi(x) < 0$

$\therefore \quad g'(x) < 0$ for $x \in]1, \infty[$

(ii) Ans. (c).

$f(x) + 2x = (1-x)^2 \sin^2 x + x^2 + 2x$

$f(x) + 2x = 2(1 + x^2)$

$\Rightarrow \quad (1-x)^2 \sin^2 x + x^2 + 2x = 2 + 2x^2$

$\Rightarrow \quad (1-x)^2 \sin^2 x = x^2 - 2x + 1 + 1 = (1-x)^2 + 1$

$\Rightarrow \quad (1-x)^2 \cos^2 x = -1,$

which can never be possible

$\Rightarrow \quad P$ is not true

Let $H(x) = 2f(x) + 1 - 2x(1 + x)$

$H(0) = 2f(0) + 1 - 0 = 1$

$H(1) = 2f(1) + 1 - 4 = -3$

$\Rightarrow \quad H(z)$ has a solution

Hence Q is true.

Fascinatng Facts

- A function f is said to be monotonic in an interval if it is either increasing or decreasing in that interval.
- If $f(x)$ is strictly increasing function on an interval $(a b]$ then f^{-1} exists, which is also strictly increasing function.
- If $f(x)$ is strictly increasing function on an interval $[a, b]$ such that it is continuous then f^{-1} is continuous on $[f(a), f(b)]$
- If $f(x)$ is continuous on $[a, b]$ such that $f'(c) \le 0$ $[f'(c) < 0]$ for each $c \in [a, b]$ then $f(x)$ is monotonically (strictly) decreasing function on $[a, b]$.
- If $f(x)$ is continous on $[a, b]$ such that $f'(c) \ge 0$ $(f'(c) > 0]$ for each $c \in [a, b[$ then $f(x)$ is monotonically (strictly) increasing on $[a, b]$.
- If $f(x)$ and $g(x)$ are monotonically (or strictly) increasing (or decreasing) function on $[a, b]$ then $gof(x)$ is monotonically (or strictly) increasing function on $[a, b]$

❑

CHAPTER 28

Differential Calculus

Limits, Continuity and Differentiability

§1. Limits.

Consider the function $y = (x^2 - 1)/(x - 1)$. the value of the function at $x = 1$ is of the form 0/0 which is meaningless. In this case we cannot divide the numerator by denominator since $(x - 1)$ is zero.

Now suppose x is not actually equal to 1 but very nearly equal to 1 then $(x - 1)$ is not equal to zero. Hence in this case we can divide the numerator by denominator

$$\therefore \quad \frac{x^2 - 1}{x - 1} = x + 1$$

Now if x is little greater than 1; then value of y will be greater than 2 and as x gets nearer to 1, y comes nearer to 2. Now the difference between y and 2 is

$$\frac{x^2 - 1}{x - 1} - 2 = \frac{x^2 - 2x + 1}{x - 1} = \frac{(x - 1)^2}{x - 1} = x - 1 \quad (x \neq 1)$$

This difference $(x - 1)$ can be made as small as we please by letting x tend to 1.

Thus we see that when x has fixed value 1, the value of y is meaningless but when x tends to 1, y tends to 2 and we say that the limit of y is 2 when x tends to 1. This we write as

$$\lim_{x \to 1} \frac{(x^2 - 1)}{(x - 1)} = 2.$$

Definition of limit. *The number A is said to be the limit of $f(x)$ at $x = a$ if for any arbitrarily chosen positive number ε, however small but not zero, there exists a corresponding number δ greater than zero such that*

$$|f(x) - A| < \varepsilon$$

For all values of x for which

$$0 < |x - a| < \delta$$

where $|x - a|$ means the absolute value of $(x - a)$ without any regard to sign.

Right hand and Left hand limits.

If x approaches a from the right, that is, from larger values of x than a, the limit of f as defined before is called the right hand limit of $f(x)$ and is written as

$$\lim_{x \to a+0} f(x) \quad \text{or} \quad f(a + 0)$$

The working rule for finding the right hand limit is : "Put $a + h$ for x in $f(x)$ and make h approach zero".

In short, we have $f(a + 0) = \lim\limits_{h \to 0} f(a + h)$

Similarly if x approaches a from the left, that is, from smaller values of x than a, the limit of f is called the left hand limit and is written as $\lim\limits_{x \to a-0} f(x)$ or $f(a - 0)$.

In this case, we have $f(a - 0) = \lim\limits_{h \to 0} (a - h)$

If both right hand and left hand limits of $f(x)$, as $x \to a$, **exist and are equal in value**, their common value, evidently, will be the limit of $f(x)$ as $x \to a$. **If, however, either or both of these limits do not exist, the limit of $f(x)$ as $x \to a$ does not exist. Even if both these limits exist but are not equal in value then also the limit of $f(x)$ as $x \to a$ does not exist.**

Algebra of Limits.

$$\underset{x \to a}{\text{Lt}} [f(x) \pm g(x)] = \underset{x \to a}{\text{Lt}} f(x) \pm \underset{x \to a}{\text{Lt}} g(x)$$

$$\underset{x \to a}{\text{Lt}} [f(x)\, g(x)] = \underset{x \to a}{\text{Lt}} f(x) \cdot \underset{x \to a}{\text{Lt}} g(x)$$

$$\underset{x \to a}{\text{Lt}} \frac{f(x)}{g(x)} = \underset{x \to a}{\text{Lt}} f(x) \div \underset{x \to a}{\text{Lt}} g(x)$$

provided $\quad \text{Lt}\, g(x) \neq 0$

§2. Indeterminate forms and L' Hospital's Rule.

If a function $f(x)$ takes the form $\frac{0}{0}$ or $\frac{\infty}{\infty}$ at $x = a$, then we say that $f(x)$ is indeterminate at $x = a$. Other indeterminate forms are $\infty - \infty, 0 \times \infty, 1^{\infty}, 0^0, \infty^0$

L' Hospital's Rule. If $\phi(x)$, and $\psi(x)$ are functions of x such that $\phi(a) = 0$, and $\psi(a) = 0$, then

$$\lim_{x \to a} \frac{\phi(x)}{\psi(x)} = \lim_{x \to a} \frac{\phi'(x)}{\psi'(x)}.$$

Important Note : While applying L' Hospital's rule, we are not to differentiate $\frac{\phi(x)}{\psi(x)}$ by the rule for finding the differential coefficient of the quotient of two functions. But we are to differentiate the numerator and denominator separately.

Before applying this rule ensure that $f(x)$ is of the form $\frac{0}{0}$ or $\frac{\infty}{\infty}$. Continue differentiation as above till you get a definite limit.

***Some Important expansions.**

(i) $\sin x = x - \frac{x^3}{3!} + \frac{x^5}{5!} - ....$ (odd + −)

$\sinh x = x + \frac{x^3}{3!} + \frac{x^5}{5!} + ...$ (odd + +)

(ii) $\cos x = 1 - \frac{x^2}{2!} + \frac{x^4}{4!} - ....$ (Even + −)

$\cosh x = 1 + \frac{x^2}{2!} + \frac{x^4}{4!} + ...$ (Even + +)

(iii) $\tan x = x + \frac{1}{3}x^3 + \frac{2}{15}x^5 + ...$

(iv) $\tan^{-1} x = x - \frac{1}{3}x^3 + \frac{1}{5}x^5 - ...$

In $\sin x, \cos x, \tan x$, x is measured in radians in the above expansions.

(v) $e^x = 1 + x + \frac{x^2}{2!} + \frac{x^3}{3!} + ...$ (All + +)

$e^{-x} = 1 - x + \frac{x^2}{2!} - \frac{x^3}{3!} + ...$ (Alt. + −)

(vi) If $|x| < 1$, then

$\log_e (1+x) = x - \frac{1}{2}x^2 + \frac{1}{3}x^3 - \frac{1}{4}x^4 + ...$

(vii) $\log(1-x) = -\left\{x + \frac{x^2}{2} + \frac{x^3}{3} + ...\right\}$

Certain Limits : For indeterminate forms we can find the limit by L' Hospital's rule. Besides this, we should use expansions of various functions given above or else apply algebra of limits given above.

The following limits should be remembered.

(1) $\underset{x\to 0}{\text{Lt}} \frac{\sin x}{x} = 1$. In other words $\sin x = x$ when x is very small and so also $\tan x = x$ whereas $\cos x = 1$ when x is small.

Similarly $\underset{x\to 0}{\text{Lt}} \frac{\tan x}{x} = 1$, $\underset{x\to 0}{\text{Lt}} \frac{\tan^{-1} x}{x} = 1$

$\underset{x\to 0}{\text{Lt}} \cos x = 1$, $\underset{x\to 0}{\text{Lt}} \frac{\sin^{-1} x}{x} = 1$

(2)* $\underset{x\to 0}{\text{Lt}} (1+x)^{1/x} = e$ (See **44 P. 1292-1302** for proof)

or $\underset{x\to \infty}{\text{Lt}} \left(1 + \frac{1}{x}\right)^x = e$

and $\underset{x\to 0}{\text{Lt}} (1+px)^{1/x} = e^p$

or $\underset{x\to \infty}{\text{Lt}} \left(1 + \frac{p}{x}\right)^x = e^p$

or $\underset{x\to 0}{\text{Lt}} \left(1 + \frac{x}{p}\right)^{1/x} = e^{1/p}$

or $\underset{x\to \infty}{\text{Lt}} \left(1 + \frac{1}{px}\right)^x = e^{1/p}$

(3)* $\underset{x\to 0}{\text{Lt}} \frac{a^x - 1}{x} = \log a$ Form $\left(\frac{0}{0}\right)$

$= \underset{x\to 0}{\text{Lt}} \frac{a^x \log a}{1} = \log a$ $a > 0$

$\underset{x\to 0}{\text{Lt}} \frac{e^x - 1}{x} = \log e = 1$, as above.

(4)* $\underset{x\to 0}{\text{Lt}} \frac{(1+x)^n - 1}{x} = n$

$= \underset{x\to 0}{\text{Lt}} \frac{1 + nx + \frac{n(n-1)}{2}x^2 + ... - 1}{x} = n$

(5) $\underset{x\to a}{\text{Lt}} \frac{x^n - a^n}{x - a} = na^{n-1}$ $\left(\frac{0}{0}\right)$

$\underset{x\to a}{\text{Lt}} \frac{nx^{n-1}}{1} = na^{n-1}$

§3 Various Methods for evaluation of limits.

1. Factorisation or Substitution.

$\underset{x\to a}{\text{Lt}} \frac{x^2 - a^2}{x - a} = \underset{x\to a}{\text{Lt}} (x+a) = 2a$

We have cancelled the factor $x - a$ as $x - a \neq 0$ because $x \neq a$ but $x \to a$.

2nd Method.

Put $x = a + h$ where $h \to 0$ as $x \to a$

$\therefore \underset{h\to 0}{\text{Lt}} \frac{(h+a)^2 - a^2}{h + a - a} = \underset{h\to 0}{\text{Lt}} \frac{h^2 + 2ah}{h}$

$= \underset{h\to 0}{\text{Lt}} (h + 2a) = 2a$

2. L'Hospital Rule :

$\underset{x\to 0}{\text{Lt}} x \log \sin x$ $(0 \times \infty)$

$= \underset{x\to 0}{\text{Lt}} \frac{\log \sin x}{1/x}$ $\left(\frac{\infty}{\infty}\right)$

We have to make $f(x)$ take the form either $\frac{0}{0}$ or $\frac{\infty}{\infty}$. Now differentiate N^r and D^r separately.

$= \underset{x\to 0}{\text{Lt}} \frac{\frac{1}{\sin x} . \cos x}{-1/x^2} = \underset{x\to 0}{\text{Lt}} -\frac{x^2}{\tan x}$ $\left(\frac{0}{0}\right)$

$= \underset{x\to 0}{\text{Lt}} -\frac{2x}{\sec^2 x} = \frac{0}{1} = 0$

3. Expansion Rule.

$\underset{x\to 0}{\text{Lt}} \frac{1}{x} - \frac{1}{x^2} \log(1+x)$

$= \underset{x\to 0}{\text{Lt}} \frac{x - \log(1+x)}{x^2}$ $\left(\frac{0}{0}\right)$

Instead of L' Hospital rule we shall follow expansion method.

$$= \underset{x \to 0}{\text{Lt}} \frac{x - \left\{x - \frac{x^2}{2} + \frac{x^3}{3} - \ldots\right\}}{x^2}$$

$$= \underset{x \to 0}{\text{Lt}} \frac{x^2 \left\{\frac{1}{2} - \frac{1}{3} x \ldots\right\}}{x^2} = \underset{x \to 0}{\text{Lt}} \frac{1}{2} - \frac{1}{3} x \ldots = \frac{1}{2}.$$

4. Rationalisation

$$\underset{x \to 3}{\text{Lt}} \frac{x-3}{\sqrt{(x-2)} - \sqrt{(4-x)}}$$ **(M.N.R. 1991)**

$$= \underset{x \to 3}{\text{Lt}} \frac{x-3}{\sqrt{(x-2)} - \sqrt{(4-x)}} \cdot \frac{\sqrt{(x-2)} + \sqrt{(4-x)}}{\sqrt{(x-2)} + \sqrt{(4-x)}}$$

$$= \underset{x \to 3}{\text{Lt}} \frac{x-3}{(x-2)-(4-x)} \cdot \underset{x \to 3}{\text{Lt}} \{\sqrt{(x-2)} + \sqrt{(4-x)}\}$$

$$= \underset{x \to 3}{\text{Lt}} \frac{x-3}{2(x-3)} \cdot (1+1) = 1.$$

5. Limits when $x \to \infty$ are calculated by replacing x by $1/y$ and when $x \to \infty$, $y \to 0$. Hence

$$\underset{x \to \infty}{\text{Lt}} f(x) = \underset{y \to 0}{\text{Lt}} \phi(y)$$

where $f(x)$ becomes $\phi(y)$ when x is put $1/y$.

$x = \infty$ has no meaning as ∞ is not a fixed number on the real line. Hence we always say $x \to \infty$. Also we cannot apply ordinary laws of algebra on ∞ *i.e.* $5 - 5 = 0$ or $\frac{5}{5} = 1$ but $\infty - \infty \neq 0$ and $\frac{\infty}{\infty} \neq 1$ as explained above. These are indeterminate.

However $\text{Lt} \frac{\text{finite}}{\text{infinite}} = 0$, $\text{Lt} \frac{\text{inf.}}{\text{finite}} = \infty$

and $\text{Lt} \frac{0}{\text{non-zero finite}} = 0$,

$$\text{Lt} \frac{\text{finite } a}{\text{non-zero finite } b} = \frac{a}{b}$$

6. Limit of algebraic expressions.

(i) $\underset{x \to 0}{\text{Lt}} \frac{2x^3 + 5x^2 + 7x + 3}{5x^3 - 3x^2 + 2x - 5} = \frac{3}{-5}$

(ii) $\underset{x \to 0}{\text{Lt}} \frac{2x^4 + 5x^3 + 7x^2 + 3x}{5x^3 - 3x^2 + 2x - 5} = \frac{0}{-5} = 0$

(iii) $\underset{x \to \infty}{\text{Lt}} \frac{2x^3 + 5x^2 + 7x + 3}{5x^3 - 3x^2 + 2x - 5}$ Put $x = \frac{1}{y}$

$$= \underset{y \to 0}{\text{Lt}} \frac{2 + 5y + 7y^2 + 3y^3}{5 - 3y + 2y^2 - 5y^3} = \frac{2}{5}$$

(iv) $\underset{x \to \infty}{\text{Lt}} \frac{2x^4 + 5x^3 + 7x^2 + 3x}{5x^3 - 3x^2 + 2x - 5}$

$$= \underset{x \to \infty}{\text{Lt}} x \cdot \underset{x \to \infty}{\text{Lt}} \frac{2x^3 + 5x^2 + 7x + 3}{5x^3 - 3x^2 + 2x - 5} = \infty \cdot \frac{2}{5} = \infty.$$

(v) $\underset{x \to \infty}{\text{Lt}} \frac{2x^2 + 5x + 7}{5x^3 - 3x^2 + 2x - 5}$ Put $x = \frac{1}{y}$

$$= \underset{y \to 0}{\text{Lt}} \frac{2 + 5y + 7y^2}{5 - 3y + 2y^2 - 5y^3} \cdot \text{Lt } y$$

$$= \frac{2}{5} \cdot 0 = 0.$$

Conclusions :

(a)	If the degree of algebraic expression in N^r and D^r be same, then $\underset{x \to 0}{\text{Lt}}$ = Ratio of constant terms of N^r and D^r [See (i)] $\underset{x \to \infty}{\text{Lt}}$ = Ratio of coefficients of highest powers (same) [See (iii)]
(b)	If degree of N^r is greater than degree of D^r $\underset{x \to 0}{\text{Lt}} \frac{N^r}{D^r} = 0$ [See (ii)] $\underset{x \to \infty}{\text{Lt}} \frac{N^r}{D^r} = \infty$ [See (iv)]
(c)	If degree of D^r is greater than degree of N^r $\underset{x \to \infty}{\text{Lt}} \frac{N^r}{D^r} = 0$ [See (v)] $\underset{x \to 0}{\text{Lt}} \frac{N^r}{D^r} = \infty$

7. By finding Right hand and Left hand limits.

For the limit to exist, both $R = L$.

This method is applied when the function is defined differently for $x > a, = a, < a$

Above is clear from the example below :

Consider the function $y = f(x) = \frac{|x|}{x}$

The function is not defined for $x = 0$

For $x > 0$, $f(x) = \frac{x}{x} = 1 \quad \because |x| = x$

For $x < 0$, $f(x) = \frac{-x}{x} = -1 \quad \because |x| = -x$

For $x = 0$, $f(x) = \frac{0}{0}$ not defined.

Therefore we find $\underset{x \to 0}{\text{Lt}} f(x)$. Here the function is defined differently to the right and left of $x = 0$.

R.H.L. = $\underset{h \to 0}{\text{Lt}} f(0 + h) = 1 \quad x > 0$

L.H.L. = $\underset{h \to 0}{\text{Lt}} f(0 - h) = -1 \quad x < 0$

Since R.H.L. $\neq$ L.H.L., therefore limit of the given function does not exist as $x \to 0$.

Problem Set (1)

Evaluation of limits of functions by rationalization, by trigonometric and algebraic expansions by L' Hospital's rule, by

$$\underset{x\to 0}{\text{Lt}}\ \frac{\sin x}{x}=1 \quad \text{or by} \quad \underset{x\to \infty}{\text{Lt}}\left(1+\frac{1}{x}\right)^{x}=e \quad \text{or} \quad \underset{x\to 0}{\text{Lt}}\ (1+x)^{1/x}=e$$

Limit by R.H.L. = L.H.L. *i.e.*, $R = L$

1. (a) Is the function $\dfrac{\sqrt{(1+x)}-\sqrt{(1-x)}}{x}$ defined for all values of x? Indicate the values of x for which it is defined and real. Find the limit as $x\to 0$.

   (b) Evaluate $\displaystyle\lim_{h\to 0}\frac{\sqrt{(x+h)}-\sqrt{x}}{h}$.

2. (a) Use the formula $\displaystyle\lim_{x\to 0}\frac{a^x-1}{x}=\log a$ to find $\displaystyle\lim_{x\to 0}\frac{2^x-1}{(1+x)^{1/2}-1}$.

   (b) Evaluate $\displaystyle\underset{x\to 0}{\text{Lt}}\ \frac{x.2^x-x}{1-\cos x}$

3. (a) $\displaystyle\underset{x\to 0}{\text{Lt}}\ \frac{5^x-4^x}{4^x-3^x}$ (b) $\displaystyle\underset{x\to 0}{\text{Lt}}\ \frac{8^x-4^x-2^x+1^x}{x^2}$.

4. (a)* $\displaystyle\underset{x\to 0}{\text{Lt}}\ \frac{64^x-32^x-16^x+4^x+2^x-1}{[\sqrt{(15+\cos x)}-4]\sin x}$

   (b) $\displaystyle\underset{x\to 0}{\text{Lt}}\ \frac{8^x-4^x-2^x+1}{\sqrt{2}-\sqrt{1+\cos x}}$

5. (a)* $\displaystyle\underset{x\to 0}{\text{Lt}}\left\{\frac{p^x+q^x+r^x}{3}\right\}^{2/x}$, $p,q,r>0$.

   (b) Evaluate : $\displaystyle\lim_{x\to 0}\frac{a^{\tan x}-a^{\sin x}}{\tan x-\sin x}$, $a>0$.

   (Roorkee 2002)

6.* $\displaystyle\underset{x\to a}{\text{Lt}}\ \frac{e^{\sqrt{x}}-e^{\sqrt{a}}}{x-a}$

7. Evaluate :

   (a) $\displaystyle\lim_{h\to 0}\frac{(a+h)^2\sin(a+h)-a^2\sin a}{h}$

   (b)* $\displaystyle\underset{x\to 0}{\text{Lt}}\ \frac{\sin(3x+a)-3\sin(2x+a)+3\sin(x+a)-\sin a}{x^3}$

   (M.N.R. 1997)

   (c) $\displaystyle\lim_{x\to 0}\left[\frac{\sin(x+a)+\sin(a-x)-2\sin a}{x\sin x}\right]$.

8. Evaluate the following limits :

   (a) $\displaystyle\lim_{x\to 0}\frac{\sin x}{x}$. (b) $\displaystyle\underset{x\to 0}{\text{Lt}}\ \frac{x}{\tan x}=1$

   (M.N.R. 1995)

   (c) $\displaystyle\lim_{x\to 0}\frac{\sin nx[(a-n)nx-\tan x]}{x^2}=0$, where n is non-zero positive integer, then a is equal to

   (a) $(n+1)/n$ (b) n^2
   (c) $\dfrac{1}{n}$ (d) $n+\dfrac{1}{n}$.

   (IIT-Sc. 2003)

9. (a) $\displaystyle\underset{x\to \pi/2}{\text{Lt}}\ \frac{1-\sin^3 x}{\cos^2 x}$

   (b) $\displaystyle\underset{x\to \pi/2}{\text{Lt}}\ \frac{\sin(\cos x)\cos x}{\sin x-\operatorname{cosec} x}$

   (c) $\displaystyle\underset{x\to 0}{\text{Lt}}\ \frac{\sqrt{1-\cos 2x}}{x}=$

   (a) 0 (b) 1
   (c) $\sqrt{2}$ (d) does not exist

   (AIEEE 2002)

   (d) $\displaystyle\underset{\alpha\to \beta}{\text{Lt}}\ \frac{\sin^2\alpha-\sin^2\beta}{\alpha^2-\beta^2}=$

   (a) 0 (b) 1
   (c) $\dfrac{\sin\beta}{\beta}$ (d) $\dfrac{\sin 2\beta}{2\beta}$

   (AIEEE 2002)

10. (a) $\displaystyle\underset{x\to 0}{\text{Lt}}\ \frac{1-\cos^3 x}{x\sin x\cos x}$

    (b)* $\displaystyle\underset{x\to a}{\text{Lt}}\ \frac{a\sin x-x\sin a}{ax^2-a^2x}$

11. (a) $\displaystyle\lim_{x\to 0}\frac{1-\cos 2x}{x}$

    (b) Prove that $\displaystyle\lim_{x\to 0}\frac{\log\cos x}{x}=0$

    (c) $\displaystyle\underset{x\to 0}{\text{Lt}}\ \frac{(1-\cos 2x)\sin 5x}{x^2\sin 3x}=\frac{10}{3}$

    (M.N.R. 1993)

12. (a) Show that

    $$\lim_{x\to 1}\left\{\frac{x^3+2x^2+x+1}{x^2+2x+3}\right\}^{\frac{1-\cos(x-1)}{(x-1)^2}}=\sqrt{\frac{5}{6}}$$

    (b) Evaluate $\displaystyle\underset{x\to 0}{\text{Lt}}\ \frac{e^{x^2}-\cos x}{x^2}$

    (c) $f(x)$ is the integral of $\dfrac{2\sin x-\sin 2x}{x^3}$, $x\neq 0$, find $\displaystyle\lim_{x\to 0}f'(x)$.

Evaluate the following limits :

13. (a) $\lim_{x \to 1} \frac{x-1}{2x^2 - 7x + 5}$. (b) $\lim_{\theta \to \pi/2} (\sec\theta - \tan\theta)$.

14. (a) $\lim_{x \to \infty} [x - \sqrt{(x^2 + x)}]$.

(b) $\text{Lt}_{x \to \infty} \frac{2\sqrt{x} + 3\sqrt[3]{x} + 5\sqrt[5]{x}}{\sqrt{(5x-2)} + \sqrt[3]{(3x-2)}}$

15. (a) $\text{Lt}_{x \to \infty} \frac{\sqrt{x^2+1} - \sqrt[3]{x^2+1}}{\sqrt[4]{x^4+1} - \sqrt[5]{x^4+1}}$

(b) Prove that $\lim_{x \to \infty} \sqrt{\left(\frac{x - \sin x}{x + \cos^2 x}\right)} = 1$

16. (a)* $\text{Lt}_{x \to \infty} \frac{e^{x^2} - 1}{e^{x^2} + 1} = 1$

(b) $\lim_{x \to \infty} \frac{(2+x)^{40}(4+x)^5}{(2-x)^{45}} = -1$ **(C.E.T. 1997; I.I.T. 1990)**

17.* $\lim_{x \to -\infty} \frac{x^4 \sin(1/x) + x^2}{1 + |x|^3} = -1$

Evaluate the following limits ;

18. (a) $\lim_{x \to \infty} \frac{\sin x}{x}$.

(b) $\lim_{x \to 0} \frac{\sqrt{(1+\sin x)} - \sqrt{(1-\sin x)}}{x}$.

(c) $\lim_{x \to 0} \frac{\sqrt[3]{(1+\sin x)} - \sqrt[3]{(1-\sin x)}}{x}$

19. $\text{Lt}_{x \to 2} \frac{2 - \sqrt{2+x}}{2^{1/3} - (4-x)^{1/3}}$ **(J.E.E.W.B. 1996)**

20. (a) $\text{Lt}_{x \to 1} \frac{x^m - 1}{x^n - 1}$ (b) $\text{Lt}_{x \to a} \frac{x^{3/5} - a^{3/5}}{x^{1/3} - a^{1/3}}$

(c) $\text{Lt}_{x \to a} \frac{x^m - a^m}{x^n - a^n} = \frac{m}{n} a^{m-n}$.

(d) If $\text{Lt}_{x \to 1} \frac{x^4 - 1}{x - 1} = \text{Lt}_{x \to k} \frac{x^3 - k^3}{x^2 - k^2}$ then $k =$

(a) $\frac{2}{3}$ (b) $\frac{4}{3}$

(c) $\frac{8}{3}$ (d) none

21. (a) $\text{Lt}_{x \to 2a} \frac{\sqrt{(x-2a)} + \sqrt{x} - \sqrt{2a}}{\sqrt{(x^2 - 4a^2)}}$.

(b) $\lim_{x \to a} \frac{\sqrt{a+2x} - \sqrt{3x}}{\sqrt{(3a+x)} - 2\sqrt{(x)}}$ $(a \neq 0)$.

22. Evaluate the following limits :

(a) $\text{Lt}_{x \to 0} \frac{\sqrt{4 + \sin 3x} - 2}{\log(1 + \tan 2x)}$

(b) $\text{Lt}_{x \to 1} \frac{2(x-1)}{\sqrt[3]{(7+x)} - 2}$.

23. $\text{Lt}_{x \to \pi/2} \tan^2 x [(2\sin^2 x + 3\sin x + 4)^{1/2} - (\sin^2 x + 6\sin x + 2)^{1/2}]$

24. (a) $\lim_{x \to 1} (1-x)\tan\left(\frac{\pi x}{2}\right)$

(b) $\lim_{\alpha \to \pi/4} \frac{\sin\alpha - \cos\alpha}{\alpha - \pi/4}$.

(c) $\lim_{x \to \pi/4} \frac{1 - \tan x}{1 - \sqrt{2}\sin x}$

25. (a) $\lim_{x \to 1} \frac{(2x-3)(\sqrt{x}-1)}{2x^2 + x - 3}$.

(b) $\lim_{x \to 2} \frac{x^2 - 3x + 2}{x^2 + x - 6}$.

26. Evaluate the following limits :

(a) $\lim_{x \to 0} \frac{\tan x - \sin x}{x^3}$.

(b)* $\lim_{x \to 0} \frac{x\cos x - \log(1+x)}{x^2} = \frac{1}{2}$

(c) $\lim_{x \to 0} \frac{x\tan 2x - 2x\tan x}{(1 - \cos 2x)^2}$ is

(a) 2 (b) -2

(c) $\frac{1}{2}$ (d) $-\frac{1}{2}$ **(I.I.T. 1999)**

(d) If $\text{Lt}_{x \to 0} \frac{\cos^2 x - \cos x - e^x \cos x + e^x - \frac{x^3}{2}}{x^n}$ is a finite non-zero number, then the integer n is :

(a) 2 (b) 3

(c) 4 (d) 5

27. (a) $\lim_{x \to \pi/2} \frac{2x - \pi}{\cos x}$. (b) $\lim_{x \to 0} \frac{2\sin^2 3x}{x^2}$.

(c) $\lim_{x \to 0} \frac{\tan 2x - x}{3x - \sin x}$.

(d) $\text{Lt}_{x \to 0} \frac{\log(3+x) - \log(3-x)}{x} = k$ then the value of k is :

(a) 0 (b) $-\frac{1}{3}$

(c) $\frac{2}{3}$ (d) $-\frac{2}{3}$ **(AIEEE 2003)**

28. (a)* $\lim_{x \to 0} \frac{\sin x - x}{x^3}$. (b)* $\lim_{x \to 0} \frac{x\cos x - \sin x}{x^2 \sin x}$.

(c) If $f'(a)$ exists, then show that

$\text{Lt}_{x \to a} \frac{x f(a) - a f(x)}{x - a} = f(a) - a f'(a)$

29. (a) If $f(2) = 4$ and $f'(2) = 1$, then find

$\lim\limits_{x\to 2} \dfrac{x f(2) - 2f(x)}{x-2}$. **(M.N.R. 1996)**

(b) If $f(a) = 2, f'(a) = 1, g(a) = -1, g'(a) = 2$, then the value of $\lim\limits_{x\to a} \dfrac{g(x)\ f(a) - g(a)\ f(x)}{x-a} = 5$

(Karnataka C.E.E. 1999)

(c) $f(x)$ is differentiable function given $f'(1) = 4, f'(2) = 6$, where $f'(c)$ means the derivative of function at $x = c$ then $\lim\limits_{h\to 0} \dfrac{f(2+2h+h^2) - f(2)}{f(1+h-h^2) - f(1)}$

(a) not exist (b) -3

(c) 3 (d) 3/2 **(IIT-Sc. 2003)**

(d) $f(x)$ is differentiable, increasing function, then $\lim\limits_{x\to 0} \dfrac{f(x^2) - f(x)}{f(x) - f(0)}$ is equal to

(a) 2 (b) 1

(c) -1 (d) 0 **(IIT-Sc. 2004)**

30. (a)* Suppose $f : \mathbf{R} \to \mathbf{R}$ is a differentiable function and $f(1) = 4$. Then the value of

$$\lim_{x\to 1} \int_4^{f(x)} \frac{2t}{(x-1)}\, dt = 8f'(1)$$

(I.I.T. 1990)

(b)* If $G(x) = -\sqrt{25 - x^2}$, then

$$\lim_{x\to 1} \frac{G(x) - G(1)}{x-1} = \frac{1}{\sqrt{24}}$$

31. (a)* If $f(9) = 9,\ f'(9) = 4$, then $\lim\limits_{x\to 9} \dfrac{\sqrt{f(x)} - 3}{\sqrt{(x)} - 3}$ equals ....

(Karnataka C.E.E. 1999)

(b)* $F(x) = f(x)\, g(x)\, h(x)$ for all real x, where $f(x), g(x)$ and $h(x)$ are differentiable functions. At some point x_0,

$F'(x_0) = 21\, F(x_0), f'(x_0) = 4f(x_0)$,

$g'(x_0) = -7g(x_0)$ and $h'(x_0) = kh(x_0)$.

Then $k =$ .... **(I.I.T. 1997)**

(c) If $f''(x)$ be continuous at $x = 0$ and $f''(0) = 4$ then

$$\underset{x\to 0}{\text{Lt}} \frac{2f(x) - 3f(2x) + f(4x)}{x^2} = 12$$

(d) If the normal of $f(x) = 0$ at $x = 0$ is given by $3x - y + 3 = 0$ then prove that

$$\underset{x\to 0}{\text{Lt}} \frac{x^2}{f(x^2) - 5f(4x^2) + 4f(7x^2)} = -\frac{1}{3} \quad \text{Form } \frac{0}{0}.$$

32. $\lim\limits_{x\to \pi/2} \dfrac{\sin x - (\sin x)^{\sin x}}{1 - \sin x + \log \sin x}$

33. (a) $\underset{\theta\to \pi}{\text{Lt}} \dfrac{\sqrt{(2+\cos\theta)} - 1}{(\pi - \theta)^2}$

(b) $\underset{\theta\to \frac{\pi}{4}}{\text{Lt}} \dfrac{\sqrt{2} - \cos\theta - \sin\theta}{(4\theta - \pi)^2}$

(c)* $\underset{\theta\to \pi/4}{\text{Lt}} \dfrac{2\sqrt{2} - (\cos\theta + \sin\theta)^3}{1 - \sin 2\theta}$

34. (a) Let α and β be the roots of $ax^2 + bx + c = 0$, then prove that

$$\lim_{x\to \alpha} \frac{1 - \cos(ax^2 + bx + c)}{(x-\alpha)^2} = \frac{a^2}{2}(\alpha - \beta)^2$$

(b) $\lim\limits_{x\to 0} \dfrac{\sin(\pi \cos^2 x)}{x^2}$ equals

(a) $-\pi$ (b) π

(c) $\dfrac{\pi}{2}$ (d) 1 **(I.I.T. Sc. 2001)**

Evaluate the following limits :

35. (a) $\underset{x\to \infty}{\text{Lt}}\ x \cos\left(\dfrac{\pi}{4x}\right) \sin\left(\dfrac{\pi}{4x}\right)$

(b) $\underset{x\to 0}{\text{Lt}} \dfrac{(\pi/x)}{\cot\left(\dfrac{\pi}{2} x\right)} = \dfrac{\pi^2}{2}$

36. (a)* $\underset{x\to 0}{\text{Lt}} \dfrac{\log \tan\left(\dfrac{\pi}{4} + ax\right)}{\sin bx}$

(b)* $\underset{x\to \infty}{\text{Lt}}\ x\left(\tan^{-1} \dfrac{x+1}{x+2} - \dfrac{\pi}{4}\right)$

37. (a) $\underset{x\to 0}{\text{Lt}} \dfrac{\sin^{-1} x - \tan^{-1} x}{x^3}$

(b) $\underset{x\to 0}{\text{Lt}} \dfrac{2x - \sin^{-1} x}{2x + \tan^{-1} x}$

38. (a)* If $\lim\limits_{x\to a} \dfrac{a^x - x^a}{x^x - a^a} = -1$, then prove that $a = 1$.

(b)* $\lim\limits_{h\to 0} \dfrac{\ln(1+2h) - 2\ln(1+h)}{h^2} =$ .... **(I.I.T. 1997)**

39. (a) Prove that

$$\lim_{n\to\infty} \cos\left(\frac{x}{2}\right)\cos\left(\frac{x}{4}\right)\cos\left(\frac{x}{8}\right).....\cos\left(\frac{x}{2^n}\right)$$

is $\dfrac{\sin x}{x}$.

(b) Prove that

$$\lim_{n\to\infty} \log_{n-1}(n) \log_n (n+1) \ldots \log_{n^k-1}(n^k)$$

is equal to k.

40. Find the values of a, b and c such that

(a) $\lim\limits_{x\to 0} \dfrac{x(1 + a\cos x) - b\sin x}{x^3} = 1$.

(b)* Find the values of constants a, b and c so that

$$\lim_{x\to 0} \frac{axe^x - b\log(1+x) + cxe^{-x}}{x^2 \sin x} = 2$$

(Roorkee 1997)

(c) If $\lim\limits_{x\to\infty} \left(\dfrac{x^2+1}{x+1} - ax - b\right) = 0$, then prove that $a = 1, b = -1$.

(d) If $\underset{x\to\infty}{\text{Lt}}\left[\dfrac{x^2-1}{x+1}-ax-b\right]=2$ then prove that $a=1, b=-3$

(e) If $\underset{x\to\infty}{\text{Lt}}\left[\dfrac{x^2+1}{x+1}-ax-b\right]=\infty$, find a and b.

41. (a) $\lim\limits_{x\to 0}\dfrac{\sin 2x+a\sin x}{x^3}=$ finite, find a and the limit.

(b)* $\lim\limits_{x\to 0}\dfrac{a\cos x+bx\sin x-5}{x^4}=$ finite, find a and b and the limit.

42. (a) $\lim\limits_{x\to 0}\dfrac{ae^x-b\cos x+ce^{-x}}{x\sin x}=2$.

(b) $\lim\limits_{x\to 0}\dfrac{x(a+b\cos x)-c\sin x}{x^5}=1$

(c) $\lim\limits_{x\to 0}\dfrac{a\sin x-bx+cx^2+x^3}{2x^2\log(1+x)-2x^3+x^4}=$ finite and determine it.

43. Evaluate the following limits :

(a) $\lim\limits_{x\to 0}\dfrac{\sin x-x+\frac{1}{6}x^3}{x^5}$

(b) $\lim\limits_{x\to\pi/2}\tan x\log_e\sin x$.

(c) $\lim\limits_{x\to\pi/2}[x\tan x-(\pi/2)\sec x]$

Very Important Limit :

44. $\lim\limits_{x\to 0}(1+x)^{1/x}$ and deduce

(i) $\lim\limits_{x\to 0}(1+px)^{1/x}=e^p$

(ii) $\lim\limits_{x\to 0}\left(1+\dfrac{x}{p}\right)^{1/x}=e^{1/p}$.

(iii) $\underset{x\to\infty}{\text{Lt}}\left(1+\dfrac{1}{x}\right)^x=e$, (iv) $\underset{x\to\infty}{\text{Lt}}\left(1+\dfrac{p}{x}\right)^x=e^p$,

(v) $\underset{x\to\infty}{\text{Lt}}\left(1+\dfrac{1}{px}\right)^x=e^{1/p}$.

45.* $\underset{x\to 0}{\text{Lt}}\dfrac{(1+x)^{1/x}-e+\dfrac{ex}{2}}{x^2}=\dfrac{11e}{24}$

46. (a)* $\lim\limits_{x\to 0}\left\{\tan\left(\dfrac{\pi}{4}+x\right)\right\}^{1/x}$ **(I.I.T. 1993)**

(b) $\lim\limits_{x\to\infty}\left(\dfrac{x+6}{x+1}\right)^{x+4}=$..........

(c) Let $f:\mathbf{R}\to\mathbf{R}$ be such that $f(1)=3$ and $f'(1)=6$. Then $\lim\limits_{x\to 0}\left(\dfrac{f(1+x)}{f(1)}\right)^{1/x}$ equals

(a) 1 (b) $e^{1/2}$
(c) e^2 (d) e^3 **(I.I.T. Sc. 2002)**

47. (a)* $\underset{x\to\infty}{\text{Lt}}\left(\dfrac{x+2}{x+1}\right)^{x+3}$ is .... **(M.N.R. 1994)**

(b)* $\lim\limits_{x\to 0}\left(\dfrac{1+5x^2}{1+3x^2}\right)^{1/x^2}=$....... **(I.I.T. 1996)**

(c) For $x\in R$, $\lim\limits_{x\to\infty}\left(\dfrac{x-3}{x+2}\right)^x=$

(a) e (b) e^{-1}
(c) e^{-5} (d) e^5 **(I.I.T. Sc. 2000)**

(d) If α and β are the roots of the equation $ax^2+bx+c=0$, then $\underset{x\to\alpha}{\text{Lt}}[ax^2+bx+c+1]^{2/(x-\alpha)}$ is :

(a) $2a(\alpha-\beta)$ (b) $2\log|a(\alpha-\beta)|$
(c) $e^{2a(\alpha-\beta)}$ (d) $e^{a^2|\alpha-\beta|}$

Evaluate the following limits :

48. (a) $\lim\limits_{x\to 0}\left(\dfrac{\tan x}{x}\right)^{1/x^2}$ (b) $\lim\limits_{x\to 0}\left(\dfrac{\tan x}{x}\right)^{1/x}$

(c) $\lim\limits_{x\to 0}\left(\dfrac{\tan x}{x}\right)^{1/x^3}$

49. (a) $\lim\limits_{x\to 0}\left(\dfrac{\sin x}{x}\right)^{1/x^2}$ (b) $\lim\limits_{x\to 0}\left(\dfrac{\sin x}{x}\right)^{1/x}$

Prove the following :

(c) $\underset{x\to 1}{\text{Lt}}(\log_5 5x)^{\log_x 5}=e$

(d) $\underset{x\to 1}{\text{Lt}}(\log_2 2x)^{\log_x 5}=e^{\log_2 5}$

50. (a) $\lim\limits_{x\to 0}\left(\dfrac{\sinh x}{x}\right)^{1/x^2}$

(b)* $\lim\limits_{x\to 0}\left[2\dfrac{\cosh x-1}{x^2}\right]^{1/x^2}$

(c) $\underset{x\to 0}{\text{Lt}}\left(\dfrac{\sin x}{x}\right)^{\frac{\sin x}{x-\sin x}}=\dfrac{1}{e}$

51. (a)* $\underset{x\to\infty}{\text{Lt}}\left(\dfrac{x-2}{x+3}\right)^{2x}=\underset{x\to\infty}{\text{Lt}}\left(1-\dfrac{5}{x+3}\right)^{2x}$

(b) $\underset{x\to\infty}{\text{Lt}}\left(\sin\dfrac{1}{x}+\cos\dfrac{1}{x}\right)^x$

(c)* $\underset{x\to 2}{\text{Lt}}\dfrac{\tan\pi x}{x-2}+\underset{x\to\infty}{\text{Lt}}\left(1+\dfrac{1}{x^2}\right)^x=\pi+1$

52. (a) $\underset{x\to a}{\text{Lt}}\left(\dfrac{\sin x}{\sin a}\right)^{\frac{1}{x-a}}$, $a\neq n\pi, n\in I$

(b) $\underset{x\to\alpha}{\text{Lt}}\left(\dfrac{\tan x}{\tan\alpha}\right)^{1/(x-\alpha)}=e^{2\operatorname{cosec}2\alpha}$

(c) $\underset{x\to 0}{\text{Lt}}\left(\dfrac{\sin x}{x}\right)^{\frac{\sin x}{x-\sin x}}=\dfrac{1}{e}$

53. (a) $\underset{x \to \infty}{\text{Lt}} \left(\frac{\pi}{2} - \tan^{-1} x\right)^{1/x}$

(b) $\underset{x \to \pi/2}{\text{Lt}} \left(\frac{1+\cot x}{1+\cos x}\right)^{1/\cos x}$

(c) The integer n for which $\lim_{x \to 0} \frac{(\cos x - 1)(\cos x - e^x)}{x^n}$ is a finite non-zero number is

(a) 1 (b) 2 (c) 3 (d) 4

(I.I.T. Sc. 2002)

54. (a) Evaluate $\underset{x \to \infty}{\text{Lt}} \left(\frac{x^2+5x+3}{x^2+x+2}\right)^x$

(b) Prove that $\lim_{n \to \infty} (4^n + 5^n)^{1/n} = 5$

55. (a) A function $f(x)$ is defined as under :

$$f(x) = \begin{cases} x+2, & x<1 \\ 4x-1, & 1 \le x < 3 \\ x^2+5, & x>3 \end{cases}$$

Determine Lt $f(x)$ when $x \to 1$ and $x \to 3$.

(b)* A function is defined as under :

$$f(x) = \begin{cases} \frac{\sin x}{x}, & x<0 \\ ax+b, & x>0 \end{cases}$$

If $\underset{x \to 0}{\text{Lt}} f(x)$ exists, then find a, b and the limit.

56. (a) $\underset{x \to n}{\text{Lt}} (-1)^{[x]}$ where $[x]$ stands for greatest integer not exceeding x.

(b)* Evaluate $\underset{x \to 2}{\text{Lt}} \{x + (x - [x])^2\}$

(c) If $[x]$ denotes the greatest integer less than or equal to x, then $\underset{x \to \infty}{\text{Lt}} \frac{[x]+[2x]+[3x]+\ldots+[nx]}{n^2} =$

(a) $x/2$ (b) $x/3$
(c) x (d) 0

57. (a)* Evaluate $\underset{x \to 5}{\text{Lt}} \frac{x^2-9x+20}{x-[x]}$

(b) Prove that $\lim_{x \to 0} (1 - x + [x-1] + [1-x]) = -1$.

(c) Show that $\lim_{x \to 0} \frac{\log_{\sec \frac{x}{2}} \cos x}{\log_{\sec x} \cos \frac{x}{2}}$ is equal to 16.

58.* $f(x) = \begin{cases} x^4, & x^2 < 1 \\ x, & x^2 \ge 1 \end{cases}$

Discuss the existence of limit at $x = 1$ and $x = -1$.

59.* Differentiate x^x from first principle where $x > 0$.

60. Does the following limits exist ? If they exist find their values

(a) $\lim_{x \to 0} e^{1/x}$ (b) $\lim_{x \to 0} \sin \frac{1}{x}$. **(M.N.R. 1995)**

61. (a) If $\underset{x \to a}{\text{Lt}} f(x) g(x)$ exists, then does it imply that $\underset{x \to a}{\text{Lt}} f(x)$ and $\underset{x \to a}{\text{Lt}} g(x)$ also exist ?

(b) If $\underset{x \to a}{\text{Lt}} [f(x) + g(x)]$ exists, then does it imply that $\underset{x \to a}{\text{Lt}} f(x)$ and $\underset{x \to a}{\text{Lt}} g(x)$ also exist ?

62. (a)* Draw the graph of function $f(x) = |x|/x$. Is $f(x)$ defined at $x = 0$? Does the limit of $f(x)$ exist when $x \to 0$? Explain.

(b) (i) $f(x) = \frac{x-2}{|x-2|}, x \ne 2$ $\underset{x \to 2}{\text{Lt}} f(x) = \ldots..$

(ii) $f(x) = \frac{\sin x}{|x|}, x \ne 0$ $\underset{x \to 0}{\text{Lt}} f(x) = \ldots.$

(iii) $\underset{x \to 1}{\text{Lt}} \frac{\sqrt{x} . \sin(x-1)}{|x-1|}$

63.* $f(x) = \frac{|x^3 - 3x^2 + 2x|}{x^3 - 3x^2 + 2x}$.

Find the set of points a, where $\underset{x \to a}{\text{Lt}} f(x)$ does not exist.

64. (a)* If $f(x) = \frac{\sin [x]}{[x]}, [x] \ne 0,$

$= 0, \ [x] = 0$

where $[x]$ denotes the greatest integer less than or equal to x, then prove that $\lim_{x \to 0} f(x)$ does not exist. **(I.I.T. 1995)**

(b) $\underset{x \to 0}{\text{Lt}} [x] [x+1]$

65. (a)* If $f(x) = x \sin(1/x), x \ne 0,$

$= 0, x = 0.$

then prove that $\lim_{x \to 0} f(x) = 0$.

(b) Evaluate $\lim_{x \to 0} \frac{\sin x}{x}$

A function $f(x)$ is defined as

$f(x) = \begin{cases} 1 \text{ when } x \ne 0 \\ 2 \text{ when } x = 0. \end{cases}$

Does the limit of $f(x)$ as $x \to 0$ exist ? Explain your answer.

66. (a) $\lim_{x \to 1} \frac{\sqrt{1 - \cos 2(x-1)}}{x-1}$

(a) exists and it equals $\sqrt{2}$
(b) exists and it equals $-\sqrt{2}$
(c) does not exist because $x - 1 \to 0$
(d) does not exist because left hand limit is not equal to right hand limit. **(I.I.T. 1998)**

(b) The left hand limit of $f(x) = \left\{\frac{|x|^3}{a} - \left[\frac{x}{a}\right]^3\right\}$ $(a > 0)$ where $[x]$ denotes the greatest integer less than or equal to x is

(a) a^2 (b) $a^2 - 1$
(c) $a^2 - 3$ (d) none of these

67. If $f : [-1, 1] \to R$ and $f'(0) = \lim_{n \to \infty} nf\left(\frac{1}{n}\right)$ and $f(0) = 0$. Find the value of

$$\lim_{n \to \infty} \frac{2}{\pi}(n+1)\cos^{-1}\left(\frac{1}{n}\right) - n.$$

Given that $0 < \left|\lim_{n \to \infty} \cos^{-1}\left(\frac{1}{n}\right)\right| < \frac{\pi}{2}$. **(I.I.T. 2004)**

68. Let $g(x) = \frac{(x-1)^n}{\log \cos^m (x-1)}, 0 < x < 2$, m and n are integers, $m \neq 0, n > 0$, and let p be the left hand derivative of $|x-1|$ at $x = 1$. If $\lim_{x \to 1^+} g(x) = p$, then

(a) $n = 1, m = 1$
(b) $n = 1, m = -1$
(c) $n = 2, m = 2$
(d) $n > 2, m = n$ **(I.I.T. 2008)**

Solutions to Problem Set (1)

1. (a) The given function is not defined at $x = 0$ since it takes the indeterminate form 0/0 at $x = 0$. Also $1 + x \geq 0, 1 - x \geq 0$ or $-1 \leq x \leq 1$. The value of the function is imaginary for all values of $x > 1$ and $x < -1$ and so it is also not defined for these values of x. It follows that the function is defined and real for all values of x in the interval $-1 \leq x \leq 1$ except $x = 0$. Now

$$\lim_{x \to 0} \frac{\sqrt{(1+x)} - \sqrt{(1-x)}}{x}$$

$$= \lim_{x \to 0} \frac{(1+x) - (1-x)}{x[\sqrt{(1+x)} + \sqrt{(1-x)}]}$$

$$= \lim_{x \to 0} \frac{2}{\sqrt{(1+x)} + \sqrt{(1-x)}} = \frac{2}{1+1} = 1.$$

(b) **Hint :** Rationalize the N^r. Ans. $\frac{1}{2\sqrt{(x)}}$

2. (a) $\lim_{x \to 0} \frac{2^x - 1}{(1+x)^{1/2} - 1}$

$$= \lim_{x \to 0} \frac{(2^x - 1)\{(1+x)^{1/2} + 1\}}{\{(1+x)^{1/2} - 1\}\{(1+x)^{1/2} + 1\}}$$

$$= \lim_{x \to 0} \frac{2^x - 1}{1 + x - 1}\{(1+x)^{1/2} + 1\}$$

$$= \lim_{x \to 0} \frac{2^x - 1}{x} \lim_{x \to 0} \{(1+x)^{1/2} + 1\}$$

$$= (\log 2) . 2 = 2 \log 2.$$

(b) $\text{Lt}_{x \to 0} \frac{x.2^x - x}{1 - \cos x} = \text{Lt}_{x \to 0} \frac{x(2^x - 1)}{2\sin^2 (x/2)}$

$$= \text{Lt} \frac{1}{2} \frac{x^2}{[\sin^2 (x/2)]^2} \text{Lt} \frac{2^x - 1}{x} \left(\frac{0}{0}\right)$$

$$= \frac{1}{2} \frac{x^2}{(x/2)^2} . \text{Lt}_{x \to 0} \frac{2^x \log 2}{1} \quad \because \text{Lt}_{\theta \to 0} \sin \theta = \theta$$

$$= \frac{1}{2} . 4 . \log 2 = 2 \log 2.$$

3. (a) $\text{Lt}_{x \to 0} \frac{5^x - 4^x}{4^x - 3^x}$

$$= \text{Lt}_{x \to 0} \frac{\frac{5^x - 1}{x} - \frac{4^x - 1}{x}}{\frac{4^x - 1}{x} - \frac{3^x - 1}{x}} = \frac{\log 5 - \log 4}{\log 4 - \log 3}$$

$$= \log \frac{5}{4} \Big/ \log \frac{4}{3}.$$

Note : You can use L' Hospital's rule straight away.

(b) $\text{Lt}_{x \to 0} \frac{(4^x - 1)}{x} . \frac{(2^x - 1)}{x} = \log 4 . \log 2 = 2(\log 2)^2$

$$\text{Lt}_{x \to 0} \frac{a^x - 1}{x}\left(\frac{0}{0}\right) = \text{Lt}_{x \to 0} \frac{a^x \log a}{1} = \log a.$$

4. (a) If $2^x = t$, then $N^r = t^6 - t^5 - t^4 + t^2 + t - 1$

$$= t^5(t-1) - t^2(t^2 - 1) + (t-1)$$

$$= (t-1)[t^5 - t^2(t+1) + 1]$$

$$= (t-1)(t^5 - t^3 - t^2 + 1)$$

$$= (t-1)(t^3 - 1)(t^2 - 1)$$

$$= (2^x - 1)(2^{3x} - 1)(2^{2x} - 1)$$

Rationalizing, we have to evaluate

$$\text{Lt}_{x \to 0} \frac{2^x - 1}{x} . \frac{2^{2x} - 1}{2x} . \frac{2^{3x} - 1}{3x} . 6 . \frac{x^3(\sqrt{15 + \cos x} + 4)}{(\cos x - 1)\sin x}$$

$$= \log 2 . \log 2 . \log 2 . 6 . \frac{x^3(\sqrt{15 + \cos x} + 4)}{-2\sin^2 (x/2) . \sin x}$$

$$= -6(\log 2)^3 \frac{x^2}{2\sin^2 (x/2)} . \frac{x}{\sin x} . 8$$

$$= -6(\log 2)^3 . \frac{x^2}{2(x/2)^2} . 8 = -96(\log 2)^3.$$

(b) $\text{Lt}_{x \to 0} \frac{(2^x - 1)(4^x - 1)}{2 - (1 + \cos x)}[\sqrt{2} + \sqrt{1 + \cos x}]$

$$= \text{Lt}_{x \to 0} \left\{\frac{2^x - 1}{x} . \frac{4^x - 1}{x} . \frac{x^2}{1 - \cos x} . [\sqrt{2} + \sqrt{1 + \cos x}]\right\}$$

$$= (\log 2)(\log 4) . 2\sqrt{2} \text{ Lt} \frac{x^2}{2\sin^2 (x/2)} = 8\sqrt{2}(\log 2)^2$$

5. (a) $\log y = \text{Lt}_{x \to 0} 2 . \frac{\log(p^x + q^x + r^x) - \log 3}{x} \left(\frac{0}{0}\right)$

$$= 2\frac{p^x \log p + q^x \log q + r^x \log r}{(p^x + q^x + r^x) . 1} = \frac{2}{3}\log(pqr)$$

$$\therefore \quad \log y = \log(pqr)^{2/3} \quad \text{or} \quad y = (pqr)^{2/3}.$$

(b) $$\underset{x\to 0}{\text{Lt}}\ \frac{\dfrac{(a^{\tan x}-1)}{\tan x}\tan x-\dfrac{(a^{\sin x}-1)}{\sin x}\sin x}{\tan x-\sin x}$$

$$=\underset{x\to 0}{\text{Lt}}\ \log a.\frac{(\tan x-\sin x)}{\tan x-\sin x}=\log a$$

6. $$e^{\sqrt{a}}.\underset{x\to a}{\text{Lt}}\ \frac{e^{\sqrt{x}-\sqrt{a}}-1}{(\sqrt{x}+\sqrt{a})(\sqrt{x}-\sqrt{a})}$$

$$=\frac{e^{\sqrt{a}}}{2\sqrt{a}}\underset{\theta\to 0}{\text{Lt}}\ \frac{e^{\theta}-1}{\theta},\text{ where }\theta=\sqrt{x}-\sqrt{a}\to 0\text{ as }x\to a$$

$$=\frac{e^{\sqrt{a}}}{2\sqrt{a}}\log e=\frac{e^{\sqrt{a}}}{2\sqrt{a}}.$$

7. (a) $$\lim_{h\to 0}\frac{(a+h)^2\sin(a+h)-a^2\sin a}{h}$$

$$=\lim_{h\to 0}\frac{(a+h)^2[\sin(a+h)-\sin a]+\sin a[(a+h)^2-a^2]}{h}$$

$$=\lim_{h\to 0}\frac{1}{h}(a+h)^2\,2\cos\left(a+\frac{h}{2}\right)\sin\frac{h}{2}+\lim_{h\to 0}\frac{1}{h}(\sin a)[a^2+2ah+h^2-a^2]$$

$$=\lim_{h\to 0}(a+h)^2\cos\left(a+\frac{h}{2}\right).\frac{\sin(h/2)}{(h/2)}+\lim_{h\to 0}(\sin a)(2a+h)$$

$$=a^2\cos a.1+(\sin a)(2a)$$

$$=a(a\cos a+2\sin a).$$

(b) $$\underset{x\to 0}{\text{Lt}}\ \frac{\sin(3x+a)-3\sin(2x+a)+3\sin(x+a)-\sin a}{x^3}$$

$$=\underset{x\to 0}{\text{Lt}}\ \frac{2\sin\dfrac{3x}{2}\cos\dfrac{3x+2a}{2}-3\left(2\sin\dfrac{x}{2}\cos\dfrac{3x+2a}{2}\right)}{x^3}$$

$$=\underset{x\to 0}{\text{Lt}}\ \frac{2\cos\dfrac{3x+2a}{2}\left[3\sin\dfrac{x}{2}-4\sin^3\dfrac{x}{2}-3\sin\dfrac{x}{2}\right]}{x^3}$$

$$=\underset{x\to 0}{\text{Lt}}\ 2\cos\frac{3x+2a}{2}\left\{-4\frac{(x/2)^3}{x^3}\right\}\quad\because\underset{\theta\to 0}{\text{Lt}}\ \sin\theta=\theta$$

$$=2\cos a\left(-\frac{4}{8}\right)=-\cos a.$$

(c) Ans. $-\sin a$.

8. (a) Let the circular measure of each of the angles DOA and DOB be x where $0<x<\frac{1}{2}\pi$.

Let the tangents at A and B meet OD produced in E and let the chord AB meet OD in C, O being the centre of the circle BDA. We shall assume now as an axiom the chord $ACB <$ the arc $ADB < AE + BE$. Dividing by OA, we have

$$\frac{\text{chord } ACB}{OA}<\frac{\text{arc } ADB}{OA}<\frac{AE+BE}{OA}$$

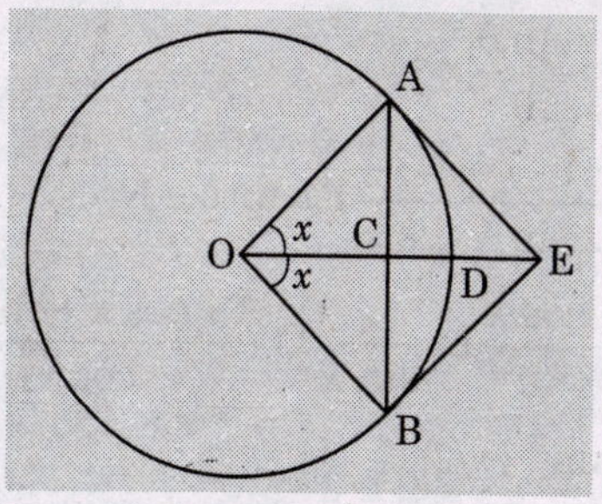

Fig. 1

or $$\frac{2AC}{OA}<\frac{2\text{ arc }AD}{OA}<\frac{2\,AE}{OA}\qquad[\because AE=BE]$$

or $\sin x<x<\tan x$ ...(1)

or $1<x/\sin x<1/\cos x$.

Now let $x\to 0$. Then $\dfrac{1}{\cos x}\to 1$. Hence $\dfrac{x}{\sin x}$ must also $\to 1$.

Therefore $$\lim_{x\to 0}\frac{\sin x}{x}=1.$$

(b) L' Hospital's Rule or

$$\text{Lt}\ \frac{x}{\sin x}\quad\text{Lt}\cos x=1\cdot 1=1$$

(c) Ans. (d)

$$\underset{x\to 0}{\text{Lt}}\ \frac{\sin nx}{x}\left[(a-n)\,n-\frac{\tan x}{x}\right]=0$$

$$\Rightarrow\quad 1[an-n^2-1]=0\quad\therefore\quad a=\frac{n^2+1}{n}=n+\frac{1}{n}.$$

9. (a) $$\underset{x\to\pi/2}{\text{Lt}}\ \frac{1-\sin^3 x}{\cos^2 x}$$

$$\underset{x\to\pi/2}{\text{Lt}}\ \frac{(1-\sin x)(1+\sin x+\sin^2 x)}{(1-\sin x)(1+\sin x)}=\frac{3}{2}$$

(b) When $x\to\pi/2, \cos x\to 0$

$\therefore$ $\sin(\cos x)=\cos x$

$$\therefore\quad\underset{x\to\pi/2}{\text{Lt}}\ \frac{\cos x.\cos x}{(\sin^2 x-1)/\sin x}=\underset{x\to\pi/2}{\text{Lt}}\ -\sin x=-1.$$

(c) Ans. (d).

$$1-\cos 2x=2\sin^2 x$$

$$\underset{x\to 0}{\text{Lt}}\ \frac{\sqrt{2}\,|\sin x|}{x}$$

$$\text{R.H.L.}=\underset{x\to 0+}{\text{Lt}}\ =\frac{\sqrt{2}\sin x}{x}=\sqrt{2}$$

$$\text{L.H.L.}=\underset{x\to 0-}{\text{Lt}}\ =-\sqrt{2}\frac{\sin x}{x}=-\sqrt{2}$$

Since R.H.L. $\neq$ L.H.L., therefore limit does not exist.

(d) Ans. (d).

$$\text{Limit}=\underset{\alpha\to\beta}{\text{Lt}}\ \frac{\sin\alpha-\sin\beta}{\alpha-\beta}\ \underset{\alpha\to\beta}{\text{Lt}}\ \frac{\sin\alpha+\sin\beta}{\alpha+\beta}$$

$$=\underset{\theta\to 0}{\text{Lt}}\ \frac{\sin\theta}{\theta}.\frac{\sin 2\beta}{2\beta}=1.\frac{\sin 2\beta}{2\beta}$$

as $\underset{\theta\to 0}{\text{Lt}} \dfrac{\sin\theta}{\theta} = 1$

10. (a) $\underset{x\to 0}{\text{Lt}} \dfrac{1-\cos^3 x}{x\sin x\cos x}$ Factorize N^r.

$= \text{Lt} \dfrac{1-\cos x}{x^2} \text{Lt} \dfrac{x}{\sin x} \text{Lt} \dfrac{1+\cos x+\cos^2 x}{\cos x}$

$= \text{Lt} \dfrac{2\sin^2 (x/2)}{x^2}.1.3$

$= \text{Lt}\ 2.\dfrac{(x/2)^2}{x^2}.3 = \dfrac{3}{2}$

(b) Write N^r as $a\sin x - x\sin x + x\sin x - x\sin a$

$\therefore \quad \underset{x\to a}{\text{Lt}} \dfrac{\sin x.(a-x)}{ax(x-a)} + \text{Lt} \dfrac{x.(\sin x-\sin a)}{ax(x-a)}$

$= -\dfrac{\sin a}{a^2} + \underset{x\to a}{\text{Lt}} \dfrac{2\sin\dfrac{x-a}{2}\cos\dfrac{x+a}{2}}{2a.\dfrac{x-a}{2}}$

$= -\dfrac{\sin a}{a^2} + \dfrac{\cos a}{a}.1 \quad \because \underset{\theta\to 0}{\text{Lt}} \dfrac{\sin\theta}{\theta} = 1$

11. (a) $\lim\limits_{x\to 0} \dfrac{1-\cos 2x}{x} = \lim\limits_{x\to 0} \dfrac{2\sin^2 x}{x}$

$= \lim\limits_{x\to 0} 2.\dfrac{\sin x}{x}.\sin x = 2.1.0 = 0$

(b) [**Hint** : Use L' Hospital Rule]

(c) $\underset{x\to 0}{\text{Lt}}\ 2\left(\dfrac{\sin x}{x}\right)^2 \text{Lt}\left(\dfrac{\sin 5x}{\sin 3x}\right) = 2.1.\dfrac{5}{3} = \dfrac{10}{3}$

12. (a) $\lim\limits_{x\to 1} \left(\dfrac{5}{6}\right)^{\frac{1-\cos(x-1)}{(x-1)^2}}$ ...(1)

Put $x-1=t$ where $t\to 0$ as $x\to 1$

$\lim\limits_{t\to 0} \dfrac{1-\cos t}{t^2} = \lim\limits_{t\to 0} \dfrac{2\sin^2(t/2)}{t^2}$

$= \lim\limits_{t\to 0} \dfrac{2}{t^2}\left(\dfrac{t}{2}\right)^2 = \dfrac{1}{2}$

$\therefore \quad \lim\limits_{x\to 1} \left(\dfrac{5}{6}\right)^{1/2} = \sqrt{\dfrac{5}{6}}$

(b) $\underset{x\to 0}{\text{Lt}} \dfrac{e^{x^2}-\cos x}{x^2} = \text{Lt} \dfrac{(e^{x^2}-1)+(1-\cos x)}{x^2}$

$= \underset{y\to 0}{\text{Lt}} \dfrac{e^y - 1}{y} + \text{Lt} \dfrac{2\sin^2\dfrac{x}{2}}{x^2}$

$\log e + 2.\dfrac{(x/2)^2}{x^2} = 1 + \dfrac{1}{2} = \dfrac{3}{2}$

(c) We are given $f(x) = \displaystyle\int \dfrac{2\sin x - \sin 2x}{x^3}\,dx, \quad x\neq 0$

Then by definition, $f'(x) = \dfrac{2\sin x-\sin 2x}{x^3}$

$\therefore \quad \lim\limits_{x\to 0} f'(x) = \lim\limits_{x\to 0} \dfrac{2\sin x - \sin 2x}{x^3}$ ...(1)

$= \underset{x\to 0}{\text{Lt}} \dfrac{2\left(x-\dfrac{x^3}{3!}+\dfrac{x^5}{5!}-....\right)-\left(2x-\dfrac{(2x)^3}{3!}+\dfrac{(2x)^5}{5!}-...\right)}{x^3}$

$= \underset{x\to 0}{\text{Lt}} \dfrac{x^3\left(-\dfrac{2}{6}+\dfrac{8}{6}\right)+x^5(\,)}{x^3} = 1$

2nd Method : You can write (1) as

$\underset{x\to 0}{\text{Lt}}\ 2\dfrac{\sin x}{x}\cdot\dfrac{(1-\cos x)}{x^2} \quad [\because \sin 2x = 2\sin x\cos x]$

$= \underset{x\to 0}{\text{Lt}}\ 2\dfrac{\sin x}{x}\cdot\dfrac{2\sin^2(x/2)}{x^2}$

$= \underset{x\to 0}{\text{Lt}} \dfrac{\sin x}{x}\cdot\left\{\dfrac{\sin(x/2)}{x/2}\right\}^2 = 1.1 = 1.$

3rd Method : You may use L' Hospital's Rule.

13. (a) $\lim\limits_{x\to 1} \dfrac{x-1}{2x^2-7x+5} = \lim\limits_{x\to 1} \dfrac{x-1}{(x-1)(2x-5)}$

$= \lim\limits_{x\to 1} \dfrac{1}{2x-5} \quad [\because x-1\neq 0 \text{ when } x\to 1]$

$= \dfrac{1}{2-5} = -\dfrac{1}{3}.$

(b) $\lim\limits_{\theta\to\pi/2} (\sec\theta - \tan\theta)$ form $(\infty-\infty)$

$= \lim\limits_{\theta\to\pi/2} \dfrac{1-\sin\theta}{\cos\theta} \quad \left(\dfrac{0}{0}\right)$

$= \underset{\theta\to\pi/2}{\text{Lim}} \dfrac{-\cos\theta}{-\sin\theta} = 0$

14. (a) Put $x = 1/h$, then $h\to 0$ as $x\to\infty$.

Then $\lim\limits_{x\to\infty} [x-\sqrt{(x^2+x)}]$

$= \lim\limits_{h\to 0}\left\{\dfrac{1}{h}-\sqrt{\left(\dfrac{1}{h^2}+\dfrac{1}{h}\right)}\right\} = \lim\limits_{h\to 0} \dfrac{1-\sqrt{(1+h)}}{h}$

$= \lim\limits_{h\to 0} \dfrac{1-(1+h)}{h[1+\sqrt{(1+h)}]} = \lim\limits_{h\to 0} \dfrac{-h}{h[1+\sqrt{(1+h)}]}$

$= \lim\limits_{h\to 0} -\dfrac{1}{1+\sqrt{(1+h)}} = -\dfrac{1}{1+1} = -\dfrac{1}{2}$

(b) Put $x = 1/y$, when $x\to\infty, y\to 0$.

$= \underset{y\to 0}{\text{Lt}} \dfrac{\dfrac{2}{y^{1/2}}+\dfrac{3}{y^{1/3}}+\dfrac{5}{y^{1/5}}}{\dfrac{1}{y^{1/2}}\sqrt{(5-2y)}+\dfrac{1}{y^{1/3}}(3-2y)^{1/3}}$

Multiply above and below by $y^{1/2}$

$= \underset{y\to 0}{\text{Lt}} \dfrac{2+3y^{1/6}+5y^{3/10}}{\sqrt{(5-2y)}+y^{1/6}(3-2y)^{1/3}} = \dfrac{2}{\sqrt{5}}$

15. (a) Here we shall do it without putting $x = 1/y$.

The various powers of x both in N^r and D^r are $(x^2)^{1/2} = 1, (x^2)^{1/3} = 2/3, (x^4)^{1/4} = 1, (x^4)^{1/5} = 4/5.$

The highest power is 1. Divide above and below each term by x^1 *i.e.* x

$$\therefore \quad \underset{x\to\infty}{\text{Lt}} \frac{\sqrt{\left(1+\frac{1}{x^2}\right)}-\sqrt[3]{\left(\frac{1}{x}+\frac{1}{x^3}\right)}}{\sqrt[4]{\left(1+\frac{1}{x^4}\right)}-\sqrt[5]{\left(\frac{1}{x}+\frac{1}{x^5}\right)}}=\frac{1-0}{1-0}=1.$$

(b) $\lim_{x\to\infty} \sqrt{\left(\frac{x-\sin x}{x+\cos^2 x}\right)}$

$$= \lim_{x\to\infty} \sqrt{\left(\frac{1-\sin x/x}{1+\cos^2 x/x}\right)} = \sqrt{\left(\frac{1-0}{1+0}\right)} = 1.$$

$$\left[\because \frac{\sin x}{x} \to 0 \text{ and } \frac{\cos^2 x}{x} \to 0 \text{ as } x\to\infty\right].$$

16. (a) $\underset{x\to\infty}{\text{Lt}} \dfrac{1-\left(\frac{1}{e}\right)^{x^2}}{1+\left(\frac{1}{e}\right)^{x^2}} = \dfrac{1-0}{1+0} = 1.$

$e>1 \ \therefore \ \frac{1}{e}<1$ and $\left(\frac{1}{e}\right)^{x^2} \to 0$ as $x\to\infty$.

(b) Put $x=\frac{1}{y}$ where $y\to 0$ as $x\to\infty$

$$\lim_{y\to 0} \frac{(2y+1)^{40}(4y+1)^{45}}{(2y-1)^{45}} = \frac{1.1}{(-1)^{45}} = -1$$

17. $\lim_{x\to-\infty} \dfrac{x^4 \sin(1/x)+x^2}{1+|x^3|}$

Put $x=-\frac{1}{y} \ \therefore \ y\to 0$

and y is + ive when $x\to-\infty$

$$= \lim_{y\to 0} \frac{(1/y^4)\sin(-y)+(1/y^2)}{1+|(-1/y)|^3}$$

$$= \lim_{y\to 0} \frac{(y^2-\sin y)/y^4}{[1+(1/y^3)]}$$

$$\because \left|-\frac{1}{y}\right|^3 = \frac{|-1|^3}{|y|^3} = \frac{1}{y^3} \quad (y>0)$$

$$= \lim_{y\to 0} \frac{y^2-\sin y}{y^4+y} \qquad \left(\text{Form } \frac{0}{0}\right)$$

$$= \lim_{y\to 0} \frac{2y-\cos y}{4y^3+1} = \frac{0-1}{0+1} = -1.$$

18. (a) $\lim_{x\to\infty} \dfrac{\sin x}{x} = \lim_{x\to\infty} \left(\dfrac{1}{x}\right) \cdot \lim_{x\to\infty} \sin x$

$= 0 \times$ (number lying between -1 and 1) $= 0$

(b) Rationalize.

$$\underset{x\to 0}{\text{Lt}} \frac{(1+\sin x)-(1-\sin x)}{x} \cdot \frac{1}{\sqrt{}+\sqrt{}}$$

$$= \underset{x\to 0}{\text{Lt}} \frac{2\sin x}{x} \cdot \frac{1}{1+1} = 1$$

(c) Ans. $\frac{2}{3}$. **Hint** : Rationalize.

Multiply above and below by a^2+ab+b^2

where $a=\sqrt[3]{(1+\sin x)}$ and $b=\sqrt[3]{(1-\sin x)}$

19. In order to rationalize we multiply above and below by $p+q$ and a^2+ab+b^2

$$\underset{x\to 2}{\text{Lt}} \frac{4-(2+x)}{2+\sqrt{(2+x)}}$$

$$\cdot \ \underset{x\to 2}{\text{Lt}} \frac{2^{2/3}+2^{1/3}(4-x)^{1/3}+(4-x)^{2/3}}{2-(4-x)}$$

$$= \underset{x\to 2}{\text{Lt}} \frac{2-x}{-(2-x)} \cdot \frac{2^{2/3}+2^{1/3}.2^{1/3}+2^{2/3}}{2+\sqrt{2}}$$

$$= -1.\frac{3.2^{2/3}}{2^2} = 3.2^{-4/3}.$$

20. (a) $\underset{x\to 1}{\text{Lt}} \dfrac{x^m-1}{x^n-1} = \text{Lt} \dfrac{x^m-1}{x-1}.\text{Lt} \dfrac{x-1}{x^n-1} = \dfrac{m}{n}.$

See (5), Page 1287.

(b) $\underset{x\to a}{\text{Lt}} \dfrac{x^{3/5}-a^{3/5}}{x-a}.\text{Lt} \dfrac{1}{\dfrac{x^{1/3}-a^{1/3}}{x-a}}$

$$= \frac{3}{5}a^{3/5-1} \div \frac{1}{3}a^{1/3-1} = \frac{9}{5}a^{3/5-1/3} = \frac{9}{5}a^{4/15}$$

by (5) P. 1287.

(c) Limit $= \underset{x\to a}{\text{Lt}} \dfrac{x^m-a^m}{x-a}.\dfrac{x-a}{x^n-a^n}$

$$= ma^{m-1}\frac{1}{na^{n-1}} = \frac{m}{n}a^{m-n}$$

(d) $\underset{x\to 1}{\text{Lt}} \dfrac{x^4-1}{x-1} = 4.1^{4-1} = 4$

$$\underset{x\to k}{\text{Lt}} \frac{x^3-k^3}{x^2-k^2} = \underset{x\to k}{\text{Lt}} \frac{x^3-k^3}{x-k} \cdot \underset{x\to k}{\text{Lt}} \frac{x-k}{x^2-k^2}$$

$$= 3k^{3-1}\frac{1}{2k^{2-1}} = \frac{3}{2}k$$

$\therefore \quad 4=\frac{3}{2}k \qquad$ or $\quad k=\frac{8}{3}$

21. (a) Split into two terms and rationalize.

$$\underset{x\to 2a}{\text{Lt}} \frac{1}{\sqrt{(x+2a)}} + \underset{x\to 2a}{\text{Lt}} \frac{x-2a}{\sqrt{x}+\sqrt{(2a)}} \cdot \frac{\sqrt{(x^2-4a^2)}}{(x^2-4a^2)}$$

$$= \frac{1}{2\sqrt{a}} + \underset{x\to 2a}{\text{Lt}} \frac{1}{\sqrt{x}+\sqrt{(2a)}} \cdot \frac{\sqrt{(x^2-4a^2)}}{x+2a} = \frac{1}{2\sqrt{a}}+0$$

(b) $\lim_{x\to a} \dfrac{\sqrt{(a+2x)}-\sqrt{3x}}{\sqrt{(3a+x)}-2\sqrt{(x)}}$

$$= \lim_{x\to a} \frac{(a+2x)-3x}{(3a+x)-4x} \times \frac{\sqrt{(3a+x)}+2\sqrt{x}}{\sqrt{(a+2x)}+\sqrt{(3x)}}$$

$$= \lim_{x \to a} \frac{a-x}{3(a-x)} \cdot \frac{\sqrt{(3a+2x)} + 2\sqrt{(x)}}{\sqrt{(a+2x)} + \sqrt{(3x)}}$$

$$= \lim_{x \to a} \frac{1}{3} \frac{\sqrt{(3a+x)} + 2\sqrt{(x)}}{\sqrt{(a+2x)} + \sqrt{(3x)}} = \frac{1}{3} \cdot \frac{\sqrt{(4a)} + 2\sqrt{(a)}}{\sqrt{(3a)} + \sqrt{(3a)}}$$

$$= \frac{1}{3} \cdot \frac{4\sqrt{a}}{2\sqrt{(3)}\sqrt{(a)}} = \frac{2}{3\sqrt{(3)}}.$$

22. (a) Rationalize and $\log(1+t) = t - \frac{t^2}{2} + \ldots$

$$\text{Lt}_{x \to 0} \frac{\sin 3x}{\sqrt{(4+\sin 3x)} + 2} \cdot \frac{1}{\tan 2x}$$

$$= \frac{1}{2+2} \cdot \frac{3x}{2x} = \frac{3}{8}$$

(b) $D^r = p^{1/3} - q^{1/3}$ $(q = 8)$. Rationalize by multiplying N^r and D^r by $p^{2/3} + q^{2/3} + (pq)^{1/3}$

$$\text{Lt}_{x \to 1} \frac{2(x-1)}{7+x-8} \times (7+x)^{2/3} + 8^{2/3} + \{8(7+x)\}^{1/3}$$

$$= 2[8^{2/3} + 8^{2/3} + (64)^{1/3}] = 2[12] = 24$$

23. Form is $\infty . (3-3)$ or $0 \times \infty$

Rationalize

$$\text{Lt}_{x \to \pi/2} \tan^2 x \frac{[(2\sin^2 x + 3\sin x + 4) - (\sin^2 x + 6\sin x + 2)]}{\sqrt{9} + \sqrt{9}}$$

$$= \text{Lt}_{x \to \pi/2} \frac{1}{6} \frac{\sin^2 x}{\cos^2 x} (\sin^2 x - 3\sin x + 2)$$

$$= \text{Lt}_{x \to \pi/2} \frac{1}{6} \cdot \frac{\sin^2 x (\sin x - 2)(\sin x - 1)}{(1-\sin x)(1+\sin x)}$$

$$= \text{Lt}_{x \to \pi/2} \frac{1}{6} \cdot \frac{-\sin^2 x(\sin x - 2)}{1 + \sin x}$$

$$= \frac{1}{6} \cdot \frac{(-1)(-1)}{2} = \frac{1}{12}$$

24. (a) $\text{Lt}_{x \to 1} (1-x) \tan\left(\frac{\pi x}{2}\right)$ [Form $0 \times \infty$]

$$= \text{Lt}_{x \to 1} \frac{1-x}{\cot(\pi x/2)} \qquad \left[\text{Form } \frac{0}{0}\right]$$

$$= \text{Lt}_{x \to 1} \frac{-1}{-\frac{\pi}{2}\text{cosec}^2\left(\frac{\pi x}{2}\right)} = \frac{2}{\pi}.$$

(b) $\lim_{\alpha \to \pi/4} \frac{\sin \alpha - \cos \alpha}{\alpha - \pi/4}$ $\left(\frac{0}{0}\right)$

$$= \lim_{\alpha \to \pi/4} \frac{\cos \alpha + \sin \alpha}{1} = \frac{1}{\sqrt{2}} + \frac{1}{\sqrt{2}} = \sqrt{2}$$

(c) Ans. 2. Use L' Hospital rule.

25. (a) $\lim_{x \to 1} \frac{(2x-3)(\sqrt{x}-1)}{2x^2+x-3} = \lim_{x \to 1} \frac{(2x-3)(\sqrt{x}-1)}{(2x+3)(x-1)}$

$$= \lim_{x \to 1} \frac{2x-3}{(2x+3)(\sqrt{x}+1)} = \frac{2-3}{(2+3)(1+1)} = -\frac{1}{10}.$$

(b) $\lim_{x \to 2} \left[\frac{x^2 - 3x + 2}{x^2 + x - 6}\right] = \lim_{x \to 2} \frac{(x-1)(x-2)}{(x+3)(x-2)}$

$$= \lim_{x \to 2} \frac{x-1}{x+3} = \frac{2-1}{2+3} = \frac{1}{5}.$$

26. (a) $\lim_{x \to 0} \frac{\tan x - \sin x}{x^3} = \lim_{x \to 0} \frac{\sin x(1-\cos x)}{x^3 \cos x}$

$$= \lim_{x \to 0} \frac{2\sin(x/2)\cos(x/2)\, 2\sin^2(x/2)}{x^3 \cos x}$$

$$= \lim_{x \to 0} \frac{4\sin^3(x/2)}{x^3} \cdot \frac{\cos(x/2)}{\cos x}$$

$$= \lim_{x \to 0} \frac{1}{2}\left(\frac{\sin(x/2)}{x/2}\right)^3 \frac{\cos(x/2)}{\cos x} = \frac{1}{2}.1.1 = \frac{1}{2}.$$

You may use expansions.

(b) **Hint :** Use the expansion of $\cos x$ and $\log(1+x)$.

(c) Ans. (c). Use expansions of $\tan \theta$

$$\lim_{x \to 0} \frac{x\left(2x + \frac{(2x)^3}{3} + \ldots\right) - 2x\left(x + \frac{x^3}{3} + \ldots\right)}{(2\sin^2 x)^2}$$

$$= \frac{8-2}{3} \cdot \frac{1}{4} \text{Lt}\left(\frac{x}{\sin x}\right)^4 = \frac{2}{4} = \frac{1}{2}$$

(d) Ans. (c).

Numerator

$$= \cos x(\cos x - 1) - e^x(\cos x - 1) - \frac{x^3}{2}$$

$$= (\cos x - 1)(\cos x - e^x) - \frac{x^3}{2}$$

$$= \left(1 - \frac{x^2}{2!} + \frac{x^4}{4!} - \ldots - 1\right)$$

$$\left\{1 - \frac{x^2}{2!} + \frac{x^4}{4!} - \ldots - \left(1 + \frac{x}{1!} + \frac{x^2}{2!} + \frac{x^3}{3!} \ldots\right)\right\} - \frac{x^3}{2}$$

$$= \left\{-\frac{x^2}{2} + \frac{x^4}{24} \ldots\right\}\left\{-x - x^2 - \frac{x^3}{6} \ldots\right\} - \frac{x^3}{2}$$

$$= x^3\left(\frac{1}{2} - \frac{1}{2}\right) + x^4\left(\frac{1}{2}\right) + x^5\left(\frac{1}{12} - \frac{1}{24}\right)$$

+ higher powers of x

$$= \frac{1}{2}x^4 + \frac{x^5}{24} + \text{higher powers of } x$$

$$\therefore \quad \text{Lt}_{x \to 0} \frac{\left\{\frac{1}{2}x^4 + \frac{x^5}{24} + \ldots\right\}}{x^n} = \text{finite}$$

Therefore n must be 4 and in that case limit $= \frac{1}{2}$.

27. (a) Do yourself. Ans. -2.

(b) $\lim_{x \to 0} \frac{2\sin^2 3x}{x^2}$

$= \lim_{x \to 0} 18 . \frac{\sin^2 3x}{9x^2} = \lim_{x \to 0} 18 \left(\frac{\sin 3x}{3x}\right)^2 = 18.$

$\left[\because \lim_{x \to 0} \frac{\sin 3x}{3x} = 1\right]$

(c) $\lim_{x \to 0} \frac{\tan 2x - x}{3x - \sin x}$ $\left[\text{Form } \frac{0}{0}\right]$

$= \lim_{x \to 0} \frac{\frac{d}{dx}(\tan 2x - x)}{\frac{d}{dx}(3x - \sin x)}$, by L' Hospital Rule

$= \lim_{x \to 0} \frac{2\sec^2 2x - 1}{3 - \cos x} = \frac{2-1}{3-1} = \frac{1}{2}.$

(d) Ans. (c).

Form $\frac{0}{0}$. Apply L'Hospital's rule.

$\text{Lt}_{x \to 0} \frac{\frac{1}{3+x} + \frac{1}{3-x}}{1} = \frac{2}{3} \Rightarrow (c)$

28. (a) Ans. $-\frac{1}{6}$. **[Hint** : Apply L' Hospital Rule]

(b) Ans. $-\frac{1}{3}$.

(c) Use L' Hospital rule.

29. (a) Form $\frac{0}{0}$. Use L' Hospital's rule.

$= \text{Lt}_{x \to 2} \frac{f(2) - 2f'(x)}{1} = f(2) - 2f'(2)$

$= 4 - 2.1 = 2.$

(b) Use L'Hospital rule.

(c) Ans. (c).

The form being $\frac{0}{0}$ the required limit by L' Hospital's rule is

$\text{Lt}_{h \to 0} \frac{f'(2+2h+h^2).(2+2h)}{f'(1+h-h^2)(1-2h)} = \text{Lt} \frac{f'(2).2}{f'(1).1} = \frac{6}{4}.2 = 3.$

(d) Ans. (c).

Apply L' Hospital rule the form being $\frac{0}{0}$

$\text{limit} = \text{Lt}_{x \to 0} \frac{2xf'(x^2) - f'(x)}{f'(x)} = -1$

because $f'(0) \neq 0$ as $f(x)$ is increasing.

30. (a) $\lim_{x \to 1} \int_4^{f(x)} \frac{2t}{x-1} dt = \lim_{x \to 1} \frac{1}{x-1} [t^2]_4^{f(x)}$

$= \lim_{x \to 1} \frac{1}{x-1} [f^2(x) - 16]$ [Form $\frac{0}{0}$, since $f(1) = 4$]

$= \lim_{x \to 1} \frac{2f(x) f'(x)}{1} = 2f(1) f'(1)$

$= 2 \times 4 f'(1) = 8 f'(1).$

[Note that since $f(x)$ is differentiable, $f'(1)$ exists.

(b) Ans. $\frac{1}{\sqrt{(24)}}$. L' Hospital rule

31. (a) Ans. 4.

We have $\lim_{x \to 9} \frac{\sqrt{f(x)} - 3}{\sqrt{(x)} - 3}$

$= \lim_{x \to 9} \frac{f(x) - 9}{\sqrt{[f(x)]} + 3} . \frac{\sqrt{x} + 3}{x - 9}.$

$= \lim_{x \to 9} \frac{f(x) - 9}{x - 9} \left(\frac{0}{0}\right) \cdot \lim_{x \to 9} \frac{\sqrt{x} + 3}{\sqrt{[f(x)]} + 3}$

$= f'(9) . \frac{\sqrt{9} + 3}{\sqrt{[f(9)]} + 3} = 4 . \frac{3+3}{3+3} = 4.$

by L' Hospital rule and $f(9) = 9$

(b) Ans. 24. $F' = f'gh + fg'h + fgh'$

Put x_0 for x and the values of F', f', g', h' at x_0 as given $\therefore$ $21F = fgh[4 - 7 + k]$

$21fgh = fgh[k - 3]$ $\therefore$ $k = 24.$

(c) The given form is $\frac{0}{0}$ as $2 + 1 - 3 = 0$

So we apply L'Hospital's rule twice

$\text{Limit} = \text{Lt}_{x \to 0} \frac{f''(x) - 6f''(2x) + 8f''(4x)}{1}$

$= (1 + 8 - 6) f''(0) = 3.4 = 12$

(d) Apply L' Hospital's rule

$\text{Limit} = \text{Lt}_{x \to 0} \frac{2x}{2xf'(x^2) - 40xf'(4x^2) + 56xf'(7x^2)}$

$= \text{Lt}_{x \to 0} \frac{1}{f'(x^2) - 20f'(4x^2) + 28f'(7x^2)}$

For $f(x) = 0$, slope of tangent is $f'(x)$ and slope of normal at $x = 0$ is $\frac{-1}{f'(0)} = 3$

$\therefore$ $f'(0) = -\frac{1}{3}$

$\therefore$ $\text{Limit} = \frac{1}{(1 + 28 - 20) f'(0)} = -\frac{3}{9} = -\frac{1}{3}$

32. Put $\sin x = t$ and as $x \to \pi/2, t \to 1$

Also $\frac{d}{dx}(x^x) = x^x (1 + \log x)$ **by Q. 1 (b) P. 1215-19.**

$\therefore$ $\lim_{t \to 1} \frac{t - t^t}{1 - t + \log t}$ $\left(\text{Form } \frac{0}{0}\right)$

$= \lim_{t \to 1} \frac{1 - t^t(1 + \log t)}{-1 + \frac{1}{t}}$ $\left(\text{Form } \frac{0}{0}\right)$

Apply L' Hospital rule.

$= \lim_{t \to 1} \frac{-\left\{t^t . \frac{1}{t} + t^t (1 + \log t)^2\right\}}{-1/t^2} = \frac{1+1}{1} = 2$

33. (a) Let $\pi - \theta = x$ $\therefore$ $-\cos\theta = \cos x$ and $x \to 0$ when $\theta \to \pi$

$\therefore$ $\text{Lt}_{x \to 0} \frac{\sqrt{(2 - \cos x)} - 1}{x^2}$ Rationalize

$$= \underset{x\to 0}{\text{Lt}} \frac{(2-\cos x)-1}{x^2}\cdot\frac{1}{\sqrt{(2-\cos x)}+1}$$

$$= \underset{x\to 0}{\text{Lt}} \frac{1-\cos x}{x^2}\cdot\frac{1}{2} = \underset{x\to 0}{\text{Lt}} \frac{2\sin^2(x/2)}{x^2}\cdot\frac{1}{2}$$

$$= \frac{1}{x^2}\cdot\left(\frac{x}{2}\right)^2 = \frac{1}{4}.$$

(b) $\cos\theta+\sin\theta=\sqrt{2}\cos(\theta-\pi/4)$.

Put $(\theta-\pi/4)=x$

$$\underset{x\to 0}{\text{Lt}} \sqrt{2}\frac{(1-\cos x)}{16x^2} = \underset{x\to 0}{\text{Lt}} \frac{2\sqrt{2}}{16}\frac{\sin^2(x/2)}{x^2}$$

$$= \frac{1}{4\sqrt{2}}\cdot\frac{1}{4}1 = \frac{1}{16\sqrt{2}}.$$

(c) $\cos\theta+\sin\theta=\sqrt{2}\cos(\theta-\pi/4)$

$$\theta-\frac{\pi}{4}=t \quad\therefore\quad \theta=\frac{\pi}{4}+t$$

or $\quad 2\theta=\frac{\pi}{2}+2t \quad\therefore\quad \sin 2\theta=\cos 2t$

When $\theta\to\pi/4, t\to 0$

$$\underset{t\to 0}{\text{Lt}} \frac{2\sqrt{2}-2\sqrt{2}\cos^3 t}{1-\cos 2t} = \underset{t\to 0}{\text{Lt}} \frac{2\sqrt{2}(1-\cos^3 t)}{2\sin^2 t}$$

$$= \underset{t\to 0}{\text{Lt}} \sqrt{2}.\frac{(1-\cos t)(1+\cos t+\cos^2 t)}{(1-\cos t)(1+\cos t)}$$

$$= \sqrt{2}.\frac{1}{1+1}(1+1+1) = \frac{3}{\sqrt{2}}.$$

34. (a) $ax^2+bx+c=a(x-\alpha)(x-\beta)$

and $1-\cos\theta=2\sin^2\frac{\theta}{2}$

and $\lim\limits_{\theta\to 0} \sin\theta=\theta$ ...(1)

$$\lim_{x\to\alpha}\frac{2\sin^2\dfrac{a(x-\alpha)(x-\beta)}{2}}{(x-\alpha)^2}$$

$$= \lim_{x\to\alpha} 2\frac{\left[\dfrac{a(x-\alpha)(x-\beta)}{2}\right]^2}{(x-\alpha)^2} \quad \text{by (1)}$$

$$= 2\frac{a^2}{4}(\alpha-\beta)^2 = \frac{1}{2}a^2(\alpha-\beta)^2$$

(b) Ans. (b).

$$\sin(\pi\cos^2 x)=\sin[\pi(1-\sin^2 x)]$$

$$=\sin(\pi-\pi\sin^2 x)=\sin(\pi\sin^2 x)$$

$$\underset{x\to 0}{\text{Lt}} \frac{\sin(\pi\sin^2 x)}{x^2} = \underset{x\to 0}{\text{Lt}} \frac{\sin(\pi\sin^2 x)}{(\pi\sin^2 x)}\pi\left(\frac{\sin x}{x}\right)^2$$

$$=\pi$$

35. (a) Put $(\pi/4x)=y \quad\therefore\quad y\to 0$ when $x\to\infty$

$$\underset{y\to 0}{\text{Lt}} \frac{\pi}{4y}\cos y\sin y = \text{Lt}\,\frac{\pi}{4}\cdot\cos y\cdot\frac{\sin y}{y}$$

$$=\frac{\pi}{4}\cdot 1\cdot 1=\frac{\pi}{4}.$$

(b) $$\underset{x\to 0}{\text{Lt}} \frac{\pi\tan\left(\dfrac{\pi}{2}x\right)}{x} \quad \left(\frac{0}{0}\right)$$

$$=\frac{\pi}{x}.\frac{\pi}{2}x=\frac{\pi^2}{2} \quad \because \underset{\theta\to 0}{\text{Lt}} \tan\theta=\theta$$

36. (a) $$\underset{x\to 0}{\text{Lt}} \frac{\log\tan\left(\dfrac{\pi}{4}+ax\right)}{\sin bx} \quad \left(\frac{0}{0}\right)$$

$$= \underset{x\to 0}{\text{Lt}} \frac{\log(1+\tan ax)-\log(1-\tan ax)}{\sin bx}$$

$$= \underset{x\to 0}{\text{Lt}} \frac{2\left[\tan ax+\dfrac{1}{3}\tan^3 ax\ldots\right]}{\sin bx}$$

$$= \underset{x\to 0}{\text{Lt}} \frac{2\tan ax}{\sin bx}\left[1+\frac{1}{3}\tan^2 ax\right]$$

$$= \underset{x\to 0}{\text{Lt}} 2\frac{ax}{bx}\left[1+\frac{1}{3}\tan^2 ax\right]=2\frac{a}{b}.$$

(b) $$\underset{x\to\infty}{\text{Lt}} x\left(\tan^{-1}\frac{x+1}{x+2}-\frac{\pi}{4}\right)$$

Put $\quad \frac{\pi}{4}=\tan^{-1}1$

$$\therefore \quad \tan^{-1}\frac{x+1}{x+2}-\tan^{-1}1=\tan^{-1}\frac{\dfrac{x+1}{x+2}-1}{1+\dfrac{x+1}{x+2}}$$

$$\tan^{-1}\frac{-1}{2x+3}=-\tan^{-1}\frac{1}{2x+3}$$

$$=-\left[\frac{1}{2x+3}-\frac{1}{3(2x+3)^3}+\ldots\right]$$

$$\therefore \quad \text{Limit} = \underset{x\to\infty}{\text{Lt}} -x\left[\frac{1}{2x+3}-\frac{1}{3(2x+3)^3}+\ldots\right]$$

$$= \underset{x\to\infty}{\text{Lt}} \frac{-1}{2+\dfrac{3}{x}}+\frac{x}{24x^3\left(1+\dfrac{3}{2x}\right)^3}+\ldots.$$

$$=-\frac{1}{2}+0=-\frac{1}{2}.$$

37. (a) Let $y=\sin^{-1}x$

$$\therefore \quad \frac{dy}{dx}=\frac{1}{\sqrt{(1-x^2)}}=(1-x^2)^{-1/2}$$

or $$\frac{dy}{dx}=1+\frac{1}{2}x^2+\frac{\dfrac{1}{2}\left(\dfrac{1}{2}+1\right)}{1.2}(x^2)^2+\ldots$$

$$\therefore \quad y=x+\frac{x^3}{6}+\frac{3}{40}x^5+\ldots$$

$$\therefore \quad \underset{x\to 0}{\text{Lt}} \frac{\left(x+\dfrac{x^3}{6}+\dfrac{3}{40}x^5\ldots\right)-\left(x-\dfrac{x^3}{3}-\dfrac{x^5}{5}\ldots\right)}{x^3}$$

$$= \text{Lt}\left(\frac{1}{6}+\frac{1}{3}\right)+\left(\frac{3}{40}-\frac{1}{5}\right)x^2 \ldots = \frac{3}{6}=\frac{1}{2}.$$

(b) $\displaystyle \underset{x\to 0}{\text{Lt}} \frac{2x-\sin^{-1}x}{2x+\tan^{-1}x}$

$$= \underset{x\to 0}{\text{Lt}} \frac{2x-\left(x+\frac{x^3}{6}+\ldots\right)}{2x+\left(x-\frac{x^3}{3}\ldots\right)} = \text{Lt} \frac{x-\frac{x^3}{6}\ldots}{3x-\frac{x^3}{3}\ldots}$$

$$= \underset{x\to 0}{\text{Lt}} \frac{1-\frac{x^2}{6}+\ldots}{3-\frac{x^2}{3}+\ldots} = \frac{1}{3}.$$

38. (a) Using L' Hospital's rule, we get

$$-1 = \lim_{x\to a}\frac{a^x - x^a}{x^x - a^a} = \lim_{x\to a}\frac{a^x \log_e a - ax^{a-1}}{x^x(1+\log_e x)-0}$$

or $\displaystyle -1 = \frac{a^a \log_e a - a.a^{a-1}}{a^a(1+\log_e a)} = \frac{\log_e a - 1}{\log_e a + 1}$

or $2\log_e a = 0 \quad \therefore \ a = 1$

(b) Ans. – 1. Use expansion.

39. (a) Choose $\dfrac{x}{2^n} = A$ or $x = 2^n A$ ...(1)

Also as $n\to\infty, A\to 0$

and $\lim\limits_{A\to 0} \sin A = A$ ...(2)

From trigonometry,

$\cos A \cos 2A \cos 4A \cos 8A \ldots n$ terms

$$= \frac{\sin 2^n A}{2^n \sin A}$$

$\therefore$ limit $= \displaystyle\lim_{n\to\infty}\frac{\sin 2^n . A}{2^n . A}$ by (2) $= \dfrac{\sin x}{x}$ by (1)

(b) Apply $\log_b a = \dfrac{\log a}{\log b}$

$$\text{Lt} = \lim_{n\to\infty}\frac{\log n}{\log(n-1)}\cdot\log\frac{(n+1)}{\log n}\cdots\frac{\log n^k}{\log n^k - 1}$$

$$= \lim_{n\to\infty}\frac{\log n^k}{\log(n-1)}$$

$$= \lim_{n\to\infty} k\frac{\log n}{\log(n-1)} \quad \left(\text{form}\ \frac{\infty}{\infty}\right)$$

Apply L' Hospital Rule $\displaystyle \lim_{n\to\infty} k\frac{\frac{1}{n}}{\frac{1}{n-1}}$

$$= \lim_{n\to\infty} k\left(1-\frac{1}{n}\right) = k$$

40. (a) Here we use the expansions

$\sin x = x - x^3/3! + x^5/5! - \ldots$

and $\cos x = 1 - x^2/2! + x^4/4! - \ldots$

Then we have $= \displaystyle\lim_{x\to 0}\frac{x(1+a\cos x)-b\sin x}{x^3}$

$$= \lim_{x\to 0}\frac{x+ax(1-x^2/2!+x^4/4!-\ldots)}{x^3} - \frac{b(x-x^3/3!+x^5/5!-\ldots)}{x^3}$$

$$= \lim_{x\to 0}\frac{(1+a-b)x+(b/6-a/2)x^3 + (a/24-b/120)x^5+\ldots}{x^3}$$

$$= \lim_{x\to 0}\frac{(1+a-b)+(b/6-a/2)x^2 + (a/24-b/120)x^4\ldots}{x^2}$$

Since the limit is given as 1, a finite quantity, we must have

$1+a-b=0$ ...(1)

and $b/6 - a/2 = 1.$ ...(2)

Solving (1) and (2),

we have $a = -5/2, b = -3/2.$

(b) Using expansions we have

$$\lim_{x\to 0}\frac{ax\left(1+x+\frac{x^2}{2!}+\ldots\right)-b\left(x-\frac{x^2}{2}+\frac{x^3}{3}\ldots\right)+cx\left(1-x+\frac{x^2}{2!}-\frac{x^3}{3!}\ldots\right)}{x^2\left(x-\frac{x^3}{3!}\ldots\right)}$$

$$\lim_{x\to 0}\frac{(a-b+c)x+x^2\left(a+\frac{b}{2}-c\right)+x^3\left(\frac{a}{2}-\frac{b}{3}+\frac{c}{2}\right)\ldots}{x^3\ldots}$$

If the limit is to be 2 then we must have

$$a-b+c=0, a+\frac{b}{2}-c=0, \frac{a}{2}-\frac{b}{3}+\frac{c}{2}=2$$

Solving them as usual, we get $a=3, b=12, c=9.$

(c) $\displaystyle\lim_{x\to\infty} f(x) = \lim_{x\to\infty}\frac{x^2(1-a)-(a+b)x-b+1}{x+1}$

The limit will be zero if the degree of N^r is less than degree of D^r.

Hence we must have $1-a=0, a+b=0$

$\therefore \quad a=1, \ b=-1.$

(d) $\displaystyle\underset{x\to\infty}{\text{Lt}}\frac{x^2(1-a)-x(a+b)-(1+b)}{x+1} = 2 =$ finite

$\therefore$ Degree of N^r = Degree of D^r

$\therefore \quad 1-a=0, \ a+b=-2 \ \therefore \ a=1, \ b=-3$

(e) $\displaystyle\underset{x\to\infty}{\text{Lt}}\frac{x^2(1-a)-x(a+b)+(1-b)}{x+1} = \infty$

Above will be possible if degree of N^r is greater than degree of D^r.

$\therefore \quad 1-a \neq 0$ *i.e.*, $a \neq 1$ and b can have any value.

41. (a) $a=-2$, Limit $=-1$.

(b) $a=5, \; b=5/2, \;$ Limit $=-5/24$.

42. (a) $a=1, \; b=2, \; c=1$.

(b) $a=120, \; b=60, \; c=180$.

(c) $a=6, \; b=6, \; c=0$.

43. (a) $\lim_{x \to 0} \dfrac{\sin x - x + (1/6)\, x^3}{x^5}$

$$= \lim_{x \to 0} \frac{[x-(1/3!)\, x^3 + (1/5!)\, x^5 - \dots] - x + (1/6)\, x^3}{x^5}$$

$$= \lim_{x \to 0} \frac{1}{x^5}\left[\frac{1}{5!}x^5 + \text{higher powers of } x\right]$$

$$= \lim_{x \to 0} \left[\frac{1}{120} + \text{powers of } x\right] = \frac{1}{120}.$$

(b) $I = \lim_{x \to \pi/2} \dfrac{\log \sin x}{\cot x} \qquad \left[\text{Form } \dfrac{0}{0}\right]$

$$= \lim_{x \to \pi/2} \frac{(1/\sin x)\cos x}{-\operatorname{cosec}^2 x}$$

$$= \lim_{x \to \pi/2} -\sin x \cos x = 0.$$

(c) $\lim_{x \to \pi/2} [x \tan x - (\pi/2) \sec x]$

$$= \lim_{x \to \pi/2} \frac{2x \sin x - \pi}{2 \cos x} \qquad \left[\text{Form } \frac{0}{0}\right]$$

$$= \lim_{x \to \pi/2} \frac{\text{d.c. of } [2x \sin x - \pi]}{\text{d.c. of } [2 \cos x]}, \text{ by L' Hospital Rule}$$

$$= \lim_{x \to \pi/2} \frac{[2 \sin x + 2x \cos x]}{-2 \sin x}$$

$$= \frac{2.1 + 2.\pi/2.0}{-2.1} = -1.$$

44. Let $y = \lim_{x \to 0} (1+x)^{1/x}$. Take log

$$\therefore \quad \log y = \lim_{x \to 0} \frac{\log(1+x)}{x}$$

$$= \lim_{x \to 0} \frac{(x - x^2/2 + x^3/3 - \dots)}{x}$$

$\therefore \quad \log y = 1$ or $y = e^1 = e$.

(i) Proceeding as above if $y = \lim_{x \to 0} (1+px)^{1/x}$,

then $\quad \log y = p$

$\therefore \quad y = e^p$ and if (ii) $y = \lim_{x \to 0} \left(1 + \dfrac{x}{p}\right)^{1/x}$,

then $\quad \log y = 1/p \quad \therefore \; y = e^{1/p}$.

We may also say that

$$\lim_{x \to 0} (1+px)^{1/x} = \lim_{x \to 0} [(1+px)^{1/px}]^p = e^p$$

and $\lim_{x \to 0} \left(1 + \dfrac{x}{p}\right)^{1/p} = \lim_{x \to 0} \left[\left(1 + \dfrac{x}{p}\right)^{p/x}\right]^{1/p} = e^{1/p}$.

Observe that in both the above cases; the limit is $e^{\text{coeff. of x}}$ *i.e.* e^p or $e^{1/p}$.

(iii), (iv), (v). Put $y = \dfrac{1}{x}$ so that $y \to 0$ as $x \to \infty$ and hence we have to evaluate

$$\operatorname{Lt}_{y \to 0} (1+y)^{1/y}, \; \operatorname{Lt}_{y \to 0} (1+py)^{1/y}. \; \operatorname{Lt}_{y \to 0} \left(1 + \frac{y}{p}\right)^y$$

which are e, e^p and $e^{1/p}$ respectively as proved above.

Note : The above results can be used as formulae.

45. Refer last Q. 44. If $y = (1+x)^{1/x}$ then

$$\log y = \frac{\left(x - \dfrac{x^2}{2} + \dfrac{x^3}{3} - \dots\right)}{x} = \left(1 - \frac{x}{2} + \frac{x^2}{3} - \dots\right)$$

$$y = e^{1 - \left(\frac{x}{2} - \frac{x^2}{3}\right)} = e . e^{-\left(\frac{x}{2} - \frac{x^2}{3}\right)}$$

$$= e\left[1 - \left(\frac{x}{2} - \frac{x^2}{3}\right) + \frac{1}{2!}\left(\frac{x}{2} - \frac{x^2}{3}\right)^2 + \dots\right]$$

$$= e\left[1 - \frac{x}{2} + x^2\left(\frac{1}{3} + \frac{1}{8}\right) + x^3(\;) + \dots\right]$$

$$\therefore \quad y - e + \frac{ex}{2} = ex^2 . \frac{11}{24} + ex^3(\;) + \dots$$

$$\therefore \quad \operatorname{Lt}_{x \to 0} \frac{(1+x)^{1/x} - e + \dfrac{ex}{2}}{x^2} = \frac{11e}{24}.$$

46. (a) Refer Q. 44 above.

$$\tan\left(\frac{\pi}{4} + x\right) = \frac{1 + \tan x}{1 - \tan x} = \frac{1+x}{1-x} \text{ app.}$$

$$\operatorname{Lt}_{x \to 0} \left(\frac{1+x}{1-x}\right)^{1/x} = \operatorname{Lt}_{x \to 0} [(1+x)(1-x)^{-1}]^{1/x}$$

$$= \operatorname{Lt}_{x \to 0} [(1+x)(1+x+\dots)]^{1/x}$$

$$= \operatorname{Lt}_{x \to 0} (1+2x)^{1/x} = e^{\text{coeff. of x}} = e^2$$

or $\operatorname{Lt}_{x \to 0} [(1+2x+\dots)^{1/2x}]^2 = e^2$

(b) Ans. e^5.

$$\text{Let } A = \lim_{x \to \infty} \left(\frac{x+6}{x+1}\right)^{x+4} = \lim_{x \to \infty} \left[1 + \frac{5}{x+1}\right]^{x+4}$$

$$= \lim_{x \to \infty} \left[\left(1 + \frac{5}{x+1}\right)^{\frac{x+1}{5}}\right]^{\frac{5(x+4)}{x+1}} = e^5$$

$$\left[\because \lim_{x \to \infty} \left(1 + \frac{5}{x+1}\right)^{\frac{x+1}{5}} = e \right.$$

$$\left. \text{and } \lim_{x \to \infty} \frac{5(x+4)}{x+1} = \lim_{x \to \infty} \frac{5(1+4/x)}{1+1/x} = 5\right]$$

(c) Ans. (c).

$$\log y = \underset{x\to 0}{\text{Lt}} = \frac{1}{x}[\log f(1+x) - \log f(1)] \quad \left(\frac{0}{0}\right)$$

$$= \underset{x\to 0}{\text{Lt}} \frac{\frac{1}{f(1+x)}\cdot f'(1+x) - 0}{1} = \frac{f'(1)}{f(1)} = \frac{6}{3} = 2$$

$\therefore \quad y = e^2.$

47. (a) Ans. e. Proceed as in last question.

(b) Ans. e^2.

$$\lim_{x\to 0} \left[(1+5x^2)(1+3x^2)^{-1}\right]^{1/x^2}$$

$$= \lim_{x\to 0} \left[(1+5x^2)(1-3x^2+....)\right]^{1/x^2}$$

$$= \lim_{x\to 0} \left[(1+2x^2)^{1/2x^2}\right]^2 = e^2$$

(c) Ans. (c).

$$\underset{x\to\infty}{\text{Lt}} \left(\frac{x+2-5}{x+2}\right)^x = \underset{x\to\infty}{\text{Lt}} \left[\left(1-\frac{5}{x+2}\right)^{\frac{x+2}{-5}}\right]^{-\frac{5x}{x+2}}$$

$$= e^{-5} \quad \because \underset{x\to\infty}{\text{Lt}} -5\frac{x}{x+2} = \underset{x\to\infty}{\text{Lt}} -5\cdot\frac{1}{1+\frac{2}{x}} = -5.$$

(d) Ans. (c).

$$ax^2 + bx + c + 1 = 1 + a(x-\alpha)(x-\beta)$$

$\therefore$ Put $a(x-\alpha)(x-\beta) = y$

$\therefore$ $y \Rightarrow 0$ as $x \Rightarrow \alpha$

$$\frac{2a(x-\beta)}{y} = \frac{2}{x-\alpha}$$

$\therefore$ Required limit $= \underset{y\to 0}{\text{Lt}} [1+y]^{\frac{2a(x-\beta)}{y}}$

$$= \underset{y\to 0}{\text{Lt}} \left[\{1+y\}^{1/y}\right]^{2a(x-\beta)} = e^{2a(\alpha-\beta)}$$

48. (a) $\tan x = x + \dfrac{x^3}{3} + \ldots$

$$\text{Limit} = \lim_{x\to 0}\left(1+\frac{x^2}{3}\right)^{1/x^2} = e^{\text{coeff. of } x^2} = e^{1/3}$$

$$\text{or} \quad \lim_{x\to 0}\left[\left(1+\frac{x^2}{3}\right)^{3/x^2}\right]^{1/3} = e^{1/3}$$

(b) $$\lim_{x\to 0}\left[\left(1+\frac{x^2}{3}\right)^{3/x^2}\right]^{x/3} = e^0 = 1.$$

(c) $\lim_{x\to 0} e^{1/3x} = e^{\infty} = \infty.$

Use expansion of $\sin x, \sinh x, \cosh x$ as given **on P. 591.**

49. (a) $e^{-1/6}$ (b) 1

(c) $\text{Limit} = \underset{x\to 1}{\text{Lt}} [\log_5 5 + \log_5 x]^{\log_x 5}$

Let $y = \log_5 x \to 0$ as $x \to 1$

$\therefore$ $\text{Limit} = \underset{y\to 0}{\text{Lt}} [1+y]^{1/y} = e,$

(d) $\text{Limit} = \underset{x\to 1}{\text{Lt}} [1+\log_2 x]^{\log_2 5}$

$$= \underset{x\to 1}{\text{Lt}} \left[\{1+\log_2 x\}^{\log_x 2}\right]^{\log_2 x \log_x 5}$$

$= e^{\log_2 5}$ as above.

50. (a) $e^{1/6}$ (b) $e^{1/12}$.

(c) $$\text{Limit} = \underset{x\to 0}{\text{Lt}} \left[1+\frac{\sin x - x}{x}\right]^{\frac{\sin x}{-(\sin x - x)}}$$

$$= \underset{x\to 0}{\text{Lt}} [1+t]^{1/t\left(-\frac{\sin x}{x}\right)}$$

where $t = \underset{x\to 0}{\text{Lt}} \dfrac{\sin x - x}{x} = \underset{x\to 0}{\text{Lt}} \dfrac{\cos x - 1}{1} = 0$

and $\underset{x\to 0}{\text{Lt}} \dfrac{\sin x}{x} = 1$

$\therefore$ Required limit $= e^{-1} = \dfrac{1}{e}$

51. (a) Put $-\dfrac{5}{x+3} = y \quad \therefore \quad y \to 0$ as $x \to \infty$

Also $-5 = xy + 3y \quad \therefore \quad -\dfrac{(5+3y)}{y} = x$

or $2x = -\dfrac{10}{y} - 6$

$$\therefore \quad \underset{y\to 0}{\text{Lt}} (1+y)^{-\frac{10}{y}-6}$$

$$= \underset{y\to 0}{\text{Lt}} \left[(1+y)^{1/y}\right]^{-10} \cdot \underset{y\to 0}{\text{Lt}} (1+y)^{-6}$$

$$= e^{-10} \cdot 1^{-6} = e^{-10}.$$

(b) Put $x = \dfrac{1}{y} \quad \therefore \quad x \to \infty \Rightarrow y \to 0$

$$\underset{y\to 0}{\text{Lt}} (\sin y + \cos y)^{1/y}$$

$$= \underset{y\to 0}{\text{Lt}} \left[\left(y - \frac{y^3}{3!} + \ldots\right) + \left(1 - \frac{y^2}{2!} - \ldots\right)\right]^{1/y}$$

$$= \underset{y\to 0}{\text{Lt}} (1+y+\ldots)^{1/y} = e$$

(c) 1st limit is π by L'Hospital rule and 2nd is

$$\underset{x\to\infty}{\text{Lt}} \left[\left(1+\frac{1}{x^2}\right)^{x^2}\right]^{1/x} = \underset{x\to\infty}{\text{Lt}} e^{1/x} = e^0 = 1$$

52. (a) Let $y = \underset{x\to a}{\text{Lt}} \left(\dfrac{\sin x}{\sin a}\right)^{\frac{1}{x-a}}$ (form 1^∞)

$$\therefore \quad \log y = \underset{x\to a}{\text{Lt}} \frac{\log \sin x - \log \sin a}{x-a} \quad \left(\frac{0}{0}\right)$$

$$= \underset{x\to a}{\text{Lt}} \frac{\frac{1}{\sin x}.\cos x}{1} = \cot a \quad \therefore \quad y = e^{\cot a}$$

(b) Proceed as in last part.

(c) Limit $= \underset{x\to 0}{\text{Lt}} \left(1+\frac{\sin x - x}{x}\right)^{\frac{\sin x}{-(\sin x - x)}}$

$= \underset{x\to 0}{\text{Lt}} (1+t)^{\frac{1}{t}\left(-\frac{\sin x}{x}\right)}$,

where $t = \underset{x\to 0}{\text{Lt}} \frac{\sin x - x}{x} = \underset{x\to 0}{\text{Lt}} \frac{\cos x - 1}{1} = 0$

and $\underset{x\to 0}{\text{Lt}} \frac{\sin x}{x} = 1 \quad \therefore$ Limit $= e^{-1} = \frac{1}{e}$

53. (a) As above

$\log y = \underset{x\to\infty}{\text{Lt}} \frac{\log\left(\frac{\pi}{2} - \tan^{-1} x\right)}{x} \quad \left(\frac{\infty}{\infty}\right)$

$= \underset{x\to\infty}{\text{Lt}} \frac{1}{\left(\frac{\pi}{2} - \tan^{-1} x\right)}\left\{-\frac{1}{(1+x^2)}\right\} \quad \left(\frac{0}{0}\right)$

$= \underset{x\to\infty}{\text{Lt}} \frac{2x}{(1+x^2)^2} \Big/ -\frac{1}{(1+x^2)} = \underset{x\to\infty}{\text{Lt}} -\frac{2x}{1+x^2}$

$= \underset{x\to\infty}{\text{Lt}} \frac{-2/x}{1+1/x^2} = \frac{0}{1} = 0 \quad \therefore \quad y = e^0 = 1.$

(b) The given limit is of the form 1^∞. If the limit be y, then

$\log y = \underset{x\to\pi/2}{\text{Lt}} \frac{\log(1+\cot x) - \log(1+\cos x)}{\cos x} \quad \left(\frac{0}{0}\right)$

$= \underset{x\to\pi/2}{\text{Lt}} \frac{-\frac{\text{cosec}^2 x}{1+\cot x} + \frac{\sin x}{1+\cos x}}{-\sin x} = \frac{-1+1}{-1} = 0$

$\therefore \quad y = e^0 = 1.$

Alternative method.

$\lim_{x\to\frac{\pi}{2}} \left[(1+\cot x)^{\frac{1}{\cot x}}\right]^{\cot x \cdot \frac{1}{\cos x}}$

$\div \lim_{x\to\frac{\pi}{2}} (1+\cos x)^{\frac{1}{\cos x}} = e \div e = 1$

$\because \quad \cot x \cdot \frac{1}{\cos x} = \frac{1}{\sin x} = 1$ as $x \to \frac{\pi}{2}$

Another form :

$\lim_{x\to 0}\left[\frac{1+\tan x}{1+\sin x}\right]^{\text{cosec } x} = 1$

(c) Ans. (c).

$y = \underset{x\to 0}{\text{Lt}} \left(1 - \frac{x^2}{2!} + \frac{x^4}{4!} \ldots - 1\right) \times$

$\left[1 - \frac{x^2}{2!} + \frac{x^4}{4!} \ldots - \left(1 + x + \frac{x^2}{2!} + \frac{x^3}{3!} \ldots\right)\right] \div x^n$

$= \underset{x\to 0}{\text{Lt}} \left(-\frac{x^2}{2} - \frac{x^4}{24} \ldots\right)(-x - x^2 \ldots) \div x^n$

The least power of x in N^r is 3 and if the limit is to be finite then n must be 3.

54. (a) $\frac{x^2+5x+3}{x^2+x+2} = 1 + \frac{4x+1}{x^2+x+2} = 1 + y$ say

where $y = \frac{4x+1}{x^2+x+2} = \frac{\frac{4}{x}+\frac{1}{x^2}}{1+\frac{1}{x}+\frac{2}{x^2}} \to 0 \quad$ as $x \to \infty$

Also $xy = \frac{4x^2+x}{x^2+x+2} = \frac{4+1/x}{1+\frac{1}{x}+\frac{1}{x^2}} \to 4 \quad$ as $x \to \infty$

$\therefore \quad$ limit $= \lim_{y\to 0} (1+y)^x$

$= \lim [(1+y)^{1/y}]^{xy} = e^{xy} = e^4 \quad$ as $xy \to 4$

(b) When $n \to \infty$, $\left(\frac{4}{5}\right)^n = y$ say $\to 0$

$\therefore \quad \lim_{y\to 0} 5[1+y]^{(1/y).\,y.(1/n)}$

where $y \cdot \frac{1}{n} = \left(\frac{4}{5}\right)^n \cdot \frac{1}{n} \to 0$ as $n \to \infty$

$\therefore \quad$ limit $= 5 . e^0 = 5 . 1 = 5.$

55. (a) Lt at $x = 1$

$\underset{h\to 0}{\text{Lt}} f(1-h) = \text{Lt}(1-h+2) = 3$

$\underset{h\to 0}{\text{Lt}} f(1+h) = \text{Lt}(4+4h-1) = 3$

Since R.H.L. = L.H.L. $\quad \therefore \quad$ Limit exists and is 3.

Lt at $x = 3$

$\underset{h\to 0}{\text{Lt}} f(3-h) = \underset{h\to 0}{\text{Lt}} (12-4h-1) = 11.$

$\underset{h\to 0}{\text{Lt}} f(3+h) = \underset{h\to 0}{\text{Lt}} (9+6h+h^2)+5 = 14$

Since R.H.L. $\neq$ L.H.L. therefore $\underset{x\to 3}{\text{Lt}} f(x)$ does not exist.

(b) R.H.L. $= b$,

L.H.L. $= \underset{h\to 0}{\text{Lt}} \frac{\sin(0-h)}{(0-h)} = \underset{h\to 0}{\text{Lt}} \frac{\sin h}{h} = 1$

Hence $b = 1$ and limit $= 1$. There is no condition for a and as such a may be any real number.

56. (a) We know $[n+h] = n$, $[n-h] = n-1$

$\therefore \quad$ R.H.L. $= \underset{h\to 0}{\text{Lt}} (-1)^n = (-1)^n$

$\therefore \quad$ L.H.L. $= \underset{h\to 0}{\text{Lt}} (-1)^{n-1} = (-1)^{n-1} = -(-1)^n$

$\therefore \quad$ R.H.L. $\neq$ L.H.L. Hence limit does not exist.

(b) $[2+h] = 2$, $[2-h] = 1$

$R = \underset{h\to 0}{\text{Lt}} \{2+h+(2+h-2)^2\} = 2$

$L = \underset{h\to 0}{\text{Lt}} \{2-h+(2-h-1)^2\} = 3$

$R \neq L \quad \therefore \quad$ Limit does not exist.

(c) Ans. (a).

$(kx-1) < [kx] \leq (kx+1)$ for any integral value of x.

Putting $k = 1, 2, 3, \ldots n$ and adding the n inequalities, we get

$$x \sum_{k=1}^{n} k - n < \sum_{k=1}^{n} [kx] < x \sum_{k=1}^{n} k + n$$

or $$x \frac{n(n+1)}{2} - n < \sum_{k=1}^{n} [kx] < x \frac{n(n+1)}{2} + n$$

Dividing throughout by n^2,

$$\frac{x}{2}\left(1 + \frac{1}{n}\right) - \frac{1}{n} < \sum_{k=1}^{n} \frac{[kx]}{n^2} < \frac{x}{2}\left(1 + \frac{1}{n}\right) + \frac{1}{n}$$

Taking limit as $n \to \infty$

$$\frac{x}{2} \le \underset{n \to \infty}{\text{Lt}} \sum_{k=1}^{n} \frac{[kx]}{n^2} \le \frac{x}{2}$$

$$\therefore \quad \underset{n \to \infty}{\text{Lt}} \sum_{k=1}^{n} \frac{[kx]}{n^2} = \frac{x}{2} \Rightarrow \text{(a)}$$

57. (a) Limit does not exist as $x = 5 + h \Rightarrow [x] = 5$ and $x = 5 - h \Rightarrow [x] = 4$ $\therefore$ R.H.L. = 1, L.H.L. = 0

(b) $\lim_{h \to 0} [h] = 0$, $\lim_{h \to 0} [-h] = -1$

Replacing x by $1 + h$ for R.H.L. and by $1 - h$ for L.H.L. where $h \to 0$ and using the above results we have

R.H.L. $= \lim_{h \to 0} [-h + [h] + [-h]] = 0 + 0 - 1 = -1$

L.H.L. $= \lim_{h \to 0} [h + [-h] + [h]] = 0 - 1 + 0 = -1$

Since R.H.L. = L.H.L. = -1 $\therefore$ limit exists and is equal to -1.

(c) $\log_b a = \dfrac{\log a}{\log b}$, $\log \dfrac{1}{x} = -\log x$

$$\therefore \quad f(x) = \frac{-\log \cos x}{\log \cos \frac{x}{2}} \div \frac{-\log \cos \frac{x}{2}}{\log \cos x}$$

or $$f(x) = \left[\frac{\log \cos x}{\log \cos \frac{x}{2}}\right]^2 \qquad \ldots(1)$$

Now $\lim_{x \to 0} \dfrac{\log \cos x}{\log \cos \frac{x}{2}}$ form $\dfrac{0}{0}$

$$= \lim_{x \to 0} \frac{-\tan x}{-\frac{1}{2} \tan \frac{x}{2}} = \lim_{x \to 0} \frac{x}{\frac{1}{2} \cdot \frac{x}{2}} = 4$$

$$\therefore \quad \lim_{x \to 0} f(x) = (4)^2 = 16$$

58. $x^2 < 1 \Rightarrow x^2 - 1 = -$ ive

$\Rightarrow \quad (x - (-1))(x - 1) = -$ ive.

$\therefore \quad x$ lies between -1 and 1 *i.e.* $-1 < x < 1$ ...(1)

$x^2 \ge 1 \Rightarrow (x - (-1))(x - 1) \ge 0$ *i.e.* $+$ ive

$\therefore \quad x$ does not lie between -1 and 1.

$\therefore \quad x \le -1$ or $x \ge 1$ ...(2)

$\left\{\begin{array}{l} f(x) = x^4 \\ \quad\;\; = x \end{array}\right\}$ $\begin{array}{l} x^2 < 1 \\ x^2 \ge 1 \end{array}$ may be defined as

$\left\{\begin{array}{l} f(x) = x^4 \\ \quad\;\; = x \end{array}\right\}$ $\begin{array}{ll} -1 < x < 1 & \text{by (1)} \\ x \le -1, x \ge 1 & \text{by (2)} \end{array}$ ...(A) ...(B)

Limit at $x = 1$.

$\text{Lt } f(1 - h) = \text{Lt } (1 - h)^4 = 1$

$\text{Lt } f(1 + h) = \text{Lt } (1 + h) \quad = 1$

Since right hand and left hand limits are equal, therefore limit exists and is equal to 1.

Limit at $x = -1$

$\text{Lt } f(-1 - h)$ $\therefore$ $\text{Lt } (-1 - h) = -1$ from (B)

$\text{Lt } f(-1 + h)$ $\therefore$ $(-1 + h)^4 = 1$ from (A).

Since these limits are not equal, therefore limit does not exist at $x = -1$.

59. $$\frac{dy}{dx} = \underset{h \to 0}{\text{Lt}} \frac{(x+h)^{x+h} - x^x}{h}$$

$$= \underset{h \to 0}{\text{Lt}} \frac{1}{h} [(x+h)^{x+h} - x^{x+h} + x^{x+h} - x^x] \qquad \textbf{Note}$$

$$= \underset{h \to 0}{\text{Lt}} \frac{1}{h} \left[x^{x+h} \left\{ \left(\frac{x+h}{x}\right)^x \cdot \left(\frac{x+h}{x}\right)^h - 1 \right\} + x^x (x^h - 1) \right]$$

$$= x^x \underset{h \to 0}{\text{Lt}} \frac{1}{h} \left[\left\{ \left(1 + \frac{h}{x}\right)^{x/h} \right\}^h - 1 \right] + \text{Lt} \left[\frac{x^h - 1}{h} \right]$$

$$= x^x \left[\text{Lt } \frac{e^h - 1}{h} + \text{Lt } \frac{x^h - 1}{h} \right]$$

$= x^x [\log e + \log x]$ **by Q. 44 P. 1282-1302.**

$= x^x [1 + \log x]$

$\therefore \quad \underset{h \to 0}{\text{Lt}} \dfrac{a^x - 1}{x} = \log a$ **by Q. 2 (a) P. 1289-94.**

60. (a) Let $f(x) = e^{1/x}$. Then

$$f(0 + 0) = \lim_{h \to 0} e^{1/(0+h)} = \lim_{h \to 0} = e^{(1/h)} = e^{\infty} = \infty,$$

and $$f(0 - 0) = \lim_{h \to 0} e^{1/(0-h)}$$

$$= \lim_{h \to 0} e^{(-1/h)} = e^{-\infty} = \frac{1}{e^{\infty}} = \frac{1}{\infty} = 0.$$

Since the right hand and the left hand limits are unequal, the $\lim_{x \to 0} e^{1/x}$ does not exist.

(b) As $x \to 0$, the value of $\sin(1/x)$ oscillates between $+1$ and -1, passing through zero and intermediate values, an infinite number of times. Evidently there is no definite number A to which $\sin(1/x)$ tends as x tends to zero from the right. So the limit on the right does not exist. Similarly the limit on the left does not exist. Hence the ordinary limit of $\sin(1/x)$ as $x \to 0$ does not exist. This is also

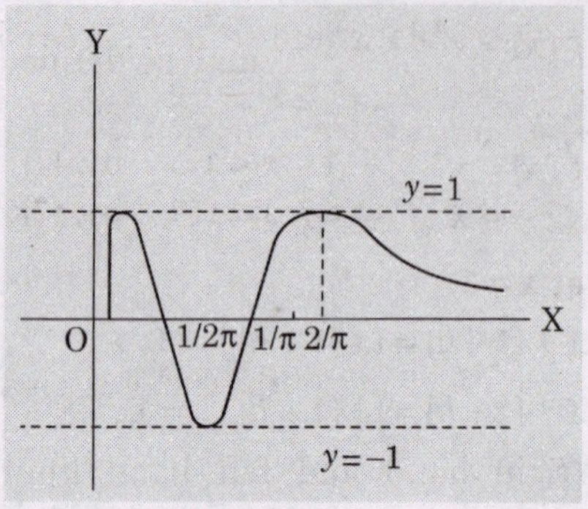

Fig. 2

evident from the graph of the function. Considering only positive values of x, we find that

$$f(x) = 0 \text{ for } x = \frac{1}{\pi}, \frac{1}{2\pi}, \frac{1}{3\pi}, \ldots \frac{1}{n\pi}.$$

and between consecutive zeros $f(x)$ is alternatively negative and positive. Thus there are an infinite number of oscillations which get closer and closer as we approach the origin. Each oscillation extends upto the line $y = +1$ and $y = -1$. For $x > (1/\pi), f(x)$ positive. After reaching the maximum value $+1$ at $x = 2/\pi$, the curve continually approaches the axis of x as x tends to infinity.

The graph has been drawn on the right of the origin. The students can verify that the curve on the left is exactly of the same type.

From the graph it is clear that the function makes an infinite number of oscillations between −1 and 1 in the neighbourhood of 0 on the right. Similarly it makes an infinite number of oscillations between −1 and 1 on the left of 0. Hence the limit on the right as well as the limit on the left does not exist at the origin.

61. (a) No. Let us choose $f(x) = x, g(x) = \frac{1}{x}$

$$\underset{x \to 0}{\text{Lt}} f(x) g(x) = \underset{x \to 0}{\text{Lt}} 1 = 1.$$

$$\underset{x \to 0}{\text{Lt}} f(x) = \underset{x \to 0}{\text{Lt}} x = 0. \text{ Limit exists.}$$

But $\underset{x \to 0}{\text{Lt}} g(x) = \underset{x \to 0}{\text{Lt}} \frac{1}{x}$.

This limit does not exist as R.H.L. $= \infty$, L.H.L. $= -\infty$.

(b) No. Let $f(x) = \frac{1}{x}$ and $g(x) = -\frac{1}{x}$ then

$$\underset{x \to 0}{\text{Lt}} [f(x) + g(x)] = \underset{x \to 0}{\text{Lt}} 0 = 0, \text{ exists.}$$

But as shown above the limits of both the functions do not exist as $x \to 0$.

62. (a) To draw the graph we consider two cases

(i) $x > 0$ (ii) $x < 0$.

In case (i), we have $f(x) = (x/x) = 1$.

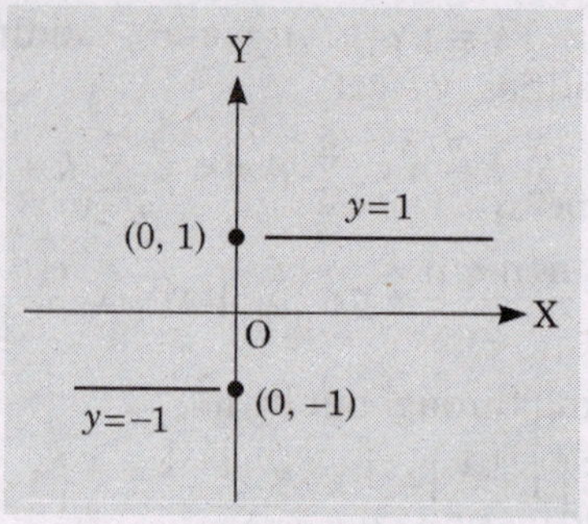

Fig. 3

Thus in this case, graph is the ray $y = 1$ parallel to x-axis extending from the neighbourhood of 0 to ∞.

In case (ii), we have $f(x) = (-x)/x = -1$.

Hence in this case, the graph is the ray $y = -1$ extending from the neighbourhood of 0 to $-\infty$.

Thus the graph is as shown in the adjoining figure.

The function $f(x)$ is not defined at $x = 0$ since it takes the indeterminate form 0/0 at $x = 0$.

To see whether $\lim_{x \to 0} f(x)$ esists or not we find the right hand and left hand limits at $x = 0$.

$$\text{Thus } f(0+0) = \frac{|0+h|}{0+h} = \lim_{h \to 0} \frac{h}{h} = 1$$

$$f(0-0) = \lim_{h \to 0} \frac{|0-h|}{0-h}$$

$$= \lim_{h \to 0} \frac{h}{-h} = -1.$$

Since $f(0+0) \neq f(0-0)$, the limit of $f(x)$ as $x \to 0$ does not exist.

(b) Proceed as in (a). $L \neq R$ and hence limit does not exist.

(iii) Limit does not exist as R.H.L. $= 1$, L.H.L. $= -1$.

63. $f(x) = \dfrac{|x(x-1)(x-2)|}{x(x-1)(x-2)} = \dfrac{|x|}{x} \dfrac{|x-1|}{x-1} \dfrac{|x-2|}{x-2}$

Consider the points $x = 0, 1, 2$; we redefine the function

$$f(x) = \begin{cases} -1, & x < 0 & (-1)(-1)(-1) = -1 \\ 1, & 0 < x < 1 & (1)(-1)(-1) = 1 \\ -1, & 1 < x < 2 & (1)(1)(-1) = -1 \\ 1, & x > 2 & (1)(1)(1) = 1 \end{cases}$$

Lt $f(x)$ as $x \to 0, 1, 2$ does not exist as both R.H.L. and L.H.L. will be different. Hence $a = 0, 1, 2$.

64. (a) First note that by def. of $[x]$, we have

$[x] = -1$ when $-1 \leq x < 0$

and $[x] = 0$ when $0 \leq x < 1$.

Hence by def. of f, the function is re-defined as under :

$$f(x) = \frac{\sin(-1)}{-1} = \sin 1 \text{ when } -1 \leq x < 0$$

and $f(x) = 0$ when $0 \leq x < 1$.

Change point is 0 and so we consider limit when $x \to 0$

$$\therefore \quad f(0-0) = \lim_{h \to 0} \sin 1 = \sin 1.$$

and $f(0+0) = \lim_{h \to 0} 0 = 0.$

Since $f(0-0) \neq f(0+0)$, the limit of $f(x)$ at $x = 0$ does not exist.

(b) L.H.L. $= \text{Lt}_{h \to 0} [0-h][0-h+1] = -1.0 = 0$

R.H.L. $= \text{Lt}_{h \to 0} [0+h][0+h+1] = 0.1 = 0$

Since L.H.L. = R.H.L. = 0, limit exists and is equal to 0.

65. (a) $R = L = 0$ as $\sin\frac{1}{x}$ is oscillating and $\text{Lt}\ h \sin\frac{1}{h} = 0$

(b) For the first part, see **Q. 8 (a), P. 1289-92.**

For the second part we see that

$f(0+0) = \lim_{h \to 0} [1] = 1$ and $f(0-0) = \lim_{h \to 0} [1] = 1.$

Hence the limit of $f(x)$ as $x \to 0$ exists and its value is 1.

66. (a) Ans. (d). $R = \sqrt{2}, L = -\sqrt{2} \quad \therefore \quad R \neq L$

(b) Ans. (a).

For left hand limit $x < a$ *i.e.* $x = a - h$, where $h \to 0$ and $a > 0$

$\therefore$ x is + ive $|x| = x$. Also $\frac{x}{a} < 1$ but it is + ive,

$\frac{x}{a}$ lies between 0 and 1 so that $\left[\frac{x}{a}\right] = 0$

$\therefore \quad \lim f(x) = \frac{a^3}{a} - 0 = a^2$

67. Given $f'(0) = \text{Lt}_{n \to \infty} nf\left(\frac{1}{n}\right)$ ...(1)

and $f(0) = 0$ ...(2)

Now $\text{Lt}_{n \to \infty} \left[\frac{2}{\pi}(n+1)\cos^{-1}\left(\frac{1}{n}\right) - n\right]$

$= \text{Lt}_{n \to \infty} n\left[\frac{2}{\pi}\left(1+\frac{1}{n}\right)\cos^{-1}\left(\frac{1}{n}\right) - 1\right]$

$= \text{Lt}_{n \to \infty} n\left[f\left(\frac{1}{n}\right)\right] = f'(0)$ by (1)

where $f(x) = \frac{2}{\pi}(1+x)\cos^{-1} x - 1$ ...(3)

Also $f(0) = \frac{2}{\pi}(1+0)\cos^{-1} 0 - 1 = \frac{2}{\pi}.\frac{\pi}{2} - 1 = 1 - 1 = 0.$

$$f'(x) = \frac{2}{\pi}\left[(1+x)\left(-\frac{1}{\sqrt{1-x^2}}\right) + 1 \cdot \cos^{-1} x\right]$$

$$\therefore \quad f'(0) = \frac{2}{\pi}\left[-1 + \frac{\pi}{2}\right] = -\frac{2}{\pi} + 1 = 1 - \frac{2}{\pi}.$$

68. Ans. (c). $y = x - 1, x \geq 1,$

$y = -(x-1), x < 1$

Clearly left hand derivative of $g(x)$ at $x = 1$ is $-1 = p$ (given) ...(1)

$$\text{Lt}_{x \to 1^+} g(x) = \text{Lt}_{h \to 0} \frac{h^n}{m \log \cos h} \quad \text{Form}\left(\frac{0}{0}\right)$$

$$= \text{Lt}_{h \to 0} \frac{n}{m} \frac{h^{n-1}}{(-\tan h)} = p = -1$$

or $\quad \text{Lt}_{h \to 0} \frac{n}{m} \frac{h^{n-1}}{\tan h} = 1$

Above is possible when $n = m = 2$ as we know that

$$\text{Lt}_{h \to 0} \frac{h}{\tan h} = \text{Lt}_{h \to 0} \frac{h}{\sin h} . \text{Lt}_{h \to 0} \cos h = 1.1 = 1$$

Continuity and Differentiability

§4 Continuity.

$f(x)$ is said to be continuous at $x = a$ if $R = L = V$ *i.e.*

$$\text{Lt}_{h \to 0} f(a+h) = \text{Lt}_{h \to 0} f(a-h) = f(a)$$

In case the function is not defined at $x = a$, *i.e.* $f(a)$ does not exist or in case the R.H.L. ≠ L.H.L., then we say that the function is discontinuous at $x = a$. Its graph will show a break at $x = a$.

Continuity in the open interval

(a, b)* or *]a, b[i.e., a < x < b

$f(x)$ will be continuous if it is continuous at every point of the interval.

Continuous in the closed interval [*a, b*] *i.e.* $a \leq x \leq b$. It will satisfy the following three conditions :

(i) $f(x)$ will be continuous in the open interval (a, b)

(ii) It is continuous at a from the right *i.e.*

$\text{Lt}_{x \to a+0} f(x)$ or $\text{Lt}_{h \to 0} f(a+h) = f(a)$ and

(iii) It is continuous at b from the left *i.e.*

$\text{Lt}_{x \to b-0} f(x)$ or $\text{Lt}_{h \to 0} f(b-h) = f(b)$

A continuous function in the closed interval $a \leq x \leq b$ has the following properties :

(a) If $f(a)$ and $f(b)$ are of opposite signs, then there exits at least one and in general odd solutions of the equation $f(x) = 0$ for any x in the open interval (a, b).

(b) If λ is any real number between $f(a)$ and $f(b)$, then there exists at least one solution of the equation $f(x) = \lambda$ in the open interval (a, b).

Examples : (i) $f(x) = \frac{x^2 - a^2}{x - a}$ is discontinuous at $x = a$

as $f(a)$ does not exist. Similarly if $y = 1/x$, it is also discontinuous at $x = 0$ as it is not defined.

(ii) $f(x) = \frac{1}{1 + 2^{1/x}}$, $x \neq 0, f(0) = 0$

is discontinuous at $x = 0$ because

$$\text{R.H.Lt.} = \text{Lt}_{h \to 0} \frac{1}{1 + 2^{1/h}} = \frac{1}{\infty} = 0$$

whereas L.H.Lt.

$$= \text{Lt}_{h \to 0} \frac{1}{1 + 2^{-1/h}} = \text{Lt}_{h \to 0} \frac{1}{1 + \frac{1}{\infty}} = \frac{1}{1} = 1$$

$\therefore \quad R \neq L$

(iii) $f(x) = 1 - \cos e^{1/x}$ is discontinuous at $x = 0$ because $f(0) = 1 - \cos e^{1/0}$ is undefined. It is oscillating.

(iv) $f(x) = \dfrac{x^3 - x^2 - 3x + 3}{1 - x}$

Here $f(x) = \dfrac{(x^2 - 3)(x - 1)}{1 - x}$

It is not defined for $x = 1$ as it takes the form $\dfrac{0}{0}$ but

$\underset{x \to 1}{\text{Lt}} \; f(x) = 2$. Hence it is discontinuous at $x = 1$.

As a matter of fact $y = -(x^2 - 3)$ or $x^2 = -(y - 3)$ *i.e.* a parabola (inverted) with vertex at (0, 3) with a break at $x = 1$.

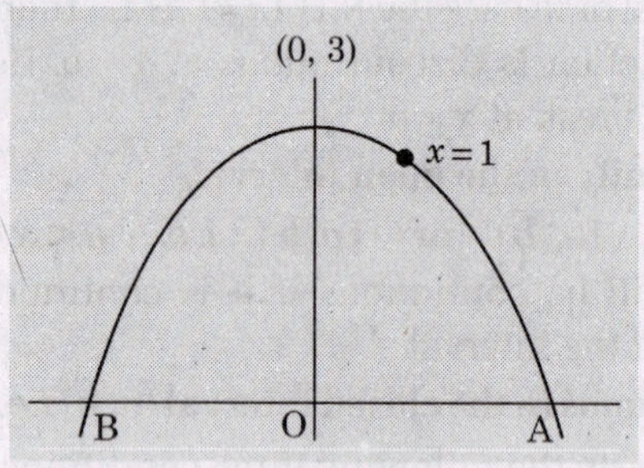

Fig. 4

However if we redefine the function as

$$f(x) = \frac{x^3 - x^2 - 3x + 3}{1 - x}, \quad x \neq 1$$
$$= 2, \quad x = 1$$

then it will be continuous at $x = 1$, as in that case limit will be equal to value at $x = 1$.

Types of discontinuities

(1) Discontinuity of First kind : The point $x = a$ will be a point of discontinuity of first type if both right hand and left hand limits at $x = a$ exist but are not equal *i.e.*

$$\underset{h \to 0}{\text{Lt}} \; f(a - h) \neq \underset{h \to 0}{\text{Lt}} \; f(a + h).$$

(2) Discontinuity of Second kind : The point $x = a$ will be point of discontinuity of second type if either or both the right hand and left hand limits do not exist or if either or both the limits $\underset{h \to 0}{\text{Lt}} \; f(a - 0)$ or $\underset{h \to 0}{\text{Lt}} \; f(a + 0)$ are infinite.

(3) Removable discontinuity : If $\underset{h \to 0}{\text{Lt}} \; f(a + 0) = \underset{h \to 0}{\text{Lt}} \; f(a - 0)$ *i.e.* limit exists but is not equal to $f(a)$ *i.e.* value, then the function is said to have a removable discontinuity. We can re-define the function at $x = a$ so that limit = value and thus the discontinuity has been removed and the function has become continuous now.

§5 Differentiability.

$f(x)$ is said to be differentiable at $x = a$ if $R' = L' =$ **finite**

i.e. $\underset{h \to 0}{\text{Lt}} \; \dfrac{f(a + h) - f(a)}{h} = \underset{h \to 0}{\text{Lt}} \; \dfrac{f(a - h) - f(a)}{-h}$

An important point :

A function which is differentiable at a point $x = a$ must also be continuous at that point. On the other hand if a function is continuous at a point $x = a$, it is not necessarily differentiable at $x = a$.

(A) Differentiability implies continuity always.

Since the function is differentiable

$\therefore \quad L' = R' =$ finite

$\underset{h \to 0}{\text{Lt}} \; \dfrac{f(a + h) - f(a)}{h}$ exists and is finite ...(1)

or $\underset{h \to 0}{\text{Lt}} \; f(a + h) = \underset{h \to 0}{\text{Lt}} \; [f(a + h) - f(a)] + f(a)$

$$= \underset{h \to 0}{\text{Lt}} \; h \left[\frac{f(a + h) - f(a)}{h} \right] + f(a)$$

$$= \text{Lt}\; h \,.\, \text{Lt} \; \frac{f(a + h) - f(a)}{h} + f(a) = 0 + f(a) = f(a).$$

Similarly $\underset{h \to 0}{\text{Lt}} \; f(a - h) = f(a)$

Since $\text{Lt}\; f(a + h) = \text{Lt}\; f(a - h) = f(a)$, the function is continuous.

(B) Continuity does not necessarily imply differentiability.

We will illustrate the above by the following example :

$$\text{Consider } f(x) = \begin{cases} x \sin \dfrac{1}{x}, & x \neq 0 \\ 0, & x = 0 \end{cases}$$

Consider its differentiability at $x = 0$

$$R'(0) = \underset{h \to 0}{\text{Lt}} \; \frac{f(0 + h) - f(0)}{h}$$

$$= \underset{h \to 0}{\text{Lt}} \; \frac{h \sin(1/h)}{h} = \underset{h \to 0}{\text{Lt}} \; \sin \frac{1}{h}$$

The above limit does not exist as $\sin \dfrac{1}{h}$ is an oscillating function. Similarly $L'(0)$ does not exist. Hence the function is not differentiable at $x = 0$.

Continuity. $R = L = V$

$$R = \underset{h \to 0}{\text{Lt}} \; h \sin \frac{1}{h} = 0$$

$$L = \underset{h \to 0}{\text{Lt}} \; (-h) \sin \left(-\frac{1}{h} \right) = 0$$

$$V = 0$$

Since $R = L = V$ the function is continuous but as shown above, it is not differentiable. But a function which is differentiable at a point must be continuous at that point.

Note : Continuity and differentiability is estabilished at change points.

Differentiability of $f(x)$ on closed interval $[a, b]$.

(1) It should be differentiable at every point on the open interval $]a, b[$ *i.e.* (a, b)

(2) **Right hand** derivative R' at a and **left hand** derivative at b exist finitely.

If both the above are satisfied then we say that $f(x)$ is differentiable in the closed interval $[a, b]$.

Note : L' cannot exist at $x = a$ and R' does not exist at $x = b$ for the closed interval $[a, b]$.

Problem Set (2)

Continuity, $R = L = V$, Differentiability by $R' = L'$.

1. (a) A function f is defined as

$$f(x) = \frac{x^2 - 4x + 3}{x^2 - 1} \text{ for } x \neq 1.$$
$$= 2 \text{ for } x = 1$$

Test the continuity of the function at $x = 1$.

(b) A function f is defined as

$$f(x) = \frac{x^2 - 4x + 3}{x^2 + 2x - 3} \quad \text{for } x \neq 1$$
$$= -1/2 \quad \text{for } x = 1.$$

Show that $f(x)$ is differentiable at $x = 1$ and find its value. **(J.E.E. W.B. 1992)**

2. (a)* Determine the values of a, b, c for which the function

$$f(x) = \frac{\sin(a+1)x + \sin x}{x} \text{ for } x < 0$$
$$= c \text{ for } x = 0$$
$$= \frac{(x + bx^2)^{1/2} - x^{1/2}}{bx^{3/2}} \text{ for } x > 0$$

is continuous at $x = 0$.

(b) The function $\dfrac{\log(1+ax) - \log(1-bx)}{x}$ is not defined at $x = 0$. The value which should be assigned to f at $x = 0$ so that it is continuous at $x = 0$ is $a + b$. True or false. **(Karnataka C.E.E. 1999)**

3. (a)* In order that the function $f(x) = (x+1)^{\cot x}$ is continuous at $x = 0$, $f(0)$ must be defined as $f(0) = e$. Prove this.

(b) Let $f(x) = \dfrac{x^3 + x^2 - 16x + 20}{(x-2)^2}$ if $x \neq 2$,

$= k$, if $x = 2$.

If $f(x)$ is continuous for all x, then $k = \dots\dots$

(c) If $f(x) = \begin{cases} x + \lambda, & -1 < x < 3 \\ 4, & x = 3 \\ 3x - 5, & x > 3 \end{cases}$

is continuous at 3 then $\lambda =$

(a) 1 (b) -1
(c) 0 (d) none **(AIEEE 2002)**

(d) Let $f(x) = \dfrac{1 - \tan x}{4x - \pi}$, $x \neq \dfrac{\pi}{4}$, $x \in \left[0, \dfrac{\pi}{2}\right]$. If $f(x)$ is continuous in $\left[0, \dfrac{\pi}{2}\right]$ then $f\left(\dfrac{\pi}{4}\right) =$

(a) 1 (b) $1/2$
(c) $-1/2$ (d) -1 **(AIEEE 2004)**

4. (a)* Find the values of a and b so that the function

$$f(x) = \begin{cases} x + a\sqrt{2} \sin x, & 0 \le x < \pi/4 \\ 2x \cot x + b, & \pi/4 \le x \le \pi/2 \\ a \cos 2x - b \sin x, & \pi/2 < x \le \pi \end{cases}$$

is continuous for $0 \le x \le \pi$.

(b) $f(x) = \begin{cases} a \tan^{-1} \dfrac{1}{x-4}, & 0 \le x < 4 \\ \pi/2, & x = 4 \\ b \tan^{-1} \dfrac{2}{x-4}, & 4 < x < 6 \\ \sin^{-1}(7 - x) + a\pi/4, & 6 \le x \le 8 \end{cases}$

Determine the values of a and b if $f(x)$ is continuous in the interval $[0, 8]$.

(c) Let $f(x) = \begin{cases} \dfrac{a + 3\cos x}{x^2}, & x < 0 \\ b \tan \left\{ \dfrac{\pi}{[x+3]} \right\}, & x \ge 0 \end{cases}$

where [ ] represents the greatest integer function. If $f(x)$ is continuous at $x = 0$, then prove that $a = -3$ and $b = -\dfrac{1}{2}\sqrt{3}$.

5. (a)* $f(x) = \dfrac{1 - \cos 4x}{x^2}$, $\quad x < 0$

$= a$, $\quad x = 0$

$= \dfrac{\sqrt{x}}{\sqrt{[16 + \sqrt{(x)}]} - 4}$, $\quad x > 0$. **(I.I.T. 1990)**

If possible find the value of a so that the function may be continuous at $x = 0$

(b) $f(x) = \begin{cases} (8^x - 4^x - 2^x + 1)/x^2, & x > 0 \\ e^x \sin x + \pi x + a \log 4, & x \le 0 \end{cases}$

If $f(x)$ is continuous at $x = 0$, then prove that $a = \log 2$.

(c) Discuss the continuity of the function

$$f(x) = \operatorname*{Lt}_{n \to \infty} \frac{\log(2+x) - x^{2n} \sin x}{1 + x^{2n}} \text{ at } x = 1$$

(d) Prove that the function

$$f(x) = \operatorname*{Lt}_{n \to \infty} \frac{(1 + \sin \pi x)^n - 1}{(1 + \sin \pi x)^n + 1}$$

is not continuous at $x = 1$.

(e) Discuss the continuity of the function

$$f(x) = \begin{cases} \dfrac{a^{[x]+x} - 1}{[x] + x}, & x \neq 0 \\ \log_e a, & x = 0 \end{cases}$$

at $x = 0$, $a > 0$.

6. (a)* Let $f(x) = \begin{cases} (1 + |\sin x|)^{a/|\sin x|} & -\pi/6 < x < 0 \\ b & x = 0 \\ e^{\tan 2x / \tan 3x} & 0 < x < \pi/6 \end{cases}$

Determine a and b such that f is continuous at $x = 0$. **(I.I.T. 1994)**

(b) If $f(x) = \dfrac{\sin 2x + a \sin x + b \cos x}{x^3}$

is continuous at $x=0$, find the values of a and b. What is $f(0)$?

(c) If

$$f(x)=\begin{cases}\dfrac{\sin 3x+a\sin 2x+b\sin x}{x^5} & x\neq 0\\ c, & x=0\end{cases}$$

is continuous at $x=0$, find the values of a,b,c.

7. (a) Determine the constants a,b and c for which the function

$$f(x)=\begin{cases}(1+ax)^{1/x} & , x<0\\ b & , x=0\\ \dfrac{(x+c)^{1/3}-1}{(x+1)^{1/2}-1} & , x>0\end{cases}$$

is continuous at $x=0$. **(Roorkee 1999)**

(b) Prove that the value of $f(0)$, so that the function

$$f(x)=\frac{\sqrt{a^2-ax+x^2}-\sqrt{a^2+ax+x^2}}{\sqrt{(a+x)}-\sqrt{(a-x)}}$$

becomes continuous for all x, is given by $-\sqrt{a}$.

8. (a) Function $f(x)=(\sin 2x)^{\tan^2 2x}$ is not defined at $x=\dfrac{\pi}{4}$. If $f(x)$ is continuous at $x=\dfrac{\pi}{4}$ then show that $f\left(\dfrac{\pi}{4}\right)$ is equal to $\sqrt{e}$.

(b) If $f(x)=\dfrac{2-(256-7x)^{1/8}}{(5x+32)^{1/5}-2}$ $(x\neq 2)$, then for f to be continuous everywhere, $f(0)$ is equal to 7/64.

(c) If $f(x)=x^{\alpha}\log x$ and $f(0)=0$, then the value of α for which Rolle's theorem can be applied in [0, 1] is

(a) -2 (b) -1

(c) 0 (d) 1/2 **(Screening 2004)**

(d) If $p(x)=51x^{101}-2323x^{100}-45x+1035$, using Rolle's Theorem, prove that atleast one root lies between $(45^{1/100}, 46)$. **(I.I.T. 2004)**

9. (a) $f(x)=\begin{cases}-2\sin x, & -\pi\le x\le -\pi/2\\ a\sin x+b, & -\pi/2<x<\pi/2\\ \cos x, & \pi/2\le x\le \pi\end{cases}$

If $f(x)$ is continuous on $[-\pi,\pi]$, then prove that $a=-1, b=1$

(b) Determine a and b if the function defined as under be continuous at $x=\pi/2$.

$$f(x)=\begin{cases}\dfrac{1-\sin^3 x}{3\cos^2 x} & , x<\pi/2\\ a & , x=\pi/2\\ \dfrac{b(1-\sin x)}{(\pi-2x)^2} & , x>\pi/2\end{cases}$$

10. (a) $f(x)=\dfrac{(3^x-1)^2}{\sin x\log(1+x)}$, $x\neq 0$ is continuous at $x=0$ then find $f(0)$.

(b) If $f(x)=\begin{cases}3x-4, & 0\le x\le 2\\ 2x+a, & 2<x\le 3\end{cases}$ and $f(x)$ be continuous at $x=2$ then prove that $a=-2$.

11. (a)* $f(x)=\begin{cases}ax^2-b, & |x|<1\\ -\dfrac{1}{|x|}, & |x|\ge 1\end{cases}$

The above function is continuous and differentiable, then prove that $a=\dfrac{1}{2}, b=\dfrac{3}{2}$.

(b) Discuss the continuity and differentiability of the function :

$f(x)=\dfrac{x}{1+|x|}, |x|\ge 1$, $\dfrac{x}{1-|x|}, |x|<1$. **(Roorkee 2000)**

12. (a)* Discuss the continuity and differentiability of the function

$$f(x)=\begin{cases}2+\sqrt{(1-x^2)}, & |x|\le 1\\ 2e^{(1-x)^2}, & |x|>1.\end{cases}$$

(Roorkee 1998)

(b) If $f(x)=\begin{cases}6x^5, & x<0\\ 2a+x, & x>0\end{cases}$ be continuous at $x=0$, then show that $a=3$.

13. (a)* $f(x)=\dfrac{1-\sin x}{(\pi-2x)^2}\cdot\dfrac{\log\sin x}{\log(1+\pi^2-4\pi x+4x^2)}$, $x\neq\pi/2$

What value be assigned to function at $x=\pi/2$ in order that it may be continuous at $x=\pi/2$?

(b) $f(x)=\dfrac{1-\sin x}{(\pi-2x)^4}.\cos x.(8x^3-\pi^3)\left(x\neq\dfrac{\pi}{2}\right)$

Determine $f(\pi/2)$ if $f(x)$ is continuous at $x=\pi/2$

14. (a) If $f(x)=\dfrac{(a^x-1)^3}{\sin(x\log a)\log(1+x^2\log a^2)}$ is continuous everywhere then determine $f(0)$.

(b) If the derivative of the function

$$f(x)=\begin{cases}ax^2+b, & x<-1\\ bx^2+ax+4, & x\ge -1\end{cases}$$

is everywhere continuous, then show that $a=2, b=3$.

Test the following functions for continuity.

15. (a) $f(x)=x\sin 1/x, x\neq 0, f(0)=0$ at $x=0$.

(b) $f(x)=2^{1/x}$ when $x\neq 0, f(0)=0$ at $x=0$.

16. (a)* $f(x)=\dfrac{2^{1/x}}{1+2^{1/x}}, x\neq 0$ and $f(0)=1$

(b) $f(x)=1/(1-e^{-1/x}), x\neq 0, f(0)=0$ at $x=0$

17. (a) $f(x)=\dfrac{e^{1/x}-1}{e^{1/x}+1}, x\neq 0, f(0)=-1$

(b) Discuss the continuity of the function

$$f(x) = \begin{cases} \dfrac{e^{1/(x-1)} - 2}{e^{1/(x-1)} + 2}, & x \neq 1 \\ 1, & x = 1 \end{cases} \quad \text{at } x = 1.$$ **(Roorkee 2001)**

(c) A function $f(x)$ is defined by

$$f(x) = \begin{cases} \dfrac{[x^2] - 1}{x^2 - 1} & \text{for } x^2 \neq 1 \\ 0 & \text{for } x^2 = 1 \end{cases}$$

Discuss the continuity of $f(x)$ at $x = 1$.

18. (a)* Let $f(x) = \begin{cases} xe^{-\left(\frac{1}{|x|} + \frac{1}{x}\right)}, & x \neq 0 \\ 0, & x = 0. \end{cases}$

Test whether

(i) $f(x)$ is continuous at $x = 0$

(ii) $f(x)$ is differentiable at $x = 0$. **(I.I.T. 1997)**

(b) The function $f(x) = [x]^2 - [x^2]$ (where $[y]$ is the greatest integer less than or equal to y), is **discontinuous** at

(a) all integers

(b) all integers except 0 and 1

(c) all integers except 0

(d) all integers except 1 **(I.I.T. 1999)**

19. (a) Show that the function ϕ defined as

$$\phi(x) = \begin{cases} 0 & \text{for } x = 0 \\ \frac{1}{2} - x & \text{for } 0 < x < \frac{1}{2} \\ \frac{1}{2} & \text{for } x = \frac{1}{2} \\ \frac{3}{2} - x & \text{for } \frac{1}{2} < x < 1 \\ 1 & \text{for } x = 1 \end{cases}$$

has three points of discontinuity which you are required to find. Also draw the graph of the function.

(b) Construct the graph of the function given below :

$$f(x) = \begin{cases} x - 1, & x < 0 \\ \frac{1}{4}, & x = 0 \\ x^2, & x > 0 \end{cases}$$

Find $\lim\limits_{x \to 0+} f(x)$ and $\lim\limits_{x \to 0-} f(x)$. Discuss the continuity of $f(x)$ at $x = 0$.

20. (a) Determine the number of points where the function

(i) $f(x) = \dfrac{1}{\log |x|}$ is discontinuous

(ii) $f(x) = \dfrac{4 - x^2}{4x - x^3}$ is discontinuous

(b) Prove that $f(x) = |\log x|$ is continuous at $x = 1$ but is not differentiable at $x = 1$.

21. (a)* Show that the function $f(x) = [x] + [-x]$ has removable discontinuity for integral values of x.

(b)* Consider the function f defined by $f(x) = x - [x]$, where x is a positive variable, and $[x]$ denotes the integral part of x and show that it is discontinuous for integral values of x, and continuous for all others. Is the function periodic ? If periodic, what is its period ? Draw its graph.

22. (a) Let $f(x)$ be a function of x defined as

$$f(x) = \frac{x^2 - 1}{x^2 - 2|x - 1| - 1}, \; x \neq 1$$
$$= 1/2, \quad x = 1$$

Discuss the continuity of function at $x = 1$

(b)* Determine the point of discontinuity of the function $f(x) = x + \dfrac{x + 2}{|x + 2|}$. Also find the jump of the function at this point.

23. Find the points of discontinuity of

(a) $f(x) = \dfrac{1}{x - [x]}$ (b) $f(x) = \dfrac{1}{x - |x|}$

24. (a) $f(x) = [\tan^2 x]$ is continuous at $x = 0$. **(I.I.T. 1993)**

(b) The number of points where $f(x) = [\sin x + \cos x]$ (where [•] denotes the greatest integer function) $x \in (0, 2\pi)$ is discontinuous is

(a) 3 (b) 4

(c) 5 (d) 6

25. (a)* Given the function $f(x) = 1/(1 - x)$. Find the points of discontinuity of the function $f(x)$ and the composite function $f\{f(x)\}$ and $f[f\{f(x)\}]$.

(b) If $f(x) = \dfrac{1}{x - 1}$, then determine the points of discontinuity of $f[f\{f(x)\}]$.

(c) Given the function $f(x) = \dfrac{1}{1 - x}$, the number of points of discontinuity of the composite function $y = f^{3n}(x)$, where $f^n(x) = fofof \ldots (n \text{ times}) \; (n \in N)$ are 0, 1.

26. (a)* Let $f(x) = [x] \sin\left(\dfrac{\pi}{[x + 1]}\right)$, where [•] denotes the greatest integer function. The domain of f is .... and the points of discontinuity of f in the domain are .... **(I.I.T. 1996)**

(b) The left-hand derivative of $f(x) = [x] \sin(\pi x)$ at $x = k$, k an integer, is

(a) $(-1)^k (k - 1)\pi$ (b) $(-1)^{k-1} (k - 1)\pi$

(c) $(-1)^k k\pi$ (d) $(-1)^{k-1} k\pi$

(I.I.T. Sc. 2001)

27. (a) If $f(x) = (1/x) \sin x^2, x \neq 0, f(0) = 0$, discuss the continuity and differentiability of $f(x)$ at $x = 0$.

(b) Find the derivative of

$$f(x)=\begin{cases}\dfrac{x-1}{2x^2-7x+5} & \text{when } x\neq 1\\ -1/3 & \text{when } x=1\end{cases}$$

at $x=1$.

28. (a) Investigate the following function from the point of view of its differentiability. Does the differential coefficient of the function exist at $x=0$ and $x=1$?

$$f(x)=\begin{cases}-x & \text{if } x<0\\ x^2 & \text{if } 0\le x\le 1\\ x^3-x+1 & \text{if } x>1\end{cases}$$

(b) Test the continuity and differentiability of the function defined as under at $x=1$ and $x=2$.

$$f(x)=\begin{cases}x & , \ x<1\\ 2-x & , \ 1\le x\le 2\\ -2+3x-x^2 & , \ x>2\end{cases}$$

29. (a)* If $f(x)=1$ for $x<0$

$=1+\sin x$ for $0\le x<\pi/2$,

then at $x=0$, the derivative $f'(x)$ does not exist. True or false.

(b) Show that the value of the derivative of $|x-1|+|x-3|$ at $x=2$ is 0. **(M.N.R. 1993)**

(c) If $f:[-2a,2a]\to R$ be an odd function such that left hand derivative at $x=a$ is zero and $f(x)=f(2a-x)$, $x\in(a,2a)$ then find left hand derivaitve of f at $x=-a$. **(I.I.T. 2003)**

30. Discuss the differentiablility of

(a) $\sin(\pi[x])$ and

(b)* $\sin\{\pi(x-[x])\}$ in $(-\pi/2,\pi/2)$. **(I.I.T. 1992)**

31.* Discuss the continuity of $f(x)$ in $[0,2]$

$$f(x)=\begin{cases}[\cos\pi x], & x\le 1\\ |2x-3|[x-2], & x>1\end{cases}$$

where $[t]$ represents the greatest integer function.

32. (a) If $f(x)=\dfrac{x}{1+e^{1/x}}$, $x\neq 0$, $f(0)=0$, show that f is continuous at $x=0$ but $f'(x)$ does not exist.

(b)* Discuss the limit, continuity and differentiability of the function

$$f(x)=\begin{cases}\dfrac{x(3e^{1/x}+4)}{(2-e^{1/x})} & x\neq 0\\ 0 & x=0\end{cases}$$

at $x=0$ **(Roorkee 1995)**

33. (a) Prove that the function $f(x)=\sin\pi|x|$ is continuous at $x=0$ but is not differentiable there.

(b) $$f(x)=\begin{cases}\dfrac{x(e^{1/x}-e^{-1/x})}{(e^{1/x}+e^{-1/x})} & , \ x\neq 0\\ 0 & , \ x=0\end{cases}$$

Prove that $f(x)$ is not differentiable at $x=0$.

34. (a) If $f(x)=x^2\sin(1/x)$ for $x\neq 0$, show that f is continuous and differentiable everywhere and that $f'(0)=0$. Show further that the function $f'(x)$ is discontinuous at the origin.

(b) Prove that the function $f(x)=|x|$ is continuous at $x=0$, but not differentiable at $x=0$ where $|x|$ means the numerical value of x.

35. (a)* Sketch the function $y=|x-2|$ in the interval $(-1,3)$. Is this function

(i) continuous

(ii) differentiable at $x=2$?

(b) Discuss the continuity and differentiablity of the function $f(x)=|x-2|$ at $x=2$

36. (a) If $f(x)=x[\sqrt{x}-\sqrt{x+1}]$, then $f(x)$ is continuous and differentiable at $x=0$.

(b)* Discuss the continuity and differentiability of

$$f(x)=\begin{cases}|x-3|, & x\ge 1\\ x^2/4-3x/2+13/4, & x<1\end{cases}$$ at $x=1,3$.

37. (a) If $$f(x)=\begin{cases}3x^2+12x-1, & -1\le x\le 2\\ 37-x, & 2<x\le 3\end{cases}$$

then prove the following

(a) $f(x)$ is increasing on $[-1,2]$

(b) $f(x)$ is continuous on $[-1,3]$

(c) $f'(2)$ does not exist. **(I.I.T. 1993)**

(b)* If $f(x)=\int_{-1}^{x}|t|\,dt$, $x\ge -1$ then f and f' are continuous for $x+1>0$. **(M.N.R. 1994)**

38. $$f(x)=\begin{cases}\int_0^x\{1+|(1-t)|\}\,dt & , \ x>2\\ 5x-7 & , \ x\le 2\end{cases}$$

then show that f is continuous but not differentiable at $x=2$.

39. (a)* $f(x)$ is defined as under :

$$f(x)\begin{cases}=ax(x-1)+b & , \ x<1\\ =x-1 & , \ 1\le x\le 3\\ =cx^2+dx+2 & , \ x>3\end{cases}$$

Determine the constants a,b,c and d, given that

(i) $f(x)$ is continuous for all x

(ii) $f'(1)$ does not exist

(iii) $f'(x)$ is continuous at $x=3$.

(b) A function ϕ is defined as follows :

$\phi(x)=-x$ for $x\le 0$; $\phi(x)=x$ for $x\ge 0$.

Test the character of the function at $x=0$ as regards continuity and differentiability.

40. Examine the following curve for continuity and differentiability :

$y=x^2$ for $x\le 0$; $y=1$ for $0<x\le 1$

and $y=1/x$ for $x>1$.

Also draw the graph of the function.

41. (a) Discuss the continuity and differentiability of the following function

$f(x) = x^2$ for $x < -2$;

$f(x) = 4$ for $-2 \le x \le 2$

and $f(x) = x^2$ for $x > 2$.

Also draw the graph.

(b) Prove that the function $f(x) = |x^2 - 4|$ is not differentiable at $x = 2$.

(c) Determine the values of x for which the following function fails to be continuous or differentiable :

$$f(x) = \begin{cases} 1 - x, & x < 1 \\ (1-x)(2-x), & 1 \le x \le 2 \\ 3 - x, & x > 2 \end{cases}$$

Justify your answer. **(I.I.T. Re-ex. 1997)**

42. Examine the continuity and differentiability in $-\infty < x < \infty$ of the following function :

$f(x) = 1$ in $-\infty < x < 0$,

$f(x) = 1 + \sin x$ in $0 \le x \le \pi/2$,

$f(x) = 2 + (x - \pi/2)^2$ in $\pi/2 \le x < \infty$.

43. (a) A function f is defined as follows :

$f(x) = x$ for $0 \le x \le 1$

and $f(x) = 2 - x$ for $x \ge 1$.

Test the character of the function at $x = 1$ as regards its continuity and differentiability. Also draw the graph.

(b) The function $f(x)$ is defined as

$f(x) = \frac{1}{3} - x, x < \frac{1}{3}$

$= \left(\frac{1}{3} - x\right)^2, x \ge \frac{1}{3}$

then in the interval (0, 1), the mean value, theorem is not true because

(a) $f(x)$ is not continuous

(b) $f(x)$ is not differentiable

(c) $f(0) \ne f(1)$

(d) none **(Screening 2003)**

44. Show that the function f defined by

$f(x) = x\left\{1 + \frac{1}{3}\sin(\log x^2)\right\}$, $x \ne 0$, and $f(0) = 0$, is everywhere continuous but has no differential coefficient at the origin.

45. (a)* A function f is defined as follows :

$f(x) = x^p \cos(1/x)$, $x \ne 0$, $f(0) = 0$.

What conditions should be imposed on p so that

(i) f may be continuous at $x = 0$,

(ii) f may have a differential coefficient at $x = 0$?

(b) If $f(x) = \dfrac{(e^x - 1)^4}{\sin\left(\dfrac{x^2}{\lambda^2}\right)\log\left(1 + \dfrac{x^2}{2}\right)}$, $x \ne 0$

and $f(0) = 8$ be a continuous function then show that $\lambda = \pm 2$.

(c) If $f(x) = \begin{cases} \dfrac{(4^x - 1)^3}{\sin\dfrac{x}{4}\log\left(1 + \dfrac{x^2}{3}\right)}, & x \ne 0 \\ p, & x = 0 \end{cases}$

be continuous at $x = 0$ then prove that $p = 12(\log 4)^3$

46. Let $f(x) = \sqrt{x}\{1 + x\sin(1/x)\}$ for $x > 0$,

$= -\sqrt{(-x)}\{1 + x\sin(1/x)\}$ for $x < 0$, $f(0) = 0$.

Show that $f'(x)$ exists everywhere and is finite except at $x = 0$ where its value is $+\infty$.

47. (a)* Draw the graph of the function $y = |x - 1| + |x - 2|$ in the interval [0, 3] and discuss the continuity and differentiability of the function in this interval.

(b)* Draw the graph of the following function and discuss its continuity and differentiability at $x = 1$.

$y = 3^x$, $-1 \le x \le 1$

$= 4 - x$, $1 < x < 4$ **(Roorkee 1994)**

(c) If $f(x) = \begin{cases} xe^{-\left[\frac{1}{|x|} + \frac{1}{x}\right]}, & x \ne 0 \\ 0, & x = 0 \end{cases}$, then $f(x)$ is :

(a) continuous and differentiable $\forall$ x

(b) continuous for $\forall$ x but not differentiable at $x = 0$

(c) neither differentiable nor continuous at $x = 0$

(d) discontinuous everywhere **(AIEEE 2003)**

48. (a) Let $h(x) = \min\{x, x^2\}$, for every real number of x. Then

(a) h is continuous for all x

(b) h is differentiable for all x

(c) $h'(x) = 1$, for all $x > 1$

(d) h is not differentiable at two values of x.

(I.I.T. 1998)

(b) Let $f : R \to R$ be a function defined by $f(x) = \max\{x, x^3\}$. The set of all points where $f(x)$ is not differentiable is

(a) $\{-1, 1\}$ (b) $\{-1, 0\}$

(c) $\{0, 1\}$ (d) $\{-1, 0, 1\}$ **(I.I.T. Sc. 2001)**

49. (a)* Let $f(x) = x^3 - x^2 + x + 1$

and $g(x) = \max\{f(t) : 0 \le t \le x\}$, $0 \le x \le 1$

$= 3 - x$, $1 < x \le 2$.

Discuss the continuity and differentiability of the function $g(x)$ in the interval (0, 2).

(b) $f(x) = \cos x$ and

$g(x) = \begin{cases} \min\{f(t) : 0 \le t \le x\}, & 0 \le x \le \pi \\ \sin x - 1, & x > \pi \end{cases}$

Discuss the continuity of $g(x)$ in $[0, \infty)$.

(c) Let $f(x) = \min\{1, x^2, x^3\}$, then :

(a) $f(x)$ is continuous $\forall$ $x \in R$

(b) $f'(x) > 0$, $\forall$ $x > 1$

(c) continuous but not differentiable $\forall\ x \in R$

(d) differentiable everywhere **(I.I.T. 2006)**

50.* A function is defined as follows :

$$f(x) = \begin{cases} x^3 & ; \quad x^2 < 1 \\ x & ; \quad x^2 \geq 1 \end{cases}$$

Draw the graph of the function and discuss limit, continuity and differentiability at $x = 1$. **(Roorkee 1993)**

51.* Let $f(x)$ be defined in the interval $[-2, 2]$ such that

$f(x) = -1, \quad -2 \leq x \leq 0$

$= x - 1, \quad 0 < x \leq 2$

and $g(x) = f(|x|) + |f(x)|$.

Test the differentiability of $g(x)$ in $(-2, 2)$.

52.* Let $f(x) = 1 + x$ for $0 \leq x \leq 2$

$= 3 - x$ for $2 < x \leq 3$.

Determine the form of $g(x) = f(f(x))$ and hence find the points of discontinuity of g, if any.

53. (a)* Draw a graph of the function

$y = [x] + |1 - x|, \quad -1 \leq x \leq 3$

Determine the points, if any, where this is not differentiable.

(b) Discuss the continuity and differentiability of the function $f(x)$ in $(0, 3)$ where

$$f(x) = \begin{cases} |2x - 3|\,[x], & 0 \leq x \leq 2 \\ x^2/2, & 2 < x \leq 3 \end{cases}$$

(c) $$f(x) = \begin{cases} (x-2)\,.\,2^{-\left[\frac{1}{|(x-2)|} + \frac{1}{(x-2)}\right]} & x \neq 2 \\ 0 & x = 2 \end{cases}$$

Prove that the above function is not differentiable at $x = 2$.

54. (a) The function

$f(x) = (x^2 - 1)\,|x^2 - 3x + 2| + \cos(|x|)$

is not differentiable at

(a) -1 (b) 0

(c) 1 (d) 2 **(I.I.T. 1999)**

(b) Which of the following functions is differentiable at $x = 0$?

(a) $\cos(|x|) + |x|$ (b) $\cos(|x|) - |x|$

(c) $\sin(|x|) - |x|$ (d) $\sin(|x|) + |x|$

(I.I.T. Sc. 2001)

55.* The number of points at which the function

$f(x) = |x - 0{\cdot}5| + |x - 1| + \tan x$

does not have a derivative in the interval $(0, 2)$ is 3.

(M.N.R. 1995)

56. (a)* Determine the set of all points where the function $f(x) = \dfrac{x}{1 + |x|}$ is differentiable.

(b) Find the set of points where $f(x) = x^2\,|x|$ is thrice differentiable.

(c) Let $f(x) = x\,|x|$

The set of points where $f(x)$ is twice differentiable is .... **(I.I.T. 1992)**

57. (a) Let $f : \mathbf{R} \to \mathbf{R}$ be any function. Define $g : \mathbf{R} \to \mathbf{R}$ by $g(x) = |f(x)|$ for all x. Then g is

(a) onto if f is onto

(b) one-one if f is one-one

(c) continuous if f is continuous

(d) differentiable if f is differentiable

(I.I.T. Sc. 2000)

(b) Consider the following statements S and R :

S : Both $\sin x$ and $\cos x$ are decreasing functions in the interval $(\pi/2, \pi)$.

R : If a differentiable function decreases in an interval (a, b), then its derivative also decreases in (a, b).

Which of the following is true ?

(a) Both S and R are wrong.

(b) Both S and R are correct, but R is not the correct explanation for S.

(c) S is correct and R is the correct explanation for S.

(d) S is correct and R is wrong. **(I.I.T. Sc. 2000)**

58. Draw a graph of the function

$f(x) = x - |x - x^2|, \quad -1 \leq x \leq 1$

and discuss its continuity or discontinuity in the interval $-1 \leq x \leq 1$. Graph is to be drawn on a page of your answer book.

59. $$f(x) \begin{cases} = \dfrac{|x^2 - x|}{x^2 - x}, & x \neq 0, x \neq 1 \\ = 1, & x = 0 \\ = -1, & x = 1 \end{cases}$$

Discuss its continuity in $0 < x \leq 1$.

60.* The function f is defined by $y = f(x)$ where

$x = 2t - |t|, y = t^2 + t|t|, t \in R.$

draw the graph of f for the interval $-1 \leq x \leq 1$. Also discuss its continuity and differentiability at $x = 0$.

61.* If $f(x) = \sqrt{|x - 1|}$ and $g(x) = \sin x$ then calculate $(f \circ g)\,x$ and $(g \circ f)\,x$ and discuss differentiability of $(g \circ f)\,x$ at $x = 1$. **(Roorkee 1992)**

62. If the functions f, g, h are defined from the set of real numbers R to R such that

$f(x) = x^2 - 1, g(x) = \sqrt{x^2 + 1},$

$$h(x) = \begin{cases} 0, & \text{if } x \leq 0 \\ x, & \text{if } x \geq 0 \end{cases}$$

then find the composite function $hofog$ and determine whether the function (fog) is invertible and the function h is the identity function. **(Roorkee 1997)**

63. (a) If $f(x) = -1 + |x - 1|, \quad -1 \leq x \leq 3$

$g(x) = 2 - |x + 1|, \quad -2 \leq x \leq 2,$

then calculate $(fog)(x)$ and $(gof)(x)$. Draw their graphs (on sheet of your answer book). Discuss the continuity of $(fog)(x)$ at $x = -1$ and differentiability of $(gof)(x)$ at $x = 1$. **(Roorkee 1990)**

(b) Let $f(x) = \begin{cases} x+a & \text{if} \quad x<0 \\ |x-1| & \text{if} \quad x \geq 0, \end{cases}$

and $g(x) = \begin{cases} x+1 & \text{if} \quad x<0 \\ (x-1)^2+b & \text{if} \quad x \geq 0, \end{cases}$

where a and b are non-negative real numbers. Determine the composite function $g \circ f$. If $(g \circ f)(x)$ is continuous for all real x, determine the values of a and b. Further, for these values of a and b, is $g \circ f$ differentiable at $x=0$? Justify your answer. **(I.I.T. 2002)**

64. Let a function $f: \mathbf{R} \to \mathbf{R}$ satisfy the equation $f(x+y) = f(x) + f(y)$ for all $x, y \in \mathbf{R}$, show that

(i) if f is continuous at the point $x=a$, then it is continuous for all $x \in \mathbf{R}$.

(ii) if f is continuous at $x=0$, then it is continuous for all $x \in \mathbf{R}$.

(iii) if f is continuous, then $f(x) = x f(1)$ for all $x \in \mathbf{R}$.

65. Let $f(xy) = f(x) f(y)$ for all x and y. If the function $f(x)$ is continuous at $x=1$ then prove that $f(x)$ is continuous for all $x \neq 0$.

66. Suppose the function f satisfies the conditions :

(a)* (i) $f(x+y) = f(x) f(y)$ for all x and y.

(ii) $f(x) = 1 + x g(x)$ where $\lim_{x \to 0} g(x) = 1$.

Show that the derivative $f'(x)$ exists and $f'(x) = f(x)$ for all x.

(b)* A function $f: \mathbf{R} \to \mathbf{R}$ satisfies the equation $f(x+y) = f(x) f(y)$ for all values of x and y and for any $x \in \mathbf{R}, f(x) \neq 0$. Suppose the function is differentiable at $x=0$ and $f'(0) = 2$. Prove that for all $x \in \mathbf{R}, f'(x) = 2f(x)$. Hence find the value of $f(x)$. **(I.I.T. 1990)**

67. (a)* If f is twice differentiable function such that

$$f''(x) = -f(x), \quad \text{and} \quad f'(x) = g(x),$$

and $h(x) = [f(x)]^2 + [g(x)]^2$,

find $h(10)$ if $h(5) = 11$.

(b) Let $f(x)$ be a continuous function defined for $1 \leq x \leq 3$. If $f(x)$ takes rational values for all x and $f(2) = 10$, then $f(1.5) = \ldots\ldots$ **(I.I.T. Re-ex. 1997)**

68. (a)* Let $f(x+y) = f(x) f(y)$ for all x and y. Suppose $f(5) = 2$ and $f'(0) = 3$. Find $f'(5)$.

(b) $f(x+y+z) = f(x) f(y) f(z) \; \forall \; x, y, z \in R$

If $f(2) = 4, f'(0) = 3$, then prove that $f(0) = 1$ and $f'(2) = 12$.

69.* Let $f\left(\dfrac{x+y}{2}\right) = \dfrac{f(x)+f(y)}{2}$ for all real x and y.

If $f'(0)$ exists and equals -1 and $f(0) = 1$, find $f(2)$. **(I.I.T. 1995)**

70. (a) Let $f(x)$ be a continuous function and $g(x)$ be discontinuous function. Prove that $f(x) + g(x)$ is a discontinuous function.

(b)* Let $f(x)$ be function satisfying the condition $f(-x) = f(x)$ for all real x. If $f'(0)$ exists, find its value.

71. Give an example of each of the following types of functions :

(a) The function which possesses a limit at $x=1$ but is not defined at $x=1$.

(b) The function which is neither defined at $x=1$ nor has a limit at $x=1$.

(c) The function which is defined at two points but is nevertheless discontinuous at both the points.

72. Let $y = E(x)$, where $E(x)$ denotes the integral part of x. Prove that the function is discontinuous where x has an integral value. Also draw the graph.

73. Let (x) denote the positive or negative excess of x over the nearest integer, and when x exceeds an integer by $\frac{1}{2}$, let $(x) = 0$. What do you say about the continuity of (x)? Draw the graph.

74. Let $f(x), x \geq 0$, be a non-negative continuous function, and let $F(x) = \int_0^x f(t)\,dt, \; x \geq 0$. If for some $c > 0$, $f(x) \leq cF(x)$ for all $x \geq 0$, then show that $f(x) = 0$ for all $x \geq 0$. **(I.I.T. 2001)**

75. Let $\alpha \in R$. Prove that a function $f: R \to R$ is differentiable at α if and only if there is a function $g: R \to R$ which is continuous at α and satisfies $f(x) - f(\alpha) = g(x)(x-\alpha)$ for all $x \in R$. **(I.I.T. 2001)**

76. Let $\mathbf{R}$ be the set of real numbers and $f: \mathbf{R} \to \mathbf{R}$ such that for all x and y in $\mathbf{R}$, $|f(x) - f(y)| \leq |x-y|^3$. Prove that $f(x)$ is a constant.

77. Let $f: [0, 4] - R$ be differentiable function

(i) For some $a, b \in (0, 4)$, show that

$$f^2(4) - f^2(0) = 8f(a) \,.\, f'(b)$$

(ii) Show $\int_0^4 f(t)\,dt = 2[\alpha f(\alpha^2) + \beta f(\beta^2)]$, for some $0 < \alpha; \beta < 2$. **(I.I.T. 2003)**

(iii) Let f be a non-negative function defined on the interval $[0, 1]$. If $\int_0^x \sqrt{1-(f'(t))^2}\,dt = \int_0^x f(t)\,dt$, $0 \leq x \leq 1$, and $f(0) = 0$, then

(a) $f\left(\frac{1}{2}\right) < \frac{1}{2}$ and $f\left(\frac{1}{3}\right) > \frac{1}{3}$

(b) $f\left(\frac{1}{2}\right) > \frac{1}{2}$ and $f\left(\frac{1}{3}\right) > \frac{1}{3}$

(c) $f\left(\frac{1}{2}\right) < \frac{1}{2}$ and $f\left(\frac{1}{3}\right) < \frac{1}{3}$

(d) $f\left(\frac{1}{2}\right) > \frac{1}{2}$ and $f\left(\frac{1}{3}\right) < \frac{1}{3}$ **(I.I.T. 2009)**

78. $f(x) = \begin{cases} b \sin^{-1}\left(\dfrac{x+c}{2}\right), & -\dfrac{1}{2} < x < 0 \\ \dfrac{1}{2}, & x = 0 \\ \dfrac{e^{\frac{a}{2}x} - 1}{x}, & 0 < x < \dfrac{1}{2} \end{cases}$

If $f(x)$ is differentiable at $x=0$ and $|c|<\frac{1}{2}$ then find the value of 'a' and prove that $64b^2=(4-c^2)$. **(I.I.T. 2004)**

79. Let $g(x)=\log(f(x))$ where $f(x)$ is a twice differentiable positive function on $(0,\infty)$ such that $f(x+1)=x f(x)$. Then, for $N=1,2,3,\ldots$

(a) $-4\left\{1+\frac{1}{9}+\frac{1}{25}+\ldots+\frac{1}{(2N-1)^2}\right\}$

(b) $4\left\{1+\frac{1}{9}+\frac{1}{25}+\ldots+\frac{1}{(2N-1)^2}\right\}$

(c) $-4\left\{1+\frac{1}{9}+\frac{1}{25}+\ldots+\frac{1}{(2N+1)^2}\right\}$

(d) $4\left\{1+\frac{1}{9}+\frac{1}{25}+\ldots+\frac{1}{(2N+1)^2}\right\}$ **(I.I.T. 2008)**

Solutions to Problem Set (2)

1. (a) We have, $f(1)=2$

$$f(x)=\frac{(x-1)(x-3)}{(x-1)(x+1)}=\frac{x-3}{x+1}, x\neq 1$$

$$\text{R.H.L.}=\lim_{x\to 0}\frac{1+h-3}{1+h+1}=\frac{-2}{2}=-1$$

Since $f(1)\neq f(1+0)$, the function is discontinuous at $x=1$.

(b) Proceed as above. Ans. 3/8.

2. (a) $f(0-0)=\lim_{h\to 0}\dfrac{\sin(a+1)(0-h)+\sin(0-h)}{-h}$

$$=\lim_{h\to 0}\frac{\sin(a+1)h+\sin h}{h}$$

$$=\frac{(a+1)h+h}{h}=a+2 \qquad \because \lim_{\theta\to 0}\sin\theta=\theta$$

and $f(0+0)=\lim_{h\to 0}\dfrac{(h+bh^2)^{1/2}-h^{1/2}}{bh^{3/2}}$

$$=\lim_{h\to 0}\frac{(1+bh)^{1/2}-1}{bh}$$

$$=\lim_{h\to 0}\frac{1+\frac{1}{2}bh\ldots-1}{bh}=\frac{1}{2},$$

which is independent of b and so b may have any real value.

Again by continuity at $x=0$,

we have $a+2=\frac{1}{2}=c$.

$\therefore \quad a=-3/2$ and $c=1/2$.

(b) Ans. True.

3. (a) For continuity actual value must be equal to the limiting value *i.e.* $L=R=V$

Let $A=\lim_{x\to 0}(x+1)^{\cot x}$

$\therefore \quad \log A=\lim_{x\to 0}\cot x\log(1+x)$

$$=\lim_{x\to 0}\frac{\log(1+x)}{\tan x}\quad\left(\frac{0}{0}\right)$$

$$=\lim_{x\to 0}\frac{1/(1+x)}{\sec^2 x}=1 \text{ by L' Hospital's Rule}$$

Hence $A=e^1=e$.

$\therefore \quad f(0)$ must be defined as $f(0)=e$.

(b) Ans. $k=7$.

(c) Ans. (a).

For continuity $L=R=V$

$\therefore \quad \text{Lt}\, f(3-\lambda)=\text{Lt}\, f(3+\lambda)=f(3)$

$3+\lambda=3.3-5=4$

$\therefore \quad \lambda=4-3=1$

(d) Ans. (c).

For continuity, limit = value at $x=\pi/4$

$$\operatorname*{Lt}_{x\to\pi/4}\frac{1-\tan x}{4(x-\pi/4)} \quad \text{form } \frac{0}{0}$$

$$=\operatorname*{Lt}_{x\to\pi/4}-\frac{\sec^2(\pi/4)}{4}=-\frac{2}{4}=-\frac{1}{2}$$

$\therefore \quad f\left(\frac{\pi}{4}\right)=-\frac{1}{2}=\text{limit}.$

4. (a) We apply the test of continuity at $x=\pi/4$ and $x=\pi/2$ to get the values of a and b.

At $x=\pi/4$, we have

$$f\left(\frac{\pi}{4}\right)=2.\frac{\pi}{4}\cot\frac{\pi}{4}+b=\frac{\pi}{2}+b$$

$$f\left(\frac{\pi}{4}-0\right)=\lim_{h\to 0}\left[\frac{\pi}{4}-h+a\sqrt{2}\sin\left(\frac{\pi}{4}-h\right)\right]$$

$$=\frac{\pi}{4}+a\sqrt{2}.\frac{1}{\sqrt{(2)}}=a+\frac{\pi}{4}$$

and $f\left(\frac{\pi}{4}+0\right)=\lim_{h\to 0}\left[2\left(\frac{\pi}{4}+h\right)\cot\left(\frac{\pi}{4}+h\right)+b\right]$

$$=\frac{\pi}{2}.1+b=\frac{\pi}{2}+b.$$

$\therefore \quad$ For continuity at $x=\pi/4$, we have

$$\frac{\pi}{2}+b=a+\frac{\pi}{4} \quad\text{or}\quad a-b=\frac{\pi}{4}. \qquad \ldots(1)$$

At $x=\pi/2$, we have

$$f\left(\frac{\pi}{2}\right)=2.\frac{\pi}{2}\cot\frac{\pi}{2}+b=b$$

$$f\left(\frac{\pi}{2}-0\right)=\lim_{h\to 0}\left[2\left(\frac{\pi}{2}-h\right)\cot\left(\frac{\pi}{2}-h\right)+b\right]=b$$

$$f\left(\frac{\pi}{2}+0\right)=\lim_{h\to 0}\left[a\cos 2\left(\frac{\pi}{2}+h\right)-b\sin\left(\frac{\pi}{2}+h\right)\right]$$

$$=-a-b.$$

$\therefore \quad$ For continutity at $x=\pi/2$, we have

$$b=-a-b \quad\text{or}\quad a+2b=0 \qquad \ldots(2)$$

Solving (1) and (2), we get

$$a=\frac{\pi}{6}, b=-\frac{\pi}{12}.$$

(b) Continuity at $x=4$; $L=R=V=\pi/2$

$a(-\pi/2)=b.\pi/2=\pi/2$

$\therefore \quad a = -1, b = 1$

With these values of a and b we must show that function is continuous at $x = 6$ also because we have to show that $f(x)$ is continuous in the interval [0, 8]. i.e. $L = R = V$

V at $x = 6, = \sin^{-1} 1 + a.\frac{\pi}{4} = \frac{\pi}{2} - \frac{\pi}{4} = \frac{\pi}{4}$ as $a = -1$

$$L = \text{Lt}\; b \tan^{-1} \frac{2}{6-h-4} = \text{Lt}\; b \tan^{-1} 1$$

$$= b.\frac{\pi}{4} = \frac{\pi}{4} \text{ as } b = 1$$

$R = \frac{\pi}{4}$, as above. Hence continuous at $x = 6$ also.

(c) For continuity $R = L = V$ at $x = 0$

Now for $x = 0$ and $x = 0 + h$; $[x + 3] = 3$

$$V = b \tan \frac{\pi}{3} = b\sqrt{3}$$

$$\text{R.H.L.} = \underset{h\to 0}{\text{Lt}}\; b \tan \frac{\pi}{[h+3]} = b \tan \frac{\pi}{3} = b\sqrt{3}$$

$$\text{L.H.L.} = \underset{h\to 0}{\text{Lt}} \frac{a + 3\cos(0-h)}{(-h)^2} = \underset{h\to 0}{\text{Lt}} \frac{a + 3\cos h}{h^2}$$

$$= \underset{h\to 0}{\text{Lt}} \frac{a + 3\left(1 - \frac{h^2}{2!} + \frac{h^4}{4!} - \ldots\right)}{h^2}$$

$$= \underset{h\to 0}{\text{Lt}} \left[\frac{(a+3)}{h^2} - \frac{3}{2} + \text{powers of } h\right]$$

For left hand limit to exist we must have $a + 3 = 0$

$\therefore \quad a = -3$ and in that case the L.H.L. $= -\frac{3}{2}$

For continuity $R = L = V$

$$\therefore \quad b\sqrt{3} = -\frac{3}{2} = b\sqrt{3}$$

$$\therefore \quad a = -3 \text{ and } b = -\frac{1}{2}\sqrt{3}$$

5. (a) $f(0-0) = \lim\limits_{h\to 0} \frac{1 - \cos 4(0-h)}{(0-h)^2}$

$$= \lim_{h\to 0} \frac{1 - \cos 4h}{h^2}$$

$$= \lim_{h\to 0} \frac{2\sin^2 2h}{h^2} = \lim_{h\to 0} \left(\frac{\sin 2h}{2h}\right)^2 .8 = 8.$$

$$\left[\because \lim_{h\to 0} \frac{\sin 2h}{2h} = 1\right]$$

and $f(0+0) = \lim\limits_{h\to 0} \frac{(0+h)^{1/2}}{[16 + (0+h)^{1/2}]^{1/2} - 4}$

$$= \lim_{h\to 0} h^{1/2} \frac{\sqrt{16 + \sqrt{h}} + 4}{16 + \sqrt{(h)} - 16}, \text{ on rationalizing}$$

$$= \lim_{h\to 0} \sqrt{16 + \sqrt{(h)}} + 4 = 4 + 4 = 8$$

Also $f(0) = a$ (given).

Since $f(x)$ is continuous at $x = 0$, we must have

$$f(0-0) = f(0+0) = f(0)$$

or $\quad 8 = 8 = a$. Hence $a = 8$.

(b) Since $f(x)$ is continuous at $x = 0$

$\therefore \quad R = L = V$

$V = a \log 4 = 2a \log 2$

$$= \underset{h\to 0}{\text{Lt}}\; (8^h - 4^h - 2^h + 1)/h^2$$

$$= \underset{h\to 0}{\text{Lt}} \frac{(2^h - 1)}{h} \frac{(4^h - 1)}{h} = \log 2 . \log 4 = 2(\log 2)^2$$

$$L = \underset{h\to 0}{\text{Lt}}\; e^{-h} \sin(-h) - \pi h + a \log 4 = 2a \log 2$$

Since $R = L = V$

$\therefore \quad 2a \log 2 = 2(\log 2)^2 = 2a \log 2$

$\therefore \quad a = \log 2.$

(c) First we have to define $f(x)$ for $\underset{n\to\infty}{\text{Lt}}$ and then define $f(x)$ for $x < 1, x > 1$ and at $x = 1$ for continuity at $x = 1$

$$\underset{n\to\infty}{\text{Lt}}\; x^{2n} = \underset{n\to\infty}{\text{Lt}}\; (x^2)^n = \infty \text{ if } x^2 > 1$$

$$= 0 \text{ if } x^2 < 1$$

$$\therefore \quad \underset{n\to\infty}{\text{Lt}} \left(\frac{1}{x^2}\right)^n = 0 \text{ if } x^2 > 1 \qquad \ldots(1)$$

i.e., when $x < -1$ or $x > 1$

and $\underset{n\to\infty}{\text{Lt}}\; (x^2)^n = 0$ if $x^2 < 1$ i.e., $-1 < x < 1$ ...(2)

Also at $x = 1$, $f(x) = \frac{\log 3 - \sin 1}{2}$ ...(3)

$$\therefore \quad f(x) = \frac{\log(2+x) - 0}{1 + 0} \text{ if } x < 1 \text{ by (2)} \qquad \ldots(4)$$

and $f(x) = \frac{(1/x^{2n}) \log(2+x) - \sin x}{1/x^{2n} + 1} = -\sin x$ ...(5)

if $x > 1$ by (1)

For continuity at $x = 1$, we redefine the function as shown above

$$f(x) = \begin{cases} \log(2+x); x < 1 & \text{by (4)} \\ \frac{\log 3 - \sin 1}{2}; x = 1 & \text{by (3)} \\ -\sin x; \quad x > 1 & \text{by (5)} \end{cases}$$

$$\text{L.H.L.} = \underset{h\to 0}{\text{Lt}}\; \log(2 + 1 - h) = \log 3$$

$$\text{R.H.L.} = \underset{h\to 0}{\text{Lt}}\; -\sin(1+h) = -\sin 1$$

and $V = \frac{1}{2}(\log 3 - \sin 1)$

$\therefore \quad R \neq L \neq V$

$\therefore \quad f(x)$ is not continuous at $x = 1$.

(d) We must have $L = R = V$ at $x = 1$

$$V \text{ at } x = 1, f(x) = \underset{n\to\infty}{\text{Lt}} \frac{(1 + \sin \pi)^n - 1}{(1 + \sin \pi)^n + 1} = \frac{1-1}{1+1} = 0$$

$$\text{R.H.L.} = \underset{h\to 0}{\text{Lt}} \cdot \underset{n\to\infty}{\text{Lt}} \frac{[1+\sin(\pi+\pi h)]^n - 1}{[1+\sin(\pi+\pi h)]^n + 1}$$

$$= \underset{h\to 0}{\text{Lt}} \cdot \underset{n\to\infty}{\text{Lt}} \frac{(1-\sin\pi h)^n - 1}{(1-\sin\pi h)^n + 1}$$

$\because \quad \sin(\pi+\theta) = -\sin\theta$

Again $1-\sin\pi h < 1$

$\therefore \quad (1-\sin\pi h)^n \to 0$ as $n\to\infty$.

$\therefore \quad \text{R.H.L.} = \dfrac{0-1}{0+1} = -1.$

$$\text{L.H.L.} = \underset{h\to 0}{\text{Lt}} \cdot \underset{n\to\infty}{\text{Lt}} \frac{[1+\sin(\pi-\pi h)]^n - 1}{[1+\sin(\pi-\pi h)]^n + 1}$$

$$= \underset{h\to 0}{\text{Lt}} \cdot \underset{n\to\infty}{\text{Lt}} \frac{(1+\sin\pi h)^n - 1}{(1+\sin\pi h)^n + 1}$$

Now $1+\sin\pi h > 1 \;\therefore\; \dfrac{1}{1+\sin\pi h} < 1$

$$\therefore \quad \text{L.H.L.} = \underset{h\to 0}{\text{Lt}} \cdot \underset{n\to\infty}{\text{Lt}} \frac{1-\dfrac{1}{(1+\sin\pi h)^n}}{1+\dfrac{1}{(1+\sin\pi h)^n}}$$

$$= \frac{1-0}{1+0} = 1$$

$\therefore \quad R=-1,\; L=1,\; V=0$

Hence the function is not continuous at $x=1$.

(e) $\text{R.H.L.} = \underset{h\to 0}{\text{Lt}} \dfrac{a^{[h]+h}-1}{[h]+h}$; Put $[h]=0$

$$= \underset{h\to 0}{\text{Lt}} \frac{a^h-1}{h} = \log_e a = \text{value}$$

$\text{L.H.L.} \Rightarrow \underset{h\to 0}{\text{Lt}} \dfrac{a^{[-h]-h}-1}{[-h]-h}$; put $[-h]=-1$

$$= \underset{h\to 0}{\text{Lt}} \frac{a^{-h-1}-1}{-1-h} = \frac{a^{-1}-1}{-1} = 1-a^{-1}$$

$\therefore \quad R = V \neq L$

Hence $f(x)$ is not continuous.

6. (a) $L=R=V=b$ at $x=0$ for continiuty at $x=0$

$\text{R.H.L.} = \underset{h\to 0}{\text{Lt}}\; f(0+h) = \text{Lt}\; e^{(\tan 2h)/(\tan 3h)}$

$= \text{Lt}\; e^{2h/3h} = e^{2/3} \qquad \because \underset{\theta\to 0}{\text{Lt}} = \tan\theta = \theta$

$\text{L.H.L.} = \underset{h\to 0}{\text{Lt}}\; f(0-h)$

$= \text{Lt}\,(1+|\sin(-h)|)^{a/|\sin(-h)|}$

$= \text{Lt}\,(1+\sin h)^{a/\sin h}$

$\because \quad |-\sin h| = \sin h = y$, say

$= \underset{y\to 0}{\text{Lt}}\,(1+y)^{a/y} = e^a \qquad$ as $h\to 0,\, y\to 0$

$\therefore \quad e^a = e^{2/3} = b$

$\therefore \quad a = 2/3,\, b = e^{2/3}$

(b) Using expansion,

$$\underset{x\to 0}{\text{Lt}}\; f(x) = \underset{x\to 0}{\text{Lt}} \frac{\left(2x - \dfrac{(2x)^3}{3!} + \ldots\right) + a\left(x - \dfrac{x^3}{3!} + \ldots\right) + b\left(1 - \dfrac{x^2}{2!} + \ldots\right)}{x^3}$$

$$= \underset{x\to 0}{\text{Lt}} \frac{(2+a)\,x - \dfrac{bx^2}{2} + x^3\left(-\dfrac{8}{6} - \dfrac{a}{6}\right) + \ldots}{x^3} = \text{finite}$$

Above is posible only when $2+a=0$ and $b=0$

$\therefore \quad a=-2, b=0$ and limit is

$$-\frac{8}{6} - \frac{a}{6} = -\frac{8}{6} + \frac{2}{6} = -1.$$

Since the function is to be continuous therefore

Limit = value $\;\therefore\; f(0) = -1.$

(c) If the function is continuous at $x=0$, then $\underset{x\to 0}{\text{Lt}}\; f(x) = \text{value} = c$

Using expansion $\underset{x\to 0}{\text{Lt}}\; f(x)$

$$= \underset{x\to 0}{\text{Lt}} \frac{x(3+2a+b) + x^3\left(-\dfrac{9}{2} - \dfrac{4a}{3} - \dfrac{b}{6}\right) + \dfrac{x^5}{5!}(3^5 + 2^5 a + b)}{x^5}$$

Above limit will be equal to value c if

$$3+2a+b=0,\; -\frac{9}{2} - \frac{4a}{3} - \frac{b}{6} = 0$$

and $\dfrac{1}{120}(243+32a+b) = c$

The first two relations give $a=-4, b=5$.

and hence from third

$$c = \frac{1}{120}(243-128+5) = \frac{120}{120} = 1$$

7. (a) Apply the criteria $R=L=V$ at $x=0$.

$L = \underset{h\to 0}{\text{Lt}}\; (1-ah)^{-1/h} = e^a,\; V = b = \text{finite}$

$R = \underset{h\to 0}{\text{Lt}} \dfrac{(h+c)^{1/3}-1}{(h+1)^{1/2}-1} = \dfrac{\text{finite}}{0}$ *i.e.* infinite

It must take the form $\dfrac{0}{0}$ and hence $c=1$.

$$\therefore \quad R = \underset{h\to 0}{\text{Lt}} \frac{(h+1)^{1/3}-1}{(h+1)^{1/2}-1}\left(\frac{0}{0}\right)$$

$$= \underset{h\to 0}{\text{Lt}} \frac{\frac{1}{3}(1+h)^{-2/3}}{\frac{1}{2}(1+h)^{-1/2}} = \frac{2}{3}$$

$\therefore \quad e^a = b = \dfrac{2}{3}$ and $c=1$

or $\quad a = \log\dfrac{2}{3},\; b = \dfrac{2}{3}, c = 1.$

(b) For continuity, limit = value.

Rationalize the given function.

$$\lim_{x\to 0}\frac{-2ax[\sqrt{a+x}+\sqrt{a-x}]}{2x[\sqrt{(a^2-ax+x^2)}+\sqrt{(a^2+ax+x^2)}]}$$

$$=-a\frac{2\sqrt{a}}{2a}=-\sqrt{a}.$$

8. (a) For continuity we know Limit = Value

$$\therefore\quad f\left(\frac{\pi}{4}\right)=\lim_{x\to\pi/4}(\sin 2x)^{\tan^2 2x}\quad[(1^\infty)\text{ form}]$$

$$=\lim_{x\to\pi/4}(\sin^2 2x)^{\frac{1}{2}\tan^2 2x}$$

$$=\lim_{x\to\pi/4}(1-\cos^2 2x)^{\frac{1}{2}\tan^2 2x}$$

$$=\lim_{x\to\pi/4}\left[(1-\cos^2 2x)^{1/\cos^2 2x}\right]^{\frac{1}{2}\sin^2 2x}$$

$$=e^{1/2.1}=\sqrt{e}$$

(b) For continuity, limit = value.

$$\lim_{x\to 0}f(x)=\lim_{x\to 0}\frac{2-2\left[1-\frac{7x}{256}\right]^{1/8}}{2\left(1+\frac{5x}{32}\right)^{1/5}-2}$$

$$=\lim_{x\to 0}\frac{1-\left(1-\frac{1}{8}\cdot\frac{7x}{256}+\ldots\right)}{\left(1+\frac{1}{5}\cdot\frac{5x}{32}\ldots\right)-1}=\frac{\frac{1}{8}\cdot\frac{7}{256}}{\frac{1}{32}}=\frac{7}{64}$$

(c) Ans. (d). We must have

(i) $f(1)=f(0)=0$ (given)

(ii) $f(x)$ is continuous in $[0,1]$

i.e., $f(0)=\underset{x\to 0^+}{\text{Lt}}\ f(z)=0$

(iii) $f(x)$ is differentiable in (0, 1) i.e. $f'(x)=0$

$f'(x)=x^{\alpha-1}(1+\alpha\log x)=0\Rightarrow 1+\alpha\log x=0$

$\therefore\quad \alpha=-\dfrac{1}{\log x}\quad\therefore$ But $\log x$ is – ive in [0, 1]

$\therefore\quad \alpha=+$ive $\quad\therefore\quad \alpha=\dfrac{1}{2}$

(d) Let $f(x)=\int p(x)\,dx$

$$=51\frac{x^{102}}{102}-2323\frac{x^{101}}{101}-45\frac{x^2}{2}+1035x+c$$

or $\quad f(x)=\dfrac{x^{102}}{2}-23x^{101}-\dfrac{45}{2}x^2+1035x+c$

$(a,b)=(45^{1/100},46)$

$$f(a)=\frac{1}{2}(45)^{\frac{102}{100}}-23(45)^{\frac{101}{100}}-\frac{45}{2}(45)^{\frac{2}{100}}+1035(45)^{\frac{1}{100}}+c$$

$$=\frac{1}{2}45\cdot(45)^{\frac{2}{100}}-23(45)(45)^{\frac{1}{100}}$$

$$-\frac{45}{2}(45)^{\frac{2}{100}}+23(45)(45)^{\frac{1}{100}}+c=0+c=c.$$

$$f(b)=f(46)=\frac{1}{2}(46)^{102}-23(46)^{101}-\frac{45}{2}(46)^2+1035(46)+c$$

$$=\left[\frac{1}{2}.46(46)^{101}-23(46)^{101}\right]-(45)(46)\left[\frac{46}{2}-23\right]+c=0-0+c=c.$$

Hence $f(a)=f(b)$. Therefore $f'(x)$ *i.e.* $p(x)$ is zero for at least one point in the interval (a,b). In other words, the equation $p(x)=0$ has at least one root in (a,b).

9. (a) Consider continuity at $x=-\pi/2$ and $\pi/2$

At $x=-\pi/2\Rightarrow -a+b=2$

At $x=\pi/2\Rightarrow a+b=0\quad\therefore\quad a=-1,b=1$

(b) $R=L=V$ at $x=\dfrac{\pi}{2}\Rightarrow\dfrac{1}{2}=\dfrac{b}{8}=a$

$\therefore\quad a=\dfrac{1}{2},b=4$

$$\because\quad R=\underset{h\to 0}{\text{Lt}}\ b\frac{1-\sin(\pi/2+h)}{[\pi-(\pi+2h)]^2}$$

$$=\text{Lt}\frac{b(1-\cos h)}{4h^2}=\text{Lt}\frac{2b\sin^2\frac{h}{2}}{4h^2}$$

$$=\text{Lt}\frac{b(h/2)^2}{2h^2}=\frac{b}{8}$$

$$L=\underset{h\to 0}{\text{Lt}}\frac{1-\sin^3\left(\frac{\pi}{2}-h\right)}{3\cos^2\left(\frac{\pi}{2}-h\right)}=\text{Lt}\frac{1-\cos^3 h}{3\sin^2 h}$$

$$=\text{Lt}\frac{(1-\cos h)(1+\cos h+\cos^2 h)}{3(1-\cos h)(1+\cos h)}=\frac{1}{2}$$

10. (a) For continuity Lt = Value = $f(0)$

$$\underset{x\to 0}{\text{Lt}}\frac{(3^x-1)^2}{\sin x\log(1+x)}=\frac{(3^x-1)^2}{x\left\{x-\frac{x^2}{2}\ldots\right\}}$$

$$=\left(\frac{3^x-1}{x}\right)^2=(\log 3)^2$$ Q. 2 (a) P. 1289-91

$\therefore\quad f(0)=(\log 3)^2$

(b) Do yourself.

11. (a)
$$f(x)=\begin{cases}-\dfrac{1}{|x|}, & |x|\geq 1\text{ or }x^2-1\geq 0\\ & \text{or }x\leq -1,\ x\geq 1\\ ax^2-b, & |x|<1\text{ or }x^2-1<0\end{cases}\quad\ldots(1)$$

or $\quad -1<x<1$ ...(2)

Also $|x|=x$ when $x=+$ive ...(3)

$|x|=-x$ when $x=-$ive ...(4)

Hence we redefine the function as under

$$f(x)=\begin{cases} ax^2-b & , \; x<1 \quad \text{by (2)} \\ -\dfrac{1}{+x}=-\dfrac{1}{x} & , \; x\ge 1 \quad \text{by (1)} \end{cases} \quad \text{...(A)}$$

$$f(x)=\begin{cases} -\dfrac{1}{-x}=\dfrac{1}{x} & , \; x\le -1 \quad \text{by (1)} \\ ax^2-b & , \; x>-1 \quad \text{by (2)} \end{cases} \quad \text{... (B)}$$

At $x=1$, for continiuty $R=L=V$

$\therefore \quad a-b=1$

For differentiability $R'=L'$

$\therefore \quad 2a=1$

Solving $a=1/2, b=3/2$

At $x=-1$, for continiuty $R=L=V$

$\therefore \quad a-b=-1$

For differentiability $R'=L'$

$$-1=-2a \quad \therefore \quad a=\frac{1}{2}, b=\frac{3}{2}$$

(b) $|x|\ge 1 \Rightarrow x^2-1\ge 0, \; (x+1)(x-1)\ge 0$

$x\ge 1$ or $x\le -1$ ...(1)

$|x|<1 \Rightarrow x^2-1<0 \Rightarrow -1<x<1$ ...(2)

$$f(x)=\frac{x}{1+|x|}, \; |x|\ge 1 \quad \text{...(3)}$$

$$=\frac{x}{1-|x|}, \; |x|<1 \quad \text{...(4)}$$

Hence we redefine the function

$$f(x)=\frac{x}{1-x} \; \forall \; x\le -1 \text{ by (1), (3)}$$

$$=\frac{x}{1-(-x)}=\frac{x}{1+x}, \; -1<x<0 \text{ by (2), (4)}$$

$$=\frac{x}{1-x}, \; 0\le x<1 \quad \text{by (2), (4)}$$

$$=\frac{x}{1+x}, x\ge 1$$

Now as usual discuss C and D at $x=-1,0,1$ by evaluating right hand and left hand limits.

Ans. C and D at $x=0$ and neither at $x=-1$ and 1.

12. (a) Redefine the function when $x=+$ive or $x=-$ive as in part (e) and then consider continuity and differentiability at $x=1, x=-1$.

x = + ive. $\quad \therefore \quad |x|=x$

$$f(x)=\begin{cases} 2+\sqrt{1-x^2}, & x\le 1 \\ 2e^{(1-x)^2} & x>1. \end{cases}$$

$$f(1)=2, \; \underset{h\to 0}{\text{Lt}} \; f(1+h)=\underset{h\to 0}{\text{Lt}} \; 2e^{h^2}=2.1=2.$$

$$\underset{h\to 0}{\text{Lt}} \; f(1-h)=\text{Lt}\,\{2+\sqrt{1-(1-h)^2}\}=2$$

Since $R=L=V$ $\therefore$ continuous.

Differentiability at x = 1.

$$R'=\underset{h\to 0}{\text{Lt}}\frac{f(1+h)-f(1)}{h}=\underset{h\to 0}{\text{Lt}}\frac{2e^{h^2}-2}{h}$$

$$=\text{Lt}\,\frac{2\left[\left(1+h^2+\dfrac{h^4}{2!}...\right)-1\right]}{h}$$

$$=\text{Lt}\,2\left[h+\frac{h^3}{2!}+...\right]=0$$

You can also say

$$\underset{h\to 0}{\text{Lt}} \; 2\frac{(e^{h^2}-1)}{h^2}\cdot h=2(\log e).0=0$$

$$L'=\underset{h\to 0}{\text{Lt}}\frac{f(1-h)-f(1)}{-h}$$

$$=\underset{h\to 0}{\text{Lt}}\frac{2+\sqrt{1-(1-h)^2}-2}{-h}$$

$$=\text{Lt}\frac{\sqrt{2h-h^2}}{-h}=\text{Lt}-\sqrt{\frac{2}{h}-1}=-\infty.$$

Since $R'\ne L'$ hence not differentiable.

x = − ive. $\quad |x|=-x$

$\therefore \quad |x|\le 1 \Rightarrow -x\le 1$ or $x\ge -1$

and $|x|>1 \Rightarrow -x>1$ or $x<-1$

$$\therefore \quad f(x)=2e^{(1-x)^2}, \quad x<-1$$

$$=2+\sqrt{1-x^2}, \; x\ge -1$$

Show as above that $L=2e^4, R=2$ hence not continuous and consequently not differentiable also.

(b) Do yourself.

13. (a) For continuity at $x=\pi/2$, we must have Lt = Value

$$f(x)=\frac{1-\sin x}{4\left(\dfrac{\pi}{2}-x\right)^2}\cdot\frac{\log\sin x}{\log\left\{1+4\left(\dfrac{\pi}{2}-x\right)^2\right\}}$$

Put $\dfrac{\pi}{2}-x=t$ or $x=\dfrac{\pi}{2}-t$

As $x\to\pi/2, t\to 0$

$$\therefore \quad \underset{x\to\pi/2}{\text{Lt}} f(x)=\underset{t\to 0}{\text{Lt}}\frac{1-\cos t}{4t^2}\cdot\underset{t\to 0}{\text{Lt}}\frac{\log\cos t}{\log(1+4t^2)}$$

$$=\underset{t\to 0}{\text{Lt}}\frac{2\sin^2\dfrac{t}{2}}{4t^2}\cdot\underset{t\to 0}{\text{Lt}}\frac{\log\left(1-\dfrac{t^2}{2!}+...\right)}{\log(1+4t^2)}$$

$$=\underset{t\to 0}{\text{Lt}}\frac{2}{4}\cdot\frac{(t/2)^2}{t^2}\cdot\underset{t\to 0}{\text{Lt}}\frac{-\dfrac{t^2}{2}-\dfrac{1}{2}\left(\dfrac{t^2}{2}\right)^2...}{4t^2-\dfrac{1}{2}(4t^2)^2}$$

$$=\frac{1}{8}\left(-\frac{1}{8}\right)=-\frac{1}{64}$$

Hence $f\left(\frac{\pi}{2}\right) = -\frac{1}{64}$.

(b) Proceed as in last part. Put $\frac{\pi}{2} - x = t$ etc.

Ans. $-3\pi^2/16$.

$$\operatorname*{Lt}_{t\to 0} \frac{1-\cos t}{(2t)^4} . \sin t \{(\pi - 2t)^3 - \pi^3\}$$

Applying factors of $a^3 - b^3$

$$= \operatorname*{Lt}_{t\to 0} \frac{2\sin^2(t/2).t}{16t^4} [-2t\{(\pi-2t)^2 + \pi^2 + \pi(\pi - 2t)]$$

$$= -\frac{1}{4}\frac{(t/2)^2}{t^2} . \{3\pi^2 - 6\pi t + 4t^2\} = -\frac{3\pi^2}{16}.$$

14. (a) Ans. $\frac{1}{2}\log a$. Let us consider continuity at $x = 0$.

$\therefore \quad \operatorname*{Lt}_{x\to 0} f(x) = V = f(0)$

$$\operatorname*{Lt}_{x\to 0} f(x) = \operatorname*{Lt}_{x\to 0} \frac{\left(\frac{a^x - 1}{x}\right)^3}{\frac{\sin(x\log a)}{x} . \frac{\log(1 + x^2\log a^2)}{x^2}}$$

$$= \frac{(\log a)^3}{\log a . \left\{\frac{x^2\log a^2 \dots}{x^2}\right\}} = \frac{(\log a)^2}{2\log a} = \frac{1}{2}\log a$$

(b) $f'(x) = \begin{cases} 2ax & , x < -1 \\ 2bx + a, & x \geq -1 \end{cases}$

We must have two equations in a, b.

Since $f(x)$ is differentiable, it must be continuous at $x = -1$.

$\therefore \quad R = L = V$ at $x = -1$ for $f(x)$

$\Rightarrow \quad b - a + 4 = a + b = a + b$

$\therefore \quad 2a = 4$ *i.e.* $a = 2$

Again $f'(x)$ is continuous, it must be continuous at $x = -1$.

$\therefore \quad R = L = V$ at $x = -1$ for $f'(x)$

$-2b + a = -2a$. Putting $a = 2$, we get

$-2b + 2 = -4 \quad \therefore \quad 2b = 6$ or $b = 3$.

15. (a) Here

$$f(0+0) = \lim_{h\to 0} (0+h)\sin\frac{1}{0+h} = \lim_{h\to 0} h\sin\frac{1}{h}.$$

$= 0 \times$ a finite quantity $= 0$.

[$\because \sin(1/h)$ is bounded lying between -1 and 1]

Similarly $f(0-0) = \lim_{h\to 0} (0-h) \sin\frac{1}{0-h}$

$= \lim_{h\to 0} h\sin(1/h) = 0$ as before.

Also $\quad f(0) = 0$.

Since $\quad f(0+0) = f(0-0) = f(0)$

The function $x\sin(1/x)$ is continuous at $x = 0$. Although the function is continuous at the origin, yet the graph of the function in the vicinity of the origin cannot be drawn, since the function oscillates infinitely often in any interval containing the origin (see figure).

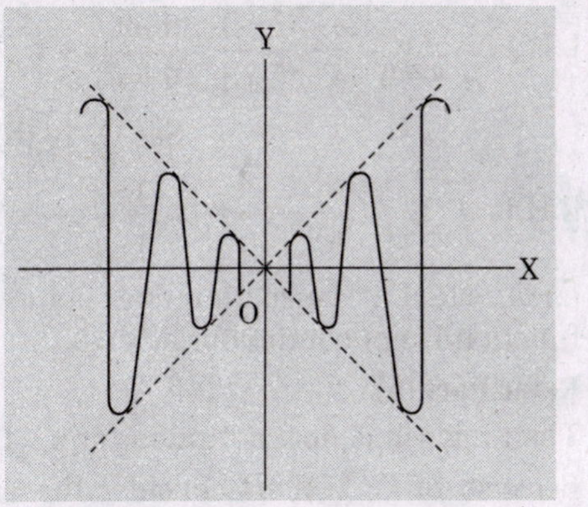

Fig. 5

From the graph it is clear that the function makes an infinite number of oscillations in the neighbourhood of $x = 0$. The oscillations, however, go on diminishing in length as x approaches zero.

(b) Here $f(x) = 2^{1/x}$

$\therefore \quad f(0+0) = \lim_{h\to 0} 2^{1/(0+h)} = 2^{\infty} = \infty$

and $f(0-0) = \lim_{h\to 0} 2^{1/(0-h)} = 2^{-\infty} = 0$

and $f(0) = 0$.

Since $f(0+0) \neq f(0-0)$,

the function is discontinuous at the origin.

16. (a) $f(x) = \frac{1}{2^{-1/x} + 1}, x \neq 0$

$$f(0+0) = \operatorname*{Lt}_{h\to 0} \frac{1}{2^{-1/h} + 1} = \frac{1}{0+1} = 1$$

$$f(0-0) = \operatorname*{Lt}_{h\to 0} \frac{1}{2^{1/h} + 1} = \frac{1}{\infty + 1} = 0 \neq f(0+0)$$

Hence discontinuous at $x = 0$.

(b) Here $f(x) = \frac{1}{1 - e^{-1/x}}$

$$\therefore \quad f(0+0) = \lim_{h\to 0} \frac{1}{1 - e^{-1/(0+h)}} = \lim_{h\to 0} \frac{1}{1 - e^{-1/h}}$$

$$= \frac{1}{1 - e^{-\infty}} = \frac{1}{1-0} = 1.$$

and $f(0-0) = \lim_{h\to 0} \frac{1}{1 - e^{-1/(0-h)}} = \lim_{h\to 0} \frac{1}{1 - e^{1/h}}$

$$= \lim_{h\to 0} \frac{1}{1 - e^{\infty}} = \frac{1}{1 - \infty} = 0.$$

Also $\quad f(0) = 0$.

Hence f is discontinuous at $x = 0$.

The function has a jump of one unit at 0 since

$f(0+0) - f(0-0) = 1$.

17. (a) L.H.L. $= \underset{h\to 0}{\text{Lt}} \dfrac{e^{-1/h}-1}{e^{-1/h}+1} = \dfrac{0-1}{0+1} = -1$

See Q. 16 (b), P. 1321.

R.H.L. $= \underset{h\to 0}{\text{Lt}} \dfrac{e^{1/h}-1}{e^{1/h}+1} = \text{Lt} \dfrac{1-e^{-1/h}}{1+e^{-1/h}} = \dfrac{1}{1} = 1$

L.H.L. $\neq$ R.H.L. Hence limit does not exist and so function is not continuous at $x=0$.

(b) **Refer Part (a).**

The function is not continuous at $x=1$.

(c) Because of $[x^2]$ let us consider the case when $x^2<1$ and when $1<x^2<2$ for continuity at $x=1$.

$\therefore$ $[x^2]=0$ when $x^2<1$ *i.e.*, $-1<x<1$

$[x^2]=1$ when $1<x^2<2$ *i.e.*, $x>1$

Hence we redefine the function as under.

$$f(x) = \begin{cases} \dfrac{-1}{x^2-1}, & x<1 \\ 0, & x=1 \\ \dfrac{1-1}{x^2-1}=0, & x>1 \end{cases}$$

$R=V=1$ but $L = \underset{h\to 0}{\text{Lt}} \dfrac{-1}{(1-h)^2-1}$

$= \underset{h\to 0}{\text{Lt}} \dfrac{-1}{-2h+h^2} = -\infty$

Since $R\neq L$ therefore $f(x)$ is not continuous at $x=1$.

18. (a) (i) **Continuity :** $R=L=V=0$ at $x=0$

$\therefore$ continuous.

$R = \lim\limits_{h\to 0} he^{-\infty} = 0$

$L = \lim\limits_{h\to 0} -he^{-0} = 0 = V.$

(ii) **Differentiability :**

$R' = \lim \dfrac{he^{-\infty}-0}{h} = \lim e^{-\infty} = 0$

$L' = \lim \dfrac{-he^{-0}-0}{-h} = 1$

Since $R'\neq L'$ $\therefore$ Not differentiable.

(b) Ans. (d). Apply $R=L=V$ at $x=0$ and $x=1$

At $x=1, V=0, R=1-1=0, L=0-0=0 \therefore C.$

At $x=0, V=0, R=0-0=0, L=(-1)^2-0=1 \therefore D.$

Hence $f(x)$ is **discontinuous** at all integers except 1.

19. (a) We test the function for continuity at $x=0, \dfrac{1}{2}$ and 1.

For $x=0$, we have $\phi(0)=0$

$\phi(0+0) = \lim\limits_{h\to 0}\left[\dfrac{1}{2}-(0+h)\right] = \dfrac{1}{2}.$

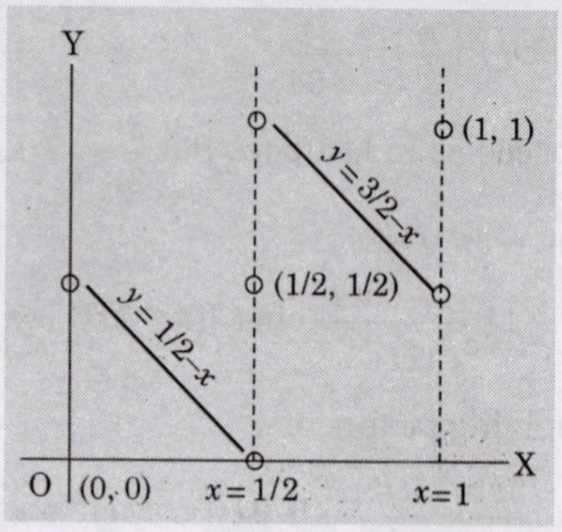

Fig. 6

Since, $\phi(0)\neq\phi(0+0)$, the function ϕ is discontinuous at $x=0$.

For $x=\dfrac{1}{2}$, we have

$\phi\left(\dfrac{1}{2}\right) = \dfrac{1}{2}.$

$\phi\left(\dfrac{1}{2}-0\right) = \lim\limits_{h\to 0}\left[\dfrac{1}{2}-\left(\dfrac{1}{2}-h\right)\right] = 0.$

$\phi\left(\dfrac{1}{2}+0\right) = \lim\limits_{h\to 0}\left[\dfrac{3}{2}-\left(\dfrac{1}{2}+h\right)\right] = 1.$

Since $\lim\phi\left(\dfrac{1}{2}-0\right)\neq\phi\left(\dfrac{1}{2}\right)\neq\lim\phi\left(\dfrac{1}{2}+0\right)$, the function is discontinuous at $x=\dfrac{1}{2}$.

Finally, we consider $x=1$

$\phi(1)=1,$

$\phi(1-0) = \lim\limits_{h\to 0}\left[\dfrac{3}{2}-(1-h)\right] = \dfrac{1}{2}.$

Since $\phi(1-0)\neq\phi(1)$, the function is discontinuous at $x=1$.

Hence the function ϕ is discontinuous at $x=0$, $\dfrac{1}{2}$ and 1.

The graph of the function consists of the point (0, 0), the segment of the line

$y=\dfrac{1}{2}-x,\quad 0<x<\dfrac{1}{2};$

The point $\left(\dfrac{1}{2},\dfrac{1}{2}\right)$ the segment of the line

$y=\dfrac{3}{2}-x, \dfrac{1}{2}<x<1$ and the point (1, 1).

Thus the graph is as shown.

From the graph it is clear that the function is discontinuous at $x=0, \dfrac{1}{2}$ and 1.

(b) The graph consists of the straight line $y=x-1$ for $x<0$, the point (0, 1/4) and the parabola $y=x^2$ for $x>0$.

Now $\lim\limits_{x\to 0+} f(x) = \lim\limits_{h\to 0}(0+h)^2 = 0$

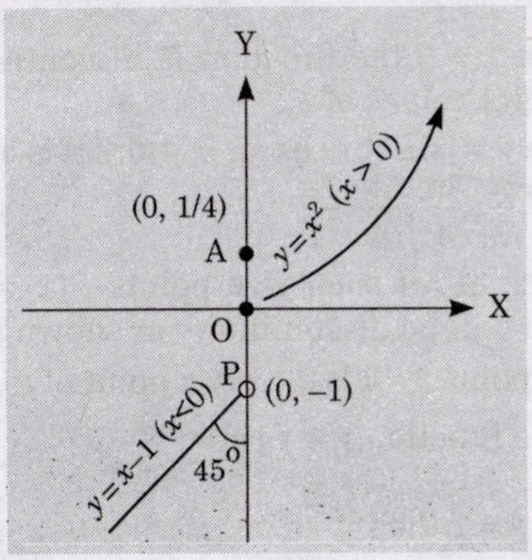

Fig. 7

and $\lim_{x \to 0-} f(x) = \lim_{h \to 0} (0 - h - 1) = -1.$

Since $\lim_{x \to 0+} f(x) \neq \lim_{x \to 0-} f(x)$, the function $f(x)$ is discontinuous at $x = 0$.

20. (a) (i) The function is not defined for $x = 0$ and hence it is a point of discontinuity. Further if $\log |x| = 0$ or $|x| = 1$ or $x = \pm 1$ then also function is not defined. Hence it has three points of discontinuity at $x = 0, 1, -1$.

(ii) Three points at $x = 0, 2, -2$.

(b) We know that $\log t = 0$, if $t = 1; > 0$ if $t > 1, < 0$, if $t < 1, |y| = y$, if $y > 0, |y| = -y$, if $y < 0$

$$\text{R.H.L.} = \underset{h \to 0}{\text{Lt}} \; |\log(1+h)| = \underset{h \to 0}{\text{Lt}} \; \log(1+h) = 0$$

$$\text{L.H.L.} = \underset{h \to 0}{\text{Lt}} \; |\log(1-h)|$$

$$= \underset{h \to 0}{\text{Lt}} \; -[\log(1-h)] = 0$$

$V = |\log 1| = 0. \therefore R = L = V \therefore$ continuous

$$R' = \underset{h \to 0}{\text{Lt}} \frac{|\log(1+h)| - |\log 1|}{h} = \underset{h \to 0}{\text{Lt}} \frac{\log(1+h)}{h}$$

$$= \underset{h \to 0}{\text{Lt}} \frac{h - \frac{h^2}{2} + \ldots}{h} = h = 0$$

$L' = -1$ as above. Since $R' \neq L'$ therefore the function is not differentiable at $x = 1$.

21. (a) Let $x = p$ be any integral value of x

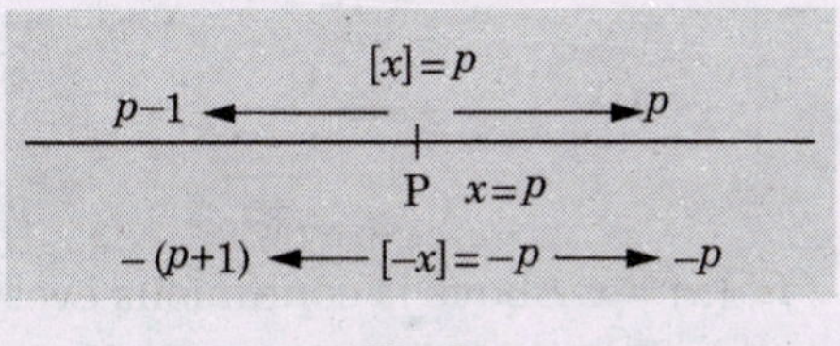

Fig. 8

$\therefore \quad [p] = p$ and $[-p] = -p \quad \therefore \quad f(x) = 0$ at $x = p$

$$R = \underset{h \to 0}{\text{Lt}} \; f(p+h)$$

$$= \text{Lt}\; [p+h] + \text{Lt}\; [-p-h]$$

$$= p - (p+1) = -1$$

$$L = \underset{h \to 0}{\text{Lt}} \; f(p-h)$$

$$= \text{Lt}\; [p-h] + \text{Lt}\; [-p+h]$$

$$= (p-1) - p = -1$$

$\therefore \quad L = R = -1$

But $V = 0$.

If $\quad p = 5, [5] = 5, [5 \cdot 1] = 5, [4 \cdot 99] = 4$

$[-5] = -5, [-4 \cdot 99] = -5, [-5 \cdot 1] = -6$

Hence the function is not continuous at $x = p$. If however we define $f(p) = -1$ then $R = L = V$ and the function becomes continuous at $x = p$. Hence the function has a removable discontinuity for integral values of x.

(b) From the definition of the function it follows that

$f(x) = x - (n-1)$ for $n - 1 < x < n$. ...(1)

$f(x) = 0$ for $x = n$, ...(2)

$f(x) = x - n$ for $n < x < n + 1$ ...(3)

where n is an integer.

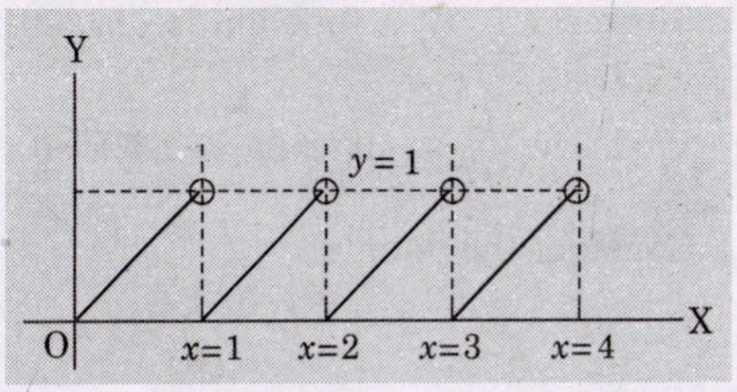

Fig. 9

We test the function for continuity at $x = n$. We have

$f(n) = 0.$ by (2)

$f(n-0) = \lim_{x \to n-0} [x - (n-1)]$

$L = \lim_{h \to 0} [(n-h) - (n-1)] = 1$ by (1)

and $f(n+0) = \lim_{x \to n+0} (x - n)$

$R = \lim_{h \to 0} (n + h - n) = 0$, by (3)

Hence f is discontinuous at $x = n$ *i.e.* for all integral values of x. It is obviously continuous for all other values.

Since x is positive variable, putting $n = 1, 2, 3, 4, 5, \ldots$

we see that the graph consists of the following :

$y = x$	when	$0 < x < 1$
$y = 0$	when	$x = 1$
$y = x - 1$	when	$1 < x < 2$
$y = 0$	when	$x = 2$
$y = x - 2$	when	$2 < x < 3$
$y = 0$	when	$x = 3$
$y = x - 3$	when	$3 < x < 4$
$y = 0$	when	$x = 4$

and so on. The graph is shown by thick lines from $x = 0$ to $x = 4$.

Remark : From the graph the following facts are evident :

(i) The function is discontinuous for all integral values and continuous for all others.

(ii) In every range which includes an integer, it is bounded between 0 and 1.

(iii) The lower bound zero is attained but the upper bound 1 is not attained since $f(x) \neq 1$ for any value of x whatsoever.

22. (a) $\text{Lt } f(1-h) = \text{Lt } \dfrac{(1-h)^2 - 1}{(1-h)^2 - 2|(1-h)-1| - 1}$

$$= \frac{h(h-2)}{h(h-4)} = \frac{1}{2}, \quad f(1) = 1/2$$

$$\text{Lt } f(1+h) = \text{Lt } \frac{(1+h)^2 - 1}{(1+h)^2 - 2|(1+h-1)| - 1}$$

$$= \text{Lt } \frac{h^2 + 2h}{h^2} = \underset{h \to 0}{\text{Lt}} \left(1 + \frac{2}{h}\right) = \infty$$

Since $R \neq L = V$ $\therefore$ function is discontinuous at $x = 1$.

(b) We know $\dfrac{t}{|t|} = 1$, if $t > 0$; $= -1$, if $t < 0$

Consider the point $x = -2$.

$$\therefore \quad R = \underset{h \to 0}{\text{Lt}} \quad (-2+h) + \frac{h}{|h|} = -2 + 1 = -1$$

$$L = \underset{h \to 0}{\text{Lt}} \quad -2 - h + \frac{(-h)}{|-h|} = -2 - 1 = -3$$

Thus $R \neq L$ at $x = -2$. Besides this the function is also not defined at $x = -2$. Hence $x = -2$ is a point of discontinuity, the jump at which is $R - L = (-1) - (-3) = 2$

Similarly

If $f(x) = \dfrac{|2x-1|}{2x-1}$ then $x = \dfrac{1}{2}$ is a point of discontinuity because at $x = \dfrac{1}{2}$, $R = 1$, $L = -1$.

23. (a) The functions are not defined for $x = 0$ and for integral values of x as $[x] = x$.

$\therefore$ $x = 0$ and integral values of x are all points of discontinuity.

(b) As above $x = 0$ is a point of discontinuity.

Again $|x| = x$ when $x > 0$

Hence it is discontinuous for $x = 0$ and all $x > 0$

24. (a) $\underset{h \to 0}{\text{Lt}} \quad [\tan^2(0-h)] = \underset{h \to 0}{\text{Lt}} \quad [\tan^2(0+h)]$

$$= [\tan^2 0] = 0$$

Since L.H.Lt. = R.H.Lt. = value.

$\therefore$ $f(x)$ is continuous at $x = 0$.

(b) Ans. (c).

$y = [x]$. Consider the continuity of $f(x)$ at $x = n$

$\therefore$ $L = R = V$

$$L = \lim_{h \to 0} \quad [n-h] = n - 1,$$

$$R = \lim_{h \to 0} \quad [n+h] = n$$

$$V = [n] = n$$

Since $L \neq R$ the function is discontinuous at all integral values of x.

Here $y = [\sin x + \cos x]$, $x \in (0, 2\pi)$ is an integer at $x = 0, \dfrac{\pi}{2}, \dfrac{3\pi}{4}, \dfrac{5\pi}{4}, \dfrac{7\pi}{4}$.

Hence at all such **five** points $f(x) = [\text{Integer } x]$ there will be discontinuity as shown above.

25. (a) The point $x = 1$ is clearly a point of discontinuity of the function $y = f(x) = \dfrac{1}{1-x}$.

If $\quad x \neq 1$, then

$$v(x) = f[f(x)] = f\left(\frac{1}{1-x}\right) = \frac{1}{1 - [1/(1-x)]} = \frac{x-1}{x}$$

Hence, the point $x = 0$ is a discontinuity of the function v.

If $\quad x \neq 0$, $x \neq 1$, then $w(x) = f[f\{f(x)\}]$

$$= f\left[f\left(\frac{1}{1-x}\right)\right] = f\left(\frac{x-1}{x}\right) = \frac{1}{1-(x-1)/x} = x.$$

Hence w is clearly continuous everywhere. Thus, the points of discontinuity of the composite function $f[f\{f(x)\}]$ are $x = 0$, $x = 1$ and the composite function $f\{f(x)\}$ has a discontinuity at $x = 1$ only.

(b) $f(x) = \dfrac{1}{x-1}$, $f\{f(x)\} = \dfrac{x-1}{2-x}$

$$f[f\{f(x)\}] = \frac{2-x}{2x-3}$$

Clearly $x = 1$, $x = 2$, $x = 3/2$. are points of discontinuity.

(c) Clearly $x = 1$ is a point of discontinuity of the function $f(x) = \dfrac{1}{1-x}$. Now $f[f(x)]$

$$= f\left[\frac{1}{1-x}\right] = \frac{1}{1 - \dfrac{1}{1-x}} = \frac{1-x}{-x} = \frac{x-1}{x}$$

Hence, $x = 0$ is a point of discontinuity of function $(fof)\,x$. Again

$$(fofof)\,x = fo\,[fof]\,x = f\left(\frac{x-1}{x}\right)$$

$$= \frac{1}{1 - \dfrac{x-1}{x}} = x$$

$\therefore$ $f^3(x) = x$. Above is continuous every where

$\therefore$ $y = f^{3n}(x) = \{f^3(x)\}^n = x$ which is continuous everywhere.

26. (a) The function is not defined for those values of x for which $[x+1] = 0$. In other words it means that

$$0 \leq x + 1 < 1 \quad \text{or} \quad -1 \leq x < 0 \qquad \text{...(1)}$$

Hence the function is defined outside the region given by (1). In other words for $x \geq 0$ and $x < -1$ or $x \in]-\infty, -1[\cup [0, \infty[$.

Now consider integral values of x say $x = n$.

R.H.L. $= \lim_{h\to 0} [n+h] \sin \dfrac{\pi}{[n+1+h]} = n \sin \dfrac{\pi}{n+1}$

L.H.L. $= \lim_{h\to 0} [n-h] \sin \dfrac{\pi}{[n+1-h]} = (n-1) \sin \dfrac{\pi}{n}$

$V = n \sin \dfrac{\pi}{n+1}$

Since $R \neq L = V$. Hence the given function is not continuous for integral values of n $(n \neq 0, -1)$.

At $x = 0$ $\qquad f(0) = 0$

$\lim f(0+h) = \lim_{h\to 0} [h] \sin \dfrac{\pi}{[h+1]} = 0$

The function is not defined for $x < 0$. Hence we cannot find $\lim f(0-h)$. Thus $f(x)$ is continuous at $x = 0$. Hence the point of discontinuity are given by $I - \{0\}$ where I is set of integers n except $n = -1$.

(b) Ans. (a).

L' at $x = k$ is $\text{Lt}_{h\to 0} \dfrac{[k-h] \sin \pi (k-h)}{-h}$

$= \text{Lt}_{h\to 0} (k-1) [\sin \pi k \cos \pi h - \cos \pi k \sin \pi h]$

as $[k-h]$ when k is an integer is $k-1$

Put $\sin \pi k = 0, \cos \pi k = (-1)^k$

$\therefore \quad L' = \text{Lt}_{h\to 0} (k-1) \dfrac{[0-(-1)^k \sin \pi h]}{-h}$

$= (k-1)(-1)^k \pi \because \text{Lt}_{h\to 0} \dfrac{\sin(\pi h)}{h} = \pi$

27. (a) $f(0) = 0$

$f(0+0) = \lim_{h\to 0} \dfrac{\sin(0+h)^2}{(0+h)}$

$= \lim_{h\to 0} \dfrac{\sin h^2}{h^2} . h = 1 \times 0 = 0.$

and $f(0-0) = \lim_{h\to 0} \dfrac{\sin(0-h)^2}{0-h}$

$= \lim_{h\to 0} \dfrac{\sin h^2}{h^2} (-h) = 1 \times 0 = 0.$

Hence $f(x)$ is continuous at $x = 0$.

Now $Rf'(0) = \lim_{h\to 0} \left(\dfrac{\sin(0+h)^2}{0+h} - 0 \right) \Big/ h$

$= \lim_{h\to 0} \dfrac{\sin h^2}{h^2} = 1$

and $Lf'(0) = \lim_{h\to 0} \left(\dfrac{\sin(0-h)^2 - 0}{0-h} \right) \Big/ (-h),$

$= \lim_{h\to 0} \dfrac{\sin h^2}{h^2} = 1.$

Hence $f(x)$ is differentiable at $x = 0$ and $f'(0) = 1$.

(b) $f(x) = \dfrac{x-1}{(x-1)(2x-5)} = \dfrac{1}{2x-5}, \quad x \neq 1$

$f(x) = -1/3, x = 1$

$Rf'(1) = \lim_{h\to 0} \dfrac{f(1+h) - f(1)}{h}$

$= \lim_{h\to 0} \dfrac{\dfrac{1}{2h-3} + \dfrac{1}{3}}{h}$

$= \lim_{h\to 0} \dfrac{2h}{3h(2h-3)} = -\dfrac{2}{9}$

Similarly $Lf'(1) = -2/9 \quad \therefore \quad f'(1) = -2/9$

28. (a) We test the function $f(x)$ for differentiability at $x = 0$ and $x = 1$ only. For other values of x, $f(x)$ can be easily seen to be differentiable. Students can check that $f(x)$ is continuous at $x = 0$ and $x = 1$. We now first test the differentiability at $x = 0$.

$Lf'(0) = \lim_{h\to 0} \dfrac{f(0-h) - f(0)}{-h}$

$= \lim_{h\to 0} \dfrac{-(0-h) - 0}{-h} = -1.$

and $Rf'(0) = \lim_{h\to 0} \dfrac{f(0+h) - f(0)}{h}$

$= \lim_{h\to 0} \dfrac{(0+h)^2 - 0}{h} = \lim_{h\to 0} h = 0.$

Since $Lf'(0) \neq Rf'(0)$, the function is not differentiable at $x = 0$.

Again $Lf'(1) = \lim_{h\to 0} \dfrac{f(1-h) - f(1)}{-h}$

$= \lim_{h\to 0} \dfrac{(1-h)^2 - 1}{-h} = \lim_{h\to 0} \dfrac{-2h + h^2}{-h}$

$= \lim_{h\to 0} (2-h) = 2$

and $Rf'(1) = \lim_{h\to 0} \dfrac{f(1+h) - f(1)}{h}$

$= \lim_{h\to 0} \dfrac{(1+h)^3 - (1+h) + 1 - 1}{h}$

$= \lim_{h\to 0} \dfrac{2h + 3h^2 + h^3}{h}$

$= \lim_{h\to 0} (2 + 3h + h^2) = 2.$

Hence $f'(1)$ exists *i.e.*, function is differentiable at $x = 1$.

(b) Continuous at both points but differentiable only at $x = 2$.

29. (a) True.

We have $f(0) = 1 + \sin 0 = 1$. Then

$Rf'(0) = \lim_{h\to 0} \dfrac{1 + \sin(0+h) - 1}{h}$

$= \lim_{h\to 0} \dfrac{\sin h}{h} = 1$

and $Lf'(0) = \lim_{h\to 0} \dfrac{1-1}{-h} = 0$

Hence $f'(0)$ does not exist.

(b) R.H.D. = L.H.D. = 0

$$\text{R.H.D.} = \underset{h\to 0}{\text{Lt}} \frac{|2+h-1|+|2+h-3| - [|(2-1)|+|(2-3)|]}{h}$$

$$= \underset{h\to 0}{\text{Lt}} \frac{(1+h)-(h-1)-(1+1)}{h} = 0,$$

$|x| = -x$ if x is – ive.

Similarly L.H.D. = 0.

(c) Given $f(-x) = -f(x)$ ...(1)

$$Lf'(a) = \underset{h\to 0}{\text{Lt}} \frac{f(a-h)-f(a)}{-h} = 0 \quad ...(2)$$

since left hand derivative is zero.

$$f(x) = f(2a-x), x \in (a, 2a) \quad ...(3)$$

We have to find $Lf'(-a)$.

$$Lf'(-a) = \underset{h\to 0}{\text{Lt}} \frac{f(-a-h)-f(-a)}{-h}$$

$$= \underset{h\to 0}{\text{Lt}} \frac{-f(a+h)+f(a)}{-h}, \text{ by (1)}$$

$$= \underset{h\to 0}{\text{Lt}} \frac{-f\{2a-(a-h)\}+f(a)}{-h}$$

$$= \underset{h\to 0}{\text{Lt}} \frac{-f(a-h)+f(a)}{-h}, \text{ by (3)}$$

$$= \underset{h\to 0}{\text{Lt}} -\frac{f(a-h)-f(a)}{-h} = 0, \text{ by (2)}.$$

30. Beacuse of $[x]$ divide the given interval $(-\pi/2, \pi/2)$ into four intervals as shown in fig. D-38 and redefine the function as under in these intervals

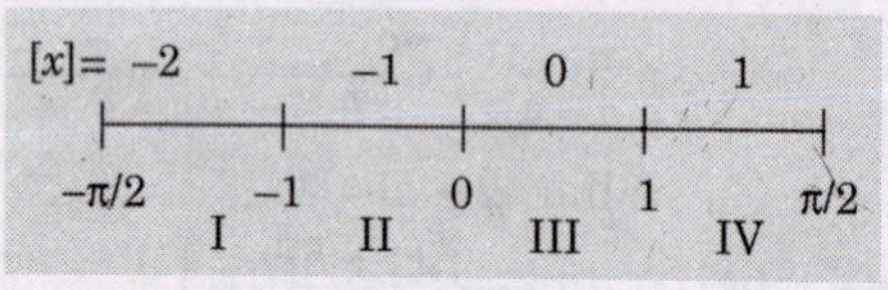

Fig. 10

(a) $f(x) = \sin\{\pi[x]\}$

$$f(x) = \begin{cases} \sin(-2\pi) = 0 & \text{in I} \\ \sin(-\pi) = 0 & \text{in II} \\ \sin(0) = 0 & \text{in III} \\ \sin(\pi) = 0 & \text{in IV} \end{cases}$$

$f(x) = 0$ throughout and hence it is differentiable.

(b) $f(x) = \sin[\pi(x - \{x\})]$

$$f(x) = \begin{cases} \sin\pi(x+2) = \sin(2\pi+\pi x) = \sin\pi x, & \text{I} \\ \sin\pi(x+1) = \sin(\pi+\pi x) = -\sin\pi x, & \text{II} \\ \sin\pi(x-0) = \sin(\pi x - 0) = \sin\pi x, & \text{III} \\ \sin\pi(x-1) = -\sin(\pi-\pi x) = -\sin\pi x, & \text{IV} \end{cases}$$

Consider $x = 1$, $x = -1$

$$L'(1) = \frac{\sin\pi(1-h)-0}{-h} = \frac{\sin\pi h}{-h} = -\pi, \text{ III}$$

$$R'(1) = \frac{-\sin\pi(1+h)-0}{h} = \frac{\sin\pi h}{h} = \pi, \text{ IV}$$

Since $L'(1) \neq R'(1)$

∴ function is not differentiable at $x = 1$.

Similarly it can be shown that

$$L'(-1) = -\pi, R'(-1) = \pi$$

hence not differentiable at $x = -1$ also.

31. Let us redefine the function f into two intervals $[0, 1]$ and $(1, 2]$

Case I. $x \in [0, 1]$

$$f(x) = [\cos\pi x] = [\cos 0] \left[\cos\frac{\pi}{2}\right] [\cos\pi]$$

$$= 1 \quad 0 \quad -1 \quad \text{at } x = 0, \frac{1}{2}, 1$$

Case II. $x \in (1, 2]$

Here the critical points in $(1, 2]$ on which the function will depend are 3/2 and 2 because of $2x - 3$ and $[x - 2]$.

$(1, 2] = (1, 3/2] + (3/2, 2) + 2$

$2x - 3 = \quad - \quad + \quad +$

$[x - 2] = \quad -1 \quad -1 \quad 0$

Hence we are now in a position to redefine the function as under :

$$f(x) = \begin{cases} 1 & x = 0 \\ 0 & 0 < x \leq 1/2 \\ -1 & 1/2 < x \leq 1 \\ -1 \times -(2x-3) = 2x-3 & 1 < x \leq 3/2 \\ -1 \times (2x-3) & 3/2 < x < 2 \\ 0 & x = 2 \end{cases}$$

Hence we shall discuss continuity at $x = 0, \frac{1}{2}, 1, \frac{3}{2}$ and 2.

It can be easily shown that $f(x)$ is continuous only at $x = 1, 3/2$. At all other points it is discontinuous.

32. (a) We have $f(0+0) = \lim\limits_{h\to 0} \dfrac{0+h}{1+e^{1/(0+h)}}$

$$= \lim_{h\to 0} \frac{h}{1+e^{1/h}} = 0.$$

Similarly $f(0-0) = \lim\limits_{h\to 0} \dfrac{-h}{1+e^{-1/h}} = 0$

Since $f(0+0) = f(0) = f(0-0)$, the function is continuous at $x = 0$.

We now proceed to find the derivative of $f(x)$ at $x = 0$. We have

$$Rf'(0) = \lim_{h\to 0} \frac{h/(1+e^{1/h})-0}{h}$$

$$= \lim_{h\to 0} \frac{1}{1+e^{1/h}} = \frac{1}{1+e^{\infty}} = 0.$$

and $$Lf'(0) = \lim_{h\to 0} \frac{-h/(1+e^{-1/h})-0}{-h}$$

$$= \lim_{h\to 0} \frac{1}{1+e^{-1/h}} = \frac{1}{1+e^{-\infty}} = \frac{1}{1+0} = 1.$$

Since $Rf'(0) \neq Lf'(0)$,

the derivative of f at $x = 0$ does not exist.

(b) For continuity, $R = L = V$ at $x = 0$.

$\text{Lt.}\, e^{1/h} = \infty$, $\quad \text{Lt}\ 1/e^{1/h} = 0$

$$R = \underset{h\to 0}{\text{Lt}} \frac{h\,(3e^{1/h}+4)}{2-e^{1/h}}$$

$$= \text{Lt} \frac{h\left(3+\frac{4}{e^{1/h}}\right)}{\left(\frac{2}{e^{1/h}}-1\right)} = \text{Lt}\; h\left(\frac{3}{-1}\right) = 0$$

$$L = \underset{h\to 0}{\text{Lt}} \; -\frac{h\,(3e^{-1/h}+4)}{2-e^{-1/h}} = \underset{h\to 0}{\text{Lt}} \; -h\left(\frac{4}{2}\right) = 0$$

Since R.H.Lt = L.H.Lt

$\therefore$ Lt exists at $x=0$ and limit is equal to value and hence the function is continuous.

Differentiability :

$$R' = \underset{h\to 0}{\text{Lt}} \frac{f\,(0+h)-f\,(0)}{h}$$

$$L' = \underset{h\to 0}{\text{Lt}} \frac{f\,(0-h)-f\,(0)}{-h}$$

$$R = \underset{h\to 0}{\text{Lt}} \frac{1}{h}\left[\frac{h\,(3e^{1/h}+4)}{(2-e^{1/h})} - 0\right] = \frac{3}{-1}$$

$$L = \underset{h\to 0}{\text{Lt}} \; -\frac{1}{h}\left[\frac{-h\,(3e^{-1/h}+4)}{(2-e^{-1/h})}\right] = \frac{4}{2} = 2$$

Since $R' \neq L'$ therefore the given function is not differentiable at $x=0$.

33. (a) $f\,(x) = \begin{cases} -\sin \pi x, & x<0 \\ 0 & x=0 \\ \sin \pi x & x>0 \end{cases}$

For continuity, $L = R = V = 0$

For Differentiability $L' = R'$ at $x=0$

$$L' = \text{Lt} \frac{f\,(0-h)-f\,(0)}{-h}$$

$$\text{Lt} \frac{-\sin \pi\,(-h)-0}{-h} = \text{Lt} \frac{\sin \pi h}{-h} = \text{Lt} \frac{\pi h}{-h} = -\pi$$

$R' = \pi$ as above

Since $L' \neq R'$ at $x=0$ therefore function is not differentiable at $x=0$.

(b) $R' = 1, L' = -1$. Not differentiable.

$$e^{-\infty} = \frac{1}{e^{\infty}} = 0$$

Write $f\,(x) = \dfrac{x\,(1-e^{-2/x})}{(1+e^{-2/x})}$ for R or $\dfrac{x\,(e^{2/x}-1)}{(e^{2/x}+1)}$ for L

34. (a) We have $f\,(0+0) = \lim_{h\to 0} (0+h)^2 \sin \dfrac{1}{0+h}$

$$= \lim_{h\to 0} h^2 \sin \frac{1}{h} = 0.$$

Similarly $f\,(0-0) = 0$.

Since $f\,(0+0) = f\,(0-0) = f\,(0)$,

the function is continuous at $x=0$.

Now $Rf\,'(0) = \lim_{h\to 0} \dfrac{(0+h)^2 \sin[1/(0+h)] - 0}{h}$

$$= \lim_{h\to 0} h \sin(1/h) = 0.$$

Similarly $Lf\,'(0) = 0$.

Hence f is differentiable at $x=0$. The derivative of f at $x=0$ has the value zero. At all other points f is easily seen to be continuous and differentiable.

Now $f\,'(x) = 2x \sin(1/x) - \cos(1/x)$ at $x \neq 0$ and $f\,'(0) = 0$.

$\therefore \quad f\,'(0+0) = \lim_{h\to 0} [2h \sin(1/h) - \cos(1/h)]$,

which does not exist.

Similarly $f\,'(0-0)$ does not exist. Hence $f\,'$ is discontinuous at the origin.

(b) We have $f\,(0) = |0| = 0$.

$$f\,(0+0) = \lim_{h\to 0} |0+h| = 0$$

and $f\,(0-0) = \lim_{h\to 0} |0-h| = 0$

Hence $f\,(x)$ is continuous at $x=0$.

As regard differentiability, we have

$$Rf\,'(0) = \lim_{h\to 0} \frac{f\,(0+h)-f\,(0)}{h} = \lim_{h\to 0} \frac{|h|-0}{h}$$

$$= \lim_{h\to 0} \frac{h}{h} \quad (h \text{ being positive}) = 1.$$

And $Lf\,'(0) = \lim_{h\to 0} \dfrac{f\,(0-h)-f\,(0)}{-h} = \lim_{h\to 0} \dfrac{|-h|-0}{-h}$

$$= \lim_{h\to 0} \frac{h}{-h} \quad (h \text{ being positive}) = -1$$

Since $Rf\,'(0) \neq Lf\,'(0)$, the function f is not differentiable at $x=0$.

35. (a) $y = \begin{cases} -(x-2), & x<2 \\ 0 & , x=2 \\ x-2 & , x>2 \end{cases}$

It consists of two straight lines and a point (2, 0). Sketch the graph yourself. Continuous but not differentiable at $x=2$.

(b) Do yourself.

36. (a) It is easy to see that

$f\,(0+0) = f\,(0-0) = f\,(0) = 0$.

(This is left for the students). Hence $f\,(x)$ is continuous at $x=0$.

Now

$$Lf\,'(0) = \lim_{h\to 0} \frac{(0-h)\,[\sqrt{0-h} - \sqrt{0-h+1}] - 0}{-h}$$

$$= \lim_{h\to 0} [\sqrt{-h} - \sqrt{-h+1}] = 0 - \sqrt{1} = -1.$$

and $Rf\,'(0) = \lim_{h\to 0} \dfrac{(0+h)\,[\sqrt{0+h} - \sqrt{0+h+1}] - 0}{h}$

$$= \lim_{h\to 0} [\sqrt{h} - \sqrt{h+1}] = 0 - \sqrt{1} = -1.$$

Since $Lf'(0) = Rf'(0) = -1$, the function $f(x)$ is differentiable at $x = 0$.

(b) We write the given function as :

$$f(x) = \begin{cases} x-3, & x \geq 3 \\ 3-x, & 1 \leq x \leq 3 \\ x^2/4 - 3x/2 + 13/4, & x < 1. \end{cases}$$

Now it can be easily seen that $f(x)$ is continuous at $x = 1$ and $x = 3$, differentiable at $x = 1$ but non-differentiable at $x = 3$.

37. (a) $\dfrac{dy}{dx} = 6x + 12$ and $6(x+2) = +$ ive on $[-1, 2]$

$\therefore$ $f(x)$ is an increasing function on $[-1, 2]$.

$$\underset{h\to 0}{\text{Lt}}\ f(2-h) = \underset{h\to 0}{\text{Lt}}\ f(2+h) = f(2) = 35$$

$\therefore$ continuous at $x = 2$ in $[-1, 3]$.

$$\underset{h\to 0}{\text{Lt}}\ f'(2+h) = \underset{h\to 0}{\text{Lt}}\ \frac{f(2+h)-f(2)}{h} = \frac{37-(2+h)-35}{h} = -1$$

$$\underset{h\to 0}{\text{Lt}}\ f'(2-h) = \underset{h\to 0}{\text{Lt}}\ \frac{f(2-h)-f(2)}{-h} = \underset{h\to 0}{\text{Lt}}\ \frac{3h^2-24h}{-h} = 24 \quad \therefore \quad L' \neq R'$$

$\therefore$ $f'(2)$ does not exist.

(b) Let us divide the interval to two sub-intervals $I_1, -1 \leq x < 0$ so that x is $-$ ive and $I_2, x \geq 0$ so that x is +ive

For I_1,

$$f(x) = \int_{-1}^{x} (-t)\,dt = -\frac{1}{2}(x^2-1) \quad ...(1)$$

For I_2,

$$f(x) = \int_{-1}^{0} (-t)\,dt + \int_0^x t\,dt$$

$$= -\frac{1}{2}[t^2]_{-1}^{0} + \frac{1}{2}[t^2]_0^x = \frac{1}{2}(1+x^2) \quad ...(2)$$

Hence the function can be defined as follows :

$$f(x) = \begin{cases} -\dfrac{1}{2}(x^2-1), & -1 \leq x < 0 \\ \dfrac{1}{2}(x^2+1), & x \geq 0 \end{cases}$$

$$f'(x) = \begin{cases} -x, & -1 < x < 0 \\ 0, & x = 0 \\ x, & x > 0 \end{cases}$$

for f, $L = R = V = \dfrac{1}{2}$ at $x = 0$ so f is continuous at $x = 0$ for f', $L = R = V = 0$ at $x = 0$ so f' is also continuous at $x = 0$. Thus both f and f' are continuous at $x = 0$ and hence both are continuous for $x > -1$ *i.e.* $x + 1 > 0$.

38. Let us redefine the function

$$f(x) = \int_0^1 \{1 + (1-t)\}\,dt + \int_1^x \{1-(1-t)\}\,dt$$

$$= \left[2t - \frac{t^2}{2}\right]_0^1 + \left[\frac{t^2}{2}\right]_1^x = \left(2 - \frac{1}{2}\right) + \left(\frac{x^2}{2} - \frac{1}{2}\right)$$

$\therefore$ $f(x) = 1 + \dfrac{x^2}{2}$

$$\therefore \quad f(x) = \begin{cases} 5x-7, & x \leq 2 \\ 1 + \dfrac{x^2}{2}, & x > 2 \end{cases}$$

$L = R = V = 3$ at $x = 2$ $\therefore$ continuous

$$L' = \lim_{h\to 0} \frac{f(2-h)-f(2)}{-h} = \lim_{h\to 0} \frac{5(2-h)-7-3}{-h} = 5$$

$$R' = \lim_{h\to 0} \frac{f(2+h)-f(2)}{h} = \lim_{h\to 0} \frac{1 + \frac{1}{2}(2+h)^2 - 3}{h} = \lim_{h\to 0} \frac{2h + \frac{1}{2}h^2}{h} = 2$$

Since $L' \neq R'$ so the function is not differentiable at $x = 2$. Hence at $x = 2$ function is continuous but not differentiable.

39. (a) We shall make use of all the given conditions to find the values of four constants

$$f'(x) = \begin{cases} a(2x-1), & x < 1 \\ 1, & 1 \leq x \leq 3 \\ 2cx + d, & x > 3. \end{cases}$$

(i) $f(x)$ is continuous for all x.

$\therefore$ consider $x = 1$

$\therefore$ $L = R = V$; $V = 0, L = b, R = 0$ $\quad \therefore \quad b = 0$ ...(1)

Now consider $x = 3$; $L = R = V$

$V = 2, L = \text{Lt}\ (3-h-1) = 2$

$R = \underset{h\to 0}{\text{Lt}}\ c(3+h)^2 + d(3+h) + 2 = 9c + 3d + 2$

$\therefore$ $9c + 3d + 2 = 2$ or $3c = -d$ ...(2)

(ii) $f'(1)$ does not exist means that the function $f(x)$ is not differentiable at $x = 1$.

$\therefore$ $L' \neq R'$ at $x = 1$ for $f(x)$.

$$L' = \underset{h\to 0}{\text{Lt}}\ \frac{a(1-h)(-h)-0}{-h} = a;$$

$$R' = \underset{h\to 0}{\text{Lt}}\ \frac{h-0}{h} = 1. \quad \therefore \quad a \neq 1 \quad ...(3)$$

(iii) $f'(x)$ is continuous at $x = 3$

$\therefore$ $L = R = V$ at $x = 3$ for $f'(x)$

$L = 1, R = \underset{h\to 0}{\text{Lt}}\ 2c(3+h) + d = 6c + d$

$\therefore$ $6c + d = 1$ or $-2d + d = 1$, by (2)

$\therefore$ $d = -1$ and hence $c = 1/3$

Hence $a \neq 1, b = 0, c = 1/3, d = -1$ are the required values.

(b) Do yourself.

40. Let $y = f(x)$. We consider $x = 0, 1$.

At $x = 0$, we have $f(0) = 0$.

$$f(0-0) = \lim_{h\to 0} (0-h)^2 = 0,$$

$$f(0+0) = \lim_{h\to 0} 1 = 1$$

Since $f(0-0) \neq f(0+0)$, the function is discontinuous at $x = 0$.

It is, therefore, non-differentiable also.

At $x = 1$, we have, $f(1) = 1$.

$$f(1-0) = 1$$

and $f(1+0) = \lim_{h\to 0} 1/(1+h) = 1$.

Hence $f(1+0) = f(1-0) = f(1) = 1$.

It follows that f is continuous at $x = 1$.

Now $Lf'(1) = \lim_{h\to 0} \dfrac{1-1}{-h} = 0$,

$$Rf'(1) = \lim_{h\to 0} \frac{1/(1+h) - 1}{h}$$

$$= \lim_{h\to 0} \frac{1-1-h}{h(1+h)}$$

$$= \lim_{h\to 0} -\frac{1}{1+h} = -1.$$

Since $Lf'(1) \neq Rf'(1)$, the function is non-differentiable at $x = 1$.

To draw the graph, we proceed as follows.

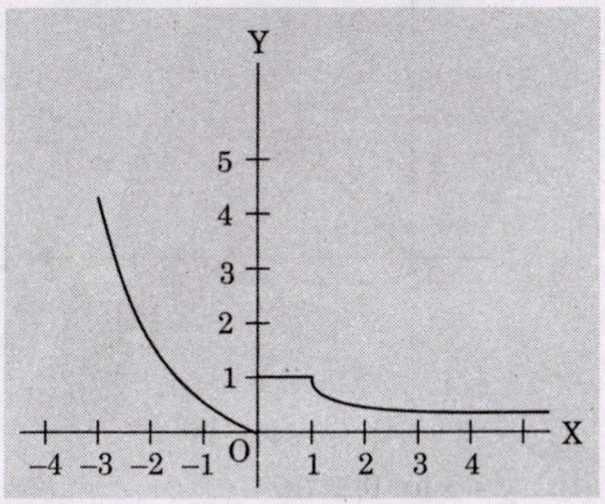

Fig. 11

(i) For $x \le 0$, We have the parabola $y = x^2$.

We construct the following table for this portion of the graph :

x	0	–1	–2	–3	–4...
y	0	1	4	9	16...

(ii) For $0 < x < 1$, we have $y = 1$ which is a straight line parallel to x-axis.

(iii) For $x > 1$, we have $y = 1/x$ and table for this is as follows :

x	1	2	4	8 .... $\to \infty$
y	1	$\frac{1}{2}$	$\frac{1}{4}$	$\frac{1}{8}$ .... $\to 0$

Hence the graph is as shown above.

41. (a) We consider $x = -2, 2$.

At $x = -2$, we have $f(-2) = 4$

$$f(-2-0) = \lim_{h\to 0} [-2-h]^2 = 4$$

and $f(-2+0) = \lim_{h\to 0} 4 = 4$

Since $f(-2+0) = f(-2-0) = f(-2)$, the function is continuous at $x = -2$.

Now $Lf'(-2) = \lim_{h\to 0} \dfrac{(-2-h)^2 - 4}{-h}$

$$= \lim_{h\to 0} \frac{4 + 4h + h^2 - 4}{-h} = \lim_{h\to 0} [-4-h] = -4.$$

And $Rf'(-2) = \lim_{h\to 0} \dfrac{4-4}{h} = 0$.

Since $Lf'(-2) \neq Rf'(-2)$, the function is non-differentiable at $x = -2$.

At $x = 2$, we have $f(2) = 4$.

$$f(2-0) = \lim_{h\to 0} 4 = 4$$

and $f(2+0) = \lim_{h\to 0} [2+h]^2 = 4$.

Hence f is continuous at $x = 2$.

$$Lf'(2) = \lim_{h\to 0} \frac{4-4}{-h} = 0.$$

$$Rf'(2) = \lim_{h\to 0} \frac{(2+h)^2 - 4}{h}$$

$$= \lim_{h\to 0} \frac{4 + 4h + h^2 - 4}{h} = \lim_{h\to 0} [4+h] = 4$$

Since $Lf'(2) \neq Rf'(2)$, the function is non-differentiable at $x = 2$.

Hence the function is continuous throughout and non-differentiable at $x = -2, 2$.

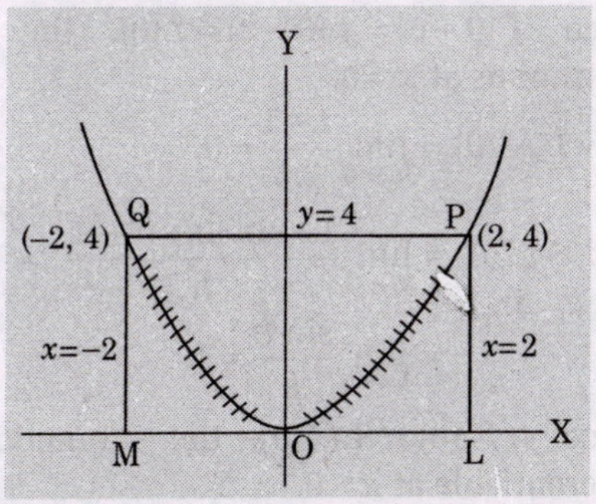

Fig. 12

The graph consists of

(i) The parabola $y = x^2$ for $x < -2$.

(ii) The straight line $y = 4$ for $-2 \le x \le 2$, and

(iii) The parabola $y = x^2$ for $x > 2$.

Hence the graph is as drawn. From the graph it is evident that the function is continuous throughout and non-differentiable at $x = -2, 2$, since the slopes on the two sides of these points are different.

(b) $x^2 - 4 = (x+2)(x-2)$

Redefine as under :

$$f(x) = \begin{cases} x^2 - 4 & x \le -2 \\ -(x^2 - 4) & -2 < x < 2 \\ x^2 - 4 & x > 2 \end{cases}$$

$Lf'(2) = -4,\ Rf'(2) = 4.$

Hence not differentiable at $x = 2$.

(c) Consider $x = 1, 2$

$\text{Lt } f(1-h) = \underset{h\to 0}{\text{Lt}}\ 1-(1-h) = \text{Lt } h = 0$

$\text{Lt } f(1+h) = \underset{h\to 0}{\text{Lt}}\ -h(1-h) = 0, f(1) = 0$

Since $L = R = V = 0$

$\therefore$ f is continuous at $x = 1$

Consider differentiability

$L'\quad f'(1) = \underset{h\to 0}{\text{Lt}}\ \dfrac{f(1-h)-f(1)}{-h} = \dfrac{h-0}{-h} = -1$

$R'\quad f'(1) = \underset{h\to 0}{\text{Lt}}\ \dfrac{f(1+h)-f(1)}{h}$

$= \dfrac{-h(1-h)-0}{h} = -1$

$\therefore$ $f(x)$ is differentiable at $x = 1$

At $x = 2$ $L = 0$ $R = 1$ $V = 0$

Hence $f(x)$ is not continuous at $x = 2$ and as such it is not differentiable also at $x = 2$.

42. We consider $x = 0, \pi/2$.

At $x = 0$, we have $f(0) = 1 + \sin 0 = 1$.

$f(0-0) = \lim_{h\to 0} 1 = 1$

and $f(0+0) = \lim_{h\to 0} [1 + \sin(0+h)] = 1.$

Since $f(0+0) = f(0-0) = f(0)$, the function is continuous at $x = 0$.

Now $Lf'(0) = \lim_{h\to 0} \dfrac{1-1}{-h} = 0.$

And $Rf'(0) = \lim_{h\to 0} \dfrac{1+\sin(0+h)-1}{h}$

$= \lim_{h\to 0} \dfrac{\sin h}{h} = 1.$

Since $Lf'(0) \ne Rf'(0)$, the function is non-differentiable at $x = 0$.

At $x = \pi/2$, we have

$f(\pi/2) = 2 + (\pi/2 - \pi/2)^2 = 2$

$f(\pi/2 - 0) = \lim_{h\to 0} \{1 + \sin(\pi/2 - h)\}$

$= \lim_{h\to 0} (1 + \cos h) = 2$

$f\left(\dfrac{\pi}{2}+0\right) = \lim_{h\to 0} \left\{2 + \left(\dfrac{\pi}{2} + h - \dfrac{\pi}{2}\right)^2\right\} = 2,$

Since $f(\pi/2 + 0) = f(\pi/2 - 0) = f(\pi/2)$, the function is continuous at $x = \pi/2$.

Now $Lf'\dfrac{\pi}{2} = \lim_{h\to 0} \dfrac{1+\sin(\pi/2-h)-2}{-h}$

$= \lim_{h\to 0} \dfrac{1-\cos h}{h}\ \left[\text{form } \dfrac{0}{0}\right]$

$= \lim_{h\to 0} \dfrac{\sin h}{1} = 0$

And $Rf'\dfrac{\pi}{2} = \lim_{h\to 0} \dfrac{2+(\pi/2+h-\pi/2)^2-2}{h}$

$= \lim_{h\to 0} h = 0.$

Since $Rf'(\pi/2) = Lf'(\pi/2)$, the function is differentiable at $x = \pi/2$.

43. (a) We have $f(1) = 1$.

$f(1-0) = \lim_{h\to 0} [1-h] = 1$

and $f(1+0) = \lim_{h\to 0} [2-(1+h)] = 1.$

Since $f(1+0) = f(1-0) = f(1)$, the function is continuous at $x = 1$.

Now $Lf'(1) = \lim_{h\to 0} \dfrac{(1-h)-1}{-h} = \lim_{h\to 0} \dfrac{-h}{-h} = 1.$

And $Rf'(1) = \lim_{h\to 0} \dfrac{2-(1+h)-1}{h} = \lim_{h\to 0} \dfrac{-h}{h} = -1.$

Since $Rf'(1) \ne Lf'(1)$, the function is non-differentiable at $x = 1$.

The graph consists of the segments of the two straight lines

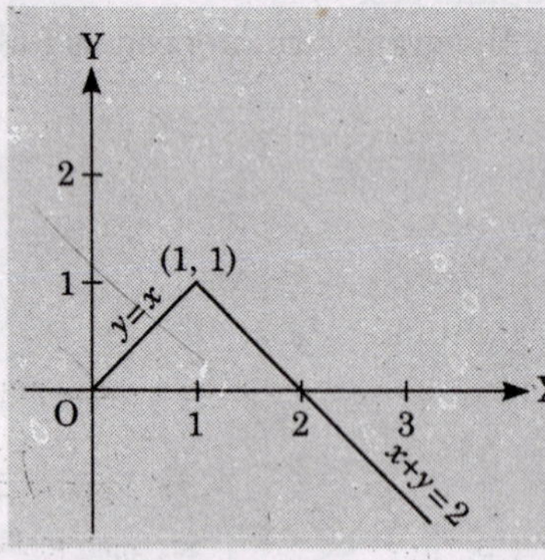

Fig. 13

(i) $y = x$ for $0 \le x \le 1$.

(ii) $y = 2 - x$ for $x \ge 1$.

Hence the graph is as drawn. From the graph, it is evident that the function is continuous at $x = 1$ but non-differentiable since the slope on the two sides are different.

(b) Ans. (b), (c).

The function given in (a) is not differentiable at $x = \dfrac{1}{3}$ in $[0, 1]$ as $Lf'(1) = 1$ and $Rf'(1) = -1$. Hence it does not satisfy the mean value theorem $\Rightarrow$ (b).

Also $f(0) \ne f(1)$ $\Rightarrow$ (c).

44. We consider $x = 0$, we have $f(0) = 0$.

$f(0+0) = \lim_{h\to 0} \left\{(0+h)\left(1 + \tfrac{1}{3}\sin\log(0+h)^2\right\}\right.$

$= \lim_{h\to 0} [h + (h/3)\sin\log h^2].$

$= 0 + 0 \times \text{a finite quantity} = 0$

[$\because \sin \log h^2$ oscillates between -1 and 1 as $h \to 0$ hence finite]

and $f(0-0) = \lim_{h \to 0} (0-h) . \left\{1 + \frac{1}{3} \sin \log (0-h)^2 \right\}$

$= \lim_{h \to 0} [-h - (h/3) \sin \log h^2] = 0$ as before.

Hence f is continuous at $x = 0$.

Now, $Lf'(0) = \lim_{h \to 0} \dfrac{(0-h)\left\{1 + \frac{1}{3} \sin \log (0-h)^2\right\} - 0}{-h}$

$= \lim_{h \to 0} [1 + \frac{1}{3} \sin \log h^2]$

Now $\sin \log h^2$ oscillates between -1 and 1 as $h \to 0$ so that $\lim_{h \to 0} \sin (\log h^2)$ does not exist.

Hence $Lf'(0)$ does not exist.

Similarly

$Rf'(0) = \lim_{h \to 0} \dfrac{(0+h)\left\{1 + \frac{1}{3} \sin \log (0+h)^2\right\} - 0}{h}$

$= \lim_{h \to 0} \left\{1 + \frac{1}{3} \sin \log h^2\right\}$,

which does not exist as before.

Hence f has no differential coefficient at $x = 0$.

45. (a) $f(0+0) = \lim_{h \to 0} (0+h)^p \cos \dfrac{1}{0+h}$

$= \lim_{h \to 0} h^p \cos \dfrac{1}{h}$ ...(1)

And $f(0-0) = \lim_{h \to 0} (-h)^p \cos \left(\dfrac{1}{-h}\right)$

$= \lim_{h \to 0} (-h)^p \cos \dfrac{1}{h}$ ...(2)

Now in order that the function may be continuous at $x = 0$, the limits given in (1) and (2) must both tend to zero. This will be the case if $p > 0$ which is the required condition.

Again, $Rf'(0) = \lim_{h \to 0} \dfrac{h^p \cos(1/h) - 0}{h}$

$= \lim_{h \to 0} h^{p-1} \cos \dfrac{1}{h}$ ...(3)

And $Lf'(0) = \lim_{h \to 0} \dfrac{(-h)^p \cos(-1/h) - 0}{-h}$

$= \lim_{h \to 0} -(-1)^p h^{p-1} \cos(1/h)$. ...(4)

Now in order that $f'(0)$ may exist, it is necessary that the limits in (3) and (4) must tend to the same quantity. This will be the case when $p > 1$ for in that case both $Rf'(0)$ and $Lf'(0)$ will be zero. Hence in order that f may have a differential coefficient at $x = 0$, p should be greater than 1.

(b) Since $f(x)$ is continuous

$\therefore \lim_{x \to 0} f(x) = f(0) = 8$ ...(1)

Now $\underset{x \to 0}{\text{Lt}} f(x) = \underset{x \to 0}{\text{Lt}} \dfrac{(e^x - 1)^4}{\left(\dfrac{x^2}{\lambda^2}\right)\left(\dfrac{x^2}{2}\right)}$

$= 2\lambda^2 . \underset{x \to 0}{\text{Lt}} \left(\dfrac{e^x - 1}{x}\right)^4$

$= 2\lambda^2 (\log e)^4 = 2\lambda^2 \quad \because \lim_{x \to 0} \dfrac{a^x - 1}{x} \log a$

Hence from (1) we have

$2\lambda^2 = 8 \Rightarrow \lambda^2 = 4 \quad \therefore \lambda = 2, -2$

(c) $\underset{x \to 0}{\text{Lt}} \dfrac{x^3 \left(\dfrac{4^x - 1}{x}\right)^3}{\left(\dfrac{x}{4} . \dfrac{x^2}{3} \ldots\right)} = \dfrac{12x^3}{x^3} (\log 4)^3 = 12 (\log 4)^3$

For continuity limit = value at $x = 0$

$\therefore \quad p = 12 (\log 4)^3$.

46. $Rf'(0) = \lim_{h \to 0} \dfrac{\sqrt{h}\{1 + h \sin(1/h)\} - 0}{h}$

$= \lim_{h \to 0} \left[\dfrac{1}{\sqrt{(h)}} + \sqrt{h} \sin \dfrac{1}{h}\right] = \infty + 0 = +\infty$.

And $Lf'(0) = \lim_{h \to 0} \dfrac{-\sqrt{-(0-h)}\,[1 + (0-h)\sin 1/(0-h)] - 0}{-h}$

$= \lim_{h \to 0} [1/\sqrt{h} + \sqrt{h} \sin(1/h)]$

$= \infty + 0 = +\infty$.

Since $Rf'(0) = Lf'(0) = +\infty$, the derivative of f at $x = 0$ is $+\infty$.

For values of x, other than zero, we have

$f'(x) = \dfrac{1}{2\sqrt{(x)}} + \dfrac{3}{2}\sqrt{x} \sin \dfrac{1}{x} - \dfrac{1}{\sqrt{(x)}} \cos \dfrac{1}{x}$

where $x > 0$

and $f'(x) = \dfrac{1}{2\sqrt{(-x)}} + \dfrac{3}{2}\sqrt{-x} \sin \dfrac{1}{x} - \dfrac{1}{\sqrt{(-x)}} \cos \dfrac{1}{x}$

when $x < 0$.

Hence $f'(a)$ is finite for $a \neq 0$.

47. (a) We know that $|x| = x$ when x is +ive and $|x| = -x$ when x is negative.

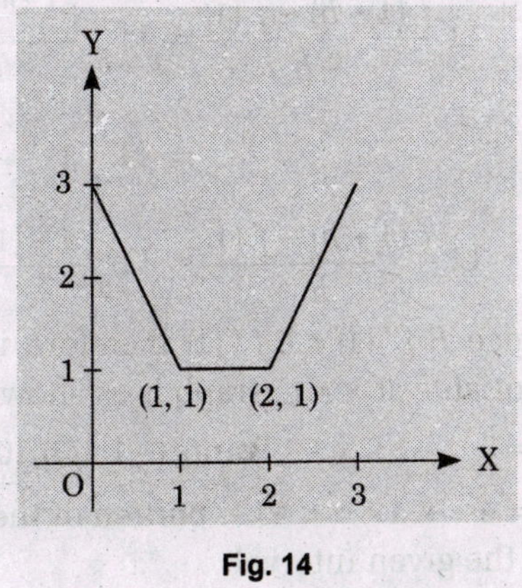

Fig. 14

From the definition of function, we have

$$y = -(x-1) - (x-2) = 3 - 2x \text{ when } x \le 1$$
$$= (x-1) - (x-2) = 1 \quad \text{when } 1 \le x \le 2$$
$$= (x-1) + (x-2) = 2x - 3 \quad \text{when } x > 2.$$

Thus the function has been defined for [0, 1], [1, 2] and [2, 3] respectively. Hence the graph drawn for the interval [0, 3] is as shown.

From the graph it is clear that the function is continuous throughout the interval but is not differentiable at $x = 1, 2$ since the slopes at these points are different on the left hand and right hand sides.

To test it analytically, we have

$$f(x) = 3 - 2x \text{ when } x \le 1$$
$$= 1 \text{ when } 1 \le x \le 2$$
$$= 2x - 3 \text{ when } x > 2.$$

It is easy to show that

$\lim f(1-0) = \lim (1+0) = f(1) = 1$

$\lim f(2-0) = \lim f(2+0) = f(2) = 1$

Hence continuous both at $x = 1$ and $x = 2$

Again $Rf'(1) = 0, \; Lf'(1) = -2$

and $Rf'(2) = 2, \; Lf'(2) = 0$

Hence not differentiable at $x = 1$ and $x = 2$.

(b) L.H.L. $= \underset{h \to 0}{\text{Lt}} f(1-h) = \text{Lt } 3^{1-h} = 3$

R.H.L. $= \underset{h \to 0}{\text{Lt}} f(1+h) = \text{Lt } 4 - (1+h) = 3$

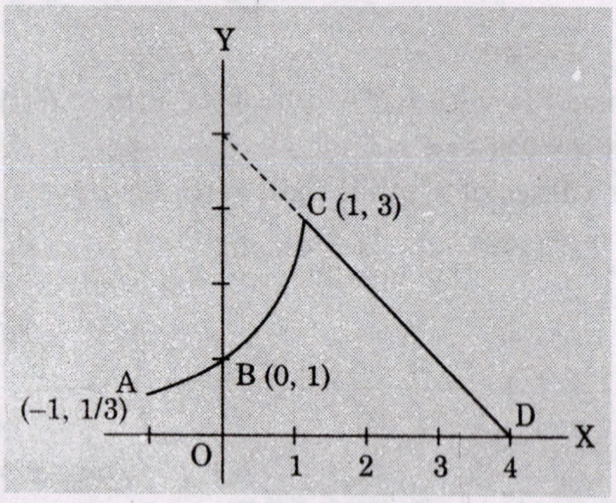

Fig. 15

Also $f(1) = 3 \;\therefore\; R = L = V$. Hence continuous.

$$\text{Lt} \frac{f(1-h) - f(1)}{-h} = \underset{h \to 0}{\text{Lt}} \frac{3^{1-h} - 3}{-h}$$

$$= \underset{y \to 0}{\text{Lt}} \; 3 \cdot \frac{3^{y} - 1}{y} = 3 \log 3$$

$$\text{Lt} \frac{f(1+h) - f(1)}{h} = \underset{h \to 0}{\text{Lt}} \frac{4 - (1+h) - 3}{h} = -1$$

Since $Rf'(1) \ne Lf'(1)$ therefore it is not differentiable at $x = 1$. Graph is as shown

$y = 3^x, -1 \le x \le 1$ Points $(-1, 1/3), (0, 1), (1, 3)$ etc.

$y = 4 - x, 1 < x < 4$ *i.e.* portion of the line $x + y = 4$ in the given interval.

(c) Ans. (b).

Let us redefine the function $|x| = -x$, $x < 0, |x| = x, x > 0$

$$\therefore \quad f(x) = \begin{cases} xe^{-\left[-\frac{1}{x} + \frac{1}{x}\right]} = xe^{0} = x & x < 0 \\ xe^{-\left[\frac{1}{x} + \frac{1}{x}\right]} = xe^{-2/x} & x > 0 \\ = 0 & x = 0 \end{cases}$$

$$f(0-h) = 0, f(0+h) = \underset{h \to 0}{\text{Lt}} \frac{h}{e^{2/h}}$$

$$= \underset{h \to 0}{\text{Lt}} \frac{h}{1 + \frac{2}{h} + \frac{1}{2!}\left(\frac{2}{h}\right)^2 + \ldots} = 0$$

$\therefore \quad f(0) = 0$

From above we conclude that $\text{Lt } f(0+h) = \text{Lt } f(0-h) = f(0)$. Hence $f(x)$ is continuous $\forall \; x$.

For differentiability we have

$$Lf'(0) = \underset{h \to 0}{\text{Lt}} \frac{(0-h) - 0}{-h} = 1$$

$$Rf'(0) = \underset{h \to 0}{\text{Lt}} \frac{h.e^{-2/h}}{h} = \underset{h \to 0}{\text{Lt}} \frac{1}{e^{2/h}} = \frac{1}{\infty} = 0$$

Since $Lf'(0) \ne Rf'(0)$ so the function is not differentiable at $x = 0$.

48. (a) Ans. (a), (c), (d).

Let us consider continuity and differentiabilitv for $x = 0, 1$. Hence we define the function $h(x) = \min\{x, x^2\}$ as under :

$$h(x) = \begin{cases} x, & x < 0 \\ 0, & x = 0 \\ x^2, & 0 < x < 1 \\ x, & x > 1 \end{cases}$$

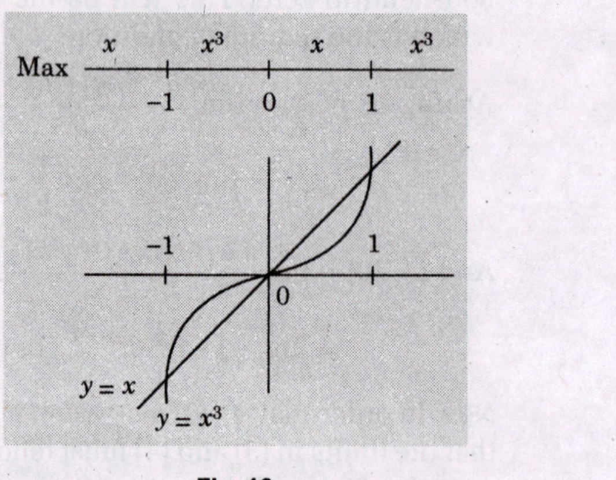

Fig. 16

Clearly $h(x)$ being a polynomial in x is continuous for all $x \Rightarrow$ (a).

Also $h'(x) = 1 \;\; \forall \; x > 1 \;\Rightarrow$ (c).

Again both at $x = 0$ and $x = 1$, $h(x)$ is not differentiable as $L' \ne R' \;\Rightarrow$ (d).

(b) Ans. (d).

Let us redefine the function in $[-1, 1]$

$$f(x) = \begin{cases} x & x \le -1 \\ x^3 & -1 < x \le 0 \\ x & 0 < x \le 1 \\ x^3 & x > 1 \end{cases}$$

$y = x$ represents a straight line and $y = x^3$ represents a semi-cubical parabola. From the figure it is clear that $f(x)$ is not differentiable at $x = 1, 0, -1$ as L' and R' are different.

49. (a) We are given $f(x) = x^3 - x^2 + x + 1$

$\therefore \quad f'(x) = 3x^2 - 2x + 1 = 3\left(x^2 - \frac{2}{3}x + \frac{1}{3}\right)$

$= 3\left[\left(x - \frac{1}{3}\right)^2 - \frac{1}{9} + \frac{1}{3}\right]$

$= 3\left[\left(x - \frac{1}{3}\right)^2 + \frac{2}{9}\right] > 0$ for all real x.

Hence $f(x)$ is an increasing function of x for all real values of x.

Note : The sign of a quadratic $ax^2 + bx + c$ is same as of a except when its roots α and β are real and unequal and x has a value lying between them $\alpha < x < \beta$ (§ 6. Algebra, Quadratic Eqns.)

Here $\Delta = B^2 - 4AC = 4 - 12 = -$ ive $\therefore$ Roots are imaginary, hence the sign of quadratic is same as of $a = 3$ *i.e.* +ive for all real x.

$\therefore \quad \max[f(t) : 0 \le t \le x] = x^3 - x^2 + x + 1.$

[Note that here max $f(t)$ means the greatest value of $f(t)$ in the interval $0 \le t \le x$ which is obtained at $t = x$ since the function $f(t)$ is increasing for all t.]

Hence the function g is defined as follows :

$g(x) = x^3 - x^2 + x + 1$ when $0 \le x \le 1$

and $g(x) = 3 - x$ when $1 < x \le 2$

It is sufficient to discuss the continuity and differentiability of $g(x)$ at $x = 1$ since for all other values of x, $g(x)$ is clearly continuous and differentiable, being a polynomial function of x.

We have

$g(1) = 2,$

$g(1 - 0) = \lim_{h \to 0} [(1 - h)^3 - (1 - h)^2 + (1 - h) + 1] = 2$

and $g(1 + 0) = \lim_{h \to 0} [3 - (1 + h)] = 2$

hence $g(x)$ is continuous at $x = 1$

Now $Lg'(1) = \lim_{h \to 0} \dfrac{[(1 - h)^3 - (1 - h)^2 + (1 - h) + 1] - 2}{-h}$

$$= \lim_{h \to 0} \frac{1 - 3h + 3h^2 - h^3 - 1 + 2h - h^2 + 1 - h + 1 - 2}{-h}$$

$$= \lim_{h \to 0} \frac{-2h + 2h^2 - h^3}{-h} = \lim_{h \to 0} [2 - 2h + h^2] = 2$$

and $Rg'(1) = \lim_{h \to 0} \dfrac{[3 - (1 + h)] - 2}{h} = \lim_{h \to 0} \dfrac{-h}{h} = -1.$

Since $Lg'(1) \ne Rg'(1)$, the function $g(x)$ is not differentiable at $x = 1$.

Hence $g(x)$ is continuous throughout the interval $(0, 2)$. It is also diffferentiable throughout the interval $(0, 2)$ except at $x = 1$ where it is non-differentiable.

(b) $y = \cos x, \dfrac{dy}{dx} = -\sin x = -$ ive in $[0, x]$.

$\therefore$ $\cos x$ is a decreasing function and hence its minimum will occur at $x = x$ *i.e.* at end point.

$\therefore \quad g(x) = \begin{cases} \cos x & 0 \le x \le \pi \\ \sin x - 1 & x > \pi \end{cases}$

Now consider $x = \pi$.

$L = R = V = -1.$ Hence continuous.

(c) Ans. (a), (c).

Let us redefine the function

$f(x) = \begin{cases} x^3, & x < 1 \\ 1, & x \ge 1 \end{cases}$ by definition

$f'(x) = \begin{cases} 3x^2, & x < 1 \\ 0, & x \ge 1 \end{cases}$

Let us consider continuity at $x = 1$.

$\text{Lt } f(1 + h) = \text{Lt } f(1 - h) = f(1) = 1$

Hence continuous $\forall\, x \in R$

$R' = \text{Lt } \dfrac{f(1 + h) - f(1)}{h} = \dfrac{1 - 1}{h} = 0$

$L' = \text{Lt } \dfrac{f(1 - h) - f(1)}{-h} = \dfrac{(1 - h)^3 - 1}{-h} = 3$

Hence $L' \ne R'$, therefore not differentiable.

50. Refer Q. 58 P. 1293-1305.

$f(x) = x^3, -1 < x < 1$

$= x, x \le -1$ or $x \ge 1$

R.H.L. = Lt $(1 + h) = 1$,

L.H.L. = Lt $(1 + h)^3 = 1$, value = 1

R.H.L. = L.H.L. = 1 = value $\therefore$ cont. at $x = 1$

Also R.H.D. = 1, L.H.D. = 3

It is not differentiable at $x = 1$.

Graph is shown in the above figure.

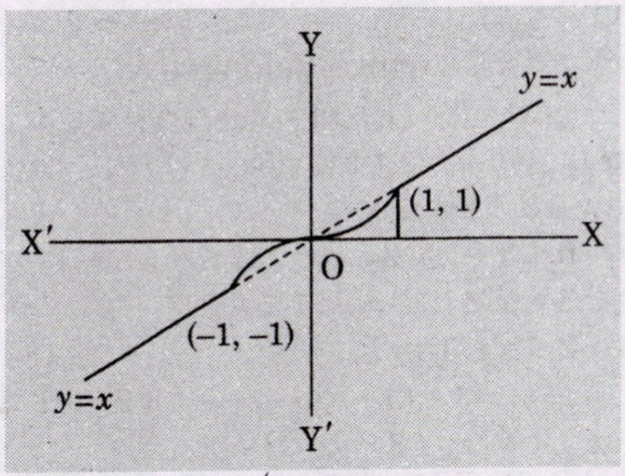

Fig. 17

It consists of semi-cubical parabola $y = x^3$ and portion of line $y = x$ as the intervals.

51. $f(x) = -1, \quad -2 \le x \le 0$ ...(1)
$\qquad = x - 1, \quad 0 < x \le 2$ ...(2)
$\qquad g(x) = f(|x|) + |f(x)|$ ...(3)
Hence $g(x)$ involves $|x|$ and $|x - 1|$ or $|-1| = 1$.
Therefore we should divide the given interval $(-2, 2)$ into the following intervals

	I_1	I_2	I_3
$[-2, 2] =$	$[-2, 0[\ +$	$[0, 1[\ +$	$[1, 2]$
$x =$	$-$	$+$	$+$
$|x| =$	$+$	$+$	$+$
$f(x) =$	-1	$x - 1$	$x - 1$
$f(|x|) =$	$|x| - 1$	$|x| - 1$	$|x| - 1$
	$= -x - 1$	$x - 1$	$x - 1$ ...(1)
$|f(x)| =$	$|-1|$	$|x - 1|$	$|x - 1|$
	$= 1$	$-(x - 1)$	$x - 1$ ...(2)

$\therefore \quad g(x) = f(|x|) + |f(x)|$ use (1), (2)
$\qquad = -x - 1 + 1 = -x \quad$ in I_1
$\qquad = x - 1 - (x - 1) = 0 \quad$ in I_2
$\qquad = (x - 1) + (x - 1) = 2(x - 1)$ in I_3.
Hence $g(x)$ is defined as under :
$\qquad g(x) = -x, \qquad\qquad -2 \le x \le 0$
$\qquad\qquad = 0, \qquad\qquad\quad 0 < x < 1$
$\qquad\qquad = 2(x - 1), \qquad 1 \le x \le 2$
Clearly $g'(x) = -1, 0, 2$ respectively as $g(x)$ is a polynomial in x.
$\qquad L\, g'(0) = -1, R\, g'(0) = 0$ not equal
$\qquad L\, g'(1) = 0, R\, g'(1) = 2$ not equal
Hence $g(x)$ is not differentiable both at $x = 0$ and $x = 1$.

52. By definitions of the functions f and g, we have
$\qquad g(x) = f(f(x)) = 1 + f(x)$ for $0 \le f(x) \le 2$
$\qquad\qquad = 3 - f(x)$ for $2 < f(x) \le 3$.
Now we find the form of $g(x)$ as a function of x. We consider two sub-intervals $I_1 (0 \le x \le 2)$ and $I_2 (2 < x \le 3)$ of the interval $I (0 \le x \le 3)$.
(i) On I_1, we have $f(x) = 1 + x$
Now $0 \le f(x) \le 2 \Rightarrow 0 \le 1 + x \le 2$
$\qquad \Rightarrow \quad -1 \le x \le 1 \Rightarrow 0 \le x \le 1$ on I_1.
$\qquad \therefore \quad g(x) = 1 + f(x) = 1 + (1 + x) = 2 + x$
$\qquad\qquad\qquad\qquad\qquad\qquad$ for $0 \le x \le 1$.
and $2 < f(x) \le 3 \quad \Rightarrow \quad 2 < 1 + x \le 3$
$\qquad \Rightarrow \quad 1 < x \le 2$ which belong to I_1
$\qquad \therefore \quad g(x) = 3 - (1 + x) = 2 - x, \ 1 < x \le 2$.
(ii) On I_2, we have $f(x) = 3 - x$.
Now $0 \le f(x) \le 2$
$\qquad \Rightarrow \quad 0 \le 3 - x \le 2 \Rightarrow -3 \le -x \le -1$
$\qquad \Rightarrow \quad 3 \ge x \ge 1 \quad \Rightarrow \quad 1 \le x \le 3$
$\qquad \Rightarrow \quad 2 \le x \le 3$ on I_2.
$\qquad \therefore \quad g(x) = 1 + (3 - x) = 4 - x$ for $2 < x \le 3$.
and $2 < f(x) \le 3 \Rightarrow 2 < 3 - x \le 3$.
$\qquad \Rightarrow \quad -1 < -x \le 0 \Rightarrow 0 \le x < 1 \notin I_2$.

$\therefore \quad g(x)$ is not defined in this case.
Thus g is defined as follows :
$\qquad g(x) = 2 + x$ for $0 \le x \le 1$
$\qquad\qquad = 2 - x$ for $1 < x \le 2$
$\qquad\qquad = 4 - x$ for $2 < x \le 3$.
We test the function g for continuity at $x = 1$ and $x = 2$ only.
$\qquad g(1) = 3, g(1 - 0) = \lim_{h \to 0} [2 + (1 - h)] = 3$
and $g(1 + 0) = \lim_{h \to 0} [2 - (1 + h)] = 1$.
Hence g is discontinuous at $x = 1$
$\qquad g(2) = 2 - 2 = 0,$
$\qquad g(2 - 0) = \lim_{h \to 0} [2 - (2 - h)] = 0$
and $g(2 + 0) = \lim_{h \to 0} [4 - (2 + h)] = 2$.
Hence g is also discontinuous at $x = 2$.

53. (a) $|1 - x|$ depends on whether $x > 1$ or $x < 1$ and $[x]$ is greatest integer function. We divide the given interval $[-1, 3]$ into various intervals keeping these two in view.

$[-1, 3] =$	$[-1, 0[\ +$	$[0, 1[\ +$	$[1, 2[\ +$	$[2, 3[\ +$	3
$[x] =$	-1	0	1	2	3
$1 - x =$	$+$	$+$	$-$	$-$	$-$
$|1 - x| =$	$1 - x$	$1 - x,$	$-(1 - x),$	$-(1 - x),$	$|-2|$

Hence y is defined as follows :
$\qquad y = -1 + 1 - x = -x \qquad$ if $-1 \le x < 0$.
$\qquad y = 0 + 1 - x = 1 - x \qquad$ if $0 \le x < 1$,
$\qquad y = 1 + x - 1 = x \qquad\qquad$ if $1 \le x < 2$,
$\qquad y = 2 + x - 1 = x + 1 \qquad$ if $2 \le x < 3$,
and $y = [3] + |1 - 3| = 3 + 2 = 5$ if $x = 3$.
Hence the graph of the function is as shown.

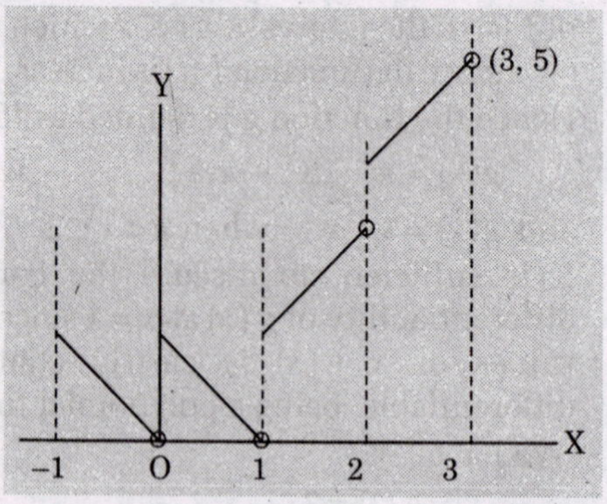

Fig. 18

From the graph it is clear that the function y is not continuous at $x = 0, 1, 2$ and 3 and so it is non-differentiable at these points. Note that y is continuous and differentiable on the right at $x = -1$, y is continuous and differentiable at all other points in the domain of definition.

(b) As in part (a), we redefine the function $|2x - 3| = 2 \left| x - \dfrac{3}{2} \right|$ depends upon whether
$\qquad\qquad\qquad x > \dfrac{3}{2} \quad$ or $\quad x < \dfrac{3}{2}$.

$$[0,2] = [0,1[+\left[1,\frac{3}{2}\right[+\left[\frac{3}{2},2\right[+2$$

$[x]$ =	0	1	1	2
$2x-3$ =	$-$	$-$	+	+

$$f(x)=\begin{cases}0, & 0\le x<1\\ -2\left(x-\frac{3}{2}\right), & 1\le x<\frac{3}{2}\\ 2\left(x-\frac{3}{2}\right), & \frac{3}{2}\le x<2\\ 1\cdot 2, & x=2\\ x^2/2, & 2<x<3\end{cases}$$

We shall consider the points $x=1, 3/2, 2$.

It is left for the reader to establish that it is discontinuous and hence non-differentiable at $x=1,2$ but at $x=3/2$ it is continuous but not differentiable as $L'=-2$ and $R'=2$.

(c) $R'=\text{Lt}\, e^{-2/h}=0, L'=2^0=1.$ $\therefore$ Not diff.

54. (a) $(x^2-3x+2)=(x-1)(x-2)=+\text{ive}$

when $x<1$ or >2, $=-\text{ive}$ when $1\le x\le 2$

Also $\cos|x|=\cos x$ $\qquad\because \cos(-x)=\cos x$

$\therefore\ f(x)=-(x^2-1)(x^2-3x+2)+\cos x, 1\le x\le 2$

$\qquad=(x^2-1)(x^2-3x+2)+\cos x,\ x>2\ \ldots$(A)

Evidently $f(x)$ is not differentiable at $x=2$ as $L'\neq R'$

Note : For all other values like $x<0, 0\le x<1, f(x)$ is same as given by (A).

(b) Ans. (c).

$|x|$ is non-differentiable function at $x=0$ as

$L'=-1$ and $R'=1$

i.e. $\lim\limits_{h\to 0}\dfrac{|-h|-0}{-h}=-1,\ \lim\limits_{h\to 0}\dfrac{|h|-0}{h}=1$

or $y=x, x>0, y=-x, x<0$

But $\cos|h|$ is differentiable

Now any combination of two such functions will be non-differentiable, hence the options (a) and (b) are ruled out.

Now consider $\sin|x|-|x|$

$$L'=\lim_{h\to 0}\frac{\sin|-h|-|-h|}{-h}=\lim\frac{\sin h}{-h}=-1$$

$$R'=\lim_{h\to 0}\frac{\sin|h|-|h|}{h}=\lim=\frac{\sin h}{h}=1$$

55. $f(x)=\left|x-\frac{1}{2}\right|+|x-1|+\tan x$ in $(0, 2)$.

The function is not defined at $x=\pi/2$ because of the term tan x. Further it involves $|x-1/2|$ and $|x-1|$ which depend upon whether $x>\frac{1}{2}$ or $<\frac{1}{2}$ and $x>1$ or $x<1$ in the given interval $(0, 2)$.

Hence we divide the interval $(0, 2)$ into various intervals excluding the point $\pi/2$.

$$(0,2)=\left[0,\frac{1}{2}\right[+\left[\frac{1}{2},1\right[+\left[1,\frac{\pi}{2}\right[+\left[\frac{\pi}{2},2\right[$$

$x-\frac{1}{2}$ =	$-$	+	+	+
$x-1$ =	$-$	$-$	+	+

Let us re-define it in various sub-intervals as under

$$f(x)=\begin{cases}-\left(x-\frac{1}{2}\right)-(x-1)+\tan x & \text{in } 0<x<\frac{1}{2}\\ \left(x-\frac{1}{2}\right)-(x-1)+\tan x & \text{in } \frac{1}{2}\le x<1\\ \left(x-\frac{1}{2}\right)+(x-1)+\tan x & \text{in } 1\le x<\frac{\pi}{2}\\ \left(x-\frac{1}{2}\right)+(x-1)+\tan x & \text{in } \frac{\pi}{2}<x<2\end{cases}$$

We consider the point $x=1/2$, 1 and $\pi/2$. For the derivative to exist $Lf'(a)=Rf'(a)$

At $x=\frac{1}{2}$ L.H.D. $=\sec^2\frac{1}{2}-2$, R.H.D. $=\sec^2\frac{1}{2}$

At $x=1$ L.H.D. $=\sec^2 1$, R.H.D. $=2+\sec^2 1$

At $x=\frac{\pi}{2}$ the function is not defined and hence discontinuous and hence derivative does not exist.

Thus there are three points where the function is non-differentiable.

56. (a) $|x|=x, x>0, |x|=-x, x<0, |x|=0,\ x=0$

$\therefore\quad f(x)=\dfrac{x}{1-x}, x<0; f(x)=0, x=0,$

$\qquad f(x)=\dfrac{x}{1+x}, x>0$

Consider $x=0$

For continuity :

Lt $f(0-h)=$ Lt $f(0+h)=f(0)$.

Lt $-\dfrac{h}{1+h}=0$, Lt $\dfrac{h}{1+h}=0, f(0)=0.$

Since limit = value $\therefore$ function is continuous.

For differentiability :

$$\text{Lt}\frac{f(0-h)-f(0)}{-h}=\text{Lt}\frac{f(0+h)-f(0)}{h}$$

Lt $1/(1+h)=1$, Lt $1/(1+h)=1$.

Hence both left hand and right hand derivatives exist so the function is differentiable at $x=0$ and hence for all other real values of x it is differentiable. Therefore it is differentiable in the interval $(-\infty,\infty)$.

(b) Since $f(x)$ involves $|x|$ so we consider the function for $x<0, =0, >0$.

$f(x)$ =	$-x^3$,	0,	x^3
$f'(x)$ =	$-3x^2$,	0,	$3x^2$
$f''(x)$ =	$-6x$,	0,	$6x$
$f'''(x)$ =	-6,	0,	6

$$\therefore\quad f'''(x)=\begin{cases}-6 & x<0\\ 0 & x=0\\ 6 & x>0\end{cases}$$

R.H.L. and L.H.L. of $f'''(x)$ at $x=0$ are $+6$ and -6 hence $f'''(x)$ is not differentiable at $x=0$

$\therefore$ Hence the required set of points is given by $R-\{0\}$.

(c) $f(x)=x|x|$.

$\therefore \quad f(x)=x(-x)=-x^2, \quad x<0$

$\quad = x(x)=x^2, \quad x>0$

$\quad = 0 \quad x=0$

Clearly $f(x)$ is twice differentiable in $(-\infty, 0)$ and $(0, \infty)$.

Hence we have to discuss the differentiablility at $x=0$.

$$Rf'(0)=\operatorname*{Lt}_{h\to 0}\frac{(0+h)^2-0}{h}=\operatorname*{Lt}_{h\to 0} h=0$$

$$Lf'(0)=\operatorname*{Lt}_{h\to 0}\frac{-(0-h)^2-0}{-h}=\operatorname*{Lt}_{h\to 0} h=0$$

Since $Rf'(0)=Lf'(0)$, so the function is differentiable once at $x=0$ and $f'(0)=0$.

$F(x)=f'(x)=-2x, \quad x<0$

$\quad =f'(x)=2x, \quad x>0$

$\quad =f'(0)=0$

$$RF'(0)=\operatorname*{Lt}_{h\to 0}\frac{2(0+h)-0}{h}=2$$

$$LF'(0)=\operatorname*{Lt}_{h\to 0}\frac{-2(0-h)-0}{-h}=-2$$

Since $RF'(0)\neq LF'(0)$ so the function $F(x)$ is not differentiable at $x=0$. In other words, $f(x)$ is not twice differentiable at $x=0$. But it is twice differentiable at $R-\{0\}$ *i.e.* the set of all real numbers except 0.

57. (a) Ans. (c). f is continuous at $x=a$ if limit = value.

i.e. $\lim_{h\to 0} f(a-h)=\lim_{h\to 0} f(a+h)=f(a)$.

$g(x)=|f(x)|$

$$g(a-0)=\lim_{h\to 0} g(a-h)=\lim_{h\to 0}|f(a-h)| =|f(a)|$$

Similarly $g(a+0)=\lim_{h\to 0} g(a+h)$

$=\lim_{h\to 0}|f(a+h)|=|f(a)|=-g(a)$.

$\therefore$ g is continuous at $x=a$.

Hence g is continuous if f is continuous.

(b) Ans. (d).

$$\frac{dy}{dx}=\cos x \quad \text{or} \quad -\sin x$$

Both are – ive in $(\pi/2, \pi)$. Hence S is correct.

Again if a differentiable function $f(x)$ decreases then its derivative $f'(x)=-$ ive.

It is not necessary that its derivative $f''(x)$ may be + ive and hence it may be increasing or decreasing. Hence R is not correct.

58. Keeping in view $|x|$ and $|1-x|$ we divide the given interval as under

$[-1, 1] = [-1, 0]+[0, 1]$

$|x| \quad = \quad - \quad +$

$|1-x| = \quad + \quad +$

Hence we re-define the function as under

$y=x-(-x)(1-x)=2x-x^2$ in $[-1, 0]$

$y=x-(x)(1-x)=x^2$ in $[0, 1]$

Clearly it is continuous at $x=0$ as $L=R=V=0$

Graph consists of parabolas $x^2=y$ and $(x-1)^2=-(y-1)$ in respective regions as shown.

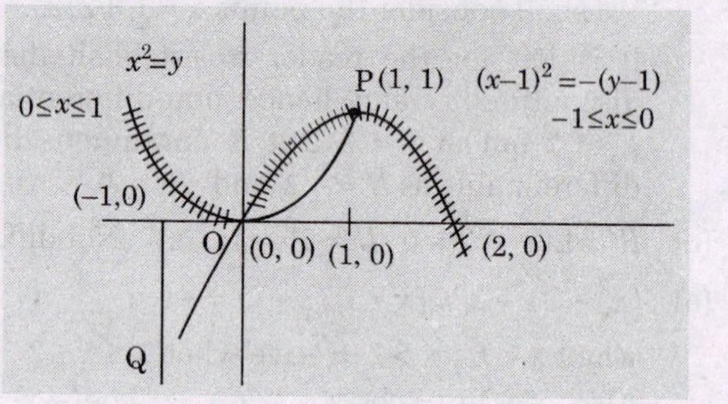

Fig. 19

59. $x^2-x=x(x-1) \quad \therefore \quad x=0, 1$.

$\therefore \quad |x^2-x|=x^2-x$ when $x<0$ or $x>1$

$\quad =-(x^2-x)$ when $0<x<1$.

$$\therefore \quad f(x)\begin{cases} =1, & x<0 \text{ or } x>1 \\ =-1, & 0<x<1 \\ =1, & x=0 \\ =-1, & x=1 \end{cases}$$

At $x=1, R=1, L=-1, V=-1$

$\therefore$ Discontinuous.

At $x=0, R=-1, L=1, V=1$

$\therefore$ Discontinuous.

Hence $f(x)$ is continuous $\forall$ x except at $x=0$ and $x=1$.

60. Here $x=2t-|t|$, $y=t^2+t|t|$

Let $t\geq 0$, then $x=2t-t=t$, $y=t^2+t^2=2t^2$

$\therefore \quad y=2x^2, x\geq 0 \quad [\because t\geq 0 \Rightarrow x\geq 0]$

And for $t\leq 0$, $x=2t+t=3t$, $y=t^2-t^2=0$

$\therefore \quad t=x/3$ and $t\leq 0 \Rightarrow x\leq 0$

Thus $y=0$, when $x\leq 0$.

Hence the function is defined by

$f(x)=y=2x^2, \; x\geq 0$

and $f(x)=y=0, \quad x\leq 0$

The function f is continuous at $x=0$, since

$$f(0+0)=\operatorname*{Lt}_{h\to 0} 2(0+h)^2=0,$$

$f(0-0)=0$ and $f(0)=0$

f is also differentiable at $x=0$, for we have

$$Rf'(0)=\operatorname*{Lt}_{h\to 0}\frac{2(0+h)^2-0}{h}=\operatorname*{Lim}_{h\to 0} 2h=0$$

and $Lf'(0) = \underset{h\to 0}{\text{Lt}} \dfrac{0-0}{-h} = 0.$

Thus the function f is continuous and differentiable for all real x.

The graph of the function is shown below.

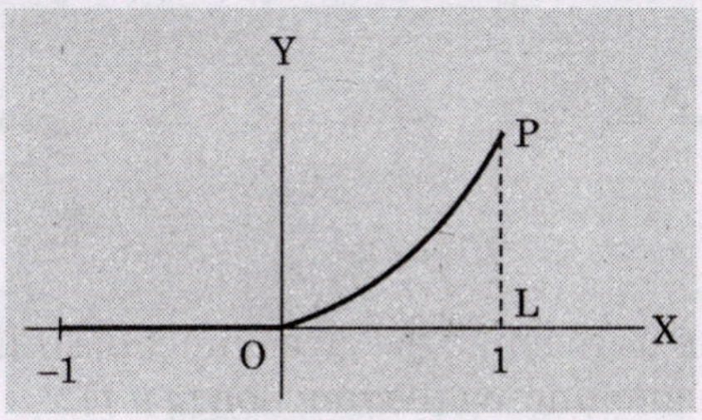

Fig. 20

61. $f(x) = \sqrt{|x-1|}$ and $g(x) = \sin x$ for all $x \in R$

$\therefore \quad f(x) = \sqrt{(x-1)}, x \ge 1, f(x) = \sqrt{(1-x)}, x \le 1$

$\therefore \quad (fog)\, x = f(g(x)) = f(\sin x)$ for all $x \in R$

Since $\sin x \le 1$ for all $x \in R$ therefore by definition of $f(x)$, we have

$f(\sin x) = \sqrt{(1-\sin x)}$ for all $x \in R$.

$\therefore \quad (fog)\, x = \sqrt{(1-\sin x)}$ ...(1)

$(gof)\, x = g(f(x)) = g(\sqrt{x-1})$ for all $x \ge 1$

$= g(\sqrt{1-x})$ for all $x \le 1$

$= \sin\sqrt{x-1}$ for all $x \ge 1$. ...(2)

$= \sin\sqrt{1-x}$ for all $x \le 1$. ...(3)

Differentiability of $F(x) = (gof)\, x$ at $x = 1$

$RF'(1) = \lim_{h\to 0} \dfrac{F(1+h) - F(1)}{h}$

$= \lim_{h\to 0} \dfrac{\sin\sqrt{(1+h-1)} - 0}{h}$ by (2)

$= \lim_{h\to 0} \dfrac{\sin\sqrt{h}}{\sqrt{h}} \cdot \dfrac{1}{\sqrt{h}} = \infty$

$LF'(1) = \lim_{h\to 0} \dfrac{F(1-h) - F(1)}{-h}$

$= \lim_{h\to 0} \dfrac{\sin\sqrt{1-(1-h)} - 0}{-h}$ by (3)

$= \lim_{h\to 0} \dfrac{\sin\sqrt{h}}{-h} = \lim_{h\to 0} \dfrac{\sin\sqrt{h}}{\sqrt{h}} \cdot \dfrac{-1}{\sqrt{h}} = -\infty$

Since $RF'(1) \ne LF'(1)$ therefore $F(x)$ i.e. $(gof)\, x$ is not differentiable at $x = 1$.

62. $(f\,o\,g)\, x = f(g(x)) = f(\sqrt{x^2+1}) = (\sqrt{x^2+1})^2 - 1$

$= x^2 + 1 - 1 = x^2$

Let $F = f\,o\,g$ so that $F(x) = x^2$

Since F is many-one (both x and $-x$ have the same image) hence $F = f\,o\,g$ is not invertible.

Again $(h\,o\,f\,o\,g)\, x = h(x^2) = \begin{bmatrix} 0, & x^2 \le 0 \\ x^2, & x^2 \ge 0 \end{bmatrix}$

or $h(x^2) = \begin{bmatrix} 0, & x = 0 \\ x^2, & x \ne 0 \text{ or } x > 0 \end{bmatrix}$

By definition of identity function

$I(x) = x \;\forall\; x$

Here $h(x) = \begin{bmatrix} 0, & x \le 0 \\ x; & x \ge 0 \end{bmatrix}$

Hence h is not an identity function.

63. (a) We are given :

$f(x) = -1 + |x-1|, \; -1 \le x \le 3,$

$g(x) = 2 - |x+1|, -2 \le x \le 2.$

Using the definition of modulus function, we write the above relations as :

$f(x) = -1 - (x-1) = -x, \qquad -1 \le x \le 1$

$= -1 + (x-1) = x - 2, \qquad 1 \le x \le 3$

and $g(x) = 2 - [-(x+1)] = 3 + x, \qquad -2 \le x \le -1.$

$= 2 - (x+1) = 1 - x, \qquad -1 \le x \le 2.$

To find fog, we consider the following sub-intervals :

(i) $-2 \le x \le -1$ (ii) $-1 \le x \le 0$

(iii) $0 \le x \le 1$ (iv) $1 \le x \le 2$

(v) $2 \le x \le 3$

On the interval $-2 \le x \le -1$, we have

$(fog)(x) = f(g(x)) = f(3+x),$

$= (3+x) - 2 = 1 + x,$

$[\because -2 \le x \le -1 \Rightarrow 1 \le 3 + x \le 2]$

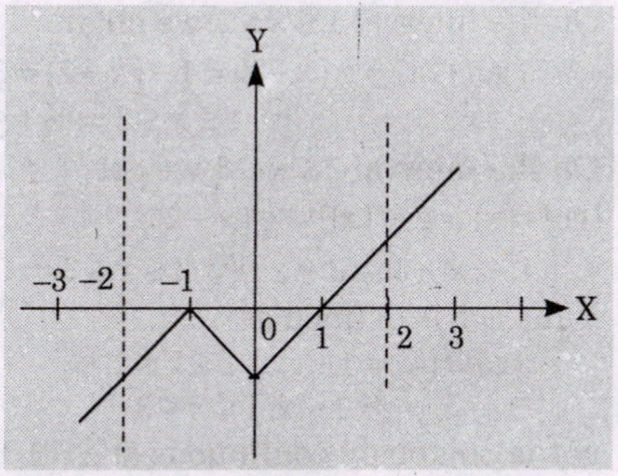

Fig. 21

On the interval $-1 \le x \le 0$, we get

$(fog)(x) = f(g(x))$

$= f(1-x) = 1 - x - 2 = -1 - x$

$[\because -1 \le x \le 0 \Rightarrow 0 \le -x \le 1 \Rightarrow 1 \le 1 - x \le 2]$

On the interval $0 \le x \le 1$, we obtain

$(fog)\, x = f(g(x)) = f(1-x)$

$= -(1-x) = x - 1.$

$[\because \; 0 \le x \le 1 \Rightarrow -1 \le -x \le 0 \Rightarrow 0 \le 1 - x \le 1]$

On the interval $1 \le x \le 2$, we have

$(fog)\, x = f(g(x)) = f(1-x)$

$= -(1-x) = x - 1 \qquad [\because \; 1 \le x \le 2]$

$\Rightarrow -2 \le -x \le -1$

$\Rightarrow -1 \le 1 - x \le 0]$

On the interval $1 \le x \le 3$, $g(x)$ is undefined and fog is also undefined.

Hence *fog* is defined as follows :

$$(fog)(x) = 1 + x, \quad -2 \le x \le -1$$
$$= -1 - x, \quad -1 \le x \le 0$$
$$= x - 1 \quad 0 \le x \le 2$$

To test *fog* for continuity at

$x = -1$, we have

$(fog)(-1) = 1 - 1 = 0,$

$(fog)(-1-0) = \lim_{h \to 0} [1 + (-1-h)] = 0$

and $(fog)(-1+0) = \lim_{h \to 0} [-1-(-1+h)] = 0$

$\therefore \quad fog(-1-0) = (fog)(-1) = (fog)(-1+0),$

The function *fog* is continuous at $x = -1$

To draw the graph of *fog*, we write $(fog)(x) = y$. Then

$$y = 1 + x, \quad -2 \le x \le -1$$
$$y = -1 - x, \quad -1 \le x \le 0$$
$$y = x - 1, \quad 0 \le x \le 2$$

We now find (gof).

On the interval $-2 \le x \le -1$, $f(x)$ is undefined and so $(gof)(x)$ is also undefined.

On the interval $-1 \le x \le 0$, we have

$(gof)(x) = g(f(x)) = g(-x)$

$= 1 - (-x) = 1 + x \quad [\because -1 \le x \le 0 \Rightarrow 0 \le -x \le 1]$

On the interval $0 \le x \le 1$, we get

$(gof)(x) = g(f(x)) = g(-x) = 1 - (-x) = 1 + x$

$[\because \ 0 \le x \le 1 \Rightarrow -1 \le -x \le 0]$

On the interval $1 \le x \le 2$, we obtain

$(gof)(x) = g(x-2) = 1 - (x-2) = 3 - x$

$[\because \ 1 \le x \le 2 \Rightarrow -1 \le x - 2 \le 0]$

On the interval $2 \le x \le 3$, we get

$(gof)(x) = g(f(x)) = g(x-2)$

$= 1 - (x-2) = 3 - x \quad [\because \ 2 \le x \le 3 \Rightarrow 0 \le x - 2 \le 1]$

Thus *gof* is defined as

$$(gof)(x) = 1 + x, -1 \le x \le 1,$$
$$= 3 - x, 1 \le x \le 3.$$

gof is obviously continuous at $x = 1$. We now test *gof* for differentiability at $x = 1$. We have

$$L(gof)'(1) = \lim_{h \to 0} \frac{(gof)(1-h) - (gof)(1)}{-h}$$

$$= \lim_{h \to 0} \frac{1 + (1-h) - 2}{-h} = \lim_{h \to 0} \frac{-h}{-h} = 1$$

and $R(gof)'(1) = \lim_{h \to 0} \dfrac{(gof)(1+h) - (gof)(1)}{h}$

$$= \lim_{h \to 0} \frac{3 - (1+h) - 2}{h} = \lim_{h \to 0} \frac{-h}{h} = -1$$

Since $R(gof)'(1) \ne L(gof)'(1)$,

the function *gof* is not differentiable at $x = 1$.

To draw graph of *gof*, we write $(gof)(x) = y$.

Then $\quad y = 1 + x, \ -1 \le x \le 1$

$\quad = 3 - x, \ 1 \le x \le 3.$

The graph consists of two line segments *AB* and *BC* as shown in the fig.

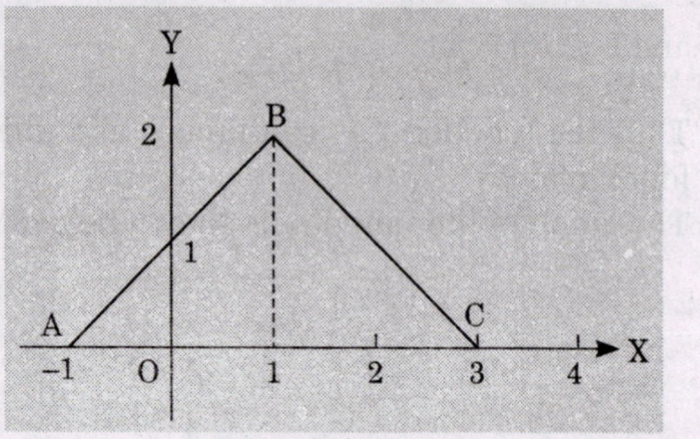

Fig. 22

(b) Let us redefine the given functions $f(x)$ and $g(x)$ before finding the function $(g \circ f)\,x$

$$f(x) = \begin{cases} x + a, & x < 0 \\ |x - 1|, & x \ge 0 \end{cases}$$

$$= \left.\begin{array}{l} x + a, \ x < 0 \\ x - 1, \ x > 1 \\ -(x-1), 0 \le x \le 1 \\ = 1 - x \end{array}\right\} \quad ...(A)$$

$$g(x) = \left\{\begin{array}{ll} x + 1 & \forall \, x < 0 \\ (x-1)^2 + b & \forall \, x \ge 0 \end{array}\right\} \quad ...(B)$$

$\therefore \quad (g \circ f)\, x = g[f(x)]$ Apply definition of g

$$= \left\{\begin{array}{l} f(x) + 1, f(x) < 0 \\ [f(x) - 1]^2 + b, f(x) \ge 0 \end{array}\right\} \quad ...(C)$$

by (B).

Now combine (A) and (C) by putting for the values of $f(x)$ in different intervals of (A).

$$= \begin{cases} (x + a) + 1, x + a < 0, x < 0 \\ (1 - x) + 1, (1 - x) < 0, 0 \le x \le 1 \\ (x - 1) + 1, (x - 1) < 0, x > 1 \\ (x + a - 1)^2 + b, x + a \ge 0, x < 0 \\ (1 - x - 1)^2 + b, 1 - x \ge 0, 0 \le x \le 1 \\ (x - 1 - 1)^2 + b, x - 1 \ge 0, x > 1 \end{cases}$$

$$\therefore (g \circ f)\, x = \left\{\begin{array}{ll} x + a + 1, & x < -a \\ (x + a - 1)^2 + b, & -a \le x < 0 \\ x^2 + b, & 0 \le x \le 1 \\ (x - 2)^2 + b & x > 1 \end{array}\right\} \quad ...(D)$$

Now $F(x) = (g \circ f)\, x$ is continuous at $x = a$ if $L = R = V$ at $x = -a, x = 0$ for $F = g \circ f$

At $x = -a, 1 = 1 + b = 1 + b \Rightarrow b = 0$

At $x = 0, (a - 1)^2 + b = b$

$\Rightarrow \quad (a-1)^2 = 0 \quad \because \ b = 0 \ \Rightarrow \ a = 1.$

Now putting the values of a and b in (D), we get

$$(g \circ f)\, x = \begin{cases} x + 2 & , \quad x < -1 \\ x^2 & , \quad -1 \le x \le 1 \\ (x-2)^2 & , \quad x > 1 \end{cases}$$

Clearly $F(x) = (g \circ f)\, x$ is differentiable at $x = 0$.

64. (i) Since f is continuous at a, we have

Value = R.H.L.

$f(a) = \lim_{h \to 0} f(a + h) = \lim_{h \to 0} [f(a) + f(h)]$

[see definition of f]

$= \lim_{h\to 0} f(a) + \lim_{h\to 0} f(h) = f(a) + \lim_{h\to 0} f(h)$

Hence $\lim_{h\to 0} f(h) = 0.$ ...(1)

Similarly Value = L.H.L.

$\therefore \quad f(a) = \lim_{h\to 0} f(a-h) = f(a) + \lim_{h\to 0} f(-h)$

$\therefore \quad \lim_{h\to 0} f(-h) = 0.$ ...(2)

Now let α be any member of **R**. To show that f is continuous at α. We have R.H.L.

$\lim_{h\to 0} f(\alpha+h) = \lim_{h\to 0} [f(\alpha) + f(h)]$

$= \lim_{h\to 0} f(\alpha) + \lim_{h\to 0} f(h)$

$= f(\alpha) + \lim_{h\to 0} f(h) = f(\alpha)$, by (1)

Similarly by using (2), we shall have

L.H.L. $f(\alpha - h) = f(\alpha)$

Hence R.H.L. = L.H.L = Value

It follows that f is continuous at α. Since α is arbitrary, the function f is continuous for all $x \in \mathbf{R}$.

(ii) It is a particular case of (i) with $a = 0$.

(iii) **Case I :** First let $x = 0$.

Since $f(x+x) = f(x) + f(x)$, we have

$f(0) = f(0) + f(0)$

and so $f(0) = 0$.

Thus $f(x) = kx$ is satisfied for all constants k in this case.

In particular $f(x) = x f(1)$.

Case II : Let x be any positive integer. Then

$f(x) = f(1 + 1 + \ldots x \text{ times})$

$= f(1) + f(1) + \ldots x \text{ times} = x f(1)$.

Case III : Let x be any negative integer. Put $x = -y$ so that y is a positive integer.

Now $f(0) = f(y - y) = f(y) + f(-y)$

or $f(y) + f(-y) = 0$, by case I.

Hence $f(x) = f(-y) = -f(y)$

$= -y f(1)$ by case II $= x f(1)$

Case IV : Let x be any rational number. Put $x = \frac{p}{q}$ where q is a positive integer and p is any integer, positive, negative or zero. Then

$f\{q(p/q)\} = f(p/q + p/q + \ldots\ldots\ldots q \text{ times})$

$= f(p/q) + f(p/q) + \ldots\ldots\ldots q$ times

$\therefore \quad f(p) = q f(p/q)$.

But $f(p) = p f(1)$ by previous cases.

Hence $q f(p/q) = p f(1)$

or $f(p/q) = (p/q) f(1)$

or $f(x) = x f(1)$ in this case also.

Case V : Finally let x be any real number, and let $\{x_n\}$ be a sequence of rational numbers which represents x. Since f is continuous at x, the sequence $\{f(x_n)\}$ converges to $f(x)$.

Thus $\lim_{n\to\infty} x_n = x$ and $\lim_{n\to\infty} f(x_n) = f(x)$

Since x_n is a rational number, we have by case IV,

$f(x_n) = x_n f(1)$

$\therefore \quad \lim_{n\to\infty} f(x_n) = f(1) \lim_{n\to\infty} x_n$

or $f(x) = x f(1)$.

Thus we have shown that

$f(x) = x f(1) \cdot x \in \mathbf{R}$.

65. For continuity at $x = 1$, we must know $f(1)$.

Hence put $x = y = 1 \quad \therefore \quad f(1) = f(1) f(1)$

or $f(1)[f(1) - 1] = 0$

$\therefore \quad f(1) = 0$ or $f(1) = 1$

Case I. $f(1) = 0$; then $f(x) = f(x.1) = f(x) f(1)$

or $f(x) = f(x).0 = 0 \quad \forall \; x \in R$.

Thus $f(x)$ is a constant function and hence it is continuous.

Case II. $f(1) = 1$; then $f(x)$ is continuous at $x = 1$

$\therefore \quad R = L = V$ at $x = 1$

$\therefore \quad \text{Lt}_{h\to 0} f(1+h) = \text{Lt}_{h\to 0} f(1-h) = f(1) = 1$ ...(1)

We have to prove that $f(x)$ is continuous at any aribitrary point $x = a$

$R = \text{Lt}_{h\to 0} f(a+h) = \text{Lt}_{h\to 0} f\left\{a\left(1+\frac{h}{a}\right)\right\}$

$= \text{Lt}_{h\to 0} f(a) f\left(1+\frac{h}{a}\right) = f(a) f(1) = f(a)$, by (1)

Similarly $L = f(a)$

Thus $R = L = V = f(a)$

Hence the function is continuous at $x = a$ but a being arbitrary we conclude $f(x)$ is continuous at all points $x \neq 0$.

66. (a) Writing δx for y in the given condition (a), we have

$f(x + \delta x) = f(x) f(\delta x)$.

Then $f(x+\delta x) - f(x) = f(x) f(\delta x) - f(x)$

or $\frac{f(x+\delta x) - f(x)}{\delta x} = \frac{f(x)[f(\delta x) - 1]}{\delta x}$

$= \frac{f(x)\,\delta x\, g(\delta x)}{\delta x}$, by condition (b)

$= f(x) g(\delta x)$.

Hence $\lim_{\delta x\to 0} \frac{f(x+\delta x) - f(x)}{\delta x} = \lim_{\delta x\to 0} f(x) g(\delta x)$

$= f(x).1$,

since by hypothesis $\lim_{\delta x\to 0} g(\delta x) = 1$.

It follows that $f'(x) = f(x)$.

Since $f(x)$ exists, $f'(x)$ also exists and

$f'(x) = f(x)$.

(b) We are given :

$f(x+y) = f(x) f(y)$ for all real x and y ...(1)

For $x = y = 0$, we get from (1),

$f(0) = f(0) f(0) \Rightarrow f(0) = 1$ ...(2)

$[\because f(0) \neq 0]$

Now $f'(x) = \lim_{h\to 0} \frac{f(x+h) - f(x)}{h}$

$= \lim_{h \to 0} \frac{f(x) f(h) - f(x)}{h}$, by (1)

$= f(x) \lim_{h \to 0} \frac{f(h) - 1}{h} = f(x) \lim_{h \to 0} \frac{f(h) - f(0)}{h}$ by (2)

$= f(x) f'(0) = f(x) . 2$ $[\because f'(0) = 2]$

Thus $f'(x) = 2 f(x) \ \forall \ x$.

Again $\frac{f'(x)}{f(x)} = 2$. On integrating both sides we have

$\log f(x) = 2x + \log A,$

When $x = 0, \log f(0) = 0 + \log A$.

$\Rightarrow$ $\log 1 = \log A \Rightarrow \log A = 0$.

$\therefore$ $\log f(x) = 2x$ or $f(x) = e^{2x}$.

67. (a) Differentiating the given relation

$h(x) = [f(x)]^2 + [g(x)]^2,$

with respect to x, we get

$h'(x) = 2 f(x) f'(x) + 2g(x) g'(x)$. ...(1)

But we are given $f''(x) = - f(x)$ and $f'(x) = g(x)$ so that $f''(x) = g'(x)$.

Then (1) may be re-written as

$h'(x) = - 2f''(x) f'(x) + 2f'(x) f''(x) = 0$.

Thus $h'(x) = 0$,

Whence by intergrating, we get

$h(x) = \text{constant} = c$, say

Hence $h(x) = c$, for all x.

In particular, $h(5) = c$. But we are given $h(5) = 11$.

It follows that $c = 11$ and we have $h(x) = 11$ for all x.

Therefore $h(10) = 11$.

(b) $f(x)$ is continuous and takes all rational values $\forall \ x$ s.t. $1 \le x \le 3$.

Therefore $f(x)$ must be a constant function. Between any two rational numbers there exist infinite number of irrational numbers. If $f(x)$ is not constant then it cannot be continuous.

$\therefore$ $f(x) = c \ \ \forall \ x$ but $f(2) = 10$ $\therefore$ $f(1 \cdot 5) = 10$

68. (a) We are given $f(x + y) = f(x) f(y)$ ...(1) for all x and y.

In the identity (1), we put $x = 5, y = 0$.

Then $f(5) = f(5) f(0)$.

This gives $f(0) = 1$ $[\because f(5) = 2 \neq 0]$.

Now $f'(5) = \lim_{h \to 0} \frac{f(5 + h) - f(5)}{h}$

$= \lim_{h \to 0} \frac{f(5) f(h) - f(5)}{h}$,

by the given identity

$= f(5) \lim_{h \to 0} \frac{f(h) - 1}{h} = f(5) \lim_{h \to 0} \frac{f(h) - f(0)}{h}$

$[\because f(0) = 1]$

$= f(5) f'(0), = 2 \times 3 = 6$

by definition of differential coefficient.

(b) Put $y = z = - 1$

$\therefore$ $f(x - 2) = f(x) f(-1) f(-1) = f(x) [f(-1)]^2$

Now put $x = 2$ to find $f(0)$

$\therefore$ $f(0) = f(2) [f(-1)]^2 = 4 [f(-1)]^2 = +\text{ive}$...(1)

Above shows that $f(0)$ is +ive.

Now put $y = 0, z = 0$

$\therefore$ $f(x) = f(x) \{f(0)\}^2$ $\therefore$ $[f(0)]^2 = 1$.

$\therefore$ $f(0) = \pm 1$ but by (1) $f(0)$ is +ive

$\therefore$ We choose $f(0) = 1$ ...(2)

Now we have to find $f'(2)$. Put $y = 2, z = 0$.

$\therefore$ $f(x + 2) = f(x) f(2) . f(0) = 4 f(x)$ by (2)

$\therefore$ $f'(x + 2) = 4f'(x)$

Now put $x = 0$. $f'(2) = 4f'(0) = 4.3 = 12$.

69. $f\left(\frac{x + y}{2}\right) = \frac{f(x) + f(y)}{2}$ ...(1)

Value at mean of two points =

Mean of values at those points ...(1)

Putting $y = 0$ and $f(0) = 1$ in (1)

$f\left(\frac{x}{2}\right) = \frac{1}{2}[f(x) + 1]$

$\therefore$ $f(x) = 2 . f\left(\frac{x}{2}\right) - 1$ ...(2)

Now $f'(x) = \underset{h \to 0}{\text{Lt}} \frac{f(x + h) - f(x)}{h}$

$= \underset{h \to 0}{\text{Lt}} \frac{1}{h}\left[\frac{f(2x) + f(2h)}{2} - f(x)\right]$ by (1)

$= \underset{h \to 0}{\text{Lt}} \frac{1}{h}\left[\frac{(2 f(x) - 1) + (2f(h) - 1)}{2} - f(x)\right]$ by (2)

$= \underset{h \to 0}{\text{Lt}} \frac{1}{h}[f(h) - 1] = \underset{h \to 0}{\text{Lt}} \frac{f(h) - f(0)}{h} = f'(0) = - 1$

Hence $f'(x) = - 1$ integrating

$f(x) = - x + c$. Putting $x = 0$

$f(0) = c = 1$ by (1) $\therefore$ $f(x) = 1 - x$

$f(2) = 1 - 2 = - 1$

70. (a) Let $F(x) = f(x) + g(x)$ where $f(x)$ is continuous and $g(x)$ is discontinuous. Let us suppose that $F(x)$ be continuous so that $F(x) - f(x)$ is also continuous *i.e.* $g(x)$ is also continuous.

But it is a contradiction as $g(x)$ is given to be discontinuous.

$\therefore$ $F(x)$ must be discontinuous.

(b) $f(-x) = f(x)$ given. Also $f'(0)$ exists

$\therefore$ $\text{Lt} \frac{f(0 - h) - f(0)}{- h} = \text{Lt} \frac{f(0 + h) - f(0)}{h}$,

by definition

or $\text{Lt} \frac{f(h) - f(0)}{- h} = \text{Lt} \frac{f(h) - f(0)}{h}$,

by given condition.

$\therefore$ $2 \, \text{Lt} \frac{f(h) - f(0)}{h} = 0$ or $2 f'(0) = 0$

$\therefore$ $f'(0) = 0$.

71. (a) Consider the function f defined as follows :

$f(x) = x^2$ for $x > 1, f(x) = x^3$ for $x < 1$.

This function is not defined at $x = 1$.

Now $f(1+0) = \lim_{h \to 0} (1+h)^2 = 1$

$f(1-0) = \lim_{h \to 0} (1-h)^3 = 1$

Hence $f(1+0) = f(1-0) = 1$.

This shows that the function has the limit 1 as $x \to 1$.

(b) Consider the function ϕ defined as follows :

$\phi(x) = -x^2$ for $x < 1, \phi(x) = x^2$ for $x > 1$.

This function is not defined at $x = 1$. Moreover

$\phi(1-0) = \lim_{h \to 0} -(1-h)^2 = -1$

and $\phi(1+0) = \lim_{h \to 0} (1+h)^2 = 1$.

Since $\phi(1-0) \neq \phi(1+0)$,

the limit does not exist at $x = 1$.

(c) Consider the function ϕ defined as follows :

$\phi(x) = 0$ for $x \le 0$,

$\phi(x) = \frac{3}{2} - x$ for $0 < x \le \frac{1}{2}$,

$\phi(x) = \frac{3}{2} + x$ for $x > \frac{1}{2}$.

The function is defined for $x = 0$ and $x = \frac{1}{2}$ but is discontinuous at both these points as can be easily seen.

72. From the definition of $E(x)$, we have

$E(x) = n - 1$ for $n - 1 \le x < n$

$E(x) = n$ for $n \le x < n + 1$

$E(x) = n + 1$ for $n + 1 \le x \le n + 2$

and so on where n is an integer.

We consider $x = n$.

We have $E(n) = n$.

$E(n-0) = n - 1$ and $E(n+0) = n + 1$

Since $E(n+0) \neq E(n-0) \neq E(n)$.

The function $E(x)$ is discontinuous when $x = n$ *i.e.* when x has an integral value.

To draw the graph, we put

$n = \ldots, -4, -3, -2, -1, 0, 1, 2, 3, 4, \ldots$

$y = -5$ when $-5 \le x < -4$

$y = -4$ when $-4 \le x < -3$

$y = -3$ when $-3 \le x < -2$

$y = -2$ when $-2 \le x < -1$

$y = -1$ when $-1 \le x < 0$

$y = 0$ when $0 \le x < 1$

$y = 1$ when $1 \le x < 2$

$y = 2$ when $2 \le x < 3$

$y = 3$ when $3 \le x < 4$

$y = 4$ when $4 \le x < 5$

and so on.

The graph is shown by thick lines in the figure given below.

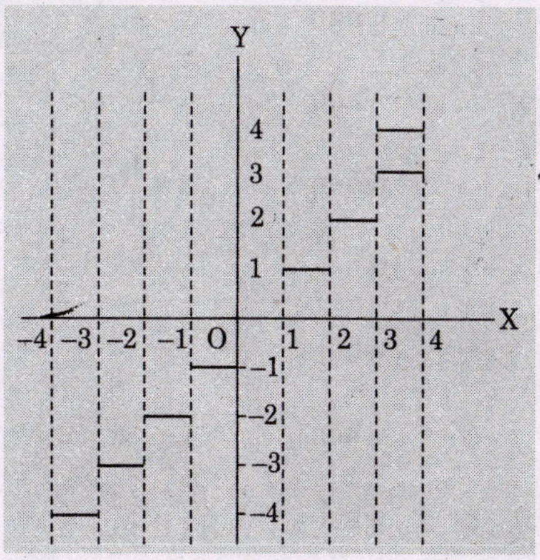

Fig. 23

73. From the definition of (x), we get

$(x) = x - n$ when $n - \frac{1}{2} < x < n + \frac{1}{2}$

$(x) = 0$ when $x = n + \frac{1}{2}$

$(x) = x - (n+1)$ when $n + \frac{1}{2} < x < n + \frac{3}{2}$,

where n is an integer.

We consider $x = n + \frac{1}{2}$. Then $\left(n + \frac{1}{2}\right) = 0$,

$$\left(n + \frac{1}{2} - 0\right) = \lim_{x \to n + \frac{1}{2} - 0} [x - n]$$

$$= \lim_{h \to 0} \left[n + \frac{1}{2} - h - n\right] = \frac{1}{2}$$

$$\left(n + \frac{1}{2} + 0\right) = \lim_{x \to n + \frac{1}{2} + 0} [x - (n+1)]$$

$$= \lim_{h \to 0} \left[n + \frac{1}{2} + h - (n+1)\right] = -\frac{1}{2}$$

Since $\left(n + \frac{1}{2} + 0\right) \neq \left(n + \frac{1}{2} - 0\right) \neq \left(n + \frac{1}{2}\right)$,

The function (x) is discontinuous when $x = n + \frac{1}{2}$ where n is an integer.

To draw the graph, we put

$n = \ldots, -3, -2, -1, 0, 1, 2, 3, \ldots$

Then putting $(x) = y$, we have

$y = x + 3$ when $-3\frac{1}{2} < x < -2\frac{1}{2}$

$y = 0$ when $x = -2\frac{1}{2}$

$y = x + 2$ when $-2\frac{1}{2} < x < -1\frac{1}{2}$

$y = 0$ when $x = -1\frac{1}{2}$

$y = x + 1$ when $-1\frac{1}{2} < x < -\frac{1}{2}$

$y = 0$ when $x = -\frac{1}{2}$

$y = x$ when $-\frac{1}{2} < x < \frac{1}{2}$

$y = 0$ when $x = \frac{1}{2}$

$y = x - 1$ when $\frac{1}{2} < x < 1\frac{1}{2}$

$y = 0$ when $x = 1\frac{1}{2}$

$y = x - 2$ when $1\frac{1}{2} < x < 2\frac{1}{2}$

$y = 0$ when $x = 2\frac{1}{2}$

$y = x - 3$ when $2\frac{1}{2} < x < 3\frac{1}{2}$

$y = 0$ when $x = 3\frac{1}{2}$

and so on. The following graph consists of segment of parallel straight lines.

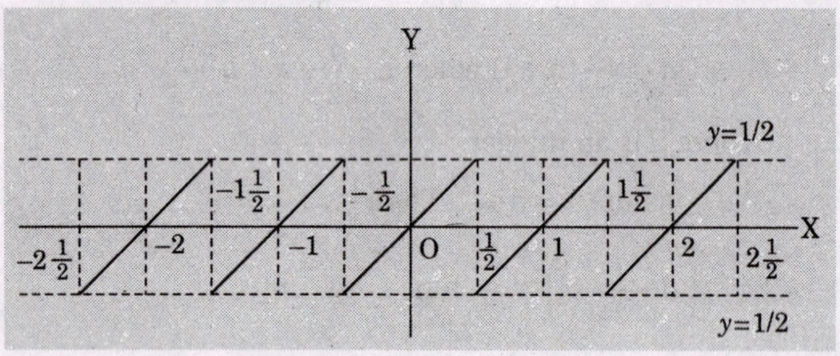

Fig. 24

$x - y = -2;\ x - y = -1;\ x - y = 0$

$x - y = 1;\ x - y = 2.$

and so on between open intervals of

$]-2\frac{1}{2}, -1\frac{1}{2}[,]-1\frac{1}{2}, -\frac{1}{2}[,]-\frac{1}{2}, \frac{1}{2}[$

$]\frac{1}{2}, 1\frac{1}{2}[,]1\frac{1}{2}, 2\frac{1}{2}[$

and so on and the points $x = \pm\frac{1}{2}, \pm\frac{3}{2}, \pm\frac{5}{2}, \ldots$ on x-axis.

The graph is shown by thick lines and thick dots or x-axis. From the graph, it is evident that the function (x) is discontinuous at

$$x = \pm\frac{1}{2}, \pm\frac{3}{2}, \pm\frac{5}{2}, \ldots \text{ and so on.}$$

74. $F(x) = \int f(t)\, dt$

$\therefore \quad F'(x) = f(x).1 - f(0).0$

We are given that $\forall x \geq 0$, $f(x)$ is a non-neg. continuous function.

$\therefore \quad f(x) \geq 0$ ...(1)

Also $f(x) \leq c\,F(x)\ \forall\ x \geq 0, c > 0$

Taking limit of both sides when $c \to 0$

$$\lim_{c \to 0+} f(x) \leq \lim_{c \to 0+} F(x) \lim_{c \to 0+} c = 0$$

$\therefore \quad f(x) \leq 0 \Rightarrow f(x) = 0$ by (1) ...(2)

75. Since g is continuous at $x = \alpha$

$\therefore \quad R = L = V$

or $\lim_{h \to 0} g(\alpha + h) = \lim_{h \to 0} g(\alpha - h) = g(\alpha)$ ...(1)

Also $\dfrac{f(x) - f(\alpha)}{x - \alpha} = g(x)$ ...(2)

Now for differentiability of $f(x)$ at $x = \alpha$ we must have $R' = L'$ *i.e.* $\lim_{h \to 0} \dfrac{f(\alpha + h) - f(\alpha)}{h}$

$$= \lim_{h \to 0} \frac{f(\alpha - h) - f(\alpha)}{-h}$$

$$R' = \lim \frac{f(\alpha) + g(\alpha + h).h - f(\alpha)}{h}$$

$= \lim g(\alpha + h) = g(\alpha)$ by (1)

$$L' = \lim \frac{f(\alpha) + g(\alpha - h)(-h) - f(\alpha)}{-h}$$

$= \lim g(\alpha - h) = g(\alpha)$ by (1)

Since $R' = L'$ hence $f(x)$ is differentiable at $x = \alpha$.

76. We are given that f is a function from **R** to **R** such that

$$|f(x) - f(y)| \leq |x - y|^3$$

...(1)

where (1) holds for all real numbers x and y. Let x be any real number and let y be chosen arbitrarily close to x but not equal to x. Then writing (1) as

$$\left|\frac{f(x) - f(y)}{x - y}\right| \leq |x - y|^2$$

and letting $y \to x$, we get

$$\lim_{y \to x} \left|\frac{f(x) - f(y)}{x - y}\right| \leq \lim_{y \to x} |x - y|^2 \quad \ldots(2)$$

Since $\lim_{y \to x} \dfrac{f(x) - f(y)}{x - y} = f'(x)$, we see from (2) that

$$|f'(x)| = 0 \to f'(x) = 0.$$

Hence $f(x)$ is constant.

77. (i) Using *LMVT*, there exists $b \in (0, 4)$ such that

$$f'(b) = \frac{f(4) - f(0)}{4} \quad \ldots(1)$$

Now $(f(4))^2 - (f(0))^2 = \left[\dfrac{(f(4) - f(0))}{4}\right]$

$[f(4) + f(0)] \times 4$ From (1)

$(f(4))^2 - (f(0))^2 = f'(b)(f(4) + f(0)) \times 4$

$\Rightarrow \quad \dfrac{f(0) + f(4)}{2} = f(a)$

Range of function f must contain the interval

$[f(0), f(4)]$ or $[f(4), f(0)]$

according as

$f(0) \leq f(4)$ or $f(0) \geq f(4)$

Now $\dfrac{f(0) + f(4)}{2}$ is the mean value of $f(0)$ and $f(4)$ $\therefore$ $\left(\dfrac{f(0) + f(4)}{2}\right) \in$ Range of the function

$\Rightarrow \quad a \in [0, 4]$ for which $f(a) = \dfrac{f(0) + f(4)}{2}$

Hence Proved.

(ii) Let $\sqrt{t} = x \Rightarrow t = x^2$

$\Rightarrow \quad dt = 2x\,dx.$

Thus $\int_0^4 f(t)\,dt = 2\int_0^2 xf(x^2)\,dx = 2(2-0)\,f(\varepsilon)$

for some $\varepsilon \in (0, 2)$,

[Using mean value theorem for definite integral of a differentiable function]

Thus $\int_0^4 f(t)\,dt = 2(f(\varepsilon) + f(\varepsilon))$

$= 2(\alpha f(\alpha^2) + \beta f(\beta^2))$,

where $\alpha = \beta = \varepsilon$.

(iii) Ans. (c). Differentiate both sides w.r.t. x.

$$1 - [f'(x)]^2 = f(x) \geq 0 \text{ given}$$

$\therefore \quad |f'(x)| \leq 1$

Apply Lagranges mean value theorem on $f(x)$ in $\left[0, \dfrac{1}{2}\right]$

$$|f'(x)| \left| \frac{f\left(\frac{1}{2}\right) - f(0)}{\frac{1}{2} - 0} \right| < 1$$

$\therefore \quad f\left(\dfrac{1}{2}\right) < \dfrac{1}{2}$ as $f(0) = 0$

Again apply Lagranges mean value theorem on $f(x)$ in $\left[0, \dfrac{1}{3}\right]$

$$|f'(x)| = \left| \frac{f\left(\frac{1}{3}\right) - f(0)}{\frac{1}{3} - 0} \right| < 1$$

or $\quad f\left(\dfrac{1}{3}\right) < \dfrac{1}{3}$ as $f(0) = 0$

78. For differentiability at $x = 0$, we must have $R' = L'$

or $\quad \operatorname*{Lt}_{h \to 0} \dfrac{f(0+h) - f(0)}{h} = \operatorname*{Lt}_{h \to 0} \dfrac{f(0-h) - f(0)}{-h}$

$$R' = \operatorname*{Lt}_{h \to 0} \frac{\frac{e^{\frac{a}{2}h} - 1}{h} - \frac{1}{2}}{h} = \operatorname*{Lt}_{h \to 0} \frac{\left(e^{\frac{a}{2}h} - 1\right) - \frac{h}{2}}{h^2}$$

$$= \operatorname*{Lt}_{h \to 0} \frac{\left[1 + \left(\frac{a}{2}h\right) + \frac{1}{2!}\left(\frac{a}{2}h\right)^2 + \ldots - 1\right] - \frac{h}{2}}{h^2}$$

$$= \operatorname*{Lt}_{h \to 0} \frac{(a-1)\frac{h}{2} + \frac{a^2}{8}h^2 + \ldots}{h^2}$$

For the limit to exist we must have $a - 1 = 0$ *i.e.*, $a = 1$ and in that case

$$R' = \operatorname*{Lt}_{h \to 0} \frac{\frac{1}{8}h^2 + \ldots}{h^2} = \frac{1}{8}$$

$$L' = \operatorname*{Lt}_{h \to 0} \frac{b \sin^{-1}\frac{c-h}{2} - \frac{1}{2}}{-h} = R' = \frac{1}{8}$$

By expansion of $\sin^{-1} x$ the L.H.S. is

$$\operatorname*{Lt}_{h \to 0} \frac{b\left\{\frac{c-h}{2} + \frac{1^2}{3!}\left(\frac{c-h}{2}\right)^3 + \frac{1^2 \cdot 3^2}{5!}\left(\frac{c-h}{2}\right)^5 \ldots\right\} - \frac{1}{2}}{-h}$$

The constant term in N^r will be zero and the coefficient of $-h$ in the N^r will be

$$\frac{b}{2}\left\{1 + \frac{1^2}{3!}3\left(\frac{c}{2}\right)^2 + \frac{1^2 \cdot 3^2}{5!} \cdot 5\left(\frac{c}{2}\right)^4 + \ldots\right\}$$

Above is clearly differentiation of $b \sin^{-1}\dfrac{x}{2}$ at $x = c$ which must be equal to $\dfrac{1}{8} = R'$

$\therefore \quad \dfrac{b}{2} \dfrac{1}{\sqrt{1 - \frac{x^2}{4}}}$ at $x = c = \dfrac{1}{8}$

$\therefore \quad 64b^2 = 4\left(1 - \dfrac{c^2}{4}\right) = 4 - c^2.$

79. Ans. (a).

$$g(x) = \log f(x) \qquad \ldots(1)$$

Given $f(x+1) = x f(x)$

$g(x+1) = \log f(x+1) = \log\{x f(x)\}$

$= \log x + \log f(x)$

$\therefore \quad g(x+1) = \log x + g(x)$ by (1)

$\therefore \quad g(x+1) - g(x) = \log x$

$g'(x+1) - g'(x) = \dfrac{1}{x}$

$$g''(x+1) - g''(x) = -\frac{1}{x^2} \qquad \ldots(1)$$

Replace x by $y - \dfrac{1}{2}$

$\therefore \quad g''\left(y + \dfrac{1}{2}\right) - g''\left(y - \dfrac{1}{2}\right) = -\dfrac{1}{\left(y - \frac{1}{2}\right)^2} = -\dfrac{2^2}{(2y-1)^2}$

Now put $y = 1, 2, 3, \ldots, N$ and add. The terms will cancel diagonally.

$\therefore \quad g''\left(N + \dfrac{1}{2}\right) - g''\left(\dfrac{1}{2}\right)$

$$= -4\left[1 + \frac{1}{9} + \frac{1}{25} + \ldots + \frac{1}{(2N-1)^2}\right]$$

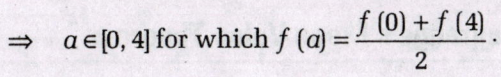

§ 5. Rolle's Theorem

If a function f defined on $[a,b]$ is such that it is

(i) continuous in the closed interval $[a,b]$,

(ii) differentiable in the open interval $]a,b[$,

(iii) $f(a)=f(b)$, then there exists at least one value of x, say $c, (a<c<b)$ such that $f'(c)=0$.

Remarks :

- Converse of Rolle's theorem is not true *i.e.*,. $f'(x)$ may vanish at a point $c\in[a,b]$ without $f(x)$ satisfying the three conditions of Roll's theorem.
- There may be more than one point like c at which $f'(x)$ vanishes but Rolle's theorem ensures the existence of at least one such c.
- Rolle's theorem will not hold good if
  (a) $f(x)$ is discontinuous at some point in the interval $[a,b]$
  (b) $f(x)$ does not exist at some point in the interval $[a,b]$
  (c) $f(a)\neq f(b)$.
- The hypothesis of Rolle's theorem can not be weakened.

  For example, if $f(x)=1-|x|, -1\le x\le 1$, then $f(-1)=f(1)=0$ and f is continuous on $[-1,1]$. Also if $f'(x)$ exist $\forall\ x\in]-1,1[$ except at $x=0$. Thus, f satisfies all the condition of Rolle's theorem except that f is not differentiable at $x=0$. For this f, there is no c in $]-1,1[$ for which $f'(c)=0$.

Geometrical Interpretation of Rolle's Theorem :

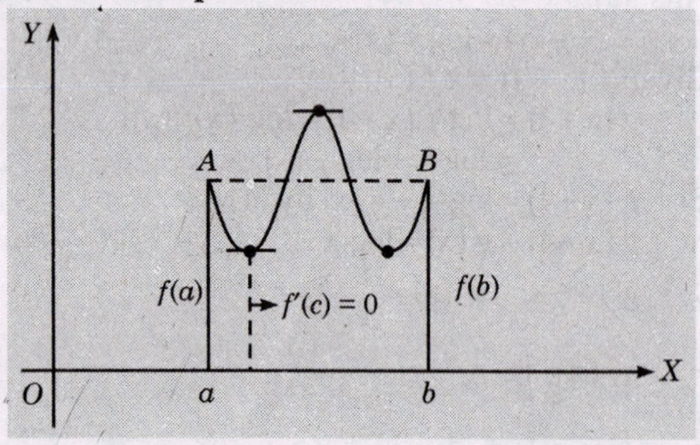

Fig. 25

Geometrically, Rolle's theoorem means that if the curve $y=f(x)$ is continuous from $x=a$ and $x=b$ has a definite tangent at each point of $[a,b]$ and the ordinates at the extremities are equal, then there exists at least one point between a and b at which the tangent is parallel to x-axis.

Algebraic Interpretation of Rolle's Theorem :

Algebraically, Rolle's theorem means that if $f(x)$ is a polynomial function in x and $x=a$ and $x=b$ are two roots of the equation $f(x)=0$, then, there is at least one root of the equation $f'(x)=0$ which lies between a and b.

§ 6. Lagrange's Mean Value Theorem

Let f be a function defined on $[a,b]$ such that

(i) f is continuous an $[a,b]$

(ii) f is differentiable an $]a,b[$

Then, there exists a real number $c\in]a,b[$ such that

$$\frac{f(b)-f(a)}{b-a}=f'(c)$$

Remarks :

- Another form of Lagrange's theorem is given below :

  If we take $b=a+h$ and c can be written as $a+\theta h$, where θ is same real number such that $0<\theta<1$. Lagrange's theorem then read as follows:

  "Let f be defined and continuous on $[a,a+h]$ and differentiable on $]a,a+h[$, then for some real number $\theta\,(0<\theta<1)$

  $$\frac{f(a+h)-f(a)}{h}=f'(a+\theta h)$$

- The hypothesis of the Lagrange's mean value theorem can not be weakened, as it is clear from the following examples

  "Let f be the function defined on $[-1,2]$ by setting

  $$f(x)=|x|,\ \forall\ x\in[-1,2].$$

  Here, f is continuous on $[-1,2]$ and differentiable at all points of $]-1,2[$ except at $x=0$ (so that second condition is violated)

  Now $f'(x)=\begin{cases}-1\ if\ x\in]-1,2[\\ \ \ 1\ if\ x\in]0,2[\end{cases}$

  Also $\dfrac{f(2)-f(-1)}{2-(-1)}\neq f'(x)$ for any x in $]-1,2[$.

- Lagrange's mean value theorem is known as first mean value theorem.
- The result $f(b)-f(b-a)\,f'(c)$ is also known as the formula for finite increment.

  For $f(a)=f(b)$, the Lagrange's mean value theorem yields Rolle's theorem

Geometrical Interpretation of Lagrange's Mean Value Theorem :

If the curve $y=f(x)$ is continuous from $x=a$ and $x=b$ and has a definite tangent at each point on the curve

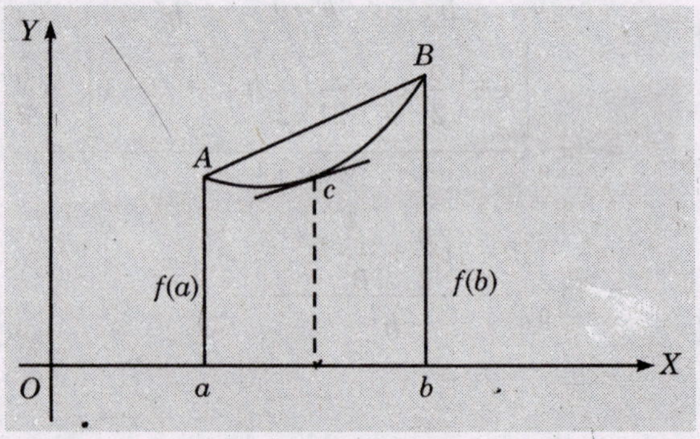

Fig. 26

between $x=0$ and $x=b$, then, geometrically, the first mean value theorem mean that there is at least one point between $x=a$ and $x=b$ on the curve where the tangent to the curve parallel to the chord joining the points $(a, f(a))$ and $(b, f(b))$.

Let ACB be the graph of the function $y=f(x)$ then the co-ordinate of the points A and B are given by $(a, f(a))$ and $(b, f(b))$ respectively. If the chord AB makes an angle θ with the x-axis, then

$$\tan\theta = \frac{f(b)-f(a)}{b-a} = f'(c), \text{ where } a<c<b.$$

Deduction from the First Mean Value Theorem :

If a function $f(x)$ satisfies the conditions of mean value theorem then

(i) $f'(x)=0 \;\forall\; x\in]a,b[\Rightarrow f$ is constant on $[a,b]$

(ii) $f'(x)>0 \;\forall\; x\in]a,b[\Rightarrow f$ is strictly decreasing on $[a,b]$,

(iii) $f'(x)<0 \;\forall\; x\in]a,b[\Rightarrow f$ is strictly decreasing on $[a,b]$,

Remark:

- For a strictly increasing function f, the derivative $f'(x)$ need not be strictly positive. For example, consider $f(x)=x^3, x\in]-1,1[$. Here, $f(x)$ is strictly increasing but $f'(x)=3x^2$, which is zero at $x=0\in]-1,1[$.

Problem Set (3)

1. Discuss the applicability of Rolle's theorem in the interval $[-1,1]$ to the function $f(x)=|x|$.
2. Verify Rolle's theorem the function $f(x)=x^3-4x$ on $[-2,2]$.
3. Discuss the applicability of Rolle's theorem to
$$f(x)=\log\left[\frac{x^2+ab}{(a+b)\,x}\right], \text{ in the interval } [a,b].$$
4. Verify Rolle's theorem for the following function
$$f(x)=2x^3+x^2-4x-2$$
5. Verify Rolle's theorem for $f(x)=x(x+3)\,e^{-x/2}$ in $[-3,0]$.
6. Show that there is no real number p for which the equation $x^2-3x+p=0$ has two distinct roots in $]0,1[$.
7. Verify the Rolle's theorem for the function $f(x)=x^2$ in $[-1,1]$.
8. Verify the Rolle's theorem for the function $f(x)=x^2-3x+2$ on the interval $[1,2]$.
9. If $a+b+c=0$, then show that the quadratic equation $3ax^2+2bx+c=0$ has at least one root in $]0,1[$.
10. Discuss the applicapibility of Rolle's Theorem to the function $f(x)=x^{2/3}$ in $(-1,1)$.
11. Discuss the applicability of Rolle's theorem to the function
$$f(x)=\begin{cases} x^2+1, \text{ when } 0\le x<1 \\ 3-x, \text{ when } 1<x\le 2 \end{cases}$$
12. Discuss the application of Rolle's theorem to the function $f(x)=\log\left[\dfrac{(x^2+ab)}{\{(a+b)\,x\}}\right]$ in (a,b).
13. Verify Rolle's theorem for the function $f(x)=x^2-6x^2+11x-6$.
14. Verify Rolle's Theorem for the function $f(x)=10x-x^2$
15. (a) Find 'c' of the mean value theorem, if $f(x)=x(x-1)(x-2); a=0, b=1/2$

    (b) If $f(x)=\log x$ find all numbers strictly between e^2 and e^3 such that $f'(x)=\dfrac{f(e^3)-f(e^2)}{e^3-e^2}$
16. Separate the intervals in which the polynomial $2x^3-15x^2+36x+1$ is increasing or decreasing.
17. Use the function $f(x)=x^{1/x}, x>0$ show that $e^\pi>\pi^e$.
18. Show that Lagrange's mean value theorem does not holds for the function $f(x)=|x|$ in the interval $[-1,1]$.
19. Verify Lagrange's mean value theorem for the function $f(x)=\sin x$ in $\left[0,\dfrac{\pi}{2}\right]$
20. If $f''(x)$ exist for all points in $[a,b]$ and $\dfrac{f(c)-f(a)}{c-a}=\dfrac{f(b)-f(c)}{b-c}$ where $a<c<b$, then, there is a number l such that
$$a<l<b \text{ and } f''(l)=0.$$
21. If $f(x)=(x-1)(x-2)$ and $a=0, b=4$, find 'c' using Langrange's mean value theorem.
22. Examine if Mean Value Theorem applies to $f(x)=x^2+3x^2-5x$ in the interval $[1,2]$. If it does, then find the intermediate point whose existence is asserted by theorem.

Solution to Problem Set (3)

1. We have $f(x)=|x|$
$$\left.\begin{matrix}\Rightarrow & f(-1)=1 \\ \text{and} & f(1)=1\end{matrix}\right\} \Rightarrow f(1)=f(-1).$$
Now, the function $f(x)$ is continuous throughout the closed interval $[-1,1]$ but $f(x)$ is not differentiable at $x=0\in]-1,1[$. Hence, Rolle's theorem is not satisfied (due to the second condition).

2. The function $f(x) = x^3 - 4x$ is a polynomial and so it is continuous and differentiable at all $x \in \mathbf{R}$. In particular it is continuous in the closed interval $[-2, 2]$ and differentiable in the open interval $]-2, 2[$. Also $f(-2) = 0 = f(2)$.

Thus, $f(x)$ satisfies all the three conditions of Rolle's theorem in $[-2, 2]$.

Therefore, there must exist at least one real number 'x' in the open interval $]-2, 2[$ for which $f'(x) = 0$.

Also $f'(x) = 3x^2 - 4$.

Now $f'(x) = 0$ gives $3x^2 - 4 = 0$

or $x = \pm\frac{2}{\sqrt{3}} = \pm 1.55$.

Both these value lie in the open interval $]-2, 2[$ and thus the conclusion of Rolle's theorem is verified.

3. We have

$$f(a) = \log\left[\frac{a^2 + ab}{(a+b)\,a}\right] = \log 1 = 0$$

and $f(b) = \log\left[\frac{b^2 + ab}{(a+b)\,b}\right] = \log 1 = 0$

$\Rightarrow \quad f(a) = f(b) = 0.$

Also, it can be easily seen that $f(x)$ is continuous on $[a, b]$ and differentiable on $]a, b[$.

Thus all the three conditions of Rolle's theorem are satisfied.

Hence $f'(x) = 0$ for at least one value of x in $]a, b[$.

Now $f'(x) = 0 \quad \Rightarrow \quad \frac{2x}{x^2 + ab} - \frac{1}{x} = 0$

$\Rightarrow \quad 2x^2 - (x^2 + ab) = 0 \Rightarrow \quad x^2 = ab$ or $x = \sqrt{ab}$.

Obviously $\sqrt{ab} \in]a, b[$

[being the geometric mean of a and b]

Hence, the Rolle's theorem is verified.

4. Since, $f(x)$ is a rational integral function of x, therefore it is continuous and differentiable for all real values of x.

Hence, the first two conditions of Rolle's theorem are satisfied in any interval.

Hence, $f(x) = 0$ gives $2x^3 + x^2 - 4x - 2 = 0$

i.e,. $x = \pm\sqrt{2}, -\frac{1}{2}$

$\Rightarrow \quad f(\sqrt{2}) = f(-\sqrt{2}) = f\left(-\frac{1}{2}\right) = 0$

Now, take the interval $[-\sqrt{2}, \sqrt{2}]$, then all the conditions of Rolle's theorem are satisfied in this interval. Then, $\exists$ at least one value of c in $]-\sqrt{2}, \sqrt{2}[$. such that $f'(c) = 0$

$$f'(x) = 0 \quad \Rightarrow \quad 6x^2 + 2x - 4 = 0$$

$\Rightarrow \quad x = -1, \frac{2}{3}$.

Since, both the points -1 and $\frac{2}{3}$ lie in the open interval $]-\sqrt{2}, \sqrt{2}[$. Hence, Rolle's theorem is verified.

5. We have

$$f(x) = x\,(x+3)\,e^{-x/2}$$

$$\therefore \quad f'(x) = (2x+3)\,e^{-x/2} + (x^2 + 3x)\,e^{-x/2}\left(-\frac{1}{2}\right)$$

$$= e^{-x/2}\left[2x + 3 - \frac{1}{2}[x^2 + 3x]\right]$$

$$= -\frac{1}{2}[x^2 - x - 6]\,e^{-x/2}$$

$\Rightarrow$ $f'(x)$ exist for every value of x in the interval $[-3, 0]$. Hence, $f(x)$ is differentiable and hence, continuous in the interval $[-3, 0]$.

Also, we have

$$f(-3) = f(0) = 0$$

$\Rightarrow$ All the three conditions of Rolle's theorem are satisfied. So

$f'(x) = 0 \quad \Rightarrow \quad \frac{1}{2}(x^2 - x - 6)\,e^{-x/2} = 0$

$\Rightarrow \quad x^2 - x - 6 = 0 \quad \Rightarrow \quad x = 3, -2.$

Since, the value $x = -2$ lies in the open interval $]-3, 0[$. the Rolle's theorem is verified.

6. Let, if possible, there are two distinct roots a and b of the given equation in $]0, 1[$, such that $0 < a < b < 1$.

Now, let $f(x) = x^3 - 3x - p$

Obviously, $f(x)$ is continuous and differentiable for all values of x (being a polynomial)

Also, we have $f(a) = f(b) = 0$

$\Rightarrow$ f satisfies all the conditions of Rolle's theorem in $[a, b]$ hence, $\exists$ a point $c \in]a, b[$ such that $f'(c) = 0$.

Now $f'(x) = 0 \Rightarrow 3x^2 - 3 = 0$

$\Rightarrow \quad x = \pm 1$

which is a contradiction $[\because a < c < b$ as $0 < a < b < 1]$

$\Rightarrow$ our assumption is wrong. Hence , there can not be two distinct roots of $f(x) = 0$ in $]0, 1[$ for any value of p.

7. Here, it can be easily seen that the function $f(x) = x^2$ is continuous as well as differentiable on $\mathbf{R}$

$\Rightarrow$ $f(x)$ is continuous and differentiable in $[-1, 1]$.

Also, we have $f(1) = f(-1) = 1$.

Thus, $f(x)$ satisfies all the conditions of Rolle's theorem in $[-1, 1]$.

$\Rightarrow$ $\exists$ at least one number, say c, in $]-1, 1[$ such that $f'(c) = 0$.

Now $f'(x) = 2x$

$$f'(x) = 0 \Rightarrow x = 0.$$

Since, the root $x = 0$ lies in the interval $]-1, 1[$. Hence, the Rolle's theorem is satisfied.

8. It can be easily seen that $f(x) = x^2 - 3x + 2$ is continuous as well as differentiable on **R** (being a polynomial)

$\Rightarrow$ $f(x)$ is continuous in $[1, 2]$ and differentiable in $]1, 2[$.

Also, we have $f(1) = f(2) = 0$.

Thus, $f(x)$ satisfies all the conditions of Rolle's theorem in $[1, 2]$

$\Rightarrow$ $\exists$ at least one number, say, c in $[1, 2]$ such that $f'(c) = 0$.

Now, $f'(x) = 2x - 3$

$$f'(x) = 0 \Rightarrow x = \frac{3}{2}$$

Since, the root $x = \frac{3}{2}$ lies in the interval $(1, 2)$. Hence, Rolle's theorem is verified.

9. Let us define a function $f(x)$ such that $f(x) = ax^3 + bx^2 + cx + d$.

Here we have $f(0) = d$ and $f(1) = a + b + c + d = d$ ($\because a + b + c = 0$)

Obviously, $f(x)$ is continuous and differentiable in $]0, 1[$ (being a polynomial).

Thus, $f(x)$ satisfies all the three conditions of Rolle's theorem in $[0, 1]$. Hence, there is at least one value of x in the open interval $]0, 1[$ where $f'(x) = 0$

i.e.,. $3ax^2 + 2bx + c = 0$ has at least one root in $]0, 1[$.

10. We have $f(x) = x^{2/3}$

$$\Rightarrow \quad f'(x) = \frac{2}{3} x^{-1/3}$$

$$\therefore \quad \lim_{z \to 0} f'(x) = \lim_{h \to 0} \frac{2}{3} (0 + h)^{-1/3} = +\infty$$

$$Rf'(0) = \lim_{h \to 0} \left\{ \frac{f(0 + h) - f(0)}{h} \right\} = \lim_{h \to 0} \left\{ \frac{h^{2/3} - 1}{h} \right\} = +\infty$$

$$Lf'(0) = \lim_{h \to 0} \left\{ \frac{f(0 + h) - f(0)}{-h} \right\} = \lim_{h \to 0} \left\{ \frac{(-h)^{2/3}}{-h} \right\} = +\infty$$

$\therefore$ $Lf'(0) \neq Rf'(0)$

$\therefore$ $f'(0)$ does not exist showing that $f'(x)$ does not exist in the open interval $(-1, 1)$.

Hence, Rolle's theorem is not applicable although $f(-1) = f(1) = 1$ and $f(x)$ is continuous in the closed interval $(-1, 1)$.

11. Here $f(0) = 0^2 + 1$ and $f(2) = 3 - 2 = 1$.

We shall show that $f(x)$ is continuous for all x in the range $(0, 2)$ except at $x = 1$

Also $f(1) = 1^2 = 2$

Again, when $h \to 0$ $\quad f(1 + 0) = \lim_{x \to 1+0} (3 - x) = \lim_{x \to 1+h} [3 - (1 + h)]$

$$= \lim_{h \to 0} (2 - h) = 2$$

and $f(1 - 0) = \lim_{x \to 1-0} (x^2 + 1) = \lim_{x \to (1+h)} [(1 - h)^2 + 1]$, when $h \to 0$

$$= \lim_{h \to 0} [2 - 2h + h^2] = 2.$$

Hence, $f(1 - 0) = f(1) = f(1 + 0)$ and so the function $f(x)$ is continuous at $x = 1$, and the continuous in the whole interval $(0, 2)$.

Again $f'(x) = \begin{cases} 2x, \text{ when } 0 \le x \le 1 \\ -1, \text{ when } 1 < x \le 2 \end{cases}$

$\therefore$ $f(x)$ is differentiable in the interval $(0,2)$ except at $x = 1$.

$$\text{Now } Rf'(1) = \lim_{h \to 0} \frac{f(1 + h) - f(1)}{h}$$

$$= \lim_{h \to 0} \frac{\{3(1 + h)\} - 2}{h}$$

$$= \lim_{h \to 0} \frac{2 - h - 2}{h} = \lim_{h \to 0} (-1) = -1.$$

$$\text{and } Lf'(1) = \lim_{h \to 0} \frac{f(1 + h) - f(1)}{h}$$

$$\lim_{h \to 0} \frac{\{(1 + h)^2 + 1\} - 2}{h}$$

$$\lim_{h \to 0} \frac{2h - h^2}{h} = \lim_{h \to 0} (2 - h) = 2.$$

$\therefore$ Thus $Rf'(1) \neq Lf'(1)$ and so $f'(1)$ does not exist.

Hence, the function $f(x)$ is not differentiable in the entire range $(0, 2)$ and therefore Rolle's theorem is not applicable to the given function $f(x)$ in $(0, 2)$.

12. We have $f(x) = \log \left\{ \frac{x^2 + ab}{(a + b)\, x} \right\}$

$$f(a) = \log \left\{ \frac{a^2 + ab}{(a + b)\, a} \right\} = \log (1) = 0$$

$$\text{and } f(b) = \log \left\{ \frac{b^2 + ab}{(a + b)\, b} \right\} = \log (1) = 0$$

$\therefore$ $f(a) = f(b) = 0$

$$\text{Also } Rf'(x) = \lim_{h \to 0} \frac{f(x + h) - f(x)}{h}$$

$$= \lim_{h \to 0} \frac{1}{h} \left[\log \left\{ \frac{(x + h)^2 + ab}{(a + b)(x + h)} \right\} - \log \left\{ \frac{x^2 + ab}{(a + b)\, x} \right\} \right]$$

$$= \lim_{h \to 0} \frac{1}{h} \left[\log \frac{(x^2 + 2xh + h^2 + ab)(a + b)x}{(a + b)(x + h)(x^2 + ab)} \right]$$

$$= \lim_{h \to 0} \frac{1}{h} \left[\log \left\{ \frac{(x^2 + 2xh + h^2 + ab}{(x^2 + ab)} \times \frac{x}{x + h} \right\} \right]$$

$$= \lim_{h \to 0} \frac{1}{h} \left[\log \left\{ 1 + \frac{2hx + h^2}{x^2 + ab} \right\} - \log \left\{ 1 + \frac{h}{x} \right\} \right]$$

$$= \lim_{h\to 0} \frac{1}{h}\left[\frac{2hx}{x^2+ab} - \frac{h}{x} + \ldots\right]$$

$$\left[\because \log(1+x) = x - \frac{x^2}{2} + \frac{x^3}{3} \ldots\right]$$

$$= \left[\frac{2x}{(x^2+ab)}\right] - \left(\frac{1}{x}\right).$$

Also $Lf'(x) = \lim_{h\to 0}\left\{\frac{f(x-h)-f(x)}{-h}\right\}$

$$= \lim_{h\to 0}\frac{1}{(-h)}\left\{\frac{-2hx}{x^2+ab} - \frac{(-h)}{x} + \ldots\right\}$$

$\therefore \quad Lf'(x) = Rf'(x)$

Thus $Lf'(x) = Rf'(x)$.

$\therefore \quad f'(x)$ exists for all values of x in (a, b).

Also $f(x)$ is continuous for all values of x in (a, b) since $f(x)$ is differentiable for all values of x in (a, b).

Hence, all the three conditions of Rolle's theorem are satisfied.

$\therefore \quad f'(x) = 0$ for at least one value of x where $a < x < b$.

Equating $f'(x)$ to zero, we have

$$\left[\frac{2x}{(x^2+ab)}\right] - \left(\frac{1}{x}\right) = 0$$

or $2x^2 - (x^2+ab) = 0$ or $x^2 = ab$

or $x = \sqrt{ab}$

which clearly lies in (a, b) as $\sqrt{ab}$ is the G.M. of a and b

13. Here, we have $f(x) = x^3 - 6x^2 + 11x - 6$, if $f(x) = 0$. Then

$$x^3 - 6x^2 + 11x - 6 = 0$$

$\Rightarrow \quad (x-1)(x-2)(x-3) = 0 \quad \therefore \; x = 1, 2, 3.$

$\Rightarrow \quad f(1) = 0 = f(2) = f(3)$

Also $\quad f'(x) = 3x^2 - 12x + 11 \qquad \ldots(1)$

Now $Rf'(x) = \lim_{h\to 0}\frac{f(x+h)-f(x)}{h}$

$$= \lim_{h\to 0}\frac{[(x+h)^3 + 6(x+h)^2 + 11(x+h) - 6] - [x^3 - 6x^2 + 11x - 6]}{h}$$

$$= \lim_{h\to 0}\frac{\{(x+h)^3 - x^3\} - 6\{(x+h)^2 - x^2\} + 11\{(x+h) - x\}}{h}$$

$$= \lim_{h\to 0}\frac{(x+h)^3 - x^3}{h} - 6\lim_{h\to 0}\frac{[(x+h)^2 - x^2]}{h} + 11\lim_{h\to 0}\frac{(x+h)-x}{h}$$

$$= 3x^2 - 12x + 11.$$

Similarly $Lf'(x) = \lim_{h\to 0}\frac{f(x-h)-f(x)}{-h}$

$$= \lim_{h\to 0}\frac{(x-h)^3 - x^3}{-h} - 6\lim_{h\to 0}\frac{(x-h)^2 - x^2}{-h} + 11\lim_{h\to 0}\frac{(x-h)-x}{-h}$$

$$= 3x^2 - 12x + 11.$$

Since $Lf'(x) = Rf'(x)$, therefore $f'(x)$ exists for all values of x in $[1, 3]$.

Also $f(x)$ is continuous. Hence, all conditions of Rolle's Theorem are satisfied, and so $f'(x) = 0$ for at least one value of x in $[1, 3]$.

From (1), equating $f'(x) = 0$ where $3x^2 - 12x + 11 = 0$

$\Rightarrow \quad x = 2 \pm \frac{\sqrt{3}}{3} \qquad \therefore \qquad x = 2.577, 1423.$

Both these above values lie in $[1, 3]$.

14. $f(x) = 0 \;\Rightarrow\; 10x - x^2 = 0 \;\Rightarrow\; x(10-x) = 0$

$\Rightarrow \quad x = 0, 10.$

Now, $f(0) = 0, f(10) = 0 \Rightarrow f(0) = 0 = f(10)$.

Also, $f'(x) = 10 - 2x$

Now $Rf'(x) \lim_{h\to 0}\frac{f(x+h)-f(x)}{h}$

$$= \lim_{h\to 0}\frac{(10(x+h) - (x+h)^2] - (10x - x^2)}{h}$$

$$= \lim_{h\to 0}\frac{(10x + 10h - x^2 - 2xh - h^2] - (10x - x^2)}{h}$$

$$= \lim_{h\to 0}\frac{10h - 2xh + h^2}{h}$$

$$= \lim_{h\to 0}(10 - 2x - h) = 10 - 2x$$

Similarly, $Lf'(x) = \lim_{h\to 0}\frac{f(x-h)-f(x)}{-h}$

$$= \lim_{h\to 0}\frac{[10(x-h) - (x-h)^2] - (10x - x^2)}{-h}$$

$$= \lim_{h\to 0}\frac{-10h + 2xh - h^2}{-h} = 10 - 2x$$

Thus $Lf'(x) = Rf'(x)$. Therefore $f'(x)$ exists for all values of x in $[0, 10]$. Also $f(x)$ is continuous for all values of x in $[0, 10]$.

Also, since every differentiable function is continuous.

Hence, all the three conditions of Rolle's Theorem are satisfied.

$\therefore \quad f'(x) = 0$ for at least one value of x in $[0, 10]$.

From (1), equating $f'(x) = 0 = 2x = 10 \Rightarrow x = 5$ which is lies in $[0, 10]$.

15. (a) We have $f(a) = f(0) = 0$

$$f(b) = f\left(\frac{1}{2}\right) = \frac{3}{8}$$

$$\therefore \qquad \frac{f(b) - f(a)}{b - a} = \frac{\frac{3}{8} - 0}{\frac{1}{2} - 0} = \frac{3}{4}$$

Now $f(x) = x^3 - 3x^2 + 2x$

$\therefore \quad f'(x) = 3x^2 - 6x + 2 \quad \Rightarrow \quad f'(c) = 3c^2 - 6c + 2.$

Putting all these value in the Lagrange's mean value theorem

$$\frac{f(b) - f(a)}{b - a} = f'(c), (a < c < b)$$

we get $\frac{3}{4} = 3c^2 - 6c + 2$ or $c = 1 \pm \frac{\sqrt{21}}{6}$

Hence $c = \frac{1 - \sqrt{21}}{6}$ lies in the open interval $\left]0, \frac{1}{2}\right[$ therefore, it is the required value.

(b) Obviously $f(x) = \log x$ is continuous in $[e^3, e^2]$ and differentiable in $]e^2, e^3]$.

Then by Lagrange's mean value theorem. There exist $c \in]e^2, e^3]$, such that

$$f'(c) = \frac{f(e^3) - f(e^2)}{e^3 - e^2}$$

$$\frac{1}{c} = \frac{3 - 2}{e^3 - e^2}$$

$$c = (e^3 - e^2).$$

There exist only one value $c = (e^3 - e^2)$ in $]e^2, e^3[$.

16. We have

$$f(x) = 2x^3 - 15x^2 + 36x + 1$$

$\therefore \quad f'(x) = 6x^2 - 30x + 36 = 6(x - 2)(x - 3)$

Here $f'(x) > 0$ for $x < 2$ or for $x > 3$

$f'(x) < 0$ for $2 < x < 3$

and $f'(x) = 0$ for $x = 2, 3$

$f''(x)$ is positive in the intervals $]-\infty, 2]$ and $[3, \infty[$ and negative in the interval $]2, 3[$.

Hence, the function $f(x)$ is monotonically increasing in the interval $]-\infty, 2]$, $[3, \infty[$ and monotonically decreasing in $]2, 3[$.

17. Here $f(x) = x^{1/x}, x > 0$

$\therefore \quad \log f(x) = \frac{1}{x} \log_e x.$

Differentiating w.r.t. x, we get

$$\frac{1}{f(x)} f'(x) = \frac{1}{x} \cdot \frac{1}{x} - \frac{1}{x^2} \log_e x$$

$\Rightarrow \quad f'(x) = \frac{x^{1/x}}{x^2} [1 - \log_e x].$

For $x > e, f'(x) < 0 \qquad (\because \log_e x > 1 \text{ for } x > e)$

$\therefore \quad f(x)$ is a decreasing function of x for $x > e$.

Two Important Resuts

(i) $\frac{x}{1 + x} < \log(1 + x) < x, \ \forall \ x > 0$

(ii) $(1 + x) < e^x < 1 + xe^x, \ \forall \ x > 0$

Hence, $\pi > e \Rightarrow f(\pi) < f(e) \Rightarrow \pi^{1/\pi} < e^{1/e}$

$\Rightarrow \quad (\pi^{1/\pi})^{e\pi} < (e^{1/e})^{e\pi} \quad \Rightarrow \quad \pi^e < e^\pi$

$\Rightarrow \quad e^\pi > \pi^e$

18. Since $f(x) = |x|$ is a continuous function on $[-1, 1]$ but it is not differentiable at $x = 0 \in]-1, 1[$. Hence, Lagrange's mean value theorem does not hold for the function $f(x) = |x|$ in the interval $[-1, 1]$.

19. The function $f(x) = \sin x$ is continuous and differentiable on **R**. Hence it is continuous as well as differentiable in $\left[0, \frac{\pi}{2}\right]$. Then, by Lagrange's mean value theorem, there must exists at least one c in $\left]0, \frac{\pi}{2}\right[$ such that

$$\frac{f\left(\frac{\pi}{2}\right) - f(0)}{\frac{\pi}{2} - 0} = f'(c).$$

Here $f(0) = 0, f\left(\frac{\pi}{2}\right) = 1$

$f'(x) = \cos x \Rightarrow f'(c) = \cos c.$

Put all these values in (1), we have

$$\frac{1 - 0}{\frac{\pi}{2}} = \cos c \quad \Rightarrow \quad \cos c = \frac{2}{\pi}$$

$\Rightarrow \quad c = \cos^{-1}\left(\frac{2}{\pi}\right)$

Since, $0 < \frac{2}{\pi} < 1$, therefore the value of $c = \cos^{-1}\left(\frac{2}{\pi}\right)$ lies in $\left]0, \frac{\pi}{2}\right[$, so the required value of c. Hence, Lagrange's mean value theorem is satisfied.

20. Since $f''(x)$ exists for all points in $[a, b]$,

$\Rightarrow \quad f'(x)$ is continuous in $[a, b]$

$\Rightarrow \quad f(x)$ is continuous in $[a, b]$.

Now, applying Lagrange's mean value theorem to $f(x)$ in $[a, c]$ and $[c, b]$ respectively, we get

$$\frac{f(c) - f(a)}{c - a} = f'(l_1), a < l_1 < c \qquad \ldots(1)$$

and $$\frac{f(b) - f(c)}{b - c} = f'(l_2), c < l_2 < b \qquad \ldots(2)$$

Then, from (1) and (2), we get

$$f'(l_1) = f'(l_2) \qquad \left[\because \frac{f(c) - f(a)}{c - a} = \frac{f(b) - f(c)}{b - c}\right]$$

Now $f'(x)$ satisfies all the condition of Rolle's theorem in the interval $[l_1, l_2]$. Hence $f''(l) = 0$ where $l \in]l_1, l_2[$ and $l \in]a, b[$.

21. We have

$$f(x) = (x - 1)(x - 2)(x - 3) = x^3 - 6x^2 + 11x - 6$$

$$f(a) = f(0) = -6 \text{ and } f(b) = f(4) = 6$$

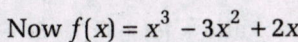

$\therefore \quad \dfrac{f(b)-f(a)}{b-a}=\dfrac{6-(-6)}{4-0}=\dfrac{12}{4}=3.$

Also $f'(x)=3x^2-12x+11$ gives $f'(c)=3c^2-12c+11$

Putting these value in Lagrange's mean value theorem,

$\dfrac{f(b)-f(a)}{b-a}=f'(c)$, where $a<c<b$

we get $\quad 3=3c^2-12c+11$ or $3c^2-12c+8=0$

$c=\dfrac{12\pm\sqrt{(144-96)}}{6}=2\pm\dfrac{2\sqrt{3}}{3}$

As the value of c lies in the open interval $]0,4[$. Hence both of these are the required values of c.

22. Given $\quad f(x)=x^3+3x^2-5x \quad$ ...(1)

$\therefore \quad f'(x)=3x^2+6x-5$ and $f'(c)=3x^2+6c-5.$ ...(2)

Let $a=1$ and $b=2$, then from (1), we have

$f(a)=f(1)=1^3+3(1)^2-5(1)=-1$

$f(b)=f(2)=2^3+3(2)^2-5(2)=10$

From Mean Value Theore, we have

$f(b)-f(a)=(b-a)\,f'(c)$

$\Rightarrow \quad f(2)-f(1)=(2-1)\,f'(c)$

$\Rightarrow \quad 10-(-1)=(2-1)\,f'(c)$

$\Rightarrow \quad 3c^2+6c-5=11$ [using (2)]

$\Rightarrow \quad 3c^2+6c-16=0$

$\therefore \quad c=-1\pm 2.55;$

$c=-3.55, 1.55.$

Problem Set (4)

1. Discuss the applicability of Rolle's theorem of the following functions:

(a) $f(x)=2+(x-1)^{3/2}$ in the interval $[0,2]$

(b) $f(x)=x^2$ in $2\le x\le 3$

(c) $f(x)=\tan x$ in $0\le x\le \pi$

(d) $f(x)=x^4-3x^2+4$ in the interval $[-4,4]$

(e) $f(x)=\dfrac{1}{(x^2+1)}$ in the interval $[-3,3]$

(f) $f(x)=e^x\sin x$ in the interval $[0,\pi]$

(g) $f(x)=|x|$ in the interval $[-1,1]$

(h) $f(x)=(x-2)\sqrt{x}$ in the interval $[0,2]$

(i) $f(x)=(x-a)^m(x-b)^n, m,n\in \mathbf{Z}^+$ in the interval $[a,b]$.

2. Show that between any two roots of $e^x\cos x=1$, there exists at least one root of $e^x\sin x-1=0$.

3. Let $\dfrac{a_0}{n+1}+\dfrac{a_1}{n}+\dfrac{a_2}{n-1}+\ldots+\dfrac{a_{n-1}}{2}+a_n=0$. Show that there exists at least one real x between 0 and 1 such that

$$a_0x^n+a_1x^{n-1}+\ldots+a_n=0.$$

4. Verify the Rolle's theorem for the following functions :

(a) $f(x)=x^4-1$ on the interval $[-1,1]$

(b) $f(x)=e^x(\sin x-\cos x)$ in $\left(\dfrac{\pi}{4},\dfrac{5\pi}{4}\right)$.

5. $f(x)=\begin{vmatrix}\sin x & \sin\alpha & \sin\beta\\ \cos x & \cos\alpha & \cos\beta\\ \tan x & \tan\alpha & \tan\beta\end{vmatrix}$ where $0<\alpha<\beta<\dfrac{\pi}{2}$ show that $f'(l)=0$, where $\alpha<l<\beta$

6. A function $f(x)$ is continuous in the closed interval $[0,1]$ and differentiable in the open interval $]0,1[$ prove that

$$f'(x_1)=f(1)-f(0),\ 0<x_1<1$$

7. Show that the set of all x for which $\log(1+x)\le x$ is equal to $[0,\infty[$.

8. Compute the value of θ in the first mean value theorem

$$f(x+h)=f(x)+hf'(x+\theta h)$$

if $\quad f(x)=ax^2+bx+c.$

9. Show that $x^n-a=0$ has at most one real positive root if n is a positive integer.

10. Show that the function f' if it exists in an interval, can not have an ordinary or removable discontinuity in that interval.

11. Verify the Lagrange's theorem for the following functions:

(a) $f(x)=x^3$ in $[-1,1]$

(b) $f(x)=\sin x$ in $\left[0,\dfrac{\pi}{2}\right]$

(c) $f(x)=x^n$ in $[-1,1], n\in \mathbf{Z}^+$

(d) $f(x)=2x^2-7x+10,\ x\in[2,5]$.

12. Find the value of c, of mean value theorem, when

(a) $f(x)=\sqrt{x^2-4}$ in the interval $[2,4]$

(b) $f(x)=2x^2+3x+4$ in the interval $[1,2]$

(c) $f(x)=x(x-1)$ in the interval $[1,2]$.

Hints / Solution to Problem Set (4)

1. (a) $f(x)=2+(x-1)^{2/3}$

Here we have

$f'(x)=\dfrac{2}{3}(x-1)^{-1/3}=\dfrac{2}{3(x-)^{1/3}}$

$\therefore \quad \lim\limits_{x\to 0}f'(x)=\lim\limits_{h\to 0}\left[\dfrac{2}{3(1+0-1)^{\frac{1}{3}}}\right]=+\infty.$

$\therefore \quad f'(x)$ does not exist *i.e.,* it is not finite at $x=1$ $1\in(0,2)$. So $f'(x)$ does not exist at each point in open interval $(0,2)$. Thus second condition of Rolle's theorem is not satisfied.

Hence, Rolle's theorem is not applicable for the function $f(x)=2+(x-1)^{\frac{2}{3}}$ in interval $[0,2]$.

(b) $f(x)=x^2$ in $2 \le x \le 3$

$f'(x)=2x$

$\therefore \lim_{h\to 0} f'(x)=\lim_{h\to 0}[2x]=0.$

Therefore, IInd condition of Rolle's theorem is satisfied.

Also $f(2)=4,\ f(3)=9$

$f(2)\ne f(3) \Rightarrow$ Third condition of Rolle's theorem is not satisfied.

$f(x)=x^2$ is continuous and differentiable in $2\le x<3$.

Thus the first two conditions of Rolle's theorem are satisfied and third condition is not satisfied.

Hence, Rolle's theorem is not applicable.

(c) $f(x)=\tan x$ in $0\le x\le \pi$

We have $f(x)=\tan x$

At $x=\frac{\pi}{2}$

$$f\left(\frac{\pi}{2}+0\right)\ne f\left(0-\frac{\pi}{2}\right)\ne f\left(\frac{\pi}{2}\right)$$

$f(x)$ is not continuous at $x=\frac{\pi}{2}$ and not differentiable, therefore Rolle's first two conditions are not satisfied.

Hence, Rolle's theorem is not applicable.

(d) $f(x)=x^4-3x^2+4$ in interval $[-4,4]$

Since $f(x)$ is a polynomial, therefore it is continuous as well as differentiable in the given interval. Also $f(-4)=f(4)$.

Therefore, all conditions of Rolle's theorem are satisfied.

Hence, Rolle's theorem is applicable.

(e) Do as above (d).

(f) $f(x)=e^x \sin x$ in the interval $[0,\pi]$.

$f(0)=e^0 \sin 0=0$

$f(\pi)=e^\pi \sin\pi=0$

$f(0)=0=f(\pi)$.

$$Rf'(0)=\lim_{h\to 0}\frac{f(x+h)-f(x)}{h}$$

$$=\lim_{h\to 0}\frac{e^{x+h}\sin(x+h)-e^x\sin x}{h}$$

$$=\lim_{h\to 0}\frac{e^x[e^h\sin(x+h)-\sin x]}{h}$$

$$=\lim_{h\to 0}\frac{1}{h}\left[\left(1+h+\frac{h^2}{2!}+\ldots\right)\sin(x-h)-\sin x\right]$$

$$=e^x\lim_{h\to 0}\frac{1}{h}[(\sin(x+h)-\sin x\}+h\sin(x+h)$$

$$+\left(\frac{h^2}{2!}+\ldots\right)\sin(x+h)\Bigg]$$

$$=e^x\left[\lim_{h\to 0}\frac{\sin(x+h)-\sin x}{h}+\lim_{h\to 0}\sin(x+h)+\lim_{h\to 0}\left\{\left(\frac{h}{2!}+\frac{h^2}{3!}+\ldots\right)\sin(x+h)\right\}\right]$$

$$=e^x\left[\frac{d}{dx}(\sin x)+\sin x+0\right]=e^x(\cos x+\sin x)$$

Similarly, we can find $Lf'(0)$

$$Lf'(x)=\lim_{h\to 0}\frac{f(x-h)-f(x)}{-h}=e^x(\cos x+\sin x)$$

$Rf'(x)=Lf'(x)$.

$\therefore$ $f'(x)$ exist for all values of x in $[a,\pi]$ and $f(x)$ is continuous for all values of x in $[0,\pi]$.

$f'(x)=e^x(\cos x+\sin x),\ f'(x)=0$

$e^x(\cos x+\sin x)=0,\ \sin x+\cos x=0$

$\tan x+1=0 \quad \Rightarrow \tan x=-1,\ x=\frac{3\pi}{3},\ x\in[0,\pi]$

Hence, Rolle's theorem is verified.

(g) $f(x)=|x|$ in interal $[-1,1]$

We show that $f(x)$ is continuous in $[-1,1]$

$f(1)=|1|=1,\ f(-1)=|-1|=1,\ f(1)=f(-1)=1.$

Also $f(x)$ is continuous in $[-1,1]$, for all values of x

Now, $Rf'(0)=\text{Lim}_{h\to 0}\frac{f(0+h)-f(0)}{h}$

$$=\lim_{h\to 0}\frac{|0+h|-|0|}{h}\lim_{h\to 0}=\frac{h-0}{h}=1$$

and $Lf'(0)=\lim_{h\to 0}\frac{f(0-h)-f(0)}{-h}$

$$=\lim_{h\to 0}\frac{|0+h|-|0|}{-h}=\lim_{h\to 0}\frac{h-0}{-h}=-1$$

$Rf'(0)\ne Lf'(0)$. Therefore $f'(0)$ does not exist.

Hence, the function $f(x)$ is not differentiable in open interval $(0,2)$ and so Rolle's theorem is not applicable to given function $f(x)$ in $[-1,1]$.

(h) Same as (g).

(i) Same (g).

2. Let a,b are two distinct roots of $e^x\sin x-1=0$

$e^a\cos a=1$ and $e^b\cos b=1$. ...(1)

Let function $f(x)$ be defined as $f(x)=e^{-x}-\cos x$, then we observe that

(i) $f(x)$ is continuous in $[a,b]$ as both e^{-x} and $\cos x$ are continuous.

(ii) $f'(x)=-e^{-x}+\sin x$ for all $x\in]a,b[$. So it is differentiable in $]a,b[$.

(iii) $f(a)=e^{-a}-\cos a=e^{-a}-e^{-a}=0$ [from (1)]

$f(b)=e^{-b}-e^{-b}=0$ [from (1)]

$f(a)=f(b)=0.$

Thus $f(x)$ satisfies all the conditions of Rolle's theorem in $[a, b]$.

Therefore, $f'(c) = 0, c \in]a, b[$

$\Rightarrow \quad -e^{-c} + \sin c - 1 = 0$

$\Rightarrow \quad c$ is root of equation of $e^x \sin x - 1 = 0$.

Hence, between any two roots of equation $e^x \cos x = 1$ there exists at least one root of equation $e^x \sin x - 1 = 0$

3. Let us consider the function

$$f(x) = a_0 \frac{x^{n+1}}{n+1} + \frac{a_1 x^n}{n} + \ldots + a_{n-1} \frac{x^2}{2} + a_n x$$

Here $f(x)$ is a polynomial function therefore, $f(x)$ is continuous and differentiable for all x.

$\Rightarrow$ $f(x)$ is continuous in closed interval $[0, 1]$ and differentiable in open interval $(0, 1)$.

Also $f(0) = 0$

$$f(1) = \frac{a_0}{n+1} + \frac{a_1}{n} + \ldots + \frac{a_{n-1}}{2} + a_n = 0 \quad \ldots(1)$$

$\Rightarrow \quad f(0) = 0 = f(1)$.

Hence, all the conditions of Rolle's theorem are satisfied and therefore $f'(x) = 0$ for at least one value of x in $(0, 1)$

$$f'(x) = a_0 x^n + a_1 x^{n-1} + \ldots + a_{n-1} x + a_n \quad \ldots(2)$$

[From (1)]

Hence, from (2) we conclude that $a_0 x^n + a_1 x^{n-1} + \ldots + a_n$ vanishes at least once in $(0, 1)$.

4. (a) We have $f(x) = x^4 - 1$ in $[-1, 1]$

$\Rightarrow \quad f'(x) = 4x^3$

Now, $f(x) = x^4 - 1 = 0 \Rightarrow x = \pm 1$.

Also, $f(-1) = (-1)^4 - 1 = 0$

$f(+1) = (1)^4 - 1 = 0$

$\Rightarrow \quad f(-1) = f(+1) = 0$

Now, we check the differentiability of $f(x)$

$$Rf'(x) = \lim_{h \to 0} \frac{f(x+h) - f(x)}{h}$$

$$= \lim_{h \to 0} \frac{\{(x+h)^4 - 1\} - (x^4 - 1)}{h} = 4x^3$$

$Lf'(x) = 4x^3$

$\Rightarrow \quad Rf'(x) = Lf'(x)$.

Therefore all conditions of Rolle's theorem are satisfied. Hence $f'(x)$ exists

$\therefore \quad f'(x) = 0$ for at least one $x \in [-1, 1]$

$f'(x) = 4x^3 = 0 \Rightarrow x = 0 \in [-1, 1]$.

Hence, Rolle's theorem is verified.

(b) We have $f(x) = e^x (\sin x - \cos x)$ in $\left(\frac{\pi}{4}, \frac{5\pi}{4}\right)$

$$f'(x) = 2e^x \sin x \quad \ldots(1)$$

$$Rf'(x) = \lim_{h \to 0} \frac{f(x+h) - f(x)}{h}$$

$$= \lim_{h \to 0} \frac{2e^{x+h} \sin(x+h) - 2e^x \sin x}{h}$$

$$= 2e^x (\cos x + \sin x)$$

$$Lf'(x) = \lim_{h \to 0} \frac{f(x-h) - f(x)}{-h} = 2e^x (\cos x + \sin x)$$

$\Rightarrow \quad Lf'(x) = Rf(x)$

$\Rightarrow \quad f'(x)$ exists for all values of x in $[\pi/4, 5\pi/4]$

Now, $f\left(\frac{\pi}{4}\right) = e^{\frac{\pi}{4}}\left[\sin\left(\frac{\pi}{4}\right) - \cos\left(\frac{\pi}{4}\right)\right] = 0$

$f\left(\frac{5\pi}{4}\right) = e^{\frac{5\pi}{4}}\left[\sin\left(\frac{5\pi}{4}\right) - \cos\left(\frac{5\pi}{4}\right)\right] = 0$

$\therefore \quad f\left(\frac{\pi}{4}\right) = f\left(\frac{5\pi}{4}\right)$.

Since $f(x)$ is differentiable for all values of x in $\left[\frac{\pi}{4}, \frac{5\pi}{4}\right]$.

Hence, all three conditions of Rolle's theorem are satisfied. Therefore, there exists a point $c \in \left(\frac{\pi}{4}, \frac{5\pi}{4}\right)$ such that $f'(c) = 0$.

5. Since, we have

$$f(x) = \begin{vmatrix} \sin x & \sin\alpha & \sin\beta \\ \cos x & \cos\alpha & \sin\beta \\ \tan x & \tan\alpha & \sin\beta \end{vmatrix}$$

$$= \sin x(\cos\alpha \tan\beta - \cos\beta \tan\alpha)$$
$$- \sin\alpha(\cos x \tan\beta - \tan x \cos\beta)$$
$$+ \sin\beta(\cos x \tan\alpha - \tan x \cos\alpha)$$

$\therefore \quad f(x) = (\cos\alpha \tan\beta - \cos\beta \tan\alpha) \sin x$
$\quad -(\sin\alpha \tan\beta - \sin\beta \tan\alpha) \cos x$
$\quad + (\sin\alpha \cos\beta - \sin\beta \cos\alpha) \tan x$

Since $\sin x, \cos x, \tan x$ have finite derivative in $\left(0, \frac{\pi}{2}\right)$ so $f'(x)$ exist in $\left(0, \frac{\pi}{2}\right)$ and we have $0 < \alpha < \beta < \frac{\pi}{2}$ therefore, $f(x)$ is continuous in $[\alpha, \beta]$ and is differentiable in $]\alpha, \beta[$. Further, we have

$$f(\alpha) = \begin{vmatrix} \sin\alpha & \sin\alpha & \sin\beta \\ \cos\alpha & \cos\alpha & \sin\beta \\ \tan\alpha & \tan\alpha & \sin\beta \end{vmatrix} = 0$$

$$f(\beta) = \begin{vmatrix} \sin\beta & \sin\alpha & \sin\beta \\ \cos\beta & \cos\alpha & \sin\beta \\ \tan\beta & \tan\alpha & \sin\beta \end{vmatrix} = 0$$

$\therefore \quad f(\alpha) = f(\beta)$

Hence, all the conditions of Rolle's theorem are satisfied for given function. Then by Rolle's theorem, there exist a point $l \in (\alpha, \beta)$ such that $f'(l) = 0$.

6. Since, the given function is continuous in $[0, 1]$ and differentiable in $]0, 1[$, then by Lagrange's theorem, we have

$$f'(c) = \frac{f(b) - f(a)}{b - a}$$

Take $a=0, b=1$ and $c=x$ we have

$$f'(x_1)=\frac{f(1)-f(0)}{1-0}, 0<x_1<1$$

$\Rightarrow$ $f'(x)=f(1)-f(0)$, $0<x_1<1$

7. Let us suppose $f(x)=\log(1+x)-x$

then $f(0)=\log(1+0)-0=0$

Now $f'(x)=\frac{1}{1+x}-1=-\frac{x}{1+x}\le 0$ for $x\ge 0$.

$\therefore$ $f(x)$ is a decreasing function in $[0,\infty[$.

$\Rightarrow$ $f(x)\le f(0)$ for all $x\ge 0$

$\Rightarrow$ $\log(1+x)-x\le 0$ or $\log(1+x)\le x$ for $x\in[0,\infty[$.

8. We have $f(x)=ax^2+bx+c$

$\Rightarrow$ $f(x+h)=a(x+h)^2+b(x+h)+c$

Also, $f'(x)=2ax+b$

$\Rightarrow$ $f'(x+\theta h)=2a(x+\theta h)+c$

Putting these values in Lagrange's mean value theorem we get

$\therefore$ $f(x+h)=f(x)+hf'(x+\theta h)$

$$a(x+h)^2+b(x+h)+c=ax^2+bx+c+h[2a(x+\theta h)+b]$$

when $x\to 0$. we have $ah^2+bh+c=c+h[2a\theta h+b]$

$$ah^2=2a\theta h^2 \text{ or } \theta=\frac{1}{2}$$

which is the required value of θ.

9. We have $f(x)=x^n-a$ then $f'(x)=nx^{n-1}$.

Now, we can easily show that $f'(x)>0$ for $x>0$

Therefore, f is an increasing function in $[0,\infty[$.

Let $x_1, x_2, \in]0,\infty[$ and $0<x_1,<r<x_2$ such that $f(r)=0$.

Then $f(x_1)<f(r)<f(x_2)$ or $f(x_1)<0<f(x_2)$ which shows that it $x\ne r$, $f(x)\ne 0$ on $[0,\infty[$ *i.e.*, $x^n-a=0$ has at most one real positive root.

10. Let f' exist in $[a,b]$ and therefore, $f'(x)$ exists in $]a,b[$. Assume that x_0 and x_0+h are two neighboring points in $]a,b[$. By mean value theorem, we have

$$\lim_{h\to 0}\frac{f(x_0+h)-f(x_0)}{h}\lim_{h\to 0}f'(x_0+\theta h), 0<\theta<1.$$

$\Rightarrow$ $f'(x_0-0)=f'(x_0)$, under the assumption that $f'(x_0+0)$ exist in $]a,b[$

$$\lim_{h\to 0}\frac{f(x_0-h)-f(x_0)}{-h}$$

$\Rightarrow$ $f'(x_0-\theta_1 h), 0<\theta<1$

$\Rightarrow$ $f'(x_0-0)=f'(x_0)$ if $f'(x_0-0)$ exist

$\Rightarrow$ $f'(x_0+0)=f'(x_0-0)=f(x_0)=f'$

is continuous on $[a,b]\Rightarrow f'$ cannot have an ordinary or removable discontinuity in $]a,b[$ under our assumption that $f(x_0+0)$ and $f'(x_0-0)$ exist. If $f'(x_0+0)$ and $f'(x_0-0)$ do not exist f' can have a discontinuity of second kind.

11. (a) $f(x)=x^3, f'(x)=3x^2$ and $f'(c)=3c^2$

Let $a=-1, b=1$, $f(a)=f(-1)=(-1)^3=-1$

$f(b)=f(1)=(1)^3=+1.$

By Lagrange's mean value theorem, we have

$$f(b)=f(a)+(b-a)\ f'(c)$$
$$f(1)=f(-1)+(1+1)\ f'(c)$$
$$1=-1+2f'(c)$$
$$\Rightarrow\ 1=-1+2(3c^2)$$
$$\Rightarrow\ 1=-1+6c^2$$
$$2=6c^2\Rightarrow c^2=\frac{1}{3}, c=\frac{1}{\sqrt{3}}\in[-1,1]$$

Hence, Lagrange's mean theorem is verified.

(b) $f(x)=\sin x$ in $\left[0,\frac{\pi}{2}\right]$

$\Rightarrow$ $f'(x)=\cos x$

$\Rightarrow$ $f(0)=\sin 0=0$

and $f\left(\frac{\pi}{2}\right)=\sin\left(\frac{\pi}{2}\right)=1.$

Since $f(x)=\sin x$ which is continuous and differentiable for all values of $x\in\mathbf{R}$. So in particular $f(x)=\sin x$ is continuous in $\left[0,\frac{\pi}{2}\right]$ and differentiable in $\left(0,\frac{\pi}{2}\right)$. Thus Lagrange's theorem is applicable. Then by Lagrange's mean value theorem, there must exist $c\in\left(0,\frac{\pi}{2}\right)$ such that

$$\frac{f\left(\frac{\pi}{2}\right)-f(0)}{\frac{\pi}{2}-0}=f'(c)$$

$$\Rightarrow\ \frac{1-0}{\frac{\pi}{2}}=\cos c\Rightarrow \cos c=\frac{2}{\pi}\Rightarrow c=\cos^{-1}\left(\frac{2}{\pi}\right)$$

Now we know that $0\le\frac{\pi}{2}<1$ so $c=\cos^{-1}\left(\frac{2}{\pi}\right)$ exists in $\left(0,\frac{\pi}{2}\right)$. Hence,

Lagrange's mean value theorem is verified.

(c) $f(x)=x^n$ in $[-1,1]$,

$f'(x)=nx^{n-1}, f'(c)=nc^{n-1}$

$f(-1)=(-1)^n, f(1)=(1)^n.$

Since x^n is a polynomial of degree n so it is continuous and differentiable for all $x\in\mathbf{R}$. So in particular $f(x)=x^n$ is continuous in $[-1,1]$ and differentiable in $(-1,1)$. Then by Lagrange's mean value theorem, there exist $c\in(-1,1)$. Now, there are two cases :

(I) if n is even, then $(-1)^n=1\Rightarrow c=0\in(-1,1)$.

(II) if n is odd, then $(-1)^n=-1\Rightarrow c^{n-1}=\frac{2}{2n}=\frac{1}{n}$

$$\Rightarrow\ c=\left(\frac{1}{n}\right)^{\frac{1}{n-1}}\in(-1,1)\ \forall \text{ odd value of } n.$$

Hence, the Lagrange's theorem is verified.

12. (a) We have $f(x)=\sqrt{x^2-4}$

$$f'(x)=\frac{1}{2}\frac{1}{\sqrt{x^2-4}}(2x)=\frac{x}{\sqrt{x^2-4}}$$

$\therefore$ $$f'(c)=\frac{c}{\sqrt{c^2-4}}$$

For $a=2, b=4$ $f(2)=f(a)=\sqrt{2^2}-4=0$

$$f(4)=f(b)=\sqrt{4^2-4}=\sqrt{12}.$$

By mean value theorem, we have $f(b)=f(a)+(b-a)f'(c)$

$$\sqrt{12}=0+(2)\frac{c}{\sqrt{c^2-4}}c=\pm\sqrt{6}\in(2,4]$$

(b) We have $f(x)=2x^2+3x+4 \Rightarrow f'(x)=4x+3$

$$f'(c)=4c+3$$

For $a=1, b=2$ $f(a)=f(1)=2.1^2+3.1+4=9$

and $f(b)=f(2)=2.2^2+3.2+4=8+6+4=18.$

Then, by mean value theorem, we have

$$18=9+(2-1)(4c+3)$$

$$9=4c+3 \Rightarrow c=\frac{3}{2}.$$

(c) We have $f(x)=x(x-1)$ in interval $[1,2]$

$\Rightarrow$ $f(x)=x^2-x$

and $f'(x)=2x-1$ and $f'(c)=2c-1.$

For $a=1, b=2$ $f(a)=1-1=0$

and $f(b)=f(2)=4-2=2.$

By mean value theorem, we have

$$2=1+(2-1).(2c-1)$$

$$1=2c-1, c=1.$$

Problem Set (5)

Multiple Choice Questions

1. $\lim_{x\to\pi/4}\frac{\sqrt{2}\cos x-1}{\cot x-1}$ equals

(a) $\frac{1}{\sqrt{(2)}}$ (b) $\frac{1}{2}$ (c) $\frac{1}{2\sqrt{(2)}}$ (d) 1

2. $\lim_{x\to\pi/4}\frac{1-\tan x}{1-\sqrt{2}\sin x}$ equals

(a) $\frac{1}{\sqrt{(2)}}$ (b) $\frac{1}{2}$ (c) $\frac{1}{2\sqrt{(2)}}$ (d) 1

3. $\lim_{x\to 0}\frac{\sin 2x}{x}$ is equal to

(a) 0 (b) 1 (c) 1/2 (d) 2

(M.N.R. 1990)

4. The function f defined as $f(x)=(\sin x^2)/x$ for $x\neq 0$ and $f(0)=0$ is

(a) continuous and derivable at $x=0$,

(b) neither continuous nor derivable at $x=0$,

(c) continuous but not derivable at $x=0$,

(d) none of these.

5. For a real number y, let $[y]$ denote the greatest integer less than or equal to y. Then $f(x)=\frac{\tan(\pi[x-\pi])}{1+[x]^2}$ is

(a) discontinuous at some x,

(b) continuous at all x, but the derivative $f'(x)$ does not exist for some x.

(c) $f'(x)$ exists for all x but second derivative $f''(x)$ does not exist.

(d) $f'(x)$ exists for all x.

6. There exists a function $f(x)$ satisfying

$f(0)=1$, $f'(0)=-1$, $f(x)>0$ for all x and

(a) $f'(x)<0$ for all x.

(b) $-1<f''(x)<0$ for all x.

(c) $-2\le f''(x)\le -1$ for all x.

(d) $f''(x)<-2$ for all x.

7. The function $f(x)=1+|\sin x|$ is

(a) continuous nowhere,

(b) continuous everywhere,

(c) differentiable nowhere,

(d) not differentiable at $x=0$,

(e) not differentiable at an infinite number of points.

8. Let $[x]$ denote the greatest integer less than or equal to x. If $f(x)=[x\sin\pi x]$, then $f(x)$ is

(a) continuous at $x=0$,

(b) continuous in $(-1,0)$,

(c) differentiable at $x=1$,

(d) differentiable in $(-1,1)$,

(e) none of these.

9. The following functions are continuous on $(0,\pi)$

(a) $\tan x$

(b) $\int_0^x t\sin\frac{1}{t}\,dt$

(c) $\begin{cases}1, & 0<x\le\frac{3\pi}{4}\\ 2\sin\frac{2}{9}x, & \frac{3\pi}{4}<x<\pi\end{cases}$

(d) $\begin{cases}x\sin x, & 0<x\le\pi/2\\ \frac{\pi}{2}\sin(\pi+x), & \frac{\pi}{2}<x<\pi\end{cases}$

(I.I.T. 1991)

10. (i) If $f(x)=\frac{1}{2}x-1$, then, on the interval $[0,\pi]$

(a) $\tan[f(x)]$ and $1/f(x)$ are both continuous,

(b) $\tan[f(x)]$ and $1/f(x)$ are both discontinuous,

(c) $\tan[f(x)]$ and $f^{-1}(x)$ are both continuous,

(d) $\tan[f(x)]$ is discontinuous but $1/f(x)$ is not.

(ii) If $f(x)=3x-5$, then $f^{-1}(x)$

(a) is given by $\frac{1}{3x-5}$

(b) is given by $\frac{x+5}{3}$

(c) does not exist because f is not one-one

(d) does not exist because f is not onto.

(I.I.T. 1998)

11. If $\lim_{x\to 0}[1+x\log(1+b^2)]^{1/x} = 2b\sin^2\theta, b>0$ and $\theta \in]-\pi, \pi[$. Then the value of θ is

(a) $\pm\frac{\pi}{4}$ (b) $\pm\frac{\pi}{3}$ (c) $\pm\frac{\pi}{6}$ (d) $\pm\frac{\pi}{2}$

(IIT JEE 2011)

12. $\lim_{x\to 2}\left(\frac{\sqrt{1-\cos\{2(x-2)\}}}{x-2}\right)$

(a) does not exist (b) equals $\sqrt{2}$

(c) equals $-\sqrt{2}$ (d) equals $\frac{1}{\sqrt{2}}$

(AIEEE 2011, IIT 1998)

13. Let $f:\mathbf{R}\to\mathbf{R}$ be a positive increasing function with $\lim_{x\to\infty}\frac{f(3x)}{f(x)} = 1$ Then $\lim_{x\to\infty}\frac{f(2x)}{f(x)} =$

(a) 1 (b) $\frac{2}{3}$ (c) $\frac{3}{2}$ (d) 3

(AIEEE 2010)

14. If $\lim_{x\to\infty}\left(\frac{x^2+x+1}{x+1} - ax - b\right) = 4$ then

(a) $a=1, b=4$ (b) $a=1, b=-4$

(c) $a=2, b=-3$ (d) $a=2, b=3$

(IIT JEE 2012)

15. The value of p and q for which the function

$$f(x) = \begin{cases} \frac{\sin(p+1)x + \sin x}{x} ; & x<0 \\ \frac{9}{} ; & x=0 \\ \frac{\sqrt{x+x^2}-\sqrt{x}}{x^{3/2}} ; & x>0 \end{cases}$$

is continuous for all $x\in\mathbf{R}$ are

(a) $p=\frac{1}{2}, q=\frac{-3}{2}$ (b) $p=\frac{5}{2}, q=\frac{1}{2}$

(c) $p=\frac{-3}{2}, q=\frac{1}{2}$ (d) $p=\frac{1}{2}, q=\frac{3}{2}$

(AIEEE 2011)

16. Let $f:[-1,1[\to\mathbf{R}$ be a differentiable function with $f(0)=-1$ and $f'(0)=1$. Let $g(x) = [f(2)f(x)+2)]^2$ Then $g'(0) =$

(a) 4 (b) −4 (c) 0 (d) −2

(AIEEE 2010)

17. If $f:\mathbf{R}\to\mathbf{R}$ is a function defined by $f(x) = [x]\cos\left(\frac{2x-1}{2}\right)\pi$, where $[x]$ denotes the greatest integer function then f is

(a) continuous for every real **R**

(b) discontinuous only at $x=0$

(c) discontinuous only at non zero integral values of k

(d) continuous only at $x=0$ **(AIEEE 2012; IIT 1995)**

18. Let $L = \lim_{x\to 0}\frac{a-\sqrt{a^2-x^2}-x^2/4}{x^4}, a>0$. If L is finite then

(a) $a=2$ (b) $a=1$ (c) $L=\frac{1}{64}$ (d) $L=\frac{1}{32}$

(IIT-JEE 2004)

19. Let $f:\mathbf{R}\to\mathbf{R}$ be a function such that $f(x+y)=f(x)+f(y)\ \forall\ x,y\in\mathbf{R}$. If $f(x)$ is differentiable at $x=0$ then

(a) $f(x)$ is differentiable only in a finite interval containing 0

(b) $f(x)$ is continuous $\forall\ x\in\mathbf{R}$

(c) $f'(x)$ is constant $\forall\ x\in\mathbf{R}$

(d) $f(x)$ is differentiable except at finitely many points

(IIT-JEE 2011)

20. If $f(x) = \begin{cases} -x-\frac{\pi}{2} ; & x\le -\frac{\pi}{2} \\ -\cos x & -\frac{\pi}{2} < x \le 0, \\ x-1 & 0<x\le 1 \\ \log x & x>1 \end{cases}$ then

(a) $f(x)$ is continuous at $x=-\frac{\pi}{2}$

(b) $f(x)$ isnot differentiable at $x=0$

(b) $f(x)$ is differentiable at $x=1$

(d) $f(x)$ is differentiable at $x=-\frac{3}{2}$ **(IIT-JEE 2011)**

21. Let $f:[0,1[\to\mathbf{R}$ be defined by $f(x)=\frac{b-x}{1-bx}$, where b is a constant such that $0<b<1$. Then

(a) f is not invertible on $[0,1[$

(b) $f\ne f^{-1}$ on $[0,1[$ and $f'(b)=\frac{1}{f'(0)}$

(b) $f=f^{-1}$ on $[0,1[$ and $f'(b)=\frac{1}{f'(0)}$

(d) f^{-1} is differentiable on $[0,1[$ **(IIT-JEE 2011)**

22. Let f be a real valued function defined on the interval $[0,\infty[$ by $f(x)=\log x+\int_0^x\sqrt{1+\sin t}\,.dt$ then which is (are) true

(a) $f''(x)$ exists $\forall\ x\in[0,\infty[$

(b) $f'(x)$ exists $\forall\ x\in[0,\infty[$ and f' is continuous on $]0,\infty[$ but not differentiable on $[0,\infty[$

(c) $\exists\alpha>1$ such that $|f'(x)|<|f(x)|\ \forall\ x\in[\alpha,\infty[$

(d) $\exists\beta>0$ such that $|f(x)|+|f'(x)|\le\beta\ \forall\ x\in[0,\infty[$

(IIT-JEE 2010)

23. For every integer n let a_n and b_n be real numbers. Let function $f: \mathbf{R} \to \mathbf{R}$ be given by

$$f(x) = \begin{cases} a_n + \sin \pi x & \text{for } x \in [2n, 2n+1] \\ b_n + \cos \pi x, & \text{for } x \in]2n-1, 2n[\end{cases} \text{for all integer}$$

n. If f is continuous, then which case is true :

(a) $a_{n-1} - b_{n-1} = 0$ (b) $a_n - b_n = 1$

(c) $a_n - b_{n+1} = 1$ (d) $a_{n-1} - b_n = -1$

(IIT JEE 2012)

24. (a) Let $f :]-1, 1[\to \mathbf{R}$ be such that $f(\cos 4\theta) = \dfrac{2}{2 \sec^2 \theta}$ for $\theta \in \left]0, \dfrac{\pi}{4}\right[\cup \left]\dfrac{\pi}{4}, \dfrac{\pi}{2}\right[$ then the value of $f\left(\dfrac{1}{3}\right)$ is

(a) $1 - \sqrt{\dfrac{3}{2}}$ (b) $1 + \sqrt{\dfrac{3}{2}}$

(c) $1 - \sqrt{\dfrac{2}{3}}$ (d) $1 + \sqrt{\dfrac{2}{3}}$ **(IIT JEE 2012)**

(b) If $f(x) = \left\{ x^2 \left| \cos \dfrac{\pi}{x} \right| \; x \neq 0, x \in \mathbf{R} \right.$ then f is

(a) diff. at $x = 0$ and $x = 2$

(b) diff. at $x = 0$ but not at $x = 2$

(c) not diff at $x = 0$, but diff. at $x = 2$

(d) differentiable neither $x = 0$ nor $x = 2$ **(IIT JEE 2012)**

True and False Type Questions :

Find whether the following statements are True or False.

25. If $f(x)$ and $g(x)$ have no derivative at a point, then $f(x)\, g(x)$ has no derivative at that point.

Fill in the blanks :

26. A discontinuous function $y = f(x)$ satisfying $x^2 + y^2 = 4$ is given by $f(x) = \ldots$..

27. Let $f(x) = (x-1)^2 \sin [1/(x-1)] - |x|$, if $x \neq 1$,

$= -1$, if $x = 1$.

be a real valued function. Then the set of points where $f(x)$ is not diffrentiable is ....

28. Let A be a set of n distinct elements, then the total number of distinct functions from A to A is .... and out of these .... are onto functions.

29. If $f(x) = \sin x, x \neq n\pi, n = 0, \pm 1, \pm 2, \pm 3, \ldots$

$= 2$, otherwise

and $g(x) = x^2 + 1, x \neq 0, 2,\; g(0) = 4, g(2) = 5$, then $\lim\limits_{x \to 0} g[f(x)]$ is ...

Solutions to Problem Set (5)

1. Ans. (b). **2.** Ans. (d).

3. Ans. (d).

We have $\lim\limits_{x \to 0} \dfrac{\sin 2x}{x} = \lim\limits_{x \to 0} \dfrac{\sin 2x}{2x} . 2 = 1.2 = 2.$

4. Ans. (a).

We have, $f(0) = 0$

$$f(0+0) = \lim_{h \to 0} \frac{\sin (0+h)^2}{0+h} = \lim_{h \to 0} \frac{\sin h^2}{h}$$

$$= \lim_{h \to 0} \frac{\sin h^2}{h^2} . h = 1 \times 0 = 0.$$

Similarly $f(0-0) = 0$.

Hence $f(x)$ is continuous at $x = 0$.

$$\text{Now } Rf'(0) = \lim_{h \to 0} \frac{\sin (0+h)^2 / (0+h) - 0}{h}$$

$$= \lim_{h \to 0} \frac{\sin h^2}{h^2} = 1.$$

$$\text{and } Lf'(0) = \lim_{h \to 0} \frac{\sin (0-h)^2 / (0-h) - 0}{-h}$$

$$= \lim_{h \to 0} \frac{\sin h^2}{h^2} = 1$$

Since $Rf'(0) = Lf'(0)$, the function $f(x)$ is derivable at $x = 0$.

5. Ans. (d).

By definition $[x - \pi]$ is an integer whatever x may be and so $\pi [x - \pi]$ is an integral multiple of π. Consequently $\tan (\pi [x - \pi]) = 0$ for all x.

And since $1 + [x]^2 \neq 0$ for any x, we conclude that $f(x) = 0$.

Thus $f(x)$ is constant function and so it is continuous and differentiable any number of times, that is $f'(x), f''(x), f'''(x) \ldots, f^n(x), \ldots$, all exist for every x, their value being 0 at every point x. Hence of all the given alternatives only (d) is correct.

6. Ans. (a).

$f(x) = e^{-x}$ is one such function. It can be shown that there exists no function satisfying the conditions (b) or (c) or (d) and the given conditions $f(0) = 1,\; f'(0) = -1, f(x) > 0$ for all x.

7. Ans. (b), (d), (e).

The function is clearly continuous everywhere. For if a is any real number, then

$$f(a) = 1 + |\sin a|$$

$$f(a+0) = \lim_{h \to 0} [1 + |\sin (a+h)|]$$

$$= 1 + |\sin a|$$

$$\text{and } f(a-0) = \lim_{h \to 0} [1 + |\sin (a-h)|]$$

$$= 1 + |\sin a|.$$

The function is not differentiable at $x = n\pi, n = 0, \pm 1, \pm 2, \ldots$ as shown below :

$$f(n\pi) = 1 + |\sin n\pi| = 1 + |0| = 1$$

$$\text{Now } Rf'(n\pi) = \lim_{h \to 0} \frac{1 + |\sin (n\pi + h)| - 1}{h} \quad (h > 0)$$

$$= \lim_{h \to 0} \frac{|\pm \sin h|}{h} = \lim_{h \to 0} \frac{\sin h}{h} = 1$$

[$\because$ h is small and > 0 and as such $\sin h > 0$]

and $\quad Lf'(n\pi) = \lim_{h\to 0} \frac{1+|\sin(n\pi - h)|-1}{-h}$

$= \lim_{h\to 0} \frac{|\pm\sin h|}{-h} = \lim_{h\to 0} \frac{\sin h}{-h} = -1$

Since $Rf'(n\pi) \neq Lf'(n\pi)$, $f(x)$ is not differentiable at $x = n\pi, n = 0, \pm 1, \pm 2, \pm 3, \ldots$

At all other points $f(x)$ is clearly differentiable. For if a is any real number such that

$$n\pi < a < (n+1)\pi.$$

Then we can write $a = n\pi + \alpha$, where $0 < \alpha < \pi$. Now

$Rf'(a) = \lim_{h\to 0} \frac{\{1+|\sin(a+h)|\} - \{1+|\sin a|\}}{h}$

$= \lim_{h\to 0} \frac{|\sin(a+h)| - |\sin a|}{h}$

$= \lim_{h\to 0} \frac{|\sin(n\pi+\alpha+h)| - |\sin(n\pi+\alpha)|}{h}$

$= \lim_{h\to 0} \frac{|\pm\sin(\alpha+h)| - |\pm\sin\alpha|}{h}$

$= \lim_{h\to 0} \frac{\sin(\alpha+h) - \sin\alpha}{h}$

Note that since h is small and $0 < \alpha < \pi$, we must also have $0 < \alpha + h < \pi$ so that $\sin(\alpha+h) > 0$

$= \lim_{h\to 0} \frac{2\cos\left(\alpha + \frac{1}{2}h\right)\sin\frac{1}{2}h}{h}$

$= \lim_{h\to 0} \cos\left(\alpha + \frac{1}{2}h\right) \cdot \lim_{h\to 0} \frac{\sin\frac{1}{2}h}{\frac{1}{2}h}$

$= \cos\alpha \,.\, 1 = \cos\alpha = \cos(a - n\pi)$.

Similarly $Lf'(a) = \cos(a - n\pi)$.

Hence $f(x)$ is continuous everywhere. Also $f(x)$ is differentiable everywhere except at

$$x = n\pi, n = 0, \pm 1, \pm 2, \pm 3, \ldots$$

8. Ans. (a), (b) and (d).

By def. of $[x]$, we easily see that

$f(x) = [x \sin \pi x] = 0$ when $-1 \le x \le 1$.

[**Note that** $-1 \le x \le 1 \Rightarrow 0 \le x \sin \pi x \le \frac{1}{2}$]

and $f(x) = [x\sin\pi x] = -1$ when $1 < x < 1 + h$, (h small)

[**Note :** $x \sin \pi x$ becomes negative and numerically less than 1 when x is slightly greater than 1 and so by def. of $[x]$

$[x \sin \pi x] = -1$ when $1 < x < [1+h]$]

Thus $f(x)$ is constant and equal to 0 in the closed interval $[-1, 1]$ and so $f(x)$ is continuous and differentiable in the open interval $(-1, 1)$. At $x = 1$, $f(x)$ is clearly discontinuous since $f(1-0) = 0$ and $f(1+0) = -1$ and $f(x)$ is non-differentiable at $x = 1$. Hence (a), (b) and (d) are correct answers.

9. Ans. (b) and (c).

Let $F(x) = \int_0^x t \sin\frac{1}{t}\, dt$

Since $t\sin(1/t)$ is clearly a continuous function on $(0, \pi)$ for any $x \in (0, \pi)$, it follows that $F(x)$ is also a continuous function. Thus (b) is correct.

To prove (c), we need to test the continuity of the function

$$f(x) = \begin{cases} 1, & 0 < x \le 3\pi/4 \\ 2\sin(2x/9), & 3\pi/4 < x < \pi, \end{cases}$$

at the point $x = 3\pi/4$ alone.

We have $f(3\pi/4 - 0) = \underset{h\to 0}{\text{Lt}}\ 1 = 1$

and $f(3\pi/4 + 0) = \underset{h\to 0}{\text{Lt}}\ 2\sin\left\{\frac{2}{9}\left(\frac{3\pi}{4} + h\right)\right\}$

$= \underset{h\to 0}{\text{Lt}}\ 2\sin\left(\frac{\pi}{6} + \frac{2h}{9}\right) = 2\sin\frac{\pi}{6} = 1$

Also $f(3\pi/4) = 1$, by definition.

Hence $f(x)$ is continuous at $x = 3\pi/4$. At all points of $(0, \pi)$, $f(x)$ is clearly continuous. Hence $f(x)$ is continuous on $(0, \pi)$.

Observe that $\tan x$ is discontinuous at $x = \pi/2$ which is point of the interval $(0, \pi)$ and the function given in (d) can be shown to be discontinuous at $x = \pi/2$.

10. (i) Ans. (b).

First note that $[x]$ means the greatest integer not exceeding x, keeping this in mind we find

$[f(x)] = \left[\frac{1}{2}x - 1\right] = -1$, when $0 \le x < 2$

$= 0$, when $2 \le x \le \pi$

$\therefore \quad \tan[f(x)] = \tan(-1) = -\tan 1$, $0 \le x < 2$

$= \tan 0 = 0$, $2 \le x \le \pi$

The function $\tan[f(x)]$ is clearly discontinuous at $x = 2$.

Also the function $\frac{1}{f(x)} = \frac{1}{\left(\frac{1}{2x-1}\right)}$ is discontinuous at $x = 2$.

These two functions are continuous at all other points in the interval $[0, \pi]$.

The function $f^{-1}(x)$ is defined by

$f^{-1}(x) = y \quad \Rightarrow f(y) = x$

$\Rightarrow \quad \frac{1}{2}y - 1 = x \quad \Rightarrow \quad y = 2x + 1$.

Thus $f^{-1}(x) = 2x + 1$, which is continuous on $[0, \pi]$. Hence (b) is the only correct answer.

(ii) Ans. (b).

11. Ans. (d).

$\lim_{x\to 0} \frac{x\log(1+b^2)}{x} = 1 + b^2 = 2b\sin^2\theta$

$\Rightarrow \quad \sin^2\theta = \frac{1}{2}\left(b + \frac{1}{b}\right)$

we have $b + \frac{1}{b} \ge 2$

$\Rightarrow \quad \sin^2\theta \ge 1$ but $\sin^2\theta \le 1$

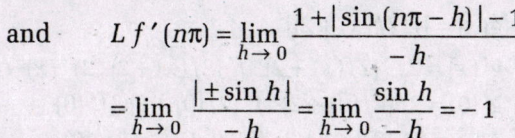

$\Rightarrow \quad \sin^2\theta = 1 \qquad \Rightarrow \quad \theta = \pm\frac{\pi}{2}$

12. Ans. (a).

$$f(2+0) = \lim_{h\to 0} f(2+h) = \lim_{h\to 0} \frac{\sqrt{1-\cos 2h}}{h}$$

$$= \lim_{h\to 0} \frac{\sqrt{2}-\sin h}{h} = \sqrt{2}$$

$$f(2-0) = \lim_{h\to 0} f(2-h) = \lim_{h\to 0} \frac{\sqrt{1-\cos(-2h)}}{-h}$$

$$= \lim_{h\to 0} \sqrt{2}\cdot\frac{\sin h}{-h} = -\sqrt{2}$$

$\Rightarrow$ limit does not exist

13. Ans. (a).

For positive numbers

$x < 2x < 3x \Rightarrow f(x) < f(2x) < f(3x)$

$$\Rightarrow \frac{f(x)}{f(x)} < \frac{f(2x)}{f(x)} < \frac{f(3x)}{f(x)}$$

$$\lim_{x\to 0}\frac{f(x)}{f(x)} < \lim_{x\to\infty}\frac{f(2x)}{f(x)} < \lim_{x\to\infty}\frac{f(3x)}{f(x)}$$

$$\Rightarrow 1 < \lim \frac{f(2x)}{f(x)} < 1$$

$\therefore$ By sandwich theorem $\lim_{x\to\infty}\frac{f(2x)}{f(x)} = 1$

14. Ans. (b).

$$\lim_{x\to\infty}\left(\frac{x^2+x+1}{x+1} - ax - b\right) = 4$$

$$\lim_{x\to\infty}\left(\frac{x^2(1-0)+x(1-a-b)+(1-b)}{x+1}\right) = 4$$ limit is finite

It exists when $1-a=0 \Rightarrow a=1$

Then $$\lim_{x\to\infty}\left(\frac{1-a-b+\frac{1-b}{x}}{1+\frac{1}{x}}\right) = 4$$

$\therefore \quad 1-a-b=4 \Rightarrow b=4$

15. Ans. (c).

$f(0) = q$

$$f(0+0) = \lim_{x\to 0^+}\frac{(1+x)^{1/2}-1}{x}$$

$$= \lim_{x\to 0^+}\frac{1+\frac{1}{2}x+\ldots-1}{x} = \frac{1}{2}$$

$$f(0-0) = \lim_{x\to 0^-}\frac{\sin(p+1)x+\sin x}{2}$$

$$= \lim_{x\to 0^-}\frac{(\cos(p+1)x)(p+1)+\cos x}{1}$$

$= (p+1)+1 = p+2$

$\therefore \quad p+2 = g = \frac{1}{2} \Rightarrow p = -\frac{3}{2}, g = \frac{1}{2}$

16. Ans. (b).

$g(x) = [f(2f(x)+2)]^2$

$g'(x) = 2f`(2f(x)+2)\,.\,f'(2f(x)+2)\,.\,2f'(x)$

$\Rightarrow \quad g'(0) = 2f(2f(0)+2)\,.\,f'(2f(0)+2)\,2f'(0)$

$= 2f(2(-1)+2)\,f'(2(-1)+2)\,2f'(0)$

$= 2f(0)\,f'(0)\,2f'(0) = 4(-1)(1)(1) = -4$

17. Ans. (a).

Doubtful points are $x = n, n \in \mathbf{I}$

$$\text{LHL} = \lim_{x\to n^-}[x]\cos\left(\frac{2x-1}{2}\right)\pi$$

$$= (n-1)\cos\left(\frac{2n-1}{2}\right)\pi = 0$$

$$\text{RHL} = \lim_{x\to n^+}[x]\cos\left(\frac{2x+1}{2}\right)\pi = n\cos\left(\frac{2n-1}{2}\right)\pi = 0$$

and $f(n) = 0$

$\Rightarrow \quad f(x)$ is continuous

18. Ans. (a) and (c).

$$L = \sin_{x\to 0}\frac{a-\sqrt{a^2-x^2}-\frac{x^2}{4}}{x^4}, a>0$$

$$= \lim_{x\to 0}\frac{a-a\left[1-\frac{1}{2}\cdot\frac{x^2}{a^2}+\frac{1}{2}\frac{\left(\frac{1}{2}-1\right)}{2}\cdot\frac{x^4}{a^4}-\ldots\right]-\frac{x^2}{4}}{x^4}$$

$$= \lim_{x\to 0}\frac{\frac{x^2}{2a}+\frac{1}{8}\frac{x^4}{a^3}+\ldots-\frac{x^2}{4}}{x^4}$$

Since L is finite $\Rightarrow 2a = 4 \Rightarrow a = 2$

$\therefore$ Required limit $L = \lim_{x\to 0}\frac{1}{8a^3} = \frac{1}{64}$

19. Ans. (b) and (c).

$f(x) = kx$, clearly $f(x)$ is continuous and differentiable at $x \in \mathbf{R}$ and $f'(x) = k$, constant

20. Ans. (a), (b), (c) and (d)

At $x = -\frac{\pi}{2}$ $Lf\left(-\frac{\pi}{2}\right) = 0 = f\left(\frac{-\pi}{2}\right)$ and $Rf\left(\frac{-\pi}{2}\right) = 0$

$\Rightarrow \quad f$ is continuous

(b) At $x=0$, $Rf'(0) = 1$ and $Lf'(0) = 0 \Rightarrow f$ is not differentiable

(c) At $x=1$, $Rf'(1) = 1$ and $Lf'(1) = 1 \Rightarrow f$ is differentiable at $x = 1$

(d) At $x = \frac{-3}{2} > -\frac{\pi}{2} \Rightarrow f(x) = -\cos x \Rightarrow f$ is differentiable at $x = -\frac{3}{2}$

21. Ans. (a) and (b).

$$f(x) = \frac{x-b}{bx-1} = \frac{1}{b} + \frac{\left(\frac{1}{b}-b\right)}{(bx-1)},\; f'(x) = \frac{-\left(\frac{1}{b}-b\right)}{(bx-1)^2}.b$$

$f'(x) < 0\ \forall\ x \in [0, 1[$

Range of $f(x)$ is $[-1,b[\Rightarrow$ range $\neq$ codomain f is not invertible

22. Ans. (b) and (c).

$$f(x)=\log x+\int_0^x \sqrt{1+\sin t}\,dt$$

$$f'(x)=\frac{1}{x}+\sqrt{1+\sin x}$$

$$f''(x)=\frac{-1}{x^2}+\frac{\cos x}{2\sqrt{1+\sin x}}$$

(a) f'' is not defined for $x=-\frac{\pi}{2}+2n\pi,\ n\in\mathbf{I}\Rightarrow$ (a) is wrong.

(b) $f'(x)$ always exists for $x>0$

(c) $|f'|<|f|$. Since $f'>0$ and $f>0\Rightarrow f'<f$

$$\frac{1}{x}+\sqrt{1+\sin x}<\log x+\int_0^x \sqrt{1+\sin x}\,dx$$

LHS is bounded and RHS is increasing with range ∞. Thus, these exists some α beyond which RHS is greater than LHS

(d) $|f|+|f'|\leq\beta$ is wrong as f is monotonically increasing and range is not bounded while β is finite

23. Ans. (b) and (d).

$$f(2n)=a_n \qquad a_n=b_{n+1}$$

$$f(2n^+)=a_n \Rightarrow a_n-b_n=1$$

$$f(2n^-)=b_{n+1}\Rightarrow \text{(b) is correct}$$

Also $\quad a_n=b_{n+1}^{-1}$

$$a_n-b_{n+1}=1$$

$\Rightarrow\ a_{n-1}-b_n=-1\Rightarrow$ (d) is correct.

24. **(a)** Ans. (a) and (b).

$$\cos 4\theta=\frac{1}{3}\Rightarrow 2\cos^2 2\theta-1=\frac{1}{3}\Rightarrow \cos^2 2\theta=\frac{2}{3}$$

$$\Rightarrow \cos 2\theta=\pm\sqrt{\frac{2}{3}}$$

Now $f(\cos 4\theta)=\dfrac{2}{2-\sec^2\theta}=\dfrac{1+\cos 2\theta}{\cos 2\theta}=1+\dfrac{1}{\cos 2\theta}$

$$\Rightarrow f\left(\frac{1}{3}\right)=1\pm\sqrt{\frac{3}{2}}$$

(b) Ans. (a).

(i) Fordifferentiability at $x=0$

$$\text{LHD}=f'(0^-)=\lim_{h\to 0^+}\frac{f(0-h)-f(0)}{-h}$$

$$=\lim_{h\to 0^+}\frac{h^2\left|\cos\left(\frac{-\pi}{h}\right)\right|-0}{-h}$$

$$=\lim_{h\to 0^+} -h\left|\cos\frac{\pi}{h}\right|=0$$

$$\text{RHD}=f'(0^+)=\lim_{h\to 0^+}\frac{f(0+h)-f(0)}{h}$$

$$=\lim_{h\to 0^+}\frac{h^2\left|\cos\left(\frac{\pi}{h}\right)\right|}{h}=0$$

$\Rightarrow\ f(x)$ is differentiable at $x=0$

(ii) For differentiability at $x=2$

$$\text{RHD}=f'(2^+)=\lim_{h\to 0^+}\frac{f(2+h)-f(2)}{h}$$

$$=\lim_{h\to 0^+}\frac{(2+h)^2\left|\cos\left(\frac{\pi}{2+h}\right)\right|-0}{h}$$

$$=\lim_{h\to 0^+}\frac{(2+h)^2\cos\left(\frac{\pi}{2+h}\right)}{h}$$

$$=\lim_{h\to 0^+}(2+h)^2\sin\left(\frac{\pi}{2}-\frac{\pi}{2+h}\right)$$

$$=\lim_{h\to 0^+}\frac{(2+h)^2.\sin\left(\frac{\pi h}{2(2+h)}\right)}{\left(\frac{\pi}{2(2+h)}\right).h}\cdot\frac{\pi}{2(2+h)}$$

$$=(2)^2.\frac{\pi}{2.2}=\pi$$

$$\text{LHD}=f'(2^-)=\lim_{h\to 0^+}\frac{f(2-h)-f(2)}{-h}$$

$$=\lim_{h\to 0^+}\frac{(2-h)^2\left|\cos\left(\frac{\pi}{2-h}\right)\right|-0}{-h}$$

$$=\lim_{h\to 0^+}\frac{(2-h)^2\left(-\cos\left(\frac{\pi}{2-h}\right)\right)-0}{-h}$$

$$=\lim_{h\to 0^+}\frac{(2-h)^2\cos\left(\frac{\pi}{2-h}\right)}{h}$$

$$=\lim_{h\to 0^+}\frac{(2-h)^2.\sin\left(\frac{\pi}{2}-\frac{\pi}{2-h}\right)}{h}$$

$$=\lim_{h\to 0^+}\frac{(2-h)^2\cos\left(\frac{\pi}{2}-\frac{\pi}{2-h}\right)}{h}$$

$$=\lim_{h\to 0^+}\frac{(2-h)^2.\sin\left(\frac{-\pi h}{2(2-h)}\right)}{\left(-\frac{\pi h}{2(2-h)}\right)}\cdot\frac{-\pi}{2(2-h)}=-\pi$$

$\Rightarrow\ f(x)$ is not differentiable at $x=2$

25. False. Take $f(x)=g(x)=|x|,\ x_0=0$.

26. Ans. $f(x)=\sqrt{4-x^2}$ for $x\geq 0$ and

$f(x)=-\sqrt{4-x^2}$ for $x<0$.

27. Ans. $\{0\}$.

28. The total number of functions is n^n and the number of onto functions is $n!$.

29. Ans. 5.

Problem Set (6)

Multiple Choice Questions

1. A value of c for which the conclusion of mean value theorem holds for the function $f(x) = \log_e x$ on the interval [1, 3] is

(a) $2\log_3 e$ (b) $\frac{1}{2}\log_e 3$ (c) $\log_3 e$ (d) $\log_e 3$ **(AIEEE 2007)**

2. In the mean value theorem $f(b) - f(a) = (b-a) f'(c)$ if $a = 4, b = 9$ and $f(x) = \sqrt{x}$ then the value of c is

(a) 8.00 (b) 5.25 (c) 4.00 (d) 6.25

(Kerela Engg. 2011, J & K 2005)

3. Rolle's theorem is not applicable to the function $f(x) = |x|$ defined on [–1, 1] because

(a) f is not continuous on [–1 1]
(b) f is nt differentiable on [1, 1]
(c) $f(-1) + f(1)$
(d) $f(-1) = f(1) \neq 0$ **(MPPET 1994, 95, WB JEE 2008)**

4. If the function $f(x) = x^3 - 6x^2 + ax + b$ satisfy's Rolle's theorem in the interval [1, 3] and $f'\left[\frac{2\sqrt{3}+1}{\sqrt{3}}\right) = 0$ then $a =$

(a) –11 (b) –6 (c) 6 (d) 11

(MP PET 2002)

5. For the function $f(x) = x + \frac{1}{x}, x \in [1, 3]$ the value of C for the mean value theorem is

(a) 1 (b) $\sqrt{3}$
(c) 2 (d) None of these

(MP PET 1997, 2007)

6. For a function $f(x) = e^x \sin x$ in $[0, \pi]$, which of the following is not correct.

(a) f is continuous in $[0, \pi]$
(b) f is differentiable in $[0\ \pi]$
(c) $f(0) = f(\pi)$
(d) Rolle's theorem is not true is $[0, \pi]$

7. The mean value theorem is $f(b) - f(a) = (b-a) f'(c)$. Then for the function $x^2 - 2x + 3$ in $\left[1, \frac{3}{2}\right]$, the value of C is

(a) $\frac{6}{5}$ (b) $\frac{5}{4}$ (b) $\frac{4}{3}$ (d) $\frac{7}{6}$

8. For the function $f(x) = e^{\cos x}$, Rolle's theorem is applicable when

(a) $\frac{\pi}{2} \le x \le \frac{3\pi}{2}$ (b) $\frac{-\pi}{2} \le x \le \frac{\pi}{2}$
(c) $0 \le x \le 2\pi$ (d) $-\frac{\pi}{4} \le x \le \frac{\pi}{4}$

(WB JEE 2011)

9. In which of the following functions, Rolle's theorem is applicable

(a) $f(x) = |x|$ in $-1 \le x \le 1$
(b) $f(x) = \tan x$ in $0 \le x < x$
(c) $f(x) = 1 - (x-2)^{2/3}$ in $1 \le x \le 3$
(d) $f(x) = x(x-2)^2$ in $0 \le x \le 2$ **(WB JEE 2010)**

10. The value of C in $]0, 2[$ satisfying the mean value theorem for the function $f(x) = x(x-1)^4, x \in [0, 2]$ is equal to

(a) $\frac{5}{4}$ (b) $\frac{4}{5}$ (c) $\frac{5}{3}$ (d) $\frac{1}{3}$

11. If $f(x)$ satisfying the conditions of Rolle's theorem in [1, 2] and $f(x)$ is continuous in [1, 2] then $\int_1^2 f'(x)\,dx =$

(a) 4 (b) 0 (c) 1 (d) 2

(DCE 2002)

12. If $f(x) = \sqrt{x-1} + \sqrt{x + 24 - 10\sqrt{x-1}}$; $1 < x < 26$ be real values function, then $f'(x)$ for $1 < x < 26$ is

(a) 0 (b) $\sqrt{x-1}$
(b) $2\sqrt{x-1}$ (d) $\sqrt{x-1} + 5$

(MPPET 2000, 06)

Hints / Solution to Problem set (6)

1. Ans. (a).

By mean value theorem

$$f'(c) = \frac{f(3) - f(1)}{3-1} \Rightarrow \frac{1}{c} = \frac{\log 3 + \log 1}{2}$$

$$\Rightarrow \quad c = \frac{2}{\log_e 3} = 2\log_3 e$$

2. Ans. (d).

$$f(x) = \sqrt{x} \Rightarrow f(a) = \sqrt{4} = 2, f(b) = \sqrt{9} = 3; f'(x) = \frac{1}{2\sqrt{x}}$$

$$f'(c) = \frac{f(b) - f(a)}{b-a} = \frac{3-2}{9-4} = \frac{1}{5}$$

so $\frac{1}{2\sqrt{c}} = \frac{1}{5} \Rightarrow c = \frac{25}{4} = 6.25$

3. Ans. (b). $f(x) = |x| = \begin{cases} -x & \text{if } -1 \le x \le 0 \\ x & \text{if } 0 \le x \le 1 \end{cases}$

$$R f'(0) = \lim_{h \to 0} \frac{f(0+h) - f(0)}{h} = \lim_{h \to 0} \frac{|h|}{h} = 1$$

similarly $Lf'(0) = -1$

$\Rightarrow$ $Rf'(0) \neq Lf'(0)$

$\Rightarrow$ $f(x)$ is not differentiable on $]-1, 1[$

4. Ans. (d).

$$f(x) = x^3 - 6x^2 + ax + b \Rightarrow f'(x) = 3x^2 - 12x + a$$

$\therefore \quad f'(c)=0 \Rightarrow f'\left(2+\frac{1}{\sqrt{3}}\right)=0$

$\Rightarrow \quad 3\left(2+\frac{1}{\sqrt{3}}\right)^2-12\left(2+\frac{1}{\sqrt{3}}\right)+a=0$

$\Rightarrow \quad a=11$

5. Ans. (b).

$f'(x)=1-\frac{1}{x^2} \Rightarrow f'(c)=1-\frac{1}{c^2}$

$\therefore \quad 1-\frac{1}{c^2}=\frac{10/3-2}{2} \Rightarrow 1-\frac{1}{c^2}-\frac{2}{3} \Rightarrow c^2=3$

6. Ans. (d).

$f(x)=e^x \sin x$ in $(0, \pi]$

$\text{LHL}=\lim_{h\to 0} f\left(\frac{\pi}{2}-h\right)=\lim_{h->0} e^{\left(\frac{\pi}{2}-h\right)}.\sin\left(\frac{\pi}{2}-h\right)$

$=\lim_{h\to 0} e^{\left(\frac{\pi}{2}-h\right)}.\cos h=e^{\pi/2}$

$\text{RHL}=\lim_{h\to 0} f\left(\frac{\pi}{2}+h\right)$

$\lim_{h\to 0} e^{\left(\frac{\pi}{2}+h\right)} \sin\left(\frac{\pi}{2}+h\right)$

$=\lim_{h\to 0} e^{\left(\frac{\pi}{2}+h\right)}(-\cos h)=-e^{\pi/2}$

$\Rightarrow$ LHL $\neq$ RHL $\Rightarrow f(x)$ is not continuous in $[0, \pi]$

$\Rightarrow$ Rolle's theorem is not applicable in $[0, \pi]$

7. Ans. (b).

$f(x)=x^2-2x+3,\ a=1,\ b=3/2 \Rightarrow f(1)=2,\ f\left(\frac{3}{2}\right)=\frac{9}{4}$

$f(b)-f(c)=(b-a)\,f'(c)$

$\Rightarrow \quad \frac{9}{4}-2=\left(\frac{3}{2}-1\right).f'(c)$

$\Rightarrow \quad f'(c)=\frac{1}{2}$

$f'(x)=2x-2=\frac{1}{2} \quad \Rightarrow \quad x=5/4$

$\Rightarrow \quad c=5/4$

8. $f\left(\frac{\pi}{2}\right)=e^0=1,\ f\left(\frac{3\pi}{2}\right)=e^0=1$

$\Rightarrow$ IIIrd conditions of Rolle's theorem is satisfied by option (a)only.

9. Ans. (d).

$f(x)=x(x-2)^2$, a polynomial which is differentiable for all $x \in \mathbf{R}$

for other cases, Rolle's theorem is not applicable.

10. Ans. (b).

$f(x)=x(x-1)^2 \Rightarrow f(0)=0,\ f(2)=2$

$\Rightarrow \quad f(0)=f(2)$

By mean value theorem $f'(x)=\frac{f(2)-f(0)}{2-0}$

$\Rightarrow \quad 3x^2-4x+1=\frac{2-0}{2-0}$

$\Rightarrow \quad 3x^2-4x=0 \Rightarrow x=4/3$

11. Ans. (b).

$\int_1^2 f'(x)\,dx=f(x)\big|_1^2=f(1)-f(1)=0$ ($\because$ By Rolle's theorem $f(1)=f(2)$)

12. Ans. (a).

$f(1)=f(26)=5$

Then by Rolle's theorem $\exists$ at least one $x \in]1, 26[$ for which $f'(x)=0$

MISCELLANEOUS EXERCISE

Matching Entries

Match the entries of List-A and List-B.

FUNCTIONS

1.

List-A	List-B
(a) If $f(x)=\frac{a^x+a^{-x}}{2}$ $(a>2)$ then $f(x+y)+f(x-y)=$	1. $\frac{1}{2}\log\left(\frac{x-1}{3-x}\right)$
(b) If $f(x)=\frac{e^x-e^{-x}}{e^x+e^{-x}}+2$, then $f^{-1}(x)=$	2. odd
(c) The period of function $\left|\sin\frac{x}{2}\right|+|\cos x|$ is	3. $2f(x)f(y)$
(d) If $f(x)=\sin[\log(x+\sqrt{x^2+1})]$, then $f(x)$ is odd or even	4. x
(e) If $f(x)=\frac{1}{1-x}$, then $(f\ o\ f\ o\ f)\ x=$	5. 2π

RANGE AND DOMAIN OF A FUNCTION

2.

	List-A		List-B
(a)	Domain of $y = \sin^{-1}\left[\log_2\left(\frac{x^2}{2}\right)\right]$ is	1.	$1 \le x < 4$
(b)	Domain of $y = \sin^{-1}\frac{x-3}{2} - \log(4-x) =$	2.	$\left]-\frac{3\pi}{2}, \frac{\pi}{2}\right[$
(c)	Range of $y = \frac{1}{2-\sin 3x}$ is	3.	$[-2,-1] \cup [1,2]$
(d)	Range of $y = \frac{x^2+x+2}{x^2+x+1}, x \in R$ is	4.	$\left[\frac{1}{3}, 1\right]$
(e)	Range of $y = \sin x - \cos x$ is	5.	$\left[1, \frac{7}{3}\right]$
(f)	Range of $\tan^{-1} x - \cot^{-1} x$ is	6.	$[-\sqrt{2}, \sqrt{2}]$

INCREASING AND DECREASING FUNCTIONS

3.

	List-A		List-B
(a)	$y = x^2 e^{-x}$ is an increasing function in the interval ...	1.	$\pi/3$
(b)	$y = \frac{x}{\log x}$ is an increasing function in the interval ...	2.	$(1, 2)$
(c)	The length of the longest interval in which $y = 3\sin x - 4\sin^3 x$ is increasing is	3.	(e, ∞)
(d)	If $f(x) = \int e^x (x-1)(x-2)\,dx$ then f decreases in the interval	4.	$(0, 2)$

LIMITS

4.

	List-A		List-B
(a)	$\underset{x\to\infty}{\text{Lt}}\ x\cos\frac{\pi}{4x}\sin\frac{\pi}{4x}$ is	1.	1
(b)	$\underset{x\to 0}{\text{Lt}}\ \frac{\tan[-\pi^2]x^2 - [\pi^2]x^2}{\sin^2 x}$	2.	4
(c)	$\underset{x\to\infty}{\text{Lt}}\ \sqrt{\left\{\frac{2x - \sin x\cos x}{x + \cos^2 x + \sin^2 x}\right\}}$	3.	$\frac{\pi}{4}$
(d)	If $f(a) = 9, f'(a) = 4$, then $\underset{x\to 9}{\text{Lt}}\ \frac{\sqrt{f(x)} - 3}{\sqrt{x} - 3}$	4.	$\sqrt{2}$
(e)	If $f(x)$ is differentiable increasing function, then $\underset{x\to 0}{\text{Lt}}\ \frac{f(x^2) - f(x)}{f(x) - f(0)}$ is	5.	0

5.

	List-A		List-B
(a)	$\underset{x\to 0}{\text{Lt}}\ \frac{\log_{\sec(x/2)} \cos x}{\log_{\sec x} \cos(x/2)}$	1.	$e^{(n-1)/2}$
(b)	$\underset{x\to 0}{\text{Lt}}\ \frac{8^x - 4^x - 2^x - 1^x}{x^2} =$	2.	16
(c)	$\underset{x\to 0}{\text{Lt}}\ \left[\frac{1+5x^2}{1+3x^2}\right]^{1/x^2} =$	3.	$2(\log 2)^2$
(d)	$\underset{x\to\infty}{\text{Lt}}\ \left[\frac{x^2+5x+3}{x^2+x+2}\right]^x =$	4.	e^2
(e)	$\underset{x\to 1}{\text{Lt}}\ \left[\frac{x^n - 1}{n(x-1)}\right]^{1/(x-1)} =$	5.	e^4

6. **List-A** **List-B**

(a) $\lim_{x \to 3} \dfrac{x-3}{|x-3|} =$ 1. $16\sqrt{2} \log 2 . \log 3$

(b) If $f(x) = \dfrac{\log(1+ax) - \log(1+bx)}{x}$ be continuous at $x = 0$, then $f(0) =$ 2. $\sqrt{e}$

(c) If $f(x) = (\sin 2x)^{\tan^2 2x}$ be continuous at $x = \pi/4$, then $f\left(\dfrac{\pi}{4}\right) =$ 3. $a + b$

(d) If $f(x) = \begin{cases} \dfrac{36^x - 9^x - 4^x + 1}{\sqrt{2} - \sqrt{1+\cos x}}, & x \neq 0 \\ k, & x = 0 \end{cases}$ be continuous at $x = 0$, then $k =$ 4. Does not exist

7. **List-A** **List-B**

(a) If $y = |x-1| + |x-3|$, then at $x = 2, \dfrac{dy}{dx} = \ldots$ 1. 32

(b) If $f(x) = \begin{cases} x^2 \sin(1/x), & x \neq 0 \\ 0, & x = 0 \end{cases}$, then the set of all points of differentiability = ... 2. 0

(c) If $f(x) = a|x|^2 + b|x| + c = 0$ and if $f'(x)$ exists at $x = 0$, then the value of b is 3. $(-\infty, \infty)$

(d) If $f'(x) = g(x)$ and $g'(x) = -f(x) \ \forall \ x$ and $f(2) = 4 = f'(2)$, then $f^2(16) + g^2(16) = \ldots$ 4. 0

8. Match the $\lim_{x \to \infty} f(x)$ of col. I with col. II

Column I	Column II
(a) $f(x) = (x+1)^{2/3} - (x-1)^{2/3}$	(p) 1
(b) $f(x) = x^{3/2} [\sqrt{x^3+1} - \sqrt{x^3-1}]$	(q) $\dfrac{3}{2}$
(c) $f(x) = \sqrt{x^2 - 2x - 1} - \sqrt{x^2 - 7x + 3}$	(r) 0
(d) $f(x) = \sqrt{(x+1)(x+2)} - x$	(s) $\dfrac{5}{2}$

9. For f to be continuous $f(a)$ is given by

Column I	Column II
(a) $f(x) = \dfrac{\log(1+4x)}{x}$	(p) $\dfrac{1}{4}$
(b) $f(x) = \dfrac{\log(4+x) - \log 4}{x}$	(q) 0
(c) $f(x) = \dfrac{1}{\sin x} - \dfrac{1}{\cos x}$	(r) 4
(d) $f(x) = \dfrac{1 - \cos^3 x}{x \sin 2x}$	(s) $\dfrac{3}{4}$

Answers

1. (a) → 3, (b) → 1, (c) → 5, (d) → 2, (e) → 4
2. (a) → 3, (b) → 1, (c) → 4, (d) → 5, (e) → 6, (f) → 2
3. (a) → 4, (b) → 3, (c) → 1, (d) → 2
4. (a) → 3, (b) → 5, (c) → 4, (d) → 2, (e) → 1
5. (a) → 2, (b) → 3, (c) → 4, (d) → 5, (e) → 1
6. (a) → 4, (b) → 3, (c) → 2, (d) → 1
7. (a) → 2, (b) → 3, (c) → 4, (d) → 1
8. (a)→ (r), (b)→ (p), (c)→ (s), (d)→ (q)
9. (a)→ (r), (b) → (p), (c)→ (q), (d)→ (s)

Solutions

1. (a) → 3. **Q. 5 P. 1241**
(b) → 1. **Q. 16 (c) P. 1241**
(c) → 5.

$$\left|\sin\frac{2\pi+x}{2}\right| = \left|\sin\left(\pi+\frac{x}{2}\right)\right| = \left|-\sin\frac{x}{2}\right| = \left|\sin\frac{x}{2}\right|$$

$$|\cos(\pi+x)| = |-\cos x| = |\cos x|$$

Above shows that 2π and π are periods of the two functions and hence their L.C.M. *i.e.* 2π is period of given function.
(d) → 2. **Q. 6 (c) P. 1266**
(e) → 4. Refer **39 (a) P. 1243**

2. (a) → 3. **Q. 8 (a) P. 1257**
(b) → 1.

$$-1 \le \frac{x-3}{2} < 1 \Rightarrow 1 \le x \le 5 \qquad ...(D_1)$$

$$4 - x > 0 \Rightarrow x > 4 \qquad ...(D_2)$$

$D_1 \cap D_2 =$ domain of $(f+g)$

$[1, 5] \cap (4, \infty) = [1, 4)$

$\therefore \quad 1 \le x < 4$

(c) → 4. **Q. 16 (b) P. 1257**
(d) → 5. **Q. 17 (d) P. 1257**
(e) → 6. $\quad y = \sqrt{2}\sin\left(x - \frac{\pi}{4}\right)$
(f) → 2.

$$y = \tan^{-1}x - \left(\frac{\pi}{2} - \tan^{-1}x\right) = 2\tan^{-1}x - \frac{\pi}{2}$$

where $-\frac{\pi}{2} < \tan^{-1}x < \frac{\pi}{2}$

$$\therefore \quad \text{Range} = 2\left]-\frac{\pi}{2}, \frac{\pi}{2}\right[- \frac{\pi}{2} =]-\pi, \pi[- \frac{\pi}{2}$$

$$= \left]-\frac{3\pi}{2}, \frac{\pi}{2}\right[.$$

3. (a) → 4.

$$\frac{dy}{dx} = -\frac{x}{e^x}(x-2) \text{ is + ive when } x(x-2) \text{ is – ive } i.e.\ x$$

lies in the interval (0, 2) exponential function as we know is always + ive.
(b) → 3. **Q. 3 (d) ii P. 1271**
(c) → 1. **Q. 6 (c) P. 1271**
(d) → 2. **Q. 15 (b) P. 1272**

4. (a) → 3. **Q. 35 (a) P. 1291**
(b) → 5.

$\pi^2 = 9 \cdot 8$

$\therefore \quad [-\pi^2] = -10$ and $\theta \Rightarrow 0, \tan\theta = \theta$

$$\therefore \quad \text{Lt} \frac{-10x^2 - (-10x^2)}{x^2} = 0$$

(c) → 4. Divide above and below by x.
(d) → 2. **Q. 31 (a) P. 1291**
(e) → 1. **Q. 29 (d) P. 1291**

5. (a) → 2. **Q. 57 (c) P. 1293**
(b) → 3. **Q. 3 (b) P. 1289**
(c) → 4. **Q. 47 (b) P. 1292**
(d) → 5. **Q. 54 (a) P. 1293**
(e) → 1. Put $x - 1 = y \quad \therefore \quad x = 1 + y$

$$\therefore \quad \underset{y\to 0}{\text{Lt}}\left[\frac{(1+y)^n - 1}{ny}\right]^{1/y}$$

$$= \underset{y\to 0}{\text{Lt}}\left[\frac{1 + ny + \frac{n(n-1)}{2}y^2 + \ldots - 1}{ny}\right]^{1/y}$$

$$= \underset{y\to 0}{\text{Lt}}\left[1 + \frac{n-1}{2}y\right]^{1/y} = e^{(n-1)/2}$$

6. (a) → 4.

$$\text{R.H.L.} = \lim_{h\to 0}\frac{3+h-3}{|3+h-3|} = \frac{h}{|h|} = \frac{h}{h} = 1$$

$$\text{L.H.L.} = \lim_{h\to 0}\frac{3-h-3}{|3-h-3|} = \frac{-h}{|-h|} = -\frac{h}{h} = -1$$

Since R.H.L. ≠ L.H.L.

$\therefore$ Limit does not exist.
(b) → 3. **Q. 2 (b) P. 1309**
(c) → 2. **Q. 8 (a) P. 1310**
(d) → 1.

$$\lim_{x\to 0}\frac{(9^x - 1)(4^x - 1)}{\sqrt{2}\left[1 - \cos\frac{x}{2}\right]}$$

$$= \lim_{x\to 0}\frac{9^x - 1}{x} \cdot \frac{4^x - 1}{x} \cdot \frac{x^2}{\sqrt{2} \cdot 2\sin^2\frac{x}{4}}$$

$$= \log 9 \cdot \log 4 \cdot \frac{1}{2\sqrt{2}} \cdot \frac{x^2}{(x/4)^2}$$

$$= \frac{16}{2\sqrt{2}}\log 3^2 \cdot \log 2^2$$

$$= 16\sqrt{2}\log 3 \log 2$$

For continuity, limit = value

$\therefore \quad 16\sqrt{2}\log 3 \cdot \log 2 = k$

7. (a) → 2. **Q. 29 (b) P. 1312**
(b) → 3. **Q. 34 (a) P. 1312**
(c) → 4. For $f'(x)$ to exist at $x = 0$, we must have $L' = R'$ at $x = 0$

$$\underset{h\to 0}{\text{Lt}}\frac{\{a|-h|^2 + b|-h| + c\} - c}{-h}$$

$$= \underset{h\to 0}{\text{Lt}}\frac{\{a|h|^2 + b|h| + c\} - c}{h}$$

or $\quad -b = b \quad$ or $\quad 2b = 0 \quad \therefore \ b = 0.$

(d) → 1.

If $h(x) = f^2(x) + g^2(x)$ then

$$h'(x) = 2ff' + 2gg' = 2f(g) + 2g(-f) = 0$$

Hence $h(x) =$ constant

$\therefore \quad f^2(16) + g^2(16) = f^2(2) + g^2(2)$

$= f^2(2) + f'^2(2) = 4^2 + 4^2 = 32$

8. (a)→ (r), (b)→ (p), (c)→ (s), (d)→ (q)

(a) Let $A = (x+1)^2$, $B = (x-1)^2$

$\therefore \quad f(x) = A^{1/3} - B^{1/3}$

Multiply above and below by $A^{2/3} + B^{2/3} + (AB)^{2/3}$

$\therefore \quad f(x) = \dfrac{A - B}{A^{2/3} + B^{2/3} + (AB)^{2/3}}$

$= \dfrac{(x+1)^2 - (x-1)^2)}{(x+1)^{4/3} + (x-1)^{4/3} + (x^2-1)^{2/3}}$

or $f(x) = \dfrac{4x}{x^{4/3}\left[\left(1+\frac{1}{x}\right)^{4/3} + \left(1-\frac{1}{x}\right)^{4/3} + \left(1-\frac{1}{x^2}\right)^{4/3}\right]}$

or $f(x) = \dfrac{4/x^{1/3}}{D^r}$

$\therefore \quad \underset{x\to\infty}{\text{Lt}} f(x) = \dfrac{0}{1+1+1} = 0$

(b) Proceeding as above, $\underset{x\to\infty}{\text{Lt}} f(x) =$

$\underset{x\to\infty}{\text{Lt}} \dfrac{2}{\left(1+\frac{1}{x^3}\right)^{1/2} + \left(1-\frac{1}{x^3}\right)^{1/2}} = \dfrac{2}{1+1} = 1$

(c) $\underset{x\to\infty}{\text{Lt}} f(x) = \dfrac{5}{2}$

(d) $\underset{x\to\infty}{\text{Lt}} f(x) = \dfrac{3}{2}$

9. (a)→ (r), (b)→ (p), (c)→ (q), (d)→ (s)

For $f(x)$ to be continuous at $x = 0$

$\underset{x\to 0}{\text{Lt}} f(x) =$ value of $f(x)$ at $x = 0$.

It is easy to calculate $\underset{x\to 0}{\text{Lt}} f(x)$, which are

(a) 4, (b) $\frac{1}{4}$, (c) 0 and (d) $\frac{3}{4}$

Assertions / Reasons

1. Let $f(x) = (x+1)^2 - 1, x \geq -1$.

Statement-1 : The set $\{x : f(x) = f^{-1}(x)\} = \{0, -1\}$.

Statement-2 : f is a bijection.

2. Let $f(x) = x|x|$ and $g(x) = \sin x$.

Statement-1 : *gof* is differentiable at $x = 0$ and its derivative is continuous at that point.

Statement-2 : *gof* is twice differentiable at $x = 0$

3. **Statement 1.**

$\underset{x\to\infty}{\text{Lt}} \dfrac{(x+1)^{10} + (x+2)^{10} + \ldots + (x+100)^{10}}{x^{10} + 9^{10}} = 100$

Statement 2. If $f(x)$ and $\phi(x)$ are polynomials of same degree, then $\underset{x\to\infty}{\text{Lt}} \dfrac{f(x)}{\phi(x)} = \dfrac{\text{Leading coeff. of f}(x)}{\text{Leading coeff. of }\phi(x)}$

Hints / Solutions

1. Both (1) and (2) are true but (2) is not the correct explanation of (1).

$f(x) = y = (x+1)^2 - 1, x \geq -1, y \geq -1$

$\therefore \quad x = \sqrt{y+1} - 1 = f^{-1}(y)$

$\therefore \quad f^{-1}(x) = \sqrt{x+1} - 1, \ x \geq -1$

[$f^{-1}(x)$ exists only when $f(x)$ is both one-one and onto, *i.e.*, f is a bijection.]

$f^{-1}(x) = f(x) \Rightarrow (\sqrt{x+1}) - 1 = (x+1)^2 - 1$

$\Rightarrow \quad (x+1) = (x+1)^4 \quad \Rightarrow \quad (x+1)[(x+1)^3 - 1] = 0$

$\Rightarrow \quad (x+1)(x^3 + 3x^2 + 3x) = 0$

$\Rightarrow \quad (x+)\,x(x^2 + 3x + 3) = 0$

$\Rightarrow \quad x = [0, -1]$

The roots of $x^2 + 3x + 3$ are imaginary as discriminant $= 9 - 12 = -3$.

2. Statement (1) is true and statement (2) is false.

Let $h(x) = (gof)\,x = g(f(x))$

$= g(x.x), x \geq 0, g(x.(-x)), x < 0$

$= \sin x^2, \ x \geq 0$

$= -\sin x^2, x < 0$

$\left.\begin{aligned} h'(x) &= 2x\cos x^2, \ x \geq 0 \\ &= -2x\cos x^2, \ x < 0 \end{aligned}\right\}$ ...(A)

$\therefore \quad h'(0^+) = h'(0^-) = 0$ from (A)

and hence (*gof*) is differentiable at $x = 0$ and its derivative is continuous at that point.

Now $h''(x) = -4x^2 \sin x^2 + 2\cos x^2, x \geq 0$

$= -[-4x^2 \sin x^2 + 2\cos x^2], \ x < 0$

$\therefore \quad h''(0^+) = 2, \ h''(0^-) = -2$

$\therefore \quad h = (gof)$ is not twice differentiable at $x = 0$.

3. Ans. (a).

Both statements 1 and 2 are true and 2 is correct explanation to 1.

See conclusion 6 **(b) P. 1388 Ex. 6 (iii) P. 1288.**

Fascinating Facts

- Limit describe the behaviour of a function $f(x)$ as its variable x approaches a particular number.
- If a function $y = f(x)$ is discontinuous at $x = a$ but LHL, RHL and $f(a)$ are finite then $f(x) . \phi(x)$ is continuous at $x = a$, provided $\phi(x)$ is continuous at $x = a$ and $\phi(a) = 0$
- **For example :**
  (i) $f(x) = [x]$ is discontinuous at $x = 0, \pm 1, \pm 2, \ldots\ldots$ but $g(x) = x[x]$ is continuous at $x = 0$, since $\phi(x) = x$ is continuous at $x = 0$ and $\phi(0) = 0$
  (ii) $f(x) = [x] \log x$ is continuous at $x = 1$ as $\phi(x) = \log x$ is continuous at $x = 1$ and $\phi(1) = 0$
- We can prove the continuity by directly showing $\lim_{\varepsilon \to 0} f(x + \varepsilon) = f(x)$, where ε can approach zero from both the sides.
- If at a point $x = a$, the LHD and RHD of a function $y = f(x)$ are finite but LHD $\neq$ RHD then $y = f(x)$ is continuous at $x = a$, although it is not differentiable at that point.
- If at least one of the derivatives of $y = f(x)$ is non-existent or infinite at the point $x = a$, then the function $y = f(x)$ may or may not be continuous at $x = a$ and the function is not differentiable.
- A function can not have derivative at points of discontinuity.
- If a function $y = f(x)$ is not differentiable at $x = a$ but its LHD and RHD are finite then $f(x) . \phi(x)$ is differentiable at $x = a$, provided $f(x)$ is continuous at $x = a$ and $\phi(a) = 0$
- **For Example :**
  (i) $f(x) = |x|$ is not differentiable at $x = 0$ but $g(x) = x|x|$ is differentiable at $x = 0$. Since, $\phi(x) = x$ is continuous at $x = 0$, $f(0) = 0$ and RHD and LHD of $f(x)$ are finite.
  (ii) $f(x) = |\log x|$ is not differentiable at $x = 1$ but RHD and LHD of $f(x)$ are finite. Hence, $g(x) = (x - 1)|\log x|$ is differentiable at $x = 1$. Since $d(x) = x - 1$ is continuous at $x = 1$ and $\phi(1) = 0$.

❑

CHAPTER 29

Differential Calculus

Tangents, Normals and Simple Applications of the Derivatives

§1. Tangent at (x, y) to $y = f(x)$.

Let $y = f(x)$ be a given curve and $P(x, y)$ and $Q(x + \delta x, y + \delta y)$ be two neighbouring points on it. Equation of the line PQ is

$$Y - y = \frac{y + \delta y - y}{x + \delta x - x}(X - x)$$

or $$Y - y = \frac{\delta y}{\delta x}(X - x) \qquad ...(1)$$

The line (1) will be a tangent to the given curve at P if $Q \to P$ which in turn means that $\delta x \to 0$ and we know that

$$\lim_{\delta x \to 0} \frac{\delta y}{\delta x} = \frac{dy}{dx}.$$

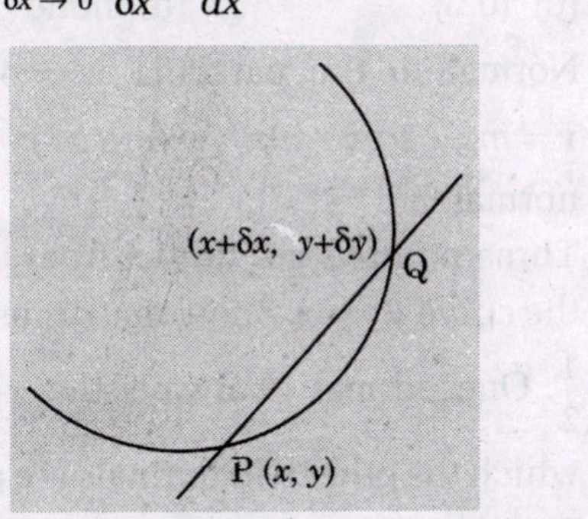

Fig. 1

Therefore the equation of the tangent is

$$Y - y = (dy/dx)(X - x) \qquad ...(2)$$

§2. Normal at (x, y).

The normal at (x, y) being perpendicular to tangent (2) will have its slope as $-\dfrac{1}{(dy/dx)}$ and hence its equation is

$$Y - y = -\frac{1}{dy/dx}(X - x) \qquad ...(3)$$

Geometrical meaning of dy/dx.

From equation (1) we observe that dy/dx represents the slope of the tangent to the given curve $y = f(x)$ at any point (x, y)

$$\therefore \quad \frac{dy}{dx} = \tan \psi$$

where ψ is the angle which the tangent to the curve makes with +ive direction of x-axis. In case we are to find the tangent at any point (x_1, y_1) then $\left(\dfrac{dy}{dx}\right)_{(x_1, y_1)}$ *i.e.* the value of dy/dx at (x_1, y_1) will represent the slope of the tangent and hence its equation in this case will be

Tangent $$y - y_1 = \left(\frac{dy}{dx}\right)_{(x_1, y_1)}(x - x_1)$$

Normal $$y - y_1 = \frac{-1}{(dy/dx)_{(x_1, y_1)}}(x - x_1) \qquad ...(4)$$

Slope of tangent $= m_1 = dy/dx$ or its value at a given point.

Slope of Normal $= -\dfrac{1}{m_1} = -\dfrac{1}{dy/dx}$ or its value at a given point.

§3. Condition for tangent to be parallel or perpendicular to x-axis :

- If a tangent is parallel to x-axis or normal is $\perp$ to x-axis then $m = 0$ so that $dy/dx = 0$.
- If the tangent is perpendicular to x-axis or normal is parallel to x-axis then $m = \infty$, $\therefore$ $dy/dx = \infty$ or its reciprocal $dx/dy = 0$.

Parametric Form :

$$\frac{dy}{dx} = \frac{dy}{dt} \div \frac{dx}{dt} = \frac{\dot{y}}{\dot{x}}$$

If the equations of the curve be $x = f(t)$, $y = \phi(t)$, then

- Tangent is $\quad y - \phi(t) = \dfrac{\dot{y}}{\dot{x}}[x - f(t)]$
- Normal is $\quad y - \phi(t) = -\dfrac{\dot{x}}{\dot{y}}[x - f(t)]$
- Tangent is parallel to x-axis if $\dot{y} = 0$
- Tangent is perpendicular to x-axis if $\dot{x} = 0$

***Partial Differentiation.**

If the equation of the curve is of the form $f(x, y) = c$ or $= 0$ then a convenient method of finding $\dfrac{dy}{dx}$ is by the help of partial derivatives $\dfrac{dy}{dx} = -\dfrac{f_x}{f_y}$, where f_x is differentiation of $f(x, y)$ w.r.t. x but treating y as constant and similarly f_y stands for differentiation of $f(x, y)$ w.r.t. y treating x as constant.

e.g. if $x^3 + y^3 - 3axy = 0 = f(x, y)$ then

$f_x = 3(x^2 - ay)$, $f_y = 3(y^2 - ax)$

or $\left(\frac{x}{a}\right)^m + \left(\frac{y}{b}\right)^m - 1 = 0$, then

$f_x = m\left(\frac{x}{a}\right)^{m-1} \cdot \frac{1}{a}$, $f_y = m\left(\frac{y}{b}\right)^{m-1} \cdot \frac{1}{b}$

With this notation the equation of the tangent can be written as

$$Y - y = -\frac{f_x}{f_y}(X - x)$$

or $\quad$ ***$(X - x) f_x + (Y - y) f_y = 0$** ... (1)

or $\quad (x - a) \underset{(a,b)}{f_x} + (y - b) \underset{(a,b)}{f_y} = 0$ at the point (a, b)

*Normal will be $\dfrac{X - x}{f_x} = \dfrac{Y - y}{f_y}$ ... (2)

or $\quad \dfrac{x - a}{\underset{(a,b)}{f_x}} = \dfrac{y - b}{\underset{(a,b)}{f_y}}$ at the point (a, b).

Problem Set (1)

Equation of tangents and normals to given curves.

1. (a)* Find the equation of the tangent to the curve at any point (x, y).

$$\frac{x^m}{a^m} + \frac{y^m}{b^m} = 1.$$

(b) Deduce the equation of tangents to

(i) $\frac{x^2}{a^2} + \frac{y^2}{b^2} = 1$ **Ellipse**

(ii) $\left(\frac{x}{a}\right)^{2/3} + \left(\frac{y}{b}\right)^{2/3} = 1$ **Hypo-cycloid Astroid**

(iii) $x^{2/3} + y^{2/3} = a^{2/3}$

(iv) $\left(\frac{x}{a}\right)^{n/(n-1)} + \left(\frac{y}{b}\right)^{n/(n-1)} = 1$

(c) Does the straight line $\frac{x}{a} + \frac{y}{b} = 2$ touch the curve $\left(\frac{x}{a}\right)^2 + \left(\frac{y}{b}\right)^2 = 2$? If it touches then determine the co-ordinates of the point of contact.

2. (a) $x = a\sin^3\theta$, $y = a\cos^3\theta$,

or $x^{2/3} + y^{2/3} = a^{2/3}$, Tangent and Normal.

(b)* Normal to $x^{2/3} + y^{2/3} = a^{2/3}$ in the form $y\cos\theta - x\sin\theta = a\cos 2\theta$.
where θ is the angle which the normal makes with the axis of x.

3. (a) Show that θ is the angle which the perpendicular from the origin on the tangent makes with the x-axis for the curve whose parametric equations are $x = a\sin^3\theta$, $y = a\cos^3\theta$.

(b) If p_1 and p_2 be the lengths of perpendiculars from the origin on the tangent and normal to the curve $x^{2/3} + y^{2/3} = a^{2/3}$ respectively, prove that $4p_1^2 + p_2^2 = a^2$.

(c) If the tangent at any point of the curve $x^{2/3} + y^{2/3} = a^{2/3}$ meets the axes of co-ordinates in A and B then locus of mid-point of AB is a circle.

4. (a) The equation of the normal to the curve $x^3 + y^3 = 6xy$ at the point (3, 3).

(b) The equation of the normal to the curve $2y = 3 - x^2$ at the point (1, 1).

(c) The values of parameter 'a' so that the line $(3 - a)x + ay + a^2 - 1 = 0$ is a normal to the curve $xy = 1$ is/are :

(a) $(3, \infty)$ (b) $(-\infty, 0)$
(c) $(0, 3)$ (d) none

5. (a) Normal to the parabola $y^2 = 4ax$ in the form $y = mx - 2am - am^3$ where m is the slope of the normal.

(b)* Three normals are drawn from the point $(c, 0)$ to the curve $y^2 = x$. Show that c must be greater than $\frac{1}{2}$. One normal is always the x-axis. Find c for which the other two normals are perpendicular to each other. **(I.I.T. 1991)**

(c)* Normal to the curve $x^2 = 4y$ which passes through the point (1, 2).

6. (a) Tangent to the parabola $y^2 = 4ax$ in the form $y = mx + a/m$ where m is the slope of the tangent. Prove also that two perpendicular tangents to a parabola meet on the directrix.

(b) The equation of the tangent at the point $P(t)$, where t is any parameter, to the parabola $y^2 = 4ax$ is

(i) $yt = x + at^2$ (ii) $y = xt + at^2$
(iii) $y = tx$ (iv) $y = tx + a/t$

7. (a) The parametric equation of a curve are $x = a\cos 2t$, $y = 2\sqrt{2}a\sin t$. Find the equation of tangent in the form $mx - y = a\left(m + \frac{1}{m}\right)$ where m is the slope of the tangent. Hence prove that two perpendicular tangents meet on the line $x = 2a$.

(b) Angle between the tangents to the curve $y = x^2 - 5x + 6$ at the points $(2, 0)$ and $(3, 0)$ is :
(a) $\pi/2$ (b) $\pi/6$
(c) $\pi/4$ (d) $\pi/3$ **(AIEEE 2006)**

8. Find tangent and normal to
(a) $y^2(a + x) = x^2(3a - x)$
(b) $y^2(2a - x) = x^3$ at the points where $x = a$.

9. Normal to $y = x^3 - 3x$ which is parallel to $2x + 18y = 9$.

10. Tangent to $3x^2 + y^2 + x + 2y = 0$ which are perpendicular to the line $4x - 2y = 1$.

11. (a) Tangent to parabola $y^2 = 4x + 5$ which is parallel to $y = 2x + 7$.
(b)* Determine the constant c such that the straight line joining the points $(0, 3)$ and $(5, -2)$ is tangent to the curve $y = \dfrac{c}{x+1}$. **(M.N.R. 1993)**

12. (a) The straight line $x + y = a$ will be a tangent to the ellipse $x^2/9 + y^2/16 = 1$ if $a =$
(i) 8 (ii) ± 5
(iii) ± 10 (iv) ± 6 **(B.I.T.S. 1992)**
(b) On the ellipse $4x^2 + 9y^2 = 1$, the points at which the tangents are parallel to the line $8x = 9y$ are
(a) $\left(\frac{2}{5}, \frac{1}{5}\right)$ (b) $\left(-\frac{2}{5}, \frac{1}{5}\right)$
(c) $\left(-\frac{2}{5}, -\frac{1}{5}\right)$ (d) $\left(\frac{2}{5}, -\frac{1}{5}\right)$ **(I.I.T. 1999)**

13. (a) Determine the equation of tangent at vertex of the parabola $(x + 4)^2 = -4(y - 2)$.
(b) If the normal to the curve $y = f(x)$ at the point $(3, 4)$ makes an angle $3\pi/4$ with the positive x-axis, then $f'(3) =$
(a) -1 (b) $-\frac{3}{4}$ (c) $\frac{4}{3}$ (d) 1 **(I.I.T. Sc. 2000)**

14. (a) Tangent and normal to the curve $x = \dfrac{2at^2}{1+t^2}$, $y = \dfrac{2at^3}{1+t^2}$ at the point for which $t = \frac{1}{2}$.
(b)* Normal at any point θ to the curve
$$x = a\cos\theta + a\theta\sin\theta,$$
$$y = a\sin\theta - a\theta\cos\theta.$$
Also show that it is at a constant distance from the origin.

15. (a)* The rectangular co-ordinates of a point on the curve are given by
$$x = 3\cos\theta - \cos^3\theta,\quad y = 3\sin\theta - \sin^3\theta.$$
Find the equation of the normal at any point on the curve and show that at the point P where $\theta = \pi/4$, the normal passes through the origin.
(b) The parametric equations of given curve are $x = a(2\cos t + \cos 2t)$, $y = a(2\sin t - \sin 2t)$. Prove that the equations of tangent and normal at any point t are $x\sin\frac{t}{2} + y\cos\frac{t}{2} = a\sin\frac{3t}{2}$ and $x\cos\frac{t}{2} - y\sin\frac{t}{2} = 3a\cos\frac{3t}{2}$ respectively. Also establish that S.T. $= y\cot\frac{t}{2}$ and S.N. $= y\tan\frac{t}{2}$.
(c) Prove that the portion of the normal to the curve
$$x = 2a\sin t + a\sin t\cos^2 t$$
$$y = -a\cos^3 t$$
which is intercepted between the co-ordinate axes is of constant length.

16. (a) Tangents to $y = (x^3 - 1)(x - 2)$ at the points where the curve cuts the x-axis.
(b) Find the equation of the tangent to the curve $y = x^2 + 1$ at the point $(1, 2)$.
(c) Find the slopes of the tangents of the curve $y = (x + 1)(x - 3)$ at the points where it cuts the axis of x.

17. (a) Tangents and normal to the curve
$$y(x - 2)(x - 3) - x + 7 = 0$$
at the point where it cuts the axis of x.
(b) Normal to the curve $y^2 = x^3$ at the point whose abscissa x is 8.
(c) Normal to the curve $y = x^3 - 2x^2 + 4$ at the point where $x = 2$.

18.* Find the points on the curve $9y^2 = x^3$ where normal to the curve makes equal intercepts with the axes. **(Roorkee 1993)**

19. (a) Find the point on the curve
$$y = x^4 - 6x^3 + 13x^2 - 10x + 5$$
where the tangent is parallel to the line $y = 2x$. Show that two of these points have the same tangent.
(b) Find the points on the curve $x^2 + y^2 - 2x - 3 = 0$ the tangents at which are parallel to x-axis.
(c) Find the points on the curve $y = x^3$, the tangents at which are inclined at an angle of 60° to x-axis.

20. (a) Normals at the points on the curve $y = x/(1 - x^2)$ where the tangent makes an angle of $\pi/4$ with x-axis.
(b) At which points on the curve $y = x/(1 - x^2)$, the tangent makes an angle of 45° with x-axis ? At what point the tangent is parallel to x-axis ? Is there any point on the curve the tangent at which is parallel to y-axis ?
(c) The point(s) on the curve $y^3 + 3x^2 = 12y$ where the tangent is vertical, is (are)

(a) $\left(\pm\frac{4}{\sqrt{3}}, -2\right)$ (b) $\left(\pm\sqrt{\frac{11}{3}}, 1\right)$

(c) $(0, 0)$ (d) $\left(\pm\frac{4}{\sqrt{3}}, 2\right)$ **(I.I.T. Sc. 2002)**

21. (a) The curve $y - e^{xy} + x = 0$ has a vertical tangent at the point

(i) (1, 1) (ii) no point

(iii) (0, 1) (iv) (1, 0)

(b) A and B are points $(-2, 0)$ and $(1, 3)$ on the curve $y = 4 - x^2$. If the tangent at P on the curve be parallel to chord AB then co-ordinates of point P are $\left(-\frac{1}{2}, \frac{15}{4}\right)$.

22. (a) Prove that all points on the curve $y^2 = 4a\,[x + a\sin(x/a)]$ at which the tangent is parallel to the x-axis lie on the parabola $y^2 = 4ax$.

(b)* Tangents are drawn from origin to the curve $y = \sin x$. Prove that their points of contact lie on $x^2y^2 = x^2 - y^2$.

(c) If the point on $y = x\tan\alpha - \frac{1}{2}\frac{ax^2}{u^2\cos^2\alpha}$ $(a > 0)$ where the tangent is parallel to $y = x$ has an ordinate $\frac{u^2}{4a}$, then prove that $\sin^2\alpha = \frac{3}{4}$.

23. (a)* Show that the line $\frac{x}{a} + \frac{y}{b} = 1$ touches the curve $y = b\,e^{-x/a}$ at the point where the curve crosses the y-axis.

(b)* The line $x/a + y/b = 1$ touches the curve $y = be^{-x/a}$ at the point

(i) $(a, b/a)$ (ii) $(-a, b/a)$

(iii) $(a, a/b)$ (iv) None of these.

24. (a) Show that the curve $\left(\frac{x}{a}\right)^n + \left(\frac{y}{b}\right)^n = 2$ touches the straight line $\frac{x}{a} + \frac{y}{b} = 2$ at the point (a, b) whatever the value of n may be.

(b) If the line $\frac{x}{a} + \frac{y}{b} = 1$ be a tangent to hyperbola $xy = c^2$ then show that $ab = 4c^2$.

(c) A function $y = f(x)$ has a second order derivative $f''(x) = 6(x - 1)$. If the graph passes through the point (2, 1) and at this point tangent to the graph is $y = 3x - 1$, then function is :

(a) $(x-1)^3$ (b) $(x-1)^2$

(c) $(x+1)^3$ (d) $(x+1)^2$ **(AIEEE 2004)**

25. (a) Show that tangents to the folium of descartes $x^3 + y^3 = 3axy$ at the point where it meets the parabola $y^2 = ax$ are parallel to the axis of y. Also determine the point on the curve at which the tangent is parallel to x-axis .

(b) Find the equation of the normal to the curve $x^3 + y^3 = 8xy$ at the point other than origin where it meets the curve $y^2 = 4x$. **(J.E.E. W.B. 1992)**

26. (a) Find the equations of the tangents drawn to the curve $y^2 - 2x^3 - 4y + 8 = 0$ from the point (1, 2). **(Roorkee 1990)**

(b) Find the equations of tangents to the curve $y = x^4$ which are drawn from the point (2, 0).

(c) Find the equations of tangents to parabola $y^2 = 4ax$ which are drawn from the point $(2a, 3a)$.

27. (a)* Find all the tangents to the curve $y = \cos(x + y), -2\pi \le x \le 2\pi$ that are parallel to the line $x + 2y = 0$.

(b) If $f(x)$ satisfies

$$|f(x_1) - f(x_2)| \le (x_1 - x_2)^2, \forall x_1, x_2 \in R,$$

then find the equation of tangent to $f(x)$ at point (1, 2). **(I.I.T. 2005)**

28. (a) Find the equation to the tangent to $x^3 = ay^2$ at $(4am^2, 8am^3)$ and also the point in which the tangent cuts the curve again.

(b)* If the tangent at the point (at^2, at^3) on the curve $ay^2 = x^3$ meets the curve again at Q, then the co-ordinates of Q are $\left(\frac{1}{4}at^2, -\frac{1}{8}at^3\right)$.

29. (a)* Show that the normal at the point $(3t, 4/t)$ of the curve $xy = 12$ cuts the curve again at the point whose parameter t_1 is given by $t_1 = -\frac{16}{9t^3}$.

(b) Show that the normal to the rectangular hyperbola $xy = c^2$ at the point t meets the curve again at the point t' such that $t^3t' = -1$

(c) Show that the tangent to the curve $3xy^2 - 2x^2y = 1$ at (1, 1) meets the curve again at the point $(-16/5, -1/20)$.

(d) If the tangent at the point (p, q) to the curve $x^3 + y^3 = k$ meets the curve again at the point (a, b), prove that $\frac{a}{p} + \frac{b}{q} = -1$

30. (a)* If the line $ax + by + c = 0$ is a normal to the curve $xy = 1$, then

(i) $a > 0, b > 0$ (ii) $a > 0, b < 0$

(iii) $a < 0, b > 0$ (iv) $a < 0, b < 0$

(v) None of these

(b) The normal drawn at the point $P(at_1^2, 2at_1)$ on the parabola meets the curve again at $Q(at_2^2, 2at_2)$, then $t_2 = -t_1 - 2/t_1$

31.* Find the equation of the straight line which is tangent at one point and normal at another point of the curve $y = 8t^3 - 1,\ x = 4t^2 + 3$. **(Roorkee 1991)**

32. Show that the normal to the curve

$$5x^5 - 10x^3 + x + 2y + 6 = 0$$

at $P(0, -3)$ meets the curve again at two points. Find the equation of tangents to the curve at these points. **(Roorkee 1992)**

33. Find the equation of the straight line which is tangent at one point and normal at another point of the curve $x = 3t^2,\ y = 2t^3$. **(Roorkee 2000)**

34. The parametric equations of a curve are given by $x = \sec^2 t,\ y = \cot t$. Tangent at $P\ t = \pi/4$ meets the curve again at Q; then $PQ = (3\sqrt{5})/2$.

35. (a)* The curve $y = ax^3 + bx^2 + cx + 5$ touches the x-axis at $P(-2, 0)$ and cuts the y-axis at a point Q where its gradient is 3. Find a, b, c. **(I.I.T. 1994)**

(b) The line $y = x$ is a tangent to the parabola $y = ax^2 + bx + c$ at the point $x = 1$. If the parabola passes through the point $(-1, 0)$, then determine a, b, c.

(c) If the tangent at any point (1, 2) on the curve $y = ax^2 + bx + 7/2$ be parallel to normal at $(-2, 2)$ on the curve $y = x^2 + 6x + 10$, then prove that $a = 1, b = -5/2$.

(d) The curve $y = ax^4 + bx^3 + cx + d$ has zero gradient at the point (0, 1) and also touches the x-axis at the point $(-1, 0)$. If the curve has negative gradient then prove that $x < -1$.

(e) If the tangent to the curve $xy + ax + by = 0$ at (1, 1) is inclined at an angle $\tan^{-1} 2$ to axis of x then show that $a = 1, b = -2$.

36. The triangle formed by the tangent to the curve $f(x) = x^2 + bx - b$ at the point (1, 1) and the co-ordinate axes, lies in the first quadrant. If its area is 2, then the value of b is

(a) -1 (b) 3 (c) -3 (d) 1 **(I.I.T. Sc. 2001)**

37. If the area of the triangle formed by the axes of co-ordinates and tangent at any point $P(x, y)$ in 1st quadrant on the ellipse $\frac{x^2}{8} + \frac{y^2}{18} = 1$ be minimum, then find the co-ordinates of P.

38.* Tangent at point P_1 [other than (0, 0)] on the curve $y = x^3$ meets the curve again at P_2. The tangent at P_2 meets the curve at P_3 and so on. Show that the abscissae of $P_1, P_2, P_3, \dots, P_n$ form a G.P. Also find the ratio (area $\Delta P_1P_2P_3$) / (area $\Delta P_2P_3P_4$). **(I.I.T. 1993)**

39.* Find the equation of the normal to the curve $y = (1 + x)^y + \sin^{-1}(\sin^2 x)$ at $x = 0$. **(I.I.T. 1993)**

40. (a)* If $x = a \sin t \sqrt{\cos 2t},\ y = a \cos t \sqrt{\sin 2t}$, then prove that tangent at $t = \pi/4$ is parallel to x-axis.

(b) If $x = a\sqrt{\cos 2t}\,.\cos t,\ y = a\sqrt{\cos 2t}\,\sin t$, then prove that tangent at $t = \pi/6$ is parallel to x-axis and its equation is $y = a/(2\sqrt{2})$.

41. The tangent to the curve $y = e^x$ drawn at the point (c, e^c) intersects the line joining the points $(c - 1, e^{c-1})$ and $(c + 1, e^{c+1})$

(a) on the left of $x = c$ (b) on the right of $x = c$

(c) at no point (d) at all points **(I.I.T. 2007)**

Solutions to Problem Set (1)

1. (a) $\frac{x^m}{a^m} + \frac{y^m}{b^m} = 1.$ ...(1)

Differentiating w.r.t. x, we get

$$m.\frac{x^{m-1}}{a^m} + m.\frac{y^{m-1}}{b^m}.\frac{dy}{dx} = 0.$$

$$\therefore \quad \frac{dy}{dx} = -\frac{1}{a}\left(\frac{x}{a}\right)^{m-1}.b\left(\frac{b}{y}\right)^{m-1}$$

$\therefore$ Equation of tangent is $Y - y = \frac{dy}{dx}(X - x)$

or $(Y - y) = -\frac{1}{a}\left(\frac{x}{a}\right)^{m-1}.b\left(\frac{b}{y}\right)^{m-1}(X - x)$

or $\frac{X}{a}\left(\frac{x}{a}\right)^{m-1} - \left(\frac{x}{a}\right)^m = -\frac{Y}{b}\left(\frac{y}{b}\right)^{m-1} + \left(\frac{y}{b}\right)^m$

or $\frac{X}{a}\left(\frac{x}{a}\right)^{m-1} + \frac{Y}{b}\left(\frac{y}{b}\right)^{m-1} = \left(\frac{x}{a}\right)^m + \left(\frac{y}{b}\right)^m$

or $\frac{X}{a}\left(\frac{x}{a}\right)^{m-1} + \frac{Y}{b}\left(\frac{y}{b}\right)^{m-1} = 1$, by (1).

(V. Imp.) ...(2)

Another method :

$$f_x = \frac{m\,x^{m-1}}{a^m},\ f_y = \frac{m\,y^{m-1}}{b^m}$$

Equation of tangent is

$(X - x) f_x + (Y - y) f_y = 0$ **(See P. 1358)**

or $(X - x)\frac{m\,x^{m-1}}{a^m} + (Y - y)\frac{m\,y^{m-1}}{b^m} = 0$

or $\frac{X}{a}\left(\frac{x}{a}\right)^{m-1} + \frac{Y}{b}\left(\frac{y}{b}\right)^{m-1} = \frac{x^m}{a^m} + \frac{y^m}{b^m}$

or $\frac{X}{a}\left(\frac{x}{a}\right)^{m-1} + \frac{Y}{b}\left(\frac{y}{b}\right)^{m-1} = 1$

(b) **Deductions. Tangent of ellipse $\frac{x^2}{a^2} + \frac{y^2}{b^2} = 1$.**

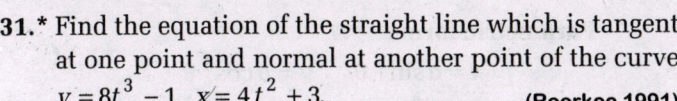

Putting $m=2$, $\frac{X}{a}\left(\frac{x}{a}\right)^{2-1}+\frac{Y}{b}\left(\frac{y}{b}\right)^{2-1}=1$

or $\frac{Xx}{a^2}+\frac{Yy}{b^2}=1.$ ...(A)

Tangent to $\left(\frac{x}{a}\right)^{2/3}+\left(\frac{y}{b}\right)^{2/3}=1.$

Putting $m=\frac{2}{3}$, $\frac{X}{a}\left(\frac{x}{a}\right)^{(2/3)-1}+\frac{Y}{b}\left(\frac{y}{b}\right)^{(2/3)-1}=1$

or $\frac{X}{a}\left(\frac{a}{x}\right)^{1/3}+\frac{Y}{b}\left(\frac{b}{y}\right)^{1/3}=1$

or $\frac{X}{x^{1/3}a^{2/3}}+\frac{Y}{y^{1/3}b^{2/3}}=1$ ...(B)

Note : You should prove it independently as in the main question.

Tangent to $x^{2/3}+y^{2/3}=a^{2/3}$.

Putting $b=a$ in (B) above, the equation of tangent becomes

$$\frac{X}{x^{1/3}}+\frac{Y}{y^{1/3}}=a^{2/3} \quad ...(C)$$

Tangent to $\left(\frac{x}{a}\right)^{n/(n-1)}+\left(\frac{y}{b}\right)^{n/(n-1)}=1.$

Putting $m=\frac{n}{n-1}$ or $m-1=\frac{n}{n-1}-1=\frac{1}{n-1}$,

we get

$$\frac{X}{a}\left(\frac{x}{a}\right)^{1/(n-1)}+\frac{Y}{b}\left(\frac{y}{b}\right)^{1/(n-1)}=1. \quad ...(D)$$

(c) As in part (a). Equation of tangent at any point (x, y) is

$$\frac{X}{a}\left(\frac{x}{a}\right)^{2-1}+\frac{Y}{b}\left(\frac{y}{b}\right)^{2-1}=2$$

or $\frac{X}{a}.\frac{x}{a}+\frac{Y}{b}.\frac{y}{b}=2$

Comparing with $\frac{X}{a}+\frac{Y}{b}=2.$

$$\frac{x}{a}=1, \frac{y}{b}=1 \quad \therefore \quad x=a, y=b$$

and equation of the tangent becomes $\frac{X}{a}+\frac{Y}{b}=2.$

Hence the given line touches and the point of contact is (a, b).

2. (a) Eliminating θ from

$$\left(\frac{x}{a}\right)^{1/3}=\sin\theta \text{ and } \left(\frac{y}{a}\right)^{1/3}=\cos\theta,$$

we get $\left(\frac{x}{a}\right)^{2/3}+\left(\frac{y}{a}\right)^{2/3}=1$ or $x^{2/3}+y^{2/3}=a^{2/3}$.

The tangent to this curve we have found in (C) above.

Parametric form :

$$x=a\sin^3\theta, \quad y=a\cos^3\theta$$

$$dx/d\theta=3a\sin^2\theta\cos\theta,$$

$$dy/d\theta=-3a\cos^2\theta\sin\theta.$$

$\therefore$ $\frac{dy}{dx}=\frac{dy}{d\theta}\div\frac{dx}{d\theta}=-\frac{\cos\theta}{\sin\theta}=-\cot\theta$

$\therefore$ Tangent is

or $y-a\cos^3\theta=-\frac{\cos\theta}{\sin\theta}(x-a\sin^3\theta)$

or $x\cos\theta+y\sin\theta=a\sin\theta\cos\theta$ $(\cos^2\theta+\sin^2\theta)$

or $x\cos\theta+y\sin\theta=(a/2)\sin 2\theta.$

Normal : Slope of the tangent is $-\cot\theta$ and hence slope of the normal will be

$+\tan\theta=\sin\theta/\cos\theta$ $\quad\because m_1m_2=-1.$

$\therefore$ Normal is

$$y-a\cos^3\theta=(\sin\theta/\cos\theta)(x-a\sin^3\theta)$$

or $y\cos\theta-x\sin\theta=a(\cos^4\theta-\sin^4\theta)$

or $y\cos\theta-x\sin\theta=a\cos 2\theta.$

$\because$ $\cos^4\theta-\sin^4\theta=(\cos^2\theta-\sin^2\theta).$ $(\cos^2\theta+\sin^2\theta)=\cos 2\theta.$

(b) $x^{2/3}+y^{2/3}=a^{2/3}$. ...(1)

$$\frac{2}{3}x^{-1/3}+\frac{2}{3}y^{-1/3}\frac{dy}{dx}=0.$$

$\therefore$ $\frac{dy}{dx}=-\frac{x^{-1/3}}{y^{-1/3}}=-\frac{y^{1/3}}{x^{1/3}}.$

$\therefore$ Slope of the normal is $x^{1/3}/y^{1/3}=\tan\theta$ (given)

(It is given that normal makes an angle θ with x-axis.)

$\therefore$ $\frac{x^{1/3}}{\sin\theta}=\frac{y^{1/3}}{\cos\theta}=\left[\frac{x^{2/3}+y^{2/3}}{\sin^2\theta+\cos^2\theta}\right]^{1/2}=a^{1/3}$, by(1).

$\therefore$ $x=a\sin^3\theta, y=a\cos^3\theta.$

Hence the normal whose slope is $\tan\theta$ is given by

$$y-a\cos^3\theta=(\sin\theta/\cos\theta)(x-a\sin^3\theta)$$

or $y\cos\theta-x\sin\theta=a\cos 2\theta$ as in Q. 2.

3. (a) $\frac{dy}{dx}=$ slope of the tangent $=-\cot\theta.$

Hence slope of a line through origin and perpendicular to the tangent is $=\tan\theta.$ $(m_1m_2=-1)$

Therefore it makes an angle θ with x-axis.

(b) Tangent is $x\cos\theta+y\sin\theta=(a/2)\sin 2\theta.$

Normal is $y\cos\theta-x\sin\theta=a\cos 2\theta$

$\therefore$ $p_1=\frac{(a/2)\sin 2\theta}{\sqrt{(\cos^2\theta+\sin^2\theta)}}=\frac{a}{2}\sin 2\theta$

$$p_2 = \frac{a\cos 2\theta}{\sqrt{(\cos^2\theta + \sin^2\theta)}} = a\cos 2\theta$$

$\therefore\quad 4p_1^2 + p_2^2 = a^2(\sin^2 2\theta + \cos^2 2\theta) = a^2.$

(c) **Tangent Cartesian form :**

$\frac{X}{x^{1/3}} + \frac{Y}{y^{1/3}} = a^{2/3}$ **Result (C) Q. 1. P. 1372.**

Tangent parametric form :

$x\cos\theta + y\sin\theta = a\sin\theta\cos\theta$

or $\frac{x}{\sin\theta} + \frac{y}{\cos\theta} = a.$ **Q. 2 (a) P. 1372.**

$\therefore\quad A(a^{2/3}x^{1/3}, 0), B(0, a^{2/3}y^{1/3})$

or $A(a\sin\theta, 0), B(0, a\cos\theta)$

If (h, k) be mid-point of AB, then

$2h = a^{2/3}x^{1/3}, 2k = a^{2/3}y^{1/3}$

Squaring and adding,

$4(h^2 + k^2) = a^{4/3}(x^{2/3} + y^{2/3}) = a^{4/3}.a^{2/3} = a^2$

$\therefore$ Locus is $x^2 + y^2 = a^2/4$, which is a circle.

In parametric

$2h = a\sin\theta, 2k = a\cos\theta$

$\therefore\quad 4(h^2 + k^2) = a^2.1$

$\therefore$ Locus is $x^2 + y^2 = a^2/4$, which is a circle.

4. (a) $\frac{dy}{dx} = -\frac{f_x}{f_y} = -\frac{3x^2 - 6y}{3y^2 - 6x} = -1$ at (3, 3)

$\therefore$ Normal is $y - 3 = 1(x - 3)$

or $x - y = 0$

(b) $x - y = 0$ as above $\frac{dy}{dx} = -1$ at (1, 1)

(c) Ans. (a), (b).

$y = \frac{1}{x} \quad \therefore \quad \frac{dy}{dx} = -\frac{1}{x^2}.$

Hence slope of the normal is x^2 which is +ive $\forall\, x \in R$. But slope of normal is given to be

$-\frac{3 - a}{a}$ or $\frac{a - 3}{a} = \frac{(a - 0)(a - 3)}{a^2} = +\text{ive}$

$\therefore\quad a < 0$ or $a > 3$

$\therefore\quad a \in (-\infty, 0)$ or $a \in (3, \infty)$

5. (a) $y^2 = 4ax.$

$\therefore\quad 2y\frac{dy}{dx} = 4a$ or $\frac{dy}{dx} = \frac{2a}{y}.$

$\therefore$ Slope of the normal $= -\frac{1}{dy/dx}$

$= -\frac{y}{2a} = m$, given. $\therefore\ y = -2am.$

Therefore $x = \frac{y^2}{4a} = \frac{4a^2m^2}{4a} = am^2.$

Hence the normal whose slope is m will be at the point $(am^2, -2am)$ so that its equation is

$y + 2am = m(x - am^2)$

or $y = mx - 2am - am^3.$

(b) Refer part (a), the equation of normal to $y^2 = 4ax$ in terms of slope m is

$y = mx - 2am - am^3.$

For $y^2 = x$ we shall put $4a = 1$ so that its equation is

$y = mx - \frac{1}{2}m - \frac{1}{4}m^3.$

It passes through $(c, 0)$

$\therefore\quad 0 = mc - \frac{1}{2}m - \frac{1}{4}m^3$

or $m(m^2 - 4c + 2) = 0$

Above gives $m = 0$ so that the normal corresponding to this value of m is $y = 0$ i.e. x-axis. The slopes of the remaining two normals are given by $m^2 + 0m + (2 - 4c) = 0.$

For reality of roots

$B^2 - 4AC \geq 0 \ \therefore\ 0 - 4(2 - 4c) \geq 0$

or $4c - 2 \geq 0$ or $c \geq \frac{1}{2}.$

Also if the normals be perpendicular, then

$m_1 m_2 = -1$ or $2 - 4c = -1$ or $3 = 4c$

$\therefore\quad c = 3/4.$

(c) From the equation of the curve $x^2 = 4y$, we get $dy/dx = x/2$. If m be the slope of the normal to $x^2 = 4y$ then $m = -1\Big/\frac{dy}{dx} = -\frac{2}{x}.$

$\therefore\quad x = -2/m$ and $y = x^2/4 = 1/m^2.$

Normal is $y - \frac{1}{m^2} = m\left(x + \frac{2}{m}\right).$

If it passes through the point (1, 2), then

$\therefore\quad 2 - \frac{1}{m^2} = m\left(1 + \frac{2}{m}\right) = m + 2$

$\therefore\quad m^3 = -1$ or $m = -1.$

$\therefore$ Required normal is $y - 1 = -1(x - 2)$

or $x + y = 3$

6. (a) Slope of the tangent to $y^2 = 4ax$ is

$\frac{dy}{dx} = \frac{2a}{y} = m$, given

$\therefore\quad y = \frac{2a}{m}.\ \therefore\ x = \frac{y^2}{4a} = \frac{1}{4a}.\frac{4a^2}{m^2} = \frac{a}{m^2}.$

Hence the tangent whose slope is m will be at the point $\left(\frac{a}{m^2}, \frac{2a}{m}\right)$ and hence its equation is

$y - \frac{2a}{m} = m\left(x - \frac{a}{m^2}\right)$ or $y = mx + \frac{a}{m}.$

If the tangent passes through the point (x_1, y_1) then $y_1 = mx_1 + \frac{a}{m}$

or $\quad m^2 x_1 - my_1 + a = 0$

Above is a quadratic in m (slope of the tangent) which shows that there will be two tangents which pass through the point (x_1, y_1). If these tangents are perpendicular then $m_1 m_2 = -1$ or $\frac{a}{x_1} = -1$ or $x_1 = -a$. Hence their point of intersection (x_1, y_1) lies on directix $x = -a$.

(b) Ans. (i).

7. (a) $\frac{dy}{dx} = \frac{\dot{y}}{\dot{x}} = \frac{2\sqrt{2}\, a\cos t}{-2a\sin 2t} = \frac{-\sqrt{2}\cos t}{2\sin t\cos t}$

$$= -\frac{1}{\sqrt{2}\sin t} = m \quad \therefore \quad \sin t = -\frac{1}{m\sqrt{2}}$$

Now $x = a\cos 2t = a(1 - 2\sin^2 t) = a\left(1 - \frac{1}{m^2}\right)$

$$y = 2\sqrt{2}\, a\sin t = 2\sqrt{2}a\left(-\frac{1}{m\sqrt{2}}\right) = -\frac{2a}{m}.$$

Hence the equation of tangent is

$$y + \frac{2a}{m} = m\left\{x - a + \frac{a}{m^2}\right\}$$

or $\quad mx - y = a\left(m + \frac{1}{m}\right)$

Above is the equation of tangent in terms of its slope m. If it passes through the point (x_1, y_1), then

$$mx_1 - y_1 = a\left(m + \frac{1}{m}\right)$$

$$m^2 x_1 - my_1 = am^2 + a$$

or $\quad m^2(x_1 - a) - my_1 - a = 0$

Above is a quadratic in m which shows that there will be two tangents which pass through (x_1, y_1). If the two tangents be perpendicular, then $m_1 m_2 = -1$

or $\quad \frac{-a}{x_1 - a} = -1$

or $\quad a = x_1 - a$ or $x_1 = 2a$

Thus the two perpendicular tangents meet at $x = 2a$.

(b) Ans. (a).

$$\frac{dy}{dx} = 2x - 5 = -1 \text{ at } (2, 0) \text{ and } = 1 \text{ at } (3, 0)$$

Clearly $m_1 m_2 = -1$ and hence the tangents are perpendicular $\therefore \quad \theta = \pi/2$.

8. (a) $y^2(a + x) = x^2(3a - x)$.

The point whose $x = a$, then $y^2(2a) = a^2 .2a$.

$\therefore \quad y^2 = a^2 \quad$ or $\quad y = a, -a$.

Hence the points are $P(a, a), Q(a, -a)$.

$$y^2 = \frac{x^2(3a - x)}{a + x}.$$

$$f(x, y) = y^2(a + x) - (3ax^2 - x^3) = 0$$

$$\therefore \quad \frac{dy}{dx} = -\frac{f_x}{f_y} = -\frac{[y^2 - 6ax + 3x^2]}{2y(a + x)}$$

$$\therefore \quad \frac{dy}{dx}_{at(a,a)} = \frac{2a^2}{4a^2} = \frac{1}{2}$$

$$\frac{dy}{dx}_{at(a,-a)} = -\frac{2a^2}{4a^2} = -\frac{1}{2}$$

$\therefore \quad$ Tangent is $y - a = \frac{1}{2}(x - a)$ or $2y - x = a$.

Since slope of tangent is $\frac{1}{2}$, therefore slope of normal will be -2. Normal is

$$y - a = -2(x - a) \quad \text{or} \quad y + 2x = 3a.$$

Similarly we can write tangent and normal at $Q(a, -a)$ as $x + 2y + a = 0$ and $2x - y - 3a = 0$ respectively.

(b) Do yourself as in (a).

9. $y = x^3 - 3x, \quad \therefore \quad \frac{dy}{dx} = 3x^2 - 3.$

$\therefore \quad$ Slope of normal is $-1\Big/\frac{dy}{dx} = -\frac{1}{3x^2 - 3}.$

Since it is parallel to $2x + 18y = 9$ whose slope is $-1/9$.

$$\therefore \quad \frac{-1}{3x^2 - 3} = -\frac{1}{9} \quad \text{or} \quad x^2 - 1 = 3$$

or $\quad x^2 = 4. \quad \therefore \quad x = 2, -2$

Hence two such points are $(2, 2)$ and $(-2, -2)$ slope of the normal at which is $-1/9$. Hence their equations are

$$y - 2 = \frac{1}{9}(x - 2) \quad \text{and} \quad y + 2 = -\frac{1}{9}(x + 2)$$

$$x + 9y = 20 \quad \text{and} \quad x + 9y = -20.$$

10. Tangent being perpendicular to given line of slope 2, will have its slope as $-\frac{1}{2}$.

$$\text{Slope of tangent} = -\frac{f_x}{f_y} = -\frac{6x + 1}{2(y + 1)} = -\frac{1}{2}$$

$\therefore \quad y = 6x.$

Solving with the given curve, we have

$$3x^2 + 36x^2 + x + 12x = 0 \quad \text{or} \quad 13x(3x + 1) = 0$$

$\therefore \quad x = 0, -1/3 \quad \therefore \quad y = 0, -2$

Hence the two points are $(0, 0), \left(-\frac{1}{3}, -2\right)$

$$\therefore \quad y = -\frac{1}{2}x \text{ and } y + 2 = -\frac{1}{2}\left(x + \frac{1}{3}\right)$$

or $2y + x = 0$ and $2y + x + \frac{13}{3} = 0.$

11. (a) $2y \frac{dy}{dx} = 4. \quad \therefore \quad \frac{dy}{dx} = \frac{2}{y} = 2$, given

$\therefore \quad y = 1$ and $x = -1$.

$\therefore$ Tangent is $y - 1 = 2(x + 1)$ or $y = 2x + 3$.

(b) Ans. $c = 4$. Equation of the line is $x + y = 3$. If it is tangent to $y(x+1) = c$, it will cut it in two coincident points $(3 - x)(x + 1) = c$

or $x^2 - 2x + c - 3 = 0$ will have equal roots.

$\therefore \quad B^2 - 4AC = 0$

or $4 - 4(c - 3) = 0$ or $c = 4$.

12. (a) Ans. (b). If the given line is a tangent to ellipse it will cut it in two coincident points. Eliminating y, we get

$25x^2 - 18ax + 9(a^2 - 16) = 0$

$\therefore \quad B^2 - 4AC = 0$

or $18 \times 18a^2 - 4 \times 25 \times 9(a^2 - 16) = 0$

$\therefore \quad 16a^2 = 400$ or $a = \pm 5$

(b) Ans. (b) and (d).

$\frac{dy}{dx} = -\frac{8x}{18y} = \frac{8}{9} \quad \Rightarrow \quad x = -2y$

Solving $16y^2 + 9y^2 = 1$

$\therefore \quad y = \pm\frac{1}{5} \qquad \therefore \quad x = \mp\frac{2}{5}$

$\left(\frac{2}{5}, -\frac{1}{5}\right)$ and $\left(-\frac{2}{5}, \frac{1}{5}\right) \Rightarrow$ (b) and (d).

13. (a) $y - 2 = 0$. Vertex is $(-4, 2)$ etc.

(b) Ans. (d). Slope of the normal at (3, 4) is the value of $-1/f'(x)$ at $x = 3$.

or $-\frac{1}{f'(3)} = \tan\frac{3\pi}{4} = -1 \quad \therefore \quad f'(3) = 1.$

14. (a) $x = \frac{2at^2}{1+t^2}, y = \frac{2at^3}{1+t^2},$

$\therefore \quad x = 2a/5, y = a/5$ at $t = 1/2$.

Again $y = tx$

$\therefore \quad \frac{dy}{dx} = t.1 + x.\frac{dt}{dx}$ ...(1)

Now $\frac{dx}{dt} = 2a.\frac{(1+t^2)\,2t - t^2\,.\,2t}{(1+t^2)^2} = \frac{4at}{(1+t^2)^2}$

$\therefore \quad \frac{dy}{dx} = t + x.\frac{(1+t^2)^2}{4at} \qquad \because \quad \frac{dx}{dt}.\frac{dt}{dx} = 1$

$\therefore \quad \frac{dy}{dx}$ at $t = \frac{1}{2}$ is $\frac{1}{2} + \frac{2}{5}a.\frac{25}{16\,.\,2a} = \frac{1}{2} + \frac{5}{16} = \frac{13}{16}.$

$\therefore$ Slope of tangent is 13/16 and that of normal is $-16/13$.

Tangent at $t = \frac{1}{2}$ is $\left(y - \frac{1}{5}a\right) = \frac{13}{16}\left(x - \frac{2}{5}a\right)$

or $13x - 16y = 2a$.

Normal at $t = \frac{1}{2}$ is $\left(y - \frac{1}{5}a\right) = -\frac{16}{13}\left(x - \frac{2}{5}a\right)$

or $16x + 13y = 9a$.

(b) $dx/d\theta = -a\sin\theta + a\theta\cos\theta + a\sin\theta = a\theta\cos\theta$

$dy/d\theta = a\cos\theta - a\cos\theta + a\theta\sin\theta = a\theta\sin\theta$

$\therefore \quad \frac{dy}{dx} = \frac{dy}{d\theta} \div \frac{dx}{d\theta} = \frac{\sin\theta}{\cos\theta}$ = solpe of tangent.

$\therefore$ Slope of normal $= -1\Big/\frac{dy}{dx} = -\frac{\cos\theta}{\sin\theta}.$

$\therefore$ Normal is $[y - (a\sin\theta - a\theta\cos\theta)] = -\frac{\cos\theta}{\sin\theta}.$

$\times [x - (a\cos\theta + a\theta\sin\theta)]$

or $y\sin\theta + x\cos\theta = a(\cos^2\theta + \sin^2\theta) = a.$

Its distance from the origin is clearly

$\frac{a}{\sqrt{(\cos^2\theta + \sin^2\theta)}} = a$ *i.e.* constant

15. (a) $x = 3\cos\theta - \cos^3\theta, y = 3\sin\theta - \sin^3\theta.$

$dx/d\theta = -3\sin\theta + 3\cos^2\theta\sin\theta$

$= -3\sin\theta(1 - \cos^2\theta) = -3\sin^3\theta$

$dy/d\theta = 3\cos\theta - 3\sin^2\theta\cos\theta$

$= 3\cos\theta(1 - \sin^2\theta) = 3\cos^3\theta$

$\therefore \quad \frac{dy}{dx} = -\frac{\cos^3\theta}{\sin^3\theta}$ = slope of tangent

and slope of the normal is

$= \frac{-1}{dy/dx} = \frac{\sin^3\theta}{\cos^3\theta}$

Hence the equation of the normal is

$y - (3\sin\theta - \sin^3\theta) = (\sin^3\theta/\cos^3\theta)$

$[x - (3\cos\theta - \cos^3\theta)]$

or $y\cos^3\theta - x\sin^3\theta = 3\sin\theta\cos^3\theta$

$-3\cos\theta\sin^3\theta$

Dividing throughout by $\sin^3\theta\cos^3\theta$, we get

$y\,\text{cosec}^3\theta - x\sec^3\theta = 3(\text{cosec}^2\theta - \sec^2\theta)$

If $\theta = \pi/4$ then $\sec(\pi/4) = \text{cosec}(\pi/4) = \sqrt{2}$.

$\therefore$ Normal is $y.2\sqrt{2} - x.2\sqrt{2} = 0$

or $y - x = 0$.

It clearly passes through the origin.

(b) $\frac{dy}{dx} = \frac{\dot{y}}{\dot{x}} = \frac{a(2\cos t - 2\cos 2t)}{-a(2\sin t + 2\sin 2t)}$

$= \frac{2a.2\sin\frac{3t}{2}\sin\frac{t}{2}}{-2a.2\sin\frac{3t}{2}\cos\frac{t}{2}} = -\frac{\sin\frac{t}{2}}{\cos\frac{t}{2}} = -\tan\frac{t}{2}.$

$\therefore$ T is $y - a(2\sin t - \sin 2t)$

$$= -\frac{\sin(t/2)}{\cos(t/2)}[x - a(2\cos t + \cos 2t)]$$

$$x \sin\frac{t}{2} + y\cos\frac{t}{2} = a\left\{2\sin\left(t+\frac{t}{2}\right) - \sin\left(2t - \frac{t}{2}\right)\right\}$$

$$= a \sin\frac{3t}{2}$$

Similarly N is $x\cos\frac{t}{2} - y\sin\frac{t}{2} = 3a\cos\frac{3t}{2}$

Also S.T. $= \frac{y}{y'} = y\cot\frac{t}{2}$

S.N. $= yy' = y\tan\frac{t}{2}$.

(c) $\frac{dy}{dx} = \frac{\dot{y}}{\dot{x}} = \frac{3a\cos^2 t \sin t}{3a\cos^3 t} = \tan t$

Hence slope of normal is $-\cot t$.

Equation of normal can be easily found to be

$y + a\cos^3 t = -\cot t\,[x - 2a\sin t - a\sin t\cos^2 t]$

or $x\cos t + y\sin t = 2a\sin t\cos t$

or $\frac{x}{2a\sin t} + \frac{y}{2a\cos t} = 1$

Intercepts on the axes are $A = 2a\sin t, B = 2a\cos t$

$\therefore$ Portion intercepted between the axes is

$\sqrt{A^2 + B^2} = 2a$ *i.e.*, constant.

16. (a) Points are $(1, 0)$ and $(2, 0)$.

Tangents are $y + 3x = 3,\ y - 7x + 14 = 0$.

(b) $y = 2x$, (c) $-3, 5$.

(c) $\frac{dy}{dx} = \frac{\dot{y}}{\dot{x}} = \frac{3a\cos^2 t \sin t}{3a\cos^3 t} = \tan t$

Hence slope of normal is $-\cot t$.

Equation of normal can be easily found to be

$y + a\cos^3 t = -\cot t\,[x - 2a\sin t - a\sin t\cos^2 t]$

or $x\cos t + y\sin t = 2a\sin t\cos t$

or $\frac{x}{2a\sin t} + \frac{y}{2a\cos t} = 1$

Intercepts on the axes are $A = 2a\sin t, B = 2a\cos t$

$\therefore$ Portion intercepted between the axes is

$\sqrt{A^2 + B^2} = 2a$ *i.e.*, constant.

17. (a) Point is $(7, 0), T, x - 20y - 7 = 0$,

$N,\ 20x + y - 140 = 0$.

(b) Putting $x = 8$ in the equation $y^2 = x^3$,

we get $y = \pm 8^{3/2} = \pm 8\sqrt{8} = \pm 16\sqrt{2}$.

Now the equation of the normals at $(8, 16\sqrt{2})$ and $(8, -16\sqrt{2})$ to $y^2 = x^3$ can be easily found as $x \pm 3\sqrt{2}\,y = 104$.

(c) Ans. $x + 4y = 18$.

18. $9y^2 = x^3$

$\therefore$ $18y\frac{dy}{dx} = 3x^2$ or $\frac{dy}{dx} = \frac{x^2}{6y}$

Slope of the normal $= \frac{-6y}{x^2} = \pm 1$ ...(1)

Any line making equal intercepts on axes will have its slope as 1 or -1. $y = \frac{x^2}{6}$ or $\frac{-x^2}{6}$. Solving these with $9y^2 = x^3$, we get the points $(4, 8/3)$ or $(4, -8/3)$.

19. (a) Tangent is parallel to $y = 2x$ and hence its slope $dy/dx = 2$

or $4x^3 - 18x^2 + 26x - 10 = 2$.

or $4x^3 - 18x^2 + 26x - 12 = 0$ $[4 + 26 = 18 + 12]$

or $(x-1)(4x^2 - 14x + 12) = 0$

$(x-1)(x-2)(4x-6) = 0$

$\therefore$ $x = 1, 2, 3/2$, $\therefore$ $y = 3, 5, 15/6$.

Clearly tangent at $(1, 3)$ and $(2, 5)$ are

$y - 3 = 2(x-1)$ and $y - 5 = 2(x-2)$.

or $y = 2x + 1$ and $y = 2x + 1$ *i.e.* same.

(b) $(1, 2), (1, -2)$

(c) $\left(\frac{1}{3^{1/4}}, \frac{1}{3^{3/4}}\right), \left(-\frac{1}{3^{1/4}}, -\frac{1}{3^{3/4}}\right)$

20. (a) $\frac{dy}{dx} = \frac{1.(1-x^2) - (-2x).x}{(1-x^2)^2} = \frac{1+x^2}{(1-x^2)^2} = \tan\frac{\pi}{4} = 1$.

$\therefore$ $(1 + x^2) = (1 - x^2)^2$

or $x^4 - 3x^2 = 0$, giving $x = 0, -\sqrt{3}, \sqrt{3}$.

$\therefore$ $y = 0, \sqrt{3}/2, -\sqrt{3}/2$.

Hence the points are : $(0,0), (-\sqrt{3}, \sqrt{3}/2)$ and $(\sqrt{3}, -\sqrt{3}/2)$.

The normals at these points are respectively

$x + y = 0, x + y = -\sqrt{3}/2$ and $x + y = \sqrt{3}/2$.

This is left for the reader.

(b) Already done in last question.

Tangent is parallel to x-axis or y-axis according as $\frac{dy}{dx} = 0$ or ∞

$\Rightarrow$ $x^2 + 1 = 0$ not possible

or $x^2 - 1 = 0$.

In this case also, we shall not get any point on the curve as y becomes infinity.

(c) Ans. (d). $f(x, y) = y^3 + 3x^2 - 12y = 0$

Slope of tangent is $\frac{dy}{dx} = -\frac{f_x}{f_y} = -\frac{6x}{3y^2 - 12}$

If the tangent is vertical

$\frac{dy}{dx} = \infty \Rightarrow y^2 = 4 \therefore y = \pm 2$

$y = -2$ is ruled out as it makes x^2 negative.

Hence $y = 2$ $\therefore$ $x = \pm\frac{4}{\sqrt{3}}$

21. (a) Ans. (iv). $\frac{dy}{dx}=-\frac{f_x}{f_y}=\infty=\frac{y\,e^{xy}-1}{1-x\,e^{xy}}$

$\therefore \quad 1-x\,e^{xy}=0$

$\therefore \quad e^{xy}=1/x.$ Also $e^{xy}=x+y.$

$\therefore \quad x+y=\frac{1}{x}.$

This relation is satisfied by (1, 0) only.

(b) $\frac{dy}{dx}=-2x=1,$ *i.e.* slope of *AB*.

$\therefore \quad x=-1/2$ and hence $y=15/4.$

22. (a) $y^2=4a\,[x+a\sin(x/a)]$ ...(1)

$\therefore \quad 2y.dy/dx=4a\,[1+\cos(x/a)]$ ...(2)

If the tangent is to be parallel to *x*-axis then $dy/dx=0$

Hence from (2), we get $\cos(x/a)=-1$

$\therefore \quad \sin(x/a)=0$

Putting in (1) we get $y^2=4a\,(x+0)$

or $\quad y^2=4ax$

Hence all such points tangent at which are parallel to *x*-axis will lie on the parabola $y^2=4ax.$

(b) Let the tangent be drawn at the point (*x, y*). Its equation is $Y-y=\frac{dy}{dx}(X-x)$

But $y=\sin x \quad \therefore \quad \frac{dy}{dx}=\cos x$

$\therefore \quad Y-y=\cos x\,(X-x).$

Since it passes through (0, 0), $\therefore \quad -y=-x\cos x$

or $\quad \frac{y}{x}=\cos x$ and $y=\sin x$

$\therefore \quad \frac{y^2}{x^2}+y^2=\cos^2 x+\sin^2 x=1$

or $\quad y^2+x^2y^2=x^2 \quad$ or $\quad x^2-y^2=x^2y^2.$

Hence the points of contact lie on

$x^2-y^2=x^2y^2.$

(c) Since the tangent to the given curve is parallel to $y=x,$ so $\frac{dy}{dx}=1$

$\therefore \quad \frac{dy}{dx}=\tan\alpha-\frac{ax}{u^2\cos^2\alpha}=1$

$\therefore \quad (\tan\alpha-1)=\frac{ax}{u^2\cos^2\alpha}$

or $\quad x=\frac{u^2}{a}\frac{\sin\alpha-\cos\alpha}{\cos\alpha}\cdot\cos^2\alpha$

or $\quad x=\frac{u^2}{a}(\sin\alpha-\cos\alpha)\cos\alpha$

Putting for *x* in the given equation, we have

$$y=\frac{u^2}{a}(\sin\alpha-\cos\alpha)\cos\alpha\,\frac{\sin\alpha}{\cos\alpha}$$
$$-\frac{1}{2}\frac{a}{u^2\cos^2\alpha}\cdot\frac{u^4}{a^2}(\sin\alpha-\cos\alpha)^2\cos^2\alpha$$

or $\quad y=\frac{u^2}{a}\left[\sin^2\alpha-\frac{1}{2}\right]=\frac{u^2}{4a}$ (given)

$\therefore \quad \sin^2\alpha=\frac{1}{2}+\frac{1}{4}=\frac{3}{4}$ **Proved.**

23. (a) $y=be^{-x/a}.$ It cuts *y*-axis at $(0,b).$

$\frac{dy}{dx}=-\frac{b}{a}e^{-x/a}$

$\therefore \quad \left(\frac{dy}{dx}\right)_{(0,b)}=-\frac{b}{a}\cdot 1=-\frac{b}{a}$

Tangent at $(0,b)$ is $y-b=-(b/a).(x-0)$

or $\quad bx+ay=ab \quad$ or $\quad x/a+y/b=1.$

(b) Ans. (iv).

$\frac{dy}{dx}=-\frac{b}{a}e^{-x/a}=-\frac{b}{a}$ (given)

$\therefore \quad e^{-x/a}=1 \Rightarrow x=0 \therefore y=b$ i.e. $(0,b)$

24. (a) Equation of tangent is

$(x-a)\,f_x{}_{(a,b)}+(y-b)\,f_y{}_{(a,b)}=0$

$f_x=n\left(\frac{x}{a}\right)^{n-1}\cdot\frac{1}{a} \quad \therefore \quad f_x{}_{(a,b)}=\frac{n}{a}$

Similarly, $f_y{}_{(a,b)}=\frac{n}{b}.$

$\therefore \quad$ Tangent is $\frac{(x-a)}{a}+\frac{(y-b)}{b}=0$

or $\quad \frac{x}{a}+\frac{y}{b}=2.$ This is independent of *n*.

(b) $y=\frac{c^2}{x} \quad \therefore \quad y'=-\frac{c^2}{x^2}=-\frac{xy}{x^2}=-\frac{y}{x}$

But slope $=-\frac{b}{a} \quad \therefore \quad -\frac{y}{x}=-\frac{b}{a}$

or $\quad \frac{x}{a}=\frac{y}{b}=\frac{\frac{x}{a}+\frac{y}{b}}{1+1}=\frac{1}{2}$

$\therefore \quad x=\frac{a}{2}, y=\frac{b}{2} \quad$ but $xy=c^2$

$\therefore \quad ab=4c^2.$

(c) Ans. (a).

$y=f(x)$ has a second order derivative of 1st degree and hence it must be a cubic.

$\therefore \quad f(x)=ax^3+bx^2+cx+d$ ...(1)

$f'(x)=3ax^2+2bx+c=3 \quad$ at (2, 1) ...(2)

$f''(x)=6ax+2b=6\,(x-1)$ ...(3)

Comparing, $a=1, 2b=-6 \quad \Rightarrow \quad b=-3$ ...(4)

From (2) we have $3a(4)+2b(2)+c=3$

$12(1)+4(-3)+c=3 \quad \therefore \quad c=3$

Again the point (2, 1) lies on $y=f(x)$

$\therefore \quad 1=8a+4b+2c+d$

or $\quad 1=8.1+4(-3)+2.3+d \quad \therefore \quad d=-1$

$\therefore \quad f(x)=x^3-3x^2+3x-1=(x-1)^3$

25. (a) $x^3+y^3-3axy=0$

$$3x^2+3y^2\, dy/dx-3a(y+x\, dy/dx)=0$$

or $\dfrac{dy}{dx}=-\dfrac{x^2-ay}{y^2-ax}$

or $\dfrac{dy}{dx}=-\dfrac{f_x}{f_y}=-\dfrac{(x^2-ay)}{(y^2-ax)}$

At the points where the curve meets $y^2=ax$, the value of $\dfrac{dy}{dx}=-\dfrac{x^2-ay}{0}=\infty$ and hence tangent is perpendicular to x-axis or parallel to y-axis.

If the tangent is to be parallel to x-axis then $dy/dx=0$.

$\therefore \quad x^2=ay.$

Solving with the given curve, we get

$$x^3+(x^6/a^3)-3x.x^2=0$$

or $\quad x^3(x^3-2a^3)=0$

$\therefore \quad x=0, 2^{1/3}a$. Now $y=x^2/a$

$\therefore \quad y=0, 2^{2/3}a.$

Hence the required points are (0, 0) and $(2^{1/3}a, 2^{2/3}a)$.

But for $(0,0)\ \dfrac{dy}{dx}=\dfrac{0}{0}$ *i.e.* indeterminate. Hence the required point is the other point.

(b) Solving the two we get (0, 0), (4, 4), (4, − 4). Out of these, first we do not require and the last does not satisfy the first curve. Hence the point under consideration is (4, 4) at which

$$\frac{dy}{dx}=\frac{8y-3x^2}{3y^2-8x}=-1.$$

Hence the equation of normal is $y-x=0$.

26. (a) We find the equation of tangent at any point (h, k) on the curve

$$\frac{dy}{dx}=-\frac{f_x}{f_y}=\frac{6x^2}{2y-4} \qquad ...(1)$$

$\therefore \quad \dfrac{dy}{dx}$ at $(h,k)=\dfrac{3h^2}{k-2}$

$\therefore$ The equation of the tangent at (h, k) is given by

$$(y-k)=\frac{3h^2}{k-2}(x-h). \qquad ...(2)$$

Now tangent (2) passes through (1, 2).

$\therefore \quad 2-k=\dfrac{3h^2}{k-2}(1-h)$

or $\quad -(k-2)^2=3h^2-3h^3$

or $\quad 3h^3-3h^2-k^2+4k-4=0. \qquad ...(3)$

Also (h, k) lies on (1). Hence

$$k^2-2h^3-4k+8=0 \qquad ...(4)$$

Adding (3) and (4), we get

$$h^3-3h^2+4=0.$$

Factorizing the L.H.S., we shall obtain

$$(h+1)(h-2)^2=0 \quad \therefore \quad h=-1, h=2.$$

But $h=-1$ gives imaginary values of k as can be seen from (4). Now putting $h=2$ in (4), we get

$$k^2-4k-8=0 \quad \therefore \quad k=2\pm 2\sqrt{3}$$

Thus the points are :

$$(2, 2+2\sqrt{3}) \text{ and } (2, 2-2\sqrt{3})$$

Putting for h, k, the slopes of tangents are $2\sqrt{3}, -2\sqrt{3}$.

Equations, $\quad y-(2+2\sqrt{3})=2\sqrt{3}(x-2)$

and $\quad y-(2-\sqrt{3})=-2\sqrt{3}(x-2).$

(b) Let the point of contact be (h, k) where

$$k=h^4 \qquad ...(1)$$

Tangent is $y-k=4h^3(x-h) \qquad ...(2)$

It passes through (2, 0)

$\therefore \quad -k=4h^3(2-h)$

or $\quad -h^4=8h^3-4h^4$ by (1) or $3h^4-8h^3=0$

$\therefore \quad h=0$ or $8/3$

$\therefore \quad k=0$ or $(8/3)^4$

$\therefore \quad$ Points are (0, 0) and $[8/3, (8/3)^4]$

Putting in (2), tangents are

$$y=0 \text{ and } y-\left(\frac{8}{3}\right)^4=4\left(\frac{8}{3}\right)^3\left(x-\frac{8}{3}\right)$$

(c) Any tangent to parabola is $y=mx+\dfrac{a}{m}$ etc.

Ans. $x-y+a=0,\ x-2y+4a=0$

27. (a) $\dfrac{dy}{dx}=-\sin(x+y).\left[1+\dfrac{dy}{dx}\right] \qquad ...(1)$

Since the tangent is parallel to $x+2y=0$ therefore $\dfrac{dy}{dx}=\text{slope}=-\dfrac{1}{2}$. Putting in (1)

or $\quad \sin(x+y)=1=\sin(\pi/2).$

$\therefore \quad \cos(x+y)=0$

$\therefore \quad y=\cos(x+y)=0$

$\therefore \quad \sin(x+y)=1 \Rightarrow \sin x=1 \quad \because \quad y=0$

$\therefore \quad x=\dfrac{\pi}{2}, -\dfrac{3\pi}{2}$ as $-2\pi<x<2\pi$

Hence the points are $[(-3\pi)/2, 0]$ and $[\pi/2, 0]$ where the tangents are parallel to the line $x+2y=0$.

$\therefore$ The equations of tangents are :

$$y-0=-\frac{1}{2}\left(x+\frac{3\pi}{2}\right)$$

and $y-0=-\frac{1}{2}\left(x-\frac{\pi}{2}\right)$

or $2x+4y+3\pi=0$ and $2x+4y-\pi=0$.

(b) $y-2=\frac{dy}{dx}(x-1)$ is the equation of tangent.

From the given relation

$$\frac{|f(x_1)-f(x_2)|}{x_1-x_2}\le|x_1-x_2|$$

Taking limit when $x_1\to x_2$

$\therefore$ $|f'(x_1)|\le 0 \quad \forall\ x_1\in R$

$\therefore$ $f'(x_1)=0$ or $\frac{dy}{dx}=0$ at $x=x_1\in R$.

Hence the equation of tangent is $y-2=0$ or $y=2$.

28. (a) Tangent at the point 'm' is

$$y-8am^3=3m(x-4am^2)$$

It meets the curve again at m' *i.e.* $(4am'^2, 8am'^3)$

$\therefore$ $8a(m'^3-m^3)=3m.4a(m'^2-m^2)$

or $2(m'^2+m'm+m^2)=3m(m'+m)$, as $m'\ne m$

or $2m'^2-m'm-m^2=0$

or $(m'-m)(2m'+m)=0$

$\therefore$ $m'=-m/2$, as $m'\ne m$

$\therefore$ other point is $[4a(-m/2)^2, 8a(-m/2)^3]$

or $(am^2,-am^3)$.

(b) Proceeding as above $t_1=-\frac{1}{2}t$

29. (a) $y=\frac{12}{x}$ $\therefore$ $\frac{dy}{dx}=-\frac{12}{x^2}=-\frac{12}{9t^2}=-\frac{4}{3t^2}$

$\therefore$ Slope of normal is $3t^2/4$.

Its equation is $y-4/t=(3t^2/4)(x-3t)$ ...(1)

If the normal meets the curve again at the point $\left(3t_1,\frac{4}{t_1}\right)$, then substituting these co-ordinates in (1), we get

$$\frac{4}{t_1}-\frac{4}{t}=\frac{3t^2}{4}(3t_1-3t)$$

or $\frac{4}{tt_1}=-\frac{9t^2}{4}$ or $t_1=-\frac{16}{9t^3}$.

(b) Proceed as in part (a).

Normal at $(ct, c/t)$ is

$$xt^3-yt+c-ct^4=0 \quad ...(1)$$

It passes through the point t' *i.e.* $(ct', c/t')$

$\therefore$ $(ct't^3-ct^4)+c-\frac{c}{t'}\cdot t=0$

$$t^3t'(1-t/t')+(1-t/t')=0$$

or $(t^3t'+1)\left(1-\frac{t}{t'}\right)=0$

$\therefore$ $t^3t'=-1$ as $t\ne t'$

(c) Do yourself. Proceed as in Q. 29 (a).

(d) $\frac{dy}{dx}=\frac{-3x^2}{3y^2}=-\frac{p^2}{q^2}=$ slope of tangent.

Slope of line joining the points (p,q) and (a,b) is

$\frac{q-b}{p-a}$. $\therefore$ $\frac{q-b}{p-a}=-\frac{p^2}{q^2}$ ...(1)

Again both the points lie on the curve

$\therefore$ $p^3+q^3=k^3=a^3+b^3$

$\therefore$ $(p^3-a^3)+(q^3-b^3)=0$

$(p-a)(p^2+pa+a^2)+(q-b)(q^2+qb+b^2)=0$

$\therefore$ $\frac{q-b}{p-a}=-\frac{p^2+pa+a^2}{q^2+qb+b^2}$ ...(2)

From (1) and (2) we have

$$\frac{p^2}{q^2}=\frac{p^2+pa+a^2}{q^2+qb+b^2}$$

or $p^2(qb+b^2)=q^2(pa+a^2)$

or $pq(pb-qa)=-(p^2b^2-q^2a^2)$

$pq=-(pb+qa)$

Divide by pq $\therefore$ $\frac{a}{p}+\frac{b}{q}=-1$

30. (a) Ans. (i) and (iii).

$y=\frac{1}{x}$ $\therefore$ $\frac{dy}{dx}=-\frac{1}{x^2}$

Hence the gradient of normal $=x^2$

$=-a/b=$ slope of given line.

Since $x^2>0$, we must have $-\frac{a}{b}>0$ or $\frac{a}{b}=-$ ive *i.e.* a and b are of opposite signs. Hence either $a>0, b<0$ or $a<0, b>0$.

(b) The normal at t_1 is easily found to be

$$y=-t_1x+2at_1+at_1^3$$

It passes through the point $(at_2^2, 2at_2)$

$\therefore$ $2at_2=-t_1at_2^2+2at_1+at_1^3$

or $2a(t_2-t_1)=-at_1(t_2^2-t_1^2)$

$\therefore$ $2=-t_1(t_2+t_1)$ $\because$ $t_2\ne t_1$

$\therefore$ $t_2=-t_1-\frac{2}{t_1}$

31. We have $\frac{dy}{dt}=24t^2$ and $\frac{dx}{dt}=8t$

$\therefore$ $\frac{dy}{dx}=\frac{24t^2}{8t}=3t$.

$\therefore$ The equation of the tangent at the point 't' is given by

$y - 8t^3 + 1 = 3t\,(x - 4t^2 - 3)$ ...(1)

Let the co-ordinates of another point where it intersects the curve be

$(4t'^2 + 3, 8t'^3 - 1)$ which must satisfy (1).

Hence $8t'^3 - 1 - 8t^3 + 1 = 3t\,(4t'^2 + 3 - 4t^2 - 3)$

or $2\,(t' - t)\,(t'^2 + t't + t^2) = 3t\,(t' + t)\,(t' - t)$

or $2\,(t'^2 + t't + t^2) = 3t\,(t' + t)$ $[\because t' \neq t]$

or $2t'^2 - t't - t^2 = 0$ or $2t'^2 - 2t't + t't - t^2 = 0$

or $(2t' + t)\,(t' - t) = 0$

$\therefore$ $t' = -\frac{1}{2}t$ $[\because t' \neq t]$

Then the co-ordinates of the other end are

$\left\{4\left(-\frac{1}{2}t\right)^2 + 3,\ 8\left(-\frac{1}{2}t\right)^3 - 1\right\}$,

that is, $(t^2 + 3,\ -t^3 - 1)$.

m of the tangent at this end t' is $3t' = -\frac{3t}{2}$

Hence equation of the normal at the other end is given by

$y + t^3 + 1 = \frac{2}{3t}(x - t^2 - 3)$ ...(2)

Now (1) and (2) must represent the same line.

Hence comparing (1) and (2), we get

$$\frac{1}{1} = \frac{3t}{2/3t} = \frac{8t^3 - 1 - 12t^3 - 9t}{-t^3 - 1 - 2t/3 - 2/t}$$

and $3t^3 + 9t - \frac{2t}{3} - \frac{2}{t} = 0$

$$3t\left(t^2 - \frac{2}{9}\right) + \frac{9}{t}\left(t^2 - \frac{2}{9}\right) = 0$$

$\therefore$ $t^2 = \frac{2}{9}$ only, as $3t + \frac{9}{t} = 0 \Rightarrow t^2 = -3$

$\therefore$ $t = \pm\frac{1}{3}\sqrt{2}$.

Substituting these values of t in (1) [or (2)] we shall get the equation of the required line as (taking $t = \frac{1}{3}\sqrt{2}$)

$$y - 8\cdot\frac{2\sqrt{2}}{27} + 1 = 3\cdot\frac{\sqrt{2}}{3}\left(x - 4\cdot\frac{2}{9} - 3\right)$$

or $27\sqrt{2}x - 27y - 89\sqrt{2} - 27 = 0.$ ...(4)

And taking $t = -\sqrt{2}/3$, the equation will be

$27\sqrt{2}x + 27y - 89\sqrt{2} + 27 = 0.$ ...(5)

Hence the equation of the required lines are given by (4) and (5).

32. $5x^5 - 10x^3 + x + 2y + 6 = 0$

$\therefore$ $25x^4 - 30x^2 + 1 + 2\frac{dy}{dx} = 0,\ P\,(0, -3)$

$\therefore$ $\frac{dy}{dx} = -\frac{1}{2}$ at P $\therefore$ Slope of normal is 2.

Its equation is $y + 3 = 2\,(x - 0)$ or $y = 2x - 3$

Solving with the given equation, we get

$5x^5 - 10x^3 + x + 4x - 6 + 6 = 0$

or $5x\,(x^4 - 2x^2 + 1) = 0$

$\therefore$ $5x\,(x^2 - 1)^2 = 0$ $\therefore$ $x = 0, 1, -1$

$\therefore$ $y = -3, -1, -5$

$\therefore$ Other points are $(1, -1)$, $(-1, -5)$; $(0, -3)$ being P.

Tangents at both these other points are easily seen to be

$y + 1 = 2\,(x - 1)$ and $y + 5 = 2\,(x + 1)$

or $y = 2x - 3$ *i.e.* same.

33. Let tangent be drawn at $A\,(3t^2, 2t^3)$ and it is normal at $B\,(3t_1^2, 2t_1^3)$.

Slope of tangent at $A = \frac{dy}{dt} \div \frac{dx}{dt} = t$

Its equation is $(y - 2t^3) = t\,(x - 3t^2)$

or $y = t\,x - t^3$ ...(1)

Slope of normal at $B = -1/t_1$

But they represent the same line.

$\therefore$ $t = -\frac{1}{t_1}$ or $tt_1 = -1$ ...(2)

Now tangent at A is $tx - y - t^3 = 0$

It passes through t_1 $\therefore$ $t\,.3t_1^2 - 2t_1^3 - t^3 = 0$

or $3t_1^2\,(t - t_1) - (t^3 - t_1^3) = 0$

or $3t_1^2 - (t^2 + tt_1 + t_1^2) = 0$

or $2t_1^2 - tt_1 - t^2 = 0$

or $(t_1 - t)\,(2t_1 + t) = 0$

$\therefore$ $t = -2t_1 = \frac{2}{t}$ by (2)

$\therefore$ $t^2 = 2$ or $t = \pm\sqrt{2}$

Putting for t in (1), equation of tangent is

$y = \pm\sqrt{2}\,(x - 2)$

34. $\frac{dy}{dx} = \frac{\dot{y}}{\dot{x}} = -\frac{1}{2}\cot^3 t = -\frac{1}{2}$ at $t = \frac{\pi}{4}$

and $P\,(2, 1)$ $\therefore$ T is $x + 2y = 4$.

Eliminating t by $\sec^2 t - \tan^2 t = 1$ the equation of the curve is $x - \frac{1}{y^2} = 1$. Solving with tangent $x + 2y = 4$, we get $(4 - 2y)\,y^2 - 1 = y^2$.

This gives $y = 1, 1, -\frac{1}{2}$.

$\therefore$ Q is $\left(5, -\frac{1}{2}\right)$ $\therefore$ $PQ = \sqrt{\frac{45}{4}} = \frac{3\sqrt{5}}{2}$.

The values of $y = 1, 1$ correspond to point P.

35. (a) Cuts y-axis $(x = 0)$ at $(0, 5)$ at which $\frac{dy}{dx} = 3$

or $3ax^2 + 2bx + c = 3$ at $(0, 5)$

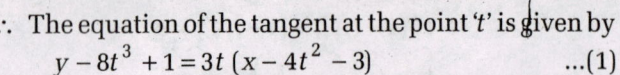

$\therefore \quad c = 3$ ...(1)

Again $\frac{dy}{dx} = 0$ at $P(-2, 0)$ as it touches x-axis

$\therefore \quad 12a - 4b + c = 0$

or $\quad 12a - 4b + 3 = 0 \quad \because \; c = 3$ ...(2)

Also P lies on the curve $-8a + 4b - 2c + 5 = 0$

or $\quad -8a + 4b - 1 = 0$ as $c = 3$ ...(3)

Solving (2) and (3), we get $a = -\frac{1}{2}, b = -\frac{3}{4}$.

(b) Parabola passes through $(-1, 0)$

$\therefore \quad a - b + c = 0$ ...(1)

$\frac{dy}{dx} = 2ax + b = 2a + b$ at $(x = 1) = 1$ (given) ...(2)

$y = x$ is a tangent at $x = 1 \quad \therefore \; y = 1$.

Hence (1, 1) lies both on tangent and parabola

$\therefore \quad a + b + c = 1$ ...(3)

Solving (1), (2) and (3), we get $a = \frac{1}{4}, b = \frac{1}{2}, c = \frac{1}{4}$.

(c) Do yourself.

(d) The points (0, 1) and $(-1, 0)$ lie on the curve.

$\therefore \quad 1 = d$ and $0 = a - b + d$

$\therefore \quad b - a = 1$ ...(I)

Also $\frac{dy}{dx} = 4ax^3 + 3bx^2 + c = 0$ at both (0, 1) and $(-1, 0)$

$\therefore \quad c = 0$ and $-4a + 3b + c = 0$

or $\quad 3b - 4a = 0$ ...(2)

Solving (1) and (2), $a = 3, b = 4, c = 0, d = 1$

$\therefore \quad$ curve is $y = 3x^4 + 4x^3 + 1$

Gradient $m = \frac{dy}{dx} = 12x^3 + 12x^2 = 12x^2(x + 1) < 0$ (given)

Above implies that $x < -1$.

(e) (1, 1) lies on the curve

$\therefore \quad a + b + 1 = 0$ ...(1)

$\frac{dy}{dx} = \tan\theta = 2 \quad$ or $\quad -\left(\frac{f_x}{f_y}\right)_{(1,1)} = 2$

or $\quad -\left(\frac{y + a}{x + b}\right)_{(1,1)} = 2$

$\therefore \quad (1 + a) + 2(1 + b) = 0$

or $\quad a + 2b + 3 = 0$ ...(2)

Solving (1) and (2), we get $a = 1, b = -2$

36. Ans. (c).

$\frac{dy}{dx} = 2x + b = 2 + b$ at (1, 1)

Equation of tangent is $y - 1 = (2 + b)(x - 1)$

Its intercepts A and B on the axes are obtained by putting $y = 0$ and then $x = 0$

$\therefore \quad A = 1 - \frac{1}{2 + b} = \frac{b + 1}{b + 2}$

$B = 1 - (2 + b) = -(b + 1)$

$\Delta = \frac{1}{2} AB = 2 \quad \therefore \; AB = 4$

$-(b + 1)(b + 1) = 4(b + 2)$

or $\quad b^2 + 6b + 9 = 0$

or $\quad (b + 3)^2 = 0 \quad \therefore \; b = -3$

37. $x = a\cos t, y = b\sin t; a^2 = 8, b^2 = 18$

Tangent is $\frac{x}{a}\cos t + \frac{y}{b}\sin t = 1$

Its intercepts on the axes are $\frac{a}{\cos t}$ and $\frac{b}{\sin t}$.

$\therefore \quad$ Area of $\Delta = \frac{1}{2}\frac{ab}{\sin t \cos t} = \frac{ab}{\sin 2t}$

It will be least if $\sin 2t$ is max. *i.e.* $2t = 90^\circ$ or $t = 45^\circ$ or 135° (rejected) as the point P lies in 1st quadrant.

$\therefore \quad P$ is $\left(\frac{a}{\sqrt{2}}, \frac{b}{\sqrt{2}}\right) = \left(\frac{2\sqrt{2}}{\sqrt{2}}, \frac{3\sqrt{2}}{\sqrt{2}}\right)$ or (2, 3).

38. Let any point P_1 on $y = x^3$ be (h, h^3).

Tangent at P_1 is $y - h^3 = 3h^2(x - h)$. It meets $y = x^3$ at P_2. $\quad \therefore \; x^3 - h^3 = 3h^2(x - h)$

or $\quad x^2 + xh + h^2 - 3h^2 = 0$

or $\quad x^2 + xh - 2h^2 = 0$

or $\quad (x - h)(x + 2h) = 0$

$\therefore \quad x = -2h$ for P_2 as $x = h$ is for the point P_1.

$\therefore \quad P_2$ is $(-2h, -8h^3)$.

Tangent at P_2 is $y + 8h^3 = 3(2h)^2(x + 2h)$. It meets $y = x^3$ at P_3.

$x^3 + 8h^3 = 12h^2(x + 2h)$

or $\quad x^2 - 2hx - 8h^2 = 0$

or $\quad (x - 4h)(x + 2h) = 0$

$\therefore \quad x = 4h$ for P_3. $\quad \therefore \quad P_3$ is $(4h, 64h^3)$

Continuing like this, we get $x = -8h$ for P_4 etc.

Hence the abscissae are $h, -2h, 4h, -8h,$ ...... which form a G.P.

$D_1 = \Delta P_1P_2P_3, \quad D_2 = \Delta P_2P_3P_4$

$$\frac{\Delta_1}{\Delta_2} = \frac{1}{2}\begin{vmatrix} h & h^3 & 1 \\ -2h & -8h^3 & 1 \\ 4h & 64h^3 & 1 \end{vmatrix} \div \frac{1}{2}\begin{vmatrix} -2h & -8h^3 & 1 \\ 4h & 64h^3 & 1 \\ -8h & -512h^3 & 1 \end{vmatrix} = \frac{D_1}{D_2}$$

Take -2 and -8 common from C_1 and C_2 of D_2 and it becomes D_1.

$\therefore \quad D_2 = 16 D_1 \quad$ or $\quad \dfrac{\Delta_1}{\Delta_2} = \dfrac{D_1}{D_2} = \dfrac{1}{16}$.

39. $y = (1+x)^y + \sin^{-1}(\sin^2 x)$ ...(1)

When $x = 0,\ y = 1^y \ \therefore \ y = 1 \ \therefore$ point P is $(0, 1)$.

Also $(1+x)^y - y + \sin^{-1}(\sin^2 x) = 0$

or $f(x, y) = 0$

$$f_x = y(1+x)^{y-1} + \frac{1}{\sqrt{(1-\sin^4 x)}} .2 \sin x . \cos x = 1$$

$f_y = (1+x)^y \log(1+x) - 1 = 0 - 1 = -1$ at P.

$\therefore$ Slope of normal is $\dfrac{f_y}{f_x} = -1$ and hence its equation is $y - 1 = -1(x - 0)$ or $x + y = 1$.

40. (a) Refer **Q. 43.**

$$\frac{dy}{dx} = \sqrt{\cot 2t} = 0 \text{ at } t = \frac{\pi}{4}.$$

Since slope of tangent $\dfrac{dy}{dx} = 0$, it is parallel to x-axis.

(b) $\dot{x} = -\dfrac{\sin 3t}{\sqrt{\cos 2t}},\ \dot{y} = \dfrac{\cos 3t}{\sqrt{\cos 2t}}$

$$\therefore \quad \frac{dy}{dx} = \frac{\dot{y}}{\dot{x}} = -\cot 3t = 0 \text{ at } t = \frac{\pi}{6}.$$

41. Ans. (a).

Slope of line AB joining the given points is

$$\tan \theta_2 = \frac{e^{c+1} - e^{c-1}}{(c+1) - (c-1)} = e^c . \frac{e^1 - e^{-1}}{2} = e^c \sinh 1$$

$$\therefore \quad \tan \theta_2 = e^c \left(1 + \frac{1}{3!} + \frac{1}{5!} \ldots\right) > e^c \quad \text{...(1)}$$

If the tangent at P to the curve $y = e^x$ at (c, e^c) makes an angle θ_1 with x-axis, then

$$\tan \theta_1 = \frac{dy}{dx} \text{ at } P = e^c \quad \text{...(2)}$$

$\therefore \quad \tan \theta_2 > \tan \theta_1 \ \Rightarrow \ \theta_2 > \theta_1$ by (1), (2)

$\therefore$ Lines AB and tangent at P meet on the left of line $x = c$. $\Rightarrow$ (a)

§4. Angle of intersection of two curves.

By angle of intersection of two curves we mean the angle between the tangents to the two curves at their common point of intersection. Hence if θ be the acute angle between the tangents then

$$\tan \theta = \left|\frac{m_1 - m_2}{1 + m_1 m_2}\right|$$

where m_1 = value of (dy/dx) at the common point for 1st curve

m_2 = value of (dy/dx) at the common point for 2nd curve.

***Condition for orthogonal intersection.**

Two curves are said to cut orthogonally if the angle between them is a right angle

i.e. $\quad \theta = 90° \ \therefore \ \tan 90° = \infty$

or $\quad 1 + m_1 m_2 = 0$ or $m_1 m_2 = -1$

or $\quad (dy/dx)_I \, (dy/dx)_{II} = -1$

***Condition for the two curves to touch.**

If the two curves touch, then $\theta = 0$,

$\therefore \quad \tan \theta = 0$

$\therefore \quad m_1 - m_2 = 0$ or $m_1 = m_2$

or $\quad (dy/dx)_I = (dy/dx)_{II}$

If the two curves be $f(x, y) = 0$ and $\varphi(x, y) = 0$ then

$$\left(\frac{dy}{dx}\right)_I = -\frac{f_x}{f_y} \text{ and } \left(\frac{dy}{dx}\right)_{II} = -\frac{\varphi_x}{\varphi_y}$$

$$\therefore \quad \tan \theta = \left|\frac{f_x \varphi_y - f_y \varphi_x}{f_x \varphi_x + f_y \varphi_y}\right|$$

***Condition for touching.**

$\theta = 0 \ \therefore \ \tan \theta = 0 \ \therefore \ f_x \varphi_y - f_y \varphi_x = 0$

or $\quad \dfrac{f_x}{f_y} = \dfrac{\varphi_x}{\varphi_y}$

***Condition to cut orthogonally.**

$\theta = 90° \ \therefore \ \tan \theta = \infty$

$\therefore \quad f_x \varphi_x + f_y \varphi_y = 0$

§5. Intercepts of tangent on the axes.

Find the equation of the tangent. Put $y = 0$ and find the value of x which will be intercept on axis of x. Then put $x = 0$ and find the value of y which will be intercept on y-axis.

Length of tangent and normal.

Length of tangent = PT, where P is the point of contact and T is the point where tangent meets the axis of x.

Length of normal = PG where P is the point of contact and G is the point where normal meets the axis of x.

From the figure $\dfrac{y}{PT} = \sin \psi$

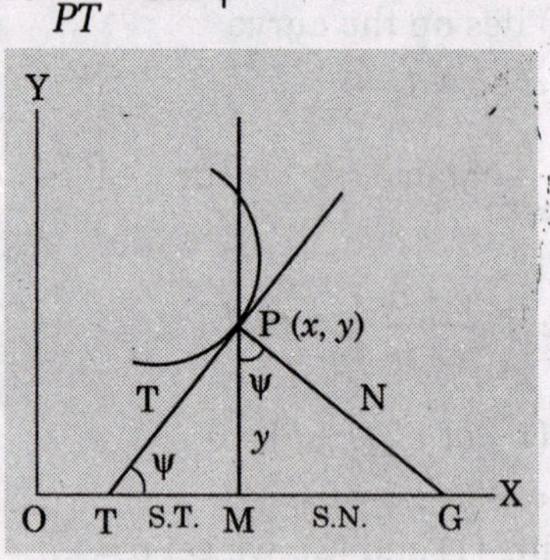

Fig. 2

$\therefore \quad PT = y \operatorname{cosec} \psi$ ...(1)

$\dfrac{y}{PG} = \cos \psi$ ...(2)

$\therefore \quad PG = y \sec \psi$

Now $\tan \psi = dy/dx = y'$, say

$\therefore \quad \sec\psi = \sqrt{1+\tan^2\psi} = \sqrt{1+y'^2}$ ...(3)

$\text{cosec}\,\psi = \sqrt{1+\cot^2\psi}$

$= \sqrt{\left(1+\frac{1}{y'^2}\right)} = \frac{\sqrt{1+y'^2}}{y'}$ ...(4)

$\therefore \quad PT = \frac{y}{y'}\sqrt{1+y'^2}$ by (1) and (4)

$PG = y\sqrt{1+y'^2}$ by (2) and (3).

Condition for a given line to touch a given curve.

Let the line be a tangent to the given curve at (x, y) then write the equation of the tangent as

$$Y - y = (dy/dx)(X - x).$$

Compare this with the given line $aX + bY + c = 0$ and then eliminate x and y.

Length of sub-tangent and sub-normal

Subtangent $= TM = y\cot\psi = y \div (dy/dx) = y / y'$

Subnormal $= MG = y\tan\psi = y\frac{dy}{dx} = yy'$.

Problem Set (2)

Angle of intersection of two curves, length of tangent, normal, sub-tangent, sub-normal and intercepts on the axes.

1. In Q. 1 to 6 find the angle of intersection of the curves :

(a)* $x^2 + y^2 = a^2\sqrt{2}$ and $x^2 - y^2 = a^2$.

(b) $x^2 y = 1$ and $y = x^2$.

2. (a) $x^2 = 4ay$ and $2y^2 = ax$,

(b)* $y^2 = 2x$ and $x^2 = 16y$, common tangent.

(c) The common tangent(s) of $y = x^2$ and $y = -x^2 + 4x - 4$ is (are) :

(a) $y = 4(x-1)$ (b) $y = -4(x-1)$

(c) $y = 0$ (d) $y = 30x - 20$ **(I.I.T. 2006)**

3. (a) $y^2 = 4ax$ and $x^2 = 4by$.

(b) $y^2 = 8x$ and $x^2 = 4y - 12$.

4. (a) $xy = a^2$ and $x^2 + y^2 = 2a^2$.

(b) $y^2 = 16x$ and $2x^2 + y^2 = 4$.

5. (a) $y = x^2$ and $6y = 7 - x^2$.

(b) $y = 4x^2$ and $y = x^2$.

6. (a)* $y = 4 - x^2$ and $y = x^2$.

(b)* $\frac{x^2}{a^2} + \frac{y^2}{b^2} = 1$, $x^2 + y^2 = ab$ **(J.E.E. W.B. 1996)**

(c)* Find the acute angles between the curves $y = |x^2 - 1|$ and $y = |x^2 - 3|$ at their points of intersection. **(Roorkee 1998)**

7. (a) If the curves $\frac{x^2}{a^2} + \frac{y^2}{4} = 1$ and $y^3 = 16x$ intersect at right angles, show that $a^2 = 4/3$.

(b) The tangent and normal at the point $P(at^2, 2at)$ to the parabola $y^2 = 4ax$ meet the x-axis in T and G respectively, then the angle at which the tangent at P to the parabola is inclined to the tangent at P to the circle through P, T, G is

(i) $\tan^{-1} t^2$ (ii) $\cot^{-1} t^2$

(iii) $\tan^{-1} t$ (iv) $\cot^{-1} t$

8. (a) Show that the curves $x^3 - 3xy^2 = -2$ and $3x^2 y - y^3 = 2$ cut orthogonally.

(b) Out of the four curves given below choose the curve which intersects the parabola $y^2 = 4ax$ orthogonally

(a) $x^2 + y^2 = a^2$ (b) $y = e^{-x/2a}$

(c) $y = ax$ (d) $x^2 = 4ay$

9. Find the condition that the following conics may cut orthogonally :

(a) $ax^2 + by^2 = 1$ and $a'x^2 + b'y^2 = 1$.

(b) $\frac{x^2}{a} + \frac{y^2}{b} = 1$ and $\frac{x^2}{a'} + \frac{y^2}{b'} = 1$.

(c) Show that $\frac{x^2}{a^2 + k_1} + \frac{y^2}{b^2 + k_1} = 1$

and $\frac{x^2}{a^2 + k_2} + \frac{y^2}{b^2 + k_2} = 1$

intersect orthogonally.

10. Show that the curves $y^2 = 4ax$ and $ay^2 = 4x^3$ intersect each other at an angle of $\tan^{-1}\frac{1}{2}$ and also if PG_1 and PG_2 be the normals to the two curves at common point of intersection (which is not origin) meeting the axis of x in G_1 and G_2, then $G_1G_2 = 4a$.

11. (a)* Prove that the curves $y = e^{-ax}\sin bx$ and $y = e^{-ax}$ touch at the points for which $bx = 2n\pi + \pi/2$.

(b) Prove that the curves $y = x^3 - 3x^2 - 8x - 4$ and $y = 3x^2 + 7x + 4$ touch each other and the equation of the common tangent is $x - y + 1 = 0$.

(c) Cosine of the angle of intersection of curve $y = (3^{x-1})\ln x$ and $y = (x^x - 1)$ is :

(a) 0 (b) 1

(c) $\frac{1}{2}$ (d) $\frac{1}{\sqrt{2}}$ **(I.I.T. 2006)**

12.* Show that the angle between the tangents at any point P and the line joining P to the origin O is the same at all points of the curve $\log(x^2+y^2)=k\tan^{-1}(y/x)$.

13. (a) Find the condition that the line $Ax+By=1$ may be a normal to the curve $a^{n-1}y=x^n$.

(b) If $ax+by=1$ is a normal to the parabola $y^2=4px$ then $pa^3+2pab^3=b^2$.

14. Find the condition that the line $x\cos\alpha+y\sin\alpha=p$ may touch the curve :

(a)* $\dfrac{x^m}{a^m}+\dfrac{y^m}{b^m}=1$ (b) $\dfrac{x^2}{a^2}+\dfrac{y^2}{b^2}=1$

(c) $\left(\dfrac{x}{a}\right)^{n/(n-1)}+\left(\dfrac{y}{b}\right)^{n/(n-1)}=1.$

15. (a) Find the condition that the line $x\cos\alpha+y\sin\alpha=p$ may touch the curve : $x^m y^n=a^{m+n}$. Prove also that the portion of the tangent intercepted between the axes is divided at its point of contact in a constant ratio.

(b) In the curve $x^m y^n=a^{m+n}$, prove that sub-tangent at any point varies as the abscissa of the point.

16. (a)* If x_1, y_1 be the parts of the axes intercepted by the tangent at any point (x,y) on the curve $\left(\dfrac{x}{a}\right)^{2/3}+\left(\dfrac{y}{b}\right)^{2/3}=1$, show that $\dfrac{x_1^2}{a^2}+\dfrac{y_1^2}{b^2}=1.$

(b) The tangent at any point on the curve $x^4+y^4=a^4$ cuts off intercepts p and q on the co-ordinate axes then show that the value of $p^{-4/3}+q^{-4/3}$ is equal to $a^{-4/3}$.

17. (a) Prove that the portion of the tangent to the curve $x^{2/3}+y^{2/3}=a^{2/3}$ which is intercepted between the axes is of constant length.
Also determine the length of tangent and normal at any point t where $x=a\sin^3 t, y=a\cos^3 t$.

(b) At a point $(a/8, a/8)$ on the curve $x^{1/3}+y^{1/3}=a^{1/3}$ $(a>0)$ tangent is drawn. If the portion of the tangent intercepted between the axes be of length $\sqrt{2}$, then $a=4$. Prove.

18. If x_1 and y_1 be the intercepts on the axes of x and y cut off by the tangent to the curve $\left(\dfrac{x}{a}\right)^n+\left(\dfrac{y}{b}\right)^n=1$, then show that $\left(\dfrac{a}{x_1}\right)^{n/(n-1)}+\left(\dfrac{b}{y_1}\right)^{n/(n-1)}=1$

19. (a)* Prove that the sum of intercepts of the tangent to the curve $\sqrt{x}+\sqrt{y}=\sqrt{a}$ upon the co-ordinate axes is of constant length.

(b)* A curve C has the property that if the tangent drawn at any point P on C meets the co-ordinate axes at A and B, then P is the mid-point of AB. The curve passes through the point $(1,1)$. Determine the equation of the curve. **(I.I.T. 1998)**

20.* Find the abscissa of the point on the curve $ay^2=x^3$, the normal at which cuts off equal intercepts from the axes.

21.* Find the abscissa of the point on the curve $xy=(c+x)^2$ the normal at which cuts off numerically equal intercepts from the axes of co-ordinates. **(J.E.E.W.B. 1995)**

22. (a)* In the curve $x=a[\cos t+\log\tan(t/2)], y=a\sin t$, show that the portion of the tangent between the point of contact and the x-axis is of constant length.

(b) Show that the portion of the tangent for the curve,
$$x=\sqrt{a^2-y^2}+\frac{a}{2}\log\frac{a-\sqrt{a^2-y^2}}{a+\sqrt{(a^2-y^2)}}$$
between the point of contact and the x-axis is a.

(c) Find the family of the curves $y=f(x)$, tangent to which makes an intercept of one unit between the point of contact and x-axis. **(I.I.T. 2005)**

23. For the curve $xy=c^2$, prove the following :

(a)* The intercept between the axes on the tangent at any point is bisected at the point of contact.

(b) The tangent at any point makes with co-ordinate axes a triangle of constant area.

24. For the catenary whose equation is $y=c\cosh\dfrac{x}{c}$ prove the following :

(i) length of normal $=y^2/c$.

(ii) perpendicular from foot of ordinate of P to the tangent at P is of constant length.

25.* Prove that in the curve $y=a\log(x^2-a^2)$, sum of the tangent and subtangent varies as the product of the co-ordinates of the point of contact.

26.* Prove that length of the normal varies inversely as perpendicular from origin on tangent to ellipse $\dfrac{x^2}{a^2}+\dfrac{y^2}{b^2}=1.$

27.* Prove that mth power of sub-tangent varies as nth power of subnormal for the curve $x^{m+n}=a^{m-n}y^{2n}$.

28. If sub-normal of the curve $xy^n=a^{n+1}$ is of constant length, then prove that $n=-2$.

29. If the tangent at P on the curve $x^m y^n=a^{m+n}$ meets the co-ordinates axes at A and B, then $AP:PB=m:n$

30. The parametric equations of a cycloid are $x=a(t+\sin t),\ y=a(1-\cos t)$. Prove that the lengths of tangent and normal at any point $t=\pi/3$ are a and $a/\sqrt{3}$ respectively.

Solutions to Problem Set (2)

1. (a) $x^2 + y^2 = a^2\sqrt{2}, \quad x^2 - y^2 = a^2$.

$$\left\{\begin{array}{l}\text{For points of intersection } 2x^2 = a^2(\sqrt{2}+1) \\ 2y^2 = a^2(\sqrt{2}-1)\end{array}\right\} \ldots\text{(A)}$$

$$2x + 2y\left(\frac{dy}{dx}\right)_I = 0, \quad \therefore \quad \left(\frac{dy}{dx}\right)_I = -\frac{x}{y} = m_1$$

$$2x - 2y\left(\frac{dy}{dx}\right)_{II} = 0, \quad \therefore \quad \left(\frac{dy}{dx}\right)_{II} = \frac{x}{y} = m_2.$$

If θ be the angle between the curves, then

$$\tan\theta = \frac{m_1 - m_2}{1 + m_1 m_2} = \frac{-2(x/y)}{1 - x^2/y^3} = \frac{-2xy}{y^2 - x^2}.$$

Now from (A), $4x^2y^2 = a^4 .1$

$\therefore \quad 2xy = a^2$. Also $y^2 - x^2 = -a^2$.

Hence $\tan\theta = \dfrac{-a^2}{-a^2} = 1 \quad \therefore \quad \theta = \dfrac{\pi}{4}$.

(b) $x^2 y = 1, y = x^2$.

Points of intersection are (1, 1) and (–1, 1) and $\theta = \tan^{-1}(4/3)$ at both the points.

2. (a) $x^2 = 4ay, \; 2y^2 = ax$.

[Ans. $\pi/2$ and $\tan^{-1}(3/5)$]

(b) The two curves meet at (0, 0) and (8, 4). Tangents are x-axis and y-axis at (0, 0) so that $\theta = \dfrac{\pi}{2}$. Slopes of tangents at (8, 4) are 2 and 1/4 so that $\tan\theta = 7/6$.

Common tangent. $y = mx + \dfrac{a}{m} = mx + \dfrac{1}{2m}$ is a tangent to parabola $y^2 = 2x$. If it is a tangent to $x^2 = 16y$ then $x^2 = 16\left(mx + \dfrac{1}{2m}\right)$ will have equal roots as the tangent will cut the curve in two coincident points.

$\therefore \quad x^2 - 16mx - \dfrac{8}{m} = 0$ has equal roots.

$\therefore \quad B^2 - 4AC = 0$

or $\quad 256m^2 + \dfrac{32}{m} = 0 \quad$ or $\quad 8m^3 = -1$

$\therefore \quad m = -1/2$

$\therefore \quad$ Common tangent is $y = -\dfrac{1}{2}x - 1$

or $\quad x + 2y + 2 = 0$

(c) Ans. (a), (c).

Any point on the parabola $x^2 = y$ is (t, t^2). Tangent at (t, t^2) is $xx_1 = \dfrac{1}{2}(y + y_1)$

or $\quad 2x.t = y + t^2$.

If it is a tangent to $y = -x^2 + 4x - 4$ then they will intersect in two coincident points.

$\therefore \quad 2xt + t^2 = -x^2 + 4x - 4$

(Equating the values of y)

or $\quad x^2 + 2x(t-2) + (4 - t^2) = 0$

should have equal roots.

$\therefore \quad D = 0, \; i.e., \; 4(t-2)^2 - 4(4 - t^2) = 0$

or $\quad 2t^2 - 4t = 0 \quad \therefore \quad t = 0, 2$

Putting for t in $2xt = y + t^2$, the equation of common tangents are $y = 0$ and $y = 4x - 4$.

3. (a) $y^2 = ax, x^2 = by$.

Ans. $\dfrac{\pi}{2}$ at (0, 0) and $\tan^{-1}\dfrac{2a^{1/3}b^{1/3}}{2(a^{2/3} + b^{2/3})}$ at $(4a^{1/3}b^{2/3}, 4a^{2/3}b^{1/3})$.

(b) $y^2 = 8x, \; x^2 = 4y - 12$. Eliminate x.

$$\left(\frac{y^2}{8}\right)^2 = 4y - 12$$

Clearly $y = 4$ satisfies it and putting in $y^2 = 8x$, we get $x = 2$.

$\therefore \quad$ Point is (2, 4).

Now $\quad 2y\dfrac{dy}{dx} = 8$

$\therefore \quad \left(\dfrac{dy}{dx}\right)_I = \dfrac{8}{2y} = 1$ at (2, 4) and $2x = 4\dfrac{dy}{dx}$

$\therefore \quad \left(\dfrac{dy}{dx}\right)_{II} = \dfrac{x}{2} = 1$ at (2, 4).

Thus their slopes are same and hence the two curves touch at the point (2, 4).

4. (a) Touch : The two curves meet where $(x^2 - a^2) = 0$

$\therefore \quad x = a, -a$ and so $y = \dfrac{a^2}{x} = a$ or $-a$.

Hence the points are (a, a) or $(-a, -a)$.

$$\frac{dy}{dx_I} = -\frac{y}{x} = -1, \; \frac{dy}{dx_{II}} = -\frac{x}{y} = -1$$

Hence the curves touch.

(b) $y^2 = 16x, \; 2x^2 + y^2 = 4$

$$2y\frac{dy}{dx} = 16 \quad \therefore \quad \left(\frac{dy}{dx}\right)_I = \frac{8}{y} = m_1$$

$$4x + 2y\frac{dy}{dx} = 0 \quad \therefore \quad \left(\frac{dy}{dx}\right)_{II} = \frac{-2x}{y} = m_2$$

$$m_1 m_2 = -\frac{16x}{y^2} = -1 \qquad \because \; y^2 = 16x.$$

Hence the curves cut orthogonally. Here we have not found the point of intersection which will lie on both the curves and hence we have used $y^2 = 16x$.

5. (a) $\theta = \tan^{-1}(7)$ at (1, 1) or (– 1, 1)

(b) The curves touch at the origin.

6. (a) The two curves meet at $(\sqrt{2}, 2)$ and $(-\sqrt{2}, 2)$ where slopes of tangents are $-2x$ and $2x$.

or $m_1 = -2\sqrt{2},\ m_2 = 2\sqrt{2}$ at $(\sqrt{2}, 2)$

or $m_1 = 2\sqrt{2},\ m_2 = -2\sqrt{2}$ at $(-\sqrt{2}, 2)$

$\therefore$ Angle between them is $\pm \tan^{-1} \dfrac{4\sqrt{2}}{7}$.

(b) Solving the equations for the point of intersection, we get

$$x^2 = \frac{a^2 b}{a+b},\ y^2 = \frac{b^2 a}{a+b} \quad \therefore \quad \frac{x^2}{y^2} = \frac{a}{b} \qquad ...(1)$$

$$m_1 = \frac{dy}{dx\,\mathrm{I}} = -\frac{f_x}{f_y} = -\frac{b^2}{a^2}\frac{x}{y}$$

$$m_2 = \frac{dy}{dx\,\mathrm{II}} = -\frac{\phi_x}{\phi_y} = -\frac{x}{y}$$

$$\therefore \quad \tan\theta = \frac{m_1 - m_2}{1 + m_1 m_2} = \frac{\frac{x}{y}\left(1 - \frac{b^2}{a^2}\right)}{1 + \frac{b^2}{a^2} \cdot \frac{x^2}{y^2}}$$

Now put for $\dfrac{x^2}{y^2}$ and $\dfrac{x}{y}$ from (1)

$$\therefore \quad \tan\theta = \frac{a-b}{\sqrt{ab}}.$$

(c) Clearly when $x^2 = 2, y = 1$ gives the point of intersection.

The given equations represent four parabolas $y = \pm(x^2 - 1)$ and $y = \pm(x^2 - 3)$ which can be traced.

The curves intersect when $1 < x^2 < 3$ or $1 < x < \sqrt{3}$ or $-\sqrt{3} < x < -1$

$\therefore \quad y = x^2 - 1$ and $y = -(x^2 - 3)$

The points of intersection are $(\pm\sqrt{2}, 1)$.

At $(\sqrt{2}, 1)$

$$m_1 = 2x = 2\sqrt{2},$$

$$m_2 = -2x = -2\sqrt{2}$$

$$\therefore \quad \tan\theta = \left|\frac{4\sqrt{2}}{1-8}\right| = \frac{4\sqrt{2}}{7}$$

$$\therefore \quad \theta = \tan^{-1}\left(\frac{4\sqrt{2}}{7}\right)$$

In a similar manner the acute angles at the other points is same as found above.

7. (a) $\dfrac{x^2}{a^2} + \dfrac{y^2}{4} = 1,\ y^3 = 16x$

$$\frac{2x}{a^2} + \frac{2y}{4}\frac{dy}{dx} = 0 \quad \therefore \quad \left(\frac{dy}{dx}\right)_I = \frac{-4x}{a^2 y} = m_1$$

$$3y^2 \frac{dy}{dx} = 16 \quad \therefore \quad \left(\frac{dy}{dx}\right)_{II} = \frac{16}{3y^2} = m_2.$$

If the curves cut at right angles, then

$$m_1 m_2 = -1.$$

$$\therefore \quad \left(\frac{-4x}{a^2 y}\right) \cdot \frac{16}{3y^2} = -1$$

or $64x = 3a^2 y^3 = 3a^2 . 16x \quad \therefore \quad a^2 = 4/3.$

(b) Ans. (iii).

Equation of tangent and normal at $P(at^2, 2at)$ to the parabola can be easily found to be

$$ty = x + at^2 \qquad ...(1)$$

and $y + tx = 2at + at^3 \qquad ...(2)$

Putting $y = 0$ in (1), we get $x = -at^2$ and putting $y = 0$ in (2), we have $x = 2a + at^2$.

Hence co-ordinates of T are $(-at^2, 0)$ and coordinates of G are $(2a + at^2, 0)$.

Since tangent PT is perpendicular to normal PG therefore TG is the diameter of the circle through P, T, G. Hence the equation of the circle is

$$(x + at^2)(x - 2a - at^2) + (y - 0)(y - 0) = 0$$

or $x^2 + y^2 - 2ax - at^2 (2a + at^2) = 0$

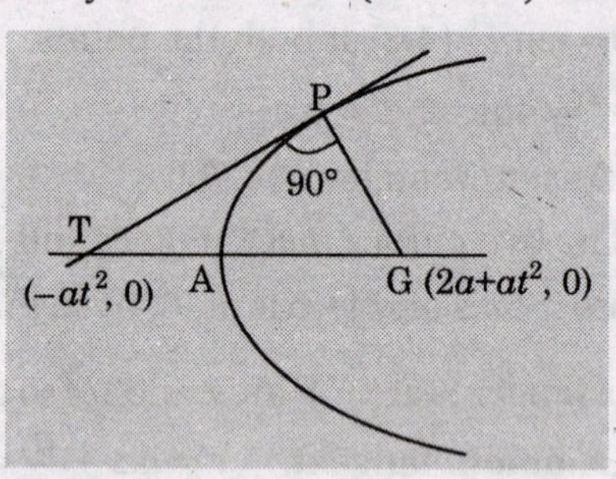

Fig. 3

$$\therefore \quad 2x + 2y\frac{dy}{dx} - 2a = 0$$

or $\dfrac{dy}{dx} = \dfrac{a-x}{y} = \dfrac{a - at^2}{2at} = \dfrac{1-t^2}{2t}$ at P

and from $y^2 = 4ax$, we get

$$\frac{dy}{dx} = \frac{2a}{y} = \frac{2a}{2at} = \frac{1}{t} \text{ at } P.$$

Hence if θ is the angle between the tangents at P to the parabola and circle, then

$$\tan\theta = \frac{(1/t) - (1-t^2)/2t}{1 + (1/t).(1-t^2)/2t}$$

$$= \frac{1+t^2}{2t} \times \frac{2t^2}{1+t^2} = t$$

or $\theta = \tan^{-1} t.$

8. (a) $x^3 - 3xy^2 = -2;\quad 3x^2 y - y^3 = 2$

$$3x^2 - 3y^2 - 6xy\frac{dy}{dx} = 0$$

$$\therefore \quad \left(\frac{dy}{dx}\right)_I = \frac{(x^2 - y^2)}{2xy} = m_1$$

$$6xy + (3x^2 - 3y^2)\frac{dy}{dx} = 0$$

$$\therefore \quad \left(\frac{dy}{dx}\right)_{II} = -\frac{2xy}{x^2 - y^2} = m_2$$

Clearly $m_1 m_2 = -1$. Hence the curves cut orthogonally.

(b) Ans. (b).

$$m_1 = \frac{dy}{dx} = \frac{4a}{2y} = \frac{2a}{y} \text{ for parabola}$$

$$m_2 = \frac{dy}{dx} = e^{-x/2a} \cdot \left(-\frac{1}{2a}\right) = -\frac{y}{2a} \text{ for } y = e^{-x/2a}$$

$m_1 m_2 = -1$. Hence the parabola intersects the curve given in (b) orthogonally.

9. (a) $ax^2 + by^2 = 1, \qquad a'x^2 + b'y^2 = 1$

$$\left(\frac{dy}{dx}\right)_I = -\frac{ax}{by} = m_1, \quad \left(\frac{dy}{dx}\right)_{II} = -\frac{a'x}{b'y} = m_2$$

If the curves cut orthogonally, then $m_1 m_2 = -1$

or $\left(-\frac{ax}{by}\right)\left(-\frac{a'x}{b'y}\right) = -1$

or $aa'x^2 + bb'y^2 = 0.$ ...(1)

We have now to put the values of x^2 and y^2 corresponding to the points of intersection of

$$ax^2 + by^2 - 1 = 0$$

and $a'x^2 + b'y^2 - 1 = 0$

$$\therefore \quad \frac{x^2}{b' - b} = \frac{y^2}{a - a'} = \frac{1}{ab' - a'b}$$

Putting the values of x^2 and y^2 in (1)

$$aa' \cdot \frac{(b' - b)}{ab' - a'b} + bb' \cdot \frac{(a - a')}{ab' - a'b} = 0$$

or $\frac{b' - b}{bb'} + \frac{a - a'}{aa'} = 0$

or $\left(\frac{1}{b} - \frac{1}{b'}\right) + \left(\frac{1}{a'} - \frac{1}{a}\right) = 0$

or $\frac{1}{a} - \frac{1}{b} = \frac{1}{a'} - \frac{1}{b'}$ is the required condition.

(b) Proceeding as above the required condition will be $a - b = a' - b'$.

(c) Put $\frac{1}{a^2 + k_1} = A, \quad \frac{1}{a^2 + k_2} = A'$

$$\frac{1}{b^2 + k_1} = B, \quad \frac{1}{b^2 + k_2} = B' \text{ etc.}$$

Hence as in part (a) question becomes

$$Ax^2 + By^2 = 1 \text{ and } A'x^2 + B'y^2 = 1.$$

The condition for their orthogonal intersection is

$$\frac{1}{A} - \frac{1}{B} = \frac{1}{A'} - \frac{1}{B'}$$

or $(a^2 + k_1) - (b^2 + k_1) = (a^2 + k_2) - (b^2 + k_2)$

or $a^2 - b^2 = a^2 - b^2$ which is true whatever k_1 and k_2 may be.

10. The two curves meet at $(a, 2a)$ and $(0, 0)$,

$$m_1 = \left(\frac{dy}{dx}\right)_I = \frac{2a}{y} = 1 \text{ at } (a, 2a)$$

$$m_2 = \left(\frac{dy}{dx}\right)_{II} = \frac{6x^2}{ay} = 3 \text{ at } (a, 2a)$$

$$\therefore \quad \tan\theta = \left|\frac{m_1 - m_2}{1 + m_1 m_2}\right| = \left|\frac{1 - 3}{1 + 3}\right| = \frac{1}{2}$$

$$\therefore \quad \theta = \tan^{-1}\frac{1}{2}.$$

Normal to 1st : $y - 2a = -1(x - a)$

or $y + x = 3a$.

Normal to 2nd : $y - 2a = -\frac{1}{3}(x - a)$

or $3y + x = 7a$.

They meet the x-axis $y = 0$ at G_1 $(3a, 0)$ and G_2 $(7a, 0)$

$\therefore \quad G_1G_2 = |7a - 3a| = 4a.$

11. (a) $y = e^{-ax} \sin bx, \; y = e^{-ax}$.

The two curves meet at the points where

$\sin bx = 1 = \sin(\pi/2)$

$\therefore \quad bx = \pi/2$ or $2n\pi + \pi/2$ ...(1)

Since $\sin bx = 1 \;\; \therefore \;\; \cos bx = 0.$ ...(2)

Now $\left(\frac{dy}{dx}\right)_I = -ae^{-ax} + be^{-ax}\cos bx = -ae^{-ax}$, by (2) ...(3)

$$\left(\frac{dy}{dx}\right)_{II} = -ae^{-ax} = \left(\frac{dy}{dx}\right)_I, \text{ by (3)}$$

Hence the two curves touch at the points given by (1).

(b) Eliminating y we get $\quad x^3 - 6x^2 - 15x - 8 = 0$

or $(x + 1)(x^2 - 7x - 8) = 0$

or $(x + 1)^2 (x - 8) = 0 \;\; \therefore \;\; x = -1, -1, 8$

$\therefore \quad y = 0, 0, 2\sqrt{2}$

Hence the points of intersection are $(-1, 0), (-1, 0), (8, 2\sqrt{2})$. Since the two points of intersection are coincident hence the two curves touch each other at $(-1, 0)$ and the common tangent is tangent to either at $(-1, 0)$.

$$y - 0 = 1(x + 1) \quad \text{or} \quad x - y + 1 = 0$$

(c) Ans. (b).

For point of intersection we have on eliminating y, $3^{x-1}\log x = x^x - 1$. Clearly $x = 1$ satisfies as each side becomes zero at $x = 1$. Hence the point of intersection is $(1, 0)$.

$$\left(\frac{dy}{dx}\right)_I = (3^{x-1}\log 3)\log x + 3^{x-1} \cdot \frac{1}{x} = 1 \text{ at } (1, 0)$$

$$\left(\frac{dy}{dx}\right)_{II} = x^x(1 + \log x) = 1 \text{ at } (1, 0) \qquad \text{by I (b)}$$

$\therefore \quad \tan\theta = \dfrac{m_1 \sim m_2}{1 + m_1 m_2} = 0$

$\therefore \quad \theta = 0$ and hence $\cos\theta = 1$.

12. $\log(x^2 + y^2) = k \tan^{-1}(y/x)$.

$$\therefore \quad \frac{1}{(x^2+y^2)}\left(2x + 2y\frac{dy}{dx}\right) = k \cdot \frac{1}{1 + y^2/x^2} \cdot \frac{x\, dy/dx - y \cdot 1}{x^2}$$

$$\text{or} \quad 2\left(x + y\frac{dy}{dx}\right) = k\left(x\frac{dy}{dx} - y\right). \quad \text{...(1)}$$

The tangent makes an angle ψ with x-axis, then

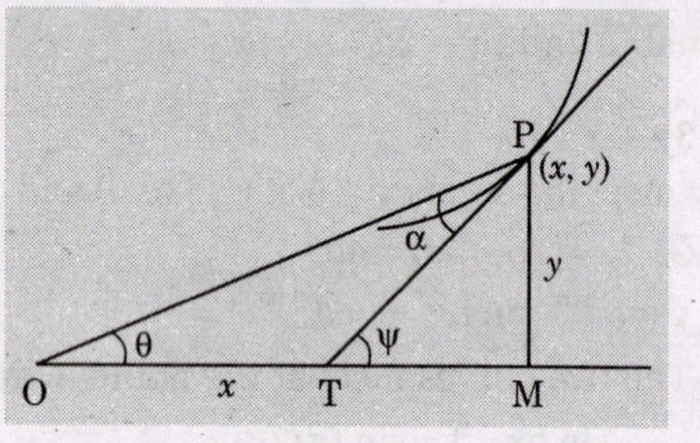

Fig. 4

$$\tan\psi = \frac{dy}{dx} \quad \text{...(2)}$$

Let OP where P is (x, y) make an angle θ with x-axis, then

$$\tan\theta = y/x. \quad \text{...(3)}$$

If α be the angle between the tangent and OP, then

$\alpha = \psi - \theta$

$$\therefore \quad \tan\alpha = \tan(\psi - \theta) = \frac{\tan\psi - \tan\theta}{1 + \tan\psi\tan\theta}$$

$$\text{or} \quad \tan\alpha = \frac{\dfrac{dy}{dx} - \dfrac{y}{x}}{1 + \dfrac{y}{x}\dfrac{dy}{dx}} = \frac{x\dfrac{dy}{dx} - y}{x + y\dfrac{dy}{dx}} = \frac{2}{k}, \text{ by (1).}$$

$\therefore \quad \alpha = \tan^{-1}(2/k)$ *i.e.* constant.

13. (a) $a^{n-1}y = x^n$

$$\therefore \quad \frac{dy}{dx} = n\frac{x^{n-1}}{a^{n-1}} = n\frac{x^n}{a^{n-1}} \cdot \frac{1}{x} = n\frac{y}{x}.$$

$$\therefore \quad \text{Normal is} : Y - y = -\frac{1}{dy/dx}(X - x)$$

$$= -\frac{x}{ny}(X - x)$$

$\therefore \quad Xx + Yny = ny^2 + x^2$.

Compare with $AX + BY = 1$

$$\therefore \quad \frac{x}{A} = \frac{ny}{B} = \frac{ny^2 + x^2}{1} = k, \text{ say.}$$

$\therefore \quad x = Ak,\ y = (Bk/n)$ and $ny^2 + x^2 = k$

or $\quad k^2[(B^2/n + A^2)] = k$

$$\therefore \quad k = \frac{n}{B^2 + nA^2}. \quad \text{..(1)}$$

Now $a^{n-1}y = x^n$. Put for x and y.

$$a^{n-1} \cdot \frac{Bk}{n} = A^n k^n \text{ or } a^{n-1}B = nA^n k^{n-1}$$

$$\text{or} \quad a^{n-1}B = nA^n \cdot \left(\frac{n}{B^2 + nA^2}\right)^{n-1}, \text{ by (1)}$$

$$\text{or} \quad a^{n-1}B(B^2 + nA^2)^{n-1} = A^n n^n.$$

Above is the required condition.

(b) Proceed as above.

14. Refer Q. 1 Set 56 Page 1368-71.

(a) The tangent to the given curve at any point (x, y) is

$$\frac{X}{a}\left(\frac{x}{a}\right)^{m-1} + \frac{Y}{b}\left(\frac{y}{b}\right)^{m-1} = 1. \quad \text{...(1)}$$

Compare with $X\cos\alpha + Y\sin\alpha = p$ ...(2)

$$\frac{(x/a)^{m-1}}{a\cos\alpha} = \frac{(y/b)^{m-1}}{b\sin\alpha} = \frac{1}{p}$$

$$\therefore \quad \frac{x}{a} = \left(\frac{a\cos\alpha}{p}\right)^{1/(m-1)}, \quad \frac{y}{b} = \left(\frac{b\sin\alpha}{p}\right)^{1/(m-1)} \quad \text{...(3)}$$

But the point (x, y) lies on

$$\left(\frac{x}{a}\right)^m + \left(\frac{y}{b}\right)^m = 1. \quad \text{...(4)}$$

Putting for $\dfrac{x}{a}$ and $\dfrac{y}{b}$ from (3) in (4), we get

$$\left(\frac{a\cos\alpha}{p}\right)^{m/(m-1)} + \left(\frac{b\sin\alpha}{p}\right)^{m/(m-1)} = 1$$

$$\text{or} \quad (a\cos\alpha)^{m/(m-1)} + (b\sin\alpha)^{m/(m-1)} = p^{m/(m-1)}.$$

Note : You have to deduce the equation of the tangent as in **Q. 1 Page 1368-71.**

(b) Choosing $m = 2$, the required condition is

$$a^2\cos^2\alpha + b^2\sin^2\alpha = p^2$$

(c) Choose $m = \dfrac{n}{n-1}$,

$$\therefore \quad m - 1 = \frac{n}{n-1} - 1 = \frac{1}{n-1} \text{ and } \frac{m}{m-1} = n.$$

Hence the required condition is

$$(a\cos\alpha)^n + (b\sin\alpha)^n = p^n.$$

Note : In the examination, do the question with power m as in part (a) and then in the result put $m = n/(n-1)$ as above.

15. (a) $x^m y^n = a^{m+n}$. Take log

$$m\log x + n\log y = (m+n)\log a$$

$$m \cdot \frac{1}{x} + n \cdot \frac{1}{y}\frac{dy}{dx} = 0 \quad \therefore \quad \frac{dy}{dx} = -\frac{m}{n}\frac{y}{x}. \quad \text{...(1)}$$

Hence the equation of the tangent is

$$Y - y = -\frac{m}{n}\frac{y}{x}(X - x)$$

$$myX + nxY = (m+n) \cdot xy. \qquad ...(2)$$

Compare with $X \cos\alpha + Y \sin\alpha = p$.

$$\therefore \quad \frac{my}{\cos\alpha} = \frac{nx}{\sin\alpha} = \frac{(m+n)\, xy}{p}$$

$(m+n)\, x = (pm/\cos\alpha)$

and $(m+n)\, y = (pn/\sin\alpha)$

Also $x^m y^n = a^{m+n}$

$$\therefore \quad \left(\frac{pm}{\cos\alpha}\right)^m \cdot \frac{1}{(m+n)^m}\left(\frac{pn}{\sin\alpha}\right)^n \cdot \frac{1}{(m+n)^n} = a^{m+n}$$

or $p^{m+n} \cdot m^m n^n = (m+n)^{m+n}\, a^{m+n} \cdot \cos^m\alpha \sin^n\alpha.$

2nd part :

Let the tangent (2) meet the axes in points A and B.

Putting $Y = 0$, we get $A = \left(\frac{(m+n)}{m} x, 0\right)$.

Putting $X = 0$, we get $B = \left(0, \frac{(m+n)}{n} y\right)$.

Point of contact $P = (x, y)$.

Let P divide AB in the ratio $\lambda : 1$

$$\therefore \quad x = \frac{\lambda \cdot 0 + 1 \cdot [(m+n)/n]\, x}{\lambda + 1},$$

$$y = \frac{\lambda \cdot [(m+n)/n]\, y + 0 \cdot 1}{\lambda + 1}$$

$$\therefore \quad (\lambda + 1)\, x = \frac{m+n}{n} x$$

or $\lambda + 1 = \frac{m}{n} + 1$ or $\lambda = \frac{m}{n}$.

Hence the required ratio is $m : n$.

Therefore the point of contact divides the portion AB of tangent intercepted between the axes in a constant ratio.

(b) We have to prove that $\frac{\text{S.T.}}{x} = \text{constant}$

or $\frac{y}{y' \cdot x} = \text{constant} = -\frac{n}{m}$, by (1) of part (d).

16. (a) Refer **eq. (B) Page 1371.** The equation of tangent for the given curve is

$$\frac{X}{x^{1/3}\, a^{2/3}} + \frac{Y}{y^{1/3}\, b^{2/3}} = 1.$$

Its intercepts on the axes are $x^{1/3} a^{2/3}, y^{1/3} b^{2/3}$ which are given to be x_1, y_1 respectively

$$x_1 = x^{1/3} a^{2/3}, \; y_1 = y^{1/3} b^{2/3}$$

$$\therefore \quad \frac{x_1}{a} = \frac{x^{1/3}}{a^{1/3}}, \frac{y_1}{b} = \frac{y^{1/3}}{b^{1/3}}.$$

Hence $\frac{x_1^2}{a^2} + \frac{y_1^2}{b^2} = \frac{x^{2/3}}{a^{2/3}} + \frac{y^{2/3}}{b^{2/3}} \quad \therefore \quad \frac{x_1^2}{a^2} + \frac{y_1^2}{b^2} = 1,$

using the equation of the curve.

(b) $(X - x) f_x + (Y - y) f_y = 0$

$(X - x)\, 4x^3 + (Y - y)\, 4y^3 = 0$

or $\quad Xx^3 + Yy^3 = x^4 + y^4 = a^4 \qquad ...(1)$

If intercepts are p and q then $(p, 0)$ and $(0, q)$ lie on (1)

$$\therefore \quad px^3 = a^4, qy^3 = a^4$$

$$p^{-4/3} + q^{-4/3} = (a^4)^{-4/3}\,(x^4 + y^4)$$

$$= a^{-16/3} \cdot a^4 = a^{-4/3}$$

17. (a) Putting $b = a$, in Q. 16, the curve becomes $x^{2/3} + y^{2/3} = a^{2/3}$ and the tangent becomes

$$\frac{X}{x^{1/3}\, a^{2/3}} + \frac{Y}{y^{1/3}\, a^{2/3}} = 1$$

It meets the axes at $A\,(x^{1/3} a^{2/3}, 0)$ and $B\,(0, y^{1/3} a^{2/3})$

$$\therefore \quad AB^2 = x^{2/3} a^{4/3} + y^{2/3} a^{4/3}$$

$$= a^{4/3}\,(x^{2/3} + y^{2/3})$$

$$= a^{4/3} \cdot a^{2/3} = a^2$$

$$\therefore \quad AB = a = \text{constant}.$$

$$\frac{dy}{dx} = y' = -\frac{y^{1/3}}{x^{1/3}} = -\frac{\cos t}{\sin t} = -\cot t$$

$$\therefore \quad T \text{ is } \frac{y}{y'}\sqrt{1 + y'^2} = y \tan t \cdot \sqrt{1 + \cot^2 t}$$

$$= \frac{y}{\cos t} = a \cos^2 t$$

Similarly N is $\frac{y}{\sin t} = a \cot t \cos^2 t$.

(b) Slope of tangent is $-\frac{f_x}{f_y} = \frac{-x^{-2/3}}{y^{-2/3}} = -\left(\frac{y}{x}\right)^{2/3}$

$= -1$ at $(a/8, a/8)$

Tangent is $y - a/8 = -1\,(x - a/8)$

or $\quad x + y = \frac{a}{4}$. Its intercepts on axes are

$$A = \frac{a}{4}, B = \frac{a}{4}$$

Portion of tangent intercepted between the axes is

$\sqrt{A^2 + B^2} = \sqrt{2}$ (given) $\quad \therefore \quad \frac{a^2}{16} + \frac{a^2}{16} = 2$

or $\quad a^2 = 16 \Rightarrow a = 4$

18. As in **Q.1 Page 1368-71**, the equation of the tangent to the curve $\left(\frac{x}{a}\right)^n + \left(\frac{y}{b}\right)^n = 1$ is

$$\frac{X}{a}\left(\frac{x}{a}\right)^{n-1} + \frac{Y}{b}\left(\frac{y}{b}\right)^{n-1} = 1$$

Putting $Y = 0$ its intercept on x-axis is

$$a\left(\frac{a}{x}\right)^{n-1} = x_1.$$

Putting $X = 0$ its intercept on y-axis is

$$b\left(\frac{b}{y}\right)^{n-1} = y_1.$$

$$\therefore \quad \frac{a}{x_1} = \left(\frac{x}{a}\right)^{n-1} \text{ or } \left(\frac{a}{x_1}\right)^{1/(n-1)} = \frac{x}{a}$$

$$\frac{b}{y_1} = \left(\frac{y}{b}\right)^{n-1} \text{ or } \left(\frac{b}{y_1}\right)^{1/(n-1)} = \frac{y}{b}.$$

But $\left(\frac{x}{a}\right)^n + \left(\frac{y}{b}\right)^n = 1.$

$$\therefore \quad \left(\frac{a}{x_1}\right)^{n/(n-1)} + \left(\frac{b}{y_1}\right)^{n/(n-1)} = 1.$$

19. (a) $\sqrt{x} + \sqrt{y} = a.$ ...(1)

$$\therefore \quad \frac{1}{2\sqrt{(x)}} + \frac{1}{2\sqrt{(y)}}\frac{dy}{dx} = 0$$

$$\therefore \quad \frac{dy}{dx} = -\frac{\sqrt{y}}{\sqrt{(x)}}.$$

or Hence tangent at (x, y) is

$$Y - y = -\frac{\sqrt{y}}{\sqrt{(x)}}(X - x)$$

or $X\sqrt{y} + Y\sqrt{x} = \sqrt{xy}\,(\sqrt{x} + \sqrt{y}) = \sqrt{axy}$

or $\dfrac{X}{\sqrt{(a)}\sqrt{(x)}} + \dfrac{Y}{\sqrt{(a)}\sqrt{(y)}} = 1.$

Clearly its intercepts on the axes are $\sqrt{a}\sqrt{x}$ and $\sqrt{a}\sqrt{y}$.

Sum of the intercepts $= \sqrt{a}\,(\sqrt{x} + \sqrt{y}) = \sqrt{a}\,.\sqrt{a} = a$ by (1) *i.e.* constant.

(b) $Y - y = \dfrac{dy}{dx}(X - x)$ is equation of tangent at $P(x, y)$.

$Y = 0 \quad \therefore \quad A = \left(x - y\Big/\dfrac{dy}{dx}, 0\right);$

$X = 0, B = \left(0, y - x\dfrac{dy}{dx}\right) \cdot P$ is mid-point of AB

$$\therefore \quad 2x = x - y\Big/\frac{dy}{dx} \text{ and } 2y = y - x\frac{dy}{dx}$$

$$\therefore \quad -\frac{y}{x} = \frac{dy}{dx} \text{ from either}$$

or $x\,dy + y\,dx = 0$ or $dx/x + dy/y = 0$

Integrating $xy = \lambda$. It passes through (1, 1).

$\therefore \quad \lambda = 1.$

$\therefore \quad x\,y = 1$ is the required equation of the curve.

20. $ay^2 = x^3$ ...(1)

$$\therefore \quad 2ay\frac{dy}{dx} = 3x^2 \text{ or } \frac{dy}{dx} = \frac{3x^2}{2ay}$$

Hence slope of the normal is $-\dfrac{1}{dy/dx} = \dfrac{-2ay}{3x^2}$

Since the normal makes equal intercepts on the axes its inclination to axis of x is either 45° or 135°. In other words its slope is tan 45° or tan 135° or 1, –1.

$$\therefore \quad -\frac{2ay}{3x^2} = \pm 1 \quad \text{or} \quad 4a^2y^2 = 9x^4$$

or $4a.x^3 = 9x^4 \quad \therefore \quad x = 4a/9$

is the abscissa of such a point.

21. Here $xy = (c + x)^2$.

$$\therefore \quad y = \frac{(c+x)^2}{x} = \frac{c^2}{x} + 2c + x$$

$$\therefore \quad \frac{dy}{dx} = -\frac{c^2}{x^2} + 1 = \frac{x^2 - c^2}{x^2}$$

Slope of the normal is $-\dfrac{x^2}{x^2 - c^2} = \pm 1.$

$$-x^2 = x^2 - c^2 \quad \text{or} \quad -x^2 = -(x^2 - c^2)$$

or $2x^2 = c^2$ as $c^2 = 0$ is not possible.

$\therefore \quad x = \pm\dfrac{c}{\sqrt{(2)}}.$

22. (a) Refer solution **Q. 34** we have

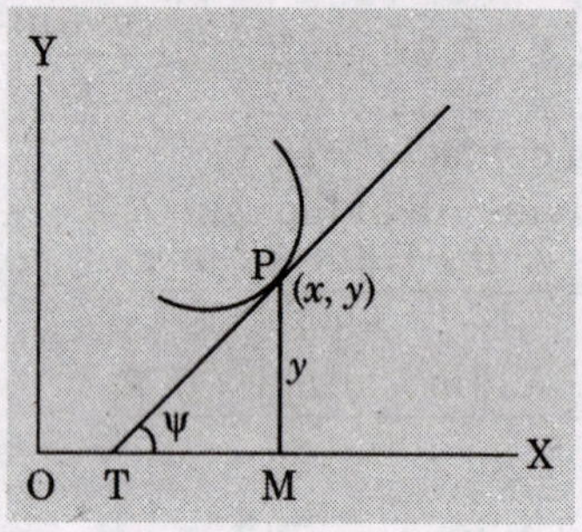

Fig. 5

$$\frac{dy}{dx} = \tan t = \tan\psi \quad \therefore \quad \psi = t.$$

If PT be the tangent intercepted between the curve and the axis of x then from the figure

$y = PT\sin\psi = PT\sin t$

But $y = a\sin t$.

$\therefore \quad a\sin t = PT\sin t. \quad \therefore \quad PT = a =$ constant

(b) Putting $y = a\sin t$, we get

$$x = a\cos t + \frac{a}{2}\log\frac{1 - \cos t}{1 + \cos t}$$

$$= a\cos t + \frac{a}{2}\log\tan^2(t/2)$$

$$= a\cos t + a\log\tan(t/2).$$

It now reduces to part (a).

(c) Given length of tangent $PT = 1$.

or $\dfrac{y}{y'}\sqrt{1 + y'^2} = 1 \quad \therefore \quad y^2 + y^2y'^2 = y'^2$

or $y'^2 = \dfrac{y^2}{1 - y^2}$ or $\left(\dfrac{dy}{dx}\right)^2 = \dfrac{y^2}{1 - y^2}$

$$\therefore \quad \int\frac{\sqrt{1 - y^2}}{y}\,dy = \int \pm\,dx$$

Put $1 - y^2 = z^2 \quad \therefore \; -2y\,dy = z\,dz$

$$\therefore \quad \int \frac{z^2\,dz}{z^2 - 1} = \pm x + k$$

$$\int \left(1 + \frac{1}{z^2 - 1}\right) dz = \pm x + k$$

or $\quad z + \frac{1}{2} \log \frac{z-1}{z+1} = \pm x + c$ where $z = \sqrt{1 - y^2}$.

23. (a) $\quad xy = c^2$ or $y = c^2/x$

$$\therefore \quad \frac{dy}{dx} = -\frac{c^2}{x^2} = -\frac{xy}{x^2} = -\frac{y}{x}$$

Tangent is : $Y - y = -\frac{y}{x}(X - x)$

or $\quad Xy + Yx = 2xy$ or $\frac{X}{2x} + \frac{Y}{2y} = 1.$

It meets the axes at $A\,(2x, 0)$ and $B\,(0, 2y)$.

Mid-point of AB is (x, y) *i.e.* the point of contact.

(b) $\Delta\, OAB$ is right angled triangle whose two sides are $2x$ and $2y$. Hence its area $= \frac{1}{2}.2x.2y$

$= 2xy = 2c^2$ *i.e.* constant.

24. (i) $\quad \frac{dy}{dx} = \sinh \frac{x}{c} = y' = \tan \psi \quad$ ...(1)

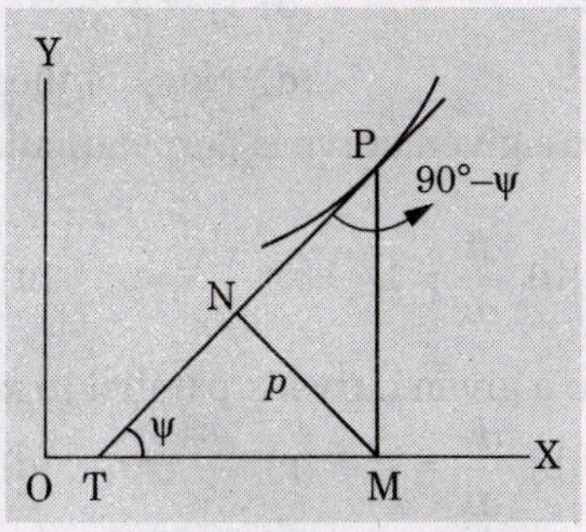

Fig. 6

$N = y . \sqrt{(1 + y'^2)}$

$= y . \sqrt{[1 + \sinh^2 (x/c)]}$

$= y . \cosh (x/c) = y . y/c = y^2/c$.

(ii) $\quad p = MN = y \sin (90^\circ - \psi) = y \cos \psi$

$= y . \frac{1}{\sqrt{(1 + y'^2)}}$, by (1)

$= \frac{y}{\cosh (x/c)} = c$ *i.e.* constant.

25. We have to prove that $\frac{\text{T} + \text{S.T.}}{xy} =$ constant

or $\quad \frac{1}{xy}\left[\frac{y}{y'}\sqrt{1 + y'^2} + \frac{y}{y'}\right] =$ constant.

or $\quad \frac{1}{xy'}[\sqrt{1 + y'^2} + 1] =$ constant. $\quad$ ...(1)

Differentiating, $y' = \frac{2ax}{x^2 - a^2}$

$$\therefore \quad \sqrt{1 + y'^2} = \frac{x^2 + a^2}{x^2 - a^2}$$

Putting in (1), we get

$$\text{L.H.S.} = \frac{x^2 - a^2}{2ax^2}\left[\frac{x^2 + a^2}{x^2 - a^2} + 1\right] = \frac{1}{a} = \text{constant.}$$

26. Tangent is $\frac{Xx}{a^2} + \frac{Yy}{b^2} = 1$

$$\therefore \quad p = \frac{1}{\sqrt{\left(\frac{x^2}{a^4} + \frac{y^2}{b^4}\right)}} = \frac{a^2 b^2}{\sqrt{(b^4 x^2 + a^4 y^2)}} \quad \text{...(1)}$$

Also $N = y\sqrt{1 + y'^2} = y\sqrt{1 + \frac{b^4 x^2}{a^4 y^2}}$

$$= \frac{y}{a^2 y}\sqrt{a^4 y^2 + b^4 x^2} \quad \text{...(2)}$$

From (1) and (2) we get $\; N . p = b^2$

Hence N varies inversely as p.

27. $\quad \frac{(\text{S.T.})^m}{(\text{S.N.})^n} = \frac{(y/y')^m}{(yy')^n} = \frac{y^{m-n}}{(y')^{m+n}} =$ constant $\quad$ ...(1)

Taking log, we get

$(m + n) \log x = (m - n) \log a + 2n \log y$

$$\therefore \quad (m + n)\frac{1}{x} = 0 + \frac{2n}{y}.y'$$

$$\therefore \quad (y')^{m+n} = \frac{(m+n)^{m+n}}{(2n)^{m+n}} \frac{y^{n+m}}{x^{n+m}}$$

$$= \lambda \frac{y^{n+m}}{a^{m-n}\,y^{2n}} = k . y^{m-n}$$

$$\therefore \quad \frac{y^{m-n}}{(y')^{m+n}} = \frac{1}{k} = \text{constant, by (1).}$$

28. Taking log and differentiating $y' = -\frac{y}{nx}$

$$\text{S.N.} = yy' = -\frac{y^2}{nx} = -\frac{y^2}{n}.\frac{y^n}{a^{n+1}}$$

$$= -\frac{y^{n+2}}{n(a^{n+1})} = \text{constant}$$

if $n + 2 = 0$ or $\quad n = -2$

Note : If the curve be $y = a^{1-n} x^n$ then prove that $n = \frac{1}{2}$ for the sub-normal to be of constant length.

29. $\quad x^m y^n = a^{m+n}$. Take log

$m \log x + n \log y = (m + n) \log a$

$$m \cdot \frac{1}{x} + n \cdot \frac{1}{y}\frac{dy}{dx} = 0$$

$$\therefore \quad \frac{dy}{dx} = -\frac{m}{n}\frac{y}{x}$$

Hence the equation of the tangent is

$$Y - y = -\frac{m}{n}\frac{y}{x}(X - x)$$

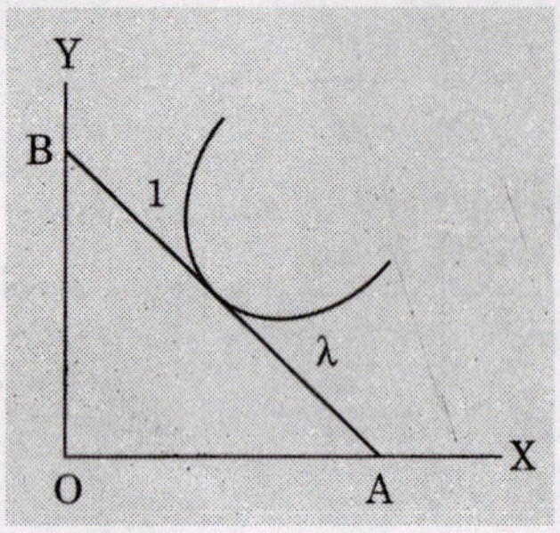

Fig. 7

$myX + nXY = (m+n) \cdot xy$ ...(1)

Let the tangent (1) meet the axes in points A and B.

Putting $Y = 0$, we get

$$A = \left[\frac{(m+n}{m} x, 0\right]$$

Putting $X = 0$ we get $B = \left(0, \frac{m+n}{m} y\right)$

Point of contact P is (x, y).

Let P divide AB in the ratio $\lambda : 1$

$$\therefore \quad x = \frac{\lambda \cdot 0 + 1 \cdot \frac{m+n}{n} x}{\lambda + 1} \quad \text{or} \quad (\lambda + 1)\, x = \left(\frac{m}{n} + 1\right) x$$

or $\lambda + 1 = \frac{m}{n} + 1 \quad \therefore \quad \lambda = \frac{m}{n}$

or $AP : PB = \lambda : 1 = m : n$

30. $y' = \frac{\dot{y}}{\dot{x}} = \frac{a \sin t}{a(1 + \cos t)} = \tan \frac{t}{2} = \frac{1}{\sqrt{3}}$ at $t = \frac{\pi}{3}$

$T = \frac{y}{y'} \sqrt{1 + y'^2}$; $N = y\sqrt{1 + y'^2}$ where $y = \frac{a}{2}$ at $t = \frac{\pi}{3}$.

Problem Set (3)

Multiple Choice Questions

1. (i)* For the curve $x = t^2 - 1$, $y = t^2 - t$, the tangent line is perpendicular to x-axis where

(a) $t = 0$ (b) $t = \infty$

(c) $t = 1/\sqrt{3}$ (d) $t = -1/\sqrt{3}$

(ii)* The slope of the tangent to the curve $x = t^2 + 3t - 8$, $y = 2t^2 - 2t - 5$ at the point $(2, -1)$ is

(a) 22/7 (b) 6/7

(c) -6 (d) None of these

(M.N.R. 1994)

2. The tangent of the curve $y = 2x^2 - x + 1$ is parallel to the line $y = 3x + 9$ at the point.

(a) (3, 9) (b) (2, −1) (c) (2, 1) (d) (1, 2)

3. The tangent to the curve $x^2 + y^2 - 2x - 3 = 0$ is parallel to x-axis at the points

(a) $(2, \pm\sqrt{3})$ (b) $(1, \pm 2)$ (c) $(\pm 1, 2)$ (d) $(\pm 3, 0)$.

4.* Let C be the curve $y^3 - 3xy + 2 = 0$. If H be the set of points on the curve C, where the tangent is horizontal and V is the set of points on the curve C where the tangent is vertical, then $H = \ldots$, $V = \ldots$. **(I.I.T. 1994)**

5. The curve $x^3 - 3xy^2 + 2 = 0$ and $3x^2 y - y^3 - 2 = 0$ cut at an angle of

(a) 45° (b) 60° (c) 90° (d) 30°

6. The angle of intersection of the curve $y = x^2$ and $6y = 7 - x^2$ at (1, 1) is

(a) $\frac{\pi}{4}$ (b) $\frac{\pi}{3}$

(c) $\frac{\pi}{2}$ (d) None of these

7. The equation of the tangent at the point $P(t)$, where t is any parameter, to the parabola $y^2 = 4ax$ is

(a) $yt = x + at^2$ (b) $y = xt + at^2$

(c) $y = tx$ (d) $y = tx + a/t$

8. The normal drawn at a point $(at_1^2, 2at_1)$ on the parabola $y^2 = 4ax$ meets it again at the point $(at_2^2, 2at_2)$, then

(a) $t_1 = 2t_2$ (b) $t_1^2 = 2t_2$

(c) $t_1 t_2 = -1$ (d) None of these.

9. The tangent to a given curve is perpendicular to x-axis if

(a) $\frac{dy}{dx} = 0$ (b) $\frac{dy}{dx} = 1$ (c) $\frac{dx}{dy} = 0$ (d) $\frac{dx}{dy} = 1$.

10. The normal to a given curve is parallel to x-axis if

(a) $\frac{dy}{dx} = 0$ (b) $\frac{dy}{dx} = 1$ (c) $\frac{dx}{dy} = 0$, (d) $\frac{dx}{dy} = 1$.

11. The point on the curve $y^2 = x$, the tangent at which makes an angle of 45° with x-axis will be given by

(a) $\left(\frac{1}{2}, \frac{1}{4}\right)$ (b) $\left(\frac{1}{2}, \frac{1}{2}\right)$ (c) (2, 4) (d) $\left(\frac{1}{4}, \frac{1}{2}\right)$

12. The tangent to the curve $y = e^{2x}$ at the point (0, 1) meets the x-axis at

(a) $(0, a)$ (b) (2, 0)

(c) $\left(-\frac{1}{2}, 0\right)$ (d) None of these.

13.* The length of sub-normal to the parabola $y^2 = 4ax$ at any point is equal to

(a) $\sqrt{2}a$ (b) $2\sqrt{2}a$ (c) $\frac{a}{\sqrt{(2)}}$ (d) $2a$

14.* The normal at the point (1, 1) on the curve $2y = 3 - x^2$, is

(a) $x + y = 0$ (b) $x + y + 1 = 0$

(c) $x - y + 1 = 0$ (d) $x - y = 0$.

15.* The normal to the curve

$x = a(\cos\theta + \theta\sin\theta),\ y = a(\sin\theta - \theta\cos\theta)$

at any θ is such that

(a) it makes a constant angle with x-axis,

(b) it passes through the origin,

(c) it is at a constant distance from the origin,

(d) None of these.

16. If the parametric equation of a curve is given by $x = e^t\cos t,\ y = e^t\sin t$ then the tangent to the curve at the point $t = \pi/4$ makes with the axis of x the angle

(a) 0 (b) $\frac{\pi}{4}$ (c) $\frac{\pi}{3}$ (d) $\frac{\pi}{2}$

17.* The angle of intersection of the curves $y = x^2$, $6y = 7 - x^3$ at (1, 1) is

(a) $\frac{\pi}{4}$ (b) $\frac{\pi}{3}$ (c) $\frac{\pi}{2}$ (d) None

(C.E.E. Andhra 1992)

18. The equation of the tangent to the curve of $y = x + \frac{4}{x^2}$ that is parallel to x-axis is

(a) $y = 0$ (b) $y = 1$ (c) $y = 2$ (d) $y = 3$

(AIEEE 2010)

Solutions to Problem Set (3)

1. (i) Ans (a).

(ii) Ans (b).

$t = 2$ for the point (2, –1).

$$\frac{dy}{dx} = \frac{\dot{y}}{\dot{x}} = \frac{4t-2}{2t+3} = \frac{6}{7} \text{ for } t = 2$$

2. Ans. (d).

We have $\frac{dy}{dx} = 4x - 1$. Hence the tangent is parallel to

$y = 3x + 9$ if $4x - 1 = 3$ or $x = 1$.

Putting $x = 1$ in the equation of the curve, we get $y = 2 - 1 + 1 = 2$. Hence the required point is (1, 2).

3. Ans. (b).

4. $\frac{dy}{dx} = -\frac{f_x}{f_y} = \frac{3y}{3(y^2 - x)} = 0$ for H; $= \infty$ for V $y = 0$ and it leads to $2 = 0$ from C. There is no point. $y^2 = x$ for V and solving with C, we get

$$xy = 1 \text{ or } y^3 = 1 \ \therefore\ y = 1, x = 1 \ \therefore\ V \text{ is } (1, 1).$$

5. Ans. (c).

6. Ans. (d). $\theta = \tan^{-1} 7$.

7. Ans. (a).

8. Ans. (d).

$\because\ t_2 = -t_1 - \frac{1}{t_1}$ is the correct answer.

9. Ans. (c). **10.** Ans. (c).

11. Ans. (d). **12.** Ans. (c).

13. Ans. (d). **14.** Ans. (d)

15. Ans. (c). **[See Q. 14 (b), Page 1369-75]**

16. Ans. (d).

$$\frac{dy}{dx} = \frac{\dot{y}}{\dot{x}} = \frac{e^t(\sin t + \cos t)}{e^t(\cos t - \sin t)} = \infty$$

at $t = \pi/4$. Hence tangent is perpendicular to x- axis.

17. Ans. (c).

$m_1 = 2, m_2 = -(1/2),\ \therefore\ m_1 m_2 = -1$

18. Ans. (d). $y = x + \frac{4}{x^2} \Rightarrow \frac{dy}{dx} = 1 - \frac{8}{x^3}$

Equation of tangent is parallel to x-axis

$\therefore\ \frac{dy}{dx} = 0 \Rightarrow 1 - \frac{8}{x^3} = 0 \Rightarrow x = 2$

At $x = 2$, $y = 2 + \frac{4}{4} = 3 \Rightarrow y_1 = 3$

$\therefore$ Equation of tangent is

$y - y_1 = 0(x - x_1) \Rightarrow y = 3$

MISCELLANEOUS EXERCISE

Matching Entries

Match the entries of List-A and List-B.

1.

List-A	List-B
(a) Tangent to $y = be^{-x/a}$ at the point where it crosses y-axis is	1. $x^2 - y^2 = x^2y^2$
(b) Tangents are drawn from origin to $y = \sin x$. Points of contact lie on the curve ...	2. $a\sin^2\theta\tan\theta$
(c) The abscissa of the point on the curve $ay^2 = x^3$ normal at which cuts off equal intercepts on the axes is ...	3. ordinate
(d) The length of normal at any point θ on the curve $x = a\cos^3\theta$, $y = a\sin^3\theta$ is	4. $\frac{x}{a} + \frac{y}{b} = 1$

(e) Length of subnormal at any point on $xy = c^2$ varies directly as cube of ...

5. $\frac{4a}{9}$

2. Match the entries of col. I with those of col. II.

Column-I	Column-II
(a) $f(x) = \frac{1-x+x^2}{1+x-x^2}$ on $[0,1]$	(p) Greatest value of $f = 1$
(b) $f(x) = 2\tan x - \tan^2 x$ on $\left[0, \frac{\pi}{2}\right]$	(q) Least value of $f = \frac{3}{5}$
(c) $f(x) = \frac{2}{\pi}(\sin 2x - x)$ on $\left[-\frac{\pi}{2}, \frac{\pi}{2}\right]$	(r) Least value of $f = -1$
(d) $f(x) = \frac{1}{2}, (x^3 - 3x^2 + 6x - 2)$ on $(-1, 1)$	(s) Least value of $f = -6$

Answers

1. (a) → 4, (b) → 1, (c) → 5, (d) → 2, (e) → 3

2. (a)→ (p, q) , (b)→ (p), (c)→ (p, r), (d)→ (p, s)

Solutions

1. (a) → 4. **Q. 23 (a) P. 1370**

(b) → 1. **Q. 22 (b) P. 1370**

(c) → 5. **Q. 20 P. 1369**

(d) → 2.

$$\frac{dy}{dx} = \frac{\dot{y}}{\dot{x}} = \frac{3a\sin^2\theta\cos\theta}{-3a\cos^2\theta\sin\theta} = -\tan\theta$$

$\therefore \quad N = y\sqrt{(1+y'^2)} = a\sin^3\theta\sec\theta = a\sin^2\theta\tan\theta$

(e) → 3. $\quad y' = -\frac{c^2}{x^2} = -\frac{xy}{x^2} = -\frac{y}{x}$

$\therefore \quad yy' = y\left(-\frac{y}{x}\right) = -y^2 \cdot \frac{y}{c^2} = ky^3$

2. (a)→ (p, q) , (b)→ (p), (c)→ (p, r), (d)→ (p, s)

(a) $f'(x) = \frac{2(2x-1)}{(1+x-x^2)^2}$ by quotient formula

$f'(x) = 0 \Rightarrow x = \frac{1}{2}$

$f(0) = 1, f(1) = 1$ but $f\left(\frac{1}{2}\right) = \frac{3}{5}$

$\therefore$ Greatest value $= 1 \Rightarrow$ (p), Least value $= \frac{3}{5} \Rightarrow$ (q)

(b) $f'(x) = 2\sec^2 x(1-\tan x) = 0$

$\Rightarrow \tan x = 1$ or $x = \frac{\pi}{4}$ and $f\left(\frac{\pi}{4}\right) = 2 - 1 = 1$

$\therefore$ (b)→ (p).

(c) $f'(x) = \frac{2}{\pi}(2\cos 2x - 1) = 0$

$\therefore \quad \cos 2x = \frac{1}{2} = \cos\frac{\pi}{3} \quad \therefore \quad x = \frac{\pi}{6}$

$f\left(-\frac{\pi}{2}\right) = 1,\ f\left(\frac{\pi}{2}\right) = -1$ and $f\left(\frac{\pi}{6}\right) = \frac{\sqrt{3}}{\pi} - \frac{1}{3} < 1$

$\therefore$ greatest value $= 1$ and least value $= -1$

$\therefore$ (c)→ (p, r)

(d) $f'(x) = \frac{3}{2}(x^2 - 2x + 2) = \frac{3}{2}[(x-1)^2 + 1] \neq 0$

But $f(-1) = -6, f(1) = 1$

$\therefore$ Least value is -6 and greatest value is 1.

$\therefore$ (d)→ (p, s)

Fascinating Facts

- If $\left(\frac{dy}{dx}\right)_{x=x}$, does not exists then the tangent is parallel to y-axis and its equation is $x = x_1$
- If $\left[\frac{dy}{dx}\right]_{dx=x_1} = 0$ then the equation of the normal at P is $x = x_1$, and if $\left(\frac{dy}{dx}\right)_{x=x_1}$ does not exist, then the equation of the normal at P is $y = y_1$

CHAPTER 30

Maxima and Minima

§ 1. Working Rule for Maxima or Minima.

From the figure it is clear that at P the function $y = f(x)$ is maximum and at Q it is minimum. At both these points tangent is parallel to x-axis so that its slope is zero.

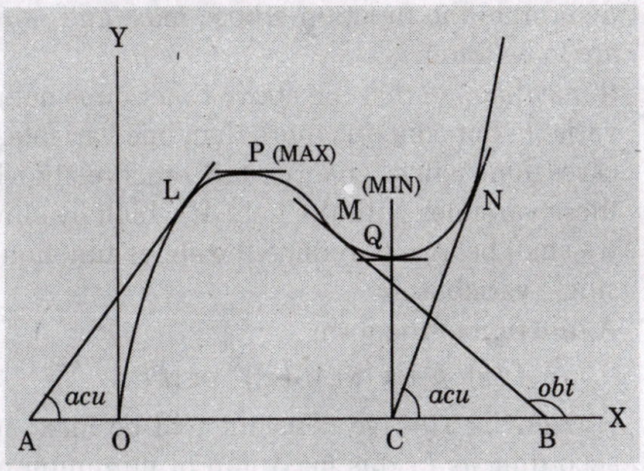

Fig. 1

$\therefore \quad \frac{dy}{dx} = 0 \quad$ **or** $\quad f'(x) = 0$

for both Max. and Min.

Above is the condition for Max. and Min.

Criteria for Max. and Min.

Let $x = a, b, c$ be the values of x given by $\frac{dy}{dx} = 0$. Consider the point $x = a$ *i.e.* P where y is Maximum. From the figure it is clear that tangent at any point $x = a - h$ will make an acute angle with x-axis just as at L, and tangent at $x = a + h$ will make an obtuse angle just as at M. Thus

for $x = a \quad \frac{dy}{dx} = 0$

for x slightly $< a, \frac{dy}{dx} = +$ ive

for x slightly $< a, \frac{dy}{dx} = -$ ive

Hence if y is max. at $x = a$ then $\frac{dy}{dx}$ changes sign from + ive to − ive for values of x less than a and greater than a in that order. Now consider the point $x = b$ *i.e.* Q where y is **Minimum**.

From the figure it is clear that tangent at any point $x = b - h$ will make an obtuse angle with x-axis just as at M and tangent at $x = b + h$ will make an acute angle just as at N. Thus

for $x = b, \quad dy/dx = 0$

for x slightly $< b$, $dy/dx = -$ ive (Obtuse)

for x slightly $> b$, $dy/dx = +$ ive (Acute).

Hence if y is minimum at $x = b$ then dy/dx changes sign from − ive to + ive for values of x less than b and greater than b in that order.

***Working rule :**

- Calculate $dy/dx = 0$ and solve for x and say $x = a, b, c$ etc.
- Put values of x slightly less than a in dy/dx and values of x slightly greater than a.

If $\frac{dy}{dx}$ changes sign from + ive to − ive, then Max. at $x = a$.

If $\frac{dy}{dx}$ changes sign from − ive to + ive, then Min. at $x = a$.

In case there is no change of sign, then neither a max. nor a minimum.

V. Imp. $(x - a)(x - b), a < b$ is + ive if either $x < a$ or $x > b$. It is − ive if x lies between a and b i.e., $a < x < b$.

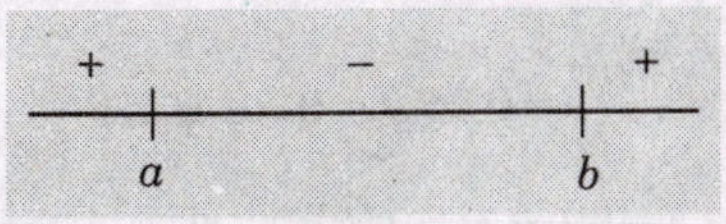

Fig. 2

Suppose $\frac{dy}{dx} = (x - 2)(x - 3)^2 (x - 5)$

$= (x - 3)^2 [(x - 2)(x - 5)]$

The critical points are 2, 3, 5. There will be no change of sign in the value of $\frac{dy}{dx}$ when x is slightly less than 3 or slightly greater than 3. Hence neither max. nor min. at $x = 3$. Plot the other points on real line. Beyond highest value of x take $+$ive and then $-, +, -$ etc. as shown below :

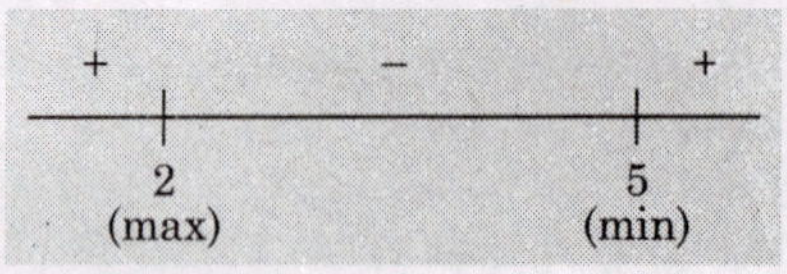

Fig. 3

At $x = 2$ there will be a change of sign from $+$ to $-$ and hence at $x = 2$ there will be maximum.

At $x = 5$ the change of sign is from $-$ to $+$ and hence there will be minimum at $x = 5$.

Note : It should be noted that max. and min. occur alternately.

Second Method :

Calculate $dy/dx = 0$ and solve for x. Suppose one root of $dy/dx = 0$ is at $x = a$.

If $\frac{d^2y}{dx^2} = -$ ive for $x = a$, then Max. at $x = a$.

If $\frac{d^2y}{dx^2} = +$ ive for $x = a$, then Min. at $x = a$.

If $\frac{d^2y}{dx^2} = 0$ at $x = a$, then find $\frac{d^3y}{dx^3}$. If $\frac{d^3y}{dx^3} \neq 0$ at $x = a$, then neither maximum nor minimum at $x = a$. If $\frac{d^3y}{dx^3} = 0$ at $x = a$, then find $\frac{d^4y}{dx^4}$. If $\frac{d^4y}{dx^4} > 0$ *i.e.* $+$ ive at $x = a$, then y is minimum at $x = a$ and if $\frac{d^4y}{dx^4} < 0$ *i.e.* $-$ ive at $x = a$, then y is max. at $x = a$ and so on.

§ 2. Parametric Form of a Function.

Let a function $y = f(x)$ be represented in parametric form by the equations

$$x = \phi(t),\ y = \psi(t).$$

where $\phi(t)$ and $\psi(t)$ have derivatives both of first and second orders within a certain interval of t, and $\phi'(t) \neq 0$.

$$\frac{dy}{dx} = \frac{\dot{y}}{\dot{x}} \quad \therefore \ \frac{dy}{dx} = 0 \Rightarrow \dot{y} = 0 \ \text{ or } \psi' = 0$$

$$\frac{d^2y}{dx^2} = \frac{d}{dx}\left(\frac{\dot{y}}{\dot{x}}\right) = \frac{d}{dt}\left(\frac{\dot{y}}{\dot{x}}\right) \cdot \frac{dt}{dx}$$

$$= \frac{\dot{x}\ddot{y} - \dot{y}\ddot{x}}{\dot{x}^2} \cdot \frac{1}{\dot{x}} \quad \text{Put } \dot{y} = 0$$

$$\therefore \ \frac{d^2y}{dx^2} = \frac{\ddot{y}}{\dot{x}^2} = \frac{\psi''}{\phi'^2}$$

$\dot{x}^2$ is $+$ive always.

$\therefore$ sign of $\frac{d^2y}{dx^2}$ depends upon ψ''.

Let at $t = t_0$, $\psi'(t) = 0$. Then

(a) if $\psi''(t_0) < 0$, $f(x)$ has a maximum at $x = x_0 = \phi(t_0)$

(b) if $\psi''(t_0) > 0$ the function $f(x)$ has a minimum at $x = x_0 = \phi(t_0)$

(c) if $\psi''(t_0) = 0$, the question of the existence of an extreme value remains open.

Note : Sometimes we also use the term **extreme values** for maximum or minimum values. The points at which $f'(x)$ does not exist are called critical points. If $f'(x) = 0$, we say that $y = f(x)$ is stationary at $x = a$.

§ 3. Important Instructions

1. According to the given conditions of the problem determine the function whose max. and min. values are to be found.

2. It may happen that the above function is not of single variable but contains more than one variable. In such cases there will be given certain other relation between these variables with the help of which by elimination we shall be able to reduce the above function to be of single variable.

A function of the form

$$k\,f(x),\ k + f(x),\ [f(x)]^k \text{ or } [f(x)]^{1/k},$$

where k is a $+$ ive constant will be max. and min. according as $f(x)$ is maximun or minimum provided $f(x) > 0$.

Also if y is max. and min. then $\log y = z$ is also max. and min. provided $y > 0$. **(Note)**

Also $y = f(x)$ is max. or min. according as $z = 1/f(x)$ is min. or max.

3. Max. and minimum occur alternately. It may be noted that maximum may be less than the minimum as will be clear from the example below :

$$y = x + \frac{1}{x} \quad \frac{dy}{dx} = 1 - \frac{1}{x^2} = 0$$

$$\therefore \quad x = 1, -1$$

$$\frac{d^2y}{dx^2} = \frac{2}{x^3} = -2 \ \textit{i.e.} - \text{ive at } x = -1$$

Hence at $x = -1$, y is max. and its max. value is -2.

Again at $x = 1$, $\frac{d^2y}{dx^2} = 2$, *i.e.* $+$ive. Hence it is minimum and its minimum value is 2 at $x = 1$, which is greater than max. value -2 at $x = -1$. When we say $f(x)$ is max. at $x = a$, we mean that it is greatest in the neighbourhood of a *i.e.* in $[a - h, a + h]$, $f(a)$ is greatest. Similarly for minimum.

§ 4. Commit to Memory : (Geometrical results)

In usual notations

Area of a square $= x^2$, its perimeter $= 4x$.
Area of rectangle $= xy$, perimeter $= 2(x+y)$.
Area of equilateral $\Delta = \frac{\sqrt{3}}{4}x^2$, x being its side and its perimeter $= 3x$
Area of a trapezium $= \frac{1}{2}$ (sum of parallel sides) × distance between them.
Area of a circle $= \pi r^2$, Perimeter $= 2\pi r$
Volume of a Sphere $= \frac{4}{3}\pi r^3$
and its Surface $= 4\pi r^2$
Volume of right cone $= \frac{1}{3}\pi r^2 h$,
Total Surface $= \pi r(r+l)$ whereas its curved surface is πrl only.
Volume of a cylinder $= \pi r^2 h$.
Total Surface $= 2\pi r^2 + 2\pi rh = 2\pi r(r+h)$
Its curved surface is $2\pi rh$.
Volume of a cuboid $= xyz$ and Surface $= 2(xy+yz+zx)$

***Greatest and least values of a function.** The reader will do well to bear in mind that a maximum value of $f(x)$ at $x = x_0$ in an interval $[a, b]$ does not mean that it is greatest value of $f(x)$ in that interval. There may be a value of the function greater than a maximum value. As a matter of fact, there may exist a minimum value of the function which is greater than or equal to some maximum value of the function in $[a, b]$.

However, if a function $f(x)$ is continuous in a closed interval $[a, b]$, then **greatest (least)** value of $f(x)$ is attained at critical points, or at the end points of the interval. Thus to find the greatest (least) value of the function, we have to compute its value at all the critical points on the interval $[a, b]$ and also the values $f(a)$, $f(b)$ and choose the greatest (least) one out of the numbers thus obtained. If the interval is not closed then the function may have neither the greatest nor the least value.

Sign of $f(x)$ for small values of x. The sign of $f(x)$ is governed by the lowest degree terms in $f(x)$. For example, for small x the sign of $-3+4x+7x^2$ will be governed by the constant term and hence – ive. Similarly the sign of $x^3 - 7x^{11} + 20x^{15}$ will be governed by x^3 and so its sign will be + ive or – ive according as x is + ive or – ive.

§ 5. Certain Important Results

(1) Max. and Min. of $\boldsymbol{y = \sin x(1+\cos x)}$

$$y = \sin x + \frac{1}{2}\sin 2x$$

$$\frac{dy}{dx} = \cos x + \cos 2x = 0$$

$\therefore\quad \cos 2x = -\cos x = \cos(\pi - x)$

$\therefore\quad 2x = \pi - x \quad \text{or} \quad x = \pi/3$

Clearly, $\dfrac{d^2y}{dx^2} = -(\sin x + 2\sin 2x)$

$$= -(\sin 60^\circ + 2\sin 120^\circ) = -\text{ive}$$

Hence y is max. at $x = \dfrac{\pi}{3}$ and its value is $\dfrac{3\sqrt{3}}{4}$.

(2) $\boldsymbol{y = \dfrac{a^2}{\cos^2 x} + \dfrac{b^2}{\sin^2 x}}$

or $\quad \boldsymbol{y = a^2\sec^2 x + b^2\operatorname{cosec}^2 x}$

1st Method : (Without differentiation)

$$y = a^2\sec^2 x + b^2\operatorname{cosec}^2 x$$
$$= a^2(1+\tan^2 x) + b^2(1+\cot^2 x)$$
$$= (a^2+b^2) + (a^2\tan^2 x + b^2\cot^2 x)$$

Add and subtract $2ab$. ...(1)

$\therefore\quad y = (a^2+b^2+2ab) + (a^2\tan^2 x + b^2\cot^2 x - 2ab)$

$$= (a+b)^2 + (a\tan x - b\cot x)^2$$
$$= (a+b)^2 + (\text{something} + \text{ive})$$

Hence the value of y is always greater than $(a+b)^2$ and hence its least value will be $(a+b)^2$ when

$$a\tan x - b\cot x = 0 \text{ or } \tan^2 x = \frac{b}{a}.$$

Warning : We could also say in step (1) that "subtract and add $2ab$".

$\therefore\quad y = (a-b)^2 + (a\tan x + b\cot x)^2$

Arguing as above we can say that the value of y is always greater than $(a-b)^2$ and hence its least value will be $(a-b)^2$ when $a\tan x + b\cot x = 0$ or $\tan^2 x = -\dfrac{b}{a} = -$ ive. It will not give real value of x.

2nd Method : (By differentiation)

$$dy/dx = 2a^2\sec x.\sec x\tan x - 2b^2\operatorname{cosec} x\operatorname{cosec} x\cot x = 0$$

$$= 2[a^2\sec^2 x\tan x - b^2\operatorname{cosec}^2 x\cot x] = 0.$$

$\therefore\quad a^2\dfrac{\sin x}{\cos^3 x} - b^2\dfrac{\cos x}{\sin^3 x} = 0.$

or $\quad \tan^4 x = b^2/a^2 \quad \therefore \quad \tan^2 x = b/a$

$$d^2y/dx^2 = 2[a^2(\sec^4 x + 2\sec x.\sec x\tan x\tan x) + b^2(\operatorname{cosec}^4 x + 2\operatorname{cosec} x\operatorname{cosec} x\cot x\cot x)].$$

Above is clearly + ive when $\tan^2 x = b/a$ and hence y is min.

Putting $\tan^2 x = b/a$ in the value of y

$$y = a^2 \sec^2 x + b^2 \operatorname{cosec}^2 x$$
$$= a^2 (1 + \tan^2 x) + b^2 (1 + \cot^2 x)$$
$$= a^2 (1 + b/a) + b^2 (1 + a/b)$$
$$= a^2 + b^2 + 2ab = (a+b)^2.$$

Hence the min. value of

$$y = a^2 \sec^2 x + b^2 \operatorname{cosec}^2 x \text{ is } (a+b)^2.$$

Note : The solutions of above two types of questions will not be given. Only reference of above two solutions will be given.

Problem Set (1)

Maxima, minima of algebraic functions. Maxima, minima of trigonometric functions.

Find the max. and min. values of the following :

1. (a) $x^5 - 5x^4 + 5x^3 - 10$.

(b) $x^3 - 9x^2 + 15x - 1$.

(c) $2x^3 - 3x^2 - 12x + 12$.

(d)* $\dfrac{x^2 + x + 1}{x^2 - x + 1}$.

(e) For all real x, the minimum value of $\dfrac{1 - x + x^2}{1 + x + x^2}$ is

(i) 0 (ii) 1/3

(iii) 1 (iv) 3 **(M.N.R. 1992)**

2. (a) The function $f(x) = \dfrac{2}{x} + \dfrac{x}{2}$ has a local minimum at $x =$

(a) -2 (b) 0

(c) 1 (d) 2 **(AIEEE 2006)**

(b) The function $f(x) = 2x^3 - 9ax^2 + 12a^2 x + 1 = 0$ has a local maximum at $x = \alpha$ and a local minimum at $x = \beta$ such that $\beta = \alpha^2$ then a is equal to :

(a) 0 (b) 1/4

(c) 2 (d) either 0 or 2

(c) If $f(x) = 2x^3 - 3x^2 - 12x + 5$ on $[-2, 4]$ then relative maximum occurs at $x =$

(a) -2 (b) -1

(c) 2 (d) 4 **(AIEEE 2002)**

3. Find max. and min. values of the following :

(a) $(x-2)^6 (x-3)^5$. (b) $(x-8)^4 (x-9)^5$.

(c)* On the interval [0, 1] the function $x^{25} (1-x)^{75}$ takes its maximum value at the point

(i) 0 (ii) 1/4

(iii) 1/2 (iv) 1/3 **(I.I.T. 1995)**

(d) $f(x) = 2x^3 - 3(a+b)x^2 + 6abx$

Determine the relative max/min of $f(x)$ when

(i) $a < b$ (ii) $a > b$

(iii) $a = b$

4. (a) $\dfrac{x}{1 + x \tan x}$ is max.

when $x = \cos x, 0 \le x \le \dfrac{\pi}{2}$.

(b)* $\sin^p \theta \cos^q \theta$ is max. when $\theta = \tan^{-1} \sqrt{p/q}$.

(c) $\sqrt{3} \sin x + 3 \cos x$ is max. at $x = \pi/6$.

(d) $\sin x + \cos x$ is max. at $x = \pi/4$.

5.* Find the min. value of $\dfrac{a^2}{\cos^2 x} + \dfrac{b^2}{\sin^2 x}$.

6. (a) $f(x) = 1 + 2 \sin x + 2 \cos^2 x, 0 \le x \le \pi/2$.

(b) Find the values of x for which the function $f(x) = 1 + 2 \sin x + 3 \cos^2 x$, $\left(0 \le x \le \dfrac{2\pi}{3}\right)$ is maximum or minimum. Also find these values of the function. **(Roorkee 1993)**

(c) A tangent is drawn at the point $(3\sqrt{3} \cos \theta, \sin \theta)$ $0 < \theta < \dfrac{\pi}{2}$ of an ellipse $\dfrac{x^2}{27} + \dfrac{y^2}{1} = 1$ the least value of the sum of the intercepts on the co-ordinate axes by this tangent is attained at $\theta =$

(a) $\dfrac{\pi}{6}$ (b) $\dfrac{\pi}{3}$

(c) $\dfrac{\pi}{8}$ (d) $\dfrac{\pi}{4}$ **(Screening 2003)**

7. (a)* If $A > 0, B > 0$ and $A + B = \pi/3$, then the maximum value of $\tan A \tan B$ is .... **(I.I.T. 1993)**

(b) $f(x) = 2 \sin x + \cos 2x, 0 \le x \le 2\pi$. **(J.E.E. W.B. 1996)**

(c) The number of values of x where the function $f(x) = \cos x + \cos(\sqrt{2}x)$ attains its maximum is

(a) 0 (b) 1

(c) 2 (d) infinite **(I.I.T. 1998)**

8. $f(x) = \cos x + \dfrac{1}{2} \cos 2x - \dfrac{1}{3} \cos 3x, 0 \le x \le 2\pi$

Determine the max. and min. values and also the greatest and least values and prove that the difference between greatest and least values is 9/4.

9. Prove that $\dfrac{1}{4} \le \sin^6 x + \cos^6 x \le 1$

10. (a) If $f(x) = \dfrac{x^2 - 1}{x^2 + 1}$, for every real number x, then the minimum value of f

(a) does not exist because f is unbounded

(b) is not attained even though f is bounded

(c) is equal to 1

(d) is equal to -1 **(I.I.T. 1998)**

(b) $(x-1)^2 e^x$.

(c) $x(1-x)^2, 0 \le x \le 2$.

11. (a) Find the max. and min. of $\dfrac{40}{3x^4+8x^3-18x^2+60}$.

(b) $f(x)=\begin{cases}-2x, & x<0\\ 3x+5 & x\ge 0\end{cases}$

Discuss the existence of max. or min. at $x=0$.

12. (a) Let $f(x)=\begin{cases}|x| & \text{for } 0<|x|\le 2\\ 1 & \text{for } x=0.\end{cases}$

Then at $x=0$, f has

(a) a local maximum (b) no local maximum

(c) a local minimum (d) no extremum

(I.I.T. Sc. 2000)

(b) The minimum value of $f(x)=|3-x|+|2+x|+|5-x|$ is

(a) 7 (b) 10

(c) 8 (d) 0

13. If $f(x)=(x^2-1)^{n+1}(x^2+x+1), n\in N$ and $f(x)$ has a local extremum at $x=1$, then $n=$

(a) 2 (b) 3 (c) 4 (d) 5

14. Find the max. and min. values of the following :

(a) $\dfrac{\log x}{x}$ in $0<x<\infty$.

(b)* $x^{1/x}$. **(Karnataka C.E.E. 1999)**

(c) x^x.

(d) $(1/x)^x$.

15. (a)* $f(x)=x^3+ax^2+bx+c$ has a max. at $x=-1$ and min. at $x=3$. Determine the constants a, b, c.

(b) $f(x)=x^2+a/x$ has a local minimum at $x=2$, then find a. Can the function attain local max. and if so what is the value of a?

(c) If the function $f(x)=2x^3-9ax^2+12a^2x+1$ attains its maximum and minimum at p and q such that $p^2=q$ then prove that a equals 2.

16.* Suppose $f(x)$ is a function satisfying the following conditions

(a) $f(0)=2, f(1)=1$,

(b) f has a minimum value at $x=\dfrac{5}{2}$, and

(c) for all x,

$$f'(x)=\begin{vmatrix}2ax & 2ax-1 & 2ax+b+1\\ b & b+1 & -1\\ 2(ax+b) & 2ax+2b+1 & 2ax+b\end{vmatrix}$$

where a, b are some constants. Determine the constants a, b and the function $f(x)$. **(I.I.T. 1998)**

17. (a) The function $y=\dfrac{ax+b}{(x-1)(x-4)}$ has turning point at $P(2,-1)$. Find the values of a and b and show that y is maximum at P.

(b)* Find the values of a and b, if
$$y=a\log|x|+bx^2+x$$
has its extreme values at $x=-1$ and $x=2$.

(c) Let $f(x)=(1+b^2)x^2+2bx+1$ and let $m(b)$ be the minimum value of $f(x)$. As b varies, the range of $m(b)$ is

(a) $[0,1]$ (b) $\left]0,\frac{1}{2}\right]$

(c) $\left[\frac{1}{2},1\right]$ (d) $]0,1]$

(I.I.T. Sc. 2001)

(d) If minimum value of $f(x)=x^2+2bx+2c^2$ is greater than maximum value of $g(x)=-x^2-2cx+b^2$ then for x is real

(a) $|c|>|b|\sqrt{2}$ (b) $|c|\sqrt{2}>b$

(c) $0<c<\sqrt{2}\,b$ (d) no real value of a.

(Screening 2003)

(e) Let $f(x)=\frac{1}{3}\sin a\tan^3 x+(\sin a-1)\tan x+\sqrt{\dfrac{a-2}{8-a}}$

where $a\in(\pi, 2\pi)$. Prove that $f(x)$ has no critical points.

(f) The set of all values of x for which the function $f(x)=(k^2-3k+2)\left(\cos^2\frac{x}{4}-\sin^2\frac{x}{4}\right)+(k-1)x+\sin 1$

does not possess critical points is given by $(0,1)\cup(1,4)$.

(g) The set of values of λ for which the function $f(x)=(4\lambda-3)(x+\log 5)+2(\lambda-7).\ \cot\frac{x}{2}\sin^2\frac{x}{2}$

does not possess critical point is :

(a) $[1,\infty)$ (b) $(2,\infty)$

(c) $(-\infty,-4/3)$ (d) $(-\infty,-1)$

(h) If $f(x)=x^3+3(a-7)x^2+3(a^2-9)x-2$ where $a>0$, has +ive point of maximum then a varies over an interval of length

(a) $\frac{8}{7}$ (b) $\frac{6}{7}$

(c) $\frac{4}{7}$ (d) $\frac{3}{7}$

18. (a) Divide 20 into two parts such that the product of one part and the cube of the other is maximum.

(b) Find the maximum value of the product of two numbers whose sum is 12. **(J.E.E. W.B. 1990)**

(c)* The maximum value of xy subject to $x+y=8$ is 16. **(M.N.R. 1995)**

19. (a) Divide 10 into two parts such that the sum of twice of one part and square of the other is a minimum.

(b) Divide 20 into two parts such that the product of the cube of one and the square of the other shall be maximum.

(c)* Divide 64 into two parts such that the sum of the cubes of two parts is minimum.

20. (a) Let x and y be two variables such that $x > 0$ and $xy = 1$. Find the minimum value of $x + y$.

(b) Does the function $y = x - \sin x$ have a maxima or a minima ?

(c) Define 'maximum'. Show that $x = \pi/2$ gives a maximum of $y = \sin x$. Is $y = [x - (\pi/2)]^5$ a maximum or a minimum at $x = \pi/2$?

21. (a) The perimeter of a rectangle is 100 metres. Find the length of its side when the area is maximum.

(b)* Let (h, k) be a fixed point, where $h > 0, k > 0$. A straight line passing through this point cuts the positive direction of the co-ordinate axes at the points P and Q. Find the minimum area of the triangle OPQ, O being the origin. **(I.I.T. 1995)**

22. (a)* A straight line is drawn through a given point $P(1, 4)$. Determine the least value of the sum of its intercepts on the axes of co-ordinates.
Also determine the length of the larger side if the area of the triangle formed by the line and co-ordinate axes be least.

(b) A straight line L with negative slope passes through the point (8, 2) and cuts the positive co-ordinate axes at points P and Q. Find the absolute minimum value of $OP + OQ$, as L varies, where O is the origin. **(I.I.T. 2002)**

23. (a)* A particle is moving in a straight line such that its distance at any time t is given by

$$s = \frac{1}{4}t^4 - 2t^3 + 4t^2 - 7.$$

Find when its velocity is maximum and acceleration minimum.

(b) The space s described in time t by a particle moving in a straight line is given by $s = t^5 - 40t^3 + 30t^2 + 80t - 250$. Find the minimum value of acceleration. **(J.E.E. W.B. 1990)**

24. (a) The angle which the tangent to a curve at any point (x, y) on it makes with axis of x is $\tan^{-1}(x^2 - 2x)$ for all values of x and it passes through the point (2, 0). Determine the point on it whose ordinate is maximum.

(b) What is the maximum slope of the curve $y = -x^3 + 3x^2 + 2x - 27$?

25. (a)* Find the co-ordinates of the points on the curve $y = x/(1 + x^2)$ where the tangent to the curve has greatest slope.

(b) Find the co-ordinates of the point(s) on the curve $y = \dfrac{x^2 - 1}{x^2 + 1}, x > 0$ such that tangent at these point(s) have the greatest slope.

26. (a) Find the co-ordinates of a point on the parabola $y = x^2 + 7x + 2$ which is closest to the straight line $y = 3x - 3$.

(b) Find the co-ordinates of points on the parabola $y = x^2$ closest to the point $A(0, a)$.

(c) Find the point on the curve $x^2 = 2y$ which is closest to the point (0, 5).

(d) Find the point on $x^2 + 2y^2 = 6$, which is nearest to the line $x + y = 7$. **(I.I.T. 2003)**

27. (a)* What normal to the curve $y = x^2$ forms the shortest chord ? **(I.I.T. 1992)**

(b) Find the point of the hyperbola $\dfrac{x^2}{24} - \dfrac{y^2}{18} = 1$ which is nearest to the line $3x + 2y + 1 = 0$. Compute the distance between the point and the line. **(J.E.E. W.B. 1992)**

28. The total area of a page is 150 square inches. The combined width of the margin at the top and bottom is 3″ and the side is 2″. What must be the dimensions of the page in order that the area of the printed matter may be maximum ?

29. (a) Two towns are to get their water supply from a river. Both towns are on the same side of the river at distance of 6 km and 18 km from the river bank. If the distance between the points on the river bank nearest to the two towns be 10 km., find (a) where a single pumping station may be located requiring the least amount of pipe, (b) how much pipe be needed.

(b)* Towns A and B are situated on the same side of a straight road at distances a and b respectively from it. Perpendiculars drawn from A and B meet the road at the points C and D respectively. The distance between C and D is c. A hospital is to be built at a point P on the road such that the distance APB is minimum. Find the position of P. **(Roorkee 1992)**

30. (a) A firm has a branch store in each of the three cities A, B and C. A and B are 320 km. apart and C is 200 km. from each of them. A godown is to be built equidistant from A and B. In order to minimize the time of transportation it should be located so that sum of the distances from the godown to each of the cities is minimum. Where should the godown be built ?

(b) A company has its branches located in three cities A, B and C. The distance of A from B and C is 100 km each, while the distance between B and C is 60 km. A godown is to be built at a place equidistant from B and C such that the sum of its distances from the three cities is minimum. Find the location of the godown. **(Roorkee 2000)**

31. (a) A factory D is to be connected by a road with a straight railway line on which a town A is situated. The distance DB of the factory to the railway line is $5\sqrt{3}$ km. Length AB of the railway line is 20 km. Freight charges on the road are twice the charges on the railway. At what point P ($AP < AB$) on the railway line should the road DP be connected so as to ensure minimum freight charges from the factory to the town ?

(b) Two roads OA and OB intersect at an angle of 60°. A car driver approaches O from A, where $AO = 800$ metres, at a uniform speed of 20 metres per second. Simultaneously a runner starts running from O towards B at uniform speed of 5 metres per second. Find the time when the car and the runner are closest.

32. (a)* In a submarine telegraph-cable the speed of signalling varies as $x^2 \log(1/x)$ where x is the ratio of the radius of the case to that of covering. Show that the greatest speed is attained when this ratio is $1 : \sqrt{e}$.

(b) The efficiency of a screw jack is given by $E = \dfrac{\tan\theta}{\tan(\theta+\alpha)}$ where α is constant. Prove that max. efficiency is $\dfrac{1-\sin\alpha}{1+\sin\alpha}$ and it occurs when $\theta = 45^o - \alpha/2$.

33. (a) The fuel charges for running a train are proportional to the square of the speed generated in miles per hour and costs Rs. 48 per hour at 16 miles per hour. What is the most economical speed if the fixed charges *i.e.* salaries etc. amount to Rs. 300 per hour.

(b)* Assuming the petrol burnt in driving a motor boat varies as the cube of its velocity, show that the most economical speed when going against a current of c miles per hour is $\left(\dfrac{3c}{2}\right)$ m.p.h.

(c) When travelling x km./hour, a truck burns diesel at the rate of $\dfrac{1}{300}\left(\dfrac{900}{x} + x\right)$ litres per km. If the diesel oil costs 40 p. per litre and driver is paid Rs. 1·50 per hour, find the steady speed that will minimise the total cost of the trip of 500 km.

34. (a) A telephone company in a town has 500 subscribers on its list and collects fixed charges of Rs. 300 per subscriber per year. The company proposes to increase the annual subscription and it is believed that for every increase of Rs. 1/-, one subscriber will discontinue the service.

Find what increase will bring maximum income to the company. **(Bihar C.E.E. 1999)**

(b) The total cost of producing x pocket radio sets per day is Rs. $\left(\dfrac{1}{4}x^2 + 35x + 25\right)$ and the price per set at which they may be sold is Rs. $\left(50 - \dfrac{1}{2}x\right)$. What should be the daily output to obtain a maximum total profit ?

(c) A private telephone company serving a small community makes a profit of Rs. 12·00 per subscriber, if it has 725 subscribers. It decides to reduce the rate by a fixed amount for each subscriber over 725, thereby reducing the profit by 1 paisa per subscriber. Thus there will be profit of Rs. 11·99 on each of the 726 subscribers, Rs. 11·98 on each of the 727 subscribers etc. What is the number of subscribers which will give the company the maximum profit ? **(Roorkee 1990)**

35. (a)* A figure consists of a semi-circle with a rectangle on its diameter. Given that the perimeter of the figure is 20 feet, find its dimensions in order that its area may be maximum.

(b) A window in the form of a rectangle is surmounted by a semi-circular opening. The total perimeter of the window is 10 m. Find the dimensions of the rectangular part of the window to admit maximum light through the whole opening.

(c)* A window of fixed perimeter (including the base of the arc) is in the form of a rectangle surmounted by a semi-circle. The semi-circular portion is fitted with coloured glass while the rectangular part is fitted with clear glass. The clear glass transmits three times as much light per square metre as the coloured glass does. What is the ratio of the sides of the rectangle so that the window transmits the maximum light ? **(I..I.T. 1991)**

36. (a) The section of a window consists of a rectangle surmounted by an equilateral triangle. If the perimeters be given as 16 m. find the dimensions of the window in order that the maximum amount of light may be admitted.

(b) Given the sum of the perimeters of a square and a circle, show that sum of their areas is least when one side of the square is equal to diameter of the circle.

37.* An open tank is to be constructed with a square base and vertical sides so as to contain a given quantity of water. Show that the expenses of lining with lead will be least if the depth is made half of the width.

38. (a) A closed rectangular box with a square base is to be made so as to contain 1000 cubic feet. The cost of the material per sq. foot for the bottom is 15 paisa, for the top 25 paisa, and for the sides 20 paisa. The labour charges for making the box are Rs. 3. Find the dimensions of the box when the cost is minimum.

(b) A square tank of capacity 250 cubic m. has to be dug out. The cost of land is Rs. 50 per sq. m. The cost of digging increases with the depth and for the whole tank is 400 (depth)² rupees. Find the dimensions of the tank for the least total cost.

39. (a) A box of constant volume c is to be twice as long as it is wide. The material on the top and four sides cost three times as much per square metre as that in the bottom. What are the most economical dimensions ?

(b) If 40 square feet of sheet metal are to be used in the construction of an open tank with square base, find the dimensions so that the capacity of the tank is max.

40. A box is constructed from a rectangular metal sheet of 21 cm. by 16 cm, by cutting equal squares of sides x from the corners of the sheet and then turning up the projected portions. For what values of x the volume of the box will be maximum ?

41. (a) The three sides of a trapezium are equal, each being 6″ long. Find the area of the trapezium when it is maximum.

(b) LL' is the latus rectum of the parabola $y^2 = 4ax$ and PP' is a double ordinate between the vertex and the latus rectum. Show that the area of the trapezium $PP'LL'$ is maximum when the distance of PP' from vertex is $a/9$.

42. (a) Prove that the maximum rectangle inscribed in a circle is a square.

(b) Find the dimensions of the rectangle of greatest area that can be inscribed in a semi-circle of radius r. **(M.N.R. 1992)**

43. (a)* Find the area of the greatest isosceles triangle that can be inscribed in a given ellipse having its vertex coincident with one extremity of major axis. **(Roorkee 1994)**

(b)* Find the point on the curve $4x^2 + a^2y^2 = 4a^2$; $4 < a^2 < 8$ that is farthest from the point $(0, -2)$.

44. (a)* If the sum of the lengths of the hypotenuse and another side of a right angled triangle is given, show that the area of the triangle is max. when the angle between these is $\pi/3$.

(b) Find the volume of the greatest right circular cone obtained by rotating a right angled triangle of hypotenuse of 1 foot about a side.

45. (a)* The strength of a beam varies as the product of its breadth and square of its depth. Find the dimensions of the strongest beam which can be cut from a circular log of radius a.

(b)* Assuming that the stiffness of a beam of rectangular cross-section varies as the breadth and as the cube of the depth, prove that for the stiffest beam, breadth must be equal to half the diameter of the log.

46. (a) Show that a triangle of max. area that can be inscribed in a circle of radius a is an equilateral triangle.

(b)* A point P is given on the circumference of a circle of radius r. The chord QR is parallel to the tangent line at P. Find the maximum area of the triangle PQR. **(I.I.T. 1990)**

(c) AB is the chord of contact of tangents drawn from a point $(6, 8)$ to the circle $x^2 + y^2 = r^2$. If the area of the triangle PAB be maximum, then radius r of the circle is 5.

47.* The circle $x^2 + y^2 = 1$ cuts the x-axis at P and Q. Another circle with centre at Q and variable radius intersects the first circle at R above the x-axis and the line segment PQ at S. Find the maximum area of triangle QSR. **(I.I.T. 1994)**

48. A running track of 440 ft. is to be laid out enclosing a football field, the shape of which is a rectangle with a semi-circle at each end. If the area of the rectangular portion is to be maximum find the lengths of its sides.

49. (a) The perimeter of a rectangle is 100 metres. Find the length of its sides when the area is maximum.

(b) Find the dimensions of the rectangle of perimeter 36 cm which will sweep out a volume as large as possible when revolved about one of its sides.

(c) How should a wire 20 cm long be divided into two parts, if one part is to be bent into a circle, the other part is to be bent into a square and the two plane figures are to have areas the sum of which is minimum ?

50. Find the greatest and least values of the following functions on the indicated intervals :

(a)* $f(x) = 2x^3 - 3x^2 - 12x + 1$ on $[-2, 5/2]$;

(b)* $f(x) = x^2 \log x$ on $[1, e]$;

(c) $f(x) = xe^{-x}$ on $[0, \infty]$.

51. (a) $f(x) \begin{cases} = 2x^2 + \dfrac{2}{x^2} \text{ for } -2 \le x < 0 \text{ and } 0 < x \le 2 \\ = 1 \text{ for } x = 0. \end{cases}$

Determine the greatest and least values. What is the minimum value of the function ?

(b) The difference between the greatest and least values of the function $f(x) = \sin 2x - x$ on $[-\pi/2, \pi/2]$ is π.

52. (a) $y = (x-8)^4 (x-9)^5, 0 \le x \le 10$

(b)* The largest value of $2x^3 - 3x^2 - 12x + 5$ for $-2 \le x \le 4$ occurs at $x =$

(i) -2 (ii) -1

(iii) 2 (iv) 4 **(M.N.R. 1993)**

53. (a) Find the maximum and minimum values of $y = |4 - x^2|$, $-3 \le x \le 3$. Also determine the greatest and least values.

(b)* A function $y = f(x)$ is represented parametrically as follows :

$x = \phi(t) = t^5 - 5t^3 - 20t + 7,$

$y = \psi(t) = 4t^3 - 3t^2 - 18t + 3.$

Find the extrema of this function. $(-2 < t < 2)$

54. (i)* Investigate for maxima and minima the functions

$$f(x) = \int_1^x [2(t-1)(t-2)^3 + 3(t-1)^2 (t-2)^2]\, dt.$$

(ii) The function

$$f(x) = \int_{-1}^x t(e^t - 1)(t-1)(t-2)^3 (t-3)^5\, dt$$

has a local minimum at $x =$

(a) 0 (b) 1

(c) 2 (d) 3 **(I.I.T. 1999)**

55. (a)* A cubic $f(x)$ vanishes at $x = -2$ and has a relative min./max. at $x = -1$ and $x = 1/3$. If $\int_{-1}^{1} f(x)\, dx = 14/3$, find the cubic $f(x)$. **(I. I.T. 1992)**

(b) $P(x)$ is a cubic polynomial such that it has a local maxima at $x = -1$ and $P'(x)$ has minima at $x = 1$. If $P(1) = -6, P(-1) = 10$, find $P(x)$. Also find the distance between the point of maxima and minima of curve $y = P(x)$. **(I.I.T. 2005)**

(c) Let three-degree polynomial function $f(x)$ has local maximum at $x = -1$ and $f(-1) = 2, f(3) = 18$, $f'(x)$ has a minima at $x = 0$, then :

(a) the distance between $(-1, 2)$ and $(a, f(a))$ where a denotes point where function has local max/min is $2\sqrt{5}$

(b) the function decreases from 1 to $2\sqrt{5}$

(c) the function increases from 1 to $2\sqrt{5}$

(d) the function decreases from -1 to 1

(I.I.T. 2006)

56. (a)* A biquadratic $f(x)$ has a local max./min. at $x = 1, 2$ and 3; $f(-1) = 0$. If $\int_{-2}^{2} f(x)\, dx = -\frac{1348}{15}$, then prove that $f(x) = x^4 - 8x^3 + 22x^2 - 24x - 55$.

(b) A biquadratic $f(x)$ has a relative max./min. at $x = 0$, $x = \pm 1$, $f(0) = 3$ and $\int_{-2}^{2} f(x)\, dx = \frac{556}{45}$, prove that $f(x) = \frac{1}{6}(x^4 - 2x^2 + 18)$.

57. Prove that $\sin x + 2x \geq \frac{3x \cdot (x+1)}{\pi}\ \forall\ x \in \left[0, \frac{\pi}{2}\right]$.

(Justify the inequality, if any used). **(I.I.T. 2004)**

Solutions to Problem Set (1)

1. (a) $y = x^5 - x^4 + 5x^3 - 10$

$\therefore \quad \frac{dy}{dx} = 5x^2 (x^2 - 4x + 3) = 0$

$\frac{dy}{dx} = 5x^2 (x-1)(x-3) = f'(x)$

$\therefore \quad x = 0, 1, 3.$

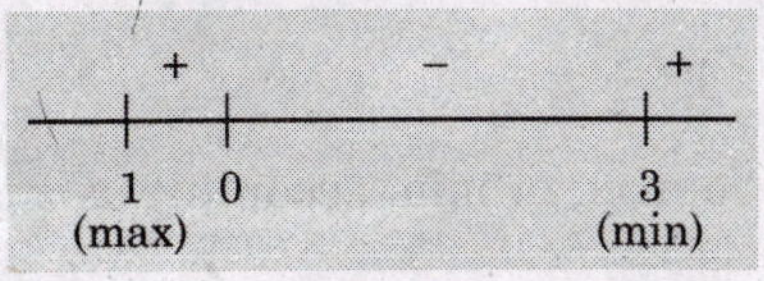

Fig. 4

Consider the point x = 1. $5x^2$ is + ive always

For $x < 1, \frac{dy}{dx} = +$ ive; for $x > 1, \frac{dy}{dx} = -$ ive.

Since the change is from +ive to − ive therefore $f(x)$ is max. at $x = 1$.

Consider the point x = 3.

For $x < 3, \frac{dy}{dx} = -$ ive ; for $x > 3, \frac{dy}{dx} = +$ ive

Since the change is from − ive to +ive therefore $f(x)$ is min. at $x = 3$.

Consider the point x = 0.

For $x < 0, \frac{dy}{dx} = +$ ive ; for $x > 0, \frac{dy}{dx} = +$ ive

Since there is no change of sign hence the function is neither maximum nor minimum at $x = 0$.

Alternative Method :

$\frac{dy}{dx} = 5x^2 (x-3)(x-1)$

$= 5x^4 - 20x^3 + 15x^2 = 0.$

$\therefore \quad x = 0, 3, 1$

$\frac{d^2 y}{dx^2} = 20x^3 - 60x^2 + 30x$

$= 10x(2x^2 - 6x + 3)$

and $\frac{d^3 y}{dx^3} = 10(6x^2 - 12x + 3)$

For $x = 0, \frac{d^2 y}{dx^2} = 0$ and $\frac{d^3 y}{dx^3} \neq 0$

$\therefore$ neither max. nor min.

For $x = 3, \frac{d^2 y}{dx^2} = 30(18 - 18 + 3) = 90 = +$ ive

$\therefore$ min.

For $x = 1, \frac{d^2 y}{dx^2} = 10(2 - 6 + 3) = -10 = -$ ive

$\therefore$ max.

(b) Proceed as above. $x = 1, 5$. At $x = 1$ max., $x = 5$ min.

(c) At $x = -1$, max. value 19. At $x = 2$ min. value -8.

(d) $y = \frac{x^2 + x + 1}{x^2 - x + 1} = \frac{x^2 - x + 1 + 2x}{x^2 - x + 1} = 1 + 2 . \frac{x}{x^2 - x + 1}$

or $y = 1 + \frac{2}{\frac{1}{x}(x^2 - x + 1)} = 1 + \frac{2}{x - 1 + \frac{1}{x}}$

or $\quad y = 1 + \dfrac{2}{z}$

y will be max. or min. according as z is min. or max.

$$z = x - 1 + \frac{1}{x} \quad \therefore \quad \frac{dz}{dx} = 1 - \frac{1}{x^2} = 0$$

$\therefore \quad x = 1, -1$

$$\frac{d^2 z}{dx^2} = \frac{2}{x^3} = +\text{ive for } x = 1, -\text{ive for } x = -1$$

Hence z is min. for $x = 1$ and max. at $x = -1$.

$\therefore$ y is max. for $x = 1$ and min. at $x = -1$ and these values are 3 and 1/3 respectively.

(e) Ans. (ii). Let $z = \dfrac{1 - x + x^2}{1 + x + x^2}$

$$\therefore \quad y = \frac{1}{z} = \frac{1 + x + x^2}{1 - x + x^2}$$

By part (d) y is max. at $x = 1$ and max. value is 3.

$\therefore$ $z = \dfrac{1}{y}$ is min. at $x = 1$ and its min. value is 1/3.

2. (a) Ans. (d).

$$\frac{dy}{dx} = -\frac{2}{x^2} + \frac{1}{2}$$

$$\frac{dy}{dx} = 0 \quad \Rightarrow \quad x^2 - 4 = 0 \quad \therefore \quad x = 2, -2$$

$$\frac{d^2 y}{dx^2} = \frac{4}{x^3} = +\text{ive at } x = 2 \text{ and hence minimum.}$$

(b) Ans. (c).

$f'(x) = 0$

$\Rightarrow \quad 6(x^2 - 3ax + 2a^2) = 0$

or $\quad 6(x - a)(x - 2a) = 0 \quad \therefore \quad x = a, 2a$

$f''(x) = 6(2x - 3a) = +$ive for $x = 2a$ and hence **local minimum** at $x = 2a = \beta$ say

$f''(x) = 6(2x - 3a) = -$ive for $x = a$ and hence **local maximum** at $x = a = \alpha$ say.

But $\beta = \alpha^2 \quad \Rightarrow \quad 2a = a^2 \quad$ or $\quad a(a - 2) = 0$

$\therefore \quad a = 2 \quad \Rightarrow \quad$ (c)

$a = 0$ is ruled out as $f(x) = 2x^3 + 1$ and $f'(x) = 6x^2$ which is always +ive and hence $f(x)$ is an increasing function in this case.

(c) Ans. (d).

$$\frac{dy}{dx} = 6(x^2 - x - 2) = 6(x - 2)(x + 1) = 0$$

$\therefore \quad x = 2, -1$

$$\frac{d^2 y}{dx^2} = 6(2x - 1) = +\text{ive} \quad \text{for } x = 2 \quad \therefore \quad \text{Min.}$$

$$= -\text{ive} \quad \text{for } x = -1 \quad \therefore \quad \text{Max.}$$

Hence $f(x)$ is max. at $x = -1$ and its value is $f(-1) = 12$

For relative maximum let us calculate the values of $f(x)$ at the end points of the interval $[-2, 4]$.

$$f(-2) = 1, f(4) = 37 \text{ and } f(-1) = 12$$

Hence relative max. value is 37 at $x = 4$.

3. (a) $y = (x - 2)^6 (x - 3)^5$. Differentiating, we get

$$\frac{dy}{dx} = 6(x - 2)^5 (x - 3)^5 + 5(x - 3)^4 (x - 2)^6$$

$$= (x - 2)^5 (x - 3)^4 (11x - 28)$$

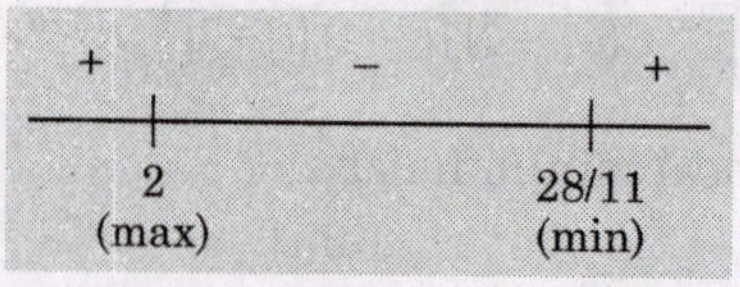

Fig. 5

$$\therefore \quad \frac{dy}{dx} = (x - 2)^4 (x - 3)^4 . 11(x - 2)\left(x - \frac{28}{11}\right)$$

$$= +\text{ive}.(x - 2)\left(x - \frac{28}{11}\right)$$

Now $\dfrac{dy}{dx} = 0$ gives $x = 2, 3, \dfrac{28}{11}$

At $\quad x = 2, \dfrac{dy}{dx}$ changes from + ive to − ive.

$\therefore \quad$ Max. at $x = 2$ and

Max. value of $y = 0$.

At $\quad x = \dfrac{28}{11}, \dfrac{dy}{dx}$ changes from − ive to + ive

$\therefore \quad$ Min. at $x = \dfrac{28}{11}$

$$\therefore \quad \text{Min. value of } y = \left(\frac{28}{11} - 2\right)^6 \left(\frac{28}{11} - 3\right)^5$$

$$= \left(\frac{6}{11}\right)^6 \left(\frac{-5}{11}\right)^5 = -\frac{5^5\, 6^6}{11^{11}}$$

At $\quad x = 3, \dfrac{dy}{dx}$ changes from + ive to + ive.

$\therefore \quad$ Neither min. nor max. at $x = 3$.

(b) Proceed as above.

Max. at $x = 8$, value 3,

Min. at $x = \dfrac{76}{9}$, value $-\left(\dfrac{4}{9}\right)^4 \left(\dfrac{5}{9}\right)^5$

(c) Ans. (ii). $\dfrac{dy}{dx} = 25x^4 (1 - x)^{74} (1 - 4x)$

$$= -100x^4 (x - 1)^{74} (x - 1/4)$$

Use change of sign of $\dfrac{dy}{dx}$ for $x < \dfrac{1}{4}$ and $x > \dfrac{1}{4}$.

$x < \dfrac{1}{4}$, + ive, $x > \dfrac{1}{4}$, − ive $\quad \therefore \quad$ Max. at $x = \dfrac{1}{4}$

$\dfrac{dy}{dx}$ does not change sign for $x = 0$ and $x = 1$

(d) $y = 2x^3 - 3(a + b)x^2 + 6abx$

$$\frac{dy}{dx} = 6x^2 - 6(a + b)x + 6ab = 0$$

$$x^2 - x(a+b) + ab = 0$$

or $\dfrac{dy}{dx} = (x-a)(x-b) = 0$ gives $x = a, b$

We shall use the rule of change of sign for max. and min. at $x = a, b$

Case I : $a < b$

At $x = a, dy/dx$ changes from + to − and hence max at $x = a$ and reverse is the case of at $x = b$ where dy/dx changes sign from − ive to + ive and hence minimum.

Case II : $a > b$ or $b < a$

$\therefore \quad \dfrac{dy}{dx} = (x-b)(x-a), \quad b < a$

As above in case I at $x = b$ is max and at $x = a$ it will be minimum.

Case III : $a = b$, $\dfrac{dy}{dx} = (x-a)^2$ or $(x-b)^2$

It does not change sign in the neighbourhood of a or b. Hence neither maximum nor minimum.

4. (a) $y = \dfrac{x}{1 + x\tan x}$

y will be maximum when its reciprocal

$$\frac{1}{y} = \frac{1 + x\tan x}{x} = \frac{1}{x} + \tan x \text{ is min.}$$

Let $z = (1/x) + \tan x$

$\therefore \quad dz/dx = -1/x^2 + \sec^2 x = 0.$

$\therefore \quad 1/x^2 = \sec^2 x$

$\therefore \quad x = \cos x$

$$\frac{d^2 z}{dx^2} = +\frac{2}{x^3} + 2\sec x \sec x \tan x = +\text{ive},$$

and hence z is min. when $x = \cos x$, that is, y is max. at $x = \cos x$.

(b) $y = \sin^p \theta \cos^q \theta$.

Now y will be max. or min. according as $z = \log y = p\log\sin\theta + q\log\cos\theta$ is max. or min.

$z = p\log\sin\theta + q\log\cos\theta$

$$\frac{dz}{d\theta} = p.\frac{1}{\sin\theta}.\cos\theta + \frac{q}{\cos\theta}(-\sin\theta) = 0$$

or $\quad p\cot\theta - q\tan\theta = 0.$

$\therefore \quad \tan^2\theta = p/q$ or $\theta = \tan^{-1}\sqrt{p/q}$

$$d^2z/d\theta^2 = -p\,\text{cosec}^2\,\theta - q\sec^2\theta$$

which is clearly − ive when $\tan^2\theta = p/q$ and hence z is max.

or $\quad \log y$ is max. or y is max.

$$d^2z/d\theta^2 = -p(1+\cot^2\theta) - q(1+\tan^2\theta)$$

$$= -p\left(1+\frac{q}{p}\right) - q\left(1+\frac{p}{q}\right)$$

$$= -p-q-q-p = -2(p+q).$$

We need not calculate the value of $\dfrac{d^2z}{d\theta^2}$ as we are only concerned with its sign.

(c) $\sqrt{3}(\sin x + \sqrt{3}\cos x)$. Divide and multiply by $\sqrt{1+3} = 2.$

$$= 2\sqrt{3}\left(\frac{1}{2}\sin x + \frac{\sqrt{3}}{2}\cos x\right) = 2\sqrt{3}\sin\left(x+\frac{\pi}{3}\right).$$

Clearly it is max. when $x + \pi/3 = \pi/2$ *i.e.* $x = \pi/6$ and Max. value is $2\sqrt{3}$.

(d) As in part (c), Max. when $x = \pi/4$ and Max. value is $\sqrt{2}$.

5. **See result (2) P. 1397 for solution.**

6. (a) We have $f'(x) = 2\cos x - 4\cos x\sin x = 0$ for max. or min. This gives $\cos x = 0$

or $\quad \sin x = 1/2$. The solution in the interval $0 \le x \le \pi/2$ is $\pi/2$ and $\pi/6$ respectively.

Now $f''(x) = -2\sin x - 4\cos 2x$

$\therefore \quad f''(x) > 0$ at $x = \pi/2$

and $f''(x) < 0$ at $x = \pi/6$.

Hence $f(x)$ is min. at $x = \pi/2$ and max. at $x = \pi/6$.

(b) $y = 1 + 2\sin x + 3\cos^2 x$

$$\frac{dy}{dx} = 2\cos x - 6\cos x\sin x = 0$$

$\therefore \quad \cos x = 0$ or $\sin x = 1/3$

$\therefore \quad x = 90^\circ$ or $\sin^{-1}(1/3)$

$$\frac{d^2y}{dx^2} = -2\sin x - 6(\cos^2 x - \sin^2 x)$$

$$= 2 + 6 = 4 \text{ at } x = 90^\circ$$

$\therefore \quad$ min. and its value is $1 + 2 = 3$.

or $\quad \dfrac{d^2y}{dx^2} = -2.\sin x - 6(1 - 2\sin^2 x)$

$$= -2.\frac{1}{3} - 6 + 12.\frac{1}{9} = +\frac{2}{3} - 6 = -\text{ive}.$$

at $\sin x = 1/3$

Max. at $x = \sin^{-1}(1/3)$ and value is 13/3.

(c) Ans. (a). Tangent is $\dfrac{x\cos\theta}{3\sqrt{3}} + \dfrac{y\sin\theta}{1} = 1$

y = sum of intercepts $= 3\sqrt{3}\sec\theta + \text{cosec}\,\theta$

For min., $\dfrac{dy}{d\theta} = 0$

$\therefore \quad 3\sqrt{3}\sec\theta\tan\theta - \text{cosec}\,\theta.\cot\theta = 0$

$\therefore \quad \tan^3\theta = \dfrac{1}{3\sqrt{3}} \quad \therefore \quad \tan\theta = \dfrac{1}{\sqrt{3}} \Rightarrow \theta = \dfrac{\pi}{6}.$

7. (a) Ans. $\dfrac{1}{3}, A = B = 30^\circ$.

When $A + B = 60^\circ \quad \therefore \quad B = 60^\circ - A$

$\therefore \quad \tan B = \tan(60^\circ - A) = \dfrac{\sqrt{3} - \tan A}{1 + \sqrt{3}\tan A}$

Now $z = \tan A \tan B$

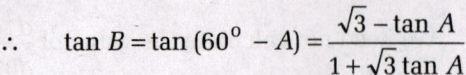

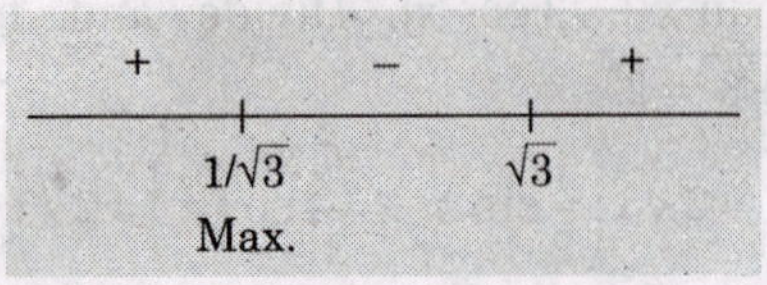

Fig. 6

or $z = \dfrac{t(\sqrt{3} - t)}{1 + \sqrt{3}t} = \dfrac{\sqrt{3}t - t^2}{1 + \sqrt{3}t}$

where $\quad t = \tan A$

$\dfrac{dz}{dt} = -\dfrac{(t + \sqrt{3})(\sqrt{3}t - 1)}{(1 + \sqrt{3}t)^2} = 0 \quad \therefore \quad t = \dfrac{1}{\sqrt{3}}$

$\therefore \quad t = \tan A = \tan 30^\circ$

$\therefore \quad B = 60^\circ - A = 30^\circ.$

The other value is rejected as both A and B are + ive acute angles.

If $t < \dfrac{1}{\sqrt{3}}, \dfrac{dz}{dt} = +$ ive and if $t > \dfrac{1}{\sqrt{3}}, \dfrac{dz}{dt} = -$ ive.

Hence max. when $t = \dfrac{1}{\sqrt{3}}$ and max. value $= \dfrac{1}{3}$.

(b) $f'(x) = 0 \Rightarrow 2\cos x - 2\sin 2x = 0$

$\therefore \quad \sin 2x = \cos x \quad$ or $\quad 2\sin x \cos x - \cos x = 0$

$\therefore \quad \cos x = 0 \quad$ or $\quad \sin x = 1/2.$

$\therefore \quad x = \pi/2, 3\pi/2$ or $x = \pi/6, 5\pi/6$

where $0 \le x \le 2\pi$

Critical points are $\pi/6, \pi/2, 5\pi/6, 3\pi/2$

$f''(x) = -2\sin x - 4\cos 2x$

$= -$ ive at $x = \pi/6$. $\therefore$ Max. at $\pi/6$,

Min. at $\pi/2$, Max. at $5\pi/6$ and Min. at $3\pi/2$ as Max. and Min. occur **alternately**.

(c) Ans. (b).

8. The given function is periodic of period 2π.

$\dfrac{dy}{dx} = -\sin x - \sin 2x + \sin 3x$

$= -\left(2\sin\dfrac{3x}{2}\cos\dfrac{x}{2} - 2\sin\dfrac{3x}{2}\cos\dfrac{3x}{2}\right)$

$= -2\sin\dfrac{3x}{2}\left(\cos\dfrac{x}{2} - \cos\dfrac{3x}{2}\right)$

$= -4\sin\dfrac{x}{2}\sin x \sin\dfrac{3x}{2}$

Now $\sin\theta = 0$ when $\theta = 0, \pi, 2\pi$

$\dfrac{dy}{dx} = 0 \quad \therefore \quad x = 0, \dfrac{2\pi}{3}, \pi, \dfrac{4\pi}{3}, 2\pi$ in $(0, 2\pi)$

$\dfrac{d^2y}{dx^2} = -\cos x - 2\cos 2x + 3\cos 3x$

$= 0$ at $x = 0$. $\therefore$ Neither

$= \dfrac{1}{2} + 1 + 3 = \dfrac{9}{2}$ at $x = \dfrac{2\pi}{3} = +$ ive $\quad \therefore$ Min.

$= 1 - 2 - 3 = -4$ at $x = \pi = -$ ive. $\quad \therefore$ Max.

$= \dfrac{1}{2} + 1 + 3 = +$ ive at $x = \dfrac{4\pi}{3} \quad \therefore$ Min.

$= -1 - 2 + 3 = 0$ at $x = 2\pi$. $\quad \therefore$ Neither

Hence the function is max. (local max.) at $x = \pi$ and max. value is -4 and it is minimum (local min.) at $x = \dfrac{2\pi}{3}$ and $x = \dfrac{4\pi}{3}$ and its minimum value is 9/2 or 0.

(Observe that minimum is greater than maximum)

Greatest and Least Values. Consider the values of function at critical and end points of the interval $(0, 2\pi)$ *i.e.* at $x = 0, \dfrac{2\pi}{3}, \pi, \dfrac{4\pi}{3}, 2\pi$.

$y = f(0) = 1 + \dfrac{1}{2} - \dfrac{1}{3} = \dfrac{7}{6}$

$f\left(\dfrac{2\pi}{3}\right) = -\dfrac{1}{2} - \dfrac{1}{4} - \dfrac{1}{3} = -\dfrac{13}{12}$ (Min.)

$f(\pi) = -1 + \dfrac{1}{2} + \dfrac{1}{3} = -\dfrac{1}{6}$ (Max.)

$f\left(\dfrac{4\pi}{3}\right) = -\dfrac{1}{2} - \dfrac{1}{4} - \dfrac{1}{3} = -\dfrac{13}{12}$ (Min.)

$f(2\pi) = f(0) = 7/6.$

Greatest value is 7/6 and least value is $-13/12$. Difference between greatest and least value is

$\dfrac{7}{6} - \left(-\dfrac{13}{12}\right) = \dfrac{27}{12} = \dfrac{9}{4}.$

9. Let $y = \sin^6 x + \cos^6 x$ ...(1)

$= (\sin^2 x + \cos^2 x)^3 - 3\sin^2 x \cos^2 x(\sin^2 x + \cos^2 x)$

$= 1 - \dfrac{3}{4}\sin^2 2x$ ...(2)

[**By Trigonometry** max. value is 1 when $\sin 2x = 0$

$\therefore \quad x = 0$ and least value is $1 - \dfrac{3}{4} = \dfrac{1}{4}$ when $\sin 2x = 1 \quad \therefore \quad x = \pi/4$.]

By Differential Calculus

$\dfrac{dy}{dx} = -\dfrac{3}{4} \cdot 2\sin 2x \cdot \cos 2x \cdot 2 = -\dfrac{3}{2}\sin 4x = 0$ by (2)

$\therefore \quad 4x = 0, \pi, 2\pi$ in $(0, 2\pi)$

$\therefore \quad x = 0, \pi/4, \pi/2.$

$\dfrac{d^2y}{dx^2} = -\dfrac{3}{2} \cdot 4\cos 4x = -6\cos 4x$

$= -6$ at $x = 0, \pi/2 \quad \therefore$ Max.

$= 6$ at $x = \pi/4 \quad \therefore$ Min.

$\therefore \quad y = 1$ (Max.), $y = \left(\dfrac{1}{\sqrt{2}}\right)^6 + \left(\dfrac{1}{\sqrt{2}}\right)^6$

$= \dfrac{1}{8} + \dfrac{1}{8} = \dfrac{1}{4}$ (Min.) from (1)

$\therefore \quad \frac{1}{4} \le \sin^6 x + \cos^6 x \le 1.$

10. (a) Ans. (d).

$y = 1 - \frac{2}{x^2+1}, \frac{dy}{dx} = \frac{4x}{(x^2+1)^2} = 0 \Rightarrow x = 0$

Change of sign of $\frac{dy}{dx}$ is from – to + and hence min.

when $x = 0, y = -1$.

(b) $y = (x-1)^2 e^x$

$dy/dx = (x-1)^2 . e^x + 2(x-1) e^x$

$= e^x (x^2 - 2x + 1 + 2x - 2)$

$= e^x (x^2 - 1) = 0$

$\therefore \quad x = -1, 1$

By change of sign rule at $x = 1, -1$.

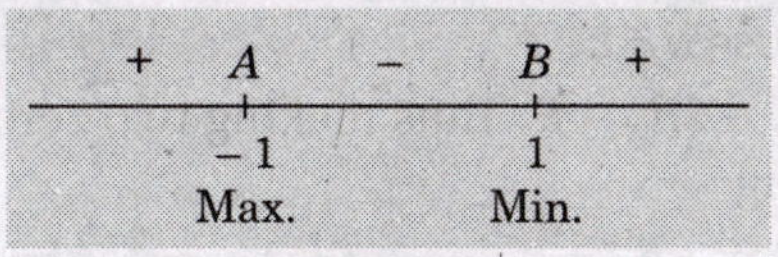

Fig. 7

Hence min. at $x = 1$ and max. at $x = -1$.

Min. value = 0, max. value is $4e^{-1} = 4/e$.

(c) Min. at $x = 1$, max. at $x = 1/3$.

11. (a) Let $z = \frac{1}{y} = \frac{1}{40}(3x^4 + 8x^3 - 18x^2 + 60)$

$\frac{dz}{dy} = \frac{12}{40}(x^3 + 2x^2 - 3x) = 0$

or $\quad x(x+3)(x-1) = 0$

By change of sign rule.

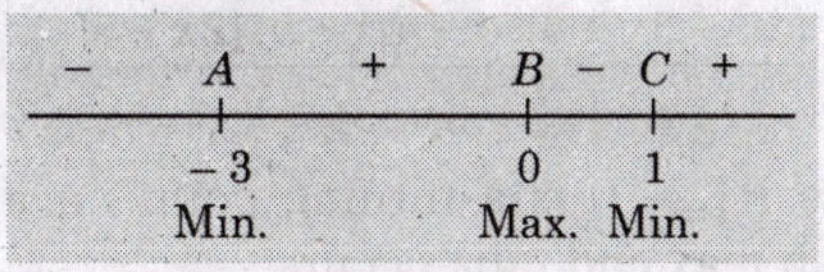

Fig. 8

At $\quad x = -3, 0, 1, z$ is Min., Max., Min.

or $\quad y$ is Max., Min., Max.

(b) $f'(x) = -2, x < 0 \qquad \text{...(1)}$

$= 3, x \ge 0$

$\therefore \quad \frac{dy}{dx} = f'(x)$ does not exist at $x = 0$. Hence we consider change of sign of $\frac{dy}{dx}$ at $x = 0$

$\therefore \quad$ From (1), $\quad L' = f'(0-h) = -2 = -$ ive,

and $R' = f'(0+h) = 3 = +$ ive.

Thus $f'(x)$ or $\frac{dy}{dx}$ changes sign from – ive to + ive showing that $f(x)$ is minimum at $x = 0$.

12. (a) Ans. (d).

Let us redefine the function

x + ive $\quad \therefore \ |x| = x$ for $0 < x < 2$

x – ive $\quad \therefore \ |x| = -x$ for $0 < -x < 2$ or $-2 < x < 0$

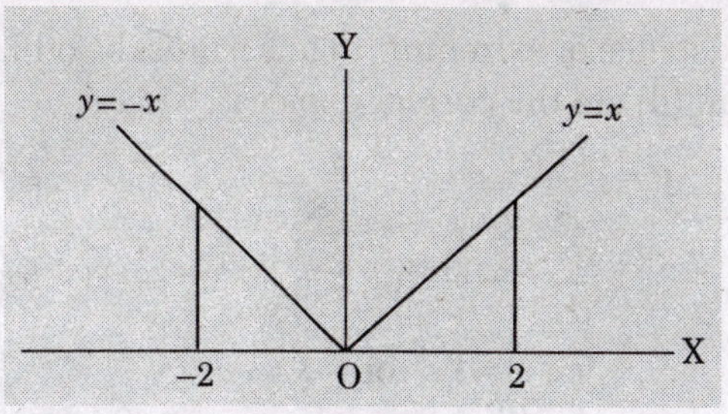

Fig. 9

$\therefore \quad f(x) = \begin{cases} -x, & -2 < x < 0 \\ 0, & x = 0 \\ x, & 0 < x < 2 \end{cases}$

$\frac{dy}{dx}$ does not exist as L.H.D. = – 1.

and R.H.D. = 1 at $x = 0$.

(b) Ans. (a).

Let us redefine $f(x)$ for considering values less than or greater than $-2, 3$ and 5 because of different mods appearing in it.

Consider the following case

$x \le -2, \ -2 \le x < 3, \ 3 \le x < 5, \ x \ge 5$

$f(x) = y = \begin{cases} 6 - 3x & x \le -2 \\ 10 - x & -2 \le x < 3 \\ x + 4 & 3 \le x < 5 \\ 3x - 6 & x \ge 5 \end{cases}$

$\frac{dy}{dx} = -$ ive for $x \le -2, -2 \le x < 3$ or in $(-\infty, 3)$

so $f(x)$ is decreasing function in $(-\infty, 3)$

$\frac{dy}{dx} = +$ ive for $3 \le x < 5, x \ge 5$ or in $(3, \infty)$

so that $f(x)$ is an increasing function in $(3, \infty)$.

Hence $x = 3$ is a point of minimum value of $f(x)$ as the function changes from decreasing to increasing.

$\therefore \quad f(3) = 0 + 5 + 2 = 7$ is minimum value of $f(x)$.

13. Ans. (b), (d).

$\frac{dy}{dx} = (x^2 - 1)^{n+1}(2x + 1)$

$+ (n+1)(x^2 - 1)^n . 2x(x^2 + x + 1)$

$= (x^2 - 1)^n [(x^2 - 1)(2x + 1) + 2x(n+1)(x^2 + x + 1)]$

Since $f(x)$ has a local extremum $\frac{dy}{dx}$ must change sign *i.e.* $f(1^+)$ and $f(1^-)$ should be of opposite signs.

Now we know that $x^2 + x + 1$ is always + ive ($b^2 - 4ac = -$ ive) and the first term tends to zero as $x \to 1$. Hence the sign of $\frac{dy}{dx}$ will depend upon $(x^2 - 1)^n$.

But $x^2 - 1 = (x+1)(x-1)$ is + ive for $x > 1$ and – ive for $x < 1$. Hence if n is even then $f(1^+)$ and $f(1^-)$ will have the same sign, but they must be of opposite sign for the existence of extremum. Thus n must be odd. Hence (b) and (d) are the correct choices.

14. (a) $y = \dfrac{\log x}{x}$

$\dfrac{dy}{dx} = -\dfrac{1}{x^2}\log x + \dfrac{1}{x}\cdot\dfrac{1}{x} = \dfrac{1}{x^2}(1-\log x) = 0$

$\therefore$ $\log x = 1$ or $x = e$

At $x = e$, $\dfrac{dy}{dx}$ changes sign from + ive to – ive and hence y is max. at $x = e$ and its value is

$\dfrac{\log e}{e} = e^{-1}$. $\because \log e = 1.$

Note : $x < e \Rightarrow \log x < 1, x > e \Rightarrow \log x > 1$. You may follow $\dfrac{d^2y}{dx^2}$ method.

(b) $y = x^{1/x}$

Now y will be max. or min. according as $z = \log y = (1/x)\log x$ is max. or min.

$\therefore$ $z = \dfrac{1}{x}\log x$ and it is max. when $x = e$ by part (a)

hence y is max. when $x = e$ and its max. value is $e^{1/e}$.

(c) $y = x^x$

Min. for $\log x = -1$ or $x = e^{-1} = 1/e$.

(d) Ans. Max. value $= e^{1/e}$

15. (a) $\dfrac{dy}{dx} = 3x^2 + 2ax + b = 0$ at $x = -1$ and $x = 3$

$\therefore$ $3 - 2a + b = 0$ and $27 + 6a + b = 0$

Solving we get $a = -3, b = -9$

Also $\dfrac{d^2y}{dx^2} = 6x + 2a = 6x - 6$

$= 6(-1) - 6 = -12 = -$ ive at $x = -1$

$\therefore$ Max.

$= 6(3) - 6 = 12 = +$ ive at $x = 3$

$\therefore$ Min.

There is no condition on c which therefore can assume any real value $\therefore$ $a = -3, b = -9, c \in R$.

(b) $\dfrac{dy}{dx} = 2x - \dfrac{a}{x^2} = 4 - \dfrac{a}{4} = 0$ at $x = 2$.

$\therefore$ $a = 16$.

Also $\dfrac{d^2y}{dx^2} = 2 + \dfrac{2a}{x^3} = 2 + \dfrac{2.16}{8} = 6$ *i.e.* +ive and hence it has a local minimum

Now $\dfrac{dy}{dx} = 0$ when $x^3 = \dfrac{a}{2}$ and for this

$\dfrac{d^2y}{dx^2} = 2 + \dfrac{2a}{x^3} = 2 + 4 = 6 = +$ive

Hence min. whatever a may be. Hence it cannot have a maximum.

(c) $f'(x) = 6x^2 - 18ax + 12a^2 = 6(x-a)(x-2a)$

$f''(x) = 6(2x - 3a)$

By given condition

$f'(p) = 0, f''(p) = -$ ive for max.

$f'(q) = 0, f''(q) = +$ ive for min.

$f'(p) = 0 \Rightarrow p = a, 2a, f'(q) = 0 \Rightarrow q = a, 2a.$

$f''(p) < 0 \Rightarrow p < \dfrac{3a}{2}$ $\therefore$ $p = a$

$f''(q) > 0 \Rightarrow q > \dfrac{3a}{2}$ $\therefore$ $q = 2a.$

Now $p^2 = q$ $\Rightarrow$ $a^2 - 2a = 0.$

$\therefore$ $a(a-2) = 0$ or $a = 0, 2.$

But for $a = 0$, $f(x) = 2x^3 + 1$

and $f'(x) = 6x^2 = +$ive

$f'(x)$ can never be – ive for any real value of x. so that $f(x)$ is not maximum anywhere. Hence we choose $a = 2$

16. Apply $R_3 - 2R_2 - R_1$ thus making two zeros in R_3 and expanding

$f'(x) = 2ax + b$ $\therefore$ $f(x) = ax^2 + bx + c$

$f(0) = 2 \Rightarrow a = 2$ $\therefore$ $f(x) = ax^2 + bx + 2$

$f(1) = 1 \Rightarrow a + b = -1$

f is max. at $x = 5/2 \Rightarrow f'(x) = 0$ at $x = 5/2$

$\Rightarrow$ $5a + b = 0$

Solving $a = \dfrac{1}{4}, b = -\dfrac{5}{4}$ $\therefore$ $f(x) = \dfrac{1}{4}x^2 - \dfrac{5}{4}x + 2$

17. (a) $y = \dfrac{ax + b}{(x-1)(x-4)}$

$P(2, -1)$ lies on it $\therefore$ $2a + b = 2$ ...(1)

$\dfrac{dy}{dx} = \dfrac{(x^2 - 5x + 4).a - (ax + b)(2x - 5)}{(x^2 - 5x + 4)^2}$

Since $P(2, -1)$ is a turning point *i.e.* a point at which max and min. occurs.

$\therefore$ $\dfrac{dy}{dx} = 0$ at $(2, -1)$

$\therefore$ $\dfrac{(4 - 10 + 4)a - (2a + b)(4 - 5)}{(4 - 10 + 4)^2} = 0$

or $-2a + 2a + b = 0$ $\therefore$ $b = 0.$

Hence from (1), $a = 1.$

$\therefore$ $y = \dfrac{x}{x^2 - 5x + 4} = \dfrac{1}{x - 5 + 4/x}$ ...(2)

Now let $z = x - 5 + 4/x$

$\therefore$ $\dfrac{dz}{dx} = 1 - \dfrac{4}{x^2} = 0$

$\therefore$ $x = 2, -2$

When $x = 2, y = -1$ $\therefore$ P is $(2, -1)$.

$\dfrac{d^2z}{dx^2} = \dfrac{8}{x^3} = 1$ *i.e.* +ive at P

$\therefore$ z is Min. at P and hence y is Max. at P by (1).

(b) $\dfrac{d}{dx}\log|x| = \dfrac{1}{x}$

See. Q. 48.

$$\frac{dy}{dx} = a.\frac{1}{x} + 2bx + 1 = 0 \text{ at } x = -1, 2.$$

Ans. $a = 2,\ b = -1/2$.

(c) Ans. (d).

$$f'(x) = 2x(1+b^2) + 2b = 0 \quad \therefore\ x = -\frac{b}{(1+b^2)}$$

$f''(x) = 2(1+b^2)$ is always +ive so that $f(x)$ is minimum when $x = -\frac{b}{1+b^2}$

$$\therefore\quad \text{min. } f(x) = (1+b^2)\frac{b^2}{(1+b^2)^2} - \frac{2b^2}{(1+b^2)} + 1$$

$$= \frac{(1+b^2) - b^2}{1+b^2} = \frac{1}{(1+b^2)} = m(b)$$

$$1 + b^2 > 1 \quad \therefore\ \frac{1}{1+b^2} < 1$$

$$\therefore\quad m(b) = \frac{1}{1+b^2} = +\text{ive but less than 1.}$$

Clearly $m(b)$ is always greater than zero and less than or equal to 1.

$\therefore$ Range of $m(b)$ is $(0, 1]$.

(d) Ans. (a). $f(x) = (x+b)^2 + (2c^2 - b^2)$

$$g(x) = (b^2 + c^2) - (x+c)^2$$

min. $f(x) = 2c^2 - b^2$ when $x = -b$

max. $g(x) = b^2 + c^2$ when $x = -c$

By given condition $2c^2 - b^2 > b^2 + c^2$

$\Rightarrow\ c^2 > 2b^2 \Rightarrow |c| \ge |b|\sqrt{2}$.

(e) $f'(x) = \sin a \tan^2 x \sec^2 x + (\sin a - 1)\sec^2 x = 0$

$$\therefore\quad \tan^2 x = \frac{1 - \sin a}{\sin a}$$

Since $a \in (\pi, 2\pi)$, $\sin a = -$ ive

$$\therefore\quad \tan^2 x = \frac{+}{-} = -\text{ive}$$

Above is not possible and as such $f(x)$ has no critical points.

(f) $f(x) = (k^2 - 3x + 2)\cos\frac{x}{2} + (k-1)x + \sin 1$

$$f'(x) = (k-1)(k-2)\left(-\frac{1}{2}\sin\frac{x}{2}\right) + (k-1)$$

$$= (k-1)\left[1 - \frac{k-2}{2}\sin\frac{x}{2}\right]$$

Since $f(x)$ does not possess critical points therefore $f'(x)$ is not equal to zero.

i.e., $k \ne 1$ or $1 - \frac{k-2}{2}\sin\frac{x}{2} = 0$ does not possess a solution or $\sin\frac{x}{2} = \frac{2}{k-2}$ does not have a solution.

Hence we must have $\left|\frac{2}{k-2}\right| > 1$ as $\left|\sin\frac{x}{2}\right| < 1$.

Above implies that $|k-2|^2 \le 4$

or $\quad -2 < (k-2) < 2$

$\because\quad x^2 < a^2 \Rightarrow (x^2 - a^2) = -$ ive or $-a < x < a$

$\therefore\quad 0 < k < 4. \qquad$ Also $k \ne 1$.

$\therefore\quad k \in (0, 1) \cup (1, 4)$

(g) Ans. (b) and (c).

$$2\cot\frac{x}{2}\sin^2\frac{x}{2} = 2\cos\frac{x}{2}\sin\frac{x}{2} = \sin x$$

$$\therefore\quad f(x) = (4\lambda - 3)(x + \log 5) + (\lambda - 7)\sin x$$

$$f'(x) = (4\lambda - 3) + (\lambda - 7)\cos x = 0 \qquad \text{...(1)}$$

$$\therefore\quad \cos x = \frac{4\lambda - 3}{\lambda - 7} \qquad \text{...(2)}$$

Now $-1 \le \cos x \le 1 \quad \therefore\ -1 \le \frac{4\lambda - 3}{\lambda - 7} \le 1$

Above gives us two inequalities

$$-1 - \frac{4\lambda - 3}{\lambda - 7} \le 0 \quad \text{or} \quad \frac{4\lambda - 3}{\lambda - 7} - 1 \le 0$$

$$\frac{-5\lambda + 10}{\lambda - 7} \le 0 \quad \text{or} \quad \frac{3\lambda + 4}{\lambda - 7} \le 0$$

$$\text{or} \quad \frac{5(\lambda - 2)}{\lambda - 7} \ge 0 \quad \text{or} \quad \frac{3(\lambda + 4/3)}{\lambda - 7} \le 0$$

Above are the conditions for $f(x)$ to have critical points. But the function does not possess critical points. Therefore we must have

$$\frac{5(\lambda - 2)}{\lambda - 7} < 0 \quad \text{or} \quad \frac{3(\lambda + 4/3)}{\lambda - 7} > 0$$

$$\text{or} \quad \frac{5(\lambda - 2)(\lambda - 7)}{(\lambda - 7)^2} < 0 \quad \text{or} \quad \frac{3(\lambda + 4/3)(\lambda - 7)}{(\lambda - 7)^2} > 0$$

$\therefore\quad \lambda \in (2, 7)$ or $\lambda < -4/3$ or > 7

$\therefore\quad \lambda \in (2, 7)$ and $\lambda \in (-\infty, -4/3)$ or $(7, \infty)$

$\therefore\quad \lambda \in (2, \infty)$ or $\lambda \in (-\infty, -4/3)$

(h) Ans. (a).

$$f'(x) = 0 \quad \Rightarrow\ x^2 + 2(a-7)x + (a^2 - 9) = 0$$

$$\therefore\quad x = \frac{-2(a-7) \pm \sqrt{4(a-7)^2 - 4(a^2 - 9)}}{2}$$

$$x = 7 - a \pm \sqrt{58 - 14a}$$

$$58 - 4a > 0 \quad \Rightarrow\ a < \frac{29}{7} \qquad \text{...(1)}$$

Also smaller root is

$(7 - a) - \sqrt{58 - 14a} = +$ ive

$\therefore\quad (7-a)^2 > 58 - 4a \quad \Rightarrow\ a^2 - 9 > 0$

$(a+3)(a-3) > 0 \quad \Rightarrow\ a > 3$ as a is +ive ...(2)

$\therefore\quad a \in \left(3, \frac{29}{7}\right)$ by (1) and (2)

$\therefore\quad$ Length of interval is $\frac{29}{7} - 3 = \frac{8}{7} \quad \Rightarrow$ (a).

18. (a) $x + y = 20$ and $z = xy^3$ is max.

$$\therefore\quad z = y^3(20 - y) = 20y^3 - y^4$$

$$dz/dy = 60y^2 - 4y^3 = 0$$

$\therefore \quad 4y^2 (15-y)=0 \quad \therefore \quad y=0, 15$

$d^2z/dy^2 = 120y - 12y^2$

$= 12y(10-y) = -\text{ive } i.e.$ max.

when $y = 15$.

Hence the two parts are 5 and 15.

(b) 6, 6. $P = 36$

(c) $z = xy = x(8-x) = 8x - x^2$,

$\frac{dz}{dx} = 8 - 2x = 0$

$\therefore \quad x = 4, y = 4, \frac{d^2z}{dx^2} = -2 \therefore$ Max.

19. (a) Ans. 9, 1.

(b) Ans. 12, 8.

(c) Ans. 32, 32.

20. (a) $z = x + y = x + \frac{1}{x}$ etc.

$x = 1, y = 1$, min. value $= 2$.

(b) $y = x - \sin x$,

$\therefore \quad \frac{dy}{dx} = 1 - \cos x = 0$ gives

$\cos x = 1 \Rightarrow x = 0$ or 2π.

Now $\frac{d^2y}{dx^2} = \sin x = 0$ at $x = 0$ or 2π

and $\frac{d^3y}{dx^3} = \cos x$,

whence $\frac{d^3y}{dx^3} \neq 0$ at $x = 0, 2\pi$.

Hence y has neither Max. nor Min. at $x = 0$ or 2π.

(c) Neither Max. nor Min. at $x = \pi/2$

21. (a) $P = 2(x+y) = 100. \quad \therefore \quad x + y = 50$.

$A = xy = x(50-x)$ etc.

$x = 25, y = 25$ *i.e.* rectangle is a square.

(b) Let the line in intercepts form be $\frac{x}{a} + \frac{y}{b} = 1$

It passes through $(h, k) \quad \therefore \quad \frac{h}{a} + \frac{k}{b} = 1$

$\therefore \quad \frac{k}{b} = 1 - \frac{h}{a} = \frac{a-h}{a} \quad \therefore \quad b = \frac{ak}{a-h}$

$\Delta = \frac{1}{2}ab = \frac{1}{2}a.\frac{ak}{a-h} = \frac{1}{2}\frac{k}{\frac{a-h}{a^2}}$ ...(1)

Δ is min. when $y = \frac{a-h}{a^2} = \frac{1}{a} - \frac{h}{a^2}$ is max.

$\therefore \quad \frac{dy}{da} = -\frac{1}{a^2} + \frac{2h}{a^3} = 0 \quad \therefore \quad a = 2h.$ ...(2)

$\frac{d^2y}{da^2} = \frac{2}{a^3} - \frac{6h}{a^4} = \frac{2}{a^3} - \frac{3}{a^3}$ by (2)

$\frac{d^2y}{da^2} = -\frac{1}{a^3} = -\text{ive} \quad \therefore \quad$ max.

Now put $a = 2h$ in (1).

$\Delta = \frac{1}{2}.4h^2.\frac{k}{h} = 2hk.$

22. (a) Any line through (1, 4) is $y - 4 = m(x-1)$

or $\quad mx - y = m - 4$ where $m = \tan\theta = -$ ive

Its intercepts on the axes are $\frac{m-4}{m}, -(m-4)$

If S be the sum of these intercepts, then

$S = \frac{m-4}{m} - (m-4)$

$S = -m + 5 - \frac{4}{m}$

$\frac{dS}{dm} = -1 + \frac{4}{m^2} \quad \therefore \quad m^2 = 4$

$\therefore \quad m = 2, -2.$

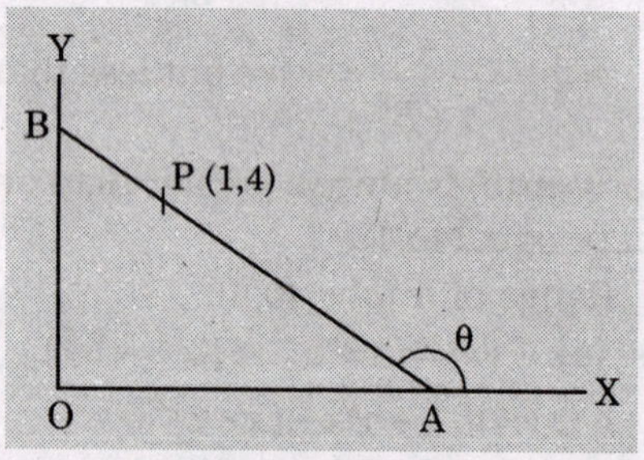

Fig. 10

From the figure, m must be $-$ ive as the line makes an obtuse angle with +ive direction of x-axis. Hence we choose $m = -2$.

Also $\frac{d^2S}{dx^2} = \frac{-8}{m^3} = +1$ for $m = -2 \quad \therefore$ Minimum

2nd part : Area will be least when $m^2 = 16$

$\therefore \; m = -4$ (only) and the intercepts are 2 and 8. Hence the larger side is 8.

(b) Any line through (8, 2) with –ive slope, say $-m$, is $y - 2 = -m(x-8)$ (m + ive)

If it cuts the axes in points P and Q, then

$OP = x = 8 + \frac{2}{m}, OQ = y = 2 + 8m$

$\therefore \quad OP + OQ = 10 + \frac{2}{m} + 8m = z$, say.

For max. or min.,

$\frac{dz}{dm} = -\frac{2}{m^2} + 8 = 0 \quad \therefore \; m^2 = \frac{1}{4}$

or $\quad m = \frac{1}{2}$ (only + ive value)

Clearly, $\frac{d^2z}{dm^2} = \frac{4}{m^3} = 4 \times 8 = 32 = +$ ive, hence minimum.

Putting $m = \frac{1}{2}, z = 18$.

23. (a) $s=\frac{1}{4}t^4-2t^3+4t^2-7$

$v=ds/dt=t^3-6t^2+8t, a=dv/dt=3t^2-12t+8$

v is maximum at $t=2-2/\sqrt{3}$, a is min. when $t=2$.

(b) Min. at $t=2$ and $a=-260$

24. (a) $\psi=\tan^{-1}(x^2-2x)$ $\therefore$ $\tan\psi=\frac{dy}{dx}=x^2-2x$

$\therefore$ $y=\frac{x^3}{3}-x^2+c$. It passes through (2, 0)

$\therefore$ $0=\frac{8}{3}-4+c$ $\therefore$ $c=\frac{4}{3}$ $\therefore$ $y=\frac{x^3}{3}-x^2+\frac{4}{3}$.

We have to find the point for which y is maximum.

$\therefore$ $\frac{dy}{dx}=x^2-2x=0$ $\therefore$ $x=0, 2$.

$\frac{d^2y}{dx^2}=2x-2=-2$ at $x=0$ $\therefore$ Max.

When $x=0, y=4/3$ $\therefore$ Point is (0, 4/3).

(b) Slope $S=dy/dx=-3x^2+6x+2$ etc.

Ans. 5 at (1, – 23)

25. (a) Here slope

$S=dy/dx=\{1.(1+x^2)-2x.x\}/(1+x^2)^2$

$=(1-x^2)/(1+x^2)^2$

$\therefore$ $\frac{dS}{dx}=\{-2x(1+x^2)^2-2(1+x^2).$

$2x(1-x^2)\}/(1+x^2)^4$

$=\frac{-2x(1+x^2)(3-x^2)}{(1+x^2)^4}$

$=\frac{2x[x-(-\sqrt{3})][x-\sqrt{3}]}{(1+x^2)^3}$.

For max. or min. of S, $dS/dx=0$.

This gives $x=-\sqrt{3}, 0, \sqrt{3}$.

It can be checked that for $x=0, dS/dx$ changes from + ive to – ive

At $x=\pm\sqrt{3}$, it changes from – ive to + ive.

Hence slope S is maximum when $x=0$ and min. when $x=\pm\sqrt{3}$. Thus for greatest slope, we have $x=0$ and $y=0$.

Hence the required point is (0, 0), that is, the origin.

(b) $y=\frac{x^2-1}{x^2+1}=\frac{x^2+1-2}{x^2+1}=1-\frac{2}{x^2+1}$

$S=\text{slope}=\frac{dy}{dx}=\frac{4x}{(x^2+1)^2}$

For max. and min. of S, $\frac{dS}{dx}=0$

$\frac{dS}{dx}=4\frac{(x^2+1)^2.1-x.2(x^2+1).2x}{(x^2+1)^4}$

$=4\frac{x^2+1-4x^2}{(x^2+1)^3}$

or $\frac{dS}{dx}=4\frac{1-3x^2}{(1+x^2)^3}=\frac{-12\left(x+\frac{1}{\sqrt{3}}\right)\left(x-\frac{1}{\sqrt{3}}\right)}{(1+x^2)^3}$

$\therefore$ $x=\frac{1}{\sqrt{3}}, -\frac{1}{\sqrt{3}}$

Now consiser change of sign at $x=\frac{1}{\sqrt{3}}$, $\frac{dz}{dx}$ changes from + to – and hence max. at $x=\frac{1}{\sqrt{3}}$. When $x=\frac{1}{\sqrt{3}}$ the value of $y=-\frac{1}{2}$.

Hence the point is $\left(\frac{1}{\sqrt{3}}, -\frac{1}{2}\right)$.

26. (a) Let the point $P(x, y)$ be on the parabola $y=x^2+7x+2$

Its distance from the line

$y=3x-3$ or $3x-y-3=0$ is

$D=\left|\frac{3x-y-3}{\sqrt{(10)}}\right|=\left|\frac{3x-(x^2+7x+2)-3}{\sqrt{(10)}}\right|$

$=\left|\frac{-x^2-4x-5}{\sqrt{(10)}}\right|$

$D=\left|\frac{x^2+4x+5}{\sqrt{(10)}}\right|=\left|\frac{(x+2)^2+1}{\sqrt{(10)}}\right|$

$=\frac{(x+2)^2+1}{\sqrt{(10)}}$ as $\frac{N^r}{D^r}$ is + ive

$\frac{dD}{dx}=\frac{2(x+2)}{\sqrt{(10)}}=0$, $\therefore$ $x=-2$

and hence y is – 8 *i.e.* point is (– 2, – 8).

$\frac{d^2D}{dx^2}=\frac{2}{\sqrt{(10)}}=+\text{ive}$

and hence min. at (– 2, – 8).

(b) Let $P(h, k)$ be any point on the parabola $x^2=y$ $\therefore$ $h^2=k$

If $D=PA$

$z=D^2=h^2+(k-a)^2=k+(k-a)^2$

$\frac{dz}{dk}=1+2(k-a)=0$ $\therefore$ $k=\frac{2a-1}{2}$

$\frac{d^2z}{dk^2}=+2$ $\therefore$ Min. Also $h=\pm\sqrt{k}$

$\therefore$ P is (h, k) *i.e.* $\left(\pm\sqrt{\frac{2a-1}{2}}, \frac{2a-1}{2}\right)$.

(c) Do yourself.

Ans. $(\pm 2\sqrt{2}, 4)$.

(d) Standard form : $\frac{x^2}{6}+\frac{y^2}{3}=1\left[\frac{x^2}{a^2}+\frac{y^2}{b^2}=1\right]$

Any point on the ellipse is

$(\sqrt{6}\cos\theta, \sqrt{3}\sin\theta), a=\sqrt{6}, b=\sqrt{3}$.

The given line $x+y=7$ has slope $=-1$

The distance of any point P on the ellipse tangent at which is parallel to the line will be least from the line.

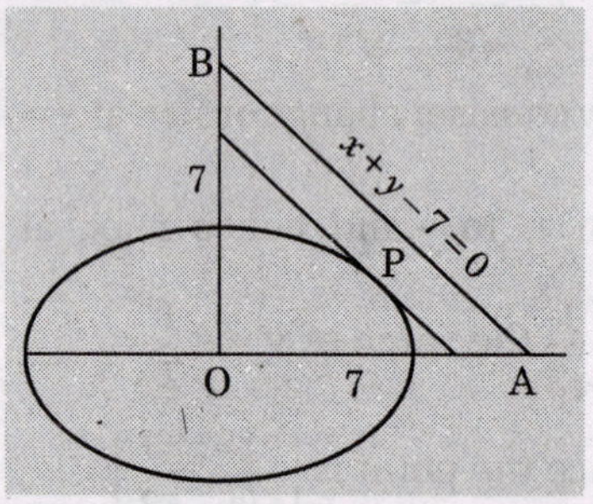

Fig. 11

In other words $\frac{dy}{dx}$ at $P=-1$

$\frac{2x}{6}+\frac{2y}{3}\cdot\frac{dy}{dx}=0 \quad \therefore \quad \frac{dy}{dx}=-\frac{x}{2y}=-1$

$\therefore \quad x=2y \quad$ or $\quad \sqrt{6}\cos\theta=2\sqrt{3}\sin\theta$

$\therefore \quad \tan\theta=\frac{1}{\sqrt{2}}$

or $\quad \sin\theta=\frac{1}{\sqrt{3}}, \cos\theta=\sqrt{\frac{2}{3}}$.

$\therefore$ Point P is (2, 1) on putting for $\sin\theta$ and $\cos\theta$.

27. (a) Let $P(t, t^2)$ be the parametric co-ordinates of any point on the parabola $y=x^2$.

$\therefore \quad \frac{dy}{dx}=2x=2t$.

Hence the normal at P is

$y-t^2=-\frac{1}{2t}(x-t)$ ...(1)

If it meets the curve again at Q whose parameter is say t' then the point (t', t'^2) will satisfy (1).

$\therefore \quad t'^2-t^2=-\frac{1}{2t}(t'-t)$

or $\quad t'+t=-\frac{1}{2t}$ (as $t\neq t'$) ...(2)

$\therefore \quad t'=-t-\frac{1}{2t}$.

If l be the length of normal chord, then

$z=l^2=PQ^2=(t-t')^2+(t^2-t'^2)^2$

$z=(t-t')^2\,[1+(t+t')^2]$.

Put for t' from (2)

$\therefore \quad z=\left(t+t+\frac{1}{2t}\right)^2\left[1+\left(\frac{-1}{2t}\right)^2\right]$

or $\quad z=\frac{(4t^2+1)^2}{4t^2}\cdot\frac{4t^2+1}{4t^2}=\frac{(4t^2+1)^3}{16t^4}$

Now put $4t^2=p$ where p is +ive.

$\therefore \quad z=\frac{(p+1)^3}{p^2}=p+3+\frac{3}{p}+\frac{1}{p^2}$

$\frac{dz}{dp}=1-\frac{3}{p^2}-\frac{2}{p^3}=0$

or $\quad p^3-3p-2=0$ or $(p+1)(p^2-p-2)=0$

or $\quad (p+1)(p+1)(p-2)=0$

$\therefore \quad p=2$ as $p\neq -1$

$\frac{d^2z}{dp^2}=\frac{6}{p^3}+\frac{6}{p^4}=$ +ive for $p=2=4t^2$

Hence z is minimum when $t^2=\frac{1}{2}$ or $t=\pm\frac{1}{\sqrt{2}}$

$z=l^2=\frac{(2+1)^3}{2^2}=\frac{27}{4} \quad \therefore \quad l=\frac{3\sqrt{3}}{2}$

Hence from (1), the equations of normal are

$y-\frac{1}{2}=\pm\frac{1}{\sqrt{2}}x+1$.

Another form :

The normal at the point $(at^2, 2at)$ on the parabola $y^2=4ax$ cuts the curve again in Q. Prove that the minimum length of PQ is $6\sqrt{3}a$.

Proceed as above. $t'=-t-\frac{2a}{t}$.

(b) Any point on the hyperbola is $(a\sec\theta, b\tan\theta)$ where $a=2\sqrt{6}, b=3\sqrt{2}$. If p be its distance from the line $3x+2y+1=0$ then $p=\left|\frac{3a\sec\theta+2b\tan\theta+1}{\sqrt{13}}\right|$

Now p will be max. or min. if $z=p^2$ is max. or min.

$\therefore \quad z=\frac{1}{13}(3a\sec\theta+2b\tan\theta+1)^2$

$\frac{dz}{d\theta}=2p\frac{dp}{d\theta}=0 \quad \therefore \quad \frac{dp}{d\theta}=0$ as $p\neq 0$

or $\quad 3a\sec\theta\tan\theta+2b\sec^2\theta=0$

$\therefore \quad \sin\theta=-\frac{2b}{3a} \quad$ or $\quad \sin\theta=-\frac{2}{3}\frac{3\sqrt{2}}{2\sqrt{6}}=-\frac{1}{\sqrt{3}}$

$\therefore \quad \cos\theta=\pm\sqrt{\frac{2}{3}}$

Putting the values of $\sin\theta, \cos\theta$ the points are $(6,-3)$ and $(-6,3)$.

The distances of these points from the given line are respectively $\sqrt{13}$ and $11/\sqrt{13}$. Clearly the distance from second point $(-6, 3)$ is least.

28. Let the dimensions of the page be x (length) and y (breadth).

After leaving the margins these dimensions are $x-3$ and $y-2$, where $xy=150$ ...(1)

Area A of printed matter is given by

$$A=(x-3)(y-2)=xy-3y-2x+6$$

or $A=150-\dfrac{450}{x}-2x+6$, by (1).

Rest as before ; $x=15$ for A to be maximum.

$\therefore\quad y=10$ by (1).

29. (a) Let P be the pumping station at a distance x from A the point nearest to the town T_1. Also $AB=10$.

$\therefore\quad PB=10-x.$

Let p be the length of the pipe required.

$$p=T_1P+T_2P$$
$$=\sqrt{36+x^2}+\sqrt{18^2+(10-x)^2}.$$

We want p to be minimum.

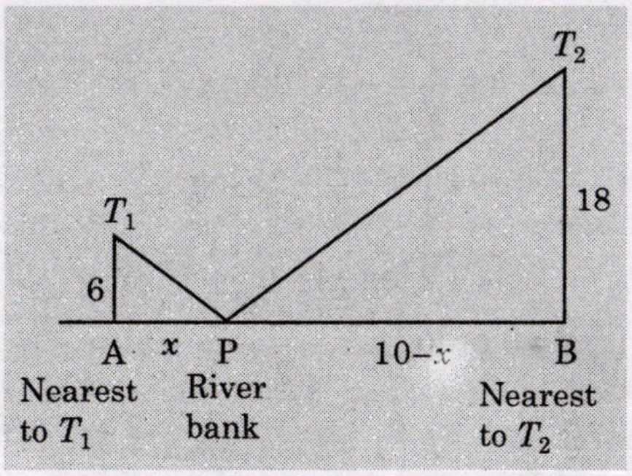

Fig. 12

$$\therefore\quad \frac{dp}{dx}=\frac{2x}{2\sqrt{(36+x^2)}}-\frac{2(10-x)}{2\sqrt{[18^2+(10-x)^2]}}=0$$

$$\therefore\quad \frac{x}{\sqrt{(36+x^2)}}=\frac{10-x}{\sqrt{[18^2+(10-x)^2]}}.\ \text{Square}$$

$$x^2[18^2+(10-x)^2]=(10-x)^2(36+x^2)$$
$$18^2x^2=(10-x)^2[36+x^2-x^2]$$
$$=36(10-x)^2$$
$$18x=\pm 6(10-x)$$

or $18x=60-6x$ or $18x=-60+6x$

or $24x=+60$ or $12x=-60$

$\therefore\quad x=5/2$ or -5.

The value of x cannot be – ive and hence we shall consider $x=5/2$.

It is easy to observe that

$$\frac{d^2p}{dx^2}=\frac{36}{(36+x^2)^{3/2}}+\frac{18}{\{18^2+(10-x)^2\}^{3/2}}.$$

Above is + ive for $x=5/2$ and hence p is minimum.

Putting $x=5/2$ in (1) the minimum length of pipe is

$$p=\sqrt{\left(36+\frac{25}{4}\right)}+\sqrt{\left(324+\frac{225}{4}\right)}$$
$$=\frac{13}{2}+\frac{39}{2}=\frac{52}{2}=26\text{ km.}$$

(b) $p=AP+PB=\sqrt{(a^2+x^2)}+\sqrt{b^2+(c-x)^2}$

$$\therefore\quad \frac{dp}{dx}=\frac{x}{\sqrt{(a^2+x^2)}}-\frac{(c-x)}{\sqrt{b^2+(c-x)^2}}$$

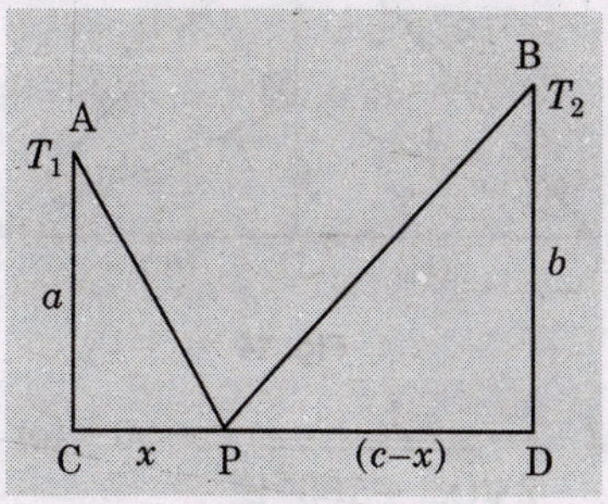

Fig. 13

$$\frac{dp}{dx}=0\ \Rightarrow\ x^2\{b^2+(c-x)^2\}=(c-x)^2[a^2+x^2]$$
$$x^2b^2=(c-x)^2[a^2+x^2-x^2]=a^2(c-x)^2$$

$\therefore\quad \pm bx=a(c-x)$

$(a\pm b)\,x=ac\quad\therefore\quad x=\dfrac{ac}{a+b},\neq\dfrac{ac}{a-b}$

The other value is rejected as

$$x=\frac{ac}{a-b}>c\text{ but }x<c.$$

When $\quad x=\dfrac{ac}{a+b},\ c-x=\dfrac{bc}{a+b}$ ...(1)

Differentiate $\dfrac{dp}{dx}$ by product (not as Quotient)

$$\frac{d^2p}{dx^2}=\frac{1}{\sqrt{(a^2+x^2)}}+\frac{1}{\sqrt{b^2+(c-x)^2}}$$
$$-x.\frac{1}{2}.\frac{2x}{(a^2+x^2)^{3/2}}+(c-x).\frac{1}{2}.\frac{2(c-x)(-1)}{\sqrt{b^2+(c-x)^2}}$$
$$=\frac{a^2+x^2-x^2}{(a^2+x^2)^{3/2}}+\frac{b^2+(c-x)^2-(c-x)^2}{[b^2+(c-x)^2]^{3/2}}$$
$$=\frac{a^2}{(a^2+x^2)^{3/2}}+\frac{b^2}{[b^2+(c-x)^2]^{3/2}}\quad ...(2)$$

Now putting the value of x and $c-x$ from (1) in (2), we get

$$\frac{d^2p}{dx^2}=\frac{(a+b)^3}{\{(a+b)^2+c^2\}^{3/2}}\left[\frac{1}{a}+\frac{1}{b}\right]$$
$$=\frac{(a+b)^4}{ab\{(a+b)^2+c^2\}^{3/2}}=+\text{ive}.$$

Hence minimum.

30. (a) Let G be the position of godown at a distance x each from A and B.

Also $\quad CD=\sqrt{200^2-160^2}=120$

$$GD=\sqrt{x^2-160^2}$$

$\therefore\quad GC=DC-DG=120-\sqrt{x^2-160^2}$

If $\quad y=GA+GB+GC$, then

$$y=2x+120-\sqrt{x^2-160^2}$$

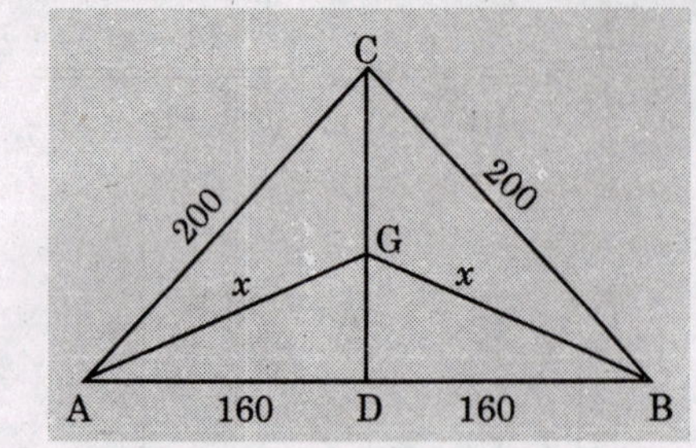

Fig. 14

$$\frac{dy}{dx} = 2 - \frac{1}{2\sqrt{(x^2 - 160^2)}} . 2x = 0 \quad \text{for max. or min.}$$

$$\therefore \quad \frac{2}{x} = \frac{1}{\sqrt{(x^2 - 160^2)}} \qquad \text{...(1)}$$

or $\quad 4(x^2 - 160^2) = x^2 \quad \therefore \quad x = \dfrac{320}{\sqrt{(3)}}$

$$\frac{d^2y}{dx^2} = -\left[1 . \frac{1}{\sqrt{(x^2 - 160^2)}} + x \cdot \frac{-1}{2(x^2 - 160^2)^{3/2}} 2x\right]$$

$$= -\left[\frac{2}{x} - x^2 \cdot \frac{8}{x^3}\right] \text{by (1)}$$

$$= \frac{6}{x} = + \text{ive}$$

$\therefore$ y is minimum when $x = \dfrac{320}{\sqrt{(3)}}$ and G is on the perpendicular bisector of AB.

(b) **See part (a).**

Ans. $x = 10\sqrt{3}$ km.

31. (a) If R rupees per km be the freight for rail, then that by road will be $2R$ per km. If C be the total cost, then

$$C = R\,[2\sqrt{x^2 + 75} + (20 - x)] \text{ etc.}$$

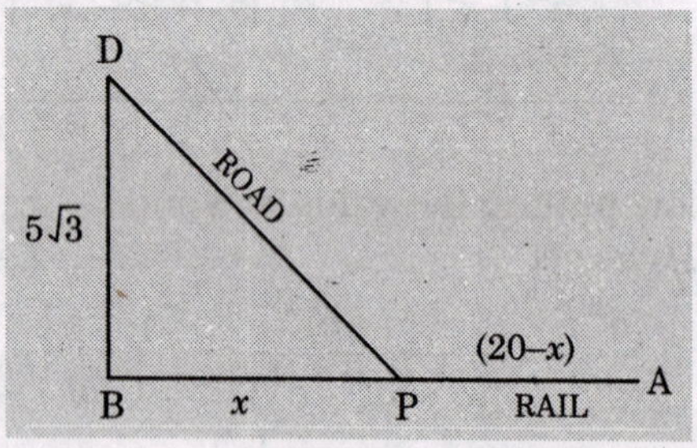

Fig. 15

$x = 5$ for C to be minimum.

(b) $PQ^2 = OP^2 + OQ^2 - 2OP.OQ \cos 60°$

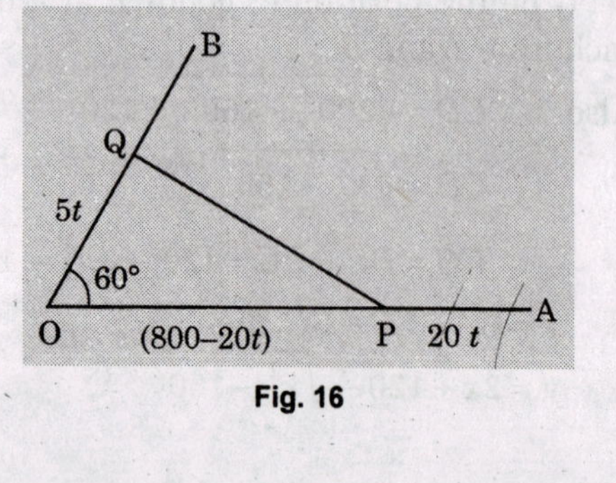

Fig. 16

PQ will be minimum when $z = PQ^2$ is minimum.

$$\therefore \quad PQ^2 = z = (800 - 20t)^2 + 25t^2 - 2.(800 - 20t)(5t) . \frac{1}{2}$$

or $\quad z = (800 - 20t)^2 + 25t^2 - 5(800t - 20t^2)$

$$\frac{dz}{dt} = -40(800 - 20t) + 50t - 5(800 - 40t) = 0$$

$$1050t - 36000 = 0$$

$$t = \frac{36000}{1050} = \frac{240}{7} .$$

Clearly $\dfrac{d^2z}{dt^2} = 1050 = +$ ive and hence z is min. when $t = \dfrac{240}{7}$ sec.

32. (a) $S = k.x^2 \log \dfrac{1}{x} = -kx^2 \log x$

$$\frac{dS}{dx} = -k\left[x^2 . \frac{1}{x} + 2x \log x\right] = 0$$

or $\quad -kx(1 + 2\log x) = 0$

$\therefore \quad x = 0$ or $\log x = -\dfrac{1}{2} \quad \therefore \quad x = e^{-1/2} = 1/\sqrt{e}$

$$\frac{d^2S}{dx^2} = -k\left(1 + 2\log x + x.\frac{2}{x}\right)$$

$$= -k(3 + 2\log x)$$

$$= -k(3 - 1) = -2k = -\text{ive}$$

and hence S is maximum when $x = 1/\sqrt{e}$.

Hence the required ratio x is $1 : \sqrt{e}$ for speed to be max.

(b) For max. or min. we must have $\dfrac{dE}{d\theta} = 0$

$$\frac{dE}{d\theta} = \frac{\tan(\theta + \alpha)\sec^2\theta - \tan\theta \sec^2(\theta + \alpha)}{\tan^2(\theta + \alpha)} = 0$$

$$= \frac{\tan(\theta + \alpha)\cos^2(\theta + \alpha) - \tan\theta . \cos^2\theta}{\cos^2\theta . \cos^2(\theta + \alpha) . \tan^2(\theta + \alpha)} = 0$$

$\therefore \quad N^r = 0$

or $\quad \tan(\theta + \alpha)\cos^2(\theta + \alpha) = \tan\theta . \cos^2\theta$

or $\quad 2\sin(\theta + \alpha)\cos(\theta + \alpha) = 2\sin\theta\cos\theta$

$\therefore \quad \sin(2\theta + 2\alpha) - \sin 2\theta = 0$

or $\quad 2\sin\alpha\cos(2\theta + \alpha) = 0 \qquad$ ...(1)

α is constant so that $\sin\alpha \neq 0$

$\therefore \quad \cos(2\theta + \alpha) = 0$

$\therefore \quad 2\theta + \alpha = \dfrac{\pi}{2}$ or $\theta = \dfrac{\pi}{4} - \dfrac{\alpha}{2}$

To find $\dfrac{d^2E}{d\theta^2}$ will be difficult. Hence we adopt the rule of change of sign of $\dfrac{dE}{d\theta}$.

$$\frac{dE}{d\theta} = \frac{1}{2} . \frac{2\sin\alpha\cos(2\theta + \alpha)}{+\text{ive}}, \text{ by (1)} \qquad \text{...(2)}$$

If $\theta < \frac{\pi}{4} - \frac{\alpha}{2}$ or $2\theta + \alpha < \frac{\pi}{2}$ $\therefore$ $\frac{dE}{d\theta} = +\text{ive}$.

$\theta > \frac{\pi}{4} - \frac{\alpha}{2}$ or $2\theta + \alpha > \frac{\pi}{2}$ $\therefore$ $\frac{dE}{d\theta} = -\text{ive}$.

Thus $\frac{dE}{d\theta}$ changes sign from +ive to – ive and hence E is maximum when $\theta = \frac{\pi}{4} - \frac{\alpha}{2}$

We have to find E for $\theta = \frac{\pi}{4} - \frac{\alpha}{2}$

or $\theta + \alpha = \frac{\pi}{4} + \frac{\alpha}{2}$

$$\therefore \quad E = \frac{\tan\theta}{\tan(\theta+\alpha)} = \frac{\tan\left(\frac{\pi}{4} - \frac{\alpha}{2}\right)}{\tan\left(\frac{\pi}{4} + \frac{\alpha}{2}\right)}$$

$$= \frac{1 - \tan(\alpha/2)}{1 + \tan(\alpha/2)} \cdot \frac{1 - \tan(\alpha/2)}{1 + \tan(\alpha/2)}$$

$$= \frac{(\cos\alpha/2 - \sin\alpha/2)^2}{(\cos\alpha/2 + \sin\alpha/2)^2}$$

$$= \frac{1 - 2\sin\alpha/2\cos\alpha/2}{1 + 2\sin\alpha/2\cos\alpha/2} = \frac{1 - \sin\alpha}{1 + \sin\alpha}$$

33. (a) Let the speed of the train be v and distance to be covered be s so that total time taken is s/v hours.

Cost of fuel per hour $= kv^2$ (k is constant)

Also $48 = k.16^2$ by given condition $\therefore k = 3/16$.

$\therefore$ Cost of fuel per hour $= \frac{3}{16}v^2$.

Other charges per hour are 300.

$\therefore$ Charges per hour are $\frac{3}{16}v^2 + 300$.

$\therefore$ Total expenses for the journey

$$E = \left(\frac{3}{16}v^2 + 300\right)\frac{S}{v}$$

or $$E = S\left(\frac{3}{16}v + \frac{300}{v}\right)$$

$$\frac{dE}{dv} = S\left(\frac{3}{16} - \frac{300}{v^2}\right) = 0$$

$\therefore$ $v^2 = 1600$ or $v = 40$

$$\frac{d^2E}{dv^2} = S\left(\frac{600}{v^3}\right) = +\text{ive for } v = 40$$

and hence E is minimum.

Hence the most economical speed is 40 m.p.h.

(b) When the meter of the boat shows a speed of v m.p.h. then consumption of petrol is kv^3 per hour where k is constant.

If s be the distance to be covered then it will be covered with effective speed of $v - c$ as it is going against a current of c miles per hour. Hence the total time is $s/(v - c)$ hours.

$\therefore$ $P =$ petrol burnt for the entire journey is

$$\frac{s}{v-c}.(kv^3) \quad \therefore \quad P = ks.\frac{v^3}{v-c}.$$

Now P will be minimum if $z = 1/P$ is maximum.

$$\therefore \quad z = \frac{1}{ks}.\frac{v-c}{v^3} = \frac{1}{ks}\left[\frac{1}{v^2} - \frac{c}{v^3}\right]$$

$$\frac{dz}{dv} = \frac{1}{ks}\left[-\frac{2}{v^3} + \frac{3c}{v^4}\right] = 0 \quad \therefore \quad v = \frac{3c}{2}$$

$$\frac{d^2z}{dv^2} = \frac{1}{ks}\left[\frac{6}{v^4} - \frac{12c}{v^5}\right]$$

$$= \frac{6}{ks.v^4}\left[1 - \frac{2c}{v}\right] = -\text{ive for } v = \frac{3c}{2}.$$

Hence $z = 1/P$ is maximum so that P is minimum for $v = 3c/2$.

(c) Total hours are $500/x$.

Diesel cost in rupees

$$= \frac{1}{300}\left(\frac{900}{x} + x\right) \times 500 \times \frac{40}{100} = \frac{2}{3}\left(\frac{900}{x} + x\right)$$

Payment to driver $= \frac{500}{x}.\frac{3}{2} = \frac{750}{x}$.

If E be the expenses then

$$E = \left(\frac{600}{x} + \frac{2}{3}x\right) + \frac{750}{x} = \frac{1350}{x} + \frac{2}{3}x \text{ etc.}$$

$x = 45$ km. p.h. is the most economical speed.

34. (a) If the increase be Rs. x per subscriber then the rate will be $300 + x$ and subscribers left will be $500 - x$ according to the given condition. If I be the new income, then

$$I = (300 + x)(500 - x) = 150000 + 200x - x^2.$$

$$\therefore \quad \frac{dI}{dx} = 200 - 2x = 0, \quad \therefore \quad x = 100$$

$$\frac{d^2I}{dx^2} = -2 = -\text{ive}.$$

and hence I is max. for $x = 100$.

(b) If daily output is x sets and P the total profit, then

$$P = x\left(50 - \frac{1}{2}x\right) - \left(\frac{1}{4}x^2 + 35x - 25\right)$$

$$= -\frac{3}{4}x^2 + 15x - 25.$$

Then $\frac{dP}{dx} = -\frac{3}{2}x + 15$

or $x = 10$ for max. or min.

Also $\frac{d^2P}{dx^2} = -\frac{3}{2} < 0 \therefore$ max. Hence for max. profit, the daily output must be 10 radio sets.

(c) Let n be the number of subscribers besides 725 subscribers so that the total number of subscribers is $(725 + n)$. If P denotes the total profit, then from the given conditions, we have $P = (725 + n)(1200 - n)$ paise.

Now see Q. 34 part (a).

Here P is maximum when $n = 237 \cdot 5 = 238$ *i.e.* the total number of subscribers is $725 + 238 = 963$.

35. (a) Perimeter of the figure = 20

or $2x + 2r + \frac{1}{2}(2\pi r) = 20$

or $2x = 20 - \pi r - 2r$ ...(1)

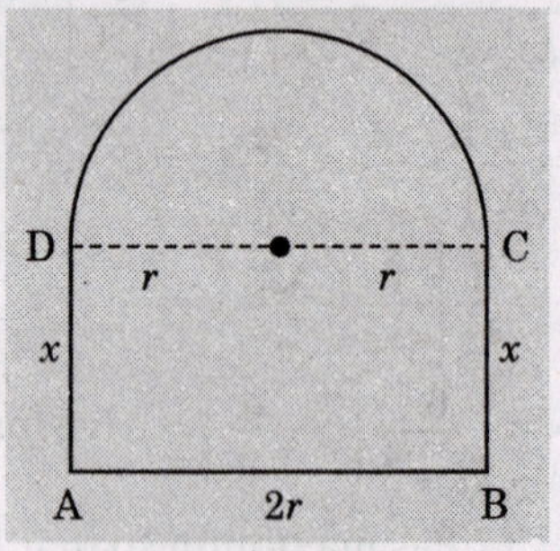

Fig. 17

$A = \frac{1}{2}\pi r^2 + 2r.\,x = \frac{1}{2}\pi r^2 + r(20 - \pi r - 2r)$, by (1)

or $A = 20r - \frac{1}{2}\pi r^2 - 2r^2$.

For max. value of A,

$\frac{dA}{dr} = 20 - \pi r - 4r = 0, \quad \therefore \quad r = \frac{20}{\pi + 4}$

$\frac{d^2A}{dr^2} = -\pi - 4 = -$ ive $\quad \therefore \quad A$ is max.

$\therefore \quad r = \frac{20}{\pi + 4}$ and $2x = \frac{40}{\pi + 4}$, by (1)

(b) Proceed as in (a).

Ans. length $= \frac{20}{\pi + 4}$, breadth $= \frac{10}{\pi + 4}$

(c) Let $2r$ be the diameter of circular arc and x be length of the other side of rectangular portion.

Total perimeter $= 2(2r + x) + \pi r = k$, say ...(1)

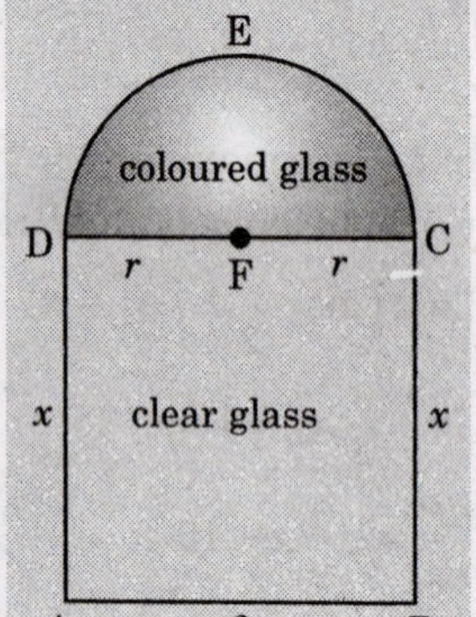

Fig. 18

Let the amount of light per square metre for the coloured glass be c; then for the clear glass it is $3c$ per square metre. Let s denote the total amount of light. Then

$S = (2rx)\,3c + \frac{1}{2}\pi r^2.c = \frac{c}{2}[12rx + \pi r^2]$

$= \frac{c}{2}[6r(k - 4r - \pi r) + \pi r^2]$, by (1)

$= \frac{c}{2}[6rk - 24r^2 - 5\pi r^2]$

$\therefore \quad \frac{dS}{dr} = \frac{c}{2}[6k - 48r - 10\pi r] = 0$

$\therefore \quad r = \frac{6k}{48 + 10\pi}$ ...(2)

$\therefore \quad \frac{d^2S}{dr^2} = \frac{c}{2}[-48 - 10\pi] < 0 \quad \therefore$ Max.

$\therefore \quad 48r + 10\pi r = 6[4r + 2x + \pi r]$, by (1) and (2)

$r(24 + 4\pi r) = 12x \quad \therefore \quad 2r(6 + \pi) = 6x$

$\therefore \quad$ Ratio $= \frac{2r}{x} = \frac{6}{6 + \pi}$.

36. (a) $P = 2y + 3x = 16$ given

$A = xy + \frac{1}{2}x.x.\sin 60^\circ = \frac{\sqrt{3}}{4}x^2 + x\left(\frac{16 - 3x}{2}\right)$

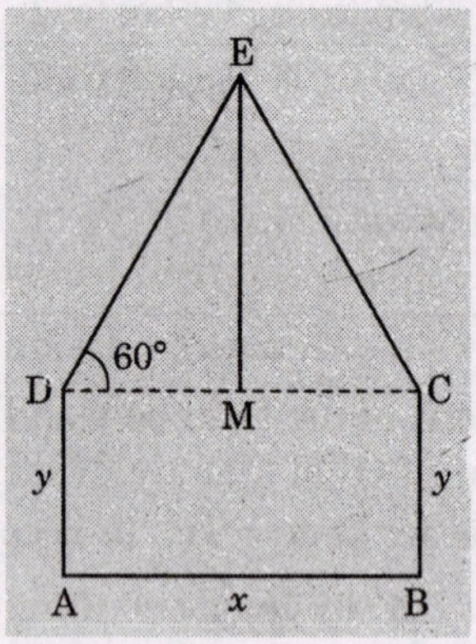

Fig. 19

$A = 8x + \left(\frac{\sqrt{3}}{4} - \frac{3}{2}\right)x^2$

$\frac{dA}{dx} = 8 + \left(\frac{\sqrt{3}}{4} - \frac{3}{2}\right)2x = 0$

or $4 - \frac{(6 - \sqrt{3})}{4}x = 0$.

$\therefore \quad x = \frac{16}{6 - \sqrt{(3)}} = \frac{16(6 + \sqrt{3})}{36 - 3} = \frac{16(6 + 1\cdot73)}{33}$

$= \frac{16(7\cdot73)}{33} = \frac{123\cdot68}{33} = 3\cdot75$ nearly.

Clearly $d^2A/dx^2 = -$ ive and hence A is maximum.

(b) $2\pi r + 4x = k$, $A = \pi r^2 + x^2$ etc.

37. Let x be the depth and y the width of the square base so that

$V = y^2 x$ (given).

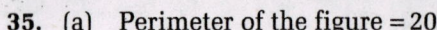

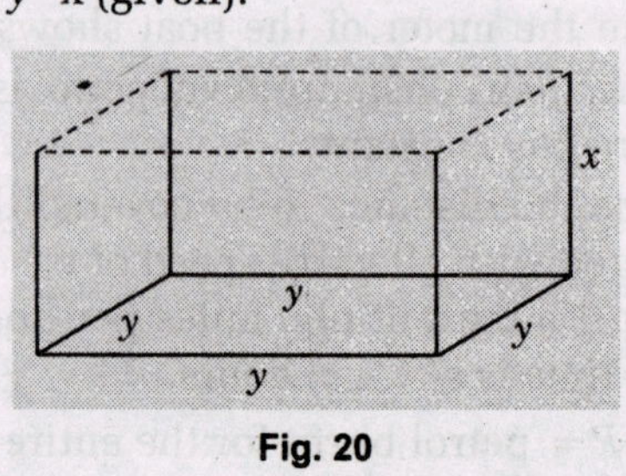

Fig. 20

$S = y^2 + 4(xy)$
base sides

$= y^2 + 4y \cdot \frac{V}{y^2} = y^2 + \frac{4V}{y}$

$\frac{dS}{dy} = 2y - \frac{4V}{y^2} \quad \therefore \quad y^3 = 2V$

$\frac{d^2S}{dy^2} = 2 + \frac{8V}{y^3} = +\text{ive}$

$\therefore$ S is minimum when $y^3 = 2V$

or $y^3 = 2y^2 x \quad \therefore \quad y = 2x$ or $x = y/2$,

i.e. depth is made half of the width.

38. (a) $x^2 h = 1000$, Top $= x^2$, Base $= x^2$,

Sides $= 4xh$

$E = 15x^2 + 25x^2 + 20(4xh) + 300$

bottom top sides labour.

or $E = 40x^2 + 80x\left(\frac{1000}{x^2}\right) + 300$

$= 40x^2 + \frac{80 \times 1000}{x} + 300$

$\frac{dE}{dx} = 0 \quad \therefore \quad 80x - \frac{80 \times 1000}{x^2} = 0$

$\therefore \quad x^3 = 1000$ or $x = 10$

$\frac{d^2E}{dx^2} = 80 + \frac{2 \times 80 \times 1000}{x^3} = +\text{ive}$

$\therefore$ Min. when $x = 10 \quad \therefore \quad h = \frac{1000}{x^2} = 10.$

Hence the box should be a cube of edge 10 feet.

(b) $x^2 h = 250$. Area of base $= x^2$, cost of land $= 50x^2$.

Cost of digging $= 400h^2$.

$E = 400h^2 + 50x^2 = 400h^2 + 50 \cdot \frac{250}{h}$ etc.

$\therefore \quad h = 2{\cdot}5$ and $x = 10.$

39. (a) Dimensions are x breadth, $2x$ length, h height

$V = x \cdot 2x \cdot h = c.$

Area of bottom $= 2x^2 =$ Area of top

and Area of sides $= 2xh + 2xh + xh + xh = 6xh.$

If R rupees be the cost of material for bottom then for the top and sides is $3R$.

$\therefore \quad E = R(2x^2) + 3R(2x^2 + 6xh) = R(8x^2 + 18xh)$

or $E = R\left(8x^2 + 18x \cdot \frac{c}{2x^2}\right) = R\left(8x^2 + \frac{9c}{x}\right)$

where R and c are constants.

$\frac{dE}{dx} = R\left(16x - \frac{9c}{x^2}\right) \quad \therefore \quad x = \left(\frac{9c}{16}\right)^{1/3}$

$\frac{d^2E}{dx^2} = R\left(16 + \frac{18c}{x^3}\right) = +\text{ive}$

and hence minimum.

$\therefore$ dimensions are

$\left[\frac{9c}{16}\right]^{1/3}, \; 2\left[\frac{9c}{16}\right]^{1/3}$ and $\left[\frac{32c}{81}\right]^{1/3}$.

(b) $x^2 + 4hx = 40. \quad V = x^2 h$ etc.

$x = 2\sqrt{\frac{10}{3}}, \; h = \sqrt{\frac{10}{3}}.$

40. The dimensions of the box after cutting equal squares of side x on the corner will be

$21 - 2x$, $16 - 2x$ and height x

$V = x(21 - 2x)(16 - 2x) = x(336 - 74x + 4x^2)$

or $V = 4x^3 - 74x^2 + 336x$

$\frac{dV}{dx} = 12x^2 - 148x + 336 = 0$

or $3x^2 - 37x + 84 = 0.$

$\therefore \quad (x - 3)(3x + 28) = 0 \quad \therefore \quad x = 3$

$\frac{d^2V}{dx^2} = 6x - 37 = 18 - 37$

$= -19 = -\text{ive}$ for $x = 3.$

Hence V is max. when $x = 3.$

41. (a) $AP = BQ = 6 \sin \alpha$

$DP = QC = 6 \cos \alpha.$

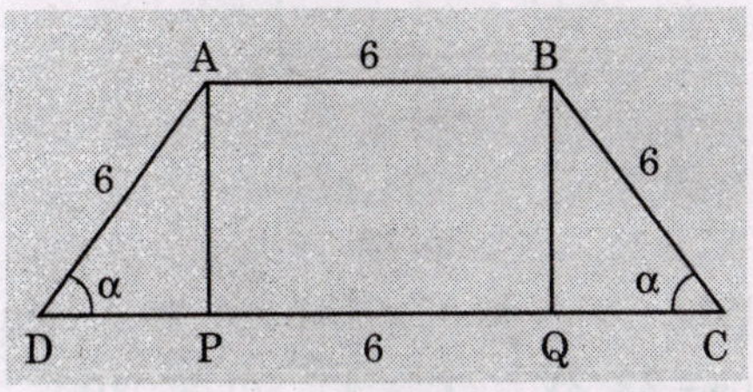

Fig. 21

$A =$ area of the trapezium $= \frac{1}{2}[AB + DC] \cdot BQ$

$= \frac{1}{2}(6 + 6 + 12\cos\alpha) \cdot 6 \sin \alpha$

$= 36 \sin \alpha (1 + \cos \alpha)$

A will be maximum when $\alpha = \pi/3$ **by (1).**

$\therefore \quad A = 36\left(\sin 60^\circ + \frac{1}{2}\sin 120^\circ\right)$

$= 36\left[\frac{\sqrt{3}}{2} + \frac{1}{2} \cdot \frac{\sqrt{3}}{2}\right] = 27\sqrt{3}$ sq. inch.

(b) $P(at^2, 2at)$, $L(a, 2a)$

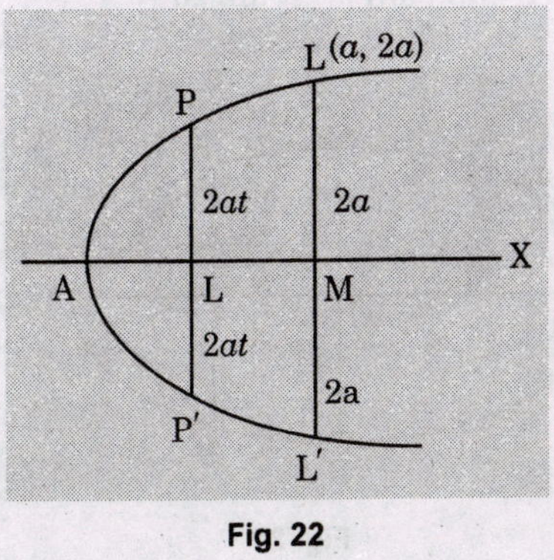

Fig. 22

$LM = AM - AL = a - at^2$

$A =$ area of trapezium $PP'L'L$

$= \frac{1}{2}(PP' + LL') \cdot LM = \frac{1}{2}(4at + 4a)\, a(1 - t^2)$

$A = 2a^2(1 + t)(1 - t^2) = 2a^2(1 + t - t^2 - t^3)$

$\frac{dA}{dt} = 2a^2(1 - 2t - 3t^2) = 0,$

or $2a^2(1 - 3t)(1 + t) = 0 \quad \therefore \quad t = \frac{1}{3}, \; -1$

$\frac{d^2A}{dt^2} = 2a^2(-2 - 6t) = -$ ive for $t = \frac{1}{3}$.

Hence area is maximum when $t = \frac{1}{3}$.

$\therefore \quad LA = at^2 = a \cdot \frac{1}{9} = \frac{a}{9}.$

42. (a) $x^2 + y^2 = a^2$.

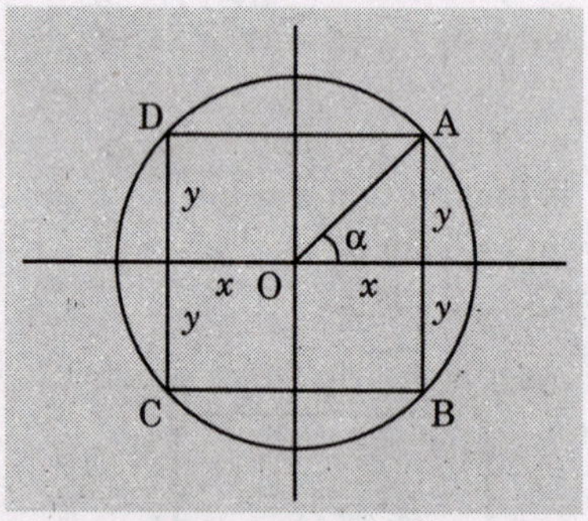

Fig. 23

Let $A(x, y)$ when $x = a\cos\alpha$, $y = a\sin\alpha$.

Area $= 2x \cdot 2y = 4xy = 4a^2 \sin\alpha\cos\alpha$

$A = 2a^2 \sin 2\alpha$.

A is clearly maximum when $\sin 2\alpha = 1$

i.e. $2\alpha = \pi/2$ or $\alpha = \pi/4$.

In that case $x = a\cos 45^\circ = a/\sqrt{2}$

$y = a\sin 45^\circ = a/\sqrt{2}$

i.e. Rectangle is a square.

(b) Proceed as above.

Ans. Length $= \sqrt{2}r$ and breadth $= r/\sqrt{2}$

43. (a) Area $= \frac{1}{2} PP' \cdot AM = \frac{1}{2}(2b\sin\theta)(a - a\cos\theta)$

or $A = ab\left(\sin\theta - \frac{1}{2}\sin 2\theta\right)$

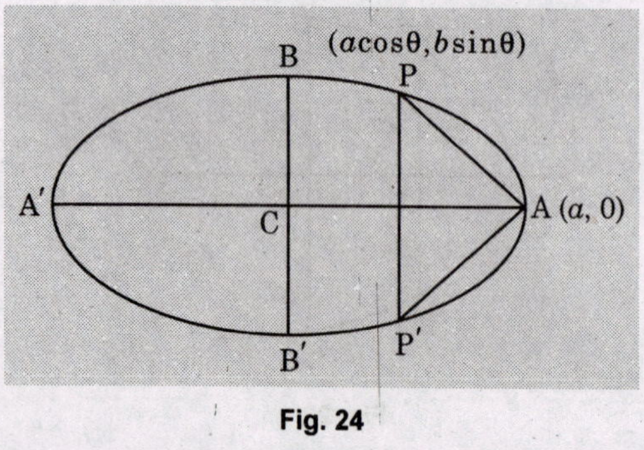

Fig. 24

$dA/d\theta = ab(\cos\theta - \cos 2\theta) = 0$

$\therefore \quad \cos 2\theta = \cos\theta \quad \therefore \quad 2\theta = 2\pi - \theta$

or $\theta = 2\pi/3 = 120^\circ$, $P'(a\cos\theta, -b\sin\theta)$

$\frac{d^2A}{d\theta^2} = ab(-\sin\theta + 2\sin 2\theta)$

$= ab(-\sin 120^\circ + 2\sin 240^\circ)$

$= ab\left[-\frac{\sqrt{3}}{2} + 2\left\{-\frac{\sqrt{3}}{2}\right\}\right] = -$ ive

and hence A is max.

$\therefore \quad A = ab\left(\sin 120^\circ - \frac{1}{2} \cdot \sin 240^\circ\right)$

$= ab\left[\frac{\sqrt{3}}{2} - \frac{1}{2}\left\{-\frac{\sqrt{3}}{2}\right\}\right] = \frac{3\sqrt{3}}{4} ab.$

(b) The given equation is $\frac{x^2}{a^2} + \frac{y^2}{4} = 1$, which represents an ellipse on which any point may be taken as $(a\cos\phi, 2\sin\phi)$.

If d be its distance from $(0, -2)$ then let

$z = d^2 = a^2\cos^2\phi + 4(1 + \sin\phi)^2$

$\frac{dz}{d\phi} = -2a^2\cos\phi\sin\phi + 8(1 + \sin\phi)\cos\phi = 0$ ...(1)

$= (4 - a^2)\sin 2\phi + 8\cos\phi$

From (1), we get $\cos\phi = 0$

or $\sin\phi = \frac{4}{a^2 - 4} = \frac{1}{a^2/4 - 1} > 1$ **(rejected)**

by the given condition $4 < a^2 < 8$

or $1 < a^2/4 < 2$ and this value is rejected.

We choose $\cos\phi = 0 \quad \therefore \quad \phi = \frac{\pi}{2}$, so the point becomes $(0, 2)$.

Also $\frac{d^2z}{d\phi^2} = (4 - a^2)\, 2\cos 2\phi - 8\sin\phi$.

$= (4 - a^2)(-2) - 8 = 2(a^2 - 8) = -$ ive,

as $4 < a^2 < 8$

Hence $z = d^2$ is maximum.

44. (a) $AB + AC =$ constant $= k$

If $AB = x$ then $AC = k - x$

$\therefore \quad BC^2 = (k - x)^2 - x^2 = k^2 - 2kx$

$\therefore \quad \Delta = \frac{1}{2} BC \cdot AB = \frac{1}{2} \cdot x \cdot \sqrt{(k^2 - 2kx)}$

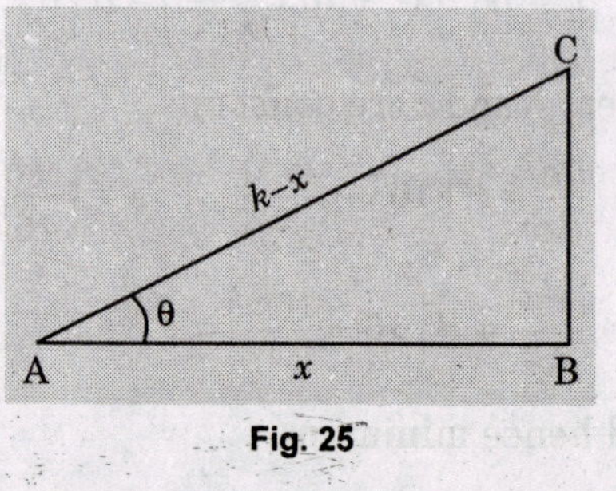

Fig. 25

Let $Z = \Delta^2 = \frac{1}{4} x^2 (k^2 - 2kx) = \frac{1}{4}(k^2 x^2 - 2kx^3)$

Z will be max. when $x = k/3$

$\therefore \quad \cos\theta = \frac{x}{k-x} = \frac{k/3}{k - k/3} = \frac{1}{2} \quad \therefore \quad \theta = 60^\circ$.

(b) **Refer fig. Part (a)** let $AC = 1$ and if its height be $AB = x$ then radius $= BC = \sqrt{(1-x^2)} = r$

$\therefore \quad V = \frac{1}{3}\pi r^2 h = \frac{1}{3}\pi(1-x^2).x$ etc.

For maximum volume

$x = \frac{1}{\sqrt{(3)}}$ and $V = \frac{2\pi}{9\sqrt{(3)}}$ cu. ft.

45. (a) Let the breadth of the beam be x and depth be y where $x^2 + y^2 = 4a^2$.

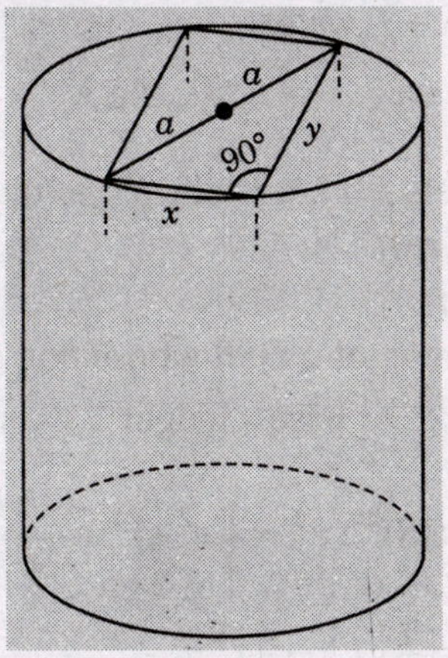

Fig. 26

Strength $= S = kxy^2$ given

or $\quad S = kx(4a^2 - x^2) = k(4a^2 x - x^3)$.

S is max. when $x = \frac{2a}{\sqrt{(3)}}$

and therefore $y = 2a\sqrt{\left(\frac{2}{3}\right)}$.

(b) Here $S = kxy^3$ where $x^2 + y^2 = d^2$

$\therefore \quad S = kx(d^2 - x^2)^{3/2}$.

$z = S^2 = k^2 x^2 (d^2 - x^2)^3$

$\frac{dz}{dx} = k^2 [2x(d^2 - x^2)^3 + x^2 .3(d^2 - x^2)^2(-2x)]$

$= k^2 .2x(d^2 - x^2)^2 [d^2 - 4x^2]$

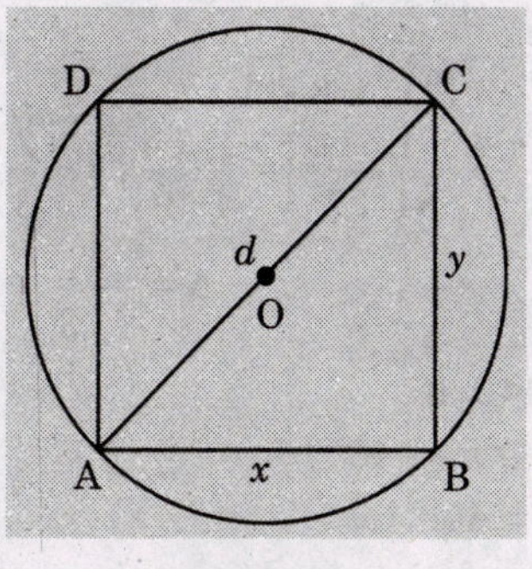

Fig. 27

$= -8k^2 x(d^2 - x^2)^2 [x - (-d/2)][x - (d/2)]$

Above gives $x = d/2$ as x cannot be zero or – ive.

If $x < \frac{d}{2}$, then $\frac{dz}{dx} = -(-) = +$ ive.

If $x > \frac{d}{2}$, then $\frac{dz}{dx} = -(+) = -$ ive.

Thus $\frac{dz}{dx}$ changes sign from +ive to –ive and hence

z i.e. S^2 is minimum when $x = d/2$. *i.e.* breadth $= \frac{1}{2}$ (diameter).

46. (a) Let AB be one of the sides and for the vertex C, it should be in such a position that the altitude CD is max. for greatest area. Hence C is as shown in the figure. Clearly such a triangle is isosceles. Now in order to prove it to be equilateral we must show that

$\angle C = 2\alpha = 60^\circ$. $\quad \therefore \quad \alpha = 30^\circ$.

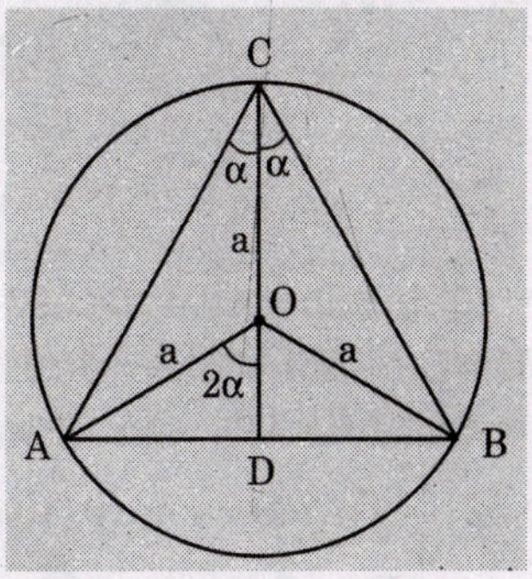

Fig. 28

$A = \Delta\, ABC = \frac{1}{2} AB.CD$

$= \frac{1}{2}.2\,AD\,(CO + OD) = a\sin 2\alpha\,(a + a\cos 2\alpha)$

Now by **result (1) P. 1397,** A is max. when $2\alpha = \frac{\pi}{3}$ or $\alpha = \frac{\pi}{6}$.

Since $\alpha = \pi/6$ or $\quad 2\alpha = \angle C = 60^\circ$

and triangle being isosceles and hence it is an equilateral triangle.

(b) Refer figure as in part (i) if A be the area of triangle PQR then

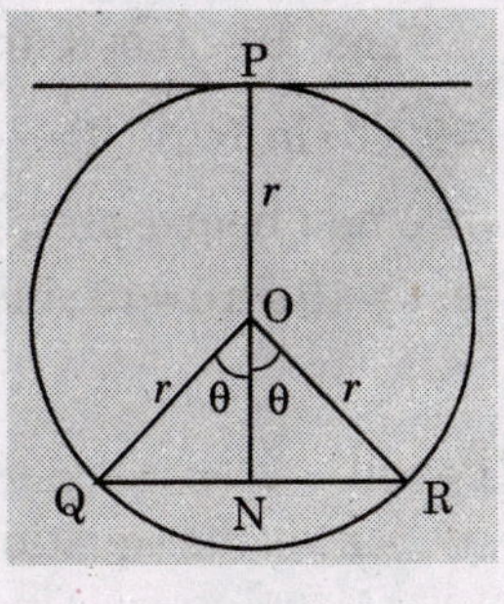

Fig. 29

$$A=\frac{1}{2}QR.PN=\frac{1}{2}\cdot 2QN\,(PO+ON)$$
$$=r\sin\theta.r(1+\cos\theta)$$
$$A=r^2\left(\sin\theta+\frac{1}{2}\sin 2\theta\right)$$

A will be maximum when $\theta=\pi/3$ by **result (1) P. 1397.** In this case the triangle will be equilateral and its area will be

$$r^2\left(\sin\frac{\pi}{3}+\frac{1}{2}\sin\frac{2\pi}{3}\right)=\frac{3\sqrt{3}}{4}r^2$$

(c) Let $\angle APB=2\theta$, $CP=\sqrt{36+64}=10$

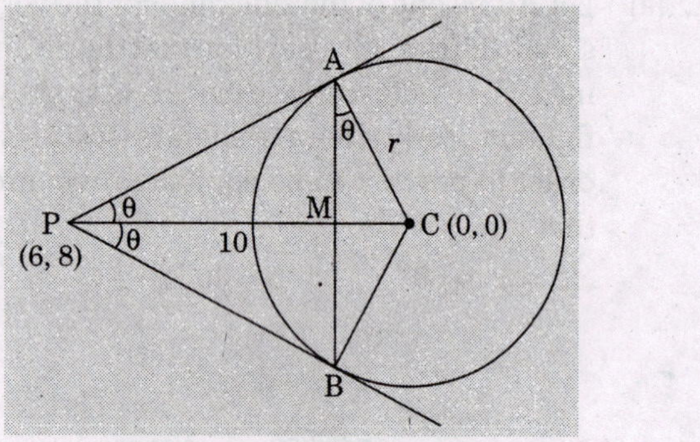

Fig. 30

$\therefore$ $r=10\sin\theta$ and $AP=10\cos\theta$

$PM=CP-CM=10-r\sin\theta$

$A=$ Area of $\Delta\,APB=2\Delta\,APM$

$$A=2\cdot\frac{1}{2}AM.PM=r\cos\theta\,(10-r\sin\theta)$$

Now put $r=10\sin\theta$

$$A=100\,[\sin\theta\cos\theta\,(1-\sin^2\theta)]=100\,[\sin\theta\cos^3\theta] \quad ...(1)$$

Now A will be maximum when $z=\sin\theta\cos^3\theta$ is max.

$$\therefore\ \frac{dz}{d\theta}=\cos^4\theta-3\sin^2\theta\cos^2\theta=0$$

or $\cos^2\theta\,(\cos^2\theta-3\sin^2\theta)=0$

$\therefore$ $\cos\theta=0$ or $\tan^2\theta=\frac{1}{3}$ $\therefore\ \theta=90°$ or $\theta=30°$

Clearly, $\theta=30°$

$$\frac{d^2z}{d\theta^2}=-2\cos\theta\sin\theta\,(\cos^2\theta-3\sin^2\theta)$$
$$+\cos^2\theta\,[-2\cos\theta\sin\theta-6\sin\theta\cos\theta]$$
$$=0-8\sin\theta\cos^3\theta=-\text{ive for }\theta=30°$$

$\therefore$ z is max. and hence, area A is maximum.

$\therefore$ Hence, $r=10\sin\theta=10\sin 30°=5$

47. $x^2+y^2=1$

$\therefore$ $P\,(1,0)$, $Q\,(-1,0)$

Also $(x+1)^2+y^2=r^2$ is the equation of second circle centred at Q and of radius r.

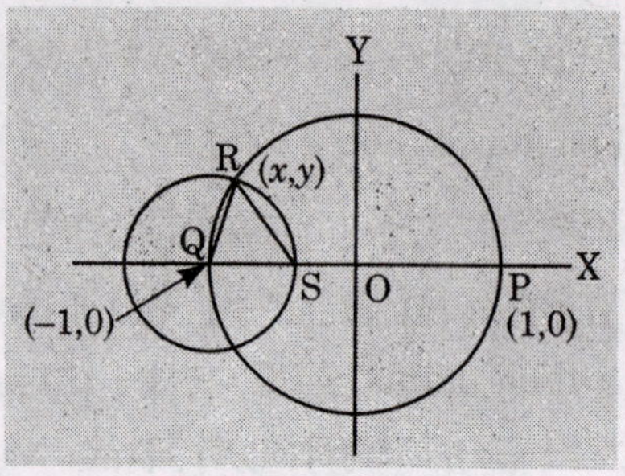

Fig. 31

Solving these, we get

$x^2+y^2+2x+1=r^2$ or $1+2x+1=r^2$

$\therefore$ $x=\frac{r^2}{2}-1$ or $x+1=\frac{r^2}{2}$

Putting for $x+1$, we get

$$y^2=r^2-(x+1)^2=r^2-\frac{r^4}{4} \quad ...(1)$$

Again it meets PQ *i.e.* x-axis or $y=0$ at $S\,(-1\pm r,0)$.

$$\therefore\ QS=\pm r. \quad ...(2)$$

If Δ be the area of $\Delta\,QSR$ whose one side QS is along x-axis, then $\Delta=\frac{1}{2}$ base $\times$ height

$$\therefore\ \Delta^2=\frac{1}{4}(QS)^2\cdot y^2=\frac{1}{4}r^2\left(r^2-\frac{r^4}{4}\right) \text{ by (1) and (2)}$$

$$\text{or}\quad Z=\Delta^2=\frac{1}{4}\left(r^4-\frac{1}{4}r^6\right) \quad ...(3)$$

$$\frac{dZ}{dr}=\frac{1}{4}\left(4r^3-\frac{3}{2}r^5\right)=0\ \therefore\ r^2=\frac{8}{3}$$

$$\therefore\ \frac{d^2Z}{dr^2}=\frac{1}{4}\left(12r^2-\frac{15}{2}r^4\right)=\frac{1}{4}\cdot 3r^2\left(4-\frac{5}{2}r^2\right)$$
$$=\frac{3}{4}\cdot\frac{8}{3}\left[4-\frac{5}{2}\cdot\frac{8}{3}\right]=-\text{ive}$$

$\therefore$ Δ is max. when $r^2=8/3$. Also for this value of r^2 we have from (1)

$$y^2=r^2\left(1-\frac{r^2}{4}\right)=\frac{8}{3}\left(1-\frac{1}{4}\cdot\frac{8}{3}\right)=\frac{8}{3}\cdot\frac{1}{3}=+\text{ive}.$$

$$\therefore\ y=\pm\frac{2\sqrt{2}}{3}$$

or $y=\frac{2\sqrt{2}}{3}$ as R is above PQ, i.e. x-axis.

Putting for r^2 in (3), we get

$$\Delta^2=\frac{1}{4}\cdot\left(\frac{64}{9}-\frac{1}{4}\frac{512}{27}\right)=\frac{1}{4}\cdot\frac{64}{9}\left(1-\frac{2}{3}\right)$$

$$\Delta^2=\frac{16}{27} \qquad \therefore\ \Delta=\frac{4}{3\sqrt{3}}$$

48. Perimeter $=440$ ft.

$2x+\pi r+\pi r=440$

$$\text{or}\quad 2x+2\pi r=440. \quad ...(1)$$

$A=$ Area of rectangular portion $=x.2r$

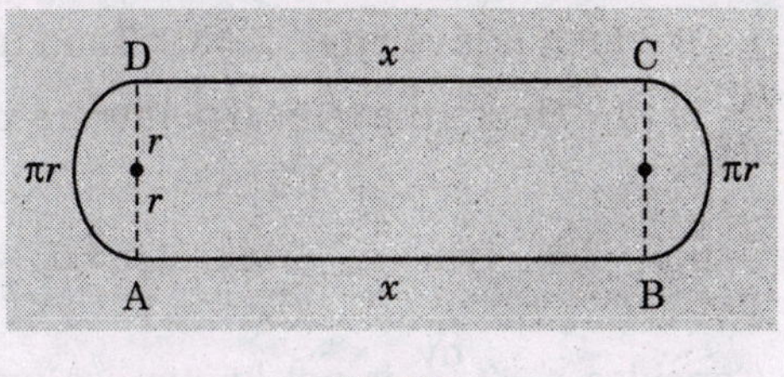

Fig. 32

$$A = x\frac{(440-2x)}{\pi} = \frac{1}{\pi}(440x - 2x^2)$$

$$\frac{dA}{dx} = \frac{1}{\pi}(440-4x) \quad \therefore \quad x = 110$$

$$\frac{d^2A}{dx^2} = -\text{ive}$$

$\therefore$ A is max. when $x = 110$.

$$\therefore \quad 2r = \frac{440-2x}{\pi} = \frac{440-220}{22/7} = 70.$$

Hence the lengths of the sides are 110′ and 70′ for max. area.

49. (a) $2(x+y) = 100,\ A = xy = x(50-x)$

A will be maximum when $x = 25$,

$\therefore \quad y = 25$ *i.e.,* it is a square.

(b) $2(x+y) = 36 \quad \therefore \quad x + y = 18$.

When revolved about side y, it will generate a cylinder of height y and radius x so that

$$V = \pi r^2 h = \pi x^2 y$$

$$V = \pi x^2(18-x) = \pi(18x^2 - x^3)$$

$$\therefore \quad \frac{dV}{dx} = \pi(36x - 3x^2) \quad \therefore \quad x = 12$$

$$\frac{d^2V}{dx^2} = \pi(36-6x) = -\text{ive}$$

when $x = 12 \ \therefore \ y = 6$.

(c) If x be the side of the square and r the radius of the circle then the sum of the perimeter

$$= 4x + 2\pi r = 20 \quad \text{...(1)}$$

If A be the sum of the areas, then

$$A = A_1 + A_2 = x^2 + \pi r^2$$

$$= \left\{\frac{20-2\pi r}{4}\right\}^2 + \pi r^2$$

or $\quad A = \frac{1}{4}\{10 - \pi r\}^2 + \pi r^2$

$$\frac{dA}{dr} = \frac{1}{4}.2\{10-\pi r\}(-\pi) + 2\pi r = 0$$

or $\quad 4r = 10 - \pi r = 2x$ by (1)

$\therefore \quad 4r = 2x$ or $x = 2r$

i.e. the diameter of the circle is equal to side of the square.

Also $\frac{d^2A}{dr^2} = \frac{\pi^2}{2} + 2\pi = +$ive so that A is minimum.

50. (a) Here $f'(x) = 0$ gives $6x^2 - 6x - 12 = 0$, whence $x = -1$ or 2. Both these values lie inside the interval $[-2, 5/2]$. To find the greatest and least values of $f(x)$, it is necessary to compute its values at $x = -1$ and $x = 2$, and also at the end points $x = -2$ and $x = 5/2$. Thus

$$f(-2) = -3,\ f(-1) = 8,\ f(2) = -19,$$
$$f(5/2) = -33/2.$$

Hence the greatest value is $f(-1) = 8$ and the least value is $f(2) = -19$.

(b) Here $f'(x) = x(1 + 2\log x) = 0$ gives $x = 0$ or $x = e^{-1/2}$.

Since $0 < e^{-1/2} < 1$, none of these critical points lies in the interval $[1, e]$. So we only compute the values of $f(x)$ at the end points 1 and e. We have

$$f(1) = 0,\ f(e) = e^2.$$

Thus $f(1) = 0$ is the least value and $f(e) = e^2$ the greatest value of the function.

(c) Do yourself. The greatest value is $f(1) = 1/e$, and the least value is $f(0) = 0$.

51. (a) $f'(x) = 0 \Rightarrow 4x - \frac{4}{x^3} = 0 \quad \therefore \quad x^4 = 1$

$\therefore \quad x = \pm 1$.

The function is neither continuous nor differentiable at $x = 0$. For greatest and least values, we tabulate the values at end points and at critical points.

$$x = -2, \quad 0, \quad 1, \quad -1, \quad 2$$
$$f(x) = \frac{17}{2}, \quad 1, \quad 4, \quad -4, \quad \frac{17}{2}$$

Hence the least value is 1 and greatest value is $\frac{17}{2}$.

Also $\frac{d^2y}{dx^2} = 4 + \frac{12}{x^4} = 16 = +$ive at $x^4 = 1$

$\therefore \quad$ Min. at $x = \pm 1$.

(b) $f\left(\frac{\pi}{2}\right) = -\frac{\pi}{2}, f\left(-\frac{\pi}{2}\right) = \frac{\pi}{2}$

$$\frac{dy}{dx} = 2\cos 2x - 1 = 0 \quad \therefore \quad \cos 2x = \frac{1}{2}$$

$\therefore \quad 2x = -\frac{\pi}{3}, \frac{\pi}{3}$ or $x = -\frac{\pi}{6}, \frac{\pi}{6}$ in $\left[-\frac{\pi}{2}, \frac{\pi}{2}\right]$

$$\frac{d^2y}{dx^2} = -4\sin 2x = +\text{ive for } -\frac{\pi}{6}$$

$\therefore \quad$ Min. at $x = -\frac{\pi}{6}$ and Min. value $= -\frac{\sqrt{3}}{2} + \frac{\pi}{6}$

$$\frac{d^2y}{dx^2} = -\text{ive for } x = \frac{\pi}{6}$$

$\therefore \quad$ Max. at $x = \frac{\pi}{6}$ and Max. value $= \frac{\sqrt{3}}{2} - \frac{\pi}{6}$

$$x = -\frac{\pi}{2} \qquad -\frac{\pi}{6} \qquad \frac{\pi}{6} \qquad \frac{\pi}{2}$$

$$\text{value} = \frac{\pi}{2}, \left(-\frac{\sqrt{3}}{2} + \frac{\pi}{6}\right), \left(\frac{\sqrt{3}}{2} - \frac{\pi}{6}\right), -\frac{\pi}{2}$$

$\frac{\pi}{2}$ is greatest and $-\frac{\pi}{2}$ is least value and their difference is π.

52. (a) $\frac{dy}{dx} = 4(x-8)^3 (x-9)^5 + 5(x-8)^4 (x-9)^4$

$= (x-8)^3 (x-9)^4 [4x - 36 + 5x - 40]$

$= 9(x-8)^3 (x-9)^4 (x - 76/9)$

$\frac{dy}{dx} = 0$ when $x = 8, \frac{76}{9}, 9$ in $0 \le x \le 10$

Apply the test of change of sign of $\frac{dy}{dx}$. We observe that y is max. at $x = 8$, min. at $x = 76/9$ and neither max. nor min. at $x = 9$.

Max. value at $x = 8$ is 0, min. value at $x = 76/9$ is $-\left(\frac{4}{9}\right)^4 \left(\frac{5}{9}\right)^5$. At the end points we have

$f(0) = -8^4 . 9^5$ which is least

$f(10) = 2^4 = 16$ which is greatest.

(b) Ans. (iv). Proceed as in last part.

Max. at $x = -1$.

Min. at $x = 2$ by sign of $\frac{d^2y}{dx^2} = 12x - 6$. But

$f(-2) = -1, f(-1) = 3, f(2) = -15, f(4) = 37.$

Hence the largest value in the interval is 37 which occurs at $x = 4$.

53. (a) $|4 - x^2| = |x^2 - 4| = |(x+2)(x-2)|$.

Hence consider three different cases

$x < -2$, +ive; $-2 \le x < 2$, –ive; $x \ge 2$, +ive

$\therefore \quad y = x^2 - 4, x < -2$

$= -(x^2 - 4) = 4 - x^2, -2 \le x < 2$

$= x^2 - 4, x \ge 2$

$$\therefore \quad \frac{dy}{dx} = \begin{cases} 2x, \quad x < -2 & \quad ...(1) \\ \text{does not exist at } x = -2 & \\ -2x, \quad -2 < x < 2 & \quad ...(2) \\ \text{does not exist at } x = 2 & \\ 2x, \quad x > 2 & \quad ...(3) \end{cases}$$

$\left(\frac{dy}{dx}\right)_{x=2} \quad R' = \lim_{h \to 0} \frac{f(2+h) - f(2)}{h}$

$= \text{Lt} \frac{(2+h)^2 - 4 - 0}{h} = 4$

$L' = \lim_{h \to 0} \frac{f(2-h) - f(2)}{-h}$

$= \text{Lt} \frac{4 - (2-h)^2 - 0}{-h} = -4$

Since $R' \ne L'$

$\therefore \quad \frac{dy}{dx}$ does not exist at $x = 2$. Similarly it does not exist at $x = -2$. For max. or min. $\frac{dy}{dx} = 0$ so that $x = 0$ which is given by $-2 < x < 2$ and in that case $\frac{dy}{dx} = -2x$. Hence the critical points are $x = 0, -2, 2$.

$\frac{d^2y}{dx^2} = -2 = -$ ive $\quad \therefore \quad$ Max. at $x = 0, -2 < x < 2$

Consider $x = 2$, $\frac{dy}{dx}$ is not known, so we consider change of sign of $\frac{dy}{dx}$.

$x = 2 - h, \frac{dy}{dx} = -2(2-h) = -4 + 2h = -$ ive, by (2)

$x = 2 + h, \frac{dy}{dx} = 2(2+h) = 4 + 2h = +$ ive, by (2)

Since $\frac{dy}{dx}$ changes sign from – ive to +ive

$\therefore \quad y$ is min. at $x = 2$.

Similarly at $x = -2$, y is again minimum.

Thus we have min. at $x = -2$, max. at $x = 0$, min. at $x = 2$.

Values are 0, 4, 0 respectively.

Again $f(-3) = f(3) = |4 - 9| = 5$

Hence the greatest value in the given interval is 5, whereas the least value is 0 at $x = 2, -2$. It is also minimum at $x = 2, -2$.

The above results can be exhibited in tabular form as under :

$x =$	-3	-2	0	2	3
$y =$	5	0	4	0	5
	greatest	least as well as local min.	local max.	least as well as local min.	greatest

(b) $x = \varphi(t) = t^5 - 5t^3 - 20t + 7$

$\therefore \quad \dot{x} = 5t^4 - 15t^2 - 20$

$= 5(t^4 - 3t^2 - 4) = 5(t^2 - 4)(t^2 + 1)$

Clearly $\dot{x} \ne 0 \quad$ when $\quad -2 < t < 2 \quad ...(1)$

$y = \psi(t) = 4t^3 - 3t^2 - 18t + 3$

$\dot{y} = 12t^2 - 6t - 18 = 6(2t^2 - t - 3)$

$= 6(2t - 3)(t + 1)$

$\therefore \quad \dot{y} = 0$ gives $t = -1, 3/2$

Both these values satisfy the condition

$-2 < t < 2 \quad ...(2)$

Now $\frac{dy}{dx} = \frac{\dot{y}}{\dot{x}} = 0 \quad (x \ne 0)$

$\therefore \quad \dot{y} = 0 \quad \therefore \quad t = -1, 3/2 \quad$ by (1) and (2)

$\therefore \quad \frac{d^2y}{dx^2} = \frac{d}{dx}\left(\frac{\dot{y}}{\dot{x}}\right) = \frac{d}{dt}\left(\frac{\dot{y}}{\dot{x}}\right)\frac{dt}{dx}$

$= \frac{\dot{x}\ddot{y} - \dot{y}\ddot{x}}{\dot{x}^2} \cdot \frac{1}{\dot{x}} = \frac{\dot{x}\ddot{y}}{\dot{x}^2} \cdot \frac{1}{\dot{x}}$

$\because \dot{y} = 0$ and $\dot{x} \ne 0$

or $\frac{d^2y}{dx^2} = \frac{\ddot{y}}{\dot{x}^2} = \frac{6(4t-1)}{\dot{x}^2}$

$= -$ ive at $t = -1$ and $+$ ive at $t = 3/2$

Hence y is max. at $t = -1$ (i.e. $y = 14, x = 31$) and is minimum at $t = 3/2$

$\left(i.e., \quad y = -17\frac{1}{4}, \; x = -\frac{1033}{32}\right)$.

54. (a) We have

$f(x) = \int_1^x [2(t-1)(t-2)^3 + 3(t-1)^2(t-2)^2]\,dt$

$= \int_1^x (t-1)(t-2)^2 [2(t-2) + 3(t-1)]\,dt$

$= \int_1^x (t-1)(t-2)^2 (5t-7)\,dt$

$\therefore \quad f'(x) = (x-1)(x-2)^2(5x-7)$

Now for max. or min., $f'(x) = 0$. This gives $x = 1, 7/5, 2$

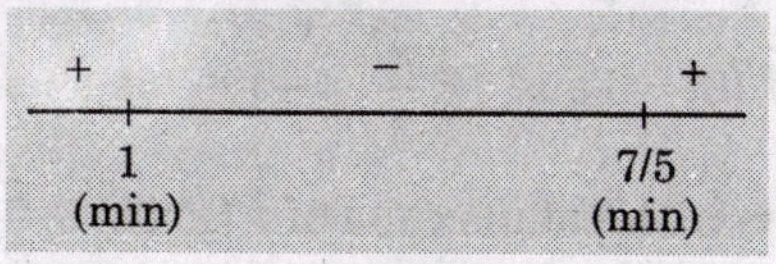

Fig. 33

$f'(x) = \frac{dy}{dx} = 5\left[(x-1)\left(x-\frac{7}{5}\right)\right](x-2)^2$

By change of sign rule at $x = 1$ and $7/5$, we observe that y is max. at $x = 1$ and min. at $x = \frac{7}{5}$. At $x = 2$, $\frac{dy}{dx}$ does not change sign hence it is neither max. nor min. at $x = 2$.

(b) Ans. (b), (d).

$\frac{dy}{dx} = f'(x) = x(e^x - 1)(x-1)(x-2)^3(x-3)^5 = 0$

Critical points are 0, 1, 2, 3.

Consider change of sign of $\frac{dy}{dx}$ at $x = 3$.

$x < 3, \frac{dy}{dx} = -$ ive and $x > 3, \frac{dy}{dx} = +$ ive

Change is from $-$ ive to $+$ ive, hence min. at $x = 3$.

Again min. and max. occur alternately.

$\therefore$ 2nd min. is at $x = 1$.

55. (a) Since $f(x)$ the cubic curve vanishes at $x = -2$ therefore we can choose

$y = f(x) = (x+2)(ax^2 + bx + c)$.

$\frac{dy}{dx} = (x+2)(2ax+b) + 1 \cdot (ax^2 + bx + c) = 0$

at $x = -1$ and $x = 1/3$

$\therefore \quad -a + c = 0$ and $15a + 24b + 9c = 0$

or $\quad 24a + 24b = 0$ or $a + b = 0$

$\therefore \quad c = a, \; b = -a,$

$\therefore \quad y = f(x) = a(x+2)(x^2 - x + 1)$.

Again $\int_{-1}^{1} f(x)\,dx = \frac{14}{3}$ (given)

$\therefore \quad \int_{-1}^{1} a(x+2)(x^2 - x + 1)\,dx = \frac{14}{3}$

$= a\int_{-1}^{1}(x^3 + x^2 - x + 2)\,dx = \frac{14}{3}$

$= 2a\int_0^1 (x^2 + 2)\,dx = \frac{14}{3}$ (Prop. V)

$2a\left[\frac{x^3}{3} + 2x\right]_0^1 = \frac{14}{3}$ or $\frac{14}{3}a = \frac{14}{3}$

$\therefore \quad a = 1, \; b = -1, \; c = 1$

Hence the cubic equation is

$(x+2)(x^2 - x + 1) = 0$.

(b) Let $P(x) = ax^3 + bx^2 + cx + d$.

$P(1) = -6 \quad \therefore \quad a + b + c + d = -6$

$P(-1) = 10 \quad \therefore \quad -a + b - c + d = 10$

$\therefore \quad b + d = 2$ and $a + c = -8$

Also $P'(-1) = 0 \; \therefore \; 3a - 2b + c = 0$

$P'(x)$ has a minima at $x = 1$

$\therefore \quad 3ax^2 + 2bx + c$ has a minima at $x = 1$.

$\therefore \quad P''(x) = 0$, i.e., $6a + 2b = 0$ or $3a + b = 0$.

Solving the above four equations, we have

$a = 1, \; b = -3, \; c = -9, \; d = 5$.

$\therefore \quad P(x) = x^3 - 3x^2 - 9x + 5,$

$P'(x) = 3x^2 - 6x - 9 = 3(x+1)(x-3)$

Hence $x = -1$ is a point of maximum and $x = 3$ is a point of minimum by the rule of change of sign.

For $x = -1, \; y = 10$, and for $x = 3, \; y = -22$.

Hence the points are $(-1, 10)$ and $(3, -22)$ and distance between them is $4\sqrt{65}$ units.

(c) Ans. (a).

Let $f(x) = ax^3 + bx^2 + cx + d$

$f(-1) = 2, f(3) = 18, f'(x)$ has a min. at $x = 0$, so that $f''(x) = 0$ at $x = 0$, $f(x)$ has a local max. at $x = -1$.

$\therefore \quad f'(-1) = 0$

$\therefore$ These conditions imply $-a + b - c + d = 2$

$27a + 9b + 3c + d = 18$

$\therefore \quad 28a + 8b + 4c = 16$

$f'(x) = 3ax^2 + 2bx + c, f''(x) = 6ax + 2b$

$f'(-1) = 0 \quad \Rightarrow \quad 3a - 2b + c = 0,$

$f''(0) = 0 \quad \Rightarrow \quad b = 0$

Putting $b = 0, \quad 7a + c = 4, \quad 3a + c = 0$

$\therefore \quad a = 1, c = -3, b = 0 \quad \therefore \quad d = 0$

Hence $f(x) = x^3 - 3x$

$\therefore \quad f'(x) = 3(x^2 - 1), f''(x) = 6x$

$f'(x) = 0 \quad \Rightarrow \quad x = 1, -1 \quad \therefore \quad y = -2, 2$

$\therefore \quad (1, -2)$ or $(-1, 2) = (a, f(a))$

$f''(x) = 6x = 6 \quad$ at $x = 1$,

$= -6 \quad$ at $x = -1$

$\therefore$ at $(1,-2)$, $f(x)$ is min. and at $(-1,2)$, $f(x)$ is max.

$\therefore \quad d^2 = \sqrt{4+16} = 2\sqrt{5}$

56. (a) Since $f(x)$ has a local max./min. at $x = 1, 2, 3$ hence $f'(x) = 0$ at $x = 1, 2, 3$.

$\therefore \quad f'(x) = a(x-1)(x-2)(x-3)$
$= a(x^3 - 6x^2 + 11x - 6)$

Integrating

$$f(x) = a\left(\frac{x^4}{4} - 2x^3 + \frac{11}{2}x^2 - 6x\right) + b$$

$$f(x) = \frac{a}{4}(x^4 - 8x^3 + 22x^2 - 24x) + b$$

Again $f(-1) = 0 \Rightarrow 0 = \frac{a}{4}(55) + b = 0$

$\therefore \quad b = -\frac{55}{4}a$

$\therefore \quad f(x) = \frac{a}{4}(x^4 - 8x^3 + 22x^2 - 24x - 55) \quad \ldots(1)$

We have to find the value of a and we are given only one condition *i.e.* $\int_{-2}^{2} f(x)\,dx = -\frac{1348}{15}$

or $\frac{a}{4}\left[0 + 2\int_0^2 (x^4 + 22x^2 - 55)\,dx\right] = -\frac{1348}{15}$

by Prop. V of definite integrals

or $\frac{a}{2}\left[\frac{x^5}{5} + 22\frac{x^3}{3} - 55x\right]_0^2 = -\frac{1348}{15}$

or $\frac{a}{2}\left[\frac{32}{5} + \frac{176}{3} - 110\right] = -\frac{1348}{15}$

$\therefore \quad -337a = -1348$ or $a = 4$

Putting for a in (1)

$$f(x) = x^4 - 8x^3 + 22x^2 - 24x - 55.$$

(b) Proceed as above.

Ans. $f(x) = \frac{1}{6}(x^4 - 2x^2 + 18)$

57. Let $f(x) = 3x(x+1) - \pi(\sin x + 2x)$

or $\quad f(x) = 3x^2 + (3 - 2\pi)x - \pi \sin x$

Clearly $f(0) = 0$

and $f\left(\frac{\pi}{2}\right) = 3\cdot\frac{\pi^2}{4} + (3-2\pi)\cdot\frac{\pi}{2} - \pi\cdot 1$

or $\quad f\left(\frac{\pi}{2}\right) = 3\frac{\pi^2}{4} - \pi^2 + \frac{3\pi}{2} - \pi$

$= -\frac{\pi^2}{4} + \frac{\pi}{2} = \frac{\pi}{2}\left(1 - \frac{\pi}{2}\right)$

Since $\frac{\pi}{2} > 1 \quad \therefore \quad f\left(\frac{\pi}{2}\right) = -$ ive.

Now $f(0) = 0$ and $f\left(\frac{\pi}{2}\right) = -$ ive, we shall establish that there is no local maxima of $f(x)$ in $\left[0, \frac{\pi}{2}\right]$ *i.e.*, $f'(x) \neq 0$ in $\left[0, \frac{\pi}{2}\right]$.

$f'(x) = 6x + (3 - 2\pi) - \pi\cos x$

$f''(x) = 6 + \pi \sin x = +$ ive in $\left[0, \frac{\pi}{2}\right]$

Hence $f'(x)$ is an increasing function in $\left[0, \frac{\pi}{2}\right]$ which means that $f'(x)$ is never zero in $\left[0, \frac{\pi}{2}\right]$. Hence $f(x)$ is always $-$ ive in $\left[0, \frac{\pi}{2}\right] \quad \therefore \quad f(x) \le 0$.

or $\quad 3x(x+1) < \pi(\sin x + 2x)$

or $\quad \sin x + 2x \ge \frac{3x(x+1)}{\pi}$.

Problem Set (2)

Geometrical problems on maxima and minima.

1. (a)* A person being in a boat a miles from the nearest point of the beach, wishes to reach as quickly as possible a point b miles from that point along the shore. The ratio of his rate of walking to his rate of rowing is $\sec\alpha$. Prove that he should land at a distance $(b - a\cot\alpha)$ from the place to be reached.

(b) A swimmer S is in the sea at a distance d km from the closest point A on a straight shore. The house of the swimmer is on the shore at a distance L km from A. He can swim at a speed of u km/hr and walk at a speed of v km/hr. At what point on the shore should he land so that he reaches his house in the shortest possible time ?

2.* A lane runs at right angles out of a road a feet wide. Find how many feet wide the lane must be if it is just possible to carry a pole b feet long $(b > a)$ from the road into the lane keeping it horizontal.

3.* A ladder is to be carried in a horizontal position round a corner formed by two streets a ft and b ft. wide meeting at right angles. Prove that the length of the longest ladder that will pass round the corner without jamming is $(a^{2/3} + b^{2/3})^{3/2}$.

4. A tall electric pole is to be kept in vertical position by a stretched straight wire from the pole to the ground. The wire has to clear a wall 6 m high and 4 m from the pole. What is the least length of the wire that can be used between the pole and the ground ?

5. (a)* One corner of long rectangular sheet of paper of width 1 ft. is folded over so as to reach the opposite edge of the sheet. Find the minimum length of the crease.

(b) The lower corner of a leaf in a book is folded over so as to reach the inner edge of the page. Show that the fraction of the width folded over when the area of the folded part is min. is 2/3.

6. (a) Area of the greatest rectangle that can be inscribed in the ellipse $\frac{x^2}{a^2}+\frac{y^2}{b^2}=1$ is :

(a) $\sqrt{ab}$ (b) a/b

(c) $2ab$ (d) ab **(AIEEE 2005)**

(b) Rectangle of maximum area that can be inscribed in an equilateral triangle of side a will have area =

(a) $\frac{a^2\sqrt{3}}{2}$ (b) $\frac{a^2\sqrt{3}}{4}$

(c) $\frac{a^2\sqrt{3}}{8}$ (d) none

7.* A rectangular sheet of metal has four equal square portions removed at the corner and the sides are then turned up so as to form an open rectangular box. Show that when the volume contained in the box is max. the depth will be

$$\frac{1}{6}[(a+b)-(a^2-ab+b^2)^{1/2}]$$

where a and b $(a>b)$ are the sides of the original rectangle. Find the corresponding result if the given metal sheet be a square.

8. Show that the semi-vertical angle of a right cone of given total surface (including area of base) and max. volume is $\sin^{-1}\frac{1}{3}$.

9. (a)* Show that the semi-vertical angle of a cone of max. volume and given slant height is $\tan^{-1}\sqrt{2}$.

(b)* A conical vessel is to be prepared out of a circular sheet of gold of unit radius. How much sectorial area is to be removed from the sheet so that the vessel has maximum volume ? **(Roorkee 1997)**

10. Show that a conical tent of given capacity will require the least amount of canvas if its height is $\sqrt{2}$ times its base radius.

11.* For a given curved surface of a right circular cone, show that the volume is max. when semi-vertical angle of the cone is $\sin^{-1}(1/\sqrt{(3)})$. **(M.N.R. 1995)**

12.* Find the cylinder of greatest volume which can be inscribed in a cone.

13. Show that the radius of the right circular cylinder of greatest curved surface which can be inscribed in a given cone is half that of the cone.

14. Show that the right circular cylinder of given surface and max. volume is such that its height is equal to the diameter of the base.

15. (a)* An open cylindrical can of given capacity is to be made from a metal sheet of uniform thickness. If no allowance is to be made for waste material, what will be the most economical ratio of the radius to the height of the can ?

(b) A cylindrical vessel of volume $25\frac{1}{7}$ cubic metres, which is open at the top is to be manufactured from a sheet of metal. Find the dimensions of the vessel so that the amount of sheet used in manufacturing it is the least possible.

(c) An open tank of given volume V has a square base. If the inner surface is least then prove that its depth is to the width as 1 : 2.

16. (a) A cylindrical gas container is closed at the top and open at the bottom ; if the iron plate of the top is 5/4 times as thick as the plate forming the cylindrical sides, find the ratio of the radius to the height of the cylinder using minimum material for the same capacity.

(b) A manufacturer plans to construct a cylindrical can to hold one cubic metre of liquid. If the cost of constructing the top and bottom of the can is twice the cost of constructing the sides, what are the dimensions of the most economical can ?

(c)* It is desired to construct a cylindrical vessel of capacity 500 cubic metres open at the top. What should be the dimensions of the vessel so that the material used is minimum, given that the thickness of the material used is 2 cm.

17.* A given quantity of metal is to be cast into a half cylinder, *i.e.* with a rectangular base and semi-circular ends. Show that in order that the total surface area may be minimum the ratio of the height of the cylinder to the diameter of the semi-circular ends is $\frac{\pi}{\pi+2}$.

18.* A thin closed rectangular box is to have one rectangular edge of n-times the length of another edge and the volume of the box is given to be V. Prove that the least surface S is given by

$$nS^3=54(n+1)^2V^2.$$

19.* A tree trunk l feet long is in the shape of a frustum of a cone, the radii of its ends being a and b $(a>b)$. It is required to cut from it a beam of uniform square section. Prove that the beam of greatest volume that can be cut is $\frac{al}{3(a-b)}$ feet long.

20. (a)* A cone is circumscribed to a sphere of radius r. Show that volume of the cone is minimum if its altitude is $4r$ and its semi-vertical angle is $\sin^{-1}\left(\frac{1}{3}\right)$.

(b)* Find the vertical angle of a right circular cone of minimum curved surface that circumscribes a given sphere. **(M.N.R. 1996)**

21.* Prove that the least perimeter of an isosceles triangle in which a circle of radius r can be inscribed is $6r\sqrt{3}$.

22.* The cone of greatest volume which can be inscribed in a given sphere has an altitude equal to (2/3) rd the diameter of the sphere. Prove also that the curved surface of the cone is maximum for the same value of altitude.

23. Show that the height of the cylinder of max. volume that can be inscribed in a sphere of radius a is $\frac{2a}{\sqrt{(3)}}$. Also find its radius.

24. (a) Find the max. value of the total surface of a right circular cylinder which can be inscribed in a sphere of radius a.

(b)* A chord of length $2L$ divides a circular area of radius R into two segments. Find the sides of the rectangle with largest area that can be inscribed in the smaller segment. **(Roorkee 1991)**

(c) Tangents are drawn from $P(6,8)$ to the circle $x^2+y^2=r^2$. Find the radius of the circle such that the area of the Δ formed by tangents and chord of contact is maximum. **(IIT 2003)**

25. Tangents are drawn to the ellipse $\frac{x^2}{a^2}+\frac{y^2}{b^2}=1$ and the auxiliary circle of the ellipse at points where a common ordinate cuts them. Show that if θ be the greatest inclination of these tangents then $\tan\theta=\frac{a-b}{2\sqrt{(ab)}}$.

26. (a)* Prove that the min. intercept made by the axes on the tangent to the ellipse $\frac{x^2}{a^2}+\frac{y^2}{b^2}=1$ is $a+b$.

Prove further that it is divided at the point of contact into parts which are equal to semi-axes respectively.

(b) The shortest distance between the line $y-x=1$ and the curve $x=y^2$ is

(a) $\frac{\sqrt{3}}{4}$ (b) $\frac{3\sqrt{2}}{8}$

(c) $\frac{2\sqrt{3}}{8}$ (d) $\frac{3\sqrt{2}}{5}$ **(AIEEE 2009)**

27. (a) From a variable point of an ellipse

$$\frac{x^2}{a^2}+\frac{y^2}{b^2}=1$$

normal is drawn to the ellipse. Find the maximum distance of the normal from the centre of the ellipse.

(b) Find the normals to the ellipse $\frac{x^2}{9}+\frac{y^2}{4}=1$ which are farthest from its centre. **(Roorkee 1999)**

28.* Prove that the min. radius vector of the curve $\frac{a^2}{x^2}+\frac{b^2}{y^2}=1$ is of length $a+b$.

29. (a) Find the max. and min. radii vectors of the curve

$$\frac{c^4}{r^2}=\frac{a^2}{\sin^2 t}+\frac{b^2}{\cos^2 t}.$$

(b)* Find the points on the curve $ax^2+2bxy+ay^2=c; c>b>a>0$, whose distance from the origin is minimum. **(Roorkee 1998)**

30. If $xy(y-x)=2a^3$, show that y has a minimum when $x=a$. Determine the minimum value. Show that y has a second value at $x=a$ which is less than the minimum. How do you explain this paradox ?

31.* Prove that the minimum value of

$$\frac{(a+x)(b+x)}{(c+x)},\ x>-c \text{ is } [\sqrt{a-c}+\sqrt{b-c}]^2$$

32.* Let $f(x)=\sin^3 x+\lambda\sin^2 x,\ -\pi/2<x<\pi/2$. Find the intervals in which λ should lie in order that $f(x)$ has exactly one minimum and one maximum.

33.* Let $A(p^2,-p)$, $B(q^2,q)$, $C(r^2,-r)$ be the vertices of the triangle ABC. A parallelogram $AFDE$ is drawn with D, E and F on the line segments BC, CA and AB respectively. Using calculus show that maximum area of such a parallelogram is $\frac{1}{4}(p+q)(q+r)(p-r)$.

34. Find the point (α,β) on the ellipse $4x^2+3y^2=12$ in the first quadrant, so that the area enclosed by the lines $y=x, y=\beta, x=\alpha$ and the x-axis is maximum. **(Roorkee 1995)**

35. At what point $P(x,y)$ of the curve $y=e^{-|x|}$ should a tangent be drawn so that the area of the triangle bounded by the tangent and the co-ordinate axes be greatest ?

36. A figure is bounded by the curve $y=x^2+1$, the axes of co-ordinates and the line $x=1$. Determine the co-ordinates of a point P at which a tangent be drawn to the curve so as to cut off a trapezium of greatest area from the figure.

37.* Find all the values of the parameter a for which the point of minimum of the function $f(x)=1+a^2x-x^3$ satisfy the inequality $\frac{x^2+x+2}{x^2+5x+6}<0$.

38.* Determine the points of maxima and minima of the function $f(x)=\frac{1}{8}\log x-bx+x^2, x>0$, where $b\ge 0$ is a constant. **(I.I.T. 1996)**

39. P is a point inside the triangle ABC from which the length of perpendiculars drawn on the sides of lengths a,b,c are respectively p,q and r. Determine the position of P if $\frac{a}{p}+\frac{b}{q}+\frac{c}{r}$ is minimum.

Solutions to Problem Set (2)

1. (a) Suppose he lands at D a point at a distance x from B or at distance $b - x$ from the place to be reached *i.e.* C. Thus he will have to row a distance $\sqrt{a^2 + x^2}$ and walk a distance $b - x$ along the shore to reach C. If he rows at the rate of k miles per hour, then he will walk at the rate of $k \sec \alpha$ m.p.h. If T be the time taken then
$T = t_1$ for rowing $+ t_2$ for walking.

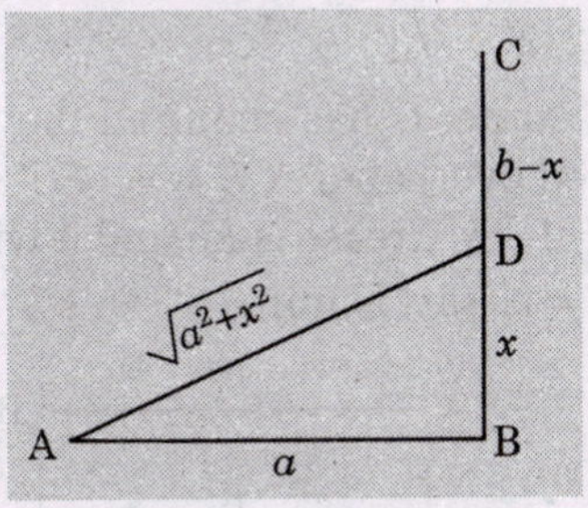

Fig. 34

$$\therefore \quad T = \frac{\sqrt{a^2 + x^2}}{k} + \frac{(b - x)}{k \sec \alpha}$$

$$\frac{dT}{dx} = \frac{1}{k}\left[\frac{2x}{2\sqrt{(a^2 + x^2)}} - \frac{1}{\sec \alpha}\right] = 0.$$

$$\therefore \quad x^2 \sec^2 \alpha = a^2 + x^2$$

$$\text{or} \quad x^2 (\sec^2 \alpha - 1) = a^2$$

$$\text{or} \quad x^2 \tan^2 \alpha = a^2. \quad \therefore \quad x = a \cot \alpha.$$

$$\frac{d^2T}{dx^2} = \frac{1}{k}\frac{\left[\sqrt{(a^2 + x^2)}\,.\,1 - x\,.\,\frac{2x}{2\sqrt{(a^2 + x^2)}}\right]}{(a^2 + x^2)}$$

$$= \frac{1}{k}\frac{a^2}{(a^2 + x^2)^{3/2}} = +\text{ive}$$

for $x = a \cot \alpha$ and hence T is minimum. Hence he should land at a distance

$$b - x = b - a \cot \alpha$$

from the place to be reached *i.e.*, C.

(b) Rate of swimming $= u$
Rate of walking $= v,\ u < v$

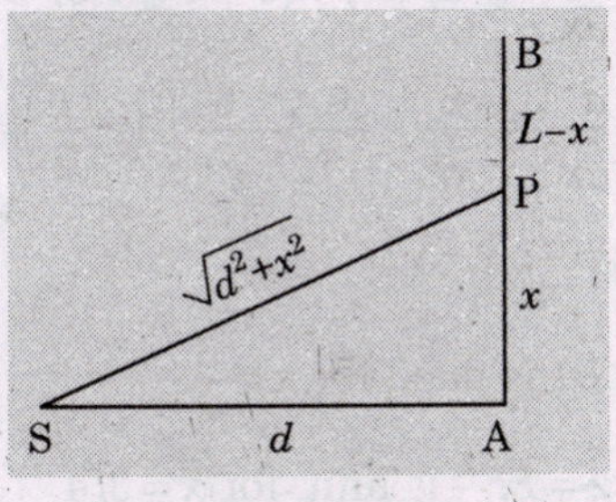

Fig. 35

$$T = t_1 + t_2$$

$$T = \frac{\sqrt{(d^2 + x^2)}}{u} + \frac{L - x}{v}$$

$$\frac{dT}{dx} = \frac{x}{u\sqrt{(d^2 + x^2)}} - \frac{1}{v} = 0$$

$$v^2 x^2 = u^2 (d^2 + x^2)$$

$$\therefore \quad x^2 (v^2 - u^2) = u^2 d^2$$

$$\therefore \quad x = \frac{ud}{\sqrt{(v^2 - u^2)}}$$

$$PB = L - x = L - \frac{ud}{\sqrt{(v^2 - u^2)}}$$

$$\frac{d^2T}{dx^2} = \frac{1}{u}\left[\frac{1}{\sqrt{(d^2 + x^2)}} - \frac{1}{2}\frac{2x}{(d^2 + x^2)^{3/2}}\right]$$

$$= \frac{1}{u}\left[\frac{d^2 + x^2 - x^2}{(d^2 + x^2)^{3/2}}\right] = \frac{1}{u}\frac{d^2}{(d^2 + x^2)^{3/2}} = +\text{ive}$$

Hence minimum.

2. Here AB is the pole of length b feet which is just taken into the lane from the road. Its end A will rest on the side of the road and the end B will rest in contact with the side of the lane. A point C of its length will be at the turning C as shown. If it is just possible to carry the pole from the road into the lane, keeping it horizontal then the width CD of the lane should not exceed its maximum value. Let $CD = y$.

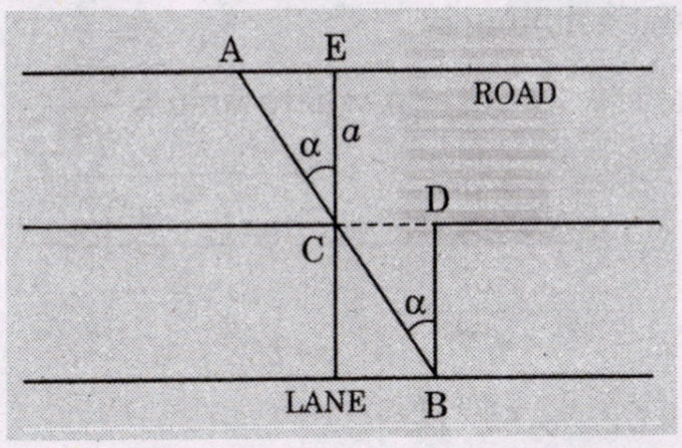

Fig. 36

$$b = AC + CB \quad \text{or} \quad b - a \sec \alpha = CB.$$

$$\therefore \quad y = CD = CB \sin \alpha = (b - a \sec \alpha) \sin \alpha$$

$$= b \sin \alpha - a \tan \alpha \qquad \text{...(1)}$$

For y to be maximum $dy/d\alpha = 0$.

$$dy/d\alpha = b \cos \alpha - a \sec^2 \alpha = 0.$$

$$\therefore \quad \cos^3 \alpha = (a/b) \quad \text{or} \quad \cos \alpha = (a/b)^{1/3}$$

$$d^2 y/d\alpha^2 = -b \sin \alpha - 2a \sec \alpha\,.\sec \alpha \tan \alpha = -\text{ive}.$$

Hence y is max. when $\cos \alpha = a^{1/3}/b^{1/3}$

$$\therefore \quad \sin \alpha = (1 - \cos^2 \alpha)^{1/2} = \frac{\sqrt{b^{2/3} - a^{2/3}}}{b^{1/3}}$$

$$\therefore \quad \tan \alpha = \frac{\sqrt{b^{2/3} - a^{2/3}}}{a^{1/3}}.$$

$$\therefore \quad y = b \sin \alpha - a \tan \alpha, \text{ by (1)}$$

$$=\sqrt{b^{2/3}-a^{2/3}}\left[b.\frac{1}{b^{1/3}}-a.\frac{1}{a^{1/3}}\right]$$

$$=\sqrt{b^{2/3}-a^{2/3}}\,[b^{2/3}-a^{2/3}]=[b^{2/3}-a^{2/3}]^{3/2}.$$

3. Refer figure of Q.2. Here road is a feet wide, lane is b feet wide *i.e.*, $CE=a$ and $CD=b$.

Let x be the length of the ladder, then

$$x=AC+CB=a\sec\alpha+b\operatorname{cosec}\alpha.$$

For max. or min. value of x.

$$dx/d\alpha=a\sec\alpha\tan\alpha-b\operatorname{cosec}\alpha\cot\alpha=0.$$

$\therefore\quad \tan^3\alpha=b/a.$

$$d^2x/d\alpha^2=a\sec^3\alpha+b\operatorname{cosec}^3\alpha+(a\sec\alpha\tan^2\alpha+b\operatorname{cosec}\alpha\cot^2\alpha)$$

$$=+\text{ive when }\tan^3\alpha=b/a.$$

Hence the minimum length of the ladder AB is attained for

$$\tan\alpha=\frac{b^{1/3}}{a^{1/3}}\quad\text{or}\quad\sin\alpha=\frac{b^{1/3}}{\sqrt{(a^{2/3}+b^{2/3})}},$$

$$\cos\alpha=\frac{a^{1/3}}{\sqrt{(a^{2/3}+b^{2/3})}}$$

Since the ladder is just to pass through the two roads without jamming, its length should not exceed the minimum value of AB.

Therefore the length of largest ladder in order to pass it without jamming is

$$x=a\sec\alpha+b\operatorname{cosec}\alpha\text{ where }\tan\alpha=\frac{b^{1/3}}{a^{1/3}}$$

or $$x=a.\frac{\sqrt{a^{2/3}+b^{2/3}}}{a^{1/3}}+b.\frac{\sqrt{a^{2/3}+b^{2/3}}}{b^{1/3}}$$

$$=\sqrt{a^{2/3}+b^{2/3}}\,.(a^{2/3}+b^{2/3})$$

$$=(a^{2/3}+b^{2/3})^{3/2}$$

4. Let $y=OP$ and $\angle POQ=\theta$. Then from the figure, it is clear that

$$y=6\operatorname{cosec}\theta+4\sec\theta.$$

$$\therefore\quad\frac{dy}{d\theta}=-6\operatorname{cosec}\theta\cot\theta+4\sec\theta\tan\theta=0$$

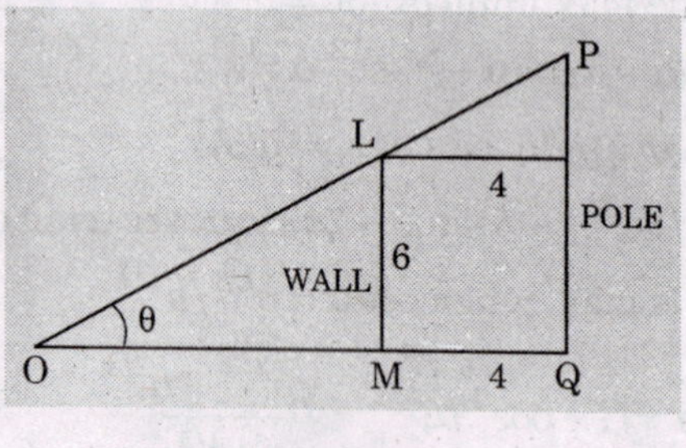

Fig. 37

for max. or min.

or $\tan^3\theta=6/4=3/2$

$\therefore\quad \tan\theta=3^{1/3}/2^{1/3}.$

$$\frac{d^2y}{d\theta^2}=+6\operatorname{cosec}\theta\cot^2\theta+6\operatorname{cosec}^3\theta+4\sec\theta\tan^2\theta+4\sec^3\theta>0$$

since θ is an acute angle.

Hence y is minimum when

$\tan\theta=3^{1/3}/2^{1/3}.$

$\therefore$ Min. value of y is given by

$$y=\sqrt{[(2^{2/3}+3^{2/3})]}\left[\frac{3.2}{3^{1/3}}+\frac{2.2}{2^{1/3}}\right]$$

$$=2(2^{2/3}+3^{2/3})^{3/2}.$$

5. (a) The corner C has acquired the position C' when folded over where $CE=x=EC'$ so that $DE=1-x$. Crease is EF and it will be minimum if $EF^2=z$, say, is min.,

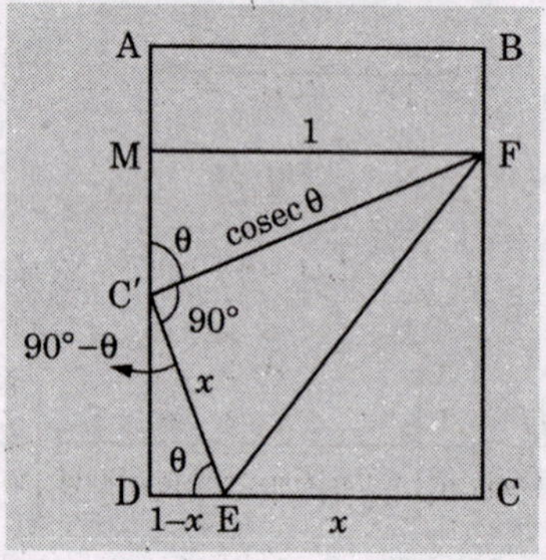

Fig. 38

$$z=EF^2=C'E^2+C'F^2$$

$$=x^2+(FM\operatorname{cosec}\theta)^2,$$

$$z=x^2+1.\operatorname{cosec}^2\theta. \quad\quad ...(1)$$

Again from $\Delta C'ED$, $\cos\theta=\frac{1-x}{x}.$

$$\therefore\quad\sin\theta=\frac{\sqrt{x^2-(1-x)^2}}{x}=\frac{\sqrt{2x-1}}{x}.$$

$$\therefore\quad z=x^2+\frac{x^2}{2x-1}=\frac{2x^3}{2x-1}=\frac{1}{(1/x^2)-(1/2x^3)}$$

$\therefore$ z will be minimum when

$t=(1/x^2)-(1/2x^3)$ is maximum

$$\frac{dt}{dx}=(-2/x^3)+(3/2x^4)=0,\quad\therefore\quad x=3/4,$$

$$\frac{d^2t}{dx^2}=\frac{6}{x^4}-\frac{6}{x^5}=\frac{6}{x^4}\left(1-\frac{1}{x}\right)=-\text{ive}$$

for $x=\frac{3}{4}.$

Hence t is max. for $x=\frac{3}{4}.$

$\therefore\quad z=EF^2$ is min. for $x=3/4$

$$z=\frac{2x^3}{2x-1}=2.\frac{27}{64}.2=EF^2.$$

$\therefore \quad EF = \dfrac{3\sqrt{3}}{4}.$

(b) Proceed as above.

6. (a) Ans. (c).

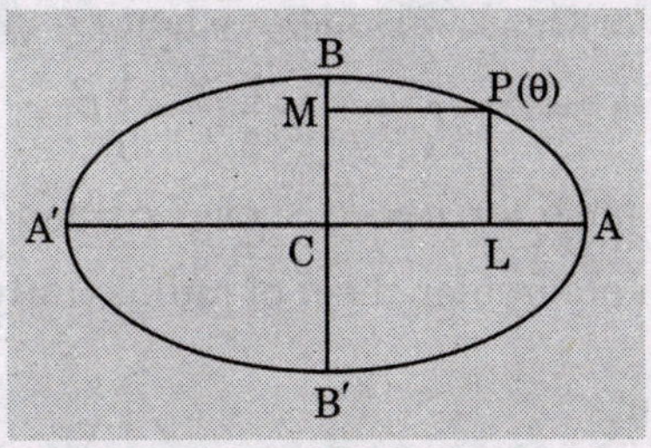

Fig. 39

Let $P(a\cos\theta, b\sin\theta)$ be any point on the ellipse. $CLPM$ is the rectangle inscribed in the 1st quadrant. Its area $= CL \, . \, PL$

$$A = a\cos\theta \, . \, b\sin\theta = \frac{1}{2}ab\sin 2\theta$$

A will be maximum when $\sin 2\theta = 1$, *i.e.*, $\theta = \dfrac{\pi}{4}$

$\therefore \quad A = \dfrac{1}{2}ab$

Hence area of rectangle inscribed in the whole of ellipse $= 4A = 2ab$.

(b) Ans. (c).

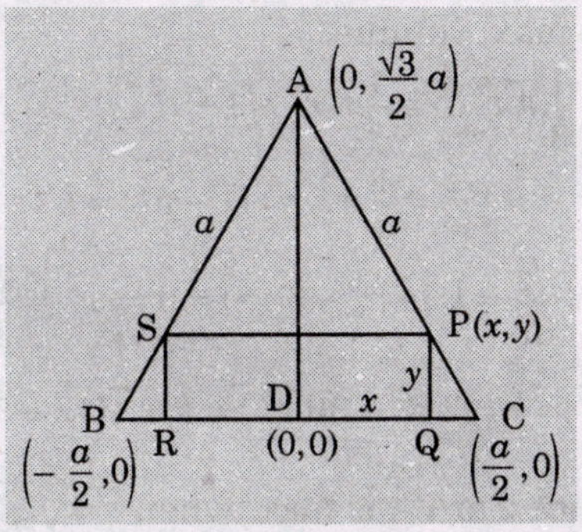

Fig. 40

Let the side $BC = a$ be chosen along x-axis and altitude AD be along y-axis.

$$AD^2 = AC^2 - DC^2 = a^2 - \frac{a^2}{4} = \frac{3a^2}{4}$$

$\therefore \quad AD = \dfrac{a\sqrt{3}}{2}$

Let $QPSR$ be the rectangle inscribed in the triangle. If A be its area, then $A = 2xy$ where (x, y) are the co-ordinates of vertex P which lies on line AC whose equation by intercepts form is

$$\frac{x}{a/2} + \frac{y}{\sqrt{3}\,a/2} = 1 \text{ or } \frac{2x}{a} + \frac{2y}{a\sqrt{3}} = 1 \quad ...(1)$$

Area $A = 2xy = x\left(1 - \dfrac{2x}{a}\right)a\sqrt{3}$ by (1)

$$\frac{dA}{dx} = a\sqrt{3}\left(1 - \frac{4x}{a}\right) = 0 \quad \therefore \quad x = \frac{a}{4}$$

$\dfrac{d^2A}{dx^2} = -$ ive and A is maximum.

$$\therefore \quad A = \frac{a}{4}\left(1 - \frac{1}{2}\right)a\sqrt{3} = \frac{a^2\sqrt{3}}{8} \Rightarrow \text{(c)}$$

7. **Refer Q 40. Page 1402-1417**

From the figure it is clear that dimensions of the box are

$$L = a - 2x, \; B = b - 2x, \; H = x$$

$$\therefore \quad V = L \times B \times H$$
$$= (a - 2x)(b - 2x)\,x$$

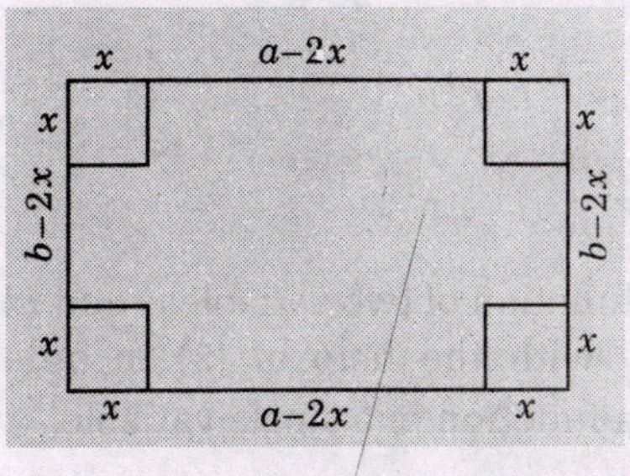

Fig. 41

or $\quad V = 4x^3 - 2x^2(a + b) + abx \quad (a > b)$

$$\frac{dV}{dx} = 12x^2 - 4x(a + b) + ab = 0.$$

$$\therefore \quad x = \frac{4(a+b) \pm \sqrt{16(a+b)^2 - 48ab}}{24}$$
$$= \frac{1}{6}[(a + b) \pm \sqrt{a^2 + b^2 - ab}]$$

Now since $a > b$, the value of x taking + ive sign with the radical will be greater than

$$\frac{1}{6}[(b + b) + \sqrt{b^2 - b^2 + b^2}]$$

or $\quad \dfrac{1}{6} . 3b$ or $b/2$

or $\quad 2x > b$ or $2x - b \;\; = +$ ive or $b - 2x$ is $-$ ive.

This is not possible as $b - 2x$ is breadth. Hence we shall consider the $-$ ive sign with the radical.

$$\therefore \quad x = \frac{1}{6}[(a + b) - \sqrt{a^2 + b^2 - ab}] \quad ...(1)$$

$$\frac{d^2V}{dx^2} = 24x - 4(a + b)$$
$$= 4[(a + b) - \sqrt{a^2 + b^2 - ab} - (a + b)]$$
$$= -4\sqrt{a^2 + b^2 - ab}.$$

i.e. $-$ ive and hence V is max.

Note : $a^2 + b^2 - ab = (a - b)^2 + ab$ i.e. + ive showing that the value of x given by (1) is real.

For Square Box : $a = b$, then from (1)

$$x = \frac{1}{6}(2a - a) = \frac{a}{6}.$$

8. $\quad S = \pi r(r + l) = $ constant. $\quad ...(2)$

$$V = \frac{1}{3}\pi r^2 h$$

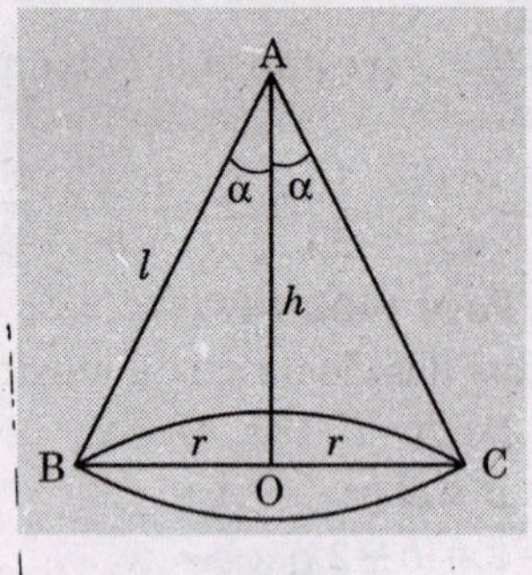

Fig. 42

$\therefore \quad z = V^2 = \frac{1}{9}\pi^2 r^4 h^2$

or $\quad z = \frac{1}{9}\pi^2 r^4 (l^2 - r^2)$.

Here z is a function of two variables r and l and we will eliminate l with the help of (2) in order to make z (i.e., V^2) a function of a single variable.

From (2),

$[(S/\pi r) - r] = l.$

$\therefore \quad z = \frac{1}{9}\pi^2 r^4 [((S/\pi r) - r)^2 - r^2]$

or $\quad z = \frac{1}{9}\pi^2 r^4 \left[\frac{S^2}{\pi^2 r^2} - \frac{2S}{\pi}\right]$

or $\quad z = \frac{1}{9}\pi^2 \left[\frac{S^2}{\pi^2} r^2 - \frac{2S}{\pi} r^4\right] = \frac{S}{9}[Sr^2 - 2\pi r^4]$.

Now V is max. when V^2 i.e. z is max.

$\therefore \quad dz/dr = (S/9)[2Sr - 8\pi r^3] = 0.$

$\therefore \quad r = 0$ or $r^2 = S/4\pi$ ...(1)

$r = 0$ is obviously rejected.

Now $d^2z/dr^2 = (S/9)[2S - 24\pi r^2]$

$= (S/9)[2S - 6S] = -(4S^2/9) = -$ ive

When $r^2 = S/4\pi$. Hence z i.e. V^2 is max.

or V is max. Now

$r^2 = S/4\pi$ or $4\pi r^2 = S = \pi r^2 + \pi r l$ by (1)

$3\pi r^2 = \pi r l. \quad \therefore \quad \frac{r}{l} = \frac{1}{3}$ or $\sin\alpha = \frac{1}{3}$.

$\therefore \quad \alpha = \sin^{-1}\frac{1}{3}$.

9. (a) $V = \frac{1}{3}\pi r^2 h$, l is given.

$z = V^2 = \frac{1}{9}\pi^2 r^4 (l^2 - r^2) = \frac{1}{9}\pi^2 (l^2 r^4 - r^6)$

$\frac{dz}{dr} = \frac{1}{9}\pi^2 (4l^2 r^3 - 6r^5) = 0$

$\therefore \quad r = 0$ or $r^2 = \frac{2}{3}l^2$

or $\quad r = \sqrt{(2/3)}\, l, \ -\sqrt{(2/3)}\, l$

Clearly $r = 0$ and $r = -\sqrt{(2/3)}\, l$ are rejected. Hence we consider $r = \sqrt{(2/3)}\, l$.

$d^2z/dr^2 = (\pi^2/9)(12l^2 r^2 - 30r^4)$

$= (\pi^2/9)[12l^2 . (2/3) l^2 - 30 . (4/9) l^4]$

$= (1/9)\pi^2 l^4 . (-16/3) = -$ ive

Hence z i.e. V^2 is max. when $r = \sqrt{(2/3)}\, l$.

$\therefore \quad h^2 = l^2 - r^2 = l^2 - \frac{2}{3}l^2 = \frac{1}{3}l^2 \quad \therefore \quad h = (1/\sqrt{3}) . l$

$\therefore \quad \tan\alpha = r/h = \sqrt{2}$ or $\alpha = \tan^{-1}\sqrt{2}$.

(b) Area of circular sheet of radius unity is $\pi a^2 = \pi$

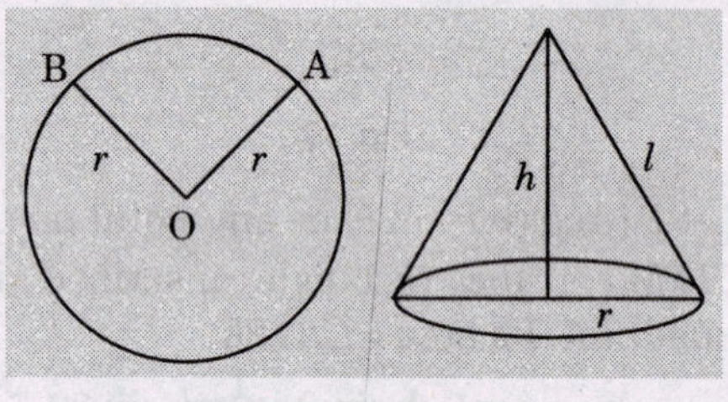

Fig. 43

Sector OAB is removed and the remaining portion is folded over so as to form a conical vessel of max. volume (its surface area will be $\pi r . l = \pi r . 1$

Sector to be removed

$= $ Total $-$ surface area of vessel

$= \pi - \pi r$ ...(1)

Now r is to be found out so that the conical vessel has max. volume.

$V = \frac{1}{3}\pi r^2 h = \frac{1}{3}\pi r^2 \sqrt{1 - r^2}$

$\therefore \quad z = V^2 = \frac{1}{9}\pi^2 r^4 (1 - r^2) = k(r^4 - r^6)$

$\frac{dz}{dr} = k(4r^3 - 6r^5) = 0 \Rightarrow r^2 = \frac{2}{3}$

$\frac{d^2z}{dr^2} = k(12r^2 - 30r^4) = kr^2(12 - 30r^2) = -$ ive

Hence z or V^2 is max. when $r = \sqrt{2/3}$.

Putting in (1), the area of sector to be removed $= \pi(1 - r) = \pi(1 - \sqrt{2/3})$ sq. units.

10. $V = \frac{1}{3}\pi r^2 h$. (given) $\quad \therefore \quad h^2 = 9V^2/\pi^2 r^4$

Here because of the tent, we are concerned only with the curved surface $\pi r l$ and not that of the base.

$S = \pi r l$

$\therefore \quad S^2 = z = \pi^2 r^2 l^2 = \pi^2 r^2 (r^2 + h^2)$.

or $\quad z = \pi^2 r^2 \left[r^2 + \frac{9V^2}{\pi^2 r^4}\right] = \pi^2 r^4 + \frac{9V^2}{r^2}$

$\therefore \quad \frac{dz}{dr} = 4\pi^2 r^3 - \frac{18V^2}{r^3} \quad \therefore \quad r^6 = \frac{9V^2}{2\pi^2}$

$\frac{d^2z}{dr^2} = 12\pi^2 r^2 + \frac{54V^2}{r^4} = \frac{12\pi^2 r^6 + 54V^2}{r^4}$

$= \frac{6(9V^2) + 54V^2}{r^2} = +$ ive

when $r^6 = \dfrac{9V^2}{2\pi^2}$.

Hence z *i.e.* S^2 is minimum or S is minimum

when $2\pi^2 r^6 = 9V^2$ or $2\pi^2 r^6 = 9 \cdot \frac{1}{9}\pi^2 r^4 h^2$

or $2r^2 = h^2$ or $h = r\sqrt{2}$.

Another form :

$\therefore \quad l = \sqrt{(r^2 + h^2)} = \sqrt{(r^2 + 2r^2)} = r\sqrt{3}$.

$\therefore \quad \sin\alpha = r/l = 1/\sqrt{3}$ or $\alpha = \sin^{-1} 1/\sqrt{3}$.

11. $S = \pi r l$ (given) where S is curved surface only.

$V = \frac{1}{3}\pi r^2 h \quad \therefore \quad z = V^2 = \frac{1}{9}\pi^2 r^4 (l^2 - r^2)$

$z = \frac{1}{9}\pi^2 r^4 \left[\frac{S^2}{\pi^2 r^2} - r^2\right] = \frac{1}{9}[S^2 r^2 - \pi^2 r^6]$

$\frac{dz}{dr} = \frac{1}{9}[2S^2 r - 6\pi^2 r^5]$

$\therefore \quad r^4 = \frac{1}{3}\frac{S^2}{\pi^2}$ or $r = 0$

$\frac{d^2 z}{dr^2} = \frac{1}{9}[2S^2 - 30\pi^2 r^4]$

$= \frac{1}{9}[2S^2 - 10S^2] = -$ ive

hence max. when

$r^4 = \frac{S^2}{3\pi^2}$ or $3\pi^2 r^4 = \pi^2 r^2 l^2$

$\frac{r}{l} = \frac{1}{\sqrt{(3)}}$ or $\sin\alpha = \frac{1}{\sqrt{(3)}}$

or $\alpha = \sin^{-1}\frac{1}{\sqrt{(3)}}$.

12. Let b be the height of the cone and α be its semi-vertical angle.

$LD = x =$ radius of the inscribed cylinder and $LM = h$ be its height

$LM = OM - OL = b - x\cot\alpha$.

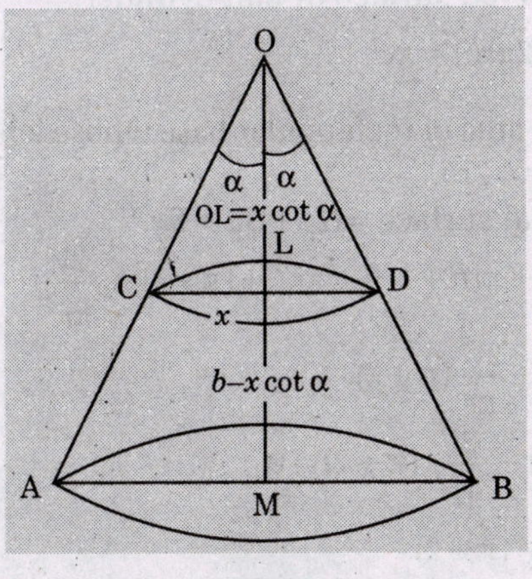

Fig. 44

$V =$ volume of cylinder $= \pi r^2 h$

$= \pi x^2 (b - x\cot\alpha)$

$V = \pi(bx^2 - x^3\cot\alpha)$.

$dV/dx = \pi(2bx - 3x^2 \cot\alpha)$

$\therefore \quad x = 0$ or $x = \frac{2}{3}b\tan\alpha$.

Clearly $x = 0$ is inadmissible and hence we consider the value $x = \frac{2}{3}b\tan\alpha$.

$\frac{d^2V}{dx^2} = \pi(2b - 6x\cot\alpha)$

$= \pi(2b - 4b) = -$ ive and hence

max. when $x = \frac{2}{3}b\tan\alpha$

$h = b - x\cot\alpha = b - \frac{2}{3}b = \frac{1}{3}b$

$\therefore$ Max. volume is

$\pi r^2 h = \pi x^2 h = \pi \cdot \frac{4}{9}b^2\tan^2\alpha \cdot \frac{1}{3}b$

or $V = \frac{4}{27}\pi b^3 \tan^2\alpha$.

13. $S = 2\pi r h =$ curved surface.

$S = 2\pi x(b - x\cot\alpha)$ as in Q.12

or $S = 2\pi(bx - x^2\cot\alpha)$

$\therefore \quad dS/dx = 2\pi(b - 2x\cot\alpha) = 0$

$\therefore \quad x = (b/2)\tan\alpha$

or $x = \frac{1}{2}(b\tan\alpha) = \frac{1}{2}(r_1)$

or Radius of cylinder $= \left(\frac{1}{2}\right)$. (radius of cone.)

14. $S = 2\pi r^2 + 2\pi r h$ (given)

$\therefore \quad \frac{S - 2\pi r^2}{2\pi r} = h \qquad ...(1)$

$V = \pi r^2 h = \pi r^2 \cdot \frac{S - 2\pi r^2}{2\pi r}$

$= \frac{1}{2}(Sr - 2\pi r^3)$

$\frac{dV}{dr} = \frac{1}{2}(S - 6\pi r^2) = 0 \quad \therefore \quad r = \sqrt{(S/6\pi)}$

$\frac{d^2V}{dr^2} = -6\pi r$

$= -6\pi\sqrt{(S/6\pi)} = -\sqrt{(6\pi S)} = -$ ive and

hence max. when $r = \sqrt{(S/6\pi)}$ or $6\pi r^2 = S$

or $6\pi r^2 = 2\pi r^2 + 2\pi r h$ or $2r = h$

i.e. its height is equal to diameter of the base.

15. (a) The curved surface of the cylindrical can be made by rolling the sheet and there will be no waste of material. But in order to have the base of the can, which will be circular of radius r we will have to cut it from a

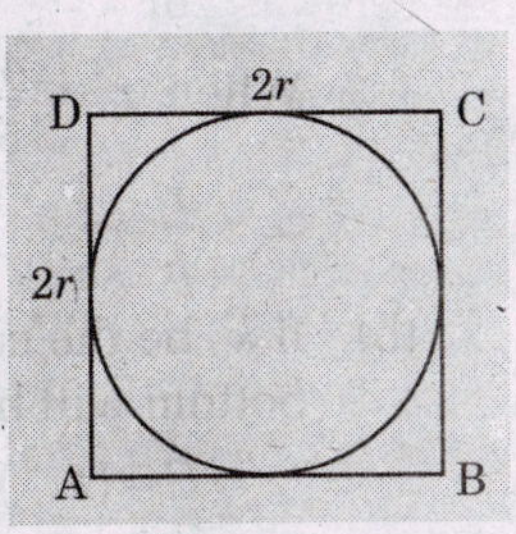

Fig. 45

square metal sheet $2r$ by $2r$ and whose area will be $4r^2$ whereas the actual area of the base is only πr^2. But no allowance is to be made for waste of material. Hence the total surface area of the sheet used for making the open cylindrical can is $S = 2\pi rh + 4r^2$.

Also $\quad V = \pi r^2 h$ (given) $\therefore \; h = V/\pi r^2$

$$\therefore \quad S = 2\pi r \cdot \frac{V}{\pi r^2} + 4r^2 = \frac{2V}{r} + 4r^2$$

$$\therefore \quad \frac{dS}{dr} = -\frac{2V}{r^2} + 8r = 0 \text{ or } 4r^3 = V$$

$$\frac{d^2S}{dr^2} = \frac{4V}{r^3} + 8 = 4 \cdot 4 + 8 = 24 = +\text{ive};$$

hence minimum

when $4r^3 = V = \pi r^2 h \quad \therefore \quad r/h = \pi/4$

is the required ratio.

(b) Do yourself. Ans. $r = h = 2$ metre.

(c) $V = x^2 h$, where h is depth and x is width.

$$S = x^2 + 4(xh) = x^2 + \frac{4V}{x}$$

$$\frac{dS}{dx} = 2x - \frac{4V}{x^2} \quad \therefore \quad x^3 = 2V = 2x^2 h$$

$$\therefore \quad x = 2h.$$

$$\frac{d^2S}{dx^2} = 2 + \frac{8V}{x^3} = 2 + 4 = 6 = +\text{ive}.$$

Hence minimum.

16. (a) $V = \pi r^2 h$.

If k be the thickness of the sides then that of the top will be $\frac{5}{4}k$.

$$\therefore \quad S = (2\pi rh)\, k + (\pi r^2) \cdot \frac{5}{4} k$$

$$\text{or} \quad S = 2\pi r \cdot \frac{V}{\pi r^2} k + \frac{5}{4} \pi r^2 k = k\left(\frac{2V}{r} + \frac{5}{4}\pi r^2\right)$$

Note : We have taken into consideration the actual material used and not as in last question in which the base was made from a square sheet thus wasting the material.

$$\therefore \quad \frac{dS}{dr} = k\left(\frac{-2V}{r^2} + \frac{5}{2}\pi r\right), \quad \therefore \quad r^3 = \frac{4V}{5\pi}$$

$$\frac{d^2S}{dr^2} = k\left(\frac{4V}{r^3} + \frac{5}{2}\pi\right) = \pi\left(5\pi + \frac{5}{2}\right) = +\text{ive}.$$

When $r^3 = \frac{4V}{5\pi}$ or $5\pi r^3 = 4\pi r^2 h$

$$\therefore \quad \frac{r}{h} = \frac{4}{5}.$$

(b) If k be the cost for the side then that of top and bottom will be $2k$ per square unit.

$$C = (\pi r^2)\, 2k + (\pi r^2)\, 2k + (2rh)\, k$$

where $1 = \pi r^2 h$

$$C = 2\pi k\left[2r^2 + \frac{1}{\pi r}\right] \text{ etc.}$$

$$r = \frac{1}{(4\pi)^{1/3}}, \quad h = \left(\frac{16}{\pi}\right)^{1/3}.$$

(c) Let r and h be the internal radius and height of the cylindrical vessel and let V denote the volume of the material. Then according to the given conditions in the question, we have

$$\pi r^2 h = 500 = V \qquad \text{... (1)}$$

$$S = (2\pi rh + \pi r^2) \cdot \frac{2}{100}, \text{ as } \frac{2}{100} \text{ is thickness}$$

$$= \left(\frac{2V}{r} + \pi r^2\right) \cdot \frac{2}{100}$$

$$\frac{dS}{dr} = \left(-\frac{2V}{r^2} + 2\pi r\right) \cdot \frac{1}{50} = 0$$

$$\therefore \quad \pi r^3 = V = 500 = \pi r^2 h$$

$$\text{or} \quad r = \left(\frac{500}{\pi}\right)^{1/3} = h$$

$$\text{Clearly } \frac{d^2S}{dr^2} = \left(\frac{4V}{r^3} + 2\pi\right) \cdot \frac{1}{50}$$

$$= +\text{ive} \quad \therefore \text{ Minimum.}$$

17. V = Volume of half cylinder $= \frac{1}{2} \cdot \pi r^2 h$. ...(1)

Fig. 46

We want the total surface to be minimum. It will consist of the following surfaces.

S_1 = Surface of semi-circular ends

$$= \frac{1}{2}\pi r^2 + \frac{1}{2}\pi r^2 = \pi r^2$$

S_2 = Curved surface of half cylinder

$$= \frac{1}{2}(2\pi rh) = \pi rh$$

S_3 = Surface area of rectangular base whose length is h and width $2r = 2rh$.

S = Total surface $= S_1 + S_2 + S_3$.

$$S = \pi r^2 + \pi rh + 2rh = \pi r^2 + (\pi + 2)\, r \cdot \frac{2V}{\pi r^2} \quad \text{by (1)}$$

$$\text{or} \quad S = \pi r^2 + \frac{2V}{\pi r}(\pi + 2).$$

$$\frac{dS}{dr} = 2\pi r - \frac{2V}{\pi r^2}(\pi + 2) = 0$$

$$\therefore \quad \pi^2 r^3 = V(\pi + 2) \qquad \text{...(2)}$$

$$\frac{d^2S}{dr^2} = 2\pi + \frac{4V(\pi + 2)}{\pi r^3}$$

$$= 2\pi + 4\pi = 6\pi = +\text{ ive and hence}$$

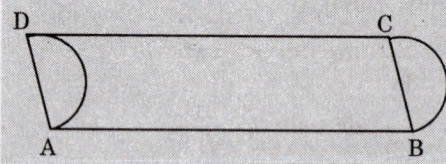

S is minimum when $\pi^2 r^3 = V(\pi + 2)$

or $\pi^2 r^3 = \frac{1}{2}\pi r^2 h(\pi+2)$ $\therefore$ $\frac{h}{2r} = \frac{\pi}{\pi+2}$.

18. Let the edges of the box according to given condition be x, nx, y.

$\therefore$ $V = nx^2 y$ (given) ...(1)

$S = 2(x \cdot nx + nxy + yx)$

[Formula $S = 2(xy + yz + zx)$]

$$S = 2\left[nx^2 + (n+1)\,x \cdot \frac{V}{nx^2}\right], \quad \text{by (1)} \quad ...(2)$$

$$\frac{dS}{dx} = 2\left[2nx - \frac{(n+1)}{n} \cdot \frac{V}{x^2}\right] = 0,$$

$$\therefore \quad x^3 = \frac{(n+1)}{2n^2} V$$

$$\frac{d^2S}{dx^2} = 2\left[2n + 2 \cdot \frac{(n+1)}{n}\,\frac{V}{x^3}\right]$$

which is clearly +ive and hence S is minimum when $x^3 = \frac{(n+1)}{2n^2} V$. ...(3)

$$\therefore \quad S = 2\left[nx^2 + \frac{(n+1)}{n}\,\frac{V}{x}\right]$$

$$= 2\left[\frac{n^2x^3 + (n+1)\,V}{nx}\right], \quad \text{by (2)}$$

$$\text{or} \quad S = \frac{2}{nx}\left[\frac{(n+1)}{2} V + (n+1)\,V\right]$$

$$= \frac{2}{nx} \cdot \frac{3(n+1)\,V}{2}, \quad \text{by (3)}$$

$$\therefore \quad S^3 n^3 x^3 = 27(n+1)^3 V^3$$

$$S^3 n^3 \cdot (n+1)\frac{V}{2n^2} = 27(n+1)^3 V^3, \text{ by (3)}$$

$$\text{or} \quad nS^3 = 54(n+1)^2 V^2.$$

19. $OM = x$ so that the length of the diagonal of the square cross-section is $2x$ and so its area is $2x^2$. [Note that area of a square

$= \frac{1}{2}(\text{diagonal})^2 = \frac{1}{2}(2x)^2 = 2x^2$]

$O'C = OL = b$, $OB = a$,

If h be the height of the beam then its volume is $2x^2 h$.

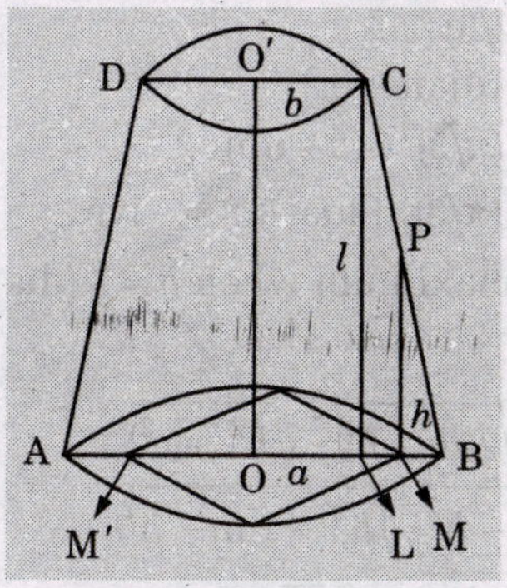

Fig. 47

Thus $V = 2x^2 h$ ...(1)

We have to eliminate the variable h and find its value in terms of x so that V is a function of single variable x.

Now from similar triangles CLB and PMB we have

$$\frac{CL}{PM} = \frac{LB}{MB} \quad \text{or} \quad \frac{l}{h} = \frac{OB - OL}{OB - OM} = \frac{a-b}{a-x}$$

$\therefore$ $h = [l/(a-b)] \cdot (a-x)$ ...(2)

Hence from (1) by the help of (2) the volume is

$V = 2x^2 \cdot [l/(a-b)](a-x)$

$= [2l/(a-b)](ax^2 - x^3)$ ...(3)

$dV/dx = [2l/(a-b)\}(2ax - 3x^2) = 0$

$\therefore$ $x = 0, \frac{2a}{3}$

$d^2V/dx^2 = [2l/(a-b)](2a - 6x)$

$= [2l/(a-b)](2a - 4a) = -$ ive

and hence V is max. when $x = 2a/3$.

Hence from (2) the height of the beam of max. volume is

$$h = \frac{l}{(a-b)}\left(a - \frac{2a}{3}\right) = \frac{al}{3(a-b)}.$$

20. (a) Let R be the radius of the cone, l its slant height and h be the height.

$$V = \frac{1}{3}\pi R^2 h$$

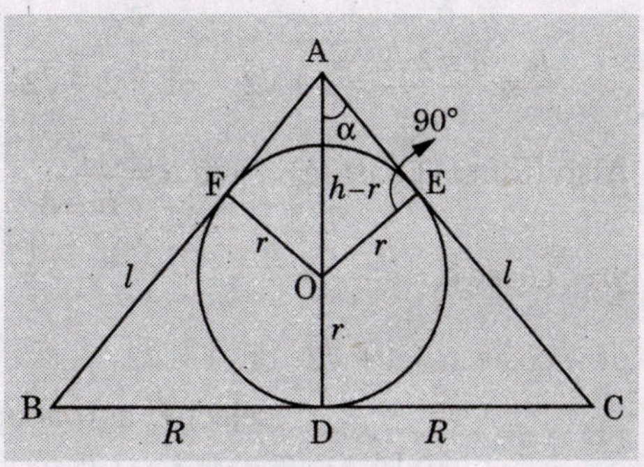

Fig. 48

We have to make V a function of single variable.

$$\frac{r}{h-r} = \frac{R}{l} = \sin\alpha \quad ...(1)$$

$$\text{or} \quad \frac{r}{h-r} = \frac{R}{\sqrt{R^2 + h^2}}$$

$$\therefore \quad r^2(R^2 + h^2) = R^2(h^2 - 2hr + r^2)$$

$$\text{or} \quad r^2h^2 = R^2 h(h - 2r)$$

$$\therefore \quad R^2 h = \frac{r^2h^2}{h - 2r} \quad ...(2)$$

$\therefore$ $V = \frac{1}{3}\pi\frac{r^2h^2}{h-2r}$, where r is given

$$\therefore \quad V = \frac{1}{3}\pi\frac{r^2}{\frac{1}{h} - \frac{2r}{h^2}}$$

Now V will be minimum if $z = \frac{1}{h} - \frac{2r}{h^2}$ is max.

$\frac{dz}{dh} = \frac{-1}{h^2} + \frac{4r}{h^3} = 0 \quad \therefore \quad h = 4r.$

$\frac{d^2z}{dh^2} = \frac{2}{h^3} - \frac{12r}{h^4} = \frac{2}{h^3}\left[1 - \frac{6r}{h}\right] = \frac{2}{h^3}\left(1 - \frac{6}{4}\right) = -\text{ive}$

$\therefore$ z is max. and hence V is minimum when $h = 4r$.

$\therefore \quad \sin\alpha = \frac{r}{h-r} = \frac{1}{3} \quad \because \quad h = 4r.$ by (1)

(b) S = curved surface $= \pi Rl$

or $S = \pi R \cdot \frac{R(h-r)}{r} = \pi \frac{h-r}{r} \cdot \frac{r^2 h}{h-2r}$

$\therefore \quad S = \pi r \cdot \left[\frac{h^2 - rh}{h-2r}\right]$, by (1) and (2) of part (a)

Thus S is a function of single variable h and for minimum value of S, we must have

$\frac{dS}{dh} = 0$ and $\frac{d^2S}{dh^2} = +\text{ive}$

$\frac{dS}{dh} = \pi r\left[\frac{h^2 - 4rh + 2r^2}{(h-2r)^2}\right] = 0$ ...(3)

$\therefore \quad h^2 - 4rh + 2r^2 = 0$ or $\frac{h^2}{r^2} - 4\frac{h}{r} + 2 = 0$

$\therefore \quad \frac{h}{r} = \frac{4 \pm 2\sqrt{2}}{2} = 2 + \sqrt{2}$ or $2 - \sqrt{2}$

Also from (1) part (a), $\sin\alpha = \frac{r}{h-r}$

or $\operatorname{cosec}\alpha = \frac{h-r}{r} = \frac{h}{r} - 1$

or $\operatorname{cosec}\alpha = 1 + \sqrt{2}$ or $1 - \sqrt{2}$

(rejected as α is not obtuse)

$\therefore \quad \sin\alpha = \frac{1}{\sqrt{2}+1} = \sqrt{2} - 1$ where $\frac{h}{r} = 2 + \sqrt{2}$ ...(4)

$\therefore \quad \frac{d^2S}{dh^2} = \pi r\left[-\frac{2}{(h-2r)^3}(h^2 - 4rh + 2r^2) + \frac{1}{(h-2r)^2}(2h - 4r)\right]$

$= \pi r\left[0 + \frac{2}{h-2r}\right] = \pi r\left[\frac{2}{\frac{h}{r} - 2}\right] = +\text{ive}$

when $\frac{h}{r} = 2 + \sqrt{2}$

$\therefore \sin\alpha = \sqrt{2} - 1.$ by (4)

21. **Refer Q. 20 (a) P. 1425-1433.**

$2s = 2l + 2R \quad \therefore \quad s = l + R$

or $s = R\frac{(h-r)}{r} + R = R \cdot \frac{h}{r}$, by (1)

$\therefore \quad z = s^2 = \frac{h^2}{r^2} \cdot R^2 = \frac{h^2}{r^2} \cdot \frac{r^2 h}{(h-2r)} = \frac{h^3}{h-2r}$ by (2)

or $z = \frac{1}{\frac{1}{h^2} - \frac{2r}{h^3}}$

Now z will be minimum if $u = \frac{1}{h^2} - \frac{2r}{h^3}$ is maximum.

$\frac{du}{dh} = 0 \Rightarrow -\frac{2}{h^3} + \frac{6r}{h^4} \quad \therefore \quad h = 3r$

$\frac{d^2u}{dh^2} = \frac{6}{h^4} - \frac{24r}{h^5} = \frac{6}{h^4}\left[1 - \frac{4r}{h}\right] = \frac{6}{h^4}\left[1 - \frac{4}{3}\right] = -\text{ive}.$

$\therefore$ u is max. and hence z is minimum when $h = 3r$.

$\therefore \quad z = s^2 = \frac{27r^3}{3r - 2r} = 27r^2$

$\therefore \quad 2s = 2(3\sqrt{3}r) = 6\sqrt{3}r$

Also $\sin\alpha = \frac{r}{h-r} = \frac{1}{2}$ or $\alpha = \frac{\pi}{6}$.

22. Let h be the height of the cone and r be its radius.

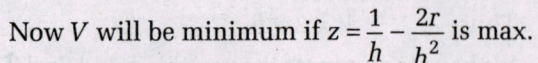

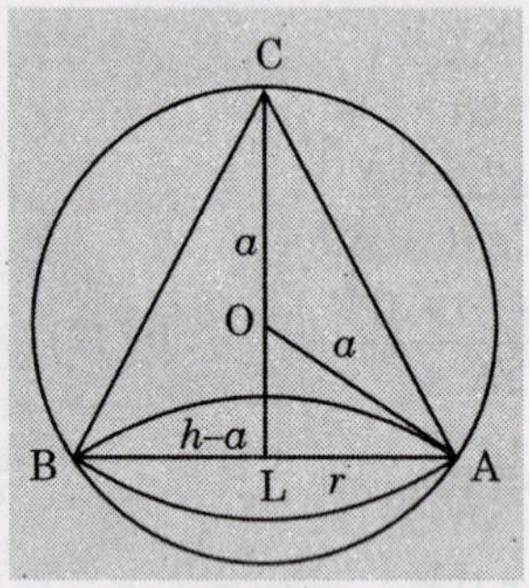

Fig. 49

$\therefore \quad h = CL = CO + OL = a + OL$

$\therefore \quad OL = h - a.$

$r = LA = \sqrt{OA^2 - OL^2}$

or $r = \sqrt{a^2 - (h-a)^2} = \sqrt{2ah - h^2}$

$V = \frac{1}{3}\pi r^2 h = \frac{1}{3}\pi(2ah - h^2)h$

$= \frac{1}{3}\pi(2ah^2 - h^3)$

$dV/dh = (\pi/3)(4ah - 3h^2) = 0$

$\therefore \quad h = 0$ or $4a/3$

$h = 0$ is rejected

$\therefore \quad h = 4a/3 = (2/3)(2a)$

$= 2/3$ (diameter)

$d^2V/dh^2 = (\pi/3).(4a - 6h)$

$= (\pi/3).(4a - 8a) = -\text{ive}$

and hence V is maximum when $h = \frac{2}{3}$ (diameter)

2nd part :

$S = \pi rl = \pi\sqrt{2ah - h^2} \cdot \sqrt{h^2 + r^2}$

$= \pi\sqrt{2ah - h^2}\sqrt{h^2 + 2ah - h^2}$

$= \pi\sqrt{2ah - h^2} \cdot \sqrt{2ah}.$

Let $Z = S^2 = \pi^2 . 2a(2ah^2 - h^3)$.

S will be maximum when $S^2 = Z$ is max.

$\therefore \quad \dfrac{dZ}{dh} = 2\pi^2 a(4ah - 3h^2) = 0$

$\therefore \quad h = 0,\ 4a/3$

$h = 0$ is rejected and hence

$h = 4a/3 = (2/3)\,2a = (2/3)$ diameter.

Also $d^2Z/dh^2 = 2\pi^2 a(4a - 6h)$

$= 2\pi^2 a(4a - 8a) = -$ ive and

hence S is max. when $h = \dfrac{2}{3}$ of diameter.

23. If r be the radius and h the height, then from the figure

$r^2 + (h^2/4) = a^2 \quad \therefore \quad h^2 = 4(a^2 - r^2)$

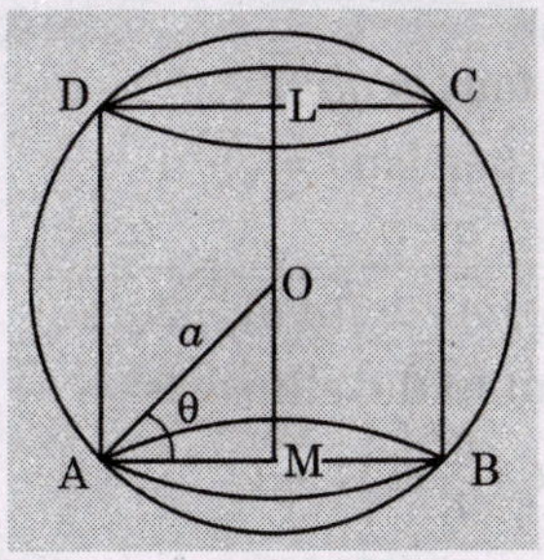

Fig. 50

Now $V = \pi r^2 h = \pi\left(a^2 - \dfrac{1}{4}h^2\right)h$

$= \pi\left(a^2 h - \dfrac{1}{4}h^3\right)$

$\therefore \quad \dfrac{dV}{dh} = \pi\left(a^2 - \dfrac{3}{4}h^2\right) = 0$ for max. or min.

This gives $h = (2/\sqrt{3})\,a$.

$d^2V/dh^2 = -6h/4 < 0$.

Hence V is max. when $h = 2a/\sqrt{3}$.

24. (a) Refer figure 107 above.

$S = 2\pi r^2 + 2\pi rh.$

$r = a\cos\theta$ and $h/2 = a\sin\theta$

$\therefore \quad h = 2a\sin\theta$

$\therefore \quad S = 2\pi.(a^2\cos^2\theta + a\cos\theta . 2a\sin\theta)$

$S = 2\pi a^2(\cos^2\theta + \sin 2\theta)$.

$dS/d\theta = 2\pi a^2\,[-2\cos\theta\sin\theta + 2\cos 2\theta]$

$= 2\pi a^2\,[2\cos 2\theta - \sin 2\theta] = 0$

$\therefore \quad \tan 2\theta = 2$ or $\cos 2\theta = \dfrac{1}{\sqrt{(5)}}$

or $\quad \sin 2\theta = \dfrac{2}{\sqrt{(5)}}$

$\dfrac{d^2S}{d\theta^2} = 2\pi\,[-4\sin 2\theta - 2\cos 2\theta] = -$ ive

and hence max. when $\tan 2\theta = 2$

$\therefore \quad S = 2\pi a^2\,(\cos^2\theta + \sin 2\theta)$

$= 2\pi a^2\left[\dfrac{1 + \cos 2\theta}{2} + \sin 2\theta\right]$

$= 2\pi a^2\left[\dfrac{1}{2} + \dfrac{1}{2\sqrt{(5)}} + \dfrac{2}{\sqrt{(5)}}\right]$

$= 2\pi a^2\left[\dfrac{1}{2} + \dfrac{5}{2\sqrt{(5)}}\right] = \pi a^2\,(1 + \sqrt{5})$

(b) From the figure we see that

$OS = R\cos\theta,\ MP = MQ = L$

$OM = \sqrt{[OQ^2 - QM^2]} = \sqrt{(R^2 - L^2)}$.

Also $\quad CD = 2\,CS = 2R\sin\theta$.

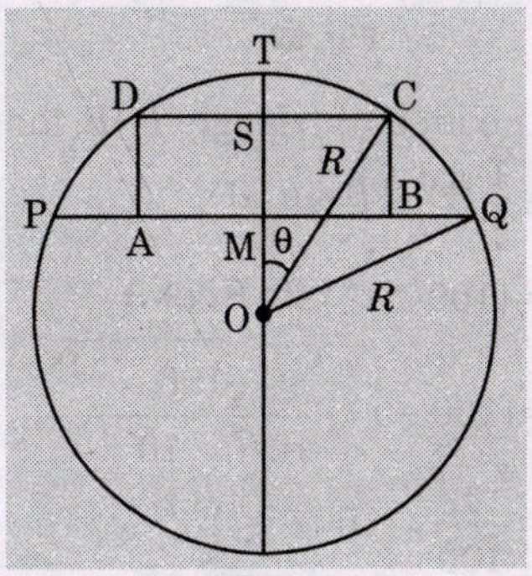

Fig. 51

If y denotes the area of rectangle $ABCD$, then

$y = BC \cdot CD = MS \cdot CD = (OS - OM) . CD$

$= [R\cos\theta - \sqrt{(R^2 - L^2)}]\,.\,2R\sin\theta \qquad \text{...(1)}$

or $\quad y = R\,[R\sin 2\theta - 2\sqrt{(R^2 - L^2)}\sin\theta] = 0$

Now $\quad \dfrac{dy}{d\theta} = 0$ for max. or min.

$\therefore \quad \dfrac{dy}{d\theta} = R\,[2R\cos 2\theta - 2\sqrt{(R^2 - L^2)}\cos\theta] = 0$

...(2)

or $\quad R(2\cos^2\theta - 1) - \sqrt{(R^2 - L^2)}\cos\theta = 0$

or $\quad 2R\cos^2\theta - \sqrt{(R^2 - L^2)}\cos\theta - R = 0$

$\therefore \quad \cos\theta = \dfrac{\sqrt{(R^2 - L^2)} \pm \sqrt{[R^2 - L^2 + 8R^2]}}{4R}$

Since θ is an acute angle, $\cos\theta$ cannot be negative. Hence we must have

$\cos\theta = \dfrac{\sqrt{(R^2 - L^2)} + \sqrt{(9R^2 - L^2)}}{4R} \qquad \text{...(3)}$

$\dfrac{d^2y}{d\theta^2} = 2R\,[-2R\sin 2\theta + \sqrt{(R^2 - L^2)}\cdot\sin\theta]$ by (2)

$= 2R\sin\theta\,[-4R\cos\theta + \sqrt{(R^2 - L^2)}] < 0$

since $\sin\theta > 0$ and $4R\cos\theta > \sqrt{(R^2 - L^2)}$, by (3).

Hence y is max. and the max. value is given by (1) when θ is given by (3).

(c) $S = x^2 + y^2 - r^2 = 0$

$PA =$ length of tangent from $P(6, 8)$

$= \sqrt{S'} = \sqrt{100 - r^2} = PB$

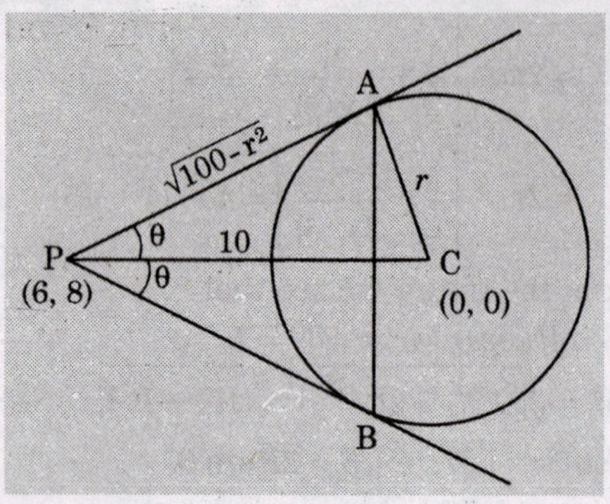

Fig. 52

If Δ be the area of triangle PAB, then

$$\Delta = \frac{1}{2} PA \cdot PB \sin 2\theta$$

$$= (100 - r^2) \sin\theta \cos\theta$$

or $$\Delta = (100 - r^2)\frac{r}{10}\frac{\sqrt{100-r^2}}{10}$$

$$= \frac{1}{100} r (100 - r^2)^{3/2}$$

For max. value of area $\frac{d\Delta}{dr} = 0$

or $$\frac{1}{100}[1 \cdot (100 - r^2)^{3/2} + r \cdot \frac{3}{2}(100 - r^2)^{1/2}(-2r)] = 0$$

or $$\frac{\sqrt{100-r^2}}{100}[100 - r^2 - 3r^2] = 0$$

$\therefore \quad r^2 = 25 \quad$ or $\quad r = 5.$

$\frac{d\Delta}{dr}$ changes sign from + ive to – ive for values of $r < 5$ to $r > 5$. Hence Δ is maximum when $r = 5$.

25. Let P be $(a\cos t, b\sin t)$ on the ellipse and the corresponding point on the auxiliary circle $x^2 + y^2 = a^2$ is $P'(a\cos t, a\sin t)$

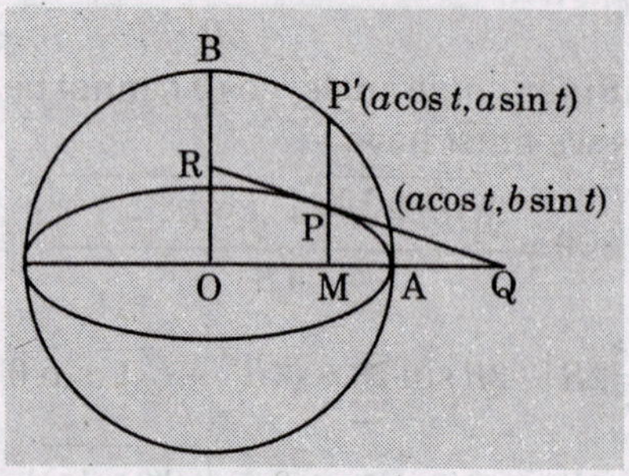

Fig. 53

$$T_p = \frac{x}{a}\cos t + \frac{y}{b}\sin t = 1$$

$\therefore \quad m_1 = -(b/a)\cot t$

$$T_{p'} = \frac{x}{a}\cos t + \frac{y}{a}\sin t = 1$$

$\therefore \quad m_2 = -\cot t.$

If θ be the angle between the tangents then

$$\tan\theta = \frac{m_1 - m_2}{1 + m_1 m_2} = \frac{\cot t\,(1 - b/a)}{1 + (b/a)\cot^2 t}$$

Now θ will be max. when $\tan\theta = y$ is maximum

$$y = \tan\theta = \frac{(a-b)\cot t}{a + b\cot^2 t} = \frac{a-b}{a\tan t + b\cot t}$$

Now N^r of y is constant and hence it will be maximum when its denominator $Z = a\tan t + b\cot t$ is min.

$\therefore \quad \frac{dZ}{dt} = a\sec^2 t - b\,\mathrm{cosec}^2\, t = 0$

$\therefore \quad \tan^2 t = b/a$

or $\quad \tan t = \sqrt{b/a}$ or $\cot t = \sqrt{a/b}$ ...(1)

$$d^2Z/dt^2 = 2a\sec^2 t\tan t + 2b\,\mathrm{cosec}^2\, t\cot t = +\text{ ive}$$

and hence

Z is min. when $\tan t = \sqrt{b/a}$

or $\quad y$ is max. when $\tan t = \sqrt{b/a}$

or $$\tan\theta = \frac{a-b}{a\sqrt{(b/a)} + b\sqrt{(a/b)}} = \frac{a-b}{2\sqrt{(ab)}},\quad \text{by (1).}$$

26. (a) Any tangent to the ellipse is

$$\frac{x}{a}\cos t + \frac{y}{b}\sin t = 1$$

or $$\frac{x}{a\sec t} + \frac{y}{b\,\mathrm{cosec}\, t} = 1.$$

It meets the axes at $Q(a\sec t, 0)$, $R(0, b\,\mathrm{cosec}\, t)$

$$y = QR^2 = a^2\sec^2 t + b^2\,\mathrm{cosec}^2\, t.$$

Now refer result **(2) P. 1397**

Min. value of $y = (a+b)^2$

or $\quad QR^2 = (a+b)^2$ or $QR = (a+b)$.

(b) Ans. (b).

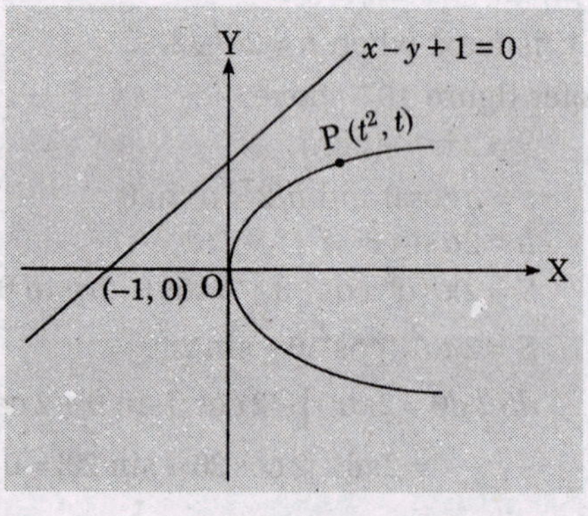

Fig. 54

Let $P(t^2, t)$ be any point on the parabola $x = y^2$.

$$1 = 2y\frac{dy}{dx} \quad \text{or} \quad \frac{dy}{dx} = \frac{1}{2y} = \frac{1}{2t}$$

Hence slope of the normal at P is $-2t$.

Slope of given line is 1, hence slope of a line perpendicular to it is – 1. The shortest distance between the curves (line and parabola) occurs along common normal.

$\therefore \quad -2t = -1 \quad$ or $\quad t = 1/2.$

$\therefore$ Point P is $\left(\frac{1}{4}, \frac{1}{2}\right)$ and S.D. is its distance from the given line.

$$\therefore \quad \text{S.D.} = \frac{\frac{1}{4} - \frac{1}{2} + 1}{\sqrt{2}} = \frac{3}{4\sqrt{2}} = \frac{3\sqrt{2}}{8}$$

27. (a) Any normal to the ellipse is
$ax \sec t - by \operatorname{cosec} t = a^2 - b^2$.
If p be the length of perpendicular from $(0, 0)$, then

$$p = \frac{a^2 - b^2}{\sqrt{(a^2 \sec^2 t + b^2 \operatorname{cosec}^2 t)}}$$

Now p will be maximum if its denominator $\sqrt{a^2 \sec^2 t + b^2 \operatorname{cosec}^2 t}$ is minimum as its numerator is constant.

Now as in **(2) P. 1397**, the minimum value of $\sqrt{a^2 \sec^2 t + b^2 \operatorname{cosec}^2 t}$ is $a + b$.

$\therefore$ Maximum value of
$p = (a^2 - b^2)/(a + b) = a - b.$

(b) Normal $ax \sec t - by \operatorname{cosec} t = a^2 - b^2$ is farthest from centre $(0, 0)$ where $\tan^2 t = \frac{b}{a} = \frac{2}{3}$

or $\tan t = \sqrt{\frac{2}{3}} \quad \therefore \quad \sec t = \sqrt{\frac{5}{3}}, \; \operatorname{cosec} t = \sqrt{\frac{5}{2}}$

$$\therefore \quad 3 . \sqrt{\frac{5}{3}}\, x - 2 . \sqrt{\frac{5}{2}}\, y = 5$$

$$x\sqrt{3} - y\sqrt{2} = \sqrt{5}$$

28. Since $x = r\cos\theta$, $y = r\sin\theta$, where r is the radius vector

$$\therefore \quad \frac{a^2}{x^2} + \frac{b^2}{y^2} = 1, \quad \text{or} \quad \frac{a^2}{r^2\cos^2\theta} + \frac{b^2}{r^2\sin^2\theta} = 1.$$

or $\quad r^2 = a^2\sec^2\theta + b^2\operatorname{cosec}^2\theta.$

The min. value of r^2 as shown in **(2) P. 1397** is $(a+b)^2$ or min. value of r is $a + b$.

29. (a) $\frac{c^4}{r^2} = a^2 \operatorname{cosec}^2 t + b^2 \sec^2 t$

$$\therefore \quad r^2 = \frac{c^4}{a^2 \operatorname{cosec}^2 t + b^2 \sec^2 t}.$$

Now $a^2 \operatorname{cosec}^2 t + b^2 \sec^2 t = a^2 (1 + \cot^2 t) + b^2 (1 + \tan^2 t)$

$= (a^2 + b^2 + 2ab) + (a^2 \cot^2 t + b^2 \tan^2 t - 2ab)$

$= (a + b)^2 + (a \cot t - b \tan t)^2$

The value of $a^2 \operatorname{cosec}^2 t + b^2 \sec^2 t$ or c^4/r^2 is always greater than $(a+b)^2$ and hence its least value is $(a+b)^2$ when $a \cot t - b \tan t = 0$

i.e. $\tan^2 t = a/b$.

Taking reciprocal the greatest value of

$$\frac{r^2}{c^4} = \frac{1}{(a+b)^2}$$

or greatest value of r is $c^2/(a+b)$

Again $c^4/r^2 = a^2 \operatorname{cosec}^2 t + b^2 \sec^2 t$

$= (a^2 + b^2) + (a^2 \cot^2 t + b^2 \tan^2 t)$

$= (a^2 + b^2 - 2ab) + (a^2 \cot^2 t + b^2 \tan^2 t + 2ab)$

$= (a - b)^2 + (a \cot t + b \tan t)^2.$

Now R.H.S. can be made as great as we please, *i.e.*, c^4/r^2 has no maximum value which in turn means that its reciprocal r^2/c^4 and in turn r has no minimum value.

(b) Put $x = r\cos\theta$, $y = r\sin\theta$, where r is the distance of point (r, θ) from origin.

$r^2 (a + b \sin 2\theta) = c.$

$$\therefore \quad z = r^2 = \frac{c}{a + b\sin 2\theta}$$

z will be minimum if $a + b \sin 2\theta$ is maximum or $\sin 2\theta = 1 \quad \therefore \quad 2\theta = \pi/2$ or $5\pi/2$

or $\theta = \pi/4$ or $5\pi/4$

$$\therefore \quad r^2 = \frac{c}{a+b}$$

and $\cos\theta = \sin\theta = 1/\sqrt{2}$, $\theta = \pi/4$

or $\cos\theta = \sin\theta = -1/\sqrt{2}$, $\theta = 5\pi/4$

$\therefore$ Points are $(r\cos\theta, r\sin\theta)$

or $\left(\frac{r}{\sqrt{2}}, \frac{r}{\sqrt{2}}\right)$ and $\left(\frac{-r}{\sqrt{2}}, \frac{-r}{\sqrt{2}}\right)$

where $r = \sqrt{\frac{c}{(a+b)}}$

30. The given relation is :

$$xy(y - x) = 2a^3. \qquad \text{...(1)}$$

Differentiating (1) with respect to x, we get

$$x . 2y\frac{dy}{dx} + 1 . y^2 - x^2\frac{dy}{dx} - 2x . y = 0$$

$$(2xy - x^2)\frac{dy}{dx} + y^2 - 2xy = 0 \qquad \text{...(2)}$$

For max. or min., we have $\frac{dy}{dx} = 0.$

Then (2) gives $y(y - 2x) = 0$ or $y = 2x$.

Since $y = 0$ does not satisfy (1), putting $y = 2x$ in (1), we get

$$2x^2(2x - x) = 2a^3 \quad \text{or} \quad x = a.$$

Then $y = 2a$.

Differentiating (2) again and putting $\frac{dy}{dx} = 0$,

$$(2xy - x^2)\frac{d^2y}{dx^2} + 0 + 0 - 2y = 0$$

In this, putting $x = a$, $y = 2a$, we get

or $3a^2 \dfrac{d^2y}{dx^2} - 4a = 0$ or $\dfrac{d^2y}{dx^2} = \dfrac{4}{3a} > 0.$

Provided $a > 0$. Hence y is minimum when $x = a$ and the minimum value of y is $2a$. To see whether y has another value at $x = a$ less than the minimum, we put $x = a$ in (1). We then get

$$ay(y - a) - 2a^3 = 0$$

or $y^2 - ay - 2a^2 = 0$ or $(y + a)(y - 2a) = 0.$

Hence $y = -a, 2a$.

Thus we get a value $-a$ of y which is less than the minimum value $2a$ of y. The reason simply is that the minimum value of a function does not mean its least value in an interval. [See 'Greatest and least values of a function' before **Page 1397**].

31. Put $c + x = y$. Then the expression

$$z = \frac{(a - c + y)(b - c + y)}{y}$$

$$= \frac{(a - c)(b - c)}{y} + y + a - c + b - c \quad ...(1)$$

$$\frac{dz}{dy} = -\frac{(a - c)(b - c)}{y^2} + 1 = 0$$

$\therefore \quad y^2 = (a - c)(b - c). \quad ...(2)$

Clearly $\dfrac{d^2z}{dy^2} = +$ ive and hence z is minimum. Putting for y from (2) in (1), we get the minimum value

$$= a - c + b - c + 2\sqrt{(a - c)(b - c)}$$

i.e., $(\sqrt{a - c} + \sqrt{b - c})^2$

32. $f(x) = \sin^3 x + \lambda \sin^2 x$

$$f'(x) = 3\sin^2 x \cos x + 2\lambda \sin x \cos x = 0$$

$\therefore \quad \sin x \cos x (3 \sin x + 2\lambda) = 0 \quad ...(1)$

$\therefore \quad \sin x = 0$ or $\cos x = 0$ or $\sin x = -2\lambda/3$

$\cos x = 0$ is ruled out as $-\pi/2 < x < \pi/2$

$\therefore \quad \sin x = 0$ i.e. $x = 0$ or $\sin x = -2\lambda/3$

provided $-1 < -\dfrac{2\lambda}{3} < 1$

or $-3 < -2\lambda < 3$ or $3 > 2\lambda > -3$

or $-\dfrac{3}{2} < \lambda < \dfrac{3}{2}$

$\therefore \quad \lambda \in (-3/2, 3/2)$. In case $\lambda = 0$, then from (1) we get $x = 0$ i.e., there is only one solution.

$\therefore \quad \lambda \in (-3/2, 0) \cup (0, 3/2).$

When λ lies in the above intervals, there are two distinct solutions, one gives maximum and the other minimum.

33. Let $AF = x = ED$

and $AE = y = FD$.

Then from similar Δ^s CED and CAB, we have

$$\frac{CE}{ED} = \frac{CA}{AB}$$

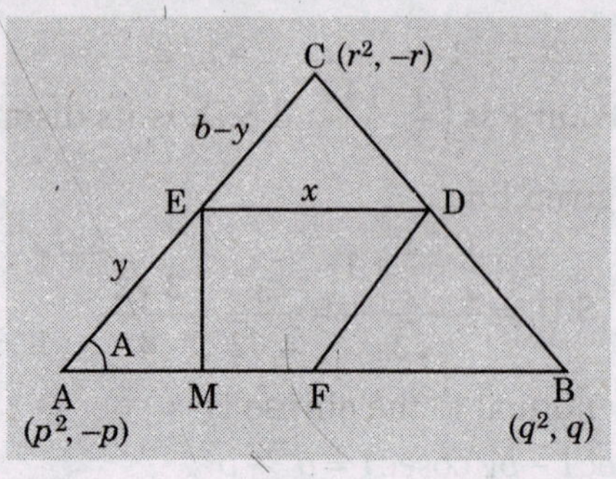

Fig. 55

or $\dfrac{b - y}{x} = \dfrac{b}{c}. \quad ...(1)$

Let u denote the area of parallelogram $AFDE$. Then

$$u = 2\Delta\, AEF = 2 \cdot \frac{1}{2} xy \sin A$$

$$= y \frac{c}{b}(b - y) \sin A, \quad \text{by (1)}$$

or $u = \dfrac{c}{b} \sin A (by - y^2)$

$\therefore \quad \dfrac{du}{dy} = \dfrac{c}{b} \sin A (b - 2y) = 0$

Above gives $y = \dfrac{b}{2}$ and

$$\frac{d^2u}{dy^2} = \frac{c}{b} \sin A(-2) = -\text{ive}$$

Hence area is maximum when $y = b/2$ and its value is

$$u = \frac{b}{2} \cdot \frac{c}{b}\left(b - \frac{b}{2}\right) \sin A$$

$$= \frac{1}{4} bc \sin A = \frac{1}{2} \Delta\, ABC$$

Now $\Delta = \dfrac{1}{2}\begin{vmatrix} p^2 & -p & 1 \\ q^2 & q & 1 \\ r^2 & -r & 1 \end{vmatrix}$

$$= \frac{1}{2}\begin{vmatrix} p^2 & -p & 1 \\ q^2 - p^2 & q + p & 0 \\ r^2 - p^2 & p - r & 0 \end{vmatrix}$$

by $R_2 - R_1$ and $R_3 - R_1$.

$$= \frac{1}{2}(q + p)(p - r)\begin{vmatrix} q - p & 1 \\ -(r + p) & 1 \end{vmatrix}$$

$$= \frac{1}{2}(q + p)(p - r)(q + r).$$

Thus max. area of parallelogram $AFDE$

$$= \frac{1}{2}\Delta = \frac{1}{4}(p + q)(q + r)(p - r).$$

34. Point (α, β) lies on the ellipse

$\therefore \quad \dfrac{\alpha^2}{3} + \dfrac{\beta^2}{4} = 1 \quad ...(1)$

Q lies on $y = x$, PQ is $y = \beta \quad \therefore \quad Q$ is (β, β)

$\therefore \quad P$ is (α, β) where $\alpha > \beta$

The area enclosed by the given lines is area of trapezium $= \dfrac{1}{2}(OR + QP)\, PR$

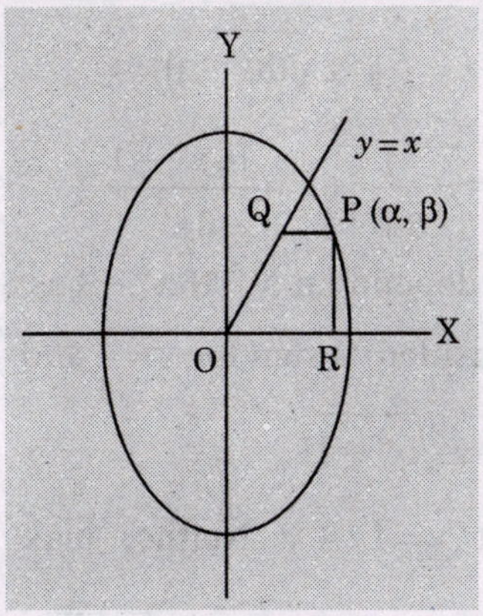

Fig. 56

or $\frac{1}{2}(\alpha + \alpha - \beta)\,\beta = \frac{1}{2}\beta\,(2\alpha - \beta)$

$A = \frac{1}{2}\beta\,[\sqrt{(12 - 3\beta^2)} - \beta]$

$\because \quad 4\alpha^2 = 12 - 3\beta^2$, by (1)

$A = \frac{1}{2}[\beta\sqrt{(12 - 3\beta^2)} - \beta^2]$

$\therefore \quad \frac{dA}{d\beta} = \frac{1}{2}\left\{\sqrt{(12 - 3\beta^2)}\,.\,1 + \beta\,.\,\frac{1}{2\sqrt{(12 - 3\beta^2)}}(-6\beta) - 2\beta = 0\right\}$

$\therefore \quad 12 - 3\beta^2 - 3\beta^2 = 2\beta\sqrt{(12 - 3\beta^2)}$

or $[6(2 - \beta^2)]^2 = 4\beta^2\,.\,3(4 - \beta^2)$

$36(4 - 4\beta^2 + \beta^4) = 12(4\beta^2 - \beta^4)$

$12 - 12\beta^2 + 3\beta^4 = 4\beta^2 - \beta^4$

or $4\beta^4 - 16\beta^2 + 12 = 0$

or $\beta^4 - 4\beta^2 + 3 = 0 \quad \therefore \quad \beta^2 = 1, 3$

$\therefore \quad \beta = 1, \sqrt{3}$ as point (α, β) being in Ist quadrant both α and β are + ive

$\therefore$ points are $\left(\frac{3}{2}, 1\right)$ and $\left(\frac{\sqrt{3}}{2}, \sqrt{3}\right)$ by (1)

We choose only the first point as $\alpha > \beta$ from the figure. Thus under given conditions there is only one point $\left(\frac{3}{2}, 1\right)$ at which area is maximum. It may be verified that $\frac{d^2A}{d\beta^2} = -$ ive for this point

35. The equation of the curve does not change if x be + ive or –ive. Hence we consider only +ive values of x, *i.e.* $x > 0$.

$\therefore \quad |x| = x \quad \therefore \quad y = e^{-x}$

Consider any point (x, y) tangent at which is

$Y - y = -e^{-x}(X - x)$

It meets the axis $Y = 0$ at $(x + ye^x, 0)$

It meets the axis $X = 0$ at $(0, y + x/e^x)$

Area of the triangle $= \frac{1}{2}AB$

$$\Delta = \frac{1}{2}(x + ye^x)\left(y + \frac{x}{e^x}\right)$$

$$= \frac{1}{2}\left(xy + xy + y^2e^x + \frac{x^2}{e^x}\right)$$

Put $y = \frac{1}{e^x}$

$$\therefore \quad \Delta = \frac{1}{2}\left[\frac{2x}{e^x} + \frac{e^x}{e^{2x}} + \frac{x^2}{e^x}\right] = \frac{1}{2}e^{-x}(x + 1)^2$$

For max. value of Δ, we have

$\frac{d\Delta}{dx} = 0 \quad \therefore \quad \frac{1}{2}e^{-x}[-(x + 1)^2 + 2(x + 1)] = 0$

or $\frac{1}{2}(x + 1)(1 - x)e^{-x} = \frac{1}{2}e^{-x}(1 - x^2)$

$\therefore \quad \frac{d\Delta}{dx} = 0 \Rightarrow x = 1, -1$. We shall consider only $x = 1$ as x is +ive.

$$\frac{d^2\Delta}{dx^2} = \frac{1}{2}e^{-x}[-(1 - x^2) - 2x]$$

$$= -\frac{x}{e^x} = -\frac{1}{e} = -\text{ ive at } x = 1$$

Hence Δ is max. when $x = 1 \quad \therefore \quad y = e^{-1} = 1/e$.

$\therefore$ Required point is $(1, 1/e)$.

We have already stated that if x be changed to $-x$, the equation of the curve does not change. Hence the required points are $(\pm 1, 1/e)$.

36. The given equation $x^2 = y - 1$ represents a parabola with vertex at (0, 1). Let the co-ordinates of any point P on the curve $y = 1 + x^2$ be $(h, 1 + h^2)$.

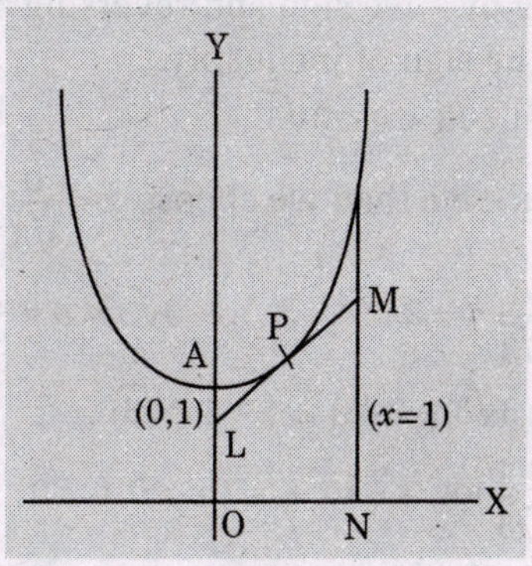

Fig. 57

Now $\frac{dy}{dx} = 2x = 2h$

Tangent at P is $y - (1 + h^2) = 2h(x - h)$

or $y - 2xh = 1 - h^2$

Putting $x = 0$, we get $y = (1 - h^2) = OL$

Putting $x = 1$, we get $y = 1 + 2h - h^2$

$\therefore \quad M$ is $(1, 1 + 2h - h^2)$, $N(1, 0)$

$A =$ area of trapezium $= \frac{1}{2}(OL + MN).ON$

$= \frac{1}{2}[1 - h^2 + 1 + 2h - h^2].1$

$A = (1 + h - h^2)$

$\therefore \quad \frac{dA}{dh} = 1 - 2h = 0 \quad \therefore \quad h = \frac{1}{2}$

and $\frac{d^2A}{dh^2} = -2 = -$ ive

Hence max. $\therefore$ Point P is $\left(\frac{1}{2}, \frac{5}{4}\right)$.

37. We first solve the inequality

$\frac{x^2 + x + 2}{x^2 + 5x + 6} < 0$, that is, $\frac{x^2 + x + 2}{(x+3)(x+2)} < 0$.

Since $x^2 + x + 2 = \left(x + \frac{1}{2}\right)^2 + \frac{7}{4} > 0$

for $x \in \mathbf{R}$, the inequility is satisfied if

$(x+3)(x+2) < 0$ whence $-3 < x < -2$ ...(1)

We now find the extrema of the function

$f(x) = 1 + a^2x - x^3$.

For max. or min.,

$f'(x) = a^2 - 3x^2 \quad \therefore \quad x = \frac{a}{\sqrt{3}}, -\frac{a}{\sqrt{3}}$

$f''(x) = -6x = +$ ive as x is $-$ ive by (1)

Hence minimum.

When a is $+$ ive we choose $x = -\frac{a}{\sqrt{3}}$

$\therefore \quad -3 < -\frac{a}{\sqrt{3}} < -2,$ by (1)

Multiplying by $-$ ive sign and reversing and hence no change in the sign of inequality.

Thus we get $2\sqrt{3} < a < 3\sqrt{3}$

Again if a is $-$ ive then we choose $x = \frac{a}{\sqrt{3}}$

$\therefore \quad -3 < \frac{a}{\sqrt{3}} < -2 \quad \therefore \quad -3\sqrt{3} < a < -2\sqrt{3}$.

Thus $a \in (-3\sqrt{3}, -2\sqrt{3}) \cup (2\sqrt{3}, 3\sqrt{3})$.

38. $f(x) = \frac{1}{8}\log x - bx + x^2, x > 0, b \geq 0$

$f'(x) = \frac{1}{8x} - b + 2x = 0$ ...(1)

$f'(x) = 0 \Rightarrow 16x^2 - 8bx + 1 = 0$ for max or min.

$\therefore \quad x = \frac{1}{4}[b \pm \sqrt{(b^2 - 1)}]$ ...(3)

Above will give real values of x if $b^2 - 1 = +$ ive *i.e.* $b \geq 1$ or $b \leq -1$. But b is given to be $+$ ive. Hence we choose $b \geq 1$.

If $b = 1$ then $x = \frac{1}{4}$

If $b > 1$ then $x = \frac{1}{4}[b \pm \sqrt{(b^2 - 1)}]$

$f''(x) = -\frac{1}{8x^2} + 2 = \frac{16x^2 - 1}{8x^2}$

Its sign will depend on N^r $16x^2 - 1$ as $8x^2$ is $+$ive.

We shall consider its sign for $x = \frac{1}{4}$ and

$x = \frac{1}{4}[b \pm \sqrt{b^2 - 1}]$

$f''(x) = 0$ at $x = 1/4$ $\therefore$ Neither max. nor min. as $f'''(x) \neq 0$.

N^r of $f''(x) = 16x^2 - 1 = (b + \sqrt{b^2 - 1})^2 - 1$

$= +$ ive for $b > 1 \quad \therefore$ Min.

or $= (b - \sqrt{b^2 - 1})^2 - 1$

$= -$ ive for $b > 1 \quad \therefore$ Max.

39. $\Delta = \Delta PBC + \Delta PCA + \Delta PAB$

$= \frac{1}{2}(ap + bq + cr) = k$

$=$ constant as Δ is given

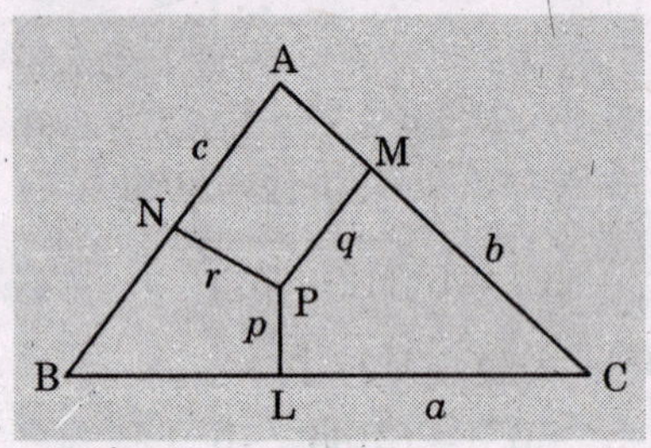

Fig. 58

Now $z = \frac{a}{p} + \frac{b}{q} + \frac{c}{r}$ will be minimum if

$y = k\left(\frac{a}{p} + \frac{b}{q} + \frac{c}{r}\right)$

or $\frac{1}{2}(ap + bq + cr)\left(\frac{a}{p} + \frac{b}{q} + \frac{c}{r}\right)$ is minimum.

or $y = \frac{1}{2}\left[a^2 + b^2 + c^2 + ab\left(\frac{p}{q} + \frac{q}{p}\right) + bc\left(\frac{q}{r} + \frac{r}{q}\right) + ca\left(\frac{r}{p} + \frac{p}{r}\right)\right]$

Now we know that $\frac{p}{q} + \frac{q}{p} \geq 2\left(\frac{p}{q} \times \frac{q}{p}\right)^{1/2} = 2$

Equality when $\frac{p}{q} = \frac{q}{p}$ *i.e.* $p^2 = q^2$ or $p = q$

$\therefore \quad y \geq \frac{1}{2}[a^2 + b^2 + c^2 + 2ab + 2bc + 2ca]$

Hence the minimum value of y is $\frac{1}{2}(a + b + c)^2$ when $p = q = r$. In this case point P will be at the incentre of ΔABC.

Problem Set (3)

1. A curve passes through the point $(2, 0)$ and its gradient at the point (x, y) is $x^2 - 2x$ for all values of x, then the point of maximum ordinate on the curve is $\left(0, \frac{4}{3}\right)$.
(a) True (b) False.

2. From a fixed point P on the circumference of a circle of radius a the perpendicular PR is drawn to the tangent at Q (a variable point), then the maximum area of the $\Delta\, PQR$ is ....

3. At $x = 5\pi/6$, $2 \sin 3x + 3 \cos 3x$ is
(a) maximum (b) minimum
(c) zero (d) none of these.

4. $f(x) = (3 - x) e^{2x} - 4x e^x - x$ has
(a) a maximum at $x = 0$
(b) a minimum at $x = 0$
(c) neither of two at $x = 0$
(d) $f(x)$ is not derivable at $x = 0$.

5. The function $f(x) = x^5 - 5x^4 + 5x^3 - 1$ has
(a) one minimum and two maxima,
(b) two minima and one maximum,
(c) two minima and two maxima,
(d) one minimum and one maximum.

6. $f(x) = \sin x + \cos 2x$ $(x > 0)$ has minima for $x =$
(a) $\frac{n\pi}{2}$ (b) $\frac{3(n+1)\pi}{2}$
(c) $\frac{(2n+1)\pi}{2}$ (d) none of these.
(P.E.T. Raj. 1990)

7. If a function $f(x)$ has $f'(a) = 0$ and $f''(a) = 0$, then
(a) $x = a$ is a maximum for $f(x)$,
(b) $x = a$ is a minimum for $f(x)$,
(c) It is difficult to say (a) and (b),
(d) $f(x)$ is necessarily a constant function.

8. If $y = a \log x + bx^2 + x$ has its extremum values at $x = -1$ and $x = 2$, then
(a) $a = 2, b = -1$ (b) $a = 2, b = -1/2$
(c) $a = -2, b = 1/2$ (d) none of these.

9. Let $P(x) = a_0 + a_1 x^2 + a_2 x^4 + \ldots + a_n x^{2n}$ be a polynomial in a real variable x with $0 < a_0 < a_1 < a_2 < \ldots < a_n$. The function $P(x)$ has
(a) neither a max. nor a min.
(b) only one maximum
(c) only one minimum
(d) none of these

10. N characters of information are held on magnetic tape, in batches of x characters each, the batch processing time is $\alpha + \beta x^2$ seconds, α and β are constants. The optical value of x for fast processing is,
(a) α/β (b) β/α (c) $\sqrt{\alpha/\beta}$ (d) $\sqrt{\beta/\alpha}$.

11. The maximum value of $(\log x)/x$ is
(a) 1 (b) $2/e$ (c) e (d) $1/e$

12. For the curve $y = x e^x$, the point
(a) $x = -1$ is a minimum (b) $x = 0$ is a minimum,
(c) $x = -1$ is a maximum (d) $x = 0$ is a maximum
(M.N.R. 1990)

13. The point $(0, 5)$ is closest to the curve $x^2 = 2y$ at
(a) $(2\sqrt{2}, 0)$ (b) $(0, 0)$
(c) $(2, 2)$ (d) none of these

14. The ratio of the altitude of the cone of greatest volume which can be inscribed in a given sphere, to the diameter of the sphere is
(a) 2/3 (b) 3/4 (c) 1/3 (d) 1/4

15. The function $f(x) = |px - q| + r|x|$, $x \in (-\infty, \infty)$ where $p > 0, q > 0, r > 0$, assumes its maximum value at the point if
(a) $p \neq q$ (b) $r \neq q$ (c) $r \neq p$ (d) $p = q = r$
(I.I.T. 1995)

16. (a) The minimum value of $5^{(x^2-2)^3+8}$ is ...
(b) Max. value of $(x+1)^2 (x+3)$ is ....
(c) If the area of the triangle formed by the tangent at any point P to ellipse $\frac{x^2}{a^2} + \frac{y^2}{b^2} = 1$ and axes of ellipse be minimum then point P is $\left(\frac{a}{\sqrt{2}}, \frac{b}{\sqrt{2}}\right)$.

17. The total number of local maxima and local minima of the function $f(x) = \begin{cases} (2+x)^3, & -3 < x \le -1 \\ x^{2/3}, & -1 < x < 2 \end{cases}$ is
(a) 0 (b) 1 (c) 2 (d) 3
(I.I.T. 2008)

18. For $x \in \left]0, \frac{5\pi}{2}\right[$ define $f(x) = \int_0^x \sqrt{t} \,.\sin t \, dt$. Then f has
(a) local maximum at π and 2π
(b) local minimum at π and 2π
(c) local minimum at π and local maximum at 2π
(d) local maximum at π and local minimum at 2π
(AIEEE 2011)

19. If $f(x) = x^4 + ax^3 + bx^2 + cx + d$ such that $x = 0$ is the only real root of $P'(x) = 0$. If $P(-1) < P(1)$ then in the interval $[-1, 1]$
(a) $P(-1)$ is minimum and $P(1)$ is maximum of P
(b) $P(-1)$ is not minimum but $P(1)$ is the maximum of P
(c) $P(-1)$ is the minimum but $P(1)$ is not the maximum of P

(d) neither $P(-1)$ is the minimum nor $P(1)$ is the maximum of P. **(AIEEE 2009)**

20. Let f, g, h be real valued functions defined on the interval $[0, 1]$ by $f(x) = e^{x^2} + e^{-x^2}$, $g(x) = xe^{x^2} + e^{-x^2}$ and $h(x) = x^2 e^{x^2} + e^{-x^2}$. If a, b and c denote respectively the absolute maximum of f, g and h on $[0, 1]$ then

(a) $a = b$ and $c \neq b$ (b) $a = c$ and $a \neq b$
(c) $a \neq b$ and $c \neq d$ (d) $a = b = c$ **(IIT-JEE 2010)**

21. The shortest distance between the line $y - x = 1$ and the curve $x = y^2$ is

(a) $\frac{3\sqrt{2}}{8}$ (b) $\frac{2\sqrt{3}}{8}$ (c) $\frac{3\sqrt{2}}{5}$ (d) $\frac{\sqrt{3}}{4}$ **(AIEEE 2009, 11)**

22. If $f(x) = \int_0^x t^2 (t-2)(t-3)\, dt$ for $x \in [0, \infty[$ then

(a) f has a local maximum at $x = 2$
(b) f is decreasing on $]2, 3[$
(b) $\exists$ some $c \in]0, \infty[$ such that $f'(c) = 0$
(d) f has a local minimum at $x = 3$ **(IIT-JEE 2012)**

23. Let $f : \mathbf{R} \to \mathbf{R}$ be defined as $f(x) = |x| + |x^2 - 1|$. The total number of points at which f attains either a local maximum or a local minimum is

(a) 5 (b) 4 (c) 3 (d) 2 **(IIT-JEE 2012)**

24. Let $p(x)$ be a real polynomial of least degree which has a local maximum at $x = 1$ and a local minimum at $x = 3$. If $p(1) = 6$, $p(3) = 2$ then $p'(0)$ is

(a) 9 (b) 8 (c) 7 (d) 6 **(IIT-JEE 2012)**

25. Let f be a function defined on $\mathbf{R}$ such that

$$f'(x) = 2010\,(x-2009)(x-2010)^2\,(x-2011)^3\,(x-2012)^4 \;\forall\, x \in \mathbf{R}$$

If g is a function defined on $\mathbf{R}$ with values in the interval $]0, \infty[$ such that $f(x) = \log(g(x))\ \forall\, x \in \mathbf{R}$ then the number of points in $\mathbf{R}$ at which g has a local maximum is

(a) 1 (b) 2 (c) 3 (d) 4 **(IIT-JEE 2010)**

26. Let $f(\theta) = \sin\left(\tan^{-1}\left(\frac{\sin\theta}{\sqrt{\cos 2\theta}}\right)\right)$ where $\frac{-\pi}{4} < \frac{\pi}{4}$. Then the value of $\frac{d}{d(\tan\theta)}(f(\theta))$ is

(a) 1 (b) 2 (c) 3 (d) 4 **(IIT-JEE 2011)**

27. The minimum value of the sum of real numbers $a^{-5}, a^{-4}, 3a^{-3}, 1, a^8$ and $a^{10}, a > 0$ is

(a) 8 (b) 10 (c) 4 (d) 1 **(IIT-JEE 2011)**

Solutions to Problem Set (3)

1. Ans. (a). We have $\frac{dy}{dx} = x^2 - 2x$. Integrating,

$$y = \frac{1}{3}x^3 - x^2 + c.$$

Since the curve passes through $(2, 0)$, we get

$$0 = \frac{1}{3} \times 2^3 - 2^2 + c \quad \text{or} \quad c = \frac{4}{3}.$$

Hence the equation of the curve is

$$y = \frac{1}{3}x^3 - x^2 + \frac{4}{3}$$

Now for max. or min., we have

$$\frac{dy}{dx} = 0, \text{ i.e. } x^2 - 2x = 0; \quad \therefore \quad x = 0, 2.$$

and $\frac{d^2y}{dx^2} = 2x - 2 = -2$ at $x = 0$.

Hence y is max. at $x = 0$. When $x = 0$, we get from (1), $y = 4/3$.

Hence the point of maximum ordinate on the curve is $(0, 4/3)$.

2. Ans. $\frac{3\sqrt{3}}{8}a^2$.

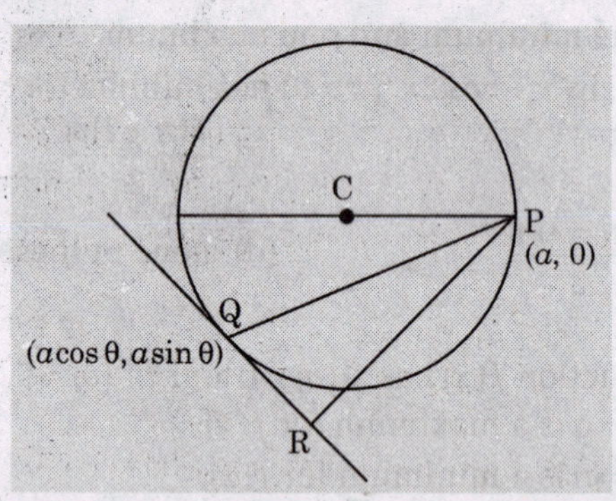

Fig. 59

Let the circle be $x^2 + y^2 = a^2$. We take the point P at $(a, 0)$ and Q at $(a\cos\theta, a\sin\theta)$. Equation of tangent at Q is easily seen to be

$$x\cos\theta + y\sin\theta = a \quad \text{...(1)}$$

Let PR be perpendicular from P on (1).

Then $PR = \frac{a - a\cos\theta}{\sqrt{(\cos^2\theta + \sin^2\theta)}} = 2a\sin^2\frac{\theta}{2}$

Also $PQ = \sqrt{(a - a\cos\theta)^2 + a^2\sin^2\theta}$

$= \sqrt{a^2(1 + \cos^2\theta - 2\cos\theta + \sin^2\theta)}$

$= a\sqrt{2(1 - \cos\theta)} = 2a\sin\frac{\theta}{2}$.

Hence $QR = \sqrt{PQ^2 - PR^2}$

$= \sqrt{4a^2\sin^2(\theta/2) - 4a^2\sin^4(\theta/2)}$

$= 2a\sin(\theta/2)\cos(\theta/2)$.

If A denotes the area of $\Delta\, PQR$, then

$$A = \frac{1}{2} PR \cdot QR$$
$$= \frac{1}{2} . 2a \sin^2 \frac{\theta}{2} . 2a \sin \frac{\theta}{2} \cos \frac{\theta}{2}$$
$$= \frac{1}{2} a^2 \,(1 - \cos \theta) \sin \theta$$
$$= \frac{1}{2} a^2 \left(\sin \theta - \frac{1}{2} \sin 2\theta \right).$$

For maxima or minima, we have

$$\frac{dA}{d\theta} = \frac{1}{2} a^2 \,(\cos \theta - \cos 2\theta) = 0.$$

This gives $\cos \theta = \cos 2\theta = \cos (2\pi - 2\theta)$

or $\theta = 2\pi - 2\theta$ *i.e.* $\theta = \frac{2\pi}{3}$

$$\frac{d^2 A}{d\theta^2} = \frac{1}{2} a^2 \,(-\sin \theta + 2 \sin 2\theta)$$
$$= \frac{1}{2} a^2 \left(\frac{-\sqrt{3}}{2} - \frac{2\sqrt{3}}{2} \right) < 0 \text{ at } \theta = \frac{2\pi}{3}.$$

Hence A is maximum when $\theta = \frac{2\pi}{3}$.

$\therefore$ Maximum value of

$$A = \frac{1}{2} a^2 \left[\sin \frac{2\pi}{3} - \frac{1}{2} \sin \frac{4\pi}{3} \right]$$
$$= \frac{1}{2} a^2 \left[\frac{\sqrt{3}}{2} + \frac{\sqrt{3}}{4} \right] = \frac{3\sqrt{3}}{8} a^2$$

3. Ans. (d).

4. Ans. (c).

We have $f'(x) = (3 - x) . 2e^{2x} - e^{2x} - 4e^x - 4xe^x - 1$

$= 0$ for maxima or minima

or $f'(x) = (5 - 2x) e^{2x} - 4(1 + x) e^x - 1 = 0.$

This is satisfied for $x = 0$.

Now $f''(x) = (5 - 2x) . 2e^{2x} - 2e^{2x} - 4e^x - 4(1 + x) e^x$

$= 10 - 2 - 4 - 4 = 0$ at $x = 0$.

So we find $f'''(x)$. We have

$f''(x) = (8 - 4x) e^{2x} - 4(2 + x) e^x$

$\therefore$ $f'''(x) = (8 - 4x) . 2e^{2x} - 4e^{2x} - 4e^x - 4(2 + x) e^x$

$= 16 - 4 - 4 - 8 = 0$ at $x = 0$.

So we find the next differential coefficient $f^{iv}(x)$.

We have

$f'''(x) = (12 - 8x) e^{2x} - 4(3 + x) e^x$.

$\therefore$ $f^{iv}(x) = (12 - 8x) . 2e^{2x} - 8e^{2x} - 4e^x - 4(3 + x) e^x$

$= 24 - 8 - 4 - 12 = 0$ at $x = 0$.

Now $f^{v}(x) = (12 - 8x) 4e^{2x} - 8 . 2e^{2x}$

$- 8 . 2e^{2x} - 4e^x - 4 . e^x - 4(3 + x) e^x$

$= 48 - 16 - 16 - 4 - 4 - 12$ at $x = 0$

$= -4 \neq 0.$

Hence $f(x)$ has neither maximum nor minimum at $x = 0$.

5. Ans. (d).

Max. at $x = 1$, Min. at $x = 3$.

6. Ans. (c).

We have $f'(x) = \cos x - 2 \sin 2x = 0$

or $\cos x \,(1 - 4 \sin x) = 0$

$\cos x = 0$ gives $x = n\pi + \frac{\pi}{2} = \frac{(2n + 1)\pi}{2}$

$f''(x) = -\sin x - 4 \cos 2x$

$= -\sin (n\pi + \pi/2) - 4 \cos (2n\pi + \pi)$ at $x = n\pi + \pi/2$

$= -\sin (n\pi + \pi/2) + 4$ [$\because \cos (2n\pi + \pi) = \cos \pi = -1$]

$> 0.$ [$\because$ $\sin (n\pi + \pi/2) = \pm 1$]

Hence $f(x)$ is minimum at $x = \frac{1}{2}(2n + 1)\pi$.

7. Ans. (c).

8. Ans. (b).

9. Ans. (c).

$$P'(x) = 2x\,(a_1 + 2a_2 x^2 + \ldots + na_n x^{2n-2})$$

$= 0$ for max. or min.

This gives $x = 0$, since other factor cannot be zero because of the condition $0 < a_0 < a_1 < a_2 < \ldots < a_n$.

Now $P''(x) = 2\,(a_1 + 6a_2 x^2 + \ldots + n(2n - 1)\, a_n x^{2n-2})$

$\therefore$ $P''(x) = 2a_1 > 0$ at $x = 0$.

Hence $P(x)$ has only one minimum at $x = 0$.

10. Ans. (c).

Number of batches $= \frac{N}{x}$.

and time per batch $= (\alpha + \beta x^2)$ seconds.

Hence total time T is given by

$$T = \frac{N}{x}(\alpha + \beta x^2) = N\left(\frac{\alpha}{x} + \beta x\right) \text{ seconds.}$$

For fast processing T must be least.

Now $\frac{dT}{dx} = N\left(-\frac{\alpha}{x^2} + \beta\right) = 0$ for max. or min.

or $x = \sqrt{\left(\frac{\alpha}{\beta}\right)}$ and $\frac{d^2 T}{dx^2} = N . \frac{2\alpha}{x^3} > 0.$

$\therefore$ T is least when $x = \sqrt{\left(\frac{\alpha}{\beta}\right)}$.

11. Ans. (d).

12. Ans. (a).

13. Ans. (d).

14. Ans. (a).

Refer **Q. 22 P. 1425-1434.**

15. Ans. (d).

16. (a) $a^t\ (a > 1)$ is min. when t is min.

$\therefore$ $(x^2 - 2)^3 + 8$ is min. when $y = x^2 - 2$ is min.

$$\frac{dy}{dx} = 2x = 0 \quad \therefore \quad x = 0$$

and $\frac{d^2y}{dx^2} = 2, +\text{ive} \quad \therefore$ min.

$\therefore \quad z = 5^{(-2)^3 + 8} = 5^0 = 1.$

(b) Ans. $\frac{32}{27}$.

(c) Area $= \frac{ab}{\sin 2\theta}$

For minimum, $\sin 2\theta$ is max.

$\therefore \quad 2\theta = 90^o$ or $\theta = 45^o$

17. Ans. (c).

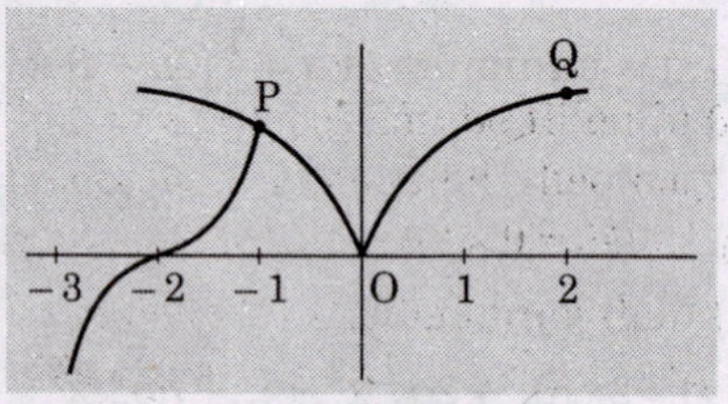

Fig. 60

$y = (2 + x)^3, -3 < x \le -1$

$y = x^{2/3}$ or $x^2 = y^3, -1 < x < 2$

From the graph it is clear that there is only point of local maxima *i.e.*, $x = -1$ and one point of local minima, *i.e.*, $x = 0$.

18. Ans. (d).

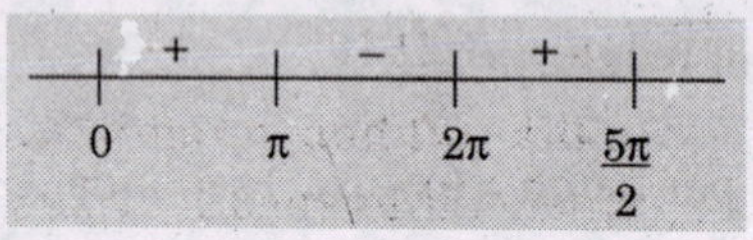

Fig. 61

$f(x) = \int_0^x \sqrt{t}\,.\sin t\, dt$

$f'(x) = \sqrt{x} \sin x$

local maximum at π and local minimum at 2π

19. Ans. (b).

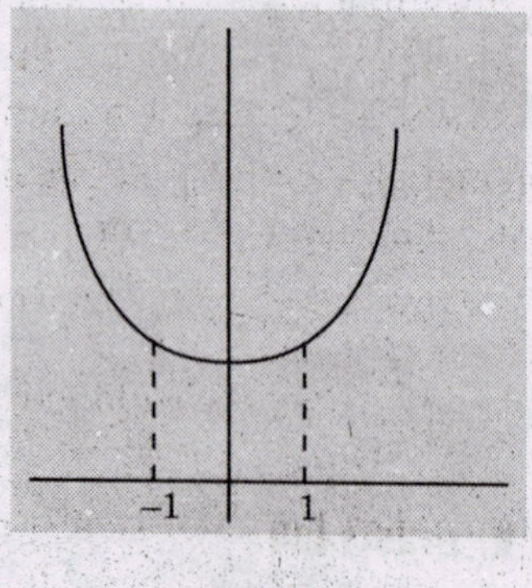

Fig. 62

$y' = x(4x^2 + 3ax + 2b) + c$

Since $y' = 0$ has only one root $x = 0$

$\Rightarrow \quad c = 0$

since D of $4x^2 + 3ax + 2b < 0$ and $4x^2 + 3ax + 2b > 0$ $\forall\, x \in \mathbf{R}$

$y' < 0$ for $x \in [-1, 0[$ and $y' > 0$ for $x \in [0, 1]$

20. Ans. (d).

$f(x) = e^{x^2} + e^{-x^2}$

$\Rightarrow f'(x) = 2x\left(x^{x^2} - e^{-x^2}\right) \ge 0$

$\Rightarrow f(x)$ is increasing

$\therefore \quad f_{max} = f(1) = e + \frac{1}{e}$ and $g(x) = xe^{x^2} + e^{-x^2}$

$\Rightarrow g'(x) = e^{x^2} + 2x^2e^{x^2} - 2xe^{-x^2} > 0$

$\Rightarrow g(x)$ is increasing

$\therefore \quad g_{max} = g(1) = e + \frac{1}{e}$

and $h(x) = x^2e^{x^2} + e^{-x^2}$

$\Rightarrow h'(x) = 2xe^{x^2} + 2x^3e^{x^2} - 2xe^{-x^2}$

$= 2x\left(e^{x^2} + x^2e^{x^2} - e^{-x^2}\right) > 0$

$\therefore \quad h_{max} = h(1) = e + \frac{1}{e}$

$\Rightarrow \quad a = b = c$

21. Ans. (a).

$y^2 = x$

Let at any point $\left(\frac{1}{4}t^2, \frac{t}{2}\right)$

Distance between $\left(\frac{t^2}{4}, \frac{t}{2}\right)$ and $x - y + 1 = 0$ is

$$D = \frac{\frac{1}{4}t^2 - \frac{t}{2} + 1}{\sqrt{2}} = \frac{t^2 - 2t + 4}{4\sqrt{2}}$$

$\Rightarrow \quad \frac{dD}{dt} = \frac{2t - 2}{4\sqrt{2}} = 0 \;\therefore t = 1 \Rightarrow \frac{d^2D}{dt^2} = \frac{2}{4\sqrt{2}} > 0$

$\therefore \quad$ Point $\left(\frac{1}{4}, \frac{1}{2}\right)$

Hence, minimum distance

$$= \frac{1 - 2 + 4}{4\sqrt{2}} = \frac{3 \times \sqrt{2}}{4\sqrt{2} \times \sqrt{2}} = \frac{3\sqrt{2}}{8}$$

22. Ans. (a), (b), (c) and (d).

$f(x) = \int_0^x e^{t^2}\,(t-2)(t-3)\,dt$

$\Rightarrow f'(x) = 1.e^{x^2}.(x-2)(x-3)$

(i) $x = 2$ is local maxima (ii) $x = 3$ is local minima

(iii) It is decreasing in $x \in]2, 3[$

(iv) $f'(x) = e^{x^2}(x-2) + e^{x^2}(x-3) + 2xe^{x^2}(x-2)(x-3)$

$= e^{x^2}[x - 2 + x - 3 + 2x(x-2)(x-3)]$

$f''(x) = 0, \quad f''(x) = e^{x^2}[2x^3 - 10x^2 + 14x - 5]$

$f''(0) < 0$ and $f''(1) > 0$

$\Rightarrow \quad f''(c) = 0, \quad c \in]0, 1[$

23. Ans. (a).

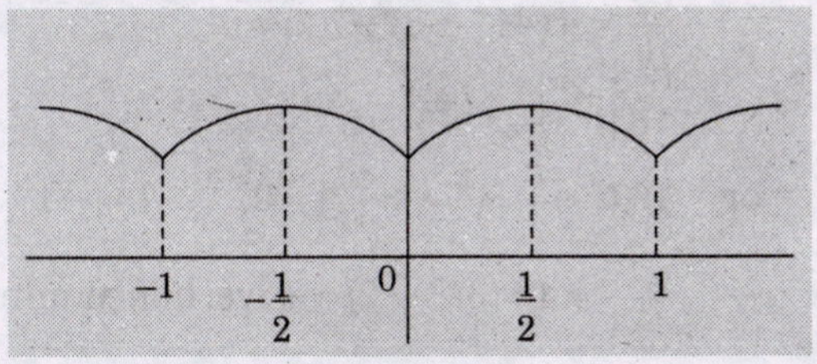

Fig. 63

$$f(x) = |x| + |x^2 - 1|$$

$$= \begin{cases} -x + x^2 - 1 & x < -1 \\ -x - x^2 + 1 & -1 \le x \le 0 \\ x - x^2 + 1 & 0 < x < 1 \\ x + x^2 - 1 & x \ge 1 \end{cases}$$

$$= \begin{cases} x^2 - x - 1 & x < -1 \\ -x^2 - x + 1 & -1 \le x \le 0 \\ -x^2 + x + 1 & 0 < x < 11 \\ x^2 + x - 1 & x \ge 1 \end{cases}$$

24. Ans. (a).

$$p' - \lambda(x-1)(x-3) = \lambda(x^2 - 4x + 3)$$

$$p(x) = \lambda\left(\frac{x^3}{3} - 2x^2 + 3x\right) + \mu$$

$$p(1) = 6 \qquad \Rightarrow \quad 6 = \lambda\left(\frac{1}{3} - 2 + 3\right) + 4$$

$$6 = \lambda\left(\frac{1}{3} + 1\right) + \mu \qquad \Rightarrow \quad 18 = 4\lambda + 3\mu \qquad \ldots(1)$$

$$p(3) = 2 \qquad \Rightarrow \quad 2 = \lambda\left(\frac{27}{3} - \frac{2}{9} + 9\right) + \mu$$

$\Rightarrow \quad \mu = 2$

$\lambda = 3$

$$p'(x) = 3(x-1)(x-3)$$

$$p'(0) = 3(-1)(-3) = 9$$

25. Ans. (a).

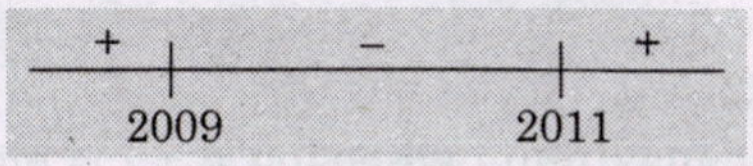

Fig. 64

$$f'(x) = 2010\,(x - 2009)\,(x - 2010)^2$$

$$(x - 2011)^3\,(x - 2012)^4$$

$f(x) = \log g(x)$ where $g(x) = e^{f(x)}$

$$g'(x) = e^{f(x)} \cdot f'(x)$$

26. Ans. (a).

$$\sin\left(\tan^{-1}\left(\frac{\sin\theta}{\sqrt{\cos 2\theta}}\right)\right), \theta \in \left]\frac{-\pi}{4}, \frac{\pi}{4}\right[$$

$$= \sin\left(\tan^{-1}\left(\frac{\sin\theta}{\sqrt{2\cos^2\theta - 1}}\right)\right)$$

$$= \sin(\sin^{-1}(\tan\theta)) = \tan\theta$$

$$\therefore \quad \frac{d(f(\theta))}{d(\tan\theta)} = 1$$

27. Ans.(a).

$$\text{AM} > \text{GM} \Rightarrow \frac{\frac{1}{a^5} + \frac{1}{a^4} + \frac{1}{a^3} + \frac{1}{a^3} + \frac{1}{a^3} + 1 + a^8 + a^{10}}{8}$$

$$\ge \left(\frac{1}{a^5} \cdot \frac{1}{a^4} \cdot \frac{1}{a^3} \cdot \frac{1}{a^3} \cdot \frac{1}{a^3} \cdot 1 \cdot a^8 \cdot a^{10}\right)^{1/8}$$

$$\Rightarrow \quad \frac{1}{a^5} + \frac{1}{a^4} + \frac{3}{a^3} + 1 + a^8 + a^{10} \ge 8(1)^{1/8}$$

$\Rightarrow$ Minimum value of

$$\frac{1}{a^5} + \frac{1}{a^4} + \frac{3}{a^3} + 1 + a^3 + a^{10} = 8 \text{ at } a = 1$$

MISCELLANEOUS EXERCISE

Matching Entries

Match the entries of List-A and List-B.

1.

List-A	List-B
(a) The max. value of $\left(\frac{1}{x}\right)^{2x^2}$ is	1. ab
(b) P is a point on the parabola $y^2 = 8x$ such that its distance from the circle $x^2 + (y+6)^2 = 1$ is minimum is	2. $e^{1/e}$
(c) Minimum area of triangle formed by any tangent to ellipse $\frac{x^2}{a^2} + \frac{y^2}{b^2} = 1$ and the axes of co-ordinates is	3. $\tan^{-1}\sqrt{(p/q)}$
(d) $\sin^p x \cos^q x$ where p, q are +ive and x acute is maximum at $x =$	4. $(2, -4)$

Answers

1. (a) → 2, (b) → 4, (c) → 1, (d) → 3

Solutions

1. (a) → 2.

y is maximum when $\log y = z$ is max.

$\therefore \quad z = 2x^2 \log \frac{1}{x} = -2x^2 \log x$

$\frac{dz}{dx} = -2[x + 2x \log x] = 0$

$= -2x(1 + 2\log x) = 0$

$\therefore \quad \log x = -\frac{1}{2}$ or $x = e^{-1/2} = \frac{1}{\sqrt{e}}$

$\frac{d^2z}{dx^2} = -2\left[(1 + 2\log x) . 1 + x . \frac{2}{x}\right]$

$= -2[0 + 2] = -4 = \text{ive} \quad \therefore$ Max.

$\therefore \quad y = \left(\frac{1}{x}\right)^{2x^2} = (\sqrt{e})^{2.(1/e)} = e^{1/e}.$

(b) → 4.

Any point on the parabla $y^2 = 8x\,(4a = 8$ or $a = 2)$ is $(at^2, 2at)$ or $(2t^2, 4t)$. Its distance from the circle means its distance from the centre $(0, -6)$ of the circle. If D be the distance, then

$Z = D^2 = (2t^2)^2 + (4t + 6)^2$

$= 4(t^4 + 4t^2 + 12t + 9)$

$\therefore \quad \frac{dz}{dt} = 4(4t^3 + 8t + 12) = 0$

$\therefore \quad 16(t^3 + 2t + 3) = 0$

or $\quad 16(t + 1)(t^2 - t - 3) = 0 \quad \therefore \quad t = -1$

$\frac{d^2z}{dt^2} = 16(3t^2 + 2) = +\text{ive}$, hence minimum.

$\therefore$ Point is $(2, -4)$.

(c) → 1.

Any tangent to ellipse at $P(a\cos t, b\sin t)$ is

$\frac{x}{a}\cos t + \frac{y}{b}\sin t = 1.$

Its intercepts on the axes are

$OA = \frac{a}{\cos t}, OB = \frac{b}{\sin t}.$

$\therefore \quad \Delta OAB = \frac{1}{2}\frac{ab}{\sin t \cos t} = \frac{ab}{\sin 2t} =$ minimum

when denominator $\sin 2t$ is maximum and is equal to 1.

$\therefore$ Area $= ab$.

(d) → 3. **Q. 4 (b) P. 1498-1405.**

Comprehension

1. Pessage

1. Consider the function

$f :]-\infty, \infty[\to]-\infty, \infty[$ defined by

$f(x) = \frac{x^2 - ax + 1}{x^2 + ax + 1}, \quad 0 < a < 2$ **(IIT 2008)**

(i) Which of the following is true

(a) $(2 + a)^2 f''(1) + (2 - a)^2 f''(1) = 0$

(b) $(2 - a)^2 f''(1) - (2 + a)^2 f''(-1) = 0$

(c) $f'(1) f'(-1) = (2 - a)^2$

(d) $f'(1) f'(-1) = -(2 + a)^2$

(ii) Which of the following is true

(a) $f(x)$ is decreaseing on $[-1, 1[$ and has a local minimum at $x = 1$

(b) $f(x)$ is increasing on $]-1, 1[$ and has a local maximum at $x = 1$

(c) $f(x)$ is increasing on $]-1, 1[$ but has neither a local maximum nor a local minimum at $x = 1$

(d) $f(x)$ is decreasing on $]-1, 1[$ but has neither a local maximum nor a local minimum at $x = 1$

(iii) If $g(x) = \int_0^{e^x} \frac{f'(t)}{1 + t^2} dt$, which of the following is true

(a) $g'(x)$ is positive on $]-\infty, 0[$ and negative on $]0, \infty[$

(b) $g'(x)$ is negative on $]-\infty, 0[$ and positive on $]0, \infty[$

(b) $g'(x)$ changes sign on both $]-\infty, 0[$ and $]0, \infty[$

(d) $g'(x)$ does not change sign on $]-\infty, \infty[$

Sol. (i) Ans. (a).

$f(x) = \frac{x^2 - ax + 1}{x^2 + ax + 1}, \quad 0 < a < 2$

Discriminant of denominator of $a^2 - 4 < 0$

$\Rightarrow$ Denommeter $\neq 0 \ \forall \ x \in \mathbf{R}$

$f'(x) = \frac{(x^2 + ax + 1)(-2a) + 2ax(2x + a)}{(x^2 + ax + 1)^2}$

$= \frac{2ax^2 - 2a}{(x^2 + ax + 1)^2} = \frac{2a(x^2 - 1)}{(x^2 + ax + 1)^2}$

$f'(1) = f'(-1) = 0 \Rightarrow$ (c) and (d) are not true.

$f''(x) = \frac{2a(x^2 + ax + 1)^2 (2x) - 2a(x^2 - 1) \, 2(x^2 + ax + 1)(2x + a)}{(x^2 + ax + 1)^4}$

$$\Rightarrow \quad f''(1) = \frac{2a[2(2+a)]}{(2+a)^3} = \frac{4a}{(2+a)^2}$$

and $f''(-1) = -\dfrac{4a}{(2-a)^2}$

$$\Rightarrow \quad f''(1)(2+a)^2 + f''(-1)(2-a)^2 = 0$$

(ii) Ans. (b).

$$f'(x) = \frac{2a(x+1)(x-1)}{(x^2+ax+1)^2}$$

$$f'(x) > 0 \text{ in }]-\infty, -1[\cup]1, \infty[$$

and $f'(x) < 0$ in $]-1, 1[$

$\Rightarrow$ $f(x)$ is decreasing in $]-1, 1[$ as $f(x)$ is continuous function for $0 < a < 2$

(iii) Ans. (b).

$$g(x) = \int_0^{e^x} \frac{f'(t)}{1+t^2}\, dt$$

$$\Rightarrow \quad g'(x) = \frac{f'(e^x)}{(1+e^{2x})} e^x = \frac{2a(e^{2x}-1)e^x}{(1+e^{2x})(e^{2x}+ae^x+1)^2}$$

$g'(x) > 0$ for $x > 0$ and $g'(x) < 0$ for $x < 0$

Fascinating Facts

- If $f(x)$ is continuous function in its domain, then at least one maxima and one minima must lie between two equal values of x.
- Maxima and minima occur alternately *i.e.* between two maxima there is one minimum and vice-versa.
- A function may have a number of local maxima or local minima in a given interval and even a local minimum may be greater than a relative maxima *i.e.*, a local maximum value may not be the greatest and a local minimum value may not be the least value of the function in any given interval.
- If a function $f(x)$ is continuous in a closed interval $[a, b]$ then it attains the absolute maximum (absolute minimum) at critical points or at the end points of the interval $[a, b]$
- A function may have an extreme value at a point without being derivative there at.

❑

CHAPTER 31

Integral Calculus

Integration

§1. Indefinite Integrals.

If $\frac{d}{dx}[F(x)+c]=f(x)$, then we say that $F(x)+c$ is an *indefinite integral or antiderivative* of $f(x)$ and we write

$$\int f(x)\,dx = F(x)+c.$$

Fundamental Formulae. To be committed to memory.

Differential Calculus :

(i) $\frac{d}{dx}(x^{n+1})=(n+1)\,x^n$

Integral Calculus :

$\therefore \int x^n\,dx = \frac{x^{n+1}}{n+1} \quad (n \neq -1).$

Note : The above formula is the most important one and shall be frequently used in the book and we shall henceforth speak it as **power formula**. It should be remembered as follows :

Increase the power of x by one and divide by the increased power.

e.g. $\int x^5\,dx = \frac{x^6}{6}$, $\int x^{3/2}\,dx = \frac{x^{5/2}}{5/2} = \frac{2}{5}x^{5/2}$.

Deductions from above :

(a) $\int \frac{1}{x^n}\,dx = \int x^{-n}\,dx = \frac{x^{-n+1}}{-n+1}$

$= \frac{1}{-(n-1)\,x^{n-1}} \quad (n \neq 1).$

In other words it means that when x^n is in the denominator then decrease the power of x in the D^r by one and multiply the denominator by the decreased power with sign changed.

i.e. $\int \frac{1}{x^5}\,dx = \frac{1}{-4x^4}$, $\int \frac{1}{x^{7/2}}\,dx = \frac{1}{-(5/2)\,x^{5/2}} = \frac{-2}{5\,x^{5/2}}$.

(b) $\int \frac{1}{\sqrt{(x)}}\,dx = \int \frac{1}{x^{1/2}}\,dx = \frac{1}{\frac{1}{2}x^{-1/2}} = 2\sqrt{x}.$ **(V. Imp.)**

(c) $\int dx = \int 1\,.\,dx = \int x^0\,dx = \frac{x^{0+1}}{0+1} = x.$

Thus $\int 7\,dx = 7x$, $\int \frac{1}{2}\,dx = \frac{1}{2}x.$

In other words it means that integral of any constant w.r.t. x is that constant multiplied by x

(ii) $\frac{d}{dx}(\log x) = \frac{1}{x}$ $\quad \therefore \int \frac{1}{x}\,dx = \log x$

(iii) $\frac{d}{dx}(e^x) = e^x$ $\quad \therefore \int e^x\,dx = e^x$

(iv) $\frac{d}{dx}(a^x) = a^x \log a$ $\quad \therefore \int a^x\,dx = \frac{a^x}{\log a}$

(v) $\frac{d}{dx}(\sin x) = \cos x$ $\quad \therefore \int \cos x\,dx = \sin x$

(vi) $\frac{d}{dx}(\cos x) = -\sin x$ $\quad \therefore \int \sin x\,dx = -\cos x$

(vii) $\frac{d}{dx}(\tan x) = \sec^2 x$ $\quad \therefore \int \sec^2 x\,dx = \tan x$

(viii) $\frac{d}{dx}(\cot x) = -\operatorname{cosec}^2 x$

$\int \operatorname{cosec}^2 x\,dx = -\cot x$

(ix) $\frac{d}{dx}(\sec x) = \sec x \tan x$

$\therefore \int \sec x \tan x\,dx = \sec x$

(x) $\frac{d}{dx}(\operatorname{cosec} x) = -\operatorname{cosec} x \cot x,$

$\therefore \int \operatorname{cosec} x \cot x\,dx = -\operatorname{cosec} x.$

(xi) $\frac{d}{dx}(\sin^{-1} x) = \frac{1}{\sqrt{(1-x^2)}},$

$\therefore \int \frac{1}{\sqrt{(1-x^2)}}\,dx = \sin^{-1} x$

(xii) $\frac{d}{dx}(\tan^{-1} x) = \frac{1}{1+x^2}$ $\quad \therefore \int \frac{1}{1+x^2}\, dx = \tan^{-1} x$

(xiii) $\frac{d}{dx} \sec^{-1} x = \frac{1}{x\sqrt{(x^2-1)}}$

$\therefore \int \frac{1}{x\sqrt{(x^2-1)}}\, dx = \sec^{-1} x$

(xiv) $\frac{d}{dx} \sinh x = \cosh x$ $\quad \therefore \int \cosh x\, dx = \sinh x$

(xv) $\frac{d}{dx} \cosh x = \sinh x$ $\quad \therefore \int \sinh dx = \cosh x$

(xvi) $\frac{d}{dx} \tanh x = \text{sech}^2 x$ $\quad \therefore \int \text{sech}^2 x\, dx = \tanh x$

(xvii) $\frac{d}{dx} \coth x = -\text{cosech}^2 x,$

$\therefore \int \text{cosech}^2 x\, dx = -\coth x$

(xviii) $\frac{d}{dx} \text{sech}\, x = -\text{sech}\, x \tanh x,$

$\therefore \int \text{sech}\, x \tanh x\, dx = -\text{sech}\, x$

(xix) $\frac{d}{dx} \text{cosech}\, x = -\text{cosech}\, x \coth x,$

$\therefore \int \text{cosech}\, x \coth x\, dx = -\text{cosech}\, x.$

Extension of the above formulae

$\because \frac{d}{dx} \tan(2x+3) = \sec^2(2x+3)$. d.c. of $(2x+3)$

$= 2\sec^2(2x+3).$

$\therefore \int \sec^2(2x+3)\, dx = \frac{1}{2}\tan(2x+3)$

$\because \frac{d}{dx} \sin(q-px) = \cos(q-px).$ d.c. of $(q-px) = -p\cos(q-px)$

$\therefore \int \cos(q-px)\, dx = -\frac{1}{p}\sin(q-px)$

$\frac{d}{dx}\tan^{-1}\frac{x}{a} = \frac{1}{1+(x^2/a^2)}$ d.c. of $\frac{x}{a}$

$= \frac{1}{a}\cdot\frac{a^2}{x^2+a^2} = \frac{a}{x^2+a^2}$

$\therefore \int \frac{1}{x^2+a^2}\, dx = \frac{1}{a}\tan^{-1}\frac{x}{a}$

Similarly $\int \frac{1}{\sqrt{(a^2-x^2)}}\, dx = \sin^{-1}\frac{x}{a}$

Important rule : In any of the standard results if in place of x we have got **a linear expression of x of the form $ax + b$**, then the same formula is applicable but we must divide by the d.c. of $ax+b$ *i.e.* by a which is a constant and is **coefficient of x.**

Integrals of squares of trigonometrical functions

(a) $\because \sin^2 x = \frac{1}{2}(1-\cos 2x), \cos^2 x = \frac{1}{2}(1+\cos 2x)$

$\therefore \int \sin^2 x\, dx = \frac{1}{2}\left(x - \frac{1}{2}\sin 2x\right),$

$\int \cos^2 x\, dx = \frac{1}{2}\left(x + \frac{1}{2}\sin 2x\right)$

(b) $\because \tan^2 x = \sec^2 x - 1, \ \cot^2 x = \text{cosec}^2 x - 1$

$\therefore \int \tan^2 x\, dx = \tan x - x, \int \cot^2 x\, dx = -\cot x - x.$

Constant of Integration :

$\frac{d}{dx}(x^5) = 5x^4 \quad \therefore \int 5x^4\, dx = x^5.$

Again $\frac{d}{dx}(x^5 + c) = 5x^4. \quad \therefore \int 5x^4\, dx = x^5 + c.$

From above we observe that

$\int 5x^4\, dx = x^5$ as well as $x^5 + c.$

This c is called constant of integration and it should be written by students in all the integrals though we shall not write the same in the answer.

§2. Evaluation of Definite Integrals.

We use the following formula, known as the Newton-Leibnitz formula

$$\int_a^b f(x)\, dx = [F(x)]_a^b = F(b) - F(a),$$

where $F(x)$ is one of the anti-derivatives of the function $f(x)$,

i.e., $F'(x) = f(x) \quad (a \le x \le b).$

Remark : When evaluating integrals with the help of the above formula, the students should keep in mind the condition for its legitimate use. This formula is used to compute the definite integral of a function *continuous* on the interval $[a, b]$ only when the equality $F'(x) = f(x)$ is fulfilled in the *whole* interval $[a, b]$, where $F(x)$ is anti-derivative of the function $f(x)$. In particular, the anti-derivative must be a function continuous on the whole interval $[a, b]$. A discontinuous function used as an anti-derivative will lead to wrong result.

Problem Set (1)

Integration based on standard formulae

Integrate the following :

1. $\frac{(4x^2-2\sqrt{x})}{x}+\frac{1}{1+x^2}-5\operatorname{cosec}^2 x.$

2. $\frac{(x+a)^3}{x^3}+\frac{1-x^4}{1-x}-\frac{7}{x\sqrt{(x^2-1)}}+\frac{x+2}{(x+1)^2}+\frac{(1+x)^3}{\sqrt{(x)}}.$

3. (a) $\frac{5\cos^3 x+2\sin^3 x}{2\sin^2 x\cos^2 x}+\sqrt{1+\sin 2x}+\frac{1+2\sin x}{\cos^2 x}+\frac{1-\cos 2x}{1+\cos 2x}+\sqrt{\left(1+\sin\frac{x}{2}\right)}+\frac{\sin^2 x}{(1+\cos x)^2}+(\tan x+\cot x)^2.$

(b)* $\frac{\cos 2x-\cos 2\alpha}{\cos x-\cos\alpha}$

(c) $\int_0^{\pi/2}\frac{(\sin x+\cos x)^2}{\sqrt{1+\sin 2x}}\,dx=$

(a) 0 (b) 1
(c) 2 (d) 3 **(AIEEE 2004)**

4. $(2x-3)^5+\frac{1}{(7x-5)^3}+\frac{1}{\sqrt{(5x-4)}}+\frac{1}{2-3x}+\sqrt{3x+2}.$

5. $e^{2x-3}+7^{4-3(x/2)}+\sin\left(3x-\frac{1}{2}\right)+\cos\left(\frac{2}{5}x-2\right)+a^{3x+2}.$

6. $\sec^2(2-3x)+\frac{1}{\sin^2(3-4x)}+\frac{\sin(2-3x)}{\cos^2(2-3x)}+\cos x\operatorname{cosec}^2 x+\operatorname{cosec}(3x-2)\cot(3x-2)$

7. $\frac{1}{\sqrt{(4-3x^2)}}+\frac{1}{\sqrt{[3-(x^2/4)]}}+\frac{1}{(5+4x^2)}+\frac{1}{5+(2-3x)^2}.$

8. $\frac{1}{\sqrt{(3x+4)}-\sqrt{(3x+1)}}+\frac{8x+13}{\sqrt{(4x+7)}}+(7x-2)\sqrt{3x+2}.$

9. $\frac{1+x+x^2}{x^3(1+x)}+\frac{2x-1}{(x+1)^2}+\frac{4-5\sin x}{\cos^2 x}+\frac{1}{\sin^2 x\cos^2 x}+\sin 2x\cos 3x.$

10. $\frac{\sin x}{1+\sin x}+\sin x\sin 2x\sin 3x+\sec^2 x\cos^2 2x+\sin^4 x\cos^4 x.$

11. (a)* $\frac{1+\cos 4x}{\cot x-\tan x}$

(b) $\frac{\cos 7x-\cos 8x}{1+2\cos 5x}$

12. $\frac{(p^x+q^x)^2}{p^x.q^x}+\frac{e^{5\log_e x}-e^{4\log_e x}}{e^{3\log_e x}-e^{2\log_e x}}+\frac{\sin^6 x+\cos^6 x}{\sin^2 x\cos^2 x}$

Solution to Problem Set (1)

1. Ans. $2x^2-4\sqrt{x}+\tan^{-1}x+5\cot x.$

2. Ans. $x+3a\log x-3\frac{a^2}{x}-\frac{a^3}{2x^2}+x+\frac{x^2}{2}+\frac{x^3}{3}+\frac{x^4}{4}-7\sec^{-1}x+\log(x+1)-\frac{1}{x+1}+2\sqrt{x}+2x^{3/2}+\frac{6}{5}x^{5/2}+\frac{2}{7}x^{7/2}.$

3. (a) Let $f(x)=\frac{5\cos x}{2\sin^2 x}+\frac{\sin x}{\cos^2 x}+\sqrt{\cos^2 x+\sin^2 x+2\sin x\cos x}+\frac{1}{\cos^2 x}+\frac{2\sin x}{\cos^2 x}+\frac{2\sin^2 x}{2\cos^2 x}+\sqrt{\left(\cos^2\frac{x}{4}+\sin^2\frac{x}{4}+2\sin\frac{x}{4}\cos\frac{x}{4}\right)}+\frac{(1-\cos x)(1+\cos x)}{(1+\cos x)^2}+\tan^2 x+\cot^2 x+2$

$=\frac{5}{2}\operatorname{cosec}x\cot x+3\sec x\tan x+(\cos x+\sin x)+\sec^2 x+(\sec^2 x-1)+\left(\cos\frac{x}{4}+\sin\frac{x}{4}\right)+\left(\sec^2\frac{x}{2}-1\right)+(\sec^2 x+\operatorname{cosec}^2 x)$

$=\frac{5}{2}\operatorname{cosec}x\cot x+3\sec x\tan x+\cos x+\sin x+3\sec^2 x+\left(\cos\frac{x}{4}+\sin\frac{x}{4}\right)+\operatorname{cosec}^2 x+\sec^2\frac{x}{2}-2$

∴ $\int f(x)\,dx=-\frac{5}{2}\operatorname{cosec}x+3\sec x+(\sin x-\cos x)+3\tan x+4[\sin(x/4)-\cos(x/4)]-\cot x+2\tan(x/2)-2x.$

(b) $\frac{(2\cos^2 x-1)-(2\cos^2\alpha-1)}{\cos x-\cos\alpha}=2(\cos x+\cos\alpha)$

$I=2(\sin x+x\cos\alpha)$ as $\cos\alpha$ is a constant.

(c) Ans. (c).

$1+\sin 2x=(\sin x+\cos x)^2$

∴ $I=\int_0^{\pi/2}(\sin x+\cos x)\,dx=[-\cos x+\sin x]_0^{\pi/2}$
$=1-(-1)=2.$

4. $\frac{1}{2}\cdot\frac{(2x-3)^{5+1}}{5+1}+\frac{1}{7}\frac{1}{(-2)(7x-5)^{3-1}}+\frac{1}{5}.2\sqrt{5x-4}+\left(-\frac{1}{3}\right)\log(2-3x)+\frac{1}{3}\frac{(3x+2)^{(1/2)+1}}{\frac{1}{2}+1}$

$$= \frac{1}{12}(2x-3)^6 - \frac{1}{14}\cdot\frac{1}{(7x-5)^2} + \frac{2}{5}\sqrt{5x-4}$$

$$- \frac{1}{3}\log(2-3x) + \frac{2}{9}(3x+2)^{3/2}.$$

5. $\frac{1}{2}e^{2x-3} - \frac{2}{3}\cdot 7^{4-3(x/2)}\ \frac{1}{\log 7} - \frac{1}{3}\cos\left(3x - \frac{1}{2}\right)$

$$+ \frac{5}{2}\sin\left(\frac{2}{5}x - 2\right) + \frac{1}{3}\frac{a^{3x+2}}{\log a}.$$

6. $-\frac{1}{3}\tan(2-3x) - \frac{1}{4}[-\cot(3-4x)]$

$$- \frac{1}{3}\sec(2-3x) - \text{cosec}\ x - \frac{1}{3}\text{cosec}\,(3x-2).$$

7. $\frac{1}{\sqrt{[2^2 - (\sqrt{3}\,x)^2]}} + \frac{1}{\sqrt{[(\sqrt{3})^2 - (x/2)^2]}}$

$$+ \frac{1}{(\sqrt{5})^2 + (2x)^2} + \frac{1}{\sqrt{[(\sqrt{5})^2 + (2-3x)^2]}}$$

Ans. $\frac{1}{\sqrt{(3)}}\sin^{-1}\frac{x\sqrt{3}}{2} + 2\sin^{-1}\frac{x}{2\sqrt{(3)}}$

$$+ \frac{1}{\sqrt{(5)}}\cdot\frac{1}{2}\tan^{-1}\frac{2x}{\sqrt{(5)}} + \frac{1}{\sqrt{(5)}}\left(-\frac{1}{3}\right)\tan^{-1}\frac{2-3x}{\sqrt{(5)}}$$

8. (i) $\frac{1}{\sqrt{(3x+4)} - \sqrt{(3x+1)}} = \frac{\sqrt{3x+4} + \sqrt{3x+1}}{(3x+4)-(3x+1)}$

$$= \frac{1}{3}[\sqrt{3x+4} + \sqrt{3x+1}].$$

(ii) $\frac{8x+13}{\sqrt{(4x+7)}} = \frac{2(4x+7)-1}{\sqrt{(4x+7)}} = 2\sqrt{4x+7} - \frac{1}{\sqrt{(4x+7)}}$

(iii) $(7x-2)\sqrt{(3x+2)} = \frac{7}{3}\left(3x - \frac{6}{7}\right)\sqrt{3x+2}$

$$= \frac{7}{3}\left(3x + 2 - \frac{6}{7} - 2\right)\sqrt{3x+2}$$

$$= \frac{7}{3}\left[(3x+2)^{3/2} - \frac{20}{7}\sqrt{3x+2}\right].$$

Ans. $\frac{1}{3}\left[\frac{1}{3}\cdot\frac{2}{3}(3x+4)^{3/2} + \frac{1}{3}\cdot\frac{2}{3}(3x+1)^{3/2}\right]$

$$+ 2\cdot\frac{1}{4}\cdot\frac{2}{3}(4x+7)^{3/2} - \frac{1}{4}\cdot 2\sqrt{4x+7}$$

$$+ \frac{7}{3}\left[\frac{1}{3}\cdot\frac{2}{5}(3x+2)^{5/2} - \frac{20}{7}\cdot\frac{1}{3}\cdot\frac{2}{3}(3x+2)^{3/2}\right].$$

9. We have

(i) $\frac{1+x+x^2}{x^2(1+x)} = \frac{1+x}{x^2(1+x)} + \frac{x^2}{x^2(1+x)} = \frac{1}{x^2} + \frac{1}{1+x}$

(ii) $\frac{2x-1}{(x+1)^2} = \frac{2(x+1)-3}{(x+1)^2} = \frac{2}{x+1} - \frac{3}{(x+1)^2},$

(iii) $\frac{4-5\sin x}{\cos^2 x} = \frac{4}{\cos^2 x} - \frac{5\sin x}{\cos^2 x}$

$$= 4\sec^2 x - 5\sec x\tan x,$$

(iv) $\sin 2x\cos 3x = \frac{1}{2}(\sin 5x - \sin x)$

(v) $\frac{1}{\sin^2 x\cos^2 x} = 4\cdot\frac{1}{(2\sin x\cos x)^2} = 4\,\text{cosec}^2\,2x$

Alternative :

$$\frac{1}{\sin^2 x\cos^2 x} = \frac{\sin^2 x + \cos^2 x}{\sin^2 x\cos^2 x}$$

$$= \frac{1}{\cos^2 x} + \frac{1}{\sin^2 x} = \sec^2 x + \text{cosec}^2 x \text{ etc.}$$

Ans. $-\frac{1}{x} + \log(1+x) + 2\log(x+1)$

$$+ \frac{3}{(x+1)} + 4\tan x - 5\sec x$$

$$+ \frac{1}{10}\cos 5x + \frac{1}{2}\cos x - 4\cdot\frac{1}{2}\cot 2x.$$

10. (i) $\frac{\sin x}{1+\sin x} = \frac{1+\sin x - 1}{1+\sin x}$

$$= 1 - \frac{1}{1+\sin x}\cdot\frac{1-\sin x}{1-\sin x}$$

$$= 1 - \frac{1-\sin x}{\cos^2 x} = 1 - (\sec^2 x - \sec x\tan x)$$

(ii) $\sin x\sin 2x\sin 3x = \frac{1}{2}(2\sin x\sin 3x)\sin 2x$

$$= \frac{1}{2}(\cos 2x - \cos 4x)\sin 2x$$

$$= \frac{1}{4}(2\sin 2x\cos 2x - 2\sin 2x\cos 4x)$$

$$= \frac{1}{4}[\sin 4x - (\sin 6x - \sin 2x)]$$

$$= \frac{1}{4}(\sin 2x + \sin 4x - \sin 6x)$$

(iii) $\sec^2 x\cos^2 2x = \left(\frac{\cos 2x}{\cos x}\right)^2 = \left(\frac{2\cos^2 x - 1}{\cos x}\right)^2$

$$= \left(2\cos x - \frac{1}{\cos x}\right)^2 = 4\cos^2 x + \frac{1}{\cos^2 x} - 4$$

$$= 2(1+\cos 2x) + \sec^2 x - 4$$

$$= 2\cos 2x + \sec^2 x - 2.$$

(iv) $\sin^4 x\cos^4 x = \frac{1}{16}(2\sin x\cos x)^4$

$$= \frac{1}{16}\sin^4 2x = \frac{1}{64}(2\sin^2 2x)^2$$

$$= \frac{1}{64}(1-\cos 4x)^2 = \frac{1}{64}(1 - 2\cos 4x + \cos^2 4x)$$

$$= \frac{1}{64}\left(1 - 2\cos 4x + \frac{1+\cos 8x}{2}\right)$$

$$= \frac{1}{128}(3 - 4\cos 4x + \cos 8x).$$

Ans. $(x - \tan x + \sec x)$

$$+ \frac{1}{4}\left(-\frac{\cos 2x}{2} - \frac{\cos 4x}{4} + \frac{\cos 6x}{6}\right)$$

$$+ (\sin 2x + \tan x - 2x)$$

$$+ \frac{1}{128}\left(3x - \sin 4x + \frac{1}{8}\sin 8x\right)$$

11. (a) $I = \int \frac{2\cos^2 2x}{\cos^2 x - \sin^2 x} \sin x \cos x \, dx$

$= \int 2\cos 2x . \frac{1}{2} \sin 2x \, dx$

$= \frac{1}{2} \int \sin 4x \, dx = -\frac{1}{8} \cos 4x.$

(b) $I = \int \frac{2\sin \frac{15x}{2} \sin \frac{x}{2}}{1 + 2\cos 5x} dx$

Multiply above and below by $\sin \frac{5x}{2}$

$\therefore \quad D^r = \sin \frac{5x}{2} + 2\cos 5x \sin \frac{5x}{2}$

$= \sin \frac{5x}{2} + \sin \frac{15x}{2} - \sin \frac{5x}{2} = \sin \frac{15x}{2}$

$\therefore \quad \int \frac{2\sin \frac{15x}{2} \sin \frac{x}{2} \sin \frac{5x}{2}}{\sin \frac{15x}{2}} dx$

$\int 2\sin \frac{x}{2} \sin \frac{5x}{2} dx$

$= \int (\cos 2x - \cos 3x) \, dx = \frac{1}{2} \sin 2x - \frac{1}{3} \sin 3x$

12. $I_1 = \left(\frac{p}{q}\right)^x + \left(\frac{q}{p}\right)^x + 2, \int a^x \, dx = \frac{a^x}{\log a}$

$I_2 = e^{a \log_e x} = e^{\log_e x^a} = x^a$

$\therefore \quad I_2 = \frac{x^5 - x^4}{x^3 - x^2} = \frac{x^4 (x-1)}{x^2 (x-1)} = x^2$

I_3. Use $a^3 + b^3 = (a+b)^3 - 3ab(a+b)$

$= \frac{1 - 3\sin^2 x \cos^2 x}{\sin^2 x \cos^2 x} \quad \because a + b = 1$

$= \frac{\sin^2 x + \cos^2 x}{\sin^2 x \cos^2 x} - 3 = \sec^2 x + \operatorname{cosec}^2 x - 3$

Ans. $\frac{(p/q)^x}{\log (p/q)} + \frac{(q/p)^x}{\log (q/p)} + 2x + \frac{x^3}{3}$

$+ \tan x - \cot x - 3x$

§3. Method of Substitution.

The *method of substitution* (or *change of variable*) consists in substituting $\varphi(t)$ for x where $\varphi(t)$ is a *continuously differentiable* function of t. On substituting, we have

$$\int f(x) \, dx = \int f[\varphi(t)] \varphi'(t) \, dt$$

and after integration we return to the old variable by inverse substitution $t = \varphi^{-1}(x)$.

Read the following examples in which we shall show that by a proper substitution and changing the variable of integration the question is reduced to a standard form whose integral we know.

Ex. 1. (a) $\int \frac{\sin^{-1} x}{\sqrt{(1 - x^2)}} dx$

(b) $\int_0^1 \frac{\tan^{-1} x}{(1 + x^2)} dx = \frac{\pi^2}{32}$

(M.N.R. 1990)

(a) d.c. of $\sin^{-1} x$ is $\frac{1}{\sqrt{(1 - x^2)}}$ and hence we put $\sin^{-1} x = t$.

$\therefore \quad \frac{1}{\sqrt{(1 - x^2)}} dx = dt,$

$\therefore \quad I = \int t \, dt = \frac{t^2}{2} = \frac{1}{2} (\sin^{-1} x)^2.$

(b) Put $\tan^{-1} x = t \;\therefore\; \frac{1}{(1 + x^2)} dx = dt.$

Also when $x = 1$, $t = \pi/4$

and when $x = 0$, $t = 0$

$\therefore \quad I = \int_0^{\pi/4} t \, dt = \left[t^2/2\right]_0^{\pi/4} = \frac{1}{2} . \frac{\pi^2}{16} = \frac{\pi^2}{32}.$

Ex. 2. $\int \frac{(1 + \log x)^2}{x} dx$

Put $1 + \log x = t \;\therefore\; \frac{1}{x} dx = dt.$

$\therefore \quad I = \int t^2 \, dt = \frac{1}{3} t^3 = \frac{(1 + \log x)^3}{3}$

***Remark.**

In general $\int [f(x)]^n f'(x) \, dx = \frac{[f(x)]^{n+1}}{n+1}.$

If $f(x) = t$ then $f'(x) \, dx = dt$.

$\therefore \quad I = \int t^n \, dt = \frac{t^{n+1}}{n+1} = \frac{[f(x)]^{n+1}}{n+1}.$

*Similarly, $\int \frac{f'(x)}{f(x)} dx = \log f(x).$

Put $f(x) = t \;\therefore\; f'(x) \, dx = dt$

$\therefore \quad I = \int \frac{1}{t} dt = \log t = \log f(x)$

Ex. 3. (a)* $\int \frac{\sin 2x}{a^2 + b^2 \sin^2 x} dx.$

Put $a^2 + b^2 \sin^2 x = t$,

$\therefore \quad b^2 . 2\sin x \cos x \, dx = dt$

$\therefore \quad I = \frac{1}{b^2} \int \frac{dt}{t} = \frac{1}{b^2} \log t$

$= \frac{1}{b^2} \log (a^2 + b^2 \sin^2 x).$

(b) $\int e^{3 \log x} . (x^4 + 1)^{-1} \, dx =$

(a) $\log (x^4 + 1)$ (b) $3 \log (x^4 + 1)$

(c) $-\log(x^4+1)$ (d) $\frac{1}{4}\log(x^4+1)$

(AIEEE 2002)

Ans. (d).

$$I=\int \frac{x^3}{x^4+1}dx=\frac{1}{4}\log(x^4+1)$$

$\because$ d.c. of $x^4+1=4x^3$.

***Remark :**

Note that $\int \frac{f'(x)}{\sqrt{[f(x)]}}dx=2\sqrt{f(x)}$.

Put $f(x)=t \therefore f'(x)\,dx=dt$.

$\therefore \quad I=\int \frac{1}{\sqrt{(t)}}dt=2\sqrt{t}=2\sqrt{f(x)}$.

Ex. 4. (a) $\int \frac{\sec^2 x\,dx}{\sqrt{(\tan x)}}$

(b)* $\int \frac{1}{x\sqrt{(1+\log x)}}dx$.

(a) Here d.c. of $\tan x$ is $\sec^2 x$.

$\therefore$ Put $\tan x=t$. $\therefore \sec^2 x\,dx=dt$.

$\therefore \quad I=\int \frac{dt}{\sqrt{(t)}}=2\sqrt{t}=2\sqrt{\tan x}$

Another form : $I=\int \frac{\sqrt{\tan x}}{\sin x\cos x}dx$.

Divide above and below by $\cos^2 x$.

$\therefore \quad I=\int \frac{\sec^2 x}{\tan x}\sqrt{\tan x}\,dx$

$=\int \frac{\sec^2 x}{\sqrt{(\tan x)}}dx=2\sqrt{\tan x}$.

(b) $2\sqrt{1+\log x}$

§4. Four Important Formulae

Integration of tan x, cot x, sec x, cosec x.

(i) $\int \tan x\,dx=\int \frac{\sec x\tan x}{\sec x}dx$.

D.C. of $\sec x$ is $\sec x\tan x$.

Put $\sec x=t$. $\therefore \sec x\tan x\,dx=dt$.

$\therefore \quad I=\int \frac{1}{t}dt=\log t=\log\sec x=-\log\cos x$.

* $\quad \boldsymbol{I=\int \tan x\,dx=\log\sec x=-\log\cos x}$. ...(1)

Alternative Method :

$\int \tan x\,dx=\int \frac{\sin x}{\cos x}dx$.

Put $\cos x=t$. $\therefore -\sin x\,dx=dt$.

$\therefore \quad I=-\int \frac{dt}{t}=-\log t=-\log\cos x=\log\sec x$.

(ii)* $\int \cot x\,dx=\int \frac{\text{cosec}\,x\cot x}{\text{cosec}\,x}dx$.

Now D.C. of cosec x is $-\text{cosec}\,x\cot x$.

Put $\text{cosec}\,x=t$. $\therefore -\text{cosec}\,x\cot x\,dx=dt$.

$\therefore \quad I=-\int \frac{dt}{t}=-\log t=-\log\text{cosec}\,x=\log\sin x$.

$\therefore \quad \boldsymbol{\int \cot x\,dx=\log\sin x=-\log(\text{cosec}\,x)}$ ...(2)

Alternative Method :

$$\int \cot x\,dx=\int \frac{\cos x}{\sin x}dx$$

D.C. of $\sin x$ is $\cos x$.

Put $\sin x=t$. $\therefore \cos x\,dx=dt$.

$\therefore \quad I=\int \frac{1}{t}dt=\log t=\log\sin x=-\log\text{cosec}\,x$.

(iii) $\int \sec x\,dx=\int \frac{\sec x(\sec x+\tan x)}{(\sec x+\tan x)}dx$.

$=\int \frac{\sec^2 x+\sec x\tan x}{\sec x+\tan x}dx$.

Put $\sec x+\tan x=t$.

$\therefore \quad (\sec x\tan x+\sec^2 x)\,dx=dt$.

$\therefore \quad I=\int \frac{1}{t}dt=\log t=\log(\sec x+\tan x)$.

*$\therefore \quad \boldsymbol{\int \sec x\,dx=\log(\sec x+\tan x)}$ ...(3)

(iv) $\int \text{cosec}\,x\,dx=\int \frac{1}{\sin x}dx$

$=\int \frac{1}{2\sin(x/2)\cos(x/2)}dx$.

Divide above and below by $\cos^2(x/2)$.

$\therefore \quad I=\int \frac{\sec^2(x/2)\,dx}{2\tan(x/2)}$.

Now d. c. of $\tan(x/2)=\frac{1}{2}\sec^2(x/2)$.

$\therefore$ Put $\tan(x/2)=t$, $\therefore \frac{1}{2}\sec^2(x/2)\,.dx=dt$.

$\therefore \quad I=\int \frac{1}{t}dt=\log t=\log\tan\left(\frac{x}{2}\right)$.

* $\quad \boldsymbol{\int \text{cosec}\,x\,dx=\log\tan\left(\frac{x}{2}\right)}$. ...(4)

Some More Examples :

1. $\int \frac{e^{\sqrt{x}}\cos e^{\sqrt{x}}}{\sqrt{(x)}}dx$.

Put $e^{\sqrt{x}} = t$. ∴ $e^{\sqrt{x}} \cdot \frac{1}{2\sqrt{(x)}} dx = dt$.

∴ $I = 2\int \cos t \, dt = 2 \sin t = 2 \sin e^{\sqrt{x}}$.

2. $\int \frac{x^2}{16+25x^6} dx = \int \frac{x^2}{4^2 + (5x^3)^2} dx$.

We put $5x^3 = t$. ∴ $15x^2 \, dx = dt$.

∴ $I = \frac{1}{15}\int \frac{dt}{4^2+t^2} = \frac{1}{15} \cdot \frac{1}{4} \tan^{-1} \frac{t}{4}$

$= \frac{1}{60} \tan^{-1} \frac{5x^3}{4}$.

3.* $\int \frac{e^x (1+x)}{\sin^2 (xe^x)} dx = \int e^x (1+x) \operatorname{cosec}^2 (xe^x) \, dx$.

Here we think of $\int \operatorname{cosec}^2 x \, dx = -\cot x$.

∴ Put $xe^x = t$.

∴ $(xe^x + e^x . 1) \, dx = dt$

or $e^x (1+x) \, dx = dt$

∴ $I = \int \operatorname{cosec}^2 t \, dt = -\cot t = -\cot (xe^x)$.

Similarly, $\int \frac{e^x (x+1) \, dx}{\cos^2 (xe^x)} = \tan (xe^x)$

4. $\int \frac{x^3 \tan^{-1} x^4}{1+x^8} dx$.

Put $\tan^{-1} x^4 = t$, ∴ $\frac{1}{1+(x^4)^2} (4x^3) \, dx = dt$.

∴ $I = \frac{1}{4}\int t \, dt = \frac{1}{4} \cdot \frac{t^2}{2} = \frac{1}{8} (\tan^{-1} x^4)^2$.

5.* $\int \frac{x \tan^{-1} x^2}{1+x^4} dx$.

Put $\tan^{-1} x^2 = t$ etc.

Ans. $\frac{1}{4} (\tan^{-1} x^2)^2$

6. $I = \int x^2 \sec x^3 \, dx$

Put $x^3 = t$ ∴ $3x^2 \, dx = dt$

∴ $I = \frac{1}{3}\int \sec t \, dt = \frac{1}{3} \log (\sec t + \tan t)$

$= \frac{1}{3} \log (\sec x^3 + \tan x^3)$

§5. Integral of $\int \frac{1}{a \sin x + b \cos x} dx$.

Here we put $a = r \cos \alpha$, $b = r \sin \alpha$.

∴ $I = \frac{1}{r}\int \frac{dx}{\sin (x+\alpha)} = \frac{1}{r}\int \operatorname{cosec} (x+\alpha) \, dx$.

$= \frac{1}{r} \log \tan \frac{x+\alpha}{2}$

where $r = \sqrt{a^2+b^2}$ and $\tan \alpha = b/a$.

Note : If we put $b = r \cos \alpha$, $a = r \sin \alpha$.

Then $I = \frac{1}{r}\int \frac{dx}{\cos (x-\alpha)} = \frac{1}{r}\int \sec (x-\alpha) \, dx$.

$= \frac{1}{r} [\log \{\sec (x-\alpha) + \tan (x-\alpha)\}]$

where $r = \sqrt{a^2+b^2}$ and $\tan \alpha = a/b$.

Problem Set (2)

Integration by method of substitution.

Integrate the following :

1. $\frac{1-\tan x}{1+\tan x}$. **2.** $\frac{\cos x + \sin x}{\cos x - \sin x}$.

3. (a) $\operatorname{cosec}^2 x \sqrt{\cot x}$. (b) $x^2 \sec x^3$.

4. $\frac{\cos \sqrt{x}}{\sqrt{(x)}}$. **5.** $\frac{\sin x \cos x}{a^2 \cos^2 x + b^2 \sin^2 x}$.

6. $\frac{1}{a^2 \cos^2 x + b^2 \sin^2 x}$. **7.** $\frac{\sin 2x}{1+\sin^2 x}$.

8. $\frac{1}{\sin^{-1} x \sqrt{(1-x^2)}}$. **9.*** $\frac{1}{e^x+1}$.

10. (i) $\frac{e^x - 1}{e^x + 1}$. (ii)* $\frac{1}{e^x + e^{-x}}$.

(iii)* If $\int \frac{4e^x + 6e^{-x}}{9e^x - 4e^{-x}} dx = Ax + B \log_e (9e^{2x} - 4) + C$,

then $A = \ldots\ldots$, $B = \ldots\ldots$, $C = \ldots\ldots$ **(I.I.T. 1990)**

11. $\frac{a}{b+ce^x}$. **12.** $\frac{\cot x}{\log \sin x}$.

13. $\frac{\tan x}{\log \sec x}$. **14.*** $\frac{\sec x}{\log (\sec x + \tan x)}$.

15. $\frac{\operatorname{cosec} x}{\log \tan (x/2)}$. **16.*** $\frac{\sec x \operatorname{cosec} x}{\log \tan x}$.

17. $\frac{1}{\sqrt{(x)} [\sqrt{(x)} + 1]}$. **18.** $\frac{1}{x + x \log x}$.

19. (i) $\frac{1+x}{1+x^2}$. (ii) $\frac{x^2}{x^3+1}$.

20. $\frac{2-x^2}{1+x^2}$. **21.** $\frac{(\sin^{-1} x)^3}{\sqrt{(1-x^2)}}$.

22.* $\frac{1}{\cos^2 x (1-\tan x)^2}$.

23. (a) $\dfrac{e^{x-1}+x^{e-1}}{e^x+x^e}$. (b)* $\dfrac{10x^9+10^x\log_e 10}{10^x+x^{10}}$.

(c)* $\displaystyle\int_0^1 \frac{2^{x+1}-3^{x-1}}{6^x}\,dx$

24. (a) $\dfrac{\cos^2 x}{\sin^4 x}$. (b) $\dfrac{\operatorname{cosec}^2 x}{1+\cot x}$

(c) $\sec^4 x \operatorname{cosec}^2 x$

25. (a) $\tan^m x\sec^2 x$ (b) $\dfrac{\sqrt{2+x^{10}}}{x^{16}}$

(c) $\sqrt[3]{\dfrac{\sin^n x}{\cos^{n+6} x}}$ (d) $\dfrac{1}{\sqrt{e^{5x}}\,.\sqrt[4]{(e^{2x}+e^{-2x})^3}}$

26. $\dfrac{e^x}{\sqrt{(a+be^x)}}$.

27. (a)* $\dfrac{1}{(e^x+e^{-x})^2}$.

(b) Prove that $\displaystyle\int_0^\infty \frac{dx}{[x+\sqrt{x^2+1}]^3}=\frac{3}{8}$

28. (a)* $\dfrac{1}{x(\log x)^2}$. (b) $\dfrac{(1+\log x)^2}{x}$.

29. (a) $\tan x\log\sec x$ (b) $\cot x\log\sin x$

30. (a) $\sec x\log(\sec x+\tan x)$.

(b) $\operatorname{cosec} x\log[\tan(x/2)]$.

31. $\dfrac{\cot x}{\sqrt{(\sin x)}}$. **32.** $\dfrac{\sec^4 x}{\sqrt{(\tan x)}}$.

33. $\tan^4 x$. **34.** $\dfrac{1}{x^2\cos^2(1/x)}$.

35. $\dfrac{\sin\sqrt{x}}{\sqrt{(x)}}$.

36. (a) $\left(1-\dfrac{1}{x^2}\right)e^{x+1/x}$. (b) $\displaystyle\int_1^2\left(x+\frac{1}{x}\right)^{3/2}\frac{x^2-1}{x^2}\,dx$

(c)* $\displaystyle\int_{\sqrt{3}}^{2\sqrt{3}} x^3(x^2-3)^{3/2}\,dx=\frac{16038}{35}$

37.* $\sec^p x\tan x$.

38. $\dfrac{1}{x\log x\log(\log x)}$. **39.** $a^x e^x$.

40. (a)* $\dfrac{1}{2\sqrt{(x)}\,[1+x]}$. (b)* $\dfrac{x}{1+x^4}$.

41. (a) $\dfrac{x^4+1}{x^6+1}$ (b) $\dfrac{x^{24}}{x^{10}+1}$

42.* $\dfrac{a^{x+\tan^{-1}a^x}}{1+a^{2x}}$

43. (a) $x\cos^3 x^2\sin x^2$. (b) $\dfrac{1}{2\sqrt{(x)}}\tan\sqrt{x}\sec^2\sqrt{x}$.

(c) $\dfrac{\log x.\sin[1+(\log x)^2]}{x}$.

44. (a) $\dfrac{x}{\sqrt{(1-x^2)}\cos^2\sqrt{(1-x^2)}}$.

(b) $\tan x\sec^2 x\sqrt{1-\tan^2 x}$.

45.* (a) $\sqrt{\left(\dfrac{x}{a^3-x^3}\right)}$. (b) $\dfrac{x}{\sqrt{(4-x^4)}}$.

(c) $\dfrac{a^x}{\sqrt{(1-a^{2x})}}$.

46. (a)* $\dfrac{1}{x^2(x^4+1)^{3/4}}$ (b) $\displaystyle\int\frac{2+\sqrt{x}}{(x+\sqrt{x}+1)^2}\,dx$

(c) $\displaystyle\int\frac{\log[x+\sqrt{1+x^2}]}{\sqrt{1+x^2}}\,dx$

(d) $\displaystyle\int\frac{5x^8+7x^6}{(x^2+1+2x^7)^2}\,dx$

47.* $\dfrac{1}{(2ax+x^2)^{3/2}}$ 48. $\dfrac{\sqrt{(x^2+1)}}{x^4}$

49. (a) $\dfrac{1}{\sin x+\cos x}$. (b) $\dfrac{1}{\sec x+\operatorname{cosec} x}$

50. $\dfrac{\sec x}{a\tan x+b}$.

51. (a) $\dfrac{1}{\sin x+\sqrt{(3)}\cos x}$.

(b) $\displaystyle\int x.\sqrt{\left[\frac{2\sin(x^2-1)-\sin 2(x^2-1)}{2\sin(x^2-1)+\sin 2(x^2-1)}\right]}\,dx$

where $x^2-1\neq n\pi$

52. (a) $\dfrac{1}{\sqrt{(1+\sin x)}}$. (b) $\dfrac{\sin x+\cos x}{\sqrt{(1+\sin 2x)}}$.

(c) For what values of a and b the following equations are correct :

(i)* $\displaystyle\int\frac{dx}{1+\sin x}=\tan\left(\frac{x}{2}+a\right)+b$

(ii)* $\displaystyle\int(\sin 2x-\cos 2x)\,dx$

$=\dfrac{1}{\sqrt{(2)}}\sin(2x-a)+b$.

53. $\dfrac{\sin x}{\sqrt{(1+\sin x)}}$. **54.** $\dfrac{1+\cos x}{\sin x\cos x}$.

55. $\dfrac{1}{4\cos^3 x-3\cos x}$. **56.** $\dfrac{1}{3\sin x-4\sin^3 x}$.

57.* $\tan^3 2x\sec 2x$. **58.** $\cot^3 x\operatorname{cosec}^4 x$.

59. $\sqrt{2+\sin 3x}\cos 3x$

60. $\sqrt{1+\sin\frac{1}{2}x}$.

61. (a) $\frac{1}{x\sin^2(\log x)}$. (b)* $\frac{\cot(\log x)}{x}$.

62. $\frac{\operatorname{cosec}(\tan^{-1}x)}{1+x^2}$.

63. (a)* $\frac{1}{\sin(x-a)\sin(x-b)}$.

(b) Prove that

$$\int_0^{\pi/2}\operatorname{cosec}\left(x-\frac{\pi}{3}\right)\operatorname{cosec}\left(x-\frac{\pi}{6}\right)dx=-2\log 3.$$

(c) $\int\frac{\sin x}{\sin\left(x-\frac{\pi}{6}\right)\sin\left(x+\frac{\pi}{6}\right)}dx=$

(a) $\frac{1}{\sqrt{3}}\left[\log\tan\frac{x}{2}+\log\tan\left(\frac{x}{2}-\frac{\pi}{12}\right)\right]$

(b) $\frac{1}{\sqrt{3}}\left[\log\tan\left(\frac{x}{2}+\frac{\pi}{12}\right)+\log\tan\left(\frac{x}{2}-\frac{\pi}{12}\right)\right]$

(c) $\frac{1}{\sqrt{3}}\left[\log\cot\left(\frac{x}{2}+\frac{\pi}{12}\right)\right]$

(d) none

(d) $\int\frac{1}{\cos x-\sin x}dx=$

(a) $\frac{1}{\sqrt{2}}\log\tan\left(\frac{x}{2}-\frac{\pi}{8}\right)$

(b) $\frac{1}{\sqrt{2}}\log\cot\frac{x}{2}$

(c) $\frac{1}{\sqrt{2}}\log\tan\left(\frac{x}{2}-\frac{3\pi}{8}\right)$

(d) $\frac{1}{\sqrt{2}}\log\tan\left(\frac{x}{2}+\frac{3\pi}{8}\right)$ **(AIEEE 2004)**

64. (a)* $\frac{1}{\cos(x-a)\cos(x-b)}$.

(b) $\frac{1}{\cos(x+a)\sin(x+b)}$

(c) $1+\tan x.\tan(x-a)$

65. (a)* $\frac{\cos x}{\cos(x-a)}$ (b) $\frac{\sin x}{\sin(x-a)}$.

(c) $\tan(x-a)\tan(x+a)\tan 2x$

66. (a) $\frac{\cos 5x+\cos 4x}{1-2\cos 3x}$

(b) $\frac{\cos 7x-\cos 8x}{1+2\cos 5x}$

67. (a)* $\frac{1}{\sqrt{[\sin^3 x\sin(x+a)]}}$.

(b)* $\frac{\sec x}{\sqrt{\{\sin(2x+\alpha)+\sin\alpha\}}}$

(c) $\frac{\sin^{3/2}x+\cos^{3/2}x}{\sqrt{\sin^3 x\cos^3 x\sin(x+\alpha)}}$

(d) $\frac{1}{\tan x+\cot x+\sec x+\operatorname{cosec} x}$

68. (a)* $\frac{\sin 2x}{\sin^4 x+\cos^4 x}$ (b) $\frac{\cos^3 x}{\sin^2 x+\sin x}$

(c) $\int\frac{\sin 2x+2\tan x}{\cos^6 x+6\cos^2 x+4}dx=$

(a) $2\sqrt{\frac{1+\cos^2 x}{\cos^7 x}}$

(b) $\tan^{-1}\frac{1}{\sqrt{2}}\left(\frac{1+\cos^2 x}{\cos^7 x}\right)$

(c) $\frac{1}{12}\log\left(1+\frac{6}{\cos^4 x}+\frac{4}{\cos^6 x}\right)$

(d) none

69. (a)* $x^{13/2}(1+x^{5/2})^{1/2}$.

(b) For any natural number m, evaluate

$\int(x^{3m}+x^{2m}+x^m)(2x^{2m}+3x^m+6)^{1/m}dx,\ x>0$

(I.I.T. 2002)

70. $[1+2\tan x(\tan x+\sec x)]^{1/2}$.

71. (a)* $\int_a^\infty\frac{dx}{x^4\sqrt{(a^2+x^2)}}=\frac{2-\sqrt{2}}{3a^4}$

(b)* If for non-zero x,

$af(x)+bf\left(\frac{1}{x}\right)=\frac{1}{x}-5$ where $a\neq b$, then

$\int_1^2 f(x)\,dx=$........

(I.I.T. 1996)

72. (a) For $x>0$, let $f(x)=\int_1^x\frac{\ln t}{1+t}dt$.

Find the function $f(x)+f\left(\frac{1}{x}\right)$ and show that $f(e)+f\left(\frac{1}{e}\right)=\frac{1}{2}$. Here $\ln t=\log_e t$.

(I.I.T. 2000)

(b) If a be a positive integer, prove that the number of values of a satisfying

$$\int_0^{\pi/2}\left[a^2\left(\frac{\cos 3x}{4}+\frac{3}{4}\cos x\right)+a\sin x-20\cos x\right]dx\leq-\frac{a^2}{3}$$ is 1, 2, 3, 4, *i.e.* four values.

73. (a) Consider the integrals $I_1=\int_0^1 e^{-y}\cos^2 y\,dy$

$I_2=\int_0^1 e^{-y^2}\cos^2 y\,dy, I_3=\int_0^1 e^{-y^2}dy$

$I_4=\int_0^1 e^{-\frac{1}{2}y^2}dy$, where $0<y<1$. If I be the greatest amongst I_1, I_2, I_3, I_4 then prove that $I=I_4$.

(b) If $I_1 = \int_0^1 2^{x^2}\,dx;\ I_2 = \int_0^1 2^{x^3}\,dx;\ I_3 = \int_1^2 2^{x^2}\,dx,$

$I_4 = \int_1^2 2^{x^3}\,dx$ then show that $I_1 > I_2$ and $I_3 < I_4$.

(c) The value of the integral $\int_0^1 e^{y^2}\,dy$ lies between 1 and e.

(d) Let $I_1 = \int_1^2 \frac{1}{\sqrt{(1+x^2)}}\,dx$ and $I_2 = \int_1^2 \frac{1}{x}\,dx$.

Then prove that $I_2 > I_1$.

(e) If $I_1 = \int_0^{\pi/2} \frac{x}{\sin x}\,dx$ and $I_2 = \int_0^1 \frac{\tan^{-1} x}{x}\,dx$, then $\frac{I_1}{I_2} =$

(a) $\frac{1}{2}$ (b) 1

(c) 2 (d) $\frac{\pi}{2}$

74. If $I = \int_0^1 \cos\left(2\cot^{-1}\sqrt{\frac{1-x}{1+x}}\right)dx$, then prove that $I = -\frac{1}{2}$.

75. (a) $\int \frac{\cos 4x - 1}{\cot x - \tan x}\,dx$

(b) $\int \frac{(1+\log x)^2}{1+\log x^{x+1} + (\log x^{\sqrt{x}})^2}\,dx$

76. $\int \left[\frac{1-\sqrt{x}}{1+\sqrt{x}}\right]^{1/2} \frac{dx}{x}$

77. If $\int_{\log 2}^{x} \frac{dy}{\sqrt{(e^y - 1)}} = \frac{\pi}{6}$ then prove that $x = \log 4$.

78. (a) $\int \frac{\sin x}{\sin 4x}\,dx = -\frac{1}{8}\log\frac{1+\sin x}{1-\sin x} + \frac{1}{4\sqrt{2}}\log\frac{1+\sqrt{2}\sin x}{1-\sqrt{2}\sin x}$.

(b) $\int \frac{dx}{x^4\sqrt{a^2+x^2}}$

$= \frac{1}{a^4}\left[\frac{1}{x}\sqrt{a^2+x^2} - \frac{1}{3x^3}(a^2+x^2)^{3/2}\right]$

Solution to Problem Set (2)

1. We know that

$$\tan\left(\frac{\pi}{4} - x\right) = \frac{\tan(\pi/4) - \tan x}{1 + \tan(\pi/4)\tan x} = \frac{1-\tan x}{1+\tan x}$$

$$I = \int \tan(\pi/4 - x)\,dx$$

$$= -\log\sec(\pi/4 - x) = \log\cos(\pi/4 - x).$$

2. Divide above and below by $\cos x$.

$$\therefore \quad I = \int \frac{1+\tan x}{1-\tan x}\,dx.$$

$$= \int \tan(\pi/4 + x)\,dx = \log\sec(\pi/4 + x).$$

3. (a) Put $\cot x = t$. $\therefore -\text{cosec}^2 x\,dx = dt$.

$$\therefore \quad I = -\int \sqrt{t}\,dt = -\frac{2}{3}t^{3/2} = -\frac{2}{3}(\cot x)^{3/2}.$$

(b) Ans. $\frac{1}{3}\log(\sec x^3 + \tan x^3)$.

4. Put $\sqrt{x} = t$. $\therefore \frac{1}{2\sqrt{(x)}}\,dx = dt$,

$$\therefore \quad I = 2\int \cos t\,dt = 2\sin t = 2\sin\sqrt{x}.$$

5. d.c. of $\cos^2 x = -2\cos x\sin x$,

d.c. of $\sin^2 x = 2\sin x\cos x$.

Put $a^2\cos^2 x + b^2\sin^2 x = t$.

$\therefore \quad 2(b^2 - a^2)\sin x\cos x\,dx = dt$

$$\therefore \quad I = \frac{1}{2(b^2-a^2)}\int\frac{dt}{t} = \frac{1}{2(b^2-a^2)}\log t$$

$$= \frac{1}{2(b^2-a^2)}\log(a^2\cos^2 x + b^2\sin^2 x).$$

6. Divide N^r and D^r by $\cos^2 x$.

$$\therefore \quad I = \int \frac{\sec^2 x\,dx}{a^2 + b^2\tan^2 x}.$$

Put $b\tan x = t$. $\therefore b\sec^2 x\,dx = dt$.

$$\therefore \quad I = \frac{1}{b}\int\frac{dt}{a^2+t^2} = \frac{1}{b}\cdot\frac{1}{a}\tan^{-1}\frac{t}{a}$$

$$= \frac{1}{ab}\tan^{-1}\left(\frac{b}{a}\tan x\right)$$

7. As in Q.5 d.c. of $\sin^2 x = 2\sin x\cos x = \sin 2x$.

$\therefore$ Put $1 + \sin^2 x = t$.

$\therefore \quad 2\sin x\cos x\,dx = dt$

$$\therefore \quad I = \int\frac{dt}{t} = \log t = \log(1+\sin^2 x).$$

8. Ans. $\log\sin^{-1} x$. Put $\sin^{-1} x = t$.

Note : In all the questions involving e^x, multiply above and below by e^x and then put $e^x = t$.

9. $I = \int \frac{e^x\,dx}{e^x(e^x+1)}$. Put $e^x = t$. $\therefore e^x\,dx = dt$.

$$\therefore \quad I = \int \frac{dt}{t(t+1)} = \int\left(\frac{1}{t} - \frac{1}{t+1}\right)dt.$$

By partial fractions.

$= \log t - \log(t+1)$

$= \log e^x - \log(e^x+1) = x - \log(e^x+1)$.

10. (i) $I = \int \frac{e^x(e^x-1)}{e^x(e^x+1)}\,dx.$

Put $e^x = t$. $\therefore e^x\,dx = dt$.

$\therefore \quad I = \int \frac{t-1}{t(t+1)} dt = \int \left(\frac{2}{t+1} - \frac{1}{t} \right) dt.$ (P.F's.)

$= 2 \log (t+1) - \log t = 2 \log (e^x + 1) - \log e^x$

$= 2 \log (e^x + 1) - x.$

(ii) $I = \int \frac{dx}{e^x + e^{-x}} = \int \frac{e^x \, dx}{e^{2x} + 1}$

$= \int \frac{dt}{t^2 + 1}$ where $e^x = t$

$= \tan^{-1} t = \tan^{-1} e^x.$

(iii) $I = \int \frac{2(2e^{2x} + 3)}{(9e^{2x} - 4)} \cdot \frac{e^{2x}}{e^{2x}} dx.$

Put $e^{2x} = t$.

$\therefore \quad I = \int \frac{(2t+3)}{t(9t-4)} dt$

$= \int \left[-\frac{3}{4t} + \frac{35}{4(9t-4)} \right] dt$ (P.F^s.)

$= -\frac{3}{4} \log e^{2x} + \frac{35}{4.9} \log (9e^{2x} - 4) + c$

$= -\frac{3}{4} . 2x + \frac{35}{36} \log (9e^{2x} - 4) + c$

$\therefore \quad A = -\frac{3}{4} . 2 = -\frac{3}{2}, \quad B = \frac{35}{36}$ and c

is any real constant.

11. Ans. $\frac{a}{b} [x - \log (b + ce^x)].$

12. We know $\int \cot x \, dx = \log \sin x$.

$\therefore \quad \frac{d}{dx} (\log \sin x) = \cot x.$

Put $\log \sin x = t$. $\quad \therefore \cot x \, dx = dt$

$\therefore \quad I = \int \frac{dt}{t} = \log t = \log (\log \sin x)$

13. Ans. $\log (\log \sec x)$.

14. Ans. $\log [\log (\sec x + \tan x)]$.

15. Ans. $\log [\log \tan (x/2)]$.

16. Put $\log \tan x = t$. $\quad \therefore \frac{1}{\tan x} . \sec^2 x \, dx = dt$

or $\frac{\cos x}{\sin x} \cdot \frac{1}{\cos^2 x} dx = dt$

or $\sec x \operatorname{cosec} x \, dx = dt$

$\therefore \quad I = \int \frac{dt}{t} = \log t = \log (\log \tan x).$

17. Put $\sqrt{x} + 1 = t$. $\quad \therefore \frac{1}{2\sqrt{(x)}} dx = dt.$

$\therefore \quad I = \int \frac{2dt}{t} = 2 \log t = 2 \log (1 + \sqrt{x}).$

18. $I = \int \frac{1}{x(1 + \log x)} dx = \log (1 + \log x).$

19. (i) $I = \int \left[\frac{1}{1+x^2} + \frac{x}{1+x^2} \right] dx$

$= \int \left[\frac{1}{1+x^2} + \frac{1}{2} . \frac{2x}{1+x^2} \right] dx.$

$= \tan^{-1} x + \frac{1}{2} \log (1 + x^2).$

(ii) Ans. $\frac{1}{3} \log (1 + x^3)$

20. $I = \int \frac{-x^2 - 1 + 3}{x^2 + 1} dx = \int \left(-1 + \frac{3}{x^2 + 1} \right) dx.$

$= -x + 3 \tan^{-1} x$

21. Ans. $\frac{1}{4} (\sin^{-1} x)^4$. Put $\sin^{-1} x = t$.

22. $I = \int \frac{\sec^2 x \, dx}{(1 - \tan x)^2}$. Put $1 - \tan x = t$.

$\therefore \quad -\sec^2 x \, dx = dt$

$\therefore \quad I = -\int \frac{1}{t^2} dt = -\left(-\frac{1}{t} \right) = \frac{1}{t} = \frac{1}{1 - \tan x}.$

23. (a) Multiply above and below by e.

$\therefore \quad I = \frac{1}{e} \int \frac{ee^{x-1} + e\,x^{e-1}}{e^x + x^e} dx$

$= \frac{1}{e} \int \frac{e^x + ex^{e-1}}{e^x + x^e} dx.$

$\therefore \quad$ Put $e^x + x^e = t$. $\quad \therefore (e^x + ex^{e-1}) dx = dt.$

$\therefore \quad I = \frac{1}{e} \int \frac{dt}{t} = \frac{1}{e} \log t = \frac{1}{e} \log (e^x + x^e).$

(b) Ans. $\log (10^x + x^{10})$.

(c) $I = \int_0^1 \left(\frac{2.2^x}{2^x.3^x} - \frac{1}{3} \frac{3^x}{2^x.3^x} \right) dx$

$= \int_0^1 \left(2.3^{-x} - \frac{1}{3} 2^{-x} \right) dx = \left[-2 \frac{3^{-x}}{\log 3} + \frac{1}{3} \frac{2^{-x}}{\log 2} \right]_0^1$

$= -\frac{2}{\log 3} \left(\frac{1}{3} - 1 \right) + \frac{1}{3 \log 2} \left(\frac{1}{2} - 1 \right)$

$= \frac{4}{3} \log_3 e - \frac{1}{6} \log_2 e.$

24. (a) $I = \int \cot^2 x \operatorname{cosec}^2 x \, dx = -\frac{1}{3} \cot^3 x.$

(b) Ans. $-\log (1 + \cot x)$.

(c) $I = \int \frac{1}{\cos^4 x \sin^2 x} dx = \int \frac{(\sin^2 x + \cos^2 x)^2}{\cos^4 x \sin^2 x} dx$

$= \int \left[\frac{\sin^2 x}{\cos^4 x} + \frac{1}{\sin^2 x} + \frac{2}{\cos^2 x} \right] dx$

$$= \int (\sec^2 x \tan^2 x + \operatorname{cosec}^2 x + 2\sec^2 x)\, dx$$

$$= \frac{1}{3}\tan^3 x - \cot x + 2\tan x$$

Alt. Divide above and below by $\cos^{4+2} x = \cos^6 x$

$$\therefore \quad = \int \frac{\sec^4 x . \sec^2 x}{\tan^2 x}\, dx = \int \frac{(1+\tan^2 x)^2}{\tan^2 x} \sec^2 x\, dx$$

$$= \int \frac{(1+t^2)^2}{t^2}\, dt = \int \left(t^2 + 2 + \frac{1}{t^2}\right) dt$$

$$= \frac{1}{3}t^3 + 2t - \frac{1}{t} \text{ etc.}$$

25. (a) Ans. $\dfrac{\tan^{m+1} x}{m+1}$. Put $\tan x = t$.

(b) $I = \int \sqrt{2 + x^{10}} . \dfrac{1}{x^5} . \dfrac{1}{x^{11}}\, dx$

$$= \int \sqrt{\frac{2+x^{10}}{x^{10}}} . \frac{1}{x^{11}}\, dx = \int \sqrt{\left(\frac{2}{x^{10}} + 1\right)} . \frac{1}{x^{11}}\, dx$$

Put $\sqrt{\dfrac{2}{x^{10}} + 1} = t$ etc.

(c) $I = \int \dfrac{\tan^{n/3} x}{\cos^2 x}\, dx = \int \tan^{n/3} x \sec^2 x\, dx$ etc.

(d) $I = \int \dfrac{1}{e^{5x/2} . e^{6x/4} (1 + e^{-4x})^{3/4}}\, dx$

$$= \int \frac{e^{-4x}}{(1+e^{-4x})^{3/4}}\, dx. \text{ Put } 1 + e^{-4x} = t \text{ etc.}$$

26. Put $a + be^x = dt$. $\therefore$ $be^x\, dx = dt$.

$$\therefore \quad I = \frac{1}{b}\int \frac{dt}{\sqrt{(t)}} = \frac{2}{b}\sqrt{t} = \frac{2}{b}\sqrt{a + be^x}.$$

27. (a) $I = \int \dfrac{1}{e^{-2x}(e^{2x}+1)^2}\, dx = \int \dfrac{e^{2x}}{(e^{2x}+1)^2}\, dx.$

Put $e^{2x} + 1 = t$. $\therefore$ $2e^{2x}\, dx = dt$.

$$\therefore \quad I = \frac{1}{2}\int \frac{dt}{t^2} = \frac{1}{2}\left(-\frac{1}{t}\right) = -\frac{1}{2(e^{2x}+1)}.$$

(b) Put $x = \tan\theta$ and adjust the limits

$$\therefore \quad I = \int_0^{\pi/2} \frac{\cos\theta}{(1+\sin\theta)^3}\, d\theta = \int_1^2 \frac{1}{t^3}\, dt = \frac{3}{8}$$

28. (a) Ans. $-\dfrac{1}{\log x}$. Put $\log x = t$.

(b) Ans. $\dfrac{1}{3}(1 + \log x)^3$

29. (a) Put $\log \sec x = t$

$$\therefore \quad \frac{1}{\sec x} . \sec x \tan x\, dx = dt$$

or $\tan x\, dx = dt$.

$$\therefore \quad I = \int t\, dt = \frac{1}{2}t^2 = \frac{1}{2}(\log \sec x)^2.$$

(b) Ans. $\dfrac{1}{2}(\log \sin x)^2$.

30. (a) We know that $\int \sec x\, dx = \log(\sec x + \tan x)$.

$$\therefore \quad \frac{d}{dx}\log(\sec x + \tan x) = \sec x.$$

Put $\log(\sec x + \tan x) = t$. $\therefore$ $\sec x\, dx = dt$.

$$\therefore \quad I = \int t\, dt = \frac{1}{2}t^2 = \frac{1}{2}[\log(\sec x + \tan x)]^2.$$

(b) Ans. $\dfrac{1}{2}[\log \tan(x/2)]^2$.

31. $I = \int \dfrac{\cos x}{\sin x \sqrt{(\sin x)}}\, dx.$ Put $\sin x = t$.

$$\therefore \quad I = \int \frac{dt}{t^{3/2}} = \int t^{-3/2}\, dt = \frac{-2}{\sqrt{(t)}} = \frac{-2}{\sqrt{(\sin x)}}.$$

32. $I = \int \dfrac{\sec^2 x \sec^2 x\, dx}{\sqrt{(\tan x)}}.$

Put $\tan x = t$. $\therefore$ $\sec^2 x\, dx = dt$.

$$\therefore \quad I = \int \frac{1+t^2}{\sqrt{(t)}}\, dt = \int \left(\frac{1}{\sqrt{(t)}} + t^{3/2}\right) dt.$$

$$= 2\sqrt{t} + \frac{2}{5}t^{5/2} = \frac{2}{5}\sqrt{t}\,(5 + t^2)$$

$$= \frac{2}{5}\sqrt{\tan x}\,(5 + \tan^2 x).$$

33. $\int \tan^4 x\, dx = \int \tan^2 x (\sec^2 x - 1)\, dx$

$$= \int [\tan^2 x \sec^2 x - (\sec^2 x - 1)]\, dx$$

$$= \frac{1}{3}\tan^3 x - \tan x + x.$$

Similarly $\int \tan^3 x\, dx = \dfrac{1}{2}\tan^2 x - \log \sec x.$

34. $I = \int \dfrac{1}{x^2}\sec^2 \dfrac{1}{x}\, dx.$ Put $\dfrac{1}{x} = t$.

$$\therefore \quad -\frac{1}{x^2}\, dx = dt$$

$$\therefore \quad I = -\int \sec^2 t\, dt = -\tan t = -\tan(1/x).$$

35. $\int \dfrac{\sin\sqrt{x}}{\sqrt{(x)}}\, dx.$ Put $\sqrt{x} = t$.

$$\therefore \quad \frac{1}{2\sqrt{(x)}}\, dx = dt.$$

$$\therefore \quad I = 2\int \sin t\, dt = -2\cos t = -2\cos\sqrt{x}.$$

36. (a) $I=\int\left(1-\frac{1}{x^2}\right)e^{x+1/x}\,dx.$ Put $x+\frac{1}{x}=t.$

$\therefore\quad I=\int e^t\,dt=e^t=e^{x+1/x}.$

(b) Put $x+\frac{1}{x}=t$ and adjust the limits

$\therefore\quad I=\int_2^{5/2}t^{3/2}\,dt=\frac{2}{5}t^{5/2}=\frac{2}{5}\left[\left(\frac{5}{2}\right)^{5/2}-2^{5/2}\right]$

$=\frac{2}{5}\left[\left(\frac{5}{2}\right)^2\sqrt{\left(\frac{5}{2}\right)}-2^2\sqrt{2}\right]=\frac{5}{2}\sqrt{\left(\frac{5}{2}\right)}-\frac{8}{5}\sqrt{2}$

(c) Put $x^2-3=t^2$ $\therefore$ $x\,dx=t\,dt$

and adjust the limits

$\therefore\quad I=\int_0^3(3+t^2)\,t^3\,.t\,dt$ etc.

37. $I=\int\sec^p x\tan x\,dx=\int\sec^{p-1}x\sec x\tan x\,dx.$

Put $\sec x=t.$ $\therefore$ $\sec x\tan x\,dx=dt.$

$I=\int t^{p-1}\,dt=t^p/p=(1/p)\sec^p x.$

38. $I=\int\frac{1}{x\log x\log(\log x)}dx$

Put $\log(\log x)=t.$ $\therefore$ $\frac{1}{\log x}\frac{1}{x}dx=dt$

$I=\int\frac{1}{t}dt=\log t=\log[\log(\log x)].$

39. $I=\int(ae)^x\,dx=\frac{(ae)^x}{\log ae}=\frac{a^x e^x}{\log a+1}$ $\because\log e=1$

40. (a) $I=\int\frac{1}{2\sqrt{(x)}\,[1+x]}dx.$ Put $\sqrt{x}=t.$

$\therefore\quad\frac{1}{2\sqrt{(x)}}dx=dt$

$\therefore\quad I=\int\frac{dt}{1+t^2}=\tan^{-1}t=\tan^{-1}\sqrt{x}.$

(b) Ans. $\frac{1}{2}\tan^{-1}x^2.$ Put $x^2=t$ etc.

41. (a) The factors of x^6+1 are $(x^2+1)(x^4-x^2+1)$

$\therefore$ Add and subtract x^2 in the N^r.

$\therefore\quad I=\int\frac{x^4-x^2+1+x^2}{x^6+1}dx$

$=\int\frac{1}{x^2+1}dx+\frac{1}{3}\int\frac{3x^2}{(x^3)^2+1}dx$

$=\tan^{-1}x+\frac{1}{3}\tan^{-1}x^3.$

(b) $I=\int\frac{x^{20}.x^4\,dx}{(x^5)^2+1}$

Put $x^5=t$ $\therefore$ $5x^4\,dx=dt$

$\therefore\quad I=\frac{1}{5}\int\frac{t^4\,dt}{t^2+1}=\frac{1}{5}\int\frac{t^4-1+1}{t^2+1}dt$

$=\frac{1}{5}\int\left(t^2-1+\frac{1}{t^2+1}\right)dt$

$=\frac{1}{5}\left[\frac{t^3}{3}-t+\tan^{-1}t\right]$ where $t=x^5$

42. Put $a^x=t$ $\therefore$ $a^x\log a\,dx=dt$

$\therefore\quad I=\int\frac{a^x\cdot a^{\tan^{-1}a^x}}{1+a^{2x}}dx=\int\frac{a^{\tan^{-1}t}}{(1+t^2)}\frac{dt}{\log a}$

Now put $\tan^{-1}t=z$ $\therefore$ $\frac{1}{1+t^2}dt=dz$

$\therefore\quad I=\int\frac{a^z\,dz}{\log a}=\frac{a^z}{(\log a)^2}=\frac{a^{\tan^{-1}a^x}}{(\log a)^2}$

43. (a) $I=\int x\cos^3x^2\sin x^2\,dx.$

Put $\cos x^2=t.$ $\therefore$ $-(\sin x^2).(2x)\,dx=dt$

$\therefore\quad I=-\frac{1}{2}\int t^3\,dt=-\frac{1}{2}\frac{t^4}{4}=-\frac{1}{8}\cos^4x^2.$

(b) $I=\int\frac{1}{2\sqrt{(x)}}\tan^4\sqrt{x}\sec^2\sqrt{x}\,dx.$

Put $\tan\sqrt{x}=t.$ $\therefore$ $(\sec^2\sqrt{x}).\frac{1}{2\sqrt{(x)}}dx=dt$

$\therefore\quad I=\int t^4\,dt=\frac{1}{5}t^5=\frac{1}{5}\tan^5\sqrt{x}.$

(c) $I=\int\frac{\log x\sin[1+(\log x)^2]}{x}dx.$

Put $1+(\log x)^2=t.$ $\therefore$ $\frac{2\log x}{x}dx=dt.$

$\therefore\quad I=\frac{1}{2}\int\sin t\,dt=-\frac{1}{2}\cos t$

$=-\frac{1}{2}\cos[1+(\log x)^2]$

44. (a) $I=\int\frac{x\,dx}{\sqrt{(1-x^2)}\cos^2\sqrt{(1-x^2)}}$

$=\int\frac{x}{\sqrt{(1-x^2)}}\sec^2\sqrt{1-x^2}\,dx.$

Put $\sqrt{1-x^2}=t$

$\therefore\quad\frac{1}{2\sqrt{(1-x^2)}}(-2x)\,dx=dt.$

$\therefore\quad I=-\int\sec^2t\,dt=-\tan t=-\tan\sqrt{1-x^2}.$

(b) $I=\int\tan x\sec^2x\sqrt{1-\tan^2x}\,dx.$

Put $1-\tan^2 x = t$. ∴ $-2\tan x \sec^2 x\,dx = dt$

∴ $I = -\frac{1}{2}\int t^{1/2}\,dt = -\frac{1}{2}\times\frac{2}{3}.t^{3/2}$

$= -\frac{1}{3}(1-\tan^2 x)^{3/2}$.

45. (a) $I=\int\sqrt{\left(\frac{x}{(a^3-x^3)}\right)}\,dx = \int\frac{\sqrt{x}}{\sqrt{[(a^{3/2})^2-(x^{3/2})^2]}}\,dx$

Put $x^{3/2}=t$ ∴ $\frac{3}{2}\sqrt{x}\,dx = dt$.

∴ $I=\frac{2}{3}\int\frac{dt}{\sqrt{[(a^{3/2})^2-t^2]}} = \frac{2}{3}\sin^{-1}\frac{t}{a^{3/2}}$

$=\frac{2}{3}\sin^{-1}\frac{x^{3/2}}{a^{3/2}}$.

(b) $\frac{1}{2}\sin^{-1}\frac{x^2}{2}$

(c) $\frac{1}{\log a}\sin^{-1}(a^x)$

46. (a) $I=\int\frac{dx}{x^2.x^3.[1+(1/x^4)]^{3/4}}$.

Put $1+\frac{1}{x^4}=t$ ∴ $-\frac{4}{x^5}\,dx = di$

∴ $I=-\frac{1}{4}\int\frac{dt}{t^{3/4}} = -\frac{1}{4}.4t^{1/4}$

$=-t^{1/4} = -\left(1+\frac{1}{x^4}\right)^{1/4} = -\frac{1}{x}(1+x^4)^{1/4}$

(b) $I=\int\frac{(2+\sqrt{x})}{x^2\left(1+\frac{1}{\sqrt{x}}+\frac{1}{x}\right)^2}\,dx = \int\frac{\left(\frac{2}{x^2}+\frac{1}{x^{3/2}}\right)}{\left(1+\frac{1}{x}+\frac{1}{\sqrt{x}}\right)^2}\,dx$

Now put $1+\frac{1}{x}+\frac{1}{\sqrt{x}}=t$

∴ $\left(-\frac{1}{x^2}-\frac{1}{2x^{3/2}}\right)dx=dt$

∴ $I=-2\int\frac{dt}{t^2}=\frac{2}{t}=\frac{2x}{x+\sqrt{x}+1)}$

(c) We know that $\int\frac{1}{\sqrt{1+x^2}}\,dx=\log(x+\sqrt{1+x^2})$

∴ $\frac{d}{dx}\log(x+\sqrt{1+x^2}) = \frac{1}{\sqrt{(1+x^2)}}$

∴ $I=\int t\,dt=\frac{1}{2}t^2=\frac{1}{2}[\log(x+\sqrt{1+x^2}]^2$

(d) $I=\int\frac{5x^8+7x^6}{x^{14}\left[\frac{1}{x^5}+\frac{1}{x^7}+2\right]^2}\,dx$

$=\int\frac{\left[\frac{5}{x^6}+\frac{7}{x^8}\right]}{\left[\frac{1}{x^5}+\frac{1}{x^7}+2\right]^2}\,dx$

Put $\frac{1}{x^5}+\frac{1}{x^7}+2=t$ ∴ $-\left[\frac{5}{x^6}+\frac{7}{x^8}\right]dx=dt$

∴ $I=\int-\frac{1}{t^2}\,dt=\frac{1}{t}$

$=\left[\frac{1}{x^5}+\frac{1}{x^7}+2\right]^{-1}=\left[\frac{2x^7+x^2+1}{x^7}\right]^{-1}$

$=\frac{x^7}{2x^7+x^2+1}$

47. $I=\int\frac{1}{[(x+a)^2-a^2]^{3/2}}\,dx$

Put $x+a=a\sec\theta$

∴ $I=\int\frac{a\sec\theta\tan\theta}{a^3(\tan^2\theta)^{3/2}}\,d\theta$

$I=\frac{1}{a^2}\int\frac{1}{\cos\theta}\cdot\frac{\cos^2\theta}{\sin^2\theta}\,d\theta=\frac{1}{a^2}\int\frac{\cos\theta}{\sin^2\theta}\,d\theta$

$=\frac{1}{a^2}\cdot\frac{-1}{\sin\theta}=-\frac{1}{a^2}\cdot\frac{x+a}{\sqrt{x^2+2ax}}$

Make a triangle for $\cos\theta=\frac{a}{x+a}$ and find $\sin\theta$.

48. Put $x=\tan\theta$

∴ $I=\int\frac{\sec\theta.\sec^2\theta}{\tan^4\theta}\,d\theta$

$I=\int\frac{\cos\theta}{\sin^4\theta}\,d\theta=-\frac{1}{3\sin^3\theta}=-\frac{1}{3}\frac{(1+x^2)^{3/2}}{x^3}$

49. (a) $I=\int\frac{1}{\sin x+\cos x}\,dx$

$=\int\frac{1}{\sqrt{2}\left(\frac{1}{\sqrt{(2)}}\sin x+\frac{1}{\sqrt{(2)}}\cos x\right)}\,dx.$

$=\frac{1}{\sqrt{(2)}}\int\frac{1}{\sin(x+\pi/4)}\,dx$

$=\frac{1}{\sqrt{(2)}}\int\text{cosec}\left(x+\frac{\pi}{4}\right)dx=\frac{1}{\sqrt{(2)}}\log\tan\left(\frac{x}{2}+\frac{\pi}{8}\right)$

(b) $I=\int\frac{\sin x\cos x}{(\sin x+\cos x)}\,dx$

$=\frac{1}{2}\int\frac{\sin 2x\,dx}{(\sin x+\cos x)}=\frac{1}{2}\int\frac{(\sin x+\cos x)^2-1}{\sin x+\cos x}\,dx$

$=\frac{1}{2}\int(\sin x+\cos x)\,dx-\frac{1}{2}\int\frac{dx}{\sin x+\cos x}$

$$= \frac{1}{2}[-\cos x + \sin x] - \frac{1}{2\sqrt{2}} \log \tan\left(\frac{x}{2} + \frac{\pi}{8}\right)$$

by part (a)

50. $I = \int \frac{\sec x \, dx}{a \tan x + b} = \int \frac{dx}{a \sin x + b \cos x}$.

Now see **§5 Page 739.**

51. (a) $\int \frac{dx}{\sin x + \sqrt{(3)} \cos x}$

Put $1 = r\cos\alpha$, $\sqrt{3} = r \sin \alpha$.

$\therefore \quad r^2 = 1 + 3 = 4$ or $r = 2$ and $\tan \alpha = \sqrt{3}$

$\therefore \quad \alpha = \pi/3$.

$$\therefore \quad I = \int \frac{dx}{r \sin(x + \alpha)} = \int \frac{1}{2} \operatorname{cosec}\left(x + \frac{\pi}{3}\right) dx.$$

$$= \frac{1}{2} \log \tan\left(\frac{x}{2} + \frac{\pi}{6}\right).$$

(b) Put $x^2 - 1 = t \quad \therefore 2x\,dx = dt$

and $(N^r)^2 \Rightarrow 2 \sin t - \sin 2t = 2 \sin t (1 - \cos t)$

and $(D^r)^2 \Rightarrow 2 \sin t (1 + \cos t)$

and $\frac{1 - \cos t}{1 + \cos t} = \frac{2 \sin^2 (t/2)}{2 \cos^2 (t/2)} = \tan^2 \frac{t}{2}$

$$\therefore \quad I = \frac{1}{2} \int \tan \frac{t}{2} dt = \log \sec \frac{t}{2}$$

$$I = \log \sec \frac{x^2 - 1}{2}.$$

52. (a) $\int \frac{dx}{\sqrt{(1 + \sin x)}}$

$$= \int \frac{dx}{\sqrt{[\sin^2 (x/2) + \cos^2 (x/2) + 2 \sin (x/2) \cos (x/2)]}}$$

$$= \int \frac{dx}{\sin \frac{x}{2} + \cos \frac{x}{2}}$$

$$= \int \frac{1}{\sqrt{2}\left(\frac{1}{\sqrt{(2)}} \sin \frac{x}{2} + \frac{1}{\sqrt{(2)}} \cos \frac{x}{2}\right)} dx$$

$$= \int \frac{1}{\sqrt{(2)} \sin (x/2 + \pi/4)} dx$$

$$= \frac{1}{\sqrt{(2)}} \int \operatorname{cosec} (x/2 + \pi/4)\, dx$$

$$= (1/\sqrt{2}) \,.\, 2 \log \tan (x/4 + \pi/8)$$

$$= \sqrt{2} \log \tan (x/4 + \pi/8).$$

(b) $I = \int \frac{\sin x + \cos x}{\sqrt{(\cos x + \sin x)^2}} dx = \int dx = x.$

(c) (i) $1 + \sin x = \left(\cos \frac{x}{2} + \sin \frac{x}{2}\right)^2$

$$= 2\left(\frac{1}{\sqrt{(2)}} \cos \frac{x}{2} + \frac{1}{\sqrt{(2)}} \sin \frac{x}{2}\right)^2$$

$$= 2 \cos^2 \left(\frac{x}{2} - \frac{\pi}{4}\right).$$

$$\therefore \quad I = \frac{1}{2} \int \sec^2 \left(\frac{x}{2} - \frac{\pi}{4}\right) dx$$

$$= \frac{1}{2} . 2 \tan \left(\frac{x}{2} - \frac{\pi}{4}\right) + \text{constant}$$

$$= \tan \left(\frac{x}{2} - \frac{\pi}{4}\right) + b.$$

$\therefore \quad a = -\pi/4$ and b is any constant.

(ii) $I = \sqrt{2} \int \left(\frac{1}{\sqrt{(2)}} \sin 2x - \frac{1}{\sqrt{(2)}} \cos 2x\right) dx$

$$= -\sqrt{2} . \int \cos \left(2x + \frac{\pi}{4}\right) dx$$

$$= -\sqrt{2} . \frac{1}{2} \sin \left(2x + \frac{\pi}{4}\right) + \text{constant.}$$

$$= \frac{1}{\sqrt{(2)}} \sin \left(\pi + 2x + \frac{\pi}{4}\right) + b,$$

$\because \sin(\pi + \theta) = -\sin\theta$

$$= \frac{1}{\sqrt{(2)}} \sin \left(2x - \left(-\frac{5\pi}{4}\right)\right) + b$$

$\therefore \quad a = -\frac{5\pi}{4}$, b is any constant.

53. $I = \int \frac{\sin x}{\sqrt{(1 + \sin x)}} dx = \int \frac{(1 + \sin x) - 1}{\sqrt{(1 + \sin x)}} dx,$

$$= \int \sqrt{1 + \sin x}\, dx - \int \frac{1}{\sqrt{(1 + \sin x)}} dx$$

$$= \int \left(\cos \frac{x}{2} + \sin \frac{x}{2}\right) dx - \int \frac{dx}{\cos (x/2) + \sin (x/2)} \text{ etc.}$$

54. $\int \frac{1 + \cos x}{\sin x \cos x} dx = \int \frac{1}{\sin x \cos x} dx + \int \frac{\cos x}{\sin x \cos x} dx,$

$$= 2 \int \operatorname{cosec} 2x\, dx + \int \operatorname{cosec} x\, dx$$

$$= 2 . \frac{1}{2} \log \tan (2x/2) + \log \tan (x/2).$$

$$= \log \tan x + \log \tan (x/2) = \log [\tan x \tan (x/2)].$$

55. $I = \int \frac{1}{4 \cos^3 x - 3 \cos x} dx = \int \frac{1}{\cos 3x} dx$

$$= \int \sec 3x\, dx = \frac{1}{3} \log (\sec 3x + \tan 3x)$$

56. $I = \int \operatorname{cosec} 3x\, dx = \frac{1}{3} \log \tan \frac{3x}{2}.$

57. $I = \int \tan^3 2x \sec 2x\, dx = \int \tan^2 2x \tan 2x \sec 2x\, dx.$

$$= \int (\sec^2 2x - 1) \sec 2x \tan 2x\, dx.$$

Put $\sec 2x = t \quad \therefore \; 2\sec 2x \tan 2x \, dx = dt$

$\therefore \quad I = \frac{1}{2}\int (t^2 - 1)\, dt = \frac{1}{2}\left(\frac{t^3}{3} - t\right)$

$= \frac{1}{6}(\sec^3 2x - 3\sec 2x).$

58. $I = \int \cot^3 x \operatorname{cosec}^4 x \, dx$

$= \int \cot^3 x \operatorname{cosec}^2 x \operatorname{cosec}^2 x \, dx.$

$I = \int \cot^3 x (1 + \cot^2 x) \operatorname{cosec}^2 x \, dx.$

Put $\cot x = t \quad \therefore \; -\operatorname{cosec}^2 x \, dx = dt.$

$\therefore \quad I = -\int (t^3 + t^5)\, dt = -\left(\frac{t^4}{4} + \frac{t^6}{6}\right)$

$= -\left(\frac{1}{4}\cot^4 x + \frac{1}{6}\cot^6 x\right).$

59. $I = \int \sqrt{2 + \sin 3x} \cos 3x \, dx.$

Put $2 + \sin 3x = t \quad \therefore \; 3\cos 3x \, dx = dt.$

$\therefore \quad I = \frac{1}{3}\int \sqrt{t}\, dt = \frac{1}{3} \cdot \frac{2}{3} t^{3/2} = \frac{2}{9}(2 + \sin 3x)^{3/2}.$

60. $\because \quad \left(\cos\frac{1}{4}x + \sin\frac{1}{4}x\right)^2 = 1 + \sin\frac{1}{2}x$

$\therefore \quad I = \int \sqrt{1 + \sin\frac{1}{2}x}\, dx = \int \left(\cos\frac{1}{4}x + \sin\frac{1}{4}x\right) dx$

$= 4\left[\sin\frac{1}{4}x - \cos\frac{1}{4}x\right]$

61. (a) $I = \int \frac{1}{x}\operatorname{cosec}^2 \log x \, dx.$

Put $\log x = t. \quad \therefore \; \frac{1}{x}dx = dt.$

$\therefore \quad I = \int \operatorname{cosec}^2 t \, dt = -\cot t = -\cot(\log x).$

(b) Ans. $\log(\sin \log x)$.

62. $I = \int \frac{\operatorname{cosec}(\tan^{-1} x)}{1 + x^2} dx.$

Put $\tan^{-1} x = t. \quad \therefore \; \frac{1}{1 + x^2} dx = dt$

$\therefore \; I = \int \operatorname{cosec} t \, dt = \log \tan\left(\frac{t}{2}\right) = \log\tan\left(\frac{1}{2}\tan^{-1} x\right).$

63. (a) $I = \int \frac{1}{\sin(x - a)\sin(x - b)} dx.$

Put $a - b = (x - b) - (x - a)$

$\sin(a - b) = \sin(x - b)\cos(x - a) - \cos(x - b)\sin(x - a)$

$\therefore \quad I = \frac{1}{\sin(a - b)} \cdot \int \frac{\sin(x - b)\cos(x - a) - \cos(x - b)\sin(x - a)}{\sin(x - a)\sin(x - b)} dx$ by (1)

$= \frac{1}{\sin(a - b)}\int [\cot(x - a) - \cot(x - b)]\, dx$

$= \frac{1}{\sin(a - b)}[\log\sin(x - a) - \log\sin(x - b)]$

$= \frac{1}{\sin(a - b)}\log\frac{\sin(x - a)}{\sin(x - b)}.$

(b) $I = \int \frac{1}{\sin\left(x - \frac{\pi}{3}\right)\sin\left(x - \frac{\pi}{6}\right)} dx$

$\left(x - \frac{\pi}{6}\right) - \left(x - \frac{\pi}{3}\right) = \frac{\pi}{6}$ and $\sin\frac{\pi}{6} = \frac{1}{2}$

$I = 2\int \left[\frac{\sin\left\{\left(x - \frac{\pi}{6}\right) - \left(x - \frac{\pi}{3}\right)\right\}}{\sin\left(x - \frac{\pi}{3}\right)\sin\left(x - \frac{\pi}{6}\right)}\right] dx$

$I = 2\left[\cot\left(x - \frac{\pi}{3}\right) - \cot\left(x - \frac{\pi}{6}\right)\right]$ etc.

$\int \cot\theta \, . d\theta = \log\sin\theta$

(c) Sol. Ans. (b).

$N^r = \sin x = \frac{1}{2\cos(\pi/6)} . 2\sin x \cos\frac{\pi}{6}$

$= \frac{1}{\sqrt{3}}\left[\sin\left(x + \frac{\pi}{6}\right) + \sin\left(x - \frac{\pi}{6}\right)\right]$

$\therefore \quad I = \frac{1}{\sqrt{3}}\int\left[\operatorname{cosec}\left(x - \frac{\pi}{6}\right) + \operatorname{cosec}\left(x + \frac{\pi}{6}\right)\right] dx$

$= \frac{1}{\sqrt{3}}\left[\log\tan\left(\frac{x}{2} - \frac{\pi}{12}\right) + \log\tan\left(\frac{x}{2} + \frac{\pi}{12}\right)\right]$

(d) Ans. (d).

$\cos x - \sin x = \sqrt{2}\left(\frac{1}{\sqrt{2}}\cos x - \frac{1}{\sqrt{2}}\sin x\right)$

$= \sqrt{2}\cos\left(x + \frac{\pi}{4}\right)$

$\therefore \quad I = \frac{1}{\sqrt{2}}\int \sec\left(x + \frac{\pi}{4}\right) dx = \frac{1}{\sqrt{2}}\log\tan\left(\frac{\pi}{4} + \frac{x + \pi/4}{2}\right)$

$= \frac{1}{\sqrt{2}}\log\tan\left(\frac{x}{2} + \frac{3\pi}{8}\right)$

$\because \quad \int \sec x \, dx = \log\tan\left(\frac{\pi}{4} + \frac{x}{2}\right)$

64. (a) Proceed as above.

$I = \frac{1}{\sin(a - b)}\log\frac{\sec(x - b)}{\sec(x - a)}.$

(b) $\cos(a - b) = \cos(\underline{x + a} - \underline{x + b})$

$$I = \frac{1}{\cos(a-b)}$$

$$\cdot \int \frac{\cos(x+a)\cos(x+b)+\sin(x+a)\sin(x+b)}{\cos(x+a)\sin(x+b)}\,dx$$

$$= \sec(a-b) \int [\cot(x+b)+\tan(x+a)]\,dx$$

$$= \sec(a-b)\,[\log\sin(x+b)+\log\sec(x+a)]$$

(c) $1+\tan x.\tan(x-a)$

$$= \frac{\cos x\cos(x-a)+\sin x\sin(x-a)}{\cos x\cos(x-a)}$$

$$= \frac{\cos a}{\cos x\cos(x-a)} = \frac{\cos a}{\sin a}\cdot\frac{\sin a}{\cos x\cos(x-a)}$$

$$= \frac{\cos a}{\sin a}\,\frac{\sin[x-(x-a)]}{\cos x\cos(x-a)}$$

$$= \cot a\,[\tan x - \tan(x-a)]$$

$I = \cot a \log.\dfrac{\cos x}{\cos(x-a)}$ as in part (a).

65. (a) $I = \displaystyle\int \frac{\cos x}{\cos(x-a)}\,dx.$

Put $x-a=t.$ $\therefore$ $x=a+t$ and $dx=dt$

$$\therefore\quad I = \int \frac{\cos(a+t)}{\cos t}\,dt.$$

$$= \int \frac{\cos a\cos t - \sin a\sin t}{\cos t}\,dt$$

$$= \int (\cos a - \sin a\tan t)\,dt$$

$$= t\cos a - \sin a\log\sec t$$

$$= (x-a)\cos a - \sin a\log\sec(x-a)$$

(b) Proceed as above.

$I = (x-a)\cos a + \sin a\log\sin(x-a).$

(c) $2x = (x+a)+(x-a)$

$$\therefore\quad \tan 2x = \frac{\tan(x+a)+\tan(x-a)}{1-\tan(x+a)\tan(x-a)}$$

$$\therefore\quad \tan 2x - \tan(x+a) - \tan(x-a) = \tan 2x\tan(x+a)\tan(x-a)$$

$$\therefore\quad I = \int [\tan 2x - \tan(x+a) - \tan(x-a)]\,dx$$

$$= \frac{1}{2}\log\sec 2x - \log\sec(x+a) - \log\sec(x-a)$$

$$= \log\{\sqrt{\sec 2x}\cos(x+a)\cos(x-a)\}$$

$\because$ $\log\dfrac{1}{x} = -\log x.$

66. (a) Multiply above and below by $\sin 3x$.

Use $\sin 2A = 2\sin A\cos A$

$$I = \int \frac{\left(2\sin\frac{3x}{2}\cos\frac{3x}{2}\right)\left(2\cos\frac{9x}{2}\cos\frac{x}{2}\right)}{\sin 3x - \sin 6x}\,dx$$

$$D^r = -2\sin\frac{3x}{2}\cos\frac{9x}{2}$$

$$\therefore\quad I = \int -\left(2\cos\frac{3x}{2}\cos\frac{x}{2}\right)dx = -\int(\cos x + \cos 2x)\,dx$$

$$= -\left(\sin x + \frac{1}{2}\sin 2x\right)$$

(b) Multiply above and below by $2\sin\dfrac{5x}{2}$.

$$\therefore\quad I = \frac{1}{2}\int \frac{2\sin\frac{5x}{2}\cos 7x - 2\sin\frac{5x}{2}\cos 8x}{\sin\frac{5x}{2} + 2\sin\frac{5x}{2}\cos 5x}\,dx$$

Now $2\sin A\cos B = \sin(A+B)+\sin(A-B)$

$\therefore$ $I =$

$$\frac{1}{2}\int \frac{\sin\frac{19x}{2} + \sin\left(-\frac{9x}{2}\right) - \left\{\sin\frac{21x}{2} + \sin\left(-\frac{11x}{2}\right)\right\}}{\sin\frac{5x}{2} + \sin\frac{15x}{2} + \sin\left(-\frac{5x}{2}\right)}$$

Now note $19+11 = 21+9 = 30$

$$= \frac{1}{2}\int \frac{\left(\sin\frac{19x}{2} + \sin\frac{11x}{2}\right) - \left(\sin\frac{21x}{2} + \sin\frac{9x}{2}\right)}{\sin\frac{15x}{2}}\,dx$$

$$= \frac{1}{2}\int \frac{2\sin\frac{15x}{2}\cos 2x - 2\sin\frac{15x}{2}\cos 3x}{\sin\frac{15x}{2}}\,dx$$

$$= \int(\cos 2x - \cos 3x)\,dx = \frac{1}{2}\sin 2x - \frac{1}{3}\sin 3x$$

67. (a) $I = \displaystyle\int \frac{1}{\sqrt{[\sin^3 x\sin(x+\alpha)]}}\,dx.$

$$I = \int \frac{1}{\sqrt{[\sin^3 x(\sin x\cos\alpha + \cos x\sin\alpha)]}}\,dx$$

$$= \int \frac{1}{\sqrt{[\sin^4 x(\cos\alpha + \sin\alpha\cot x)]}}\,dx$$

$$= \int \frac{\text{cosec}^2 x\,dx}{\sqrt{(\cos\alpha + \sin\alpha\cot x)}}.$$

Put $\cos\alpha + \sin\alpha\cot x = t$

$\therefore$ $-\sin\alpha\,\text{cosec}^2 x\,dx = dt.$

$$\therefore\quad I = -\frac{1}{\sin\alpha}\int\frac{dt}{\sqrt{(t)}} = -2\sqrt{t}\,\text{cosec}\,\alpha$$

$$= -2\,\text{cosec}\,\alpha.\sqrt{\cos\alpha + \sin\alpha\cot x}$$

$$= -2\,\text{cosec}\,\alpha.\sqrt{\left(\frac{\cos\alpha\sin x + \sin\alpha\cos x}{\sin x}\right)}$$

$$= -2\,\text{cosec}\,\alpha.\sqrt{\left(\frac{\sin(x+\alpha)}{\sin x}\right)}.$$

(b) $\sin(2x+\alpha) + \sin\alpha = 2\sin(x+\alpha)\cos x$

$$= 2\cos x\,[\sin x\cos\alpha + \cos x\sin\alpha]$$

$$= 2\cos^2 x\,[\tan x\cos\alpha + \sin\alpha]$$

$$I = \int \frac{\sec x\,dx}{\sqrt{2}\cos x\,[\tan x\cos\alpha + \sin\alpha]^{1/2}}$$

$$= \frac{1}{\sqrt{2}} \int \frac{\sec^2 x\,dx}{[\tan x\cos\alpha + \sin\alpha]^{1/2}}$$

Put $\tan x\cos\alpha + \sin\alpha = t$

$\therefore \quad \sec^2 x\cos\alpha\,dx = dt$

$$\therefore \quad I = \frac{1}{\sqrt{2}\cos\alpha}\int \frac{dt}{\sqrt{t}} = \frac{1}{\sqrt{2}\cos\alpha}.2\sqrt{t}$$

$$= \sqrt{2}\left[\frac{\tan x\cos\alpha + \sin\alpha}{\cos^2\alpha}\right]^{1/2}$$

$$= \sqrt{2}\,[\tan x\sec\alpha + \sec\alpha\tan\alpha]^{1/2}$$

$$= \sqrt{2}\,[(\tan x + \tan\alpha)\sec\alpha]^{1/2}$$

(c) $I = I_1 + I_2$

$$I_1 = \int \frac{1}{\sqrt{\cos^3 x}\sqrt{\sin x\cos\alpha + \cos x\sin\alpha}}\,dx$$

$$= \int \frac{\sec^2 x.dx}{\sqrt{(\sin\alpha + \cos\alpha\tan x)}}$$

Now put $\sin\alpha + \cos\alpha\tan x = t$ etc.

Similarly express I_2 in terms of $\cot x$ and $\operatorname{cosec}^2 x$.

Ans. $\quad \dfrac{2}{\cos\alpha}\sqrt{\sin\alpha + \cos\alpha\tan x}$

$$- \frac{2}{\sin\alpha}\sqrt{\cos\alpha + \sin\alpha\cot x}$$

(d) Change in terms of $\sin x$ and $\cos x$

$$I = \int \frac{\sin x\cos x}{1 + \sin x + \cos x}\,dx = \int \frac{\sin x\,dx}{\sec x + \tan x + 1}$$

Multiply above and below by $(1 + \tan x) - \sec x$

$$\therefore \quad I = \int \frac{\sin x(1 + \tan x - \sec x)}{(1 + \tan x)^2 - \sec^2 x}\,dx$$

$$D^r = (1 + \tan^2 x) - \sec^2 x + 2\tan x$$

$$= 0 + 2\sin x/\cos x$$

$$\therefore \quad I = \frac{1}{2}\int \cos x\left(1 + \frac{\sin x}{\cos x} - \frac{1}{\cos x}\right)dx$$

$$= \frac{1}{2}\int (\cos x + \sin x - 1)\,dx$$

$$= \frac{1}{2}(\sin x - \cos x - x)$$

68. (a) $I = \displaystyle\int \frac{\sin 2x}{\sin^4 x + \cos^4 x}\,dx = \int \frac{2\sin x\cos x}{\sin^4 x + \cos^4 x}\,dx.$

Divide N^r and D^r by $\cos^4 x$.

$$\therefore \quad I = \int \frac{2\tan x\sec^2 x\,dx}{1 + \tan^4 x}$$

Put $\tan^2 x = t. \quad \therefore\ 2\tan x\sec^2 x\,dx = dt$

$$\therefore \quad I = \int \frac{dt}{1 + t^2} = \tan^{-1} t = \tan^{-1}(\tan^2 x).$$

(b) $I = \displaystyle\int \frac{(1 - \sin^2 x)\cos x}{\sin x(1 + \sin x)}\,dx = \int \frac{1 - \sin x}{\sin x}\cos x\,dx$

$$= \int \left(\frac{1}{t} - 1\right)dt, \text{ where } t = \sin x$$

$$= \log t - t = \log\sin x - \sin x$$

(c) Ans. (c).

$$I = \int \frac{\left(\cos x + \dfrac{1}{\cos x}\right)2\sin x\,dx}{\cos^6 x + 6\cos^2 x + 4}$$

Now put $\cos x = t \quad \therefore \quad -\sin x\,dx = dt$

$$\therefore \quad I = -2\int \frac{1 + t^2}{t^7 + 6t^3 + 4t}\,dt$$

Divide above and below each term by t^7

$$\therefore \quad I = -2\int \frac{\left(\dfrac{1}{t^5} + \dfrac{1}{t^7}\right)dt}{\left(1 + \dfrac{6}{t^4} + \dfrac{4}{t^6}\right)}$$

Now put $1 + \dfrac{6}{t^4} + \dfrac{4}{t^6} = z$

$$\therefore \quad -24\left(\frac{1}{t^5} + \frac{1}{t^7}\right)dt = dz$$

$$\therefore \quad I = \frac{1}{12}\int \frac{dz}{z} = \frac{1}{12}\log z$$

where $z = \dfrac{t^6 + 6t^2 + 4}{t^6}$ and $t = \cos x$

69. (a) Put $1 + x^{5/2} = t$

Then $\dfrac{5}{2}x^{3/2}\,dx = dt$

$$\therefore \quad \int x^{13/2}(1 + x^{5/2})^{1/2}\,dx$$

$$= \int (1 + x^{5/2})^{1/2}.x^5.x^{3/2}\,dx$$

$$= \int t^{1/2}.(t - 1)^2.\frac{2}{5}\,dt$$

$$= \frac{2}{5}\int t^{1/2}(t^2 - 2t + 1)\,dt$$

$$= \frac{2}{5}\int (t^{5/2} - 2t^{3/2} + t^{1/2})\,dt$$

$$= \frac{2}{5}\left[\frac{2}{7}.t^{7/2} - \frac{4}{5}.t^{5/2} + \frac{2}{3}t^{3/2}\right] + c$$

$$= \frac{2}{5}t^{3/2}\left[\frac{2}{7}t^2 - \frac{4}{5}t + \frac{2}{3}\right] + c$$

$$= \frac{2}{5}(1+x^{5/2})^{3/2}\left[\frac{2}{7}(1+x^{5/2})^2 - \frac{4}{5}(1+x^{5/2}) + \frac{2}{3}\right] + c$$

(b) **It is a very simple question based upon**

$$\int [f(x)]^n \cdot f'(x)\,dx = \frac{[f(x)]^{n+1}}{n+1} + c.$$

Consider $(2x^{2m} + 3x^m + 6)^{1/m}$.

Multiply above and below by x^m.

$$\left[\frac{2x^{3m} + 3x^{2m} + 6x^m}{x^m}\right]^{1/m}$$

$$= \frac{1}{x}[2x^{3m} + 3x^{2m} + 6x^m]^{1/m}$$

$$\therefore \quad I = \int (x^{3m} + x^{2m} + x^m) \cdot \frac{1}{x}[2x^{3m} + 3x^{2m} + 6x^m]^{1/m}\,dx$$

$$= \int (x^{3m-1} + x^{2m-1}\ x^{m-1})\,[2x^{3m} + 3x^{2m} + 6x^m]^{1/m}\,dx$$

Now put $2x^{3m} + 3x^{2m} + 6x^m = y$

$$\therefore \quad 6m(x^{3m-1} + x^{2m-1} + x^{m-1})\,dx = dy$$

$$\therefore \quad I = \frac{1}{6m}\int y^{1/m}\,dy = \frac{1}{6m}\frac{y^{(1/m)+1}}{(1/m)+1} + c$$

$$= \frac{1}{6}\frac{y^{\frac{m+1}{m}}}{m+1} + c \text{ etc.}$$

70. The given expression is

$$(1 + 2\tan^2 x + 2\tan x \sec x)^{1/2}$$

$$= (\sec^2 x + \tan^2 x + 2\tan x \sec x)^{1/2}$$

$$= \sec x + \tan x$$

$$\therefore \quad I = \int (\sec x + \tan x)\,dx$$

$$= \log(\sec x + \tan x) + \log \sec x + c$$

$$= \log \sec x(\sec x + \tan x) + c.$$

71. (a) Put $x = a\tan\theta$ and adjust the limits

$$I = \int_{\pi/4}^{\pi/2} \frac{a\sec^2\theta\,d\theta}{a^4\tan^4\theta \cdot a\sec\theta} = \frac{1}{a^4}\int_{\pi/4}^{\pi/2}\frac{\cos^3\theta\,d\theta}{\sin^4\theta}$$

$$= \frac{1}{a^4}\int_{\pi/4}^{\pi/2}\frac{(1-\sin^2\theta)\cos\theta}{\sin^4\theta}\,d\theta$$

Again put $\sin\theta = z$ and adjust the limits

$$I = \frac{1}{a^4}\int_{1/\sqrt{2}}^{1}\left(\frac{1-z^2}{z^4}\right)dz = \frac{1}{a^4}\int\left(\frac{1}{z^4} - \frac{1}{z^2}\right)dz$$

$$= \frac{1}{a^4}\left[-\frac{1}{3z^3} + \frac{1}{z}\right]_{1/\sqrt{2}}^{1} = \frac{2-\sqrt{2}}{3a^4}$$

(b) $af(x) + bf\left(\frac{1}{x}\right) = \frac{1}{x} - 5$ ...(1)

Integrating both sides

$$a\int_1^2 f(x)\,dx + b\int_1^2 f\left(\frac{1}{x}\right)dx = [\log x - 5x]_1^2$$

$$= \log 2 - 5 \quad \text{...(2)}$$

Replacing x by $\frac{1}{x}$ in (1), we get

$$af\left(\frac{1}{x}\right) + bf(x) = x - 5$$

Integrating both sides, we get

$$a\int_1^2 f\left(\frac{1}{x}\right)dx + b\int_1^2 f(x)\,dx = \left[\frac{x^2}{2} - 5x\right]_1^2 = -\frac{7}{2}$$

...(3)

Eliminate $\int_1^2 f\left(\frac{1}{x}\right)$ between (2) and (3)

by multiplying (2) by a and (3) by b and subtracting

$$\therefore \quad (a^2 - b^2)\int_1^2 f(x)\,dx = a(\log 2 - 5) + b\cdot\frac{7}{2}$$

$$\therefore \quad \int_1^2 f(x)\,dx = \frac{1}{(a^2-b^2)}\left[a(\log 2 - 5) + \frac{7b}{2}\right]$$

72. (a) $f(x) = \int_1^x \frac{\log t}{1+t}\,dt$ ...(1)

$$f\left(\frac{1}{x}\right) = \int_1^{1/x}\frac{\log t}{1+t}\,dt$$

Put $t = \frac{1}{z}$ $\therefore$ $dt = -\frac{1}{z^2}dz$ and adjust the limits.

$$\therefore \quad f\left(\frac{1}{x}\right) = \int_1^x -\frac{\log z}{(z+1)/z}\left(-\frac{1}{z^2}dz\right)$$

$$= \int_1^x \frac{\log z}{z(z+1)}\,dz = \int_1^x \frac{\log t}{t(1+t)}\,dt$$

$$f(x) + f\left(\frac{1}{x}\right) = \int_1^x \frac{\log t}{1+t}\left(1 + \frac{1}{t}\right)dt$$

$$= \int_1^x \frac{\log t}{t} = \left[\frac{1}{2}(\log t)^2\right]_1^x = \frac{1}{2}(\log x)^2$$

Now put $x = e$ in both sides

$$\therefore \quad f(e) + f\left(\frac{1}{e}\right) = \frac{1}{2}[(\log e)^2] = \frac{1}{2}$$

(b) On integrating and putting the limits, we get

$$\Rightarrow \quad a^2\left(-\frac{1}{12} + \frac{3}{4}\right) - 0 - 20 + a \le -\frac{a^2}{3}$$

$$\Rightarrow \quad \frac{2}{3}a^2 + a - 20 + \frac{a^2}{3} \le 0 \quad \Rightarrow \quad a^2 + a - 20 \le 0$$

$$\Rightarrow \quad (a+5)(a-4) \le 0 \quad \Rightarrow \quad -5 \le \alpha \le 4$$

Since $a \in I^+$ $\therefore$ $a = 1, 2, 3, 4$ *i.e.* four values.

73. (a) Since $0 < y < 1$ *i.e.* y is + ive but less than 1.

Then $y > y^2 > \frac{1}{2}y^2$

$\Rightarrow \; -y < -y^2 < -\frac{1}{2}y^2$. Also $e > 1$

$\therefore \; e^{-y} < e^{-y^2} < e^{-\frac{1}{2}y^2}$ ...(1)

Also $\cos^2 y \le 1$ ...(2)

$\therefore \; e^{-y}\cos^2 y \le e^{-y^2}\cos^2 y < e^{-y^2} < e^{-\frac{1}{2}y^2}$

by (1) and (2)

$\therefore \; I_1 < I_2 < I_3 < I_4$

Hence I_4 is greatest.

(b) $0 < x < 1 \Rightarrow x^2 - x^3 = x^2(1-x) > 0$

$\therefore \; x^2 > x^3 \quad \therefore \; 2^{x^2} > 2^{x^3} \quad \therefore \; I_1 > I_2$

$1 < x < 2 \Rightarrow x^2 - x^3 = x^2(1-x) < 0$

$\therefore \; x^2 < x^3 \quad \therefore \; 2^{x^2} < 2^{x^3} \Rightarrow I_3 < I_4$

(c) $0 < y < 1 \Rightarrow 0 < y^2 < 1$ and $e > 1$

$\therefore \; e^0 < e^{y^2} < e$

or $\int_0^1 1\,dy < \int_0^1 e^{y^2}\,dy < \int_0^1 e\,dy$

$1 < I < e \quad \therefore \; I < e$ and $I > 1$

(d) $\sqrt{1+x^2} > x \quad \forall \; x \in [1, 2]$

$\therefore \; \int \frac{dx}{\sqrt{(1+x^2)}} < \int \frac{dx}{x} \Rightarrow I_1 < I_2$ or $I_2 > I_1$

(e) Ans. (c).

Put $x = \tan\theta$

$\therefore \; I_2 = \int_0^{\pi/4} \frac{\theta}{\tan\theta}.\sec^2\theta\,d\theta$

or $I_2 = \int_0^{\pi/4} \frac{2\theta}{2\sin\theta\cos\theta}\,d\theta = \int_0^{\pi/4} \frac{2\theta}{\sin 2\theta}\,d\theta$

Now put $2\theta = t \quad \therefore \; I_2 = \frac{1}{2}\int_0^{\pi/2} \frac{t}{\sin t}\,dt = \frac{1}{2}I_1$

$\therefore \; \frac{I_1}{I_2} = 2 \Rightarrow$ (c)

74. Put $x = \cos\theta$ and adjust the limits

$$I = \int_{\pi/2}^{0} \cos\left[2\cot^{-1}\left(\tan\frac{\theta}{2}\right)\right](-\sin\theta\,d\theta)$$

$$= \int_0^{\pi/2} \cos\left[2\left(\frac{\pi}{2} - \frac{\theta}{2}\right)\right]\sin\theta.d\theta$$

$$= \int_0^{\pi/2} \cos(\pi - \theta)\sin\theta\,d\theta$$

$$= \int_0^{\pi/2} -\cos\theta\sin\theta\,d\theta = \frac{1}{2}[\cos^2\theta]_0^{\pi/2} = -\frac{1}{2}$$

75. (a) $D^r = \frac{\cos^2 x - \sin^2 x}{\sin x.\cos x} = \frac{2\cos 2x}{\sin 2x}$

$\therefore \; I = \int \frac{-(2\sin^2 2x)}{2\cos 2x}\cdot\sin 2x\,dx$

Put $\cos 2x = t \quad \therefore \; -2\sin 2x\,dx = dt$

$I = \int \frac{1-t^2}{2t}\,dt = \int \frac{1}{2t}\,dt - \int \frac{t}{2}\,dt$

$I = \frac{1}{2}\log\cos 2x - \frac{1}{4}\cos^2 2x + c$

(b) $D^r = 1 + (x+1)\log x + (\sqrt{x}\log x)^2$

$= 1 + \log x + x\log x + x(\log x)^2$

$= (1 + \log x) + x\log x(1 + \log x)$

$= (1 + \log x)(1 + x\log x)$

$\therefore \; I = \int \frac{1 + \log x}{1 + x\log x}\,dx$

Now put

$1 + x\log x = t \quad \therefore \; (1 + \log x)\,dx = dt$

$\therefore \; I = \int \frac{1}{t}\,dt = \log t = \log(1 + x\log x)$

76. Put $x = \cos^2 2\theta$ and $\frac{1-\cos 2\theta}{1+\cos 2\theta} = \tan^2\theta$

$dx = -4\cos 2\theta.\sin 2\theta\,d\theta$

$$I = -4\int \frac{\sin\theta}{\cos\theta}\cdot\frac{\cos 2\theta\,(2\sin\theta.\cos\theta)}{\cos^2 2\theta}\,d\theta$$

$$= -4\int \frac{2\sin^2\theta}{\cos 2\theta}\,d\theta = -4\int \frac{(1-\cos 2\theta)}{\cos 2\theta}\,d\theta$$

$$= -4\int(\sec 2\theta - 1)\,d\theta$$

$$= -4\left[\frac{1}{2}\log(\sec 2\theta + \tan 2\theta) - \theta\right]$$

$$I = 4\theta - 2\log[\sec 2\theta + \sqrt{\sec^2 2\theta - 1}]$$

Now put $\cos 2\theta = \sqrt{x}$ or $\sec 2\theta = \frac{1}{\sqrt{x}}$

$\Rightarrow \; \theta = \frac{1}{2}\sec^{-1}\frac{1}{\sqrt{x}} = \frac{1}{2}\cos^{-1}\sqrt{x}$

$\therefore \; I = 2\cos^{-1}\sqrt{x} - 2\log\left[\frac{1}{\sqrt{x}} + \sqrt{\frac{1}{x} - 1}\right]$

$I = 2\cos^{-1}\sqrt{x} - 2\log\left[\frac{1 + \sqrt{1-x}}{\sqrt{x}}\right]$

77. Put $e^y - 1 = z^2 \quad \therefore \; e^y\,dy = 2z\,dz$ and adjust the limits.

Also $e^y = z^2 + 1$

$\therefore \; I = \int_1^{\sqrt{(e^x - 1)}} \frac{2z}{e^y.z}\,dz = 2\int \frac{dz}{z^2 + 1} = 2\tan^{-1} z$

$$= 2\left[\tan^{-1}\sqrt{e^x - 1} - \tan^{-1} 1\right] = \frac{\pi}{6} \quad \text{given}$$

$$2\tan^{-1}\sqrt{e^x - 1} = \left(\frac{\pi}{6} + \frac{\pi}{2}\right) = \frac{2\pi}{3}$$

$$\sqrt{e^x - 1} = \tan\frac{\pi}{3} = \sqrt{3} \quad \therefore \; e^x - 1 = 3$$

or $e^x = 4 \quad \therefore \quad x = \log 4.$

78. (a) $I = \int \frac{\sin x}{2\sin 2x \cos 2x} dx = \int \frac{dx}{4\cos x \cos 2x}$

$$= \int \frac{\cos x \, dx}{4(1 - \sin^2 x)(1 - 2\sin^2 x)} \quad \text{Put } \sin x = t$$

$$\therefore \quad I = \int \frac{dt}{4(1 - t^2)(1 - 2t^2)}$$

$$= \frac{1}{4}\int \left[\frac{2}{1 - 2t^2} - \frac{1}{1 - t^2}\right] dt$$

$$= \frac{1}{2} \cdot \frac{1}{2\sqrt{2}} \log \frac{1 + \sqrt{2}\,t}{1 - \sqrt{2}\,t} - \frac{1}{4.2} \log \frac{1 + t}{1 - t},$$

where $t = \sin x$

$$\left[\because \int \frac{1}{a^2 - x^2} dx = \frac{1}{2a} \log \frac{a + x}{a - x}\right]$$

(b) $\int \frac{dx}{x^5 \sqrt{\left(\frac{a}{x}\right)^2 + 1}} = \int \frac{dx}{x^3 \cdot x^2 \sqrt{\frac{a^2}{x^2} + 1}}$

Put $\frac{a^2}{x^2} + 1 = t^2 \quad \therefore \quad -\frac{2a^2}{x^3} dx = 2t\, dt$

$$\therefore \quad I = \int -\frac{1}{a^2} t \cdot \frac{(t^2 - 1)}{a^2} \cdot \frac{1}{t} dt$$

$$= -\frac{1}{a^4}\left(\frac{t^3}{3} - t\right) = \frac{1}{a^4}\left[t - \frac{t^3}{3}\right],$$

where $t = \sqrt{\frac{a^2}{x^2} + 1} = \frac{\sqrt{a^2 + x^2}}{x}$

*§ 6. Nine Standard Results

1. $\int \frac{1}{x^2 + a^2} dx = \frac{1}{a} \tan^{-1} \frac{x}{a}.$

2. $\int \frac{1}{x^2 - a^2} dx = \frac{1}{2a} \log \frac{(x - a)}{(x + a)}$ when $x > a.$

3. $\int \frac{1}{a^2 - x^2} dx = \frac{1}{2a} \log \frac{a + x}{a - x}$ when $x < a.$

4. $\int \frac{1}{\sqrt{(x^2 + a^2)}} dx = \log\left[x + \sqrt{x^2 + a^2}\right]$ or $\sinh^{-1}\left(\frac{x}{a}\right).$

5. $\int \frac{1}{\sqrt{(x^2 - a^2)}} dx = \log\left[x + \sqrt{x^2 - a^2}\right]$ or $\cosh^{-1} \frac{x}{a}.$

6. $\int \frac{1}{\sqrt{(a^2 - x^2)}} dx = \sin^{-1} \frac{x}{a}$

7. $\int \sqrt{x^2 + a^2}\, dx = \frac{x}{2}\sqrt{x^2 + a^2} + \frac{1}{2} a^2 \log\left[x + \sqrt{x^2 + a^2}\right].$

or $= \frac{x}{2}\sqrt{x^2 + a^2} + \frac{1}{2} a^2 \sinh^{-1} \frac{x}{a}.$

8. $\int \sqrt{x^2 - a^2}\, dx = \frac{x}{2}\sqrt{x^2 - a^2} - \frac{1}{2} a^2 \log\left[x + \sqrt{x^2 - a^2}\right].$

or $= \frac{x}{2}\sqrt{x^2 - a^2} - \frac{1}{2} a^2 \cosh^{-1} \frac{x}{a}.$

9. $\int \sqrt{a^2 - x^2}\, dx = \frac{x}{2}\sqrt{a^2 - x^2} + \frac{1}{2} a^2 \sin^{-1} \frac{x}{a}.$

§7. Application of above formulae to the Integrals : $\int \frac{dx}{ax^2 + bx + c}, \int \frac{dx}{\sqrt{(ax^2 + bx + c)}}, \int \sqrt{ax^2 + bx + c}\, dx.$

Express $ax^2 + bx + c$ as sum or difference of two squares and apply formulae no. (1) to (9) as the case may be.

Rule to express a quadratic as sum or difference of two squares.

$$3x^2 + 4x - 7 = 3\left[x^2 + \frac{4}{3}x - \frac{7}{3}\right]$$

$$= 3\left[\left(x^2 + \frac{4}{3}x + \frac{4}{9}\right) - \frac{7}{3} - \frac{4}{9}\right] = 3\left[\left(x + \frac{2}{3}\right)^2 - \left(\frac{5}{3}\right)^2\right]$$

$$4 - 3x - 2x^2 = -2\left[x^2 + \frac{3}{2}x - 2\right]$$

$$= -2\left[\left(x^2 + \frac{3}{2}x + \frac{9}{16}\right) - 2 - \frac{9}{16}\right]$$

$$= -2\left[\left(x + \frac{3}{4}\right)^2 - \left(\frac{\sqrt{41}}{4}\right)^2\right]$$

$$= 2\left[\left(\frac{\sqrt{41}}{4}\right)^2 - \left(x + \frac{3}{4}\right)^2\right]. \quad \textbf{(Note)}$$

***Rule :** Make the coefficient of x^2 equal to $+1$ by taking out the constant and then add and subtract square of half the coefficient of x.

Solved Examples

Ex. 1. $\int \frac{1}{4x^2 + 4x + 5} dx$

$$4x^2 + 4x + 5 = 4(x^2 + x + 5/4)$$

$$= 4\left(x^2 + x + \frac{1}{4} + \frac{5}{4} - \frac{1}{4}\right) = 4\left[\left(x + \frac{1}{2}\right)^2 + 1^2\right]$$

$$\therefore \quad I = \frac{1}{4}\int \frac{dx}{\left(x + \frac{1}{2}\right)^2 + 1^2} = \frac{1}{4} \tan^{-1}\left(x + \frac{1}{2}\right)$$

formula (1)

Ex. 2. $\int \frac{1}{x^2 + 4x - 5} dx = \int \frac{1}{(x + 5)(x - 1)} dx$

$$I=\int \frac{1}{x^2+4x+4-5-4}\,dx=\int \frac{1}{(x+2)^2-3^2}\,dx$$

$$=\frac{1}{2.3}\log\frac{(x+2)-3}{(x+2)+3}=\frac{1}{6}\log\frac{x-1}{x+5}. \quad \text{formula (2)}$$

Note : You should better do it by partial fractions method.

Ex. 3. $\int \frac{dx}{1+3x-x^2}$

$1+3x-x^2=-(x^2-3x-1)$

$=-(x^2-3x+9/4-1-9/4)$

$=-[(x-3/2)^2-(\sqrt{13}/2)^2]=(\sqrt{13}/2)^2-(x-3/2)^2.$

$$\therefore \quad I=\int \frac{dx}{(\sqrt{13}/2)^2-(x-3/2)^2}$$

$$=\frac{1}{2.\sqrt{(13)}/2}\log\frac{[\sqrt{13}/2+(x-3/2)]}{[\sqrt{(13)}/2-(x-3/2)]}. \quad \text{formula (3), § 6.}$$

$$=\frac{1}{\sqrt{(13)}}\log\frac{[\sqrt{13}-3]+2x}{[\sqrt{(13)}+3]-2x}.$$

Ex. 4. $\int \frac{dx}{\sqrt{(4x^2+4x+5)}}$

$$I=\frac{1}{2}\int \frac{dx}{\sqrt{\left[\left(x+\frac{1}{2}\right)^2+1^2\right]}} \quad \text{as in Ex. (1)}$$

$$=\frac{1}{2}\log\left[\left(x+\frac{1}{2}\right)+\sqrt{\left(x+\frac{1}{2}\right)^2+1^2}\right] \quad \text{formula (4), § 6.}$$

Ex. 5. $\int \frac{dx}{\sqrt{(x^2+4x-5)}}$

$$I=\int \frac{dx}{\sqrt{[(x+2)^2-3^2]}} \quad \text{as in Ex. (2)}$$

$$=\log[(x+2)+\sqrt{(x+2)^2-3^2}] \quad \text{formula (5), § 6.}$$

Ex. 6. $\int \frac{dx}{\sqrt{(1+3x-x^2)}}$

$$I=\int \frac{dx}{\sqrt{[(\sqrt{13}/2)^2-(x-3/2)^2]}}$$

$$=\sin^{-1}\frac{x-3/2}{\sqrt{(13)}/2}=\sin^{-1}\frac{2x-3}{\sqrt{(13)}} \quad \text{formula (6), § 6.}$$

Ex. 7. $\int \sqrt{4x^2+4x+5}\,dx$

$$I=2\int \sqrt{\left\{\left(x+\frac{1}{2}\right)^2+1^2\right\}}\,dx \text{ as in Ex. (1)}$$

$$=2\left[\frac{1}{2}\left(x+\frac{1}{2}\right)\sqrt{\left\{\left(x+\frac{1}{2}\right)^2+1^2\right\}}+\frac{1}{2}\log\left\{\left(x+\frac{1}{2}\right)+\sqrt{\left(x+\frac{1}{2}\right)^2+1^2}\right\}\right]$$

formula (7), § 6.

Ex. 8. $\int \sqrt{x^2+4x-5}\,dx$

$$=\int \sqrt{(x+2)^2-3^2}\,dx \text{ as in Ex. (3)}$$

$$=\frac{1}{2}(x+2)\sqrt{(x+2)^2-3^2}-\frac{1}{2}.3^2\log[(x+2)+\sqrt{(x+2)^2-3^2}]$$

formula (8), § 6.

Ex. 9. $\int \sqrt{1+3x-x^2}\,dx$

$$I=\int \sqrt{[(\sqrt{13}/2)^2-(x-3/2)^2]}\,dx$$

$$=\frac{x-3/2}{2}\sqrt{[(\sqrt{13}/2)^2-(x-3/2)^2]}+\frac{1}{2}\left(\frac{\sqrt{13}}{2}\right)^2\sin^{-1}\frac{x-3/2}{\sqrt{(13)}/2}. \quad \text{formula (9), § 6.}$$

§8. Application to the integrals $\int \frac{px+q}{ax^2+bx+c}dx, \int \frac{px+q}{\sqrt{(ax^2+bx+c)}}, \int (px+q)\sqrt{ax^2+bx+c}\,dx.$

Here we should write

$$px+q=l\,[\text{d.c.of }(ax^2+bx+c)]+m. \quad ...(1)$$

Find the values of l, m by comparing the coefficients of x and constant term on both sides of (1). In this way the question will reduce to sum of two integrals one of which will be done as explained in the last nine examples and other will be done as under :

$$\int \frac{f'(x)}{f(x)}dx=\log f(x) \text{ by putting } f(x)=t \quad \text{for 1st}$$

$$\int \frac{f'(x)}{\sqrt{[f(x)]}}dx=2\sqrt{f(x)}. \text{ Putting } f(x)=t \text{ for 2nd}$$

$$\int f'(x)\sqrt{f(x)}\,dx=\frac{2}{3}[f(x)]^{3/2}$$

by putting $f(x)=t$ for 3rd

Ex. 10. $\int \frac{3x+2}{4x^2+4x+5}dx$

$3x+2=l\,(\text{d.c.of }4x^2+4x+5)+m$

or $\quad 3x+2=l\,(8x+4)+m.$

Compare x and constant

$\therefore \quad 8l = 3$ and $4l + m = 2.$

$\therefore \quad l = \frac{3}{8},\ m = 2 - 4l = 2 - \frac{3}{2} = \frac{1}{2},$

$$\therefore \quad I = \frac{3}{8}\int \frac{(8x+4)\,dx}{4x^2+4x+5} + \frac{1}{2}\int \frac{dx}{4x^2+4x+5}.$$

For first integral put

$4x^2 + 4x + 5 = t \quad \therefore \quad (8x+4)\,dx = dt$

$$\therefore \quad I = \frac{3}{8}\int \frac{dt}{t} + \frac{1}{2}\int \frac{dx}{4x^2+4x+5}$$

$$= \frac{3}{8}\log(4x^2+4x+5) + \frac{1}{2}\cdot\frac{1}{4}\tan^{-1}\left(x+\frac{1}{2}\right)$$

as in – **Ex. 1. P. 1468.**

Ex. 11. $\displaystyle\int \frac{(3x+2)}{\sqrt{(4x^2+4x+5)}}\,dx.$

As in Ex. 10. $\quad 3x + 2 = l(8x+4) + m$ etc.

$$\therefore \quad I = \frac{3}{8}\int \frac{8x+4}{\sqrt{(4x^2+4x+5)}}\,dx + \frac{1}{2}\int \frac{dx}{\sqrt{(4x^2+4x+5)}}$$

Put $4x^2 + 4x + 5 = t \quad \therefore \quad (8x+4)\,dx = dt.$

$$\therefore \quad I = \frac{3}{8}\int \frac{dt}{\sqrt{(t)}} + \frac{1}{2}\cdot\int \frac{dx}{\sqrt{(4x^2+4x+5)}}$$

$$= \frac{3}{8}\cdot 2\sqrt{t} + \frac{1}{2}\cdot\frac{1}{2}\log\left[\left(x+\frac{1}{2}\right) + \sqrt{\left\{\left(x+\frac{1}{2}\right)^2 + 1\right\}}\right]$$

as in **Ex. 4. P. 1469.**

$$= \frac{3}{4}\sqrt{4x^2+4x+5} + \frac{1}{4}\log\left[\left(x+\frac{1}{2}\right) + \sqrt{\left\{\left(x+\frac{1}{2}\right)^2 + 1\right\}}\right].$$

Ex. 12. $\displaystyle\int (3x+2)\sqrt{4x^2+4x+5}\,dx$

$$I = \frac{3}{8}\int (8x+4)\sqrt{4x^2+4x+5}\,dx + \frac{1}{2}\int \sqrt{4x^2+4x+5}\,dx$$

as in Ex. 10.

Put $4x^2 + 4x + 5 = t \quad \therefore \quad (8x+4)\,dx = dt.$

$$\therefore \quad I = \frac{3}{8}\int \sqrt{t}\,dt + \frac{1}{2}\int \sqrt{4x^2+4x+5}\,dx$$

$$= \frac{3}{8}\cdot\frac{2}{3}t^{3/2} + \frac{1}{2}\int \sqrt{4x^2+4x+5}\,dx$$

$$= \frac{1}{4}(4x^2+4x+5)^{3/2} + \frac{1}{2}\cdot 2\left[\frac{1}{2}\left(x+\frac{1}{2}\right) \times \sqrt{\left\{\left(x+\frac{1}{2}\right)^2 + 1^2\right\}} + \frac{1^2}{2}\log\left\{\left(x+\frac{1}{2}\right) + \sqrt{\left(x+\frac{1}{2}\right)^2 + 1^2}\right\}\right]$$

as in **Ex. 7. P. 1469.**

§ 9. Application to the integrals

$$\int \frac{dx}{a\cos^2 x + 2b\sin x\cos x + c\sin^2 x}$$

$$\int \frac{dx}{a\cos^2 x + b},\ \int \frac{dx}{a + b\sin^2 x}.$$

***Rule :** In above type of questions divide above and below by $\cos^2 x$. The numerator will become $\sec^2 x$ and in the denominator we will have a quadratic in $\tan x$ (change $\sec^2 x$ into $1 + \tan^2 x$).

Putting $\tan x = t$ the question will reduce to the form

$$\int \frac{dt}{at^2 + bt + c}.$$

The integral of above has been explained in application (1).

§10. Application to the integrals

1. $\displaystyle\int \frac{1}{a\cos x + b\sin x + c}\,dx,$

2. $\displaystyle\int \frac{1}{a + b\cos x}\,dx,$

3. $\displaystyle\int \frac{1}{a + b\sin x}\,dx,$

4. $\displaystyle\int \frac{p\cos x + q\sin x + r}{a\cos x + b\sin x + c}\,dx,$

5. $\displaystyle\int \frac{p\cos x + q\sin x}{a\cos x + b\sin x}\,dx.$

***Rule for 1, 2 and 3.**

Write $\cos x = \cos^2(x/2) - \sin^2(x/2)$,

$\sin x = 2\sin(x/2)\cos(x/2)$.

Then divide above and below by $\cos^2(x/2)$. The numerator will become $\sec^2(x/2)$ and the denominator will be a quadratic in $\tan(x/2)$ [change $\sec^2(x/2)$ into $1 + \tan^2(x/2)$]. Putting $\tan(x/2) = t$ the question will reduce to the form

$$\int \frac{dt}{at^2 + bt + c}.$$

***Rule for 4.**

Express numerator as $l(D^r) + m(\text{d.c. of } D^r) + n$.

Find l, m, n by comparing the coefficients of $\sin x, \cos x$ and constant term and split the integral into sum of three integrals as

$$l\int dx + m\int \frac{(\text{d.c. of } D^r)}{D^r}\,dx + n\int \frac{dx}{a\cos x + b\sin x + c}$$

$= lx + m\log(D^r) + n$ (as explained in rule above).

***Rule for 5.**

Here express numerator as $l(D^r) + m$ (d.c. of D^r) and find l and m by comparing the coefficients of sin x and cos x. Now split the integral into sum of two integrals

$$l\int dx + m\int \frac{(\text{d.c. of } D^r)}{D^r}dx = lx + m\log(D^r).$$

We shall illustrate the above by giving suitable examples.

Ex. 13. $\displaystyle\int \frac{dx}{4\sin^2 x + 4\sin x\cos x + 5\cos^2 x}$.

Divide above and below by $\cos^2 x$.

$$\therefore \quad I = \int \frac{\sec^2 x\,dx}{4\tan^2 x + 4\tan x + 5}.$$

Put $\tan x = t$.

$$\therefore \quad I = \int \frac{dt}{4t^2 + 4t + 5} = \frac{1}{4}\int \frac{dt}{t^2 + t + 5/4}$$

$$= \frac{1}{4}\int \frac{dt}{\left(t + \frac{1}{2}\right)^2 + 1^2} = \frac{1}{4}\tan^{-1}\left(t + \frac{1}{2}\right), \text{ as in Ex. 1.}$$

$$= \frac{1}{4}\tan^{-1}\left(\tan x + \frac{1}{2}\right),$$

Ex. 14. **(a)** $\displaystyle\int \frac{dx}{1 + 3\sin^2 x}$.

Divide above and below by $\cos^2 x$.

$$\therefore \quad I = \int \frac{\sec^2 x\,dx}{\sec^2 x + 3\tan^2 x} = \int \frac{\sec^2 x\,dx}{1 + \tan^2 x + 3\tan^2 x}$$

$$= \int \frac{\sec^2 x\,dx}{1 + 4\tan^2 x}$$

Put $2\tan x = t$. $\quad \therefore \; 2\sec^2 x\,dx = dt$.

$$\therefore \quad I = \frac{1}{2}\int \frac{dt}{1 + t^2} = \frac{1}{2}\tan^{-1} t = \frac{1}{2}\tan^{-1}(2\tan x)$$

(b)* $\displaystyle\int \frac{1}{1 - \sin^4 x}dx$

$$\int \frac{1}{(1 - \sin^2 x)(1 + \sin^2 x)}dx \quad \text{P.F.s}$$

$$= \int \left[\frac{1}{2(1 - \sin^2 x)} + \frac{1}{2(1 + \sin^2 x)}\right]dx$$

$$= \frac{1}{2}\int \left[\sec^2 x + \frac{\sec^2 x}{1 + \tan^2 x + \tan^2 x}\right]dx$$

$$= \frac{1}{2}\left[\tan x + \frac{1}{\sqrt{2}}\tan(\sqrt{2}\tan x)\right]$$

***Ex. 15.** $\displaystyle\int \frac{d\theta}{(\sin\theta - 2\cos\theta)(2\sin\theta + \cos\theta)}$.

If we multiply the factors in D^r it becomes of the form of Ex. 13, but we need not multiply. Divide above and below by $\cos^2\theta$.

$$\therefore \quad I = \int \frac{\sec^2\theta\,d\theta}{(\tan\theta - 2)(2\tan\theta + 1)}$$

Put $\tan\theta = t$.

$$\therefore \quad I = \int \frac{dt}{(t - 2)(2t + 1)}$$

Split into partial fractions

$$I = \int \left[\frac{1}{5(t - 2)} - \frac{2}{5(2t + 1)}\right]dt$$

$$= \frac{1}{5}\log(t - 2) - \frac{1}{5}\log(2t + 1)$$

$$= \frac{1}{5}\log\frac{t - 2}{2t + 1} = \frac{1}{5}\log\frac{\tan\theta - 2}{2\tan\theta + 1}.$$

***Ex. 16.** $\displaystyle\int \frac{dx}{4 + 5\cos x}$

$$I = \int \frac{dx}{4 + 5[\cos^2(x/2) - \sin^2(x/2)]}.$$

Divide above and below by $\cos^2(x/2)$.

$$I = \int \frac{\sec^2(x/2)\,dx}{4\sec^2(x/2) + 5[1 - \tan^2(x/2)]}.$$

$$\therefore \quad I = \int \frac{\sec^2(x/2)\,dx}{9 - \tan^2(x/2)} \quad \because \; \sec^2\left(\frac{x}{2}\right) = 1 + \tan^2\left(\frac{x}{2}\right)$$

Put $\tan\left(\frac{x}{2}\right) = t \quad \therefore \; \frac{1}{2}\sec^2\left(\frac{x}{2}\right)dx = dt$.

$$\therefore \quad I = \int \frac{2\,dt}{9 - t^2} = 2\frac{1}{2.3}\log\frac{3 + t}{3 - t} = \frac{1}{3}\log\frac{3 + \tan(x/2)}{3 - \tan(x/2)}.$$

***Ex. 17.** $\displaystyle\int \frac{dx}{5 + 4\sin x}$ or $\displaystyle\int \frac{dx}{4 + 5\sin x}$.

$$I = \int \frac{dx}{5 + 4[2\sin(x/2)\cos(x/2)]}$$

$$\text{or} \quad \int \frac{dx}{4 + 5[2\sin(x/2)\cos(x/2)]}$$

Divide above and below by $\cos^2(x/2)$

$$I = \int \frac{\sec^2(x/2)\,dx}{5[1 + \tan^2(x/2)] + 8\tan(x/2)}$$

$$\text{or} \quad \int \frac{\sec^2(x/2)\,dx}{4[1 + \tan^2(x/2)] + 10\tan(x/2)}$$

Put $\tan(x/2) = t$. $\quad \therefore \; \frac{1}{2}\sec^2(x/2)\,dx = dt$

$$I = \int \frac{2\,dt}{5t^2 + 8t + 5} \quad \text{or} \quad \int \frac{2\,dt}{4t^2 + 10t + 4}$$

$$= \frac{2}{5}\int \frac{dt}{t^2 + \frac{8}{5}t + 1} \quad \text{or} \quad \frac{2}{4}\int \frac{dt}{t^2 + \frac{5}{2}t + 1}$$

$$=\frac{2}{5}\int \frac{dt}{\left(t+\frac{4}{5}\right)^2+\left(\frac{3}{5}\right)^2} \text{ or } \frac{1}{2}\int \frac{dt}{\left(t+\frac{5}{4}\right)^2-\left(\frac{3}{4}\right)^2}$$

$$=\frac{2}{5}\cdot\frac{1}{3/5}\tan^{-1}\frac{t+\frac{4}{5}}{3/5}$$

or $\frac{1}{2}\cdot\frac{1}{2(3/4)}\log\frac{(t+5/4)-3/4}{(t+5/4)+3/4}$ formula 1 and 2

$$=\frac{2}{3}\tan^{-1}\frac{5\tan(x/2)+4}{3}$$

or $\frac{1}{3}\log\frac{2\tan(x/2)+1}{2[\tan(x/2)+2]}$

***Ex. 18 (a).** $\int \frac{2+3\cos\theta}{\sin\theta+2\cos\theta+3}\,d\theta.$

Write $N^r = l(D^r)+m(\text{d.c. of } D^r)+n.$

Let $2+3\cos\theta = l(\sin\theta+2\cos\theta+3)$
$+m(\cos\theta-2\sin\theta)+n.$

Comparing coefficients of constant $\sin\theta$ and $\cos\theta$, we get

$3l+n=2,\quad 2l+m=3,\quad l-2m=0.$

$\therefore\quad l=6/5,\quad m=3/5,\quad n=-8/5.$

$$\therefore\quad I=\int l\,d\theta+m\int\frac{\cos\theta-2\sin\theta}{\sin\theta+2\cos\theta+3}\,d\theta$$
$$+n\int\frac{d\theta}{\sin\theta+2\cos\theta+3}$$

$=l\theta+m\log(\sin\theta+2\cos\theta+3)+nI_3.$

Now $I_3=\int\frac{d\theta}{\sin\theta+2\cos\theta+3}$

$$=\int\frac{d\theta}{2\sin(\theta/2)\cos(\theta/2)+2[\cos^2(\theta/2)-\sin^2(\theta/2)]+3}.$$

Divide above and below by $\cos^2(\theta/2)$.

$$\therefore\quad I_3=\int\frac{\sec^2(\theta/2)\,d\theta}{2\tan(\theta/2)+2[1-\tan^2(\theta/2)]+3[1+\tan^2(\theta/2)]}$$

Put $\tan\left(\frac{\theta}{2}\right)=t$ so that $\frac{1}{2}\sec^2\left(\frac{\theta}{2}\right)d\theta=dt.$

$$\therefore\quad I_3=\int\frac{2\,dt}{t^2+2t+5}=2\int\frac{dt}{(t+1)^2+2^2}$$

$$=2\cdot\frac{1}{2}\tan^{-1}\frac{t+1}{2}=\tan^{-1}\left(\frac{\tan(\theta/2)+1}{2}\right)$$

$$\therefore\quad I=l\theta+m\log(\sin\theta+2\cos\theta+3)+n\tan^{-1}\left(\frac{\tan(\theta/2)+1}{2}\right)$$

where $l=6/5,\quad m=3/5,\quad n=-8/5.$

***(b)** If $0<a<1$, then find

$\int\frac{dx}{1-2a\cos x+a^2}$ **(M.N.R. 1997)**

$$I=\int\frac{dx}{(1+a^2)-2a(\cos^2 x/2-\sin^2 x/2)}$$

Divide above and below by $\cos^2(x/2)$ and put $\tan(x/2)=t.$

$$\therefore\quad I=\int\frac{2\,dt}{(1+a^2)(1+t^2)-2a(1-t^2)}$$

$$=\int\frac{2\,dt}{(1-a)^2+(1+a)^2t^2}=\frac{2}{(1+a)^2}\int\frac{dt}{\left(\frac{1-a}{1+a}\right)^2+t^2}$$

$$=\frac{2}{(1+a)^2}\cdot\frac{1}{\frac{(1-a)}{1+a}}\tan^{-1}\left[t\,\frac{(1+a)}{1-a}\right]$$

$$=\frac{2}{1-a^2}\tan^{-1}t\,\frac{(1+a)}{(1-a)}$$

Ex. 19. $\int\frac{3\sin x+2\cos x}{3\cos x+2\sin x}\,dx.$

Write $N^r=l(D^r)+m(\text{d.c. of } D^r).$

Let $3\sin x+2\cos x=l(3\cos x+2\sin x)$
$+m(-3\sin x+2\cos x).$

Comparing coefficients of $\sin x$ and $\cos x$ on both sides

$3=2l-3m,\quad 2=3l+2m.$

Solving we get $l=12/13,\quad m=-5/13.$

$$\therefore\quad I=l\int dx+m\int\frac{-3\sin x+2\cos x}{3\cos x+2\sin x}\,dx.$$

$=lx+m\log(3\cos x+2\sin x).$

$=\frac{12}{13}x-\frac{5}{13}\log(3\cos x+2\sin x).$

***Ex. 20. (a)** $\int\frac{dx}{p+q\tan x}=\int\frac{\cos x\,dx}{p\cos x+q\sin x}.$

Write $N^r=l(D^r)+m(\text{d.c. of } D^r)$

$\cos x=l(p\cos x+q\sin x)+m(-p\sin x+q\cos x).$

Compare $\cos x$ and $\sin x$

$\therefore\quad 1=lp+mq,\quad 0=lq-pm.$

Solving $l=\frac{p}{p^2+q^2},\quad m=\frac{q}{p^2+q^2}$

$$\therefore\quad I=l\int dx+m\int\frac{-p\sin x+q\cos x}{p\cos x+q\sin x}\,dx.$$

$$\frac{p}{p^2+q^2}x+\frac{q}{p^2+q^2}\log(p\cos x+q\sin x).$$

Note : Putting $p=q=1$, we get

$$\int\frac{dx}{1+\tan x}=\frac{1}{2}x+\frac{1}{2}\log(\cos x+\sin x).$$

(b)* $\int\frac{dx}{\sin x(2+\cos x-2\sin x)}$

$$I=\frac{dx}{2\sin\frac{x}{2}\cos\frac{x}{2}\left(2+\cos^2\frac{x}{2}-\sin^2\frac{x}{2}-4\sin\frac{x}{2}\cos\frac{x}{2}\right)}$$

Divide above and below by $\cos^4 \frac{x}{2}$.

$$I = \int \frac{\sec^2 \frac{x}{2} \sec^2 \frac{x}{2} dx}{2\tan\frac{x}{2}\left[2\left(1+\tan^2\frac{x}{2}\right)+\left(1-\tan^2\frac{x}{2}\right)-4\tan\frac{x}{2}\right]}$$

Put $\tan\frac{x}{2} = t \quad \therefore \quad \frac{1}{2}\sec^2\frac{x}{2}dx = dt$

or $I = \int \frac{(1+t^2)\,2\,dt}{2t\,[t^2-4t+3]} = \int \frac{1+t^2}{t\,(t-3)\,(t-1)} dt$

$= \int \left[\frac{1}{3t} + \frac{5}{3\,(t-3)} - \frac{1}{(t-1)}\right] dt$ by P.F's

$= \frac{1}{3}\log\tan\frac{x}{2} + \frac{5}{3}\log\left(\tan\frac{x}{2}-3\right) - \log\left(\tan\frac{x}{2}-1\right)$

Problem Set (3)

Application

Integrate the following :

1. (a) $\frac{3x^2}{4+5x^6}$, (b) $\frac{3x^2}{x^6+1}$.

2. $\frac{1}{e^x+e^{-x}}$.

3. $\frac{x^3}{25x^8-16}$.

4. $\frac{\cos x}{4-\sin^2 x}$.

5. (i) $\frac{3x^2}{\sqrt{(9-16x^6)}}$. (ii) $\frac{x}{\sqrt{(4-x^4)}}$

6. $\frac{1}{(1+x^2)\sqrt{[p^2+q^2(\tan^{-1}x)^2]}}$.

7. $\frac{x^3}{\sqrt{(x^8+1)}}$.

8. $\frac{1}{[(1-x^2)\{(2\sin^{-1}x)^2-9\}]^{1/2}}$.

9. $\sec x\tan x\sqrt{\sec^2 x+1}$.

10. $\cos x\sqrt{4-\sin^2 x}$.

11.* $x^3\sqrt{q^2x^8-p^2}$.

12. $\frac{\cos x}{\sin^2 x+4\sin x+5}$.

13. $\frac{1}{x[(\log x)^2+4\log x-1]}$.

14. $\frac{x}{x^4+x^2+1}$.

15. $\frac{3x+1}{2x^2+x+1}$.

16. $\frac{2x^2+3x+4}{x^2+6x+10}$.

17. $\frac{1-x}{4x^2-4x-3}$.

18. $\frac{3x+4}{x^2+4x+2}$.

19. $\frac{1}{\sqrt{(1-4x-x^2)}}$.

20. $\frac{1}{\sqrt{(x^2+3x+1)}}$.

21. $\frac{1}{\sqrt{(3x^2+3x+4)}}$.

22.* $\frac{x}{\sqrt{(9+8x-x^2)}}$.

23. $\frac{x+3}{\sqrt{(x^2+2x+2)}}$.

24.* $\frac{x+2}{\sqrt{(4x-x^2)}}$.

25. $\sqrt{\left(\frac{a+x}{a-x}\right)}$

26. $\int_0^1 \sqrt{\left(\frac{1-x}{1+x}\right)}$. (Screening 2004)

27.* $x\sqrt{\left(\frac{a^2-x^2}{a^2+x^2}\right)}$

28. $\sqrt{4+8x-5x^2}$.

29. $\sqrt{x^2-x+1}$.

30.* $(x-2)\sqrt{2x^2-6x+5}$.

31. $\frac{1}{3-2\cos^2 x}$.

32. $\frac{1}{4\sin^2 x+9\cos^2 x}$.

33. $\frac{1}{2-3\cos 2x}$.

34.* $\frac{1}{\sin^2 x+\sin 2x}$.

35.* $\frac{1}{(2\sin x+3\cos x)^2}$.

36. $\frac{1}{\cos x(\sin x+2\cos x)}$.

37. $\frac{1}{2+\sin x+\cos x}$.

38.* $\frac{2-\sin x}{2\cos x+3}$.

39. $\frac{\cos x}{5-3\cos x}$.

40.* $\frac{\sin x}{\sin x-\cos x}$ or $\frac{1}{1-\cot x}$.

41. $\frac{\sin x+2\cos x}{2\sin x+\cos x}$.

42.* Evaluate $\int_0^{\pi/2}\frac{dx}{3+4\sin x}$

43.* Let $f:[0,\pi/2]\to R$ such that $f(0)=3$ and $f'(x)=\frac{1}{1+\cos x}$, then prove that

$$3+\frac{\pi}{4}\le f\left(\frac{\pi}{2}\right)\le 3+\frac{\pi}{2}$$

(C.E.E. Bihar 1995)

44. $\int \sin\left\{2\tan^{-1}\sqrt{\frac{3-x}{3+x}}\right\}dx$

Solutions to Problem Set (3)

1. (a) Put $\sqrt{5}x^3 = t$

$\therefore \quad I = \frac{1}{\sqrt{(5)}}\int\frac{dt}{4+t^2} = \frac{1}{2\sqrt{(5)}}\tan^{-1}\frac{t}{2}$

$= \frac{1}{2\sqrt{(5)}}\tan^{-1}\frac{\sqrt{5}x^3}{2}$.

(b) $\tan^{-1}x^3$.

2. Change e^{-x} to $\frac{1}{e^x}$ $\therefore$ $I = \int\frac{e^x\,dx}{1+e^{2x}}$.

Put $e^x = t$ etc.

Ans. $\tan^{-1} e^x$.

3. Put $5x^4 = t \therefore 20x^3\, dx = dt$

$\therefore\ I = \frac{1}{20}\int \frac{dt}{t^2 - 4^2}$

or $I = \frac{1}{20} \cdot \frac{1}{2.4} \log \frac{t-4}{t+4} = \frac{1}{160} \log \frac{5x^4 - 4}{5x^4 + 4}$.

4. Put $\sin x = t \therefore \cos x\, dx = dt$

$\therefore\ I = \int \frac{dt}{2^2 - t^2} = \frac{1}{2.2} \log \frac{2+t}{2-t} = \frac{1}{4} \log \frac{2 + \sin x}{2 - \sin x}$.

5. (i) Put $4x^3 = t \therefore 12x^2\, dx = dt$

$\therefore\ I = \frac{1}{4}\int \frac{dt}{\sqrt{(3^2 - t^2)}} = \frac{1}{4} \sin^{-1} \frac{t}{3} = \frac{1}{4} \sin^{-1} \frac{4}{3} x^3$.

(ii) Ans. $\frac{1}{2} \sin^{-1} \left(\frac{1}{2} x^2\right)$.

6. Put $q \tan^{-1} x = t \therefore q \cdot \frac{1}{1+x^2} dx = dt$.

$I = \frac{1}{q}\int \frac{dt}{\sqrt{(p^2 + t^2)}} = \frac{1}{q} \log [t + \sqrt{p^2 + t^2}]$

where $t = q \tan^{-1} x$.

7. Put $x^4 = t$

$\therefore\ I = \frac{1}{4}\int \frac{dt}{\sqrt{(t^2+1)}} = \frac{1}{4} \log [t + \sqrt{t^2 + 1}]$

$= \frac{1}{4} \log [x^4 + \sqrt{x^8 + 1}]$

8. Put $2 \sin^{-1} x = t \therefore \frac{2}{\sqrt{(1-x^2)}} dx = dt$

$\therefore\ I = \frac{1}{2}\int \frac{dt}{\sqrt{(t^2 - 9)}} = \frac{1}{2} \log [t + \sqrt{t^2 - 9}]$

$= \frac{1}{2} \log [2 \sin^{-1} x + \sqrt{(2 \sin^{-1} x)^2 - 9}]$.

9. Put $\sec x = t \therefore \sec x \tan x\, dx = dt$

$\therefore\ I = \int \sqrt{t^2 + 1}\, dt = \frac{1}{2} t \sqrt{t^2 + 1} + \frac{1}{2} \log [t + \sqrt{t^2 + 1}]$.

10. Put $\sin x = t \therefore \cos x\, dx = dt$

$I = \int \sqrt{4 - t^2}\, dt = \frac{t}{2} \sqrt{4 - t^2} + \frac{1}{2} \cdot 4 \sin^{-1} \frac{t}{2}$.

11. Put $qx^4 = t \therefore 4qx^3\, dx = dt$

$\therefore\ I = \frac{1}{4q}\int \sqrt{t^2 - p^2}\, dt$

$= \frac{1}{4q}\left[\frac{t}{2}\sqrt{t^2 - p^2} - \frac{1}{2} p^2 \log (t + \sqrt{t^2 - p^2})\right]$.

12. Put $\sin x = t \therefore \cos x\, dx = dt$

$\therefore\ I = \int \frac{dt}{t^2 + 4t + 5} = \int \frac{dt}{(t+2)^2 + 1} = \tan^{-1} \frac{(t+2)}{1}$

$= \tan^{-1} [\sin x + 2]$.

13. Put $\log x = t \therefore \frac{1}{x} dx = dt$

$\therefore\ I = \int \frac{1}{t^2 + 4t - 1} dt = \int \frac{dt}{(t+2)^2 - (\sqrt{5})^2}$

$= \frac{1}{2\sqrt{(5)}} \log \frac{(t+2) - \sqrt{5}}{(t+2) + \sqrt{(5)}}$ where $t = \log x$.

14. Put $x^2 = t \therefore 2x\, dx = dt$

$\therefore\ I = \frac{1}{2}\int \frac{dt}{t^2 + t + 1}$

$= \frac{1}{2}\int \frac{dt}{t^2 + t + \frac{1}{4} + \left(1 - \frac{1}{4}\right)} = \frac{1}{2}\int \frac{dt}{\left(t + \frac{1}{2}\right)^2 + \left(\frac{\sqrt{3}}{2}\right)^2}$

$= \frac{1}{2 \cdot \frac{\sqrt{(3)}}{2}} \tan^{-1} \frac{t + \frac{1}{2}}{\sqrt{(3)}/2} = \frac{1}{\sqrt{(3)}} \tan^{-1} \frac{2x^2 + 1}{\sqrt{(3)}}$.

15. $I = \int \frac{3x + 1}{2x^2 + x + 1} dx$

$N^r = l(\text{d.c. of } D^r) + m$.

$\therefore\ 3x + 1 = l(4x + 1) + m$. Compare

$4l = 3,\ l + m = 1 \therefore l = \frac{3}{4},\ m = \frac{1}{4}$

$\therefore\ I = l\int \frac{4x + 1}{2x^2 + x + 1} dx + m \cdot \int \frac{dx}{2x^2 + x + 1}$.

Put $2x^2 + x + 1 = t$ for first

$\therefore\ (4x + 1)\, dx = dt$

$\therefore\ I = l\int \frac{dt}{t} + \frac{m}{2}\int \frac{dx}{x^2 + \frac{1}{2}x + \frac{1}{2}}$

$= l \log t + \frac{m}{2}\int \frac{dx}{\left(x + \frac{1}{4}\right)^2 + \frac{1}{2} - \frac{1}{16}}$

$= l \log (2x^2 + x + 1) + \frac{m}{2}\int \frac{dx}{\left(x + \frac{1}{4}\right)^2 + \left(\frac{\sqrt{7}}{4}\right)^2}$

$= \frac{3}{4} \log (2x^2 + x + 1) + \frac{1}{8} \cdot \frac{1}{\sqrt{(7)/4}} \tan^{-1} \frac{x + \frac{1}{4}}{\sqrt{(7)/4}}$

$= \frac{3}{4} \log (2x^2 + x + 1) + \frac{1}{2\sqrt{(7)}} \tan^{-1} \frac{4x + 1}{\sqrt{(7)}}$.

16. $I = \int \frac{2x^2 + 3x + 4}{x^2 + 6x + 10} dx$

Write $N^r = l(D^r) + m(\text{d.c.of } D^r) + n.$

$\therefore \quad 2x^2 + 3x + 4 = l(x^2 + 6x + 10) + m(2x + 6) + n.$

Compare $l = 2,\ 6l + 2m = 3,\ 10l + 6m + n = 4.$

$\therefore \quad l = 2,\ m = -9/2,\ n = 11.$

$$\therefore \quad I = l\int dx + m\int \frac{2x+6}{x^2+6x+10}\,dx + n\int \frac{dx}{(x+3)^2+1^2}$$

$$= lx + m\log(x^2+6x+10) + n.\frac{1}{1}\tan^{-1}\frac{(x+3)}{1}$$

$$= 2x - \frac{9}{2}\log(x^2+6x+10) + 11\tan^{-1}(x+3).$$

17. Ans. $-\dfrac{1}{8}\log(4x^2-4x-3) + \dfrac{1}{16}\log\dfrac{2x-3}{2x+1}.$

18. Ans. $\dfrac{3}{2}\log(x^2+4x+2) - \dfrac{1}{\sqrt{(2)}}\log\dfrac{x+2-\sqrt{2}}{x+2+\sqrt{(2)}}.$

19. $I = \displaystyle\int \frac{dx}{\sqrt{[5-(x+2)^2]}} = \sin^{-1}\frac{x+2}{\sqrt{(5)}}.$

20. $I = \displaystyle\int \frac{dx}{\sqrt{\{[x+(3/2)]^2 - \sqrt{(5/2)]^2}\}}}.$

$$= \log[(x+3/2) + \sqrt{\{(x+3/2)^2 - (\sqrt{5}/2)^2\}}].$$

21. $I = \dfrac{1}{\sqrt{(3)}}\displaystyle\int \frac{dx}{\sqrt{(x^2+x+4/3)}} = \frac{1}{\sqrt{(3)}}\int \frac{dx}{\sqrt{\left[\left(x+\frac{1}{2}\right)^2 + \frac{13}{12}\right]}}$

$$= \frac{1}{\sqrt{3}}\log\left[\left(x+\frac{1}{2}\right) + \sqrt{\left\{\left(x+\frac{1}{2}\right)^2 + \left(\frac{13}{12}\right)\right\}}\right].$$

22. $\displaystyle\int \frac{x}{\sqrt{(9+8x-x^2)}}\,dx$

We write $\quad x = l(8-2x) + m.$ Compare

$-2l = 1,\ 8l + m = 0:\ \therefore\ l = -\dfrac{1}{2},\ m = 4.$

$$\therefore \quad I = l\int \frac{8-2x}{\sqrt{(9+8x-x^2)}}\,dx + m\int \frac{dx}{\sqrt{[25-(x^2-8x+16)]}}.$$

Put $9+8x-x^2 = t;\ \therefore\ (8-2x)\,dx = dt.$

$$\therefore \quad I = l\int \frac{1}{\sqrt{(t)}}\,dt + m\int \frac{dx}{\sqrt{[5^2-(x-4)^2]}}$$

$$= l.2\sqrt{t} + m\sin^{-1}\frac{x-4}{5}$$

$$= -\sqrt{9+8x-x^2} + 4\sin^{-1}\frac{x-4}{5}.$$

23. Proceed as in Q. 22.

$$I = \sqrt{x^2+2x+2} + 2\log[(x+1) + \{(x+1)^2+1\}^{1/2}].$$

24. $I = -\sqrt{4x-x^2} + 4\sin^{-1}\dfrac{x-2}{2}.$

25. $I = \displaystyle\int \sqrt{\left(\frac{a+x}{a-x}\right)}\,dx = \int \frac{a+x}{\sqrt{(a^2-x^2)}}\,dx$

$$= \int \frac{a}{\sqrt{(a^2-x^2)}}\,dx - \frac{1}{2}\int\left(\frac{-2x}{\sqrt{(a^2-x^2)}}\right)dx$$

$$= a\sin^{-1}\frac{x}{a} - \frac{1}{2}\int \frac{dt}{\sqrt{(t)}},\ \text{where } a^2 - x^2 = t$$

$$= a\sin^{-1}\frac{x}{a} - \frac{1}{2}.2\sqrt{t} = a\sin^{-1}\frac{x}{a} - \sqrt{a^2-x^2}$$

26. $I = \displaystyle\int \sqrt{\left(\frac{1-x}{1+x}\right)}\,dx = \int \frac{1-x}{\sqrt{(1-x^2)}}\,dx$

$$= \int \frac{1}{\sqrt{(1-x^2)}}\,dx + \frac{1}{2}\int \frac{-2x}{\sqrt{(1-x^2)}}\,dx$$

$$= \left[\sin^{-1}x + \sqrt{1-x^2}\right]_0^1 = \frac{\pi}{2} = 1.$$

27. $I = \displaystyle\int x\sqrt{\left(\frac{a^2-x^2}{a^2+x^2}\right)}\,dx.$

Put $x^2 = t;\ \therefore\ 2x\,dx = dt.$

$$\therefore \quad I = \frac{1}{2}\int \sqrt{\left(\frac{a^2-t}{a^2+t}\right)}\,dt = \frac{1}{2}\int \frac{a^2-t}{\sqrt{(a^4-t^2)}}\,dt$$

$$= \frac{1}{2}\int \frac{a^2}{\sqrt{(a^4-t^2)}}\,dt + \frac{1}{4}\int \frac{-2t}{\sqrt{(a^4-t^2)}}\,dt$$

$$= \frac{a^2}{2}\sin^{-1}\frac{t}{a^2} + \frac{1}{4}.2\sqrt{a^4-t^2}$$

$$= \frac{a^2}{2}\sin^{-1}\frac{x^2}{a^2} + \frac{1}{2}\sqrt{a^4-x^4}.$$

28. $I = \displaystyle\int \sqrt{4+8x-5x^2}\,dx = \sqrt{5}\int\sqrt{\left[-\left(x^2-\frac{8}{5}x-\frac{4}{5}\right)\right]}\,dx$

$$= \sqrt{5}\int\sqrt{\left[-\left(x^2-\frac{8}{5}x+\frac{16}{25}-\frac{4}{5}-\frac{16}{25}\right)\right]}\,dx$$

$$= \sqrt{5}\int\sqrt{\left[\left(\frac{6}{5}\right)^2 - \left(x-\frac{4}{5}\right)^2\right]}\,dx$$

$$= \sqrt{5}\left[\frac{x-4/5}{2}\sqrt{\left\{\left(\frac{6}{5}\right)^2 - \left(x-\frac{4}{5}\right)^2\right\}} + \frac{1}{2}\left(\frac{6}{5}\right)^2\sin^{-1}\frac{x-4/5}{6/5}\right]$$

$$= \sqrt{5}\left[\frac{5x-4}{10\sqrt{(5)}}\sqrt{4+8x-5x^2} + \frac{18}{25}\sin^{-1}\frac{5x-4}{6}\right]$$

29. $I = \displaystyle\int \sqrt{x^2-x+1}\,dx$

$$= \int \sqrt{\left(x-\frac{1}{2}\right)^2 + \left(\frac{\sqrt{3}}{2}\right)^2}\,dx = \frac{x-\frac{1}{2}}{2}\sqrt{\left(x-\frac{1}{2}\right)^2+\left(\frac{\sqrt{3}}{2}\right)^2}$$

$$+\frac{1}{2}\left(\frac{\sqrt{3}}{2}\right)^2 \log\left\{\left(x-\frac{1}{2}\right)+\sqrt{\left(x-\frac{1}{2}\right)^2+\left(\frac{\sqrt{3}}{2}\right)^2}\right\}$$

$$=\frac{2x-1}{4}\sqrt{x^2-x+1}+\frac{3}{8}\log\left\{\frac{2x-1}{2}+\sqrt{x^2-x+1}\right\}.$$

30. $I=\int (x-2)\sqrt{2x^2-6x+5}\,dx.$

Put $x-2=l(4x-6)+m.$ Compare

$4l=1,\ -6l+m=-2,$

$\therefore\quad l=\frac{1}{4},\ m=-\frac{1}{2}.$

$$\therefore\quad I=l\int (4x-6)\sqrt{2x^2-6x+5}\,dx$$

$$+m\int \sqrt{2x^2-6x+5}\,dx.$$

Put $2x^2-6x+5=t\quad \therefore\ (4x-6)\,dx=dt.$

$$\therefore\quad I=l\int \sqrt{t}\,dt+m\sqrt{2}\int\sqrt{x^2-3x+5/2}\,dx$$

$$=l.\frac{2}{3}t^{3/2}+m\sqrt{2}\int\sqrt{\left(x-\frac{3}{2}\right)^2+\left(\frac{1}{2}\right)^2}\,dx$$

$$=\frac{1}{4}.\frac{2}{3}(2x^2-6x+5)^{3/2}-\frac{1}{2}\sqrt{2}I_1$$

$$=\frac{1}{6}(2x^2-6x+5)^{3/2}-\frac{1}{\sqrt{2}}I_1$$

where $I_1=\dfrac{x-\frac{3}{2}}{2}\sqrt{\left(x-\frac{3}{2}\right)^2+\left(\frac{1}{2}\right)^2}$

$$+\frac{1}{2}\left(\frac{1}{2}\right)^2\log\left[\left(x-\frac{3}{2}\right)+\sqrt{\left(x-\frac{3}{2}\right)^2+\left(\frac{1}{2}\right)^2}\right]$$

31. Divide above and below by $\cos^2 x$ etc.

$$I=\frac{1}{\sqrt{(3)}}\tan^{-1}(\sqrt{3}\tan x).$$

32. As above. $I=\frac{1}{6}\tan^{-1}\left(\frac{2}{3}\tan x\right).$

33. $I=\int\dfrac{dx}{2-3\cos 2x}=\int\dfrac{dx}{2-3(2\cos^2 x-1)}$

$$=\int\frac{dx}{5-6\cos^2 x}=\int\frac{\sec^2 x\,dx}{5(1+\tan^2 x)-6}.$$

Put $\tan x=t;\ \therefore\ \sec^2 x\,dx=dt.$

$$\therefore\quad I=\int\frac{dt}{5t^2-1}=\frac{1}{5}\int\frac{dt}{t^2-[1/\sqrt{(5)}]^2}$$

$$=\frac{1}{5}.\frac{1}{2\frac{1}{\sqrt{(5)}}}\log\frac{t-\frac{1}{\sqrt{(5)}}}{t+\frac{1}{\sqrt{(5)}}}=\frac{1}{2\sqrt{(5)}}\log\frac{\sqrt{5}\tan x-1}{\sqrt{(5)}\tan x+1}.$$

34. $I=\int\dfrac{1}{\sin^2 x+\sin 2x}\,dx=\int\dfrac{dx}{\sin^2 x+2\sin x\cos x}$

Divide above and below by $\cos^2 x$

$$I=\int\frac{\sec^2 x\,dx}{\tan^2 x+2\tan x}.\qquad \text{Put } \tan x=t$$

$$\therefore\quad I=\int\frac{dt}{t^2+2t}=\int\frac{dt}{t(t+2)}$$

$$=\frac{1}{2}\int\left(\frac{1}{t}-\frac{1}{t+2}\right)dt.\ \text{Partial fractions}$$

$$=\frac{1}{2}[\log t-\log(t+2)]=\frac{1}{2}\log\frac{\tan x}{\tan x+2}.$$

35. $I=\int\dfrac{1}{(2\sin x+3\cos x)^2}\,dx.$

Here denominator consists of terms of the form $\cos^2 x,\ \sin^2 x$ and $\sin x\cos x$ but we need not open the square. Divide above and below by $\cos^2 x.$

$$\therefore\quad I=\int\frac{\sec^2 x\,dx}{(2\tan x+3)^2}.$$

Put $2\tan x+3=t;\ \therefore\ 2\sec^2 x\,dx=dt.$

$$\therefore\quad I=\frac{1}{2}\int\frac{dt}{t^2}=\frac{1}{2}\left(-\frac{1}{t}\right)=-\frac{1}{2(2\tan x+3)}.$$

36. Proceed as above

$I=\log(\tan x+2).$

37. $I=\int\dfrac{1}{2+\sin x+\cos x}\,dx$

$$=\int\frac{1}{2+2\sin(x/2)\cos(x/2)+\cos^2(x/2)-\sin^2(x/2)}\,dx$$

Divide above and below by $\cos^2(x/2).$

$$\therefore\quad I=\int\frac{\sec^2(x/2)\,dx}{2[1+\tan^2(x/2)]+2\tan(x/2)+1-\tan^2(x/2)}$$

Put $\tan\frac{x}{2}=t.$

$$\therefore\quad I=\int\frac{2\,dt}{t^2+2t+3}=2\int\frac{dt}{(t+1)^2+(\sqrt{2})^2}$$

$$=2\frac{1}{\sqrt{(2)}}\tan^{-1}\frac{t+1}{\sqrt{(2)}}=\sqrt{2}\tan^{-1}\frac{[\tan(x/2)+1]}{\sqrt{(2)}}.$$

38. $I=\int\dfrac{2-\sin x}{2\cos x+3}\,dx$

$$I=\int\frac{2}{2[\cos^2(x/2)-\sin^2(x/2)]+3}\,dx-\int\frac{\sin x\,dx}{(2\cos x+3)}$$

$$= \int \frac{2\sec^2 (x/2)\, dx}{2\,[1-\tan^2 (x/2)] + 3\,[1+\tan^2 (x/2)]}$$

$$+ \frac{1}{2}\int \frac{-2\sin x}{(2\cos x + 3)}\, dx.$$

Put $\tan (x/2) = t$ in 1st and in 2nd apply

$$\int \frac{f'(x)}{f(x)}\, dx = \log f(x)$$

$$I = \int \frac{4\, dt}{5+t^2} + \frac{1}{2}\log (2\cos x + 3)$$

$$= 4 \cdot \frac{1}{\sqrt{(5)}} \tan^{-1} \frac{t}{\sqrt{(5)}} + \frac{1}{2}\log (2\cos x + 3)$$

$$= \frac{4}{\sqrt{(5)}} \tan^{-1}\left(\frac{1}{\sqrt{(5)}}\tan \frac{x}{2}\right) + \frac{1}{2}\log (2\cos x + 3).$$

Note : We may write

$N^r = l(D^r) + m(\text{d.c.of } D^r) + n$

$2 - \sin x = l(2\cos x + 3) + m(-2\sin x) + n$

Compare coefficients of $\cos x, \sin x$ and constant

$2l = 0, \; -2m = -1, \; n = 2,$

$\therefore \quad l = 0, \; m = \frac{1}{2}, \; n = 2.$

$$\therefore \quad I = 0 + \frac{1}{2}\int \frac{-2\sin x\, dx}{2\cos x + 3} + 2\int \frac{dx}{2\cos x + 3}$$

$$= \frac{1}{2}\log (2\cos x + 3) + \text{as above.}$$

39. $\displaystyle\int \frac{\cos x}{5 - 3\cos x}\, dx$

$\cos x = l(5 - 3\cos x) + m(3\sin x) + n.$

Compare the coefficients of $\cos x, \sin x$ and constant

$-3l = 1, \; 3m = 0, \; 5l + n = 0.$

$l = -1/3, \; m = 0, \; n = 5/3$

$$\therefore \quad I = l\int \frac{5 - 3\cos x}{5 - 3\cos x}\, dx + 0 + n\int \frac{dx}{5 - 3\cos x}$$

$$= -\frac{1}{3}\int dx + \frac{5}{3}\int \frac{dx}{5 - 3\,[\cos^2 (x/2) - \sin^2 (x/2)]}$$

$$= -\frac{x}{3} + \frac{5}{3}\int \frac{\sec^2 (x/2)\, dx}{5\,[1+\tan^2 (x/2)] - 3\,[1-\tan^2 (x/2)]}$$

Put $\tan \frac{x}{2} = t \; \therefore \; \frac{1}{2}\sec^2 \frac{x}{2}\, dx = dt$

$$\therefore \quad I = -\frac{1}{3}x + \frac{5}{3}\int \frac{2\, dt}{8t^2 + 2} = -\frac{1}{3}x + \frac{5}{3} \cdot \int \frac{dt}{4t^2 + 1}$$

$$= -\frac{1}{3}x + \frac{5}{3 \cdot 4}\int \frac{dt}{t^2 + \left(\frac{1}{2}\right)^2}$$

$$= -\frac{1}{3}x + \frac{5}{12} \cdot \frac{1}{1/2}\tan^{-1} \frac{t}{1/2}$$

$$= -\frac{1}{3}x + \frac{5}{6}\tan^{-1}\left[2\tan \frac{x}{2}\right].$$

40. $\displaystyle\int \frac{\sin x}{\sin x - \cos x}\, dx$

$N^r = l(D^r) + m(\text{d.c.of } D^r).$

Here you need not write n. Even if you write n its value will be zero.

$\sin x = l(\sin x - \cos x) + m(\cos x + \sin x).$

Compare the coefficients of $\sin x$ and $\cos x$

$1 = l + m, \; -l + m = 0 \;\; \therefore \;\; l = m = 1/2$

$$\therefore \quad I = l\int \frac{(\sin x - \cos x)}{(\sin x - \cos x)}\, dx + m\int \frac{\cos x + \sin x}{\sin x - \cos x}\, dx$$

$$= lx + m\log (\sin x - \cos x)$$

$$= \frac{1}{2}x + \frac{1}{2}\log (\sin x - \cos x).$$

41. Proceed as above.

$$I = \frac{4}{5}x + \frac{3}{5}\log (2\sin x + \cos x).$$

42. We have

$$I = \int_0^{\pi/2} \frac{dx}{3 + 4\sin x} = \int_0^{\pi/2} \frac{dx}{3 + 8\sin (x/2)\cos (x/2)}$$

$$= \int_0^{\pi/2} \frac{\sec^2 (x/2)\, dx}{3\,[1+\tan^2 (x/2)] + 8\tan (x/2)}$$

$$= \int_0^{\pi/2} \frac{\sec^2 (x/2)\, dx}{3\tan^2 (x/2) + 8\tan (x/2) + 3}$$

Now put $\tan (x/2) = t$

so that $(1/2)\sec^2 (x/2)\, dx = dt$

$$\therefore \quad I = \int_0^1 \frac{2\, dt}{3t^2 + 8t + 3} = \frac{2}{3}\int_0^1 \frac{dt}{t^2 + \frac{8}{3}t + 1}$$

$$= \frac{2}{3}\int_0^1 \frac{dt}{\left(t + \frac{4}{3}\right)^2 - [\sqrt{(7)}/3]^2}$$

$$= \frac{2}{3} \cdot \frac{1}{2 \cdot [\sqrt{(7)}/3]}\left[\log \frac{t + \frac{4}{3} - (\sqrt{7}/3)}{t + \frac{4}{3} + [\sqrt{(7)}/3]}\right]_0^1$$

$$= \frac{1}{\sqrt{(7)}}\left[\log \frac{1 + \frac{4}{3} - (\sqrt{7}/3)}{1 + \frac{4}{3} + [\sqrt{(7)}/3]} - \log \frac{\frac{4}{3} - (\sqrt{7}/3)}{\frac{4}{3} + [\sqrt{(7)}/3]}\right]$$

$$= \frac{1}{\sqrt{(7)}}\log \frac{7 - \sqrt{7}}{7 + \sqrt{(7)}} - \log \frac{4 - \sqrt{7}}{4 + \sqrt{(7)}}$$

$$= \frac{1}{\sqrt{(7)}}\log \left(\frac{\sqrt{7} - 1}{\sqrt{(7)} + 1}\right) \cdot \left(\frac{4 + \sqrt{7}}{4 - \sqrt{(7)}}\right)$$

$$=\frac{1}{\sqrt{(7)}}\log\left[\frac{(\sqrt{7}-1)^2}{7-1}\times\frac{(4+\sqrt{7})^2}{16-7}\right]$$

$$=\frac{1}{\sqrt{(7)}}\log\left[\frac{4-\sqrt{7}}{3}\times\frac{23+8\sqrt{7}}{9}\right]$$

$$=\frac{1}{\sqrt{(7)}}\log\left(\frac{36+9\sqrt{7}}{27}\right)=\frac{1}{\sqrt{(7)}}\log\left(\frac{4+\sqrt{7}}{3}\right).$$

43. $f'(x)=\frac{1}{1+\cos x}=\frac{1}{2}\sec^2\frac{x}{2}$

$\therefore \quad f(x)=\int \frac{1}{2}\sec^2\frac{x}{2}\,dx=\tan\frac{x}{2}+C$

$f(0)=\tan 0+C=3$ given $\therefore\ C=3.$

$\therefore \quad f(x)=\tan\frac{x}{2}+3$

$\therefore \quad f\left(\frac{\pi}{2}\right)=1+3=4$ ...(1)

Now $\pi=\frac{22}{7}\quad \therefore\ 3+\frac{\pi}{4}=3+\frac{22}{28}=3\cdot 78$ ...(2)

$3+\frac{\pi}{2}=3+\frac{11}{7}=4\cdot 57$ ...(3)

The result is obvious from (1), (2) and (3) *i.e.*, $3\cdot 78\le 4\le 4\cdot 57$

44. Put $x=3\cos\theta$ and $\sqrt{\frac{1-\cos\theta}{1+\cos\theta}}=\tan\frac{\theta}{2}$

$\therefore \quad I=-3\int \sin\theta.\sin\theta\,d\theta=\frac{-3}{2}\int(1-\cos 2\theta)\,d\theta$

$$=\frac{-3}{2}\left\{\theta-\frac{\sin 2\theta}{2}\right\}$$

$$=\frac{-3}{2}\cos^{-1}\frac{x}{3}+\frac{3}{4}\sin\left(2\cos^{-1}\frac{x}{3}\right)$$

§ 11. Integration by Parts

Rule : If u and v be two functions of x, then

$$\int uv\,dx=u\int v\,dx-\int\left[\frac{du}{dx}\int v\,dx\right]dx.$$

The above formula can be stated as under.

The integral of the Product of two functions

= First function u multiplied by integral of 2nd function v

– integral of [d.c. of 1st function multiplied by integral of 2nd already written before].

Note : In applying the above rule care has to be taken in choosing the first and 2nd function properly. Whenever x^n where n is a +ive integer is one of the functions then it should be chosen as first function because after differentiation in the second part its power will be reduced by unity. But this is possible if we know the integral of the second function. If we choose x^n as 2nd function then it will be integrated and its power will increase *e.g.*

$$\int x^3\sin 2x\,dx$$

we will choose x^3 as 1st and choose $\sin 2x$ whose integral we know as 2nd.

$$\int x^3\log x\,dx.$$

Here we would like to choose x^3 as first but we do not know the integral of $\log x$ and hence here we shall per force choose x^3 as 2nd function and $\log x$ as first function.

$$\int\log x\,dx,\ \int\sqrt{x^2-a^2}\,dx,$$

$$\int\sqrt{a^2-x^2}\,dx,\ \int\sin^{-1}x\,dx.$$

Here in the above integrals there is only one function and as such we shall choose unity as the other function. This unity will be treated as 2nd function whose integral is to be taken.

We shall make all the above ideas clear by giving the following examples.

Solved Examples

***Ex. 1. (a)** $\int x\cos x\,dx.$

Here x will be chosen as first function and $\cos x$ whose integral we know as 2nd function.

$$\therefore \quad \int x\cos x\,dx=x\int\cos x\,dx-\int\left[\frac{d}{dx}(x)\int\cos x\,dx\right]dx$$

$$=x\sin x-\int 1.\sin x\,dx$$

$$=x\sin x+\cos x.$$

(b) Prove $\int x^3e^{x^2}\,dx=\frac{1}{2}e^{x^2}(x^2-1).$

Put $x^2=t\ \therefore\ 2x\,dx=dt\ \therefore\ I=\frac{1}{2}\int t\,e^t\,dt$

$$=\frac{1}{2}\left[t\int e^t\,dt-\int\left[\frac{d}{dt}(t)\int e^t\,dt\right]dt\right]$$

$$=\frac{1}{2}\left[t\,e^t-\int 1.e^t\,dt\right]$$

$$=\frac{1}{2}(t\,e^t-e^t)=\frac{1}{2}e^{x^2}(x^2-1).$$

Ex. 2. $\int x\log x\,dx.$

Here if we choose x as first function then $\log x$ will be second function whose integral we do not know and hence we will choose $\log x$ as 1st and x as 2nd.

$$\int x \log x\, dx = \int (\log x) . x\, dx$$

$$= \log x \int x\, dx - \int \left[\frac{d}{dx} (\log x) \int x\, dx \right] dx$$

$$= \frac{x^2}{2} (\log x) - \int \frac{1}{x} . \frac{x^2}{2} dx = \frac{x^2}{2} \log x - \frac{1}{2} \int x\, dx$$

$$= \frac{x^2}{2} \log x - \frac{x^2}{4} = \frac{x^2}{4} (2 \log x - 1).$$

Ex. 3. $\int x^2 \log x\, dx = \int (\log x)\, x^2\, dx$

$$= (\log x) \int x^2\, dx - \int \left[\frac{d}{dx} (\log x) \int x^2\, dx \right] dx$$

$$= \frac{x^3}{3} \log x - \int \frac{1}{x} . \frac{x^3}{3} dx$$

$$= \frac{x^3}{3} \log x - \frac{1}{3} . \frac{x^3}{3} = \frac{x^3}{9} (3 \log x - 1).$$

Note from Ex. 2, 3 we conclude that

$$\int x^n \log x\, dx = \frac{x^{n+1}}{(n+1)^2} [(n+1) \log x - 1].$$

***Ex. 4. (a)** $\int \log x\, dx.$ **(B.I.T.S. 1992)**

Here there is only one function whose integral we do not know and we choose the other function as unity which will be taken as 2nd function.

$$\int \log x\, dx = \int (\log x) . 1\, dx$$

$$= \log x . \int 1\, dx - \int \left[\frac{d}{dx} (\log x) \int 1\, dx \right] dx$$

$$= x \log x - \int \frac{1}{x} . x\, dx = x (\log x - 1).$$

(b) $\int \log (x+1)\, dx.$

$$I = x \log (x+1) - \int \frac{x}{x+1} dx.$$

$$= x \log (x+1) - \int \left(1 - \frac{1}{x+1}\right) dx$$

$$= x \log (x+1) - x + \log (x+1)$$

$$= (x+1) \log (x+1) - x.$$

(c) $\int x \log (1+x)\, dx = \frac{x^2}{2} \log (1+x) - \frac{1}{2} \int \frac{x^2}{x+1} dx$

$$= \frac{x^2}{2} \log (1+x) - \frac{1}{2} \int \frac{x^2 - 1 + 1}{x+1} dx$$

$$= \frac{x^2}{2} \log (1+x) - \frac{1}{2} \int \left\{ (x-1) + \frac{1}{x+1} \right\} dx$$

$$= \frac{x^2}{2} \log (1+x) - \frac{1}{2} \left[\frac{x^2}{2} - x + \log (x+1) \right]$$

$$= \frac{x^2 - 1}{2} \log (1+x) - \frac{x^2}{4} + \frac{x}{2}.$$

(d) $\int \log_{10} x\, dx.$

$$= \int \log_e x \log_{10} e\, dx = x (\log x - 1) \log_{10} e$$

by part (a).

(e) $\int [\log (\log x)/x]\, dx$

Put $\log x = t$. $\therefore$ $(1/x)\, dx = dt$

$\therefore$ $I = \int \log t\, dt$ etc.

Ans. $\log x [\log \log x - 1]$, by (a).

***Ex. 5. (a)** $\int \tan^{-1} x\, dx.$

Here also there is one function and the other be chosen as unity,

$$\therefore \int \tan^{-1} x\, dx = \int (\tan^{-1} x) . 1\, dx$$

$$= (\tan^{-1} x) \int 1\, dx - \int \left[\frac{d}{dx} (\tan^{-1} x) \int 1\, dx \right] dx$$

$$= x \tan^{-1} x - \int \frac{1}{1+x^2} x\, dx$$

$$= x \tan^{-1} x - \frac{1}{2} \int \frac{2x}{(1+x^2)} dx$$

$[\because 2x \text{ is d.c. of } 1 + x^2]$

$$= x \tan^{-1} x - \frac{1}{2} \log (1+x^2). \quad ...(1)$$

$$\because \int \frac{f'(x)}{f(x)} dx = \log f(x).$$

(b) $\int_0^1 \cot^{-1} (1 + x^2 - x) = \frac{\pi}{2} - \log 2$

$$I = \int_0^1 \tan^{-1} \frac{1}{1 - x(1-x)} dx$$

$$= \int_0^1 \tan^{-1} \frac{x + (1-x)}{1 - x(1-x)} dx$$

$$= \int_0^1 \tan^{-1} x\, dx + \int_0^1 \tan^{-1} (1-x)\, dx$$

$$= \int_0^1 \tan^{-1} x + \int_1^0 \tan z\, (-dz), \quad \text{where } z = 1 - x$$

$$= \int_0^1 \tan^{-1} x + \int_0^1 \tan^{-1} x\, dx = 2 \int_0^1 \tan^{-1} x\, dx$$

$$= 2\left[x\tan^{-1}x - \frac{1}{2}\log(1+x^2)\right]_0^1 \quad \text{by (1) of (a)}$$

$$= 2\left[\frac{\pi}{4} - \frac{1}{2}\log 2\right] = \frac{\pi}{2} - \log 2.$$

***Ex. 6.** $\int \sin^{-1} x\,dx = \int (\sin^{-1} x).1\,dx$ **(B.I.T.S. 1999)**

$$= (\sin^{-1} x)\int 1\,dx - \int\left[\frac{d}{dx}(\sin^{-1} x)\int 1\,dx\right]dx$$

$$= x\sin^{-1} x - \int \frac{1}{\sqrt{(1-x^2)}}.x\,dx$$

$$= x\sin^{-1} x + \frac{1}{2}\int \frac{-2x}{\sqrt{(1-x^2)}}dx.$$

$[\because\ -2x \text{ is d.c. of } 1-x^2]$

$$= x\sin^{-1} x + \frac{1}{2}.2\sqrt{1-x^2} = x\sin^{-1} x + \sqrt{1-x^2}.$$

$$\because \int \frac{f'(x)}{\sqrt{[f(x)]}}dx = 2\sqrt{[f(x)]}.$$

Reappearance of original integral.

Ex. 7. $\int \sqrt{x^2 - a^2}\,dx.$

Here also there is one function and as such we choose the other as unity.

$$\therefore \quad I = \int \sqrt{x^2 - a^2}\,dx = \int \sqrt{x^2 - a^2}.1\,dx$$

$$= \sqrt{x^2 - a^2}.\int 1\,dx - \int\left[\frac{d}{dx}[\sqrt{x^2 - a^2}]\int 1\,dx\right]dx$$

$$= x\sqrt{x^2 - a^2} - \int \frac{1}{2\sqrt{(x^2 - a^2)}}.2x.x\,dx$$

$$= x\sqrt{x^2 - a^2} - \int \frac{x^2}{\sqrt{(x^2 - a^2)}}dx$$

$$= x\sqrt{x^2 - a^2} - \int \frac{x^2 - a^2 + a^2}{\sqrt{(x^2 - a^2)}}dx$$

Split into two

$$= x\sqrt{x^2 - a^2} - \int \sqrt{x^2 - a^2}\,dx - \int \frac{a^2}{\sqrt{(x^2 - a^2)}}dx$$

or $\quad I = x\sqrt{x^2 - a^2} - I - a^2.\log[x + \sqrt{x^2 - a^2}].$

$\therefore \quad 2I = x\sqrt{x^2 - a^2} - a^2\log[x + \sqrt{x^2 - a^2}]$

or $\quad I = \dfrac{x}{2}\sqrt{x^2 - a^2} - \dfrac{a^2}{2}\log[x + \sqrt{x^2 - a^2}].$

***Ex. 8.** $\int \sqrt{a^2 - x^2}\,dx = \int \sqrt{a^2 - x^2}.1\,dx.$

$$= \sqrt{a^2 - x^2}\int 1\,dx - \int\left[\frac{d}{dx}[\sqrt{a^2 - x^2}]\int 1\,dx\right]dx$$

$$= x\sqrt{a^2 - x^2} - \int \frac{1}{2\sqrt{(a^2 - x^2)}}(-2x).x\,dx$$

$$= x\sqrt{a^2 - x^2} - \int \frac{-x^2}{\sqrt{(a^2 - x^2)}}dx$$

$$= x\sqrt{a^2 - x^2} - \int \frac{a^2 - x^2 - a^2}{\sqrt{(a^2 - x^2)}}dx. \text{ Split into two}$$

$$= x\sqrt{a^2 - x^2} - \int \sqrt{a^2 - x^2}\,dx + \int \frac{a^2}{\sqrt{(a^2 - x^2)}}dx$$

or $\quad I = x\sqrt{a^2 - x^2} - I + a^2\sin^{-1}(x/a).$

$\therefore \quad 2I = x\sqrt{a^2 - x^2} + a^2\sin^{-1}(x/a)$

or $\quad I = \dfrac{x}{2}\sqrt{a^2 - x^2} + \dfrac{a^2}{2}\sin^{-1}\dfrac{x}{a}.$

Note : We may similarly prove that

$$I = \int \sqrt{x^2 + a^2}\,dx$$

$$= \frac{x}{2}\sqrt{x^2 + a^2} + \frac{a^2}{2}\log[x + \sqrt{x^2 + a^2}]$$

****Successive integration by parts.**

Ex. 9. $\int x^3 \sin 2x\,dx$

$$= x^3\int \sin 2x\,dx - \int\left[\frac{d}{dx}(x^3)\int \sin 2x\,dx\right]dx$$

$$= -\frac{x^3\cos 2x}{2} - \int 3x^2\left(\frac{-\cos 2x}{2}\right)dx$$

$$= -\frac{x^3}{2}\cos 2x + \frac{3}{2}\int x^2\cos 2x\,dx. \qquad ...(1)$$

Again $\int x^2\cos 2x\,dx = x^2\dfrac{\sin 2x}{2} - \int 2x.\dfrac{\sin 2x}{2}dx$

$$= \frac{x^2}{2}\sin 2x - \int x\sin 2x\,dx.$$

Putting in (1),

$$I = -\frac{x^3}{2}\cos 2x + \frac{3}{4}x^2\sin 2x - \frac{3}{2}\int x\sin 2x. \qquad ...(2)$$

Again $\int x\sin 2x\,dx = x\left(-\dfrac{\cos 2x}{2}\right) - \int 1.\left(-\dfrac{\cos 2x}{2}\right)dx$

$$= -\frac{x\cos 2x}{2} + \frac{1}{2}\int \cos 2x\,dx$$

$$= -\frac{x\cos 2x}{2} + \frac{\sin 2x}{4}.$$

Putting in (2),

$$I = -\frac{x^3}{2}\cos 2x + \frac{3}{4}x^2\sin 2x + \frac{3}{4}x\cos 2x - \frac{3}{8}\sin 2x. \qquad ...(3)$$

Ex. 10. (a) $\int x^3 e^{4x}\,dx = x^3\dfrac{e^{4x}}{4} - \int 3x^2\dfrac{e^{4x}}{4}dx$

$$= \frac{x^3}{4} e^{4x} - \frac{3}{4} \int x^2 e^{4x}\, dx \quad ...(1)$$

Now $\int x^2 e^{4x}\, dx = x^2 . \frac{e^{4x}}{4} - \int 2x . \frac{e^{4x}}{4}\, dx$

$$= \frac{x^2}{4} e^{4x} - \frac{1}{2} \int x e^{4x}\, dx.$$ Putting in (1)

$$I = \frac{x^3}{4} e^{4x} - \frac{3}{16} x^2 e^{4x} + \frac{3}{8} \int x e^{4x}\, dx \quad ...(2)$$

Again $\int x e^{4x}\, dx = x . \frac{e^{4x}}{4} - \int 1 . \frac{e^{4x}}{4}\, dx$

$$= \frac{x}{4} e^{4x} - \frac{e^{4x}}{16}$$

Putting in (2), we get

$$I = \frac{x^3}{4} e^{4x} - \frac{3}{16} x^2 e^{4x} + \frac{3}{32} x e^{4x} - \frac{3}{128} e^{4x}.$$

Note : You have seen that in examples 9 and 10 we had to integrate successively thrice by parts. Below we give a method with the help of which we can straight away write down the answer.

***Rule :** Start as usual and then go on successively integrating one function and successively differentiating the other and attach alternately + and − signs. The successive integration and differentiation be written within brackets.

$$\int x^3 \sin 2x\, dx.$$

Here $\sin 2x$ will be successively integrated and x^3 will be successively differentiated.

$$= x^3 \left(\frac{-\cos 2x}{2}\right) - (3x^2)\left(\frac{-\sin 2x}{4}\right) + (6x)\left(\frac{\cos 2x}{8}\right) - (6)\left(\frac{\sin 2x}{16}\right) + 0.$$

We have stopped here because differentiation of 6 will be zero.

$$\therefore \quad \int x^3 \sin 2x\, dx = \frac{-x^3}{2} \cos 2x + \frac{3}{4} x^2 \sin 2x + \frac{3}{4} x \cos 2x - \frac{3}{8} \sin 2x.$$

Above is same as result (3) of Ex. 9.

Similarly $\int x^3 e^{4x}\, dx$.

Here e^{4x} will be successively integrated and x^3 will be successively differentiated

$$\therefore \quad \int x^3 e^{4x}\, dx = x^3 \left(\frac{e^{4x}}{4}\right) - (3x^2)\left(\frac{e^{4x}}{16}\right) + (6x)\left(\frac{e^{4x}}{64}\right) - 6\left(\frac{e^{4x}}{256}\right) + 0$$

$$= \frac{1}{4} x^3 e^{4x} - \frac{3}{16} x^2 e^{4x} + \frac{3}{32} x e^{4x} - \frac{3}{128} e^{4x}.$$

Above is same as result (3) of Ex. 10.

Similarly $\int x^2 \cos x\, dx = x^2 (\sin x)$

$$- (2x) . (-\cos x) + 2(-\sin x)$$

$$= x^2 \sin x + 2x \cos x - 2 \sin x$$

and $\int x^2 e^{2x}\, dx = e^{2x} \left(\frac{x^2}{2} - \frac{x}{2} + \frac{1}{4}\right)$.

$$\int x^2 \sqrt{(x + 2a)}\, dx$$

$$= x^2 \left[\frac{2}{3} (x + 2a)^{3/2}\right] - 2x \left[\frac{2}{3} \cdot \frac{2}{5} (x + 2a)^{5/2}\right] + 2\left[\frac{2}{3} . \frac{2}{5} . \frac{2}{7} (x + 2a)^{7/2}\right]$$

***(Imp.)** Thus successive integration by parts can be performed when one of the functions is x^n (n +ive integer) which will be successively differentiated and the other is either of the following $\sin ax, \cos ax, e^{ax}, e^{-ax}, (x + a)^m$ which will be successively integrated.

(b)* $\int_1^e (\log x)^3\, dx$

Put $\log x = t \quad \therefore \quad x = e^t \quad \therefore \quad dx = e^t\, dt$

When $x = e, t = 1$, and when $x = 1, t = 0$

$$I = \int_0^1 e^t . t^3\, dt = [e^t . t^3 - e^t (3t^2) + e^t (6t) - e^t . 6]_0^1$$

$$= e^t [t^3 - 3t^2 + 6t - 6] = -2e + 6$$

(c)* Determine a positive integer $n \le 5$ such that

$$\int_0^1 e^x (x - 1)^n\, dx = 16 - 6e.$$

(I.I.T. 1992)

$$I_1 = \int_0^1 e^x (x - 1)\, dx = [e^x (x - 1) - e^x . 1]_0^1$$

$$= 1 - (e - 1) = 2 - e \quad ...(1)$$

$$I_n = [e^x (x - 1)^n]_0^1 - \int_0^1 e^x . n (x - 1)^{n-1}\, dx$$

$$= 0 - (-1)^n - n I_{n-1} = (-1)^{n+1} - n I_{n-1}$$

Putting $n = 2, 3, 4, ...$ in the above, we get

$$I_2 = (-1)^3 - 2I_1 = -1 - 2(2 - e) = 2e - 5$$

$$I_3 = (-1)^4 - 3I_2 = 1 - 3(2e - 5) = 16 - 6e \quad \therefore \ n = 3$$

(d)* $\int_0^a \sqrt{a^2 - x^2} \left(\cos^{-1} \frac{x}{a}\right)^2 dx = \frac{\pi a^2}{48} (\pi + 6)$

Put $x = a \cos \theta$ and adjust the limits

$$I = \int_{\pi/2}^0 (a \sin \theta)\, \theta^2\, (-a \sin \theta)\, d\theta$$

$$= a^2 \int_0^{\pi/2} \frac{\theta^2}{2}(1-\cos 2\theta)$$

$$= \frac{a^2}{2}\left[\frac{\theta^3}{3} - \int \theta^2 \cos 2\theta \, d\theta\right] \quad \text{Integrate by parts}$$

$$= \frac{a^2}{2}\left[\frac{\pi^3}{24} - \left\{\theta^2 \frac{\sin 2\theta}{2} - (2\theta)\left(-\frac{\cos 2\theta}{4}\right) + 2\left(-\frac{\sin 2\theta}{8}\right)\right\}_0^{\pi/2}\right]$$

The first and the last terms vanish on putting the limits

$$I = \frac{a^2}{2} \cdot \frac{\pi^3}{24} - \frac{a^2}{4}\left[\theta \cos 2\theta\right]_0^{\pi/2}$$

$$= \frac{\pi^3 a^2}{48} - \frac{a^2}{4}\left[-\frac{\pi}{2}\right] = \frac{\pi a^2}{48}[\pi^2 + 6]$$

(e) Evaluate $\int (\sin^{-1} x)^4 \, dx$

Put $x = \sin\theta \quad \therefore \quad dx = \cos\theta \, d\theta$

$$\therefore \quad I = \int \theta^4 \cos\theta \, d\theta.$$

$$= \theta^4 \sin\theta - (4\theta^3)(-\cos\theta) + (12\theta^2)(-\sin\theta) - (24\theta)(\cos\theta) + 24(\sin\theta)$$

$$= \sin\theta\,[\theta^4 - 12\theta^2 + 24] + 4\theta\cos\theta\,[\theta^2 - 6]$$

where $\theta = \sin^{-1} x$, $x = \sin\theta$, $\sqrt{1-x^2} = \cos\theta$.

Ex. 11. (a) $\int x \sec^2 x \, dx$.

$$= x\int \sec^2 x \, dx - \int \left[\frac{d}{dx}(x) \int \sec^2 x \, dx\right] dx$$

$$= x\tan x - \int 1 . \tan x \, dx = x \tan x - \log \sec x.$$

Note : $\int x \tan^2 x \, dx = \int x(\sec^2 x - 1)\, dx$

$$= \int x \sec^2 x \, dx - \int x \, dx$$

$$= x\tan x - \log\sec x - \frac{x^2}{2} \text{ by Ex. 11 (a).}$$

(b) Evaluate $\int \sin^{-1}\left(\frac{2x+2}{\sqrt{4x^2+8x+13}}\right) dx.$ **(I.I.T. 2001)**

$$I = \sin^{-1}\left[\frac{2x+2}{[(2x+2)^2+9]^{1/2}}\right] dx$$

Put $2x + 2 = 3\tan\theta$

$\therefore \quad 2\,dx = 3\sec^2\theta \, d\theta$

$$\therefore \quad I = \int \sin^{-1}\left[\frac{3\tan\theta}{3\sec\theta}\right] \cdot \frac{3}{2}\sec^2\theta \, d\theta$$

$$= \int \frac{3}{2}\sin^{-1}(\sin\theta)\sec^2\theta \, d\theta$$

$$= \frac{3}{2}\int \theta \sec^2\theta \, d\theta = \frac{3}{2}\left[\theta\tan\theta - \int \tan\theta \, d\theta\right]$$

$$= \frac{3}{2}[\theta\tan\theta - \log\sec\theta]$$

where $\tan\theta = \dfrac{2x+2}{3}$

$$\therefore \quad \sec\theta = \frac{1}{3}\sqrt{4x^2+8x+13}$$

(c)* $\int x\frac{(\sec 2x - 1)}{(\sec 2x + 1)} dx = \int x \frac{(1-\cos 2x)}{(1+\cos 2x)} dx$

$$= \int x . \frac{(2\sin^2 x)}{(2\cos^2 x)} dx$$

$$= \int x \tan^2 x \, dx. \text{ etc. as done above.}$$

(d) $\int \frac{x\,dx}{(1-\cos x)^2}$

$$I = \int \frac{x}{\left(2\sin^2 \frac{x}{2}\right)^2} dx$$

$$= \frac{1}{4}\int x\left(1+\cot^2\frac{x}{2}\right)\operatorname{cosec}^2\frac{x}{2}\, dx$$

$$I = \frac{1}{4}\int x\left(\operatorname{cosec}^2\frac{x}{2} + \operatorname{cosec}^2\frac{x}{2}\cot^2\frac{x}{2}\right) dx$$

Put $\frac{x}{2} = t$

$$I = \int t\,[\operatorname{cosec}^2 t + \cot^2 t \operatorname{cosec}^2 t]\, dt$$

$$= t\left[-\cot t - \frac{1}{3}\cot^3 t\right] + \int\left[\cot t + \frac{1}{3}\cot^3 t\right] dt$$

$$= -t\left(\cot t + \frac{1}{3}\cot^3 t\right) + \log\sin t$$

$$+ \frac{1}{3}\int \cot t . (\operatorname{cosec}^2 t - 1)\, dt$$

The last integral is

$$\frac{1}{3}\left[-\frac{1}{2}\cot^2 t - \log\sin t\right]$$

$$\therefore \quad I = -t\left(\cot t + \frac{1}{3}\cot^3 t\right) + \frac{2}{3}\log\sin t - \frac{1}{6}\cot^2 t$$

Put $t = \frac{x}{2}$ etc.

Ex. 12. $\int \tan^{-1} x \, dx.$

We have already done this question in **Ex. 5, P. 1479.** Here we shall do it by alternative method.

Put $x = \tan\theta$.

$dx = \sec^2\theta \, d\theta$ and $\tan^{-1}\tan\theta = \theta$.

$\therefore \quad I = \int \tan^{-1} x\, dx = \int \tan^{-1} (\tan \theta) . \sec^2 \theta\, d\theta$

$= \int \theta \sec^2 \theta.$ Integrate by parts.

$= \theta \tan \theta - \log \sec \theta$ by Ex. 11

$= x \tan^{-1} x - \log \sqrt{1 + \tan^2 \theta}$

$= x \tan^{-1} x - \frac{1}{2} \log (1 + x^2).$

Same as in Ex. 5.

***Ex. 13. (a)** $\int e^{ax} \sin bx\, dx.$

$I = e^{ax} \left(\frac{-\cos bx}{b}\right) - \int ae^{ax} \left(\frac{-\cos bx}{b} dx\right)$

$= -\frac{e^{ax} \cos bx}{b} + \frac{a}{b} \int e^{ax} \cos bx\, dx$

$= -\frac{e^{ax} \cos bx}{b} + \frac{a}{b}\left[e^{ax} \left(\frac{\sin bx}{b}\right) - \int ae^{ax} \left(\frac{\sin bx}{b}\right) dx\right]$

$= -\frac{e^{ax} \cos bx}{b} + \frac{a}{b^2} e^{ax} \sin bx - \frac{a^2}{b^2} I.$

Transpose the term of I to the other side.

$\therefore \quad I\left(1 + \frac{a^2}{b^2}\right) = e^{ax} \frac{(a \sin bx - b \cos bx)}{b^2}$

or $\quad I(a^2 + b^2) = e^{ax} (a \sin bx - b \cos bx)$

or $\quad I = \frac{e^{ax}}{a^2 + b^2} (a \sin bx - b \cos bx)$.

Another form : If we put $a = r \cos \alpha$, $b = r \sin \alpha$, then $a^2 + b^2 = r^2$

and $\tan \alpha = \frac{b}{a}$ or $\alpha = \tan^{-1} \frac{b}{a}$

$\therefore \quad I = \int e^{ax} \sin bx\, dx$

$= \frac{e^{ax}}{r^2} (r \cos \alpha \sin bx - r \sin \alpha \cos bx)$

$= \frac{e^{ax}}{r} \sin (bx - \alpha)$

Similarly $I = \int e^{ax} \cos bx\, dx$

$= \frac{e^{ax}}{a^2 + b^2} (a \cos bx + b \sin bx)$

$= \frac{e^{ax}}{r} \cos (bx - \alpha).$

$\therefore \quad \int e^{4x} \sin 3x\, dx = \frac{e^{4x}}{4^2 + 3^2} (4 \sin 3x - 3 \cos 3x)$

$= \frac{e^{4x}}{r} \sin (3x - \alpha).$

where $r = \sqrt{4^2 + 3^2} = 5, \quad \tan \alpha = b/a = 3/4.$

(b) $\int_0^{\pi/2} e^x \sin x\, dx.$

Put $a = b = 1$ in the above.

(c) $\int \cos \left\{b \log \left(\frac{x}{a}\right)\right\} dx$

Put $\log \left(\frac{x}{a}\right) = t \quad \therefore \quad x = ae^t \quad \therefore \quad dx = ae^t\, dt$

$\therefore \quad I = a \int e^t \cos bt\, dt$

$= \frac{ae^t}{(1 + b^2)} [(\cos bt + b \sin bt)]$

Cancellation of integrals

***Ex. 14. (a)** $\int e^x [f(x) + f'(x)]\, dx = e^x f(x)$

[Remember]

Note the above form.

$I = \int e^x f(x)\, dx + \int e^x f'(x)\, dx.$

Integrate 1st by parts

$I = f(x) \int e^x\, dx - \int \left[\frac{d}{dx} f(x) \int e^x\, dx\right] dx + \int e^x f'(x)\, dx$

$= f(x) . e^x - \int f'(x) . e^x\, dx + \int e^x f'(x)\, dx$

$= e^x f(x).$ The last two integrals cancel.

Hence (a) $\int e^x (\sin x + \cos x)\, dx = e^x \sin x$

$\because \quad f(x) = \sin x, \quad f'(x) = \cos x.$

(b)* $\int e^{x/2} \sin \left(\frac{x}{2} + \frac{\pi}{4}\right) dx$

$= \frac{1}{\sqrt{(2)}} \int e^t (\sin t + \cos t)\, (2\, dt)$

$= \sqrt{2} \int e^t (\sin t + \cos t)\, dt$

$= \sqrt{2}\, e^t \sin t,$ where $\frac{x}{2} = t$

$= \sqrt{2}\, e^{x/2} \sin (x/2)$.

(c) $\int e^x (\tan x + \sec^2 x)\, dx = e^x \tan x.$

$\because \quad f(x) = \tan x, \quad f'(x) = \sec^2 x$

$\int e^x \left(\log x + \frac{1}{x}\right) dx = e^x \log x$

$\because \quad f(x) = \log x, \quad f'(x) = \frac{1}{x}.$

(d) $\int e^x (\cot x - \operatorname{cosec}^2 x)\, dx = e^x \cot x,$

$\because \quad f(x) = \cot x, \quad f'(x) = -\operatorname{cosec}^2 x.$

(e)* $\int_1^2 e^x\left(\frac{1}{x}-\frac{1}{x^2}\right)dx = e\left(\frac{e}{2}-1\right)$

$\because \quad f(x)=\frac{1}{x},\ f'(x)=-\frac{1}{x^2}. \quad \therefore \quad I=\left[e^x \cdot \frac{1}{x}\right]_1^2$

(M.N.R. 1990)

(f) Prove that $\int_0^\infty e^{-2x}(\sin 2x+\cos 2x)\,dx=\frac{1}{2}$

Put $-2x=t \qquad \therefore \quad dx=-\frac{1}{2}dt$

$\therefore \quad I=\int e^t[\cos(-t)+\sin(-t)]\left(-\frac{1}{2}dt\right)$

$=-\frac{1}{2}\int e^t[\cos t+(-\sin t)]\,dt$

$=-\frac{1}{2}[e^t\cos t]=-\frac{1}{2}[e^{-2x}\cos(-2x)]_0^\infty$

$=-\frac{1}{2}[0-1]=\frac{1}{2}$

***Ex. 15. (a)** $\int e^x\frac{1+\sin x}{1+\cos x}dx=e^x\tan\frac{x}{2}$

$I=\int\frac{e^x}{1+\cos x}dx+\int e^x\frac{\sin x}{1+\cos x}dx$

$=\int\frac{e^x}{2\cos^2(x/2)}dx+\int e^x\frac{2\sin(x/2)\cos(x/2)}{2\cos^2(x/2)}dx$

$=\int e^x\left[\tan\frac{x}{2}+\frac{1}{2}\sec^2\frac{x}{2}\right]dx=e^x\tan(x/2).$

$\because \quad f(x)=\tan\frac{x}{2},\quad f'(x)=\frac{1}{2}\sec^2\frac{x}{2}.$

Proceeding directly

$I=\int e^x\tan\frac{x}{2}dx+\int\frac{1}{2}e^x\sec^2\frac{x}{2}dx$

$=\tan(x/2)\int e^x\,dx$

$-\int\left[\frac{d}{dx}\tan\frac{x}{2}\cdot\int e^x\,dx\right]dx+\int\frac{1}{2}e^x\sec^2\frac{x}{2}dx$

$=\tan\frac{x}{2}\cdot e^x-\int\frac{1}{2}\sec^2\frac{x}{2}\cdot e^x\,dx+\int\frac{1}{2}e^x\sec^2\frac{x}{2}dx$

$=e^x\tan(x/2)$. The last two cancel.

(b)* $\int\frac{(x-1)e^x}{(x+1)^3}dx$

$I=\int\frac{(x+1-2)}{(x+1)^3}e^x\,dx$

$=\int e^x\left[\frac{1}{(x+1)^2}+\frac{-2}{(x+1)^3}\right]dx$

$=e^x\cdot\frac{1}{(x+1)^2}$ by Ex. 14

Here $f(x)=\frac{1}{(x+1)^2}$ and $f'(x)=\frac{-2}{(x+1)^3}$.

Ex. 16. $\int[\sin(\log x)+\cos(\log x)]\,dx$

Put $\log x=t$

$\therefore \quad x=e^t$ and $dx=e^t\,dt$

$\therefore \quad I=\int e^t(\sin t+\cos t)\,dt$

$=e^t\sin t=x\sin(\log x)$

Ex. 17. $\int\sec^3 x\,dx.$

$I=\int\sec^3 x\,dx=\int\sec x.\sec^2 x\,dx$

$=\sec x.\tan x-\int\left[\frac{d}{dx}(\sec x).\int\sec^2 x\,dx\right]dx$

$=\sec x\tan x-\int\sec x\tan x.\tan x\,dx$

$=\sec x\tan x-\int\sec x(\sec^2 x-1)\,dx$

$=\sec x\tan x-\int\sec^3 x\,dx+\int\sec x\,dx$

$\therefore \quad 2\int\sec^3 x\,dx=\sec x\tan x+\log(\sec x+\tan x)$

$\therefore \quad \int\sec^3 x\,dx=\frac{1}{2}\sec x\tan x+\frac{1}{2}\log(\sec x+\tan x).$

Ex. 18. $\int\sin\sqrt{x}\,dx.$

Put $x=t^2 \quad \therefore \quad dx=2t\,dt$

$\therefore \quad I=\int 2t\sin t\,dt$. Integrate by parts

$=2t(-\cos t)-\int 2.(-\cos t)\,dt$

$=-2t\cos t+2\sin t$. Now put $t=\sqrt{x}$

$=2[\sin\sqrt{x}-\sqrt{x}\cos\sqrt{x}].$

Similarly $\int\cos\sqrt{x}\,dx=2(\cos\sqrt{x}+\sqrt{x}\sin\sqrt{x}).$

Ex. 19. $\int x\sin^{-1}x\,dx$

$I=(\sin^{-1}x)\frac{x^2}{2}-\int\frac{1}{\sqrt{(1-x^2)}}\frac{x^2}{2}dx$

$=\frac{1}{2}x^2\sin^{-1}x+\frac{1}{2}\int\frac{1-x^2-1}{\sqrt{(1-x^2)}}$. Split into two

$=\frac{1}{2}x^2\sin^{-1}x+\frac{1}{2}\left[\int\sqrt{1-x^2}\,dx\right]-\int\frac{1}{\sqrt{(1-x^2)}}dx$

$=\frac{1}{2}x^2\sin^{-1}x+\frac{1}{2}\left[\frac{x}{2}\sqrt{1-x^2}+\frac{1}{2}\sin^{-1}x-\sin^{-1}x\right]$

$=\frac{1}{2}x^2\sin^{-1}x+\frac{x}{4}\sqrt{1-x^2}-\frac{1}{4}\sin^{-1}x.$

Ex. 20. (a) $\int u\frac{d^2v}{dx^2}dx-\int v\frac{d^2u}{dx^2}dx=u\frac{dv}{dx}-v\frac{du}{dx}$

Is the above statement true ?

Yes, true. Integrate by parts.

$I_1=u\frac{dv}{dx}-\int\frac{dv}{dx}\frac{du}{dx}dx \qquad ...(1)$

$I_2=v\frac{du}{dx}-\int\frac{du}{dx}\frac{dv}{dx}dx \qquad ...(2)$

$\therefore \quad I_1-I_2=u\frac{dv}{dx}-v\frac{du}{dx}$

(b)* $\int_a^b x f''(x)\,dx = [bf'(b) - af'(a)] - [f(b) - f(a)]$

where $f''(x)$ is continuous on the interval $[a,b]$.

Integrating by parts, we get

$I = [x f'(x)]_a^b - \int_a^b f'(x).1.dx$

$= [x f'(x) - f(x)]_a^b$ etc. on putting limits.

Problem Set (4)

Integration by parts.

Integrate the following :

1. (a) $x^2 \sin 2x$ (b) $\int_0^{\pi/2} x^2 \sin x\,dx$

2. $x \sin x \cos x$

3. (a) $x \tan^{-1} x$

(b) $\int_0^{\pi/2} \sin 2x . \tan^{-1}(\sin x)\,dx$

4. $x \sec^2 2x$ **5.** $(\log x)^2$.

6. $\sin(\log x)$ **(J.E.E.W.B. 1993)**

7. $e^x \sin x$. **8.** $x^2 a^x$.

9. $\frac{1}{x^2}\log(x^2 + a^2)$ **10.** $\frac{x^2 \tan^{-1} x}{1+x^2}$

11.* $\frac{\sin^{-1} x}{(1-x^2)^{3/2}}$.

12. $\sin^{-1}\frac{2x}{1+x^2}$; $\cos^{-1}\frac{1-x^2}{1+x^2}$; $\tan^{-1}\frac{2x}{1-x^2}$.

13. $\frac{x}{1+\cos x}$.

14. (i) $\frac{x \sin^{-1} x}{\sqrt{(1-x^2)}}$. (ii)* $\int_0^{1/2} \frac{x \sin^{-1} x}{\sqrt{(1-x^2)}}$.

(C.E.E. Andhra 1992)

15. $x^3 \cos x^2$. **16.*** $\frac{x \tan^{-1} x}{(1+x^2)^{3/2}}$.

17. $x \sin^2 x$, $x \cos^2 x$ **18.** $\cos\sqrt{x}$.

19. (a) $x^3 (\log x)^2$. (b) $\sqrt{x}(\log x)^2$.

20. $\sin x \log(\sec x + \tan x)$.

21. (a) $\cos x \log\tan(x/2)$.

(b)* $\int \cos 2\theta \log\left(\frac{\cos\theta + \sin\theta}{\cos\theta - \sin\theta}\right) d\theta$ **(I.I.T. 1994)**

(c)* $\int \cos 2x \log(1 + \tan x)\,dx$

22. $\log(1+x^2)$. **23.*** $\log\{x + \sqrt{x^2 + a^2}\}$.

24. $e^x \frac{1-\sin x}{1-\cos x}$. **25.** $e^x \left[\frac{1+\sqrt{1-x^2}\sin^{-1} x}{\sqrt{(1-x^2)}}\right]$

26.* $e^x \frac{2+\sin 2x}{1+\cos 2x}$.

27. (a)* $\frac{x e^x}{(x+1)^2}$. (b)* $\frac{\log x}{(1+\log x)^2}$

28. (a)* $\frac{e^x (x^3 + x + 1)}{(x^2+1)^{3/2}}$ (b)* $e^x \left(\frac{x+2}{x+4}\right)^2$

(c) Prove that

$\int e^{\tan^{-1} x}\left(\frac{1+x+x^2}{1+x^2}\right) dx = x e^{\tan^{-1} x} + c$

29. (a) If $\int [(1+x) e^x f(x) + x e^x f'(x)]\,dx = e^x$, then $f(x) =$

(a) 1 (b) x

(c) $1/x$ (d) e^x

(b) $\int 4^x [g'(x) + g(x)\log 4]\,dx =$

(a) $\frac{4^x}{\log 4} g(x)$ (b) 4^x

(c) $4^x \log 4 . g(x)$ (d) $4^x g(x)$

(c) $\int \left\{\frac{\log x - 1}{1+(\log x)^2}\right\}^2 dx =$

(a) $\frac{x e^x}{1+x^2}$ (b) $\frac{x}{(\log x)^2 + 1}$

(c) $\frac{\log x}{(\log x)^2 + 1}$ (d) $\frac{x}{x^2+1}$ **(AIEEE 2005)**

30. (a) $\int \frac{x^2 (x\sec^2 x + \tan x)}{(x\tan x + 1)^2} dx$

(b) Show that $\int_2^{e^2} \frac{1}{\log x} dx = \int_1^2 \frac{e^x}{x} dx$,

(c)* Show that $\int_t^1 \frac{dx}{1+x^2} = \int_1^{1/t} \frac{dx}{1+x^2}$

31. (a) $\frac{x - \sin x}{1 - \cos x}$

(b)* $\log(1+\cos x) - x\tan(x/2)$

32. $\frac{2x + \sin 2x}{1+\cos 2x}$ or $\frac{x + \sin x}{1+\cos x}$.

33. $\int (e^{\log x} + \sin x)\cos x\,dx$

34. (a) $\int \frac{\log x}{x^2} dx =$

(a) $\frac{1}{x}(\log x + 1)$ (b) $-\frac{1}{x}(\log x + 1)$

(c) $\frac{1}{x}(\log x - 1)$ (d) $\log(x+1)$ **(AIEEE 2002)**

(b)* $\int \frac{\log_e x}{x^3} dx$. (c)* $\int \frac{\log(1-x)}{x^2} dx$

(J.E.E. W.B. 1992)

35.* Evaluate $\int_0^1 \log[\sqrt{1-x} + \sqrt{1+x}]\,dx$.

36. Prove that $\int_0^{\pi/4} x \cos x \cos 3x\, dx = (\pi - 3)/16$

(J.E.E. W.B. 1990)

37. Let $f(x)$ be a function satisfying $f'(x) = f(x)$ with $f(0) = 1$ and g be the function satisfying $f(x) + g(x) = x^2$. Prove that the value of the integral $\int_0^1 f(x)\, g(x)\, dx$ is $-\frac{1}{2}(e^2 - 2e + 3)$.

38. (a) If $I_m = \int_1^e (\log x)^m\, dx$, then show that $I_m + I_{m-1} = e$.

(b) If $I(m, n) = \int_0^1 t^m (1+t)^n\, dt$ $m, n \in R$, then $I(m, n)$ is

(a) $\frac{n}{1-m} I[(m+1), (n-1)]$

(b) $\frac{m}{n+1} I[(m+1), (n-1)]$

(c) $\frac{2^n}{1+m} - \frac{n}{1+m} I[(m+1), (n-1)]$

(d) $\frac{2^n}{1+m} - \frac{m}{1+n} I[(m+1), (n-1)]$

(Screening 2003)

39. (a) If $I_{10} = \int_0^{\pi/2} x^{10} \sin x\, dx$ then show that the value of $I_{10} + 90 I_8$ is $10(\pi/2)^9$.

(b) If $I_n = \int_0^1 x^n \tan^{-1} x\, dx$, then show that $(n+1) I_n + (n-1) I_{n-2} = \frac{\pi}{2} - \frac{1}{n}$

(c) If $I = \int_0^1 \frac{e^t}{1+t}\, dt$, then $P = \int_0^1 e^t \log(1+t)\, dt =$

(a) I (b) $2I$

(c) $e \log 2 - I$ (d) none

(d) Let $I = \int_0^{\pi/2} \frac{dx}{1 + \sin x}$, then $\int_0^{\pi} \frac{x^2 \cos x}{(1+\sin x)^2}\, dx$

(a) $-\pi^2$ (b) $\pi^2 - 2\pi I$

(c) $2\pi I$ (d) $2\pi I - \pi^2$

40. $\int x e^x \cos x\, dx$

41. (a) $\int \sqrt{x^6 + 1} \cdot \frac{\log(x^6 + 1) - 6 \log x}{x^{10}}\, dx$

(b) $\int \frac{\sqrt{1 + x^{2n}}\, \{\log(1 + x^{2n}) - 2n \log x\}}{x^{3n+1}}\, dx$

42. (a) $\int \sin^{-1} \left\{ \frac{2x + 2}{\sqrt{4x^2 + 8x + 13}} \right\} dx$

(b) If $R = \frac{5050 \int_0^1 (1 - x^{50})^{100}\, dx}{\int_0^1 (1 - x^{50})^{101}\, dx}$, then find the value of R. (I.I.T. 2006)

Passage : $\int e^x [f(x) + f'(x)]\, dx = e^x f(x)$

43. (a) $I = \int \frac{e^x (1 + n x^{n-1} - x^{2n})}{(1 - x^n)\sqrt{1 - x^{2n}}} = e^x \sqrt{\frac{1 + x^n}{1 - x^n}}$

(b) $\int \frac{\operatorname{cosec}^2 x - 203}{(\cos x)^{203}}\, dx = \frac{-\cot x}{(\cos x)^{203}}$

44. Prove that $\int \frac{dx}{x^3 \sqrt{x^2 - 1}} = \frac{1}{2} \left[\frac{\sqrt{x^2 - 1}}{x^2} + \tan^{-1} \sqrt{x^2 - 1} \right]$

Solution to Problem Set (4)

1. Proceed as in **Ex. 9, P. 1480** by any of the two methods.

$$\int x^2 \sin 2x\, dx = x^2 \left(-\frac{\cos 2x}{2}\right) - (2x)\left(-\frac{\sin 2x}{4}\right) + (2)\left(\frac{\cos 2x}{8}\right)$$

$$= -\frac{1}{2} x^2 \cos 2x + \frac{1}{2} x \sin 2x + \frac{1}{4} \cos 2x.$$

(b) Do yourself.

2. $I = \int x \sin x \cos x\, dx = \frac{1}{2} \int x \sin 2x\, dx$

$$= \frac{1}{2} \left[x\left(-\frac{\cos 2x}{2}\right) - \int 1 \cdot \left(-\frac{\cos 2x}{2}\right) dx \right]$$

$$= -\frac{1}{4} x \cos 2x + \frac{1}{4} \cdot \frac{\sin 2x}{2}$$

$$= -\frac{1}{4} x \cos 2x + \frac{1}{8} \sin 2x.$$

3. (a) $I = \int x \tan^{-1} x\, dx$

$$= (\tan^{-1} x)\left(\frac{x^2}{2}\right) - \int \frac{1}{1 + x^2} \frac{x^2}{2}\, dx.$$

$$= \frac{1}{2} x^2 \tan^{-1} x - \frac{1}{2} \int \frac{x^2 + 1 - 1}{x^2 + 1}\, dx$$

$$= \frac{1}{2} x^2 \tan^{-1} x - \frac{1}{2} \int \left(1 - \frac{1}{x^2 + 1}\right) dx$$

$$= \frac{1}{2} x^2 \tan^{-1} x - \frac{1}{2} [x - \tan^{-1} x]$$

$$= \frac{1}{2}(x^2 + 1) \tan^{-1} x - \frac{1}{2} x.$$

(b) $I = \int_0^{\pi/2} 2 \cdot \sin x \cos x \tan^{-1} (\sin x)\, dx$

Put $\sin x = \theta$ $\therefore$ $\cos x\, dx = d\theta$

$$\therefore \quad I = 2 \int_0^1 \theta \cdot \tan^{-1} \theta\, d\theta = \frac{\pi}{2} - 1 \text{ by part (a)}$$

4. $I = \int x \sec^2 2x\, dx = x \cdot \frac{\tan 2x}{2} - \int 1 \cdot \frac{\tan 2x}{2}\, dx$

$$= \frac{1}{2} x \tan 2x - \frac{1}{2} \cdot \frac{1}{2} \log \sec 2x$$

$= \frac{1}{2} x \tan 2x - \frac{1}{4} \log \sec 2x.$

5. $I = \int (\log x)^2 \, dx = \int 1.(\log x)^2 \, dx$

$= (\log x)^2 . x - \int 2 (\log x) . \frac{1}{x} . x \, dx$

$= x (\log x)^2 - 2 \int 1 . \log x \, dx$

$= x (\log x)^2 - 2 \left[x \log x - \int \frac{1}{x} . x \, dx \right]$

$= x (\log x)^2 - 2x \log x + 2x.$

6. $I = \int \sin (\log x) \, dx$

Put $\log x = t \quad \therefore \quad x = e^t$ and $dx = e^t \, dt$

$\therefore \quad I = \int e^t \sin t \, dt$

$= e^t (-\cos t) - \int e^t (-\cos t) \, dt$

$= -e^t \cos t + \int e^t \cos t \, dt$

$= -e^t \cos t + [e^t \sin t - \int e^t \sin t \, dt]$

Transpose

$\therefore \quad 2 \int e^t \sin t \, dt = -e^t \cos t + e^t \sin t$

$\therefore \quad \int e^t \sin t \, dt = \frac{1}{2} e^t (\sin t - \cos t)$

$= \frac{1}{2} x [\sin (\log x) - \cos (\log x)].$

7. Do yourself. Ans. $\frac{e^x}{2} (\sin x - \cos x).$

8. $\int x^2 a^x \, dx.$

We know that $\int a^x \, dx = \frac{a^x}{\log a}$

$\therefore \quad I = x^2 \frac{a^x}{\log a} - \int 2x . \frac{a^x}{\log a} dx$

$= \frac{x^2 a^x}{\log a} - \frac{2}{\log a} \left[x . \frac{a^x}{\log a} - \int 1 . \frac{a^x}{\log a} dx \right]$

$= x^2 \frac{a^x}{\log a} - \frac{2x \, a^x}{(\log a)^2} + \frac{2}{(\log a)^2} \int a^x \, dx.$

$= \frac{x^2 a^x}{\log a} - \frac{2x \, a^x}{(\log a)^2} + \frac{2a^x}{(\log a)^3}$

$= \frac{a^x}{(\log a)^3} [x^2 (\log a)^2 - 2x \log a + 2].$

Note : We could have straight away written the answer by applying successive integration.

$\int x^2 a^x \, dx = x^2 \left(\frac{a^x}{\log a} \right) - (2x) \left(\frac{a^x}{(\log a)^2} \right)$

$+ 2 \left(\frac{a^x}{(\log a)^3} \right) - 0$

$= \frac{a^x}{(\log a)^3} [x^2 (\log a)^2 - 2x (\log a) + 2].$

9. $I = \frac{-1}{x} \log (x^2 + a^2) + \int \frac{1}{x} . \frac{1}{x^2 + a^2} . 2x \, dx$

$= \frac{-1}{x} \log (x^2 + a^2) + 2 \int \frac{1}{x^2 + a^2} dx$

$= \frac{-1}{x} \log (x^2 + a^2) + 2 . \frac{1}{a} \tan^{-1} \frac{x}{a}.$

10. $I = \int \frac{x^2 \tan^{-1} x}{1 + x^2} dx.$

Put $x = \tan \theta \qquad dx = \sec^2 \theta \, d\theta$

$\therefore \quad I = \int \frac{(\tan^2 \theta) \, \theta}{\sec^2 \theta} \sec^2 \theta \, d\theta = \int \theta \tan^2 \theta \, d\theta$

$= \theta \tan \theta - \log \sec \theta - \frac{\theta^2}{2}$ by note to **Ex.11 P. 1482.**

$= x \tan^{-1} x - \log \sqrt{1 + \tan^2 \theta} - \frac{1}{2} (\tan^{-1} x)^2.$

$= x \tan^{-1} x - \frac{1}{2} \log (1 + x^2) - \frac{1}{2} (\tan^{-1} x)^2.$

11. $I = \int \frac{\sin^{-1} x}{(1 - x^2)^{3/2}} dx.$ Put $x = \sin \theta;$

$\therefore \quad dx = \cos \theta \, d\theta$

$\therefore \quad I = \int \frac{\theta \cos \theta \, d\theta}{\cos^3 \theta} = \int \theta \sec^2 \theta \, d\theta$

$= \theta \tan \theta - \log \sec \theta$ **by Ex. 11. P. 1482.**

$= \theta \tan \theta + \log \cos \theta.$

Now since $\sin \theta = x; \quad \therefore \quad \cos \theta = \sqrt{1 - x^2}$

and $\tan \theta = \frac{x}{\sqrt{(1 - x^2)}}$

$\therefore \quad I = \frac{x}{\sqrt{(1 - x^2)}} \sin^{-1} x + \frac{1}{2} \log (1 - x^2).$

12. By definition each is equal to $2 \tan^{-1} x.$

$\therefore \quad I = 2 \int \tan^{-1} x \, dx$

$= 2 \left[x \tan^{-1} x - \frac{1}{2} \log (1 + x^2) \right]$

by Ex. 5 Page 1479.

13. $I = \int \frac{x}{1 + \cos x} dx = \int \frac{x}{2 \cos^2 (x/2)} dx$

$= \int x \left[\frac{1}{2} \sec^2 \frac{x}{2} \right] dx = x \tan \frac{x}{2} - \int 1 . \tan \frac{x}{2} dx$

$= x \tan (x/2) - 2 \log \sec (x/2).$

14. (i) $I = \int \frac{x \sin^{-1} x}{\sqrt{(1 - x^2)}} dx.$ Put $x = \sin \theta;$

$\therefore \quad dx = \cos \theta \, d\theta.$

$\therefore \quad I=\int \frac{\theta \sin \theta . \cos \theta \, d\theta}{\cos \theta}=\int \theta \sin \theta \, d\theta$

$=\theta(-\cos \theta)-\int 1(-\cos \theta) \, d\theta$

$=-\theta \cos \theta+\sin \theta$

$=-\sqrt{1-x^2} \sin^{-1} x+x$.

(ii) $I=\left[x-\sqrt{1-x^2} \sin^{-1} x\right]_0^{1/2}$

$=\left[\frac{1}{2}-\frac{\sqrt{3}}{2} . \frac{\pi}{6}\right]=\left[\frac{1}{2}-\frac{\sqrt{3}}{12} \pi\right]$.

15. $I=\int x^3 \cos x^2 \, dx$. Put $x^2=t$,

$\therefore \quad 2x \, dx=dt$.

$\therefore \quad I=\int x^2 \cos x^2 . x \, dx=\frac{1}{2} \int t \cos t \, dt$

$=\frac{1}{2}\left[t \sin t-\int 1 . \sin t \, dt\right]$

$=\frac{1}{2}[t \sin t+\cos t]$

$=\frac{1}{2}[x^2 \sin x^2+\cos x^2]$.

16. $I=\int \frac{x \tan^{-1} x}{(1+x^2)^{3/2}} dx$. Put $x=\tan \theta$;

$\therefore \quad dx=\sec^2 \theta \, d\theta$.

$\therefore \quad I=\int \frac{\theta \tan \theta}{\sec^3 \theta} \sec^2 \theta \, d\theta=\int \theta \sin \theta \, d\theta$

$=\theta(-\cos \theta)-\int 1 .(-\cos \theta) \, d\theta$

$=-\theta \cos \theta+\sin \theta$.

Now $\tan \theta=x$, $\quad \therefore \sin \theta=\frac{x}{\sqrt{(1+x^2)}}$,

$\cos \theta=\frac{1}{\sqrt{(1+x^2)}} \quad \therefore \quad I=\frac{x-\tan^{-1} x}{\sqrt{(1+x^2)}}$

17. $\sin^2 x=\frac{1-\cos 2x}{2}, \cos^2 x=\frac{1+\cos 2x}{2}$

$\therefore \quad I=\int x \sin^2 x \, dx=\int \frac{x(1-\cos 2x)}{2} dx$

$=\int \frac{x}{2} dx-\frac{1}{2} \int x \cos 2x \, dx$

$=\frac{x^2}{4}-\frac{1}{2}\left[\frac{x \sin 2x}{2}-\int 1 . \frac{\sin 2x}{2} dx\right]$

$=\frac{x^2}{4}-\frac{1}{4} x \sin 2x+\frac{1}{2}\left[-\frac{\cos 2x}{4}\right]$

$=\frac{x^2}{4}-\frac{1}{4} x \sin 2x-\frac{1}{8} \cos 2x$.

Similarly $\int x \cos^2 x \, dx=\frac{x^2}{4}+\frac{1}{4} x \sin 2x+\frac{1}{8} \cos 2x$.

18. $I=\int \cos \sqrt{x} \, dx$.

Put $\sqrt{x}=t$ so that $\frac{1}{2\sqrt{(x)}} dx=dt$

$\therefore \quad I=\int (\cos t) \, 2t \, dt=2\int t \cos t \, dt$

Integrating by parts, we get

$I=2[t \sin t-\int 1 . \sin t \, dt]$

$=2[t \sin t+\cos t]$

$=2[\sqrt{x} \sin \sqrt{x}+\cos \sqrt{x}]$.

19. (a) $I=\int x^3 (\log x)^2 \, dx$

$=\frac{x^4}{4}(\log x)^2-\int 2(\log x) . \frac{1}{x} . \frac{x^4}{4} dx$

$=\frac{x^4}{4}(\log x)^2-\frac{1}{2} \int x^3 \log x \, dx$

$=\frac{x^4}{4}(\log x)^2-\frac{1}{2}\left[\frac{x^4}{4} \log x-\int \frac{1}{x} \frac{x^4}{4} dx\right]$

$=\frac{x^4}{4}(\log x)^2-\frac{1}{8} x^4 \log x+\frac{1}{8} \int x^3 \, dx$

$=\frac{x^4}{4}(\log x)^2-\frac{1}{8} x^4 \log x+\frac{1}{32} x^4 \, dx$

(b) Ans. $\frac{2}{3} x^{3/2}\left[(\log x)^2-\frac{4}{3} \log x+\frac{8}{9}\right]$.

20. $I=\int \sin x \log (\sec x+\tan x) \, dx$

$I=(-\cos x) \log (\sec x+\tan x)$

$-\int\left[\frac{d}{dx} \log (\sec x+\tan x) .(-\cos x)\right] dx$.

Now $\int \sec x \, dx=\log (\sec x+\tan x)$;

$\therefore \quad \frac{d}{dx} \log (\sec x+\tan x)=\sec x$

$\therefore \quad I=-\cos x \log (\sec x+\tan x)-\int \sec x(-\cos x) \, dx$

$=-\cos x \log (\sec x+\tan x)+\int 1 \, dx$

$=x-\cos x \log (\sec x+\tan x)$.

21. (a) $I=\int \cos x \log \tan \frac{x}{2} dx$

$\int \operatorname{cosec} x \, dx=\log \tan \frac{x}{2}$;

$\therefore \quad \frac{d}{dx}\left(\log \tan \frac{x}{2}\right)=\operatorname{cosec} x$.

Hence as in Q. 20, $I=\sin x \log \tan (x/2)-x$.

(b) We know the following

$\log\left(\frac{\cos \theta+\sin \theta}{\cos \theta-\sin \theta}\right)=\log\left(\frac{1+\tan \theta}{1-\tan \theta}\right)$

$=\log \tan\left(\frac{\pi}{4}+\theta\right)$

$\int \sec \theta \, d\theta=\log \tan\left(\frac{\pi}{4}+\frac{\theta}{2}\right)$

$\therefore \quad \int \sec 2\theta \, d\theta=\frac{1}{2} \log \tan\left(\frac{\pi}{4}+\theta\right)$

$\therefore \quad 2\sec 2\theta = \dfrac{d}{d\theta}\log\tan\left(\dfrac{\pi}{4}+\theta\right)$ ...(1)

Integrating the given expression by parts

$$I=\frac{1}{2}\sin 2\theta\log\tan\left(\frac{\pi}{4}+\theta\right)-\frac{1}{2}\int\sin 2\theta\,.\,2\sec 2\theta\,d\theta,$$

by (1)

$$=\frac{1}{2}\sin 2\theta\log\tan\left(\frac{\pi}{4}+\theta\right)-\int\tan 2\theta\,d\theta$$

$$=\frac{1}{2}\sin 2\theta\log\tan\left(\frac{\pi}{4}+\theta\right)-\frac{1}{2}\log\sec 2\theta$$

(c) $I=\dfrac{\sin 2x}{2}\log(1+\tan x)$

$$-\frac{1}{2}\int\sin 2x\,.\,\frac{1}{1+\tan x}\sec^2 x\,dx$$

or $\quad I=\dfrac{1}{2}\sin 2x\log(1+\tan x)-\dfrac{1}{2}I_1$ ...(A)

where $I_1=\displaystyle\int\frac{2\tan x}{1+\tan^2 x}\,.\,\frac{1}{1+\tan x}(1+\tan^2 x)\,dx$

$=2\displaystyle\int\left(1-\frac{1}{1+\tan x}\right)dx$ **See Note Ex. 20 P. 1472**

$$=\int\left(2-\frac{2\cos x}{\cos x+\sin x}\right)dx$$

$$=2x-\int\frac{(\cos x+\sin x)+(\cos x-\sin x)\,dx}{\cos x+\sin x}$$

$$=2x-\int\left[1+\frac{\cos x-\sin x}{\cos x+\sin x}\right]dx$$

$$=2x-x-\log(\cos x+\sin x)$$

$$=x-\log(\cos x+\sin x)$$

Now put the value of I_1 in (A)

$\therefore \quad I=\dfrac{1}{2}\sin 2x\log(1+\tan x)$

$$-\frac{1}{2}x+\frac{1}{2}\log(\cos x+\sin x)$$

22. $I=\int\log(1+x^2)\,dx=\int 1\,.\log(1+x^2)\,dx$

$$=x\log(1+x^2)-\int x\,.\,\frac{1}{1+x^2}\,.\,2x\,dx$$

$$=x\log(1+x^2)-2\int\frac{x^2+1-1}{x^2+1}dx$$

$$=x\log(1+x^2)-2\int\left[1-\frac{1}{1+x^2}\right]dx$$

$$=x\log(1+x^2)-2x+2\tan^{-1}x.$$

23. $I=\displaystyle\int\log[x+\sqrt{x^2+a^2}]\,dx.$

We know that

$$\int\frac{1}{\sqrt{(x^2+a^2)}}dx=\log\left\{x+\sqrt{x^2+a^2}\right\}$$

$$\therefore \quad \frac{d}{dx}\log\left\{x+\sqrt{x^2+a^2}\right\}=\frac{1}{\sqrt{(x^2+a^2)}}$$

Choosing 1 as the other function

$\therefore \quad I=x\log\left\{x+\sqrt{x^2+a^2}\right\}$

$$-\int x\,.\,\frac{d}{dx}\log\left\{x+\sqrt{x^2+a^2}\right\}dx$$

$$=x\log\left\{x+\sqrt{x^2+a^2}\right\}-\int x\,.\,\frac{1}{\sqrt{(x^2+a^2)}}dx$$

$$=x\log[x+\sqrt{x^2+a^2}]-\frac{1}{2}\int\frac{2x}{\sqrt{(x^2+a^2)}}dx$$

$$=x\log[x+\sqrt{x^2+a^2}]-\frac{1}{2}\,.\,2\sqrt{(x^2+a^2)}$$

$$=x\log[x+\sqrt{x^2+a^2}]-\sqrt{x^2+a^2}$$

$$\because \int\frac{f'(x)}{\sqrt{[f(x)]}}dx=2\sqrt{f(x)}\,.$$

24. $I=\displaystyle\int e^x\frac{(1-\sin x)}{(1-\cos x)}dx$

$$=\int\left[\frac{e^x}{2\sin^2(x/2)}-e^x\frac{2\sin(x/2)\cos(x/2)}{2\sin^2(x/2)}\right]dx$$

$$=\int e^x\left(\frac{1}{2}\operatorname{cosec}^2\frac{x}{2}\right)dx-\int e^x\cot\frac{x}{2}dx.$$

Integrate first by parts

$$\therefore \quad I=e^x\left(-\cot\frac{x}{2}\right)-\int e^x\left(-\cot\frac{x}{2}\right)dx-\int e^x\cot\frac{x}{2}dx$$

$$=-e^x\cot(x/2).$$

The last two integrals cancel.

25. $I=\displaystyle\int e^x\left[\frac{1+\sqrt{1-x^2}\sin^{-1}x}{\sqrt{(1-x^2)}}\right]dx$

$$=\int e^x\,.\,\frac{1}{\sqrt{(1-x^2)}}dx+\int e^x\sin^{-1}x\,dx.$$

Integrate 1st by parts

$I=e^x\,.\sin^{-1}x-\int e^x\sin^{-1}x\,dx+\int e^x\sin^{-1}x\,dx$

$I=e^x\sin^{-1}x.\quad$ The last two integrals cancel.

Note : Above is also of the form

$$\int e^x[f(x)+f'(x)]\,dx=e^x f(x)$$

$$f(x)=\sin^{-1}x \text{ and } f'(x)=\frac{1}{\sqrt{(1-x^2)}}.$$

26. $I=\displaystyle\int e^x\frac{(2+\sin 2x)}{(1+\cos 2x)}dx.$

$$=\int\left[\frac{e^x\,.\,2}{2\cos^2 x}+e^x\frac{2\sin x\cos x}{2\cos^2 x}\right]dx$$

$\int e^x \sec^2 x\,dx + \int e^x \tan x\,dx$.

Integrate first by parts

$I = e^x \tan x - \int e^x \tan x\,dx + \int e^x \tan x\,dx$.

$= e^x \tan x$. The last two integrals cancel.

Above is of the form

$\int e^x [f(x) + f'(x)]\,dx = e^x f(x)$,

where $f(x) = \tan x$ and $f'(x) = \sec^2 x$.

27. (a) $\int \frac{xe^x}{(1+x)^2}\,dx = \int e^x \frac{(x+1-1)}{(x+1)^2}\,dx$

$= \int e^x \left[\frac{1}{x+1} + \frac{-1}{(x+1)^2}\right] dx$

$= \int e^x\ [f(x) + f'(x)]\,dx$,

where $f(x) = \frac{1}{x+1}$ and $f'(x) = \frac{-1}{(x+1)^2}$

$= e^x f(x) = e^x \cdot \frac{1}{x+1}$.

(b) Put $\log x = t$; $\therefore$ $x = e^t$ and $dx = e^t\,dt$.

$\therefore$ $I = \int \frac{\log x}{(1+\log x)^2}\,dx$

$= \int \frac{t\,e^t\,dt}{(1+t)^2} = e^t \cdot \frac{1}{t+1}$, by part (a).

$= \frac{x}{1+\log x}$.

28. (a) $I = \int e^x \frac{x(x^2+1)+1}{(x^2+1)^{3/2}}\,dx$

$= \int e^x \left[\frac{x}{\sqrt{x^2+1}} + \frac{1}{(x^2+1)^{3/2}}\right]$

It can be easily seen that

$\frac{d}{dx}\left\{\frac{x}{\sqrt{(x^2+1)}}\right\} = \frac{1}{(x^2+1)^{3/2}}$

$\therefore$ $I = \int e^x\ [f(x) + f'(x)]\,dx = e^x f(x)$

$\therefore$ $I = e^x \cdot \frac{x}{\sqrt{(x^2+1)}}$

(b) $I = \int e^x \frac{(x^2+4x+4)}{(x+4)^2}\,dx$

$= \int e^x \left[\frac{x(x+4)}{(x+4)^2} + \frac{4}{(x+4)^2}\right] dx$

$= \int e^x \left[\frac{x}{x+4} + \frac{4}{(x+4)^2}\right] dx$

Above is of the form $\int e^x\ [f(x) + f'(x)]\,dx$

$\therefore$ $I = e^x \cdot f(x) = e^x \cdot \frac{x}{x+4}$.

(c) Put $x = \tan t, 1 + \tan^2 t = \sec^2 t$

$\therefore$ $I = \int e^t (\tan t + \sec^2 t)\,dt = e^t \tan t + c$

$= x e^{\tan^{-1} x} + c$

29. (a) Ans. (c).

$\frac{d}{dx}(xe^x) = (1+x)\,e^x$

$\therefore$ $I = \int \frac{d}{dx}(xe^x)\,f(x)\,dx + \int xe^x f'(x)\,dx$

Integrating 1st by parts

$xe^x f(x) - \int xe^x f'(x)\,dx + \int xe^x f'(x)\,dx$

$= xe^x f(x) = e^x$ $\therefore$ $x f(x) = 1$

or $f(x) = 1/x \Rightarrow$ (c).

(b) Ans. (d).

$I = \int 4^x g'(x)\,dx + \int g(x)\,4^x \log 4\,dx$

Integrate 1st by parts, the second integral cancels

$\therefore I = 4^x g(x)$.

(c) Ans. (b).

Put $\log x = t$ $\therefore$ $x = e^t$ and $dx = e^t\,dt$

$I = \int \frac{(t-1)^2}{(1+t^2)^2} e^t\,dt = \int e^t \left[\frac{1+t^2-2t}{(1+t^2)^2}\right] dt$

$= \int e^t \left[\frac{1}{1+t^2} + \frac{-2t}{(1+t^2)^2}\right] dt$

$= \int e^t\ [f(t) + f'(t)]\,dt = e^t f(t)$

$= e^t \cdot \frac{1}{1+t^2} = \frac{x}{1+(\log x)^2}$

30. (a) Note that d.c. of $x \tan x + 1$ is $x \sec^2 x + \tan x$.

Hence integrating by parts, we get

$x^2 \left[-\frac{1}{x\tan x + 1}\right] + 2\int \frac{x}{x\tan x + 1}\,dx$

Now write $I = 2\int \frac{x\cos x}{x\sin x + \cos x}$

$= 2\log(x\sin x + \cos x)$

$\because$ d.c. of $x\sin x + \cos x = x\cos x$ etc.

(b) Put $\log x = t$ $\therefore$ $x = e^t$ and $dx = e^t$

When $x = e, t = 1, x = e^2, t = 2$

$I = \int_1^2 \frac{e^t}{t}\,dt = \int_1^2 \frac{e^x}{x}\,dx$, by Prop. I

(c) L.H.S. $= [\tan^{-1} 1 - \tan^{-1} t] = \frac{\pi}{4} - \tan^{-1} t$

R.H.S. $= \tan^{-1}\frac{1}{t} - \tan^{-1} 1 = \cot^{-1} t - \frac{\pi}{4}$

$= \left(\frac{\pi}{2} - \tan^{-1} t\right) - \frac{\pi}{4} = \frac{\pi}{4} - \tan^{-1} t$

Alt. Put $x = 1/y$ and adjust the limits.

31. (a) Split into two as in Q.24 $I = -x\cot(x/2)$.

(b) $\log(1+\cos x) - x\tan(x/2)$

$$I = x\log(1+\cos x) + \int x\frac{\sin x}{1+\cos x}dx - \int x\tan\frac{x}{2}$$

$$= x\log(1+\cos x) \qquad \because \frac{\sin x}{1+\cos x} = \tan\frac{x}{2}$$

32. Split into two as in Q. 26. $I = x\tan x$.

33. $I = \int x\cos x\,dx + \int \sin x\cos x\,dx$

$$= x\sin x + \cos x + \frac{1}{2}\sin^2 x.$$

34. (a) Ans. (b). Integrating by parts,

$$I = -\frac{1}{x}\log x - \int -\frac{1}{x}\cdot\frac{1}{x}dx$$

$$= -\frac{1}{x}\log x - \frac{1}{x} = -\frac{1}{x}(\log x + 1)$$

(b) Ans. $-\frac{1}{4x^2}(2\log_e x + 1) + c$.

[**Hint** : Integrate by parts].

(c) $\left(1-\frac{1}{x}\right)\log(1-x) - \log x$.

Integrate by parts.

35. $I = [x\log\{\sqrt{(1-x)} + \sqrt{(1+x)}\}]_0^1$

$$= -\int_0^1 x\cdot\frac{1}{\sqrt{(1-x)}+\sqrt{(1+x)}}\cdot\left\{\frac{-1}{2\sqrt{(1-x)}} + \frac{1}{2\sqrt{(1+x)}}\right\}dx$$

$$= \log\sqrt{2} - \int_0^1 \frac{x}{2\sqrt{(1-x^2)}}\frac{\sqrt{(1-x)}-\sqrt{(1+x)}}{\sqrt{(1-x)}+\sqrt{(1+x)}}dx$$

Rationalize

$$= \log\sqrt{2} - \int_0^1 \frac{x}{2\sqrt{(1-x^2)}}\frac{[\sqrt{1-x}-\sqrt{1+x}]^2}{(1-x)-(1+x)}$$

$$= \log\sqrt{2} - \int_0^1 \frac{x}{2\sqrt{(1-x^2)}}\cdot\frac{(1-x)+(1+x)-2\sqrt{(1-x^2)}}{-2x}dx$$

$$= \log\sqrt{2} + \int_0^1 \frac{1}{4\sqrt{(1-x^2)}}\left\{2 - 2\sqrt{(1-x^2)}\right\}dx$$

$$= \log\sqrt{2} + \frac{1}{2}\int_0^1\left\{\frac{1}{\sqrt{(1-x^2)}} - 1\right\}dx$$

$$= \log\sqrt{2} + \frac{1}{2}[\sin^{-1}x - x]_0^1$$

$$= \log\sqrt{2} + \frac{1}{2}\left[\frac{\pi}{2} - 1\right] = \frac{1}{2}\log 2 + \frac{\pi}{4} - \frac{1}{2}$$

36. $I = \frac{1}{2}\int_0^{\pi/4} x(\cos 4x + \cos 2x)\,dx.$

$$= \frac{1}{2}\left[x\left(\frac{\sin 4x}{4} + \frac{\sin 2x}{2}\right) - (1)\left(-\frac{\cos 4x}{16} - \frac{\cos 2x}{2}\right)\right]_0^{\pi/4}$$

etc.

37. $f'(x) = f(x)$

$$\therefore \int\frac{f'(x)}{f(x)}dx = \int 1.dx$$

or $\log f(x) = x + k$

Putting $x = 0$ and $f(0) = 1$, $\log 1 = 0 + k$

$\therefore$ $k = 0$ $\therefore$ $\log f(x) = x$

or $f(x) = e^x$ $\therefore$ $g(x) = x^2 - f(x) = x^2 - e^x$

$\therefore$ $I = \int_0^1 f(x)\,g(x)\,dx = \int_0^1 e^x(x^2 - e^x)\,dx$

$$= \left[e^x(x^2 - 2x + 2) - \frac{1}{2}e^{2x}\right]_0^1 \quad \text{etc.}$$

38. (a) $I_m = [x(\log x)^m]_1^e$

$$- m\int_1^e x.(\log x)^{m-1}.\frac{1}{x}dx = e - mI_{m-1}$$

$\therefore$ $I_m + mI_{m-1} = e$

(b) Ans. (c). Integrating by parts

$$I(m,n) = \left[\frac{t^{m+1}}{m+1}(1+t)^n\right]_0^1 - \frac{n}{m+1}\int t^{m+1}(1+t)^{n-1}\,dt$$

$$= \frac{2^n}{m+1} - \frac{n}{m+1}I(m+1, n-1)$$

39. (a) Integrating by parts,

$I_{10} = \int_0^{\pi/2} x^{10}\sin x\,dx$

$$= [x^{10}(-\cos x)_0^{\pi/2}] + 10\int_0^{\pi/2} x^9\cos x\,dx$$

$$= 0 + 10\,[(x^9\sin x)^{\pi/2} - 9\int_0^{\pi/2} x^8\sin x\,dx]$$

$$I_{10} = 10\left(\frac{\pi}{2}\right)^9 - 90I_8$$

$\therefore$ $I_{10} + 90I_8 = 10\left(\frac{\pi}{2}\right)^9$.

(b) $I_n = \left[\frac{x^{n+1}}{n+1}\tan^{-1}x\right]_0^1 - \frac{1}{n+1}\int\frac{x^{n+1}}{1+x^2}dx$

$\therefore$ $(n+1)I_n = \frac{\pi}{4} - \int\frac{x^{n+1}}{1+x^2}dx$ ...(1)

Replace n by $(n-2)$ in (1)

$\therefore$ $(n-1)I_{n-2} = \frac{\pi}{4} - \int\frac{x^{n-1}}{1+x^2}dx$ ...(2)

Adding (1) and (2), we get

$$\text{L.H.S.} = \left(\frac{\pi}{4} + \frac{\pi}{4}\right) - \int_0^1 x^{n-1}\frac{1+x^2}{1+x^2}dx$$

$$= \frac{\pi}{2} - \left[\frac{x^n}{n}\right]_0^1 = \frac{\pi}{2} - \frac{1}{n}$$

(c) Ans. (c).

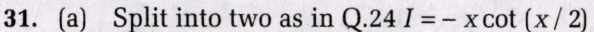

Integrating by parts,

$$P = [e^t \log(1+t)]_0^1 - \int e^t \cdot \frac{1}{1+t}\, dt = e \log 2 - I \Rightarrow \text{(c)}.$$

(d) Ans. (d).

Let $P = \int_0^{\pi} x^2 \cdot \frac{\cos x}{(1+\sin x)^2}\, dx$. Integrate by parts.

$$\therefore \quad P = \left[x^2 \left\{ -\frac{1}{1+\sin x} \right\} \right]_0^{\pi} + 2\int_0^{\pi} x \frac{1}{1+\sin x}\, dx$$

$$= -\pi^2 + 2Q \text{ where} \qquad \ldots(1)$$

$$Q = \int_0^{\pi} x \frac{1}{1+\sin x}\, dx = \int_0^{\pi} (\pi - x) \cdot \frac{1}{1+\sin x}\, dx$$

(Prop IV)

$$\therefore \quad 2Q = \pi \int_0^{\pi} \frac{1}{1+\sin x}\, dx = 2\pi \int_0^{\pi/2} \frac{1}{1+\sin x}\, dx = 2\pi I$$

$$\therefore \quad P = -\pi^2 + 2\pi I \text{ by (1).}$$

40. $\cos x$ is R.P. of e^{ix} *i.e.* of $\cos x + i \sin x$

$$\therefore \quad I = \text{R.P. of} \int x e^x e^{ix}\, dx = \int x e^{(1+i)x}\, dx$$

Integrating by parts

$$I = x \cdot \frac{e^{(1+i)x}}{(1+i)} - \frac{1}{(1+i)} \int e^{(1+i)x} \cdot 1\, dx$$

$$= x \cdot \frac{e^{(1+i)x}}{(1+i)} - \frac{1}{(1+i)^2} e^{(1+i)x}$$

$$= \frac{e^{(1+i)x}}{(1+i)^2} [x(1+i) - 1] = \frac{e^x \cdot e^{ix}}{2i} [x + xi - 1]$$

$$= \frac{e^x [(x-1) + ix](\cos x + i \sin x)}{2i}$$

Real part of above is imaginary part of N^r

$$\therefore \quad I = \frac{e^x}{2} [(x-1)\sin x + x \cos x]$$

41. (a) Write $\frac{1}{x^{10}} = \frac{1}{x^7 \cdot x^3} = \frac{1}{x^7 \cdot \sqrt{x^6}}$

$$I = \int \sqrt{\frac{x^6+1}{x^6}} \log \frac{x^6+1}{x^6} \cdot \frac{1}{x^7}\, dx$$

Put $\frac{x^6+1}{x^6} = 1 + \frac{1}{x^6} = t \quad \therefore \quad \frac{-6}{x^7}\, dx = dt$

$$\therefore \quad I = \int -\frac{1}{6} \sqrt{t} \log t\, dt$$

$$= \frac{-1}{6} \left[\frac{2}{3} t^{3/2} \log t - \frac{2}{3} \int t^{3/2} \frac{1}{t}\, dt \right]$$

$$= -\frac{1}{6} \left[\frac{2}{3} t^{3/2} \log t - \frac{4}{9} t^{3/2} \right] \text{etc.}$$

(b) $I = \int \log \left\{ \frac{1+x^{2n}}{x^{2n}} \right\} \cdot \frac{\sqrt{1+x^{2n}}}{x^n \cdot x^{2n+1}}\, dx$

Put $\frac{1+x^{2n}}{x^{2n}} = 1 + \frac{1}{x^{2n}} = t \quad \therefore \quad -\frac{2n}{x^{2n+1}}\, dx = dt$

$$\therefore \quad I = -\frac{1}{2n} \int \sqrt{t} \cdot \log t\, dt = -\frac{1}{2n} \left[\frac{2}{3} t \sqrt{t} \log t - \frac{4}{9} t \sqrt{t} \right]$$

as in part (a).

42. (a) $4x^2 + 8x + 13 = (2x+2)^2 + 9$

If we put $2x + 2 = t$ then $dx = \frac{1}{2} dt$

$$\therefore \quad I = \frac{1}{2} \int \sin^{-1} \frac{t}{\sqrt{t^2+9}}\, dt$$

Now put $t = 3\tan\theta \quad \therefore \; 3\sec^2\theta\, d\theta = dt$

$$\therefore \quad I = \frac{1}{2} \int \sin^{-1} \frac{3\tan\theta}{3\sec\theta} \cdot 3\sec^2\theta\, d\theta$$

$$= \frac{3}{2} \int \sin^{-1} \sin\theta \sec^2\theta\, d\theta$$

$$= \frac{3}{2} \int \theta \sec^2\theta\, d\theta$$

$$= \frac{3}{2} \left[\theta \tan\theta - \int \tan\theta\, d\theta \right]$$

$$= \frac{3}{2} [\theta \tan\theta - \log\sec\theta] \quad \text{where } \tan\theta = \frac{t}{3} = \frac{2x+2}{3}.$$

(b) $D^r = \int_0^1 (1 - x^{50})^{101}\, 1\, dx.$

Integrating by parts,

$$D^r = [x(1-x^{50})^{101}]_0^1 - \int_0^1 x(101)[1-x^{50}]^{100} (-50x^{49})\, dx$$

$$= 0 + 5050 \int (1-x^{50})^{100} x^{50}\, dx$$

$$= (5050) \int_0^1 (1-x^{50})^{100} [x^{50} - 1 + 1]\, dx$$

$$= (5050) [-\int (1-x^{50})^{101} + \int_0^1 (1-x^{50})^{100}\, dx$$

$$= N^r - (5050) D^r$$

$$\therefore \quad R = \frac{N^r}{D^r} = \frac{N^r}{N^r - (5050) D^r} = \frac{1}{1 - (5050) \frac{D^r}{N^r}}$$

$$\therefore \quad R \left[1 - \frac{5050}{R} \right] = 1 \text{ or } R - 5050 = 1$$

$$\therefore \quad R = 5050 + 1 = 5051$$

43. (a) $I = \int e^x \left[\frac{1 - x^{2n}}{(1-x^n)\sqrt{1-x^{2n}}} + \frac{nx^{n-1}}{(1-x^n)\sqrt{1-x^{2n}}} \right]$

$$T_1 = \frac{\sqrt{1-x^{2n}}}{1-x^n} = \frac{\sqrt{(1-x^n)(1+x^n)}}{1-x^n} = \sqrt{\frac{1+x^n}{1-x^n}}$$

It is easy to observe that d.c. of $T_1 = T_2$ etc.

(b) $I = \int (\cos^{-203} x) \operatorname{cosec}^2 x\, dx - \int \frac{203}{(\cos x)^{203}}\, dx$

$$= I_1 - I_2$$

Integrate I_1 by parts

$\therefore \quad I_1 = (\cos^{-203} x)(-\cot x)$
$\quad - \int \cot x . 203 \cos^{-204} x (-\sin x)\, dx$

$I_1 = -\frac{\cot x}{(\cos x)^{203}} + \int \frac{203}{(\cos x)^{203}} dx$ i.e., I_2

$\therefore \quad I_1 - I_2 =$ as given.

44. $I = \int \frac{x\,dx}{x^4 \sqrt{x^2 - 1}}$. Put $x^2 - 1 = t^2$

$\therefore \quad x\,dx = t\,dt$

$\therefore \quad I = \int \frac{t\,dt}{(t^2+1)^2 t} = \int \frac{1}{(t^2+1)^2} dt \quad \ldots(1)$

Now, $\int \frac{1}{t^2+1} dt = \tan^{-1} t$

$\therefore \quad \tan^{-1} t = \int 1 \cdot \frac{1}{(t^2+1)} dt$. Integrate by parts

$\tan^{-1} t = t \cdot \frac{1}{(t^2+1)} - \int \frac{t \cdot (-2t)}{(t^2+1)^2} dt$

$= \frac{t}{t^2+1} + 2 \int \frac{(t^2+1) - 1}{(t^2+1)^2}$

$= \frac{t}{t^2+1} + 2 \tan^{-1} t - 2I$

or $\quad 2I = \frac{t}{t^2+1} + \tan^{-1} t$

or $\quad I = \frac{1}{2}\left[\frac{t}{t^2+1} + \tan^{-1} t\right]$, where $t^2 = x^2 - 1$

$= \frac{1}{2}\left[\frac{\sqrt{x^2-1}}{x^2} + \tan^{-1} \sqrt{x^2-1}\right]$

§12. Integration of Rational and Irrational fractions.

Students are fully conversant with the process of splitting a given fraction into partial fractions. In the case of irrational fractions we make such substitution so that the fractional powers are removed. The process will be clear from the following examples.

Solved Examples

Ex. 1. (a) $\int_0^{\pi/2} \frac{\cos x\,dx}{(1+\sin x)(2+\sin x)}$

Here we know that d.c. of $\sin x$ is $\cos x$. Hence we put
$\sin x = t \quad \therefore \quad \cos x\,dx = dt$.
Also when $x = \pi/2, t = 1$ and when $x = 0, t = 0$.

$\therefore \quad I = \int_0^1 \frac{dt}{(1+t)(2+t)}$.

Now split into partial fractions by the method of suppression

$I = \int_0^1 \left(\frac{1}{1+t} - \frac{1}{2+t}\right) dt$

$= [\log\{(1+t) - \log(2+t)\}]_0^1 = \left[\log \frac{1+t}{2+t}\right]_0^1$

$= \log \frac{2}{3} - \log \frac{1}{2} = \log\left[\frac{2}{3} \div \frac{1}{2}\right] = \log \frac{4}{3}$.

(b) Prove :

$\int_0^1 \frac{2e^{2x}\,dx}{e^{3x} - 6e^{2x} + 11e^x - 6} = \log \frac{(e^x - 1)(e^x - 3)^3}{(e^x - 2)^4}$

Put $e^x = t \quad \therefore \quad e^x\,dx = dt$

$\therefore \quad I = \int \frac{2t\,dt}{(t-1)(t-2)(t-3)}$

Now split into partial fractions and integrate.

Ex. 2. $\int \frac{1 - \cos x}{\cos x (1 + \cos x)} dx$.

Here we have $\cos x$ but its d.c. *i.e.,* $-\sin x$ is not present in the numerator and as such we cannot make the substitution of $\cos x = t$. But we simply put $\cos x = t$ to split the integrand into partial fractions.

$\frac{1-\cos x}{\cos x (1+\cos x)} = \frac{1-t}{t(1+t)}$ (say)

$= \left(\frac{1}{t} - \frac{2}{1+t}\right) = \left(\frac{1}{\cos x} - \frac{2}{1+\cos x}\right)$

$\therefore \quad I = \int \left(\frac{1}{\cos x} - \frac{2}{1+\cos x}\right) dx = \int \left(\sec x - \sec^2 \frac{x}{2}\right) dx$

$= \log(\sec x + \tan x) - 2\tan(x/2)$.

***Ex. 3. (a)** $\int \frac{dx}{x(x^n + 1)}$. **(Important)**

Here we multiply above and below by x^{n-1}

$\therefore \quad I = \int \frac{x^{n-1}\,dx}{x^n (x^n + 1)}$.

Now d.c. of x^n is nx^{n-1} which is present in the numerator.
Therefore we make the substitution

$x^n = t \quad \therefore \quad nx^{n-1}\,dx = dt$

$\therefore \quad I = \frac{1}{n} \int \frac{dt}{t(t+1)} = \frac{1}{n} \int \left(\frac{1}{t} - \frac{1}{t+1}\right) . dt$

$= \frac{1}{n}[\log t - \log(t+1)] = \frac{1}{n} \log \frac{x^n}{x^n + 1}$.

Similarly, $\int \frac{dx}{x(x^3+1)} = \frac{1}{3} \log \frac{x^3}{x^3+1}$

and $\int \frac{dx}{x(x^4+1)} = \frac{1}{4} \log \frac{x^4}{x^4+1}$ etc.

(b) $\int \frac{dx}{(x+1)(2+2x+x^2)}$

$I = \int \frac{dx}{(x+1)\{(x+1)^2 + 1\}}$

$$=\int \frac{dt}{t(t^2+1)}=\int \frac{t\,dt}{t^2(1+t^2)}=\frac{1}{2}\int \frac{dz}{z(z+1)}$$

$$=\frac{1}{2}\int\left(\frac{1}{z}-\frac{1}{z+1}\right)dz=\frac{1}{2}\log\frac{z}{z+1}$$

$$=\frac{1}{2}\log\frac{t^2}{t^2+1}, \qquad \text{where } t=x+1$$

(c) $\int_1^{\sqrt[7]{2}} \frac{1}{x(2x^7+1)}dx=\frac{1}{7}\log\frac{6}{5}$.

Multiply above and below by x^6 and put $x^7=t$ and adjust the limits.

***Ex. 4. (a)** $\int \frac{dx}{\sin x+\sin 2x}$

$$I=\int \frac{dx}{\sin x(1+2\cos x)}=\int \frac{\sin x\,dx}{\sin^2 x(1+2\cos x)}$$

$$=\int \frac{\sin x\,dx}{(1-\cos x)(1+\cos x)(1+2\cos x)}.$$

Now d.c. of $\cos x$ is $-\sin x$ which is given in numerator and hence we make the substitution

$\cos x=t \quad \therefore \quad -\sin x\,dx=dt$

$$\therefore \quad I=-\int \frac{dt}{(1-t)(1+t)(1+2t)}.$$

We split the integrand into partial fractions by the method of suppression.

$$\therefore \quad I=-\int\left[\frac{1}{6(1-t)}-\frac{1}{2(1+t)}+\frac{4}{3(1+2t)}\right]dt$$

$$=\int\left[\frac{1}{6}\left(\frac{-1}{1-t}\right)+\frac{1}{2}\cdot\frac{1}{1+t}-\frac{2}{3}\cdot\frac{2}{1+2t}\right]dt$$

$$=\frac{1}{6}\log(1-t)+\frac{1}{2}\log(1+t)-\frac{2}{3}\log(1+2t)$$

$$=\frac{1}{6}\log(1-\cos x)+\frac{1}{2}\log(1+\cos x)$$

$$-\frac{2}{3}\log(1+2\cos x).$$

(b) $\int_0^{\pi/2} \frac{\sin x\cos x}{\cos^2 x+3\cos x+2}dx=\log\frac{9}{8}$.

Put $\cos x=t$

$$\therefore \quad I=-\int_1^0 \frac{t\,dt}{(t+1)(t+2)}=\int_0^1\left(\frac{2}{t+2}-\frac{1}{t+1}\right)dt$$

$$=\left[\log\frac{(t+2)^2}{(t+1)}\right]_0^1=\log\frac{9}{2}-\log 4=\log\frac{9}{8}.$$

(c)* Evaluate : $\int_0^{\pi/4} \frac{\sec x}{1+2\sin^2 x}dx$ **(M.N.R. 1994)**

$$I=\int_0^{\pi/4} \frac{\cos x}{\cos^2 x(1+2\sin^2 x)}dx$$

$$=\frac{1}{3}\int_0^{1/\sqrt{2}}\left(\frac{1}{1-t^2}+\frac{2}{1+2t^2}\right)dt$$

by partial fractions where $t=\sin x$

$$=\frac{1}{3}\left[\frac{1}{2.1}\log\frac{1+t}{1-t}+\frac{2}{\sqrt{2}}\tan^{-1}t\sqrt{2}\right]_0^{1/\sqrt{2}}$$

$$=\frac{1}{3}\left[\frac{1}{2}\log\frac{\sqrt{2}+1}{(\sqrt{2}-1)}+\sqrt{2}\tan^{-1}1\right]$$

$$=\frac{1}{3}\left[\frac{1}{2}\log(\sqrt{2}+1)^2+\sqrt{2}\cdot\frac{\pi}{4}\right]=\frac{1}{3}\left[\log(\sqrt{2}+1)+\frac{\pi}{2\sqrt{2}}\right]$$

(d) $\int \frac{dx}{1-\sin^4 x}$

$$I=\int \frac{1}{(1-\sin^2 x)(1+\sin^2 x)}dx \text{ P.F. in } \sin^2 x$$

$$=\int\left[\frac{1}{2(1-\sin^2 x)}+\frac{1}{2(1+\sin^2 x)}\right]dx$$

$$=\frac{1}{2}\int\left[\sec^2 x+\frac{\sec^2 x}{(1+\tan^2 x+\tan^2 x)}\right]dx$$

$$=\frac{1}{2}\left[\tan x+\int\frac{dt}{1+2t^2}\right]=\frac{1}{2}\left[\tan x+\frac{1}{\sqrt{2}}\tan^{-1}\sqrt{2}t\right]$$

$$=\frac{1}{2}\left[\tan x+\frac{1}{\sqrt{2}}\tan^{-1}\sqrt{2}\tan x\right]$$

Ex. 5. $\int \frac{x^2\,dx}{(a+bx)^2}$

Put $a+bx=t \quad \therefore \quad b\,dx=dt$.

Also $\quad x=\frac{t-a}{b}$

$$\therefore \quad I=\int \frac{1}{t^2}\frac{(t-a)^2}{b^2}\frac{dt}{b}=\frac{1}{b^3}\int\frac{t^2-2at+a^2}{t^2}dt$$

$$=\frac{1}{b^3}\int\left(1-\frac{2a}{t}+\frac{a^2}{t^2}\right)dt=\frac{1}{b^3}\left[t-2a\log t-\frac{a^2}{t}\right]$$

Now put $t=a+bx$

Ex. 6. $\int \frac{x^3}{(1+x^2)^2}dx$.

Now $x^3=x^2.x$ and d.c. of x^2 is $2x$.

Hence we put $1+x^2=t \quad \therefore \quad 2x\,dx=dt$

and $\quad x^2=t-1$

$$\therefore \quad I=\int \frac{x^2}{(1+x^2)^2}x\,dx=\int\frac{t-1}{t^2}\frac{1}{2}dt$$

$$=\frac{1}{2}\int\left(\frac{1}{t}-\frac{1}{t^2}\right)dt=\frac{1}{2}\left[\log t+\frac{1}{t}\right]$$

$$= \frac{1}{2}\left[\log(x^2+1) + \frac{1}{x^2+1}\right].$$

***Ex. 7.** $\int \frac{1}{x\sqrt{(1+x^n)}}\,dx$. See also **Ex. 3. P. 1493**

Here we multiply above and below by x^{n-1}.

$$\therefore \quad I = \int \frac{x^{n-1}\,dx}{x^n\sqrt{(1+x^n)}}$$

Now d.c. of x^n is nx^{n-1}.

Also in order to remove the fractional powers we put $1+x^n = t^2$.

$\therefore \quad nx^{n-1}\,dx = 2t\,dt$. Also $x^n = t^2-1$

$$\therefore \quad I = \frac{1}{n}\int \frac{2t\,dt}{(t^2-1).t} = \frac{2}{n}\int \frac{dt}{t^2-1} = \frac{2}{n}\frac{1}{2}\log\frac{t-1}{t+1}$$

$$= \frac{1}{n}\log\frac{\sqrt{1+x^n}-1}{\sqrt{(1+x^n)}+1}$$

$$\therefore \quad \int \frac{1}{x\sqrt{(1+x^3)}}\,dx = \frac{1}{3}\log\frac{\sqrt{1+x^3}-1}{\sqrt{(1+x^3)}+1}.$$

Ex. 8. $\int \frac{x^2\,dx}{\sqrt{(1-x)}}$.

Put $1-x=t^2$, $\therefore\ dx = -2t\,dt$.

Also $x = 1-t^2$.

$$\therefore \quad I = \int \frac{(1-t^2)^2(-2t\,dt)}{t} = -2\int (1-2t^2+t^4)\,dt$$

$$= -2\left[t - \frac{2}{3}t^3 + \frac{1}{5}t^5\right] = -2t\left[1 - \frac{2}{3}t^2 + \frac{1}{5}t^4\right]$$

Now put $t = \sqrt{1-x}$

$$= -\frac{2\sqrt{1-x}}{15}[15 - 10(1-x) + 3(1-2x+x^2)]$$

$$= -\frac{2\sqrt{1-x}}{15}[8+4x+3x^2].$$

Similarly, $\int \frac{x^2}{\sqrt{(x+1)}}\,dx = \frac{1}{15}\sqrt{1+x}\,[8-4x+3x^2]$.

Ex. 9. $\int \frac{x^5}{\sqrt{(1+x^3)}}\,dx$.

Here $x^5 = x^3 . x^2$ and d.c. of x^3 is $3x^2$.

In order to remove fractional powers we put

$1 + x^3 = t^2$

$\therefore \quad 3x^2\,dx = 2t$. Also $x^3 = t^2 - 1$

$$\therefore \quad I = \int \frac{x^5}{\sqrt{(1+x^3)}}\,dx = \int \frac{x^3 . x^2\,dx}{\sqrt{(1+x^3)}}$$

$$= \int \frac{(t^2-1)}{t}\left(\frac{2}{3}t\,dt\right) = \frac{2}{3}\int (t^2-1)\,dt$$

$$= \frac{2}{3}\left(\frac{t^3}{3} - t\right) = \frac{2}{9}t\,(t^2-3) = \frac{2}{9}\sqrt{1+x^3}\,(1+x^3-3)$$

$$= \frac{2}{9}\sqrt{1+x^3}\,.(x^3-2).$$

Ex. 10. $\int \frac{x^5}{\sqrt{(1+x^2)}}\,dx$.

As above $x^5 = x^4 . x$ and d.c. of x^2 is $2x$.

Put $1+x^2 = t^2 \quad \therefore\ 2x\,dx = 2t\,dt$

and $x^2 = t^2 - 1$

$$\therefore \quad I = \int \frac{x^4 . x\,dx}{\sqrt{(1+x^2)}} = \int \frac{(t^2-1)^2\,t\,dt}{t}$$

$$= \int (t^4 - 2t^2 + 1)\,dt = \left(\frac{t^5}{5} - 2\frac{t^3}{3} + t\right)$$

$$= \frac{1}{15}t\,(3t^4 - 10t^2 + 15)$$

$$= \frac{1}{15}\sqrt{1+x^2}\,[3(1+x^4+2x^2) - 10(1+x^2) + 15]$$

$$= \frac{1}{15}\sqrt{1+x^2}\,[3x^4 - 4x^2 + 8].$$

Ex. 11. $\int \frac{1}{(x+1)\sqrt{(x-1)}}\,dx$.

Put $x - 1 = t^2 \quad \therefore\ dx = 2t\,dt$.

Also $\quad x = t^2 + 1$

$$\therefore \quad I = \int \frac{2t\,dt}{(t^2+2)\,t} = 2\int \frac{1}{t^2 + (\sqrt{2})^2}\,dt$$

$$= 2.\frac{1}{\sqrt{(2)}}\tan^{-1}\frac{t}{\sqrt{(2)}} = \sqrt{2}\tan^{-1}\frac{t}{\sqrt{(2)}}.$$

$$= \sqrt{2}\tan^{-1}\sqrt{\left(\frac{x-1}{2}\right)}$$

Ex. 12. $\int \frac{1+x^2}{\sqrt{(1-x^2)}}\,dx.$

Numerator $1+x^2$ is written as

$-[1-x^2-2] = 2-(1-x^2)$

$$\therefore \quad I = \int \frac{2-(1-x^2)}{\sqrt{(1-x^2)}}\,dx = \int \frac{2}{\sqrt{(1-x^2)}}\,dx - \int \sqrt{1-x^2}\,dx$$

$$= 2\sin^{-1}x - \left\{\frac{x}{2}\sqrt{1-x^2} + \frac{1}{2}\sin^{-1}x\right\}$$

$$= \frac{3}{2}\sin^{-1}x - \frac{x}{2}\sqrt{1-x^2}.$$

***Ex. 13.** $\int x\sqrt{\frac{1-x}{1+x}}\,dx$

$$I = \int \frac{x(1-x)}{\sqrt{(1-x^2)}}\,dx = \int \frac{x}{\sqrt{(1-x^2)}}\,dx + \int \frac{-x^2}{\sqrt{(1-x^2)}}$$

$$= -\frac{1}{2}\int \frac{-2x}{\sqrt{(1-x^2)}}\,dx + \int \frac{1-x^2-1}{\sqrt{(1-x^2)}}\,dx$$

$$= -\frac{1}{2}\cdot 2\sqrt{1-x^2} + \int \sqrt{1-x^2}\, dx - \int \frac{1}{\sqrt{(1-x^2)}}\, dx$$

$\because \quad \int \frac{f'(x)}{\sqrt{[f(x)]}}\, dx = 2\sqrt{f(x)}$

$$= -\sqrt{1-x^2} + \left[\frac{x}{2}\sqrt{1-x^2} + \frac{1}{2}\sin^{-1} x\right] - \sin^{-1} x$$

$$= \left(\frac{x}{2} - 1\right)\sqrt{1-x^2} - \frac{1}{2}\sin^{-1} x.$$

Ex. 14. $\int \frac{dx}{(2x+3)\sqrt{(4x+5)}}$

and hence deduce the integral of

$$\int \frac{8x^2 + 22x + 17}{(2x+3)\sqrt{(4x+5)}}\, dx.$$

Put $4x+5 = t^2 \quad \therefore \quad 4\,dx = 2t\,dt$ and $x = \frac{t^2-5}{4}$

$\therefore \quad 2x + 3 = \frac{t^2-5}{2} + 3 = \frac{t^2+1}{2}$

$\therefore \quad I = \frac{1}{2}\int \frac{t\,dt}{(t^2+1)/2 . t}$

$$= \int \frac{dt}{t^2+1} = \tan^{-1} t = \tan^{-1}\sqrt{4x+5}$$

Now $8x^2 + 22x + 17 = (2x+3)(4x+5) + 2$

$\therefore \quad I = \int \frac{8x^2 + 22x + 17}{(2x+3)\sqrt{(4x+5)}}\, dx$

$$= \int \frac{(2x+3)(4x+5) + 2}{(2x+3)\sqrt{(4x+5)}}\, dx.$$

$$= \int \sqrt{4x+5} + 2\int \frac{dx}{(2x+3)\sqrt{(4x+5)}}$$

$$= \frac{1}{4}\cdot\frac{2}{3}(4x+5)^{3/2} + 2\tan^{-1}\sqrt{4x+5}$$

as proved above.

$$= \frac{1}{6}(4x+5)^{3/2} + 2\tan^{-1}\sqrt{4x+5}.$$

***Ex. 15. (a)** $\int_0^{1/\sqrt{3}} \frac{dx}{(1+x^2)\sqrt{(1-x^2)}}$

Put $x = \frac{1}{t} \quad \therefore \quad dx = -\frac{1}{t^2}\,dt$

Also when $x = \frac{1}{\sqrt{(3)}}$, $t = \sqrt{3}$

and when $\quad x = 0, t = \infty$

$\therefore \quad I = \int_\infty^{\sqrt{3}} \frac{-1/t^2\,dt}{(1+t^2)/t^2 . \sqrt{(t^2-1)}/t}$

$$= \int_\infty^{\sqrt{3}} \frac{-t\,dt}{(1+t^2)\sqrt{(t^2-1)}}$$

Now differentiation of t^2 is $2t$ which is present and in order to remove fractional power we put $t^2 - 1 = z^2$

$\therefore \quad 2t\,dt = 2z\,dz$ and $t^2 = 1 + z^2$

Also when $\quad t = \sqrt{3}$ then $z = \sqrt{2}$

and when $\quad t = \infty, z = \infty$

$\therefore \quad I = -\int_\infty^{\sqrt{3}} \frac{z\,dz}{(z^2+2)\,z} = -\int_\infty^{\sqrt{2}} \frac{dz}{z^2+2}$

$$= -\frac{1}{\sqrt{(2)}}\left[\tan^{-1}\frac{z}{\sqrt{(2)}}\right]_\infty^{\sqrt{2}}$$

$$= -\frac{1}{\sqrt{(2)}}[\tan^{-1} 1 - \tan^{-1}\infty]$$

$$= -\frac{1}{\sqrt{(2)}}\left[\frac{\pi}{4} - \frac{\pi}{2}\right] = -\frac{1}{\sqrt{(2)}}\left[-\frac{\pi}{4}\right] = \frac{\pi}{4\sqrt{(2)}}.$$

(b)* Prove that :

$$\int_0^{1/2} \frac{dx}{(1-2x^2)\sqrt{(1-x^2)}} = \frac{1}{2}\log(2+\sqrt{3})$$

Put $x = \frac{1}{t}$ and adjust the limits

$$I = -\int_\infty^{2} \frac{t\,dt}{(t^2-2)\sqrt{t^2-1}}$$

Now put $t^2 - 1 = z^2 \quad \therefore \quad 2t\,dt = 2z\,dz$

$$I = \int_{\sqrt{3}}^{\infty} \frac{z\,dz}{(z^2-1)\,z} = \frac{1}{2.1}\left[\log\frac{z-1}{z+1}\right]_{\sqrt{3}}^{\infty}$$

$$= \frac{1}{2}\left[\log\frac{\left(1-\frac{1}{z}\right)}{\left(1+\frac{1}{z}\right)}\right]_{\sqrt{3}}^{\infty} = \frac{1}{2}\left[\log 1 - \log\frac{\sqrt{3}-1}{\sqrt{3}+1}\right]$$

$$= \frac{1}{2}\log\frac{\sqrt{3}+1}{\sqrt{3}-1} = \frac{1}{2}\log\frac{(\sqrt{3}+1)^2}{2} = \frac{1}{2}\log(2+\sqrt{3}).$$

(c) Evaluate the integral $\int_0^{\pi/6} \frac{\sqrt{3\cos 2x - 1}}{\cos x}\, dx.$

(Roorkee 1999)

Multiply above and below by $\cos x$ and change in terms of $\sin x$ and put $\sin x = t$ so that $\cos x\,dx = dt$. Also adjust the limits as 0 to 1/2.

$$I = \int_0^{1/2} \frac{\sqrt{2-6t^2}}{1-t^2}\, dt = \sqrt{2}\int_0^{1/2} \frac{1-3t^2}{(1-t^2)\sqrt{(1-3t^2)}}\, dt.$$

$$= \sqrt{2}\int_0^{1/2} \frac{3(1-t^2) - 2}{(1-t^2)\sqrt{(1-3t^2)}}\, dt$$

$$= \sqrt{2}\left[\int_0^{1/2} \frac{3}{\sqrt{(1-3t^2)}}\, dt - \int_0^{1/2} \frac{2}{(1-t^2)\sqrt{(1-3t^2)}}\, dt\right]$$

$$= \sqrt{2}\,[I_1 - I_2] \qquad \ldots(1)$$

$$I_1 = \frac{3}{\sqrt{3}}[\sin^{-1} t\sqrt{3}]_0^{1/2} = \sqrt{3}\sin^{-1}\frac{\sqrt{3}}{2} = \sqrt{3}\cdot\frac{\pi}{3} = \frac{\pi}{\sqrt{3}} \qquad \text{...(2)}$$

For I_2 put $t = \frac{1}{z}$ and adjust the limits

$$I_2 = 2\int_\infty^2 \frac{z^2}{(z^2-1)}\frac{z}{\sqrt{(z^2-3)}}\cdot\left(-\frac{1}{z^2}dz\right)$$

$$= 2\int_2^\infty \frac{z}{(z^2-1)\sqrt{(z^2-3)}}dz$$

Put $z^2 - 3 = u^2$ $\therefore$ $z\,dz = u\,du$ and adjust the limits

$$I_2 = 2\int_1^\infty \frac{u\,du}{(u^2+2)u} = 2.\frac{1}{\sqrt{2}}\left[\tan^{-1}\frac{u}{\sqrt{2}}\right]_1^\infty$$

$$= \sqrt{2}\left[\frac{\pi}{2} - \tan^{-1}\frac{1}{\sqrt{2}}\right] = \sqrt{2}\cot^{-1}\frac{1}{\sqrt{2}}$$

$$= \sqrt{2}\tan^{-1}\sqrt{2}$$

$$\therefore \quad I = \sqrt{2}\left[\frac{\pi}{\sqrt{3}} - \sqrt{2}\tan^{-1}\sqrt{2}\right]$$

$$= \pi\sqrt{\frac{2}{3}} - 2\tan^{-1}\sqrt{2} \qquad \text{...(3)}$$

Ex. 16. (a)* $\displaystyle\int \frac{dx}{(1+x)^{1/2} - (1+x)^{1/3}}$

(b) $\displaystyle\int \frac{x^{1/2}}{x^{1/2} - x^{1/3}}dx.$

(a) In order to remove the fractional powers $\frac{1}{2}$ and $\frac{1}{3}$ we should put $(1+x) = t^6$ where 6 is the L.C.M. of 2 and 3 .

$$\therefore \quad I = \int \frac{6t^5\,dt}{t^3 - t^2} = 6\int \frac{t^3}{t-1}dt = 6\int \frac{t^3 - 1 + 1}{t-1}dt$$

$$= 6\int\left\{(t^2+t+1) + \frac{1}{t-1}\right\}dt$$

$$= 6\left[\frac{t^3}{3} + \frac{t^2}{2} + t + \log(t-1)\right]$$

where $t = (1+x)^{1/6}$.

(b) Do yourself.

Ex. 17. (a)* $\displaystyle\int_0^{\pi/4} \frac{\sin x + \cos x}{9 + 16\sin 2x}dx.$ **(V. Imp.)**

N^r is d.c. of $\sin x - \cos x$

Put $\sin x - \cos x = t$

$\therefore$ $(\cos x + \sin x)\,dx = dt$

Also squaring, we get $1 - 2\sin x\cos x = t^2$

or $1 - t^2 = \sin 2x$

Again when $x = \pi/4, t = 0$

when $x = 0, t = -1$

$$\therefore \quad I = \int_{-1}^0 \frac{dt}{9 + 16(1-t^2)} = \int_{-1}^0 \frac{dt}{5^2 - (4t)^2}$$

$$= \frac{1}{4}\cdot\frac{1}{2.5}\left[\log\frac{5+4t}{5-4t}\right]_{-1}^0$$

$$\because \quad \int \frac{1}{a^2 - x^2}dx = \frac{1}{2a}\log\frac{a+x}{a-x}$$

$$= \frac{1}{40}\cdot\left[\log 1 - \log\frac{1}{9}\right] = \frac{1}{40}\log 3^2 = \frac{1}{20}\log 3.$$

(b) $\displaystyle\int \frac{(\sin\theta - \cos\theta)}{\sqrt{(\sin 2\theta)}}d\theta$

N^r is d.c. of $\sin\theta + \cos\theta$

Put $\sin\theta + \cos\theta = t$ ...(1)

$\therefore$ $(\cos\theta - \sin\theta)\,d\theta = dt$

Also $1 + \sin 2\theta = t^2$ $\therefore$ $\sin 2\theta = t^2 - 1$ ...(2)

$$\therefore \quad I = \int \frac{-dt}{\sqrt{(t^2-1)}} = -\log\{t + \sqrt{t^2-1}\}$$

$$= -\log(\sin\theta + \cos\theta + \sqrt{\sin 2\theta}) \qquad \text{by (1), (2)}$$

18. (a)* $\displaystyle I = \int_0^{\pi/4} \frac{\sin x + \cos x}{\cos^2 x + \sin^4 x}dx$ **(Roorkee 1991)**

$$I = \int_0^{\pi/4} \frac{4(\sin x + \cos x)\,dx}{2(1+\cos 2x) + (1-\cos 2x)^2}$$

$$= 4\int_0^{\pi/4} \frac{(\sin x + \cos x)}{3 + \cos^2 2x} = 4\int_0^{\pi/4} \frac{\sin x + \cos x}{4 - \sin^2 2x}dx$$

Now put $\sin x - \cos x = t$ so that

$(\cos x + \sin x)\,dx = dt$

and on squaring $1 - \sin 2x = t^2$. Also adjust the limits for t.

$$\therefore \quad I = 4\int_{-1}^0 \frac{dt}{4 - (1-t^2)^2} = 4\int_{-1}^0 \frac{dt}{(3-t^2)(1+t^2)}$$

$$= 4\int_{-1}^0 \left[\frac{1}{4(3-t^2)} + \frac{1}{4(1+t^2)}\right]dt \qquad \text{P.F's}$$

$$= \frac{1}{2\sqrt{(3)}}\left[\log\left(\frac{\sqrt{3}+t}{\sqrt{(3)}-t}\right)\right]_{-1}^0 + \left[\tan^{-1} t\right]_{-1}^0$$

$$= \frac{1}{2\sqrt{(3)}}\left[0 - \log\frac{\sqrt{3}-1}{\sqrt{(3)}+1}\right] + \left[0 - \left(-\frac{\pi}{4}\right)\right]$$

$$= \frac{1}{2\sqrt{(3)}}\log\frac{\sqrt{3}+1}{\sqrt{(3)}-1} + \frac{\pi}{4}$$

$$= \frac{1}{2\sqrt{(3)}}\log\frac{(\sqrt{3}+1)^2}{2} + \frac{\pi}{4} = \frac{1}{\sqrt{(3)}}\log\frac{(\sqrt{3}+1)}{\sqrt{(2)}} + \frac{\pi}{4}.$$

Note : See Q. 30 (a, b) P. 1515-20 for similar questions.

(b) $\int \frac{\sin x + \cos x}{\sin^4 x + \cos^4 x} dx$

Proceed as in part (a).

$$I = \int \frac{2\,dt}{2-(1-t^2)^2} = \int \frac{2\,dt}{(\sqrt{2}-1+t^2)(\sqrt{2}+1-t^2)}$$

$$= \int \frac{1}{\sqrt{2}}\left[\frac{1}{\sqrt{2}+1-t^2} + \frac{1}{\sqrt{2}-1+t^2}\right] dt \text{ etc.}$$

19.* $\int \frac{\cos^3 x + \cos^5 x}{\sin^2 x + \sin^4 x} dx$

$$I = \int \frac{\cos^3 x\,(1+\cos^2 x)}{\sin^2 x\,(1+\sin^2 x)} dx$$

Put $\sin x = t \quad \therefore \cos x\,dx = dt$

and $\cos^2 x = 1 - \sin^2 x = 1 - t^2$

$$I = \int \frac{(1-t^2)(2-t^2)}{t^2(1+t^2)} dt = \int \frac{t^4 - 3t^2 + 2}{t^4 + t^2} dt$$

$$= \int \frac{t^4 + t^2 - 4t^2 + 2}{t^4 + t^2} dt = \int \left[1 - 2 \cdot \frac{2t^2 - 1}{t^2(t^2+1)}\right] dt$$

$$= \int \left[1 - 2\left\{-\frac{1}{t^2} + \frac{3}{t^2+1}\right\}\right] dt \text{ P.F's. in } t^2$$

$$= t - \frac{2}{t} - 6\tan^{-1} t$$

$$= \sin x - 2(\sin x)^{-1} - 6\tan^{-1}(\sin x)$$

20. $\int \frac{\sin x}{\sin 4x} dx$

$$I = \int \frac{\sin x\,dx}{2(2\sin x \cos x)\cos 2x} = \frac{1}{4}\int \frac{\cos x\,dx}{\cos^2 x \cdot \cos 2x}$$

Now change denominator to $\sin^2 x$ as (d.c.) of $\sin x$ is present in N^r

$$\therefore \quad I = \frac{1}{4}\int \frac{\cos x\,dx}{(1-\sin^2 x)(1-2\sin^2 x)}.$$

Put $\sin x = t \quad \therefore I = \frac{1}{4}\int \frac{dt}{(1-t^2)(1-2t^2)}$

Now split into partial fractions in t^2

$$\therefore \quad I = \frac{1}{4}\int \left[\frac{-1}{(1-t^2)} + \frac{2}{1-2t^2}\right] dt$$

$$= \frac{1}{4}\int \left[\frac{-1}{1-t^2} + \frac{1}{\left(\frac{1}{\sqrt{2}}\right)^2 - t^2}\right] dt$$

Now use $\int \frac{1}{a^2 - x^2} dx = \frac{1}{2a} \log \frac{a+x}{a-x}$

Ex. 21. (a)* $\int \frac{dx}{(x+1)^2 (x^2+1)}$ **(M.N.R. 1997)**

Let $\frac{1}{(x+1)^2(x^2+1)} = \frac{A}{(x+1)^2} + \frac{B}{x+1} + \frac{Cx+D}{x^2+1}$

$\therefore \quad 1 = A(x^2+1) + B(x+1)(x^2+1) + (Cx+D)(x+1)^2$

Put $x = -1 \quad \therefore \quad 1 = 2A \quad$ or $\quad A = 1/2$

Put $x^2 = -1$

$\therefore \quad 1 = (Cx+D)(x^2+2x+1) = (Cx+D)\,2x$

or $\quad 1 = 2Cx^2 + 2Dx = -2C + 2Dx \quad \because x^2 = -1$

$\therefore \quad C = -\frac{1}{2}, D = 0.$

Comparing coefficient of x^3, we get

$0 = B + C \quad \therefore \quad B = -C = 1/2$

$$\therefore \quad \int \frac{1}{(x+1)^2(x^2+1)} dx$$

$$= \int \left[\frac{1}{2} \cdot \frac{1}{(x+1)^2} + \frac{1}{2} \cdot \frac{1}{x+1} - \frac{1}{2} \frac{x}{x^2+1}\right] dx$$

$$= \frac{1}{2}\left[-\frac{1}{x+1} + \log(x+1) - \frac{1}{2}\log(x^2+1)\right]$$

(b)* Evaluate $\int_2^3 \frac{2x^5 + x^4 - 2x^3 + 2x^2 + 1}{(x^2+1)(x^4-1)} dx$ **(I.I.T. 1993)**

$N^r = 2x^3(x^2-1) + (x^2+1)^2$

$I = I_1 + I_2$

$$I_1 = \int_2^3 \frac{2x^3(x^2-1)}{(x^2+1)(x^4-1)} dx = \int_2^3 \frac{x^2 \cdot 2x}{(x^2+1)^2} dx$$

Put $x^2 + 1 = t$

$$\therefore \quad I_1 = \int_5^{10} \frac{(t-1)\,dt}{t^2} = \int_5^{10} \left(\frac{1}{t} - \frac{1}{t^2}\right) dt$$

$$= \left(\log t + \frac{1}{t}\right)_5^{10} = \log \frac{10}{5} + \left(\frac{1}{10} - \frac{1}{5}\right) = \log 2 - \frac{1}{10}$$

$$I_2 = \int_2^3 \frac{(x^2+1)^2\,dx}{(x^2+1)(x^2+1)(x^2-1)}$$

$$= \frac{1}{2}\left[\log \frac{x-1}{x+1}\right]_2^3 = \frac{1}{2}\left[\log \frac{1}{2} - \log \frac{1}{3}\right] = \frac{1}{2}\log \frac{3}{2}$$

$$\therefore \quad I = I_1 + I_2 = \log 2 - \frac{1}{10} + \frac{1}{2}\log \frac{3}{2}$$

$$= \frac{1}{2}\left[2\log 2 + \log \frac{3}{2} - \frac{1}{5}\right] = \frac{1}{2}\left[\log \frac{3}{2} \times 4 - \frac{1}{5}\right]$$

$$= \frac{1}{2}\left[\log 6 - \frac{1}{5}\right].$$

22. (a)* $\int \frac{\sin x}{\sin^3 x + \cos^3 x} dx$

Divide above and below by $\cos^3 x$

$\therefore \quad I=\int \frac{\tan x \sec^2 x}{1+\tan^3 x} dx$

$=\int \frac{t\, dt}{(1+t)(t^2-t+1)}$, where $t=\tan x$

Now $\frac{t}{(t+1)(t^2-t+1)}=\frac{A}{t+1}+\frac{Bt+C}{t^2-t+1}$,

where $A=-1/3$ on putting $t=-1$.

Also $t=A(t^2-t+1)+(Bt+C)(t+1)$

Comparing the coefficients of t^2 and constant,

we get $A+B=0 \quad \therefore \quad B=-A=1/3$

$A+C=0 \quad \therefore \quad C=-A=1/3$.

$\therefore \quad I=-\frac{1}{3}\int \frac{1}{t+1} dt+\frac{1}{3}\int \frac{t+1}{t^2-t+1} dt$

$=-\frac{1}{3}\log(t+1)+\frac{1}{6}\int \frac{2t-1+3}{t^2-t+1} dt$

$=-\frac{1}{3}\log(t+1)+\frac{1}{6}\log(t^2-t+1)$

$+\frac{1}{2}\int \frac{dt}{\left(t-\frac{1}{2}\right)^2+\left(\frac{\sqrt{3}}{2}\right)^2}$

$=-\frac{1}{3}\log(t+1)+\frac{1}{6}\log(t^2-t+1)$

$+\frac{1}{2}\cdot\frac{2}{\sqrt{3}}\tan^{-1}\frac{2t-1}{\sqrt{3}}$,

where $t=\tan x$.

(b)* $\int \frac{x^5}{x^9-1} dx$

$x^5=x^3 \cdot x^2$ Put $x^3=t \quad \therefore \quad 3x^2\, dx=dt$

$\therefore \quad I=\frac{1}{3}\int \frac{t\, dt}{t^3-1}=\frac{1}{3}\int \frac{t\, dt}{(t-1)(t^2+t+1)}$

$=\frac{1}{3}\left[\frac{1}{3}\cdot\frac{1}{t-1}+\frac{1}{3}\frac{-t+1}{t^2+t+1}\right]$ P.F's.

Now as in part (c).

$I=\frac{1}{9}\log(x^3-1)-\frac{1}{18}\log(x^6+x^3+1)$

$+\frac{2}{6\sqrt{3}}\tan^{-1}\frac{2x^3+1}{\sqrt{3}}$

Special Type :

****Ex. 23. (a) (i)** $\int \frac{x^2+1}{x^4+1} dx$, **(ii)** $\int \frac{x^2+1}{x^4+x^2+1} dx$,

(iii) $\int \frac{x^2+1}{x^4-x^2+1} dx$. **(iv)** $\int \frac{x^2+1}{(x^2-1)^2} dx$

(i) Divide above and below by x^2.

$I=\int \frac{[1+(1/x^2)]\, dx}{x^2+(1/x^2)}$

Now $1+\frac{1}{x^2}$ is differentiation of $x-\frac{1}{x}$ as

$\int\left(1+\frac{1}{x^2}\right) dx=x-\frac{1}{x}$

$\therefore$ We write

$x^2+\frac{1}{x^2}$ as $x^2+\frac{1}{x^2}-2+2=\left(x-\frac{1}{x}\right)^2+2$

$\therefore \quad I=\int \frac{(1+1/x^2)\, dx}{(x-1/x)^2+2}$. Put $x-\frac{1}{x}=t$

$\therefore \quad \left(1+\frac{1}{x^2}\right) dx=dt$

$\therefore \quad I=\int \frac{dt}{t^2+2}=\frac{1}{\sqrt{(2)}}\tan^{-1}\frac{t}{\sqrt{(2)}}$.

or $\quad I=\frac{1}{\sqrt{(2)}}\tan^{-1}\frac{x-\frac{1}{x}}{\sqrt{(2)}}=\frac{1}{\sqrt{(2)}}\tan^{-1}\frac{x^2-1}{x\sqrt{(2)}}$.

Another form :

$\int \frac{1+(\sin x)^{2/3}}{1+(\sin x)^{4/3}} d(\sin^{1/3} x)=$

(a) $\sin^{-1}(1+\sin^{1/3} x)$

(b) $\sin^{-1}(\sin x)^{1/3}$

(c) $\frac{1}{\sqrt{2}}\tan^{-1}\frac{(\sin^2 x)^{1/3}-1}{\sqrt{2}\sin^{1/3} x}$

(d) $\frac{1}{\sqrt{2}}\tan^{-1}\frac{\sin^{1/3} x}{\sqrt{2}}$

Sol. Ans. (c).

$\sin^{1/3} x=t$

$\therefore \quad I=\int \frac{1+t^2}{1+t^4} dt=\frac{1}{\sqrt{2}}\tan^{-1}\frac{t^2-1}{t\sqrt{2}} \to$ (c)

as $t=\sin^{1/3} x$.

Proceeding as above.

(ii) $\int \frac{x^2+1}{x^4+x^2+1} dx=\int \frac{dt}{t^2+3}=\frac{1}{\sqrt{(3)}}\tan^{-1}\frac{x^2-1}{x\sqrt{(3)}}$.

(iii) $\int \frac{x^2+1}{x^4-x^2+1} dx=\int \frac{dt}{t^2+1}=\tan^{-1}\frac{x^2-1}{x}$.

(iv) $I=\int \frac{\left(1+\frac{1}{x^2}\right)}{\left(x-\frac{1}{x}\right)^2} dx=\int \frac{1}{t^2} dt$

$=-\frac{1}{t}=-\frac{1}{\left(x-\frac{1}{x}\right)}=\frac{-x}{x^2-1}$

(b) Evaluate $\int_0^1 \frac{(x^2+1)\,dx}{x^4+x^2+1}$ and deduce that

$$1-\frac{1}{5}+\frac{1}{7}-\frac{1}{11}+\frac{1}{13}-\ldots=\frac{\pi}{2\sqrt{3}}$$

From part (ii), $I=\frac{1}{\sqrt{3}}\left[\tan^{-1}\frac{x^2-1}{x\sqrt{3}}\right]_0^1$

$$=\frac{1}{\sqrt{3}}[\tan^{-1}0-\tan^{-1}(-\infty)]=\frac{\pi}{2\sqrt{3}} \quad \ldots(1)$$

Again $I=\int_0^1 \frac{(1+x^2)(1-x^2)\,dx}{(1-x^2)(1+x^2+x^4)}=\int_0^1 \frac{1-x^4}{1-x^6}\,dx$

$$=\int_0^1 (1-x^4)(1-x^6)^{-1}\,dx$$

$$=\int_0^1 (1-x^4)[1+x^6+(x^6)^2+(x^6)^3+\ldots]\,dx$$

$$=\int_0^1 (1-x^4+x^6-x^{10}+x^{12}-\ldots)\,dx$$

$$=\left[x-\frac{x^5}{5}+\frac{x^7}{7}-\frac{x^{11}}{11}+\frac{x^{13}}{13}-\ldots\right]_0^1$$

$$=1-\frac{1}{5}+\frac{1}{7}-\frac{1}{11}+\frac{1}{13}-\ldots\infty \quad \ldots(2)$$

From (1) and (2) we prove the result.

Ex. 24. (A) (i)* $\int \frac{x^2-1}{x^4+1}\,dx$, **(ii)** $\int \frac{x^2-1}{x^4+x^2+1}$,

(iii) $\int \frac{x^2-1}{x^4-x^2+1}\,dx$ **(iv)** $\int \frac{x^2-1}{(x^2+1)^2}\,dx$

(i) Divide above and below by x^2.

$$I=\int \frac{[1-(1/x^2)]\,dx}{x^2+(1/x^2)}.$$

Now $1-\frac{1}{x^2}$ is differentiation of $x+\frac{1}{x}$ as

$$\int\left(1-\frac{1}{x^2}\right)dx=x+\frac{1}{x}$$

$\therefore$ We write $x^2+\frac{1}{x^2}=x^2+\frac{1}{x^2}+2-2=\left(x+\frac{1}{x}\right)^2-2.$

$$\therefore \quad I=\int \frac{[1-(1/x^2)]\,dx}{[x+(1/x)]^2-(\sqrt{2})^2}.$$

Put $x+\frac{1}{x}=t \quad \therefore \quad \left(1-\frac{1}{x^2}\right)dx=dt$

$$\therefore \quad I=\int \frac{dt}{t^2-(\sqrt{2})^2}=\frac{1}{2\sqrt{(2)}}\log\frac{t-\sqrt{2}}{t+\sqrt{(2)}}$$

or $I=\frac{1}{2\sqrt{(2)}}\log\frac{[x+(1/x)]-\sqrt{2}}{[x+(1/x)]+\sqrt{(2)}}$

$$=\frac{1}{2\sqrt{(2)}}\log\frac{x^2-x\sqrt{2}+1}{x^2+x\sqrt{(2)}+1}$$

Proceeding as above

(ii) $\int \frac{x^2-1}{x^4+x^2+1}\,dx=\int \frac{dt}{t^2-1}=\frac{1}{2}\log\frac{x^2-x+1}{x^2+x+1}$

(iii) $\int \frac{x^2-1}{x^4-x^2+1}\,dx=\int \frac{dt}{t^2-3}$

$$=\frac{1}{2\sqrt{(3)}}\log\frac{x^2-x\sqrt{3}+1}{x^2+x\sqrt{(3)}+1}$$

As in Q. 23 (iv) put $x+\frac{1}{x}=t$

(iv) $I=\int \frac{dt}{t^2}=-\frac{1}{t}=-\frac{1}{x+\frac{1}{x}}=\frac{-x}{x^2+1}$

Deduction I :

$$\int \frac{x^2}{x^4+1}\,dx,\ \int \frac{x^2\,dx}{x^4+x^2+1},\ \int \frac{x^2\,dx}{x^4-x^2+1}$$

Write $x^2=\frac{1}{2}[(x^2+1)+(x^2-1)].$

Hence each integral is

$\frac{1}{2}$ [Ans. of Q. 23 + Ans. of Q. 24].

***Deduction II :**

$$\int \frac{1}{x^4+1}\,dx,\ \int \frac{1}{x^4+x^2+1}\,dx,$$

(M.N.R. 1995)

$$\int \frac{1}{x^4-x^2+1}$$

write $1=\frac{1}{2}[(x^2+1)-(x^2-1)]$

Hence each integral is $\frac{1}{2}$ [Ans. of Q. 23 – Ans. of Q. 24].

24. (B) Let $I=\int \frac{e^x}{e^{4x}+e^{2x}+1}\,dx,\ J=\int \frac{e^{-x}}{e^{-4x}+e^{-2x}+1}\,dx$

Then, for an arbitrary constant C, the value of $J-I$ equals

(a) $\frac{1}{2}\log\left(\frac{e^{4x}-e^{2x}+1}{e^{4x}+e^{2x}+1}\right)+C$

(b) $\frac{1}{2}\log\left(\frac{e^{2x}+e^x+1}{e^{2x}-e^x+1}\right)+C$

(c) $\frac{1}{2}\log\left(\frac{e^{2x}-e^x+1}{e^{2x}+e^x+1}\right)+C$

(d) $\frac{1}{2}\log\left(\frac{e^{4x}+e^{2x}+1}{e^{4x}-e^{2x}+1}\right)+C$

Sol. Ans. (c).

$$J=\int \frac{1}{e^x}\cdot\frac{e^{4x}}{e^{4x}+e^{2x}+1}\,dx$$

$$\therefore\quad J-I=\int \frac{1}{e^{4x}+e^{2x}+1}(e^{3x}-e^x)\,dx$$

Now put $e^x=t \quad \therefore\ e^x\,dx=dt$

$$J-I=\int\frac{(t^2-1)}{t^4+t^2+1}dt$$ **[Now see 24 (iii) P. 1500]**

$$=\int\frac{1-\dfrac{1}{t^2}}{\left(t^2+\dfrac{1}{t^2}+1\right)}dt$$

$$t+\frac{1}{t}=z\ \therefore\ 1-\frac{1}{t^2}\,dt=dz$$

$$\therefore\quad J-I=\int\frac{dz}{z^2-1}=\frac{1}{2}\log\frac{z-1}{z+1}$$

***Ex. 25.** $\displaystyle\int\frac{(x^2-1)\,dx}{x\sqrt{(x^4+3x^2+1)}}$ **(J.E.E.W.B. 1991)**

$$I=\int\frac{(x^2-1)\,dx}{x\,.\,x\sqrt{\left(x^2+\dfrac{1}{x^2}+3\right)}}=\int\frac{(1-1/x^2)\,dx}{\sqrt{\{(x+1/x)^2+1\}}}$$

$$=\int\frac{dt}{\sqrt{(t^2+1)}}=\log\{t+\sqrt{(t^2+1)}\}$$

where $t=x+\dfrac{1}{x}=\log[\{(x^2+1)+\sqrt{(x^4+3x^2+1)}\}/x]$.

Ex. 26. (a) $\displaystyle\int\frac{x^4-1}{x^2\sqrt{x^4+x^2+1}}dx$

$$I=\int\frac{x^4-1}{x^2\,.\,x\sqrt{x^2+\dfrac{1}{x^2}+1}}=\int\frac{\left(x-\dfrac{1}{x^3}\right)dx}{\sqrt{x^2+\dfrac{1}{x^2}+1}}$$

Put $x^2+\dfrac{1}{x^2}+1=t \qquad \therefore\ 2\left(x-\dfrac{1}{x^3}\right)dx=dt$

$$\therefore\quad I=\frac{1}{2}\int\frac{dt}{\sqrt{t}}=\frac{1}{2}.2\sqrt{t}=\sqrt{t}$$

$$I=\sqrt{x^2+\frac{1}{x^2}+1}=\frac{\sqrt{x^4+x^2+1}}{x}$$

(b) $\displaystyle\int\frac{x^2-1}{x^3\sqrt{2x^4-2x^2+1}}dx$ is equal to :

(a) $\dfrac{\sqrt{2x^4-2x^2+1}}{x(x^2-1)}+c$

(b) $\dfrac{\sqrt{2x^4-2x^2+1}}{x^3}+c$

(c) $\dfrac{\sqrt{2x^4-2x^2+1}}{x^2}+c$

(d) $\dfrac{\sqrt{2x^4-2x^2+1}}{2x^2}+c$

(I.I.T. 2006)

Sol. Ans. (d).

$$I=\int\frac{(x^2-1)\,dx}{x^3\,.\,x^2\sqrt{2-\dfrac{2}{x^2}+\dfrac{1}{x^4}}}=\frac{\left(\dfrac{1}{x^3}-\dfrac{1}{x^5}\right)dx}{\sqrt{2-\dfrac{2}{x^2}+\dfrac{1}{x^4}}}$$

Put $2-\dfrac{2}{x^2}+\dfrac{1}{x^4}=z \qquad \therefore\ \left(\dfrac{4}{x^3}-\dfrac{4}{x^5}\right)dx=dz$

$$\therefore\quad I=\frac{1}{4}\int\frac{dz}{\sqrt{z}}=\frac{1}{4}.2\sqrt{z}=\frac{1}{2}\sqrt{z}$$

$$=\frac{1}{2}\frac{\sqrt{2x^4-2x^2+1}}{x^2}+c\Rightarrow\text{(d).}$$

Ex. 27. $\displaystyle\int\sqrt{(x+\sqrt{x^2+1})}\,dx$

Put $x=\tan\theta \qquad \therefore\ dx=\sec^2\theta\,d\theta$

$$\therefore\quad I=\int\sqrt{(\tan\theta+\sec\theta)}\,.\sec^2\theta\,d\theta$$

Integrate by parts

$$I=\tan\theta\,.\sqrt{\tan\theta+\sec\theta}-\int\tan\theta\,.\frac{1.(\sec^2\theta+\sec\theta\,.\tan\theta)}{2\sqrt{\tan\theta+\sec\theta}}d\theta$$

$$=\tan\theta\,.\sqrt{\tan\theta+\sec\theta}-\frac{1}{2}\int\tan\theta\sec\theta(\sqrt{\sec\theta+\tan\theta})\,d\theta$$

$$=x\sqrt{x+\sqrt{1+x^2}}-\frac{1}{2}I_1$$

Now for I_1 put $\sec\theta+\tan\theta=z^2$ ...(1)

$\therefore\quad (\sec\theta\,.\tan\theta+\sec^2\theta)\,d\theta=2z\,dz$

or $\quad \sec\theta\,.z^2\,d\theta=2z\,dz \ \therefore\ \sec\theta\,d\theta=\dfrac{2}{z}dz$ by (1) ...(2)

Also $\sec\theta-\tan\theta=\dfrac{1}{\sec\theta+\tan\theta}=\dfrac{1}{z^2}$

$\therefore\quad 2\tan\theta=z^2-\dfrac{1}{z^2}$ by (1), (2) ...(3)

$$\therefore\quad I_1=\int\frac{1}{2}\left(z^2-\frac{1}{z^2}\right).z.\frac{2}{z}dz=\frac{z^3}{3}+\frac{1}{z}$$

$$\therefore\quad I=x\sqrt{x+\sqrt{1+x^2}}-\frac{1}{2}\left[\frac{1}{3}\{x+\sqrt{x^2+1}\}^{3/2}+\frac{1}{\sqrt{x+\sqrt{x^2+1}}}\right]$$

Problem Set (5)

Integration of rational and irrational functions.

1. (a) Prove $\int \frac{1}{(e^x - 1)} dx = \log(e^x - 1) - x.$

(b) If $\int_{\log 2}^{x} \frac{1}{e^x - 1} dx = \log \frac{3}{2}$ then $x = \log 4.$

(c) Evaluate $\int \frac{x-1}{(x-3)(x-2)} dx.$

2. Show that $\int_0^{\log 5} \frac{\sqrt{e^x - 1} \cdot e^x}{e^x + 3} dx = 4 - \pi$

3. (a) Evaluate $\int \frac{e^x - 2}{e^{2x} + 4} dx$

(b) Prove :

$$\int \frac{e^{2x} - 2e^x}{e^{2x} + 1} dx = \frac{1}{2} \log(e^{2x} + 1) - 2\tan^{-1}(e^x)$$

4. (a)* Prove $\int \frac{1}{(e^x - 1)^2} dx = x - \log(e^x - 1) - \frac{1}{e^x - 1}.$

(b) Evaluate $\int_1^2 \frac{dx}{x(x+1)^2}.$

(c) Evaluate $\int \frac{e^x}{(1+e^x)} dx.$

Prove the following :

5. (a) $\int \frac{dx}{x\{6(\log x)^2 + 7\log x + 2\}} = \log \frac{1 + \log x^2}{2 + \log x^3}.$

(b) $\int \frac{x\,dx}{(x^2 - a^2)(x^2 - b^2)} = \frac{1}{2(a^2 - b^2)} \cdot \log \frac{x^2 - a^2}{x^2 - b^2}.$

6. (a) $\int \frac{(x^2 + 1)\,dx}{(x^2 + 2)(2x^2 + 1)}$

$$= \frac{1}{3\sqrt{(2)}} \left\{ \tan^{-1} \frac{x}{\sqrt{(2)}} + \tan^{-1} x\sqrt{2} \right\}.$$

(b) $\int_0^{\pi/2} \frac{\cos^2 \theta\, d\theta}{\cos^2 \theta + 4\sin^2 \theta} = \frac{\pi}{6}.$

7. (a) $\int \frac{dx}{\sin x(5 + 4\cos x)} = \frac{1}{18} \log(1 - \cos x)$

$$- \frac{1}{2} \log(1 + \cos x) + \frac{4}{9} \log(5 + 4\cos x).$$

(b) $\int \frac{dx}{\log x^x [(\log x)^2 - 3\log x - 10]}$

$$= -\frac{1}{10} \log(\log x) + \frac{1}{35} \log(\log x - 5) + \frac{1}{14} \log(\log x + 2).$$

8. $\int \frac{x-1}{(x+1)(x^2+1)} dx = -\log(x+1) + \frac{1}{2} \log(x^2+1).$

9. (a) $\int \frac{x\,dx}{(1+x)(1+x^2)} = -\frac{1}{2} \log(1+x)$

$$+ \frac{1}{4} \log(1+x^2) + \frac{1}{2} \tan^{-1} x$$

(b)* Evaluate $\int \frac{x^4}{(x-1)(x^2+1)} dx.$

10. (a) $\int \frac{dx}{(1+x)(1+x^2)} = \frac{1}{2} \log(1+x)$

$$- \frac{1}{4} \log(1+x^2) + \frac{1}{2} \tan^{-1} x$$

(b) $\int \frac{x^2 + x + 3}{(x-2)(x+1)} dx = x + 3\log(x-2) - \log(x+1).$

(c) Evaluate $\int \frac{1}{(x-1)(x^2+1)} dx.$

11.* Evaluate $\int \frac{x^3 - 1}{x^3 + x} dx.$

12.* Evaluate $\int \frac{f(x)}{x^3 - 1} dx$ where $f(x)$ is a polynomial of second degree in x such that $f(0) = f(1) = 3f(2) = -3.$ **(Roorkee 1993)**

13.* Evaluate $\int \frac{(x+1)}{x(1+xe^x)^2} dx.$ **(I.I.T. 1996)**

14. Prove $\int \frac{dx}{x + \sqrt{(x-1)}} = \log[x + \sqrt{x-1}]$

$$- \frac{2}{\sqrt{(3)}} \tan^{-1} \frac{2\sqrt{x-1} + 1}{\sqrt{(3)}}.$$

15. (a) $\int \sqrt{\left(\frac{x+1}{x-1}\right)} dx = \sqrt{x^2 - 1} + \log[x + \sqrt{x^2 - 1}].$

(b) $\int \sqrt{\left(\frac{1+x}{1-x}\right)} dx = \sin^{-1} x - \sqrt{1-x^2}.$

(c) $\int x \sqrt{\left(\frac{1-x^2}{1+x^2}\right)} dx = \frac{1}{2} [\sin^{-1} x^2 + \sqrt{1-x^4}].$

16. (a) $\int \frac{x\,dx}{\sqrt{(x+a)} + \sqrt{(x+b)}}$

$$= \frac{1}{a-b} \left\{ \frac{2}{5}(x+a)^{5/2} - \frac{2a}{3}(x+a)^{3/2} - \frac{2}{5}(x+b)^{5/2} + \frac{2b}{3}(x+b)^{3/2} \right\}.$$

(b) $\int \frac{x\,dx}{(px+q)^{3/2}} = \frac{2}{p^2}\left\{\sqrt{px+q} + \frac{q}{\sqrt{(px+q)}}\right\}$.

17. (i) Prove $\int \frac{1+x^{1/2}-x^{2/3}}{1+x^{1/3}}\,dx$

$= -\frac{3}{4}t^8 + \frac{6}{7}t^7 + t^6 - \frac{6}{5}t^5 + 2t^3 - 6t + 6\tan^{-1} t$

where $t = x^{1/6}$.

(ii)* Evaluate $\int \frac{x^{1/2}}{x^{1/2}-x^{1/3}}\,dx$.

(iii)* $\int \frac{x+\sqrt[3]{x^2}+2\sqrt[6]{x}}{x(1+\sqrt[3]{x})}\,dx$ **(J.E.E. W.B. 1993)**

18. Prove $\int x^5\sqrt{a^3+x^3}\,dx$

$= \frac{2}{3}\left\{\frac{1}{5}(a^3+x^3)^{5/2} - \frac{a^3}{3}(a^3+x^3)^{3/2}\right\}$.

19.* $\int \frac{x\sqrt{a^2-x^2}}{a^2+x^2}\,dx$

$= \sqrt{a^2-x^2} - \frac{a}{\sqrt{(2)}}\log\frac{a\sqrt{2}+\sqrt{a^2-x^2}}{a\sqrt{(2)}-\sqrt{(a^2-x^2)}}$

20. $\int \frac{dx}{(x+2)\sqrt{(x-1)}} = \frac{2}{\sqrt{(3)}}\tan^{-1}\sqrt{\left(\frac{x-1}{3}\right)}$.

21. $\int \frac{dx}{(x+2)\sqrt{(3x+4)}} = \sqrt{2}\tan^{-1}\sqrt{\left(\frac{3x+4}{2}\right)}$ and hence

prove $\int \frac{3x^2+13x+9}{(x+2)\sqrt{(3x+4)}}\,dx$

$= \frac{2}{9}(3x+4)^{3/2} + \sqrt{2}\tan^{-1}\sqrt{\left(\frac{3x+4}{2}\right)}$.

22.* $\int_0^1 \frac{dx}{(1+x^2)\sqrt{(2+x^2)}} = \frac{\pi}{6}$.

23.* $\int_0^{\pi/4} \sqrt{\tan\theta}\,d\theta = \frac{1}{\sqrt{(2)}}\log(\sqrt{2}-1) + \frac{\pi}{2\sqrt{(2)}}$.

24. (a) $\int_0^{\pi/4} \frac{dx}{\cos^4 x - \cos^2 x\sin^2 x + \sin^4 x} = \frac{\pi}{2}$.

(b) Evaluate $\int \frac{dx}{\cos^6 x + \sin^6 x}$

25. (a) $\int_0^{\pi/2} \frac{\cos x\,dx}{1-\sin^2 x + \sin^4 x} = \frac{\pi}{2} - \frac{1}{2\sqrt{(3)}}\log(2-\sqrt{3})$.

(b)* Evaluate $\int \frac{1}{x^4+4}\,dx$

(c)* $\int \frac{x^4(x^{10}-1)}{(x^{20}+3x^{10}+1)}\,dx = \frac{1}{5}\tan^{-1}\left(x^5+\frac{1}{x^5}\right)$

26.* $\int \frac{\sin^{-1}\sqrt{x}-\cos^{-1}\sqrt{x}}{\sin^{-1}\sqrt{(x)}+\cos^{-1}\sqrt{(x)}}\,dx$ **(J.E.E.W.B. 1992)**

27. (a)* Evaluate $\int \frac{(x-1)\,dx}{(x+1)\sqrt{(x^3+x^2+x)}}$.

(b)* $\int \frac{(x^2-1)\,dx}{(x^4+3x^2+1)\tan^{-1}\left(x+\frac{1}{x}\right)}$

(c) $\int \frac{x^2-2}{(x^4+5x^2+4)\tan^{-1}\left(\frac{x^2+2}{x}\right)}\,dx$

(d) $\int \frac{x(x-1)}{(x^2+1)(x+1)\sqrt{x^3+x^2+x}}\,dx$

(e)* $\int \left(\frac{1}{\sqrt{1-x^8}}\right)\left[\cos^{-1}\frac{2x}{1+x^2} + \tan^{-1}\frac{2x}{1-x^2}\right]dx$

(f) $\int \frac{dx}{x+\sqrt{x^2-x+1}}$

28. (a) Prove that

$\int \frac{x^2-1}{x^2+1}\cdot\frac{dx}{\sqrt{(1+x^4)}} = \frac{1}{\sqrt{(2)}}\cos^{-1}\frac{x\sqrt{2}}{x^2+1} + c.$

(b) Prove that $\int \frac{1+x^2}{(1-x^2)\sqrt{1+x^2+x^4}}\,dx$

$= \frac{-1}{2\sqrt{3}}\log\frac{t-\sqrt{3}}{t+\sqrt{3}}$ where $t^2 = x^2 + \frac{1}{x^2} + 1$

29.* Evaluate $\int \frac{1+x^{-2/3}}{1+x}\,dx$.

30. (a) Evaluate $\int \frac{dx}{\sqrt[4]{(1+x^4)}}$. (b) $\int \frac{dx}{\sqrt{x}(\sqrt[4]{\sqrt{x}}+1)^{10}}$

31. (a)* Evaluate $\int \frac{3x+1}{(x-1)^3(x+1)}\,dx$. **(Roorkee 1992)**

(b) $\int \frac{1}{(x^6-1)}\,dx$

32.* $\int \left\{\frac{1}{(\sqrt[3]{x}+\sqrt[4]{x})} + \frac{\log(1+\sqrt[6]{x})}{\sqrt[3]{x}+\sqrt{x}}\right\}dx$ **(I.I.T. 1992)**

33. $\int_0^{\pi/2} \frac{\cos^2 x\sin x}{\sqrt{(1+\cos^2 x)}}\,dx = \frac{1}{2}[\sqrt{2} - \log(\sqrt{2}+1)]$

Evaluate the following :

34.* $\int \sqrt{\left(\frac{1-\sqrt{x}}{1+\sqrt{x}}\right)}\,dx$ **35.** $\int \frac{1}{(x^2+a^2)^2}\,dx$

[Q. 36, 37 are good questions for practice]

36.* $\int \frac{x^4-x^3+5x^2+x+3}{(x+1)(x^2-x+1)^2}\,dx$

37. (a)* $\int \frac{x^4+4x^3+11x^2+12x+8}{(x^2+2x+3)^2\,(x+1)}\,dx$

(b) $\int \frac{2x^4+x^3-4x^2+4x+2}{(x^2+4)\,(x^2-1)^2}\,dx$

38. $\int_0^1 \frac{2x^2+3x+3}{(x+1)\,(x^2+2x+2)}\,dx$

$= 2\log 2 - \tan^{-1}\frac{1}{3} = \log 4 - \cot^{-1} 3$

39.* Evaluate $\int \frac{\cos 2x . \sin 4x}{\cos^4 x\,(1+\cos^2 2x)}\,dx.$ **(Roorkee 1996)**

40. (a)* Evaluate $\int \frac{x^4}{(x^2+1)^2}\,dx$

***Note :** $\int \frac{dx}{P\sqrt{Q}}$ and $\frac{dx}{P^2\sqrt{Q}}$ where P is of 1st degree and Q of 2nd degree is performed by putting $P=\frac{1}{t}$, as explained in solutions of questions below.

(b) $\int \frac{x^3+3x+2}{(x^2+1)^2\,(x+1)}\,dx$ **(I.I.T. 1999)**

41. $\int \frac{dx}{(1+x)\sqrt{(1+2x-x^2)}}$

42. $\int_0^1 \frac{dx}{(1+x)\sqrt{(2+x-x^2)}} = \frac{1}{3}\sqrt{2}$

43.* $\int \frac{dx}{(x^2-6x+9)\sqrt{(x^2-6x+4)}}$

44.* $\int \left(\frac{1-\sqrt{x}}{1+\sqrt{x}}\right)^{1/2} \frac{dx}{x}$ **(I.I.T. 1997)**

45. $\int \frac{dx}{(1+\sqrt{x})\sqrt{x-x^2}}$

Solutions to Problem Set (5)

1. (a) Multiply above and below by e^x and then put $e^x = t$ and now split into partial fractions.

(b) $I = \int_{\log 2}^{x} \frac{e^x}{e^x\,(1-e^x)}\,dx$

Put $e^x = t$ and adjust the limits

$$I = \int_2^{e^x} \frac{dt}{t\,(t-1)} = \int\left(\frac{1}{t-1}-\frac{1}{t}\right)dt = \left[\log\frac{t-1}{t}\right]_2^{e^x}$$

$\therefore \quad \log\frac{e^x-1}{e^x} - \log\frac{1}{2} = \log\frac{3}{2}$ (given)

$\therefore \quad \log\frac{e^x-1}{e^x} = \log\frac{3}{2} + \log\frac{1}{2} = \log\frac{3}{4}$

$\therefore \quad \frac{e^x-1}{e^x} = \frac{3}{4} \Rightarrow e^x = 4 \quad \therefore\ x = \log 4$

(c) Ans. $2\log(x-3) - \log(x-2)$

2. Put $e^x - 1 = t^2$ and adjust the limits, $e^{\log 5} = 5$

$$\therefore \quad I = \int_0^2 \frac{t . 2t\,dt}{t^2+4} = 2\int_0^2 \left(1-\frac{4}{t^2+4}\right)dt$$

3. (a) Multiplying above and below by e^x and put $e^x = t$

$$\therefore \quad I = \int \frac{t-2}{t\,(t^2+4)}\,dt \quad \text{P.F's.} = \int\left[-\frac{1}{2t}+\frac{1}{2}\frac{t+2}{t^2+4}\right]dt$$

$$= \int\left[-\frac{1}{2t}+\frac{1}{4}.\frac{2t}{t^2+4}+\frac{1}{t^2+4}\right]dt$$

$$= -\frac{1}{2}\log e^x + \frac{1}{4}\log(t^2+4) + \frac{1}{2}\tan^{-1}\left(\frac{t}{2}\right)$$

$$= -\frac{1}{2}x + \frac{1}{4}\log(e^{2x}+4) + \frac{1}{2}\tan^{-1}\left(\frac{e^x}{2}\right)$$

(b) Do yourself.

4. (a) Prove yourself.

(b) Ans. $\log\frac{4}{3} - \frac{1}{6}$

(c) Ans. $\log(1+e^x)$

5. (a) Put $\log x = t$ and then split into partial fractions.

(b) Put $x^2 = t$ and partial fractions.

6. (a) Write $x^2 = t$ and split $\frac{t+1}{(t+2)(2t+1)}$ into partial fractions.

(b) Divide above and below by $\cos^2\theta$

$$I = \int \frac{d\theta}{1+4\tan^2\theta} = \int \frac{\sec^2\theta\,d\theta}{(1+\tan^2\theta)\,(1+4\tan^2\theta)}$$

Now put $\tan\theta = t. \quad \therefore\ \sec^2\theta\,d\theta = dt.$

$$\therefore \quad I = \int \frac{dt}{(1+t^2)\,(1+4t^2)}.$$

Now split into partial fractions as in (a) above.

7. (a) Mulitply above and below by $\sin x$ and put $\cos x = t, \sin^2 x = (1-\cos x)\,(1+\cos x)$.

(b) Write $\log x^x = x\log x$ and then put

$\log x = t \quad \therefore\ (1/x)\,dx = dt$

$$\therefore \quad I = \int \frac{dt}{t\,(t^2-3t-10)} = \int \frac{dt}{t\,(t-5)\,(t+2)}.$$

Now split into partial fractions.

8, 9, 10. Split into partial fractions :

$$\int \frac{x^4}{(x-1)\,(x^2+1)}\,dx = \int \frac{x^4-1+1}{(x-1)\,(x^2+1)}\,dx$$

$$= \int\left[(x+1) + \frac{1}{(x-1)\,(x^2+1)}\right]dx$$

$$= \int \left[x + 1 + \frac{1}{2(x-1)} - \frac{x+1}{2(x^2+1)} \right] dx \quad \text{P.F's.}$$

$$= \frac{1}{2}x^2 + x + \frac{1}{2}\log(x-1) - \frac{1}{4}\log(x^2+1) - \frac{1}{2}\tan^{-1} x + c.$$

11. $\int \frac{x^3-1}{x^3+x} dx = \int \frac{x^3+x-(x+1)}{x^3+x} dx$

$$= \int \left[1 - \frac{x+1}{x(x^2+1)} \right] dx$$

$$= \int \left(1 - \frac{1}{x} + \frac{x}{x^2+1} - \frac{1}{x^2+1} \right) dx$$

$$= x - \log x + \frac{1}{2}\log(x^2+1) - \tan^{-1} x + c.$$

12. Let $f(x) = ax^2 + bx + c$. By given condition, we get, $c = -3, a+b+c = -3, 3(4a+2b+c) = -3$

These give $a = 1, b = -1, c = -3$

$\therefore \quad f(x) = x^2 - x - 3$

$$\therefore \quad \frac{x^2-x-3}{(x-1)(x^2+x+1)} = -\frac{1}{x-1} + \frac{2(x+1)}{x^2+x+1}$$

Partial Fractions

$$\therefore \quad \int \frac{f(x)}{x^3-1} dx$$

$$= \left[-\frac{1}{x-1} + \frac{2x+1}{x^2+x+1} + \frac{1}{\left(x+\frac{1}{2}\right)^2 + \left(\frac{\sqrt{3}}{2}\right)^2} dx \right]$$

$$= -\log(x-1) + \log(x^2+x+1) + \frac{2}{\sqrt{3}}\tan^{-1}\frac{2x+1}{\sqrt{3}} + k$$

13. Multiply above and below by e^x

$$I = \int \frac{e^x(1+x)}{xe^x(1+xe^x)^2} dx$$

Now $1 + xe^x = t \quad \therefore \quad e^x(x+1)\,dx = dt$

$$\therefore \quad I = \frac{dt}{t^2(1-t)} = \int \left(\frac{1}{1-t} + \frac{1}{t} + \frac{1}{t^2} \right) dt \quad \text{(P.F's.)}$$

$$= \log \frac{t}{1-t} - \frac{1}{t}$$

14. Put $x - 1 = t^2 \quad \therefore \quad dx = 2t\,dt.$

$$\therefore \quad I = \int \frac{2t\,dt}{t^2+1+t} = \frac{(2t+1)-1}{t^2+t+1} dt$$

$$= \int \frac{(2t+1)}{t^2+t+1} dt - \int \frac{1}{(t+1/2)^2 + (\sqrt{3}/2)^2} dt \quad \text{etc.}$$

15. (a) $I = \int \frac{x+1}{\sqrt{(x^2-1)}} dx$

$$= \int \left[\frac{x}{\sqrt{(x^2-1)}} + \frac{1}{\sqrt{(x^2-1)}} \right] dx \text{ etc.}$$

(b) $I = \int \frac{1+x}{\sqrt{(1-x^2)}} dx$

$$= \int \left[\frac{1}{\sqrt{(1-x^2)}} + \frac{x}{\sqrt{(1-x^2)}} \right] dx \text{ etc.}$$

(c) Put $x^2 = t$ first and then as in (a), (b).

16. (a) Multiply above and below by $\sqrt{x+a} - \sqrt{x+b}$.

$$\therefore \quad I = \int \frac{x[\sqrt{x+a} - \sqrt{x+b}]}{(x+a)-(x+b)} dx$$

$$= \frac{1}{(a-b)} \int [(x+a-a)\sqrt{x+a} - (x+b-b)\sqrt{x+b}]\,dx$$

$$I = \frac{1}{a-b} \int [(x+a)^{3/2} - a(x+a)^{1/2} - (x+b)^{3/2} + b(x+b)^{1/2}\,dx].$$

(b) Put $px + q = t^2$.

17. (i) & (ii). Put $x = t^6$.

(iii) Put $x = t^6 \therefore I = \int \frac{(2+t^3+t^5).6\,dt}{t^2+1}$

$$= 6\int \frac{t^3(t^2+1)+2}{t^2+1} dt = 6\int \left(t^3 + \frac{2}{t^2+1} \right) dt$$

Now integrate term by term etc.

18. (i) Write $x^5 = x^3 . x^2$ and put $a^3 + x^3 = t^2$,

(ii) Ans. $x + (6/5)x^{5/6} + (3/2)x^{2/3} + 2x^{1/2} + 3x^{1/3} + 6x^{1/6} + 6\log(x^{1/6} - 1).$

19. Put $a^2 - x^2 = t^2 \quad \therefore \quad a^2 - t^2 = x^2.$

and $-2x\,dx = dt.$

$$\therefore \quad I = -\int \frac{t.t\,dt}{2a^2-t^2} = \int \frac{2a^2-t^2-2a^2}{2a^2-t^2} dt$$

$$= \int \left[1 - \frac{2a^2}{[a\sqrt{(2)}]^2 - t^2} \right] dt \text{ etc.}$$

20. **Hint :** Put $x - 1 = t^2$.

21. **Hint :** Put $3x + 4 = t^2$.

and $3x^2 + 10x + 9 = (3x+4)(x+2) + 1.$

22. Proceed as in solved **Ex. 15 P. 1496.**

23. Put $\tan\theta = t^2 \quad \therefore \quad \sec^2\theta\,d\theta = 2t\,dt$

or $d\theta = \frac{2t\,dt}{1+\tan^2\theta} = \frac{2t\,dt}{1+t^4}$

and limits are adjusted as 0 to 1.

$$\therefore \quad I = \int_0^1 \left[\frac{t.2t\,dt}{t^4+1} \right] = \int_0^1 \frac{2t^2\,dt}{t^4+1}$$

$$= \int_0^1 \left[\frac{(t^2+1)+(t^2-1)}{t^4+1} \right] dt$$

It has been calculated in **Q. 23, 24 P. 1499-1500.**

24. (a) Divide above and below by $\cos^4 x$

$$\therefore \quad I=\int_0^{\pi/4}\frac{\sec^2 x\sec^2 x\,dx}{1-\tan^2 x+\tan^4 x}$$

Put $\tan x=t \;\therefore\; \sec^2 x\,dx=dt$

and adjust the limits

$$I=\int_0^1\frac{(1+t^2)}{t^4-t^2+1}\,dt \text{ etc. as in } \textbf{Q. 23 P. 1499.}$$

$$=\left[\tan^{-1}\frac{t^2-1}{t}\right]_0^1=\tan^{-1}0-\tan^{-1}(-\infty)$$

$$=0-(-\pi/2)=\pi/2.$$

(b) $I=\int\frac{1}{1.(\cos^4 x+\sin^2 x\cos^2 x+\sin^4 x)}\,dx$

It reduces to (a).

Ans. $\tan^{-1}\left(\frac{t^2-1}{t}\right)=\tan^{-1}(\tan x-\cot x)$

25. (a) Put $\sin x=t \;\therefore\; \cos x\,dx=dt$

and adjust the limits

$$\therefore \quad I=\int_0^1\frac{dt}{t^4-t^2+1}=\frac{1}{2}\int_0^1\frac{(t^2+1)-(t^2-1)}{t^4-t^2+1}\,dt$$

It has been calculated in **Q. 23, 24 P. 1499-1500.**

(b) $I=\frac{1}{4}\int\frac{(x^2+2)-(x^2-2)}{(x^4+4)}\,dx=\frac{1}{4}[I_1+I_2]$

$$I_1=\int\frac{\left(1+\frac{2}{x^2}\right)dx}{x^2+\frac{4}{x^2}-4+4}=\int\frac{dt}{t^2+4}=\frac{1}{2}\tan^{-1}\frac{t}{2}$$

$$=\frac{1}{2}\tan^{-1}\frac{\left(x-\frac{2}{x}\right)}{2}=\frac{1}{2}\tan^{-1}\frac{x^2-2}{2x}$$

$$I_2=\frac{1}{16}\log\frac{x^2+2x+2}{x^2-2x+2}.$$

Here $t=x+\frac{2}{x}$.

(c) Put $x^5=t \;\therefore\; I=\frac{1}{5}\int\frac{t^2-1}{t^4+3t^2+1}\,dt$ etc.

$$=\frac{1}{5}\tan^{-1}\left(t+\frac{1}{t}\right).$$

26. $I=\int\frac{\sin^{-1}\sqrt{x}-\cos^{-1}\sqrt{x}}{\sin^{-1}\sqrt{x}+\cos^{-1}\sqrt{x}}\,dx$

$$=\int\frac{\sin^{-1}\sqrt{x}-(\pi/2-\sin^{-1}\sqrt{x})}{\pi/2}\,dx$$

$\because \quad [\sin^{-1}\sqrt{x}+\cos^{-1}\sqrt{x}]=\pi/2$

$$=\frac{4}{\pi}\int\sin^{-1}\sqrt{x}\,dx-\int dx$$

$$=\frac{4}{\pi}\int\sin^{-1}\sqrt{x}\,dx-x+c. \qquad \text{...(1)}$$

Now put $x=\sin^2\theta$.

Then $\quad dx=2\sin\theta\cos\theta\,d\theta$

Then $\int\sin^{-1}\sqrt{x}\,dx=\int\theta.2\sin\theta\cos\theta\,d\theta$

$$I=\theta\sin^2\theta-\int\sin^2\theta\,d\theta$$

$$=\theta\sin^2\theta-\frac{1}{2}\int(1-\cos 2\theta)\,d\theta$$

$$=\theta\sin^2\theta-\frac{1}{2}\left[\theta-\frac{\sin 2\theta}{2}\right]$$

$$=\frac{\theta}{2}(2\sin^2\theta-1)+\frac{1}{4}\cdot 2\sin\theta\cos\theta$$

$$=\frac{1}{2}\sin^{-1}\sqrt{x}\cdot(2x-1)+\frac{1}{2}\sqrt{x}\sqrt{(1-x)} \qquad \text{...(2)}$$

$$\therefore \quad I=\frac{2}{\pi}[(2x-1)\sin^{-1}\sqrt{x}+\sqrt{x(1-x)}]-x+c$$

by (1) and (2)

27. (a) We write the integral as

$$I=\int\frac{x^2-1}{(x+1)^2}\cdot\frac{dx}{\sqrt{(x^3+x^2+x)}}$$

$$=\int\frac{(x^2-1)}{(x^2+2x+1)}\cdot\frac{dx}{\sqrt{(x^3+x^2+x)}}$$

$$=\int\frac{(1-1/x^2)}{(x+2+1/x)}\cdot\frac{dx}{\sqrt{(x+1+1/x)}}$$

on dividing both N^r and D^r by x^2.

Putting $x+1+\frac{1}{x}=t^2 \;\therefore\; \left(1-\frac{1}{x^2}\right)dx=2t\,dt$

$$\therefore \quad I=\int\frac{2t\,dt}{(t^2+1).t}=\int\frac{2\,dt}{(t^2+1)}$$

$$=2\tan^{-1}t=2\tan^{-1}\sqrt{\left(x+1+\frac{1}{x}\right)}.$$

(b) Divide above and below by x^2 and make D^r a function of $x+\frac{1}{x}$.

$$\therefore \quad I=\int\frac{\left(1-\frac{1}{x^2}\right)dx}{\left[\left(x+\frac{1}{x}\right)^2+1\right]\tan^{-1}\left(x+\frac{1}{x}\right)}$$

Put $x+\frac{1}{x}=t$

$$\therefore \quad I=\int\frac{dt}{(1+t^2)\tan^{-1}t}=\log\tan^{-1}t$$

(c) Proceed as in part (b).

Ans. $\log\tan^{-1}\left(x+\frac{2}{x}\right)$

(d) Multiply above and below by $x+1$

$$I=\int \frac{x(x^2-1)}{(x^2+1)(x+1)^2\sqrt{x^3+x^2+x}}$$

$$=\int \frac{x.x^2(1-1/x^2)}{x\left(x+\frac{1}{x}\right).(\sqrt{x})^2\left(\sqrt{x}+\frac{1}{\sqrt{x}}\right)^2.x\sqrt{x+\frac{1}{x}+1}}dx$$

Note the above step and cancel x^3.

Now put $x+\frac{1}{x}+1=t^2$

$$\therefore \quad I=\int \frac{2t\,dt}{(t^2-1)(t^2+1).t}=\int \frac{2\,dt}{(t^2-1)(t^2+1)}$$

$$=\int\left(\frac{1}{t^2-1}-\frac{1}{t^2+1}\right)dt=\frac{1}{2}\log\frac{t-1}{t+1}-\tan t \text{ etc.}$$

(e) $\cos^{-1}\frac{2x}{1+x^2}=\frac{\pi}{2}-\sin^{-1}\frac{2x}{1+x^2}=\frac{\pi}{2}-2\tan^{-1}x$

$$\therefore\ I=\frac{\pi}{2}\int\frac{1}{1-x^8}dx$$

$$=\frac{\pi}{2}.\frac{1}{2}\int\left[\frac{1}{1-x^4}+\frac{1}{1+x^4}\right]dx$$

$$=\frac{\pi}{4}.\frac{1}{2}\int\left[\left(\frac{1}{1+x^2}+\frac{1}{1-x^2}\right)+\frac{(x^2+1)-(x^2-1)}{x^4+1}\right]dx$$

$$=\frac{\pi}{8}\left[\tan^{-1}x+\frac{1}{2}\log\frac{1+x}{1-x}+\text{Deduction II } \mathbf{P.\ 1500}\right]$$

(f) $\{x+\sqrt{x^2-x+1}\}\{x-\sqrt{x^2-x+1}\}=x-1 \quad ...(A)$

Now let $z=x+\sqrt{x^2-x+1}$

$$\frac{x-1}{z}=x-\sqrt{x^2+1} \text{ by (A)}$$

$$\therefore \quad z+\frac{x-1}{z}=2x \text{ or } z^2+(x-1)=2xz$$

or $\quad z^2-1=x(2z-1)$

$$\therefore \quad x=\frac{z^2-1}{2z-1} \text{ or } \frac{dx}{dz}=\frac{2z^2-2z+2}{(2z-1)^2}$$

$$\therefore \quad I=\int\frac{1}{z}\frac{2z^2-2z+2}{(2z-1)^2}dz=2\int\frac{z^2-z+2}{z(2z-1)^2}dz$$

Split into partial fractions

$$\therefore \quad I=2\int\left[\frac{1}{z}-\frac{3}{2(2z-1)}+\frac{3}{2(2z-1)^2}\right]dz$$

$$=2\log z-\frac{3}{2}\log(2z-1)-\frac{3}{4}\frac{1}{(2z-1)}$$

where $z=x+\sqrt{x^2-x+1}$.

28. (a) Dividing both N^r and D^r by x^2, we get

$$I=\int\frac{(1-1/x^2)\,dx}{(x+1/x)\sqrt{(1/x^2+x^2)}}=\int\frac{dt}{t\sqrt{(t^2-2)}}$$

We have put $x+\frac{1}{x}=t, \quad \therefore \left(1-\frac{1}{x^2}\right)dx=dt$ etc.

$$I=\frac{1}{\sqrt{2}}\sec^{-1}\frac{t}{\sqrt{2}}=\frac{1}{\sqrt{2}}\cos^{-1}\frac{\sqrt{2}}{t}$$

$$=\frac{1}{\sqrt{2}}\cos^{-1}\frac{\sqrt{2}}{x+(1/x)}=\frac{1}{\sqrt{2}}\cos^{-1}\frac{x\sqrt{2}}{x^2+1}.$$

(b) $I=\int\frac{(1+1/x^2)\,dx}{(1/x-x)\sqrt{x^2+1/x^2+1}}$

Put $x-\frac{1}{x}=z$

$$\therefore \quad I=-\int\frac{dz}{z\sqrt{z^2+3}}=- \text{ Now put } z^2+3=t^2$$

or $\left(x-\frac{1}{x}\right)^2+3=t^2$ or $x^2+\frac{1}{x^2}+1=t^2$

$$\therefore \quad I=-\int\frac{1}{t^2-3}dt \text{ etc.}$$

29. Put $x=t^3 \quad \therefore \ I=3\int\frac{t^2+1}{(t^3+1)}dt$

$$I=3\int\frac{(t^2+1)}{(t+1)(t^2-t+1)} \quad \text{P.F's.}$$

Integration of Miscellaneous Questions

$$=3\int\left\{\frac{2}{3}.\frac{1}{(t+1)}+\frac{1}{3}.\frac{t+1}{t^2-t+1}\right\}dt$$

$$=2\log(t+1)+\frac{1}{2}\int\frac{2t-1+3}{(t^2+t+1)}dt$$

$$=2\log(t+1)+\frac{1}{2}\log(t^2-t+1)+\frac{3}{2}\int\frac{dt}{\left(t-\frac{1}{2}\right)^2+\left(\frac{\sqrt{3}}{2}\right)^2}$$

$$=\frac{1}{2}[4\log(t+1)+\log(t^2-t+1)]+\frac{3}{2}.\frac{2}{\sqrt{(3)}}\tan^{-1}\frac{t-\frac{1}{2}}{\sqrt{(3)}/2}$$

$$=\frac{1}{2}[\log(t+1)^4(t^2-t+1)]+\sqrt{3}.\tan^{-1}\frac{2t-1}{\sqrt{(3)}}$$

where $t=x^{1/3}$.

30. (a) We write the given integral as

$$I=\int\frac{x^4\,dx}{x^5.\sqrt[4]{(1+1/x^4)}}, \text{ put } 1+\frac{1}{x^4}=t^4$$

so that $-\frac{4}{x^5}dx=4t^3\,dt$

$$\therefore \quad I=-\int\frac{t^3}{(t^4-1)t}dt=-\int\frac{t^2\,dt}{(t^2-1)(t^2+1)}$$

$$=-\frac{1}{2}\left[\int\frac{dt}{t^2-1}+\int\frac{dt}{t^2+1}\right]$$

$$=-\frac{1}{2}\left[\frac{1}{2}\log\frac{t-1}{t+1}+\tan^{-1}t\right]$$

$$= -\frac{1}{4}\left[\log \frac{\sqrt[4]{1+1/x^4}-1}{\sqrt[4]{(1+1/x^4)}+1} + 2\tan^{-1}\left(1+\frac{1}{x^4}\right)^{\frac{1}{4}}\right]$$

(b) Put $x^{1/4}=t$ $\therefore$ $x=t^4$ and $dx=4t^3\,dt$

$$\therefore \quad I=\int \frac{4t^3\,dt}{t^2\,(t+1)^{10}} = 4\int \frac{t+1-1}{(t+1)^{10}}\,dt$$

$$=4\int\left[\frac{1}{(t+9)^{10}}-\frac{1}{(t+1)^{10}}\right]dt$$

$$=4\left[\frac{-1}{8}\,\frac{1}{(t+1)^8}+\frac{1}{9}\cdot\frac{1}{(t+1)^9}\right]\text{etc.}$$

31. (a) $\dfrac{3x+1}{(x-1)^3\,(x+1)}=\dfrac{A}{(x-1)^3}+\dfrac{B}{(x-1)^2}+\dfrac{C}{x-1}+\dfrac{D}{x+1}$

$\therefore$ $(3x+1)=A\,(x+1)+B\,(x-1)\,(x+1)$
$+C\,(x-1)^2\,(x+1)+D\,(x-1)^3$

Putting $x=1,-1$ we get

$2A=4$ $\therefore$ $A=2,\ -2=-8D$ $\therefore$ $D=1/4$

Comparing coeff. of x^3, we have

$0=C+D$ $\therefore$ $C=-D=-1/4$

Comparing const, we have

$1=A-B+C-D$ $\therefore$ $B=\frac{1}{2}$

$$\therefore \int \frac{(3x+1)}{(x-1)^3\,(x+1)}\,dx=-\frac{A}{2\,(x-1)^2}$$
$$-\frac{B}{(x-1)}+C\log(x-1)+D\log(x+1),$$

where A, B, C, D have values written above.

(b) $I=\frac{1}{2}\int\left(\frac{1}{x^3-1}-\frac{1}{x^3+1}\right)dx=I_1+I_2$

For I_1 and I_2 **see Ex. 22 (a), (b) P. 1498-1499.**

$$I_1=\frac{1}{3}\log(x-1)-\frac{1}{6}\log(x^2+x+1)-\frac{1}{\sqrt{3}}\tan^{-1}\frac{2x+1}{\sqrt{3}}$$

$$I_2=\frac{1}{3}\log(x+1)-\frac{1}{6}\log(x^2-x+1)+\frac{1}{\sqrt{3}}\tan^{-1}\frac{2x-1}{\sqrt{3}}$$

32. Put $x=t^{12}$ $\therefore$ $dx=12\cdot t^{11}\,dt$.

$$\therefore \quad I=\int\left[\frac{1}{(t^4+t^3)}+\frac{\log(1+t^2)}{t^4+t^6}\right]12\cdot t^{11}\,dt$$

$$=12\int\left[\frac{t^8-1+1}{t+1}+\frac{t^7\log(1+t^2)}{(1+t^2)}\right]dt$$

Put $1+t^2=z$ for 2nd $\therefore$ $2t\,dt=dz$

$$\therefore \quad I=12\int\left(\frac{t^8-1}{t+1}+\frac{1}{t+1}\right)dt+\frac{12}{2}\int\frac{\log z}{z}(z-1)^3\,dz.$$

$$=12\int\left(t^7-t^6+t^5-t^4+t^3-t^2+t-1+\frac{1}{t+1}\right)dt$$
$$+6\int\left(z^2-3z+3-\frac{1}{z}\right)\log z\,dz$$

$$=12\left[\frac{t^8}{8}-\frac{t^7}{7}+\frac{t^6}{6}-\frac{t^5}{5}+\frac{t^4}{4}-\frac{t^3}{3}+\frac{t^2}{2}-t+\log(t+1)\right]$$
$$+6\left[\left(\frac{z^3}{3}-\frac{3}{2}z^2+3z-\log z\right)\log z\right.$$
$$\left.-\int\left(\frac{z^3}{3}-\frac{3}{2}z^2+3z-\log z\right)\frac{1}{z}\,dz\right]$$

$$=12[\quad]+6[\quad]\log z-6\int\left(\frac{z^2}{3}-\frac{3}{2}z+3-\frac{\log z}{z}\right)dz$$

$$=12[\quad]+6[\quad]\log z-6\left[\frac{z^3}{9}-\frac{3}{4}z^2+3z\right.$$
$$\left.-\frac{1}{2}(\log z)^2\right]+c$$

33. In order to remove the radical let us put $\cos x=\tan t$

$\therefore$ $-\sin x\,dx=\sec^2 t\,dt$

and adjust the limits.

$$\therefore \quad I=-\int_{\pi/4}^{0}\frac{\tan^2 t\,.\sec^2 t}{\sec t}\,dt$$

or $I=\int_0^{\pi/4}\tan t\,.\sec t\tan t\,dt$

$=\int_0^{\pi/4}\sqrt{(\sec^2 t-1)}\sec t\tan t\,dt$

Now put $\sec t=z$ and adjust the limits

$I=\int_1^{\sqrt{2}}\sqrt{(z^2-1)}\,dz$

$$=\left[\frac{z}{2}\sqrt{z^2-1}-\frac{1}{2}\log\{z+\sqrt{z^2-1}\}\right]_1^{\sqrt{2}}$$

$=\frac{1}{2}\sqrt{2}-\frac{1}{2}[\log(\sqrt{2}+1)-0]$

$=\frac{1}{2}[\sqrt{2}-\log(\sqrt{2}+1)]$

Alt. You may put $\cos x=t$ and adjust the limits.

$$\therefore \quad I=\int_0^1\frac{t^2}{\sqrt{1+t^2}}\,dt$$

$$=\int_0^1\left[\sqrt{1+t^2}-\frac{1}{\sqrt{1+t^2}}\right]dt \quad \text{etc.}$$

34. $I=\int\dfrac{1-\sqrt{x}}{\sqrt{1-x}}\,dx$, on rationalization.

Now put $\sqrt{x}=\cos\theta$ or $x=\cos^2\theta$

$\therefore$ $dx=-2\cos\theta\sin\theta\,d\theta$

$$\therefore \quad I=\int\frac{1-\cos\theta}{\sin\theta}(-2\sin\theta\cos\theta\,d\theta)$$

$$=\int -2\cos\theta+(1+\cos 2\theta)\,d\theta$$

$$=-2\sin\theta+\theta+\frac{1}{2}\sin 2\theta$$

$$=-2\sin\theta+\theta+\sin\theta\cos\theta$$

$$=-2\sqrt{1-x}+\cos^{-1}\sqrt{x}+\sqrt{x}\sqrt{1-x}$$

35. Put $x=a\tan\theta$

$\therefore \quad I = \int \frac{a \sec^2 \theta \, d\theta}{a^4 \sec^4 \theta} = \frac{1}{a^3} \int \cos^2 \theta \, d\theta$

$= \frac{1}{2a^3} \int (1 + \cos 2\theta) \, d\theta = \frac{1}{2a^3} \left[\theta + \frac{1}{2} \sin 2\theta \right]$

$= \frac{1}{4a^3} \left[2\theta + \frac{2 \tan \theta}{1 + \tan^2 \theta} \right]$

$= \frac{1}{4a^3} \left[2 \tan^{-1} \frac{x}{a} + \frac{2ax}{x^2 + a^2} \right]$

$= \frac{1}{2a^3} \left[\tan^{-1} \frac{x}{a} + \frac{ax}{x^2 + a^2} \right]$

Note : For alternative method, see solution **Q. 40 (a) P. 1510.**

36. Let the given fraction be

$\frac{A}{x+1} + \frac{Bx + C}{x^2 - x + 1} + \frac{Dx + E}{(x^2 - x + 1)^2}$

$\therefore \quad x^4 - x^3 + 5x^2 + x + 3 = A(x^2 - x + 1)^2$

$+ (Bx + C)(x + 1)(x^2 - x + 1) + (Dx + E)(x + 1) \quad ...(1)$

Put $x = -1$, we get $9A = 9 \quad \therefore \quad A = 1$

Again put $x^2 - x + 1 = 0$ or $x^2 = x - 1$ in both sides

$(x - 1)^2 - x(x - 1) + 5(x - 1) + x + 3$

$= Dx^2 + x(D + E) + E$

$5x - 1 = D(x - 1) + x(D + E) + E$

or $\quad 5x - 1 = (2D + E)x + (E - D)$

Comparing,

$2D + E = 5$ and $E - D = -1$

Solving, we get $D = 2, E = 1$

Now comparing coefficients of x^4 and constant in (1),

$1 = A + B \quad \therefore \quad B = 0$ as $A = 1$

$3 = A + C + E \quad \therefore \quad C = 1$ as $A = 1, E = 1$

$$\therefore \quad I = \int \left[\frac{1}{x+1} + \frac{1}{\left(x - \frac{1}{2}\right)^2 + (\sqrt{3}/2)^2} + \frac{2x + 1}{(x^2 - x + 1)^2} \right] dx$$

$$= \log(x + 1) + \frac{2}{\sqrt{3}} \tan^{-1} \frac{2x - 1}{\sqrt{3}} + \int \frac{2x - 1 + 2}{(x^2 - x + 1)^2} dx$$

$$= \log(x + 1) + \frac{2}{\sqrt{3}} \tan^{-1} \frac{2x - 1}{\sqrt{3}} - \frac{1}{x^2 - x + 1} + 2\int \frac{1}{(x^2 - x + 1)^2} dx \quad ...(2)$$

Now let $I_3 = \int \frac{1}{(x^2 - x + 1)^2} dx$

$$= \int \frac{1}{\left[\left(x - \frac{1}{2}\right)^2 + \left(\frac{\sqrt{3}}{2}\right)^2\right]^2} dx = \int \frac{dx}{(X^2 + A^2)^2}$$

where $X = x - \frac{1}{2}$ and $A = \sqrt{3}/2$

Now proceeding as in part (d),

$$I_3 = \frac{1}{2A^3} \left[\tan^{-1} \frac{X}{A} + \frac{AX}{X^2 + A^2} \right]$$

$$= \frac{1}{2 \cdot \left(\frac{\sqrt{3}}{2}\right)^3} \left[\tan^{-1} \frac{2x - 1}{\sqrt{3}} + \frac{\frac{\sqrt{3}}{2}\left(x - \frac{1}{2}\right)}{x^2 - x + 1} \right]$$

$$= \frac{4}{3\sqrt{3}} \left[\tan^{-1} \frac{2x - 1}{\sqrt{3}} + \frac{\sqrt{3}}{4} \frac{(2x - 1)}{x^2 - x + 1} \right]$$

$\therefore \quad$ Putting in (2), we get

$$I = \log(x + 1) + \frac{2}{\sqrt{3}} \tan^{-1} \frac{2x - 1}{\sqrt{3}} - \frac{1}{x^2 - x + 1} + \frac{8}{3\sqrt{3}} \tan^{-1} \frac{2x - 1}{\sqrt{3}} + \frac{2}{3} \frac{2x - 1}{x^2 - x + 1}$$

$$= \log(x + 1) + \frac{14}{3\sqrt{3}} \tan^{-1} \frac{2x - 1}{\sqrt{3}} + \frac{1}{x^2 - x + 1} \left[\frac{2}{3}(2x - 1) - 1 \right]$$

$$= \log(x + 1) + \frac{14}{3\sqrt{3}} \tan^{-1} \frac{2x - 1}{\sqrt{3}} + \frac{4x - 5}{3(x^2 - x + 1)}$$

37. (a) $(x^2 + 2x + 3)^2 = x^4 + 4x^2 + 9 + 4x^3 + 12x + 6x^2$

$= x^4 + 4x^3 + 10x^2 + 12x + 9$

$= N^r - (x^2 - 1)$

$\therefore \quad N^r = (x^2 + 2x + 3)^2 + (x^2 - 1)$

$$I = \int \left[\frac{1}{x+1} + \frac{x - 1}{(x^2 + 2x + 3)^2} \right] dx$$

$$= \log(x + 1) + \int \frac{l(2x + 2) + m}{(x^2 + 2x + 3)^2} dx$$

where $2l = 1, 2l + m = -1 \quad \therefore \quad l = \frac{1}{2}, m = -2$

$$\therefore \quad I = \log(x + 1) - \frac{l}{(x^2 + 2x + 3)} + m\int \frac{1}{[(x + 1)^2 + (\sqrt{2})^2]^2} dx$$

$$= \log(x + 1) - \frac{1}{2(x^2 + 2x + 3)} - 2I_1$$

$\because \quad l = 1/2, m = -2 \quad ...(1)$

Put $x + 1 = \sqrt{2} \tan \theta$

$\therefore \quad I_1 = \int \frac{\sqrt{2}\sec^2\theta\, d\theta}{4\sec^4\theta} = \frac{1}{4\sqrt{2}}\int 2\cos^2\theta\, d\theta$

$= \frac{1}{4\sqrt{2}}\int (1+\cos 2\theta)\, d\theta = \frac{1}{4\sqrt{2}}\left[\theta + \frac{\sin 2\theta}{2}\right]$

$= \frac{1}{4\sqrt{2}}\left[\tan^{-1}\frac{x+1}{\sqrt{2}} + \sin\theta\cos\theta\right]$

$2I_1 = \frac{1}{2\sqrt{2}}\left[\tan^{-1}\frac{x+1}{\sqrt{2}} + \frac{(x+1)\sqrt{2}}{(x^2+2x+3)}\right]$

$= \frac{1}{2\sqrt{2}}\tan^{-1}\frac{x+1}{\sqrt{2}} + \frac{1}{2}\frac{x+1}{x^2+2x+3}$

Putting for $2I_1$ in (1), we get

$I = \log(x+1) - \frac{1}{2(x^2+2x+3)}$

$- \frac{1}{2\sqrt{2}}\tan^{-1}\frac{x+1}{\sqrt{2}} - \frac{1}{2}\cdot\frac{x+1}{x^2+2x+3}$

$= \log(x+1) - \frac{x+2}{2(x^2+2x+3)} - \frac{1}{2\sqrt{2}}\tan^{-1}\frac{x+1}{\sqrt{2}}$

(b) $N^r = 2(x^4 - 2x^2 + 1) + x(x^2+4)$

$= 2(x^2-1)^2 + x(x^2+4)$

$\therefore \quad I = \int\left[\frac{2}{x^2+4} + \frac{x}{(x^2-1)^2}\right]dx$

$= 2.\frac{1}{2}\tan^{-1}\frac{x}{2} + \frac{1}{2}\left(-\frac{1}{x^2-1}\right) = \tan^{-1}\frac{x}{2} - \frac{1}{2}\cdot\frac{1}{x^2-1}$

38. Do yourself.

39. $I = 4\int \frac{\cos 2x.(2\sin 2x\cos 2x)}{(1+\cos 2x)^2(1+\cos^2 2x)}dx$

Put $\cos 2x = t \quad \therefore \quad -2\sin 2x\, dx = dt$

$\therefore \quad I = -4\int \frac{t^2}{(1+t)^2(1+t^2)}$

Split into partial fractions by putting $t = -1$ and $t^2 = -1$

$I = -4\int\left[\frac{1}{2(1+t)^2} - \frac{1}{2(1+t)} + \frac{t}{2(1+t^2)}\right]dt$

$= -2\left[-\frac{1}{1+t} - \log(1+t) + \frac{1}{2}\log(1+t^2)\right]$

$= \frac{2}{2\cos^2 x} + 2\log(1+\cos 2x) - \log(1+\cos^2 2x)$

$= \sec^2 x + 2\log(1+\cos 2x) - \log(1+\cos^2 2x)$

40. (a) $I = \int \frac{x^4 - 1 + 1}{(x^2+1)^2}dx$

$= \int\left[\frac{x^2-1}{x^2+1} + \frac{1}{(x^2+1)^2}\right]dx = I_1 + I_2$

$I_1 = \int\left(1 - \frac{2}{x^2+1}\right)dx = x - 2\tan^{-1}x$

$I_2 = \int \frac{1}{(x^2+1)^2}dx$

Integrate $P = \int \frac{1}{x^2+1}dx$ by parts

$P = x.\frac{1}{(x^2+1)} + \int \frac{x}{(x^2+1)^2}.2x\, dx$

or $\quad P = \frac{x}{x^2+1} + 2\int \frac{x^2+1-1}{(x^2+1)^2}dx = \frac{x}{x^2+1} + 2P - 2I_2$

$\therefore \quad 2I_2 = P + \frac{x}{x^2+1} \quad$ or $\quad I_2 = \frac{1}{2}\tan^{-1}x + \frac{1}{2}\frac{x}{x^2+1}$

$\therefore \quad I = I_1 + I_2 = x - \frac{3}{2}\tan^{-1}x + \frac{1}{2}\cdot\frac{x}{x^2+1}$

(b) **This is a combination of two questions on integration given in the book, namely Q. 9 (a) P. 1502 and Q. 40 (a) P. 1504-1510.**

$I = \int \frac{(x^3+x) + 2(x+1)}{(x^2+1)^2(x+1)}dx$

$= \int \frac{x}{(x^2+1)(x+1)}dx + 2\int \frac{1}{(x^2+1)^2}dx = I_1 + 2I_2$

$2I_2$ is integrated as in **part (a)**

$2\left[\frac{1}{2}\tan^{-1}x + \frac{1}{2}\frac{x}{x^2+1}\right]$

I_1 is splitted into P.F's as in **Q. 9 (a) P. 1502-1505** by putting $x = -1$ and $x^2 = -1$ etc.

$I_1 = \int\left[\frac{1}{2}\frac{x+1}{(x^2+1)} - \frac{1}{2(x+1)}\right]dx$

$= \frac{1}{2}\left[\frac{1}{2}\log(x^2+1) + \tan^{-1}x - \log(x+1)\right]$

$\therefore \quad I = I_1 + 2I_2 = \frac{1}{4}\log(x^2+1)$

$-\frac{1}{2}\log(x+1) + \frac{3}{2}\tan^{-1}x + \frac{x}{x^2+1}$

41. Put $1 + x = \frac{1}{t} \quad \therefore \quad dx = -\frac{1}{t^2}dt$

Also $x = \frac{1}{t} - 1 = \frac{1-t}{t}$

$\therefore \quad 1 + 2x - x^2 = 1 + \frac{2(1-t)}{t} - \frac{(1-t)^2}{t^2}$

$= \frac{1}{t^2}(t^2 + 2t - t^2 - 1 - t^2 + 2t)$

$= \frac{1}{t^2}(-1 - 2t^2 + 4t)$

$= -\frac{2}{t^2}\left[t^2 - 2t + \frac{1}{2}\right] = -\frac{2}{t^2}\left[(t-1)^2 - \left(\frac{1}{\sqrt{2}}\right)^2\right]$

$\therefore \quad \sqrt{(1+2x-x^2)} = \frac{\sqrt{2}}{t}\sqrt{\left[\left(\frac{1}{\sqrt{2}}\right)^2 - (t-1)^2\right]}$

Note $\sqrt{a^2 - x^2}$

$\therefore \quad I = \int \frac{(-1/t^2)\,dt}{\frac{1}{t}\frac{\sqrt{2}}{t}\sqrt{\left[\left(\frac{1}{\sqrt{2}}\right)^2 - (t-1)^2\right]}}$

$\therefore \quad I = -\frac{1}{\sqrt{2}}\int \frac{dt}{\sqrt{\left[\left(\frac{1}{\sqrt{2}}\right)^2 - (t-1)^2\right]}} = -\frac{1}{\sqrt{2}}\sin^{-1}\frac{(t-1)}{\frac{1}{\sqrt{2}}}$

$= -\frac{1}{\sqrt{2}}\sin^{-1}\frac{\sqrt{2}x}{1+x}$, on putting for t.

42. Proceeding as in **Q. 41** and adjusting the limits after putting $x+1 = \frac{1}{t}$

$$I = -\int_1^{1/2} \frac{1}{\sqrt{(3t-1)}}\,dt = -2\left[\frac{1}{3}\sqrt{(3t-1)}\right]_1^{1/2} = \frac{1}{3}\sqrt{2}.$$

43. Put $x - 3 = \frac{1}{t}$

$\therefore \quad x^2 - 6x + 4 = (x-3)^2 - 5 = \frac{1}{t^2} - 5$

$$I = \int \frac{-\frac{1}{t^2}dt}{\frac{1}{t^2}\cdot\frac{1}{t}\sqrt{1-5t^2}} = \frac{1}{10}\int \frac{-10t}{\sqrt{1-5t^2}}\,dt$$

$$= \frac{1}{10}\cdot 2\sqrt{1-5t^2} = \frac{1}{5}\sqrt{\left(1 - \frac{5}{(x-3)^2}\right)}$$

$$= \frac{\sqrt{(x^2-6x+4)}}{5(x-3)}.$$

44. Put $x = t^2 \quad \therefore \quad dx = 2t\,dt$

$$I = \int \sqrt{\frac{1-t}{1+t}}\cdot\frac{2t}{t^2}\,dt = 2\int \frac{1-t}{t\sqrt{1-t^2}}\,dt$$

$$= \int 2\frac{1}{t\sqrt{1-t^2}}\,dt - 2\int \frac{1}{\sqrt{1-t^2}}\,dt = I_1 - I_2$$

For I_1 put $t = \frac{1}{z}$ as above.

Ans. $-2\log\left\{\frac{1+\sqrt{1-x}}{\sqrt{x}}\right\} - 2\sin^{-1}\sqrt{x}$.

45. $I = \int \frac{dx}{(1+\sqrt{x})\sqrt{x}\sqrt{1-x}}$

Put $\sqrt{x} = t \quad \therefore \quad \frac{1}{2\sqrt{x}}dx = dt$

$$I = 2\int \frac{dt}{(1+t)\sqrt{1-t^2}}$$

Put $1 + t = \frac{1}{z} \quad \therefore \quad t = \frac{1-z}{z}$ and $dt = -\frac{1}{z^2}dz$

$\therefore \quad I = -2\int \frac{dz}{\sqrt{(2z-1)}} = -2\sqrt{(2z-1)}$

$$= -2\sqrt{\frac{2}{1+\sqrt{x}} - 1} = -2\sqrt{\frac{1-\sqrt{x}}{1+\sqrt{x}}}$$

$$= -2\frac{(1-\sqrt{x})}{\sqrt{(1-x)}} = \frac{2(\sqrt{x}-1)}{\sqrt{(1-x)}}$$

§13. Integration of Trigonometrical Functions in Special Cases

(a) $\int \sin^n x\,dx$ **or** $\int \cos^n x\,dx$ **when *n* is odd.**

(i) $\int \sin^5 x\,dx = \int \sin^4 x \sin x\,dx$

Now put $\cos x = t \quad \therefore \quad -\sin x\,dx = dt$.

$\sin^2 x = 1 - \cos^2 x = 1 - t^2$

$\therefore \quad I = -\int (1-t^2)^2\,dt = \int (1 - 2t^2 + t^4)\,dt$

or $\quad I = \left(t - \frac{2t^3}{3} + \frac{1}{5}t^5\right)$, where $t = \cos x$.

(ii) $\int \cos^7 x\,dx = \int \cos^6 x \cos x\,dx$

Put $\sin x = t \quad \therefore \quad \cos x\,dx = dt$

Also $\cos^2 x = 1 - \sin^2 x = 1 - t^2$

$$I = \int (1-t^2)^3\,dt = \int (1 - 3t^2 + 3t^4 - t^6)\,dt$$

$= t - t^3 + \frac{3}{5}t^5 - \frac{t^7}{7}$, where $t = \sin x$.

(iii) $\int \sin^3 x \cos^4 x\,dx$

$$I = \int \sin^2 x \cos^4 x \sin x\,dx$$

Put $\cos x = t$

$\therefore \quad I = -\int t^4(1-t^2)\,dt = -\int (t^4 - t^6)\,dt = -\left[\frac{t^5}{5} - \frac{t^7}{7}\right]$

where $t = \cos x$

Similarly $\int \cos^3 x \sin^4 x\,dx$

$= \frac{t^5}{5} - \frac{t^7}{7}$, where $t = \sin x$

(b) $\int \sin^m x \cos^n x\,dx$ **when $m + n = -$ (Even integer)**

(i) $I = \int \frac{\sin^4 x}{\cos^8 x}\,dx$. Here $m + n = 4 - 8 = -4$

Change in terms of tan x and $\sec^2 x$

$$I = \int \tan^4 x \sec^4 x \, dx$$

or $$I = \int \tan^4 x (1 + \tan^2 x) \sec^2 x \, dx$$

Now put $\tan x = t \quad \therefore \quad \sec^2 x \, dx = dt$

$$\therefore \quad I = \int (t^4 + t^6) \, dt = \frac{1}{5} t^5 + \frac{1}{7} t^7$$

(ii) $$\int \sec^{4/3} x \operatorname{cosec}^{8/3} x \, dx = \int \frac{1}{\cos^{4/3} x \sin^{8/3} x} dx$$

Here $m + n = -\left(\frac{4}{3} + \frac{8}{3}\right) = -4$ *i.e.*, $-$ (Even).

Change in terms of tan x and $\sec^2 x$ for which divide above and below by

$$\cos^{m+n} x = \cos^{8/3} x \cos^{4/3} x = \cos^4 x$$

$$\therefore \quad I = \int \frac{\sec^4 x \, dx}{\tan^{8/3} x} = \int \frac{1 + \tan^2 x}{\tan^{8/3} x} \sec^2 x \, dx$$

Now put $\tan x = t$

$$\therefore \quad I = \int \frac{1 + t^2}{t^{8/3}} dt = (t^{-8/3} + t^{-2/3}) \, dt$$

$$= -\frac{3}{5t^{8/3}} + 3t^{1/3}, \text{ where } t = \tan x.$$

(iii) $$\int \sqrt{\frac{\cos^3 x}{\sin^{11} x}} \, dx.$$

Here $m + n = \frac{3}{2} - \frac{11}{2} = -\frac{8}{2} = -4$

i.e., $-$ ive even integer. So we convert in terms of cot x.

$$I = \int \cot^{3/2} x \operatorname{cosec}^4 x \, dx$$

$$= \int \cot^{3/2} x (1 + \cot^2 x) \operatorname{cosec}^2 dx$$

Put $\cot x = t \therefore - \operatorname{cosec}^2 x \, dx = dt$

$$\therefore \quad I = \int t^{3/2} (1 + t^2)(-dt) = -\int (t^{3/2} + t^{7/2}) \, dt$$

$$= -\frac{2}{5} t^{5/2} - \frac{2}{9} t^{9/2}, \quad \text{where } t = \cot x$$

(iv) $$\int \frac{(1 - \cos x)^{2/7}}{(1 + \cos x)^{9/7}} dx = \frac{7}{11} \left(\tan \frac{x}{2}\right)^{11/7}.$$

$$I = \frac{2^{2/7}}{2^{9/7}} \int \frac{\sin^{4/7} (x/2)}{\cos^{18/7} (x/2)} dx.$$

Now put $\frac{x}{2} = t$

and $m + n = \frac{4}{7} - \frac{18}{7} = -2 = -$ ive even and so convert in terms of tan t and $\sec^2 t$ etc.

(c) $\int \sin^m x \, dx$ **or** $\int \cos^n x \, dx$ **by the help of De-Moivre's theorem, when m and n are integers (Even or odd).**

$$z = \cos x + i \sin x \quad \therefore \quad \frac{1}{z} = (\cos x - i \sin x)$$

$$z + \frac{1}{z} = 2 \cos x, \; z - \frac{1}{z} = 2i \sin x$$

Also $z^n + \frac{1}{z^n} = 2 \cos nx, \; z^n - \frac{1}{z^n} = 2i \sin nx.$

Note : When n is odd then follow the rule given in (a) even though the above rule is also applicable.

(i) $$\int \sin^6 x \, dx$$

$$2i \sin x = z - \frac{1}{z}$$

$$\therefore \quad (2i \sin x)^6 = \left(z - \frac{1}{z}\right)^6$$

$$= z^6 - 6z^4 + 15z^2 - 20 + 15 \frac{1}{z^2} - 6 \frac{1}{z^4} + \frac{1}{z^6}$$

$$= \left(z^6 + \frac{1}{z^6}\right) - 6\left(z^4 + \frac{1}{z^4}\right) + 15\left(z^2 + \frac{1}{z^2}\right) - 20$$

$$= 2 [\cos 6x - 6 \cos 4x + 15 \cos 2x - 10]$$

$$\therefore \quad \int \sin^6 x \, dx = \frac{1}{(2i)^6} . 2 \int (\cos 6x - 6 \cos 4x + 15 \cos 2x - 10) \, dx$$

$$= -\frac{1}{32} \left[\frac{\sin 6x}{6} - \frac{6}{4} \sin 4x + \frac{15}{2} \sin 2x - 10x\right]$$

(ii) $$\int \cos^4 x \, dx$$

$$(2 \cos x)^4 = \left(z + \frac{1}{z}\right)^4 = z^4 + 4z^2 + 6 + 4 . \frac{1}{z^2} + \frac{1}{z^4}$$

$$= \left(z^4 + \frac{1}{z^4}\right) + 4\left(z^2 + \frac{1}{z^2}\right) + 6$$

$$\therefore \quad 2^4 \cos^4 x = 2 [\cos 4x + 4 \cos 2x + 3]$$

$$\int \cos^4 x \, dx = \frac{1}{8}\left[\frac{1}{4} \sin 4x + 2 \sin 2x + 3x\right]$$

(d) $\int \tan^n x \, dx$ **or** $\int \cot^n x \, dx$

Rule : Write

$$\tan^n x = \tan^{n-2} x \tan^2 x = \tan^{n-2} x (\sec^2 x - 1)$$

$$\therefore \quad \int \tan^n x \, dx = \int \tan^{n-2} x \sec^2 x \, dx - \int \tan^{n-2} x \, dx$$

$$I_n = \frac{\tan^{n-1} x}{n - 1} - I_{n-2}$$

Above is a reduction formula.

If the limits were 0 to $\pi/4$, then

$$I_n + I_{n-2} = \left[\frac{\tan^{n-1} x}{n-1}\right]_0^{\pi/4} = \frac{1}{n-1}$$

Replacing n by $n+1$ or proceeding as above we can prove that $I_{n+1} + I_{n-1} = \frac{1}{n}$.

Similarly $\int \cot^n x\,dx = -\frac{\cot^{n-1} x}{n-1} - I_{n-2}$

(i) $\tan^5 x\,dx = \int \tan^3 x(\sec^2 x - 1)\,dx$

$$= \frac{\tan^4 x}{4} - \tan x(\sec^2 x - 1)\,dx$$

$$= \frac{1}{4}\tan^4 x - \frac{1}{2}\tan^2 x + \int \tan x\,dx$$

$$= \frac{1}{4}\tan^4 x - \frac{1}{2}\tan^2 x + \log(\sec x + \tan x)$$

(ii) $\int \cot^6 x\,dx = \int \cot^4 x(\text{cosec}^2 x - 1)\,dx$

$$= -\frac{1}{5}\cot^5 x - \int \cot^2 x(\text{cosec}^2 x - 1)\,dx$$

$$= -\frac{1}{5}\cot^5 x + \frac{1}{3}\cot^3 x + \int (\text{cosec}^2 x - 1)\,dx$$

$$= -\frac{1}{5}\cot^5 x + \frac{1}{3}\cot^3 x - \cot x - x$$

(e) $\int \sec^n x\,dx$ or $\int \text{cosec}^n x\,dx$, when n is even.

Write $\sec^n x\,dx = \sec^{n-2} x \sec^2 x$

Now change $\sec^{n-2} x$, $(n-2)$ even into $\tan^2 x$ and then put $\tan x = t$.

(i) $\int \sec^6 x\,dx = \int \sec^4 x \sec^2 x\,dx$

$$= \int (1 + \tan^2 x)^2 \sec^2 x\,dx. \text{ Put } \tan x = t$$

$$\therefore \quad I = \int (1+t^2)^2\,dt = \int (1 + 2t^2 + t^4)\,dt$$

$$= t + \frac{2}{3}t^3 + \frac{1}{5}t^5, \text{ where } t = \tan x$$

(ii) $\int \text{cosec}^8 x\,dx = \int \text{cosec}^6 x\,\text{cosec}^2 x\,dx$

$$= \int (1 + \cot^2 x)^3 \text{cosec}^2 x\,dx$$

$$= -\int (1+t^2)^3\,dt, \text{ where } t = \cot x$$

$$= -\int (1 + 3t^2 + 3t^4 + t^6)\,dt$$

$$= -\left[t + t^3 + \frac{3}{5}t^5 + \frac{1}{7}t^7\right], \text{ where } t = \cot x$$

When n is odd, then proceed as under :

(iii) $I_n = \int \sec^n x\,dx = \int \sec^{n-2} x \sec^2 x\,dx$

Integrate by parts.

$$I_n = \sec^{n-2} x \tan x - (n-2)\int \tan x \sec^{n-3} x \sec x \tan x\,dx$$

$$= \sec^{n-2} x \tan x - (n-2)\int \sec^{n-2} x(\sec^2 x - 1)\,dx$$

$$= \sec^{n-2} x \tan x - (n-2)\,I_n + (n-2)\,I_{n-2}$$

Transpose I_n to other side.

$$\therefore \quad I_n(n-1) = \sec^{n-2} x \tan x + (n-2)\,I_{n-2}$$

or $\quad I_n = \frac{\sec^{n-2} x \tan x}{n-1} + \left(\frac{n-2}{n-1}\right) I_{n-2}$

Above is known as reduction formula.

Similarly

$$\text{cosec}^n x\,dx = \frac{-\text{cosec}^{n-2} x \cot x}{n-2} + \left(\frac{n-2}{n-1}\right) I_{n-2}$$

e.g. $\sec^5 x\,dx = \frac{\sec^3 x \tan x}{4} + \frac{3}{4}\int \sec^3 x\,dx$

$$= \frac{\sec^3 x \tan x}{4} + \frac{3}{4}\left[\frac{\sec x \tan x}{2} + \frac{1}{2}\int \sec x\,dx\right]$$

$$= \frac{\sec^3 x \tan x}{4} + \frac{3}{8}\sec x \tan x + \frac{3}{8}\log(\sec x + \tan x)$$

(f) Reduction formula for $\int \sin^n x\,dx$

$I_n = \sin^{n-1} x \sin x\,dx$

Integrate by parts.

$$= \sin^{n-1} x(-\cos x) + (n-1)\int \cos x . \sin^{n-2} x \cos x\,dx$$

$$= -\sin^{n-1} x \cos x + (n-1)\int \sin^{n-2} x(1 - \sin^2 x)\,dx$$

$$= -\sin^{n-1} x \cos x + (n-1)\,[I_{n-2} - I_n]$$

Transpose I_n to other side.

$$nI_n = -\sin^{n-1} x \cos x + (n-1)\,I_{n-2}$$

$$\therefore \quad I_n = -\frac{\sin^{n-1} x \cos x}{n} + \frac{n-1}{n}\int \sin^{n-2} x\,dx$$

Similarly

$$\int \cos^n x\,dx = \frac{\cos^{n-1} x \sin x}{n} + \frac{n-1}{n}\int \cos^{n-2} x\,dx$$

Note : $\int_0^{\pi/2} \sin^n x\,dx, \int_0^{\pi/2} \cos^n x\,dx,$ $\int_0^{\pi/2} \sin^m x \cos^n x\,dx$

See gamma function definite integral on P. 1536.

Ex. Prove that if n is a +ive integer, then

$$I_n = \int_0^{\pi/2} \cos^n x \cos nx\,dx = \frac{\pi}{2^{n+1}}$$

$$I_n = \cos^n x \frac{\sin nx}{n} - \frac{1}{n}\int \sin nx\,(n\cos^{n-1} x)(-\sin x)\,dx$$

$$= \left[\frac{\cos^n x \sin nx}{n}\right]_0^{\pi/2} + \int \cos^{n-1} x\,\{\sin nx \sin x\}\,dx \quad ...(1)$$

Now $\cos(n-1)x = \cos nx \cos x + \sin nx \sin x$

$\therefore \quad I_n = 0 + \int_0^{\pi/2} \cos^{n-1} x\,\{\cos(n-1)x - \cos nx \cos x\}\,dx$

$$I_n = 0 + I_{n-1} - I_n$$

or $2I_n = I_{n-1}$ or $I_n = \frac{1}{2} I_{n-1}$

$$I_n = \frac{1}{2}\left[\frac{1}{2} I_{n-2}\right] = \frac{1}{2^2}\left[\frac{1}{2} I_{n-3}\right] = \frac{1}{2^3} I_{n-3}$$

$$= \frac{1}{2^n} I_{n-n} = \frac{1}{2^n} I_0, \text{ where } I_0 = \int_0^{\pi/2} dx = \frac{\pi}{2}.$$

$$\therefore \quad I_n = \frac{\pi}{2^{n+1}}$$

Miscellaneous Problem Set (6)

Miscellaneous type Problems

1. $\int \frac{\tan x}{a^2 + b^2 \tan^2 x}\,dx$.

2. $\int \frac{\sqrt{\tan x}\,dx}{\sin x \cos x}$.

3. $\int \frac{e^x (1+x)\,dx}{\sin^2 (xe^x)}$.

4. $\int \frac{e^{\sqrt{x}} \cos e^{\sqrt{x}}}{\sqrt{(x)}}\,dx$.

5. $\int \frac{dx}{(x^2 - 2x\cos\theta + 1)}$.

6. $\int \frac{3 + 4\sin x + 2\cos x}{3 + 2\sin x + \cos x}\,dx$.

7. $\frac{dx}{\sqrt{[(x-a)(x-b)]}}$.

8. $\int e^{-ax} \cos bx\,dx$.

9.* If $P = \int e^{ax} \cos bx\,dx$, $Q = \int e^{ax} \sin bx\,dx$, then prove that $(P^2 + Q^2)(a^2 + b^2) = e^{2ax}$ and $\tan^{-1}\frac{Q}{P} + \tan^{-1}\frac{b}{a} = bx$.

10. $\int \frac{x}{1 + \sin x}\,dx$.

11.* $\int \frac{x}{1 + \sec x}\,dx$.

12. (a)* $\int \tan^{-1} \sqrt{\left(\frac{1-x}{1+x}\right)}\,dx$.

(b)* $\int_1^{16} \tan^{-1} \sqrt{(\sqrt{x} - 1)}\,dx$

13. $\int x^2 \tan^{-1} x\,dx$.

14. $\int x^3 \tan^{-1} x\,dx$.

15.* $\int x \sin^{-1} x\,dx$.

16. (i) $\int x \sec^{-1} x\,dx$. (ii) $\int_0^1 \tan^{-1} x\,dx$.

17.* $\int \sin^{-1} \sqrt{\left(\frac{x}{a+x}\right)}\,dx$. **(J.E.E.W.B. 1991)**

18.* $\int x \sin^{-1} \frac{1}{2} \sqrt{\left(\frac{2a - x}{a}\right)}\,dx$

19. $\int_a^b \frac{\log x}{x}\,dx$.

20.* $\int \sqrt{x^2 + 1}\,\frac{[\log(x^2 + 1) - 2\log x]}{x^4}\,dx$

21. $\int \left[\log(\log x) + \frac{1}{(\log x)^2}\right] dx$.

22. $\int (\log x)^2\,dx$.

23. $\int \frac{e^x (x^2 + 1)}{(x+1)^2}\,dx$

24. $\int e^x \left(\frac{1-x}{1+x^2}\right)^2 dx$.

25.* $\int \frac{e^x (x^3 - x + 2)}{(1 + x^2)^2}\,dx$.

26. (a) $\int \left[\frac{1}{\log x} - \frac{1}{(\log x)^2}\right] dx$

(b)* $\int a^x \left[\log x + \log a \log\left(\frac{x^x}{e^x}\right)\right] dx$

(c)* $\int e^{(x\sin x + \cos x)} \left[\frac{x^4 \cos^3 x - x\sin x + \cos x}{x^2 \cos^2 x}\right] dx$

27. (a)* $\int \frac{dx}{\sqrt[4]{[(x-1)^3 (x+2)^5]}}$.

(b) $\int \frac{dx}{(x+\alpha)^{8/7} (x-\beta)^{6/7}}$

(b_1) $\int \frac{dx}{(x+3)^{13/14} (x-4)^{15/14}}$

(c) $\int \frac{x\,dx}{(x^2+1)^{4/5} (x^2+2)^{6/5}}$

28. $\int \frac{e^{2x}\,dx}{\sqrt[4]{(e^x + 1)}}$.

29. (a)* $\int \frac{x^2}{(x\sin x + \cos x)^2}\,dx$.

(b) $\int \frac{x^2\,dx}{(x\cos x - \sin x)^2}$

30. (a)* $\int \frac{\sin\theta+\cos\theta}{\sqrt{(\sin 2\theta)}}\,d\theta$

(b) $\int_0^{\pi/4} (\sqrt{\tan x}+\sqrt{\cot x})\,dx$. **(M.N.R. 1992)**

(c) $\int \frac{(\sin x-\cos x)\,dx}{(\sin x+\cos x)\sqrt{(\sin x\cos x+\sin^2 x\cos^2 x)}}$

(d) $\int \frac{\cos x-\sin x}{\sqrt{8-\sin 2x}}\,dx$

31.* $\int \sqrt{\left(\frac{\sin(x-\alpha)}{\sin(x+\alpha)}\right)}\,dx$ **32.** $\int \frac{1-\cos x}{\cos x(1+\cos x)}\,dx$.

33. $\int \frac{1}{x(x^2+1)^3}\,dx$. **34.** $\int \frac{(e^x-1)}{(e^x+1)}\,dx$.

35. $\int \frac{e^x\,dx}{(e^x-3e^{-x}+2)}$. **36.** $\int \frac{dx}{1+3e^x+2e^{2x}}$.

37. (a) $\int \frac{1+x\sin x+\cos x}{x(1+\cos x)}\,dx$.

(b) $\int \frac{1+2x\sin x-\cos x}{x(1-\cos x)}\,dx$

38. $\int \frac{\cos x+x\sin x}{x(x+\cos x)}\,dx$.

39. (a)* If $s_n=\int_0^{\pi/2}\frac{\sin(2n-1)x}{\sin x}\,dx$,

$v_n=\int_0^{\pi/2}\left(\frac{\sin nx}{\sin x}\right)^2 dx$

and n is an integer, show that

$s_{n+1}-s_n=0,\ v_{n+1}-v_n=s_{n+1}$.

(b) If $I_n=\int_0^{\pi/2}\frac{\sin^2 nx}{\sin^2 x}\,dx$ then prove the following

(a) $I_1, I_2, I_3, ..., I_n$ are in A.P.

(b) $I_n=\frac{n\pi}{2}$ (c) $\sin(I_{16})=0$

40. (a)* If m and n are integers, show that $\int_0^{\pi}\sin mx\sin nx\,dx=0$ if $m\neq n$ and $\pi/2$ if $m=n$.

(b)* For all positive integers k, prove that

$\frac{\sin 2kx}{\sin x}=2[\cos x+\cos 3x+\ldots\ \ldots+\cos(2k-1)x]$.

Hence prove that $\int_0^{\pi/2}\sin(2kx)\cot x\,dx=\frac{\pi}{2}$. **(I.I.T. 1990)**

41.* $\int_a^b \frac{dx}{\sqrt{[(x-a)(b-x)]}}=\pi\ (b>a)$.

42.* $\int_a^b \sqrt{\left(\frac{x-a}{b-x}\right)}\,dx=\frac{\pi}{2}(b-a)$.

43. (a)* $\int_a^b \sqrt{(x-a)(b-x)}\,dx=\frac{\pi}{8}(b-a)^2$.

(b)* $\int_{\sqrt{\left(\frac{3a^2+b^2}{4}\right)}}^{\sqrt{\left(\frac{a^2+b^2}{2}\right)}} \frac{x}{\{\sqrt{(x^2-a^2)(b^2-x^2)}\}}\,dx$

44. (a)* $\int_0^{\infty}\frac{dx}{[x+\sqrt{(1+x^2)}]^n}$, where n is an integer >1. **(Roorkee 1990)**

(b) $\int [x+\sqrt{x^2+1}]^n\,dx$

45.* $\int_0^{\pi/2}\frac{\sec^2 x}{(\sec x+\tan x)^n}\,dx\ (n>1)$.

46.* $\int \left[\frac{(\cos 2x)^{1/2}}{\sin x}\right]dx$.

47. (a)* $\int \frac{dx}{\sin x+\sec x}$. (b) $\int \frac{dx}{\cos x+\operatorname{cosec} x}$.

48. (a) $\int \frac{dx}{\cos^3 x\sqrt{(\sin 2x)}}$ (b) $\int \frac{dx}{\sqrt{(\sin^3 x\cos^5 x)}}$

49. $\int \frac{dx}{\sqrt{(1+e^x+e^{2x})}}$ **50.** $\int \left\{\frac{\cos x-\cos^3 x}{(1-\cos^3 x)}\right\}^{1/2} dx$

51.* $\int e^{\sin x}\left(\frac{x\cos^3 x-\sin x}{\cos^2 x}\right)dx$

52. $\int \frac{e^{\cos x}(x\sin^3 x+\cos x)}{\sin^2 x}\,dx$

53.* $\int_0^1 \frac{2-x^2}{(1+x)\sqrt{(1-x^2)}}\,dx$ **(Roorkee 1995)**

54. (a)* Evaluate $\int_0^1 (tx+1-x)^n\,dx$, where n is a + ive integer and t is a parameter independent of x. Hence prove that

$\int_0^1 x^k(1-x)^{n-k}=\left[{}^nC_k\,(n+1)\right]^{-1}$

for $k=0, 1, 2, ..., n$.

(b) Prove that $\int_0^1 \frac{dx}{(1+x^n)^{1/n}}=\int_0^{\infty}\frac{dx}{1+x^n}$ $(n>1)$

55. $\int \sec^2 x\log(1+\sin^2 x)\,dx$

56.* If $f(x)=\begin{vmatrix}\sin x+\sin 2x+\sin 3x & \sin 2x & \sin 3x\\ 3+4\sin x & 3 & 4\sin x\\ 1+\sin x & \sin x & 1\end{vmatrix}$

then prove that $\int_0^{\pi/2} f(x)\,dx=\frac{1}{3}$.

57. The value of $\int_1^{e^{37}} \frac{\pi \sin(\pi \ln x)}{x} dx$ is ..... **(I.I.T. Re-ex. 1997)**

58.* Let $\frac{d}{dx} F(x) = \frac{e^{\sin x}}{x}, x > 0$.

If $\int_1^4 \frac{2e^{\sin x^2}}{x} dx = F(k) - F(1)$ then one of the possible values of k is ...... **(I.I.T. Re-ex. 1997)**

59. If $\int \frac{2\,dx}{[(x-5)+(x-7)]\sqrt{(x-5)(x-7)}} = f[g(x)] + c$, then

(a) $f(x) = \sin^{-1} x, g(x) = \sqrt{(x-5)(x-7)}$

(b) $f(x) = \sin^{-1} x, g(x) = (x-5)(x-7)$

(c) $f(x) = \tan^{-1} x, g(x) = \sqrt{(x-5)(x-7)}$

(d) $f(x) = \tan^{-1} x, g(x) = (x-5)(x-7)$

60. If the integral

$$\int \frac{5\tan x}{\tan x - 2} dx = x + a\log|\sin x - 2\cos x| + k$$

then a is equal to

(a) -1 (b) -2 (c) 1 (d) 2

(AIEEE 2012)

61. The integral $\int \frac{\sec^2 x}{(\sec x + \tan x)^{9/2}} dx$ equals for some arbitrary constant k

(a) $\frac{-1}{(\sec x + \tan x)^{11/2}} \left\{\frac{1}{11} - \frac{1}{7}(\sec x + \tan x)^2\right\} + k$

(b) $\frac{1}{(\sec x + \tan x)^{11/2}} \left\{\frac{1}{11} - \frac{1}{7}(\sec x + \tan x)^2\right\} + k$

(c) $\frac{-1}{(\sec x + \tan x)^{11/2}} \left\{\frac{1}{11} + \frac{1}{7}(\sec x + \tan x)^2\right\} + k$

(d) $\frac{1}{(\sec x + \tan x)^{11/2}} \left\{\frac{1}{11} + \frac{1}{7}(\sec x + \tan x)^2\right\} + k$

(IIT-JEE 2012)

Solutions to Miscellaneous Problem Set (6)

1. Change to $\sin x$ and $\cos x$ and it reduces to **Q. 5, P. 739-42.**

2. Divide above and below by $\cos^2 x$

$$I = \int \frac{\sqrt{\tan x}\sec^2 x\,dx}{\tan x} = \int \frac{\sec^2 x}{\sqrt{(\tan x)}} dx = 2\sqrt{\tan x}.$$

3. Put $xe^x = t$ $\therefore$ $(1.e^x + x.e^x)\,dx = dt$

$$I = \int \operatorname{cosec}^2 t\,dt = -\cot t = -\cot(xe^x).$$

4. Put $e^{\sqrt{x}} = t$ $\therefore$ $e^{\sqrt{x}} . \frac{1}{2\sqrt{(x)}} dx = dt.$

$$I = 2\int \cos t\,dt = 2\sin t = 2\sin e^{\sqrt{x}}.$$

5. $x^2 - 2x\cos\theta + 1 = (x - \cos\theta)^2 + (1 - \cos^2\theta)$

$$\therefore \quad I = \int \frac{dx}{(x-\cos\theta)^2 + \sin^2\theta} = \frac{1}{\sin\theta}\tan^{-1}\frac{x - \cos\theta}{\sin\theta}$$

6. $I = \int_0^\pi \left[2 - \frac{3}{3 + 2\sin x + \cos x}\right] dx$

Now see I_3 of **Ex. 18 P. 1472.**

7. $I = \int \frac{dx}{\sqrt{[(x-a)(x-b)]}} = \int \frac{dx}{\sqrt{(x-a)} . \sqrt{[x - a + (a-b)]}}$

Put $x - a = z^2$ $\therefore$ $dx = 2z\,dz$

$$\therefore \quad I = \int \frac{2z\,dz}{z\sqrt{(z^2 + a - b)}} = 2\int \frac{dz}{\sqrt{[z^2 + (a-b)]}}$$

$$= 2\log[z + \sqrt{z^2 + (a-b)}] = 2\log[\sqrt{x-a} + \sqrt{x-b}].$$

8. Proceed as in **Ex. 13 (a) P. 1483.**

$$I = -\frac{e^{-ax}}{r}\cos(bx + \alpha)$$

where $r = \sqrt{a^2 + b^2}$ and $\alpha = \tan^{-1}(b/a)$.

9. **Refer Ex. 13 (a) P. 1483. Another form.**

$$P = \frac{e^{ax}}{r}\cos(bx - \alpha), \quad Q = \frac{e^{ax}}{r}\sin(bx - \alpha).$$

Squaring and adding, we get

$$P^2 + Q^2 = \frac{e^{2ax}}{r^2}.1 \text{ or } (P^2 + Q^2)(a^2 + b^2) = e^{2ax}.$$

Dividing, we get $\frac{Q}{P} = \tan(bx - \alpha)$

or $\tan^{-1}\frac{Q}{P} + \alpha = bx$ or $\tan^{-1}\frac{Q}{P} + \tan^{-1}\frac{b}{a} = bx.$

10. $I = \int \frac{x}{1 + \sin x} dx = \int \frac{x(1 - \sin x)}{1 - \sin^2 x} dx$

$$= \int x\sec^2 x\,dx - \int x\sec x\tan x\,dx.$$

Integrate each by parts

$I = [x\tan x - \log\sec x] - [x\sec x - \log(\sec x + \tan x)].$

11. $I = \int \frac{x}{\sec x + 1} dx = \int \frac{x\cos x}{1 + \cos x} dx$

$$= \int x\frac{1 + \cos x - 1}{1 + \cos x} dx = \int \left(x - \frac{x}{2\cos^2(x/2)}\right) dx$$

$$I = \frac{x^2}{2} - x\tan\frac{x}{2} + 2\log\sec\frac{x}{2}$$

as in **Ex.11 P. 1482.**

12. (a) Put $x = \cos\theta$. $\therefore$ $\frac{1 - \cos\theta}{1 + \cos\theta} = \tan^2\frac{\theta}{2}$

and $dx = -\sin\theta\,d\theta$

$$I = \int \tan^{-1}[\tan(\theta/2)](-\sin\theta\,d\theta)$$

$= -\frac{1}{2}\int \theta \sin\theta \, d\theta = -\frac{1}{2}[-\theta\cos\theta + \sin\theta]$

$= \frac{1}{2}[x\cos^{-1} x - \sqrt{1-x^2}]$

(b) Since $\sqrt{\sec^2\theta - 1} = \tan\theta$.

hence we put $x = \sec^4\theta$

$\therefore$ $dx = 4\sec^3\theta \sec\theta \tan\theta$ and adjust the limits.

$I = \int_0^{\pi/3} \tan^{-1}(\tan\theta) \cdot 4\sec^3\theta\sec\theta\tan\theta \, d\theta$

$= \int_0^{\pi/3} \theta\,(4\sec^3\theta\sec\theta\tan\theta)\, d\theta$

Integrate by parts.

$I = \left[\theta \sec^4\theta\right]_0^{\pi/3} - \int_0^{\pi/3} \sec^4\theta \cdot 1\, d\theta$

$= \frac{\pi}{3}(2^4) - \int (1+\tan^2\theta)\sec^2\theta \, d\theta$

$= \frac{16\pi}{3} - \left(\tan\theta + \frac{\tan^3\theta}{3}\right)_0^{\pi/3} = \frac{16\pi}{3} - 2\sqrt{3}.$

13. Integrating by parts,

$I = \frac{x^3}{3}\tan^{-1} x - \frac{1}{3}\int \frac{x^3}{x^2+1}\,dx.$

$= \frac{x^3}{3}\tan^{-1} x - \frac{1}{3}\int \left(x - \frac{x}{x^2+1}\right) dx$ **(Note)**

$= \frac{x^3}{3}\tan^{-1} x - \frac{1}{6}x^2 + \frac{1}{6}\log(x^2+1).$

14. $I = \frac{x^4}{4}\tan^{-1} x - \frac{1}{4}\int \frac{x^4 - 1 + 1}{1+x^2}\,dx.$ **(Note)**

$= \frac{x^4}{4}\tan^{-1} x - \frac{1}{4}\int \left[(x^2-1) + \frac{1}{1+x^2}\right] dx.$

$= \frac{1}{4}\left[(x^4-1)\tan^{-1} x - \frac{x^3}{3} + x\right].$

15. Integrate by parts

$I = \frac{x^2}{2}\sin^{-1} x - \frac{1}{2}\int \frac{x^2}{\sqrt{(1-x^2)}}\,dx$

$= \frac{1}{2}x^2\sin^{-1} x + \frac{1}{2}\int \frac{1-x^2-1}{\sqrt{(1-x^2)}}$ **(Note)**

$= \frac{1}{2}x^2\sin^{-1} x + \frac{1}{2}\int \left(\sqrt{1-x^2} - \frac{1}{\sqrt{(1-x^2)}}\right) dx$

$= \frac{1}{2}x^2\sin^{-1} x + \frac{1}{2}\left[\frac{x}{2}\sqrt{1-x^2} + \frac{1}{2}\sin^{-1} x - \sin^{-1} x\right]$

$= \frac{1}{2}x^2\sin^{-1} x + \frac{1}{4}x\sqrt{1-x^2} - \frac{1}{4}\sin^{-1} x.$

16. (i) $I = \frac{x^2}{2}\sec^{-1} x - \frac{1}{2}\int \frac{x^2}{x\sqrt{(x^2-1)}}\,dx$

$= \frac{x^2}{2}\sec^{-1} x - \frac{1}{4}\int \frac{2x}{\sqrt{(x^2-1)}}\,dx$

Put $x^2 - 1 = t$ etc.

$\therefore$ $I = \frac{1}{2}[x^2\sec^{-1} x - \sqrt{x^2-1}].$

(ii) Ans. $\frac{\pi}{4} - \frac{1}{2}\log 2.$

17. Put $x = a\tan^2\theta$ $\therefore$ $dx = 2a\tan\theta\sec^2\theta\, d\theta.$

$\therefore$ $I = \int \sin^{-1}\sqrt{\left(\frac{a\tan^2\theta}{a\sec^2\theta}\right)} \cdot 2a\tan\theta\sec^2\theta\, d\theta.$

$= \int \sin^{-1}(\sin\theta) \cdot 2a\tan\theta\sec^2\theta\, d\theta$

$= a\int \theta\,(2\tan\theta\sec^2\theta)\, d\theta.$

Integrate by parts

$I = a[\theta\sec^2\theta - \int \sec^2\theta \cdot 1\, d\theta]$

$\because$ $\int 2\tan\theta\sec^2\theta\, d\theta$

$= \int 2\sec\theta(\sec\theta\tan\theta\, d\theta) = 2\frac{\sec^2\theta}{2}$

$= a[\theta(1+\tan^2\theta) - \tan\theta]$

$= a\left[\left(1+\frac{x}{a}\right)\tan^{-1}\sqrt{\left(\frac{x}{a}\right)} - \sqrt{\left(\frac{x}{a}\right)}\right]$

$= (a+x)\tan^{-1}\sqrt{\left(\frac{x}{a}\right)} - \sqrt{ax}.$

18. Put $x = 2a\cos\theta$ $\therefore$ $\frac{2a-x}{a} = \frac{2a(1-\cos\theta)}{a}$

$\therefore$ $\sqrt{\left(\frac{2a-x}{a}\right)} = \sqrt{4\sin^2\left(\frac{\theta}{2}\right)} = 2\sin\left(\frac{\theta}{2}\right).$

$\therefore$ $I = \int (2a\cos\theta)\sin^{-1}\left[\frac{1}{2} \cdot 2\sin\left(\frac{\theta}{2}\right)\right](-2a\sin\theta\, d\theta)$

$= \int \frac{1}{2}\theta(-4a^2\sin\theta\cos\theta)\, d\theta = -a^2\int \theta\sin 2\theta\, d\theta$

$= a^2\left[\frac{1}{2}\theta\cos 2\theta - \frac{\sin 2\theta}{4}\right],$ integrating by parts

$= \frac{a^2}{2}[\theta(2\cos^2\theta - 1) - \cos\theta\sqrt{1-\cos^2\theta}].$

Now put $\cos\theta = \frac{x}{2a}.$

$I = \left[\frac{1}{4}(x^2 - 2a^2)\cos^{-1}\frac{x}{2a} - \frac{x}{8}\sqrt{4a^2 - x^2}\right].$

19. Put $\log x = t$ $\therefore$ $(1/x)\,dx = dt$ and adjust the limits

$\therefore$ $I = \int t\, dt = \left[\frac{1}{2}t^2\right]_{\log a}^{\log b}$

$\therefore$ $I = \frac{1}{2}[(\log b)^2 - (\log a)^2]$

$= \frac{1}{2}(\log b + \log a)(\log b - \log a)$

$\therefore$ $I = \frac{1}{2}\log(ab) \cdot \log\frac{b}{a}.$

20. $I = \dfrac{x\sqrt{\left(1+\frac{1}{x^2}\right)}}{x^4}\log\frac{(x^2+1)}{x^2}\,dx$

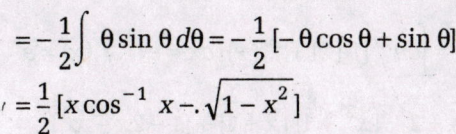

$$=\int \frac{1}{x^3}\sqrt{\left(1+\frac{1}{x^2}\right)}\log\left(1+\frac{1}{x^2}\right)dx$$

Put $1+\frac{1}{x^2}=t \quad \therefore \quad \frac{-2}{x^3}dx=dt$

$\therefore \quad I=-\frac{1}{2}\int \sqrt{t}\log t\,dt$. Integrate by parts

$$=-\frac{1}{2}\left[\frac{2}{3}t^{3/2}\log t-\frac{2}{3}\int \sqrt{t}\,dt\right]$$

$$=-\frac{1}{2}\left[\frac{2}{3}t^{3/2}\log t-\frac{2}{3}\cdot\frac{2}{3}t^{3/2}\right]=\frac{t^{3/2}}{9}[2-3\log t]$$

where $t=1+\frac{1}{x^2}=\frac{x^2+1}{x^2}$.

21. Put $\log x=t \quad \therefore \quad x=e^t$ and $dx=e^t dt$.

$$I=\int e^t\left(\log t+\frac{1}{t^2}\right)dt=\int e^t\left(\log t+\frac{1}{t}-\frac{1}{t}+\frac{1}{t^2}\right)dt$$

$$=e^t\left(\log t+\frac{1}{t}\right)dt+\int e^t\left(-\frac{1}{t}+\frac{1}{t^2}\right)dt \qquad \textbf{(Note)}$$

$$=e^t\log t+e^t\left(-\frac{1}{t}\right)=x\log(\log x)-\frac{x}{\log x}$$

22. $I=x(\log x)^2-2\int x.\log x.\frac{1}{x}dx$

$$=x(\log x)^2-2\int \log x\,dx$$

$=x(\log x)^2-2[x\log x-x]$ **Ex. 4 (a) P. 1479**

$$=x[(\log x)^2-2\log x+2].$$

23. $\frac{x^2+1}{(x+1)^2}=\frac{x^2-1+2}{(x+1)^2}=\frac{x-1}{x+1}+\frac{2}{(x+1)^2}=f(x)+f'(x)$

$\therefore \quad I=\int e^x[f(x)+f'(x)]dx=e^x f(x)=e^x.\frac{x-1}{x+1}.$

Alternative Method :

$I=\frac{e^x(x^2+1)}{(x+1)^2}.$ Integrate by parts

$$I=e^x(x^2+1)\left[-\frac{1}{x+1}\right]+\int \frac{1}{x+1}.e^x(x^2+1+2x)dx$$

$$=-e^x.\frac{x^2+1}{x+1}+\int e^x(x+1)dx=-e^x.\frac{x^2+1}{x+1}+e^x.x.$$

$$=e^x.\left[\frac{-x^2-1+x^2+x}{x+1}\right]=e^x.\frac{x-1}{x+1}.$$

24. $\left(\frac{1-x}{1+x^2}\right)^2=\frac{1+x^2-2x}{(1+x^2)^2}$

$$=\frac{1}{1+x^2}+\frac{-2x}{(1+x^2)^2}=f(x)+f'(x)$$

$\therefore \quad I=\int e^x[f(x)+f'(x)]dx=e^x.f(x)=e^x.\frac{1}{1+x^2}.$

25. $\frac{x^3-x+2}{(x^2+1)^2}=\frac{(x^2+1)(x+1)+(1-2x-x^2)}{(x^2+1)^2}$

$$=\frac{x+1}{x^2+1}+\frac{1-2x-x^2}{(x^2+1)^2}=f(x)+f'(x)$$

$\therefore \quad I=\int e^x[f(x)+f'(x)]dx=e^x f(x)=e^x.\frac{x+1}{x^2+1}$

26. (a) $I=I_1-I_2$

$$I_1=\int \frac{1}{\log x}dx=x.\frac{1}{\log x}-\int x.\left(-\frac{1}{\log x}\right)^2.\frac{1}{x}dx$$

$$I_1=x.\frac{1}{\log x}+\int\left(\frac{1}{\log x}\right)^2 dx=x.\frac{1}{\log x}+I_2$$

or $I=I_1-I_2=x(\log x)^{-1}$.

(b) $I=\int a^x\log x\,dx+\int(a^x\log a).x(\log x-1)\,dx$

We know that

$$\int \log x\,dx=x\log x-\int x.\frac{1}{x}dx=x(\log x-1)$$

Integrating Ist term by parts,

$$\therefore \quad I=a^x.x(\log x-1)-\int x(\log x-1)(a^x\log a)\,dx$$

$$+\int(a^x\log a).x(\log x-1)\,dx$$

$$=a^x.x(\log x-1)$$

(c) d.c. of $(x\sin x+\cos x)=x\cos x$

d.c. of $\frac{1}{x\cos x}=-\frac{1}{(x\cos x)^2}.(\cos x-x\sin x)$

$$\int e^{(x\sin x+\cos x)}(x^2\cos x)\,dx$$

$$-\int e^{(x\sin x+\cos x)}.\frac{d}{dx}\left(\frac{1}{x\cos x}\right)dx=I_1-I_2$$

$I_1=x[e^{(x\sin x+\cos x)}.x\cos x]$ Integrate by parts

$$=x.e^{x\sin x+\cos x}-\int e^{x\sin x+\cos x}.1.dx \qquad ...(1)$$

$$I_2=\int e^{(x\sin x+\cos x)}.\frac{1}{x\cos x}$$

$$-\int \frac{1}{x\cos x}.e^{(x\sin x+\cos x)}.x\cos x\,dx$$

$$=e^{(x\sin x+\cos x)}.\frac{1}{x\cos x}-\int e^{(x\sin x+\cos x)}dx \qquad ...(2)$$

$$\therefore \quad I=I_1-I_2=e^{(x\sin x+\cos x)}\left(x-\frac{1}{x\cos x}\right)$$

27. (a) $I=\int \frac{1}{\left[\left(\frac{x-1}{x+2}\right)^3 (x+2)^8\right]^{1/4}} dx$

$=\frac{1}{(x+2)^2\left(\frac{x-1}{x+2}\right)^{3/4}} dx$

Put $\frac{x-1}{x+2}=t$ or $1-\frac{3}{x+2}=t$

$\therefore \quad \frac{3}{(x+2)^2} dx=dt$

$\therefore \quad I=\frac{1}{3}\int t^{-3/4}\, dt=\frac{1}{3}.4t^{1/4}=\frac{4}{3}\left(\frac{x-1}{x+2}\right)^{1/4}.$

(b) $\frac{8}{7}+\frac{6}{7}=\frac{14}{7}=2$

$I=\frac{dx}{(x+\alpha)^{8/7+6/7}\cdot\left(\frac{x-\beta}{x+\alpha}\right)^{6/7}}$

$=\frac{dx}{(x+\alpha)^2\left[1-\frac{\alpha+\beta}{x+\alpha}\right]^{6/7}}$

Put $1-\frac{\alpha+\beta}{x+\alpha}=t \quad \therefore \quad \frac{\alpha+\beta}{(x+\alpha)^2}dx=dt$

$\therefore \quad I=\frac{1}{(\alpha+\beta)}\int\frac{dt}{t^{6/7}}=\frac{7}{\alpha+\beta}t^{1/7}$

$=\frac{7}{\alpha+\beta}\left[1-\frac{\alpha+\beta}{x+\alpha}\right]^{1/7}=\frac{7}{\alpha+\beta}\left(\frac{x-\beta}{x+\alpha}\right)^{1/7} \Rightarrow$ (d).

(b_1) $\frac{13}{14}+\frac{15}{14}=\frac{28}{14}=2$

$\frac{x+3}{x-4}=\frac{x-4+7}{x-4}=1+\frac{7}{x-4}$

$\therefore \quad I=\int\frac{dx}{\left(\frac{x+3}{x-4}\right)^{13/14}\cdot(x-4)^2}$

Now put $\frac{x+3}{x-4}=t$ or $1+\frac{7}{x-4}=t$

$\therefore \quad \frac{-7\,dx}{(x-4)^2}=dt$

$\therefore \quad I=\int\frac{1}{t^{13/14}}\left(-\frac{1}{7}dt\right)=-\frac{1}{7}\int t^{-13/14}\, dt$

$=-\frac{1}{7}\frac{t^{-13/14+1}}{-\frac{13}{14}+1}=-2t^{1/14}=-2\left(\frac{x+3}{x-4}\right)^{1/14}$

(c) $\frac{4}{5}+\frac{6}{5}=2$

$I=\frac{x\,dx}{(x^2+1)^2\left(\frac{x^2+2}{x^2+1}\right)^{6/5}}=\frac{x\,dx}{(x^2+1)^2\left[1+\frac{1}{x^2+1}\right]^{6/5}}$

Put $1+\frac{1}{x^2+1}=t \quad \therefore \quad \frac{-2x}{(x^2+1)^2}dx=dt$

$\therefore \quad I=-\frac{1}{2}\int t^{-6/5}\, dt=-\frac{1}{2}\frac{t^{-1/5}}{-1/5}=\frac{5}{2}t^{-1/5}$

$I=\frac{5}{2}\left(1+\frac{1}{x^2+1}\right)^{-1/5}=\frac{5}{2}\left(\frac{x^2+2}{x^2+1}\right)^{-1/5}$

or $I=\frac{5}{2}\left(\frac{x^2+1}{x^2+2}\right)^{1/5}$

28. $I=\int\frac{e^x.e^x\,dx}{(e^x+1)^{1/4}}$

Put $e^x+1=t^4 \quad \therefore \quad e^x\,dx=4t^3\,dt$

$\therefore \quad I=\int\frac{(t^4-1).4t^3}{t}dt=4\int(t^6-t^2)\,dt$

$=4\left[\frac{t^7}{7}-\frac{t^3}{3}\right]=\frac{4t^3}{21}[3t^4-7]$

$=\frac{4}{21}(e^x+1)^{3/4}[3e^x-4].$

29. (a) Differentiation of $x\sin x+\cos x$ is $x\cos x$.

Then $I=\int\frac{x^2\,dx}{(x\sin x+\cos x)^2}$

$=\int\frac{x\cos x}{(x\sin x+\cos x)^2}.\frac{x}{\cos x}dx$

Integrate by parts $\left[\int\frac{1}{t^2}dt=-\frac{1}{t}\right]$

$\therefore \quad I=\frac{-1}{(x\sin x+\cos x)}.\frac{x}{\cos x}$

$+\int\frac{1}{(x\sin x+\cos x)}\frac{\cos x.1-x(-\sin x)}{\cos^2 x}dx$

$=-\frac{1}{x\sin x+\cos x}.\frac{x}{\cos x}+\int\sec^2 x\,dx$

$=-\frac{1}{x\sin x+\cos x}.\frac{x}{\cos x}+\frac{\sin x}{\cos x}$

$=-\frac{-x+x\sin^2 x+\sin x\cos x}{(x\sin x+\cos x)\cos x}$

$=\frac{\sin x\cos x-x(1-\sin^2 x)}{(x\sin x+\cos x)\cos x}=\frac{\sin x-x\cos x}{x\sin x+\cos x}.$

(b) Ans. $\frac{x\sin x+\cos x}{x\cos x-\sin x}$

30. (a) $\sin\theta+\cos\theta$ is differential coefficient of $\sin\theta-\cos\theta$.

Hence we put $\sin\theta-\cos\theta=t$

$\therefore \quad (\cos\theta+\sin\theta)\,d\theta=dt$

Also on squaring $\sin^2\theta+\cos^2\theta-2\sin\theta\cos\theta=t^2$

(Refer **Ex. 17 P. 1497**)

or $1-t^2=\sin 2\theta$.

$\therefore \quad I=\int \frac{dt}{\sqrt{(1-t^2)}}=\sin^{-1}t=\sin^{-1}(\sin\theta-\cos\theta).$

(b) $I=\int_0^{\pi/4}\frac{(\sin x+\cos x)}{\sqrt{(\sin x\cos x)}}dx$

$=\int \frac{\sqrt{2}(\sin x+\cos x)\,dx}{\sqrt{(\sin 2x)}}.$

$=\sqrt{2}\sin^{-1}(\sin x-\cos x)$ by part (a)

$=\sqrt{2}[\sin^{-1}0-\sin^{-1}(-1)]=\sqrt{2}\cdot\frac{\pi}{2}=\frac{\pi}{\sqrt{(2)}}.$

(c) Put $\sin x+\cos x=t \quad \therefore \quad 1+\sin 2x=t^2$

so that $(\cos x-\sin x)=dt$

$I=\int \frac{-(\cos x-\sin x)\,dx}{(\sin x+\cos x)\sqrt{\left(\frac{1}{2}\sin 2x+\frac{1}{4}\sin^2 2x\right)}}$

$=-\frac{dt}{t\sqrt{\left\{\frac{1}{2}(t^2-1)+\frac{1}{4}(t^2-1)^2\right\}}}$

$=-\frac{dt}{\frac{1}{2}t\sqrt{\{(2t^2-2)+(t^4-2t^2+1)\}}}$

$=-\frac{2\,dt}{t\sqrt{(t^4-1)}}=-\int\frac{2t\,dt}{t^2\sqrt{(t^4-1)}}$ ...(A)

Put $t^2=z$

$\therefore \quad I=-\int\frac{dz}{z\sqrt{(z^2-1)}}=\text{cosec}^{-1}z$

$=\text{cosec}^{-1}t^2=\text{cosec}^{-1}(1+\sin 2x).$

Alternative : [See (A) above]

$I=-\int\frac{2t^3\,dt}{t^4\sqrt{(t^4-1)}}$, Put $t^4-1=z^2$

$\therefore \quad 4t^3\,dt=2z\,dz$

$I=-\int\frac{z\,dz}{z(z^2+1)}=-\tan^{-1}z=-\sec^{-1}\sqrt{1+z^2}$

$=-\sec^{-1}t^2=\text{cosec}^{-1}(1+\sin 2x).$

$\because \quad \sec^{-1}x+\text{cosec}^{-1}x=\pi/2$

(d) Ans. $\sin^{-1}\left(\frac{1}{3}(\sin x+\cos x)\right)$

31. $I=\int\sqrt{\left(\frac{\sin(x-\alpha)}{\sin(x+\alpha)}\right)}dx=\int\frac{\sin(x-\alpha)}{\sqrt{[\sin(x+\alpha)\sin(x-\alpha)]}}dx$

$=\int\left\{\frac{\sin x\cos\alpha}{\sqrt{(\sin^2 x-\sin^2\alpha)}}-\frac{\cos x\sin\alpha}{\sqrt{(\sin^2 x-\sin^2\alpha)}}\right\}dx$

$=\cos\alpha\int\frac{\sin x\,dx}{\sqrt{(\cos^2\alpha-\cos^2 x)}}$

$-\sin\alpha\int\frac{\cos x\,dx}{\sqrt{(\sin^2 x-\sin^2\alpha)}}$

$\cos x=t$ for 1st and $\sin x=z$ for 2nd

$=\cos\alpha\cos^{-1}(\cos x\sec\alpha)$

$-\sin\alpha\cosh^{-1}(\sin x\,\text{cosec}\,\alpha).$

32. $\frac{1-\cos x}{\cos x(1+\cos x)}=\frac{1}{\cos x}-\frac{2}{1+\cos x}$ P. F.'s

$\therefore \quad I=\int[\sec x-2/2\cos^2(x/2)]\,dx$

$=\log(\sec x+\tan x)-2\tan\frac{x}{2}.$

33. $I=\int\frac{1}{x(x^2+1)^3}dx=\int\frac{x\,dx}{x^2(x^2+1)^3}$

Put $x^2+1=t \quad \therefore \quad 2x\,dx=dt.$

$\therefore \quad I=\frac{1}{2}\int\frac{dt}{t^3(t-1)}=-\frac{1}{2}\int\frac{1}{t^3}\frac{t^3-1-t^3}{t-1}dt$

$=-\frac{1}{2}\int\frac{1}{t^3}\left[t^2+t+1-\frac{t^3}{t-1}\right]dt$

$=-\frac{1}{2}\int\left[\frac{1}{t}+\frac{1}{t^2}+\frac{1}{t^3}-\frac{1}{t-1}\right]dt$

$=-\frac{1}{2}\left[\log t-\frac{1}{t}-\frac{1}{2t^2}-\log(t-1)\right]$

where $t=x^2+1$.

34, 35, 36. In all these multiply above and below by e^x and put $e^x=t$ and split into partial fractions.

34. Ans. $2\log(e^x-1)-x$.

35. Ans. $\frac{1}{4}\log(e^x-1)(e^x+3)^3$.

36. Ans. $\log\frac{e^x(1+e^x)}{(1+2e^x)^2}$.

37. (a) $\int\frac{1+x\sin x+\cos x}{x(1+\cos x)}dx$

$=\int\left[\frac{1+\cos x}{x(1+\cos x)}+\frac{x\sin x}{x(1+\cos x)}\right]dx$

$=\int\left(\frac{1}{x}+\frac{\sin x}{1+\cos x}\right)dx=\int\left(\frac{1}{x}+\tan\frac{x}{2}\right)dx$

$=\log x+2\log\sec(x/2).$

(b) Ans. $\log x+2\log(1-\cos x)$

Split into two integrals.

38. $\int\frac{\cos x+x\sin x}{x(x+\cos x)}dx$

$I=\int\frac{(x+\cos x)-x+x\sin x}{x(x+\cos x)}dx$

$$=\int\left[\frac{1}{x}-\frac{(1-\sin x)}{(x+\cos x)}\right]dx$$

$$=\log x-\log(x+\cos x)=\log\frac{x}{x+\cos x}.$$

39. (a) $s_{n+1}-s_n$

$$\int_0^{\pi/2}\frac{\sin(2n+1)x-\sin(2n-1)x}{\sin x}dx$$

$$=\int_0^{\pi/2}\frac{2\sin x.\cos 2nx}{\sin x}dx$$

$$=\int_0^{\pi/2}2\cos 2nx\,dx=2.\left[\frac{\sin 2nx}{2n}\right]_0^{\pi/2}$$

$$=\frac{1}{n}[\sin n\pi-\sin 0]=0,$$

where n is an integer

$$v_{n+1}-v_n=\int_0^{\pi/2}\frac{\sin^2(n+1)x-\sin^2 nx}{\sin^2 x}dx$$

$$=\int_0^{\pi/2}\frac{\sin(2n+1)x\sin x}{\sin^2 x}dx$$

$$=\int_0^{\pi/2}\frac{\sin(2n+1)}{\sin x}dx=s_{n+1}.$$

$[\because\ \sin^2 A-\sin^2 B=\sin(A+B)\sin(A-B)]$

(b) Consider $I=I_{n+1}+I_{n-1}-2I_n$ for (a)

$$=\int_0^{\pi/2}\frac{\sin^2(n+1)x+\sin^2(n-1)x-2\sin^2 nx}{\sin^2 x}dx$$

write $2\sin^2 nx=\sin^2 nx+\sin^2 nx$ and apply

$\sin^2 A-\sin^2 B=\sin(A+B)\sin(A-B)$

$$I=\int_0^{\pi/2}\frac{\sin(2n+1)\sin x-\sin(2n-1)\sin x}{\sin^2 x}dx$$

$$=\int_0^{\pi/2}\frac{\sin(2n+1)x-\sin(2n-1)}{\sin x}dx$$

$$=\int_0^{\pi/2}\frac{2\sin x\cos 2nx}{\sin x}dx$$

$$=2\int_0^{\pi/2}\cos 2nx\,dx=\frac{1}{n}[\sin 2nx]_0^{\pi/2}=0$$

$\therefore\quad I_{n+1}+I_{n-1}=2I_n\ \forall\ n\geq 1$

Above implies the sequence $\{I_n\}$ is in A.P.

i.e., $I_1, I_2, I_3, \ldots$ are in A.P. $\Rightarrow$ (a).

Again $I_1=\int_0^{\pi/2}1\,dx=\frac{\pi}{2}.$

$$I_2=\int_0^{\pi/2}\frac{\sin^2 2x}{\sin^2 x}dx=4\int_0^{\pi/2}\cos^2 x=4.\frac{1}{2}.\frac{\pi}{2}=\pi$$

$\therefore\quad d=I_2-I_1=\pi-\frac{\pi}{2}=\frac{\pi}{2}$

and $a=I_1=\frac{\pi}{2}$ for A.P.

$$I_n=a+(n-1)d=\frac{\pi}{2}+(n-1)\frac{\pi}{2}=\frac{n\pi}{2}\rightarrow\text{(b)}$$

$\therefore\quad I_{16}=16.\frac{\pi}{2}=8\pi$

$\sin(I_{16})=\sin(8\pi)=0.$

40. (a) $I=\int_0^{\pi}\sin mx\sin nx\,dx$

$$=\frac{1}{2}\int_0^{\pi}[\cos(m-n)x-\cos(m+n)x]dx;\quad \boldsymbol{m\neq n}$$

$$=\frac{1}{2}\left[\frac{\sin(m-n)x}{m-n}-\frac{\sin(m+n)x}{m+n}\right]_0^{\pi}=0.$$

$\because m-n$ and $m+n$ are both integers and $\sin r\pi=0$, where r is an integer.

When $\boldsymbol{m=n}$ then

$$I=\int_0^{\pi}\sin^2 mx\,dx=\frac{1}{2}\int_0^{\pi}(1-\cos 2mx)dx$$

$$=\frac{1}{2}\left[x-\frac{\sin 2mx}{2m}\right]_0^{\pi}=\frac{\pi}{2}-0=\frac{\pi}{2}$$

(b) We have

$\sin 2kx=2\sin x[\cos x+\cos 3x+\ldots\ldots$
$+\cos(2k-1)x]$ ...(1)

Here $T_1=2\sin x\cos x=\sin 2x$
$T_2=2\sin x\cos 3x=\sin 4x-\sin 2x$
$T_3=2\sin x\cos 5x=\sin 6x-\sin 4x$
... ...
... ...
$T_k=2\sin x\cos(2k-1)x$
$=\sin 2kx-\sin(2k-2)x$

Adding, $S_k=\sin 2kx$ as required.

Now $\int_0^{\pi/2}\sin 2kx\cot x=\int_0^{\pi/2}\left(\frac{\sin 2kx}{\sin x}\right)\cos x\,dx$

$$=\int_0^{\pi/2}2\cos x[\cos x+\cos 3x+\ldots.$$

$\cos(2k-1)x]dx$ by (1)

$$\int_0^{\pi/2}(1+\cos 2x)+\int_0^{\pi/2}(\cos 4x+\cos 2x)dx+\ldots$$

$$+\int_0^{\pi/2}[\cos 2kx+\cos(2k-2)x]dx \quad \text{...(2)}$$

But for any integer $n\,(n\neq 0)$, we get

$$\int_0^{\pi/2}\cos 2nx\,dx=\left[\frac{\sin 2nx}{2n}\right]_0^{\pi/2}$$

$$=\frac{1}{2n}[\sin n\pi-\sin 0]=0 \qquad [\because\ n\neq 0]\ \text{...(3)}$$

and $\int_0^{\pi/2} 1 \cdot dx = \frac{\pi}{2}$. ...(4)

Hence from (2) $\int_0^{\pi/2} \sin 2kx \cot x\, dx = \pi/2$, by (3) and (4)

41, 42, 43. Put $x = a\cos^2 t + b\sin^2 t$

$$x - a = a\cos^2 t + b\sin^2 t - a$$

$$= b\sin^2 t - a(1-\cos^2 t) = (b-a)\sin^2 t$$

$$b - x = b - a\cos^2 t - b\sin^2 t = (b-a)\cos^2 t$$

$$dx = 2(b-a)\sin t\cos t\, dt.$$

Also when $x = a$ then $\sin t = 0 \therefore t = 0$

when $x = b$ then $\cos t = 0 \therefore t = \pi/2$.

For Q. 41.

$$\therefore \quad I = \int_0^{\pi/2} \frac{2(b-a)\sin t\cos t\, dt}{(b-a)\sin t\cos t} = 2[t]_0^{\pi/2} = \pi$$

For Q. 42.

$$I = \int_0^{\pi/2} \frac{\sin t}{\cos t} . 2(b-a)\sin t\cos t\, dt$$

$$= (b-a)\int_0^{\pi/2} 2\sin^2 t\, dt$$

$$= (b-a)\int_0^{\pi/2} (1-\cos 2t)\, dt$$

$$= (b-a)\left[t - \frac{\sin 2t}{2}\right]_0^{\pi/2} = (b-a)\frac{\pi}{2}.$$

For Q. 43 (a).

$$I = \int_0^{\pi/2} (b-a)\sin t\cos t . 2(b-a)\sin t\cos t\, dt$$

$$= 2(b-a)^2\int_0^{\pi/2} \sin^2 t\cos^2 t\, dt$$

$$= 2(b-a)^2\int_0^{\pi/2} \frac{1-\cos 2t}{2} . \frac{1+\cos 2t}{2}\, dt$$

$$= \frac{(b-a)^2}{2}\int (1-\cos^2 2t)\, dt$$

$$= \frac{(b-a)^2}{4}\int_0^{\pi/2} 2\sin^2 2t\, dt$$

$$= \frac{(b-a)^2}{4}\int_0^{\pi/2} (1-\cos 4t)\, dt$$

$$= \frac{(b-a)^2}{4} . \left[t - \frac{\sin 4t}{4}\right]_0^{\pi/2} = \frac{\pi}{8}(b-a)^2.$$

Alernative Method :

Put $x - a = t^2 \quad \therefore \quad dx = 2t\, dt$ and limits are adjusted as 0 to $b-a$. Also $b - x = b - a - t^2$.

For Q. 41.

$$I = \int_0^{\sqrt{(b-a)}} \frac{2t\, dt}{t \cdot \sqrt{(b-a-t^2)}} = 2\sin^{-1}\left\{\frac{t}{\sqrt{(b-a)}}\right\}$$

$$= 2[\sin^{-1} 1 - \sin^{-1} 0] = 2 \cdot \frac{\pi}{2} = \pi \quad \text{etc.}$$

Similarly you may try Q. 42 & 43 but this will be lengthy.

(b) It is same as Q. 41 if we put $x^2 = y$ and adjust the limits.

$$\therefore \quad I = \int_{\frac{3a^2+b^2}{4}}^{\frac{a^2+b^2}{2}} \frac{dy}{\sqrt{\{(y-a^2)(b^2-y)\}}}$$

Put $y = a^2\cos^2 t + b^2\sin^2 t$ and adjust the limits

$$\frac{a^2+b^2}{2} = a^2\cos^2 t + b^2\sin^2 t$$

or $a^2 + b^2 = 2a^2\cos^2 t + 2b^2\sin^2 t$

or $2(a^2 - b^2)\sin^2 t = a^2 - b^2$

$\therefore \quad \sin t = \frac{1}{\sqrt{2}}$ or $t = \frac{\pi}{4}$

When $y = \frac{3a^2+b^2}{4} = a^2\cos^2 t + b^2\sin^2 t$

$$3a^2 + b^2 = 4a^2(1-\sin^2 t) + 4b^2\sin^2 t$$

$$4(a^2-b^2)\sin^2 t = a^2 - b^2$$

$\therefore \quad \sin t = \frac{1}{2}$ or $t = \frac{\pi}{6}$

$$\therefore \quad I = \frac{1}{2}\int_{\pi/6}^{\pi/4} 2\, dt = [t]_{\pi/6}^{\pi/4} = \frac{\pi}{12}.$$

44. (a) Put $x + \sqrt{1+x^2} = u$ so that

$$(u-x)^2 = 1 + x^2 \quad \text{or} \quad u^2 - 2ux = 1$$

or $x = \frac{1}{2}\left(u - \frac{1}{u}\right). \quad \therefore \quad dx = \frac{1}{2}\left(1 + \frac{1}{u^2}\right)du.$

Also $u = 1$ when $x = 0$,

and $u = \infty$ when $x = \infty$.

$$\therefore \quad I = \int_1^{\infty} \frac{\frac{1}{2}(1+1/u^2)}{u^n}\, du = \frac{1}{2}\int_1^{\infty}\left(\frac{1}{u^n} + \frac{1}{u^{n+2}}\right)du$$

$$= \frac{1}{2}\left[-\frac{1}{(n-1)u^{n-1}} - \frac{1}{(n+1).u^{n+1}}\right]_1^{\infty}$$

$$= \frac{1}{2}\left\{\frac{1}{n-1} + \frac{1}{n+1}\right\} = \frac{n}{n^2-1}.$$

Note : For another method if we put $x = \tan\theta$ then $dx = \sec^2\theta\, d\theta$

$$\therefore \quad I = \int_0^{\pi/2} \frac{\sec^2\theta\, d\theta}{(\sec\theta + \tan\theta)^n}$$

Now see Q. 45 for solution by another method.

Note : See also **Ex. 7 P. 1560** for one more method.

(b) Put $t = x+\sqrt{x^2+1}, \frac{1}{t} = \frac{1}{x+\sqrt{x^2+1}} = \frac{x-\sqrt{x^2+1}}{-1}$

$\therefore \quad t-\frac{1}{t} = 2x, \quad t+\frac{1}{t} = 2\sqrt{x^2+1}$ ...(1)

Also $dt = \left(1+\frac{2x}{2\sqrt{x^2+1}}\right)dx = \frac{t}{\sqrt{x^2+1}}dx$ ...(2)

$\therefore \quad I = \int t^n \frac{dt}{t}\sqrt{x^2+1}$ by (2)

$= \int t^{n-1}\frac{1}{2}\left(t+\frac{1}{t}\right)dt$ by (1)

$= \frac{1}{2}\int (t^n + t^{n-2})\,dt = \frac{1}{2}\left[\frac{t^{n+1}}{n+1}+\frac{t^{n-1}}{n-1}\right]$

45. $\int_0^{\pi/2} \frac{\sec^2 x}{(\sec x+\tan x)^n}dx$

$= \frac{1}{2}\int_0^{\pi/2} \frac{(\sec x\tan x+\sec^2 x)-(\sec x\tan x-\sec^2 x)}{(\sec x+\tan x)^n}dx$

(Note this step)

$= \frac{1}{2}\int_0^{\pi/2} \frac{\sec x\tan x+\sec^2 x}{(\sec x+\tan x)^n}dx$

$-\frac{1}{2}\int_0^{\pi/2} \frac{(\sec x-\tan x)^n(\sec x\tan x-\sec^2 x)}{(\sec^2 x-\tan^2 x)^n}dx$

$= \frac{1}{2}\int_0^{\pi/2} \frac{\sec x\tan x+\sec^2 x}{(\sec x+\tan x)^n}dx$

$-\frac{1}{2}\int_0^{\pi/2} (\sec x-\tan x)^n(\sec x\tan x-\sec^2 x)\,dx$

$\because \quad (\sec x+\tan x)(\sec x-\tan x) = 1$ ...(1)

$= \frac{1}{2}\left[\frac{1}{(1-n)(\sec x+\tan x)^{n-1}}\right]_0^{\pi/2}$

$-\frac{1}{2}\left[\frac{(\sec x-\tan x)^{n+1}}{n+1}\right]_0^{\pi/2}$

$= \frac{1}{2}\left[\frac{1}{(1-n)(\sec x+\tan x)^{n-1}}\right]_0^{\pi/2}$

$-\frac{1}{2}\left[\frac{1}{(n+1)(\sec x+\tan x)^{n+1}}\right]_0^{\pi/2}$ by (1)

$= \frac{1}{2(1-n)}[0-1] - \frac{1}{2(n+1)}[0-1]$

$= \frac{1}{2}\left[\frac{1}{1+n}-\frac{1}{1-n}\right] = \frac{n}{n^2-1}.$

46. Put $\cos 2x = \frac{1-\tan^2 x}{1+\tan^2 x}$

$\therefore \quad I = \int \frac{\sqrt{(1-\tan^2 x)}}{\sin x.\sec x}dx = \int \frac{\sqrt{(1-\tan^2 x)}}{\tan x}dx$

Now put $1-\tan^2 x = t^2$

$\therefore \quad -2\tan x\sec^2 x\,dx = 2t\,dt$

$\therefore \quad I = \int \frac{t}{\tan x}\cdot\frac{-t\,dt}{\tan x\sec^2 x} = -\int \frac{t^2}{(1-t^2)(2-t^2)}$

$\therefore \quad \sec^2 x = 1+\tan^2 x$

Split into partial fractions by putting $t^2 = 1$ and $t^2 = 2$

$\therefore \quad I = -\int\left[\frac{1}{(1-t^2)}-\frac{2}{(2-t^2)}\right]dt$

$= -\frac{1}{2}\log\left|\frac{1+t}{1-t}\right| + 2\cdot\frac{1}{2\sqrt{2}}\log\left|\frac{\sqrt{2}+t}{\sqrt{2}-t}\right|$

where $\quad t = \sqrt{(1-\tan^2 x)}$.

47. (a) $I = \int \frac{dx}{\sin x+\sec x} = \int \frac{\cos x}{1+\sin x\cos x}dx$

$= \frac{1}{2}\int \frac{(\cos x+\sin x)+(\cos x-\sin x)}{1+\sin x\cos x}dx$

$= \frac{1}{2}\int \frac{\cos x+\sin x}{1+\frac{1}{2}\sin 2x}dx + \frac{1}{2}\int \frac{\cos x-\sin x}{1+\frac{1}{2}\sin 2x}dx$

$= I_1 + I_2.$

In I_1, put $\sin x-\cos x = t$

so that $(\cos x+\sin x)\,dx = dt$

and $1-2\sin x\cos x = t^2$, *i.e.* $\sin x\cos x = \frac{1-t^2}{2}$

In I_2, put $\sin x+\cos x = u$

so that $(\cos x-\sin x)\,dx = du$.

and $1+2\sin x\cos x = u^2$ or $\sin x\cos x = \frac{u^2-1}{2}$.

$I = \frac{1}{2}\int \frac{dt}{1+(1-t^2)/2} + \frac{1}{2}\int \frac{du}{1+(u^2-1)/2}$

$= \int \frac{dt}{3-t^2} + \int \frac{du}{1+u^2}$

$= \frac{1}{2\sqrt{(3)}}\log\frac{\sqrt{3}+t}{\sqrt{(3)}-t} + \tan^{-1}u + c$

$= \frac{1}{2\sqrt{(3)}}\log\left[\frac{\sqrt{3}+(\sin x-\cos x)}{\sqrt{(3)}-(\sin x-\cos x)}\right]$

$+\tan^{-1}(\sin x+\cos x)+c.$

(b) Proceed exactly as in part (a).

$\frac{1}{2\sqrt{3}}\log\frac{\sqrt{3}+(\sin x-\cos x)}{\sqrt{3}-(\sin x-\cos x)} + \tan^{-1}(\sin x+\cos x)$

48. (a) Put $\sin 2x = \dfrac{2\tan x}{1+\tan^2 x}$

$$I = \int \frac{\sec^2 x . \sec^2 x}{\sqrt{(2\tan x)}} dx = \int \frac{1}{\sqrt{2}} \frac{(1+t^2)}{\sqrt{t}} dt$$

$$= \frac{1}{\sqrt{2}} \int \left(\frac{1}{\sqrt{t}} + t^{3/2} \right) dt = \frac{\sqrt{2}}{5} (t^2 + 5) \sqrt{t}$$

where $t = \tan x$

(b) $\dfrac{3}{2} + \dfrac{5}{2} = 4 =$ even. Divide above and below by $\cos^4 x$

$$\therefore \; I = \int \frac{\sec^2 x . \sec^2 x}{\sqrt{(\tan^3 x)}} dx = \int \frac{(1+t^2)}{t\sqrt{t}} dt$$

$$= \frac{2}{3} \frac{(t^2+3)}{\sqrt{t}}, \text{ where } t = \tan x$$

49. $I = \displaystyle\int \frac{e^x \, dx}{e^x \sqrt{(1+e^x+e^{2x})}} = \int \frac{dt}{t\sqrt{1+t+t^2}}, t = e^x$

Now put $t = \dfrac{1}{z}$

$$\therefore \quad I = -\int \frac{dz}{\sqrt{(z^2+z+1)}} = -\frac{dz}{\sqrt{\left\{ \left(z+\frac{1}{2}\right)^2 + \left(\frac{\sqrt{3}}{2}\right)^2 \right\}}}$$

$$= -\log \left\{ \left(z + \frac{1}{2} \right) + \sqrt{(z^2+z+1)} \right\}$$

50. $I = \displaystyle\int \frac{\sin x . \sqrt{\cos x}}{\sqrt{\{1-(\cos^{3/2} x)^2\}}} dx$

Put $\cos^{3/2} x = t \quad \therefore \quad I = \dfrac{2}{3} \sin^{-1} (\cos^{3/2} x)$

51. $I = \int [x(e^{\sin x} \cos x) - e^{\sin x} (\sec x \tan x)] dx$

Integrate by parts.

$[xe^{\sin x} - \int e^{\sin x} .1.dx]$

$- [e^{\sin x} \sec x - \int e^{\sin x} \cos x \sec x \, dx]$

$= xe^{\sin x} - e^{\sin x} \sec x$. other integrals cancel

52. Proceed as in last question.

Ans. $-x e^{\cos x} - e^{\cos x}$ cosec x.

53. Put $x = \sin\theta \quad \therefore \quad dx = \cos\theta \, d\theta$

$$I = \int_0^{\pi/2} \frac{2-\sin^2\theta}{(1+\sin\theta)\cos\theta} \cos\theta \, d\theta$$

$$= \int_0^{\pi/2} \left[\frac{1-\sin^2\theta}{1+\sin\theta} + \frac{1}{1+\sin\theta} \right] d\theta$$

$$= \int_0^{\pi/2} \left[(1-\sin\theta) + \frac{1-\sin\theta}{1-\sin^2\theta} \right] d\theta$$

$$= \int_0^{\pi/2} (1 - \sin\theta + \sec^2\theta - \tan\theta\sec\theta) \, d\theta$$

$$= [(\theta + \cos\theta) + (\tan\theta - \sec\theta)]_0^{\pi/2}$$

$$= \left(\frac{\pi}{2} - 1 \right) + \left(\frac{\sin\theta - 1}{\cos\theta} \right)_0^{\pi/2} = \left(\frac{\pi}{2} - 1 \right) + [0 - (-1)] = \frac{\pi}{2}$$

$$\underset{\theta \to \frac{\pi}{2}}{\text{Lt}} \frac{\sin\theta - 1}{\cos\theta} = \frac{0}{0} = \underset{\theta \to \frac{\pi}{2}}{\text{Lt}} \frac{\cos\theta}{-\sin\theta} = 0$$

Note : $\displaystyle\int \frac{1}{1+\sin\theta} d\theta = \int \frac{d\theta}{[\cos(\theta/2) + \sin(\theta/2)]^2}$

$$= \int \frac{\sec^2(\theta/2) \, d\theta}{[1+\tan(\theta/2)]^2}$$

Now put $1 + \tan(\theta/2) = t \quad \therefore \quad \dfrac{1}{2}\sec^2(\theta/2) \, d\theta = dt$

$$\therefore \quad I = \int_1^2 \frac{2}{t^2} dt = -2 \left[\frac{1}{t} \right]_1^2 = -2 \left(\frac{1}{2} - 1 \right) = 1$$

54. (a) $I = \displaystyle\int_0^1 [(t-1)x+1]^n \, dx$

$$= \left[\frac{\{(t-1)x+1\}^{n+1}}{(n+1)(t-1)} \right]_0^1$$

$$= \frac{t^{n+1}-1}{(n+1)(t-1)} = \frac{1}{n+1} [t^n + t^{n-1} + \ldots + t + 1] \quad \ldots(1)$$

Again $I = \displaystyle\int_0^1 \{(1-x)+tx\}^n \, dx.$

Expand binomially.

$$I = \int_0^1 (1-x)^n + C_1 (1-x)^{n-1} tx + C_2 (1-x)^{n-2} t^2 x^2 + \ldots C_r (1-x)^{n-r} t^r x^r + \ldots] dx \quad \ldots(2)$$

Comparing the coefficients of t^r in (1) and (2), we get

$$\frac{1}{n+1} = \int_0^1 {}^nC_r (1-x)^{n-r} x^r \, dx$$

$$\frac{1}{(n+1)C_r} = \int_0^1 x^r (1-x)^{n-r} \, dx$$

Now replace r by k.

(b) Put $x = \dfrac{1}{y}$ in L.H.S.

$$\therefore \quad I = \int_\infty^1 \frac{-1/y^2}{\left(1 - \frac{1}{y^n}\right)^{1/n}} = \int_1^\infty \frac{dy}{y(y^n-1)^{1/n}}$$

$$= \int_1^\infty \frac{y^{n-1} \, dy}{y^n (y^n-1)^{1/n}}$$

Now put $y^n - 1 = z^n \quad \therefore \quad y^n = z^n + 1$

$$\therefore \quad I = \int_0^\infty \frac{z^{n-1} \, dz}{z(1+z^n)}$$

In order to get the required form now put $z = \dfrac{1}{t}$

$\therefore \quad I = \int_0^\infty \frac{dt}{(1+t^n)} = \int_0^\infty \frac{dx}{(1+x^n)}$

55. Integrating by parts, we get

$I = \tan x \log(1+\sin^2 x) - \int \frac{\tan x}{1+\sin^2 x} . 2\sin x \cos x\, dx$

or $\quad I = \tan x \log(1+\sin^2 x) - 2I_1$ ...(A)

where $I_1 = \int \frac{\sin^2 x}{1+\sin^2 x} dx = \int \left(1 - \frac{1}{1+\sin^2 x}\right) dx$

$= x - \int \frac{\sec^2 x\, dx}{(\tan^2 x + 1) + \tan^2 x}$

$= x - \int \frac{dt}{2t^2+1} = x - \frac{1}{\sqrt{2}} \tan^{-1} t\sqrt{2}$

Putting the value of I_1 in (A), we get

$I = \tan x \log(1+\sin^2 x) - 2x + \sqrt{2}\tan^{-1} \sqrt{2}\tan x$

56. Apply $C_1 - (C_2 + C_3)$ and expand

$\therefore \quad f(x) = \sin x(3 - 4\sin^2 x) = \sin 3x$

$\therefore \quad \int_0^{\pi/2} f(x)\,dx = \int_0^{\pi/2} \sin 3x\, dx$

$= -\frac{1}{3}[\cos 3x]_0^{\pi/2} = \frac{1}{3}$

57. Ans. 2.

Put $\pi \log x = t$ and adjust the limits.

$\therefore \quad I = \int_0^{37\pi} \sin t\, dt = [-\cos t]_0^{37\pi} - [-1-1] = 2$

58. Ans. $k = 16$.

$\int_1^4 \frac{2e^{\sin x^2}}{x} dx = F(k) - F(1) = [F(x)]_1^k$

Put $x^2 = t \quad \therefore 2x\,dx = dt$

$\therefore \quad I = \int_1^{16} \frac{e^{\sin t}}{t} dt = [F(t)]_1^{16} \quad \therefore k = 16.$

59. Ans. (c).

$(x-5) + (x-7) = 2(x-6)$

and $(x-5)(x-7) = x^2 - 12x + 35 = (x-6)^2 - 1$ ...(1)

$\therefore \quad I = \int \frac{dx}{(x-6)\sqrt{(x-6)^2 - 1}} = \sec^{-1}(x-6)$

$= \tan^{-1}[(x-6)^2 - 1]^{1/2}$

$\because \quad \sec^{-1} z = \tan^{-1}\sqrt{z^2 - 1}$

$= \tan^{-1}\sqrt{(x-5)(x-7)}$ by (1)

$= f(g(x))$

$\therefore \quad f(x) = \tan^{-1} x$ and $g(x) = \sqrt{(x-5)(x-7)}$

60. Ans. (d).

$\int \frac{5\tan x}{\tan x - 2} dx = \int \frac{5\sin x}{\sin x - 2\cos x} dx$

$= \int \frac{(\sin x - 2\cos x) + 2(\cos x + 2\sin x)}{(\sin x - 2\cos x)} dx$

$= \int dx + 2\int \frac{\cos x + 2\sin x}{\sin x - 2\cos x} dx$

$= x + 2\log|(\sin x - 2\cos x)| + k$

$\Rightarrow \quad a = 2$

61. Ans. (c).

Let $\sec x + \tan x = t \quad \Rightarrow \quad (\sec x \tan x + \sec^2 x)\,dx = dt$

$\Rightarrow \quad \sec x . t . dx = dt$

$\Rightarrow \quad \sec x - \tan x = \frac{1}{t}, \quad \sec x = \frac{t + \frac{1}{t}}{2}$

$\therefore \quad \int \frac{\sec x}{t^{9/2}} .dt = \int \frac{1}{2} \frac{\left(t + \frac{1}{t}\right)}{t . t^{9/2}} .dt = -\frac{1}{2}\left(\frac{1}{t^{9/2}} + \frac{1}{t^{13/2}}\right) dt$

$= -\frac{1}{2}\left[\frac{2}{7t^{7/2}} + \frac{2}{11 . t^{11/2}}\right] + k = \frac{-1}{t^{11/2}}\left[\frac{t^2}{7} + \frac{1}{11}\right] + k$

§ 14. Definite integral as the limit of sum.

Definition : If $f(x)$ be a single valued continuous function in the interval (a, b) where $b > a$ and if the interval (a, b) be divided into n equal parts of length h, by the points

$a + h,\; a + 2h,\; a + 3h, \ldots\ldots\ldots a + \overline{n-1}\,h$

so that $a + nh = b$ or $nh = b - a$ then

$\lim_{h \to 0} h[f(a) + f(a+h) + f(a+2h) + \ldots . f(a + \overline{n-1}\,h)]$

written as $\quad \lim_{h \to 0} h \sum_{r=0}^{n-1} f(a + rh),$

or $\quad \lim_{n \to \infty} h \sum_{r=0}^{n-1} f(a + rh). \quad \because \; h = \frac{b-a}{n}$

and when $h \to 0$; $n \to \infty$

$F(x)$ is defined as the integral of $f(x)$ w.r.t. x between the limits a to b and is written as

$\int_a^b f(x)\,dx = [F(x)]_a^b = F(b) - F(a)$

where $F(x)$ is a function whose differentiation is $f(x)$ or $F(x)$ is the integral of $f(x)$ w.r.t. x.

We shall illustrate the above by giving few examples.

Note : The above sum can also be written as under

$\lim_{n \to \infty} h \sum_{r=1}^{n} f(a + rh) \quad$ where $h = \frac{b-a}{n}$

Recollect the following : From summation of series

$\sum_{r=1}^{n} r = \frac{n(n+1)}{2};$

$\sum_{r=1}^{n} r^2 = \frac{n(n+1)(2n+1)}{6}$

$\sum_{r=1}^{n} r^3 = \left(\frac{n(n+1)}{2}\right)^2 = \frac{n^2(n+1)^2}{4},$

$\Sigma\, 1 = n$

$\sum_{r=1}^{n} x^r = \text{Sum of a G.P.} = \frac{x(x^n - 1)}{x - 1}$

$$\sum_{r=1}^{n} ax^{r-1} = \frac{a(x^n - 1)}{x - 1}$$

as first term will be a

$$\sin A + \sin(A+B) + \sin(A+2B) + \ldots + \sin(A + \overline{n-1}\,B)\ (n \text{ terms})$$

$$= \sin\left(\frac{A + A + \overline{n-1}\,B}{2}\right)\frac{\sin\frac{nB}{2}}{\sin\frac{B}{2}} \qquad \ldots(1)$$

$$\cos A + \cos(A+B) + \cos(A+2B) + \ldots + \cos(A + \overline{n-1}\,B)\ (n \text{ terms})$$

$$= \cos\left(\frac{A + A + \overline{n-1}\,B}{2}\right)\frac{\sin\frac{nB}{2}}{\sin\frac{B}{2}}. \qquad \ldots(2)$$

Here the angles are in A.P. whose first term is A and commom difference is B.

Formula for (1), (2) :

$$\sin \text{ or } \cos\left\{\frac{\text{1st angle} + \text{last angle}}{2}\right\}\frac{\sin\frac{n\,\text{Diff.}}{2}}{\sin\frac{\text{Diff.}}{2}}$$

Solved Examples

Ex. 1. $\int_a^b x^2 = \frac{1}{3}(b^3 - a^3).$

Here $f(x) = x^2 \quad \therefore \quad f(a) = a^2,$

$f(a+h) = (a+h)^2,$

$f(a+2h) = (a+2h)^2$ etc.

$$\text{Now} \int_a^b f(x)\,dx = \lim_{h \to 0} \sum_{r=0}^{n-1} h\,.\,f(a+rh)$$

$$= \lim_{n \to \infty} \sum_{r=0}^{n-1} hf(a+rh). \qquad \text{where } nh = b - a.$$

$$\therefore \quad I = \int_a^b x^2\,dx$$

$$= \lim_{n \to \infty} h\,[f(a) + f(a+h) + f(a+2h) + \ldots + f(a + \overline{n-1}\,h)]$$

$$= \lim_{n \to \infty} h\,[a^2 + (a+h)^2 + (a+2h)^2 + \ldots + (a + \overline{n-1}\,h)^2].$$

Grouping the terms of a^2, $2ah$ and h^2 in the above, we get

$$I = \lim_{n \to \infty} h\,[a^2\,\Sigma\,1 + 2ah\,.\,\{(1+2+3+\ldots(n-1)\}] + h^2\,[1^2 + 2^2 + 3^2 + \ldots(n-1)^2].$$

Now $\Sigma\,1 = n, \quad \sum_{r=1}^{n} r = \frac{n(n+1)}{2}$

and $\sum_{r=1}^{n} r^2 = \frac{n(n+1)(2n+1)}{6}.$

Replacing n by $n-1$ in the above

$$\sum_{r=1}^{n-1} r = \frac{(n-1)\,n}{2}, \quad \sum_{r=1}^{n-1} r^2 = \frac{(n-1)\,n\,(2n-1)}{6}.$$

$$\therefore \quad I = \lim_{n \to \infty} h\left\{a^2\,.\,n + 2ah\frac{(n-1)\,n}{2} + h^2\frac{(n-1)(n)(2n-1)}{6}\right\}.$$

We have to take the limit of the above sum when $n \to \infty$ or $h \to 0$ and $nh = b - a$.

Therefore we write the above as below

$$I = \lim_{n \to \infty}\left\{a^2(nh) + a(nh)^2\left(1 - \frac{1}{n}\right) + \frac{1}{6}(nh)^3\left(1 - \frac{1}{n}\right)\left(2 - \frac{1}{n}\right)\right\}.$$

Now when $n \to \infty, \frac{1}{n} \to 0$ and $nh = b - a$.

$$\therefore \quad I = \left\{a^2(b-a) + a(b-a)^2\,.\,1 + \frac{1}{6}(b-a)^3\,.\,1\,.\,2\right\}$$

$$= (b-a)\left[a^2 + a(b-a) + \frac{1}{3}(b-a)^2\right]$$

$$= \frac{b-a}{3}[3a^2 + 3(ab - a^2) + (b^2 - 2ab + a^2)]$$

$$= \frac{b-a}{3}[b^2 + ba + a^2] = \frac{1}{3}(b^3 - a^3).$$

Note : Had we started with the result

$$\int_a^b f(x)\,dx = \lim_{n \to \infty} \sum_{r=1}^{n} f(a+rh),$$

where $nh = b - a$

then also we would have obtained the same result.

Ex. 2. $\int_1^3 x^3\,dx = 20.$

Here $a = 1, b = 3, b - a = 3 - 1 = 2, f(x) = x^3$

and $h = \frac{b-a}{n} = \frac{2}{n}.$

By definition,

$$\int_1^3 x^3\,dx = \lim_{n \to \infty} h\sum_{r=1}^{n} f(a+rh)$$

$$= \lim_{n \to \infty} \frac{2}{n}\sum_{r=1}^{n} f\left(1 + \frac{2r}{n}\right) \quad \because h = \frac{2}{n}.$$

$$\text{Now } f(x) = x^3 \quad \therefore \quad f\left(1 + \frac{2r}{n}\right) = \left(1 + \frac{2r}{n}\right)^3 \qquad \ldots(1)$$

$$\text{or} \quad f\left(1 + \frac{2r}{n}\right) = 1 + 3\,.\left(\frac{2r}{n}\right) + 3\left(\frac{2r}{n}\right)^2 + \left(\frac{2r}{n}\right)^3$$

$$= 1 + \frac{6}{n}\,.\,r + \frac{12}{n^2}\,.\,r^2 + \frac{8}{n^3}\,.\,r^3 \qquad \ldots(2)$$

Hence from (1) by the help of (2),

$$\int_1^3 x^3\,dx = \lim_{n \to \infty} \frac{2}{n}\sum_{r=1}^{n}\left(1 + \frac{6}{n}\,.\,r + \frac{12}{n^2}\,.\,r^2 + \frac{8}{n^3}\,.\,r^3\right)$$

$$= \lim_{n \to \infty} \frac{2}{n}\left(\Sigma\,1 + \frac{6}{n}\,\Sigma\,r + \frac{12}{n^2}\Sigma\,r^2 + \frac{8}{n^3}\Sigma\,r^3\right)$$

$$= \lim_{n\to\infty} \frac{2}{n}\left[n + \frac{6}{n}\cdot\frac{n(n+1)}{2} + \frac{12}{n^2}\frac{n(n+1)(2n+1)}{6} + \frac{8}{n^3}\frac{n^2(n+1)^2}{4}\right]$$

$$= \lim_{n\to\infty} 2\left[1 + \frac{3}{n^2}n^2\cdot\left(1+\frac{1}{n}\right) + \frac{2}{n^3}n^3\left(1+\frac{1}{n}\right)\left(2+\frac{1}{n}\right) + \frac{2}{n^4}n^4\left(1+\frac{1}{n}\right)^2\right]$$

$$= \lim_{n\to\infty} 2\left[1 + 3\left(1+\frac{1}{n}\right) + 2\left(1+\frac{1}{n}\right)\left(2+\frac{1}{n}\right) + 2\left(1+\frac{1}{n}\right)^2\right]$$

$$= 2[1+3+2.1.2+2.1] = 2.10 = 20.$$

Note : $\int_a^b x^3\,dx = \frac{1}{4}(b^4 - a^4).$

This will be evaluated as in Ex. 1. It will be convenient if we take the definition as

$$\int_a^b f(x)\,dx = \lim_{n\to\infty} h \sum_{r=1}^{n} f(a+rh)$$

where $nh = b - a$, instead of

$$\lim_{n\to\infty} h \sum_{r=0}^{n-1} f(a+rh) \text{ where } nh = b-a.$$

Ex. 3. (a) $\int_a^b \cos x\,dx = \sin b - \sin a$

$$\int_a^b f(x)\,dx = \lim_{n\to\infty} h \sum_{r=1}^{n} f(a+rh)$$

where $nh = b - a$.

$f(x) = \cos x,\ f(a+rh) = \cos(a+rh).$

$$\therefore \int_a^b \cos x\,dx = \lim_{n\to\infty} h \sum_{r=1}^{n} \cos(a+rh)$$

$$= \lim_{n\to\infty} h[\cos(a+h) + \cos(a+2h) + \ldots + \cos(a+nh)]$$

$$= \lim_{n\to\infty} h\cos\frac{a+h+a+nh}{2}\cdot\frac{\sin(nh/2)}{\sin(h/2)}$$

See eq. (2), P. 1526

$$= \lim_{n\to\infty} h\cdot\cos\left(a+(n+1)\frac{h}{2}\right)\frac{\sin(nh/2)}{\sin(h/2)}$$

$$= \lim_{n\to\infty} 2\cdot\frac{h/2}{\sin(h/2)}\cos\left\{a+\frac{1}{2}nh\left(1+\frac{1}{n}\right)\right\}\sin\frac{nh}{2}. \quad \ldots(1)$$

Now we know that

$$\lim_{\theta\to 0}\frac{\sin\theta}{\theta} = 1 \text{ and } \lim_{n\to\infty}\frac{1}{n} = 0.$$

$$\therefore \int_a^b f(x)\,dx = 2.1\cos\left[a+\frac{1}{2}(b-a)\right]\sin\frac{b-a}{2}$$

$$= 2\cos\frac{b+a}{2}\sin\frac{b-a}{2} = \sin b - \sin a.$$

Note : $\int_0^{\pi/2} \cos x\,dx = 1.$ Here $a = 0,\ b = \pi/2$

$\therefore \quad b - a = \pi/2 = nh$

Hence from (1)

$$\int_0^{\pi/2} \cos x\,dx = \lim_{n\to\infty} 2.1\cos\left(0+\frac{1}{2}.\frac{\pi}{2}\right).\sin\frac{1}{2}.\frac{\pi}{2}.$$

$$= 2\cos(\pi/4)\sin(\pi/4) = \sin(2\pi/4) = \sin(\pi/2) = 1.$$

(b) $\int_a^b \sin x\,dx = \cos a - \cos b.$

This can be similarly proved as in part (a).

Ex. 4. $\int_a^b e^x\,dx = e^b - e^a.$

$$\int_a^b f(x)\,dx = \lim_{n\to\infty} h \sum_{r=1}^{n} f(a+rh),$$

where $nh = b - a$

$$f(x) = e^x;\ \therefore\ f(a+rh) = e^{a+rh} = e^a.e^{rh}$$

$$\therefore \int_a^b f(x)\,dx = \lim_{n\to\infty} h \sum_{r=1}^{n} e^a.e^{rh}$$

$$= \lim_{n\to\infty} he^a[e^h + e^{2h} + e^{3h} + \ldots + e^{nh}]$$

$$= \lim_{n\to\infty} h.e^a.e^h.\frac{[e^{nh}-1]}{e^h - 1}$$

$$= \lim_{n\to\infty} \frac{h}{e^h - 1}e^h.e^a(e^{nh}-1) \quad \ldots(1)$$

$$\text{Now } \lim\frac{h}{e^h - 1} = \lim\frac{h}{(1+h+h^2/2!\ldots)-1}$$

$$= \lim\frac{h}{h+h^2/2!+\ldots} = \lim\frac{1}{1+h/2!+\ldots} = 1;$$

$\because$ when $n\to\infty,\ h\to 0$

$\lim e^h = e^0 = 1.$

Hence from (1), we have

$$\int_a^b e^x\,dx = 1.1.e^a[e^{b-a} - 1] = e^b - e^a.$$

Note : $\int_0^1 e^x\,dx = e - 1$

Here $a = 0,\ b = 1,\ b - a = nh$ or $1 - 0 = nh.$

Hence proceeding as above we have from (1)

$$\int_0^1 e^x\,dx = 1.1.e^0[e^1 - 1] = e - 1.$$

Ex. 5. $\int_a^b \frac{1}{x^2}\,dx = \frac{1}{a} - \frac{1}{b}$

$$\int_a^b f(x)\,dx = \lim_{n\to\infty} h \sum_{r=1}^{n} f(a+rh),$$

where $nh = b - a.$

Here $f(x) = \frac{1}{x^2};$

$\therefore \quad f(a+rh)=\dfrac{1}{(a+rh)^2}.$

$$\therefore \quad \int_a^b \frac{1}{x^2}\,dx=\lim_{n\to\infty} h\left[\frac{1}{(a+h)^2}+\frac{1}{(a+2h)^2}+\ldots+\frac{1}{(a+nh)^2}\right] \quad \ldots(1)$$

Now $\dfrac{h}{(a+rh)\,[a+(r+1)\,h]}<\dfrac{h}{(a+rh)^2}<\dfrac{h}{(a+rh)\,[a+(r-1)\,h]}$

or $\dfrac{1}{a+rh}-\dfrac{1}{a+(r+1)\,h}<\dfrac{h}{(a+rh)^2}<\dfrac{1}{a+(r-1)\,h}-\dfrac{1}{a+rh}$

Putting $r=1, 2, 3, \ldots, n$ and adding, we get

$\therefore \quad \dfrac{1}{a+h}-\dfrac{1}{a+(n+1)\,h}\le \sum_{r=1}^{n}\dfrac{h}{(a+rh)^2}\le\dfrac{1}{a}-\dfrac{1}{a+nh}$

or $\lim\left[\dfrac{1}{a+h}-\dfrac{1}{a+(n+1)\,h}\right]<\lim\sum_{r=1}^{n}\dfrac{h}{(a+rh)^2}<\lim\left[\dfrac{1}{a}-\dfrac{1}{a+nh}\right]$

$\dfrac{1}{a}-\dfrac{1}{a+b-a}\le\lim\sum_{r=1}^{n}\dfrac{h}{(a+rh)^2}\le\dfrac{1}{a}-\dfrac{1}{a+b-a}$

$[\because \; nh=b-a$ and $h\to 0]$

$\dfrac{1}{a}-\dfrac{1}{b}\le\lim\sum_{r=1}^{n}\dfrac{h}{(a+rh)^2}\le\dfrac{1}{a}-\dfrac{1}{b}$

It follows that $\lim\sum_{r=1}^{n}\dfrac{h}{(a+rh)^2}=\dfrac{1}{a}-\dfrac{1}{b}.$

Hence from (1), we get

$$\int_a^b\frac{1}{x^2}\,dx=\frac{1}{a}-\frac{1}{b}.$$

Ex. 6. $\displaystyle\int_a^b\frac{1}{\sqrt{x}}\,dx=2(\sqrt{b}-\sqrt{a})$

$$\int_a^b f(x)\,dx=\lim_{n\to\infty} h\,.\sum_{r=1}^{n} f(a+rh)$$

where $nh=b-a$.

Here $f(x)=\dfrac{1}{\sqrt{(x)}}$ $\quad\therefore\quad f(a+rh)=\dfrac{1}{\sqrt{(a+rh)}}$

$$\therefore\quad\int_a^b\frac{1}{\sqrt{(x)}}\,dx=\lim_{n\to\infty} h\left(\frac{1}{\sqrt{(a+h)}}+\frac{1}{\sqrt{(a+2h)}}+\ldots+\frac{1}{\sqrt{(a+nh)}}\right)$$

$$=\lim_{n\to\infty}\left(\frac{h}{\sqrt{(a+h)}}+\frac{h}{\sqrt{(a+2h)}}+\ldots+\frac{h}{\sqrt{(a+nh)}}\right) \quad \ldots(1)$$

we have

$\dfrac{2h}{\sqrt{(a+rh)}+\sqrt{[a+(r+1)\,h]}}<\dfrac{2h}{2\sqrt{(a+rh)}}<\dfrac{2h}{\sqrt{(a+rh)}+\sqrt{[a+(r-1)\,h]}}$

or $\dfrac{2h[\sqrt{a+(r+1)\,h}-\sqrt{a+rh}]}{[a+(r+1)\,h]-(a+rh)}<\dfrac{h}{\sqrt{(a+rh)}}<\dfrac{2h[\sqrt{a+rh}-\sqrt{a+(r-1)\,h}]}{(a+rh)-[a+(r-1)\,h]}$

or $2\,[\sqrt{a+(r+1)\,h}-\sqrt{a+rh}]<\dfrac{h}{\sqrt{(a+rh)}}<2\,[\sqrt{a+rh}-\sqrt{a+(r-1)\,h}]$

Putting $r=1, 2, 3, \ldots, n$ and adding, we get

$2\,[\sqrt{a+(n+1)\,h}-\sqrt{a+h}]<\sum_{r=1}^{n}\dfrac{h}{\sqrt{(a+rh)}}<2\,[\sqrt{a+nh}-\sqrt{a}]$

Now proceeding to the limits as $n\to\infty$ and $h\to 0$ such that $nh=b-a$, we get from above

$2\,[\sqrt{a+b-a}-\sqrt{a}]\le\lim\sum_{r=1}^{n}\dfrac{h}{\sqrt{(a+rh)}}\le 2\,[\sqrt{a+b-a}-\sqrt{a}]$

or $2\,[\sqrt{b}-\sqrt{a}]\le\lim\sum_{r=1}^{n}\dfrac{h}{\sqrt{(a+rh)}}\le 2\,[\sqrt{b}-\sqrt{a}]$

It follows that $\lim\sum_{r=1}^{n}\dfrac{h}{\sqrt{(a+rh)}}=2\,[\sqrt{b}-\sqrt{a}]$

Hence (1) gives $\displaystyle\int_a^b\frac{1}{\sqrt{(x)}}\,dx=2\,[\sqrt{b}-\sqrt{a}].$

Problem Set (7)

Regarding integral as the limit of a sum, prove the following :

Ex. 1. $\displaystyle\int_0^1(3x-2)\,dx=-\frac{1}{2}.$

Here $a=0,\ b=1,\ nh=b-a=1,$

$a+rh=0+r\,.\dfrac{1}{n}=\dfrac{r}{n}$

$\therefore\quad f(x)=3x-2=f(a+rh)=f\left(\dfrac{r}{n}\right)=3\dfrac{r}{n}-2.$

$$\therefore\quad\int_0^1(3x-2)\,dx=\lim_{n\to\infty} h\sum_{r=1}^{n} f(a+rh)$$

$$=\lim_{n\to\infty} h\sum_{r=1}^{n}\left(3\frac{r}{n}-2\right)=\lim_{n\to\infty} h\left[\frac{3}{n}\Sigma\, r-2\Sigma\, 1\right]$$

$$= \lim_{n\to\infty} h\left[\frac{3}{n}\cdot\frac{n(n+1)}{2} - 2n\right]$$

$$= \lim_{n\to\infty}\left[\frac{3}{2}nh\left(1+\frac{1}{n}\right) - 2nh\right].$$

Put $nh = 1$

$$= \frac{3}{2}.1.1 - 2.1 = \frac{3}{2} - 2 = -\frac{1}{2}.$$

Ex. 2. $\int_1^2 (3x^2 + 2x)\, dx = 10.$ Proceed as above.

Ex. 3. $\int_1^2 (x^2 + 5)\, dx = \frac{22}{3}$

Ex. 4. $\int_0^1 x^2\, dx = \frac{1}{3}.$

Ex. 5. $\int_a^b \sin^2 x\, dx = \frac{1}{2}[(b-a) - \cos(b+a).\sin(b-a)]$

Hint : $\sin^2 x = \frac{1}{2}[1 - \cos 2x] = \frac{1}{2} - \frac{1}{2}\cos 2x.$

Now proceed as in **Ex. 3 (a), P. 1527**

Ex. 6. $\int_a^b \sqrt{x}\, dx = \frac{2}{3}(b^{3/2} - a^{3/2}).$

§15. Summation of Series.

We know that

$$\int_a^b f(x)\, dx = \lim_{n\to\infty} h \sum_{r=1}^{n} f(a + rh)$$

where $nh = b - a$.

Now put $a = 0,\ b = 1$.

$\therefore\quad nh = 1 - 0 = 1$ or $h = \frac{1}{n}$.

$$\therefore\quad \int_0^1 f(x)\, dx = \lim_{n\to\infty} \frac{1}{n} \Sigma\, f\left(\frac{r}{n}\right).$$

Rule : Express the given series in the form $\Sigma\ \frac{1}{n} f\left(\frac{r}{n}\right)$.

Replace $\frac{r}{n}$ by x and $\frac{1}{n}$ by dx and the limit of the sum is $\int_0^1 f(x)\, dx$.

Solved Examples

***Ex. 1.** $\lim_{n\to\infty}\left[\frac{1}{n+1} + \frac{1}{n+2} + \ldots + \frac{1}{2n}\right]$ **(C.E.E. Bihar 1995)**

$$= \lim_{n\to\infty} \frac{1}{n}\left[\frac{1}{1+\frac{1}{n}} + \frac{1}{1+\frac{2}{n}} + \ldots + \frac{1}{1+\frac{n}{n}}\right]$$

$$= \lim_{n\to\infty} \frac{1}{n} \sum_{r=1}^{n} \frac{1}{\left(1+\frac{r}{n}\right)}.\quad \text{Standard form}$$

Put $\frac{r}{n} = x$ and $\frac{1}{n} = dx$.

When $r = 1,\ x = \frac{1}{n} \to 0,$

when $r = n,\ x = \frac{n}{n} \to 1$ as $n \to \infty$.

$$I = \int_0^1 \frac{1}{1+x}\, dx = [\log(1+x)]_0^1$$

$$= \log 2 - \log 1 = \log 2$$

Similarly $\lim_{n\to\infty}\left[\frac{1}{n+1} + \frac{1}{n+2} + \ldots + \frac{1}{6n}\right]$

$$= \lim_{n\to\infty} \frac{1}{n} \sum_{r=1}^{5n} \frac{1}{(1 + r/n)}$$

Put $r/n = x,\ 1/n = dx$. Also when $r = 1$, $x = 1/n \to 0$ and when $r = 5n,\ x = 5n/n = 5.$

$$\therefore\quad \lim = \int_0^5 \frac{dx}{1+x} = [\log(1+x)]_0^5$$

$$= \log 6 - \log 1 = \log 6.$$

Ex. 2. (a) $\lim_{n\to\infty}\left[\frac{1}{\sqrt{(n^2 - 1^2)}} + \frac{1}{\sqrt{(n^2 - 2^2)}} + \ldots + \frac{1}{\sqrt{[n^2 - (n-1)^2]}}\right]$

$$= \lim_{n\to\infty} \frac{1}{n}\left[\frac{1}{\sqrt{\left[1 - \left(\frac{1}{n}\right)^2\right]}} + \frac{1}{\sqrt{\left[1 - \left(\frac{2}{n}\right)^2\right]}} + \ldots + \frac{1}{\sqrt{\left[1 - \left(\frac{n-1}{n}\right)^2\right]}}\right]$$

$$= \lim_{n\to\infty} \frac{1}{n} \sum_{r=1}^{n-1} \frac{1}{\sqrt{[1 - (r/n)^2]}}$$

Replace $\frac{r}{n}$ by x and $\frac{1}{n}$ by dx.

Also when $r = 1,\ x = \frac{1}{n} = 0,$

when $r = n - 1,\ x = \frac{n-1}{n} = 1 - \frac{1}{n} = 1.$

$$\therefore\quad \lim = \int_0^1 \frac{1}{\sqrt{(1 - x^2)}}\, dx = \left[\sin^{-1} x\right]_0^1$$

$$= \sin^{-1} 1 - \sin^{-1} 0 = \pi/2.$$

(b)* Find $\lim_{n\to\infty} S_n$ if $S_n = \frac{1}{2n} + \frac{1}{\sqrt{4n^2 - 1}} + \frac{1}{\sqrt{4n^2 - 4}} + \ldots + \frac{1}{\sqrt{3n^2 + 2n - 1}}$

(Roorkee 1997)

Sol. $\lim_{n\to\infty} \dfrac{1}{\sqrt{(4n^2-0)}}+\dfrac{1}{\sqrt{(4n^2-1)}}+\dfrac{1}{\sqrt{(4n^2-2^2)}}$
$+\ldots\dfrac{1}{\sqrt{[4n^2-(n-1)^2]}}$

$$\lim_{n\to\infty}\sum_{r=0}^{n-1}\frac{1}{\sqrt{(4n^2-r^2)}}=\lim_{n\to\infty}\Sigma\frac{1}{n\sqrt{\left[4-\left(\frac{r}{n}\right)^2\right]}}$$

Put $\frac{r}{n}=x \;\therefore\; \frac{1}{n}=dx$

$\therefore \quad \lim=\int_0^1\frac{dx}{\sqrt{(4-x^2)}}=\left[\sin^{-1}\frac{x}{2}\right]_0^1=\frac{\pi}{6}.$

(c)* $\lim_{n\to\infty}\frac{1}{n}\sum_{r=1}^{2n}\frac{r}{\sqrt{n^2+r^2}}$ equals

(a) $1+\sqrt{5}$ (b) $-1+\sqrt{5}$

(c) $-1+\sqrt{2}$ (d) $1+\sqrt{2}$ **(I.I.T. Re-ex. 1997)**

Sol. Ans. (b).

$$I=\int_0^2\frac{x\,dx}{\sqrt{1+x^2}}=\left[\frac{1}{2}.2\sqrt{1+x^2}\right]_0^2=\sqrt{5}-1$$

Ex. 3. Prove : $\lim_{n\to\infty}\left[\frac{n}{n^2}+\frac{n}{n^2+1^2}+\frac{n}{n^2+2^2}+\ldots.+\frac{n}{n^2+(n-1)^2}=\frac{\pi}{4}\right]$

Now $\lim_{n\to\infty}\frac{n}{n^2}\left[\frac{1}{1+0^2}+\frac{1}{1+\left(\frac{1}{n}\right)^2}+\frac{1}{1+\left(\frac{2}{n}\right)^2}+\cdots+\frac{1}{1+\left(\frac{n-1}{n}\right)^2}\right]$

$$=\lim_{n\to\infty}\frac{1}{n}\sum_{r=0}^{n-1}\frac{1}{1+(r/n)^2}.$$

Put $\frac{r}{n}=x, \frac{1}{n}=dx$

When $r=0, x=0,$

and when $r=n-1, x=\frac{n-1}{n}=1-\frac{1}{n}\to 1,$

as $n\to\infty$.

$\therefore$ Reqd. $\lim=\int_0^1\frac{dx}{1+x^2}$

$$=\left[\tan^{-1}x\right]_0^1=\tan^{-1}1-\tan^{-1}0=\pi/4-0=\pi/4.$$

***Ex. 4.** $\lim_{n\to\infty}\left(\frac{1}{1+n^3}+\frac{4}{8+n^3}+\ldots+\frac{r^2}{r^3+n^3}+\ldots+\frac{1}{2n}\right)$

Now $\frac{1}{2n}=\frac{n^2}{n^3+n^3}$.

$\therefore$ The given expression

$$=\lim_{n\to\infty}\sum_{r=1}^{n}\frac{r^2}{r^3+n^3}=A,\text{ say.}$$

We should put it in the form $\frac{1}{n}\Sigma f\left(\frac{r}{n}\right)$.

$$\therefore \quad A=\lim_{n\to\infty}\sum_{r=1}^{n}\frac{r^2}{n^3[1+(r/n)^3]}$$

$$=\lim_{n\to\infty}\sum_{r=1}^{n}\frac{1}{n}\frac{(r/n)^2}{1+(r/n)^3}.$$

Now put $r/n=x$ and $1/n=dx$ and limits for x are 0 to 1.

$$\therefore \quad \lim=\int_0^1\frac{x^2\,dx}{1+x^3}=\frac{1}{3}\int_0^1\frac{3x^2\,dx}{1+x^3}$$

$$=\frac{1}{3}[\log(1+x^3)]_0^1=\frac{1}{3}\log 2.$$

Similarly, $\lim_{n\to\infty}\sum_{r=1}^{n}\frac{r^3}{r^4+n^4}=\frac{1}{4}\log 2.$

Ex. 5. $\lim_{n\to\infty}\left[\frac{n+1}{n^2+1^2}+\frac{n+2}{n^2+2^2}+\ldots+\frac{1}{n}\right]$. **(J.E.E.W.B. 1990)**

The last term $\frac{1}{n}=\frac{n+n}{n^2+n^2}$.

The given expression $=\lim_{n\to\infty}\sum_{r=1}^{n}\frac{n+r}{n^2+r^2}$

Express in the form $\frac{1}{n}\Sigma f\left(\frac{r}{n}\right)$.

$$\therefore \quad \text{Expression}=\lim_{n\to\infty}\sum_{r=1}^{n}\frac{n(1+r/n)}{n^2(1+r^2/n^2)}$$

$$=\lim\sum_{r=1}^{n}\frac{1}{n}\left(\frac{1+r/n}{1+r^2/n^2}\right).$$

Put $\frac{r}{n}=x$ and $\frac{1}{n}=dx$ and as usual limits are adjusted as 0 to 1.

$$\therefore \quad \lim=\int_0^1\frac{1+x}{1+x^2}dx=\int_0^1\frac{1}{1+x^2}dx+\frac{1}{2}\int_0^1\frac{2x}{1+x^2}dx$$

$$=[\tan^{-1}x]_0^1+\frac{1}{2}[\log(1+x^2)]_0^1$$

$$=(\tan^{-1}1-\tan^{-1}0)+\frac{1}{2}[\log 2-\log 1]$$

$$=\frac{\pi}{4}+\frac{1}{2}\log 2.$$

Ex. 6 (a). Evaluate $\lim_{n\to\infty}\left[\frac{n!}{n^n}\right]^{1/n}$

$$\frac{n!}{n^n}=\frac{1}{n}.\frac{2}{n}.\frac{3}{n}\ldots\ldots\ldots\frac{n}{n}.$$

Let $A=\lim_{n\to\infty}\left[\frac{n!}{n^n}\right]^{1/n}=\lim_{n\to\infty}\left[\frac{1}{n}.\frac{2}{n}.\frac{3}{n}\cdots\frac{n}{n}\right]^{1/n}$

$$\therefore \quad \log A = \lim_{n\to\infty} \frac{1}{n}\left[\log\frac{1}{n} + \log\frac{2}{n} + \log\frac{3}{n} + \ldots \log\frac{n}{n}\right]$$

$$= \lim_{n\to\infty} \frac{1}{n}\sum_{r=1}^{n} \log\left(\frac{r}{n}\right).$$

Put $\frac{r}{n} = x$ and $\frac{1}{n} = dx$ and limits are adjusted as 0 to 1.

$$\therefore \quad \log A = \int_0^1 \log x\, dx$$

$$= [x\log x]_0^1 - \int_0^1 x.\frac{1}{x}dx = [x\log x - x]_0^1$$

$$= [1\log 1 - 1] - \left[\lim_{x\to 0} x\log x - 0\right] = -1.$$

$$\therefore \quad A = e^{-1} = \frac{1}{e}.$$

Note : $\lim_{x\to 0} x\log x = \lim_{x\to 0} \frac{\log x}{1/x} = \frac{1/x}{-1/x^2} = -x = 0.$

We have used the rule for limits in the case of indeterminate forms.

(b) The value of $\lim_{n\to\infty}\left[\frac{(2n)!}{n!\,n^n}\right]^{1/n}$ is equal to $\frac{4}{e}$.

$$y = \lim_{n\to\infty}\left[\frac{(2n)(2n-1)\ldots[2n-(n-1)]\,n!}{n.n\ldots(n)\,n!}\right]^{1/n}$$

$$\log y = \lim_{n\to\infty}\sum_{r=0}^{n-1}\frac{1}{n}\left[\log\frac{2n-r}{n}\right]$$

$$= \lim_{n\to\infty}\Sigma\frac{1}{n}\left[\log\left(2-\frac{r}{n}\right)\right]$$

Put $\frac{r}{n} = x$ and $\frac{1}{n} = dx$ and adjust the limits

$$\log y = \int_0^1 \log(2-x)\,dx$$

$$= [x\log(2-x)]_0^1 - \int_0^1 \frac{-x}{2-x}dx$$

$$= 0 - \int_0^1\left(1 - \frac{2}{2-x}\right)dx$$

$$\log y = [-x - 2\log(2-x)]_0^1 = -1 - 2(0 - \log 2)$$

or $\log y = -1 + \log 4$

or $\log\frac{y}{4} = -1 \quad \therefore \quad y = 4e^{-1} = \frac{4}{e}$

Ex. 7. (a)* $\lim_{n\to\infty}\left[\left(1+\frac{1}{n^2}\right)\left(1+\frac{2^2}{n^2}\right)\ldots\left(1+\frac{n^2}{n^2}\right)\right]^{1/n}$

(J.E.E.W.B. 1992, 93)

Let $A = \lim_{n\to\infty}\left[\left(1+\frac{1}{n^2}\right)\left(1+\frac{2^2}{n^2}\right)\ldots\left(1+\frac{n^2}{n^2}\right)\right]^{1/n}$.

$$\therefore \quad \log A = \lim_{n\to\infty}\frac{1}{n}\left[\log\left(1+\frac{1}{n^2}\right) + \log\left(1+\frac{2^2}{n^2}\right) + \ldots + \log\left(1+\frac{n^2}{n^2}\right)\right]$$

$$= \lim_{n\to\infty}\frac{1}{n}\sum_{r=1}^{n}\log\left(1+\frac{r^2}{n^2}\right)$$

Put $\frac{r}{n} = x$ and $\frac{1}{n} = dx$ and the limits are adjusted as from 0 to 1.

$$\therefore \quad \log A = \int_0^1 \log(1+x^2)\,dx$$

$$= [x.\log(1+x^2)]_0^1 - \int_0^1 x.\frac{1}{(1+x^2)}.2x\,dx$$

$$= [x.\log(1+x^2)]_0^1 - 2\int_0^1\frac{x^2+1-1}{x^2+1}dx$$

$$= \log 2 - 2\int_0^1\left(1 - \frac{1}{1+x^2}\right)dx$$

$$= \log 2 - 2[x - \tan^{-1}x]_0^1$$

or $\log A = \log 2 - 2 + \frac{2\pi}{4}$ or $\log A - \log 2 = \frac{\pi - 4}{2}$

or $\log\frac{A}{2} = \frac{\pi-4}{2} \quad \therefore \quad \frac{A}{2} = e^{(\pi-4)/2}$

or $A = 2e^{(\pi-4)/2}$.

(b) $\lim_{n\to\infty}\left[\left(1+\frac{1}{n^2}\right)^{2/n^2}\left(1+\frac{2^2}{n^2}\right)^{4/n^2}\ldots\left(1+\frac{n^2}{n^2}\right)^{2^n/n^2}\right]$

If A be the given limit then

$$\log A = \operatorname{Lt}_{n\to\infty}\sum_{r=1}^{n}\frac{2r}{n^2}\log\left(1+\frac{r^2}{n^2}\right)$$

$$= \operatorname{Lt}_{n\to\infty}\sum_{r=1}^{n}\frac{2r}{n}\log\left(1+\frac{r^2}{n^2}\right).\frac{1}{n}$$

$$= \int_0^1 2x\log(1+x^2)\,dx$$

$$= [x^2\log(1+x^2)]_0^1 - \int\frac{x^2}{1+x^2}.2x.dx$$

$$= \log 2 - \int_0^1\left(1 - \frac{1}{1+x^2}\right)2x\,dx$$

$$= \log 2 - [x^2 - \log(1+x^2)]_0^1 = \log 2 - 1 + \log 2$$

$$= 2\log 2 - \log 1 = \log\frac{4}{e} \quad \therefore \quad A = \frac{4}{e}$$

Ex. 8. (a) $\lim_{n\to\infty}\frac{1}{n}\left[\sin^2\frac{\pi}{2n} + \sin^2\frac{2\pi}{2n} + \sin^2\frac{3\pi}{2n} + \ldots + \sin^2\frac{n\pi}{2n}\right]$

$$= \lim_{n\to\infty}\frac{1}{n}\sum_{r=1}^{n}\sin^2\frac{r\pi}{2n}.$$

Put $\frac{r}{n} = x$, $\frac{1}{n} = dx$ and limits are 0 to 1.

$$\therefore \quad \lim = \int_0^1 \sin^2 \frac{\pi x}{2}\, dx.$$

Put $\frac{\pi x}{2} = t \quad \therefore \quad \frac{\pi}{2} dx = dt$ or $dx = \frac{2}{\pi} dt$.

Also when $x = 1$, $t = \pi/2$
and when $x = 0$, $t = 0$.

$$\therefore \quad \lim = \int_0^{\pi/2} \sin^2 t \cdot \frac{2}{\pi} dt = \frac{1}{\pi}\int_0^{\pi/2} (1 - \cos 2t)\, dt$$

$$= \frac{1}{\pi}\left[t - \frac{\sin 2t}{2}\right]_0^{\pi/2} = \frac{1}{\pi}\left[\frac{\pi}{2} - 0\right] = \frac{1}{2}.$$

(b) $\underset{n \to \infty}{\text{Lt}}$

$$\frac{1}{n^2}\left[\sin^3 \frac{\pi}{4n} + 2\sin^3 \frac{2\pi}{4n} + 3\sin^3 \frac{3\pi}{4n} + \ldots n \sin^3 \frac{n\pi}{4n}\right]$$

$$\underset{n \to \infty}{\text{Lt}} \sum_{r=1}^{n} \frac{1}{n^2} r \sin^3 \frac{r\pi}{4n} = \underset{n \to \infty}{\text{Lt}} \Sigma \frac{r}{n}\left(\sin^3 \frac{r}{n} \cdot \frac{\pi}{4}\right) \cdot \frac{1}{n}$$

$$= \int_0^1 x \sin^3 \frac{\pi}{4} x\, dx \qquad \text{Put } \frac{\pi x}{4} = t$$

$$\therefore \; I = \left(\frac{4}{\pi}\right)^2 \int_0^{\pi/4} t \sin^3 t\, dt = \frac{16}{\pi^2}\int_0^{\pi/4} t\,(3 \sin t - \sin 3t)\, dt$$

Integrate by parts etc.

Ans. $\frac{\sqrt{2}}{9\pi^2}(52 - 15\pi)$

(c) Assuming that $1 - \frac{1}{2^2} + \frac{1}{3^2} - \frac{1}{4^2} + \ldots = \frac{\pi^2}{12}$

prove that

$$\underset{n \to \infty}{\text{Lt}} \left[\left\{1 + \left(\frac{1}{n}\right)^4\right\}\left\{1 + \left(\frac{2}{n}\right)^4\right\}^{1/2} \left\{1 + \left(\frac{3}{n}\right)^4\right\}^{1/3} \ldots 2^{1/n}\right]$$

$$= e^{\pi^2/48}$$

Write $2^{1/n} = \left[1 + \left(\frac{n}{n}\right)^4\right]^{1/n}$

If A be the required limit, then

$$\log A = \underset{n \to \infty}{\text{Lt}} \sum_{r=1}^{n} \frac{1}{r} \log\left(1 + \left(\frac{r}{n}\right)^4\right)$$

$$= \underset{n \to \infty}{\text{Lt}} \sum_{r=1}^{n} \frac{n}{r} \log\left(1 + \left(\frac{r}{n}\right)^4\right)\frac{1}{n}$$

$$= \int_0^1 \frac{1}{x}\log(1 + x^4)\, dx = \int_0^1 \frac{x^3}{x^4}\log(1 + x^4)\, dx$$

$$= \frac{1}{4}\int_0^1 \frac{1}{t}\log(1 + t)\, dt, \text{ where } t = x^4$$

$$= \frac{1}{4}\int_0^1 \frac{1}{t}\left(t - \frac{t^2}{2} + \frac{t^3}{3} - \frac{t^4}{4} + \ldots\right) dt$$

$$= \frac{1}{4}\int_0^1 \left(1 - \frac{t}{2} + \frac{t^2}{3} - \frac{t^3}{4} + \ldots\right) dt$$

$$= \frac{1}{4}\left[1 - \frac{1}{2^2} + \frac{1}{3^2} - \frac{1}{4^2} + \ldots\right] = \frac{1}{4}\frac{\pi^2}{12} = \frac{\pi^2}{48}$$

Problem Set (7)

Summation of series by the help of definite integral.

Prove the following :

1. (a) $\lim_{n \to \infty}\left[\frac{\sqrt{n+1} + \sqrt{n+2} + \ldots + \sqrt{2n}}{n\sqrt{(n)}}\right] = \frac{2}{3}(2\sqrt{2} - 1)$.

(b) If $S_n = \frac{1}{1 + \sqrt{n}} + \frac{1}{2 + \sqrt{2n}} + \ldots + \frac{1}{n + \sqrt{n^2}}$, find $\lim_{n \to \infty} S_n$.

(Roorkee 2000)

$$\Sigma \lim_{n \to \infty} \frac{1}{r + \sqrt{rn}} = \Sigma \lim_{n \to \infty} \frac{1}{n\left[\frac{r}{n} + \sqrt{\frac{r}{n}}\right]}$$

$$= \int_0^1 \frac{dx}{\sqrt{x}\,(1 + \sqrt{x})} = 2\,[\log(1 + \sqrt{x})]_0^1 = 2 \log 2$$

2.* $\lim_{n \to \infty} \sum_{r=1}^{n} \frac{1}{n}\sqrt{\left(\frac{n+r}{n-r}\right)} = \frac{\pi}{2} + 1.$

Above reduces to

$$\int_0^1 \sqrt{\left(\frac{1+x}{1-x}\right)} = \int_0^1 \frac{1+x}{\sqrt{(1-x^2)}}\, dx.$$ **See Q. 15(b), P. 1502-05**

$$= \left[\sin^{-1} x - \sqrt{(1 - x^2)}\right]_0^1 = \frac{\pi}{2} + 1$$

3.* $\lim_{n \to \infty}\left[\frac{1}{n} + \frac{n^2}{(n+1)^3} + \frac{n^2}{(n+2)^3} + \ldots + \frac{1}{8n}\right] = \frac{3}{8}.$

$\frac{1}{n} = \frac{n^2}{(n+0)^3}$, $\frac{1}{8n} = \frac{n^2}{(n+n)^3}$. **(Note)**

4. $\lim_{n \to \infty} \sum_{r=1}^{n} \frac{1}{\sqrt{(n^2 + r^2)}} = \log(1 + \sqrt{2}).$

5. $\lim_{n \to \infty}\left[\frac{\sqrt{1} + \sqrt{2} + \sqrt{3} + \ldots\ldots + \sqrt{n}}{n\sqrt{(n)}}\right] = \frac{2}{3}.$

6. (a) $\lim_{n \to \infty} \frac{1}{n}\left[\sec^2 \frac{\pi}{4n} + \sec^2 \frac{2\pi}{4n} + \ldots + \sec^2 \frac{n\pi}{4n}\right] = \frac{4}{\pi}.$

(b) $\lim_{n \to \infty} \frac{1}{n}\left[\tan \frac{\pi}{4n} + \tan \frac{2\pi}{4n} + \ldots + \tan \frac{n\pi}{4n}\right] = \frac{2}{\pi}\log 2$

$$I = \lim_{n \to \infty} \Sigma \frac{1}{n} \tan \frac{\pi}{4}\frac{r}{n} = \int_0^1 \tan \frac{\pi}{4} x\, dx$$

$$= \frac{4}{\pi}\int_0^{\pi/4} \tan t\, dt = \frac{4}{\pi}[\log \sec t]_0^{\pi/4}$$

$$= \frac{4}{\pi}\log \sqrt{2} = \frac{2}{\pi}\log 2$$

7. (a) $\underset{n\to\infty}{\text{Lt}}\left[\frac{1}{n^2}\sec^2\frac{1}{n^2} + \frac{2}{n^2}\sec^2\frac{4}{n^2} + \ldots + \frac{1}{n}\sec^2 1\right] =$

(a) $\tan 1$ (b) $\frac{1}{2}\tan 1$

(c) $\frac{7}{2}\sec 1$ (d) $\frac{1}{2}\operatorname{cosec} 1$ **(AIEEE 2005)**

Ans. (b).

$$I = \underset{n\to\infty}{\text{Lt}} \sum \frac{r}{n^2}\sec^2\left(\frac{r}{n}\right)^2$$

$$= \underset{n\to\infty}{\text{Lt}} \frac{1}{n}\sum \frac{r}{n}\sec^2\left(\frac{r}{n}\right)^2$$

$$= \int_0^1 x\sec^2 x^2\, dx = \frac{1}{2}\int_0^1 \sec^2 t\, dt$$

$$= \frac{1}{2}[\tan t]_0^1 = \frac{1}{2}\tan 1$$

(b) $\underset{n\to\infty}{\text{Lt}} \frac{1+2^4+3^4+\ldots+n^4}{n^5} - \underset{n\to\infty}{\text{Lt}} \frac{1+2^3+3^3+\ldots+n^3}{n^5} =$

(a) $\frac{1}{30}$ (b) 0

(c) $\frac{1}{4}$ (d) $\frac{1}{5}$ **(AIEEE 2003)**

Ans. (d).

$$\text{Lt}\sum \frac{1}{n}\left(\frac{r}{n}\right)^4 - \text{Lt}\frac{1}{n}\sum\frac{1}{n}\left(\frac{r}{n}\right)^3 \quad \textbf{(Note)}$$

$$= \int_0^1 x^4\, dx - 0 = \left[\frac{x^5}{5}\right]_0^1 = \frac{1}{5} \quad \because \text{Lt}\frac{1}{n} = 0$$

(c) $\underset{n\to 0}{\text{Lt}}\left[\frac{1}{n^2}\sin\left(\frac{1+n^2}{n^2}\right) + \frac{2}{n^2}\sin\left(\frac{4+n^2}{n^2}\right) + \frac{3}{n^2}\sin\left(\frac{9+n^2}{n^2}\right) + \ldots \frac{2}{n}\sin(5)\right] =$

(a) $\cos 2\sin 3$ (b) $\sin 2\cos 3$

(c) $\sin 2\sin 3$ (d) $\cos 2\cos 3$

Ans. (c).

Write the last term as $\frac{2n}{n^2}\sin\left[\frac{(2n)^2+n^2}{n^2}\right]$

$$\therefore \quad \text{Lt} = \sum_{r=1}^{2n}\frac{r}{n^2}\sin\left(1+\frac{r^2}{n^2}\right)$$

$$= \frac{1}{n}\sum_{r=1}^{2n}\frac{r}{n}\sin\left(1+\frac{r^2}{n^2}\right). \text{ Put } \frac{r}{n} = x, \frac{1}{n} = dx$$

$$= \int_0^2 x\sin(1+x^2)\, dx$$

$$= \frac{1}{2}[-\cos(1+x^2)]_0^2 = \frac{1}{2}[\cos 1 - \cos 5]$$

$$= \frac{1}{2}.2\sin 2\sin 3 = \sin 2\sin 3.$$

(d) If $\underset{n\to\infty}{\text{Lt}}\sum\frac{\log(n+r)-\log n}{n} = 2\left(\log 2 - \frac{1}{2}\right)$,

then $\underset{n\to\infty}{\text{Lt}} \frac{1}{n^\lambda}[(n+1)^\lambda (n+2)^\lambda \ldots (n+n)^\lambda]^{1/n} =$

(a) $\frac{4\lambda}{e}$ (b) $\left(\frac{4}{e}\right)^{1/\lambda}$

(c) $\left(\frac{4}{e}\right)^\lambda$ (d) $\left(\frac{e}{4}\right)^\lambda$

Ans. (c).

Let the limit be y, then

$$\log y = \frac{1}{n}\underset{n\to\infty}{\text{Lt}}\left[\log\left(\frac{n+1}{n}\right)^\lambda + \log\left(\frac{n+2}{n}\right)^\lambda \ldots \log\left(\frac{n+n}{n}\right)^\lambda\right]$$

$$= \frac{1}{n}\underset{n\to\infty}{\text{Lt}}\sum_{r=1}^{n}\left[\log\left(\frac{n+r}{n}\right)^\lambda\right]$$

$$= \lambda\int_0^1 \log(1+x)\, dx = \lambda\int_1^2 \log t\, dt$$

$$= \lambda[t\log - t]_1^2 = \lambda[2\log 2 - 1]$$

$$= \lambda[\log 4 - \log e] = \lambda\log\frac{4}{e}$$

$$= \log\left(\frac{4}{e}\right)^\lambda \quad \therefore \quad y = \left(\frac{4}{e}\right)^\lambda.$$

8. $\lim_{n\to\infty}\frac{1}{n}[(n+1)(n+2)\ldots(n+n)]^{1/n} = \frac{4}{e}$

or $\lim_{n\to\infty}\left[\left(1+\frac{1}{n}\right)\left(1+\frac{2}{n}\right)\ldots\left(1+\frac{n}{n}\right)\right]^{1/n} = \frac{4}{e}$

$$\log A = \lim_{n\to\infty}\sum_{r=1}^{n}\frac{1}{n}\log\left(1+\frac{r}{n}\right)$$

$$= \int_0^1 \log(1+x)\, dx = [x\log(1+x)]_0^1 - \int_0^1\frac{x}{1+x}dx$$

$$\log A = \log 2 - \int_0^1\left(1-\frac{1}{1+x}\right)dx$$

$$\therefore \quad \log\frac{A}{2} = -[x - \log(1+x)]_0^1 = -1 + \log 2$$

or $\log\frac{A}{4} = -1 \quad \therefore \quad \frac{A}{4} = e^{-1}$ or $A = \frac{4}{e}$

9. $\lim_{n\to\infty}\frac{1}{n^{p+1}}[1^p + 2^p + \ldots + n^p], p > -1$ **(J.E.E.W.B. 1994)**

$$I = \lim_{n\to\infty}\sum\frac{r^p}{n^{p+1}} = \lim\sum_1^n\left(\frac{r}{n}\right)^p.\frac{1}{n} = \int_0^1 x^p\, dx = \frac{1}{p+1}$$

10. Evaluate :

$$\underset{n\to\infty}{\text{Lt}}\ n^{-n^2}\left[(n+1)\left(n+\frac{1}{2}\right)\left(n+\frac{1}{2^2}\right)+\ldots\left(n+\frac{1}{2^{n-1}}\right)\right]^n$$

$$n^{-n^2}=\left(\frac{1}{n^n}\right)^n$$

$$\text{Lt}=\underset{n\to\infty}{\text{Lt}}\ \frac{\left[(n+1)\left(n+\frac{1}{2}\right)\left(n+\frac{1}{2^2}\right)\ldots\left(n+\frac{1}{2^{n-1}}\right)\right]^n}{n^n}$$

$$=\underset{n\to\infty}{\text{Lt}}\left[\left(1+\frac{1}{n}\right)^n\left(1+\frac{1}{2n}\right)^n\left(1+\frac{1}{2^2\,n}\right)^n\ldots\right]$$

Now $\underset{n\to\infty}{\text{Lt}}\left(1+\frac{a}{n}\right)^n=e^a$

$\therefore\quad \text{Lt}=\underset{n\to\infty}{\text{Lt}}\ (e\,.e^{1/2}\,.e^{1/2^2}\ \ldots n\text{ terms})$

$$=e^{1+(1/2)+(1/2^2)\ldots\infty}=e^{\frac{1}{1-(1/2)}}=e^2$$

11. Let $S_n=\sum_{k=1}^{n}\frac{n}{n^2+kn+k^2}$ and $T_n=\sum_{k=0}^{n-1}\frac{n}{n^2+kn+k^2}$ for $n=1,2,3,\ldots$ Then,

(a) $S_n<\frac{\pi}{3\sqrt{3}}$ (b) $S_n>\frac{\pi}{3\sqrt{3}}$

(c) $T_n<\frac{\pi}{3\sqrt{3}}$ (d) $T_n>\frac{\pi}{3\sqrt{3}}$ **(I.I.T. 2008)**

Ans. (a), (d).

Refer summation of series. **Definite Integral.**

$$\underset{n\to\infty}{\text{Lt}}\sum_{r=1}^{n}\frac{n}{n^2+rn+r^2}.\ \text{Divide by } n^2$$

$$=\underset{n\to\infty}{\text{Lt}}\sum\frac{1}{1+\frac{r}{n}+\left(\frac{r}{n}\right)^2}.\frac{1}{n}$$

Put $\frac{r}{n}=x\quad\therefore\quad\frac{1}{n}=dx$ and limits are adjusted as 0 to 1.

$$\therefore\quad S=\int_0^1\frac{1}{x^2+x+1}dx=\int_0^1\frac{dx}{\left(x+\frac{1}{2}\right)^2+\left(\frac{\sqrt{3}}{2}\right)^2}$$

$$=\left[\frac{2}{\sqrt{3}}\tan^{-1}\frac{2x+1}{\sqrt{3}}\right]_0^1=\frac{2}{\sqrt{3}}\left[\tan^{-1}\sqrt{3}-\tan^{-1}\frac{1}{\sqrt{3}}\right]$$

$$=\frac{2}{\sqrt{3}}\left[\frac{\pi}{3}-\frac{\pi}{6}\right]=\frac{2}{\sqrt{3}}.\frac{\pi}{6}=\frac{\pi}{3\sqrt{3}}$$

$\therefore\quad S_n<\frac{\pi}{3\sqrt{3}}$ and $T_n>\frac{\pi}{3\sqrt{3}}$

§16. General Properties of Definite Integrals.

Prop. I. $\int_a^b f(x)\,dx=\int_a^b f(t)\,dt.$

i.e. change of variable does not make any difference

Prop. II. $\int_a^b f(x)\,dx=-\int_b^a f(x)\,dx.$

Interchanging the limits amounts to change of sign.

Prop. III. $\int_a^b f(x)\,dx=\int_a^c f(x)\,dx+\int_c^b f(x)\,dx.$

If $\int f(x)\,dx=F(x)+c,$

then L.H.S.

$$=[F(x)+c]_a^b=[F(b)+c]-[F(a)+c]=F(b)-F(a).$$

$$\text{R.H.S.}=[F(c)-F(a)]+[F(b)-F(c)]$$
$$=F(b)-F(a)=\text{L.H.S.}$$

***Ex.** If $g(x)=\int_0^x\cos^4 t\,dt$, then $g(x+\pi)$ equals

(a) $g(x)+g(\pi)$ (b) $g(x)-g(\pi)$

(c) $g(x)\,g(\pi)$ (d) $\frac{g(x)}{g(\pi)}$ **(I.I.T. Re-ex. 1997)**

Sol. Ans. (a).

$$g(x+\pi)=\int_0^{\pi+x}\cos^4 t\,dt$$
$$=\int_0^{\pi}\cos^4 t\,dt+\int_{\pi}^{\pi+x}\cos^4 t\,dt.$$

Put $t=\pi+\theta$ and adjust the limits in I_2

$\therefore\quad I_2=\int_0^x\cos^4\theta\,d\theta=\int_0^x\cos^4 t\,dx=g(x)$ by Prop. I

$\therefore\quad g(\pi+x)=g(\pi)+g(x)$

***Prop. IV.** $\int_0^a f(x)\,dx=\int_0^a f(a-x)\,dx$ **(V. Imp.)**

(B.I.T.S. 1992)

Proof : Put $x=a-t,\quad\therefore\quad dx=-dt$ and adjust limits

Hence $\int_0^a f(x)\,dx=-\int_0^a f(a-t)\,dt$

$=\int_0^a f(a-x)\,dx,$ by Prop. I and II.

Lower limit must be zero and in that case we can replace x by $a-x$.

Applications :

Ex. 1. $I=\int_0^{\pi/2}\frac{\sin x}{\sin x+\cos x}dx.$

Here the lower limit is zero and hence we can replace x by $a-x$ *i.e.* x by $\pi/2-x$.

$$\therefore\quad I=\int_0^{\pi/2}\frac{\sin(\pi/2-x)}{\sin(\pi/2-x)+\cos(\pi/2-x)}dx$$

$$=\int\frac{\cos x}{\cos x+\sin x}dx$$

Adding, $2I=\int_0^{\pi/2}\frac{\sin x+\cos x}{\sin x+\cos x}dx$

$$=\int_0^{\pi/2}1\,dx=[x]_0^{\pi/2}=\frac{\pi}{2}$$

$\therefore\quad I=\pi/4$

Ex. 2. $\int_0^{\pi} \frac{e^{\cos x}}{e^{\cos x} + e^{-\cos x}} dx$ **(I.I.T. 1999)**

Use Prop. IV and add.

$$2I = \int_0^{\pi} 1 . dx = \pi \quad \therefore \quad I = \frac{\pi}{2}.$$

***Prop. V.** $\int_{-a}^{a} f(x)\, dx = 2\int_0^a f(x)\, dx$ **if** $f(-x) = f(x)$ **Even**

$= 0$ **if** $f(-x) = -f(x)$ **Odd**

Proof : $I = \int_{-a}^{a} f(x)\, dx = \int_{-a}^{0} f(x)\, dx + \int_0^a f(x)\, dx.$

Putting $x = -t$ in the first integral.

$I = -\int_a^0 f(-t)\, dt + \int_0^a f(x)\, dx,$

$= \int_0^a f(-x)\, dx + \int_0^a f(x)\, dx,$ by Prop. I and II.

$= 2\int_0^a f(x)\, dx$ if $f(-x) = f(x)$

$= 0$ if $f(-x) = -f(x).$

Ex. Prove that $I = \int_0^1 x(1-x)^{2007/2}\, dx = \frac{4}{(2009)(2011)}$

$\int_0^1 (1-x)\, x^{2007/2}\, dx$, by Prop. IV.

$= \int_0^1 [x^{2007/2} - x^{2009/2}]\, dx$

$= \left[\frac{2}{2009} x^{2009/2} - \frac{2}{2011} x^{2011/2}\right]_0^1$

$= \frac{2}{2009} - \frac{2}{2011} = \frac{2.2}{(2009)(2011)}$

Applications :

Ex. 1. (a) $\int_{-a}^{a} x^3\, dx = 0$ as $f(x)$ is odd.

$\because f(x) = x^3,\ f(-x) = (-x)^3 = -x^3 = -f(x).$

(b) $\int_{-a}^{a} x^4\, dx = 2\int_0^a x^4\, dx$ as $f(x)$ is even.

$\because f(x) = x^4,\ f(-x) = (-x)^4 = x^4 = f(x).$

In other words when $f(x)$ is an odd function of x the result is zero and when $f(x)$ is an even function of x the result is $2\int_0^a f(x)\, dx.$

Ex. 2. (a) $\int_{-\pi/2}^{\pi/2} \cos^3 x\, dx = 2\int_0^{\pi/2} \cos^3 x\, dx$

$\because f(x) = \cos^3 x,$

$f(-x) = \cos^3(-x) = \cos^3 x = f(x)$

(b) $\int_{-\pi/2}^{\pi/2} \sin^3 x\, dx = 0.$

$\because f(x) = \sin^3 x,$

$f(-x) = \sin^3(-x) = (-\sin x)^3 = -\sin^3 x = -f(x).$

Ex. 3. (a) $\int_{-1}^{1} \sin^3 x \cos^2 x\, dx = 0$

$f(-x) = -f(x)$ **(M.N.R. 1991)**

(b) $\int_{-3}^{1} (x+1)(x+2)(x+3)\, dx$

Put $x + 2 = t$ and adjust the limits

$\therefore \quad I = \int_{-1}^{1} t(t-1)(t+1)\, dt = \int_{-1}^{1} (t^3 - t)\, dt = 0$

by prop V as $f(t)$ is an odd function of t.

***Prop. VI.**

$$\int_0^{2a} f(x)\, dx = 2\int_0^a f(x)\, dx \text{ if } f(2a-x) = f(x).$$

$$= 0 \text{ if } f(2a-x) = -f(x).$$

Proof : $I = \int_0^{2a} f(x)\, dx = \int_0^a f(x)\, dx + \int_a^{2a} f(x)\, dx,$

Put $x = 2a - t$ in 2nd so that $dx = -dt$ and adjust limits

$I = \int_0^a f(x)\, dx - \int_a^0 f(2a-t)\, dt,$

$I = \int_0^a f(x)\, dx + \int_0^a f(2a-x)\, dx,$ by Prop. I and II.

Hence $I = 2\int_0^a f(x)\, dx$ if $f(2a-x) = f(x).$

and $= 0$ if $f(2a-x) = -f(x)$

Applications :

Ex. 1. (a) $\int_0^{\pi} \cos^3 x\, dx = 0.$

$\because f(x) = \cos^3 x,$

$f(2a-x) = \cos^3(\pi - x) = (-\cos x)^3$

$= -\cos^3 x = -f(x).$

(b) $\int_0^{\pi} \cos^4 x\, dx = 2\int_0^{\pi/2} \cos^4 x\, dx.$

Here $f(2a-x) = f(x)$

Ex. 2. (a) $\int_0^{\pi} \sin^3 x\, dx = 2\int_0^{\pi/2} \sin^3 x\, dx.$

$\because f(2a-x) = \sin^3(\pi - x) = \sin^3 x = f(x).$

(b) $\int_0^{\pi} \sin^4 x\, dx = 2\int_0^{\pi/2} \sin^4 x\, dx$ as above.

Ex. 3. $I = \int_0^{\pi} \frac{\sin 2kx}{\sin x} dx = 0$ where k is an integer

$f(2a-x) = \frac{\sin 2k(\pi - x)}{\sin(\pi - x)} = \frac{\sin(2k\pi - 2kx)}{\sin x}.$

$= \frac{\sin(-2kx)}{\sin x} = -\frac{\sin 2kx}{\sin x} = -f(x).$

Since $f(2a-x) = -f(x)$ therefore by Prop. VI.

$$I = \int_0^{\pi} \frac{\sin 2kx}{\sin x} dx = 0.$$

Ex. 4. If $\int_0^{\pi/2} \cos^m x \sin^m x\, dx = \lambda \int_0^{\pi/2} \sin^m x\, dx$ then $\lambda = 2^{-m}$. Is it true or false ?

Ans. True.

$I = \int_0^{\pi/2} \frac{2^m \sin^m x \cos^m x}{2^m} dx$

$I = 2^{-m} \int_0^{\pi/2} (\sin 2x)^m\, dx$

Put $2x = t$ and adjust the limits

$I = 2^{-m} \int_0^{\pi} \sin^m t \frac{dt}{2} = 2^{-m} . 2\int_0^{\pi/2} \sin^m x \frac{dx}{2}$

Prop. II and VI

$= 2^{-m} \int_0^{\pi/2} \sin^m x\, dx \quad \therefore \lambda = 2^{-m}$

Gamma function : $\int_0^{\pi/2} \sin^m x \cos^n x\, dx$

$$= \frac{[(m-1)(m-3)\ldots\ldots 2 \text{ or } 1]\,[(n-1)(n-3)\ldots\ldots 2 \text{ or } 1]}{[(m+n)(m+n-2)\ldots\ldots 2 \text{ or } 1]}$$

Multiply the above by $\frac{\pi}{2}$ **only when both *m* and *n* are even.**

Ex. 1. (a) $\int_0^{\pi/2} \sin^6 x \cos^3 x\, dx = \frac{(5.3.1)\,(2)}{9.7.5.3.1} = \frac{2}{63}$

(b) $\int_0^{\pi/2} \sin^8 x \cos^2 x\, dx = \frac{(7.5.3.1)\,(1)}{10.8.6.4.2} \cdot \frac{\pi}{2}$

(c) $\int_0^{\pi/2} \sin^2 x \cos^2 x\, dx = \frac{1.1}{4.2} \cdot \frac{\pi}{2} = \frac{\pi}{16}$ **(M.N.R. 1995)**

Ex. 2. (a) $\int_0^{\pi/2} \sin^4 x\, dx = \frac{3.1}{4.2} \frac{\pi}{2} = \int_0^{\pi/2} \cos^4 x\, dx$

(b) $\int_0^{\pi/2} \sin^5 x\, dx = \frac{4.2}{5.3.1} = \int_0^{\pi/2} \cos^5 x\, dx$

Particular case when *m* or *n* = 1 **(V. Imp.)**

$$\int_0^{\pi/2} \sin^m x \cos x\, dx = \left[\frac{\sin^{m+1} x}{m+1}\right]_0^{\pi/2} = \frac{1}{m+1}$$

$$\int_0^{\pi/2} \cos^m x \sin x\, dx = \left[-\frac{\cos^{m+1} x}{m+1}\right]_0^{\pi/2} = \frac{1}{m+1}$$

When limits are 0 to π : (Use Prop. VI)

$\int_0^{\pi} \sin^m x \cos^n x\, dx = 0$

always **except when *n* the power of cos *x* is even** and in that case,

$\int_0^{\pi} \sin^m x \cos^n x\, dx = 2\int_0^{\pi/2} \sin^m x \cos^n x\, dx$

$\sin^m (\pi - x) = \sin^m x$ whether *m* is odd or even, but

$\cos^n (\pi - x) = [-\cos x]^n = \cos^n x$ **(*n* even)**

$= -\cos^n x$ **(*n* odd)**

Hence $f(2a - x) = f(x)$ **(*n* even)**

$= -f(x)$ **(*n* odd)**

Ex. 1. (a) $\int_0^{\pi} \sin^6 x \cos^2 x\, dx = 2\int_0^{\pi/2} \sin^6 x \cos^2 x\, dx,$

$= 2 \cdot \frac{(5.3.1).1}{8.6.4.2} \cdot \frac{\pi}{2} = \frac{5\pi}{128}, \quad n = 2$

(b) $\int_0^{\pi} \sin^6 x \cos^3 x\, dx = 0, n = 3$

Ex. 2. (a) $\int_0^{\pi} \cos^6 x\, dx = 2\int_0^{\pi/2} \cos^6 x\, dx = 2 \frac{5.3.1}{6.4.2} \cdot \frac{\pi}{2} = \frac{5\pi}{16}$

(b) $\int_0^{\pi} \cos^3 x\, dx = 0 \quad \because \; f(2a - x) = -f(x)$, Prop. VI

Ex. 3. Prove that :

$$\int_0^{\pi/4} \cos^{3/2} 2x \cos x\, dx = \frac{3\pi}{16\sqrt{2}}.$$

$I = \int_0^{\pi/4} (1 - 2\sin^2 x)^{3/2} \cos x\, dx$

Put $\sqrt{2} \sin x = \sin t$ and adjust the limits

$$I = \int_0^{\pi/2} (1 - \sin^2 t)^{3/2} \frac{\cos t}{\sqrt{2}}\, dt$$

$$= \frac{1}{\sqrt{2}} \int_0^{\pi/2} \cos^4 t\, dt = \frac{1}{\sqrt{2}} \frac{3.1}{4.2} \cdot \frac{\pi}{2} = \frac{3\pi}{16\sqrt{2}}.$$

***Ex. 4.** $\int_0^{\pi/6} \cos^4 3\phi \sin^2 6\phi = \frac{5\pi}{192}.$

Put $3\phi = t$ and adjust the limits.

$$\therefore \quad I = \frac{1}{3} \int_0^{\pi/2} \cos^4 t \sin^2 2t\, dt$$

$$= \frac{1}{3} \int_0^{\pi/2} \cos^4 t\, (2 \sin t \cos t)^2\, dt$$

$$= \frac{4}{3} \int_0^{\pi/2} \cos^6 t \sin^2 t\, dt = \frac{4}{3} \frac{(5.3.1).1}{8.6.4.2} \frac{\pi}{2} = \frac{5\pi}{192}.$$

***Ex. 5.** $\int_0^{a} x^{5/2} \sqrt{a - x}\, dx = \frac{5\pi a^4}{128} \cdot$ Put $x = a \sin^2 \theta$

$$\therefore \quad I = \int_0^{\pi/2} 2a^4 \sin^6 \theta \cos^2 \theta\, d\theta \text{ etc.}$$

***Ex. 6.** $\int_0^{a} x^3 (2ax - x^2)^{3/2}\, dx = a^7 \left(\frac{9\pi}{32} - \frac{23}{35}\right)$

$I = \int_0^{a} x^{9/2} (2a - x)^{3/2}\, dx$

Put $x = 2a \sin^2 \theta \quad \therefore \quad dx = 4a \sin \theta \cos \theta\, d\theta$

and adjust the limits.

$\therefore \quad I = \int_0^{\pi/4} (2a)^{9/2 + 3/2} \sin^9 \theta \cos^3 \theta\, (4a \sin \theta \cos \theta\, d\theta)$

$= 2^8 a^7 \int_0^{\pi/4} \sin^{10} \theta \cos^4 \theta\, d\theta$

$= 2a^7 \int_0^{\pi/4} (2^4 \sin^4 \theta \cos^4 \theta)\, (2 \sin^2 \theta)^3\, d\theta$

$= 2a^7 \int_0^{\pi/4} \sin^4 2\theta\, (1 - \cos 2\theta)^3\, d\theta$

Now put $2\theta = t$ and adjust the limits

$I = a^7 \int_0^{\pi/2} \sin^4 t\, (1 - \cos t)^3\, dt$

$= a^7 \int_0^{\pi/2} \sin^4 t\, (1 - 3\cos t + 3\cos^2 t - \cos^3 t)\, dt$

$$= a^7 \left[\frac{3.1}{4.2} \frac{\pi}{2} - 3 \cdot \frac{1}{5} + 3 \cdot \frac{3.1.1}{6.4.2} \frac{\pi}{2} - \frac{3.1.2}{7.5.3}\right] = a^7 \left[\frac{9\pi}{32} - \frac{23}{35}\right]$$

Similarly, we can prove that

$$\int_0^{2a} x^3 \sqrt{(2ax - x^3)}\, dx = \frac{7}{8} \pi a^5$$

and $\int_0^{2a} \sqrt{(2ax - x^2)}\, dx = \frac{\pi a^2}{2}$

Ex. 7. $\int_0^{\pi} \sin^3 x\, (1 + 2\cos x)\, (1 + \cos x)^2\, dx = \frac{8}{3}$

$I = \int_0^{\pi} \sin^3 x\, (1 + 2\cos x)\, (1 + 2\cos x + \cos^2 x)\, dx$

$$= \int_0^{\pi} \sin^3 x\,(1 + 4\cos x + 5\cos^2 x + 2\cos^3 x)\,dx$$

$$= 2\int_0^{\pi/2} \sin^3 x\,dx + 0 + 2\int_0^{\pi/2} \sin^3 x . 5\cos^2 x\,dx + 0$$

$$= 2\left(\frac{2}{3}\right) + 10\left(\frac{2.1}{5.3.1}\right) = \frac{4}{3} + \frac{4}{3} = \frac{8}{3}$$

Similarly, $\displaystyle\int_0^{\pi} \sin^5 x\,(1 - \cos x)^3\,dx = \frac{32}{21}$

Ex. 8. (a) Evaluate :

$$\int_0^{\pi/2} \frac{\cos^9 x}{\cos^3 x + \sin^3 x}\,dx.$$ **(Roorkee 2001)**

Apply prop. IV and add.

$$\therefore \quad 2I = \int_0^{\pi/2} \frac{\cos^9 x + \sin^9 x}{\cos^3 x + \sin^3 x}\,dx$$

or $\displaystyle I = \frac{1}{2}\int_0^{\pi/2} [\cos^6 x + \sin^6 x - \cos^3 x \sin^3 x]\,dx$

$$= \frac{1}{2}\left[\frac{5.3.1}{6.4.2}\frac{\pi}{2} + \frac{5.3.1}{6.4.2}\frac{\pi}{2} - \frac{2.2}{6.4.2}\right] = \frac{1}{2}\left[\frac{5}{16}\pi - \frac{1}{12}\right]$$

***Prop. VII. (i)** $\int_a^b f(x)\,dx = \int_a^b f(a + b - x)\,dx.$

Proof : Put $x = a + b - t$. Then $dx = -dt$

$\therefore \quad \int_a^b f(x)\,dx = -\int_b^a f(a + b - t)\,dt$

$= \int_a^b f(a + b - x)\,dx$, by Prop. I and II.

(ii) Prove that $\int_a^b f(x)\,dx = \int_{a+c}^{b+c} f(x - c)\,dx$

Put $x = t - c$ and adjust the limits

$I = \int_{a+c}^{b+c} f(t - c)\,dt = \int_{a+c}^{b+c} f(x - c)\,dx$

Applications :

***Ex. 1.** $\displaystyle = \int_{\pi/6}^{\pi/3} \frac{dx}{1 + \sqrt{(\tan x)}}$

$$= \int_{\pi/6}^{\pi/3} \frac{\sqrt{\cos x}}{\sqrt{(\cos x)} + \sqrt{(\sin x)}}\,dx$$

Then by Prop. VII

$$I = \int_{\pi/6}^{\pi/3} \frac{\sqrt{\sin x}}{\sqrt{(\sin x)} + \sqrt{(\cos x)}}\,dx, \quad \because a + b = \frac{\pi}{2}.$$

Hence $\displaystyle 2I = \int_{\pi/6}^{\pi/3} dx = \frac{\pi}{3} - \frac{\pi}{6} = \frac{\pi}{6}$ or $\displaystyle I = \frac{\pi}{12}.$

Ex. 2. $\displaystyle I = \int_a^b \frac{f(x)}{f(x) + f(a + b - x)}\,dx = \frac{b - a}{2}$

$$I = \int_a^b \frac{f(a + b - x)}{f(a + b - x) + f(x)}, \qquad \text{by Prop. VII}$$

Adding $2I = \int_a^b 1 . dx = [x]_a^b = b - a$

$\therefore \quad I = \dfrac{b - a}{2}.$

Ex. 3. (a) $\displaystyle\int_1^2 \frac{\sqrt{x}}{\sqrt{(3 - x)} + \sqrt{x}}\,dx = \frac{1}{2}.$

Here $a + b = 3$. Using Prop. VII,

$$I = \int_1^2 \frac{\sqrt{(3 - x)}}{\sqrt{x} + \sqrt{(3 - x)}}\,dx.$$

Adding as in Ex. 2. etc.

(b)* $\displaystyle\int_2^3 \frac{\sqrt{x}}{\sqrt{(5 - x)} + \sqrt{x}}\,dx = \frac{1}{2}$ **(I.I.T. 1994)**

Use Prop. VII. $2I = 1 \quad \therefore \quad I = \dfrac{1}{2}.$

(c)* $\displaystyle\int_2^4 x\sqrt{6 - x}\,dx = \frac{32}{5}(3 - \sqrt{2})$

$I = \int_2^4 (6 - x)\sqrt{x}$ by Prop. VII

$x \to 2 + 4 - x$

$$= 6 \cdot \frac{2}{3}x^{3/2} - \frac{2}{5}x^{5/2} = \left[x^{3/2}\left(4 - \frac{2}{5}x\right)\right]_2^4$$

$$= 8 \cdot \frac{12}{5} - 2\sqrt{2} \cdot \frac{16}{5} = \frac{32}{5}(3 - \sqrt{2})$$

***Ex. 4.** The value of $\displaystyle\int_{\pi/4}^{3\pi/4} \frac{\phi}{1 + \sin\phi}\,d\phi$ is $= \pi(\sqrt{2} - 1)$ **(I.I.T. 1993)**

$$I = \int_{\pi/4}^{3\pi/4} \frac{\phi}{1 + \sin\phi}\,d\phi.$$

Here $a + b = \pi$

$$I = \int_{\pi/4}^{3\pi/4} \frac{\pi - \phi}{1 + \sin(\pi - \phi)}\,d\phi, \qquad \textbf{Prop. VII, P. 1537}$$

$$= \int_{\pi/4}^{3\pi/4} \frac{\pi}{1 + \sin\phi}\,d\phi - I$$

$$\therefore \quad 2I = \int_{\pi/4}^{3\pi/4} \frac{\pi}{1 + \sin\phi}$$

or $\displaystyle I = \frac{\pi}{2}\int_{\pi/4}^{3\pi/4} \frac{1 - \sin\phi}{1 - \sin^2\phi}\,d\phi$

$$I = \frac{\pi}{2}\int_{\pi/4}^{3\pi/4} \left(\frac{1}{\cos^2\phi} - \frac{\sin\phi}{\cos^2\phi}\right)d\phi$$

$$= \frac{\pi}{2}\int_{\pi/4}^{3\pi/4} (\sec^2\phi - \sec\phi\tan\phi)\,d\phi$$

$$= \frac{\pi}{2}[\tan\phi - \sec\phi]_{\pi/4}^{3\pi/4} = \frac{\pi}{2}[-1 - 1 - (-\sqrt{2} - \sqrt{2})]$$

$$= \pi[\sqrt{2} - 1].$$

Ex. 5. Prove that

$$\int_a^b \frac{\sin(x - a) - \cos(x - a)}{\sin(b - x) - \cos(b - x)}\,dx$$

$$= \int_a^b \frac{\sin(b - x) - \cos(b - x)}{\sin(x - a) - \cos(x - a)}\,dx$$

It follows by putting $x = a + b - t$ and adjusting the limits. (Prop. VII)

Ex. 6. Let f be a positive function. Let

$I_1 = \int_{1-k}^{k} x f[x(1-x)]\,dx,$

$I_2 = \int_{1-k}^{k} f[x(1-x)]\,dx,$

where $2k-1>0$. Then $\dfrac{I_1}{I_2}$ is

(a) 2 (b) k (c) $\dfrac{1}{2}$ (d) 1

(I.I.T. 1997)

Ans. (c).

Use Prop. VII on I_1, $a+b=1-k+k=1$

$\therefore \quad I_1 = \int_{1-k}^{k} (1-x) f[(1-x)x]\,dx$

$= \int f[(1-x)x]\,dx - \int x f[x(1-x)]\,dx$

$\therefore \quad I_1 = I_2 - I_1 \quad \therefore 2I_1 = I_2$ etc.

Ex. 7. $\displaystyle\int_{\pi/4}^{3\pi/4} \frac{dx}{1+\cos x}$ is equal to

(a) 2 (b) -2 (c) $\dfrac{1}{2}$ (d) $-\dfrac{1}{2}$

(I.I.T. 1999)

Ans. (a). Use Prop. VII.

$$I = \int_{\pi/4}^{3\pi/4} \frac{dx}{1-\cos x} \quad \because \cos(\pi - x) = -\cos x$$

$$\therefore \quad 2I = \int_{\pi/4}^{3\pi/4} \frac{2}{1-\cos^2 x}\,dx$$

$$= 2\int_{\pi/4}^{3\pi/4} \operatorname{cosec}^2 x\,dx$$

$$= -2[\cot x]_{\pi/4}^{3\pi/4} = 4 \quad \therefore I = 2$$

Ex. 8. If $\displaystyle\int_a^b \frac{x^n}{x^n + (16-x)^n}\,dx = 6$, then prove that $a=2, b=14, n \in R$.

Sol. Choose $a+b=16$ and now apply Prop. VII and add.

$2I = \int_a^b 1\,dx = b-a$

$\therefore \quad I = \dfrac{b-a}{2} = 6$ (given)

$\therefore \quad b-a=12$

Solving with $a+b=16$, we get $b=14, a=2$.

Ex. 9. For any $t \in R$ and f be a continuous function.

Let $\displaystyle I_1 = \int_{\sin^2 t}^{1+\cos^2 t} x f(x(2-x))\,dx$

and $\displaystyle I_2 = \int_{\sin^2 t}^{1+\cos^2 t} f(x(2-x))\,dx$ then $\dfrac{I_1}{I_2} = 1$

Apply Property VII.

$\int_a^b f(x)\,dx = \int_a^b f(a+b-x)\,dx$

where $a+b = \sin^2 t + 1 + \cos^2 t = 2$

$$I_1 = \int_{\sin^2 t}^{1+\cos^2 t} (2-x) f((2-x)x)\,dx = 2I_2 - I_1$$

or $2I_1 = 2I_2 \quad \therefore I_1/I_2 = 1$

***Removal of x:**

Ex. 1. (a)* Consider $\displaystyle\int_0^{\pi} \frac{x\sin x}{1+\cos^2 x}\,dx.$

We know how to integrate

$\displaystyle I = \int_0^{\pi} \frac{\sin x}{1+\cos^2 x}\,dx$ by putting

$\cos x = t$, *i.e.* $-\sin x\,dx = dt$.

Also when $x=\pi$, $t=-1$, when $x=0$, $t=1$.

$$\therefore \quad I = \int_{+1}^{-1} \frac{-dt}{1+t^2} = -[\tan^{-1} t]_{+1}^{-1}$$

$$= -[\tan^{-1}(-1) - \tan^{-1}(1)]$$

$$= -[-\pi/4 - (\pi/4)] = \pi/2.$$

Now $\displaystyle I = \int_0^{\pi} \frac{x\sin x}{1+\cos^2 x}\,dx.$ ...(1)

In order to remove x apply Property IV *i.e.*

$$\therefore \quad I = \int_0^{\pi} \frac{(\pi-x)\sin(\pi-x)}{1+\cos^2(\pi-x)}\,dx$$

$$= \int_0^{\pi} \frac{(\pi-x)\sin x}{1+\cos^2 x}\,dx \quad \text{...(2)}$$

Adding (1) and (2), we get

$$2I = \int_0^{\pi} (x+\pi-x)\frac{\sin x}{1+\cos^2 x}\,dx$$

or $\displaystyle I = \frac{\pi}{2}\int_0^{\pi} \frac{\sin x}{1+\cos^2 x}\,dx = \frac{\pi}{2}\left(\frac{\pi}{2}\right) = \frac{\pi^2}{4}$

as calculated above.

Note : $\displaystyle\int_0^{\pi} \frac{x\sin x}{2-\sin^2 x}\,dx = \frac{\pi^2}{4}$

$\because \quad 2-\sin^2 x = 1 + (1-\sin^2 x) = 1+\cos^2 x.$

(b)* Prove that $\displaystyle\int_{-\pi}^{\pi} \frac{2x(1+\sin x)}{1+\cos^2 x}\,dx = \pi^2$

(I.I.T. Re-ex. 1997)

$$I = 0 + 2\int_0^{\pi} \frac{2x\sin x}{1+\cos^2 x}\,dx \quad \text{(Prop. V)}$$

$$= 4\int_0^{\pi} \frac{x\sin x}{1+\cos^2 x}\,dx = 4\cdot\frac{\pi^2}{4} = \pi^2,$$

by part (a), proved above.

Ex. 2. Prove $I = \int_0^{\pi} x f(\sin x)\,dx = \frac{\pi}{2}\int_0^{\pi} f(\sin x)\,dx$

$= \pi \int_0^{\pi/2} f(\sin x)\,dx$

$I = \int_0^{\pi} x f(\sin x)\,dx.$ ...(1)

We apply Property IV, *i.e.*

$\int_0^a f(x)\,dx = \int_0^a f(a-x)\,dx.$

$\therefore \quad I = \int_0^{\pi} (\pi - x) f\sin(\pi - x)\,dx$

$= \int_0^{\pi} (\pi - x) f(\sin x)\,dx.$ ...(2)

Adding (1) and (2), we get

$2I = \int_0^{\pi} (x + \pi - x) f(\sin x)\,dx = \pi \int_0^{\pi} f(\sin x)\,dx.$

$\therefore \quad I = \frac{\pi}{2}\int_0^{\pi} f(\sin x)\,dx.$

Now for the second result we shall use Property VI *i.e.*

$\int_0^{2a} f(x)\,dx = 2\int_0^a f(x)\,dx.$

if $f(2a - x) = f(x)$.

Here $2a = \pi$ and $f(x) = f(\sin x)$.

$\therefore \quad f(2a - x) = f(\sin(\pi - x)) = f(\sin x) = f(x)$

$\therefore \quad I = \frac{\pi}{2}.2\int_0^{\pi/2} f(\sin x)\,dx = \pi\int_0^{\pi/2} f(\sin x)\,dx.$

***In general $\int_0^a x\,\phi(x)\,dx = \frac{1}{2}a\int_0^a \phi(x)\,dx$, provided $\phi(a - x) = \phi(x)$.**

Ex. 3. If $\int_0^{\pi} x f(\cos^2 x + \tan^4 x)\,dx$

$= \lambda \int_0^{\pi/2} f(\cos^2 x + \tan^4 x)\,dx,$

then prove that $\lambda = \pi$.

As above $I = \frac{\pi}{2}\int_0^{\pi} f(\cos^2 x + \tan^4 x)\,dx$

$= \frac{\pi}{2}.2\int_0^{\pi/2} f(\cos^2 x + \tan^4 x)\,dx$ Prop. VI

$= \pi \int_0^{\pi/2} f(\cos^2 x + \tan^4 x)\,dx$

$\therefore \quad \lambda = \pi$

***Ex. 4.** For $n > 0$, $\int_0^{2\pi} \frac{x\sin^{2n} x}{\sin^{2n} x + \cos^{2n} x}\,dx = \ldots\ldots$ **(I.I.T. 1996)**

Ans. π^2

Apply property IV and adding,

$2I = 2\pi \int_0^{2\pi} \frac{\sin^{2n} x}{\sin^{2n} x + \cos^{2n} x}\,dx$

$\therefore \quad I = \pi.4\int_0^{\pi/2} \frac{\sin^{2n} x}{\sin^{2n} x + \cos^{2n} x}\,dx$

by applying Prop. (VI) twice.

$= 4\pi.\frac{\pi}{4} = \pi^2$ (by Prop. IV)

***Prop. VIII.**

$$\frac{d}{dt}\left[\int_{f(t)}^{\phi(t)} F(x)\,dx\right] = F(\phi(t))\,\phi'(t) - F(f(t))\,f'(t)$$

where $f(t)$ and $\phi(t)$ are defined on the interval $[a, b]$ and are differentiable at any point $t \in (a, b)$ and $F(x)$ is continuous for $f(a) \le x \le f(b)$

***Ex. 1.** $\frac{d}{dt}\int_0^t \cos x^2\,dx = (\cos t^2).1 - \cos(0).0 = \cos t^2$

Also $\lim_{t\to 0} \frac{\int_0^t \cos x^2\,dx}{t} = \lim_{t\to 0}\frac{f(t)}{g(t)} = \frac{0}{0}$ form as

$f(0) = 0, g(0) = 0 = \lim_{t\to 0}\frac{f'(t)}{g'(t)} = \lim_{t\to 0}\frac{\cos t^2}{1} = 1$

***Ex. 2.** If $f(t) = \int_{t^2}^{t^3} \frac{1}{\log x}\,dx$ then find $f'(t)$.

By prop. VIII,

$f'(t) = \frac{d}{dt}f(t) = \frac{1}{\log t^3}\frac{d}{dt}(t^3) - \frac{1}{\log t^2}\frac{d}{dt}(t^2)$

$= \frac{3t^2}{3\log t} - \frac{2t}{2\log t} = \frac{t(t-1)}{\log t}$

Ex. 3. (a) Find the points at which y has local max. and min.

where $y = \int_0^{x^2} \frac{t^2 - 5t + 4}{2 + e^t}\,dt = \int_{f(x)}^{\phi(x)} F(t)\,dt$, say

$\therefore \quad \frac{dy}{dx} = F[\phi(x)]\,\phi'(x) - F[f(x)]\,f'(x)$

$\frac{dy}{dx} = F(x^2).2x - F(0).0 = \frac{x^4 - 5x^2 + 4}{2 + e^{x^2}}\cdot 2x - 0$

For max. or min.,

$\frac{dy}{dx} = 0 \Rightarrow x(x^2 - 1)(x^2 - 4) = 0$

$\therefore$ $x = 0, 1, -1, 2, -2$ or $-2, -1, 0, 1, 2$ in order. We shall use change of sign of $\frac{dy}{dx}$ for determining max. and min.

The denominator of $\frac{dy}{dx}$ *i.e.* $2 + e^{x^2}$ is always +ive.

For $x < 0$, $\frac{dy}{dx} = -$ ive; for $x > 0$, $\frac{dy}{dx} = +$ ive.

Hence at $x = 0$, it is min. Since max. and min. occur alternately therefore we can say the function is min. at $x = -2, 0, 2$ and max. at $x = -1, 1$.

(b) Let $f(x) = \int_1^x \sqrt{2 - t^2}\,dt$. Then the real roots of the equation $x^2 - f'(x) = 0$ are :

(a) ± 1 (b) $\pm\frac{1}{\sqrt{2}}$

(c) $\pm\frac{1}{2}$ (d) 0 and 1 **(I.I.T. Sc. 2002)**

Ans. (a). $f(x) = \int_1^x \sqrt{2-t^2}\, dt$

$f'(x) = \sqrt{2-x^2}\,.1 - \sqrt{2-1}\,.0 = \sqrt{2-x^2}$

$\therefore \quad x^2 = f'(x) = \sqrt{2-x^2}$ or $x^4 + x^2 - 2 = 0$

or $(x^2+2)(x^2-1) = 0 \quad \therefore \quad x = \pm 1$ (only real)

(c)* If $\int_0^x f(t)\, dt = x + \int_x^1 t\, f(t)\, dt$, then the value of $f(1)$ is

(a) $\frac{1}{2}$ (b) 0

(c) 1 (d) $-\frac{1}{2}$ **(I.I.T. 1998)**

Ans. (A). Differentiating both sides w.r.t. x,

$f(x).1 - f(0).0 = 1 + 1.f(1).0 - x f(x).1$

$\therefore \quad (x+1) f(x) = 1$. Put $x = 1 \quad \therefore \quad f(1) = \frac{1}{2}$.

(d) Let $f : (0, \infty) \to R$ and $F(x) = \int_0^x f(t)\, dt$.

If $F(x^2) = x^2(1+x)$, then $f(4)$ equals

(a) $\frac{5}{4}$ (b) 7

(c) 4 (d) 2 **(I.I.T. Sc. 2001)**

Ans. (c).

By definition of $F(x)$ we have

$F(x^2) = \int_0^{x^2} f(t)\, dt = x^2 + x^3$ (given)

Differentiate both sides

$f(x^2).2x + 0 = 2x + 3x^2$

Put $x = 2$

$4f(4) = 16$ or $f(4) = 4$

(e) If $\int_0^{t^2} x f(x)\, dx = \frac{2}{5} t^5$, then $f(4/25) =$

(a) 2/5 (b) $-5/2$

(c) 1 (d) 5/2 **(Screening 2004)**

Ans. (a) Using property VIII **P. 1539** definite integral,

$I = t^2 f(t^2)\, 2t - 0 = \frac{2}{5} 5t^4 \quad \therefore \quad f(t^2) = t$

Now put $t = \frac{2}{5} \quad \therefore \quad f\left(\frac{4}{25}\right) = \frac{2}{5}$

***Ex. 4.** Prove that

$$\int_0^{\sin^2 x} \sin^{-1}\sqrt{t}\, dt + \int_0^{\cos^2 x} \cos^{-1}\sqrt{t}\, dt = \frac{\pi}{4}$$

$I = f(x)$ after integration and putting the limits

Now $f'(x) = \sin^{-1}\sqrt{(\sin^2 x)}\,.(2\sin x \cos x) - 0$

$+ \cos^{-1}\sqrt{\cos^2 x}\,(-2\cos x \sin x) - 0$

$\therefore \quad f'(x) = 0$. Hence $f(x) = c$ (constant)

In order to find c, the constant of integration, we evaluate $f(x)$ at $x = \pi/4$

$\therefore \quad I = \int_0^{1/2} \sin^{-1}\sqrt{t}\, dt + \int_0^{1/2} \cos^{-1}\sqrt{t}\, dt$

$= \int_0^{1/2} (\sin^{-1}\sqrt{t} + \cos^{-1}\sqrt{t})\, dt$

$= \int_0^{1/2} \frac{\pi}{2}\, dt = \frac{\pi}{4} = c$

$\therefore \quad f(x) = \frac{\pi}{4}$.

***Ex. 5. (a)** $\operatorname{Lt}_{x \to 0} \dfrac{\int_0^{x^2} \sin\sqrt{t}\, dt}{x^3}$

$I = \operatorname{Lt}_{x \to 0} \dfrac{f(x)}{g(x)}$, where $f(0) = 0, g(0) = 0$

$\therefore \quad I = \operatorname{Lt}_{x \to 0} \dfrac{f'(x)}{g'(x)}$ where

$f'(x) = \sin\sqrt{x^2}\, \frac{d}{dx}(x^2) - 0 = 2x \sin x$

$\therefore \quad I = \operatorname{Lt}_{x \to 0} \dfrac{2x \sin x}{3x^2} = \frac{2}{3}.\operatorname{Lt} \dfrac{\sin x}{x} = \frac{2}{3}$

(b) $\lim_{x \to \pi/4} \dfrac{\int_2^{\sec^2 x} f(t)\, dt}{x^2 - \frac{\pi^2}{16}}$ equals

(a) $\frac{8}{\pi} f(2)$ (b) $\frac{2}{\pi} f(2)$

(c) $\frac{2}{\pi} f\left(\frac{1}{2}\right)$ (d) $4f(2)$ **(I.I.T. 2007)**

Ans. (a).

As $\sec^2 \frac{\pi}{4} = 2 \quad \therefore$ Lt is of the form $\frac{0}{0}$

Hence by L'Hospital rule by differentiating N^r and D^r separately as explained in **Prop. VIII (Def. Integral),**

$\text{Lt} = \operatorname{Lt}_{x \to \pi/4} \dfrac{f(\sec^2 x).2\sec x.\sec x \tan x}{2x}$

$= \dfrac{2f(2)}{\pi/4} = \frac{8}{\pi} f(2)$.

Ex. 6. If $\int_0^y e^{-t^2}\, dt + \int_0^{x^2} \sin^2 t\, dt = 0$, then prove that $\frac{dy}{dx} = -2e \sin^2(1)$ at the point (1, 1).

Differentiating the given implicit function $F(x, y)$ w.r.t. x, we have

$\left(e^{-y^2}.\frac{dy}{dx} - 0\right) + (\sin^2 x^2).2x = 0$

$\therefore \quad \frac{dy}{dx} = -(\sin^2 x^2).\dfrac{2x}{e^{-y^2}}$

Put $x = 1, y = 1$.

$\therefore \quad \frac{dy}{dx} = -2e \sin^2(1)$.

***Ex. 7.** If $f(x) = \int_1^x \dfrac{t^4 \sin\frac{1}{t} + t^2}{1 + |t|^3}\, dt$

then prove that $\operatorname{Lt}_{x \to -\infty} f'(x) = -1$.

$$f'(x)=\frac{x^4\sin\frac{1}{x}+x^2}{1+|x|^3}\cdot\frac{d}{dx}(x)-0.$$

$\therefore \quad \underset{x\to-\infty}{\text{Lt}} \quad f'(x)=-1$ **See Q. 17 P. 1351-56.**

Ex. 8. $\lim\limits_{x\to 0}\frac{1}{x}\left[\int_y^a e^{\sin^2 t}\,dt-\int_{x+y}^a e^{\sin^2 t}\,dt\right]$ is equal to

(a) $e^{\sin^2 y}$ (b) $\sin 2y\, e^{\sin^2 y}$

(c) 0 (d) None of these

Ans. (a).

$$\lim_{x\to 0}\frac{1}{x}\left[\int_y^a e^{\sin^2 t}\,dt+\int_a^{x+y} e^{\sin^2 t}\,dt\right]$$

$$=\lim_{x\to 0}\frac{1}{x}\int_y^{x+y} e^{\sin^2 t}\,dt \qquad \left(\text{Form } \frac{0}{0}\right)$$

Apply L' Hospital Rule

$$=\lim_{x\to 0}\frac{e^{\sin^2(x+y)}\left(1+\frac{dy}{dx}\right)-e^{\sin^2 y}\frac{dy}{dx}}{1}$$

$$=e^{\sin^2 y}\left[1+\frac{dy}{dx}-\frac{dy}{dx}\right]=e^{\sin^2 y} \Rightarrow \text{(a)}$$

Ex. 9. If $f(x)=\int_{x^2}^{x^3}\frac{dt}{\log t}$, $x>0$ then prove that f is an increasing function

$$f'(x)=\frac{1}{\log x^3}\frac{d}{dx}(x^3)-\frac{1}{\log x^2}\frac{d}{dx}(x^2)$$

$$=\frac{3x^2}{3\log x}-\frac{2x}{2\log x}=\frac{x(x-1)}{\log x}$$

$f'(x)=0$ at $x=1$ ($x\neq 0$ as $x>0$)

$x<1,\quad f'(x)=\frac{-}{-}=+\text{ive}$

$x>1,\quad f'(x)=\frac{+}{+}=+\text{ive}$

$f'(x)$ does not change sign hence it is neither max. nor min at $x=1$

But $f'(x)=+$ ive so that $f(x)$ is an increasing function.

Ex. 10. If $y(x)=\int_{\pi^2/16}^{x^2}\frac{\cos x\cdot\cos\sqrt{\theta}}{1+\sin^2\sqrt{\theta}}\,d\theta$ then find $\frac{dy}{dx}$ at $x=\pi$.

Refer examples 1 to 5 Prop. VIII P. 1539

$$y=\int_{\pi^2/16}^{x^2}\frac{\cos x\cos\sqrt{\theta}}{1+\sin^2\sqrt{\theta}}\,d\theta$$

$$\therefore \quad \frac{dy}{dx}=-\sin x\int_{\pi^2/16}^{x^2}\frac{\cos\sqrt{\theta}}{1+\sin^2\sqrt{\theta}}\,d\theta+\cos x.\left[\frac{\cos\sqrt{x^2}}{1+\sin^2\sqrt{x^2}}.2x-0\right]$$

Now put $x=\pi$ and $\sin\pi=0, \cos\pi=-1$

$$\therefore \quad \left(\frac{dy}{dx}\right)_{x=\pi}=0+\frac{(-1)(-1)}{1+0}.2\pi=2\pi.$$

Prop. IX. If $f(x)$ is a function defined in $[a,b]$ then $\int_a^b f(x)$ lies between $L(b-a)$ and $G(b-a)$ where L and G are the least and greatest values of the function $f(x)$ in the interval $[a,b]$.

Note : If $f(x)$ is an **increasing function** in $[a,b]$ then $L=f(a)$ is least and $G=f(b)$ is greatest. In case it is a **decreasing function**, then $G=f(a)$ is greatest and $L=f(b)$ is least.

Applications :

Ex. 1. Prove that $1\le\int_0^1 e^{x^2}\,dx\le e$

$f(x)=e^{x^2} \quad \therefore f'(x)=2xe^{x^2}=+\text{ive in } [0,1]$

Hence $f(x)$ is an increasing function in $[0,1]$.

$\therefore \quad L=f(0)=1, G=f(1)=e$

Hence by Prop. IX,

$$L(1-0)\le\int_0^1 e^{x^2}\,dx\le G(1-0)$$

$$\therefore \quad 1\le\int_0^1 e^{x^2}\,dx\le e.$$

Ex. 2. Prove that $4\le\int_1^3\sqrt{3+x^3}\,dx\le 2\sqrt{30}$

Use Prop. IX and proceed as in Ex. 1.

Ex. 3. Let $g(x)=\int_0^x f(t)\,dt$, where f is such that $\frac{1}{2}\le f(t)\le 1$ for $t\in[0,1]$ and $0\le f(t)\le\frac{1}{2}$ for $t\in(1,2]$. Then $g(2)$ satisfies the inequality,

(a) $-\frac{3}{2}\le g(2)<\frac{1}{2}$ (b) $0\le g(2)<2$

(c) $\frac{3}{2}<g(2)\le\frac{5}{2}$ (d) $2<g(2)<4$

(I.I.T. Sc. 2000)

Ans. None.

$$g(2)=\int_0^2 f(t)\,dt=\int_0^1 f(t)\,dt+\int_1^2 f(t)\,dt=I_1+I_2$$

Now we know from **Prop. IX P. 1541** (definite integral) that if $f(x)$ is defined in $[a,b]$ then $\int_a^b f(x)\,dx$ lies between $L(b-a)$ and $G(b-a)$, where L and G are the least and greatest values of the function $f(x)$ in the interval $[a,b]$.

Now $\frac{1}{2}\le f(t)\le 1, t\in[0,1]$

$\therefore \quad L=\frac{1}{2}$ and $G=1, b-a=1-0=1$

$$\frac{1}{2}\cdot 1\le I_1\le 1 \qquad \ldots(1)$$

Again $0\le f(t)\le\frac{1}{2}, t\in[1,2]$

$L = 0, G = \frac{1}{2}$ and $b - a = 2 - 1 = 1$

$\therefore \quad 0.1 \le I_2 \le \frac{1}{2} \cdot 1$ or $0 \le I_2 \le \frac{1}{2}$ ...(2)

Adding the inequalities in (1) and (2), we get

$\frac{1}{2} + 0 \le I_1 + I_2 \le 1 + \frac{1}{2}$ or $\frac{1}{2} \le g(2) \le \frac{3}{2}$.

Problem Set (8)

(Definite Integration)

***Ex. 1. (a)** $I = \int_0^{\pi/2} \log \sin x \, dx = \frac{\pi}{2} \log \frac{1}{2}$. **(V. Imp.)**

By Prop. IV,

$\int_0^a f(x)\,dx = \int_0^a f(a - x)\,dx$

$\therefore \quad I = \int_0^{\pi/2} \log \sin(\pi/2 - x)\,dx = \int_0^{\pi/2} \log \cos x \, dx$

$\therefore \quad 2I = \int_0^{\pi/2} (\log \sin x + \log \cos x)\,dx$

$2I = \int_0^{\pi/2} \log(\sin x \cos x)\,dx$.

$= \int_0^{\pi/2} \log \frac{\sin 2x}{2}\,dx$.

$= \int_0^{\pi/2} \log \sin 2x \, dx - \int_0^{\pi/2} \log 2 \, dx$.

Put $2x = t$ in the 1st, $\therefore$ $2\,dx = dt$ and limits become 0 to π.

$\therefore \quad 2I = \frac{1}{2}\int_0^{\pi} \log \sin t \, dt - [x \log 2]_0^{\pi/2}$

Now apply Prop. VI in 1st. $\because f(2a - x) = f(x)$.

$2I = \frac{1}{2} . 2 \int_0^{\pi/2} \log \sin t \, dt - \frac{\pi}{2} \log 2$

or $\quad 2I = \int_0^{\pi/2} \log \sin x \, dx - (\pi/2) \log 2$, by Prop. I

or $\quad 2I = I + \frac{\pi}{2} \log \frac{1}{2}$

$\therefore \quad \boldsymbol{I = \int_0^{\pi/2} \log \sin x \, dx = \int_0^{\pi/2} \log \cos x \, dx = \frac{\pi}{2} \log \frac{1}{2}}$

The above may be taken as a standard result.

Deduction.

$\int_0^{\pi/2} \log \sec x \, dx = \int_0^{\pi/2} \log \operatorname{cosec} x \, dx$

$= -\frac{\pi}{2} \log \frac{1}{2} = \frac{\pi}{2} \log 2 \quad \because \log \sec x = -\log \cos x$

(b) Prove $\int_0^{\pi/2} \log \tan x \, dx = \int_0^{\pi/2} \log \cot x \, dx = 0$

(Karnataka C.E.E. 1999)

We have $\log \tan x = \log \frac{\sin x}{\cos x} = \log \sin x - \log \cos x$

$\therefore \quad I = \int_0^{\pi/2} \log \sin x \, dx - \int_0^{\pi/2} \log \cos x \, dx = 0$

by Prop. IV

(c) $\int_0^1 \frac{\log x}{\sqrt{(1 - x^2)}}\,dx = \frac{\pi}{2} . \log \frac{1}{2}$.

Put $x = \sin\theta$ and it becomes part (a).

(d) $\int_0^{2\pi} \log(1 + \sin x)\,dx = 2\pi \log \frac{1}{2}$

$I = \int_0^{2\pi} \log(1 + \sin(2\pi - x))\,dx$

$= \int_0^{2\pi} \log(1 - \sin x)\,dx$

$\therefore \quad 2I = \int_0^{2\pi} \log(1 + \sin x)(1 - \sin x)\,dx$

$= \int_0^{2\pi} \log(1 - \sin^2 x)\,dx$

$= \int_0^{2\pi} \log \cos^2 x \, dx = 2.2 \int_0^{\pi/2} \log \cos^2 x \, dx$

$= 4 \int_0^{\pi/2} 2 \log \cos x \, dx$

or $\quad 2I = 8 \cdot \frac{\pi}{2} \log \frac{1}{2} \quad \therefore \quad I = 2\pi \log \frac{1}{2}$

Ex. 2. (a) $\int_0^1 \log \sin\left(\frac{\pi}{2} x\right) dx = \log \frac{1}{2}$.

Put $\frac{\pi}{2} x = t$ and it becomes **Ex. 1.**

(b) $\int_0^1 \frac{\sin^{-1} x}{x}\,dx = \frac{\pi}{2} \log 2$

Other forms : $\int_0^{\pi/2} \theta \cot\theta \, d\theta = \frac{\pi}{2} \log 2$

Put $x = \sin\theta$ and adjust the limits

$I = \int_0^{\pi/2} \frac{\theta}{\sin\theta} \cos\theta \, d\theta = \int_0^{\pi/2} \theta \cot\theta \, d\theta$.

Integrate by parts

$I = \left[\theta \log \sin\theta\right]_0^{\pi/2} - \int_0^{\pi/2} \log \sin\theta . 1 \, d\theta$

$= \left(\frac{\pi}{2} \cdot 0\right) - \lim_{\theta \to 0} (\theta \log \sin\theta) - \frac{\pi}{2} \log \frac{1}{2}$

$= 0 + \frac{\pi}{2} \log 2$

$\lim_{\theta \to 0} \theta \log \sin\theta$ is of the form $0 \times \infty$ **Indeterminate form :**

$= \lim_{\theta \to 0} \frac{\log \sin\theta}{1/\theta} = \frac{\infty}{\infty} = \lim_{\theta \to 0} \frac{\frac{1}{\sin\theta} \cos\theta}{-1/\theta^2}$

$= \lim_{\theta \to 0} -\frac{\theta^2 \cos\theta}{\sin\theta} \left(\frac{0}{0}\right) = \lim_{\theta \to 0} -\frac{\theta^2}{\tan\theta} \quad \left(\frac{0}{0}\right)$

$= \lim_{\theta \to 0} -\frac{2\theta}{\sec^2\theta} = 0$

Another form :

$\int_0^{\infty} \frac{\tan^{-1} x}{x(1 + x^2)}\,dx = \frac{\pi}{2} \log 2$

Put $\tan^{-1} x = \theta$ or $x = \tan\theta$

$\therefore \quad I = \int_0^{\pi/2} \theta \cot \theta \, d\theta$ etc.

(c)* $\int_0^{\infty} (\cot^{-1} x)^2 \, dx = \pi \log 2$

Another form : $\int_0^{\pi/2} \theta^2 \operatorname{cosec}^2\theta \, d\theta = \pi \log 2$

Put $x = \cot \theta$ and adjust the limits.

$\therefore \quad I = \int_{\pi/2}^{0} \theta^2 (-\operatorname{cosec}^2 \theta) \, d\theta$

$= \int_0^{\pi/2} \theta^2 \operatorname{cosec}^2 \theta \, d\theta$

$= \left[\theta^2 (-\cot \theta)\right]_0^{\pi/2} + 2\int_0^{\pi/2} \theta \cot \theta \, d\theta$

$= 0 + 2 \cdot \frac{\pi}{2} \log 2 = \pi \log 2$, by last part

$\lim_{\theta \to 0} -\theta^2 \cot \theta = 0$ is shown in last part (b).

(d) $\int_0^{\pi/2} (2 \log \sin x - \log \sin 2x) \, dx = \frac{\pi}{2} \log \frac{1}{2}$

$I = \int_0^{\pi/2} (2 \log \sin x - \log 2 \sin x \cos x) \, dx$

$= \int_0^{\pi/2} [2 \log \sin x - \{\log 2 + \log \sin x + \log \cos x\}] \, dx$

$= \int_0^{\pi/2} [(\log \sin x - \log \cos x) - \log 2] \, dx$

$= 0 - [x \log 2]_0^{\pi/2} = -\frac{\pi}{2} \log 2 = \frac{\pi}{2} \log \frac{1}{2}$

$\because \quad \int_0^{\pi/2} \log \sin x \, dx = \int_0^{\pi/2} \log \cos x \, dx$ by Prop. IV

(e) $\int_0^{\pi/2} \sin x \log (\sin x) \, dx =$

(a) $\log_e e$ (b) $\log_e 2$

(c) $\log_e (e/2)$ (d) $\log_e (2/e)$

Ans. (d).

$I = \int_0^{\pi/2} \sin x \log (\sin x) \, dx$

$= \frac{1}{2} \int_0^{\pi/2} \sin x \log \sin^2 x \, dx$

$= \frac{1}{2} \int_0^{\pi/2} \sin x \log (1 - \cos^2 x) \, dx$

$= \frac{1}{2} \int_0^{1} \log (1 - t^2) \, dt$ where $t = \cos x$

$= \frac{1}{2} \int_0^{1} \left[-t^2 - \frac{(t^2)^2}{2} - \frac{(t^2)^3}{3} - \dots\right] dt$

$= -\left[\frac{1}{2.3} + \frac{1}{4.5} + \frac{1}{6.7} + \dots\right]$

$= -\left[\left(\frac{1}{2} - \frac{1}{3}\right) + \left(\frac{1}{4} - \frac{1}{5}\right) + \left(\frac{1}{6} - \frac{1}{7}\right) + \dots\right]$

$= -1 + \left(1 - \frac{1}{2} + \frac{1}{3} - \frac{1}{4} + \frac{1}{5} - \dots\right)$

$= -\log_e e + \log_e (1 + 1) = \log_e (2/e)$

Ex. 3. $\int_0^{\infty} \log \left(x + \frac{1}{x}\right) \frac{dx}{1 + x^2} = \pi \log 2.$

Put $x = \tan \theta$. $\therefore dx = \sec^2 \theta \, d\theta$.

$\therefore \quad I = \int_0^{\pi/2} \log (\tan \theta + \cot \theta) \, d\theta$

$= \int_0^{\pi/2} \log \frac{\sin^2 \theta + \cos^2 \theta}{\sin \theta \cos \theta} \, d\theta$

$= -\int_0^{\pi/2} \log \sin \theta \cos \theta \, d\theta$

$= -\left[\int_0^{\pi/2} \log \sin \theta \, d\theta + \int_0^{\pi/2} \log \cos \theta \, d\theta\right]$

$= -\left[\frac{\pi}{2} \log \frac{1}{2} + \frac{\pi}{2} \log \frac{1}{2}\right]$ by **Ex. 1 Page 1542.**

$= -\pi \log \frac{1}{2} = \pi \log 2.$

Ex. 4. (a) $\int_0^{\infty} \frac{\log (1 + x^2)}{1 + x^2} \, dx = \pi \log 2.$

Put $x = \tan \theta \;\; \therefore \;\; dx = \sec^2 \theta \, d\theta.$

The limits are adjusted as 0 to $\pi/2$

$\therefore \quad I = \int_0^{\pi/2} \frac{\log \sec^2 \theta}{\sec^2 \theta} \sec^2 \theta \, d\theta = \int_0^{\pi/2} \log \sec^2 \theta \, d\theta$

or $\quad I = 2\int_0^{\pi/2} \log \sec \theta \, d\theta = -2\int_0^{\pi/2} \log \cos \theta \, d\theta$

$= -2 . \frac{\pi}{2} \log \frac{1}{2}$, by **Ex. 1. P. 1542.**

$= -\pi \log \frac{1}{2} = \pi \log 2.$

(b) $\int_0^{\pi} \log (1 + \cos x) \, dx = \pi \log \frac{1}{2}$

$I = \int_0^{\pi} \log [1 + \cos (\pi - x)] \, dx$, by Prop. IV.

or $\quad I = \int_0^{\pi} \log (1 - \cos x) \, dx$

$\therefore \quad 2I = \int_0^{\pi} [\log (1 + \cos x) + \log (1 - \cos x)] \, dx$

$= \int_0^{\pi} \log (1 - \cos^2 x) \, dx = \int_0^{\pi} \log \sin^2 x \, dx$

$= 2\int_0^{\pi} \log \sin x \, dx$

$= 2 . 2\int_0^{\pi/2} \log \sin x \, dx$ (by Prop. VI)

$= 4 . \frac{\pi}{2} . \log \frac{1}{2}.$

$\therefore \quad 2I = 2\pi \log \frac{1}{2}$ or $I = \pi \log \frac{1}{2}.$

Ex. 5. (a) $\int_0^{a} \frac{dx}{x + \sqrt{(a^2 - x^2)}}$

or $\quad \int_0^{\pi/2} \frac{1}{1 + \tan \theta} \, d\theta.$

Put $x = a \sin \theta \;\; \therefore \;\; dx = a \cos \theta \, d\theta.$

When $x = a$, $\sin \theta = 1 \;\; \therefore \;\; \theta = \pi/2.$

When $x = 0$, $\sin \theta = 0 \;\; \therefore \;\; \theta = 0.$

$\therefore \quad I = \int_0^{\pi/2} \frac{a \cos \theta \, d\theta}{a \sin \theta + a \cos \theta} = \int_0^{\pi/2} \frac{\cos \theta \, d\theta}{\sin \theta + \cos \theta}$ ...(1)

Now as in **Ex. (1)** on **P. 1534** we apply Prop. IV.

$$\therefore \quad I=\int_0^{\pi/2}\frac{\cos(\pi/2-\theta)\,d\theta}{\sin(\pi/2-\theta)+\cos(\pi/2-\theta)}$$

$$=\int_0^{\pi/2}\frac{\sin\theta\,d\theta}{\cos\theta+\sin\theta}. \qquad ...(2)$$

Adding (1) and (2), we get

$$2I=\int_0^{\pi/2}\frac{\cos\theta+\sin\theta}{\cos\theta+\sin\theta}\,d\theta=\int_0^{\pi/2}1.d\theta$$

or $2I=[\theta]_0^{\pi/2}=\pi/2.$

$\therefore \quad I=\pi/4.$

The following integrals are each equal to $\pi/4$ and may be calculated as above

$$\int_0^{\pi/2}\frac{\sqrt{\sin x}}{\sqrt{(\sin x)}+\sqrt{(\cos x)}}dx,$$

$$\int_0^{\pi/2}\frac{1}{1+\tan x}dx,$$

$$\int_0^{\pi/2}\frac{1}{1+\cot x}dx,\ \int_0^{\pi/2}\frac{\tan x}{1+\tan x}dx.$$

$$\int_0^{\pi/2}\frac{\cot x}{1+\cot x}dx,\ \int_0^{\pi/2}\frac{1}{1+\sqrt{(\tan x)}}dx,$$

$$\int_0^{\pi/2}\frac{\sqrt{\cot x}}{\sqrt{(\cot x)}+\sqrt{(\tan x)}}dx.$$

Change to sin x and cos x. **(M.N.R. 1990)**

(b) The value of $\int_0^{\pi/2}\frac{dx}{1+\tan^3 x}$ is

(a) 0 (b) 1 (c) $\pi/2$ (d) $\pi/4$

(I.I.T. 1993)

Ans. (d). Proceed as in part (a).

Ex. 6. (a) $\int_0^{\infty}\frac{x\,dx}{(1+x)(1+x^2)}=\frac{\pi}{4}.$

Put $x=\tan\theta \quad \therefore \quad dx=\sec^2\theta\,d\theta.$

When $x=\infty,\ \tan\theta=\infty \quad \therefore \quad \theta=\pi/2.$

$$\therefore \quad I=\int_0^{\pi/2}\frac{\tan\theta\sec^2\theta\,d\theta}{(1+\tan\theta)(\sec^2\theta)}d\theta.$$

Now change to sin θ and cos θ.

$$\therefore \quad I=\int_0^{\pi/2}\frac{\sin\theta\,d\theta}{\cos\theta+\sin\theta}=\frac{\pi}{4}.$$

Now do as in **Prop. IV P. 819.**

(b) $I=\int_{\pi/6}^{\pi/3}\frac{1}{1+\sqrt{(\cot x)}}dx=\frac{\pi}{12}.$

$$I=\int_{\pi/6}^{\pi/3}\frac{\sqrt{\sin x}}{\sqrt{(\sin x)}+\sqrt{(\cos x)}}dx. \qquad ...(1)$$

(Use Prop. VII P. 1537)

Put $x=\pi/2-t \qquad \because a+b=\pi/6+\pi/3=\pi/2$

$$\therefore \quad I=\int_{\pi/3}^{\pi/6}\frac{\sqrt{\cos t}}{\sqrt{(\cos t)}+\sqrt{(\sin t)}}(-dt)$$

$$=\int_{\pi/6}^{\pi/3}\frac{\sqrt{\cos t}}{\sqrt{(\cos t)}+\sqrt{(\sin t)}}dt$$

or $I=\int_{\pi/6}^{\pi/3}\frac{\sqrt{\cos x\,dx}}{\sqrt{(\cos x)}+\sqrt{(\sin x)}}$, Prop I. ...(2)

Adding (1) and (2), we get

$$2I=\int_{\pi/6}^{\pi/3}1\,dx=[x]_{\pi/6}^{\pi/3}=\frac{\pi}{6} \quad \therefore \quad I=\frac{\pi}{12}.$$

(c) $\int_0^{\pi/2}\frac{a\sin x+b\cos x}{\sin x+\cos x}dx=(a+b)\frac{\pi}{4}$

Apply Prop. IV and add.

$$2I=\int_0^{\pi/2}\frac{(a+b)(\sin x+\cos x)}{\sin x+\cos x}dx=(a+b)\frac{\pi}{2}$$

Another form :

$$I=\int_0^{\pi/2}\frac{a\sec x+b\,\text{cosec}\,x}{\sec x+\text{cosec}\,x}dx=(a+b)\frac{\pi}{4}$$

***Ex. 7. (a)** $\int_0^1\frac{\log(1+x)}{1+x^2}dx=\frac{\pi}{8}.\log 2$

Put $x=\tan\theta. \quad \therefore \quad dx=\sec^2\theta\,d\theta.$

When $x=1,\ \tan\theta=1. \quad \therefore \quad \theta=\pi/4.$

$x=0,\ \tan\theta=0. \quad \therefore \quad \theta=0.$

$$\therefore \quad I=\int_0^{\pi/4}\frac{\log(1+\tan\theta)}{\sec^2\theta}\sec^2\theta\,d\theta.$$

or $I=\int_0^{\pi/4}\log(1+\tan\theta)\,d\theta.$ **(I.T.T. 1997)**

Apply Prop. IV *i.e.* $\int_0^a f(x)\,dx=\int_0^a f(a-x)\,dx.$

$$\therefore \quad I=\int_0^{\pi/4}\log[1+\tan(\pi/4-\theta)]\,d\theta$$

$$=\int_0^{\pi/4}\log\left(1+\frac{1-\tan\theta}{1+\tan\theta}\right)d\theta. \qquad \because \tan(\pi/4)=1$$

$$=\int_0^{\pi/4}\log\frac{2}{1+\tan\theta}d\theta$$

$$=\int_0^{\pi/4}\log 2\,d\theta-\int_0^{\pi/4}\log(1+\tan\theta)\,d\theta$$

or $I=[\theta\log 2]_0^{\pi/4}-I$

or $2I=\frac{\pi}{4}\log 2 \quad \therefore \quad I=\frac{\pi}{8}\log 2.$

(b)* $\int_0^{\pi/4}\log(1+\tan x)\,dx=(\pi/8).\log 2.$

We have already done this in last part.

Ex. 8. $I=\int_0^{\pi}\frac{x\tan x}{\sec x+\tan x}dx=\frac{\pi}{2}(\pi-2).$

$\sec(\pi-x)=-\sec x, \tan(\pi-x)=-\tan x$

$\therefore \quad I = \int_0^{\pi} \frac{(\pi - x)\tan(\pi - x)}{\sec(\pi - x) + \tan(\pi - x)} dx$

$= \int_0^{\pi} \frac{(\pi - x)\tan x}{\sec x + \tan x}$ (Prop. IV)

Adding , $2I = \pi \int_0^{\pi} \frac{\tan x \, dx}{\sec x + \tan x}$

$= \pi \int_0^{\pi} \frac{\tan x (\sec x - \tan x)}{1} dx$

$\therefore \quad I = \frac{\pi}{2} \int_0^{\pi} [\sec x \tan x - (\sec^2 x - 1)] \, dx$

$= \frac{\pi}{2} [x - \tan x + \sec x]_0^{\pi}$

$= \frac{\pi}{2} [(\pi - 0 - 1) - (0 - 0 + 1)] = \frac{\pi}{2}(\pi - 2).$

Another form :

$\int_0^{\pi} \frac{x \sin x}{1 + \sin x} dx = \frac{\pi}{2}(\pi - 2)$

Divide above and below by cos *x*.

Ex. 9. (a) $\int_0^{\pi} \frac{x \, dx}{1 + \cos^2 x} = \frac{\pi^2}{2\sqrt{(2)}}.$

First remove *x* and then divide above and below by $\cos^2 x$.

(b) $\int_0^{\pi} x \log \sin x = \frac{\pi^2}{2} \log \frac{1}{2}.$

Remove *x* first and apply Prop. VI to make the limits 0 to $\pi/2$ and it becomes **Ex. 1 P. 1542.**

Ex. 10. (a) $I = \int_0^{\pi} \frac{x \, dx}{a^2 \cos^2 x + b^2 \sin^2 x} = \frac{\pi^2}{2ab}$ ...(1)

In order to remove *x* apply Prop. IV.

$\therefore \quad I = \int_0^{\pi} \frac{(\pi - x) \, dx}{a^2 \cos^2 (\pi - x) + b^2 \sin^2 (\pi - x)}$

or $\quad I = \int_0^{\pi} \frac{(\pi - x) \, dx}{a^2 \cos^2 x + b^2 \sin^2 x}$ ...(2)

Adding (1) and (2), we get

$2I = \int_0^{\pi} \frac{(x + \pi - x) \, dx}{a^2 \cos^2 x + b^2 \sin^2 x}$

$= \pi \int_0^{\pi} \frac{dx}{a^2 \cos^2 x + b^2 \sin^2 x}$

$\therefore \quad I = \frac{\pi}{2} \int_0^{\pi} \frac{dx}{a^2 \cos^2 x + b^2 \sin^2 x}.$

$= 2 . \frac{\pi}{2} \int_0^{\pi/2} \frac{dx}{a^2 \cos^2 x + b^2 \sin^2 x}$ by Prop. VI

Divide above and below by $\cos^2 x$.

$\therefore \quad I = \pi \int_0^{\pi/2} \frac{\sec^2 x \, dx}{a^2 + b^2 \tan^2 x}$

Put $b \tan x = t \;\therefore\; b \sec^2 x \, dx = dt.$

$\therefore \quad I = \frac{\pi}{b} \int_0^{\infty} \frac{dt}{a^2 + t^2} = \frac{\pi}{b} . \frac{1}{a} \left[\tan^{-1} \frac{t}{a} \right]_0^{\infty}$

$= \frac{\pi}{ab} \left[\frac{\pi}{2} - 0 \right] = \frac{\pi^2}{2ab}$

(b)* $I = \int_0^{\pi/2} \frac{x \sin x \cos x}{\cos^4 x + \sin^4 x} dx$

We have $I = \int_0^{\pi/2} \frac{(\pi/2 - x) \cos x \sin x \, dx}{\sin^4 x + \cos^4 x}$

$2I = \frac{\pi}{2} \int_0^{\pi/2} \frac{\sin x \cos x}{\cos^4 x + \sin^4 x} dx$

$= \frac{\pi}{2} \int_0^{\pi/2} \frac{\tan x \sec^2 x \, dx}{1 + \tan^4 x} = \frac{\pi}{2} . \frac{1}{2} \int_0^{\infty} \frac{dt}{1 + t^2},$

putting $\tan^2 x = t$

$= \frac{\pi}{4} \left[\tan^{-1} t \right]_0^{\infty} = \frac{\pi}{4} \left[\frac{\pi}{2} - 0 \right] = \frac{\pi^2}{8}.$

$\therefore \quad I = \pi^2/16.$

(c) $\int_0^{\pi} \frac{dx}{1 + 2\sin^2 x} = \frac{\pi}{\sqrt{(3)}}$

$I = 2 \int_0^{\pi/2} \frac{dx}{1 + 2 \sin^2 x}$, by Prop. VI

$I = 2 \int_0^{\pi/2} \frac{\sec^2 x \, dx}{1 + \tan^2 x + 2 \tan^2 x}.$

Put $\tan x = t$.

$\therefore \quad I = 2 \int_0^{\infty} \frac{dt}{1 + 3t^2} = \frac{2}{\sqrt{(3)}} \left[\tan^{-1} t \sqrt{(3)} \right]_0^{\infty}$

$= \frac{2}{\sqrt{(3)}} \left(\frac{\pi}{2} - 0 \right) = \frac{\pi}{\sqrt{(3)}}$

***Ex. 11. (a)** Prove $\int_{-4}^{-5} e^{(x+5)^2} dx + 3 \int_{1/3}^{2/3} e^{9(x - 2/3)^2} dx = 0$

Put $x + 5 = t$ in I_1 and $3(x - 2/3) = y$ in I_2 and adjust the limits $I = \int_1^0 e^{t^2} dt + \int_{-1}^0 e^{y^2} dy.$

Now put $y = -z$ in 2nd etc.

$\therefore \quad I_2 = -I_1$ (Prop.I)

or $\quad I_1 + I_2 = 0$ or $I = 0$

(b) Prove that

$\int_a^b f(x) \, dx = (b - a) \int_0^1 f[(b - a) x + a] \, dx$

Put $x = (b - a) t + a$ and adjust the limits etc.

***Ex. 12. (a)** Prove that

$$\int_{1/e}^{\tan t} \frac{x\,dx}{1+x^2} + \int_{1/e}^{\cot t} \frac{dx}{x(1+x^2)} dx = 1$$

Let $I = I_1 + I_2$

Put $x = 1/z$ in I_2 and adjust the limits

$$I_2 = \int_e^{\tan t} -\frac{z\,dz}{1+z^2} = \int_{\tan t}^{e} \frac{x\,dx}{1+x^2}, \text{ Prop. I \& II}$$

$$\therefore \quad I = \int_{1/e}^{\tan t} (\ )\,dx + \int_{\tan t}^{e} (\ )\,dx = \int_{1/e}^{e} \frac{x\,dx}{1+x^2}$$

or $I = \frac{1}{2}\left[\log(1+x^2)\right]_{1/e}^{e}$

$$= \frac{1}{2}\left[\log(1+e^2) - \log\frac{(1+e^2)}{e^2}\right]$$

$$= \frac{1}{2}\log e^2 = \log e = 1.$$

(b) Prove that $\int_2^{\infty} \frac{x \log x}{(1+x^2)^2} dx = 0$

Let $I = \int_0^1 (\,)\,dx + \int_1^{\infty} (\,)\,dx = I_1 + I_2$

Put $x = \frac{1}{t}$ in I_2 and adjust the limits

$$\therefore \quad I_2 = \int_0^1 \frac{\frac{1}{t}\log\frac{1}{t}\left(-\frac{1}{t^2}\right)dt}{\left(1+\frac{1}{t^2}\right)^2}$$

$$I_2 = \int_0^1 \frac{-t\log t}{(1+t^2)^2}dt = -\int_0^1 \frac{x\log x}{(1+x^2)^2}dx = -I_1$$

$\therefore \quad I_1 + I_2 = 0$

Ex. 13. (a) $\int_0^{\pi/2} \frac{\cos x - \sin x}{1+\sin x \cos x} dx = 0$

Use Prop. IV. $I = -I$ or $2I = 0 \therefore I = 0.$

(b)* Evaluate $\int_0^{\pi/2} \frac{\sin 8x \log(\cot x)}{\cos 2x} dx$ **(Roorkee 1995)**

By application of Prop. IV,

$$I = \int_0^{\pi/2} \frac{\sin(4\pi - 8x)\log\tan x}{\cos(\pi - 2x)} dx$$

$$= \int_0^{\pi/2} \frac{-\sin 8x}{-\cos 2x}(-\log\cot x)\,dx$$

or $I = -I \quad \therefore \quad 2I = 0 \quad$ or $\quad I = 0$

(c) $\int_0^{2\pi} \log\left[\frac{a+b\sec x}{a-b\sec x}\right] dx$

$\sec(2\pi - x) = \sec x$ but $\sec(\pi - x) = -\sec x$

Hence by Prop. VI as $f(2a - x) = f(x)$

$$\therefore \quad I = 2\int_0^{\pi} \log\left[\frac{a+b\sec x}{a-b\sec x}\right] dx$$

$$= 2\int_0^{\pi} \log\left[\frac{a-b\sec x}{a+b\sec x}\right] dx \text{ by Prop. IV}$$

$$= -2\int_0^{\pi} \log\left[\frac{a+b\sec x}{a-b\sec x}\right] \quad \because \log x = -\log 1/x$$

$\therefore \quad I = -I$ or $2I = 0 \quad \therefore \quad I = 0$

Ex. 14. (a) Evaluate $\int_0^{\pi/2} \frac{\sin^2 x - \cos^2 x}{\sin^3 x + \cos^3 x} dx$

As above $I = -I \quad \therefore \quad 2I = 0$ or $I = 0.$

(b) Prove that $\int_0^1 \tan^{-1} \frac{2x-1}{1+x-x^2} dx = 0$

$$I = \int_0^1 \tan^{-1}\frac{x-(1-x)}{1+x(1-x)} dx$$

$$= \int_0^1 [\tan^{-1} x - \tan^{-1}(1-x)]\,dx$$

$$= \int_0^1 [\tan^{-1}(1-x) - \tan^{-1} x]\,dx = -I \text{ by Prop. IV}$$

$\therefore \quad I = -I \quad$ or $\quad 2I = 0$ or $I = 0.$

Ex. 15. (a) Prove that

$$\int_0^1 \cot^{-1}(1-x+x^2)\,dx = \frac{\pi}{2} - \log 2$$

$$\cot^{-1} y = \tan^{-1}\frac{1}{y}$$

$$\cot^{-1}(1-x+x^2) = \tan^{-1}\frac{x-(x-1)}{1+x(x-1)}$$

$$= \tan^{-1} x - \tan^{-1}(x-1)$$

$\therefore \quad I = \int_0^1 \tan^{-1} x\,dx - \int_0^1 \tan^{-1}(x-1)\,dx$

Apply Prop. IV on 2nd and it becomes

$+\int_0^1 \tan^{-1} x\,dx$

$\therefore \quad I = 2\int_0^1 \tan^{-1} x\,dx$

$$= 2\left[\{x\tan^{-1} x\}_0^1 - \int_0^1 x\cdot\frac{1}{1+x^2} dx\right]$$

$$I = 2\left[\frac{\pi}{4} - \left\{\frac{1}{2}\log(1+x^2)\right\}_0^1\right] = \frac{\pi}{2} - \log 2$$

(b)* $\int_{1/2}^{2} \frac{1}{x}\sin\left(x - \frac{1}{x}\right) dx$

Put $x = \frac{1}{t} \quad \therefore \quad dx = -\frac{1}{t^2}dt$

$$\therefore \quad I = \int_2^{1/2} t\sin\left(\frac{1}{t} - t\right)\left(-\frac{1}{t^2}\right) dt$$

$$= \int_{1/2}^{2} -\frac{1}{t}\sin\left(t - \frac{1}{t}\right) dt = -I$$

$2I = 0$ or $I = 0 \quad \because \quad \sin(-\theta) = -\sin\theta$

Ex. 16. (a) $\int_0^1 x(1-x)^4\, dx = \frac{1}{30}$

$I = \int_0^1 x(1-x)^4\, dx = \int_0^1 (1-x)\, x^4\, dx$

$= (x^4 - x^5)\, dx = \frac{1}{5} - \frac{1}{6} = \frac{1}{30}.$

(b)* $\int_0^{\pi/2} \frac{\cos x\, dx}{1+\cos x+\sin x} = \frac{\pi}{4} - \frac{1}{2}.\log 2$

By application of Prop. IV,

$2I = \int_0^{\pi/2} \frac{\sin x + \cos x}{1+\cos x+\sin x} dx$

$= \int_0^{\pi/2} \left[1 - \frac{1}{1+\cos x+\sin x}\right] dx$

$= [x]_0^{\pi/2} - \int_0^{\pi/2} \frac{1}{2\cos^2(x/2) + 2\sin(x/2)\cos(x/2)} dx.$

Divide above and below by $\cos^2(x/2)$.

$\therefore \quad 2I = \frac{\pi}{2} - \int_0^{\pi/2} \frac{1}{2} \frac{\sec^2(x/2)\, dx}{1+\tan(x/2)}.$

Put $1 + \tan(x/2) = t$

$\therefore \quad I = \frac{\pi}{4} - \frac{1}{2}\int_1^2 \frac{1}{t} dt = \frac{\pi}{4} - \frac{1}{2}.[\log t]_1^2 = \frac{\pi}{4} - \frac{1}{2}.\log 2$

Ex. 17. (a) The value of $\int_{-\pi/2}^{\pi/2} \frac{dx}{e^{\sin x}+1}$ is $\frac{\pi}{2}$.

$I = \int_{-\pi/2}^{0} \frac{dx}{e^{\sin x}+1} + \int_0^{\pi/2} \frac{dx}{e^{\sin x}+1}$

or $\quad I = I_1 + I_2$

Now putting $x = -y$ in I_1 we get

$I = -\int_{\pi/2}^{0} \frac{dy}{e^{-\sin y}+1} + \int_0^{\pi/2} \frac{dx}{1+e^{\sin x}}$

$I = \int_0^{\pi/2} \frac{e^{\sin x}\, dx}{e^{\sin x}+1} + \int_0^{\pi/2} \frac{dx}{e^{\sin x}+1}$

$= \int_0^{\pi/2} 1\, dx = [x]_0^{\pi/2}$

$I = [\pi/2 - 0] = \pi/2$

Alt. You may apply Prop. VII

$I = \int_{-\pi/2}^{\pi/2} \frac{dx}{e^{\sin(-x)}+1} \qquad \because a+b=0$

$= \int_{-\pi/2}^{\pi/2} \frac{e^{\sin x}}{e^{\sin x}+1} dx$

$\therefore \quad 2I = \int_{-\pi/2}^{\pi/2} 1\, dx = \pi \quad \therefore I = \frac{\pi}{2}$

(b) The value of $\int_{-\pi}^{\pi} \frac{\cos^2 x}{1+a^x} dx, a > 0,$ is

(a) π (b) $a\pi$
(c) $\frac{\pi}{2}$ (d) 2π

(I.I.T. Sc. 2001)

Ans. (c). Apply Prop. VII

$\int_a^b f(x)\, dx = \int_a^b f(a+b-x)\, dx$

$I = \int_{-\pi}^{\pi} \frac{\cos^2 x}{1+a^x} dx, a+b=0$

$I = \int_{-\pi}^{\pi} \frac{\cos^2(0-x)}{1+a^{-x}} dx = \int_{-\pi}^{\pi} \frac{a^x \cos^2 x}{1+a^x} dx$

Add $\quad 2I = \int_{-\pi}^{\pi} \frac{1+a^x}{1+a^x} \cos^2 x\, dx = 2\int_0^{\pi} \cos^2 x$

$\therefore \quad I = 2\int_0^{\pi/2} \cos^2 x\, dx = 2\cdot\frac{1}{2}\cdot\frac{\pi}{2} = \frac{\pi}{2}$

(c) $\int_{-\pi/2}^{\pi/2} \frac{\pi^{\sin x}}{1+\pi^{\sin x}} dx =$

(a) 0 (b) $\pi/4$
(c) $\pi/2$ (d) π

Ans. (c).

$a+b-x = 0-x$ and $\sin(-x) = -\sin x$

As usual adding, $2I = \int_{-\pi/2}^{\pi/2} 1\, dx = \pi \quad \therefore \quad I = \frac{\pi}{2}.$

(d) If $f(x)$ is an integrable function in $\left(\frac{\pi}{6}, \frac{\pi}{3}\right)$

and $I_1 = \int_{\pi/6}^{\pi/3} \sec^2 x\, f(2\sin 2x)\, dx$ and

$I_2 = \int_{\pi/6}^{\pi/3} \operatorname{cosec}^2 x\, f(2\sin 2x)\, dx$, then :

(a) $I_1 = 2I_2$ (b) $2I_1 = I_2$
(c) $I_1 = I_2$ (d) none

Ans. (c).

Apply $\int_a^b f(x)\, dx = \int_a^b f(a+b-x)\, dx$ on I_1 or I_2. They become I_2 or I_1.

(e) $\int_0^{\pi} \frac{dx}{1+2^{\tan x}} =$

(a) 0 (b) $\pi/4$
(c) $\pi/2$ (d) π

Ans. (c).

$I = \int_0^{\pi} \frac{dx}{1+2^{\tan(\pi-x)}} = \int_0^{\pi} \frac{dx}{1+2^{-\tan x}}$ **(Prop. IV)**

or $\quad I = \int_0^{\pi} \frac{2^{\tan x}}{1+2^{\tan x}} dx.$ Adding

$2I = \int_0^{\pi} \frac{1+2^{\tan x}}{1+2^{\tan x}} dx = \int_0^{\pi} 1\, dx = [x]_0^{\pi} = \pi$

$\therefore \quad I = \dfrac{\pi}{2}.$

(f) $\displaystyle\int_{-3\pi/2}^{-\pi/2} [(x+\pi)^3 + \cos^2(x+3\pi)]\,dx =$

(a) $\dfrac{\pi^4}{32} + \dfrac{\pi}{2}$ (b) $\dfrac{\pi}{2}$

(c) $\dfrac{\pi}{4} - 1$ (d) $\dfrac{\pi^4}{32}$ **(AIEEE 2006)**

Ans. (b).

Put $x + \pi = t$ and adjust the limits and write $\cos^2(t+2\pi) = \cos^2 t$

$$\therefore \quad I = \int_{-\pi/2}^{\pi/2} (t^3 + \cos^2 t)\,dt$$

$$= 0 + 2\int_0^{\pi/2} \cos^2 t\,dt = 2.\frac{1}{2}.\frac{\pi}{2} = \frac{\pi}{2}, \text{ by Prop. V}$$

(g) $\displaystyle\int_{-\sqrt{2}}^{\sqrt{2}} \frac{2x^7 + 3x^6 - 10x^5 - 7x^3 - 12x^2 + x + 1}{x^2+2}\,dx = \ldots$

Ans. $\dfrac{\pi}{2\sqrt{2}} - \dfrac{16\sqrt{2}}{5}$

$$I = 2\int_0^{\sqrt{2}} \frac{3x^6 - 12x^2 + 1}{x^2+2} \text{ by Prop. V}$$

Now devide and integrate.

(h) If $f(y) = e^y, g(y) = y, y > 0$ and $F(t) = \int_0^t f(t-y)\,g(y)\,dy$, then $F(t) =$

(a) $1 - e^{-t}(1+t)$ (b) $e^t - (1+t)$

(c) $t e^t$ (d) $t e^{-t}$ **(AIEEE 2003)**

Ans. (b).

$F(t) = \int_0^t e^{t-y}.\,y\,dy$ by def. of f and g

$= \int_0^t e^{t-(t-y)}(t-y)\,dy$ Prop. IV

$= \int_0^t e^y.(t-y)\,dy$. Integrate by parts

$= [e^y(t-y)]_0^t - \int e^y(-1)\,dy$

$= (0-t) + [e^y]_0^t = -t + (e^t - 1)$

$= e^t - (1+t) \Rightarrow$ (b)

Ex. 18. (a) $\int_0^{\pi/2} \sin 2x \log\tan x\,dx = 0$

Use Prop. IV, *i.e.* $\int_0^a f(x)\,dx = \int_0^a f(a-x)\,dx$

$\therefore \quad I = \int_0^{\pi/2} \sin 2(\pi/2 - x) \log\tan(\pi/2 - x)\,dx$

$= \int_0^{\pi/2} \sin 2x \log\cot x$

$= -\int_0^{\pi/2} \sin 2x \log\tan x\,dx$

$\therefore \quad I = -I$ or $2I = 0 \quad \therefore \quad I = 0.$

(b)* Prove that

$\int_0^{\pi/2} f(\sin 2x)\sin x\,dx = \int_0^{\pi/2} f(\sin 2x)\cos x\,dx.$

$= \sqrt{2}\int_0^{\pi/4} f(\cos 2x)\cos x\,dx$ **(I.I.T. 1990)**

The first part follows by Prop. IV as in part (a). Adding the two results

$2I = \int_0^{\pi/2} f(\sin 2x)(\sin x + \cos x)\,dx$

$= \sqrt{2}\int_0^{\pi/2} f(\sin 2x)\cos(x - \pi/4)\,dx$

Now put $x - \pi/4 = t \quad \therefore \quad dx = dt$

and $x = \pi/4 + t \quad \therefore \quad 2x = \pi/2 + 2t$

$\therefore \quad \sin 2x = \cos 2t$

and the limits become $-\pi/4$ to $\pi/4$

$\therefore \quad 2I = \sqrt{2}\int_{-\pi/4}^{\pi/4} f(\cos 2t)\cos t\,dt$

$= 2\sqrt{2}\int_0^{\pi/4} f(\cos 2x)\cos x\,dx$ (by Prop. V)

$\therefore \quad I = \sqrt{2}\int_0^{\pi/4} f(\cos 2x)\cos x\,dx.$

(c) If $f(x)$ is an even function, then prove that

$\int_0^{\pi/2} f(\cos 2x)\cos x\,dx$

$= \sqrt{2}\int_0^{\pi/4} f(\sin 2x)\cos x\,dx$ **(I.I.T. 2003)**

It follows from part (b) by using the fact that $f(-x) = f(x)$ as $f(x)$ is an even function.

(d) If $f(x) = \dfrac{e^x}{1+e^x}, I_1 = \displaystyle\int_{f(-a)}^{f(a)} xg\{x(1-x)\}\,dx$

and $I_2 = \displaystyle\int_{f(-a)}^{f(a)} g\{x(1-x)\}\,dx,$

then the value of $\dfrac{I_2}{I_1}$ is :

(a) 2 (b) −3

(c) −1 (d) 1 **(AIEEE 2004)**

Ans. (a).

$$f(a) = \frac{e^a}{1+e^a},$$

$$f(-a) = \frac{e^{-a}}{1+e^{-a}} = \frac{1}{1+e^a} \quad \ldots(A)$$

$$I_1 = \int_{f(-a)}^{f(a)} xg\{x(1-x)\}\,dx \quad \ldots(1)$$

Put $x = 1 - t \quad \therefore \quad dx = -dt$ and adjust the limits

$$\therefore \quad I_1 = \int_{1-f(-a)}^{1-f(a)} (1-t)\,g\{t(1-t)\}(-dt)$$

$$I_1 = -\int_{e^a/(1+e^a)}^{1/(1+e^a)} \{g\{t(1-t) - tg\{t(1-t)\}\,dt, \quad \text{by (A)}$$

$$= -\left[\int_{f(a)}^{f(-a)} \{g\{(x(1-x) - xg\{x(1-x)\}\,dx\right], \text{ by Prop. I}$$

$$= \int_{f(-a)}^{f(a)} \{g\,x(1-x) - xg\{x(1-x)\}\,dx, \quad \text{by Prop. II}$$

$= I_2 - I_1$

$\therefore \quad 2I_1 = I_2 \qquad \therefore \quad \dfrac{I_2}{I_1} = 2 \Rightarrow$ (a)

Ex. 19. (a) $\int_{-1}^{1} \frac{x \sin^{-1} x}{\sqrt{(1-x^2)}} dx = 2.$

Here $f(-x) = \frac{(-x)\sin^{-1}(-x)}{\sqrt{[1-(-x)^2]}} = \frac{x \sin^{-1} x}{\sqrt{(1-x^2)}} = f(x).$

Therefore by Prop. V,

$$I = 2\int_0^1 \frac{x \sin^{-1} x}{\sqrt{(1-x^2)}} dx. \text{ Put } x = \sin\theta.$$

$$\therefore \quad I = 2\int_0^{\pi/2} \theta \frac{\sin\theta\cos\theta \, d\theta}{\cos\theta} = 2\int_0^{\pi/2} \theta \sin\theta \, d\theta$$

Integrate by parts

$$I = 2\{\theta(-\cos\theta) + \textstyle\int_0^1 \cos\theta \, . \, 1 \, d\theta\}$$

$$= 2\{-\theta\cos\theta + \sin\theta\}_0^{\pi/2} = 2[(0+1)-(0)] = 2.$$

Note : $\int_{-1}^{1} \frac{x^2 \sin^{-1} x}{\sqrt{(1-x^2)}} dx = 0.$

Here $f(-x) = -f(x)$ and hence by Prop. V, $I = 0$.

(b) The integral $\int_{-1/2}^{1/2} \left([x] + \ln\left(\frac{1+x}{1-x}\right)\right) dx$ equals :

(a) $-\frac{1}{2}$ (b) 0 (c) 1 (d) $2\ln\left(\frac{1}{2}\right)$

(I.I.T. Sc. 2002)

Ans. (a). $\log\left(\frac{1+x}{1-x}\right)$ is an odd function of x as

$f(-x) = -f(x)$. **See next Q. 20 (a).**

$$\therefore \quad I = \textstyle\int_{-1/2}^{1/2} [x] \, dx + 0$$

$$= \textstyle\int_{-1/2}^{0} [x] \, dx + \int_0^{1/2} [x] \, dx$$

$$= \textstyle\int_{-1/2}^{0} -1 \, dx + 0$$

$$= -[x]_{-1/2}^{0} = -\left(0 + \frac{1}{2}\right) = -\frac{1}{2}$$

(c) $\int_{-a}^{a} \cos x \, . \, f(x^2) \, dx = 2\int_0^a \cos x \, f(x^2) \, dx$

Here $f(-x) = f(x)$ and hence by Prop. V, we get the result.

(d) Prove that $\int_{-\pi/4}^{\pi/4} \frac{x + (\pi/4)}{2 - \cos 2x} dx = \frac{\pi^2}{6\sqrt{3}}$

$$I = I_1 + I_2 = 0 + 2\frac{\pi}{4}\int_0^{\pi/4} \frac{1}{2-\cos 2x} dx \quad \text{by Prop. V}$$

$$\therefore \quad I = \frac{\pi}{2}\int_0^{\pi/4} \frac{\sec^2 x}{2(1+\tan^2 x) - (1-\tan^2 x)} dx$$

$$= \frac{\pi}{2}\int_0^1 \frac{dt}{1+3t^2} \text{ where } t = \tan x$$

$$= \frac{\pi}{2} \cdot \frac{1}{\sqrt{3}} [\tan^{-1} t\sqrt{3}]_0^1 = \frac{\pi}{2\sqrt{3}} \cdot \frac{\pi}{3} = \frac{\pi^2}{6\sqrt{3}}$$

(e) Evaluate $\int_{-\pi/3}^{\pi/3} \frac{\pi + 4x^3}{2 - \cos\left(|x| + \frac{\pi}{3}\right)} dx.$

(I.I.T. 2004)

$I = I_1 + I_2 = I_1$ as $I_2 = 0$ by Prop. V

and $I_1 = 2\int_0^{\pi/3} \frac{\pi \, dx}{2 - \cos\left(|x| + \frac{\pi}{3}\right)}$

$$= 2\pi\int_0^{\pi/3} \frac{dx}{2 - \cos\left(x + \frac{\pi}{3}\right)}$$

because $|x| = x$ as x is + ive in the range 0 to $\pi/3$.

Now put $x + \frac{\pi}{3} = t$ and adjust the limits.

$$\therefore \quad I = I_1 = 2\pi\int_{\pi/3}^{2\pi/3} \frac{dt}{2 - \cos t}$$

$$= 2\pi\int_{\pi/3}^{2\pi/3} \frac{\sec^2(t/2) \, dt}{2\left(1 + \tan^2 \frac{t}{2}\right) - \left(1 - \tan^2 \frac{t}{2}\right)}$$

Now put $\tan(t/2) = z$

$\therefore \quad \frac{1}{2}\sec^2 \frac{t}{2} dt = dz$ and adjust the limits.

$$\therefore \quad I = 4\pi\int_{1/\sqrt{3}}^{\sqrt{3}} \frac{dx}{1+3z^2} = \frac{4\pi}{3}\int_{1/\sqrt{3}}^{\sqrt{3}} \frac{dz}{z^2 + \left(\frac{1}{\sqrt{3}}\right)^2}$$

$$= \frac{4\pi}{3} . \sqrt{3}\left[\tan^{-1} z\sqrt{3}\right]_{1/3}^{\sqrt{3}}$$

$$= \frac{4\pi}{\sqrt{3}}\left[\tan^{-1} 3 - \tan^{-1} 1\right]$$

$$= \frac{4\pi}{\sqrt{3}} \tan^{-1} \frac{3-1}{1+3\cdot 1} = \frac{4\pi}{\sqrt{3}} \tan^{-1} \frac{1}{2}.$$

Ex. 20. (a) Evaluate $\int_{-1}^{1} \log \frac{2-x}{2+x} dx.$

Let $f(x) = \log_e \frac{2-x}{2+x}$. Then

$$f(-x) = \log \frac{2+x}{2-x} = \log\left(\frac{2-x}{2+x}\right)^{-1}$$

$$= -\log \frac{2-x}{2+x} = -f(x)$$

Hence $\int_{-1}^{1} \log_e \left(\frac{2-x}{2+x}\right) dx = 0$ by Prop. V.

(b) Evaluate :

$$\textstyle\int_{-1}^{1} [\sqrt{1+x+x^2} - \sqrt{1-x+x^2}] \, dx$$

Ans. 0 by Prop. V as $f(-x) = -f(x)$

Ex. 21. (a) $\int_{-a}^{a} x\sqrt{a^2 - x^2} \, dx = 0$

Here $f(-x) = -f(x)$ and hence by Prop. V, $I = 0$.

(b) $\int_{-1/2}^{1/2} \cos x \log\left(\frac{1+x}{1-x}\right) dx = 0$

$\because \quad f(-x) = \cos(-x) \log\left(\frac{1-x}{1+x}\right)$

$= -\cos x \log\left(\frac{1+x}{1-x}\right) = -f(x)$

***Ex. 22. (a)** Suppose $f : \mathbf{R} \to \mathbf{R}$ and $g : \mathbf{R} \to \mathbf{R}$ are continuous functions. Then the value of integral $\int_{-\pi/2}^{\pi/2} [f(x) + f(-x)][g(x) - g(-x)]\, dx$.

(a) π (b) 1 (c) -1 (d) 0

(I.I.T. 1990)

If the given function be $F(x)$, then clearly $F(-x) = -F(x)$ and hence by Prop. V, $I = 0$. $\therefore$ (d) is correct answer.

(b) $\int_{-\pi}^{\pi} \sin mx \sin nx\, dx = 0$

$I = 2\int_0^{\pi} \sin mx \sin nx\, dx = 0$, by Prop. V

and **Q. 40 (a) P. 1513-18.**

Ex. 23. (a) If $f(x) = \begin{cases} e^{\cos x} \sin x & \text{for } |x| \le 2 \\ 2 & \text{otherwise,} \end{cases}$ then

$\int_{-2}^{3} f(x)\, dx =$

(a) 0 (b) 1 (c) 2 (d) 3

(I.I.T. Sc. 2000)

Ans. (c). $|x| \le 2 \Rightarrow -2 \le x \le 2$

and $f(x) = e^{\cos x} \sin x$ is an odd function.

$I = \int_{-2}^{3} f(x)\, dx = \int_{-2}^{2} f(x)\, dx + \int_2^3 f(x)\, dx$

Since $f(x)$ is an odd function in $(-2, 2)$ so that by Prop. V, Ist integral is zero and $f(x) = 2$ in $(2, 3)$

$\therefore \quad I = 0 + \int_2^3 2\, dx = [2x]_2^3 = 2.$

(b) If f is an odd function, then

$$I = \int_{-a}^{a} \frac{f(\sin\theta)}{f(\cos\theta) + f(\sin^2\theta)} = 0. \text{ T or F ?}$$

Ans. True.

Here denominator is an even function but numerator is an odd function as

$f[\sin(-\theta)] = f(-\sin\theta) = -f(\sin\theta)$ as f is odd.

Hence by Prop. V, $\quad I = 0$

Ex. 24. (a) Prove that $\int_0^{\infty} \frac{dx}{1+x^4} = \int_0^{\infty} \frac{x^2\, dx}{1+x^4} = \frac{\pi}{2\sqrt{2}}$

Put $x = 1/z$ in any one of the integrals, say first

Then $I = \int_0^{\infty} \frac{dx}{1+x^4} = -\int_{\infty}^{0} \frac{z^2\, dz}{1+z^4}$

$= \int_0^{\infty} \frac{z^2\, dz}{1+z^4} = \int_0^{\infty} \frac{x^2\, dx}{1+x^4}$

Hence $2I = \int_0^{\infty} \frac{dx}{1+x^4} + \int_0^{\infty} \frac{x^2\, dx}{1+x^4} = \int_0^{\infty} \frac{1+x^2}{1+x^4}\, dx$

$= \int_0^{\infty} \frac{1+1/x^2}{x^2+1/x^2}\, dx$

Now put $x - \frac{1}{x} = t$ etc. **(See Ex. 23 (a) P. 1499)**

(b)* Prove that $\int_1^{\infty} \frac{(x^2-2)\, dx}{x^3\sqrt{(x^2-1)}} = 0$

Hint : Put $x^2 - 1 = t^2$ so that $x\,dx = t\,dt$

$\therefore \quad \int_0^{\infty} \frac{(t^2-1)\,t}{(t^2+1)^2 . t}\, dt$

$= \int_0^1 \frac{t^2-1}{(t^2+1)^2}\, dt + \int_1^{\infty} \frac{(t^2-1)}{(t^2+1)^2}\, dt$

$= I_1 + I_2$

Now in the second integral I_2 put $t = \frac{1}{z}$,

$dt = -\frac{1}{z^2}\, dz$

Then $I_2 = \int_1^0 \frac{(1/z^2-1)(-1/z^2)\, dz}{(1/z^2+1)^2}$

$= -\int_0^1 \frac{(z^2-1)\, dz}{(z^2+1)^2} = -I_1$

$\therefore \quad I_1 + I_2 = 0$. Hence $I = 0$.

***Ex. 25. (a)** Evaluate

$\int_0^{\sin^2 t} \sin^{-1}\sqrt{x}\, dx + \int_0^{\cos^2 t} \cos^{-1}\sqrt{x}\, dx$

$I = I_1 + I_2$

Put $\sqrt{x} = \sin\theta$

$\therefore \quad x = \sin^2\theta$ and $dx = \sin 2\theta\, d\theta$

$I_1 = \int_0^t \theta \sin 2\theta\, d\theta$

For I_2 put $\sqrt{x} = \cos\phi$

$I_2 = \int_{\pi/2}^{t} -\phi \sin 2\phi\, d\phi = \int_t^{\pi/2} \theta \sin 2\theta\, d\theta,$ Prop. I

$\therefore \quad I = \int_0^t (\,)\, d\theta + \int_t^{\pi/2} (\,)\, d\theta = \int_0^{\pi/2} \theta \sin 2\theta\, d\theta$

$= \left[\theta\left(-\frac{\cos 2\theta}{2}\right) - (1)\left(-\frac{\sin 2\theta}{4}\right)\right]_0^{\pi/2} = \frac{\pi}{2}\cdot\frac{1}{2} + 0 = \frac{\pi}{4}.$

(b) $\int_{-2}^{2} \frac{3x^5 + 4x^3 + 2x^2 + x + 20}{x^2+4}\, dx = 3\pi + 8$

$I = 0 + 2\int_0^2 \frac{2x^2+20}{x^2+4}\, dx$, by Prop. V

$= 2.2 \int_0^2 \frac{x^2+4+6}{x^2+4}\, dx$

$= 4\left[x + 6\cdot\frac{1}{2}\tan^{-1}\frac{x}{2}\right]_0^2 = 4\left[2 + 3\cdot\frac{\pi}{4}\right] = 8 + 3\pi$

(c) Prove that

$$\int_{-\sqrt{2}}^{\sqrt{2}} \frac{2x^7+3x^6-10x^5-7x^3-12x^2+x+1}{x^2+2}\,dx$$

$$=\frac{\pi}{2\sqrt{2}}-\frac{16\sqrt{2}}{5}$$

$$I=2\int_0^{\sqrt{2}} \frac{3x^6-12x^2+1}{x^2+2}\,dx \qquad \text{by Prop. V}$$

$$=2\int_0^{\sqrt{2}} \left[3x^2(x^2-2)+\frac{1}{x^2+2}\right] dx \text{ etc.}$$

***Ex. 26.** Evaluate :

(a) $\int_0^{\infty} f(x^n+x^{-n})\frac{\log x}{x}\,dx$

(b) $\int_0^{\infty} f(x^n+x^{-n})\frac{\log x}{1+x^2}\,dx$

Put $\log x=t$ and adjust the limits. Also $x=e^t$ and $dx=e^t\,dt$

(a) $I=\int_{-\infty}^{\infty} f(e^{nt}+e^{-nt})\,t=0$

as $F(t)$ is an odd function of t.

(b) $I=\int_{-\infty}^{\infty} f(e^{nt}+e^{-nt})\,t\,.\frac{e^t}{1+e^{2t}}\,dt$

$$=\int_{-\infty}^{\infty} \frac{f(e^{nt}+e^{-nt})}{(e^{-t}+e^t)}.t\,dt=0$$

As above $F(t)$ is an odd function of t.

(c) Show that the function

$F(x)=\int_a^x \log(t+\sqrt{1+t^2})\,dt$ is an even function.

$f(t)=\log\{t+\sqrt{1+t^2}\},\quad f(-t)=\log\{\sqrt{1+t^2}-t\}$

$f(t)+f(-t)=\log[1+t^2-t^2]=\log 1=0$

$\therefore\quad f(-t)=-f(t)$

Thus $f(t)$ is an odd function of x.

Now $F(x)=\int_a^x f(t)\,dt$

$F(-x)=\int_a^{-x} f(t)\,dt=\int_a^{-a} f(t)\,dt+\int_{-a}^{-x} f(t)\,dt$

The first integral is zero. Put $t=-z$ in 2nd.

$F(-x)=0+\int_a^z f(-z)(-dz)=-\int_a^z -f(z)\,dz$

$=\int_a^x f(x)\,dx$, as $f(z)$ is odd

$\therefore\quad F(-x)=F(x)$

Hence $F(x)$ is an even function.

Ex. 27. (a) The function $F(x)=\int_0^x \log\frac{(1-x)}{(1+x)}\,dx$ is a function which is

(a) even (b) odd

(c) periodic (d) none of these

Ans. (a).

$f(x)$ is an odd function as

$$f(-x)=\log\frac{1+x}{1-x}=-\log\frac{1-x}{1+x}=-f(x)$$

Hence by **Q. 26 (c)**, $F(x)$ is an even function.

(b) $\int_{-1}^{1} \frac{\sin x-x^2}{3-|x|}=2\int_0^1 \frac{-x^2}{3-|x|}\,dx$

$I=I_1+I_2$ where I_1 is an odd function of x and I_2 is an even function of x

$\therefore\quad I=2I_2$ by Prop. V

(c)* The value of $\int_{-2}^{2}(ax^3+bx+c)\,dx$ depends on

(i) the value of b (ii) the value of c

(iii) the value of a (iv) the values of a and b

Ans. (ii).

Note that the integral of x^3 and x is 0 for limits -2 to 2 so that the value of the integral is $4c$ which depends upon c.

Ex. 28. (a) $\int_0^{na} f(x)\,dx=n\int_0^a f(x)\,dx$,

if $f(x)=f(a+x)$

and hence deduce that

$\int_a^{na} f(x)=(n-1)\int_0^a f(x)\,dx$

when $f(x)=f(a+x)$.

$\int_0^{na} f(x)\,dx=\int_0^a f(x)\,dx+\int_a^{2a} f(x)\,dx+.....$

$+...+\int_{(n-1)a}^{na} f(x)\,dx.$

$\int_a^{2a} f(x)\,dx$. Put $x=a+t$ and adjust the limits

$I=\int_0^a f(a+t)\,dt$

$=\int_0^a f(a+x)\,dx=\int_0^a f(x)\,dx \qquad ...(1)$

Similarly in $I=\int_{2a}^{3a} f(x)\,dx$. Put $x=a+t$.

$I=\int_a^{2a} f(a+t)\,dt=\int_a^{2a} f(a+x)\,dx$

$=\int_a^{2a} f(x)\,dx=\int_0^a f(x)\,dx$

as shown above in (1).

Similarly each integral can be shown to be equal to $\int_0^a f(x)\,dx$.

$\therefore\quad \int_0^{na} f(x)\,dx=n\int_0^a f(x)\,dx. \qquad ...(2)$

Deduction :

$\int_a^{na} f(x)\,dx=\int_a^0 f(x)\,dx+\int_0^{na} f(x)\,dx$

$=-\int_0^a f(x)\,dx+n\int_0^a f(x)\,dx$, by (2)

$=(n-1)\int_0^a f(x)\,dx.$

(b) If $f(x)=f(x+ma)$ for all integral values of m, then prove that $\int_0^{na} f(x)\,dx=n\int_0^a f(x)\,dx$.

Proceed as above.

(c) Let $T>0$ be a fixed real number. Suppose f is a continuous function such that for all $x\in R$, $f(x+T)=f(x)$. If $I=\int_0^T f(x)\,dx$, then the value of $\int_3^{3+3T} f(2x)\,dx$ is :

(a) $\frac{3}{2}I$ (b) $2I$ (c) $3I$ (d) $6I$

(I.I.T. Sc. 2002)

Ans. (c). Put $2x = z$

$$\therefore \int_3^{3+3T} f(2x)\,dx = \int_6^{6+6T} f(z)\frac{1}{2}dz$$

$$= \frac{1}{2}\left[\int_6^6 f(z)\,dz + \int_6^{6T} f(z)\,dz\right]$$

$$= 0 + \frac{1}{2}\cdot 6\int_0^T f(z)\,dz = 3I$$

$f(z)$ is periodic function of period T.

Note : See Q. 31 P. 1552 alt. method.

Ex. 29. (a) If f and g are continuous functions on $[0, a]$ satisfying

$f(x) = f(a-x)$ and $g(x) + g(a-x) = 2$,

then show that

$\int_0^a f(x)\,g(x)\,dx = \int_0^a f(x)\,dx.$

Sol. By Property IV, we have

$\int_0^a f(x)\,g(x)\,dx = \int_0^a f(a-x)\,g(a-x)\,dx$

$= \int_0^a f(x)\,[2 - g(x)]\,dx,$

using given relations

$\therefore \quad 2\int_0^a f(x)\,g(x)\,dx = 2\int_0^a f(x)\,dx,$

or $\int_0^a f(x)\,g(x)\,dx = \int_0^a f(x)\,dx$

(b) Show that $\int_0^{n\pi+v} |\sin x|\,dx = 2n + 1 - \cos v$

where n is a +ive integer and $0 \le v < \pi$ **(I.I.T. 1994)**

Sol. $I = \int_0^{n\pi} |\sin x|\,dx + \int_{n\pi}^{n\pi+v} |\sin x|\,dx$ ...(1)

$|\sin x|$ is a periodic function of period π as

$|\sin(\pi + x)| = |-\sin x| = |\sin x|$

$\therefore \quad I = n\int_0^{\pi} |\sin x|\,dx + I_v$

$= n\int_0^{\pi} \sin x\,dx + I_v = n[-\cos x]_0^{\pi} + I_v = 2n + I_v$ ...(2)

Again $I_v = \int_{n\pi}^{n\pi+v} |\sin x|\,dx.$

Put $x = n\pi + \theta$ and adjust the limits as above

$\therefore \quad I_v = \int_0^v \sin\theta\,d\theta = 1 - \cos v$ ...(3)

Hence from (1) by (2) and (3), we have

$I = 2n + (1 - \cos v) = 2n + 1 - \cos v.$

Ex. 30. (a) Show that if $f(t)$ is an odd function, then $\int_a^x f(t)\,dt$ is an even function, *i.e.*

$\int_a^x f(t)\,dt = \int_a^{-x} f(t)\,dt.$

(b) Can $\int_a^x f(t)\,dt$ be an odd function if $f(t)$ is an even function ?

Sol. (a) Let $F(x) = \int_a^x f(t)\,dt$

$F(-x) = \int_a^{-x} f(t)\,dt$

Put $t = -u$ and adjust the limits

We are doing so in order to make use of the fact that $f(x)$ is an odd function of x.

$= \int_{-a}^{x} f(-u)(-du)$ where $t = -u$

$= \int_{-a}^{x} f(u)\,du \quad [\because f(-u) = -f(u)]$

$= \int_{-a}^{a} f(u)\,du + \int_a^x f(u)\,du$

$= 0 + \int_a^x f(x)\,dx, \quad \because f(-u) = -f(u)$

$= F(x).$

Hence $\int_a^x f(t)\,dt$ is an even function if $f(t)$ is an odd function.

(b) Ans. No if $a \ne 0$, yes if $a = 0$.

Ex. 31. Given a function $f(x)$ such that

(i) it is integrable over every interval on the real line

(ii) $f(t + x) = f(x)$ for every x and real t.

Then show that the integral $\int_a^{a+t} f(x)\,dx$ is independent of a.

Sol. Let $\int f(x)\,dx = F(x) + c.$

Then $F'(x) = f(x)$

Now $I = \int_a^{a+t} f(x)\,dx = F(a+t) - F(a)$

$\therefore \quad \frac{dI}{da} = F'(a+t) - F'(a) = f(a+t) - f(a)$

$= f(a) - f(a)$ by condition (ii)

$= 0.$

This shows that I is independent of a.

Alternative :

$\int_a^{a+t} f(x)\,dx = \int_a^0 f(x)\,dx + \int_0^t f(x)\,dx + \int_t^{a+t} f(x)\,dx$

In the last integral, put $x = t + u$ so that $dx = du$

Then $\int_t^{a+t} f(x)\,dx = \int_0^a f(t+u)\,du$

$= \int_0^a f(u)\,du \quad \because f(t+u) = f(a)$

$= \int_0^a f(x)\,dx,$

Hence $\int_a^{a+t} f(x)\,dx = -\int_0^a f(x)\,dx + \int_0^t f(x)\,dx + \int_0^a f(x)\,dx = \int_0^t f(x)\,dx,$

which is independent of a.

Ex. 32. It is known that $f(x)$ is an odd function in the interval $\left[-\frac{1}{2}T, \frac{1}{2}T\right]$ and has a period equal to T. Prove that $\int_a^x f(t)\,dt$ is also a periodic function with the same period

Sol. We have to prove

$$\int_a^x f(t)\,dt = \int_a^{x+T} f(t)\,dt$$

or $\int_a^x f(t)\,dt - \int_a^{x+T} f(t)\,dt = 0$

or $-\int_x^a f(t)\,dt - \int_a^{x+T} f(t)\,dt = 0$

or $-\int_x^{x+T} f(t)\,dt = 0.$ ...(1)

To prove (1) we write

$\int_x^{x+T} f(t)\,dt = \int_x^a f(t)\,dt + \int_a^T f(t)\,dt + \int_T^{x+T} f(t)\,dt$ ...(2)

Putting $t = T + z$ in the last integral in (2), we have

$$\int_T^{x+T} f(t)\,dt = \int_0^x f(T+z)\,dz$$
$$= \int_0^x f(z)\,dz = \int_0^x f(t)\,dt$$

$\therefore$ From (2), we have

$$\int_x^{x+T} f(t)\,dt = \int_x^a f(t)\,dt + \int_a^T f(t)\,dt + \int_0^x f(t)\,dt$$
$$= \int_0^x f(t)\,dt + \int_x^a f(t)\,dt + \int_a^T f(t)\,dt$$
$$= \int_0^T f(t)\,dt. \quad ...(3)$$

Now (3) shows that $\int_x^{x+T} f(t)\,dt$ is independent of x.

Putting $x = -\frac{1}{2}T$ in (3), we get

$$\int_x^{x+T} f(t)\,dt = \int_{-T/2}^{T/2} f(t)\,dt = 0$$

since $f(t)$ is an odd function.

Hence (1) is proved.

Ex. 33. (a) Find the value of $\int_{-1}^{3/2} |x \sin \pi x|\,dx$.

(M.N.R. 1996)

We know that $\sin\theta$ is $+$ ive when $0 \le \theta < \pi$ and $\sin\theta$ is $-$ ive when $\pi \le \theta \le 3\pi/2$.

Hence we write

$$\int_{-1}^{3/2} |x\sin\pi x|\,dx = \int_{-1}^{0} x\sin\pi x\,dx + \int_0^1 x\sin\pi x\,dx + \int_1^{3/2} -x(\sin\pi x)\,dx$$
$$= \int_{-1}^{1} x\sin\pi x\,dx + \int_1^{3/2} (-x\sin\pi x)\,dx$$
$$= 2\int_0^1 x\sin\pi x\,dx - \int_1^{3/2} x\sin\pi x\,dx$$

by Prop. V, as $f(-x) = f(x)$

Integrate by parts

$$I = 2\left[-\frac{x}{\pi}\cos\pi x + \frac{1}{\pi^2}\sin\pi x\right]_0^1 - \left[-\frac{x}{\pi}\cos\pi x + \frac{1}{\pi^2}\sin\pi x\right]_1^{3/2}$$
$$= 2\left(-\frac{\cos\pi}{\pi}\right) - \left(0 + \frac{\cos\pi}{\pi} + \frac{1}{\pi^2}\sin\frac{3\pi}{2}\right)$$
$$= -\frac{3}{\pi}(-1) - \frac{1}{\pi^2}(-1) = \frac{3}{\pi} + \frac{1}{\pi^2}.$$

(b) Find the value of $\int_0^2 |(1-x)|\,dx$

$$I = \int_0^1 |1-x|\,dx + \int_1^2 |1-x|\,dx \quad ...(I)$$

when $0 \le x < 1$, $1-x$ is $+$ive so that $|1-x| = 1-x$

when $1 \le x < 2$, $1-x$ is $-$ ive so that $|1-x| = -(1-x) = (x-1)$

$$\therefore \quad I = \int_0^1 (1-x)\,dx + \int_1^2 (x-1)\,dx \quad \text{by (I)}$$
$$= \left[x - \frac{x^2}{2}\right]_0^1 + \left[\frac{x^2}{2} - x\right]_1^2$$
$$= \left(1 - \frac{1}{2}\right) + \frac{4-1}{2} - 1 = \frac{1}{2} + \frac{3}{2} - 1 = 1$$

***Ex. 34. (a)** The value of $\int_{-2}^{2} |1-x^2|\,dx$ is ....

Ans. 4.

$$\int_{-2}^{2} |1-x^2|\,dx = 2\int_0^2 |1-x^2|\,dx \quad \text{(Prop. V)}$$
$$= 2\left[\int_0^1 |1-x^2|\,dx + \int_1^2 |1-x^2|\,dx\right]$$
$$= 2\left[\int_0^1 (1-x^2)\,dx + \int_1^2 (x^2-1)\,dx\right]$$

by def. of modulus function

$$= 2\left[\left(x - \frac{1}{3}x^3\right)_0^1 + \left(\frac{1}{3}x^3 - x\right)_1^2\right]$$
$$= 2\left[\left(1 - \frac{1}{3}\right) - 0 + \frac{1}{3}.8 - 2 - \frac{1}{3}.1 + 1\right] = 4.$$

(b)* $\displaystyle\int_{-4}^{3} |x^2 - 4|\,dx = \frac{71}{3}$

We have to determine the sign of $x^2 - 4$ in the interval $-4 \le x \le 3$.

Now $\quad x^2 - 4 = (x+2)(x-2)$

$x < -2$, $+$ ive, $-2 < x < 2$, $-$ ive, $x > 2$, $+$ ive.

$$\therefore \quad I = \int_{-4}^{-2} + \text{ive}\,dx + \int_{-2}^{2} - \text{ive}\,dx + \int_2^3 + \text{ive}\,dx$$
$$= \int_{-4}^{-2} (x^2-4)\,dx + \int_{-2}^{2} -(x^2-4)\,dx + \int_2^3 (x^2-4)\,dx$$
$$= \left(\frac{x^3}{3} - 4x\right)_{-4}^{-2} - 2\left[\frac{x^3}{3} - 4x\right]_0^2 + \left[\frac{x^3}{3} - 4x\right]_2^3$$
$$= \left\{\frac{1}{3}(-8+64) - 8\right\} - 2\left\{\frac{8}{3} - 8\right\} + \left\{\frac{19}{3} - 4\right\}$$
$$= \frac{1}{3}(56 - 16 + 19) - 8 + 16 - 4$$
$$= \frac{59}{3} + 4 = \frac{71}{3}.$$

(c) Prove that $\displaystyle\int_{-2}^{3} |x^2 - x|\,dx = \frac{55}{6}$.

Here $x^2 - x = x(x-1)$

$x < 0$ $+$ive, $0 < x < 1$ $-$ ive, $x > 1$ $+$ ive

$$\therefore \quad I = \int_{-2}^{0} (x^2-x)\,dx + \int_0^1 -(x^2-x)\,dx + \int_1^3 (x^2-x)\,dx$$
$$= 55/6.$$

(d) $\int_{-2}^{3} |1-x^2|\,dx =$

(a) $\frac{28}{3}$ (b) $\frac{14}{3}$

(c) $\frac{7}{3}$ (d) $\frac{1}{3}$

(AIEEE 2004)

Ans. (a).

$$1 - x^2 \ge 0 \Rightarrow x^2 - 1 \le 0$$
$$\Rightarrow \quad (x+1)(x-1) \le 0 \quad \Rightarrow \quad -1 \le x \le 1 \quad ...(A)$$
$$\therefore \quad |1-x^2| = 1-x^2$$
$$(1-x^2) \le 0, \quad i.e., \quad x^2 - 1 \ge 0$$
$$\Rightarrow \quad (x+1)(x-1) \ge 0$$
$$\Rightarrow \quad x \le -1 \quad \text{or} \quad x \ge 1 \quad ...(B)$$

$\therefore \quad |1-x^2| = -(1-x^2) = x^2 - 1$

$\therefore \quad I = \int_{-2}^{-1} + \int_{-1}^{1} + \int_{1}^{3}$

$= \int_{-2}^{-1} (x^2-1)\,dx + \int_{-1}^{1} (1-x^2)\,dx + \int_{1}^{3} (x^2-1)\,dx$

$x \le -1 \qquad -1 \le x \le 1 \qquad x \ge 1$

by (A) and (B)

$$= \left[\frac{x^3}{3} - x\right]_{-2}^{-1} + \left[x - \frac{x^3}{3}\right]_{-1}^{1} + \left[\frac{x^3}{3} - x\right]_{1}^{3} = \frac{28}{3}$$

(e) $\int_0^{64} [\{x^{1/3}\} - \{\sqrt{x}\}]\,dx = ...$

Ans. $\frac{8}{3}$. Let $I = I_1 - I_2$

We know that $\{x\} = x - [x]$

$$\therefore \quad I_1 = \int_0^{64} [x^{1/3} - [x^{1/3}]]\,dx$$

$$= \frac{3}{4}(x^{4/3})_0^{64} - \int_0^{64} [x^{1/3}]\,dx$$

$$= 192 - \int_0^{64} [x^{1/3}]\,dx \qquad ...(A)$$

Now $x^{1/3} = 0$ at $x = 0$ and $= 4$ at $x = 64$

In between 0 and 4 there are five integers 0, 1, 2, 3, 4.

$\therefore \quad x^{1/3} = 0, 1, 2, 3, 4 \to x = 0, 1, 8, 27, 64$

$$\therefore \quad \int_0^{64} [x^{1/3}]\,dx = \int_0^{1} 0\,dx + \int_1^{8} 1\,dx$$

$$+ \int_8^{27} \int_8^{27} 2\,dx + \int_{27}^{64} 3\,dx + \int_{64}^{64} 4\,dx$$

$= 0 + 1.7 + 2.19 + 3.37 + 0$

$= 7 + 38 + 111 = 156$

$\therefore \quad I_1 = 192 - 156 = 36$ by (A) $\qquad$ ...(I)

$$I_2 = \int_0^{64} \{\sqrt{x}\} = \int_0^{64} [\sqrt{x} - [\sqrt{x}]]\,dx$$

$$= \frac{2}{3}(x^{3/2})_0^{64} - \int_0^{64} [x^{1/2}]\,dx$$

$$= \frac{1024}{3} - \int_0^{64} [x^{1/2}]\,dx \qquad ...(B)$$

Now $x^{1/2} = 0$ at $x = 0$ and $= 8$ at $x = 64$

In between 0 and 8 there are 9 digits 0, 1, 2, ..., 8

$\therefore \quad \sqrt{x} = 0, 1, 2, ..., 8 \Rightarrow x = 0, 1, 4, 9, 16, ..., 64$

$$\therefore \quad \int_0^{64} [\sqrt{x}]\,dx = \int_0^{1} 0\,dx + \int_0^{4} 1\,dx$$

$$+ \int_4^{9} 2\,dx + ... + \int_{49}^{64} 7\,dx + \int_{64}^{64} 8\,dx$$

$= 308$

$$I_2 = \frac{1024}{3} - 308 = \frac{100}{3} \text{ by (B)} \qquad ...(2)$$

$\therefore \quad I = I_1 - I_2 = 36 - \frac{100}{3} = \frac{8}{3}$ by (1) and (2)

(f) If [.] denotes the greatest integer function, then $\int_0^{\infty} [2e^{-x}]\,dx =$

(a) 0 $\qquad$ (b) e^2

(c) $2/e$ $\qquad$ (d) log 2

Ans. (d).

Put $e^{-x} = y \therefore -e^{-x}\,dx = dy$ or $dx = \frac{dy}{-y}$ and limits are adjusted as 1 to 0.

$$\therefore \quad I = \int_1^0 [2y]\frac{dy}{-y} = \int_0^1 \frac{1}{y}[2y]\,dy$$

As y varies from 0 to 1, $2y$ varies from 0 to 2

$\therefore \quad [2y] = 0$ or 1 $\qquad$ ...(A)

$$\therefore \quad I = \int_0^{1/2} \frac{1}{y}[2y]\,dy + \int_{1/2}^{1} \frac{1}{y}[2y]\,dy$$

$$= \int_0^{1/2} \frac{1}{y}.0\,dy + \int_{1/2}^{1} \frac{1}{y}.1\,dy \text{ by (A)}$$

$$= [\log y]_{1/2}^{1} = 0 - \log\frac{1}{2} = \log 2$$

Ex. 35. (a) If $f(x) = x^2$ for $0 \le x < 1$

$= \sqrt{x}$ for $1 \le x \le 2$

Evaluate $\int_0^2 f(x)\,dx.$

$$I = \int_0^1 x^2\,dx + \int_1^2 \sqrt{x}\,dx = \frac{1}{3}(4\sqrt{2} - 1)$$

(b) $\int_{-\pi/2}^{\pi/2} \sqrt{\cos x - \cos^3 x}\,dx = \frac{4}{3}.$

$I = 2\int_0^{\pi/2} \sqrt{(\cos x - \cos^3 x)}\,dx$, Prop. VI

$= 2\int_0^{\pi/2} \sqrt{(\cos x)}\,|\sin x|\,dx$

$= 2\int_0^{\pi/2} \sqrt{(\cos x)}\sin x\,dx,$

as $\sin x$ is +ive in $(0, \pi/2)$

$= -2 \cdot \frac{2}{3}[(\cos x)^{3/2}]_0^{\pi/2} = \frac{4}{3}.$

***Ex. 36. (a)** The integral $\int_0^{1.5} [x^2]\,dx$ where [ ] denotes the greatest integer functions, equals .....

Ans. $2 - \sqrt{2}$.

x varies from 0 to 3/2, so that x^2 varies from 0 to $9/4$ *i.e.* $2 \cdot 25$. There will be three integers 0, 1, 2 which will fall in this range. Hence we split 0 to 3/2 into 0 to 1, 1 to $\sqrt{2}$ and $\sqrt{2}$ to 3/2 during each of which $[x^2]$ will have values 0, 1, 2 respectively.

By the definition of the function, we have

$$\int_0^{1.5} [x^2]\,dx = \int_0^1 [x^2]\,dx + \int_1^{\sqrt{2}} [x^2]\,dx + \int_{\sqrt{2}}^{1.5} [x^2]\,dx$$

$= \int_0^1 0 \, .dx + \int_1^{\sqrt{2}} 1 \, .dx + \int_{\sqrt{2}}^{1.5} 2 \, .dx$

$= 0 + \sqrt{2} - 1 + 2(1 \cdot 5 - \sqrt{2})$

$= 2 - \sqrt{2}.$

(b) $\int_0^2 [x^2] \, dx = 5 - \sqrt{2} - \sqrt{3}$

x varies from 0 to 2 so that x^2 varies from 0 to 4. Hence split into 0 to 1, 1 to $\sqrt{2}$, $\sqrt{2}$ to $\sqrt{3}$, $\sqrt{3}$ to 2.

$\therefore$ x^2 varies from 0 to 1, 1 to 2, 2 to 3 and 3 to 4 in various intervals. Now put $[x^2] = 0, 1, 2$ and 3 in the various integrals.

(c) $\int_1^2 \{x^{[x^2]} + [x^2]^x\} \, dx$

$$= \left(\frac{5}{4} + \sqrt{3} + \frac{1}{3}\sqrt{2}\right) + \frac{2^{\sqrt{3}} - 2^{\sqrt{2}}}{\log 2} + \frac{3^2 - 3^{\sqrt{3}}}{\log 3}$$

As x varies from 1 to 2, x^2 varies from 1 to 4 and in between there will be four integers 1, 2, 3, 4. Hence the limits for x will be 1, $\sqrt{2}$, $\sqrt{3}$.

$$\therefore \quad I = \int_1^{\sqrt{2}} dx + \int_{\sqrt{2}}^{\sqrt{3}} dx + \int_{\sqrt{3}}^{2} dx$$

$[x^2] = 1 \quad 2 \quad 3$

$$\therefore \quad I = \int_1^{\sqrt{2}} (x+1) \, dx + \int_{\sqrt{2}}^{\sqrt{3}} (x^2 + 2^x) \, dx$$

$$+ \int_{\sqrt{3}}^{2} (x^3 + 3^x) \, dx \text{ etc.}$$

Ex. 37. (a) $\int_{-2}^{2} [|x| + |x-1|] \, dx$

Keeping in view the form of modulus and limits we divide the range of limits $(-2, 2)$ into different intervals and then find out the value of

$f(x) = |x| + |x-1|$

$-2 \le x \le 0, \qquad f(x) = -x - (x-1) = 1 - 2x$

$0 \le x \le 1, \qquad f(x) = x - (x-1) = 1$

$1 \le x \le 2, \qquad f(x) = x + x - 1 = 2x - 1$

$\therefore \quad I = \int_{-2}^{0} (1-2x) \, dx + \int_0^1 1 \, dx + \int_1^2 (2x-1) \, dx = 9$

(b) $\int_0^4 \{|x-1| + |x-3|\} \, dx = 10.$

Is it true or false ?

Ans. True.

$I = I_1 + I_2$

$I_1 = \int_0^1 -(x-1) \, dx + \int_1^4 (x-1) \, dx$

$$= -\frac{1}{2}\Big[(x-1)^2\Big]_0^1 + \frac{1}{2}\Big[(x-1)^2\Big]_1^4$$

$I_1 = \frac{1}{2} + \frac{1}{2} . 9 = 5$

$I_2 = \int_0^3 -(x-3) \, dx + \int_3^4 (x-3) \, dx$

$$= -\frac{1}{2}\Big[(x-3)^2\Big]_0^3 + \frac{1}{2}\Big[(x-3)^2\Big]_3^4$$

$I_2 = \frac{9}{2} + \frac{1}{2} = 5$

$\therefore \quad I = I_1 + I_2 = 5 + 5 = 10$

(c) $\int_3^6 [|x-3| + |x-4| + |x-5|] \, dx$

$$I = \int_3^6 \underset{+}{(x-3)} \, dx + \left\{\int_3^4 -\underset{-}{(x-4)} \, dx + \int_4^6 \underset{+}{(x-4)} \, dx\right\}$$

$$+ \left\{\int_3^5 -\underset{-}{(x-5)} \, dx + \int_5^6 \underset{+}{(x-6)} \, dx\right\} = 8$$

Ex. 38. (a) $\int_0^{n^2} [\sqrt{x}] \, dx$

x varies from 0 to n^2 $\therefore \sqrt{x}$ varies from 0 to n. Split into 0 to 1^2, 1^2 to 2^2, 2^2 to 3^2, ... $(n-1)^2$ to n^2 during which $[\sqrt{x}]$ will be 0, 1, 2, 3, ..., $n-1$ respectively.

$$\therefore \quad I = \int_0^{1^2} 0 \, dx + \int_{1^2}^{2^2} 1 \, dx + \int_{2^2}^{3^2} 2 \, dx$$

$$+ \int_{3^2}^{4^2} 3 \, dx + \ldots + \int_{(n-1)^2}^{n^2} (n-1) \, dx$$

$= (2^2 - 1^2) + 2(3^2 - 2^2) + 3(4^2 - 3^2)$

$+ \ldots (n-1)\{n^2 - (n-1)^2\}$

$= (2+1) + 2(3+2) + 3(4+3) + \ldots (n-1)(n+n-1)$

$= \{1^2 + 2^2 + 3^2 + \ldots + (n-1)^2\} + \sum_2^n (n-1) \, n$

$= \frac{1}{6} N(N+1)(2N+1) + \sum_1^n (n-1) \, n$

$$= \frac{1}{6}(n-1) \, n \, (2n-1) + \frac{(n-1) \, n \, (n+1)}{3}$$

(See § 4 illustration in A.G.S. Page 1175)

$= \frac{1}{6} n(n-1)[2n - 1 + 2n + 2]$

$= \frac{1}{6} n(n-1)(4n+1)$

$\because \quad \sum_2^n = \sum_1^n$ as the term corresponding to $n = 1$ is zero.

(b) Evaluate $\int_{1/e}^{e} |\log x| \, dx$

$\log x$ is + ive for $x > 1$.

$\log x$ is – ive for $x < 1$.

Hence we split the interval $(1/e, e)$ into $(1/e, 1)$ and $(1, e)$. During the first, $\log x$ is – ive and during the second, $\log x$ is +ive.

$\therefore \quad I = \int_{1/e}^{1} -\log x \, dx + \int_1^e \log x \, dx$

Now $\int \log x \, dx = x \log x - \int x . \frac{1}{x} dx$

$= x \log x - x$

$\therefore \quad I = -[x \log x - x]_{1/e}^{1} + [x \log x - x]_1^e$

$$= -\left[0 - \frac{1}{e}\log\frac{1}{e} - \left(1 - \frac{1}{e}\right)\right] + [e \log e - 0 - (e-1)]$$

$$= \left[-\frac{1}{e} + 1 - \frac{1}{e}\right] + 1 = 2 - \frac{2}{e} = 2(1 - e^{-1}).$$

(c) Show that $\int_{-20\pi}^{20\pi} |\cos x| \, dx = 80$

$\cos(\pi + x) = -\cos x$

$\therefore \quad |\cos(\pi + x)| = |-\cos x| = \cos x$

Thus $|\cos x|$ is a periodic function of period π.

$\therefore \quad I = 2 \times \int_0^{20\pi} |\cos x| \, dx = 2 \times 20 \int_0^{\pi} |\cos x| \, dx$

$$= 40\left[\int_0^{\pi/2} \cos x + \int_{\pi/2}^{\pi} -\cos x\right] = 40[1+1] = 80$$

(d) Prove that $\int_{10}^{100} (x-|x|)\,dx = 45$

Now $(x+1)-[x+1] = x-[x]$

Thus $x-[x]$ is a periodic function of period 1.

$\therefore \quad I = (100-10)\int_0^1 [x-[x]]\,dx = 90\left[\frac{x^2}{2}-0\right]_0^1 = 45$

Ex. 39. (a) The value of the integral $\int_{e^{-1}}^{e^2}\left|\frac{\log_e x}{x}\right| dx$ is

(a) $\frac{3}{2}$ (b) $\frac{5}{2}$ (c) 3 (d) 5

(I.I.T. Sc. 2000)

Ans. (b).

Put $\log_e x = z \quad \therefore \quad x = e^z$

$\therefore \quad dx = e^z\,dz$ and limits are adjusted as -1 to 2.

$\therefore \quad I = \int_{-1}^{2}\left|\frac{z}{e^z}\right| e^z\,dz = \int_{-1}^{2} |z|\,dz,$

e^z is always +ive.

$= \int_{-1}^{0} -z\,dz + \int_0^2 z\,dz$

$= \left[-\frac{z^2}{2}\right]_{-1}^{0} + \left[\frac{z^2}{2}\right]_0^2 = \frac{1}{2}+2 = \frac{5}{2}.$

(b) $\int_{1/2}^{2} |\log_{10} x|\,dx = \frac{1}{2}\log_{10}\left(\frac{8}{e}\right)$

$\int \log x\,dx = x\log x - x$ by parts

$\log x = -$ ive for $x<1$

$\log x = +$ ive for $x>1$

Also $\log_{10} x = \frac{\log x}{\log 10}$

$\therefore \quad I\log 10 = \int_{1/2}^{1} -\log x\,dx + \int_1^2 \log x\,dx$

$= [x\log x - x]_1^2 - [x\log x - x]_{1/2}^{1}$

$= (2\log 2 - 1) - \left(-\frac{1}{2}\log\frac{1}{2}-\frac{1}{2}\right)$

$= 2\log 2 - 1 - \frac{1}{2}\log 2 + \frac{1}{2}$

$= \frac{3}{2}\log 2 - \frac{1}{2} = \frac{1}{2}[3\log 2 - 1]$

$= \frac{1}{2}[\log 2^3 - \log_e e] = \frac{1}{2}\log\frac{8}{e}$

$\therefore \quad I = \frac{1}{2}\frac{\log(8/e)}{\log 10} = \frac{1}{2}\log_{10}\frac{8}{e}$

Ex. 40. (a) The value of $\int_{-1}^{3} (|x-2|+[x])\,dx$ is equal to 7.

([x] stands for greatest integer less than or equal to x).

$I_1 = \int_{-1}^{2} -(x-2)\,dx + \int_2^3 (x-2)\,dx = 5$

$I_2 = \left[\int_{-1}^{0} -1 + \int_0^1 0 + \int_1^2 1 + \int_2^3 2\right] dx = 2$

$\therefore \quad I = I_1 + I_2 = 5+2 = 7$

(a₁) Prove that $\int_0^9 \{\sqrt{x}\}\,dx = 5.$

We know that $\{x\} = x-[x]$

$\therefore \quad I = \int_0^9 [\sqrt{x} - [x]]\,dx$

$= \left[\frac{2}{3}x^{3/2}\right]_0^9 - \left[\int_0^1 [\sqrt{x}]\,dx + \int_1^4 \sqrt{x}\,dx + \int_4^9 \sqrt{x}\,dx\right]$

$= \frac{2}{3}(3^3) - \left[0 + \int_1^4 1\,dx + \int_4^9 2\,dx\right]$

$= 18 - (3+10) = 5$

(b) If $n \in N$, then prove that $\int_{-n}^{n} (-1)^{[x]}\,dx = 0$

If $x = 5\cdot 32$, then

$[x] = [5\cdot 32] = 5,\ [-x] = [-(5\cdot 32)] = -6$

$(-1)^5 = -1, \quad (-1)^{-6} = +1$

$(-1)^{[x]} = -(-1)^{[-x]}$

$\therefore \quad f(-x) = -f(x)$

i.e., function is odd and hence $I = 0$.

(c) $I = \int_0^{\pi} [\cot x]\,dx$, where [.] denotes the greatest integer function, is equal to

(a) $-\frac{\pi}{2}$ (b) $\frac{\pi}{2}$

(c) 1 (d) -1 **(AIEEE 2009)**

Sol. Ans. (a).

$I = \int_0^{\pi} [\cot x]\,dx$

$I = \int_0^{\pi} [\cot(\pi - x)]\,dx = \int_0^{\pi} [-\cot x]\,dx$

$2I = \int_0^{\pi} [\cot x] + [-\cot x]\,dx$

Now $\left[4\frac{1}{2}\right] = 4$ but $\left[-4\frac{1}{2}\right] = -5$

$\therefore \quad 2I = \int_0^{\pi} -1\,dx = (-x)_0^{\pi} = -\pi$

$\therefore \quad I = -\frac{\pi}{2}$

Ex. 41. (a) Show that the value of $\int_{\pi}^{2\pi} [2\sin x]\,dx$, where [ ] represents the greatest integer function, is $-\frac{5\pi}{3}$.

(I.I.T. 1995)

It is a question of greatest integer function. We subdivide the interval π to 2π as under keeping in view that we have to evaluate $[2\sin x]$

We know that $\sin\frac{\pi}{6} = \frac{1}{2}$,

$\sin\left(\pi + \frac{\pi}{6}\right) = \sin\frac{7\pi}{6} = -\frac{1}{2}$

$\sin\frac{11\pi}{6} = \sin\left(2\pi - \frac{\pi}{6}\right) = -\sin\frac{\pi}{6} = -\frac{1}{2}$

$\sin\frac{9\pi}{6} = \sin\frac{3\pi}{2} = -1.$

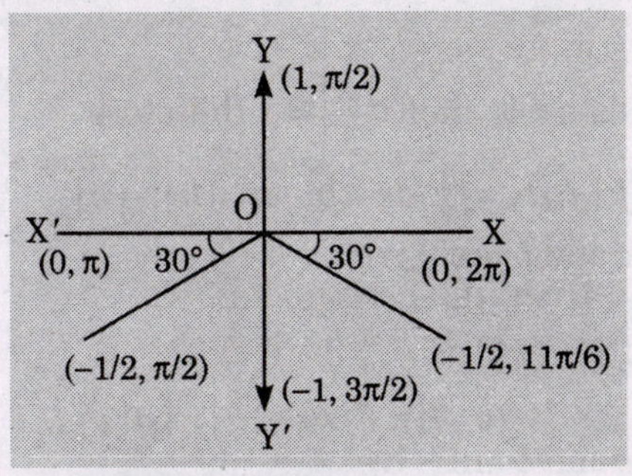

Fig. 1

Hence we divide the interval π to 2π as

$$\left(\pi, \frac{7\pi}{6}\right), \left(\frac{7\pi}{6}, \frac{11\pi}{6}\right), \left(\frac{11\pi}{6}, 2\pi\right)$$

$$\sin x = \left(0, -\frac{1}{2}\right), \left(-1, -\frac{1}{2}\right), \left(0, -\frac{1}{2}\right)$$

$2 \sin x = (0, -1), (-2, -1), (0, -1)$

$[2 \sin x] = -1 \quad -2 \quad -1$

$\therefore \quad I = I_1 + I_2 + I_3$

$= \int -1\, dx + \int -2\, dx + \int -1\, dx$

between proper limits

$$= -\frac{\pi}{6} - 2\left(\frac{4\pi}{6}\right) - \frac{\pi}{6} = -\frac{10\pi}{6} = -\frac{5\pi}{3}$$

(b) If for a real number y, $[y]$ is the greatest integer less than or equal to y, then the value of the integral $\int_{\pi/2}^{3\pi/2} [2 \sin x]\, dx$ is

(a) $-\pi$ (b) 0

(c) $-\pi/2$ (d) $\pi/2$ **(I.I.T. 1999)**

Ans. (c).

In the range $\frac{\pi}{2}$ to $\frac{3\pi}{2}$, we have to find the value of $[2 \sin x]$.

$$I_1\left(\frac{\pi}{2}, \frac{5\pi}{6}\right), \quad I_2\left(\frac{5\pi}{6}, \pi\right), \quad I_3\left(\pi, \frac{7\pi}{6}\right), \quad I_4\left(\frac{7\pi}{6}, \frac{3\pi}{2}\right)$$

$2 \sin x = (2, 1) \quad (1, 0) \quad (0, -1) \quad (-1, -2)$

$\therefore [2 \sin x] = 1 \quad 0 \quad -1 \quad -2$

$\therefore \quad I = \int 1\, dx + 0 + \int -1\, dx + \int -2\, dx$

in proper limits $= -\pi/2$.

Ex. 42. (a) Prove that the value of $\int_1^2 [2x^2 - 3]\, dx$ is

$$9 - \left\{\sqrt{\frac{3}{2}} + \sqrt{2} + \sqrt{\frac{5}{2}} + \sqrt{3} + \sqrt{\frac{7}{2}}\right\}$$

([.] denotes the greatest integer function).

$\int_1^2 [2x^2 - 3]\, dx$

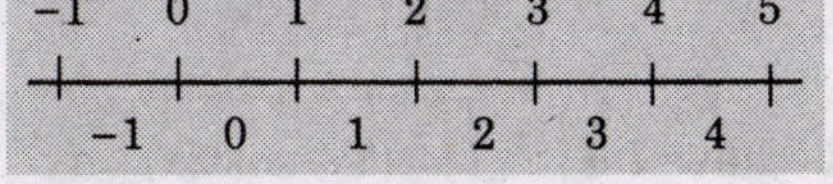

Fig. 2

at $x = 1$, value of $2x^2 - 3 = -1$

at $x = 2$, value of $2x^2 - 3 = 5$

Integers between -1 to 5 are 0, 1, 2, 3, 4

$2x^2 - 3 = 0 \qquad \therefore x = \sqrt{3/2}$

$2x^2 - 3 = 1 \qquad \therefore x = \sqrt{2}$

$2x^2 - 3 = 2 \qquad \therefore x = \sqrt{5/2}$

$2x^2 - 3 = 3 \qquad \therefore x = \sqrt{3}$

$2x^2 - 3 = 4 \qquad \therefore x = \sqrt{7/2}$

$$\therefore \quad \int_1^2 [2x^2 - 3]\, dx = \int_1^{\sqrt{3/2}} [2x^2 - 3]\, dx$$

$$+ \int_{\sqrt{3/2}}^{\sqrt{2}} dx + \int_{\sqrt{2}}^{\sqrt{5/2}} dx + \int_{\sqrt{5/2}}^{\sqrt{3}} dx + \int_{\sqrt{3}}^{\sqrt{7/2}} dx + \int_{\sqrt{7/2}}^{2} dx.$$

On evaluating this, we get

$$9 - \left\{\sqrt{\frac{3}{2}} + \sqrt{2} + \sqrt{\frac{5}{2}} + \sqrt{3} + \sqrt{\frac{7}{2}}\right\}$$

(b) Prove that $\int_0^1 (\{2x\} - 1)(\{3x\} - 1)\, dx = \frac{57}{216}$

where $\{x\}$ denotes the fractional part of x.

We know that $[x] + \{x\} = x$

$\therefore \quad \{x\} = x - [x]$

$\therefore \quad I = \int_0^1 (2x - [2x] - 1)(3x - [3x] - 1)\, dx$

$\int_0^1 [\{(2x - 1) - [2x]\}\{(3x - 1) - [3x]\}]\, dx$

At $x = 0$, both $2x, 3x$ are zero and at $x = 1$ their values are 2 and 3. Now integers between 0 and 3 are 0, 1, 2.

$$2x = 0, 1, 2 \Rightarrow x = 0, \frac{1}{2}, 1$$

$$3x = 0, 1, 2 \Rightarrow x = 0, \frac{1}{3}, \frac{2}{3}$$

$\therefore \quad x$ will vary from $0, \frac{1}{3}, \frac{1}{2}, \frac{2}{3}, 1$

Hence we split.

$I = \int_0^1 dx = \int_0^{1/3} dx + \int_{1/3}^{1/2} dx + \int_{1/2}^{2/3} dx + \int_{2/3}^{1} dx$

$= I_1 + I_2 + I_3 + I_4$

In $I_3, \frac{1}{2} < x < \frac{2}{3}$

$\therefore \quad 1 < 2x < \frac{4}{3}$ and $\frac{3}{2} < 3x < 1$

$\therefore \quad [2x] = 1$ and $[3x] = 1$

In this manner the values of $[2x]$ and $[3x]$ in various intervals are written as below. I_1, 0, 0, I_2, 0, 1, I_3, 1, 1 and I_4, 1, 2.

$\therefore \quad I = \int_0^{1/3} (2x - 1)(3x - 1)\, dx$

$+ \int_{1/3}^{1/2} (2x - 1)(3x - 2)\, dx + \int_{1/3}^{2/3} (2x - 2)(3x - 2)\, dx$

$+ \int_{2/3}^{1} (2x - 2)(3x - 3)\, dx$

$= \int_0^{1/3} (6x^2 - 5x + 1)\, dx + \int_{1/3}^{1/2} (6x^2 - 7x + 2)\, dx$

$+ \int_{1/2}^{2/3} (6x^2 - 10x + 4)\, dx + \int_{2/3}^{1} 6(x - 1)^2\, dx$

$$= \frac{29 + 5 + 8 + 16}{216} = \frac{57}{216}$$

(c) $f(x) = |2^x - 1| + |x - 1|$, then show that

$$\int_{-2}^{2} f(x)\,dx = 5 + \frac{9}{4\log 2}.$$

$f(x) = f_1(x) + f_2(x)$

Let us divide the interval – 2 to 2 into three intervals.

I_1 – 2 to 0 $f_1(x)$ is – ive $f_2(x)$ – ive

I_2 0 to 1 $f_1(x)$ is + ive $f_2(x)$ – ive

I_3 1 to 2 Both are + ive.

$\therefore \quad I = \int_{-2}^{0} [-(2^x - 1) - (x-1)\,dx]$

$+ \int_0^1 (2^x - 1) - (x-1)\,dx + \int_1^2 (2^x - 1) + (x-1)\,dx$

$= \int_{-2}^{0} (2 - x - 2^x)\,dx + \int_0^1 (2^x - x)\,dx$

$+ \int_1^2 (2^x + x - 2)\,dx$ etc.

$$\int 2^x\,dx = \frac{2^x}{\log 2}$$

Ex. 43. (a) The value of $\int_0^{[x]} \{x - [x]\}\,dx$ is

(a) $[x]$ (b) $2[x]$

(c) $\frac{1}{2[x]}$ (d) $\frac{1}{2}[x]$

Ans. (d).

We know that $f(x)$ is a periodic function of period a *i.e.* $f(a+x) = f(x)$, then

$\int_0^{na} f(x)\,dx = n\int_0^a f(x)\,dx$

Now $f(x) = x - [x]$ is a periodic function of period 1, **See Q. 57 (b) P. 1382-84**. Also $[x]$ is an integer say $n = n.1$

$\therefore \quad I = \int_0^{[x]} \{x - [x]\}\,dx = \int_0^{n.1} \{x - [x]\}\,dx$

$= n\int_0^1 \{x - [x]\}\,dx, [x] = 0$ in $(0, 1)$

$= [x]\left[\int_0^1 x\,dx - 0\right] = \frac{1}{2}[x] \Rightarrow$ (d)

(b) $\sum_{n=1}^{1000} \int_{n-1}^{n} e^{x-[x]}\,dx$ where $[x]$ is the greatest integer, is

(a) $\frac{e-1}{1000}$ (b) $1000(e-1)$

(c) $\frac{e^{1000}-1}{e-1}$ (d) $\frac{e^{1000}-1}{1000}$

Ans. (b). $I = \int_0^1 + \int_1^2 + \ldots + \int_{999}^{1000}$

$\therefore \quad I = \int_0^{1000} e^{x-[x]}\,dx$

Now $x - [x]$ is a periodic function of period 1.

$\therefore \quad I = 1000\int_0^1 e^{x-[x]}\,dx = 1000\int_0^1 e^{x-0}\,dx$

$I = 1000\,[e^x]_0^1 = 1000\,(e-1) \Rightarrow$ (b)

***Ex. 44.** Evaluate $\int_a^b \frac{|x|}{x}\,dx$ where $a < b$.

Sol. The value of $|x|$ depends on whether $x > 0$ or $x < 0$. Hence we have the following cases.

$a < b$ can be written as under :

(i) $0 \le a < b$ (ii) $a < 0 < b$

(iii) $a < b \le 0$

$|x| = x, x +$ ive, $= -x, x -$ ive

I. If $0 \le a < b$, then $\frac{|x|}{x} = 1$, therefore

$\int_a^b f(x)\,dx = \int_a^b dx = b - a = |b| - |a|$

as both a and b are + ive

III. If $a < b \le 0$, then $f(x) = -1$

and $\int_a^b f(x)\,dx = \int_a^b (-1)\,dx$

$= (-b) - (-a) = |b| - |a|$

as both a and b are – ive

II. Finally if $a < 0 < b$, then we divide the given integral into two integrals as follows :

$\int_a^b f(x)\,dx = \int_a^0 f(x)\,dx + \int_0^b f(x)\,dx$

$= \int_a^0 (-1)\,dx + \int_0^b 1\,dx = 0 - (-a) + b - 0 = |b| - |a|$

as a is – ive and b is + ive.

***Ex. 45. (a)** Evaluate $\int_0^{100\pi} \sqrt{1 - \cos 2x}\,dx$ **(Bihar C.E.E. 1999)**

Sol. We have $\sqrt{1 - \cos 2x} = \sqrt{2}\,|\sin x|$.

Since $|\sin(\pi + x)| = |-\sin x| = |\sin x|$

$\therefore$ $|\sin x|$ has a period π we have

$\int_0^{100\pi} \sqrt{1 - \cos 2x}\,dx = \sqrt{2}\int_0^{100\pi} |\sin x|\,dx$

$= 100\sqrt{2}\int_0^{\pi} |\sin x|\,dx$

$= 100\sqrt{2}\int_0^{\pi} \sin x\,dx$ **(Ex. 28 (a) P. 1551)**

$= 100\sqrt{2}\,[-\cos x]_0^{\pi} = 100\sqrt{2}\,[1 - (-1)] = 200\sqrt{2}$.

(b) Prove that $\int_{-20\pi}^{20\pi} |\cos x|\,dx = 80$

$I = 2\int_0^{20\pi} |\cos x|\,dx$, Prop. VI

$|\cos(\pi + x)| = |-\cos x| = \cos x$

$\therefore \quad f(x)$ is a periodic function of period π.

See **Q. 28 (a) P. 1551.**

$\therefore \quad I = 2 \times 20\int_0^{\pi} |\cos x|\,dx$

$= 40\int_0^{\pi/2} \cos x\,dx + 40\int_{\pi/2}^{\pi} -\cos x\,dx$

$= 40\,[\sin x]_0^{\pi/2} - 40\,[\sin x]_{\pi/2}^{\pi} = 80$

(c) $I_1 = \int_0^{n\pi} f(|\cos x|)\,dx$ and

$I_2 = \int_0^{5\pi} f|\cos x|\,dx$. then $\frac{I_1}{I_2} = \frac{n}{5}$.

$|\cos x|$ is a periodic function of period π

$\because \quad |\cos(\pi + x)| = |-\cos x| = |\cos x|$

$\therefore \quad I_1 = n\int_0^{\pi} f(|\cos x|)\,dx$

$\therefore \quad I_2 = 5\int_0^{\pi} f(|\cos x|)\,dx$

$\therefore \quad \frac{I_1}{I_2} = \frac{n}{5}$

Ex. 46. (a) Prove that $I = \int_0^{\pi} \sqrt{\left\{\frac{1}{2}(1 + \cos 2x)\right\}}\,dx = 2$.

Sol. We have $I = \int_0^{\pi} \sqrt{\left\{\frac{1}{2}(1 + \cos 2x)\right\}}\,dx$

$= \int_0^{\pi} \sqrt{\cos^2 x}\,dx = \int_0^{\pi} |\cos x|\,dx$

$= \int_0^{\pi/2} \cos x + \int_{\pi/2}^{\pi} (-\cos x)\,dx$

$= [\sin x]_0^{\pi/2} + [-\sin x]_{\pi/2}^{\pi} = 2.$

(b) $\int_0^\pi |\sin x+\cos x|\,dx=2\sqrt{2}$ **(J.E.E.W.B. 1994)**

$$I=\sqrt{2}\int_0^\pi \left|\sin\left(x+\frac{\pi}{4}\right)\right|dx$$

Put $x+\dfrac{\pi}{4}=t$

$\therefore\quad I=\sqrt{2}\int_{\pi/4}^{5\pi/4}|\sin t|\,dt$

$=\sqrt{2}\int_{\pi/4}^{\pi}\sin t\,dt+\int_{\pi}^{5\pi/4}-\sin t\,dt=2\sqrt{2}.$

Ex. 47. $\int_0^{\pi/2}\sqrt{(1-\sin 2x)}\,dx=2(\sqrt{2}-1)$

$I=\int_0^{\pi/2}|(\cos x-\sin x)|\,dx$

$$=\sqrt{2}\int_0^{\pi/2}\left|\cos\left(x+\frac{\pi}{4}\right)\right|dx$$

We have to check the sign of $\cos x-\sin x$ in the interval 0 to $\pi/2$ or 0 to $\pi/4$ and $\pi/4$ to $\pi/2$. In the Ist interval it is + ive and in the 2nd it is – ive.

Hence we write I as

$$I=\sqrt{2}\left[\int_0^{\pi/4}\cos\left(x+\frac{\pi}{4}\right)dx+\int_{\pi/4}^{\pi/2}-\cos\left(x+\frac{\pi}{4}\right)dx\right]$$

$$=\sqrt{2}\left[\left\{\sin\left(x+\frac{\pi}{4}\right)\right\}_0^{\pi/4}-\left\{\sin\left(x+\frac{\pi}{4}\right)\right\}_{\pi/4}^{\pi/2}\right]$$

$$=\sqrt{2}\left[\left(1-\frac{1}{\sqrt{2}}\right)-\left(\frac{1}{\sqrt{2}}-1\right)\right]=2(\sqrt{2}-1)$$

***Ex. 48.** Evaluate

$$\int_{-1/2}^{1/2}\left[\left(\frac{x+1}{x-1}\right)^2+\left(\frac{x-1}{x+1}\right)^2-2\right]^{1/2}dx$$

Sol.
$$I=\int_{-1/2}^{1/2}\left[\left(\frac{x+1}{x-1}-\frac{x-1}{x+1}\right)^2\right]^{1/2}dx$$

$$=\int_{-1/2}^{1/2}\left|\frac{x+1}{x-1}-\frac{x-1}{x+1}\right|dx=\int_{-1/2}^{1/2}\left|\frac{4x}{x^2-1}\right|dx$$

$$=2\int_0^{1/2}\left|\frac{4x}{x^2-1}\right|,\ \text{by Prop. V}\qquad \because |z|=|-z|$$

$$=2\int_0^{1/2}\frac{4x}{-(x^2-1)}$$

$$=2\int_0^{1/2}\frac{4x}{1-x^2}dx\ \text{by def. of modulus}$$

i.e. $|-z|=-(-z)=z$

$$=-4\,[\log(1-x^2)]_0^{1/2}=-4\left[\log\left(1-\frac{1}{4}\right)-0\right]$$

$=-4\log(3/4)=4\log(4/3).$

Ex. 49. Given $\displaystyle\int_0^1\frac{\sin t}{1+t}dt=\alpha$, find the value of

$$\int_{4\pi-2}^{4\pi}\frac{\sin(t/2)}{4\pi+2-t}dt\ \text{in terms of}\ \alpha.$$

(Roorkee 2000)

$I=-\alpha$

$$I_1=\int_{4\pi-2}^{4\pi}\frac{\sin(t/2)}{4\pi+2-t}dt$$

Put $4\pi-t=2y$ and adjust the limits

$$\therefore\quad I_1=\int_1^0\frac{\sin(2\pi-y)(-2\,dy)}{2(1+y)}$$

$$=\int_1^0\frac{\sin y}{1+y}dy\quad\because\ \sin(2\pi-y)=-\sin y.$$

$$=-\int_0^1\frac{\sin t}{1+t}dt=-\alpha$$

***Ex. 50.** If $\displaystyle A=\int_0^\pi\frac{\cos x}{(x+2)^2}dx$, then evaluate

$$I=\int_0^{\pi/2}\frac{\cos x\sin x}{(x+1)}dx\ \text{in terms of}\ A.$$

Put $x=2y$ and adjust the limits in A.

$$A=\int_0^{\pi/2}\frac{\cos 2y}{(2y+2)^2}.2\,dy$$

$$=\frac{1}{2}\int_0^{\pi/2}\frac{\cos 2y}{(y+1)^2}dy$$

or $$2A=\left[-\frac{\cos 2y}{(y+1)}\right]_0^{\pi/2}+\int_0^{\pi/2}\frac{1}{y+1}(-2\sin 2y)\,dy$$

or $$2A=\frac{1}{\left(\frac{\pi}{2}+1\right)}+1-4\int_0^{\pi/2}\frac{\sin y\cos y}{y+1}dy$$

or $$4I=\frac{2}{2+\pi}+1-2A.$$

Problem Set (9)

Miscellaneous Exercise

***Ex. 1.** Prove that

$$\int_0^1\tan^{-1}\left(\frac{1}{1-x+x^2}\right)dx=2\int_0^1\tan^{-1}x\,dx.$$

Hence or otherwise, evaluate the integral

$\int_0^1\tan^{-1}(1-x+x^2)\,dx.$ **(I.I.T. 1998)**

Refer Q. 15 (a) P. 831.

$$I=\frac{\pi}{2}-\log 2\qquad ...(1)$$

Now $\int_0^1\tan^{-1}(1-x+x^2)\,dx$

$$=\int_0^1 \cot^{-1}\frac{1}{1-x+x^2}\,dx$$

$$=\int_0^1\left(\frac{\pi}{2}-\tan^{-1}\frac{1}{1-x+x^2}\right)dx$$

$$=\left[\frac{\pi}{2}x\right]_0^1 - I=\frac{\pi}{2}-\left(\frac{\pi}{2}-\log 2\right)=\log 2, \qquad \text{by (1)}$$

***Ex. 2.** $\int_0^{\pi}\frac{x^2\cos x}{(1+\sin x)^2}dx=\pi(2-\pi)$

We know that $\int\frac{\cos x}{(1+\sin x)^2}dx=\left[-\frac{1}{1+\sin x}\right]$

Hence integrating by parts,

$$I=\left[-x^2\cdot\frac{1}{1+\sin x}\right]_0^{\pi}+2\int\frac{1}{1+\sin x}\cdot x\,dx$$

$$=-\pi^2+2I_1 \qquad \text{...(1)}$$

$$I_1=\int_0^{\pi}\frac{x}{1+\sin x}dx=\int_0^{\pi}\frac{\pi-x}{1+\sin(\pi-x)}dx, \text{Prop. IV}$$

$$2I_1=\pi\int_0^{\pi}\frac{1}{1+\sin x}dx=\pi\int_0^{\pi}\frac{1-\sin x}{\cos^2 x}dx$$

$$=\pi\int(\sec^2 x-\sec x\tan x)\,dx$$

$$=\pi[\tan x-\sec x]_0^{\pi}=\pi[2]=2\pi. \quad \text{Putting in (1)}$$

$$I=-\pi^2+2\pi=\pi(2-\pi).$$

***Ex. 3.** $I=\int_0^{\pi}\frac{x\,dx}{(a^2\cos^2 x+b^2\sin^2 x)^2}=\frac{\pi^2}{4}\frac{(a^2+b^2)}{a^3b^3}$

Applying Prop. IV $f(a-x)=f(x)$ and adding,

$$2I=\int_0^{\pi}\frac{\pi\,dx}{(a^2\cos^2 x+b^2\sin^2 x)^2}$$

$$=2\pi\int_0^{\pi/2}\frac{dx}{(a^2\cos^2 x+b^2\sin^2 x)^2}$$

$\because \quad f(2a-x)=f(x)$ (Prop. VI)

$$\therefore \quad I=\pi\int_0^{\pi/2}\frac{\sec^2 x\sec^2 x\,dx}{(a^2+b^2\tan^2 x)^2},$$

on dividing by $\cos^4 x$

Now put $b\tan x=a\tan\theta$

$\therefore \quad b\sec^2 x\,dx=a\sec^2\theta\,d\theta$

$\therefore \quad \sec^2 x\,dx=\frac{a}{b}(1+\tan^2\theta)\,d\theta$

and limits remain the same.

$$\therefore \quad I=\pi\int_0^{\pi/2}\frac{(1+\tan^2 x)\frac{a}{b}(1+\tan^2\theta)\,d\theta}{a^4(1+\tan^2\theta)^2}$$

$$=\frac{\pi}{a^3b}\int_0^{\pi/2}\left(1+\frac{a^2}{b^2}\tan^2\theta\right)\cos^2\theta\,d\theta.$$

$$=\frac{\pi}{a^3b^3}\int_0^{\pi/2}(b^2\cos^2\theta+a^2\sin^2\theta)\,d\theta$$

$$=\frac{\pi}{a^3b^3}\left[\frac{1}{2}\cdot\frac{\pi}{2}\right](b^2+a^2)=\frac{\pi^2}{4}\frac{a^2+b^2}{a^3b^3}$$

$$\int_0^{\pi/2}\cos^2 t\,dt=\int_0^{\pi/2}\sin^2 t\,dt$$

$$=\frac{1}{2}\int_0^{\pi/2}(1-\cos 2t)\,dt=\frac{1}{2}\cdot\frac{\pi}{2}.$$

Ex. 4. $\int_{3n\pi}^{\left(n+\frac{1}{n}\right)3\pi}\frac{4x\,dx}{\left[(a^2+b^2)+(a^2-b^2)\cos\frac{2nx}{3}\right]^2}$ (where $a,b>0$)

Put $\frac{nx}{3}=t$ and adjust the limits.

$$I=\int_{n^2\pi}^{(n^2+1)\pi}\frac{\left(4\cdot\frac{3t}{n}\right)\left(\frac{3}{n}dt\right)}{[a^2(1+\cos 2t)+b^2(1-\cos 2t)]^2}$$

$$=\frac{9}{n^2}\int_{n^2\pi}^{(n^2+1)\pi}\frac{4t\,dt}{4[a^2\cos^2 t+b^2\sin^2 t]^2}$$

$$I=\frac{9}{n^2}\int_{n^2\pi}^{(n^2+1)\pi}\frac{t\,dt}{[a^2\cos^2 t+b^2\sin^2 t]^2} \qquad \text{...(1)}$$

Now we know that

$$\int_a^b f(x)\,dx=\int_a^b f(a+b-x)\,dx, \text{ Prop. VII}$$

$$\therefore \quad I=\frac{9}{n^2}\int_{n^2\pi}^{(n^2+1)\pi}\frac{(2n^2+1)\pi-t}{[a^2\cos^2 t+b^2\sin^2 t]^2} \qquad \text{...(2)}$$

Adding (1) and (2), we get

$$2I=\frac{9}{n^2}(2n^2+1)\pi\cdot\int_{n^2\pi}^{(n^2+1)\pi}\frac{dt}{[a^2\cos^2 t+b^2\sin^2 t]^2}$$

Now put $t=n^2\pi+z$

$$\therefore \quad 2I=\frac{9}{n^2}(2n^2+1)\pi\int_0^{\pi}\frac{dz}{(a^2\cos^2 z+b^2\sin^2 z)^2}$$

Now proceed as in last part.

$$\therefore \quad I=\frac{9(2n^2+1)\pi}{n^2}\cdot\frac{a^2+b^2}{a^3b^3}$$

***Ex. 5. (a)** Evaluate $\int_0^{\pi}\frac{x\,dx}{1+\cos\alpha\sin x}$ $(0<\alpha<\pi)$.

(Roorkee 2001)

$$I=\int_0^{\pi}\frac{x\,dx}{1+\cos\alpha\sin x}dx$$

$$\therefore \quad I=\int_0^{\pi}\frac{(\pi-x)\,dx}{1+\cos\alpha\sin(\pi-x)}=\int_0^{\pi}\frac{(\pi-x)\,dx}{1+\cos\alpha\sin x}.$$

Adding, $2I=\int_0^{\pi}\frac{\pi\,dx}{1+\cos\alpha\sin x}$

$$=2\pi\int_0^{\pi/2}\frac{dx}{1+\cos\alpha\sin x}.$$

or $\quad I=\pi\int_0^{\pi/2}\frac{dx}{1+2\cos\alpha\sin\frac{1}{2}x\cos\frac{1}{2}x}$

$$=\pi\int_0^{\pi/2}\frac{\sec^2\frac{1}{2}x\,dx}{1+\tan^2\frac{1}{2}x+2\cos\alpha\tan\frac{1}{2}x}$$

Now put $\tan\frac{1}{2}x=t$. Then $\frac{1}{2}\sec^2\frac{1}{2}x\,dx=dt$.

$$\therefore \quad I=\pi\int_0^1\frac{2\,dt}{1+t^2+2t\cos\alpha}$$

$$=2\pi\int_0^1\frac{dt}{(t+\cos\alpha)^2+\sin^2\alpha}$$

$$=\frac{2\pi}{\sin\alpha}\left[\tan^{-1}\left(\frac{t+\cos\alpha}{\sin\alpha}\right)\right]_0^1$$

$$=\frac{2\pi}{\sin\alpha}\left[\tan^{-1}\left(\frac{1+\cos\alpha}{\sin\alpha}\right)-\tan^{-1}\left(\frac{0+\cos\alpha}{\sin\alpha}\right)\right]$$

$$=\frac{2\pi}{\sin\alpha}\left[\tan^{-1}\cot\left(\frac{1}{2}\alpha\right)-\tan^{-1}\cot\alpha\right]$$

$$=\frac{2\pi}{\sin\alpha}\left[\tan^{-1}\tan\left(\frac{1}{2}\pi-\frac{1}{2}\alpha\right)-\tan^{-1}\tan\left(\frac{1}{2}\pi-\alpha\right)\right]$$

$$=\frac{2\pi}{\sin\alpha}\cdot\frac{1}{2}\alpha=\frac{\pi\alpha}{\sin\alpha}.$$

(b)* $\int_0^{\pi}\frac{x}{1+\sin\alpha\sin x}dx=\frac{\pi}{\cos\alpha}\left(\frac{\pi}{2}-\alpha\right)$

(Roorkee 1994)

Proceed as in part (a).

$$\frac{1+\sin\alpha}{\cos\alpha}=\frac{[\cos(\alpha/2)+\sin(\alpha/2)]^2}{[\cos^2(\alpha/2)-\sin^2(\alpha/2)]}$$

$$=\frac{\cos(\alpha/2)+\sin(\alpha/2)}{\cos(\alpha/2)-\sin(\alpha/2)}=\tan\left(\frac{\pi}{4}+\frac{\alpha}{2}\right)\text{ etc.}$$

or put $\alpha=90^\circ-\beta$ and it becomes part (a).

***Ex. 6. (a)** Evaluate $\int_0^{2}\frac{\sin^2\theta}{a-b\cos\theta}d\theta,\quad a>b>0,$

$$I=\int_0^{2\pi}\frac{\sin^2\theta\,d\theta}{a-b\cos\theta}=2\int_0^{\pi}\frac{\sin^2\theta\,d\theta}{a-b\cos\theta},\quad\text{by Prop. VI}$$

Also $I=2\int_0^{\pi}\frac{\sin^2\theta\,d\theta}{a+b\cos\theta}$, by Prop. IV

$$2I=2\int_0^{\pi}\frac{2a\sin^2\theta}{a^2-b^2\cos^2\theta}d\theta$$

$$=8a\int_0^{\pi/2}\frac{\sin^2\theta\,d\theta}{a^2-b^2\cos^2\theta},\quad\text{by Prop. VI}$$

Divide above and below by $\cos^2\theta$

$$\therefore \quad 2I=8a\int_0^{\pi/2}\frac{\tan^2\theta\,d\theta}{a^2(1+\tan^2\theta)-b^2}$$

$$=8a\int_0^{\pi/2}\frac{\tan^2\theta\,d\theta}{(a^2-b^2)+a^2\tan^2\theta}$$

Put $a\tan\theta=t$ and adjust the limits.

$$\therefore \quad I=4\int_0^{\infty}\frac{(t^2/a^2)\,a^2}{[(a^2-b^2)+t^2][a^2+t^2]}$$

Split into partial fractions in t^2 by method of suppression

$$I=4\int_0^{\infty}\left[\frac{a^2}{b^2(a^2+t^2)}-\frac{a^2-b^2}{b^2\{(a^2-b^2)+t^2\}}\right]dt$$

$$=\frac{4}{b^2}\left[a^2\cdot\frac{1}{a}\tan^{-1}\frac{t}{a}-\frac{(a^2-b^2)}{\sqrt{(a^2-b^2)}}\tan^{-1}\frac{t}{\sqrt{(a^2-b^2)}}\right]_0^{\infty}$$

$$=\frac{4}{b^2}\left[a\cdot\frac{\pi}{2}-\sqrt{(a^2-b^2)}\cdot\frac{\pi}{2}\right]=\frac{2\pi}{b^2}[a-\sqrt{(a^2-b^2)}].$$

(b) Prove that $\int_0^{\pi}\frac{d\theta}{(a-\cos\theta)}=\frac{\pi}{\sqrt{a^2-1}}$

Hence or otherwise evaluate $\int_0^{\pi}\frac{d\theta}{(\sqrt{10}-\cos\theta)^3}$

Applying Prop. IV and adding,

$$2I=\int_0^{\pi}\left(\frac{1}{a-\cos\theta}+\frac{1}{a+\cos\theta}\right)d\theta$$

$$=\int_0^{\pi}\frac{2a}{a^2-\cos^2\theta}d\theta$$

$$\therefore \quad I=\int_0^{\pi}\frac{a\sec^2\theta\,d\theta}{a^2(1+\tan^2\theta)-1}$$

$$=2\int_0^{\pi/2}\frac{a\sec^2\theta\,d\theta}{(a^2-1)+a^2\tan^2\theta}$$

Put $a\tan\theta=t$

$$\therefore \quad I=2\int_0^{\infty}\frac{dt}{(a^2-1)+t^2}$$

$$= 2 \cdot \frac{1}{\sqrt{a^2 - 1}} \left[\tan^{-1} \frac{t}{\sqrt{a^2 - 1}} \right]_0^{\infty}$$

$$= \frac{2}{\sqrt{a^2 - 1}} \cdot \frac{\pi}{2} = \frac{\pi}{\sqrt{(a^2 - 1)}}$$

Deduction : $\displaystyle\int_0^{\pi} \frac{d\theta}{a - \cos\theta} = \frac{\pi}{\sqrt{a^2 - 1}}$

Differentiate both sides w.r.t. a

$$-\int_0^{\pi} \frac{d\theta}{(a - \cos\theta)^2} = \frac{-1}{2} \frac{\pi}{(a^2 - 1)^{3/2}} \cdot 2a = \frac{-\pi a}{(a^2 - 1)^{3/2}}$$

Again differentiate w.r.t. a and put $a^2 = 10$

$$\therefore \quad I = \frac{7\pi}{162}$$

***Ex. 7.** $\displaystyle\int_0^{\infty} \frac{dx}{(x + \sqrt{1 + x^2})^n}$

We have already done this question in **Q. 44, 45 P. 1512-19**. Here below we give another method.

Put $x = \tan\theta$ and adjust the limits.

$$I = \int_0^{\pi/2} \frac{\sec^2\theta \, d\theta}{(\tan\theta + \sec\theta)^n} = \int_0^{\pi/2} \frac{\cos^{n-2}\theta \, d\theta}{(1 + \sin\theta)^n}$$

$$= \int_0^{\pi/2} \frac{\sin^{n-2}\theta \, d\theta}{(1 + \cos\theta)^n} \qquad \text{(Prop. IV)}$$

$$= \int_0^{\pi/2} \frac{(2\sin\theta/2 \cos\theta/2)^{n-2}}{(2\cos^2\theta/2)^n} d\theta$$

$$= \frac{1}{4} \int_0^{\pi/2} \frac{\sin^{n-2}\theta/2}{\cos^{n+2}\theta/2} d\theta$$

$$= \frac{1}{4} \int_0^{\pi/2} \frac{\sin^{n-2}\theta/2}{\cos^{n-2}\theta/2} \cdot \frac{1}{\cos^4\theta/2} d\theta$$

$$I = \frac{1}{4} \int_0^{\pi/2} \tan^{n-2}\theta \left(1 + \tan^2\frac{\theta}{2}\right) . \sec^2\frac{\theta}{2} d\theta$$

Now put $\tan\dfrac{\theta}{2} = t$

$$\therefore \quad \frac{1}{2}\sec^2\frac{\theta}{2} d\theta = dt$$

$$= \frac{1}{4} \int_0^1 t^{n-2}(1 + t^2) . 2\,dt = \frac{1}{2} \int_0^1 (t^{n-2} + t^n)\, dt$$

$$= \frac{1}{2} \left[\frac{t^{n-1}}{n-1} + \frac{t^{n+1}}{n+1} \right]_0^1 = \frac{1}{2} \left[\frac{1}{n-1} + \frac{1}{n+1} \right] = \frac{n}{n^2 - 1}.$$

Ex. 8. If $f(x) = \int_{1/x}^{\sqrt{x}} \sin(t^2)\, dt$, then evaluate $f'(1)$.

$$f'(x) = \sin(\sqrt{x})^2 . \frac{1}{2\sqrt{x}} - \sin\left(\frac{1}{x}\right)^2 \times \left(-\frac{1}{x^2}\right)$$

Prop. VIII

$$= \frac{\sin x}{2\sqrt{x}} + \frac{1}{x^2} \sin\frac{1}{x^2}$$

$$\therefore \quad f'(1) = \frac{\sin 1}{2} + \sin 1 = \frac{3}{2}\sin 1.$$

***Ex. 9.** Evaluate $\displaystyle\int_0^1 \frac{1}{(5 + 2x - 2x^2)\{1 + e^{(2-4x)}\}} dx.$

(Roorkee 1998)

Apply Prop. IV

$$\therefore \quad I = \int_0^1 \frac{dx}{[5 + 2(1-x) - 2(1-x)^2][1 + e^{2-4(1-x)}]}$$

$$= \int_0^1 \frac{dx}{[5 + 2x - 2x^2](1 + e^{-(2-4x)})}$$

$$= \int_0^1 \frac{e^{(2-4x)}dx}{(5 + 2x - 2x)^2 (1 + e^{(2-4x)})} \text{ as } e^{-y} = \frac{1}{e^y}$$

Adding,

$$2I = \int_0^1 \frac{(1 + e^{(2-4x)})\, dx}{(5 + 2x - 2x^2)(1 + e^{(2-4x)})}$$

or $$I = \frac{1}{2} \int_0^1 \frac{dx}{2\left[\left(\frac{\sqrt{11}}{2}\right)^2 - \left(x - \frac{1}{2}\right)^2\right]}$$

$$I = \frac{1}{4} \cdot \frac{1}{2 \cdot \frac{\sqrt{11}}{2}} \left[\log \frac{\frac{\sqrt{11}}{2} + x - \frac{1}{2}}{\frac{\sqrt{11}}{2} - \left(x - \frac{1}{2}\right)} \right]_0^1 \qquad \text{Formula.}$$

$$= \frac{1}{4\sqrt{11}} \left[\log \frac{\sqrt{11} + 1}{\sqrt{11} - 1} - \log \frac{\sqrt{11} - 1}{\sqrt{11} + 1} \right]$$

$$= \frac{1}{4\sqrt{11}} \log \left(\frac{\sqrt{11} + 1}{\sqrt{11} - 1} \right)^2$$

$$\because \log m - \log n = \log(m/n)$$

$$= 2 . \frac{1}{4\sqrt{11}} \log \frac{(\sqrt{11} + 1)^2}{(\sqrt{10})^2} \qquad \text{(conj. of } D^r\text{)}$$

$$= \frac{1}{\sqrt{11}} \log \frac{\sqrt{11} + 1}{\sqrt{10}}.$$

Ex. 10. Prove that

$$\int_0^{\pi} x^3 \log \sin x \, dx = \frac{3\pi}{2} \int_0^{\pi} x^2 \log(\sqrt{2} \sin x)\, dx$$

$$I = \int_0^{\pi} (\pi - x)^3 \log \sin x \, dx \qquad \text{(Prop. IV)}$$

$$2I = \int_0^{\pi} [(\pi - x)^3 + x^3] \log \sin x \, dx$$

$$= \int_0^{\pi} (\pi^3 - 3\pi^2 x + 3\pi x^2) \log \sin x \, dx$$

$$= I_1 + I_2 + I_3$$

$$I_1 = \pi^3 \int_0^{\pi} \log \sin x \, dx = 2\pi^3 \int_0^{\pi/2} \log \sin x \, dx$$

$$= 2\pi^3 . \frac{\pi}{2} \log\frac{1}{2} = \pi^4 \log\frac{1}{2}$$

$I_2 = -3\pi^2 \int_0^\pi x \log \sin x\, dx$

$I_2 = -3\pi^2 \int_0^\pi (\pi - x) \log \sin x\, dx$ (Prop. IV)

$2I_2 = -3\pi^2 \int_0^\pi \pi \log \sin x = -3\pi^3\, \pi \log \frac{1}{2}$ as above.

$\therefore\quad I_2 = -\frac{3\pi^4}{2} \log \frac{1}{2}$

$I_1 + I_2 = \pi^4 \log \frac{1}{2} - \frac{3\pi^4}{2} \log \frac{1}{2}$

$= -\frac{1}{2}\pi^4 \log \frac{1}{2} = \frac{1}{2}\pi^4 \log 2$

$2I = \pi^4 \log \sqrt{2} + \int 3\pi x^2 \log \sin x\, dx$

$= 3\pi \left[\frac{\pi^3}{3} \log \sqrt{2} + \int_0^\pi x^2 \log \sin x\right] dx$

$= 3\pi \left[\int_0^\pi x^2 \log \sqrt{2}\, dx + \int_0^\pi x^2 \log \sin x\, dx\right]$ **(Note)**

$= 3\pi \int_0^\pi x^2 (\log \sqrt{2} + \log \sin x)\, dx$

$= 3\pi \int_0^\pi x^2 \log (\sqrt{2} \sin x)\, dx$

$\therefore\quad I =$ As given

***Ex. 11.** Evaluate

$$\int_{-\pi/2}^{\pi/2} \left\{\log \frac{px^2 + qx + r}{px^2 - qx + r} (a+b) \,|\sin x|\right\} dx$$

$$I = \int_{-\pi/2}^{\pi/2} \log \frac{px^2 + qx + r}{px^2 - qx + r} + \int_{-\pi/2}^{\pi/2} \log (a+b)\, dx + \int_{-\pi/2}^{\pi/2} \log |\sin x|\, dx$$

$= I_1 + I_2 + I_3$

Clearly $I_1 = 0$ as $-\log t = \log \frac{1}{t}$

$\therefore\quad f(-x) = -f(x)$ *i.e.* odd function

$I_2 = \log (a+b)\, x = \log (a+b)\, (\pi/2 + \pi/2)$

$= \pi \log (a+b)$

$I_3 = 2\int_0^{\pi/2} \log |\sin x|\, dx = 2\int_0^{\pi/2} \log \sin x\, dx$

$= 2 . \frac{\pi}{2} \log \frac{1}{2} = -\pi \log 2$

$\therefore\quad I = 0 + \pi \log (a+b) - \pi \log 2 = \pi \log \left(\frac{a+b}{2}\right).$

Ex. 12. Prove that

$$\int_0^\pi \frac{x \sin 2x \sin (\pi/2 \cos x)}{2x - \pi} dx = \frac{8}{\pi^2}$$

(I.I.T. 1991)

Putting $x = \frac{\pi}{2} + t \quad \therefore \quad dx = dt$ and $2x - \pi = 2t$

Adjust the limits

$\therefore\quad \sin 2x = \sin (\pi + 2t) = -\sin 2t$

$\cos x = -\sin t$

$$\therefore\quad I = \int_{-\pi/2}^{\pi/2} \frac{\left(\frac{\pi}{2} + t\right)(-\sin 2t) \sin \left(-\frac{\pi}{2} \sin t\right)}{2t} \quad ...(A)$$

$$= \int_{-\pi/2}^{\pi/2} \left(\frac{\pi}{4}\right) \frac{1}{t} \sin 2t \sin \left(\frac{\pi}{2} \sin t\right) dt + \frac{1}{2}\int_{-\pi/2}^{\pi/2} \sin 2t \sin \left(\frac{\pi}{2} \sin t\right) dt$$

$$= 0 + 2 \cdot \frac{1}{2} \int_0^{\pi/2} 2 \sin t \cos t \sin \left(\frac{\pi}{2} \sin t\right) dt$$

[using the Property V of definite integrals]

$$= 2\int_0^{\pi/2} \left(\frac{2}{\pi} z\right) \sin z \cdot \frac{2}{\pi} dz$$

Putting $\frac{\pi}{2} \sin t = z \quad \therefore \quad \frac{\pi}{2} \cos t\, dt = dz$

$$= \frac{8}{\pi^2} \int_0^{\pi/2} z \sin z\, dz$$

$$= \frac{8}{\pi^2} [z(-\cos z) + \sin z]_0^{\pi/2}$$

$$= \frac{8}{\pi^2} [(0 + 1) - 0] = \frac{8}{\pi^2}.$$

***Ex. 13.** Prove that $\int_0^\pi \frac{x^2 \sin 2x \sin \left(\frac{\pi}{2} \cos x\right)}{2x - \pi} dx = \frac{8}{\pi}$

Put $x = \frac{\pi}{2} + t,\ 2x = \pi + 2t$

$\therefore\quad dx = dt$ and adjust the limits

$$\therefore\quad I = \int_{-\pi/2}^{\pi/2} \frac{\left(\frac{\pi}{2} + t\right)^2 (-\sin 2t) \sin \left(-\frac{\pi}{2} \sin t\right) dt}{2t}$$

$$= \left[\int_{-\pi/2}^{\pi/2} \frac{\left(\frac{\pi^2}{4} + t^2\right) \sin 2t \sin \left(\frac{\pi}{2} \sin t\right)}{2t} dt + \int_{-\pi/2}^{\pi/2} \frac{\pi t \sin 2t \sin \left(\frac{\pi}{2} \sin t\right)}{2t} dt\right], \text{ by Prop. II}$$

$= I_1 + I_2$

But I_1 is clearly an odd function of t and hence is zero by Prop. V.

$$\therefore\quad I = \pi \int_{-\pi/2}^{\pi/2} \frac{t \sin 2t \sin \left(\frac{\pi}{2} \sin t\right)}{2t} dt = \pi \cdot \frac{8}{\pi^2} = \frac{8}{\pi},$$

by (A) Ex. 12 P. 1560.

***Ex. 14.** Evaluate the definite integral

$$\int_{-\frac{1}{\sqrt{3}}}^{\frac{1}{\sqrt{3}}} \left(\frac{x^4}{1 - x^4}\right) \cos^{-1} \left(\frac{2x}{1 + x^2}\right) dx$$

(I.I.T. 1995)

Sol. $\cos^{-1} y = \frac{\pi}{2} - \sin^{-1} y = \frac{\pi}{2} - \sin^{-1} \frac{2x}{1 + x^2}$

$= \frac{\pi}{2} - 2\tan^{-1} x$

$\therefore \quad I = \int_{-1/\sqrt{3}}^{1/\sqrt{3}} \left[\frac{\pi}{2} \cdot \frac{x^4}{1-x^4} - \frac{x^4}{1-x^4} 2\tan^{-1} x \right] dx$

$= I_1 - I_2$, where $I_2 = 0$ by Prop. V

$\therefore \quad I = 2 . \frac{\pi}{2} \int_0^{\frac{1}{\sqrt{3}}} \left(-1 + \frac{1}{1-x^4} \right) dx$, Prop. V

$= \frac{\pi}{2} \int_0^{\frac{1}{\sqrt{3}}} \left(-2 + \frac{1}{1-x^2} + \frac{1}{1+x^2} \right) dx$

$= \frac{\pi}{2} \left[-2x + \frac{1}{2.1} \log \frac{1+x}{1-x} + \tan^{-1} x \right]_0^{1/\sqrt{3}}$

$= \frac{\pi}{2} \left[-\frac{2}{\sqrt{3}} + \frac{1}{2} \log \frac{\sqrt{3}+1}{\sqrt{3}-1} + \frac{\pi}{6} \right]$

(b) Prove that

$$\int_{-\frac{1}{\sqrt{3}}}^{\frac{1}{\sqrt{3}}} \frac{\cos^{-1}\left(\frac{2x}{1+x^2}\right) + \tan^{-1}\left(\frac{2x}{1-x^2}\right)}{e^x + 1} dx = \frac{\pi}{2\sqrt{3}}$$

On putting $x = \tan\theta$,

$N^r = \cos^{-1}(\sin 2\theta) + \tan^{-1}(\tan 2\theta)$

$= \frac{\pi}{2} - 2\theta + 2\theta = \frac{\pi}{2}$

$\therefore \quad I = \frac{\pi}{2} \int_{-\frac{1}{\sqrt{3}}}^{\frac{1}{\sqrt{3}}} \frac{1}{e^x + 1} dx$

$= \frac{\pi}{2} \left[\int_{-\frac{1}{\sqrt{3}}}^{0} \frac{1}{e^x+1} dx + \int_0^{\frac{1}{\sqrt{3}}} \frac{1}{e^x+1} dx \right]$

Put $x = -t$ in Ist and adjust the limits

$\therefore \quad I = \frac{\pi}{2} \left[\int_0^{\frac{1}{\sqrt{3}}} \frac{1}{e^{-t}+1} dt + \int_0^{\frac{1}{\sqrt{3}}} \frac{1}{e^x+1} dx \right]$

$= \frac{\pi}{2} \int_0^{\frac{1}{\sqrt{3}}} \left[\frac{e^x}{(e^x+1)} + \frac{1}{(e^x+1)} \right] dx$

$= \frac{\pi}{2} \int_0^{\frac{1}{\sqrt{3}}} 1 . dx = \frac{\pi}{2} . \frac{1}{\sqrt{3}}$

(c) Evaluate :

$$\int_{-\frac{1}{\sqrt{2}}}^{\frac{1}{\sqrt{2}}} \frac{x^8}{1-x^4} \times [\sin^{-1}(1-2x^2) + \cos^{-1}(2x\sqrt{1-x^2})] dx$$

In N^r put $x = \sin\theta$, then

$\sin^{-1}(1 - 2\sin^2\theta) + \cos^{-1}(2\sin\theta\cos\theta)$

$= \sin^{-1}(\cos 2\theta) + \cos^{-1}(\sin 2\theta)$

$= \frac{\pi}{2} - \cos^{-1}(\cos 2\theta) + \frac{\pi}{2} - \sin^{-1}(\sin 2\theta)$

$= \pi - 2\theta - 2\theta = \pi - 4\sin^{-1} x$

$\therefore \quad I = \int_{-\frac{1}{\sqrt{2}}}^{\frac{1}{\sqrt{2}}} \frac{x^8}{1-x^4} [\pi - 4\sin^{-1} x] dx$

$= 2\int_0^{\frac{1}{\sqrt{2}}} \pi \frac{x^8}{1-x^4} dx + 0$ by Prop. V

$= 2\pi \int_0^{\frac{1}{\sqrt{2}}} \frac{x^8 - 1 + 1}{1-x^4} dx$

$= 2\pi \int_0^{\frac{1}{\sqrt{2}}} \left[-(x^4+1) + \frac{1}{(1-x^2)(1+x^2)} \right] dx$

$= 2\pi \int_0^{\frac{1}{\sqrt{2}}} -(x^4+1) + \frac{1}{2} \left\{ \frac{1}{1-x^2} + \frac{1}{1+x^2} \right\} dx$

$= 2\pi \left[-\left(\frac{x^5}{5} + x \right) + \frac{1}{4} \log \frac{1+x}{1-x} + \frac{1}{2} \tan^{-1} x \right]_0^{1/\sqrt{2}}$

$= \pi \left[\frac{1}{2} \log \frac{\sqrt{2}+1}{\sqrt{2}-1} + \tan^{-1} \frac{1}{\sqrt{2}} - \frac{21}{10\sqrt{2}} \right]$

15. Evaluate :

$$\int_0^{\pi} e^{|\cos x|} \left\{ 3\cos\left(\frac{1}{2}\cos x\right) + 2\sin\left(\frac{1}{2}\cos x\right) \right\} \sin x \, dx$$

Sol. $I = I_1 + I_2$

$I_2 = 0 \quad \because f(2a - x) = -f(x)$, by prop. VI

$\because \sin(\pi - x) = \sin x$

but $\cos(\pi - x) = -\cos x$ and $\sin(-\theta) = -\sin\theta$

and $|\cos x| = |\cos(\pi - x)| = |-\cos x| = \cos x$

$\therefore \quad I = I_1$.

Now put $\cos x = t$ and adjust the limits

$\therefore \quad I = 3\int_{-1}^{1} e^{|t|} \cos\frac{t}{2} dt = 3.2\int_0^1 e^t \cos\frac{t}{2} dt$

$\because$ $F(t)$ in an even function. Prop. VI

and $|t| = t$ in 0 to 1 and $|-t| = |t|$,

$= 6 \frac{1}{\left(1 + \frac{1}{4}\right)} \left[e^t \left\{ \cos\frac{t}{2} - \frac{1}{2}\left(-\sin\frac{t}{2} \right) \right\} \right]_0^1$

(See Q. 13 P. 1480)

From $I = \int e^{ax} \cos bx \, dx = \frac{e^{ax}}{r} \cos(bx - \alpha)$.

$= \frac{24}{5} \left[e \left\{ \cos\frac{1}{2} + \frac{1}{2}\sin\frac{1}{2} \right\} - 1 \right]$

16. Evaluate :

$\int_0^{\pi/2} (\sin x)^{\cos x} [\cos x \cot x - \log(\sin x)^{\sin x}] dx$

(I.I.T. 2006)

Sol. If $y = (\sin x)^{\cos x}$ then

$\log y = \cos x \log(\sin x)$

$$\frac{1}{y}\frac{dy}{dx} = \cos x . \frac{1}{\sin x}\cos x - \sin x \log \sin x$$

$$\therefore \quad \frac{dy}{dx} = (\sin x)^{\cos x}[\cos x . \cot x - \log(\sin x)^{\sin x}]$$

$$\therefore \quad I = \int \frac{dy}{dx}dx = [y]_0^{\pi/2} = \left[(\sin x^{\cos x})\right]_0^{\pi/2} = 1^0 = 1$$

PASSAGE :

$\int_a^b f(x)\,dx$ can be estimated by

$\left(\frac{b-a}{2}\right)[f(b) + f(a)]$.

For more accuracy $\int_a^b f(x)\,dx = \int_a^c f(x)\,dx + \int_c^b f(x)\,dx$,

then $\int_a^b f(x)\,dx = \left(\frac{c-a}{2}\right)\{f(a) + 2f(c) + f(b)\}$

for $c = \frac{a+b}{2}$.

(I.I.T. 2006)

17. (a) $\int_0^{\pi/2} \sin x\,dx$ can be approximated as

(a) $\frac{\pi}{2}(\sqrt{2}+1)$ (b) $\frac{\pi}{8}(\sqrt{2}+1)$

(c) $\frac{\pi}{8\sqrt{2}}(\sqrt{2}+1)$ (d) none of these

(I.I.T. 2006)

Ans. (b).

$$\int_0^{\pi/2} \sin x\,dx = \int_0^{\pi/4} \sin x\,dx + \int_{\pi/4}^{\pi/2} \sin x\,dx$$

$$= \frac{\left(\frac{\pi}{4} - 0\right)}{2}\left(\sin 0 + 2\sin\frac{\pi}{4} + \sin\frac{\pi}{2}\right) = \frac{\pi}{8}\left(\frac{2}{\sqrt{2}} + 1\right)$$

$$= \frac{\pi}{8}(\sqrt{2}+1)$$

(b) If $\lim_{t \to a} \frac{\int_a^t f(t)\,dt - \left(\frac{t-a}{2}\right)(f(t) + f(a))}{(t-a)^3} = 0$, then

maximum degree of $f(x)$ is :

(a) 4 (b) 3

(c) 2 (d) 1

(I.I.T. 2006)

Ans. (d).

Put $t = a + h \quad \therefore \quad t - a = h$

As $t \to a, h \to 0$

Required limit

$$= \operatorname*{Lt}_{h \to 0} \frac{\int_a^{a+h} f(t)\,dt - \frac{h}{2}[f(a+h) + f(a)]}{h^3}, \left(\frac{0}{0}\right)$$

$$= \operatorname*{Lt}_{h \to 0} \frac{f(a+h) - \frac{1}{2}[f(a+h) + f(a)] - \frac{h}{2}f'(a+h)}{3h^2}$$

$$= \operatorname*{Lt}_{h \to 0} \frac{f'(a+h) - \frac{1}{2}f'(a+h) - \frac{1}{2}f'(a+h) - \frac{h}{2}f''(a+h)}{6h}$$

$$= \operatorname*{Lt}_{h \to 0} 0 - \frac{1}{12}f''(a+h) = 0 \text{ given}$$

$\therefore \quad f''(a) = 0 \ \ \forall\, a \in R$

Hence $f(x)$ can at the most be of degree 1, so that $f'(x) =$ constant and $f''(x) = 0 \ \forall\, x \in R$.

18. (a) Let $F(x)$ be an indefinite integral of $\sin^2 x$.

STATEMENT-1 : The function $F(x)$ satisfies $F(x + \pi) = F(x)$ for all real x.

because

STATEMENT-2 : $\sin^2(x + \pi) = \sin^2 x$ for all real x.

(I.I.T. 2007)

Ans. (d).

$F(x) = \int \sin^2 x\,dx = \int (1 - \cos 2x)\,dx$

or $F(x) = x - \frac{1}{2}\sin 2x + c$

Above does not satisfy $F(x + \pi) = F(x)$. Hence statement-1 is false.

Statement-2 *i.e.,* $\sin^2(x + \pi) = \sin^2 x$ is clearly true.

Hence option (d) is correct.

(b) Let $f(x) = \frac{x}{(1 + x^n)^{1/n}}$ for $n \geq 2$ and

$g(x) = \underbrace{(f \circ f \circ \ldots \circ f)}_{f \text{ occurs } n \text{ times}}(x)$. Then $\int x^{n-2} g(x)\,dx$

(a) $\frac{1}{n(n-1)}(1 + nx^n)^{1-(1/n)} + K$

(b) $\frac{1}{n-1}(1 + nx^n)^{1-(1/n)} + K$

(c) $\frac{1}{n(n+1)}(1 + nx^n)^{1+(1/n)} + K$

(d) $\frac{1}{n+1}(1 + nx^n)^{1+(1/n)} + K$

(I.I.T. 2007)

Ans. (a).

$$f\,f(x) = \frac{f(x)}{[1 + (f(x))^n]^{1/n}} = \frac{x}{(1 + x^n)^{1/n}} \div \left[1 + \frac{x^n}{1 + x^n}\right]^{1/n}$$

$$= \frac{x}{(1 + x^n)^{1/n}} \cdot \frac{(1 + x^n)^{1/n}}{(1 + 2x^n)^{1/n}} = \frac{x}{(1 + 2x^n)^{1/n}}$$

Note $f . f$ (twice) and 2 in R.H.S.

$$\therefore \quad g(x) = (fof \ldots of)\,x = \frac{x}{(1 + nx^n)^{1/n}} \quad \ldots \text{(I)}$$

Note $f . f . f \ldots . n$ times and n in R.H.S.

$$\therefore \quad I = \int x^{n-2} g(x)\,dx = \int \frac{x^{n-1}}{(1 + nx^n)^{1/n}}dx \quad \text{by (I)}$$

Now put $1 + nx^n = t \ \therefore \ n^2 x^{n-1}\,dx = dt$

$\therefore \quad I = \dfrac{1}{n^2}\displaystyle\int \dfrac{dt}{t^{1/n}} = \dfrac{1}{n^2}\int t^{-1/n}\, dt = \dfrac{1}{n^2}\,\dfrac{t^{-\frac{1}{n}+1}}{-1/n+1}$

$= \dfrac{1}{n(n-1)}(1+nx^n)^{1-(1/n)} + c \Rightarrow$ (a).

19. If $f(-10\sqrt{2}) = 2\sqrt{2}$, then $f''(-10\sqrt{2}) =$

(a) $\dfrac{4\sqrt{2}}{7^3 3^2}$ (b) $-\dfrac{4\sqrt{2}}{7^3 3^2}$

(c) $\dfrac{4\sqrt{2}}{7^3 3}$ (d) $-\dfrac{4\sqrt{2}}{7^3 3}$ **(I.I.T. 2008)**

Ans. (b).

Given $y^3 - 3y + x = 0$ ...(1)

At $x = -10\sqrt{2},\ y = 2\sqrt{2}$ ...(2)

$3(y^2 - 1)\dfrac{dy}{dx} = -1$

$\therefore \quad \dfrac{dy}{dx} = -\dfrac{1}{3(y^2-1)} = -\dfrac{1}{21}$ at $y = 2\sqrt{2}$ ...(3)

$\dfrac{d^2y}{dx^2} = \dfrac{1}{3(y^2-1)^2}.2y.y' = \dfrac{1}{3(7)^2}.2.2\sqrt{2}\left(\dfrac{-1}{21}\right)$

$= \dfrac{-4\sqrt{2}}{3^2.7^3} \Rightarrow$ (b)

20. The area of the region bounded by the curves $y = f(x)$, the x-axis, and the lines $x = a$ and $x = b$, where $-\infty < a < b < -2$, is

(a) $\displaystyle\int_a^b \frac{x}{3((f(x))^2-1)}\,dx + bf(b) - af(a)$

(b) $-\displaystyle\int_a^b \frac{x}{3((f(x))^2-1)}\,dx + bf(b) - af(a)$

(c) $\displaystyle\int_a^b \frac{x}{3((f(x))^2-1)}\,dx - bf(b) + af(a)$

(d) $-\displaystyle\int_a^b \frac{x}{3((f(x))^2-1)}\,dx - bf(b) + af(a)$ **(I.I.T. 2008)**

Ans. (a).

$A = \int_a^b f(x)\,dx = [x\,f(x)]_a^b - \int_a^b x.f'(x)\,dx$

$= b\,f(b) - a\,f(a) - \displaystyle\int_a^b x.\left\{-\frac{1}{3(y^2-1)}\right\}dx$ by (3)

$= b\,f(b) - a\,f(a) + \displaystyle\int_a^b \frac{x}{3[f(x)^2-1]}\,dx$

21. $\int_{-1}^{1} g'(x)\,dx =$

(a) $2g(-1)$ (b) 0

(c) $-2g(1)$ (d) $2g(1)$ **(I.I.T. 2008)**

Ans. (d).

Consider $y^3 - 3y + x = 0$ where $y = g(x)$.

$\therefore \quad g^3(x) - 3g(x) + x = 0$

and $g^3(-x) - 3g(-x) - x = 0$. Add

$g^3(x) + g^3(-x) - 3\{g(x) + g(-x)\} = 0$

$[g(x) + g(-x)]\,[g^2(x) + g^2(-x) - g(x)\,g(-x) - 3] = 0$

$\Rightarrow \quad g(-x) + g(x) = 0$ or $g(-x) = -g(x)$

Thus $g(x)$ is an odd function of x.

$\therefore \quad \int_{-1}^{1} g'(x)\,dx = [g(x)]_{-1}^{1} = g(1) - g(-1)$

$= g(1) + g(1) = 2g(1) \quad \because \ g(-1) = -g(1)$

Note : The other factor for $x = 0$ gives $g^2(0) + g^2(0) - g^2(0) - 3 = 0 \quad \therefore \ g^2(0) = 3$

$\therefore \quad g(0) = \sqrt{3}$ or $-\sqrt{3}$. This is not possible as $g(0) = 0$ given.

22. Let $f(x)$ be a non-constant twice differentiable function defined on $(-\infty, \infty)$ such that $f(x) = f(1-x)$ and $f'\left(\dfrac{1}{4}\right) = 0$. Then

(a) $f''(x)$ vanishes at least twice on [0, 1]

(b) $f'\left(\dfrac{1}{2}\right) = 0$

(c) $\displaystyle\int_{-1/2}^{1/2} f\left(x+\frac{1}{2}\right)\sin x\,dx = 0$

(d) $\displaystyle\int_0^{1/2} f(t)\,e^{\sin \pi t}\,dt = \int_{1/2}^{1} f(1-t)\,e^{\sin \pi t}\,dt$ **(I.I.T. 2008)**

Ans. (a), (b), (c), (d).

Given $f(x) = f(1-x)$ ...(1)

$f'\left(\dfrac{1}{4}\right) = 0$ ...(2)

Putting $x = \dfrac{1}{2} + t$ in (1), we have

$f\left(\dfrac{1}{2}+t\right) = f\left(\dfrac{1}{2}-t\right)$ *i.e.*, $F(X) = F(-X)$

Thus $f\left(\dfrac{1}{2}+x\right)$ is an even function of x.

$\therefore \quad f\left(x+\dfrac{1}{2}\right)\sin x$ is an odd function of x.

$\therefore \quad \displaystyle\int_{-1/2}^{1/2} f\left(x+\frac{1}{2}\right)\sin x\,dx = 0 \Rightarrow$ (c).

Differentiating (1), we have

$f'(x) = -f'(1-x)$. Put $x = \dfrac{1}{2}$

$\therefore \quad f'\left(\dfrac{1}{2}\right) = -f'\left(\dfrac{1}{2}\right)$ or $2f'\left(\dfrac{1}{2}\right) = 0$

or $f'\left(\dfrac{1}{2}\right) = 0 \Rightarrow$ (b).

Again $I = \int_0^{1/2} f(t)\,e^{\sin \pi t}\,dt$

Put $t = 1 - z \quad \therefore \ dt = -dz$

$\therefore \quad \pi t = \pi - \pi z \quad \therefore \ \sin \pi t = \sin \pi z$

Also when $t = 0, z = 1$; when $t = \dfrac{1}{2}, z = \dfrac{1}{2}$

$\therefore \quad I = \int_1^{1/2} f(1-z)\, e^{\sin \pi z}\,(-dz)$

$= \int_{1/2}^{1} f(1-t)\, e^{\sin \pi t}\, dt \Rightarrow$ (d)

Differentiating (1), we have

$f'(x) = -f'(1-x)$

Put $x = \frac{1}{4} \quad \therefore \quad f'\left(\frac{1}{4}\right) = -f'\left(1-\frac{1}{4}\right) = -f'\left(\frac{3}{4}\right)$

But $f'\left(\frac{1}{4}\right) = 0$ by (2). $\therefore \quad f'\left(\frac{3}{4}\right) = 0$

Also $f'\left(\frac{1}{2}\right) = 0$

Hence $f''(x) = 0$ at least twice in [0, 1] by Rolles theorem.

$\therefore \quad F(a) = F(b)$ then $F'(c) = 0$.

Problem Set (10)

Objective Questions

1. $\int \frac{e^x(1+\sin x)}{(1+\cos x)}\,dx$ is equal to

(a) $\log \tan x$ (b) $e^x \tan(x/2)$

(c) $\sin \log x$ (d) $e^x \cot x$

2. $\int \frac{(\sec x \operatorname{cosec} x)}{(\log \tan x)}\,dx$ is equal to

(a) $\log(\tan x)$ (b) $\cot(\log x)$

(c) $\log \log(\tan x)$ (d) $\tan(\log x)$

3. $\int \frac{\sin x + \cos x}{\sqrt{(1+\sin 2x)}}\,dx$ is

(a) $\sin x$ (b) x (c) $\cos x$ (d) $\tan x$

4. $\int e^x \sin(e^x)\,dx$ is

(a) $\cos e^x$ (b) $-\cos e^x$

(c) $(\cos e^x)^{-1}$ (d) $\sin e^x$.

5. (i) For any integer n, the integral

$\int_0^{\pi} e^{\cos^2 x} \cos^3 (2n+1)\, x\, dx$

has the value

(a) π (b) 1

(c) 0 (d) None of these.

(ii) For any integer n, the integral

$\int_0^{\pi} e^{\sin^2 x} \cos^3 (2n+1)\, x\, dx$ has the value

(a) -1 (b) 0

(c) 1 (d) π **(M.N.R. 1992)**

6. The value of $\int_{-1}^{1} x|x|\,dx$ is

(a) 2 (b) 1

(c) 0 (d) None of these.

7. The value of $\int_{-\pi/2}^{\pi/2} \sqrt{\frac{1}{2}(1-\cos 2x)}\,dx$ is

(a) 0 (b) 2

(c) $\frac{1}{2}$ (d) None of these.

8. The value of $\int_{-\pi/2}^{\pi/2} \log\left(\frac{2-\sin\theta}{2+\sin\theta}\right) d\theta$ is

(a) 0 (b) 1

(c) 2 (d) None of these

9. The value of $\int_{-1/2}^{1/2} \left| x \cos \frac{1}{2}\pi x \right| dx$ is .....

10. The value of $\int_0^{1/2} \frac{dx}{\sqrt{(x-x^2)}}$ is .....

11. The value of $\int \frac{dt}{t^2+2xt+1} \quad (x^2>1)$ is .....

12. $\int \sqrt{\left(\frac{x}{1+x^3}\right)}\,dx$ is ....

13. $\int_0^1 \frac{1}{(1+x^2)^{3/2}}\,dx = \frac{3}{\sqrt{(2)}}$

(a) True (b) False

14. $\int \frac{\sin\alpha}{\sqrt{(1+\cos\alpha)}}\,d\alpha = -2\sqrt{2}\cos\frac{\alpha}{2}$

(a) True (b) False

15. $\int \frac{e^{\log(1+1/x^2)}}{x^2+1/x^2}\,dx = \frac{1}{\sqrt{(2)}}\tan^{-1}\left(x-\frac{1}{x}\right)$

(a) True (b) False.

16. The area cut off by the parabola $y^2 = 4ax$ and its latus rectum is ....

17. The area common to the curves $y^2 = x$ and $x^2 = y$ is

(a) 1 (b) $\frac{2}{3}$

(c) $\frac{1}{3}$ (d) None of these.

18. The value of the integral $\int_0^{2a} \frac{f(x)}{f(x)+f(2a-x)}\,dx$ is equal to a.

(a) True (b) False

19. (i) The value of $\int_0^{\pi/2} \frac{\sqrt{\cos x}}{\sqrt{(\sin x)}+\sqrt{(\cos x)}}\,dx$ is

(a) 0 (b) $\pi/2$

(c) $\pi/4$ (d) None of these.

(ii) The value of $\int_0^{\pi/2} \frac{\sqrt{\cot x}}{\sqrt{(\cot x)}+\sqrt{(\tan x)}}\,dx$ is

(a) $\pi/4$ (b) $\pi/2$

(c) π (d) None of these.

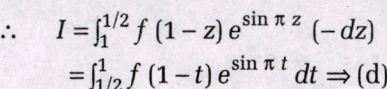

20. $\int_0^{\pi/4} \tan^2 x\,dx$ equals

(a) $\pi/4$ (b) $1+\pi/4$

(c) $1-\pi/4$ (d) None of these

21. $\int_{\pi/6}^{\pi/4} \dfrac{dx}{\sin 2x}$ is equal to

(a) $\frac{1}{2}\log(-1)$ (b) $\log(-1)$

(c) $\log 3$ (d) $\log\sqrt{3}$

22. $\int_0^{\pi/2} \dfrac{dx}{1+\sin x}$ equals

(a) 0 (b) $\frac{1}{2}$ (c) 1 (d) 3/2

23. The value of $\int_0^1 (1+e^{-x^2})\,dx$ is

(a) -1 (b) 2

(c) $1+e^{-1}$ (d) None of these.

24. $\lim_{n\to\infty}\left[\dfrac{1}{1-n^2}+\dfrac{2}{1-n^2}+\ldots\ldots+\dfrac{n}{1-n^2}\right]$ is equal to

(a) 0 (b) 2

(c) $1+e^{-1}$. (d) None of these.

25. Let $f(x)=\int_0^x t\sin t\,dt$, then $f'(x)$ is equal to

(a) $\cos x + x\sin x$. (b) $x\sin x$.

(c) $x\cos x$ (d) None of these

26. The value of $\int_3^5 \dfrac{x^2}{x^2-4}\,dx$ is

(a) $2-\log\left(\dfrac{15}{7}\right)$

(b) $2+\log\left(\dfrac{15}{7}\right)$

(c) $2-\tan^{-1}\left(\dfrac{15}{7}\right)$

(d) $2+4\log 3-4\log 7+4\log 5$

27. (i) The value of $\int_{-3}^{3} |x|\,dx$ is

(a) 3 (b) 9

(c) 18 (d) None

(ii) $\int_{-1}^{1} |1-x|\,dx$ is equal to

(a) -2 (b) 0

(c) 2 (d) 4

28. If $\int_0^{\pi/3} \dfrac{\cos\theta}{3+4\sin\theta}\,d\theta=\lambda\log\dfrac{3+2\sqrt{3}}{3}$ then λ equals

(a) 1/2 (b) 1/3 (d) 1/4 (d) 1/8

29. (i) $\int_0^{16} \dfrac{x^{1/4}\,dx}{1+\sqrt{x}}$ is equal to

(a) $4/3+\tan^{-1} 2$ (b) $8/3+4\tan^{-1} 2$

(c) $2/3+\tan^{-1} 2$ (d) None

(ii) The value of $\int \dfrac{a^{\sqrt{x}}}{\sqrt{x}}\,dx$ is

(a) $a^{\sqrt{x}}\log_e a+\lambda$ (b) $2\,a^{\sqrt{x}}\log_e a+\lambda$

(c) $2a^{\sqrt{x}}\log_{10} a+\lambda$ (d) $2a^{\sqrt{x}}\log_a e+\lambda$

30. $\int_{-\pi}^{\pi} (\cos ax-\sin bx)^2\,dx$ where a and b are integers, is

(a) $-\pi$ (b) 0 (c) π (d) 2π

31. (i) $\int_0^1 |\sin 2\pi x|\,dx$ is equal to

(a) 0 (b) $-1/\pi$

(c) $1/\pi$ (d) $2/\pi$

(ii) $\int_0^{\pi/2} |(\sin x-\cos x)|\,dx$

(a) 0 (b) $2(\sqrt{2}-1)$

(c) $2\sqrt{2}$ (d) $2(\sqrt{2}+1)$

32. The value of $\int_0^{\pi/2} \dfrac{f(x)\,dx}{f(x)+f(\pi/2-x)}$ is equal to

(a) $\pi/4$ (b) $\pi/2$ (c) π (d) None.

33. The area bounded by the curve $y=x^3$, the x-axis and the ordinates $x=-2$ and $x=1$ is

(a) -9 (b) $-15/4$ (c) $15/4$ (d) $17/4$

Hints and Solutions to Problem Set (10)

1. Ans. (b). **2.** Ans. (c).

3. Ans (b).

[**Hint :** $\sqrt{1+\sin 2x}=\sin x+\cos x$]

4. Ans. (b). **Hint** : Put $e^x = t$ etc.

5. (i) Ans. (c).

Hint : $\because$ $\cos(2n+1)(\pi-x)$

$=\cos[(2n+1)\pi-(2n+1)x]=-\cos(2n+1)x$

and $\cos^2(\pi-x)=\cos^2 x$,

so that $f(2a-x)=-f(x)$ and hence by Prop. VI of §7, we have

$\int_0^{\pi} e^{\cos^2 x}\cos^2(2n+1)x\,dx=0.$

(ii) Proceed as in part (i). Ans. (b).

6. Ans. (c). [**Hint : Use Prop. V, P. 1532**]

7. Ans. (b).

[**Hint :** $I=\int_{-\pi/2}^{\pi/2}\sqrt{\dfrac{1}{2}.2\sin^2 x}\,dx=\int_{-\pi/2}^{\pi/2}|\sin x|\,dx$

$=2\int_0^{\pi/2} |\sin x|\,dx,$ by **Prop. V, P. 1532**

$=2\int_0^{\pi/2} \sin x\,dx,$

$\because$ $|\sin x|=\sin x$ on the interval $(0,\pi/2)$

$=2(-\cos x)_0^{\pi/2}=2.$]

8. Ans. (a).

[**Hint :** If $f(\theta)=\log\left(\dfrac{2-\sin\theta}{2+\sin\theta}\right)$, then

$$f(-\theta) = \log\left(\frac{2+\sin\theta}{2-\sin\theta}\right) = \log\left(\frac{2-\sin\theta}{2+\sin\theta}\right)^{-1}$$
$$= -\log\left(\frac{2-\sin\theta}{2+\sin\theta}\right) = -f(\theta).$$

Hence by **Prop. V, P. 1532**, the value of given integral is zero]

9. Ans. $\frac{1}{\pi^2}(\pi\sqrt{2} + 4\sqrt{2} - 8)$.

Hint : If $f(-x) = |-x\cos\frac{1}{2}\pi(-x)| = |-x\cos\frac{1}{2}\pi x|$
$$= |x\cos\frac{1}{2}\pi x| = f(x).$$

Hence by **Prop. V of P. 1532**, we have

$$I = 2\int_0^{1/2} |x\cos\frac{1}{2}\pi x|\,dx$$
$$= 2\int_0^{1/2} x\cos\frac{1}{2}\pi x\,dx$$
$$= 2\left[\frac{x\sin\frac{1}{2}\pi x}{\frac{1}{2}\pi} + \frac{\cos\frac{1}{2}\pi x}{\frac{1}{4}\pi^2}\right]_0^{1/2}.$$

Successive Integration

$$= 2\left[\frac{2}{\pi}\cdot\frac{1}{2\sqrt{(2)}} + \frac{4}{\pi^2}\cdot\frac{1}{\sqrt{(2)}} - \frac{4}{\pi^2}\right]$$
$$= \frac{1}{\pi^2}(\pi\sqrt{2} + 4\sqrt{2} - 8).$$

10. Ans. $\frac{\pi}{2}$.

11. Ans. $\frac{1}{2\sqrt{(x^2-1)}}\cdot\log\frac{t + x - \sqrt{x^2-1}}{t + x + \sqrt{(x^2+1)}} + c.$

12. $I = \int\frac{x^{1/2}}{\sqrt{(1+x^3)}}\,dx.$

Put $x^{3/2} = t$ so that $\frac{3}{2}x^{1/2}\,dx = dt$

$$= \frac{2}{3}\int\frac{dt}{\sqrt{(1+t^2)}} = \frac{2}{3}\log\left\{t + \sqrt{1+t^2}\right\}.$$

13. Ans. (b). [**Hint :** $x = \tan\theta$ etc. Correct Ans. $= 1/\sqrt{2}$].

14. Ans. (a).

15. Ans. (b).

Correct Ans. is $\frac{1}{\sqrt{(2)}}\tan^{-1}\frac{x^2-1}{x\sqrt{(2)}}$.

16. Ans. $\frac{8}{3}a^2$.

17. Ans. (c).

18. Ans. (a).

Let $I = \int_0^{2a}\frac{f(x)}{f(x) + f(2a-x)}\,dx.$

Then also $I = \int_0^{2a}\frac{f(2a-x)}{f(2a-x) + f(x)}\,dx$ by Prop. IV

Adding $2I = \int_0^{2a} dx = 2a. \quad \therefore \quad I = a.$

19. (i) Ans. (c). (ii) Ans. (a).

20. Ans. (c).

21. Ans. (d).

22. Ans. (c).

23. Ans. (d).

24. Ans. (b).

25. Ans. (b).

26. Ans. (b).

$$I = \int_3^5\left(1 + \frac{4}{x^2-4}\right)dx \text{ etc.}$$

27. (i) Ans. (b).

$|-x| = |x| \quad \therefore \quad I = 2\int_0^3 |x|\,dx = 2\int_0^3 x\,dx$

or $I = \int_{-3}^0 -x\,dx + \int_0^3 x\,dx$ etc.

(ii) Ans. (c). As x varies from -1 to 1, $1 - x$ is always +ive

$\therefore \quad I = \int_{-1}^1 (1-x)\,dx = 2\int_0^1 1\,dx + 0 = 2,$ by Prop. V

28. Ans. (c).

$$I = \frac{1}{4}[\log(3 + 4\sin\theta)]_0^{\pi/3} = \frac{1}{4}\log\frac{3+2\sqrt{3}}{3}$$

29. (i) Ans. (b). Put $x = t^4$

$$\therefore \quad I = 4\int_0^2\frac{t^4 - 1 + 1}{t^2+1} \text{ etc.}$$

(ii) Ans. (d). Now $\frac{1}{\log_e a} = \log_a e.$

30. Ans. (d). $I = \int_{-\pi}^{\pi}(\cos^2 ax + \sin^2 bx)$

$$- 2\int_{-\pi}^{\pi}\cos ax \sin bx\,dx$$
$$= 2\int_0^{\pi}(\cos^2 ax + \sin^2 bx)\,dx - 0 \quad \text{Prop. VI}$$
$$= \int_0^{\pi}(1 + \cos 2ax + 1 - \cos 2bx)\,dx$$
$$= 2\pi + 0 = 2\pi$$

31. (i) Ans. (d).

$$I = \int_0^{1/2}\sin 2\pi x\,dx + \int_{1/2}^1 -\sin 2\pi x\,dx = \frac{2}{\pi}$$

(ii) Ans. (b). $I = \int_0^{\pi/4} -(\sin x - \cos x)\,dx$
$$+ \int_{\pi/4}^{\pi/2}(\sin x - \cos x)\,dx$$

Alt. $f(2a - x) = f(x)$

$\because \quad |\sin x - \cos x| = |\cos x - \sin x|$

$\therefore \quad I = 2\int_0^{\pi/4}|\sin x - \cos x|\,dx$
$$= 2\int_0^{\pi/4} -(\sin x - \cos x)\,dx = 2(\sqrt{2} - 1)$$

32. (a) Ans. (a). Use Prop IV.

$$2I = \int_0^{\pi/2} 1\,dx = \frac{\pi}{2} \therefore I = \frac{\pi}{4}$$

33. Ans. (d). y is $-$ ive for $-2 \le x \le 0$, +ive for $0 < x \le 1$

$\therefore \quad \text{Area} = \left|\int_{-2}^0 y\,dx\right| + \int_0^1 y\,dx$
$$= |-4| + \frac{1}{4} = 4 + \frac{1}{4} = \frac{17}{4}.$$

MISCELLANEOUS EXERCISE

Matching Entries

Match the entries of List-A and List-B.

1. **List-A** | **List-B**

(a) $\int \frac{e^{x-1} + x^{e-1}}{e^x + x^e} dx =$

(b) $\int e^{x \log a} . e^x \, dx =$

(c) $\int x^x \log(1+x) \, dx =$

(d) $\int \frac{\log(x+1) - \log x}{x(x+1)} dx =$

(e) $\int a^{a^{a^x}} . a^{a^x} . a^x \, dx =$

(f) $\int (e^{x \log a} + e^{a \log x}) \, dx =$

1. $-\frac{1}{2}\left[\log \frac{x+1}{x}\right]^2$
2. $a^{a^{a^x}} \div (\log a)^3$
3. $\frac{(ae)^x}{\log(ae)}$
4. x^x
5. $\frac{1}{e}\log(e^x + x^e)$
6. $\frac{a^x}{\log a} + \frac{x^{a+1}}{a+1}$

2. **List-A** | **List-B**

(a) $\int_0^{\pi/4} \frac{\sin x + \cos x}{3 + \sin 2x} dx$

(b) $\int \frac{\sin^8 x - \cos^8 x}{1 - 2\sin^2 x \cos^2 x}$

(c) If $\int \frac{dx}{\sin^4 x + \cos^4 x} = \tan^{-1} f(x)$, then $f(x) =$

(d) $\int \frac{x^2 - 1}{(x^2+1)\sqrt{(x^4+1)}} dx$

1. $\frac{1}{\sqrt{2}} \sec^{-1}\left(\frac{x^2+1}{x\sqrt{2}}\right)$
2. $\tan x - \cot x$
3. $-\frac{1}{2}\sin 2x$
4. $\frac{1}{4}\log 3$

3. **List-A** | **List-B**

(a) If $I_n = \int_0^{\pi/4} \tan^n x \, dx, (n > 0, n \in N)$, then $I_n + I_{n-2} =$

(b) $\int_0^{\pi/4} (\tan^n x + \tan^{n-2} x) \, d(x - [x])$

(c) If $I_n = \int_0^{\pi/4} \tan^n x \, dx$, then $I_{12} + 2I_{10} + I_8 =$

(d) If $I_n = \int_0^{\pi/4} \tan^n x \, dx$, then $I_2 + I_4, I_3 + I_5, I_4 + I_6$ are in which series ?

(e) If $I_n = \int_0^{\pi/2} \frac{\sin^2 nx}{\sin x} dx$, then $I_2 - I_1, I_3 - I_2, I_4 - I_3, \ldots$ are in which series ?

1. $\frac{20}{99}$
2. H.P.
3. $\frac{1}{n-1}$

4. **List-A** | **List-B**

(a) $\int \frac{x^2+1}{x^4+1} dx$

(b) $\int \frac{x^2+1}{x^4+x^2+1} dx$

(c) $\int \frac{x^2+1}{x^4-x^2+1} dx$

1. $\tan^{-1} \frac{x^2-1}{x}$
2. $\frac{1}{\sqrt{2}} \tan^{-1} \frac{x^2-1}{x\sqrt{2}}$
3. $-\frac{x}{x^2-1}$

(d) $\int \frac{x^2+1}{(x^2-1)^2}\,dx$ 4. $\frac{1}{\sqrt{3}}\tan^{-1}\frac{x^2-1}{x\sqrt{3}}$

5. **List-A**   **List-B**

(a) $\int \frac{x.e^x}{(1+x)^2}\,dx$ 1. $e^x \log(x+3)$

(b) $\int \frac{e^x}{x+3}[1+(x+3)\log(x+3)]$ 2. $\frac{e^x}{(x+2)^2}$

(c) $\int e^x . \frac{x}{(x+2)^3}\,dx$ 3. $x-\sqrt{1-x^2}\,\sin^{-1}x$

(d) $\int \frac{x\sin^{-1}x}{\sqrt{1-x^2}}\,dx$ 4. $\frac{e^x}{1+x}$

6. **List-A**   **List-B**

(a) $\int \frac{1}{x(x^n+1)}\,dx$ 1. $\frac{1}{3}\log\frac{x^3}{x^3+1}$

(b) $\int \frac{1}{x(x^3+1)}\,dx$ 2. $\frac{1}{3}\log\left\{\frac{\sqrt{1+x^3}-1}{\sqrt{1+x^3}+1}\right\}$

(c) $\int \frac{1}{x\sqrt{x^n+1}}\,dx$ 3. $\frac{1}{n}\log\frac{x^n}{x^n+1}$

(d) $\int \frac{1}{x\sqrt{x^3+1}}\,dx$ 4. $\frac{1}{n}\log\left\{\frac{\sqrt{1+x^n}-1}{\sqrt{1+x^n}+1}\right\}$

7. **List-A**   **List-B**

(a) $I_1=\int_0^{n\pi} f|\cos x|\,dx$ and $I_2=\int_0^{5\pi} f|\cos x|\,dx$ then $\frac{I_1}{I_2}=\ldots$ 1. $100(e-1)$

(b) $\int_0^{100} e^{x-[x]}\,dx=$ 2. $\frac{\pi}{8}\log 2$

(c) $\int_0^{\pi/4} \log(1+\tan x)\,dx=$ 3. $\frac{\pi}{4n}$

(d) $\int_0^{\pi/2n} \frac{dx}{1+\cot^n nx}=$ 4. $\frac{n}{5}$

8. **List-A**   **List-B**

(a) $\int_{-2}^{0} (x^3+3x^2+3x+3)+(x+1)\cos(x+1)\,dx=$ 1. 2π

(b) $\int_{\log(1/2)}^{\log 2} \sin\left[\frac{e^x-1}{e^x+1}\right]dx=$ 2. 4

(c) $\int_{-\pi}^{\pi} (\cos ax-\sin bx)^2\,dx=$ 3. 3

(d) $\int_4^{10} \frac{[x^2]}{[x^2-28x+196]+[x^2]}\,dx=$ 4. 0

9. **List-A**   **List-B**

(a) $\underset{x\to 0}{\text{Lt}}\ \frac{\int_0^{x^3}\sin\sqrt{t}\,dt}{x^3}=$ 1. $\frac{1}{2}[x]$

(b) $\int_0^1 |\sin 2\pi x| dx =$ — 2. $2/3$

(c) $\int_0^{3/2} [x^2] dx =$ — 3. $\frac{2}{\pi}$

(d) $\int_0^{[x]} [x - [x]] dx =$ — 4. $2 - \sqrt{2}$

(e) $\underset{n \to \infty}{\text{Lt}} \sum_{r=1}^{n} \frac{r^3}{r^4 + n^4} =$ — 5. $\frac{1}{4} \log 2$

10. **List-A** | **List-B**

(a) $\int_{-1}^{1} \frac{dx}{1+x^2}$ — (p) $\frac{1}{2} \log\left(\frac{2}{3}\right)$

(b) $\int_{0}^{1} \frac{dx}{\sqrt{1-x^2}}$ — (q) $2 \log\left(\frac{2}{3}\right)$

(c) $\int_{2}^{3} \frac{dx}{1-x^2}$ — (r) $\frac{\pi}{3}$

(d) $\int_{1}^{2} \frac{dx}{x\sqrt{x^2-1}}$ — (s) $\frac{\pi}{2}$ **(I.I.T. 2007)**

11. Match the statements/expressions in column-I with the open intervals in column-II.

Column-I | **Column-II**

(A) Interval contained in the domain of definition of non-zero solutions of the differential equation $(x-3)^2 y' + y = 0$ — (p) $\left(-\frac{\pi}{2}, \frac{\pi}{2}\right)$

(B) Interval containing the value of the integral $\int_1^5 (x-1)(x-2)(x-3)(x-4)(x-5)\, dx$ — (q) $\left(0, \frac{\pi}{2}\right)$

(C) Interval in which at least one of the points of local maximum of $\cos^2 x + \sin x$ lies — (r) $\left(\frac{\pi}{8}, \frac{5\pi}{4}\right)$

(D) Interval in which $\tan^{-1}(\sin x + \cos x)$ is increasing — (s) $\left(0, \frac{\pi}{8}\right)$

(t) $(-\pi, \pi)$ **(I.I.T. 2009)**

12. Match the integrals in Column-I with the values in Column-II.

Column-I | **Column-II**

(a) $\int_{-1}^{1} \frac{dx}{1+x^2}$ — (p) $\frac{1}{2} \log\left(\frac{2}{3}\right)$

(b) $\int_{0}^{1} \frac{dx}{\sqrt{1-x^2}}$ — (q) $2 \log\left(\frac{2}{3}\right)$

(c) $\int_{2}^{3} \frac{dx}{1-x^2}$ — (r) $\frac{\pi}{3}$

(d) $\int_{1}^{2} \frac{dx}{x\sqrt{x^2-1}}$ — (s) $\frac{\pi}{2}$ **(I.I.T. 2008)**

Hints / Solutions

1. (a) $\rightarrow$ 5. **Q. 23 (a) P. 1452**

(b) $\rightarrow$ 3. **Q. 39 P. 1452**

(c) $\rightarrow$ 4.

Put $x^x = t \quad \therefore \quad x \log x = \log t$

$$\left(1.\log x + \frac{1}{x}\cdot x\right) dx = \frac{1}{t}\, dt$$

or $\quad x^x (\log x + 1)\, dx = dt \qquad \because\ t = x^x$

$\therefore \quad I = \int 1.dt = t = x^x.$

(d) $\rightarrow$ 1.

$$I = \int \frac{\log\left(\frac{x+1}{x}\right)}{\frac{(x+1)}{x}} \cdot \frac{1}{x^2}\, dx$$

Now put $t = \dfrac{x+1}{x} = 1 + \dfrac{1}{x} \quad \therefore \quad dt = -\dfrac{1}{x^2}\, dx$

$\therefore \quad I = -\int \log t \,.\dfrac{1}{t}\, dt = -\dfrac{1}{2}(\log t)^2 + c$ etc.

(e) $\rightarrow$ 2.

Put $a^x = t$

$\therefore \quad I = \int \dfrac{a^{a^t} .\, a^t\, dt}{\log a}$

Again put $a^t = z$

$\therefore \quad I = \int \dfrac{a^z\, dz}{(\log a)^2} = \dfrac{a^z}{(\log a)^3} + c$

(f) $\rightarrow$ 6.

$$T_1 = e^{x \log a} = e^{\log a^x} = a^x, T_2 = x^a$$

$\therefore \quad I = \dfrac{a^x}{\log a} + \dfrac{x^{a+1}}{a+1}$

2. (a) $\rightarrow$ 4.

$\sin x + \cos x$ is d.c. of $\sin x - \cos x = t$ say,

and $t^2 = 1 - \sin 2x \quad$ or $\quad \sin 2x = 1 - t^2$

$$\therefore \quad I = \int_{-1}^{0} \frac{dt}{4 - t^2} = \frac{1}{2.2}\left[\log \frac{2+t}{2-t}\right]_{-1}^{0}$$

$$= \frac{1}{4}\left(0 - \log \frac{1}{3}\right) = \frac{1}{4} \log 3$$

(b) $\rightarrow$ 3.

$$N^r = (\sin^4 x - \cos^4 x)(\sin^4 x + \cos^4 x)$$

$$= (\sin^2 x - \cos^2 x)(1 - 2\sin^2 x \cos^2 x)$$

$\therefore \quad I = \dfrac{N^r}{D^r} = -\int \cos 2x\, dx = -\dfrac{1}{2}\sin 2x + c$

(c) $\rightarrow$ 2.

Dividing above and below by $\cos^4 x$, we have

$$I = \int \frac{(1 + \tan^2 x)\sec^2 x}{1 + \tan^4 x}\, dx$$

Now put $\tan x = t \quad \therefore \quad \sec^2 x\, dx = dt$

$$\therefore \quad I = \int \frac{1 + t^2}{1 + t^4}\, dt = \int \frac{\left(1 + \frac{1}{t^2}\right)}{\left(t - \frac{1}{t}\right)^2 + 1}\, dt$$

Now put $t - \dfrac{1}{t} = z \quad \therefore \quad \left(1 + \dfrac{1}{t^2}\right) dt = dz$

$$\therefore \quad I = \int \frac{dz}{z^2 + 1} = \tan^{-1} z = \tan^{-1}\left(t - \frac{1}{t}\right)$$

$$I = \tan^{-1}(\tan x - \cot x)$$

$\therefore \quad f(x) = \tan x - \cot x \quad$ and $\quad f\left(\dfrac{\pi}{4}\right) = 1 - 1 = 0$

(d) $\rightarrow$ 1.

Divide above and below by x^2

$$I = \int \frac{\left(1 - \frac{1}{x^2}\right)}{\left(1 + \frac{1}{x^2}\right)\sqrt{x^2 + \frac{1}{x^2}}}\, dx$$

Put $x + \dfrac{1}{x} = t \quad \therefore \quad \left(1 - \dfrac{1}{x^2}\right) dx = dt$

$$I = \int \frac{dt}{t\sqrt{t^2 - 2}} = \frac{1}{\sqrt{2}} \sec^{-1} \frac{t}{\sqrt{2}}$$

$$= \frac{1}{\sqrt{2}} \sec^{-1} \frac{\left(x + \frac{1}{x}\right)}{\sqrt{2}} = \frac{1}{\sqrt{2}} \sec^{-1}\left(\frac{x^2 + 1}{x\sqrt{2}}\right)$$

3. (a) $\rightarrow$ 3. **Q. 18 (d) P. 1510**

(b) $\rightarrow$ 3.

As x varies from 0 to $\pi/4$ *i.e.* 0 to $(3 \cdot 14)/4$ or 0 to $0 \cdot 8$ then $[x] = 0$.

Hence the function reduces to

$$\int_0^{\pi/4} \tan^{n-2} x (\tan^2 x + 1)\, dx$$

$$= \int_0^{\pi/4} \tan^{n-2} \sec^2 x\, dx$$

$$= \frac{1}{n-1}\left[\tan^{n-1} x\right]_0^{\pi/4}$$

$$= \frac{1}{n-1} - 0 = \frac{1}{n-1}$$

(c) $\rightarrow$ 1.

As proved above in (b)

$\therefore \quad I_n + I_{n-2} = \dfrac{1}{n-1} \qquad \ldots(1)$

$$I = (I_{12} + I_{10}) + (I_{10} + I_8) = \frac{1}{11} + \frac{1}{9} = \frac{20}{99},$$

putting $\quad n = 12, n = 10 \quad$ in (1)

$\therefore \quad I_{12} + 2I_{10} + I_8 = \dfrac{20}{99} \quad \Rightarrow$ (c)

(d) $\rightarrow$ 2.

As proved above in (b),

$u_n + u_{n-2} = \dfrac{1}{n-1} \quad$ Put $n = 4, 5, \ldots$

$u_2 + u_4 = \frac{1}{3}, u_3 + u_5 = \frac{1}{4}, u_4 + u_6 = \frac{1}{5}$.

which are in H.P. as their reciprocals are in A.P.

(e) $\to 2$.

$$u_n - u_{n-1} = \int_0^{\pi/2} \frac{\sin^2 nx - \sin^2 (n-1)x}{\sin x} dx$$

$$= \int_0^{\pi/2} \frac{\sin x \sin (2n-1)x}{\sin x} dx$$

$$= \left[-\frac{\cos (2n-1)x}{2n-1} \right]_0^{\pi/2}$$

or $u_n - u_{n-1} = \frac{1}{2n-1}$. Put $n = 2, 3, 4 \ldots$

$\therefore \quad u_2 - u_1 = \frac{1}{3}, u_3 - u_2 = \frac{1}{5}, u_4 = \frac{1}{7}$

which are in H.P. as their reciprocals are in A.P.

4. (a) $\to$ 2, (b) $\to$ 4, (c) $\to$ 1, (d) $\to$ 3

See Q. 23 (a) P. 1500

5. (a) $\to$ 4. **Q. 27 (a) P. 1485**

(b) $\to$ 1.

$\int e^x [f(x) + f'(x)] dx = e^x f(x)$

(c) $\to$ 2.

$x = x + 2 - 2$

$\int e^x [f(x) + f'(x)] dx = e^x f(x)$

where $f(x) = \frac{1}{(x+2)^2}$

(d) $\to$ 3. **Q. 14 (i) P. 1485**

6. (a) $\to$ 3. **Ex. 3 P. 1493**

(b) $\to$ 1. **Ex. 3 P. 1493**

(c) $\to$ 4. **Ex. 7 P. 1495**

(d) $\to$ 2. **Ex. 7 P. 1495**

7. (a) $\to$ 4. **Ex. 45 (c) P. 1558**

(b) $\to$ 1. **Q. 43 (b) P. 1558**

(c) $\to$ 2. **Ex. 7 (a) P. 1544**

(d) $\to$ 3.

Put $nx = t$ and adjust the limits and change to sin and cos.

$$I = \frac{1}{n} \int_0^{\pi/2} \frac{\sin^n t}{\sin^n t + \cos^n t} dt$$

Apply Prop. IV and add.

$$2I = \frac{1}{n} \int_0^{\pi/2} dt = \frac{1}{n} \frac{\pi}{2} \quad \therefore \quad I = \frac{\pi}{4n}.$$

8. (a) $\to$ 2.

Put $x + 1 = t$ and adjust the limits

$\therefore \quad I = \int_{-1}^{1} (t^3 + 2 + t \cos t) dt$

$= 0 + 2\int_0^1 2\, dt$ by Prop. V

$= [4t]_0^1 = 4$

(b) $\to$ 4.

$$I = \int_{-\log 2}^{\log 2} \sin\left(\frac{e^x - 1}{e^x + 1}\right) dx$$

If $f(x) = \sin\left(\frac{e^x - 1}{e^x - 1}\right)$

$$f(-x) = \sin\left(\frac{1 - e^x}{1 + e^x}\right) = -\sin\left(\frac{e^x - 1}{e^x + 1}\right) = -f(x)$$

Hence $f(x)$ is an odd function of x

$\therefore \quad I = 0$ by Prop. V.

(c) $\to$ 1.

$I = \int_{-\pi}^{\pi} (\cos^2 ax + \sin^2 bx) - 2\int_{-\pi}^{\pi} \cos ax \sin bx\, dx$

$= 2\int_0^{\pi} (\cos^2 ax + \sin^2 bx)\, dx - 0$ Prop. V and VI

$= \int_0^{\pi} (1 + \cos 2ax + 1 - \cos 2bx)\, dx$

$= \left[2x + \frac{1}{2a} \sin 2ax - \frac{1}{2b} \sin 2bx \right]_a^{\pi} = 2\pi + 0 = 2\pi$

(d) $\to$ 3.

Denominator $[(14 - x)^2] + [x^2]$

Apply Prop. VII and add

$\therefore \quad 2I = \int_4^{10} 1 . dx = 6$

$\therefore \quad I = 3$

9. (a) $\to$ 2. **Ex. 5 P. 1540**

(b) $\to$ 3.

$\sin \theta$ is + ive in 1st and 2nd quadrants and – ive in 3rd and 4th quadrants.

$$\therefore \quad I = \int_0^{1/2} \sin 2\pi x\, dx + \int_{1/2}^{1} - \sin 2\pi x\, dx = \frac{2}{\pi}$$

(c) $\to$ 4. **Q. 36 (a) P. 1554**

(d) $\to$ 1. **Q. 43 (a) P. 1558**

(e) $\to$ 5. **Ex. 4 P. 1530**

10. Ans. (a) $\to$ (s), (b) $\to$ (s), (c) $\to$ (p), (d) $\to$ (r)

(a) $I = [\tan^{-1} x]_{-1}^{1} = \tan^{-1}(1) - \tan^{-1}(-1)$

$$= \frac{\pi}{4} - \left(-\frac{\pi}{4}\right) = \frac{\pi}{2}$$

(b) $[\sin^{-1} x]_0^1 = \sin^{-1} 1 - \sin^{-1} 0 = \frac{\pi}{2}$

(c) $\left[\frac{1}{2} \log \frac{1+x}{1-x} \right]_2^3 = \frac{1}{2} \left[\log\left(\frac{4}{-2}\right) - \log\left(\frac{3}{-1}\right) \right]$

$$= \frac{1}{2} \log \frac{2}{3}$$

(d) $[\sec^{-1} x]_1^2 = \sec^{-1} 2 - \sec^{-1} 1 = \frac{\pi}{3} - 0 = \frac{\pi}{3}$

11. (A) $\to$ (p, q, s)

$(x-3)^2 \frac{dy}{dx} + y = 0$ or $\frac{dy}{y} + \frac{dx}{(x-3)^2} = 0$

Integrating, $\log y - \frac{1}{x-3} = \log k$

or $\log \frac{y}{k} = \frac{1}{x-3}$

$\therefore \quad y = k e^{1/(x-3)}$.

Hence $x \neq 3$ as $x = 3$ makes y infinite.

$\therefore$ Domain is $R - \{3\}$.

Hence (A) $\rightarrow$ (p, q, s).

(B) $\rightarrow$ (p, t). Put $x - 3 = t$ and adjust the limits.

$I = \int_{-2}^{2} (t+2)(t+1)\,t\,(t-1)(t-2)\,dt$

$= \int_{-2}^{2} t\,(t^2 - 4)(t^2 - 1)\,dt = 0$, by Prop. V as $f(t)$ is an odd function of t.

(C) $\rightarrow$ (p, q, r, t)

$y = \cos^2 x + \sin x = 1 - \sin^2 x + \sin x$

$= 1 + \frac{1}{4} - \left(\sin x - \frac{1}{2}\right)^2$

$\therefore$ y is maximum when $\sin x = \frac{1}{2}$

Alt. $\frac{dy}{dx} = -2\sin x \cos x + \cos x = 0$

$\Rightarrow$ $\cos x = 0$ or $\sin x = 1/2$

$\frac{dy}{dx} = \cos x\,(1 - 2\sin x)$

$\frac{d^2 y}{dx^2} = -\sin x\,(1 - 2\sin x) - 2\cos^2 x$

$= 0 - 2\left(1 - \frac{1}{4}\right) = -\frac{3}{2} = -$ ive

$\therefore$ y is maximum when $\sin x = \frac{1}{2}$

$\Rightarrow$ $x = n\pi + (-1)^n \frac{\pi}{6}$

Hence (C) $\rightarrow$ (p, q, r, t).

(D) $\rightarrow$ (s).

$\frac{dy}{dx} = \frac{\cos x - \sin x}{1 + (\sin x - \cos x)^2} = +$ ive for increasing

$\Rightarrow$ $\cos x > \sin x$ $\quad$ ($\because D^r$ being + ive)

$\Rightarrow$ $\tan x < 1 \Rightarrow x < \frac{\pi}{4}$ $\therefore$ $x \in \left(0, \frac{\pi}{8}\right)$

12. Ans. (a) $\rightarrow$ (s), (b) $\rightarrow$ (s), (c) $\rightarrow$ (p), (d) $\rightarrow$ (r)

(a) $I = [\tan^{-1} x]_{-1}^{1} = \tan^{-1}(1) - \tan^{-1}(-1)$

$= \frac{\pi}{4} - \left(-\frac{\pi}{4}\right) = \frac{\pi}{2}$

(b) $[\sin^{-1} x]_0^1 = \sin^{-1} 1 - \sin^{-1} 0 = \frac{\pi}{2}$

(c) $\left[\frac{1}{2}\log\frac{1+x}{1-x}\right]_2^3 = \frac{1}{2}\left[\log\left(\frac{4}{-2}\right) - \log\left(\frac{3}{-1}\right)\right]$

$= \frac{1}{2}\log\frac{2}{3}$

(d) $[\sec^{-1} x]_1^2 = \sec^{-1} 2 - \sec^{-1} 1 = \frac{\pi}{3} - 0 = \frac{\pi}{3}$

❑

§17. Area.

1. The area between the curve $y = f(x)$, x-axis and two ordinates at the points $x = a$ and $x = b$ $(b > a)$ is given by the formula

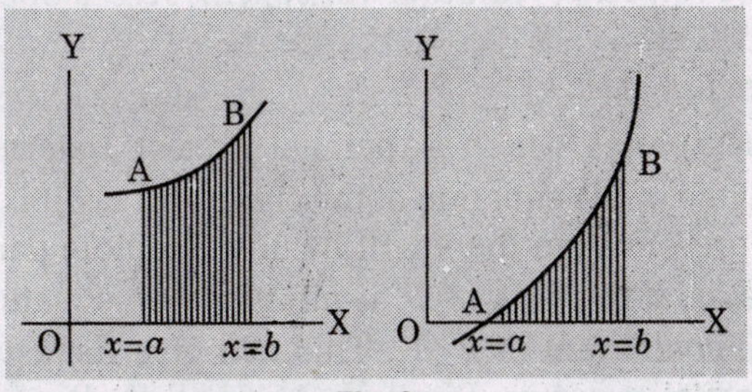

Fig. 3

$$A = \int_a^b f(x)\,dx = \int_a^b y\,dx.$$

It represents the shaded area in fig. (1, 2) and non-shaded in Fig. 3.

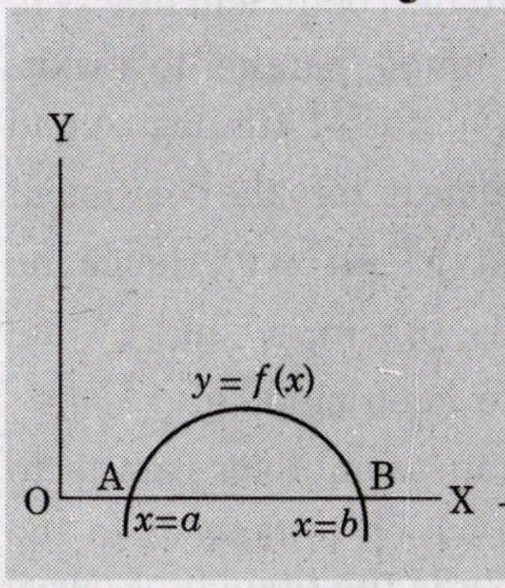

Fig. 4

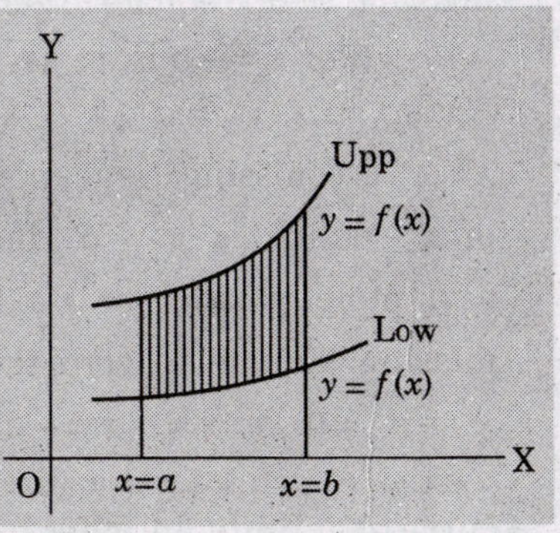

Fig. 5

2. Similarly if the area be between the curve and y-axis and two abscissas drawn at the points $y = a$ and $y = b$ $(b > a)$ then the corresponding formula will be

$A = \int_a^b x\,dy.$

3. Area between two curves $y = f(x)$ and $y = \phi(x)$ and the two ordinates drawn at the points $x = a$ and $x = b$, then

$A = \int_a^b y_1\,dx - \int_a^b y_2\,dx$

Upper $\quad$ Lower

$= \int_a^b (f(x) - \phi(x))\,dx$

where y_1 is the ordinate of $y = f(x)$ which is upper curve and y_2 is the ordinate of $y = \phi(x)$ which is lower curve.

It is shown by shaded area in the figure 5.

4. In the above results we have taken the area to be lying above x-axis. But if the area be lying below the x-axis then the value of area will be – ive if found as usual which is not true and hence we take mod.

$\therefore$ $A = \left|\int_a^b y\,dx\right|$

Similarly if the area be lying to left of y-axis, then

$A = \left|\int_a^b x\,dy\right|.$

In case the area is lying above x-axis as well as below x-axis in the interval $[a, b]$ then we divide the interval $[a, b]$ into various sub-intervals during which the area is either above x-axis or below x-axis. For below x-axis we take mod.

Consider the following graph.

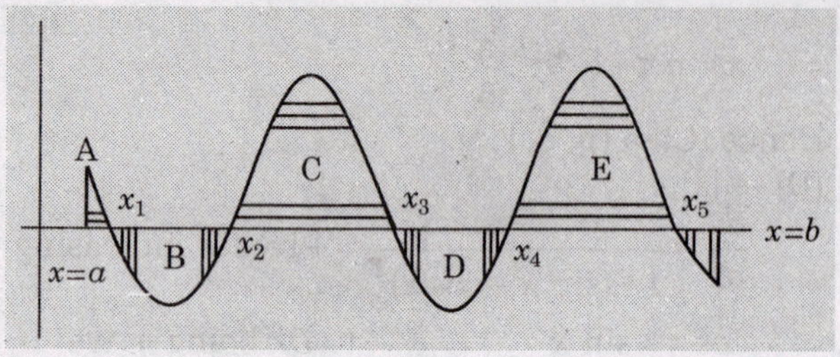

Fig. 6

We shall divide $[a, b]$ into

$[a, x_1] + [x_1, x_2] + [x_2, x_3] + [x_3, x_4] + [x_4, x_5] + [x_5, b]$

$$\therefore \int_a^b f(x)\,dx = \int_a^{x_1} \underset{+\text{ ive}}{y}\,dx + \left|\int_{x_1}^{x_2} \underset{-\text{ ive}}{y}\,dx\right|$$

$$+\int_{x_2}^{x_3} \underset{+\text{ ive}}{y}\,dx + \left|\int_{x_3}^{x_4} \underset{-\text{ ive}}{y}\,dx\right| + \int_{x_4}^{x_5} \underset{+\text{ ive}}{y}\,dx + \left|\int_{x_5}^{b} \underset{-\text{ ive}}{y}\,dx\right|$$

[Fig. 6]

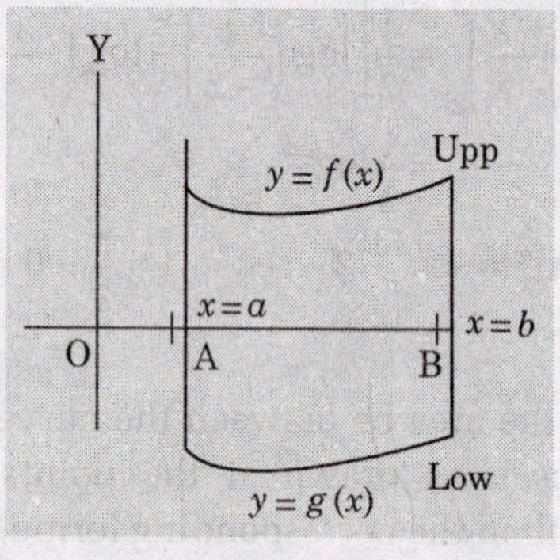

Fig. 7

Note. Area bounded by two curves.

We have shown in (3) that

$$* \quad A = \int_a^b (\underset{\text{up}}{y_1} - \underset{\text{low}}{y_2})\,dx = \int_a^b [f(x) - g(x)]\,dx \qquad \text{[Fig. 5]}$$

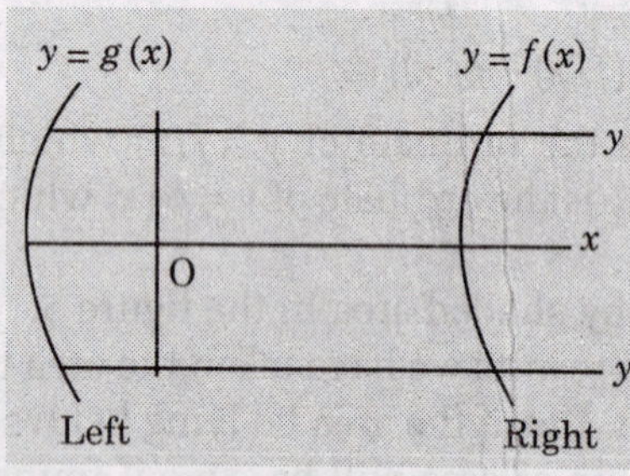

Fig. 8

The above formula does not change whether the area is above or below x-axis or both.

$$* \quad A = \int_a^b (\underset{\text{R}}{x_1} - \underset{\text{L}}{x_2})\,dy \quad \int_a^b [f(y) - g(y)]\,dy$$

R = Right, L = Left [Fig. 6]

§ 18. Rules for tracing of Cartesian Curves

1. **Symmetry :**

(a) If the equation of the curve involves **even and only even** powers of x, then that curve is **symmetrical about y-axis** because for a given value of y we will get equal and opposite values of x e.g. parabola $x^2 = 4ay$. If $y = a$, then $x^2 = 4a^2 \therefore x = 2a, -2a$. Hence this parabola is symmetrical about y-axis.

(b) Similarly if there are even and only even powers of y, then it is symmetrical about x-axis, e.g. $y^2 = 4ax$ is **symmetrical about x-axis.**

(c) If, however, the curve involves even and only even powers of both x and y then it is **symmetrical about both the axes.** Just as circle $x^2 + y^2 = a^2$ and ellipse $\frac{x^2}{a^2} + \frac{y^2}{b^2} = 1$ are symmetrical about both the axes.

(d) Again if x and y be interchanged and the equation of the curve does not change then it is symmetrical about the line $y = x$ i.e. a line through origin making an angle of 45° with x-axis.

2. **Points on the curve :** Put $y = 0$ and find x. Similarly put $x = 0$ and find y. Thus you will find the points where the curve crosses the axes of co-ordinates.

3. **Tangents :** Tangent at origin (if origin be a point on the curve) are obtained by equating to zero the lowest degree terms in the equation of the curve, $y^2 = 4ax$, $T_{(0,0)}$ is $4ax = 0$ *i.e.* $x = 0$ or y-axis. In $x^2 = 4ay$, $T_{(0,0)}$ is $4ay = 0$ *i.e.* $y = 0$ *i.e.* x-axis. In $x^3 + y^3 = 3axy$, $T_{(0,0)}$ is $3axy = 0$ *i.e.*, $x = 0$, $y = 0$ *i.e.* both the axes are tangents at the origin. Tangent at any other point is given by $\frac{dy}{dx} = -\frac{f_x}{f_y}$. Its value at (h, k) will give slope of the tangent at (h, k).

4. **Asymptotes** (which are parallel to axes) : Determine the degree of the equation of the curve and say it is n. If x^n is present then there will be no asymptote parallel to x-axis. If the term of x^n is missing then equate to zero the coefficient of x^{n-1}. This will give the asymptote parallel to x-axis. Similarly we shall find asymptotes parallel to y-axis e.g.

$$x(x^2 + y^2) = a(x^2 - y^2).$$

It is an equation of 3rd degree but x^3 is present but y^3 is missing. Hence equate to zero the coefficient of y^2 *i.e.* $x + a = 0$ or $x = -a$ is an asymptote parallel to y-axis. Again in $x^2 y^2 = a^2 (y^2 - x^2)$, it is of 4th degree and x^4, x^3 are missing. Hence equate to zero the coefficient of x^2 which is $y^2 + a^2$ but $y^2 + a^2 \neq 0$. Hence no asymptote parallel to x-axis. Again y^4 and y^3 are missing. Equate to zero the coefficient of y^2, *i.e.* $x^2 - a^2 = 0 \therefore x = a, x = -a$ are asymptotes parallel to y-axis. Asymptote is a line which is tangent to the curve at infinity. In other words the branch of curve moves almost parallel to the asymptote.

5. **Region :** Consider $y^2(2a-x)=x^3$.

If $x>2a$. Then y^2 is – ive so that y is imaginary. Hence no part of the curve will lie beyond $x=2a$. Similarly in $y^2(a+x)=x^2(a-x)$. If $x>a$, then y will be imaginary. Hence no part of the curve will lie beyond $x=a$.

Note 1 : The shapes of the standard curves,

$$y^2=4ax,\ y^2=-4ax,\ x^2=4ay,\ x^2=-4ay$$

$$\frac{x^2}{a^2}+\frac{y^2}{b^2}=1,\ a>b,\ \frac{x^2}{a^2}+\frac{y^2}{b^2}=1,\ b>a$$

may be seen in the chapters of Parabola and Ellipse respectively.

Note 2 : Evaluation of integral by Gamma function be looked on **P. 821** in the chapter of definite integral.

Figures of Certain important curves.

The four parabolas (1) $y^2=4ax$, (2) $y^2=-4ax$, (3) $x^2=4ay$, (4) $x^2=-4ay$ are traced as shown.

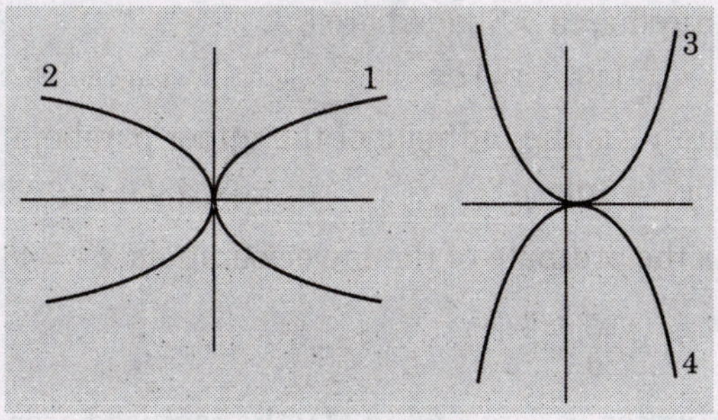

Fig. 9

$y=e^x$. The curve crosses y-axis at $x=0, y=1$. As x increases from 0, y goes on increasing beyond 1 and as x decreases from 0, y goes on decreasing but it is never negative because exponential function is always +ive. Hence its shape is shown below.

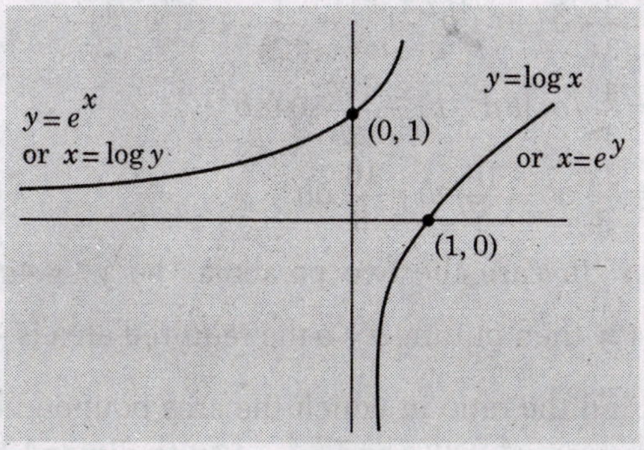

Fig. 10

$y=\log x \quad \therefore \quad x=e^y$. It is to be traced as above.

It cuts x-axis at (1, 0).

$$y=\frac{1}{e^{x^2}}$$

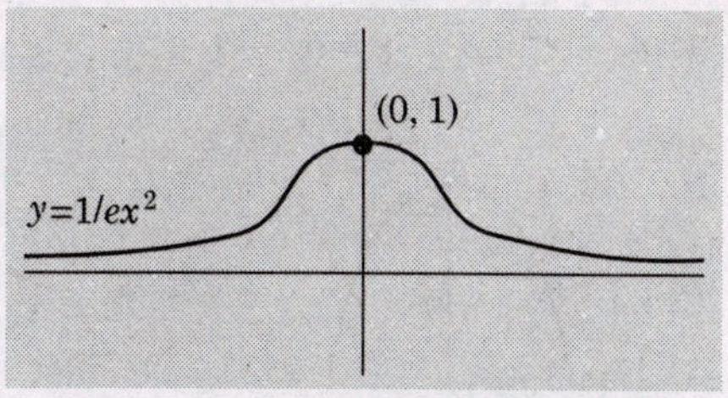

Fig. 11

$y=[x]$, greatest integer function $0<x<1$, $y=0$, $1<x<2$, $y=1$, $2<x<3$, $y=2$. Similarly $-1<x<0$, $y=-1$, $-2<x<-1$, $y=-2$.

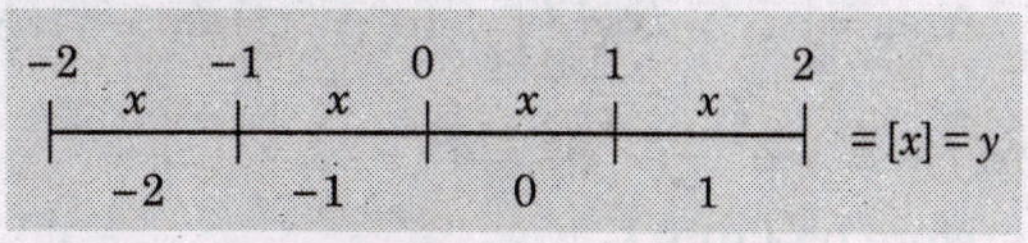

Fig. 12

Solved Examples

Ex. 1. Find the area of the ellipse $\frac{x^2}{a^2}+\frac{y^2}{b^2}=1$.

The required area is four times the area in the first quadrant shown shaded in the figure. This is the area between the curve, x-axis and two ordinates drawn at the points $x=0$ and $x=a$,

$$A=4\int_0^a y\,dx.$$

The parametric equations of ellipse are

$$x=a\cos t,\ y=b\sin t.$$

$$\therefore \quad A=4\int_{\pi/2}^{0}(b\sin t)(-a\sin t)\,dt$$

$$=4ab\int_0^{\pi/2}\sin^2 t\,dt$$

$$=4ab\cdot\frac{1}{2}\cdot\frac{\pi}{2}=\pi ab$$

Note : You can also do it by

$$A=4\int_0^a \frac{b}{a}\sqrt{(a^2-x^2)}\,dx$$

Deduction : Area of Circle

Putting $b=a$ the ellipse becomes circle $x^2+y^2=a^2$ and hence its area will be πa^2 sq. units.

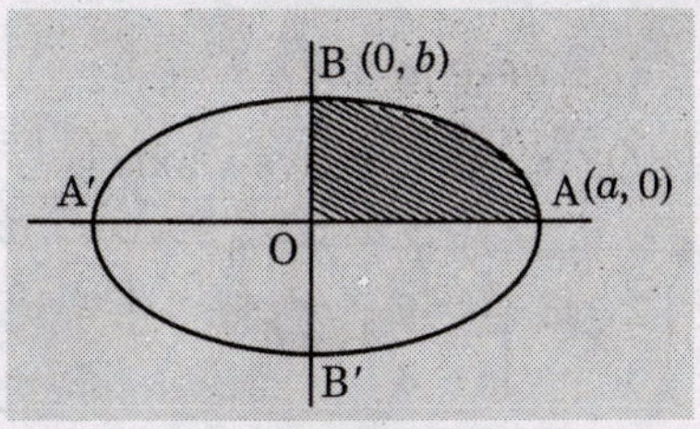

Fig. 13

Ex. 2. Find the area enclosed by the parabola

$$ay=3(a^2-x^2)$$

and the axis of x.

The parabola cuts the axis of x i.e. $y=0$ in points given by

$0 = 3(a^2 - x^2)$, $\therefore$ $x = a, -a$

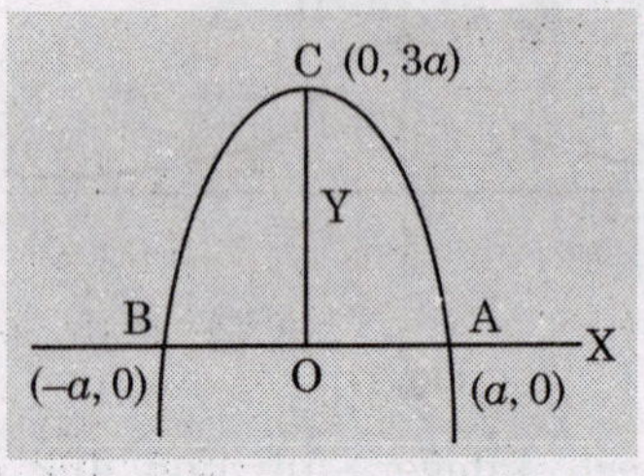

Fig. 14

$\therefore$ Area $= \int_{-a}^{a} y\,dx = \frac{3}{a}\int_{-a}^{a} (a^2 - x^2)\,dx.$

Here $f(-x) = a^2 - (-x)^2 = a^2 - x^2 = f(x)$.

Therefore by Prop. V,

$$\text{Area} = 2.\frac{3}{a}\int_0^a (a^2 - x^2)\,dx = \frac{6}{a}\left[a^2 x - \frac{x^3}{3}\right]_0^a$$

$$= \frac{6}{a}\left[a^3 - \frac{a^3}{3}\right] = \frac{6}{a}.\frac{2}{3}a^3 = 4a^2 \text{ sq. units.}$$

Ex. 3. Show that the area cut off a parabola by any double ordinate is two-thirds of the corresponding rectangle contained by that double ordinate and its distance from the vertex.

We have to prove that

Area $PAQP = \frac{2}{3}$ area of rectangle $PLMQ$.

The equation of the parabola is $y^2 = 4ax$.

Let the ordinate be drawn through $P(h, k)$.

Then $k^2 = 4ah$ or $k = 2\sqrt{ah}$

Area of rectangle $= 2k.h = 2.2\sqrt{ah}.h = 4\sqrt{ah}.h$ ...(1)

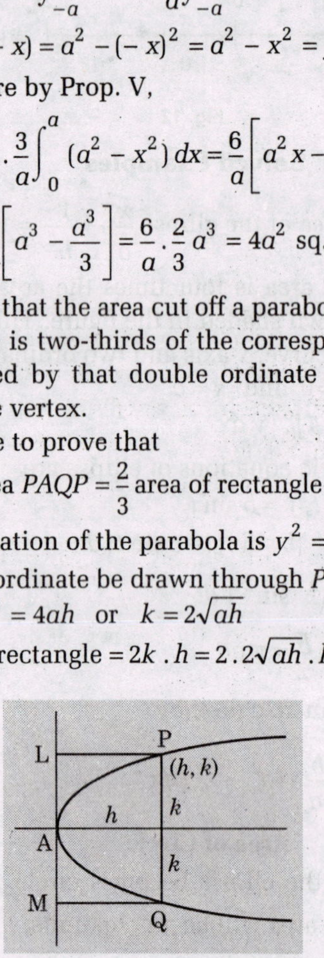

Fig. 15

Area $PAQP = 2$ [area above x-axis.]

$= 2\int_0^h y\,dx = 2\int_0^h 2\sqrt{a}\sqrt{x}\,dx$

$= 4\sqrt{a}\left[\frac{2}{3}x^{3/2}\right]_0^h = \frac{2}{3}4\sqrt{a}\,h^{3/2}$

$= \frac{2}{3}$ [Area of rectangle] by (1).

***Ex. 4. (a)** Find the area included between the parabolas $y^2 = 4ax$ and $x^2 = 4by$.

The two curves meet at P say (h, k).

Solving the two, we get

from $x^2 = 4by$, $y = \frac{x^2}{4b}$ and putting in $y^2 = 4ax$,

we have, $\left(\frac{x^2}{4b}\right)^2 = 4ax$

or $x^4 - 64b^2 ax = 0$ or $x(x^3 - 64b^2 a) = 0$

$\therefore$ $x = 0$, $x = 4a^{1/3}b^{2/3} = h$

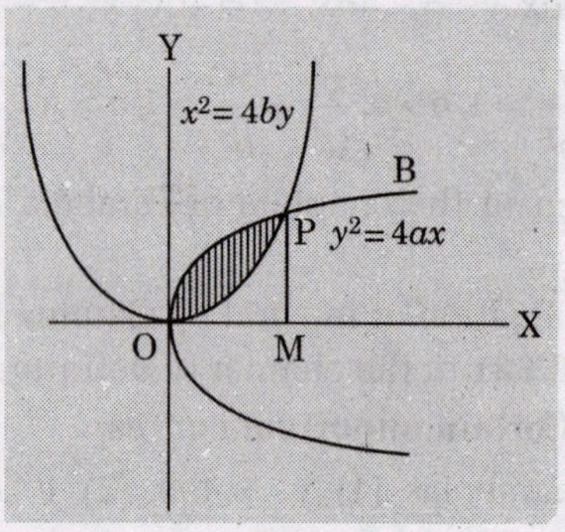

Fig. 16

Required area = Shaded area

$= \int_0^h (y_1 - y_2)\,dx$ ...(1)

where y_1 is the ordinate of the upper parabola $y^2 = 4ax$. $\therefore$ $y_1 = 2\sqrt{a}\sqrt{x}$.

y_2 is the ordinate of the lower parabola $x^2 = 4by$.

$\therefore$ $y_2 = \frac{x^2}{4b}$.

Putting for y_1 and y_2 in (1), the required area is

$$A = \int_0^h \left(2\sqrt{a}\sqrt{x} - \frac{x^2}{4b}\right)dx$$

$$= \left[2\sqrt{a}.\frac{2}{3}x^{3/2} - \frac{1}{4b}.\frac{x^3}{3}\right]_0^h = \left[4\frac{\sqrt{a}}{3}h^{3/2} - \frac{1}{12b}h^3\right].$$

Now put $h = 4a^{1/3}b^{2/3}$.

$$= \frac{4}{3}\sqrt{a}(4a^{1/3}b^{2/3})^{3/2} - \frac{1}{12b}(4a^{1/3}b^{2/3})^3$$

$$= \frac{4}{3}\sqrt{a}.(8a^{1/2}b) - \frac{1}{12b}.64ab^2$$

$$= \frac{32}{3}ab - \frac{16}{3}ab = \frac{16}{3}ab.$$

Note : In case the two parabolas be $y^2 = 4ax$ and $x^2 = 4ay$ then putting $b = a$ the required area is $\frac{16}{3}a^2$.

(b)* Find the ratio in which the area bounded by the curves $y^2 = 12x$ and $x^2 = 12y$ is divided by the line $x = 3$. **(Roorkee 1994)**

Proceed as in part (a). $a = b = 3$

The two curves meet at $P(12, 12)$

$$\therefore \quad A = \int_0^{12} (y_1 - y_2)\,dx = \int_0^{12}\left(2\sqrt{3}\,x^{1/2} - \frac{x^2}{12}\right)dx$$

$$= \left[2\sqrt{3}\cdot\frac{2}{3}x^{3/2} - \frac{x^3}{12.3}\right]_0^{12}$$

$$= \left(\frac{4}{\sqrt{3}}.12.\sqrt{12} - 48\right) = 96 - 48 = 48$$

Again Area $A_1 = \int_0^3 (y_1 - y_2)\,dx$

$$= \left[2\sqrt{3}\frac{2}{3}x^{3/2} - \frac{x^3}{12.3}\right]_0^3 = \left[\frac{4}{3}\sqrt{3}\,3\sqrt{3} - \frac{3}{4}\right] = \frac{45}{4}$$

$\therefore \quad A_2 = A - A_1 = 48 - \frac{45}{4} = \frac{3}{4} \times 49$

$\therefore \quad \frac{A_1}{A_2} = \frac{15}{49}.$

Ex. 5. Find the area between the parabola $y^2 = 4ax$ and the line $y = mx$.

The line meets the parabola where

$(mx)^2 = 4ax$ or $x(m^2x - 4a) = 0$

$\therefore \quad x = 0,\ x = \frac{4a}{m^2} = h$ say.

The required area $= \int_0^h (y_1 - y_2)\,dx.$ ...(1)

where y_1 is the ordinate of the upper curve, *i.e.* parabola $y^2 = 4ax$.

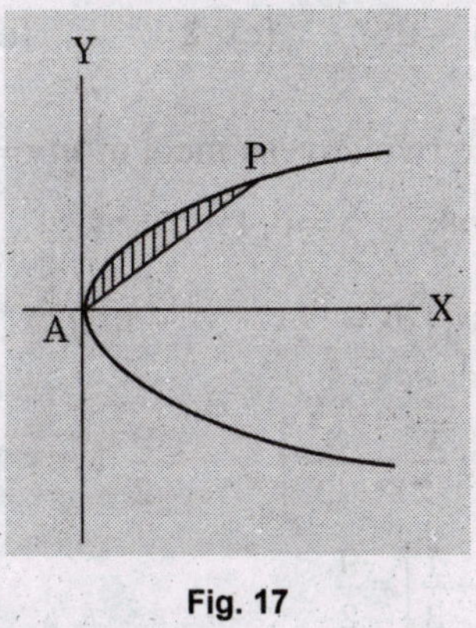

Fig. 17

$\therefore \quad y_1 = 2\sqrt{a}\sqrt{x}.$

y_2 is the ordinate of the lower curve *i.e.* straight line $y = mx$.

$\therefore \quad y_2 = mx.$

Putting for y_1 and y_2 in (1), we get

$A = \int_0^h 2\sqrt{a}\sqrt{x}\,dx - \int_0^h mx\,dx$

$$= 2\sqrt{a}\frac{2}{3}\left[x^{3/2}\right]_0^h - m\left[\frac{x^2}{2}\right]_0^h = \frac{4\sqrt{a}}{3}h^{3/2} - \frac{m}{2}h^2.$$

Now put $h = \frac{4a}{m^2}$

$$\therefore \quad A = \frac{4}{3}\sqrt{a}\left(\frac{4a}{m^2}\right)^{3/2} - \frac{m}{2}\left(\frac{4a}{m^2}\right)^2$$

$$= \frac{4}{3}\sqrt{a}.\frac{8a^{3/2}}{m^3} - \frac{m}{2}\frac{16a^2}{m^4}$$

$$= \frac{32}{3}\frac{a^2}{m^3} - 8.\frac{a^2}{m^3} = \frac{8}{3}.\frac{a^2}{m^3}.$$

Note : If the curves were $y^2 = 9x$ and $y = x$, then $4a = 9$ or $a = 9/4$ and $m = 1$.

$$\therefore \quad A = \frac{8}{3}\frac{a^2}{m^3} = \frac{8}{3}.\left(\frac{9}{4}\right)^2 = \frac{8}{3}\frac{81}{16} = \frac{27}{2} \text{ sq. units.}$$

***Ex. 6.** *AOB* is the positive quadrant of the ellipse $x^2/a^2 + y^2/b^2 = 1$ in which $OA = a$, $OB = b$. Show that the area between the arc *AB* and chord *AB* of the ellipse is $\frac{1}{4}ab(\pi - 2)$.

Area $= A_1 - A_2 = \int_0^a (y_1 - y_2)\,dx$ ...(1)

Clearly ellipse is upper curve and line is lower curve

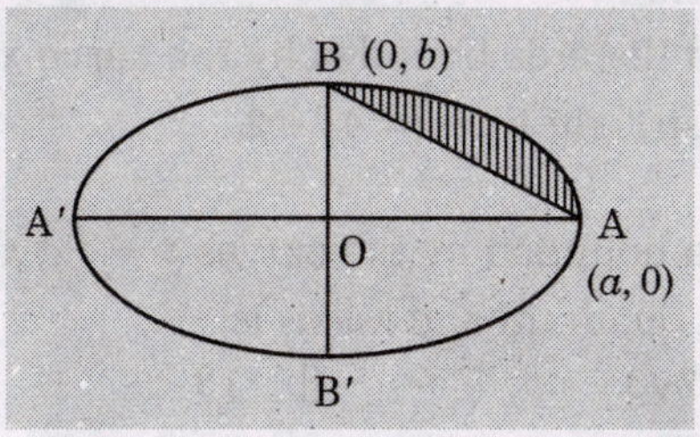

Fig. 18

Area A_1 has been calculated is **Ex. 1, P. 1477** to be $\frac{\pi ab}{4}$.

y_2 is the ordinate of the lower curve *i.e.* line *AB* whose equation in intercepts form is

$$\frac{x}{a} + \frac{y}{b} = 1. \quad \therefore \quad \frac{y_2}{b} = 1 - \frac{x}{a},$$

$$\therefore \quad A_2 = \int_0^a y_2\,dx = b\int_0^a \left(1 - \frac{x}{a}\right)dx = b\left[x - \frac{x^2}{2a}\right]_0^a$$

or $\quad A_2 = b\left[\frac{a}{2}\right] = \frac{1}{2}ab$

$$\therefore \quad A = A_1 - A_2 = \frac{\pi ab}{4} - \frac{1}{2}ab = \frac{ab}{4}\cdot(\pi - 2)$$

Note : $A_2 = \int y_2\,dx$ can also be written directly as $\Delta = \frac{1}{2}ab$.

Ex. 7. (a) Find the area cut off the parabola $4y = 3x^2$ by the straight line $2y = 3x + 12$.

Eliminating y, we get

$2(3x + 12) = 3x^2$

or $\quad 3x^2 - 6x - 24 = 0$ or $3x^2 - 12x + 6x - 24 = 0$

or $\quad 3x(x - 4) + 6(x - 4) = 0$

or $\quad (x - 4)(3x + 6) = 0;$

$\therefore \quad x = -2,\ x = 4 \quad \therefore \quad y = 3,\ y = 12.$

i.e. the points of intersection are $P(-2, 3)$ and $(4, 12)$.

$A = \int_{-2}^4 (\underset{\text{up}}{y_1} - \underset{\text{low}}{y_2})\,dx$ L = Line

L P P = Parabola

$$= \int_{-2}^4 \left\{\frac{3x + 12}{2} - \frac{3x^2}{4}\right\}dx = 27 \text{ sq. units}$$

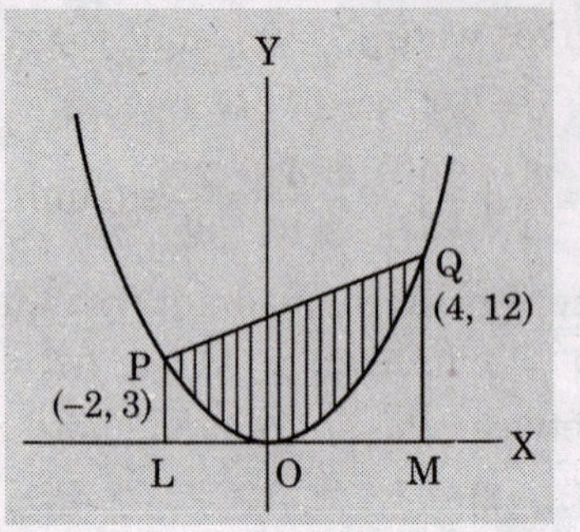

Fig. 19

Note : Area $\int y_1 \, dx$ can be written directly as the area of trapezium.

(b) Find the area bounded by the curve $x^2 = 4y$ and the straight line $x = 4y - 2$.

Ans. 9/8.

(c) Area bounded by the curves $y = \sqrt{x}, x = 2y + 3$ in first quadrant and x-axis is

(a) $2\sqrt{3}$ (b) 18

(c) 9 (d) 34/3 **(Screening 2003)**

Ans. (c). $y^2 = x, x = 2y + 3$

The line and parabola meet where $y^2 - 2y - 3 = 0$

$\therefore \quad y = 3, -1.$

$\therefore \quad x = 9, 1 \quad \therefore \quad (9, 3)$ and $(1, -1)$.

We have to find the area between the two curves and x-axis in first quadrant.

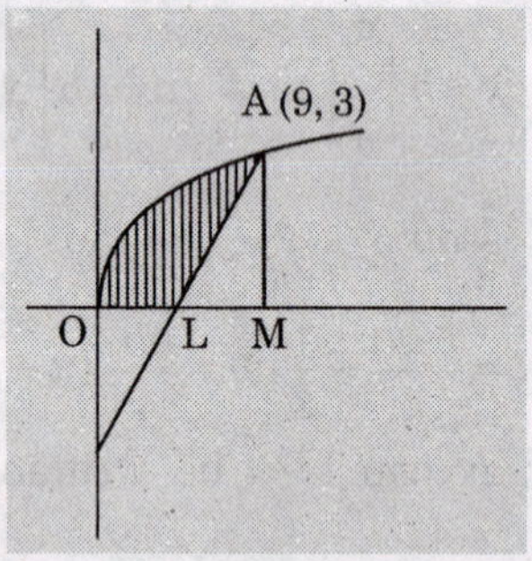

Fig. 20

$A = \int_0^9 y \, dx - \Delta ALM$

$= \frac{2}{3}[x^{3/2}]_0^9 - \frac{1}{2}.6.3 = \frac{2}{3}.27 - 9 = 18 - 9 = 9.$

***Ex. 8. (a)** Indicate the region bounded by the curves $x^2 = y$, $y = x + 2$ and x-axis and obtain the area enclosed by them. **(Roorkee 1997)**

The parabola and line meet in points $P(-1, 1)$ and $Q(2, 4)$. The line cuts the axes in $(-2, 0)$ and $B(0, 2)$.

As in parts (a) and (b) we are **not** to find the area cut off the parabola and the line and hence the formula $\int_{-1}^{2} (\underset{L}{y_1} - \underset{P}{y_2}) \, dx$ will not be used. Here we have to find the area bounded by the curves and x-axis, *i.e.* area *ORAPO*.

i.e. area *APR* + area *PRO*

$= \int_{-2}^{-1} \underset{L}{y \, dx} + \int_{-1}^{0} \underset{P}{y \, dx} = \int_{-2}^{-1} (x + 2) \, dx + \int_{-1}^{0} x^2 \, dx$

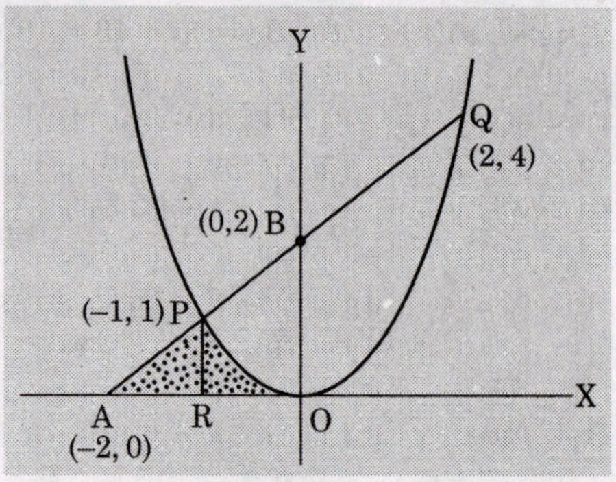

Fig. 21

$= \left[\frac{x^2}{2} + 2x\right]_{-2}^{-1} + \left[\frac{1}{3}x^3\right]_{-1}^{0} = \frac{1}{2} + \frac{1}{3} = \frac{5}{6}$ sq. units.

Note : Area $APR = \Delta = \frac{1}{2}b.h = \frac{1}{2}.1.1 = \frac{1}{2}$

(b) For which of the following values of m, is the area of the region bounded by the cruve $y = x - x^2$ and the line $y = mx$ equals 9/2 ?

(a) -4 (b) -2 (c) 2 (d) 4

(I.I.T. 1999)

Ans. (b), (d). The two curves meet at $mx = x - x^2$

or $\quad x^2 = x(1 - m) \quad \therefore \ x = 0, 1 - m.$

$A = \int (\underset{P}{y_1} - \underset{L}{y_2}) \, dx = \int (x - x^2 - mx) \, dx$

$= \left[(1 - m)\frac{x^2}{2} - \frac{x^3}{3}\right]_0^{1-m} = \frac{9}{2}$ if $m < 1$

or $\quad (1 - m)^3 \left[\frac{1}{2} - \frac{1}{3}\right] = \frac{9}{2}$

or $\quad (1 - m)^3 = 27 \quad \therefore \ m = -2$

But if $m > 1$ then $1 - m$ is – ive, then

$\left[(1 - m)\frac{x^2}{2} - \frac{x^3}{3}\right]_{1-m}^{0} = \frac{9}{2} - (1 - m)^3\left(\frac{1}{2} - \frac{1}{3}\right) = \frac{9}{2}$

$\therefore \quad (1 - m)^3 = -27$

or $\quad 1 - m = -3 \quad \therefore \quad m = 4.$

Ex. 9. Prove that the area in the first quadrant enclosed by the x-axis, the line $x = y\sqrt{3}$ and the circle $x^2 + y^2 = 4$ is $\pi/3$.

Line and the curve meet at $P(\sqrt{3}, 1)$ in Ist quadrant. Draw perpendicular PM.

$\therefore \quad A = \Delta\, OPM + \int_{\sqrt{3}}^{2} y \, dx$

Now $x = 2\cos\theta$, $y = 2\sin\theta$ and adjust the limits

$= \frac{1}{2}\sqrt{3}.1 + \int_{\pi/6}^{0} (2\sin\theta)(-2\sin\theta) \, d\theta$

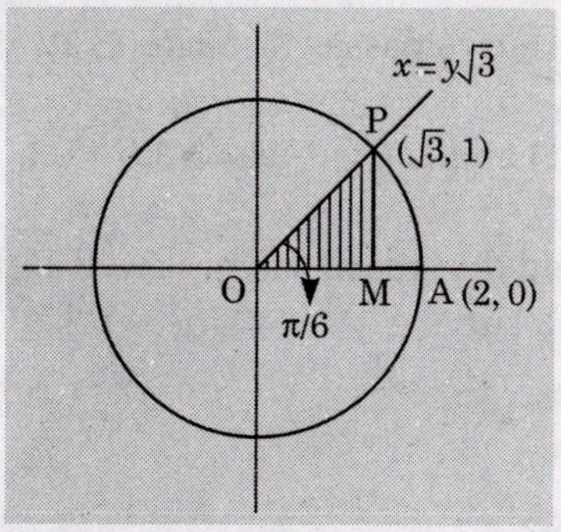

Fig. 22

$$= \frac{\sqrt{3}}{2} + 4\int_0^{\pi/6} \frac{(1 - \cos 2\theta)}{2}\, d\theta$$

$$= \frac{\sqrt{3}}{2} + 2\left[\theta - \frac{\sin 2\theta}{2}\right]_0^{\pi/6} = \frac{\sqrt{3}}{2} + 2\left[\frac{\pi}{6} - \frac{1}{2}\frac{\sqrt{3}}{2}\right] = \frac{\pi}{3}$$

Note : Another Method.

$\angle POM = \frac{\pi}{6} = \theta$

$\therefore$ A = Area of sector of a circle

$= \frac{1}{2} r^2\, \theta = \frac{1}{2}(2)^2\, \frac{\pi}{6} = \frac{\pi}{3}.$

***Ex. 10. (a)** Find the area common to the circle $x^2 + y^2 = 16a^2$ and the parabola $y^2 = 6ax$. Hence find the larger of the area into which the circle is divided by the parabola.

(b) Find the area lying above x-axis and included between the circle $x^2 + y^2 = 8x$ and the parabola $y^2 = 4x$.

(c)* Determine the area of that portion of the circle $x^2 + y^2 = 64$ which is exterior to the parabola $y^2 = 12x$.

(a) Solving the two, we get

$x^2 + 6ax - 16a^2 = 0$

$(x + 8a)(x - 2a) = 0$

$\therefore$ $x = 2a$ $\therefore$ $y = \pm 2\sqrt{3}a.$

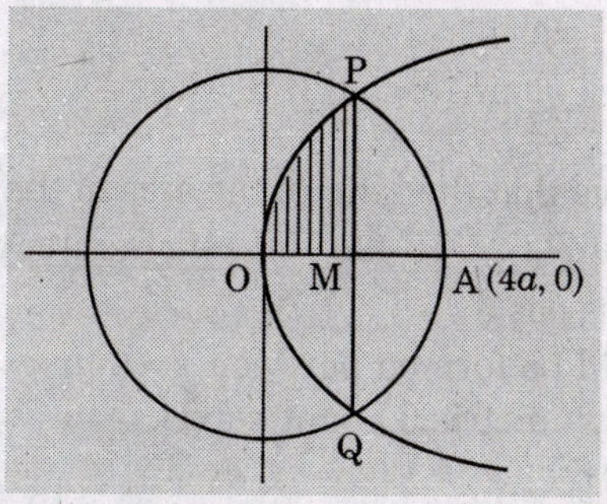

Fig. 23

The required common area

$= 2\,[APOA] = 2$ [Lined area + dotted area]

$= 2\int y\, dx + 2\int y\, dx = 2(A + B)$

Para. Circle

$$2A = 2\int_0^{2a} \sqrt{6a}\,\sqrt{x}\, dx = 2.\sqrt{6a}\,\frac{2}{3}\,[x^{3/2}]_0^{2a}$$

$$= 2.\sqrt{6a}\,\frac{2}{3}\,2a\sqrt{2a} = 2.2\sqrt{3}.\frac{4}{3}a^2 = \frac{16}{3}\sqrt{3}a^2$$

$$2B = 2\int_{2a}^{4a} \sqrt{[(4a)^2 - x^2]}\, dx$$

Put $x = 4a\sin\theta$ $\therefore$ $dx = 4a\cos\theta\, d\theta$

The limits are adjusted as $\frac{\pi}{6}$ to $\frac{\pi}{2}$

$\therefore$ $2B = 2\int_{\pi/6}^{\pi/2} 4a.\cos\theta.4a\cos\theta\, d\theta$

$$= 16a^2 \int_{\pi/6}^{\pi/2} (1 + \cos 2\theta)\, d\theta = 16a^2\left[\theta + \frac{\sin 2\theta}{2}\right]_{\pi/6}^{\pi/2}$$

$$= 16a^2\left[\frac{\pi}{3} - \frac{\sqrt{3}}{4}\right] = \frac{16}{3}\pi a^2 - 4\sqrt{3}\,a^2$$

$\therefore$ Total area $= 2A + 2B.$

$$= \frac{16}{3}\sqrt{3}a^2 - 4\sqrt{3}a^2 + \frac{16}{3}a^2\,\pi$$

$$= \frac{4\sqrt{3}a^2}{3} + \frac{16\pi a^2}{3} = \frac{4a^2}{3}(4\pi + \sqrt{3}).$$

$\therefore$ Larger area = Area of circle − Common area

$$= \pi(4a)^2 - \frac{4a^2}{3}(4\pi + \sqrt{3}) = 16\pi a^2 - \frac{4a^2}{3}(4\pi + \sqrt{3})$$

$$= \frac{4a^2}{3}[12\pi - 4\pi - \sqrt{3}] = \frac{4a^2}{3}(8\pi - \sqrt{3}).$$

(b) Ans. $\frac{4}{3}(8 + 3\pi)$, $x^2 + y^2 = 8x$ is a circle with centre at (4, 0) and radius 4. Its equation is $(x - 4)^2 + y^2 = 4^2$.

(c) Ans. $\frac{16}{3}(8\pi - \sqrt{3})$.

Ex. 11. (a) Find the area inside the parabola $5x^2 - y = 0$ but outside the parabola $2x^2 - y + 9 = 0$.

Eliminating y, we get $5x^2 - (2x^2 + 9) = 0$

or $3x^2 = 9$ $\therefore$ $x = -\sqrt{3}, \sqrt{3}.$

$\therefore$ Required area $= 2\int_0^{\sqrt{3}} (y_1 - y_2)\, dx.$ ...(1)

The two parabolas are $x^2 = \frac{1}{5}y$, $x^2 = \frac{1}{2}(y - 9)$ and clearly from the figure second parabola is upper and first is lower.

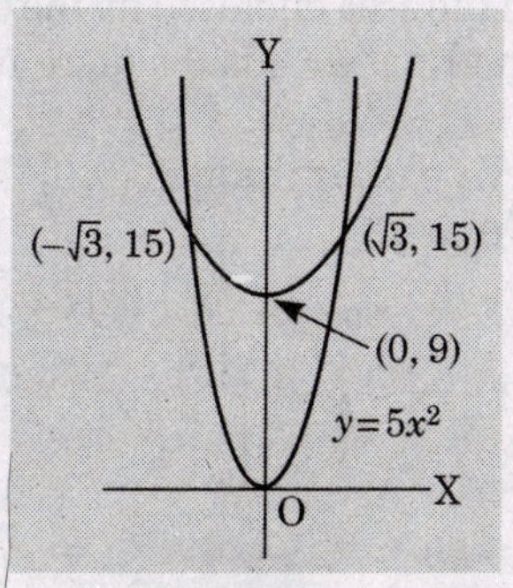

Fig. 24

Therefore from (1) the common area

$$= 2\int_0^{\sqrt{3}} (\underset{\text{Up}}{y_1} - \underset{\text{Low}}{y_2})\, dx = 2\int_0^{\sqrt{3}} [(2x^2+9) - 5x^2]\, dx$$

$$= 2\int_0^{\sqrt{3}} (9 - 3x^2)\, dx = 12\sqrt{3}$$

(b) Area enclosed between $y = ax^2$ and $x = ay^2$ $(a > 0)$ is 1, then a is

(a) $1/\sqrt{3}$ (b) $1/2$ (c) 1 (d) 1/3

(Screening 2004)

Ans. (a). The two curves meet at $O(0,0)$ and $P\left(\frac{1}{a}, \frac{1}{a}\right)$

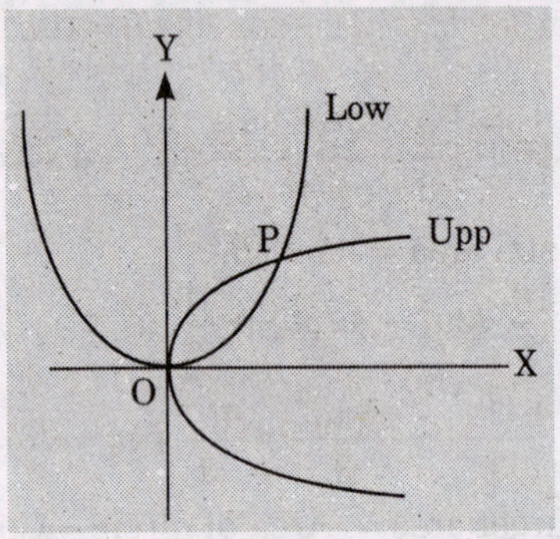

Fig. 24 (a)

$$\text{Area} = \int (\underset{\text{up}}{y_1} - \underset{\text{low}}{y_2})\, dx = \int_0^{1/a} \left(\sqrt{\frac{x}{a}} - ax^2\right) dx$$

$$= \left(\frac{2}{3} - \frac{1}{3}\right)\frac{1}{a^2} = 1 \quad \therefore \quad a = \frac{1}{\sqrt{3}}$$

(c)* Find the area bounded by the x-axis; part of the curve $y = \left(1 + \frac{8}{x^2}\right)$ and the ordinates at $x = 2$ and $x = 4$. If the ordinate at $x = a$ divides the area into two equal parts, find a.

$$A = \int_2^4 y\, dx = \int_2^4 \left(1 + \frac{8}{x^2}\right) dx = \left[x - \frac{8}{x}\right]_2^4 = 4$$

$$A_1 = \int_2^a y\, dx = \frac{1}{2}A = 2 \quad \therefore \quad \left[x - \frac{8}{x}\right]_2^a = 2$$

or $(a-2) - 8\left(\frac{1}{a} - \frac{1}{2}\right) = 2$ or $a - \frac{8}{a} = 0.$

$\therefore$ $a^2 - 8 = 0$ $\therefore$ $a = 2\sqrt{2}.$

(d) The curve $y = a\sqrt{x} + bx$ passes through the point (1, 2) and the area enclosed by the curve, the axis of x and the line $x = 4$ is 8 square units. Determine $a, b.$ **(J.E.E.W.B. 1994)**

The curve passes through (0, 0). Hence the limits of x are 0 to 4.

$$A = \int_0^4 y\, dx = \int_0^4 (a\sqrt{x} + bx)\, dx$$

or $8 = \left[a \cdot \frac{2}{3}x^{3/2} + b\frac{x^2}{2}\right]_0^4$

or $8 = \frac{16a}{3} + 8b$ ...(1)

Again the curve passes through (1, 2).

$\therefore$ $2 = a + b$ ...(2)

Solving (1) and (2), we get $a = 3, b = -1.$

Area of loops

***Ex. 12. (a)** Find the area of a loop as well as the whole area of the curve $a^2y^2 = x^2(a^2 - x^2).$

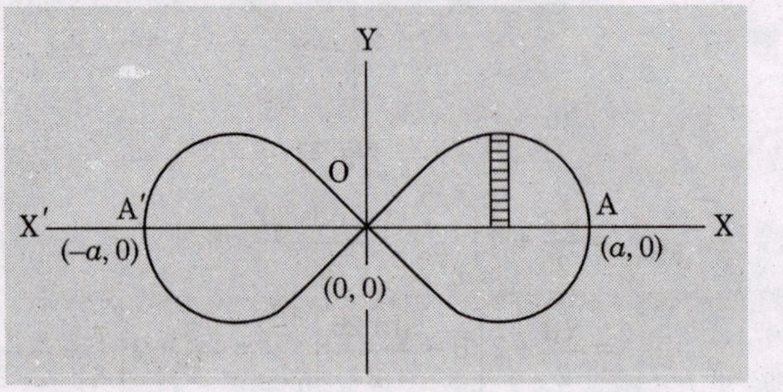

Fig. 25

The curve is symmetrical about both the axes. It cuts x-axis $y = 0$ at (0, 0), $(a, 0)$ and $(-a, 0).$

Area of a loop $= 2\int_0^a y\, dx$

$$= 2\int_0^a \frac{x}{a}\sqrt{a^2 - x^2}\, dx = -\frac{1}{a}\int_0^a \sqrt{a^2 - x^2}\,(-2x)\, dx$$

$$= -\frac{1}{a}\left[\frac{2}{3}(a^2 - x^2)^{3/2}\right]_0^a = \frac{2}{3}a^2$$

Total area $= 2 \times \frac{2}{3}a^2 = \frac{4}{3}a^2.$

Note : You can put $x = a\sin\theta$ and adjust the limits and evaluate the integral by Gamma function as in next example.

(b) $a^4y^2 = x^4(a^2 - x^2)$

$$\text{Area of a loop} = 2\int_0^a y\, dx = \frac{2}{a^2}\int_0^a x^2\sqrt{a^2 - x^2}\, dx$$

Put $x = a\sin\theta$ and adjust the limits.

$$A = \frac{2}{a^2}\int_0^{\pi/2} a^2\sin^2\theta\,(a\cos\theta)\,.\,a\cos\theta\, d\theta$$

$$= 2a^2\int_0^{\pi/2} \sin^2\theta\cos^2\theta\, d\theta = 2a^2\,\frac{1.1}{4.2}\,\frac{\pi}{2} = \frac{\pi a^2}{8}.$$

Ex. 13. (a) Prove that the ratio of the area of the loop of the curve $a^4y^2 = x^5(2a - x)$ with the area of a circle of radius a is 5 : 4.

A loop will be formed between $x = 0$ to $x = 2a$ and the curve is symmetrical about x-axis.

$$A = 2\int_0^{2a} x^{5/2}\sqrt{(2a - x)}\, dx$$

Put $x = 2a\sin^2\theta$ $\therefore$ $dx = 4a\sin\theta\cos\theta\, d\theta$

$$\therefore \quad A = \frac{2}{a^2}\int_0^{\pi/2} (2a)^{5/2}\sin^5\theta\,(2a)^{1/2}\cos\theta\,(4a\sin\theta\cos\theta)\, d\theta$$

$$= \frac{8a.(8a^3)}{a^2} \int_0^{\pi/2} \sin^6 \theta \cos^2 \theta \, d\theta$$

$$= 64a^2 \frac{(5.3.1).1}{8.6.4.2} \cdot \frac{\pi}{2} = \frac{5}{4} \pi a^2$$

Also B = area of circle of radius $a = \pi a^2$

$\therefore \quad \frac{A}{B} = \frac{5}{4}$ etc.

(b) $y^2 (a^2 + x^2) = x^2 (a^2 - x^2)$

Prove that the area of a loop of the above curve is $\frac{a^2}{2}(\pi - 2)$.

The curve is symmetrical about both axes and two loops are formed, as it cuts x-axis in points $(a, 0)$, $(0, 0)$ and $(-a, 0)$. If A be the area of one loop, then

$$A = 2\int_0^a y\,dx = 2\int_0^a x \sqrt{\frac{a^2 - x^2}{a^2 + x^2}}\,dx$$

$$= 2\int_0^a x \cdot \frac{a^2 - x^2}{\sqrt{a^4 - x^4}}\,dx$$

Put $x^2 = a^2 \sin\theta$ and adjust the limits

$$\therefore \quad A = \int_0^{\pi/2} \frac{a^2 (1 - \sin\theta)}{a^2 \cos\theta} (a^2 \cos\theta \, d\theta)$$

$$= a^2 \left[\theta + \cos\theta\right]_0^{\pi/2} = a^2 \left[\frac{\pi}{2} - 1\right].$$

Ex. 14. (a) Find the area of a loop of the curve $a^3 y^2 = x^4 (b + x)$.

The curve is symmetrical about x-axis and cuts it at $(-b, 0)$ and $(0, 0)$. Thus a loop is formed between these points.

$$\therefore \quad A = 2\int_{-b}^{0} y\,dx = \frac{2}{a\sqrt{a}} \int_{-b}^{0} x^2 \sqrt{b + x}\,dx$$

Integrating successively by parts,

$$A = \frac{2}{a\sqrt{a}} \left[x^2 \left\{\frac{2}{3}(b + x)^{3/2}\right\} - 2x \left\{\frac{2}{3} \cdot \frac{2}{5} (b + x)^{5/2}\right\} + 2\left\{\frac{2}{3} \cdot \frac{2}{5} \cdot \frac{2}{7} (b + x)^{7/2}\right\} - 0 \right.$$

$$= \frac{32b^{7/2}}{105a^{3/2}}$$

Note : The integration can also be performed by putting $x = -b\sin^2\theta$ and using Gamma function.

(b) Area of a loop of the curve $y^2 = x^2 (a + x)$ is $\frac{4}{15} a^{5/2}$.

(c) Find the area of the curve $\left(\frac{x}{a}\right)^{2/3} + \left(\frac{y}{b}\right)^{2/3} = 1$

The given equation is $\left(\frac{x^2}{a^2}\right)^{1/3} + \left(\frac{y^2}{b^2}\right)^{1/3} = 1$

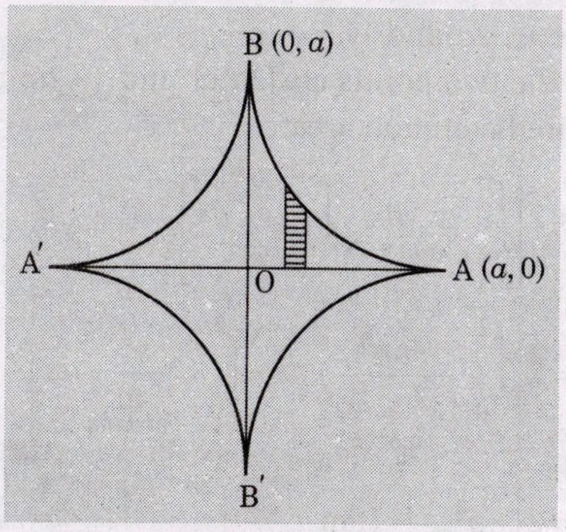

Fig. 26

It is symmetrical about both axes and cuts axes in $(\pm a, 0)$ and $(0, \pm b)$. Hence its area $= 4$ (area in 1st quadrant) $= 4\int_0^a y\,dx$

Its parametric equations are

$$x = a\cos^3 t \text{ and } y = b\sin^3 t$$

$$\therefore \quad A = 4\int_{\pi/2}^{0} (b\sin^3 t)(-3a\cos^2 t \sin t)\,dt$$

$$= 12ab \int_0^{\pi/2} \sin^4 t \cos^2 t\,dt$$

$$= 12ab \cdot \frac{(3.1).1}{6.4.2} \cdot \frac{\pi}{2} = \frac{3\pi ab}{8}$$

In case the curve be $x^{2/3} + y^{2/3} = a^{2/3}$ (Astroid) then putting $b = a$, the required area is $\frac{3\pi a^2}{8}$.

***Ex. 15. (a)** Find the area included between the parabola $y = \frac{x^2}{4a}$ and the witch of Agnesi $y = \frac{8a^3}{x^2 + 4a^2}$.

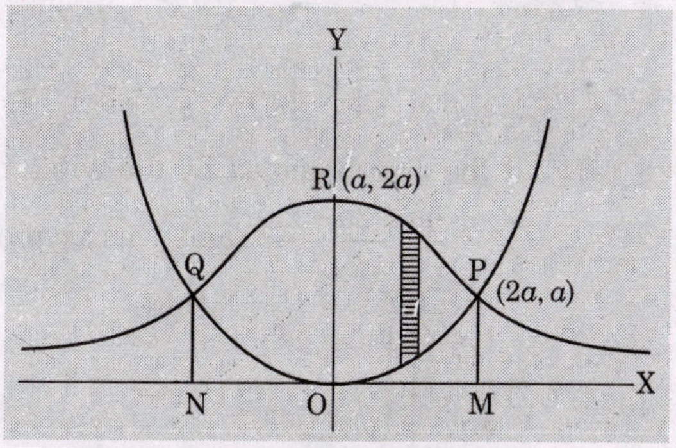

Fig. 27

$y(x^2 + 4a^2) = 8a^3$ represents a curve which is symmetrical about y-axis and cuts it at the point $(0, 2a)$ tangent at which is parallel to x-axis. Also x-axis is the asymptote. This curve meets the parabola $x^2 = 4ay$ where

$$\frac{x^2}{4a} = \frac{8a^3}{x^2 + 4a^2}$$

or $\quad x^4 + 4a^2 x^2 - 32a^4 = 0$

or $\quad (x^2 - 4a^2)(x^2 + 8a^2) = 0$

$\therefore \quad x = \pm 2a$ and $y = a$

Thus the two points are $(2a, a)$ and $(-2a, a)$.

Required common area

$$= 2\left[\int_0^{2a} \underset{\text{up}}{y_1}\, dx - \int_0^{2a} \underset{\text{low}}{y_2}\, dx\right]$$

$$= 2\left[\int_0^{2a} \underset{\text{curve}}{\frac{8a^3}{x^2 + 4a^2}}\, dx - \int_0^{2a} \underset{\text{parabola}}{\frac{x^2}{4a}}\, dx\right]$$

$$= 2\left[8a^3 \cdot \frac{1}{2a}\left\{\tan^{-1}\frac{x}{2a}\right\}_0^{2a} - \frac{1}{4a}\left\{\frac{x^3}{3}\right\}_0^{2a}\right]$$

$$= 2\left[4a^2 \cdot \frac{\pi}{4} - \frac{1}{12a} \cdot 8a^3\right]$$

$$= 2\left[\pi a^2 - \frac{2}{3}a^2\right] = a^2\left[2\pi - \frac{4}{3}\right].$$

(b)* Sketch the region bounded by the curves $y = x^2$ and $y = 2/(1 + x^2)$.

Find its area. **(I.I.T. 1992)**

The shape of the curve is exactly as of part (a) the points of intersection are given

$$x^2 = \frac{2}{1 + x^2} \text{ or } x^4 + x^2 - 2 = 0$$

or $\quad (x^2 - 1)(x^2 + 2) = 0$

$\therefore \quad x = 1, -1,\ y = 1, 1.$

$\therefore \quad P$ is $(1, 1)$ and $Q(-1, 1)$

$$A = 2\int_0^1 (\underset{\text{up}}{y_1} - \underset{\text{low}}{y_2})\, dx = 2\int_0^1 \left(\frac{2}{1 + x^2} - x^2\right) dx$$

$$= 4\left[\tan^{-1}\right]_0^1 - \frac{2}{3}\left[x^3\right]_0^1 = 4 \cdot \frac{\pi}{4} - \frac{2}{3} = \pi - \frac{2}{3}.$$

Ex. 16. (a) Find the area bounded by the witch of Agnesi $y^2 = \dfrac{4a^2(2a - x)}{x}$ and its asymptotes.

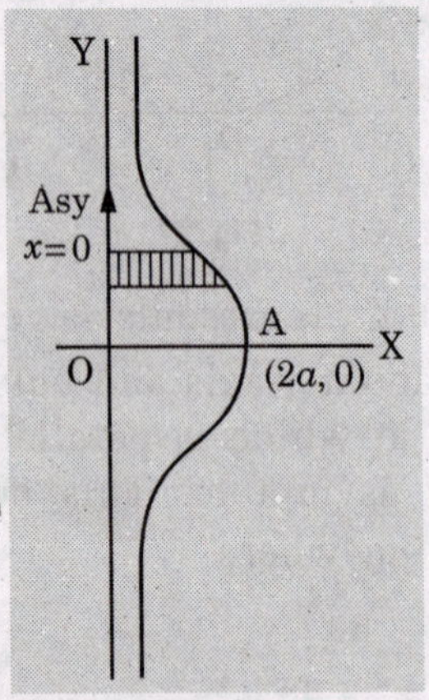

Fig. 28

The given curve is $x(y^2 + 4a^2) = 8a^3$. It has been given in part (a). Here the curve is symmetrical about x-axis as the powers of y are even and y-axis *i.e.* $x = 0$ is asymptote.

$$\text{Area} = 2\int_0^\infty x\, dy = 2\int_0^\infty \frac{8a^3}{y^2 + 4a^2}\, dy$$

$$= 16a^3 \cdot \frac{1}{2a}\left[\tan^{-1}\frac{y}{2a}\right]_0^\infty = 8a^2 \cdot \frac{\pi}{2} = 4\pi a^2$$

(b) Prove that the area enclosed by the curves $xy^2 = a^2(a - x)$ and $y^2(a - x) = a^2 x$ is $(\pi - 2)a^2$.

The first curve *i.e.* $x(y^2 + a^2) = a^3$ has been traced in part (a).

$x = 0$ is its asymptote and it passes through the point $(a, 0)$ and is symmetrical about x-axis. Its shape is same as of part (a).

The 2nd curve *i.e.* $x(y^2 + a^2) = ay^2$ is also symmetrical about x-axis and passes through origin. Tangent at origin is $x = 0$ *i.e.* y-axis. Also y^3 is missing and hence equating to zero the coefficient of y^2 we get $x = a$ as asymptote. **Point of Intersection of two curves :** Eliminating y, we get

$$\frac{a^2 x}{a - x} = \frac{a^2(a - x)}{x} \quad \therefore \quad (a - x)^2 = x^2$$

or $\quad a^2 - 2ax = 0 \quad \therefore \quad x = a/2$

$\therefore \quad y^2 = a^2$ or $y = \pm a$

Hence they meet at $P(a/2, a)$ and $Q(a/2, -a)$.

The shape of the curve is as shown below.

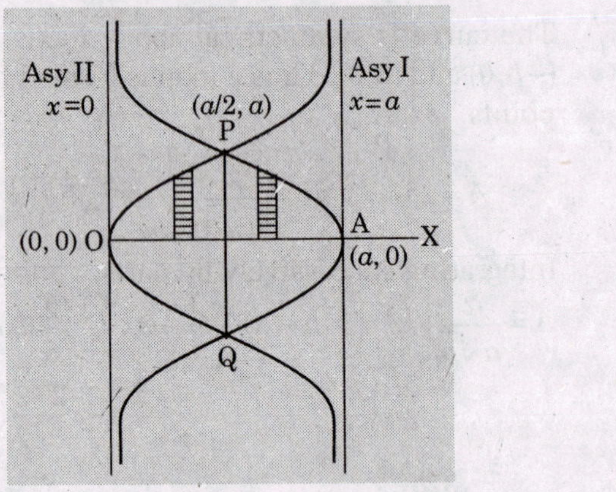

Fig. 29

The required area

$$A = 2\left[\int y_1\, dx + \int y_2\, dx\right]$$

$$= 2\left[\int_0^{a/2} a\sqrt{\frac{x}{a - x}}\, dx + \int_{a/2}^{a} a\sqrt{\frac{a - x}{x}}\, dx\right]$$

Put $x = a\sin^2\theta$

$\therefore \quad dx = 2a\sin\theta\cos\theta$

and adjust the limits for both.

$$\therefore \quad A = 2a^2\int_0^{\pi/4} 2\sin^2\theta\, d\theta + 2a^2\int_{\pi/4}^{\pi/2} 2\cos^2\theta\, d\theta$$

$$= 2a^2 \int_0^{\pi/4} (1 - \cos 2\theta)\, d\theta + 2a^2 \int_{\pi/4}^{\pi/2} (1 + \cos 2\theta)\, d\theta$$

$$= 2a^2 \left[\left\{ \theta - \frac{\sin 2\theta}{2} \right\}_0^{\pi/4} + \left\{ \theta + \frac{\sin 2\theta}{2} \right\}_{\pi/4}^{\pi/2} \right]$$

$$= 2a^2 \left[\left(\frac{\pi}{4} - \frac{1}{2} \right) + \left(\frac{\pi}{4} - \frac{1}{2} \right) \right] = a^2 (\pi - 2)$$

Ex. 17. (a) Find the whole area contained between the curve $y^2 (a - x) = x^2 (a + x)$ and its asymptotes.

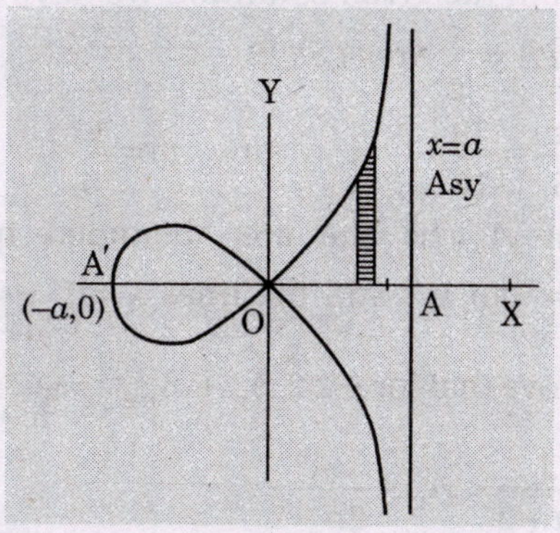

Fig. 30

The curve is symmetrical about x-axis and it cuts it at $(-a, 0)$ and $(0, 0)$. y^3 is missing, the coefficient of y^2 *i.e.* $a - x = 0$ or $x = a$ is asymptote.

$$\text{Area} = 2 \int_0^a y\, dx$$

$$= 2 \int_0^a x \sqrt{\frac{a + x}{a - x}}\, dx = 2 \int_0^a x \frac{a + x}{\sqrt{a^2 - x^2}}\, dx$$

Put $x = a \sin \theta$ and adjust the limits.

$$A = 2 \int_0^{\pi/2} a \sin \theta \frac{a(1 + \sin \theta)}{a \cos \theta} . a \cos \theta\, d\theta$$

$$= 2a^2 \int_0^{\pi/2} (\sin \theta + \sin^2 \theta)\, d\theta$$

$$= 2a^2 \left[1 + \frac{1}{2} . \frac{\pi}{2} \right] = 2a^2 \left(1 + \frac{\pi}{4} \right)$$

(b) Find the whole area contained between the curve $x^2 (x^2 + y^2) = a^2 (y^2 - x^2)$ and its asymptotes.
The given curve can be re-written as

$$y^2 (a^2 - x^2) = x^2 (a^2 + x^2)$$

It is symmetrical about both the axes and cuts them only at (0, 0). Tangent at (0, 0) are given by

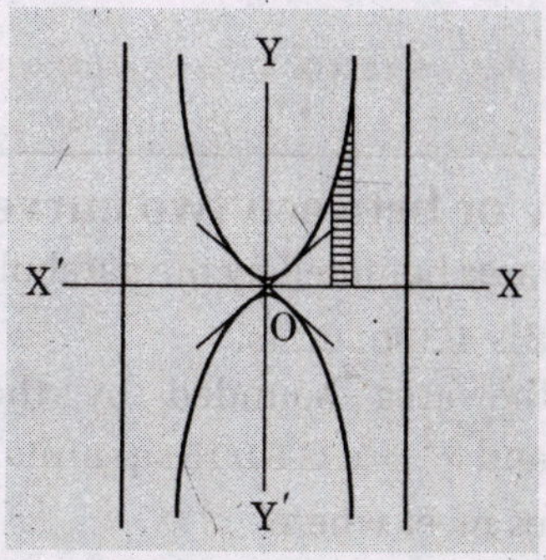

Fig. 31

$a^2 (y^2 - x^2) = 0$ or $y = \pm x$. The equation is of 4th degree and x^4 is present and hence there is no asymptote parallel to x-axis. But y^4 and y^3 both are missing.

Equate to zero the coefficient of y^2, we get $a^2 - x^2 = 0$

$\therefore$ $x = \pm a$ are asymptotes parallel to y-axis. Hence the shape of the curve is as shown in the figure.

$$\therefore \quad A = 4 \int_0^a y\, dx = 4 \int_0^a x \sqrt{\frac{a^2 + x^2}{a^2 - x^2}}\, dx$$

$$= 2 \int_0^a \frac{a^2 + x^2}{\sqrt{a^4 - x^4}} (2x)\, dx$$

Put $x^2 = a^2 \sin \theta$ and adjust the limits.

$$\therefore \quad A = 2 \int_0^{\pi/2} \frac{a^2 (1 + \sin \theta)}{a^2 \cos \theta} a^2 \cos \theta\, d\theta.$$

$$= 2a^2 \left[\theta - \cos \theta \right]_0^{\pi/2} = 2a^2 \left[\frac{\pi}{2} + 1 \right].$$

(c) Trace the curve $y^2 (a + x) = (a - x)^3$ and find the area between the curve and its asymptotes.
Symmetrical about x-axis and cuts it at $(a, 0)$, y^3 is missing, coefficient of y^2 *i.e.* $a + x = 0$ or $x = -a$ is asymptote.

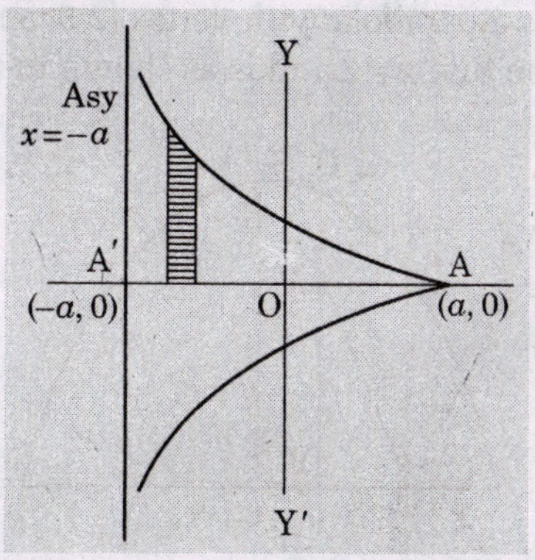

Fig. 32

$$A = 2 \int_{-a}^{a} y\, dx = 2 \int_{-a}^{a} (a - x) \sqrt{\frac{a - x}{a + x}}\, dx$$

$$= 2 \int_{-a}^{a} (a - x) \frac{a - x}{\sqrt{(a^2 - x^2)}}\, dx$$

Put $x = a \sin \theta$ and adjust the limits.

$$\therefore \quad A = 2 \int_{-\pi/2}^{\pi/2} a^2 \frac{(1 - \sin \theta)^2}{a \cos \theta} a \cos \theta\, d\theta$$

$$= 2a^2 \int_{-\pi/2}^{\pi/2} (1 + \sin^2 \theta - 2 \sin \theta)\, d\theta$$

$$= 2a^2 . 2 \int_0^{\pi/2} (1 + \sin^2 \theta)\, d\theta + 0 \text{ (Prop. V)}$$

$$= 4a^2 \left[\frac{\pi}{2} + \frac{1}{2} . \frac{\pi}{2} \right] = 3\pi a^2$$

***Ex. 18. (a)** Find the area in the first quadrant bounded by $y = 4x^2$, $x = 0$, $y = 1$ and $y = 4$. **(M.N.R. 1990)**

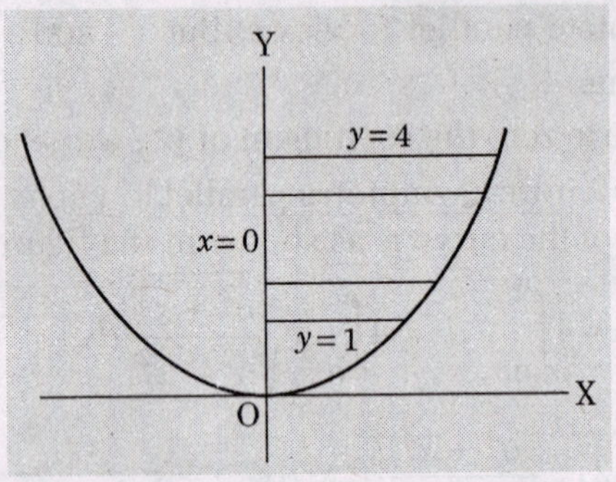

Fig. 33

The required area $= \int_1^4 x\, dy = \int_1^4 \frac{\sqrt{y}}{2}\, dy$

$$= \frac{1}{2}\left[\frac{2}{3} y^{3/2}\right]_1^4 = \frac{1}{3}[4^{3/2} - 1] = \frac{1}{3}[8 - 1] = \frac{7}{3} = 2\frac{1}{3}.$$

(b)* The line $y = mx$ bisects the area enclosed by the lines $x = 0$, $y = 0$, $x = 3/2$ and the curve $y = 1 + 4x - x^2$

Find the value of m. **(Roorkee 1991)**

The equation $y = 1 + 4x - x^2$ can be written as

$$y = -(x - 2)^2 + 5 \text{ or } (x - 2)^2 = -(y - 5)$$

which is a parabola with vertex (2, 5) and symmetrical about the line $x = 2$ and is as shown in the figure.

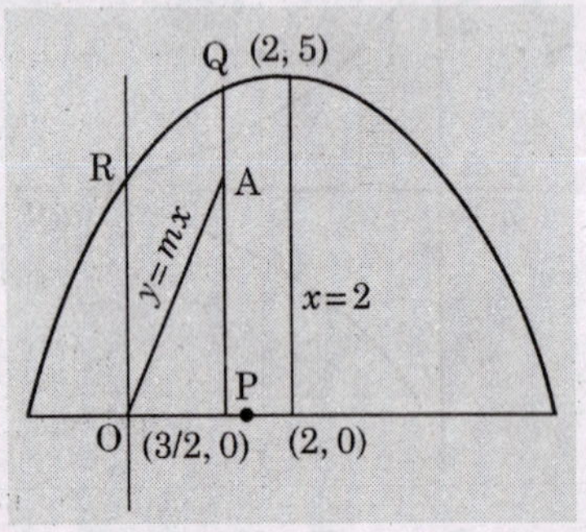

Fig. 34

Let OA represent the line $y = mx$. Then as given this line bisects the area $OPQR$ so that

Area $OPQR = 2$ Area OPA.

Now area $OPQR = \int_0^{3/2} y\, dx$

$$= \int_0^{3/2} (1 + 4x - x^2)\, dx = \left[x + 2x^2 - \frac{1}{3}x^3\right]_0^{3/2}$$

$$= \left(\frac{3}{2} + 2 \cdot \frac{9}{4} - \frac{1}{3} \cdot \frac{27}{8}\right) - 0 = 6 - \frac{9}{8} = \frac{39}{8}.$$

And area $OPA = \int_0^{3/2} y\, dx = \int_0^{3/2} mx\, dx$

$$= \frac{1}{2} m [x^2]_0^{3/2} = \frac{1}{2} m \left[\frac{9}{4} - 0\right] = \frac{9}{8} m$$

$\therefore$ From the given condition we have

Area $OPA = \frac{1}{2}$ Area $OPQR$

or $\frac{9m}{8} = \frac{39}{16}$ or $m = \frac{13}{6}$.

***Ex. 19.** Let A_n be the area bounded by the curve $y = (\tan x)^n$ and the lines $x = 0$, $y = 0$ and $x = \frac{\pi}{4}$.

Prove that for $n \geq 2, A_n + A_{n-2} = \frac{1}{n-1}$ and deduce $\frac{1}{2n+2} < A_n < \frac{1}{2n-2}$. **(I.I.T. 1996)**

$$A_n = \int_0^{\pi/4} \tan^n x\, dx$$

$$= \int_0^{\pi/4} \tan^{n-2} (\sec^2 x - 1)\, dx$$

or $A_n = \left[\frac{\tan^{n-1} x}{n-1}\right]_0^{\pi/4} - A_{n-2}$

$\therefore$ $A_n + A_{n-2} = \frac{1}{n-1}$ ...(1)

Again in the interval 0 to $\pi/4$, $\tan x$ is +ive and < 1.

$\therefore$ $\tan^n x \leq \tan^{n-2} x$

$\therefore$ $A_n < A_{n-2}$

$\therefore$ $A_n + A_n < A_n + A_{n-2} = \frac{1}{n-1}$, by (1)

$\therefore$ $A_n < \frac{1}{2(n-1)}$ ...(2)

$A_{n+2} < A_n$ $\therefore$ $A_{n+2} + A_n < A_n + A_n$

or $\frac{1}{(n+2)-1} < 2A_n$, by (1)

$\therefore$ $\frac{1}{2n+2} < A_n$ ...(3)

$\frac{1}{2n+2} < A_n < \frac{1}{2n-2}$, by (2) and (3)

Problem Set (11)

Area of curves between the curve and axis of x or axis of y or between two curves.

1. Prove that the area bounded by the hyperbola $x^2 - y^2 = a^2$ between the straight lines $x = a$ and $x = 2a$ is $2\sqrt{3}a^2 - a^2 \log(2 + \sqrt{3})$ sq. units

2. Prove that the area common to the parabolas $y = 2x^2$ and $y = x^2 + 4$ is $\frac{32}{3}$ sq. units.

3. Prove that the area bounded by the parabola $y = x^2$ and the line $y = 2x$ is 4/3 sq. units.

4. Prove that the area bounded by the parabolas $y^2 = -5x + 6$ and $x^2 = y$ is 81/15 sq. units.

The two curves meet where

$(x^2)^2 = -5x + 6$

or $x^4+5x-6=0$

or $(x-1)(x^3+x^2+x+6)=0$

or $(x-1)(x+2)(x^2-x+3)=0$

$\therefore\quad x=-2,1 \quad \therefore$ Points are $(-2,4)$ and $(1,1)$.

5. (a)* Show that the area included between the parabolas

$$y^2=4a(x+a)$$

and $y^2=4b(b-x)$ is $\frac{8}{3}\sqrt{ab}\,(a+b)$

$$y^2=4b(b-x) \quad \text{or} \quad y^2=-4b(x-b).$$

Eliminating y^2, we get x co-ordinate of their point of intersection as $x=b-a$.

$\therefore\quad y=\pm\, 2\sqrt{ab}$

The vertices of the parabolas are $(-a,0),(0,b)$ and are as shown in the figure.

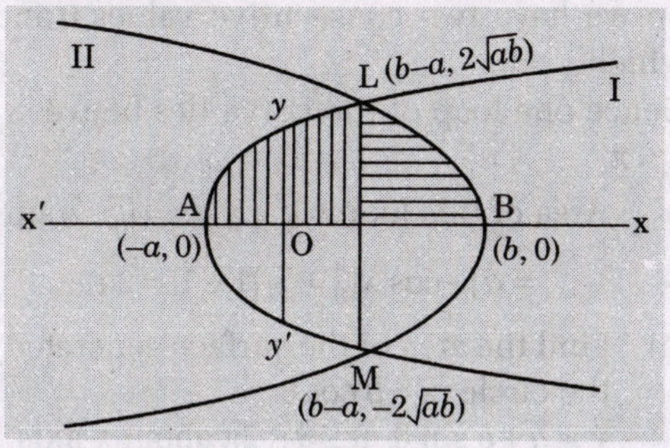

Fig. 35

Ist Method :

$$A=2\left[\int_{-a}^{b-a} y_1\,dx+\int_{b-a}^{b} y_2\,dx\right]$$

$$=2\left[2\sqrt{a}\int_{-a}^{b-a}\sqrt{x+a}\,dx+\int_{b-a}^{b}2\sqrt{b}\,\sqrt{b-x}\,dx\right]$$

$$4\sqrt{a}\cdot\frac{2}{3}\left[(x+a)^{3/2}\right]_{-a}^{b-a}+4\sqrt{b}\cdot\left(-\frac{2}{3}\right)\left[(b-x)^{3/2}\right]_{b-a}^{b}$$

$$=\frac{8}{3}\sqrt{ab}\cdot a+\frac{8}{3}\sqrt{ab}\cdot b=\frac{8}{3}\sqrt{ab}(a+b)$$

Alternative easier method by Note on P. 1576

$$A=\int_{-2\sqrt{ab}}^{2\sqrt{ab}}(\underset{R}{x_1}-\underset{L}{x_2})\,dy$$

$$=\int_{-2\sqrt{ab}}^{2\sqrt{ab}}\left[\left(b-\frac{y^2}{4b}\right)-\left(\frac{y^2}{4a}-a\right)\right]dy$$

$$=2\int_{0}^{2\sqrt{ab}}\left[(a+b)-\frac{1}{4}\frac{a+b}{ab}\,y^2\right]dy$$

$$=2(a+b)\left[y-\frac{1}{4ab}\cdot\frac{y^3}{3}\right]_0^{2\sqrt{ab}}$$

$$=2(a+b)\left[2\sqrt{ab}-\frac{1}{4ab}\cdot\frac{8}{3}\,ab\sqrt{ab}\right]$$

$$=2(a+b)\sqrt{ab}\left[2-\frac{2}{3}\right]=\frac{8}{3}(a+b)\sqrt{ab}.$$

(b)* Find the smaller of the area bounded by the parabola $4y^2-3x-8y+7=0$ and the ellipse $x^2+4y^2-2x-8y+1=0$.

C_1 is $\quad 4(y^2-2y)=3x-7$

or $\quad 4(y-1)^2=3x-3=3(x-1)$ ...(1)

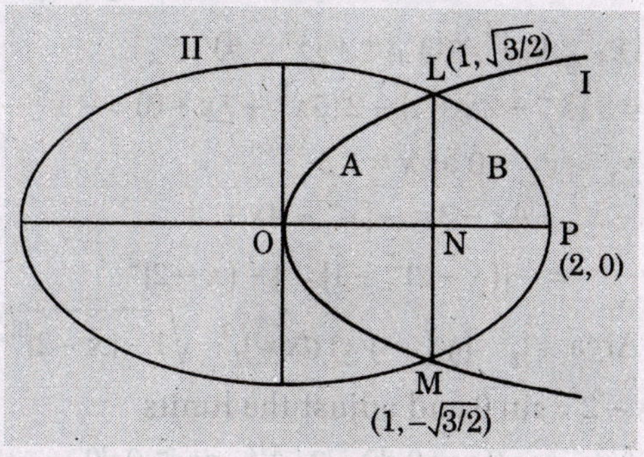

Fig. 36

Above is a parabola with vertex at $(1,1)$

C_2 is $\quad (x^2-2x)+4(y^2-2y)=-1$

or $(x-1)^2+4(y-1)^2=-1+1+4$

or $\dfrac{(x-1)^2}{2^2}+\dfrac{(y-1)^2}{1^2}=1$ ...(2)

Above represents an ellipse with centre at $(1,1)$. Shift the origin to $(1,1)$ and this will not affect the magnitude of required area but will make the calculation simpler.

Thus the two curves are

$$4Y^2=3X \quad \text{and} \quad \frac{X^2}{2^2}+\frac{Y^2}{1}=1.$$

They meet at $\left(1,\pm\dfrac{\sqrt{3}}{2}\right)$.

Ist Method : Required area $=2(A+B)$

$$=2\quad\left[\int_P Y_1\,dX+\int_E Y_2\,dX\right]$$

$$=2\left[\frac{\sqrt{3}}{2}\int_0^1 dX+\int_1^2\frac{\sqrt{4-X^2}}{2}\,dX\right]=\frac{\sqrt{3}}{6}+\frac{2\pi}{3}$$

Alternative easier method by Note P. 1576

$$A=\int_{-\sqrt{3}/2}^{\sqrt{3}/2}(\underset{E}{X_1}-\underset{P}{X_2})\,dY \quad\text{or}\quad \int(\underset{R}{X_1}-\underset{L}{X_2})\,dY$$

$$=\int_{-\sqrt{3}/2}^{\sqrt{3}/2}\left[2\sqrt{1-Y^2}-\frac{4}{3}Y^2\right]dY$$

$$=2\left[2\left\{\frac{Y}{2}\sqrt{1-Y^2}+\frac{1}{2}\sin^{-1}Y-\frac{4}{3}\frac{Y^3}{3}\right\}\right]_0^{\sqrt{3}/2} \quad \text{Prop. V}$$

$$=2\left[\left(\frac{\sqrt{3}}{2}\cdot\frac{1}{2}+\frac{\pi}{3}\right)-\frac{4}{9}\frac{3\sqrt{3}}{8}\right]=\frac{\sqrt{3}}{2}+\frac{2\pi}{3}-\frac{\sqrt{3}}{3}=\frac{\sqrt{3}}{6}+\frac{2\pi}{3}$$

(c) Find the area enclosed by the curves

$$5x^2 + 6xy + 2y^2 + 7x + 6y + 6 = 0.$$

Re-writing the given equation as a quadratic in y,

$$2y^2 + 6y(x+1) + 5x^2 + 7x + 6 = 0$$

$$y_1 + y_2 = -3(x+1),\ y_1 y_2 = \frac{5x^2 + 7x + 6}{2}$$

$\therefore \quad (y_1 - y_2)^2 = (y_1 + y_2)^2 - 4y_1 y_2$

$= 9(x^2 + 2x + 1) - 2(5x^2 + 7x + 6) = -x^2 + 4x - 3$

$y_1 - y_2 = 0$ at $x = 1, 3$

Also $-x^2 + 4x - 3 = -[x^2 - 4x + 3]$

$= -[(x-2)^2 - 1] = 1 - (x-2)^2$

$\therefore \quad \text{Area} = \int_1^3 (y_1 - y_2)\,dx = \int_1^3 \sqrt{1 - (x-2)^2}\,dx$

Put $x - 2 = \sin\theta$ and adjust the limits

$A = \int_{-\pi/2}^{\pi/2} \cos\theta \cos\theta\, d\theta = 2\int_0^{\pi/2} \cos^2\theta\, d\theta$

$= 2 \cdot \frac{1}{2} \cdot \frac{\pi}{2} = \frac{\pi}{2}.$

6. Prove that the area between the parabolas $y^2 = 4x$, $y^2 = x$ and $x = 1$, $x = 4$ is 28/3 sq. units.

$A = 2\int_1^4 (y_1 - y_2)\,dx = 2\int_1^4 (2-1)\sqrt{x}\,dx$

$= 2 \cdot \frac{2}{3}[x\sqrt{x}]_1^4 = \frac{28}{3}$

7. Find the area of the figure bounded by the curve

$$|y| = 1 - x^2$$

y is + ive $\therefore \quad y = 1 - x^2$

or $\quad x^2 = -(y-1)$ ...(1)

y is – ive $\therefore \quad -y = 1 - x^2$

or $\quad x^2 = (y+1)$ ...(2)

Both represent parabolas as shown in the figure.

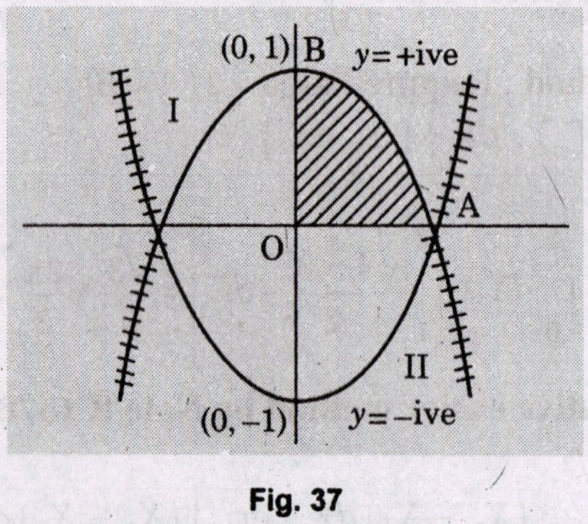

Fig. 37

For the first y is to be +ive and for the second y is to be –ive. Their vertices are at (0, 1) and (0, – 1) respectively. The required area $= 4\int_0^1 (1 - x^2)\,dx$

Ans. 8/3, since the curve is symmetrical about both the axes.

8. (a)* Find the area of the region by the method of integration bounded by the curve $y = x \sin x$ and the x-axis between $x = 0$ and $x = 2\pi$.

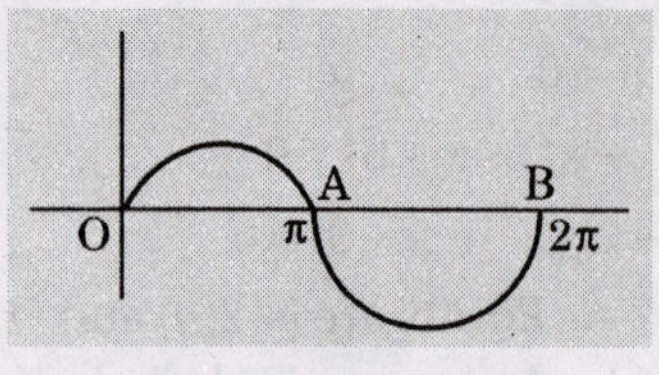

Fig. 38

$\text{Area} = \int_0^{2\pi} y\,dx = \int_0^{2\pi} |x \sin x|\,dx$

$= \int_0^{\pi} |x \sin x|\,dx + \int_{\pi}^{2\pi} |x \sin x|\,dx$

$= \int_0^{\pi} x \sin x\,dx + \int_{\pi}^{2\pi} -(x \sin x)\,dx$

$\left|[x(-\cos x) + \sin x]_0^{\pi}\right| - \left|[x(-\cos x) + \sin x]_{\pi}^{2\pi}\right|$

$= \pi - (-3\pi) = \pi + 3\pi = 4\pi.$

(b) Find the area of a loop between the curve $y = a \sin x$ and x-axis.

When $y = 0$, we have $a \sin x = 0$ whence $x = 0, \pi$.

So we have two consecutive values 0 and π of x for which $y = 0$.

Hence one loop of the curve lies between $x = 0$ and $x = \pi$.

$\therefore \quad \text{Area of this loop} = \int_0^{\pi} y\,dx = \int_0^{\pi} a \sin x\,dx$

$= a[-\cos x]_0^{\pi} = a[1 + 1] = 2a.$

9. (a) Find the area of the surface generated by rotating the circle $x = b\cos\theta$, $y = a + b\sin\theta$, $0 \le \theta \le 2\pi$ about x-axis.

$$A = \text{Area of the surface} = 2\pi \int_0^{2\pi} y \frac{ds}{d\theta} . d\theta$$

Now $\frac{dx}{d\theta} = -b\sin\theta$, $\frac{dy}{d\theta} = b\cos\theta$ so that

$$\frac{ds}{d\theta} = \sqrt{b^2 \sin^2\theta + b^2 \cos^2\theta} = b$$

Hence $A = 2\pi \int_0^{2\pi} [a + b\sin\theta] . b\,d\theta$

$= 2\pi b\,[a\theta - b\cos\theta]_0^{2\pi}$

$= 2\pi b\,[(2a\pi - 0) - b(\cos 2\pi - \cos 0)].$

$= 4\pi^2 ab.$ [Since $\cos 2\pi = \cos 0 = 1$].

(b) The straight line segment $y = x \tan\alpha$ $(0 \le x \le h)$ is rotated about the x-axis through an angle 2π radians. Find the surface area and the volume of the solid so generated. **(M.N.R. 1991)**

Let $OA = h$

$\frac{dy}{dx} = \tan\alpha$

$\therefore \quad \frac{ds}{dx} = \sqrt{\left\{1 + \left(\frac{dy}{dx}\right)^2\right\}} = \sqrt{[1 + \tan^2\alpha]} = \sec\alpha$

$\therefore \quad \text{Surface Area} = \int_0^h 2\pi y \frac{ds}{dx}\,dx$

$= 2\pi \int_0^h x \tan\alpha \sec\alpha\,dx$

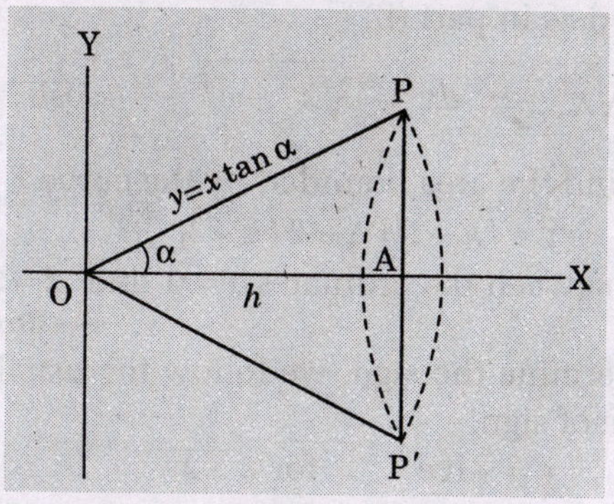

Fig. 39

$= 2\pi \tan\alpha \sec\alpha \cdot \dfrac{h^2}{2} = \pi h^2 \tan\alpha \sec\alpha.$

And volume $= \pi \int_0^h y^2\, dx = \pi \int_0^h x^2 \tan^2\alpha\, dx$

$= \pi \tan^2\alpha \cdot \dfrac{h^3}{3} = \dfrac{1}{3}\pi h^3 \tan^2\alpha.$

10. (a)* The volume of the solid obtained by revolving **about y-axis** the area enclosed between the ellipse $x^2 + 9y^2 = 9$ and the straight line $x + 3y = 3$, in the first quadrant is

(a) 3π (b) 4π

(c) 6π (d) 9π **(M.N.R. 1994)**

Ans. (a) $V = \int_0^1 \pi x^2\, dy - \int_0^1 \pi x^2\, dy$

Ellipse Line

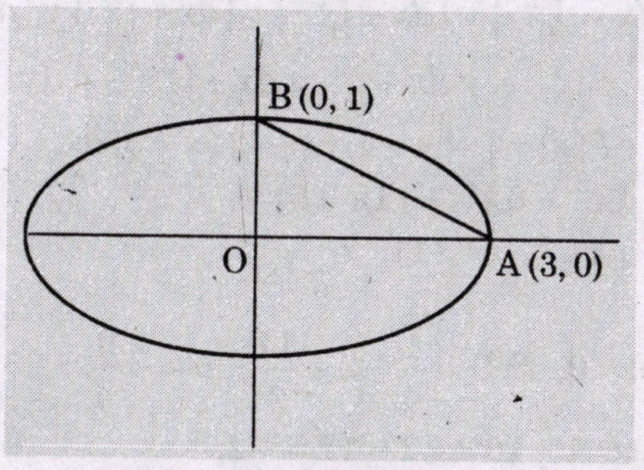

Fig. 40

$= \pi \int_0^1 9(1-y^2)\, dy - \pi \int_0^1 9(1-y)^2\, dy$

$= 9\pi \left[\left(y - \dfrac{y^3}{3}\right) + \dfrac{(1-y)^3}{3}\right]_0^1$

$= 9\pi\left[\left(1-\dfrac{1}{3}\right) + \left(0 - \dfrac{1}{3}\right)\right] = 9\pi\left(1 - \dfrac{2}{3}\right) = 9\pi \cdot \dfrac{1}{3} = 3\pi$

(b)* The volume of the solid obtained by rotating the ellipse $\dfrac{x^2}{a^2} + \dfrac{y^2}{b^2} = 1$ about axis of x is

(a) $\pi a^2 b$ (b) $\pi - b^2$

(c) $\dfrac{4}{3}\pi a^2 b$ (d) $\dfrac{4}{3}\pi a b^2$ **(M.N.R. 1995)**

Ans. (d). $V = 2\displaystyle\int_0^a \pi y^2\, dx = 2\pi b^2 \int_0^a \left(1 - \dfrac{x^2}{a^2}\right) dx$

$= 2\pi b^2 \left[x - \dfrac{x^3}{3a^2}\right]_0^a = 2\pi b^2 a\left[1 - \dfrac{1}{3}\right] = \dfrac{4}{3}\pi a b^2$

(c)* A hemispherical bowl of radius a is filled with water up to a depth h. Find the volume of water in the bowl. **(M.N.R. 1997)**

The hemisphere is obtained by revolving the semi-circular area ACB of circle $x^2 + y^2 = a^2$ about y-axis.

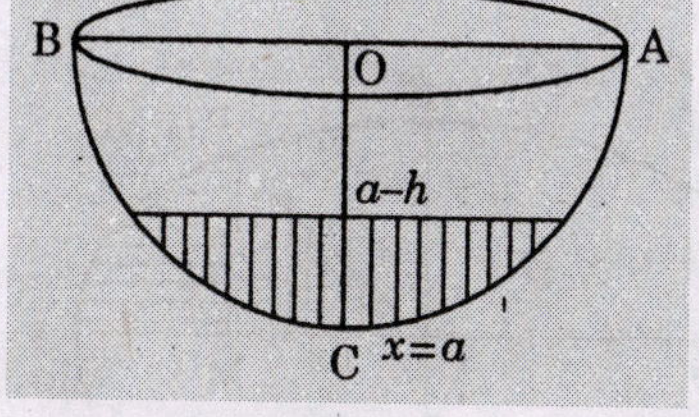

Fig. 41

Thus we get hemisphere as shown. The volume of water contained in it upto a height h is given by

$\int_{-a}^{-(a-h)} \pi x^2\, dy$

Put $y = -t$ and adjust the limits

$V = \pi \int_a^{a-h} (a^2 - t^2)(-dt)$

$= \pi\left[a^2 t - \dfrac{t^3}{3}\right]_{a-h}^{a} = \pi\left[a^2 h - \dfrac{1}{3}\{a^3 - (a-h)^3\}\right]$

$= \pi\left[a^2 h - \dfrac{1}{3}\{3a^2 h - 3ah^2 + h^3\}\right] = \pi h^2 \left(a - \dfrac{h}{3}\right)$

11. (a)* For any real t, $x = \dfrac{1}{2}(e^t + e^{-t})$, $y = \dfrac{1}{2}(e^t - e^{-t})$ is a point on the hyperbola $x^2 - y^2 = 1$. Show that the area bounded by the hyperbola and the lines joining its centre to the points corresponding to t_1 and $-t_1$ is t_1.

Hint : Let $x_1 = \cosh t_1$, $y_1 = \sinh t_1$, then (x_1, y_1) represent point P on hyperbola $x^2 - y^2 = 1$ whose centre is the origin O and let PM be perpendicular on x-axis. Then required area

$= 2[\Delta\, OPM - \int_1^{x_1} y\, dx]$

$= 2\left[\dfrac{1}{2}x_1 y_1 - \displaystyle\int_1^{x_1} \sqrt{(x^2-1)}\, dx\right]$

$= 2\left[\dfrac{1}{2}x_1 y_1 - \left\{\dfrac{x}{2}\sqrt{(x^2-1)} - \dfrac{1}{2}\log\{x + \sqrt{(x^2-1)}\}\right\}\right]_1^{x_1}$

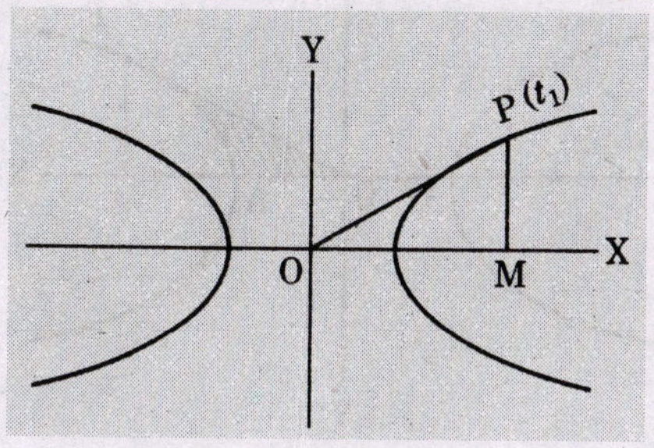

Fig. 42

$$= x_1 y_1 - 2\left\{\frac{1}{2} x_1 y_1 - \frac{1}{2}\log\{x_1 + y_1\}\right\}$$

$$= x_1 y_1 - x_1 y_1 + \log\{e^{t_1}\} = t_1$$

(b)* In the ellipse $\frac{x^2}{a^2} + \frac{y^2}{b^2} = 1$, show that

$$x = a\cos\frac{2S}{ab}, \quad y = b\sin\frac{2S}{ab}$$

where S is the sectorial area bounded by the ellipse, x-axis and the line joining (0, 0) to (x, y).

S = Area $OPLAMO$ = $\Delta\, OPM$ + Area $MPLAM$

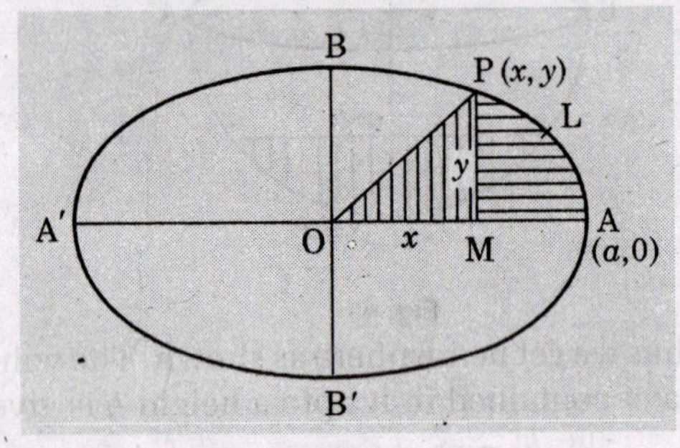

Fig. 43

$$S = \frac{1}{2}xy + \int_x^a y\,dx = \frac{1}{2}xy + \frac{b}{a}\int_x^a \sqrt{a^2 - x^2}\,dx$$

$$= \frac{1}{2}xy + \frac{b}{a}\left[\frac{x}{2}\sqrt{a^2 - x^2} + \frac{a^2}{2}\sin^{-1}\frac{x}{a}\right]_x^a$$

$$= \frac{1}{2}xy + \frac{b}{a}\left[\left(0 - \frac{x}{2}\sqrt{a^2 - x^2}\right) + \frac{a^2}{2}\left(\frac{\pi}{2} - \sin^{-1}\frac{x}{a}\right)\right]$$

$$= \frac{1}{2}xy - \frac{1}{2}xy + \frac{ab}{2}\cos^{-1}\frac{x}{a}$$

$$\therefore \frac{2S}{ab} = \cos^{-1}\frac{x}{a} \quad \therefore \frac{x}{a} = \cos\frac{2S}{ab}$$

$$\therefore \frac{y}{b} = \sqrt{1 - \frac{x^2}{a^2}} = \sin\frac{2S}{ab}.$$

(c) If A is the vertex, O the centre and P any point on the hyperbola $\frac{x^2}{a^2} - \frac{y^2}{b^2} = 1$, show that $x = a\cosh\frac{2S}{ab}$, $y = b\sinh\frac{2S}{ab}$, where S is the sectorial area OAP.

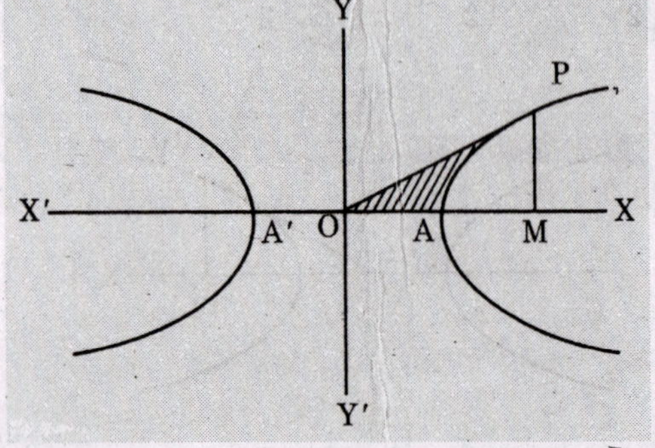

Fig. 44

Proceed as in part (b).

$$\int\sqrt{x^2 - a^2}\,dx = \frac{x}{2}\sqrt{x^2 - a^2} - \frac{a^2}{2}\cosh^{-1}\frac{x}{a}$$

12. (a)* Find the area bounded by the curve

$$y = (x-1)(x-2)(x-3)$$

lying between the ordinates $x = 0$ and $x = 3$.

(Roorkee 1993)

Sol. To determine the sign, we follow the usual rule as of change of sign.

$y = +$ive	for $x > 3$
$y = -$ive	for $2 < x < 3$
$y = +$ive	for $1 < x < 2$
$y = -$ive	for $x < 1$.

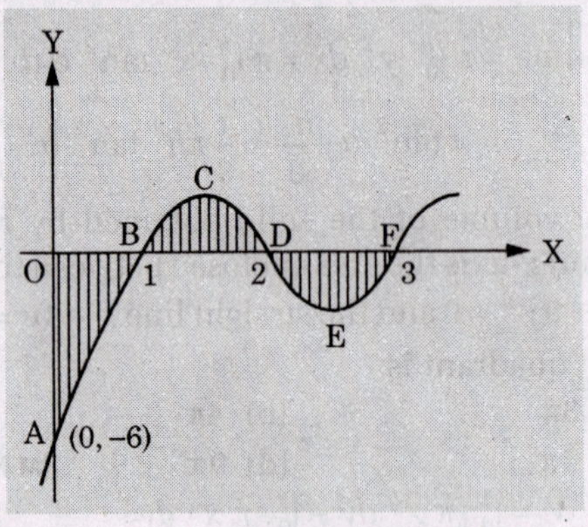

Fig. 45

$$\int_0^3 |y|\,dx = \int_0^1 |y|\,dx + \int_1^2 |y|\,dx + \int_2^3 |y|\,dx$$

$$= \int_0^1 -y\,dx + \int_1^2 y\,dx + \int_2^3 -y\,dx$$

Now let $F(x) = \int (x-1)(x-2)(x-3)\,dx$

$$= \int (x^3 - 6x^2 + 11x - 6)\,dx$$

$$= \frac{1}{4}x^4 - 2x^3 + \frac{11}{2}x^2 - 6x.$$

$$\therefore \quad F(0) = 0,\ F(1) = \frac{1}{4} - 2 + \frac{11}{2} - 6 = -\frac{9}{4}.$$

$$F(2) = 4 - 16 + 22 - 12 = -2,$$

and $F(3) = \frac{81}{4} - 54 + \frac{99}{2} - 18 = -\frac{9}{4}$.

Hence required Area

$$= -[F(1) - F(0)] + [F(2) - F(1)] - [F(3) - F(2)]$$

$$= -\left(-\frac{9}{4} - 0\right) + \left[-2 - \left(-\frac{9}{4}\right)\right] - \left[-\frac{9}{4} - (-2)\right]$$

$$= \frac{9}{4} + \frac{1}{4} + \frac{1}{4} = \frac{11}{4} = 2\frac{3}{4} \text{ units.}$$

(b)* Find the area between the curve $y = 2x^4 - x^2$, the x-axis and the ordinates of the two minima of the curve.

Sol. $y = 2x^4 - x^2 = 2x^2(x^2 - 1/2)$

or $\quad y = 2x^2\left(x + \frac{1}{\sqrt{(2)}}\right)\left(x - \frac{1}{\sqrt{(2)}}\right)$

It cuts x-axis $y = 0$ at $(0, 0)$, $\left(-\frac{1}{\sqrt{(2)}}, 0\right)$ and $\left(\frac{1}{\sqrt{(2)}}, 0\right)$.

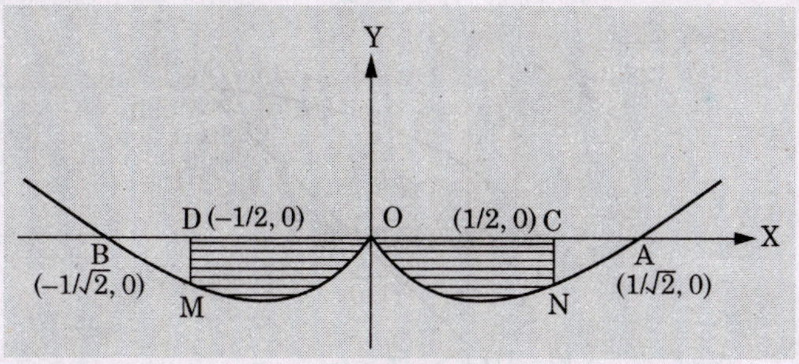

Fig. 46

Now $2x^2$ is always +ive when x lies between $-\frac{1}{\sqrt{(2)}}$ and $\frac{1}{\sqrt{(2)}}$ then y is clearly –ive. Hence the curve is below the x-axis cutting it at the three points shown below. The points of minima as found below are at $\left(-\frac{1}{2}, 0\right)$ and $\left(\frac{1}{2}, 0\right)$.

$$y = 2x^4 - x^2$$

or $\frac{dy}{dx} = 8x^3 - 2x = 0$ for max. or min.

This gives $x = 0,\ \ x = \pm\frac{1}{2}$

$\Rightarrow \quad \frac{d^2y}{dx^2} = 24x^2 - 2 > 0$ at $x = \pm\frac{1}{2}$

Hence y is min. when $x = \pm\frac{1}{2}$.

So the required area is as shown shaded in the figure. Hence

Area $A = 2\int |y|\,dx = 2\int_0^{1/2} -(2x^4 - x^2)\,dx$

as y is – ive.

$$= -2\left[2\frac{x^5}{5} - \frac{x^3}{3}\right]_0^{1/2} = -2\left[\frac{2}{5}\cdot\frac{1}{32} - \frac{1}{3}\cdot\frac{1}{8}\right]$$

$$= -\left(\frac{1}{40} - \frac{1}{12}\right) = \frac{7}{120}$$

13. (a)* Compute the area of the figure bounded by the straight lines $x = 0$, $x = 2$ and the curves $y = 2^x$, $y = 2x - x^2$.

Sol. Figure is self-explanatory.

$$y = 2^x,\ (x-1)^2 = -(y-1)$$

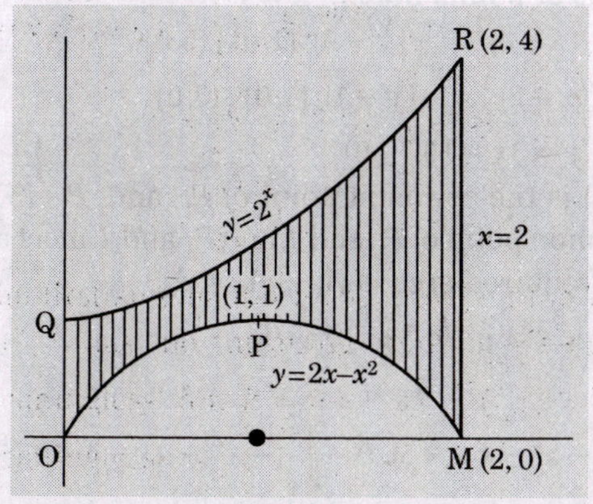

Fig. 47

The required area $= \int_0^2 (\underset{\text{Up}}{y_1} - \underset{\text{Low}}{y_2})\,dx$

where $y_1 = 2^x$ and $y_2 = 2x - x^2$

$$= \int_0^2 (2^x - 2x + x^2)\,dx = \left[\frac{2^x}{\log 2} - x^2 + \frac{1}{3}x^3\right]_0^2$$

$$= \left(\frac{4}{\log 2} - 4 + \frac{8}{3}\right) - \frac{1}{\log 2} = \frac{3}{\log 2} - \frac{4}{3}.$$

(b)* Sketch the curves and identify the region bounded by $x = \frac{1}{2}$, $x = 2$, $y = \log_e x$ and $y = 2^x$.

Find the area of this region. **(I.I.T. 1991)**

$y = \log x$ ...(1)

$y = 2^x$ ...(2)

The required area in the adjoining figure is represented by A, B and C.

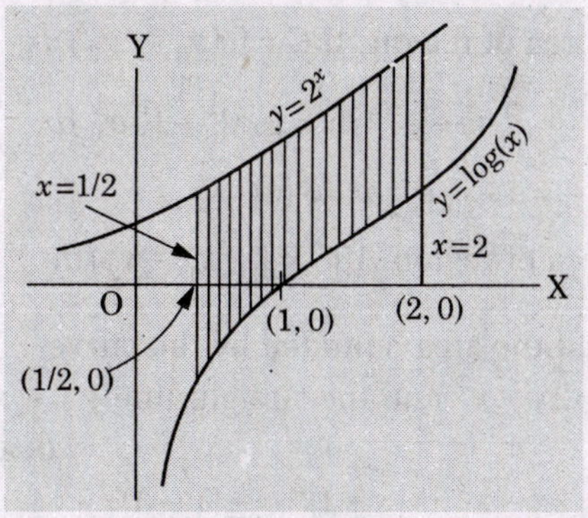

Fig. 48

We have to consider the area bounded by

$$x = \frac{1}{2} \text{ to } x = 2.$$

Required area

$$= \left|\int_{1/2}^2 (\underset{\text{up}}{y_1} - \underset{\text{low}}{y_2})\,dx\right| = \left|\int_{1/2}^2 (2^x - \log x)\,dx\right|$$

$$= \left|\left[\frac{2^x}{\log 2} - (x\log x - x)\right]_{1/2}^2\right|$$

$$= 8\left|\frac{4-\sqrt{2}}{\log 2} - (2\log 2 - 2) + \left(\frac{1}{2}\log\frac{1}{2} - \frac{1}{2}\right)\right|$$

$$= \frac{4-\sqrt{2}}{\log 2} - \frac{5}{2}\log 2 + \frac{3}{2}$$

(c) Area of the region bounded by the curve $y = e^x$ and lines $x = 0$ and $y = e$ is

(a) $e - 1$ (b) $\int_1^e \ln(e + 1 - y)\,dy$

(c) $e - \int_0^1 e^x\,dx$ (d) $\int_1^e \ln y\,dy$ **(I.I.T. 2009)**

Ans. (b), (c), (d).

We have the following curves :

$$C_1 : y = e^x, C_2 : x = 0 \text{ and } C_3 : y = e$$

C_1 and C_2 meet at $A(0,1)$, C_2 and C_3 meet at $B(0,e)$ and C_3 and C_1 meet at $C(1,e)$.

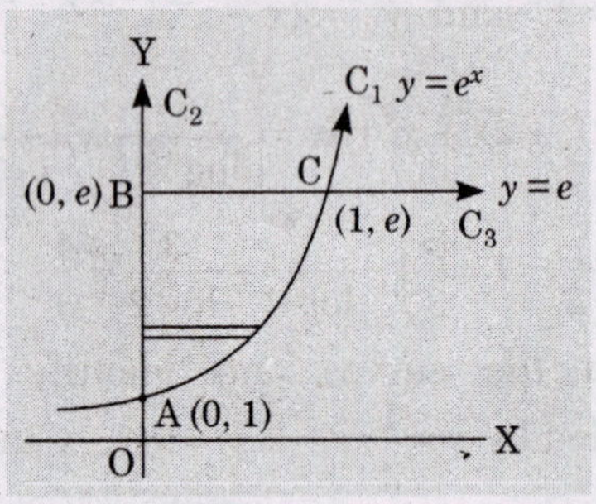

Fig. 49

$\therefore$ Required area $= \int_{y=1 \text{ for } A}^{y=e \text{ for } C} x\,dy$

From $y=e^x$, $x=\log y$

$\therefore \quad A=\int_1^e \log y\,dy \Rightarrow$ (d)

Again, area of region $ABC = \int (y_1 - y_2)\,dx$ (up, low)

$= \int_0^1 (e-e^x)\,dx = [e\,x]_0^1 - \int_0^1 e^x\,dx$

$= e - \int_0^1 e^x\,dx \Rightarrow$ (c)

Also, area of region $ABC = \int_1^e (x_1 - x_2)\,dy$ (R, L)

14. (a)* Find the area bounded by the curve $y=2x-x^2$ and the straight line $y=-x$. **(Roorkee 1992)**

$y=2x-x^2$ is $(x-1)^2=-(y-1)$

It represents a parabola with vertex at (1, 1).

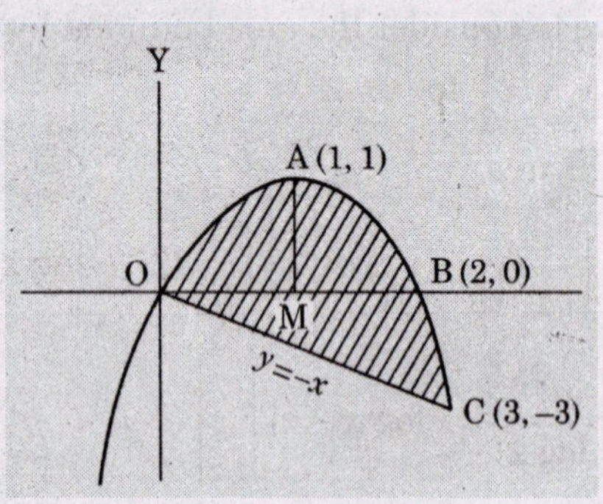

Fig. 50

$$A = \left| \int_0^3 (y_1 - y_2)\,dx \right| \quad (\text{P, L})$$

$$\left| \int_0^3 (2x-x^2)+x\,dx \right| = \left| \left(\frac{3x^2}{2} - x^3 \right) \right| = \frac{9}{2}$$

(b)* Find the area in the plane bounded by the curves $y=x-1$ and $(y-1)^2=4(x+1)$. **(J.E.E. Bihar 1995)**

Eliminating y we get the points of intersection as

$(x-2)^2=4(x+1)$ or $x^2-8x=0$

$\therefore \quad x=0,8 \quad \therefore \quad y=-1,7.$

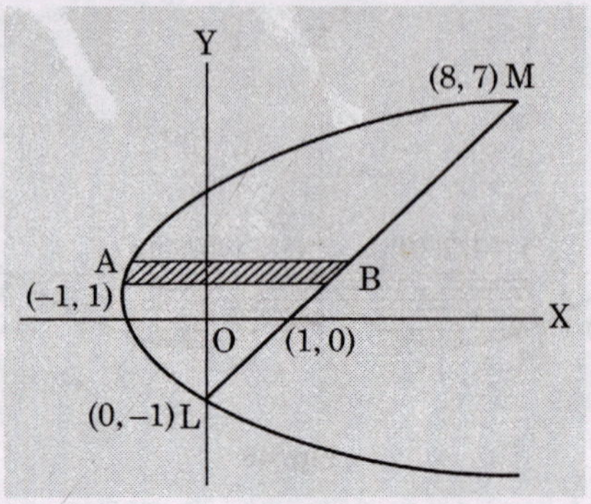

Fig. 51

Hence the points of intersection are $(0,-1)$ and $(8,7)$. The vertex of the parabola is at the point $(-1,1)$. The line cut axes at $(1,0)$ and $(0,-1)$

$\therefore \quad A = \int_{y=-1}^{7} (x_1 - x_2)\,dy$ (R L, L P)

$$= \int_{-1}^{7} \left[(y+1) - \left\{ \frac{(y-1)^2}{4} - 1 \right\} \right] dy$$

$$= \left\{ \frac{1}{2}y^2 + y - \frac{(y-1)^3}{12} + y \right\}_{-1}^{7} = \frac{64}{3} \text{ sq. units.}$$

15. (a) Find the area bounded by the curves
$y=-x^2+6x-5$, $y=-x^2+4x-3$
and the straight line $y=3x-15$.

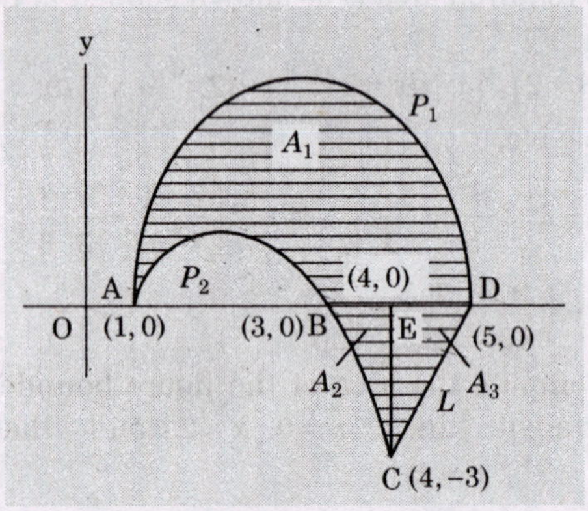

Fig. 52

The two parabolas can be re-written as and they cut x-axis at points noted.

$P_1 \quad (x-3)^2=-(y-4)$, (1, 0), (5, 0)

$P_2 \quad (x-2)^2=-(y-1)$, (1, 0), (3, 0)

$L \quad y=3x-15$, (5, 0)

(1, 0) is the common point of P_1 and P_2, (5, 0) is the common point of P_1 and L and P_2 and L meet at $(4,-3)$.

The required area is $A_1 + A_2 + A_3$.

$A_1 = \int_1^5 \underset{P_1}{y_1}\,dx - \int_1^3 \underset{P_2}{y_2}\,dx$

$$= \int_1^5 (-x^2+6x-5)\,dx - \int_1^3 (-x^2+4x-3)\,dx = \frac{28}{3}$$

$$A_2 = \int_3^4 |y_2|\, dx = \int_3^4 |-x^2 + 4x - 3|\, dx = \left|-\frac{4}{3}\right| = \frac{4}{3}$$
P_2

$$A_3 = \int_4^5 |y|\, dx = \int_4^5 |3x - 15|\, dx = \left|\frac{-3}{2}\right| = \frac{3}{2}$$
L

$\therefore$ Required area $= \frac{28}{3} + \frac{4}{3} + \frac{3}{2} = \frac{73}{6}$.

We have taken mod in A_2 and A_3 as y is – ive for these regions.

(b)* The slope of the tangent to a curve $y = f(x)$ at $\{x, f(x)\}$ is $2x + 1$. If the curve passes through the point (1, 2), then the area bounded by the curve, the x-axis and the line $x = 1$ is

(i) 5/6 (ii) 6/5
(iii) 1/6 (iv) 6 **(I.I.T. 1995)**

Ans. (i). $\frac{dy}{dx} = 2x + 1$ Integrating,

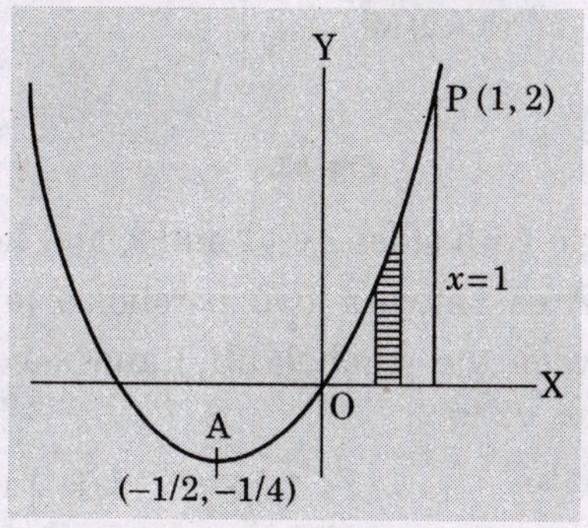

Fig. 53

$\therefore$ $y = x^2 + x + c$ It passes through (1, 2)

$\therefore$ $c = 0$

$$y + \frac{1}{4} = \left(x + \frac{1}{2}\right)^2$$

It is a parabola with vertex at $\left(-\frac{1}{2}, -\frac{1}{4}\right)$. The given lines are $x = 1$ and $y = 0$.

$$\text{Area} = \int_0^1 y\, dx = \int_0^1 (x^2 + x)\, dx = \frac{5}{6}$$

16. Find the area bounded by the parabola $y = 2 - x^2$ and the straight line $y + x = 0$.

$x^2 = -(y - 2)$ and the line $y + x = 0$ cuts it in the points

$x^2 - x - 2 = 0$

or $(x - 2)(x + 1) = 0$ $\therefore$ $x = 2, -1$

$\therefore$ Points are $(2, -2), (-1, 1)$

$$A = \left|\int_{-1}^{2} (y_1 - y_2)\, dx\right|$$

P L

$$= \left|\int_{-1}^{2} \{(2 - x^2) + 2\}\, dx\right| = \left|\left(2x + \frac{x^2}{2} - \frac{x^3}{3}\right)_{-1}^{2}\right| = \frac{9}{2}$$

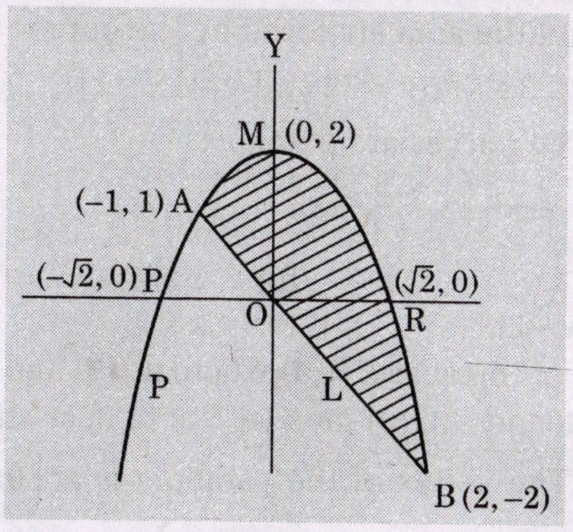

Fig. 54

17.* In what ratio does the x-axis divide the area of the region bounded by the parabolas $y = 4x - x^2$ and $y = x^2 - x$? **(I.I.T. 1994)**

P_1 is $(x - 2)^2 = -(y - 4)$, P_2 is $\left(x - \frac{1}{2}\right)^2 = \left(y + \frac{1}{4}\right)$

P_1 and P_2 meet at $(0, 0)$ and $(5/2, 15/4)$. P_1 cuts the x-axis at (0, 0), (4, 0). P_2 cuts x-axis at (0, 0) and (1, 0). The shape of the curve is as shown in the adjoining figure.

We have to find $\frac{A_1}{A_2}$ where A_1 is lined area and A_2 is dotted area.

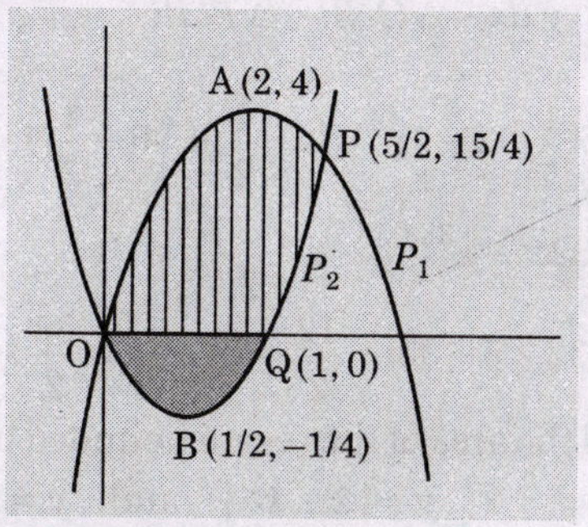

Fig. 55

$$\text{Total area} = \int_0^{5/2} (\underset{\substack{\text{Up}\\P_1}}{y_1} - \underset{\substack{\text{Low}\\P_2}}{y_2})\, dx$$

$$= \int_0^{5/2} [(4x - x^2) - (x^2 - x)]\, dx$$

$$= \int_0^{5/2} (5x - 2x^2)\, dx = \frac{125}{24}$$

Dotted area $\int_0^1 |y_2|\, dx = \int_0^1 |x^2 - x|\, dx$

$$= \left|-\frac{1}{6}\right| = \frac{1}{6}$$

Lined area = Total - Dotted $= \frac{125}{24} - \frac{1}{6} = \frac{121}{24}$

$\therefore$ Ratio $= \frac{121}{24} : \frac{1}{6} = \frac{121}{4}$

18. (a)* Find the area enclosed by the curves

$3x^2 + 5y = 32$ and $y = |x - 2|$ **(M.N.R. 1994)**

The given curves are parabola

$$x^2 = -\frac{5}{3}\left(y - \frac{32}{5}\right) \qquad ...(1)$$

$$y = x - 2 \qquad \text{for} \quad x > 2 \qquad ...(2)$$

$$y = -(x - 2) \qquad \text{for} \quad x < 2 \qquad ...(3)$$

(1) and (2) meet at $P(3, 1)$ where as (1) and (3) meet at $Q(-2, 4)$ and (2), (3) meet at R at $(2, 0)$ as shown in the figure. The vertex of the parabola is at $\left(0, \frac{32}{5}\right)$ and is downwards.

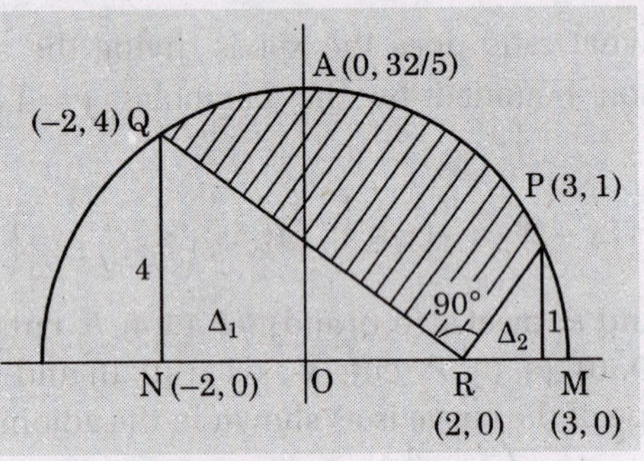

Fig. 56

Required area = Shaded area in the figure

$$= \int_{-2}^{3} y\,dx - \Delta\,QNR - \Delta\,PMR$$

$$= \int_{-2}^{3} \frac{1}{5}(32 - 3x^2)\,dx - \frac{1}{2}(4 \cdot 4) - \frac{1}{2}(1 \cdot 1)$$

$$= \frac{1}{5}[32x - x^3]_{-2}^{3} - 8 - \frac{1}{2}$$

$$= \frac{1}{5}(32 \times 5 - 35) - \frac{17}{2} = 25 - \frac{17}{2} = \frac{33}{2} \text{ sq. units.}$$

(b) Find the area of the region bounded by the curves

$y = x^2$, $y = |2 - x^2|$ and $y = 2$,

which lies to the right of the line $x = 1$. **(I.I.T. 2002)**

(A simple but lengthy question)

$2 - x^2 =$ + ive or − ive according as

$x^2 - 2 = (x + \sqrt{2})(x - \sqrt{2})$ is − ive or + ive

or $-\sqrt{2} < x < \sqrt{2}$ for − ive

and $x < -\sqrt{2}$ or $x > \sqrt{2}$ for + ive

Hence the given curves are

(a) $x^2 = y$ Parabola

(b) $y = 2 - x^2$ or $x^2 = -(y - 2)$ when $-\sqrt{2} < x < \sqrt{2}$

(b_1) $y = -(2 - x^2)$ or $x^2 = y + 2$ when $x < -\sqrt{2}$ or $x > \sqrt{2}$

(c) $y = 2$ Line

(d) $x = 1$ Line

All the above parabolas and lines are drawn in the figure below and we have to find the shaded area.

(a) intersects (b) at (1, 1), (− 1, 1).

(a) does not intersect (b_1) because of the prescribed limits. The lines $y = 2$ and $x = 1$ are marked.

We have to find the shaded area *BDEF* which is between the parabolas and the lines $x = 1$ and $y = 2$.

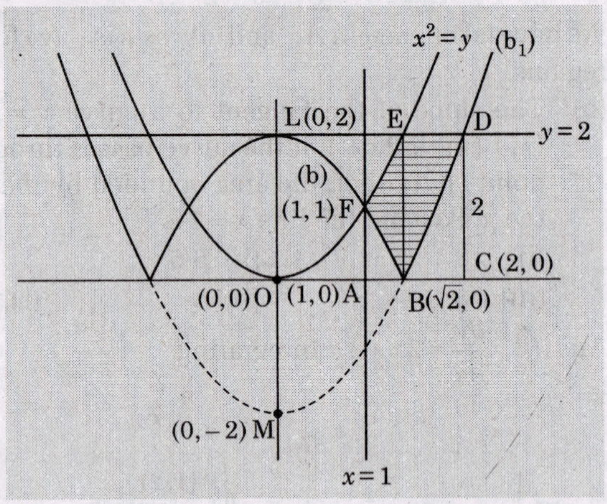

Fig. 57

A = Rectangle with sides $2 - \sqrt{2}$ and 2, and hence area $2(2 - \sqrt{2})$ + Area between two parabolas (a) and (b) − Area between the parabola (b_1) and x-axis within limits for x as $\sqrt{2}$ to 2.

$$\therefore \quad A = BC \cdot CD + \int_1^{\sqrt{2}} (\underset{a}{y_1} - \underset{b}{y_2})\,dx - \int_{\sqrt{2}}^{2} \underset{b_1}{y_3}\,dx$$

$$= 2(2 - \sqrt{2}) + \int_1^{\sqrt{2}} [\underset{y_1}{x^2} - \underset{y_2}{(2 - x^2)}]\,dx - \int_{\sqrt{2}}^{2} (x^2 - 2)\,dx$$

$$= 4 - 2\sqrt{2} + 2\left(\frac{x^3}{3} - x\right)_1^{\sqrt{2}} - \left(\frac{x^3}{3} - 2x\right)_{\sqrt{2}}^{2}$$

$$= 4 - 2\sqrt{2} + \frac{2}{3}(2\sqrt{2} - 1) - 2(\sqrt{2} - 1) - \frac{1}{3}(8 - 2\sqrt{2}) + 2(2 - \sqrt{2})$$

$$= \left(4 - \frac{2}{3} + 2 - \frac{8}{3} + 4\right) + \sqrt{2}\left(-2 + \frac{4}{3} - 2 + \frac{2}{3} - 2\right)$$

$$= \left(\frac{20}{3} - 4\sqrt{2}\right) \text{sq. units.}$$

19. The area of the region bounded by the curve $y^2 = 2x + 1$ and $x - y - 1 = 0$ is 16/3.

The line meets the parabola at (0, − 1) and (4, 3).

$$A = \left| \int_{-1}^{3} (\underset{\substack{R\\L}}{x_1} - \underset{\substack{L\\P}}{x_2})\,dy \right|$$

$$= \int_{-1}^{3} \left\{(y + 1) - \frac{1}{2}(y^2 - 1)\right\} dy$$

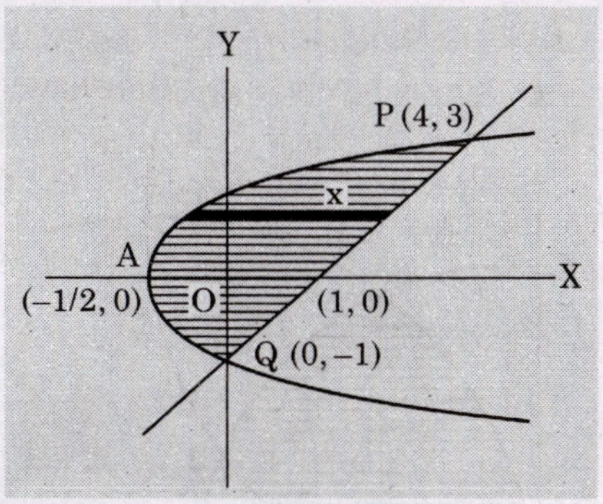

Fig. 58

$$= \frac{1}{2} \int_{-1}^{3} (3 + 2y - y^2)\, dy = \frac{16}{3}$$

20.* Find the area of the figure bounded by the parabola $(y-2)^2 = x - 1$, the tangent to it at the point with ordinate 3, and the x-axis. **(Roorkee 2000; M.N.R. 1996)**

$(y-2)^2 = x - 1$ represents a parabola with vertex at the point (1, 2). The point whose ordinate is 3 will have its x given by $(3-2)^2 = x - 1$.

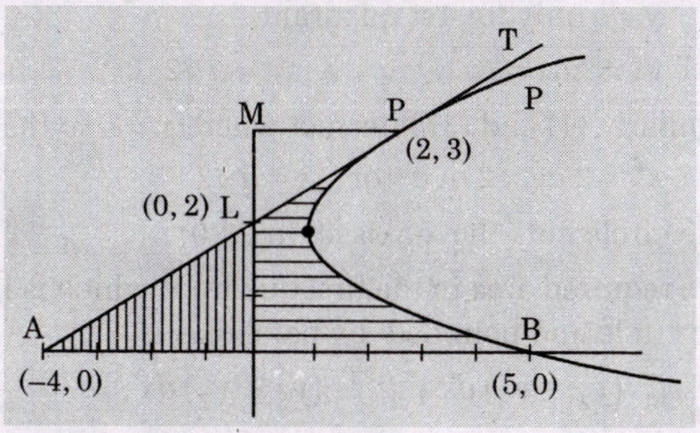

Fig. 59

$\therefore$ $x = 2$; $P(2, 3)$.

$y^2 - 4y - x + 5 = 0$ $\therefore$ Tangent at $P(2, 3)$ is

$y.3 - 2(y+3) - \frac{1}{2}(x+2) + 5 = 0$

or $2y - x = 4$ or $x = 2(y-2)$

It meets the axes at $(-4, 0)$ and $(0, 2)$. The parabola meets the x-axis at $(5, 0)$. The shape of the curve is as shown in the figure. The required area is shaded area which is between the parabola, tangent at P and x-axis, *i.e.*

$$\int_0^3 (\underset{\substack{R\\P}}{x_1} - \underset{\substack{L\\T}}{x_2})\, dy = \int_0^3 [(y-2)^2 + 1 - 2(y-2)]\, dy$$

Put $y - 2 = t$ and adjust the limits

$$\int_{-2}^{1} (t-1)^2\, dt = \left[\frac{(t-1)^3}{3}\right]_{-2}^{1} = 9.$$

21.* Let C_1 and C_2 be the graphs of the functions $y = x^2$ and $y = 2x, 0 \le x \le 1$ respectively. Let C_3 be the graph of a function $y = f(x), 0 \le x \le 1, f(0) = 0$. For a point P on C_1, let the lines through P, parallel to the axes, meet C_2 and C_3 at Q and R respectively (see figure). If for every position of P (on C_1), the areas of the shaded regions OPQ and ORP are equal, determine the function $f(x)$. **(I.I.T. 1998)**

Let P be on C_1, $y = x^2$ be (t, t^2) $\therefore$ y of Q is also t^2. Now Q on $y = 2x$, $y = t^2$ $\therefore x = t^2/2$

$\therefore$ $Q\left(\frac{t^2}{2}, t^2\right)$

For point R, $x = t$ and it is on $y = f(x)$ $\therefore$ R is $[t, f(t)]$

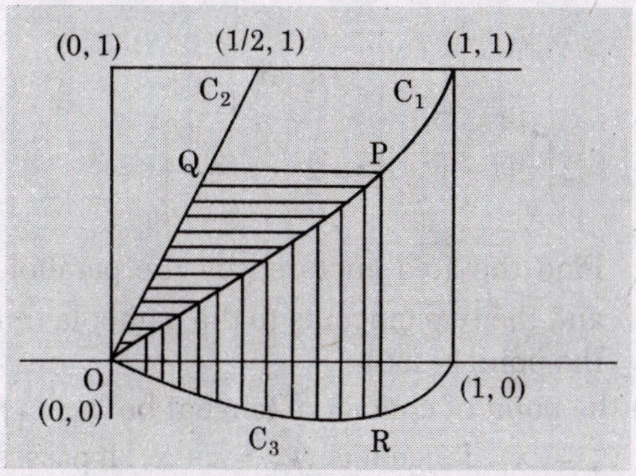

Fig. 60

$$\text{Area } OPQ = \int_0^{t^2} (\underset{C_1}{x_1} - \underset{C_2}{x_2})\, dy = \int_0^{t^2} \left(\sqrt{y} - \frac{y}{2}\right) dy$$

$$= \frac{2}{3}t^3 - \frac{t^4}{4} \qquad \text{...(1)}$$

$$\text{Area } OPR = \int_0^t \underset{C_1}{y}\, dx + \left|\int_0^t \underset{C_3}{y}\, dx\right|$$

$$= \int_0^t x^2\, dx + \left|\int_0^t f(x)\, dx\right| = \frac{t^3}{3} + \left|\int_0^t f(x)\, dx\right| \qquad \text{...(2)}$$

Equating (1) and (2), we get

$$\frac{t^3}{3} - \frac{t^4}{4} = \left|\int_0^t f(x)\, dx\right|$$

Differentiating both sides, we get

$t^2 - t^3 = -f(t)$

$\therefore$ $f(x) = x^3 - x^2$.

22. (a)* Compute the area of the figure bounded by the parabolas $x = -2y^2$, $x = 1 - 3y^2$

Sol. Solving the equations $x = -2y^2$, $x = 1 - 3y^2$ we find that ordinates of the points of intersection of the two curves as $y_1 = -1, y_2 = 1$.

The points are $(-2, -1)$ and $(-2, 1)$.

The required area $2\int_0^1 (\underset{\substack{R\\P_1}}{x_1} - \underset{\substack{L\\P_2}}{x_2})\, dy$

$$= 2\int_0^1 [(1 - 3y^2) - (-2y^2)]\, dy$$

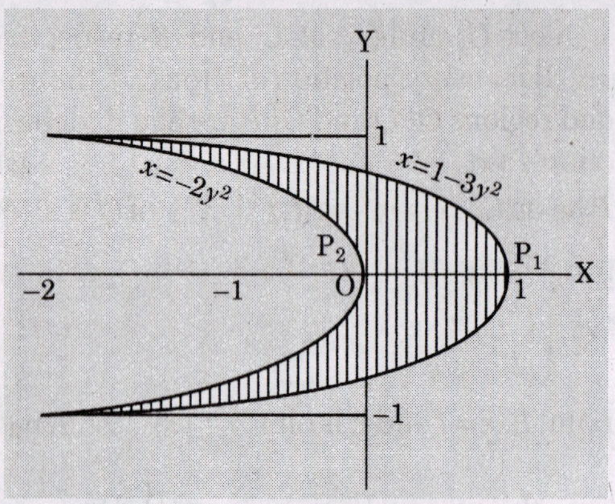

Fig. 61

$$=2\int_0^1 (1-y^2)\,dy = 2\left[y-\frac{y^3}{3}\right]_0^1 = \frac{4}{3}$$

(b) Find the area enclosed by the parabola $y^2 = 2x$ and the two tangents to the parabola drawn from the point $(-2, 0)$.

Let the point of contact of tangent be (x_1, y_1).

$\therefore\ y_1^2 = 2x_1$. Tangent is $yy_1 = x + x_1$. It passes through $(-2, 0)\ \therefore 0 = x_1 - 2$ or $x_1 = 2$

$\therefore\ y_1^2 = 4$ or $y_1 = \pm 2$

Hence the two points of contact of tangents are $(2, 2)$ and $(2, -2)$. Tangent at $(2, 2)$ is $2y = x + 2$

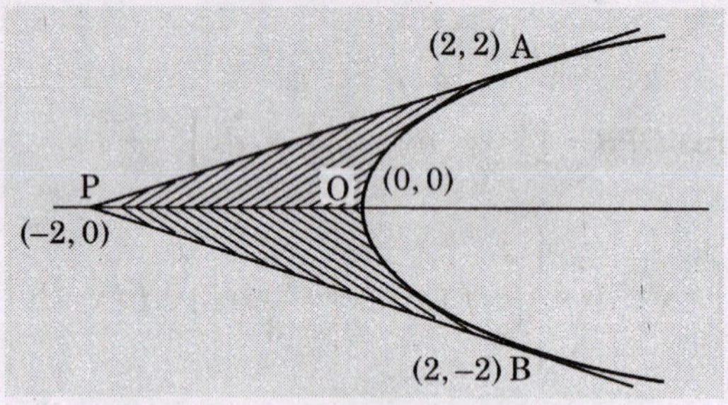

Fig. 62

Required area = shaded area

$$= 2\,[\textstyle\int (x_1\,dy - \int x_2\,dy)]$$
$$\quad\ \ R \qquad\quad L$$
$$\quad\ \ P \qquad\quad l$$

$$=2\left[\int_0^2 \frac{y^2}{2}\,dy - \int_0^2 (2y-2)\,dy\right]$$

$$=2\left[\frac{y^3}{6} - y^2 - 2y\right]_0^2 = 2.\frac{8}{6} - 0 = \frac{8}{3}.$$

Note : You can also use $2\,[\int y_1\,dx - \int y_2\,dx]$.
$\qquad\qquad\qquad\qquad\qquad$ up $\qquad$ low

23. (a)* Find the area of the figure which lies in the first quadrant inside the circle $x^2 + y^2 = 3a^2$ and bounded by the parabolas $x^2 = 2ay$ and $y^2 = 2ax$ $(a > 0)$.

C is $x^2 + y^2 = 3a^2$ ...(1)

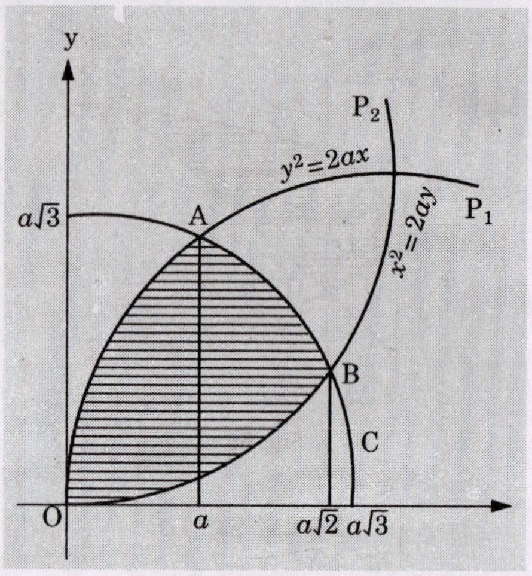

Fig. 63

P_1 is $\quad y^2 = 2ax$ ...(2)

P_2 is $\quad x^2 = 2ay$ ...(3)

(1) and (2) intersect at $x^2 + 2ax - 3a^2 = 0$

$(x + 3a)(x - a) = 0$

$\therefore\quad x = a$ only for 1st quadrant,

and $y^2 = 2ax = 2a^2 \qquad \therefore\ \ y = a\sqrt{2}$

Similarly (1) and (3) intersect where $y = a$ so that

$x^2 = 2\,ay = 2\,a\,.\,a$ or $x = a\sqrt{2}$

The circle cuts the x-axis at $(a\sqrt{3}, 0)$.

The required area in the first quadrant which is inside the circle and bounded by parabolas is

$$\int_0^a (y_1 - y_2)\,dx + \int_a^{a\sqrt{2}} (y_3 - y_2)\,dx$$
$$\qquad P_1 \quad P_2 \qquad\qquad\qquad C \quad P_2$$

$$=\int_0^a y_1\,dx + \int_a^{a\sqrt{2}} y_3\,dx - \left[\int_0^a y_2\,dx + \int_a^{a\sqrt{2}} y_2\,dx\right]$$

$$=\int_0^a \sqrt{2ax}\,dx + \int_a^{a\sqrt{2}} \sqrt{(3a^2 - x^2)}\,dx - \int_0^{a\sqrt{2}} \frac{x^2}{2a}\,dx$$

$$=\left[\sqrt{2a}\,\frac{2}{3}\,x^{3/2}\right]_0^a + \left[\frac{x}{2}\sqrt{3a^2 - x^2} + \frac{3a^2}{2}\sin^{-1}\frac{x}{a\sqrt{3}}\right]_a^{a\sqrt{2}} - \left[\frac{x^3}{6a}\right]_0^{a\sqrt{2}}$$

$$=\frac{2\sqrt{2}}{3}a^2 + \left[\left(\frac{a\sqrt{2}}{2}\cdot a + \frac{3a^2}{2}\sin^{-1}\sqrt{\frac{2}{3}}\right) - \left(\frac{a}{2}\,a\sqrt{2} + \frac{3a^2}{2}\sin^{-1}\frac{1}{\sqrt{3}}\right)\right] - \frac{a^3}{6a}(2\sqrt{2})$$

$$=\frac{a^2}{6}(4\sqrt{2} - 2\sqrt{2}) + \frac{3a^2}{2}\sin^{-1}\left[\sqrt{\frac{2}{3}}\sqrt{1-\frac{1}{3}} - \frac{1}{\sqrt{3}}\sqrt{1-\frac{2}{3}}\right]$$

$$=a^2\left[\frac{\sqrt{2}}{3} + \frac{3}{2}\sin^{-1}\left(\frac{2}{3} - \frac{1}{3}\right)\right] = a^2\left[\frac{\sqrt{2}}{3} + \frac{3}{2}\sin^{-1}\frac{1}{3}\right]$$

We have used

$$\sin^{-1}x - \sin^{-1}y = \sin^{-1}\left[x\sqrt{1-y^2} - y\sqrt{1-x^2}\right]$$

(b) Find the area bounded by the curves
$x^2 + y^2 = 4, x^2 = -\sqrt{2}\, y$ and the line $x = y$.

$$C, x^2 + y^2 = 4, P, y = -\frac{x^2}{\sqrt{2}}, L, y = x$$

We have above three curves

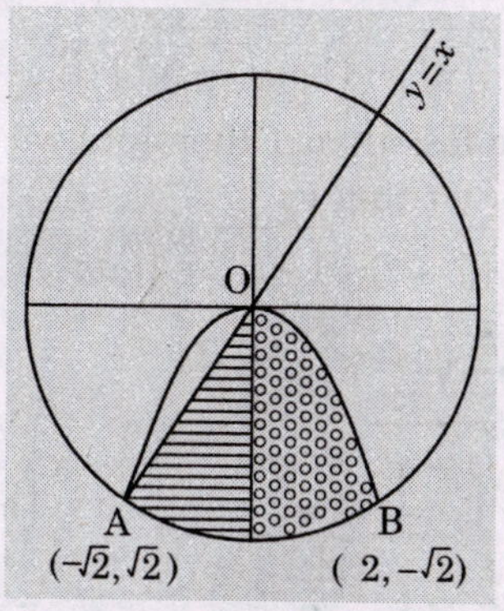

Fig. 64

Solving P and C, we get the points

$$A(-\sqrt{2}, -\sqrt{2}), B(\sqrt{2}, -\sqrt{2})$$

Also the line $y = x$ passes through $A(-\sqrt{2}, -\sqrt{2})$

$\therefore$ Required Area = shaded + dotted

$$= \int_{-\sqrt{2}}^{0} (\underset{L}{y_3} - \underset{C}{y_1})\, dx + \int_0^{\sqrt{2}} (\underset{P}{y_2} - \underset{C}{y_1})\, dx$$

$$= \int_{-\sqrt{2}}^{0} x\, dx + \int_0^{\sqrt{2}} \frac{-x^2}{\sqrt{2}}\, dx - \int_{-\sqrt{2}}^{\sqrt{2}} \sqrt{4 - x^2}\, dx$$

$$= \left[\frac{x^2}{2}\right]_{-\sqrt{2}}^{0} - \frac{1}{\sqrt{2}}\left[\frac{x^3}{3}\right]_0^{\sqrt{2}} - 2\left[\frac{x}{2}\sqrt{4 - x^2} + \frac{4}{2}\sin^{-1}\frac{x}{2}\right]_0^{\sqrt{2}}$$

$$= -1 - \frac{2}{3} - 2\left(1 + \frac{\pi}{2}\right) = -\left(\frac{3\pi + 11}{3}\right)$$

$$\therefore \quad |A| = \frac{3\pi + 11}{3}$$

24.* Find the area given by $x + y \le 6$, $x^2 + y^2 \le 6y$ and $y^2 \le 8x$. **(Roorkee 1995)**

P $\quad y^2 = 8x$ ...(1)

C $\quad x^2 + y^2 - 6y = 0$ or $x^2 + (y - 3)^2 = 3^2$ ...(2)

L $\quad x + y = 6$ ...(3)

(3) and (2) meet at $y^2 - 6y + (6 - y)^2 = 0$

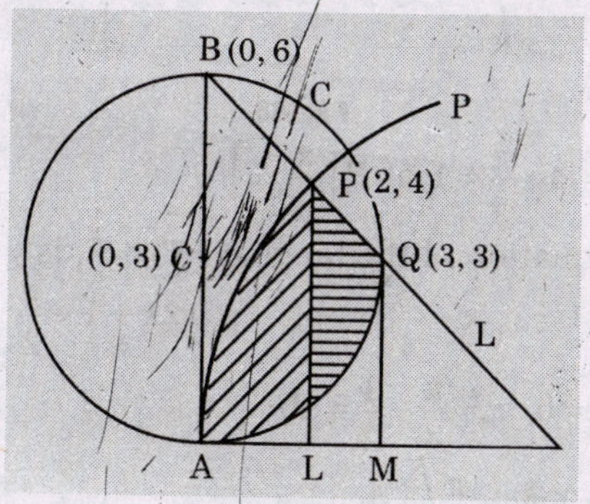

Fig. 65

or $\quad y^2 - 9y + 18 = 0, \quad (y - 6)(y - 3) = 0$

$\therefore \quad (0, 6)$ and $(3, 3)$.

(1) and (3) meet at $\quad y^2 - 8(6 - y) = 0$

or $\quad y^2 + 8y - 48 = 0, \quad (y + 12)(y - 4) = 0$

$\therefore \quad (2, 4)$ in Ist quadrant.

If P, C, L stand for parabola, circle and line then required area is shaded area

$$A = \int_0^2 (\underset{P}{y_1} - \underset{C}{y_2})\, dx + \int_2^3 (\underset{L}{y_3} - \underset{C}{y_2})\, dx \quad ...(4)$$

$$\int_0^2 y_1\, dx + \int_2^3 y_3\, dx - \left[\int_0^2 y_2\, dx + \int_2^3 y_2\, dx\right]$$

$$= \left[\int_0^2 y_1\, dx + \int_2^3 y_3\, dx - \int_0^3 y_2\, dx\right]$$

Now $\quad y_1 = 2\sqrt{(2x)}, \qquad y_3 = 6 - x$

and $x^2 + (y - 3)^2 = 9$ for C

$\therefore \quad y - 3 = \pm\sqrt{(9 - x^2)}$

But $y < 3$ for circular portion so that $y - 3$ is – ive and so we choose (Note)

$$y - 3 = -\sqrt{(9 - x^2)}$$

$\therefore \quad y_2 = 3 - \sqrt{(9 - x^2)}$

$$A = \int_0^2 2\sqrt{(2x)}\, dx + \int_2^3 (6 - x)\, dx - \int_0^3 [3 - \sqrt{(9 - x^2)}]\, dx \quad \text{by (4)}$$

$$= 2\sqrt{2}\,\frac{2}{3}\left[x^{3/2}\right]_0^2 + \left(6x - \frac{x^2}{2}\right)_2^3 - I$$

$$= \frac{16}{3} + \frac{7}{2} - \left(9 - \frac{9\pi}{4}\right) = \frac{1}{12}(27\pi - 2)$$

25.* Find the area of the region formed by $x^2 + y^2 - 6x - 4y + 12 \le 0, y \le x$ and $x \le \frac{5}{2}$. **(Roorkee 1996)**

Solving the circle and the line $y = x$, we get the points $(2, 2), (3, 3)$.

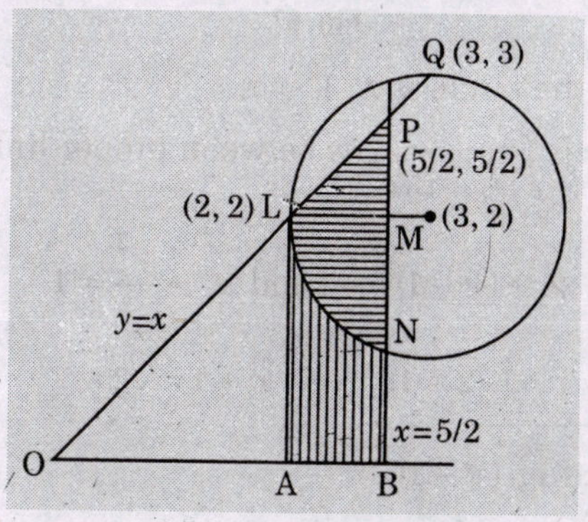

Fig. 66

The circle can be written as

$$(x - 3)^2 + (y - 2)^2 = 1 \quad \text{or} \quad (y - 2)^2 = 1 - (x - 3)^2$$

$$(y - 2) = \pm\sqrt{1 - (x - 3)^2}$$

Since $y < 2$ for circular portion, $\quad \therefore$ **$y - 2 = -$ ive.**

or $\quad (y - 2) = -\sqrt{1 - (x - 3)^2}$ **(Note)**

or $y = 2 - \sqrt{1-(x-3)^2}$

Area bounded by the three curves *i.e.* two lines and the circle is lined area $LPMNL$

= Area of trapezium – dotted area $LABNL = A_1 - A_2$

$$A_1 = \frac{1}{2}(LA + PM)\, LM = \frac{1}{2}\left(2+\frac{5}{2}\right)\frac{1}{2} = \frac{9}{8}$$

$$A_2 = \int_2^{5/2} y\,dx = \int_2^{5/2} [2 - \sqrt{1-(x-3)^2}]\,dx$$

$$= 2x - \left[\frac{x-3}{2}\cdot\sqrt{1-(x-3)^2} + \frac{1}{2}\sin^{-1}\frac{x-3}{1}\right]_2^{5/2}$$

$$= 2\cdot\frac{1}{2} - \frac{1}{2}\left(-\frac{1}{2}\right)\left(\sqrt{\frac{3}{4}}\right) - 0 - \frac{1}{2}\left[\sin^{-1}\left(-\frac{1}{2}\right) - \sin^{-1}(-1)\right]$$

$$= 1 + \frac{\sqrt{3}}{8} - \frac{1}{2}\left(-\frac{\pi}{6}+\frac{\pi}{2}\right) = 1 + \frac{\sqrt{3}}{8} - \frac{\pi}{6}$$

$$\therefore \quad A = A_1 - A_2 = \frac{9}{8} - 1 - \frac{\sqrt{3}}{8} + \frac{\pi}{6} = \frac{1}{8} - \frac{\sqrt{3}}{8} + \frac{\pi}{6}$$

26. Find the area of the region lying inside $x^2 + (y-1)^2 = 1$ and outside $c^2x^2 + y^2 = c^2$ where $c = (\sqrt{2}-1)$.

(Roorkee 1999)

Required area = Total area of circle $- 2A$ where A is shaded area between the ellipse and the circle.

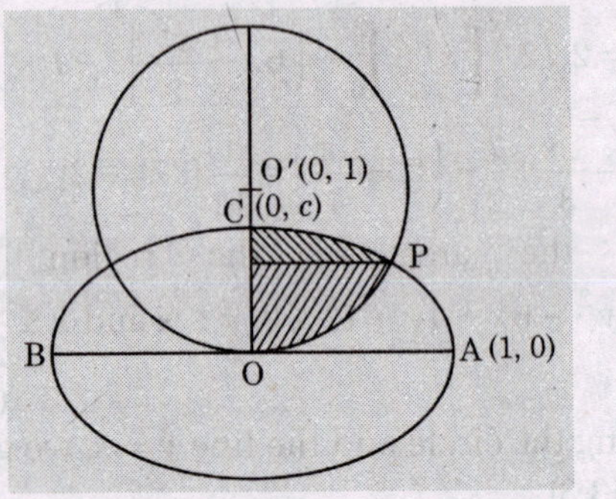

Fig. 67

Area of the circle is $\pi . 1^2 = \pi$

$A = \int (\underset{\substack{Up\\E}}{y_1} - \underset{\substack{Low\\C}}{y_2})\,dx$ between proper limits for x

Solving $x^2 + (y-1)^2 = 1$ and $x^2 + \dfrac{y^2}{c^2} = 1$

where, $c = (\sqrt{2}-1)$ or $c + 1 = \sqrt{2}$

Subtracting, $(y-1)^2 = \dfrac{y^2}{c^2}$

or $\left(\dfrac{y}{c} + y - 1\right)\left(\dfrac{y}{c} - y + 1\right) = 0$

$\therefore \quad y = \dfrac{c}{1+c}$ or $\dfrac{c}{c-1}$

But (y for P) < (y for O') *i.e.* < 1

$\therefore$ We choose $y = \dfrac{c}{c+1}$ which is < 1

$$\therefore \quad x^2 = 1 - \frac{y^2}{c^2} = 1 - \frac{1}{(c+1)^2} = 1 - \frac{1}{(\sqrt{2})^2} = \frac{1}{2}$$

$\therefore \quad x = \pm\dfrac{1}{\sqrt{2}}$. Hence x for P is $\dfrac{1}{\sqrt{2}}$.

$y - 1 = \pm\sqrt{1-x^2}$ for circle

$A = \int c\sqrt{1-x^2} - \{1 - \sqrt{1-x^2}\}\,dx$

Since y is to be less than 1 therefore we choose – ive sign out of ± for writing y_2

$$\therefore \quad A = \int_0^{1/\sqrt{2}} \{(c+1)\sqrt{1-x^2} - 1\}\,dx$$

$$= \int_0^{1/\sqrt{2}} \{\sqrt{2}\sqrt{1-x^2} - 1\}\,dx$$

$$= \sqrt{2}\left\{\left(\frac{x}{2}\sqrt{1-x^2} + \frac{1}{2}\sin^{-1}x\right) - x\right\}_0^{1/\sqrt{2}}$$

$$= \sqrt{2}\left\{\frac{1}{4} + \frac{1}{2}\cdot\frac{\pi}{4}\right\} - \frac{1}{\sqrt{2}}$$

$$\therefore \quad 2A = \frac{2\sqrt{2}}{4} + \sqrt{2}\frac{\pi}{4} - \frac{2}{\sqrt{2}}$$

Required area $= \pi - 2A = \pi - \dfrac{\pi}{2\sqrt{2}} + \dfrac{1}{\sqrt{2}}$

27.* Find the area of the region bounded by the curve $C : y = \tan x$, tangent drawn to C at $x = \pi/4$ and the x-axis.

Sol. The shape of the curve is as shown in the figure. The required area is as shown shaded in the figure and is bounded by the part OP of the curve $y = \tan x$, the tangent PT at P and the part OT of x-axis. We now first find the equation of tangent at P. We have

$$\frac{dy}{dx} = \sec^2 x = 2 \text{ at } x = \frac{\pi}{4}.$$

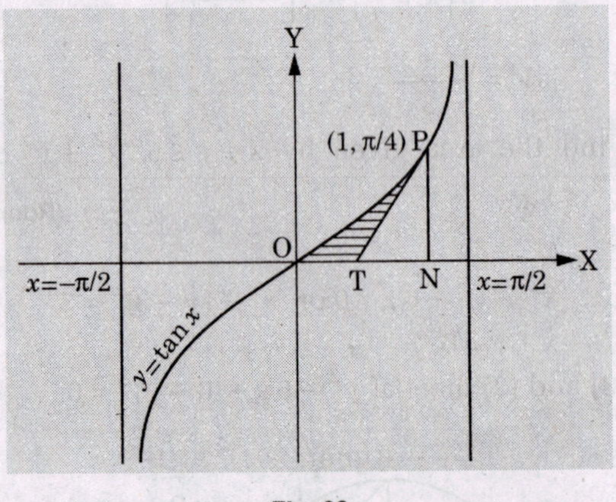

Fig. 68

Also $y = \tan\dfrac{\pi}{4} = 1$ at $P\left(\dfrac{\pi}{4}, 1\right)$

Hence equation of the tangent PT at P, is

$$y - 1 = 2\left(x - \frac{\pi}{4}\right) \quad \text{or} \quad y = 2x + 1 - \frac{\pi}{2}$$

When $y = 0$, $x = \dfrac{\pi}{4} - \dfrac{1}{2} = OT$.

Also $\quad ON = \dfrac{\pi}{4}$ so that

$$TN = ON - OT = \frac{\pi}{4} - \frac{\pi}{4} + \frac{1}{2} = \frac{1}{2}.$$

Now the required area

$$= \text{Area } OPNO - \text{Area of } \Delta\, PTN$$

$$= \int_0^{\pi/4} \tan x\, dx - \frac{1}{2} . TN . PN$$

$$= [\log \sec x]_0^{\pi/4} - \frac{1}{2} . \frac{1}{2} . 1$$

$$= (\log \sqrt{2} - 0) - \frac{1}{4} = \frac{1}{2}\left(\log 2 - \frac{1}{2}\right).$$

28. (a)* Find all maxima and minima of the function $y = x(x-1)^2,\ 0 \le x \le 2.$

Also determine the area bounded by the curve $y = x(x-1)^2$, the y-axis and the line $y = 2$

Sol. It is easy to find that y is max. at $x = \frac{1}{3}$ and min. at $x = 1$.

The curve cuts the axis of x i.e. $y = 0$ at points $(0, 0), (1, 0)$. When x increases from 1 and 2, y also increases and is +ve. When $y = 2$, $2 = x(x-1)^2$

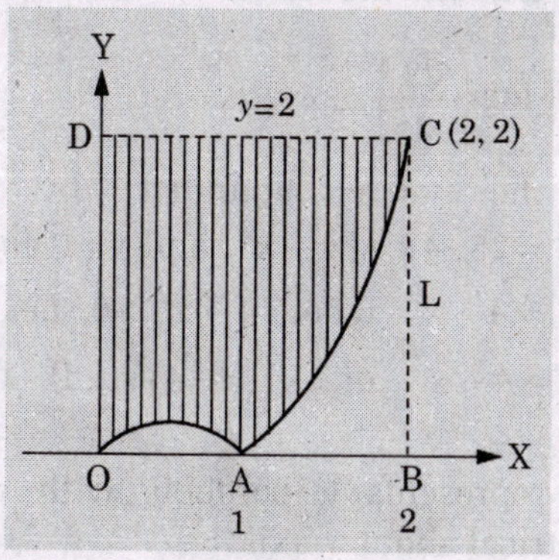

Fig. 69

or $\quad x^3 - 2x^2 + x - 2 = 0$

or $\quad (x-2)(x^2+1) = 0 \quad \therefore \quad x = 2$

$\therefore$ The required area = Shaded area

$$= \text{Area of the square } OBCD - \int_0^2 y\, dx.$$

$$= 2^2 - \int_0^2 x(x-1)^2\, dx.$$

$$= 4 - \left[x\frac{(x-1)^3}{3} - \frac{1}{3}\int (x-1)^3 . 1\, dx\right]$$

$$= 4 - \left[\frac{x}{3}(x-1)^3 - \frac{(x-1)^4}{12}\right]_0^2$$

$$= 4 - \left[\frac{1}{3}(2-0) - \frac{1}{12}(1-1)\right]$$

$$= 4 - \frac{2}{3} = \frac{10}{3} \text{ sq. units.}$$

(b)* A curve $y = f(x)$ passes through the point $P(1, 1)$. The normal to the curve at P is $a(y-1) + (x-1) = 0$. If the slope of the tangent at any point on the curve is proportional to the ordinate of the point, determine the equation of the curve. Also obtain the area bounded by the y-axis, the curve and the normal to the curve at P.

(I.I.T. 1996)

Slope of normal $= -1/a$

Hence slope of tangent or the value of $\frac{dy}{dx}$ at $P(1, 1)$ is a ...(1)

It is given $\frac{dy}{dx} = ky. \quad \therefore \quad a = k . 1$ at P

$\therefore \quad \frac{dy}{dx} = ay \quad$ or $\quad \frac{dy}{y} = a\, dx$

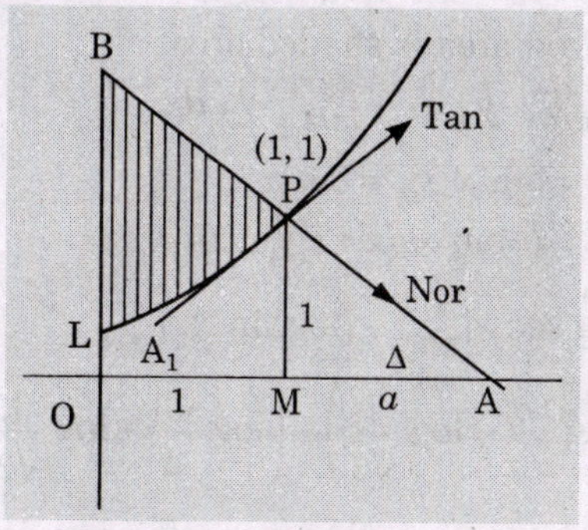

Fig. 70

Integrating, $\quad \log y = ax + \log c$

or $\quad \log(y/c) = ax \quad \therefore \quad y = ce^{ax}$

It passes through $P(1, 1)$

$\therefore \quad 1 = ce^a \quad$ or $\quad c = e^{-a}$

$\therefore \quad y = e^{a(x-1)}$ ...(2)

Required area is bounded by y-axis, the normal at P and the curve. It is the shaded area shown in the figure.

$$A = \Delta\, OAB - \Delta PMA - A_1 \quad \text{...(3)}$$

The intercepts of normal $x + ay = 1 + a$ are

$$1 + a \text{ and } \frac{1+a}{a}.$$

$$\Delta\, OAB = \frac{1}{2}\frac{(1+a)^2}{a}$$

$$\text{Area } A_1 = \int_0^1 y\, dx = \int_0^1 e^{a(x-1)}\, dx$$

$$= \frac{1}{a}[e^{a(x-1)}]_0^1 = \frac{1}{a}[1 - e^{-a}]$$

$$\Delta\, PMA = \frac{1}{2} PM . MA = \frac{1}{2} a . 1 = \frac{a}{2}$$

$\therefore$ Putting in (3), we get

$$A = \frac{(1+a)^2}{2a} - \frac{1}{a}(1 - e^{-a}) - \frac{a}{2} = 1 - \frac{1}{2a} + \frac{e^{-a}}{a}$$

29.* Find the area of the region bounded by the x-axis and the curves defined by

$$y = \tan x, -\frac{1}{3}\pi \le x \le \frac{1}{3}\pi$$

$$y = \cot x, \frac{1}{6}\pi \le x \le \frac{3}{2}\pi.$$

Sol. The curves intersect at P, where $\tan x = \cot x$, which is satisfied at $x = \pi/4$ within the given domain of x.

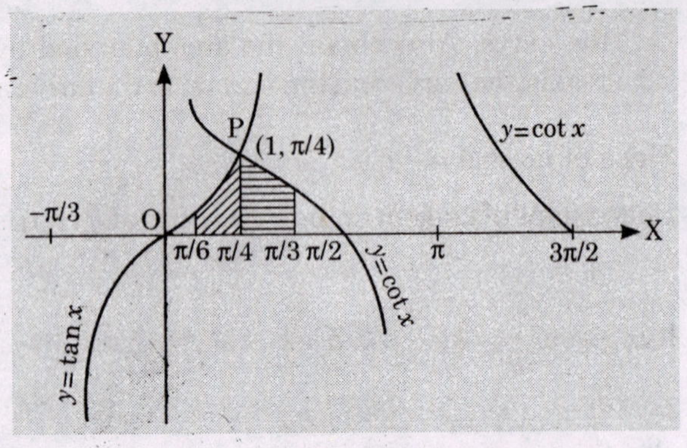

Fig. 71

The required area is shaded area

$$A=\int_{\pi/6}^{\pi/4} y_1\,dx+\int_{\pi/4}^{\pi/3} y_2\,dx,$$

where $y_1=\tan x$, $y_2=\cot x$

$$\therefore\quad A=\int_{\pi/6}^{\pi/4}\tan x\,dx+\int_{\pi/4}^{\pi/3}\cot x\,dx$$

$$=[\log\sec x]_{\pi/6}^{\pi/4}+[\log\sin x\,]_{\pi/4}^{\pi/3}$$

$$=\left(\log\sqrt{2}-\log\frac{2}{\sqrt{3}}\right)+\left(\log\frac{\sqrt{3}}{2}-\log\frac{1}{\sqrt{2}}\right)$$

$$=\left(\log\sqrt{2}+\log\frac{\sqrt{3}}{2}\right)+\left(\log\frac{\sqrt{3}}{2}+\log\sqrt{2}\right)$$

$$=2\left(\log\sqrt{2}\,.\,\frac{\sqrt{3}}{2}\right)=2\log\sqrt{\frac{3}{2}}=\log\frac{3}{2}\text{ sq. units.}$$

30. The area bounded by the curves $y=\sin x$ and $y=\cos x$ between $x=0$ and $x=2\pi$ is $4\sqrt{2}$ sq. units.

$y=\sin x$	+ive	from 0 to π	dotted curve
	−ive	from π to 2π	
$y=\cos x$	+ive	from 0 to π/2 and 3π/2 to 2π	dashes curve
	−ive	from π/2 to 3π/2	

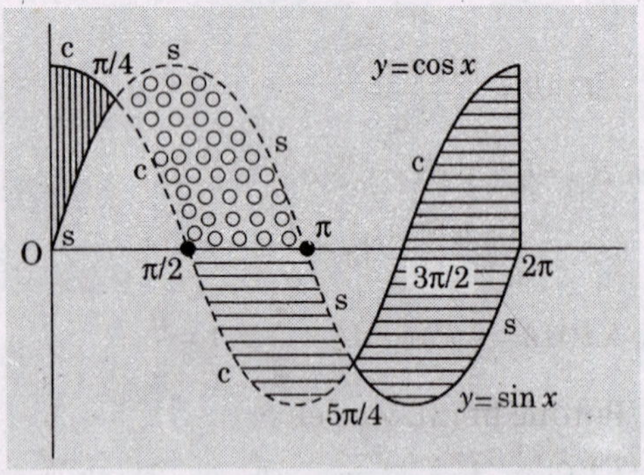

Fig. 72

Required area by $\int (y_1-y_2)\,dx$ (Up, Low)

$$=\left|\int_0^{\pi/4}(\cos x-\sin x)\,dx\right|+\left|\int_{\pi/4}^{5\pi/4}(\sin x-\cos x)\,dx\right|+\left|\int_{5\pi/4}^{2\pi}(\cos x-\sin x)\,dx\right|$$

$$=\left|\int_0^{\pi/4}\sqrt{2}\cos\left(x+\frac{\pi}{4}\right)dx\right|+\left|\sqrt{2}\int_{\pi/4}^{5\pi/4}\sin\left(x-\frac{\pi}{4}\right)dx\right|+\left|\int_{5\pi/4}^{2\pi}\sqrt{2}\cos\left(x+\frac{\pi}{4}\right)dx\right|$$

$$=\sqrt{2}\left[\left|\sin\left(x+\frac{\pi}{4}\right)\right|\right]_0^{\pi/4}+\sqrt{2}\left[\left|-\cos\left(x-\frac{\pi}{4}\right)\right|\right]_{\pi/4}^{5\pi/4}+\sqrt{2}\left[\left|\sin\left(x+\frac{\pi}{4}\right)\right|\right]_{5\pi/4}^{2\pi}$$

$$=\sqrt{2}\left|1-\frac{1}{\sqrt{2}}\right|+\sqrt{2}\,|-(-1-1)|+\sqrt{2}\left|\frac{1}{\sqrt{2}}+1\right|$$

$$=\sqrt{2}+2\sqrt{2}+\sqrt{2}=4\sqrt{2}$$

31. Compute the area of the curvilinear triangle bounded by the y-axis and the curves $y=\tan x$ and $y=\frac{2}{3}\cos x$.

Ans. $\frac{1}{3}+\log\left(\frac{\sqrt{3}}{2}\right)$.

32.* Find the area bounded by the curves $x^2+y^2=25$, $4y=|4-x^2|$ and $x=0$ above the x-axis.

$|4-x^2|=4-x^2$ when $4-x^2>0$, *i.e.* $x^2<4$

$\therefore\quad 4y=4-x^2$ or $x^2=-4(y-1)$ for $-2\le x\le 2$

Above represents a parabola with vertex at (0, 1) symmetrical about y-axis.

$|4-x^2|=-(4-x^2)$ when $4-x^2<0$ *i.e.* $x^2>4$

$4y=x^2-4$ or $x^2=4(y+1)$ $x\ge 2$, or $x\le -2$.

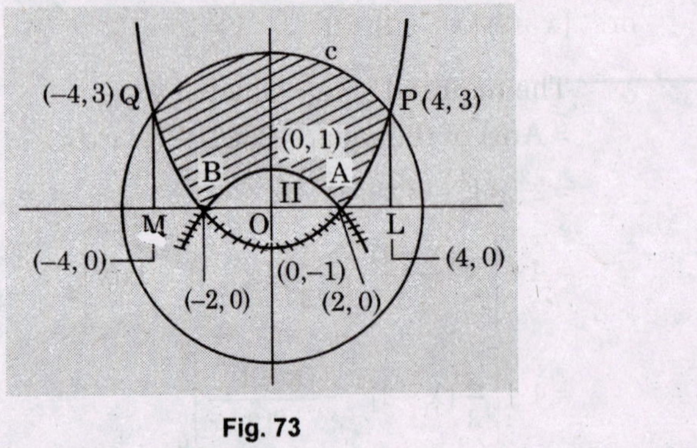

Fig. 73

Above represents a parabola with vertex at (0, − 1) symmetrical about y-axis.

Thus we have three curves :

I Circle $x^2+y^2=25$.

II $P_1=$ Parabola $x^2=-4(y-1)$ for $-2\le x\le 2$.

III $P_2=$ Parabola $x^2=4(y+1)$ for $x\ge 2$ or $x\le -2$

I and II intersect at $-4y+4+y^2=25$,

or $(y-2)^2=5^2 \quad \therefore \quad y-2=\pm 5$

$\therefore \quad y=7,\ y=-3$

$y=-3$ is rejected, since $y=-3$ is below x-axis and $y=7$ gives imaginary value of x.

I and III intersect at

$$4y+4+y^2=25 \quad \text{or} \quad (y+2)^2=5^2$$

$\therefore \quad y+2=\pm 5 \quad \therefore \quad y=3,\ -7.$

$y=-7$ is rejected; $y=3$ gives the points above x-axis. When $y=3$, $x=\pm 4$. Hence the points of intersection of I and III are $(4,3)$ and $(-4,3)$. Thus we have the shape of the curve as given.

$$\text{Required Area} = 2\left[\int_0^4 \underset{C}{y}\,dx - \int_0^2 \underset{P_1}{y}\,dx - \int_2^4 \underset{P_2}{y}\,dx\right]$$

$$\qquad\quad \text{I} \qquad\quad \text{II} \qquad\quad \text{III}$$

$$=2\left[\int_0^4 \sqrt{25-x^2}\,dx - \frac{1}{4}\int_0^2 (4-x^2)\,dx - \frac{1}{4}\int_2^4 (x^2-4)\,dx\right]$$

$$=2\left[\left\{\frac{x}{2}\sqrt{25-x^2}+\frac{25}{2}\sin^{-1}\frac{x}{5}\right\}_0^4 - \frac{1}{4}\left(4x-\frac{x^3}{3}\right)_0^2 - \frac{1}{4}\left(\frac{x^3}{3}-4x\right)_2^4\right]$$

$$=25\sin^{-1}(4/5)+4.$$

33. Find the area enclosed by the curves

$$y=2-|2-x| \text{ and } y=\frac{3}{|x|}$$

Here we have two mods $|x|$ and $|2-x|$ hence we consider the following cases

$$x>2,\quad x<2,\quad x>0,\quad x<0$$

I. $\begin{cases} y=2-(2-x)=x, & x<2 \\ y=2+(2-x)=4-x, & x>2 \end{cases}$

II. $\begin{cases} y=\dfrac{-3}{x}, x<0, y=\dfrac{3}{x}, x>0 \end{cases}$

The graph consists of two lines

$$l_1: y=x, x<2,\quad l_2: x+y=4, x>2$$

and two hyperbolas

$$xy=-3,\ x<0 \text{ and } xy=3,\ x>0$$

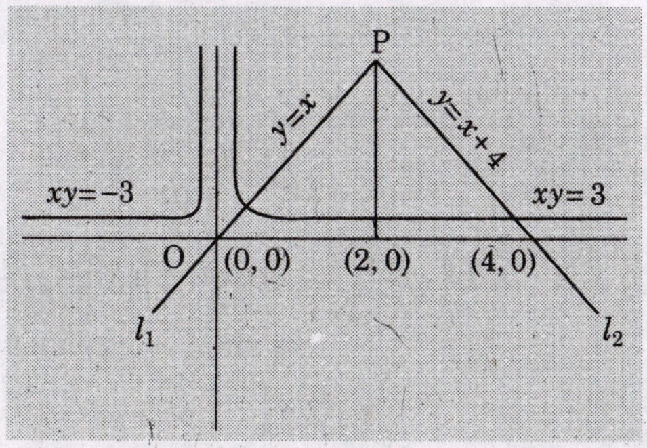

Fig. 74

The hyperbola $xy=3$ meets the lines l_1 *i.e.* $y=x$ at $x^2=3 \quad \therefore \quad x=\pm\sqrt{3}$

$\therefore \quad x=\sqrt{3}$ only as $x<2$ and $x>0$

It meets the line l_2 *i.e.* $x+y=4$ where

$$x+\frac{3}{x}=4 \quad \text{or} \quad x^2-4x+3=0 \quad \therefore \quad x=1,3$$

We choose $x=3$ only as $x>0$ and $x>2$

$$\text{Area}=\int_{\sqrt{3}}^{2}(\underset{l_1}{y_1}-\underset{hy}{y_3})\,dx+\int_2^3(\underset{l_2}{y_2}-\underset{hy}{y_3})\,dx$$

$$\text{Area}=\int_{\sqrt{3}}^{2}\left(x-\frac{3}{x}\right)dx+\int_2^3\left(4-x-\frac{3}{x}\right)dx=\frac{4-3\log 3}{2}$$

34.* Find the area bounded by the curves (I) $x^2+y^2=4$, (II) $x^2=-\sqrt{2}y$ and (III) $x=y$.

I and II meet at $-\sqrt{2}y+y^2=4$

or $\quad y^2-\sqrt{2}y-2\sqrt{2}\cdot\sqrt{2}=0$

$\quad (y-2\sqrt{2})\ (y+\sqrt{2})=0 \quad \therefore \quad y=-\sqrt{2}$

$\therefore \quad x=\pm\sqrt{2} \quad \therefore \quad A(-\sqrt{2},-\sqrt{2}), B(\sqrt{2},-\sqrt{2})$

II and III meet at $x^2=-\sqrt{2}x$

$\therefore \quad x=0, x=-\sqrt{2}$ *i.e.* $(0,0), (-\sqrt{2},-\sqrt{2})$

i.e. O and A.

III and I meet at $(\sqrt{2},\sqrt{2})$ and $(-\sqrt{2},-\sqrt{2})$ *i.e.* C and A.

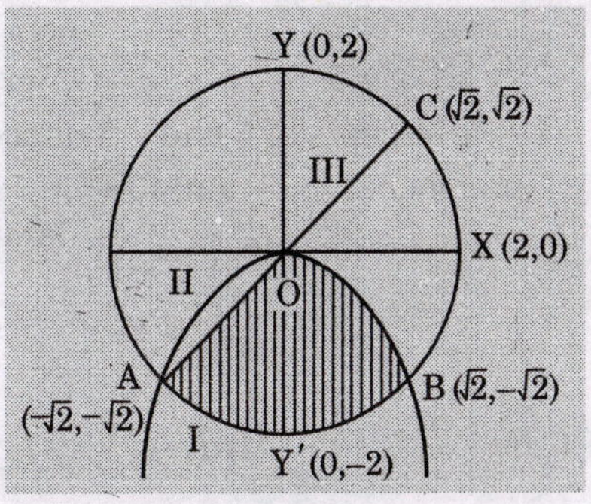

Fig. 75

Here there are two upper curves *i.e.* a line and a parabola and one lower curve *i.e.* circle.

Required area

$$\int_{-\sqrt{2}}^{0}(\underset{P}{y_2}-\underset{L}{y_3})\,dx+\int_0^{\sqrt{2}}(\underset{P}{y_2}-\underset{C}{y_1})\,dx$$

$$=\left|\int_{-\sqrt{2}}^{\sqrt{2}}\underset{P}{y_2}\,dx\right|-\left|\int_{-\sqrt{2}}^{0}\underset{L}{y_3}\,dx\right|-\left|\int_0^{\sqrt{2}}\underset{C}{y_1}\,dx\right|$$

$$=\left|\int_{-\sqrt{2}}^{0}x\,dx\right|+\left|\int_0^{\sqrt{2}}-\frac{x^2}{\sqrt{2}}\,dx\right|-2\left|\int_0^{\sqrt{2}}\sqrt{(4-x^2)}\,dx\right|$$

$$=\left|\left[\frac{x^2}{2}\right]_{-\sqrt{2}}^{0}\right|+\left|\left[-\frac{x^3}{3\sqrt{2}}\right]_0^{\sqrt{2}}\right|$$

$$-2\left|\left[\frac{x}{2}\sqrt{4-x^2}+\frac{4}{2}\sin^{-1}\frac{x}{2}\right]_0^{\sqrt{2}}\right|$$

$$=|-1|+\left|-\frac{2}{3}\right|-2\left|1+\frac{\pi}{2}\right|$$

$$=1+\frac{2}{3}-2\left(1+\frac{\pi}{2}\right)=-\left(\pi+\frac{1}{3}\right)=\pi+\frac{1}{3}$$

35. (a) Determine the area bounded by the curves $x=|y^2-1|$ and $y=x-5$.

If $y^2-1=+\text{ive}$, *i.e.* $y\le -1, y\ge 1$

$x=y^2-1$ or $y^2=(x+1)$, *i.e.* parabola ...(1)

If $y^2-1=-\text{ive}$ *i.e.* $-1\le y\le 1$

$x=-(y^2-1)$ or $y^2=-(x-1)$ ...(2)

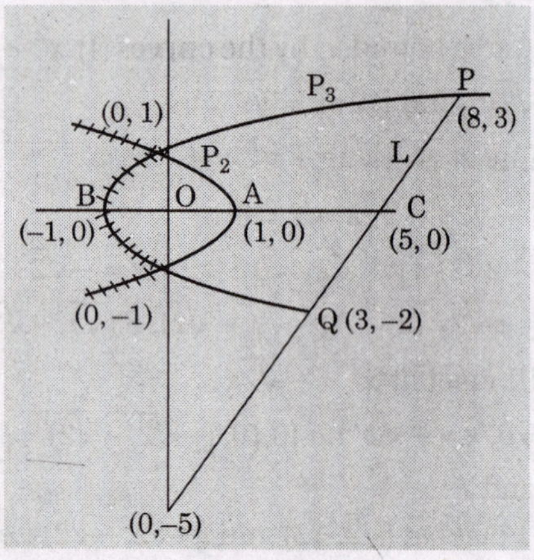

Fig. 76

Line $x-y=5$ ...(3)

which makes intercepts of 5 and – 5 on axes.

(1) and (3) intersect at (8, 3) and (3,– 2)

$A=\int_{-2}^{3}(\underset{L}{x_1}-\underset{P}{x_2})\,dy$ or up, low or R, L

$=\int_{-2}^{3}[(y+5)\,dy-|y^2-1|]\,dy$

$=\int_{-2}^{3}(y+5)\,dy-\left\{\underset{y\le -1}{\int_{-2}^{-1}(y^2-1)\,dy}+\underset{-1\le y\le 1}{\int_{-1}^{1}-(y^2-1)\,dy}\right.$

$\left.+\underset{y\ge 1}{\int_{1}^{3}(y^2-1)\,dy}.\right\}$

Ans. 109/6 sq. units.

(b) The area of the region bounded by the parabola $(y-2)^2=x-1$, the tangent to the parabola at the point (2, 3) and the x-axis is

(a) 12 (b) 3

(c) 6 (d) 9 **(AIEEE 2009)**

Sol. Ans. (d).

Equation of tangent to parabola $(y-2)^2=x-1$

at (2, 3) is $y-3=\left[\frac{dy}{dx}\right]_{(2,3)}(x-2)$

$$2(y-2)\frac{dy}{dx}=1$$

$\therefore\quad \frac{dy}{dx}=\frac{1}{2(y-2)}=\frac{1}{2}$ at (2, 3)

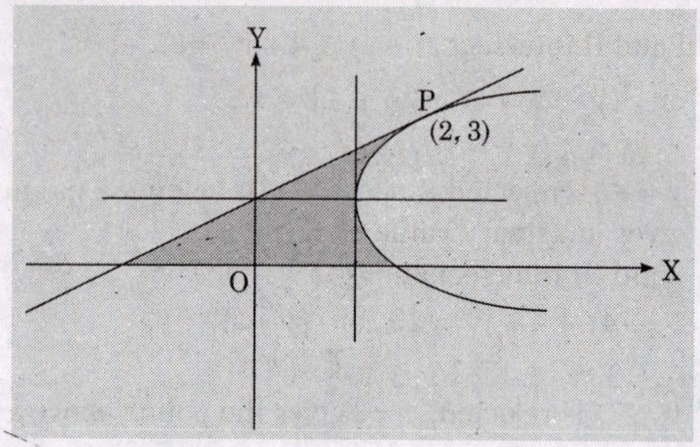

Fig. 77

$\therefore$ Equation of tangent is

$y-3=\frac{1}{2}(x-2)$ or $x=2y-4$

$\therefore\quad \text{Area}=\int_0^3(x_1-x_2)\,dy$

$=\int_0^3[\{(y-2)^2+1\}-(2y-4)]\,dy$

$=(y^2-6y+9)\,dy$

$=\frac{27}{3}=9$

36. Find the area of the parabola $y^2=1-x$ bounded by the curve $y=\frac{|x|}{x}, (x\ne 0)$ in the interval $\left[-1,\frac{1}{2}\right]$.

Parabola is $y^2=-(x-1)$. Its vertex is at (1, 0).

$y=\frac{|x|}{x}$ is $y=\frac{x}{x}=1, x>0$

$y=-\frac{x}{x}=-1, x<0$

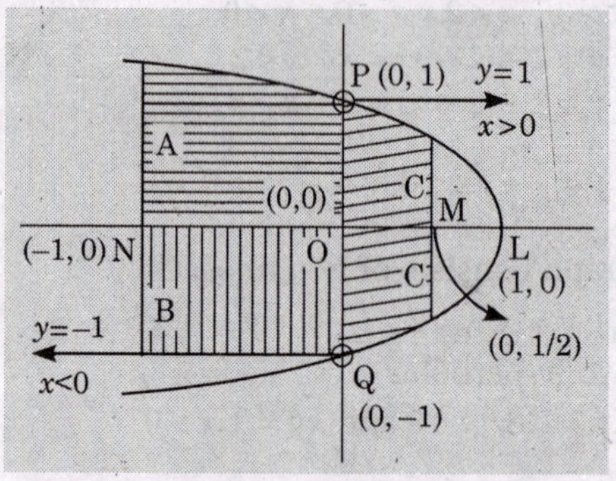

Fig. 78

Required area

$=A+B+2C$

$=\int_{-1}^{0}\underset{P}{y}\,dx+\int_{-1}^{0}\underset{L}{y}\,dx+2\int_0^{1/2}\underset{P}{y}\,dx$

$=\left|\int_{-1}^{0}\sqrt{1-x}\,dx\right|+\left|\int_{-1}^{0}(-1)\,dx\right|+2\left|\int_0^{1/2}\sqrt{1-x}\,dx\right|$

Square

$=\left|\left[-\frac{2}{3}(1-x)^{3/2}\right]_{-1}^{0}\right|+1+2\left|\left[-\frac{2}{3}(1-x)^{3/2}\right]_{0}^{1/2}\right|$

$$= \frac{2}{3}(2\sqrt{2}-1) + 1 + \frac{4}{3}\left(1 - \frac{\sqrt{2}}{4}\right) = \left(\sqrt{2} + \frac{5}{3}\right) \text{sq. units.}$$

37. Find the area of the figure bounded by the curves $y = |x-1|$ and $y = 3 - |x|$.

$x - 1 > 0$ *i.e.* $x > 1$ $\quad y = x - 1$ ...(1)

$x - 1 < 0$ *i.e.* $x < 1$ $\quad y = -(x-1)$ ...(2)

$x > 0$ $\quad y = 3 - x$ ...(3)

$x < 0$ $\quad y = 3 + x$ ...(4)

Above are two sets of parallel lines.

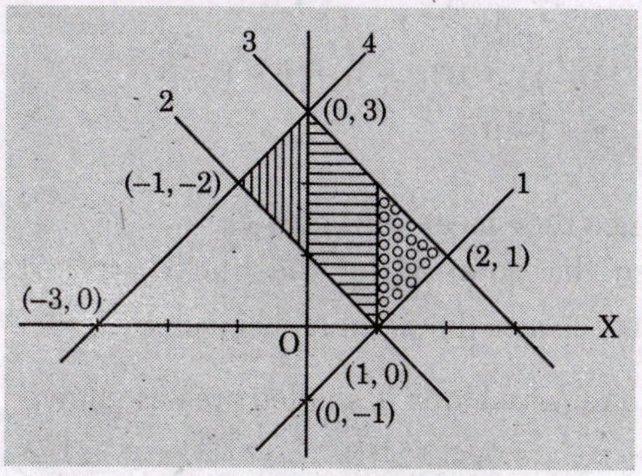

Fig. 79

Solving (1) and (3) we get (2, 1); (2) and (4) we get (– 1, 2). Trace the four lines written above by finding their intersection with axes of co-ordinates :

(1) (1, 0), (0, – 1) **(2)** (1,0), (0, 1)

(3) (3, 0), (0, 3) **(4)** (– 3,0), (0, 3)

y_p means line *p*.

$$A = \left|\int_{-1}^{0} (y_4 - y_2)\,dx\right|_{\text{vertical shaded}} + \left|\int_0^1 (y_3 - y_2)\,dx\right|_{\text{horizontal shaded}} + \left|\int_1^2 (y_3 - y_1)\,dx\right|_{\text{dotted}}$$

$$= \left|\int_{-1}^{0} \{(3+x) + (x-1)\}\,dx\right| + \left|\int_0^1 \{(3-x) + (x-1)\}\,dx\right| + \left|\int_1^2 \{(3-x) - (x-1)\}\,dx\right|$$

$$= \left|\int_{-1}^{0} (2x+2)\,dx\right| + \left|\int_0^1 2\,dx\right| + \left|\int_1^2 (4-2x)\,dx\right|$$

$$= \left|(x^2+2x)_{-1}^{0}\right| + \left|(2x)_0^1\right| + \left|(4x - x^2)_1^2\right|$$

$$= |-1| + |2| + |4-3| = 1 + 2 + 1 = 4 \text{ sq. units}$$

38.* Consider a square with vertices at (1, 1), (– 1, 1), (– 1, – 1) and (1, – 1). Let *S* be the region consisting of all points inside the square which are nearer to the origin than to any edge. Sketch the region *S* and find its area.

(I.I.T. 1995)

Sol. Let us consider any point (x, y) inside the square such that its distance from origin ≤ its disance from any of the edges say *AD*.

$\therefore \quad OP < PM \quad$ or $\quad \sqrt{(x^2 + y^2)} < 1 - x$

or $\quad x^2 + y^2 \le 1 - 2x + x^2$ or $y^2 \le 1 - 2x$

or $\quad y^2 \le -2\left(x - \frac{1}{2}\right)$ ...(1)

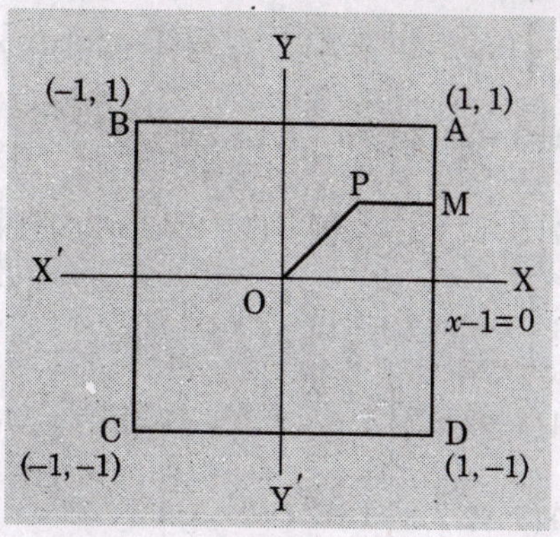

Fig. 80

Above represents all points within and on the parabola (1). If we consider the edges *BC* then $OP < PN$ will imply

$$y^2 \le 2\left(x + \frac{1}{2}\right) \quad \text{...(2)}$$

Similarly if we consider the edges *AB* and *CD*, we will have

$$x^2 \le -2\left(y - \frac{1}{2}\right) \quad \text{...(3)}$$

$$x^2 \le 2\left(y + \frac{1}{2}\right) \quad \text{...(4)}$$

Hence *S* consists of region bounded by four parabolas written above with vertices at $\left(\pm\frac{1}{2}, 0\right)$ and $\left(0, \pm\frac{1}{2}\right)$. The point *L* is intersection of P_1 and P_3 given by 1 and 3.

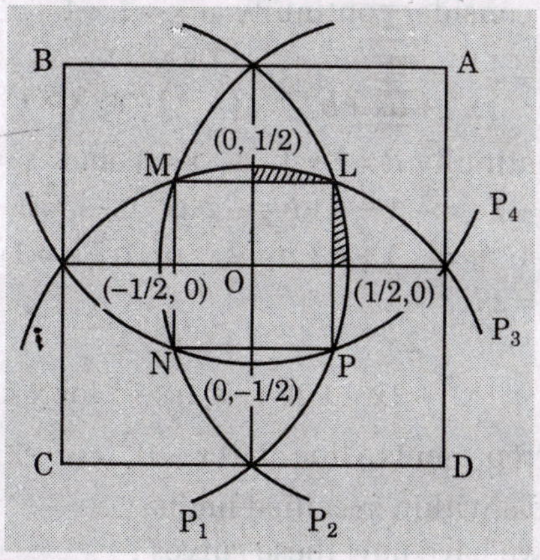

Fig. 81

$y^2 - x^2 = -2(x - y) = 2(y - x)$

$\therefore \quad y - x = 0 \quad$ or $\quad y = x$

$\therefore \quad x^2 + 2x - 1 = 0$

$\quad (x+1)^2 = 2$

$\therefore \quad x = \sqrt{2} - 1$ as x is +ive

$\therefore \quad L$ is $(\sqrt{2} - 1, \sqrt{2} - 1)$

$\therefore \quad$ Total area

$$= 4\left[\{\text{square of side } (\sqrt{2}-1)\} + 2\int_{\sqrt{2}-1}^{1/2} \underset{P_1}{y}\,dx\right]$$

$$= 4\left\{(\sqrt{2}-1)^2 + 2\int_{\sqrt{2}-1}^{1/2} \sqrt{(1-2x)}\,dx\right\}$$

$$= 4\left[3 - 2\sqrt{2} - \frac{2}{2}\cdot\frac{2}{3}\{(1-2x)^{3/2}\}_{\sqrt{2}-1}^{1/2}\right]$$

$$= 4\left[3 - 2\sqrt{2} - \frac{2}{3}\{0 - (1 - 2\sqrt{2} + 2)^{3/2}\}\right]$$

$$= 4\left\{3 - 2\sqrt{2} + \frac{2}{3}(3 - 2\sqrt{2})^{3/2}\right\}$$

$$= 4(3 - 2\sqrt{2})\left[1 + \frac{2}{3}\sqrt{\{3 - 2\sqrt{2}\}}\right]$$

$$= 4(3 - 2\sqrt{2})\left[1 + \frac{2}{3}(\sqrt{2} - 1)\right]$$

$$= \frac{4}{3}(3 - 2\sqrt{2})(1 + 2\sqrt{2})$$

$$= \frac{4}{3}[4\sqrt{2} - 5] = \frac{16\sqrt{2} - 20}{3}$$

39. Let $f(x)$ be a continuous function given by $f(x) = \begin{cases} 2x, & |x| \le 1 \\ x^2 + ax + b, & |x| > 1 \end{cases}$. Find the area of the region in the third quadrant bounded by the curves $x = -2y^2$ and $y = f(x)$ lying on the left of the line $8x + 1 = 0$. **(I.I.T. 1999)**

The second part of this question is very difficult and time consuming.

$|x| \le 1 \Rightarrow x^2 - 1 \le 0$

or $(x+1)(x-1) \le 0 \quad \Rightarrow \quad -1 \le x \le 1$

$|x| > 1 \Rightarrow x < -1$ or $x > 1$.

Let us consider continuity at $x = 1, -1$.

$$y = \begin{cases} 2x & , \; -1 \le x \le 1 \\ x^2 + ax + b & , \; x < -1 \text{ or } x > 1 \end{cases}$$

For continuity $R = L = V$ at $x = 1$ and $x = -1$

At $x = -1 \Rightarrow 1 - a + b = -2$ or $a - b = 3$

At $x = 1 \quad \Rightarrow 1 + a + b = 2$ or $a + b = 1$

$\therefore \quad a = 2, b = -1$

$$\therefore \quad y = \begin{cases} 2x & , \; -1 \le x \le 1 \\ x^2 + 2x - 1 \text{ or } (x+1)^2 - 2 \text{ for } x < -1 \text{ or } x > 1 \end{cases}$$

$y = 2x$ represents a line and $(x+1)^2 = y + 2$ represents a parabola within specified limits.

Thus we have now these curves :

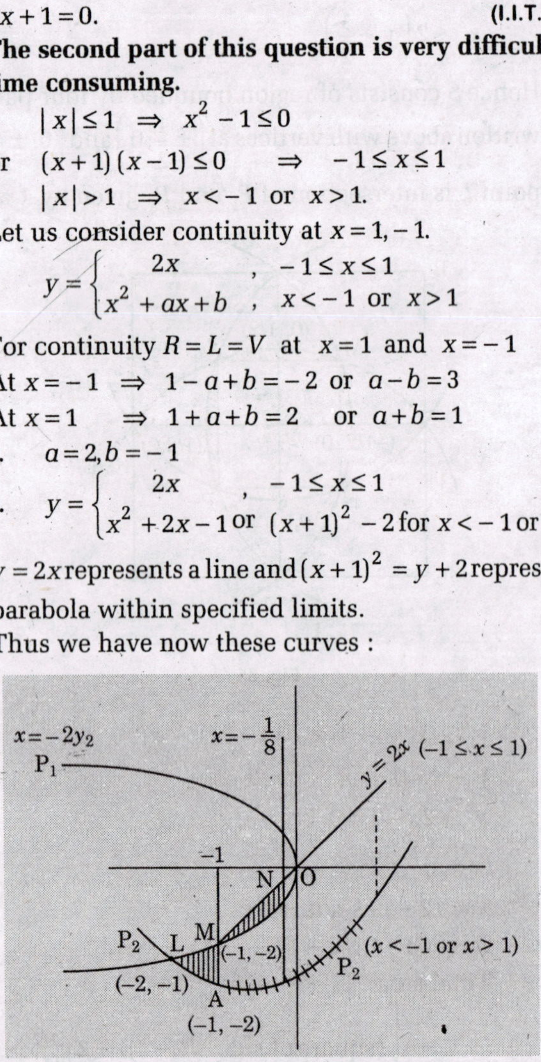

Fig. 82

$y^2 = -\frac{1}{2}x$, $y = f(x)$ and the line $x = -\frac{1}{8}$.

We have to find the area in the 3rd quadrant and lying to the left of the line $x = -\frac{1}{8}$. The curves are traced as shown below :

$$P_1 \quad y^2 = -\frac{1}{2}x \quad \text{and} \quad P_2 \quad (x+1)^2 = y + 2$$

$$(x < -1 \text{ or } x > 1)$$

meet where $(1 - 2y^2)^2 = y + 2$

or $\quad 4y^4 - 4y^2 - y - 1 = 0$

$\quad 4y^2(y+1)(y-1) - (y+1) = 0$

$\therefore \quad y + 1 = 0$

or $\quad y = -1 \quad \therefore \quad x = -2$.

Hence they meet at $L(-2, -1)$.

Also the point M for the line $y = 2x\,(-1 \le x \le 1)$ is $(-1, -2)$, and the point N is given by $x = -\frac{1}{8}$.

The required area is shaded area as shown.

$$\int_{-2}^{-1} (\underset{P_1}{y_1} - \underset{P_2}{y_2})\,dx + \int_{-1}^{-1/8} (\underset{L}{y_3} - \underset{P_1}{y_1})\,dx$$

$$= \left| \int_{-2}^{-1} \left\{ \sqrt{-\frac{x}{2}} - (x^2 + 2x - 1) \right\} dx \right|$$

$$+ \left| \int_{-1}^{-1/8} \left(2x - \sqrt{-\frac{x}{2}} \right) dx \right|$$

For $\int \sqrt{\frac{-x}{2}}\,dx$, put $-x = t$ and adjust the limits.

Ans. $\frac{257}{192}$ sq. units.

40. (a)* Find the area of the region bounded by the curves $y = \log_e x$, $y = \sin^4 \pi x$ and $x = 0$.

The first curve crosses the x-axis at $(1, 0)$ and the second crosses the x-axis when $\sin^4 \pi x = 0$ *i.e.* when $x = 0$ or $x = 1$ i.e. at point $(0, 0)$ and $(1, 0)$. The common point being $(1, 0)$. Also when $x < 1$ then y is –ive and when $x > 1$, y is +ive for first curve $y = \log_e x$ at $x = 0, y = -\infty$. Hence the two curves are as shown in the figure.

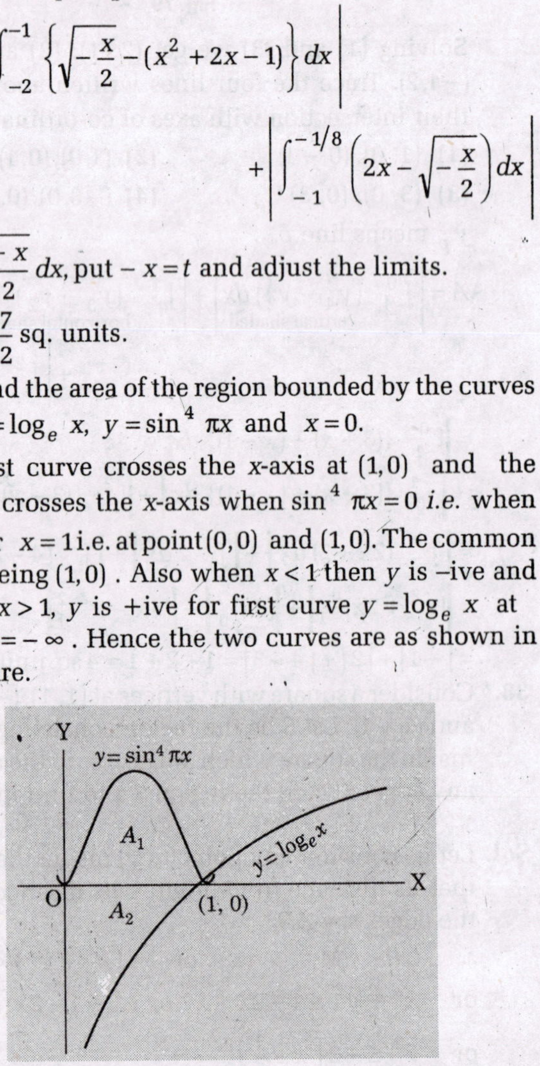

Fig. 83

$A_1 = \int_0^1 y\,dx = \int_0^1 \sin^4 \pi x\,dx$

Put $\pi x = t$

$\therefore \quad A_1 = \frac{1}{\pi}\int_0^{\pi} \sin^4 t\,dt$

$= \frac{2}{\pi}\int_0^{\pi/2} \sin^4 t\,dt = \frac{2}{\pi}.\frac{3.1}{4.2}.\frac{\pi}{2} = \frac{3}{8},$

$A_2 = \int_0^1 y\,dx = \int_0^1 \log x\,dx$

$= x\log x - \int x.(1/x)\,dx$

$= [x\log x - x]_0^1$

$= (0-1)-(0-0) = -1 \therefore |A_2| = 1.$

We can also say

$A_2 = \int_{-\infty}^0 x\,dy = \int_{-\infty}^0 e^y\,dy = (1-e^{-\infty}) = 1$

$\therefore \quad$ Required area $= \frac{3}{8} + 1 = \frac{11}{8}$

Note : $\lim_{x\to 0} x\log x = 0\times\infty = \lim_{x\to 0} \frac{\log x}{1/x} = \frac{\infty}{\infty}$

$= \lim_{x\to 0} \frac{1/x}{-1/x^2} = \lim_{x\to 0} -x = 0$

(b)* Indicate the region bounded by the curves $y = x\log x$ and $y = 2x - 2x^2$ and obtain the area enclosed by them. **(Roorkee 1998)**

Parabola is $\left(x-\frac{1}{2}\right)^2 = -\frac{1}{2}\left(y-\frac{1}{2}\right)$ and $y = x\log x$ cuts x-axis at $(1, 0)$ and y goes on increasing when $x > 1$ and y is $-$ ive when $x < 1$, and $x \neq 0$. Hence the shape of the curve is as shown.

Required area

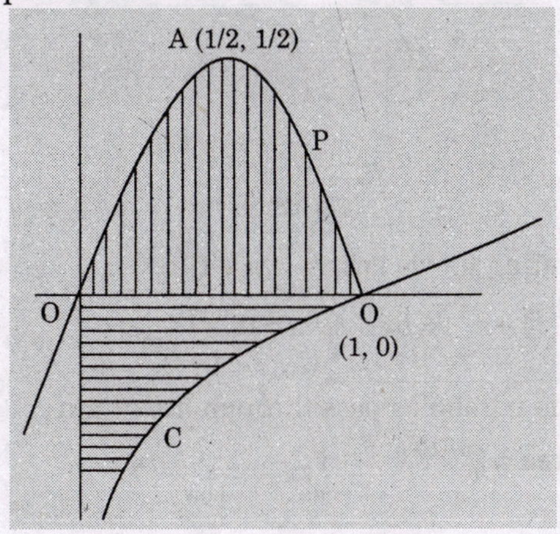

Fig. 84

$= \int_0^1 \underset{P}{y_1}\,dx + |\int_0^1 \underset{C}{y_2}\,dx|$

$= \int_0^1 (2x-2x^2)\,dx + |\int_0^1 (x\log x)\,dx|$

$= \left|x^2 - \frac{2}{3}x^3\right|_0^1 + \left|\left[\frac{x^2}{2}\log x - \frac{x^2}{4}\right]_0^1\right|$

$= \frac{1}{3} + \left|-\frac{1}{4}\right| = \frac{1}{3} + \frac{1}{4} = \frac{7}{12}$

$\text{Lt}_{x\to 0}\; x^2\log x\,(0\times\infty) = \text{Lt}_{x\to 0} \frac{\log x}{1/x^2}\left(\frac{\infty}{\infty}\right)$

$= \text{Lt}_{x\to 0} \frac{1/x}{-2/x^3} = \text{Lt}\left(-\frac{x^2}{2}\right) = 0$

41.* Find the area of region bounded by the curves $y = ex\log_e(x)$ and $y = \frac{\log_e(x)}{ex}$ where $\log_e e = 1$. **(I.I.T. 1990)**

The two curves intersect where

$ex\log x = \log x/ex$

$\Rightarrow \quad (ex - 1/ex)\log x = 0 \quad \Rightarrow \quad x = 1/e$ or $x = 1$

At $x = 1/e$ or $ex = 1$

$\log x = -\log e = -1, \; y = -1$

so that $(1/e, -1)$ is one point of intersection and at $x = 1, \log 1 = 0 \quad \therefore y = 0$

$\therefore \quad (1, 0)$ is the other common point of the curve.

Now in between, i.e., $\frac{1}{e} < x < 1$ or $1 < ex < e$

and $\log\left(\frac{1}{e}\right) < \log x < \log 1$

or $\quad -1 < \log x < 0$, *i.e.* $\log x$ is $-$ ive throughout

$\therefore \quad y_1 = ex\log_e(x), \; y_2 = \frac{\log_e(x)}{ex}$

Clearly under the condition stated above $y_1 < y_2$ both being $-$ive in the interval $\frac{1}{e} < x < 1$ just as $2(-k) < \frac{(-k)}{2}$.

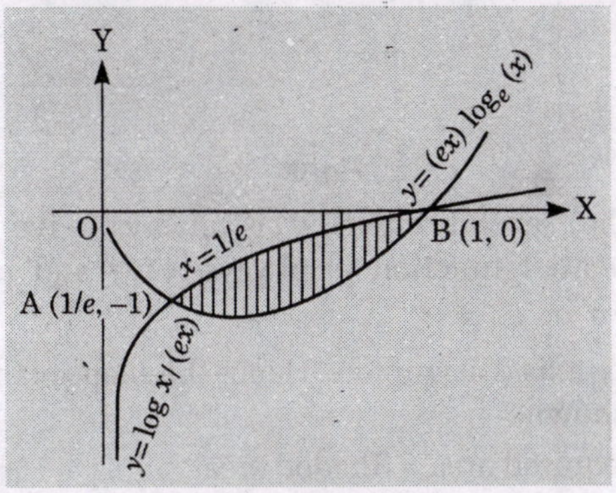

Fig. 85

The required area = Shaded area

$= \int_{1/e}^1 (y_1 - y_2)\,dx$

$= \int_{1/e}^1 [ex\log x - (\log x)/(ex)]\,dx$

$= e\int_{1/e}^1 x\log x - \frac{1}{e}\int_{1/e}^1 \frac{\log x}{x}\,dx$

$= e\left[\frac{x^2}{4}(2\log x - 1)\right]_{1/e}^1 - \left[\frac{1}{2}(\log x)^2\right]_{1/e}^1$

by **Ex. 2 P. 1478** and by power formula on putting $\log x = t$

$= e\left[\frac{1}{4}(-1) - \frac{1}{4e^2}(-2-1)\right] - \frac{1}{2e}[-1]$

$$= -\frac{e}{4} + \frac{3}{4e} + \frac{1}{2e} = \frac{5 - e^2}{4e}.$$

Note : $\log 1/e = -\log e = -1$ and $\log 1 = 0$.

42. (a)* Find the area enclosed between the curves $y = \log_e (x + e)$, $x = \log_e (1/y)$ and the x–axis.

(Roorkee 1990)

$y = \log (x + e)$ ...(1)

$x = \log \frac{1}{y}$ $\therefore \frac{1}{y} = e^x$ or $y = e^{-x}$ ...(2)

The two curves meet where $\log (x + e) = e^{-x}$ which are satisfied when $x = 0$. Hence the common point is $(0, 1)$ on y-axis.

The first curve cuts x-axis when $y = 0$ i.e.
$\log (x + e) = 0 = \log 1$

$\therefore \quad x + e = 1$ or $x = 1 - e$

when $x > 1 - e$ i.e. $x + e > 1$, y goes on increasing and is +ive and

when $x < 1 - e$ i.e. $x + e < 1$, y goes on decreasing and is –ive.

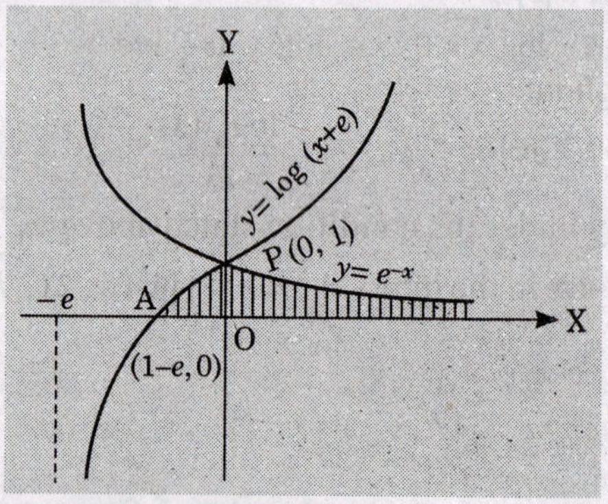

Fig. 86

For the second curve y is always +ive as the exponential function is always +ive and at $y = 0$, $e^{-x} = 0$ or $e^x = \infty$ $\therefore$ $x = \infty$.

Thus x- axis is asymptote. Hence the shape of the curve is as shown.

The required area = Shaded area
$$= \int_{1-e}^0 y_1 \, dx + \int_0^\infty y_2 \, dx,$$

where $y_1 = \log (x + e)$ and $y_2 = e^{-x}$.
$$= \int_{1-e}^0 \log (x + e) \, dx + \int_0^\infty e^{-x} \, dx \qquad ...(3)$$
$= I_1 + I_2$

Put $(x + e) = t$

$\therefore \quad I_1 = \int_1^e \log t \, dt = [t \log t - t]_1^e = 1$

$I_2 = \int_0^\infty e^{-x} \, dx = -[e^{-x}]_0^\infty = -[0 - 1] = 1$.

Hence the required area by (3) = $1 + 1 = 2$.

(b) Determine the area between the curves $y = xe^x$ and $y = xe^{-x}$ and the line $x = 1$.

The line $x = 1$ meets the curves in $A(1, e)$ and $B(1, 1/e)$. The second curve is lower curve as ordinate of B is less than ordinate of A.

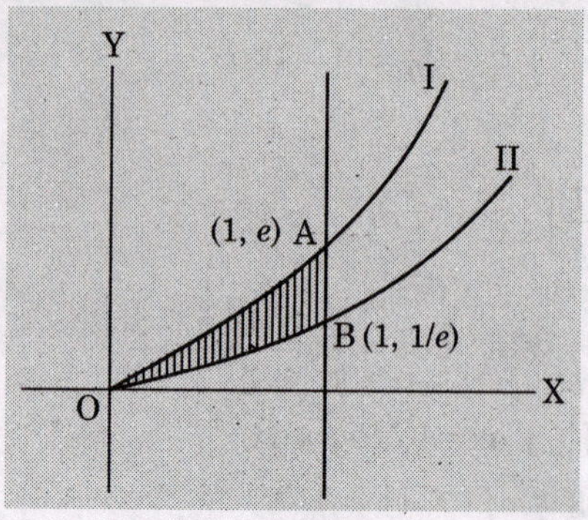

Fig. 87

Both the curves pass through origin.
$$A = \int_0^1 \underset{I}{(y_1} - \underset{II}{y_2)} \, dx = \int_0^1 (xe^x - xe^{-x}) \, dx$$
$$= x [e^x + e^{-x}]_0^1 - \int_0^1 (e^x + e^{-x}) \, 1 \, dx$$
$$= \left(e + \frac{1}{e}\right) - (e^x - e^{-x})_0^1 = \left(e + \frac{1}{e}\right) - \left(e - \frac{1}{e}\right)$$

43. (a)* Find all the possible values of $b > 0$, so that the area of the bounded region enclosed between the parabolas $y = x - bx^2$ and $y = \frac{x^2}{b}$ is maximum.

(I.I.T. 1997)

Sol. $x^2 = by$ ...(1)   and $y = x - bx^2$ ...(2)

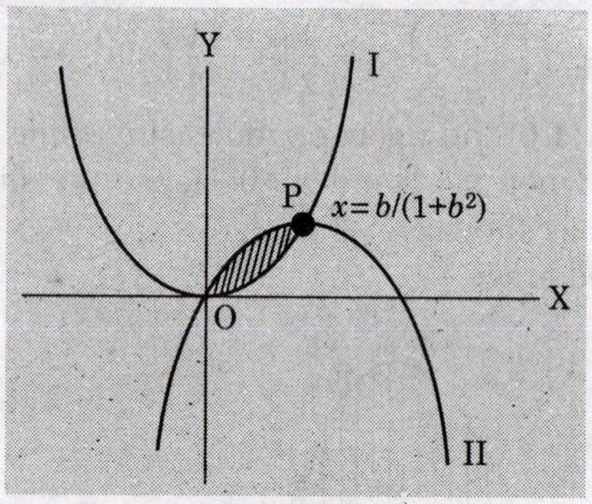

Fig. 88

Eliminating y, we get $x^2 = bx - b^2 x^2$

$\therefore \quad x^2 (1 + b^2) = bx$ $\therefore$ $x = 0, \dfrac{b}{1 + b^2}$

Both the parabolas pass through the origin

Area $= \int_0^{b/(1+b^2)} \underset{\underset{II}{up}}{(y_2} - \underset{\underset{I}{Low}}{y_1)} \, dx$

$$= \int_0^{b/1 + b^2)} \left(x - bx^2 - \frac{x^2}{b}\right) dx$$

$$= \left[\frac{x^2}{2} - \frac{1 + b^2}{b} \cdot \frac{x^3}{3}\right]_0^{b/(1+b^2)}$$

$$A = \left(\frac{b}{1 + b^2}\right)^2 \left[\frac{1}{2} - \frac{1}{3}\right] = \frac{1}{6} \frac{b^2}{(1 + b^2)^2}$$

For maximum value of A, $\frac{dA}{db} = 0$

$$\frac{dA}{db} = \frac{1}{6} \cdot \frac{(1+b^2)^2\, 2b - b^2 . 2(1+b^2) . 2b}{(1+b^2)^4}$$

$$= \frac{1}{3} \frac{b(1-b^2)}{(1+b^2)^3} = -\frac{1}{3} \frac{(b+1)\, b\, (b-1)}{(b^2+1)^3}$$

Above gives $b = -1, 0, 1$. But since $b > 0$ therefore we consider only $b = 1$. It will be difficult to find $\frac{d^2A}{db^2}$ and hence we consider change of sign of $\frac{dA}{db}$ in the neighbourhood of $b = 1$.

At $b = 1 - h$, $\frac{dA}{db} = +$ ive and at $b = 1 + h$, $\frac{dA}{db} = -$ ive

Since the change is from + ive to − ive, therefore A is maximum.

(b) The area of the region between the curves $y = \sqrt{\frac{1+\sin x}{\cos x}}$ and $y = \sqrt{\frac{1-\sin x}{\cos x}}$ bounded by the lines $x = 0$ and $x = \frac{\pi}{4}$ is

(a) $\int_0^{\sqrt{2}-1} \frac{1}{(1+t^2)\sqrt{1-t^2}}\, dt$

(b) $\int_0^{\sqrt{2}-1} \frac{4t}{(1+t^2)\sqrt{1-t^2}}\, dt$

(c) $\int_0^{\sqrt{2}+1} \frac{4t}{(1+t^2)\sqrt{1-t^2}}\, dt$

(d) $\int_0^{\sqrt{2}+1} \frac{t}{(1+t^2)\sqrt{1-t^2}}\, dt$

(I.I.T. 2008)

Sol. (b). $y_1^2 = \frac{1+\sin x}{\cos x} = \frac{\left(\cos\frac{x}{2} + \sin\frac{x}{2}\right)^2}{\cos^2\frac{x}{2} - \sin^2\frac{x}{2}} = \frac{\cos\frac{x}{2} + \sin\frac{x}{2}}{\cos\frac{x}{2} - \sin\frac{x}{2}}$

$$y_1^2 = \frac{1+\tan\frac{x}{2}}{1-\tan\frac{x}{2}}.$$

Similarly, $y_2^2 = \frac{1-\tan\frac{x}{2}}{1+\tan\frac{x}{2}}$

$$\therefore \quad y_1 - y_2 = \sqrt{\frac{1+\tan(x/2)}{1-\tan(x/2)}} - \sqrt{\frac{1-\tan(x/2)}{1+\tan(x/2)}}$$

$$= \frac{1+\tan(x/2) - (1-\tan(x/2))}{\sqrt{1-\tan^2(x/2)}}$$

$$= \frac{2\tan(x/2)}{\sqrt{1-\tan^2(x/2)}}$$

$$\therefore \quad \text{Area} = \int_0^{\pi/4} (y_1 - y_2)\, dx = \int_0^{\pi/4} \frac{2\tan(x/2)}{\sqrt{1-\tan^2(x/2)}}\, dx$$

Now put $\tan\frac{x}{2} = t \quad \therefore \quad \frac{1}{2}\sec^2\frac{x}{2}\, dx = dt$

When $x = 0, t = 0$; when $x = \frac{\pi}{4}, t = \tan\frac{\pi}{8} = \sqrt{2} - 1$

$$\therefore \quad \text{Area} = \int_0^{\sqrt{2}-1} \frac{2t}{\sqrt{1-t^2}} \cdot \frac{2\,dt}{\sec^2\frac{x}{2}}$$

$$= \int_0^{\sqrt{2}-1} \frac{4t}{(1+t^2)\sqrt{1-t^2}}\, dt \Rightarrow \text{(b)}$$

44. Let $b \neq 0$ and for $j = 0, 1, 2, \ldots, n$, let S_j be the area of the region bounded by the y-axis and the curve $xe^{ay} = \sin by$, $\frac{j\pi}{b} \le y \le \frac{(j+1)\pi}{b}$.

Show that $S_0, S_1, S_2, \ldots, S_n$ are in geometric progression. Also, find their sum for $a = -1$ and $b = \pi$.

(I.I.T. 2001)

Sol. $S_j = \int_{\frac{j\pi}{b}}^{(j+1)\frac{\pi}{b}} x\, dy = \int e^{-ay} \sin by\, dy$

$$= \left[\frac{e^{-ay}}{r} \sin(by - \alpha)\right]_{\frac{j\pi}{b}}^{(j+1)\frac{\pi}{b}}$$

where $r = \sqrt{a^2 + b^2}$, $\tan\alpha = \frac{b}{-a}$

or $\alpha = \tan^{-1}\frac{b}{-a} = -\tan^{-1}\frac{b}{a}$

$$\therefore \quad S_j = \frac{1}{r}\left[e^{-(j+1)\frac{a\pi}{b}} \sin\left\{(j+1)\pi + \tan^{-1}\frac{b}{a}\right\} - e^{-j\frac{a\pi}{b}} \sin\left(j\pi + \tan^{-1}\frac{b}{a}\right)\right]$$

Now $\sin(\pi + \theta) = -\sin\theta$, hence the above can be written as

$$S_j = \frac{e^{-j\frac{a\pi}{b}}}{r}\left[-e^{-\frac{a\pi}{b}} - 1\right] \sin\left(j\pi + \tan^{-1}\frac{b}{a}\right) \quad \ldots(1)$$

Replacing j by $j+1$ in (1) and again applying $\sin(\pi + \theta) = -\sin\theta$

$$S_{j+1} = e^{-\frac{a\pi}{b}} \cdot \frac{e^{-j\frac{a\pi}{b}}}{r}\left[-e^{-\frac{a\pi}{b}} - 1\right] \times \left\{-\sin\left(j\pi + \tan^{-1}\frac{b}{a}\right)\right\} \quad \ldots(2)$$

Dividing we get $\frac{S_{j+1}}{S_j} = -e^{-\frac{a\pi}{b}} = \text{constant}$

$\therefore \quad \Sigma S_j$ is a G.P. of common ratio $-e^{-\frac{a\pi}{b}} = R$

Now putting $a = -1, b = \pi$, i.e. $\frac{\pi}{b} = 1$

$\therefore \quad R = -e \qquad \ldots(3)$

Also putting $j = 0$ in (1) and $a = -1$, $\frac{\pi}{b} = 1$ and $r^2 = a^2 + b^2 = \pi^2 + 1$ in (1), we have

$$S_0 = -\frac{1}{r}(e+1)\sin\{\tan^{-1}(-\pi)\}$$

$$= -\frac{1}{\sqrt{(\pi^2+1)}}(e+1)\cdot\frac{-\pi}{\sqrt{\pi^2+1}}$$

or $S_0 = \frac{\pi}{(\pi^2+1)}(e+1) = \text{Ist term of G.P.} \qquad \ldots(4)$

$\therefore \; S_0 + S_1 + S_2 + \ldots S_n$ = sum of a G.P. of $(n+1)$ terms whose first term and common ratio are as given above in (3) and (4).

45. Draw rough sketches of the following curves :

[a] $y = |x|$

[b] $y = \sin^2 x$

[c] $(x-2)^2 = -4(y+1)$

[d] $9(x+2)^2 + 16(y+3)^2 = 144$

[e] $y = \log_e x$. **(M.N.R 1991)**

(a) $y = |x|$

If $x \geq 0$, then $y = x$ and if $x \leq 0$, $y = -x$.

Hence the graph in this case is as shown.

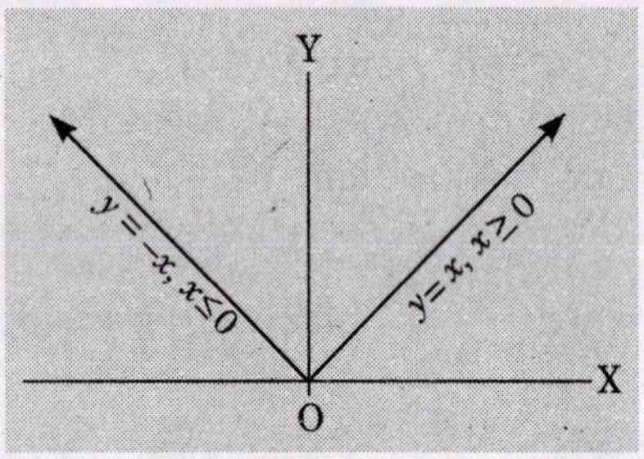

Fig. 89

(b) $y = \sin^2 x$. This is a continuous function for all real x and takes non-negative values. The function is periodic with period π. Hence the graph is shown in fig.

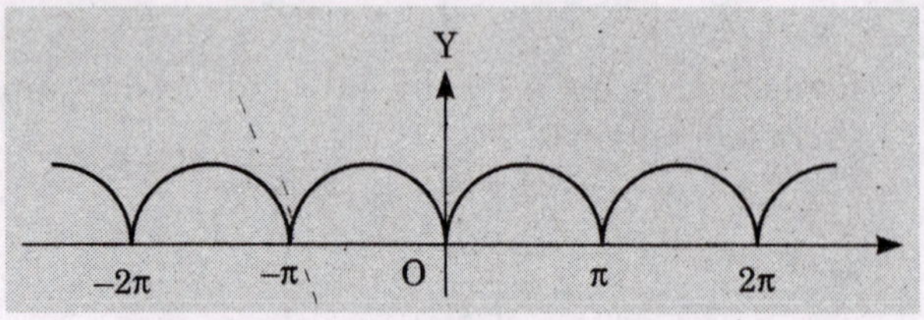

Fig. 90

(c) $(x-2)^2 = -4(y+1)$

This is a parabola with vertex $A(2, -1)$, latus-rectum having length 4 and concavity downwards. It does not intersect x-axis since $y = 0$ gives imaginary values of x. It intersects y-axis at $P(0, -2)$. Its graph is shown in fig.

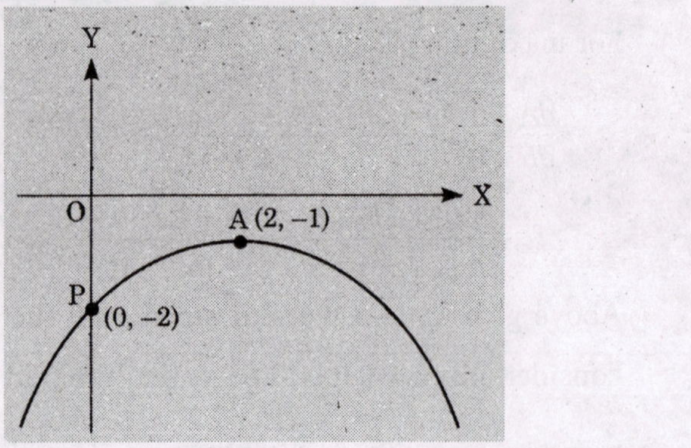

Fig. 91

(d) $9(x+2)^2 + 16(y+3)^2 = 144$

or $\frac{(x+2)^2}{16} + \frac{(y+3)^2}{9} = 1.$

This is an ellipse with centre $(-2, -3)$ and semi- axes as 4 and 3 respectively. When $y = 0$, $x = -2, -2$ that is, the ellipse touches x-axis at $(-2, 0)$,

When $x = 0$, $y = \pm\frac{3\sqrt{3}}{2} - 3 = -\cdot 4, -5\cdot 6.$

Hence the graph is as shown.

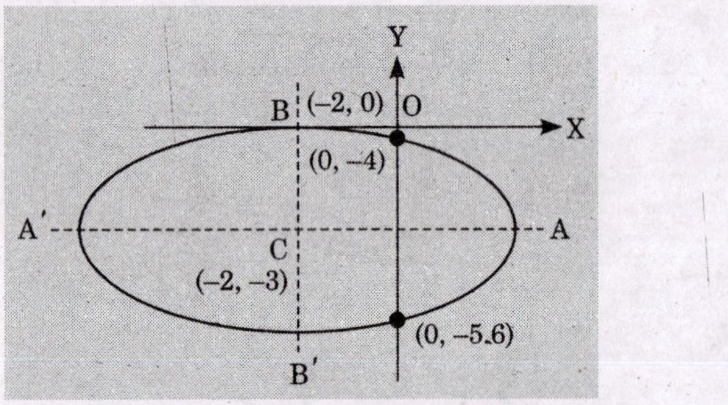

Fig. 92

(e) $y = \log_e x$

[Note that ln (x) means logarithm of x to base e]

For values of $x \leq 0$, y is meaningless.

As $x \to 0$, $y \to -\infty$.

The values of y are negative in $0 < x < 1$.

At $x = 1$, $y = 0$. And for values of $x > 1$, y takes positive values and tends to ∞ as $x \to \infty$. Hence the graph is as shown.

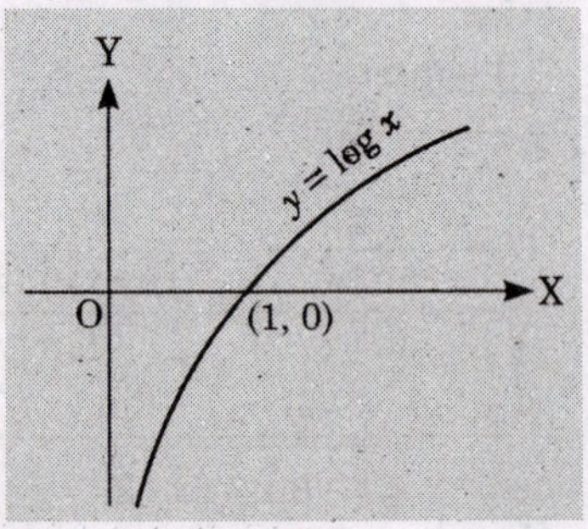

Fig. 93

Miscellaneous Problem Set (12)

1. The value of $\int_0^1 \frac{x^4(1-x)^4}{1+x^2}\,dx$ is

(a) $\frac{22}{7}-\pi$ (b) $\frac{2}{105}$ (c) 0 (d) $\frac{71}{15}-\frac{3\pi}{2}$

(IIT-JEE 2010)

2. The value of the integral $\int_{-\pi/2}^{\pi/2}\left(x^2+\log\frac{\pi+x}{\pi-x}\right)\cos x\,dx$ is

(a) 0 (b) $\frac{\pi^2}{2}-4$ (c) $\frac{\pi^2}{2}+4$ (d) $\frac{\pi^2}{2}$

(IIT-JEE 2010)

3. The value of $\int_{\sqrt{\log 2}}^{\sqrt{\log 3}} \frac{x\sin x^2}{\sin x^2+\sin(\log 6-x^2)}\,dx$ is

(a) $\frac{1}{4}\log\frac{3}{2}$ (b) $\frac{1}{2}\log\frac{3}{2}$ (c) $\log\frac{3}{2}$ (d) $\frac{1}{6}\log\frac{3}{2}$

(IIT-JEE 2011)

4. $\int_0^\pi [\cot x]\,dx$ where [ ] denote the greatest integer function, is equal to

(a) $\frac{\pi}{2}$ (b) 1 (c) -1 (d) $-\frac{\pi}{2}$

(AIEEE 2009)

5. Let $p(x)$ be a function defined on **R** such that $p'(x)=p'(1-x)\ \forall\ x\in[0,1]$, $p(0)=1$ and $p(1)=41$. Then $\int_0^1 p(x)\,dx$ equals

(a) $\sqrt{41}$ (b) 21 (c) 41 (d) 42

(AIEEE 2010)

6. If $g(x)=\int_0^x \cos 4t\,dt$, then $g(x+\pi)$ equals

(a) $\frac{g(x)}{g(\pi)}$ (b) $g(x)+g(\pi)$

(c) $g(x)-g(\pi)$ (d) $g(x).g(\pi)$ **(AIEEE 2012)**

7. Let f be a non-negative function defined on the interval [0, 1]. If $\int_0^x \sqrt{1-(f'.t)^2}\,.dt=\int_0^x f(t)\,dt, 0\le x\le 1$ and $f(0)=0$, then

(a) $f\left(\frac{1}{2}\right)<\frac{1}{2}$ and $f\left(\frac{1}{3}\right)>\frac{1}{3}$

(b) $f\left(\frac{1}{2}\right)>\frac{1}{2}$ and $f\left(\frac{1}{3}\right)>\frac{1}{3}$

(c) $f\left(\frac{1}{2}\right)<\frac{1}{2}$ and $f\left(\frac{1}{3}\right)<\frac{1}{3}$

(d) $f\left(\frac{1}{2}\right)>\frac{1}{2}$ and $f\left(\frac{1}{3}\right)<\frac{1}{3}$ **(IIT-JEE 2009)**

8. Let the straight line $x=b$ divide the area enclosed by $y=(1-x)^2$, $y=0$ and $x=0$ into two parts R_1 $(0\le x\le b)$ and R_2 $(b\le x\le 1)$ such that $R_1-R_2=\frac{1}{4}$ then b equals

(a) $\frac{3}{4}$ (b) $\frac{1}{2}$ (c) $\frac{1}{3}$ (d) $\frac{1}{4}$

(IIT-JEE 2011)

9. The area of the region bounded by the parabola $(y-2)^2=x-1$, the tangent to the parabola at the point (2, 3) and the x-axis is

(a) 3 (b) 6 (c) 9 (d) 12

(AIEEE 2009)

10. Let $f:[-1,2]\to[0,\infty[$ be a continuous function such that for all $x\in[-1,2]$. Let $R_1=\int_{-1}^2 x f(x)dx$ and R_2 be the area of the region bounded by $y=f(x)$, $x=-1$, $x=2$ and the x-axis, then

(a) $R_1=2R_2$ (b) $R_1=3R_2$ (c) $2R_1=R_2$ (d) $3R_1=R_2$

(IIT-JEE 2011)

11. The area of the region enclosed by the curves $y=x$, $x=e$, $y=\frac{1}{x}$ and the positive x-axis is

(a) $\frac{1}{2}$ sq. units (b) 1 sq. unit

(c) $\frac{3}{2}$ sq. units (d) $\frac{5}{2}$ sq. units **(AIEEE 2011)**

12. The area bounded by the curve $y=\cos x$ and $y=\sin x$ between the ordinates $x=0$ and $x=\frac{3\pi}{2}$ is

(a) $4\sqrt{2}-2$ (b) $4\sqrt{2}+2$ (c) $4\sqrt{2}-1$ (d) $4\sqrt{2}+1$

13. The value of $\lim_{x\to 0}\frac{1}{x^3}\int_0^x \frac{t.\log(1+t)}{t^4+4}\,dt$ is

(a) 0 (b) $\frac{1}{12}$ (c) $\frac{1}{24}$ (d) $\frac{1}{64}$

(ITT-JEE 2010)

14. Let S be the area of the region enclosed by $y=e^{-x^2}$, $y=0$, $x=0$ and $x=1$, then

(a) $S\ge\frac{1}{e}$ (b) $S\ge 1-\frac{1}{e}$

(c) $S\le\frac{1}{4}\left(1+\frac{1}{\sqrt{e}}\right)$ (d) $S\le\frac{1}{\sqrt{2}}+\frac{1}{\sqrt{e}}\left(1-\frac{1}{\sqrt{2}}\right)$

(IIT-JEE 2012)

15. For any real number, let $[x]$ denote the largest integer less than or equal is x let f be a real valud function defined on the interval $[-1, 1]$ by

$$f(x)=\begin{cases} x-[x]\ ; & \text{if } [x] \text{ is odd} \\ 1+[x]-x; & \text{if } [x] \text{ is even}\end{cases}$$

Then the value of $\frac{\pi^2}{10}\int_{-10}^{10} f(x)\cos\pi x\,dx$ is

(a) 4 (b) 5 (c) 6 (d) 1

(IIT-JEE 2010)

Hints / Solution to Problem Set (12)

1. Ans. (a).

$$\int_0^1 \frac{x^4(1-x)^4}{1+x^2}dx = \int_0^1 \frac{x^4(4+x^2)-(-2x)^2}{1+x^2}dx$$

$$= \int_0^1 \frac{x^4[(1+x^2)^2 - 4x(1+x^2)+4x^2]}{1+x^2}dx$$

$$= \int_0^1 x^4\left[(1+x^2) - 4x + \frac{4x^2}{1+x^2}\right]dx$$

$$= \int_0^1 \left[x^6 + x^4 - 4x^5 + \frac{4x^6}{1+x^2}\right]dx$$

On polynomial division of x^6 by $(1+x^2)$ we get

$$= \int_0^1 \left[x^6 + x^4 - 4x^5 + 4\left\{(x^4 - x^2 + 1) - \frac{1}{1+x^2}\right\}\right]dx$$

$$= \int_0^1 \left[(x^6 - 4x^5 + 5x^4 - 4x^2 + 4) - \frac{4}{(1+x^2)}\right]dx$$

$$= \left[\frac{x^7}{7} - \frac{4x^6}{6} + \frac{5x^5}{5} - \frac{4x^3}{3} + 4x\right]_0^1 - 4[\tan^{-1} x]_0^1$$

$$= \left(\frac{1}{7} - \frac{4}{6} + 1 - \frac{4}{3} + 4\right) - 4\left(\frac{\pi}{4}\right)$$

$$= \left[\frac{1}{7} - \frac{12}{6} + 5 - \pi = \left(\frac{1}{7} + 3\right) - \pi = \frac{22}{7} - \pi\right.$$

2. Ans. (b).

$$\int_{-\pi/2}^{\pi/2} \left(x^2 + \log\left(\frac{\pi+x}{\pi-x}\right)\right)\cos x\,dx = 2\int_0^{\pi/2} \cos x\,dx + 0$$

$$\left(\because \log\left(\frac{\pi+x}{\pi-x}\right) \text{ is an odd function}\right)$$

$$= 2\left[(x^2 \sin x)_0^{\pi/2} - \int_0^{\pi/2} 2x \sin x\,dx\right]$$

$$= 2\left(\frac{\pi^2}{4} - 0\right) - 4\int_0^{\pi/2} x \sin x\,dx$$

$$= \frac{\pi^2}{2} - 4\left[(-x\cos x)_0^{\pi/2} + \int_0^{\pi/2} \cos x\,dx\right] = \frac{\pi^2}{2} - 4$$

3. Ans. (a).

Let $x^2 = t \Rightarrow 2x\,dx = dt$

$$\therefore \quad I = \int_{\log 2}^{\log 3} \frac{\sin t}{\sin t + \sin(\log 6 - t)} \cdot \frac{dt}{2} \qquad \ldots(1)$$

$$= \frac{1}{2}\int_{\log 2}^{\log 3} \frac{\sin(\log 6 - t)}{\sin(\log 6 - t) + \sin t}dt \qquad \ldots(2)$$

$$\left(\because \int_a^b f(x)\,dx = \int_a^b f(a+b-x)\,dx\right)$$

On adding (1) and (2) we get

$$2I = \frac{1}{2}\int_{\log 2}^{\log 3} 1.dt \Rightarrow I = \frac{1}{4}\log\frac{3}{2}$$

4. Ans. (d).

$$I = \int_0^\pi [\cot x]\,dx = \int_0^\pi [\cot(\pi - x)] = dx$$

$$= \int_0^\pi [-\cot x]\,dx$$

$$\Rightarrow \quad 2I = \int_0^\pi \{(\cot x] + [-\cot x]\}\,dx = \int_0^\pi -1\,dx$$

$$\Rightarrow \quad 2I = -\pi \quad \Rightarrow \quad I = -\frac{\pi}{2}$$

5. Ans. (b).

$$p'(x) = p'(1-x) \Rightarrow \int p'(x)\,dx = \int p'(1-x)dx$$

$\Rightarrow \quad p(x) = -p(1-x) + c$

Put $x = 0$, $p(0) = -p(1) + c \Rightarrow 1 = -41 + c \Rightarrow c = 42$

$\therefore \quad p(x) = -p(1-x) + 42 \Rightarrow p(x) + p(1-x) = 42$

$\Rightarrow \quad \int_0^1 \{p(x) + p(1-x)]\,dx = \int_0^1 42\,dx$

(By using $\int_0^a f(x)\,dx = \int_0^a f(a-x)\,dx$)

$\Rightarrow \quad 2\int_0^1 p(x)\,dx = 42 \Rightarrow \int_0^1 p(x)\,dx = 21$

6. Ans. (b).

$$g(x+\pi) = \int_0^{x+\pi} \cos 4t\,dt$$

$$= \int_0^x \cos 4t\,dt + \int_x^{x+\pi} \cos 4t\,dt$$

$$= \int_0^x \cos 4t\,dt + \int_0^\pi \cos 4t\,dt = g(x) + g(\pi)$$

7. Ans. (c).

Given $\int_0^x \sqrt{1 - f'(t)}\,dt = \int_0^x f(t)\,dt, \qquad 0 \le x \le 1$

Apply Leibnitz theorem we get $\sqrt{1 - (f'(x)^2} = f(x)$

$\Rightarrow \quad 1 - (f'(x))^2 = f^2(x)$

$\Rightarrow \quad (f'(x))^2 = 1 - f^2(x)$

$\Rightarrow \quad f'(x) = \pm\sqrt{1 - f^2(x)}$

$\Rightarrow \quad \dfrac{dy}{dx} = \pm\sqrt{1-y^2} \qquad y = f(x)$

$\Rightarrow \quad \dfrac{dy}{\sqrt{1-y^2}} = \pm dx$

$\Rightarrow \quad \sin^{-1} y = \pm x + c$

$\because \quad f(0) = 0 \Rightarrow c = 0 \Rightarrow y = \pm \sin x$

$y = \sin x = f(x)$ given $f(x) \ge 0$ for $x \in [0, 1]$

We know that $\sin x < x \;\forall\; x \in \mathbf{R}^+$

$\therefore \quad \sin\left(\dfrac{1}{2}\right) < \dfrac{1}{2} \quad \Rightarrow \quad f\left(\dfrac{1}{2}\right) < \dfrac{1}{2}$

and $\sin\left(\dfrac{1}{3}\right) < \dfrac{1}{3} \quad \Rightarrow \quad f\left(\dfrac{1}{3}\right) < \dfrac{1}{3}$

8. Ans. (b).

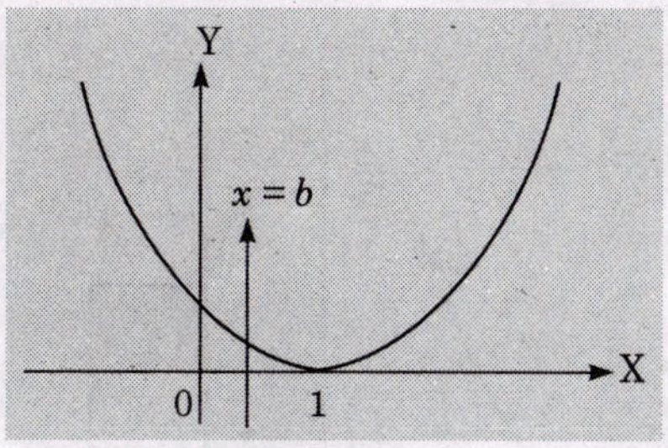

Fig. 94

$$R_1 = \int_0^b (x-1)^2\,dx = \frac{(x-1)^3}{3}\Bigg|_0^b = \frac{(b-1)^3+1}{3}$$

$$R_2 = \int_b^1 (x-1)^2\,dx = \frac{(x-1)^3}{3}\Bigg|_0^1 = -\frac{(b-1)^3}{3}$$

$$\Rightarrow\quad R_1 - R_2 = \frac{2(h-1)^3}{3} + \frac{1}{3}$$

$$\Rightarrow\quad \frac{1}{4} = \frac{2(b-1)^3}{3} \Rightarrow b = \frac{1}{2}$$

9. Ans. (c).

The equation of the tangent at (2, 3) to the given parabola is $x = 2y - 4$

$\therefore$ Required area $= \int_0^3 \{(y-2)^2 + 1 - 2y + 4\}\,dy$

$$= \left[\frac{(y-2)^3}{3} - y^2 + 5y\right]_0^3 = \frac{1}{3} - 9 + 15 + \frac{8}{3} = 9 \text{ sq. unit}$$

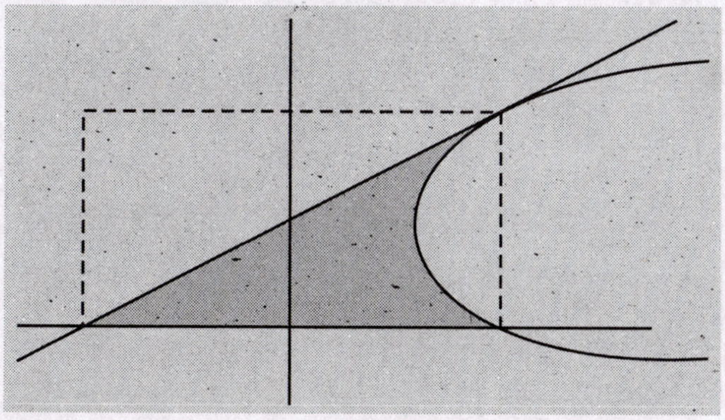

Fig. 95

10. Ans. (c).

$$R_2 = \int_{-1}^2 f(x)\,dx \text{ and } R_1 = \int_{-1}^2 x\,f(x)\,dx$$

$$= \int_{-1}^2 (1-x)\,f(1-x)\,dx$$

$$= \int_{-1}^2 (1-x)\,f(x)\,dx$$

$$\Rightarrow\quad R_1 = R_2 - R_1 \qquad \Rightarrow\quad 2R_1 = R_2$$

11. Ans. (c).

Required area $= OAB + ACDB$

$$= \frac{1}{2} \times 1 \times 1 + \int_1^x \frac{1}{x}\,dx$$

$$= \frac{3}{2} \text{ sq. units.}$$

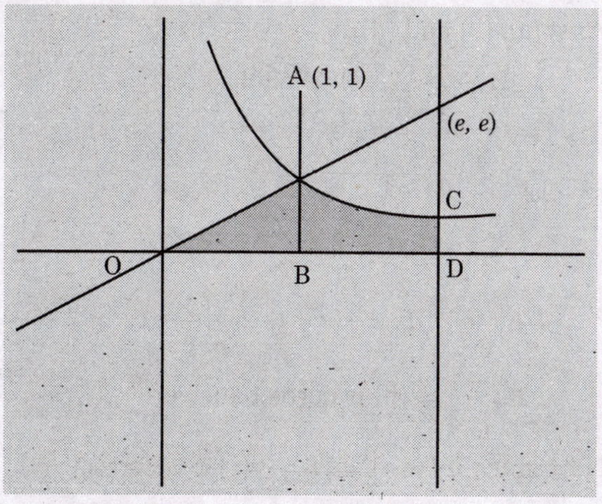

Fig. 96

12. Ans. (a).

$$A = A_1 + A_2 + A_3$$

$$A = \left|\int_0^{\pi/4}(\cos x - \sin x)\,dx\right| = \left|(\sin x + \cos x)\right|_0^{\pi/4}$$

$$= \left|\left(\frac{1}{\sqrt{2}} + \frac{1}{\sqrt{2}}\right) - (0+1)\right| = \left|\sqrt{2} - 1\right| = \sqrt{2} - 1$$

$$A_2 = \left|\int_{\pi/4}^{5\pi/4} (\sin x - \cos x)\,dx\right| = \left|(-\sin x - \cos x)_{\pi/4}^{\pi/4}\right|$$

$$= \left|-(\cos x + \sin x)_{\pi/4}^{5\pi/4}\right|$$

$$= \left|\left[\left(-\frac{1}{\sqrt{2}} - \frac{1}{\sqrt{2}}\right) - \left(\frac{1}{\sqrt{2}} + \frac{1}{\sqrt{2}}\right)\right]\right| = 2\sqrt{2}$$

and $A_3 = \left|\int_{5\pi/4}^{3\pi/4}(\cos x - \sin x)\,dx\right|$

Hence $A = A_1 + A_2 + A_3 = 4\sqrt{2} - 2$

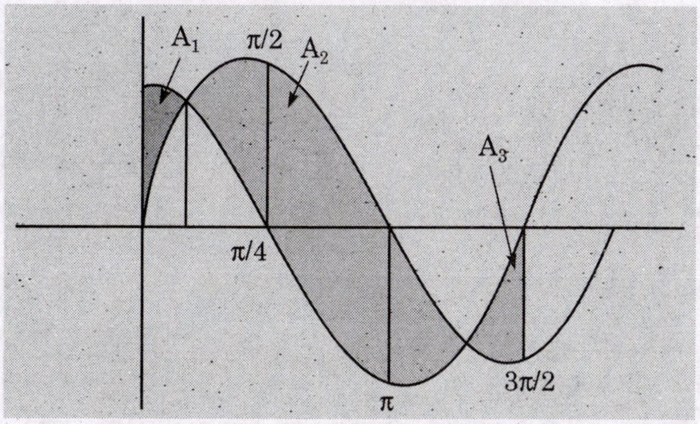

Fig. 97

13. Ans. (b).

$$\lim_{x\to 0} \frac{x \log(1+x)}{(x^4+4).3x^2} = \lim_{x\to 0} \frac{\log(1+x)}{3x(x^4+4)} \qquad \left(\frac{0}{0}\text{ from}\right)$$

$= \lim_{x\to 0} \frac{1}{3} \frac{1/(1+x)}{(x^4 + 40 + x - 4x^3} = \frac{1}{3}.\frac{1}{4} = \frac{1}{12}$

14. Ans. (a), (b) and (d).

$I = \int_0^1 e^{-x^2} dx = \begin{cases} -x^2 \le 0 \\ e^{-x^2} \le 1 \end{cases}$

$\Rightarrow \int_0^1 e^{-x^2} .dx \le 1$

$x^2 \le x \Rightarrow -x^2 \ge x \Rightarrow e^{-x^2} \ge e^{-x}$

$\therefore \quad I \ge \int_0^1 e^{-x} dx \ge -(e^{-x})_0^1 \ge -\left(\frac{1}{e} - 1\right)$

$I \ge 1 - \frac{1}{3} \Rightarrow$ (b) is correct answer

Now since if $I \ge -\frac{1}{e} \Rightarrow I > \frac{1}{e} \Rightarrow$ (a) is correct

Also, $I < \frac{1}{\sqrt{2}} \times 1 + \frac{1}{\sqrt{e}} \times \left(1 - \frac{1}{\sqrt{2}}\right) \Rightarrow$ (d) is correct.

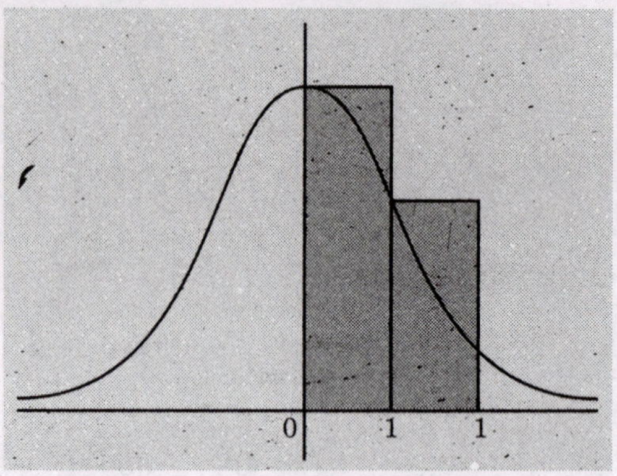

Fig. 98

15. Ans. (a).

$f(x) \begin{cases} [x]; & 2n - 1 \le x < 2n \\ 1 - [x]; & 2n \le x < 2n + 1 \end{cases}$

Clearly $f(x)$ is a periodic function with period 2

$\therefore \quad f(x) \cos \pi x$ is also periodic with period 2

Therefore,

$$\frac{\pi^2}{10} \int_{-10}^{1} f(x) \cos(\pi x) dx = \pi^2 \int_0^2 f(x) \cos(\pi x)\, dx$$

$$= \pi^2 \int_0^1 [(1 - [x]) + (-x] \cos(\pi x)\, dx$$

$$= 2\pi^2 \int_0^1 (-x \cos \pi x)\, dx$$

$$= -2\pi^2 \left(\frac{x \sin \pi x}{\pi} + \frac{\cos \pi x}{\pi^2}\right]_0^1$$

$$= -2\pi^2 \left(\frac{-2}{\pi^2}\right) = 4$$

❑

CHAPTER **32** **Differential Equations**

Differential Equations (Ist Order and Ist Degree)

§ 1. Definitions.

(a) Differential Equations.

Consider the following equations.

$$\frac{d^3y}{dx^3} - 3\frac{d^2y}{dx^2} + 3\frac{dy}{dx} - y = \sin 2x \quad ...(1)$$

$$\frac{dy}{dx} = \frac{\sqrt{(x)}}{\sqrt{(1+y^2)}}, \quad ...(2)$$

$$xy\frac{dy}{dx} = \frac{x^2+1}{y+1}, \quad ...(3)$$

$$x\frac{\partial z}{\partial x} + y\frac{\partial z}{\partial y} + z = 0, \quad ...(4)$$

$$\frac{\partial^2 y}{\partial t^2} = a^2\frac{\partial^2 y}{\partial x^2}, \quad ...(5)$$

$$\frac{\left[1+\left\{\frac{dy}{dx}\right\}^2\right]^{3/2}}{\frac{d^2y}{dx^2}} = \rho \quad ...(6)$$

All the above equations are such that they involve derivatives or differential coefficients. Some of them are with and some without variables from which the derivatives or differentials are obtained.

Such equations are called differential equations.

(b) Ordinary and partial differential equations.

Ordinary differntial equations are those which involve only one independent variable *e.g.* equations (1), (2), (3) and (6) involve only one independent variable x.

Partial differential equations are those which involve two or more than two independent variables *e.g.* in equations (4) and (5), (θ, y) and (t, x) are independent variables respectively.

We shall deal here only with ordinary differential equations.

(c) Order and degree of differential equations.

The order of differential equation is defined to be the order of the highest derivative or differential coefficient occurring in it *e.g.* equations (2) and (3) are of first order whereas equations (6) and (1) are of second and third order respectively.

Hence the equation which involves $\frac{d^2y}{dx^2}$ or its powers but not higher differential coefficient is said to be of second order.

The degree of a differential equation is the exponent of highest power of the highest differential coefficient which occurs in it after the equation has been put in the form free from radicals and fractions *e.g.*, equation (6) when freed from radicals and fractions takes the form

$$\left[1+\left\{\frac{dy}{dx}\right\}^2\right]^3 = \rho^2\left\{\frac{d^2y}{dx^2}\right\}^2$$

Hence the equation is of second order and second degree.

§ 2. Formation of differential Equations.

Consider the following examples.

Solved Examples

***Ex. 1.** Find the differential equation whose solution is

(a) $y = Ae^{2x} + Be^{-2x}$,

(b) $y = A\sin 2x + B\cos 2x$ ...(1)

(J.E.E.W.B. 1996)

(a) Eliminating the arbitrary constants A and B from the given equation

$$\frac{dy}{dx} = 2Ae^{2x} - 2Be^{-2x} \quad ...(2)$$

Differentiate again

$$\therefore \frac{d^2y}{dx^2} = 4Ae^{2x} + 4Be^{-2x} = 4y \quad ...(3)$$

The two arbitrary constants have been eliminated and we have got a differential equation of second order.

i.e. $\frac{d^2y}{dx^2} - 4y = 0$

(b) Similarly as above we will have $\frac{d^2y}{dx^2} + 4y = 0.$

(c) Prove that the degree of the differential equation satisfying $\sqrt{1-x^2}+\sqrt{1-y^2}=a(x-y)$ is one.

Refer Q. 27 (a).

$$\frac{dy}{dx}=\sqrt{\frac{1-y^2}{1-x^2}}$$

Hence the degree of the differential equation is one.

Ex. 2. Show that $Ax^2+By^2=1$ is the solution of

$$x\left[y\frac{d^2y}{dx^2}+\left(\frac{dy}{dx}\right)^2\right]=y\cdot\frac{dy}{dx}$$

Differentiating $Ax^2+By^2-1=0$, ...(1)

we get $Ax+By\frac{dy}{dx}=0$ ...(2)

Differentiating again,

$$A+B\left[y\frac{d^2y}{dx^2}+\left(\frac{dy}{dx}\right)^2\right]=0 \quad ...(3)$$

Equating the value of $-A/B$ from (2) and (3),

we get $-\frac{A}{B}=\frac{yy_1}{x}=yy_2+y_1^2$

$\therefore \quad x(yy_2+y_1^2)=yy_1$

or $x\left\{y\frac{d^2y}{dx^2}+\left(\frac{dy}{dx}\right)^2\right\}=y\frac{dy}{dx}$.

Another form :

Find the differential equation of all conics whose axes coincide with the axes of coordinates.

The general equation of a conic having axes of x and y as its axes is $Ax^2+By^2=1$ where A and B are arbitrary constants. Hence the required differential equation is as written above.

***Ex. 3.** Find the differential equation of the family of curves

(a) $xy=Ae^x+Be^{-x}+x^2$,

(b) $xy=Ae^x+Be^{-x}$ for different values of A and B.

Differentiating w.r.t. x, we get

$$x\frac{dy}{dx}+y=Ae^x-Be^{-x}+2x.$$

Differentiating again, we get

$$x\frac{d^2y}{dx^2}+2\frac{dy}{dx}=Ae^x+Be^{-x}+2=xy-x^2+2.$$

Thus two variables A and B have been eliminated and we have got a differential equation of 2nd order.

(b) $x\frac{d^2y}{dx^2}+2\frac{dy}{dx}-xy=0.$

***Ex. 4.** Find the differential equations of all circles passing through origin and having their centres on the x-axis.

If $(h,0)$ be the centre, then its radius will also be h as the circle passes through origin. Its equation therefore, is

$$(x-h)^2+y^2=h^2 \quad \text{or} \quad x^2+y^2=2hx.$$

Differentiating, we get $2x+2y\frac{dy}{dx}=2h$

or $x+y\frac{dy}{dx}=\frac{x^2+y^2}{2x}$

or $2x^2+2xy\frac{dy}{dx}=x^2+y^2$ or $\frac{dy}{dx}=\frac{y^2-x^2}{2xy}$

Ex. 5. (a) Find the differential equation of the family of curves $y=Ae^{3x}+Be^{5x}$ for different values of A and B.

$y=Ae^{3x}+Be^{5x}$ ...(1)

$\therefore \quad y_1=3Ae^{3x}+5Be^{5x}$ ...(2)

$y_2=9Ae^{3x}+25Be^{5x}$ ...(3)

Eliminating A and B from the above three, we get

$$\begin{vmatrix} e^{3x} & e^{5x} & -y \\ 3e^{3x} & 5e^{5x} & -y_1 \\ 9e^{3x} & 25e^{5x} & -y_2 \end{vmatrix}=0$$

or $$-e^{3x}\cdot e^{5x}\begin{vmatrix} 1 & 1 & y \\ 3 & 5 & y_1 \\ 9 & 25 & y_2 \end{vmatrix}=0$$

Expanding, we get

$$30y-16y_1+2y_2=0$$

or $\frac{d^2y}{dx^2}-8\frac{dy}{dx}+15y=0$

(b) Find the differential equation corresponding to $y=ae^{2x}+be^{-3x}+ce^x$ where a,b,c are arbitrary constants.

$y=ae^{2x}+be^{-3x}+ce^x$ ...(1)

$y_1=2ae^{2x}-3be^{-3x}+ce^x$ ...(2)

$y_2=4ae^{2x}+9be^{-3x}+ce^x$ ...(3)

$y_3=8ae^{2x}-27be^{-3x}+ce^x$ ...(4)

$y_1-y=ae^{2x}-4be^{-3x}$ ...(5)

$y_2-y_1=2ae^{2x}+12be^{-3x}$ ...(6)

$y_3-y_2=4ae^{2x}-36be^{-3x}$ ...(7)

Now eliminating a,b from (5) (6) and (7), we get

$$e^{2x}\cdot e^{-3x}\begin{vmatrix} 1 & -4 & -(y_1-y) \\ 2 & 12 & -(y_2-y_1) \\ 4 & -36 & -(y_3-y_2) \end{vmatrix}=0$$

or $$\begin{vmatrix} y_1-y & 1 & -1 \\ y_2-y_1 & 2 & 3 \\ y_3-y_2 & 4 & -9 \end{vmatrix}=0$$

Now expand

$$-30(y_1-y)+5(y_2-y_1)+5(y_3-y_2)=0$$

or $y_3-y_2+y_2-y_1-6y_1+6y=0$

or $\frac{d^3y}{dx^3}-7\frac{dy}{dx}+6y=0$

is the required diffrential equation.

Ex. 6. (a) Find the differential equation of all straight lines which are at a constant distance from the origin.

We know that $x\cos\theta + y\sin\theta = p$ is the equation of a straight line which is at a constant distance p from the origin. We have to eliminate the parameter θ in order to find its differential equation.

$$\cos\theta + \sin\theta \, . \, y' = 0 \quad \therefore \quad \cot\theta = -y'$$

$$\therefore \quad \sin\theta = \frac{1}{\sqrt{1+y'^2}}, \cos\theta = -\frac{y'}{\sqrt{1+y'^2}}$$

Putting in the given equation, we get

$$\frac{-xy' + y}{\sqrt{1+y'^2}} = p$$

$$\text{or} \quad \left(y - x\frac{dy}{dx}\right)^2 = p^2\left[1 + \left(\frac{dy}{dx}\right)^2\right]$$

(b) Find the differential equation of all hyperbolas whose axes are along the co-ordinate axes.

$\frac{x^2}{a^2} - \frac{y^2}{b^2} = 1$ is the standard equation of hyperbola whose transverse and conjugate axes are along the co-ordinate axes. Here we have to eliminate the two parameters a^2 and b^2. Differentiating, we have

$$\frac{2x}{a^2} - \frac{2yy'}{b^2} = 0 \qquad \text{...(1)}$$

Differentiating (1) again w.r.t. x,

$$\frac{1}{a^2} - \frac{1}{b^2}\{y'^2 + yy''\} = 0 \qquad \text{...(2)}$$

Equate the values of $\frac{b^2}{a^2}$ from (1) and (2)

$$\frac{yy'}{x} = y'^2 + yy''$$

$$\text{or} \quad y\left(\frac{dy}{dx}\right) = x\left(\frac{dy}{dx}\right)^2 + xy\frac{d^2y}{dx^2}$$

Above is a differential equation of 2nd order obtained by eliminating two parameters.

(c) Prove that the differential equation of all the conics touching y-axis at the origin and having their centres on the axis of x is

$$x^2y\frac{d^2y}{dx^2} + \left(x\frac{dy}{dx} - y\right)^2 = 0$$

The equation of a conic having centre at the origin and axes along co-ordinate axes is $ax^2 + by^2 = 1$

Since the centre is given on axis of x say $(h, 0)$, hence its equation is $a(x-h)^2 + by^2 = 1$ ...(1)

It touches y-axis, $x = 0$ at $(0, 0)$

$\therefore \quad ah^2 + by^2 = 1$ or $by^2 + 0y + (ah^2 - 1) = 0$

Above must have equal roots $\therefore ah^2 - 1 = 0$

$$\therefore \quad a = \frac{1}{h^2} \text{ Putting in (1)}$$

$$\frac{(x-h)^2}{h^2} + by^2 = 1$$

$$\text{or} \quad \frac{x^2}{h^2} - \frac{2x}{h} + by^2 = 0 \qquad \text{...(2)}$$

Above is the equation of family of conics under given condition.

Differentiating (2) w.r.t. x twice, we have

$$\frac{2x}{h^2} - \frac{2}{h} + 2byy' = 0$$

$$\text{or} \quad \frac{x}{h^2} - \frac{1}{h} + byy' = 0 \qquad \text{...(3)}$$

$$\text{and} \quad \frac{1}{h^2} + 0 + b(y'^2 + yy'') = 0 \qquad \text{...(4)}$$

Eliminating $\frac{1}{h^2}, -\frac{1}{h}$ and (b) between (2), (3) and (4), we get

$$\begin{vmatrix} x^2 & 2x & y^2 \\ x & 1 & yy' \\ 1 & 0 & (y'^2 + yy'') \end{vmatrix} = 0$$

Expanding with third row, we have

$$(2xyy' - y^2) + (y'^2 + yy'')(-x^2) = 0$$

$$\text{or} \quad (x^2y'^2 - 2xyy' + y^2) + x^2yy'' = 0$$

$$\text{or} \quad \left(x\frac{dy}{dx} - y\right)^2 + x^2y\frac{d^2y}{dx^2} = 0$$

***Ex. 7.** Transform the equation

$$(1+x^2)^2\frac{d^2y}{dx^2} + 2x(1+x^2)\frac{dy}{dx} + y = 0$$ into one in which z is independent variable, it being given that $x = \tan z$.

$$\therefore \quad \frac{dy}{dx} = \frac{dy}{dz}.\frac{dz}{dx} = \frac{dy}{dz}\frac{1}{1+x^2}$$

$\because \quad$ When $x = \tan z$, $z = \tan^{-1} x$

$$\therefore \quad \frac{dz}{dx} = \frac{1}{1+x^2} \quad \therefore \quad (1+x^2)\frac{dy}{dx} = \frac{dy}{dz}$$

Differentiate both sides again w.r.t. x

$$(1+x^2)\frac{d^2y}{dx^2} + 2x\frac{dy}{dx} = \frac{d}{dx}\left(\frac{dy}{dz}\right)$$

$$= \frac{d}{dz}\left(\frac{dy}{dz}\right)\frac{dz}{dx} = \frac{d^2y}{dz^2}\frac{1}{1+x^2}$$

$$\therefore \quad (1+x^2)^2\frac{d^2y}{dx^2} + 2x(1+x^2)\frac{dy}{dx} = \frac{d^2y}{dz^2}$$

Add y to both sides

$$\therefore \quad \frac{d^2y}{dz^2} + y = 0$$

is the required transformed equation.

Problem Set (1)

Order and degree of a differential equation and formation of differential equation.

Find the differential equations whose solutions are

1. $y = mx$

2. $y = mx + c$

3. Find the differential equations of all circles in the plane XOY which have their centres on x–axis and have given radius.

4.* Show that the differential equation of the family of circles of fixed radius r with centres on y–axis is

$$(x^2 - r^2)\left(\frac{dy}{dx}\right)^2 + x^2 = 0$$

5. Find the differential equations of all parabolas each having latus rectum $4a$ and whose axes are parallel to the x-axis.

6. Prove that the differential equation of the family of parabolas $y^2 = 4ax$ is $2x\frac{dy}{dx} - y = 0$

7.* Eliminate the constants a, b from the relation

$$y = a\sin x + b\cos x + x\sin x.$$

8. Find the differential equations of the family of curves $y = e^x (A\cos x + B\sin x)$ where A and B are arbitrary constants.

9. Prove that $v = \frac{A}{r} + B$ is a solution of $\frac{d^2v}{dr^2} + \frac{2}{r}\frac{dv}{dr} = 0.$

10. Find the differential equation corresponding to the family of curves $y = k(x - k)^2$ where k is an arbitrary constant.

11.* Form the differential equation of the circles represented by $y^2 - 2ay + x^2 = a^2$, a being arbitrary constant.

12. (a) Obtain the differential equation of which $y = ax^2 + bx$ is the general solution, a, b being arbitrary constants.

(b) $y = ax^2 + b$, a, b being constants.

13. (a) The differential equation which represents the family of curves $y = e^{cx}$ is :

(a) $y' = cy$ (b) $xy' - \log y = 0$

(c) $x\log y = yy'$ (d) $y\log y = xy'$ **(AIEEE 2002)**

(b) The degree and order of the differential equation of the family of all parabolas whose axis is axis of x are respectively :

(a) 2, 1 (b) 1, 2

(c) 3, 2 (d) 2, 3 **(AI EEE 2003)**

(c) The differential equation whose solution is $Ax^2 + By^2 = 1$, where A and B are arbitrary constants is of :

(a) 1st order, 2nd degree

(b) 1st order, 1st degree

(c) 2nd order and 1st degree

(d) 2nd order and 2nd degree **(AIEEE 2006)**

14. Obtain the differential equations whose solutions are

(a) $y = A\cos(x + 3)$, A being constant.

(b) $y = x\sin(x + A)$, A being constant.

(c) $y = a\sin(bx + c)$

(d)* The order of the differential equation whose general solution is given by

$$y = (c_1 + c_2)\cos(x + c_3) - c_4 e^{x + c_5}$$

where c_1, c_2, c_3, c_4, c_5 are arbitrary constants, is

(A) 5 (B) 4

(C) 3 (D) 2 **(I.I.T. 1998)**

(e) The differential equation representing the family of curves $y^2 = 2c(x + \sqrt{c})$, where c is a positive parameter, is of

(a) order 1 (b) order 2

(c) degree 3 (d) degree 4 **(I.I.T. 1999)**

15. Find the differential equation associated with the primitive $x^2 + y^2 + 2ax + 2by + c = 0$, where a, b, c are arbitrary constants.

16.* Find the differential equation of the family of curves whose equations are

(i) $\frac{x^2}{a^2 + \lambda} + \frac{y^2}{b^2 + \lambda} = 1$

(ii) $\frac{x^2}{a^2} + \frac{y^2}{a^2 + \lambda} = 1$, where λ is parameter.

(iii) The differential equation which represents the family of curves $y = c_1 e^{c_2 x}$, where c_1 and c_2 are arbitrary constants, is

(a) $yy'' = (y')^2$ (b) $y' = y^2$

(c) $y'' = y'y$ (d) $yy'' = y'$ **(AIEEE 2009)**

Change the independent variable from the following differential equations :

17. (a)* $(1 - x^2)\frac{d^2y}{dx^2} - x\frac{dy}{dx} + y = 0$ it being given that $x = \cos\theta$.

(b) If $y = \log(m\cos^{-1}x)$ is a solution of the differential equation

$$(1 - x^2)\frac{d^2y}{dx^2} - x\frac{dy}{dx} = ke^{-2y}, \text{ then } k =$$

(a) m^2 (b) $2m^2$

(c) $-m^2$ (d) $-2m^2$

18. (a) $\frac{d^2y}{dx^2} + \cot x\frac{dy}{dx} + 4y\,\text{cosec}^2 x = 0$

it being given that $z = \log \tan \dfrac{x}{2}$.

(b)* $\dfrac{d^2y}{dx^2}\cos x + \dfrac{dy}{dx}\sin x - 2y\cos^3 x = 2\cos^5 x$

it being given that $z = \sin x$.

19. $\sin^2 2x \dfrac{d^2y}{dx^2} + \sin 4x \dfrac{dy}{dx} + 4y = 0$

it being given that $\tan x = e^t$ or $t = \log \tan x$.

20. If $x = \sin\theta$, $y = \sin k\theta$ then show that

$$(1-x^2)\frac{d^2y}{dx^2} - x\frac{dy}{dx} + k^2 y = 0$$

Solutions to Problem Set (2)

1. Eliminate the arbitrary constant m in the given equation

$$y = mx \quad ...(1)$$

$$\frac{dy}{dx} = m = \frac{y}{x} \quad \text{from given equation}$$

$$\therefore \quad y = x\frac{dy}{dx}$$

is a differential equation of 1st order obtained by eliminating one constant m.

2. Eliminating arbitrary constants m and c from

$$y = mx + c. \quad ...(1)$$

$$\frac{dy}{dx} = m.$$

Differentiating again, $\dfrac{d^2y}{dx^2} = 0$ ...(2)

The two arbitrary constants have been eliminated and we have got a differential equation of second order.

In the light of above we can say that if an equation contains n arbitrary constants, the result of eliminating these constants will be a differential equation of nth order.

Equation (1) in the above examples are called the General solution of differential equation.

Hence we can say that by solving a differential equation of nth order, we mean to find a relation between the two variables x, y and n independent arbitrary constants, such that when these constants are eliminated the given differential equation of nth order will be formed.

3. Let the centre on x–axis be $(h, 0)$ and given radius be a so that the equation of the circle is

$$(x-h)^2 + y^2 = a^2 \quad ...(1)$$

Differentiating, $2(x-h) + 2y\dfrac{dy}{dx} = 0$

or, $\pm\sqrt{(a^2 - y^2)} + y\dfrac{dy}{dx} = 0.$ [by (1)]

We have eliminated one variable h and have got a differential equation of first order, a being constant.

4. Let the centre be $(0, k)$ on y-axis. The equation of circle is

$$x^2 + (y-k)^2 = r^2,\ k \text{ being constant} \quad ...(1)$$

$$2x + 2(y-k)y_1 = 0 \ \therefore\ y - k = -\frac{x}{y_1}$$

Putting in (1), we get

$$(x^2 - r^2) + \frac{x^2}{y_1^2} = 0$$

or $\quad (x^2 - r^2)\left(\dfrac{dy}{dx}\right)^2 + x^2 = 0.$

5. The equation of the parabola is $(y-k)^2 = 4ax$ ...(1)

$\therefore \quad 2(y-k)y_1 = 4a$ or $y - k = \dfrac{2a}{y_1}$

Putting in (1), we get

$$\frac{4a^2}{y_1^2} = 4ax \quad \text{or} \quad x\left(\frac{dy}{dx}\right)^2 = a.$$

7. Diff. twice, we get $\dfrac{d^2y}{dx^2} = -y + 2\cos x$

or $\quad \dfrac{d^2y}{dx^2} + y = 2\cos x$

8. $y = e^x(A\cos x + B\sin x)$ ...(1)

$y_1 = e^x(A\cos x + B\sin x) + e^x(-A\sin x + B\cos x)$

or $\quad y_1 - y = e^x(-A\sin x + B\cos x)$ ...(2)

Differentiating again w.r.t. x, we get

$$y_2 - y_1 = e^x(-A\sin x + B\cos x) + e^x(-A\cos x - B\sin x)$$

or $\quad y_2 - y_1 = (y_1 - y) - y$, by (1) and (2)

or $\quad \dfrac{d^2y}{dx^2} - 2\dfrac{dy}{dx} + 2y = 0$

9. $v = \dfrac{A}{r} + B$ ...(1)

$\dfrac{dv}{dr} = -\dfrac{A}{r^2}$ ...(2)

$\dfrac{d^2v}{dr^2} = \dfrac{2A}{r^3}$ ...(3)

Eliminating A between (2) and (3), we get

$$r\frac{d^2v}{dr^2} = \frac{2A}{r^2} = 2\left(-\frac{dv}{dr}\right)$$

$$\therefore \quad \frac{d^2v}{dr^2} + \frac{2}{r}\frac{dv}{dr} = 0$$

10. $y = k(x-k)^2$ ...(1)

$\therefore \quad y_1 = 2k(x-k)$ ...(2)

or $\quad y_1^2 = 4k^2(x-k)^2 = 4k^2 \cdot \dfrac{y}{k}$

$\therefore \quad \dfrac{y_1^2}{4y} = k.$

Putting the value of k in (2), we get

$$y_1 = 2.\frac{y_1^2}{4y}\left[x - \frac{y_1^2}{4y}\right]$$

$\therefore \quad 2y = y_1 x - \frac{y_1^3}{4y}$ or $8y^2 - 4xyy_1 - (y_1)^3$

or $\left(\frac{dy}{dx}\right)^3 - 4xy\frac{dy}{dx} + 8y^2 = 0$

is the required equation.

11. The given equation is $x^2 + (y-a)^2 = 2a^2$ ...(1)

Differentiate $2x + 2(y-a)y_1 = 0$

or $x + yy_1 = ay_1$ ...(2)

Putting the value of a from (2) in (1), we get

or $x^2 + \left(y - \frac{x + yy_1}{y_1}\right)^2 = 2\left(\frac{x+yy_1}{y_1}\right)^2$

or $x^2 + \frac{x^2}{y_1^2} = \frac{2}{y_1^2}(x^2 + 2xyy_1 + y^2y_1^2)$

or $x^2(y_1^2 + 1) = 2x^2 + 4xyy_1 + 2y^2y_1^2$

or $(2y^2 - x^2)\left(\frac{dy}{dx}\right)^2 + 4xy\frac{dy}{dx} + x^2 = 0$

12. (a) $y = ax^2 + bx$ ...(1)

$y_1 = 2ax + b$ ...(2)

$y_2 = 2a$ ...(3)

Eliminating (b) between (1) and (2), we get

$$xy_1 - y = ax^2 = \frac{1}{2}x^2 y_2, \quad \text{by (3)}$$

$\therefore \quad x^2\frac{d^2y}{dx^2} - 2x\frac{dy}{dx} + 2y = 0$

is the required differential equation of second order.

(b) $y_1 = 2ax, y_2 = 2a = \frac{y_1}{x}$

$\therefore \quad x\frac{d^2y}{dx^2} - \frac{dy}{dx} = 0$ is the required equation.

13. (a) Ans. (d).

$\log y = cx \log e = cx \quad \therefore \quad \frac{1}{y}y' = c$

Eliminate c

$\therefore \quad \log y = \frac{y'}{y}x$ or $y \log y = xy'$

(b) Ans. (b).

Let the equation of the parabola having axis along axis of x be $y^2 = 4a(x-h)$

$\therefore \quad 2y\frac{dy}{dx} = 4a + 0$. Differentiate again

$$y\frac{d^2y}{dx^2} + \left(\frac{dy}{dx}\right)^2 = 0$$

Clearly its degree is 1 and order 2.

(c) Ans. (d).

$2Ax + 2Byy' = 0$

$\therefore \quad \frac{yy'}{x} = -\frac{A}{B}$. Differentiate again

$\frac{1}{x^2}\{x(yy'' + y'^2) - yy'.1\} = 0$

or $xy\frac{d^2y}{dx^2} + x\left(\frac{dy}{dx}\right)^2 = y.\frac{dy}{dx}$

Above is clearly a differential equation of 2nd order and 2nd degree.

14. (a) $y_1 = -A\sin(x+3)$

$\frac{y_1}{y} = -\tan(x+3)$

or $\frac{dy}{dx} + y\tan(x+3) = 0$

(b) $y_1 = \sin(x+A) + x\cos(x+A)$

$\therefore \quad xy_1 - y = x^2\cos(x+A)$

Also $\quad xy = x^2\sin(x+A)$

$\therefore \quad (xy_1 - y)^2 + x^2y^2 = x^4.1$

$\because \quad \cos^2\theta + \sin^2\theta = 1$

(c) Here we have three arbitrary constants and the result of eliminating these will give rise to a differential equation of 3rd order.

$y = a\sin(bx+c)$ ...(1)

$y_1 = ab\cos(bx+c)$ ...(2)

$y_2 = -ab^2\sin(bx+c) = -b^2y$, by (1) ...(3)

$y_3 = -b^2y_1 = y_1\left(\frac{y_2}{y}\right)$, by (3)

$\therefore \quad yy_3 = y_1y_2$ is the required differential equation of 3rd order.

(d) Ans. (B). $a\cos(x+b) + ce^x + d$ *i.e.* 4 independent constants and hence order is 4.

(e) Ans. (a), (c). $2yy_1 = 2c \Rightarrow c = yy_1$

Eliminating c, we get

$y^2 = 2yy_1(x + \sqrt{yy_1})$

or $(y^2 - 2x\,yy_1)^2 = 4y^3y_1^3$

It involves only Ist order derivative, its order is 1 but its degree is 3 as y_1^3 is there.

15. $x^2 + y^2 + 2ax + 2by + c = 0$ ...(1)

Differentiate w.r.t. x

$\therefore \quad 2(x + yy_1) + 2(a + by_1) = 0$

or $x + yy_1 + (a + by_1) = 0$ ...(2)

Again differentiate w.r.t. x

$1 + yy_2 + y_1^2 + by_2 = 0$ ...(3)

Differentiate (3) w.r.t. x

$yy_3 + y_1y_2 + 2y_1y_2 + by_3 = 0$ ...(4)

Eliminating b between (3) and (4), we get

$$\frac{1 + yy_2 + y_1^2}{yy_3 + 3y_1y_2} = \frac{-by_2}{-by_3} = \frac{y_2}{y_3}$$

or $y_3(1+yy_2+y_1^2)=y_2(yy_3+3y_1y_2)$

Cancel the terms of yy_2y_3

$\therefore\quad y_3(1+y_1^2)=3y_1y_2^2$

or $\dfrac{d^3y}{dx^3}\left[1+\left(\dfrac{dy}{dx}\right)^2\right]=3\dfrac{dy}{dx}\left(\dfrac{d^2y}{dx^2}\right)^2$

16. Differentiating we get

$$\frac{2x}{a^2+\lambda}+\frac{2y}{b^2+\lambda}y'=0$$

or $x(b^2+\lambda)+yy'(a^2+\lambda)=0$

$$\therefore\quad \lambda=-\frac{b^2x+a^2yy'}{x+yy'}$$

Hence $a^2+\lambda=a^2-\dfrac{b^2x+a^2yy'}{x+yy'}=\dfrac{(a^2-b^2)x}{x+yy'}$

$$b^2+\lambda=-\frac{(a^2-b^2)yy'}{x+yy'}$$

Putting the values of $a^2+\lambda$ and $b^2+\lambda$ in the given equation thereby eliminating the arbitrary constant λ, we get

$$\left(x-\frac{y}{y'}\right)(x+yy')=a^2-b^2$$

(ii) Differentiating, we get $\dfrac{2x}{a^2}+\dfrac{2y}{a^2+\lambda}\dfrac{dy}{dx}=0$

$\therefore\quad (a^2+\lambda)=-a^2yy'$

Putting for $a^2+\lambda$ in the given equation, we get

$$\frac{x^2}{a^2}-\frac{y^2x}{a^2yy'}=1$$

or $-\dfrac{xy}{a^2y'}=1-\dfrac{x^2}{a^2}=\dfrac{a^2-x^2}{a^2}$

$\therefore\quad xy+(a^2-x^2)y'=0$

(iii) Ans. (a).

$y=c_1e^{c_2x}\quad\therefore\quad y_1=c_2(c_1e^{c_2x})=c_2y$

$\therefore\quad \dfrac{y_1}{y}=c_2$. Differentiating again, we get

$$\frac{yy_2-(y_1)^2}{(y)^2}=0\quad\therefore\quad yy_2=(y_1)^2\Rightarrow\text{(a)}$$

17. (a) $\theta=\cos^{-1}x\ \therefore\ \dfrac{d\theta}{dx}=-\dfrac{1}{\sqrt{1-x^2}}$ ...(1)

$$\frac{dy}{dx}=\frac{dy}{d\theta}\cdot\frac{d\theta}{dx}=-\frac{1}{\sqrt{1-x^2}}\frac{dy}{d\theta}$$

$$\sqrt{1-x^2}\,\frac{dy}{dx}=-\frac{dy}{d\theta}.$$

Differentiate, w.r.t. x

$$\therefore\quad \sqrt{1-x^2}\,\frac{d^2y}{dx^2}+\frac{dy}{dx}\frac{(-2x)}{2\sqrt{1-x^2}}=-\frac{d^2y}{d\theta^2}\cdot\frac{d\theta}{dx}$$

$$=\frac{d^2y}{d\theta^2}\cdot\frac{1}{\sqrt{1-x^2}}\qquad\text{by (1)}$$

$$\therefore\quad (1-x^2)\frac{d^2y}{dx^2}-x\frac{dy}{dx}=\frac{d^2y}{d\theta^2}$$

Add y to both sides

$$\therefore\quad \frac{d^2y}{d\theta^2}+y=0$$

(b) Ans. (c).

Differentiating the given relation,

$$\frac{dy}{dx}=\frac{1}{m\cos^{-1}x}\cdot\frac{-m}{\sqrt{1-x^2}}.\qquad\text{Square}$$

$$\therefore\quad (1-x^2)\left(\frac{dy}{dx}\right)^2=\frac{1}{(\cos^{-1}x)^2}\qquad\text{...(1)}$$

Now $e^y=m\cos^{-1}x\quad\therefore\quad \dfrac{1}{(\cos^{-1}x)^2}=m^2e^{-2y}$

Putting in (1), $(1-x^2)\left(\dfrac{dy}{dx}\right)^2=m^2e^{-2y}$

Differentiating again

$$(1-x^2)\cdot 2\left(\frac{dy}{dx}\right)\frac{d^2y}{dx^2}-2x\left(\frac{dy}{dx}\right)^2=-2m^2e^{-2y}\frac{dy}{dx}$$

Cancel $2\left(\dfrac{dy}{dx}\right)$.

or $(1-x^2)\dfrac{d^2y}{dx^2}-x\dfrac{dy}{dx}=-m^2e^{-2y}=ke^{-2y}$

Hence $k=-m^2\Rightarrow$(c).

18. (a) $z=\log\tan\dfrac{x}{2}\ \therefore\ \dfrac{dz}{dx}=\text{cosec}\,x$ ...(1)

$\because\quad \displaystyle\int\text{cosec}\,x\,dx=\log\tan\frac{x}{2}$

$\therefore\quad \dfrac{d}{dx}\left(\log\tan\dfrac{x}{2}\right)=\text{cosec}\,x$

$$\frac{dy}{dx}=\frac{dy}{dz}\cdot\frac{dz}{dx}=\text{cosec}\,x\frac{dy}{dz}=\frac{1}{\sin x}\frac{dy}{dz}$$

$$\sin x\frac{dy}{dx}=\frac{dy}{dz}$$

Diff. w. r. t. x

$$\sin x\frac{d^2y}{dx^2}+\cos x\frac{dy}{dx}=\frac{d^2y}{dz^2}\cdot\frac{dz}{dx}=\frac{1}{\sin x}\frac{d^2y}{dz^2}$$

$$\therefore\quad \sin^2x\frac{d^2y}{dx^2}+\sin x\cos x\frac{dy}{dx}=\frac{d^2y}{dz^2}$$

or $-4y=\dfrac{d^2y}{dz^2}$ or $\dfrac{d^2y}{dz^2}+4y=0.$

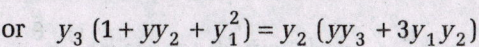

(b) $z = \sin x \quad \therefore \quad \frac{dz}{dx} = \cos x$

$$\therefore \quad \frac{dy}{dx} = \frac{dy}{dz} \cdot \frac{dz}{dx} = \cos x \frac{dy}{dz}$$

$$\frac{d^2 y}{dx^2} = -\sin x \frac{dy}{dz} + \cos x \cdot \frac{d^2 y}{dz^2} (\cos x)$$

Putting the values of $\frac{d^2 y}{dx^2}$ and $\frac{dy}{dx}$ in the given equation, we get

$$\cos x \left[-\sin x \frac{dy}{dz} + \cos^2 x \frac{d^2 y}{dz^2} \right]$$
$$+ \sin x \left(\cos x \frac{dy}{dx} \right) - 2y \cos^3 x = 2 \cos^5 x$$

or $\quad \cos^3 x \frac{d^2 y}{dz^2} - 2y \cos^3 x = 2 \cos^3 x (1 - \sin^2 x)$

or $\quad \frac{d^2 y}{dz^2} - 2y = 2(1 - z^2)$

19. $t = \log \tan x$

$$\therefore \quad \frac{dt}{dx} = \frac{1}{\tan x} \cdot \sec^2 x = \frac{1}{\sin x \cos x}$$

$$= \frac{2}{\sin 2x}$$

$$\frac{dy}{dx} = \frac{dy}{dt} \cdot \frac{dt}{dx} = \frac{2}{\sin 2x} \cdot \frac{dy}{dt}$$

$$\therefore \quad \sin 2x \cdot \frac{dy}{dx} = 2 \frac{dy}{dt}$$

Differentiate again w.r.t. x

$$2 \cos 2x \frac{dy}{dx} + \sin 2x \frac{d^2 y}{dx^2} = 2 \frac{d^2 y}{dt^2} \left[\frac{2}{\sin 2x} \right]$$

$$\therefore \quad 2 \sin 2x \cdot \cos 2x \frac{dy}{dx} + \sin^2 2x \cdot \frac{d^2 y}{dx^2} = 4 \frac{d^2 y}{dt^2}$$

Add $4y$ to both sides

or $\quad \sin^2 2x \frac{d^2 y}{dx^2} + \sin 4x \frac{dy}{dx} + 4y = 4 \frac{d^2 y}{dt^2} + 4y$

or $\quad 0 = 4 \left(\frac{d^2 y}{dt^2} + y \right) \quad$ or $\quad \frac{d^2 y}{dt^2} + y = 0$

20. $\frac{dy}{dx} = \frac{dy}{d\theta} \div \frac{dx}{d\theta} = \frac{k \cos k\theta}{\cos \theta}$

$$\therefore \quad \frac{d^2 y}{dx^2} = \frac{d}{dx} \left(\frac{k \cos k\theta}{\cos \theta} \right)$$

$$= \frac{d}{d\theta} \left(\frac{k \cos k\theta}{\cos \theta} \right) \frac{d\theta}{dx}$$

$$= k \frac{\cos \theta (-k \sin k\theta) - \cos k\theta (-\sin \theta)}{\cos^2 \theta} \cdot \frac{1}{\cos \theta}$$

Multiply by $\cos^2 \theta = 1 - x^2$

$$(1 - x^2) \frac{d^2 y}{dx^2} = -k^2 \sin k\theta + k \cos k\theta \frac{\sin \theta}{\cos \theta}$$

$$= -k^2 y + \left(\frac{dy}{dx} \right) x$$

$$\therefore \quad (1 - x^2) \frac{d^2 y}{dx^2} - x \frac{dy}{dx} + k^2 y = 0$$

§ 4. Ordinary differential equations of the first order and first degree.

An ordinary differential equation of the first order and first degree is of the form

$$M + N \frac{dy}{dx} = 0 \quad \text{or} \quad M\, dx + N\, dy = 0$$

where M and N are functions of x and y or constants. The general solution of such equation will contain only one arbitrary constant.

Note : We cannot always solve such equations. In some special cases the solution is found as follows :

Case I. VARIABLES SEPARABLE

Equations which are capable of being put in the form $f(x)\, dx + \phi(y)\, dy = 0$ will be termed as **Variables Separable.**

In other words, all such equations in which it is possible to get dx and all the terms involving x on one side and dy along with all the terms involving y on the other side will be termed as Variables Separable.

Such equations will be solved by integrating and adding one constant in any side.

Hence complete general solution of

$$f(x)\, dx + \phi(y)\, dy = 0$$

will be $\int f(x)\, dx + \int \phi(y)\, dy =$ a constant.

Solved Examples

Ex. 1. Solve $\frac{dy}{dx} = \frac{1 + y^2}{1 + x^2}$.

or $\quad \frac{dy}{1 + y^2} = \frac{dx}{1 + x^2}$. Variables have been separated.

Integrating both sides and adding a constant, we get

$$\tan^{-1} y = \tan^{-1} x + c \quad \text{or} \quad \tan^{-1} y - \tan^{-1} x = c$$

$$\tan^{-1} \frac{(y - x)}{1 + yx} = c; \qquad \therefore \quad \frac{y - x}{1 + yx} = \tan c = k$$

or $\quad y - x = k(1 + yx)$.

Note : We shall try our best to put the answer in its simplest form for which the constant of integration c shall be made to take any form i.e. it can be taken as $\log k, \sin k, \tan k$ or e^k and so on.

***Ex. 2.** $\quad \frac{ds}{dx} + x^2 = x^2 e^{3s}$

or $\quad \frac{ds}{dx} = x^2 (e^{3s} - 1); \quad \therefore \quad \int \frac{ds}{e^{3s} - 1} = \int x^2\, dx$

or $\int \frac{e^{-3s}}{1-e^{-3s}} ds = \int x^2 dx.$

Integrating, $\frac{1}{3}\log(1-e^{-3s}) = \frac{x^3}{3} + c;$

$\log(1-e^{-3s}) = x^3 + k$

or $(1-e^{-3s}) = e^{x^3+k} = e^{x^3}.e^k = Ae^{x^3}$

Ex. 3. $y - x\frac{dy}{dx} = a\left(y^2 + \frac{dy}{dx}\right).$

or $(y - ay^2) = (x+a)\frac{dy}{dx}$ $\quad\therefore\quad \frac{dy}{y(1-ay)} = \frac{dx}{x+a}$

$\left(\frac{1}{y} + \frac{a}{1-ay}\right)dy = \frac{dx}{x+a}$ P.F.'s.

Integrate $\log y - \log(1-ay) = \log(x+a) + c$

or $\log\frac{y}{1-ay} = \log k(x+a);\quad c = \log k$

$\therefore\quad y = k(1-ay)(x+a).$

Ex. 4. (a) $\frac{dy}{dx} = \frac{x(2\log x + 1)}{\sin y + y\cos y},$

(b) $\frac{dy}{dx} = \frac{\sin x + x\cos x}{y(2\log y + 1)}$

(a) $(y\cos y + \sin y)\,dy = (2x\log x + x)\,dx$

$y\sin y - \int \sin y\,dy + \int \sin y\,dy$

$= x^2\log x - \int x^2 \cdot \frac{1}{x}dx + \int x\,dx + c$

$\therefore\quad y\sin y = x^2\log x + c;$

(b) $x\sin x = y^2\log y + c.$

***Ex 5.** $(x-y)^2\frac{dy}{dx} = a^2.$

Put $x - y = v.$ $\quad\therefore\quad 1 - \frac{dy}{dx} = \frac{dv}{dx}$

or $1 - \frac{dv}{dx} = \frac{dy}{dx}$

$\therefore\quad (v^2)\left\{1 - \frac{dv}{dx}\right\} = a^2$ or $v^2 - a^2 = v^2\frac{dv}{dx}$

$\therefore\quad dx = \frac{v^2 dv}{v^2 - a^2} = \left(\frac{v^2 - a^2 + a^2}{v^2 - a^2}\right)dv$

$= \left(1 + \frac{a^2}{v^2 - a^2}\right)dv.$ Now integrate.

$x + c = v + a^2\frac{1}{2a}\log\frac{v-a}{v+a}$

Putting $v = x - y$, we get

$2y + k = a\log\frac{x-y-a}{x-y+a}$

***Ex. 6. (a)** $\frac{dy}{dx} = \sin(x+y) + \cos(x+y)$

$\frac{dv}{dx} = 1 + \cos v + \sin v$ where $v = x + y.$

$dx = \frac{dv}{1 + \cos v + \sin v} = \frac{dv}{2\cos^2\frac{v}{2} + 2\sin\frac{v}{2}\cos\frac{v}{2}}$

or $dx = \frac{\frac{1}{2}\sec^2\frac{v}{2}}{\left(1 + \tan\frac{v}{2}\right)}dv$

Integrate and put $v = x + y.$

$\log\left(1 + \tan\frac{x+y}{2}\right) = x + c.$

(b) $(y+x)^2\frac{dy}{dx} - 2(y+x)^2 + 3 = 0$

Put $y + x = v$ $\quad\therefore\quad \frac{dy}{dx} + 1 = \frac{dv}{dx}$

$\therefore\quad v^2\left[\frac{dv}{dx} - 1\right] - 2v^2 + 3 = 0$

or $v^2\frac{dv}{dx} = 3(v^2 - 1)$ or $\frac{v^2}{v^2 - 1}dv = 3\,dx$

or $\left(1 + \frac{1}{v^2 - 1}\right)dv = 3\,dx.$ Integrating

$v + \frac{1}{2}\log\frac{v-1}{v+1} = 3x + c$

$\frac{1}{2}\log\frac{v-1}{v+1} = 3x + c - x - y = 2x - y + c$

$\therefore\quad \frac{v-1}{v+1} = e^{4x-2y+2c}$

or $\frac{x+y-1}{x+y+1} = k.e^{4x-2y}$, taking $e^{2c} = k.$

(c) $\frac{dy}{dy} - x\tan(y-x) = 1$

Put $y - x = v$ $\quad\therefore\quad \frac{dy}{dx} = \frac{dv}{dx} + 1$

$\therefore\quad \frac{dv}{dx} + 1 - x\tan v = 1$

or $\cot v\,dv = x\,dx.$ Integrate

$\log\sin v = \frac{x^2}{2} + \log k$

$\therefore\quad \sin v = k\,e^{x^2/2}$

Problem Set (2)

Variables separable.

Solve the following differential equations :

1. $(1-x)\,dy - (3+y)\,dx = 0.$

2. (a) $(e^y + 1)\cos x\,dx + e^y\sin x\,dy = 0$

   (b) $(e^x + 1)\,y\,dy = (y+1)\,e^x\,dx.$

3. (a) $\sec^2 x\tan y\,dx + \sec^2 y\tan x\,dy = 0.$

   (b) $\tan y\,dx + \tan x\,dy = 0.$ **(Karnataka C.E.E. 1999)**

(c) If $y = y(x)$ and $\frac{2+\sin x}{y+1}\left(\frac{dy}{dx}\right) = -\cos x$, $y(0) = 1$, then $y(\pi/2)$ equals

(a) 1/3 (b) 2/3
(c) − 1/3 (d) 1 **(Screening 2004)**

4. (a) $\frac{dy}{dx} = e^{x-y} + x^2 e^{-y}$.

(b) $e^{x-y}\,dx + e^{y-x}\,dy = 0$

(c) $\frac{dy}{dx} = e^{x+y} + x^2 e^{x^3+y}$

5. (a) $x\cos^2 y\,dx = y\cos^2 x\,dy$

(b) $(1-x^2)(1-y)\,dx = xy(1+y)\,dy$.

6. (a) $a\left(x\frac{dy}{dx} + 2y\right) = xy\frac{dy}{dx}$

(b) $y\,dx - x\,dy = xy\,dx$

7.* $\frac{dy}{dx} + \sqrt{\left(\frac{1-y^2}{1-x^2}\right)} = 0$.

8. (a) $\frac{dy}{dx} = \frac{xy+y}{xy+x}$

(b) $(1+x)\,y\,dx + (1+y)\,x\,dy = 0$

9. (a) $(x^2 - yx^2)\frac{dy}{dx} + (y^2 + xy^2) = 0$

(b) $(xy^2 + x)\,dx + (yx^2 + y)\,dy = 0$.

(c) $y - x\frac{dy}{dx} = b\left(1 + x^2\frac{dy}{dx}\right)$.

10. (a) $3e^x \tan y\,dx + (1-e^x)\sec^2 y\,dy = 0$,

(b) $y\sec^2 x + (y+7)\tan x\frac{dy}{dx} = 0$

11. (a) $xy\frac{dy}{dx} = \frac{1+y^2}{1+x^2}(1+x+x^2)$

(b) $\log\frac{dy}{dx} = ax + by$

12. (a) $\frac{dy}{dx}\tan y = \sin(x+y) + \sin(x-y)$

(b) $\frac{dy}{dx} + \sin\left(\frac{x+y}{2}\right) = \sin\left(\frac{x-y}{2}\right)$

13. (a)* $(e^x+1)\,y\,dy + (y+1)\,dx = 0$

(b) $(2ax + x^2)\frac{dy}{dx} = a^2 + 2ax$

(c) $\frac{dy}{dx} = \frac{1+y^2}{(1+x^2)\,xy}$

14. (a) $(x+y)^2\frac{dy}{dx} = a^2$

(b)* $(3x+4y-5)^2\frac{dy}{dx} = a^2$

15. $\cos(x+y)\,dy = dx$.

16.* $\sin^{-1}\left(\frac{dy}{dx}\right) = x + y$

17. (a) The equation of the curve through the point (1, 0) whose slope is $\frac{y-1}{x^2+x}$ is :

(a) $(y-1)(x+1) + 2x = 0$
(b) $2x(y-1) + x + 1 = 0$
(c) $x(y-1)(x+1) + 2 = 0$
(d) $x(y+1) + y(x+1) = 0$ **(AIEEE 2002)**

(b).* Determine the equation of the curve passing through the origin, in the form $y = f(x)$, which satisfies the differential equation $\frac{dy}{dx} = \sin(10x + 6y)$. **(I.I.T. 1996)**

18. (a)* $\frac{dy}{dx} = (4x+y+1)^2$ (b) $\frac{dy}{dx} = (x+y)^2$

19. (a) $\frac{dy}{dx} + 1 = e^{x+y}$ (b) $\frac{dy}{dx} - x\tan(y-x) = 1$

20. (a)* $(1 + x\sqrt{x^2+y^2})\,dx + (-1 + \sqrt{x^2+y^2})\,y\,dy = 0$

(b)* $(3\tan x + 4\cot y - 7)\sin^2 y\,dx$
$- (4\tan x + 7\cot y - 5)\cos^2 x\,dy = 0$

Remember the following results to be used directly

(a)	$d\left(\frac{x}{y}\right) = \frac{y\,dx - x\,dy}{y^2}$
(b)	$d\left(\frac{y}{x}\right) = \frac{x\,dy - y\,dx}{x^2}$
(c)	$d(x^2+y^2) = 2(x\,dx + y\,dy)$
(d)	$d(x^2-y^2) = 2(x\,dx - y\,dy)$
(e)	$d(xy) = x\,dy + y\,dx$
(f)	$d\{\log(xy)\} = \frac{x\,dy + y\,dx}{xy}$
(g)	$d\left\{\log\left(\frac{x}{y}\right)\right\} = \frac{y\,dx - x\,dy}{xy}$
(h)	$d\{\log(x^2+y^2)\} = 2\left\{\frac{x\,dx + y\,dy}{x^2+y^2}\right\}$
(i)	$d\left\{\tan^{-1}\left(\frac{x}{y}\right)\right\} = \frac{y\,dx - x\,dy}{x^2+y^2}$
(j)	$d\left\{\tan^{-1}\left(\frac{y}{x}\right)\right\} = \frac{x\,dy - y\,dx}{x^2+y^2}$

21. (a) The solution of the differential equation $y\,dx + (x + x^2y)\,dy = 0$ is :

(a) $-\frac{1}{xy} = c$ (b) $-\frac{1}{xy} + \log y = c$
(c) $\frac{1}{xy} + \log y = c$ (d) $\log y = cx$ **(AIEEE 2004)**

(b) Solution of the differential equation $\frac{dy}{dx}=\frac{y(x-y\log y)}{x(x\log x-y)}$ is :

(a) $\frac{\log x}{x}-\frac{\log y}{y}=c$

(b) $\frac{\log x}{x}+\frac{\log y}{y}=c$

(c) $\frac{x\log x+y\log y}{xy}=c$

(d) $\frac{x\log x-y\log y}{xy}=c$

(c) The solution of the differential equation

$$\left\{y\left(1+\frac{1}{x}\right)+\sin y\right\}dx$$

$$+\{x+\log x+x\cos y\}\,dy=0 \text{ is :}$$

(a) $y+x\log x+x\sin y=c$

(b) $x+y\log x+y\sin x=c$

(c) $xy+y\log x+x\sin y=c$

(d) $xy+x\log x+y\sin y=c$

22. (a)* $x\,dy-y\,dx=\sqrt{(x^2\pm y^2)}\,dx$

(b) $x\,dy-y\,dx=(x^2+y^2)\,dx$

(c)* $\frac{x\,dx+y\,dy}{x\,dy-y\,dx}=\sqrt{\left(\frac{a^2-x^2-y^2}{x^2+y^2}\right)}$.

(d)* $\frac{x\,dx-y\,dy}{x\,dy-y\,dx}=\sqrt{\left\{\frac{1+x^2-y^2}{x^2-y^2}\right\}}$

23. (a)* $x\,dx+y\,dy+\frac{x\,dy-y\,dx}{x^2+y^2}=0$

(b)* $\cos\left(\frac{x}{y}\right)(y\,dx-x\,dy)=xy^3\,(x\,dy+y\,dx)$

(c) $x\cos\frac{y}{x}(y\,dx+x\,dy)=y\sin\frac{y}{x}(x\,dy-y\,dx)$

(d) $x\sin\left(\frac{y}{x}\right)dy=\left\{y\sin\left(\frac{y}{x}\right)-x\right\}dx$

(e) $(1+e^{x/y})\,dx+e^{x/y}\,(1-x/y)\,dy=0$

24. (a)* Find the equation of the curve satisfying the differential equation $y(x+y^3)\,dx=x(y^3-x)\,dy$, and passing through the point (4,2).

(b) $\frac{x+y\frac{dy}{dx}}{y-x\frac{dy}{dx}}=x^2+2y^2+\frac{y^4}{x^2}$

(c) $\frac{dy}{dx}+\frac{y}{x}=\frac{1}{(1+\log x+\log y)^2}$

25. (a) $\frac{x+y\frac{dy}{dx}}{y-x\frac{dy}{dx}}=\frac{x\cos^2(x^2+y^2)}{y^3}$

(b) $x\,dy\,(y^2e^{xy}+e^{x/y})=y\,dx\,(e^{x/y}-y^2e^{xy})$

(c) $ye^{x/y}\,dx=(xe^{x/y}+y^2\sin y)\,dy$

26. (a)* $\left(\frac{x+y-a}{x+y-b}\right)\frac{dy}{dx}=\frac{x+y+a}{x+y+b}$.

(b) Solve the following differential equation : $(x^2+4y^2+4xy)\,dy=(2x+4y+1)\,dx$.

(Roorkee 1999)

27.* Find the equation of the curve which passes through the point (α,α) and satisfies the differential equation

$$y-x\frac{dy}{dx}=\alpha\left(y^2+x^2\frac{dy}{dx}\right)$$

28.* Solve the following equation

$$x\left(\frac{dy}{dx}\right)^2+(y-x)\frac{dy}{dx}-y=0$$

(M.N.R. 1997)

29. (a) $y(2xy+1)\,dx+x(1+2xy+x^2y^2)\,dy=0$

(b) Solve the differential equation $e^{dy/dx}=x+1$ given that when $x=0$, $y=3$.

30. (a) A curve passing through the point (1, 1) is such that the intercept made by a tangent to it on x-axis is three times the x co-ordinate of the point of tangency, then the equation of the curve is :

(a) $y=\frac{1}{x^2}$ (b) $y=\sqrt{x}$

(c) $y=\frac{1}{\sqrt{x}}$ (d) none

(b) A curve passes through (1, 1) and any tangent at a point P on the curve is such that it intersect x and y axes at A and B respectively. If $PA:PB=3:1$, then differential equation of the curve is :

(a) $xy'-3y=0$

(b) $xy'+x^2=0$

(c) $xy'+3y=0$

(d) Curve passes through $\left(2,\frac{1}{8}\right)$

(I.I.T. 2006)

(c) One Indian and four American men and their wives are to be seated randomly around a cicular table. Then the conditional probability that the Indian man is seated adjacent to his wife given than each American man is seated adjacent to his wife is

(1) $\frac{1}{2}$ (b) $\frac{1}{3}$

(c) $\frac{2}{5}$ (d) $\frac{1}{5}$

(I.I.T. 2007)

31. The solution of the differential equation

$$\left(\frac{dy}{dx}\right)^2+2y\cot x\frac{dy}{dx}-y^2=0 \text{ is } y=\frac{k}{1+\cos x}$$

or $y=-k(1-\cos x)$.

Solutions to Problem Set (2)

1. By a little simplification it can be put in the form

$$\frac{dy}{3+y} = \frac{dx}{1-x}$$

in which the variables have been separated. Its general solution will be obtained by integrating both sides and adding a constant.

$$\int \frac{dy}{3+y} = \int \frac{dx}{1-x} + c$$

or $\log(3+y) = -\log(1-x) + c$,

or $\log(3+y) + \log(1-x) = c$,

or $\log(3+y)(1-x) = c$ or $\log k$.

$\therefore$ $(3+y)(1-x) = k$ is the required solution.

c being arbitrary constant, can be put equal to $\log k$ for the sake of simplification.

2. (a) $\therefore$ $\frac{\cos x}{\sin x} dx + \frac{e^y}{e^y+1} dy = 0$. Integrate

$\log \sin x + \log(e^y + 1) = \log c$

or $\sin x (e^y + 1) = c$.

(b) $y - \log(y+1) = \log(e^x + 1) + c$

or $k(y+1)(e^x+1) = e^y$. Taking $c = \log k$.

3. (a) $\tan x \tan y = k$

(b) $\sin x \sin y = c$.

$\because$ $\int \cot x \, dx = \log \sin x$.

(c) Ans. (a) Variables separable

$\frac{1}{y+1} dy = -\frac{\cos x}{2+\sin x} dx$ Integrating

$\log(y+1) + \log k + \log(2+\sin x) = 0$

$\therefore$ $k(y+1)(2+\sin x) = 1$ when $x = 0, y = 1$

$\therefore$ $4k = 1$ or $k = 1/4$

$\therefore$ $(y+1)(2+\sin x) = 4$

Now put $x = \pi/2$ $\therefore$ $(y+1).3 = 4$

$\therefore$ $y\left(\frac{\pi}{2}\right) = \frac{4}{3} - 1 = \frac{1}{3}$

4. (a) $e^y \, dy = (e^x + x^2) \, dx$.

Now integrating both sides.

$$e^y = e^x + \frac{x^3}{3} + c.$$

(b) Ans. $e^{2x} + e^{2y} = k$

(c) $e^{-y} dy = (e^x + x^2 e^{x^3}) \, dx$

$\therefore$ $-e^{-y} = e^x + \int x^2 e^{x^3} dx + c$.

Put $x^3 = t$ $\therefore$ $3x^2 \, dx = dt$

$\therefore$ $I = \frac{1}{3} \int e^t \, dt = \frac{1}{3} e^t = \frac{1}{3} e^{x^3}$

$\therefore$ $-e^{-y} = e^x + \frac{1}{3} e^{x^3} + c$.

5. (a) $x \sec^2 x \, dx = y \sec^2 y \, dy$. Integrate by parts

$x \tan x - \int \tan x \, dx = y \tan y - \int \tan y \, dy + c$

$x \tan x - \log \sec x = y \tan y - \log \sec y + c$.

(b) $\frac{1-x^2}{x} dx = \frac{y(1+y)}{1-y} dy$

$\left(\frac{1}{x} - x\right) dx = \left(-y - 2 + \frac{2}{1-y}\right) dy$, by division.

$\therefore$ $\log x - \frac{x^2}{2} = -\frac{y^2}{2} - 2y - 2\log(1-y) + k$

6. (a) $\frac{(a-y)}{y} dy = -\frac{2a}{x} dx$ or $\frac{a}{y} dy + \frac{2a}{x} dx = dy$

Integrating, we get $a \log y + a \log x^2 = y + c$

$\log yx^2 = \frac{y+c}{a}$;

$\therefore$ $yx^2 = e^{(y+c)/a} = ke^{y/a}$.

(b) $y(1-x) \, dx = x \, dy$

Ans. $x = ky \, e^x$.

7. $\sin^{-1} y + \sin^{-1} x = c$.

8. (a) $\frac{y+1}{y} dy = \frac{x+1}{x} dx$,

or $\left(1 + \frac{1}{y}\right) dy = \left(1 + \frac{1}{x}\right) dx$

$y + \log y = x + \log x + \log k$

$\therefore$ $y - x = \log \frac{kx}{y}$

(b) $\log xy + (x+y) = c$.

9. (a) $x^2(1-y)\frac{dy}{dx} + y^2(1+x) = 0$

or $\frac{1-y}{y^2} dy + \frac{1+x}{x^2} dx = 0$

or $\left(\frac{1}{y^2} - \frac{1}{y}\right) dy + \left(\frac{1}{x^2} + \frac{1}{x}\right) dx = 0$. Integrate

$\log x - \log y - \left(\frac{1}{x} + \frac{1}{y}\right) = c = \log k$ say

or $\log \frac{x}{ky} = \frac{x+y}{xy}$

(b) Ans. $(x^2+1)(y^2+1) = c$

$\because$ $\int \frac{2x}{1+x^2} dx = \log(1+x^2)$

(c) $y = k(y-b)(1+bx)$.

10. (a) Ans. $(e^x - 1)^3 = k \tan y$

(b) $\log \tan x + 7 \log y + y = c$

or $\log y^7 \tan x e^y = \log k$

or $y^7 \tan x = ke^{-y}$.

11. (a) $\int \frac{y \, dy}{1+y^2} = \int \frac{1}{x} \cdot \frac{1+x^2+x}{1+x^2} = \int \frac{1}{x}\left(1 + \frac{x}{1+x^2}\right) dx$

$\frac{1}{2}\log(1+y^2)=\log x+\tan^{-1}x+c.$

(b) $\frac{dy}{dx}=e^{ax+by}=e^{ax}.e^{by}$

or $e^{-by}\,dy=e^{ax}\,dx$

$\therefore\quad -\frac{1}{b}e^{-by}=\frac{1}{a}e^{ax}+c$

12. (a) $\tan y\,dy=2\sin x\cos y\,dx.$

or $\sec y\tan y\,dy=2\sin x\,dx.$ Integrate

or $\sec y=-2\cos x+c$

(b) $\frac{dy}{dx}=-2\cos\frac{x}{2}\sin\frac{y}{2}$

or $\int\operatorname{cosec}\frac{y}{2}\,dy=\int-2\cos\frac{x}{2}\,dx$

or $\log\tan\frac{y}{4}=c-2\sin\frac{x}{2}$

13. (a) Here $\frac{y}{y+1}dy+\frac{1}{e^x+1}dx=0$

or $\left(1-\frac{1}{y+1}\right)dy+\frac{e^{-x}}{1+e^{-x}}dx.$ Integrate

$y-\log(y+1)-\log(1+e^{-x})=c=\log k$

or $y=\log k\,(y+1)(1+e^{-x})$

or $e^y=k\,(y+1)\left(\frac{1+e^x}{e^x}\right)$

or $e^{x+y}=k\,(y+1)(1+e^x).$

(b) $dy=\frac{a(a+2x)}{x(x+2a)}dx$ Split into P.F.s.

or $dy=\frac{a}{2}\left[\frac{1}{x}+\frac{3}{x+2a}\right]dx.$ Integrate

$y+k=\frac{a}{2}[\log x+3\log(x+2a)]$

(c) $\frac{y}{1+y^2}dy=\frac{dx}{x(1+x^2)}$

or $\frac{y}{1+y^2}dy=\left(\frac{1}{x}-\frac{x}{1+x^2}\right)dx$

$\frac{2y}{1+y^2}dy+\frac{2x}{1+x^2}dx=\frac{2}{x}dx.$ Integrate

$\log(1+y^2)+\log(1+x^2)=2\log x+\log k$

or $(1+x^2)(1+y^2)=kx^2.$

Miscellaneous Type

14. (a) Put $x+y=v$ and as in **Ex. 5 P. 1621**

$\therefore\quad dx=\frac{v^2+a^2-a^2}{v^2+a^2}dv=\left(1-\frac{a^2}{v^2+a^2}\right)dv.$

$x+y=a\tan\left(\frac{y-c}{a}\right)$

(b) Put $3x+4y-5=v$

$\therefore\quad 3+4\frac{dy}{dx}=\frac{dv}{dx}$

$\therefore\quad v^2\left[\frac{dv}{dx}-3\right]=4a^2$

or $v^2\frac{dv}{dx}=3v^2+4a^2$

or $\frac{3v^2}{3v^2+4a^2}dv=3\,dx$

or $\left(1-\frac{4a^2}{3v^2+4a^2}\right)dv=3x+c$

Integrating, $v-\frac{4a^2}{\sqrt{3}}.\frac{1}{2a}\tan^{-1}\frac{v\sqrt{3}}{2a}=3x+c$

or $3x+4y-5-\frac{2a}{\sqrt{3}}\tan^{-1}\frac{v\sqrt{3}}{2a}=3x+c$

or $4y+\lambda=\frac{2a}{\sqrt{3}}\tan^{-1}\frac{(3x+4y-5)\sqrt{3}}{2a}.$

15. $\cos(x+y)\frac{dy}{dx}=1.$ Put $x+y=v.$

$\therefore\quad dx=\frac{\cos v}{1+\cos v}dv=\left(1-\frac{1}{1+\cos v}\right)dv$

or $dx=\left(1-\frac{1}{2}\sec^2\frac{v}{2}\right)dv,\quad\therefore\quad x+c=v-\tan\frac{v}{2}.$

Now replace v by $(x+y)$

$\therefore\quad y-c=\tan\left(\frac{x+y}{2}\right)$

16. $\frac{dy}{dx}=\sin(x+y).$ Put $x+y=v.$

$\therefore\quad \frac{dv}{dx}=1+\sin v=\cos^2\frac{v}{2}+\sin^2\frac{v}{2}+2\sin\frac{v}{2}\cos\frac{v}{2}$

$\frac{dv}{\left(\cos\frac{v}{2}+\sin\frac{v}{2}\right)^2}=dx$ or $\frac{\sec^2\frac{v}{2}}{\left(1+\tan\frac{v}{2}\right)^2}dv=dx$

Integrating, $\left\{\frac{-2}{\left(1+\tan\frac{v}{2}\right)}\right\}=x+c.$

Put $v=x+y.$

17. (a) Ans. (a).

$\frac{dy}{dx}=\frac{y-1}{x(x+1)}.$ Variables separable

$\therefore\quad \frac{dy}{y-1}=\frac{1}{x(x+1)}dx=\left(\frac{1}{x}-\frac{1}{x+1}\right)dx$

$\therefore\quad \log(y-1)=\log x-\log(x+1)+c$

$\log\frac{(y-1)(x+1)}{x}=\log k$

$\therefore\quad (x+1)(y-1)=kx.$ It passes through $(1,0)$

$\therefore\quad -2=k\qquad\therefore\quad k=-2$

$\therefore\quad (x+1)(y-1)+2x=0$

(b) Put $10x+6y=v \quad \therefore \quad 10+6\dfrac{dy}{dx}=\dfrac{dv}{dx}$

$\therefore \quad \dfrac{dv}{dx}-10=6\sin v \quad \therefore \quad \dfrac{dv}{6\sin v+10}=dx$

or $\quad \dfrac{dv}{12\sin\frac{v}{2}\cos\frac{v}{2}+10}=dx$

Divide above and below by $\cos^2(v/2)$ and put $\tan(v/2)=t$

$\therefore \quad \dfrac{2\,dt}{12t+10(1+t^2)}=dx$ or $\dfrac{dt}{5t^2+6t+5}=dx$

or $\quad \dfrac{dt}{\left(t+\frac{3}{5}\right)^2+\left(\frac{4}{5}\right)^2}=5\,dx$

$\dfrac{5}{4}\tan^{-1}\dfrac{5t+3}{4}=5x+5k$

or $\quad \tan^{-1}\dfrac{5t+3}{4}=4x+c$

At origin $x=0, y=0 \quad \therefore \quad v=0$

$\therefore \quad t=\tan\dfrac{v}{2}=0$

Hence from above $\tan^{-1}\dfrac{3}{4}=c$

$\therefore \quad \tan^{-1}\dfrac{5t+3}{4}-\tan^{-1}\dfrac{3}{4}=4x$

or $\quad \dfrac{\frac{5t+3}{4}-\frac{3}{4}}{1+\frac{5t+3}{4}\cdot\frac{3}{4}}=\tan 4x$

or $\quad \dfrac{20t}{25+15t}=\tan 4x$

or $\quad 4t=(5+3t)\tan 4x$

or $\quad t(4-3\tan 4x)=5\tan 4x$

or $\quad \tan\dfrac{v}{2}=\dfrac{5\tan 4x}{4-3\tan 4x}$

or $\quad \tan(5x+3y)=\dfrac{5\tan 4x}{4-3\tan 4x}$

18. (a) Put $4x+y+1=v; \quad \therefore \quad \dfrac{dy}{dx}=\dfrac{dv}{dx}-4.$

$\dfrac{dv}{v^2+4}=dx.$ Now integrate and put the value of v.

$\dfrac{1}{2}\tan^{-1}\dfrac{v}{2}=x+c.$

or $\quad 4x+y+1=2\tan(2x+k).$

Another form :

If the tangent to a curve at any point (x, y) is known to be inclined at $\tan^{-1}(4x+y+1)^2$ to x-axis, find the equation of the curve.

i.e. $\psi=\tan^{-1}(4x+y+1)^2$

or $\quad \tan\psi=\dfrac{dy}{dx}=(4x+y+1)^2$

(b) Ans. $x+y=\tan(x+c)$.

19. (a) Ans. $-1=(x+c)\,e^{x+y}$

(b) Put $y-x=v$

$\cot v\,dv=x\,dx$ Integrate

or $\quad \sin(y-x)=k\,e^{\frac{1}{2}x^2}$

20. (a) $(dx-y\,dy)+\sqrt{x^2+y^2}\,(x\,dx+y\,dy)=0$

$dx-y\,dy+\frac{1}{2}\sqrt{x^2+y^2}\,(2x\,dx+2y\,dy)=0$

Integrating, $\quad x-\dfrac{y^2}{2}+\dfrac{1}{2}\cdot\dfrac{2}{3}(x^2+y^2)^{3/2}=k.$

(b) Dividing throughout by $\sin^2 y\cos^2 x$, we get

$3\tan x\sec^2 x\,dx-7\sec^2 dx-7\cot y\,\mathrm{cosec}^2\,y\,dy$
$+5\,\mathrm{cosec}^2\,y\,dy$
$+4(\cot y\sec^2 x\,dx-\tan x\,\mathrm{cosec}^2\,y)\,dy=0$

Integrating,

$3\dfrac{\tan^2 x}{2}-7\tan x+7\dfrac{\cot^2 y}{2}-5\cot y$
$+4(\cot y\tan x)=c$

21. (a) Ans. (b).

$y\,dx+x\,dy=-(xy)\,.\,x\,dy$

Divide both sides by x^2y^2

$\therefore \quad \dfrac{y\,dx+x\,dy}{x^2y^2}=-\dfrac{dy}{y}$ or $\dfrac{d(xy)}{x^2y^2}=-\dfrac{dy}{y}.$

Integrating, $\quad -\dfrac{1}{xy}+\log y=c \Rightarrow$ (b)

(b) Ans. (c).

The given equation can be written as

$x^2\log x\,dy-xy\,dy=xy\,dx-y^2\log y\,dx$

Divide by x^2y^2

$\dfrac{\log x}{y^2}dy+\dfrac{\log y}{x^2}dx=\dfrac{1}{xy}(dy+dx)$

R.H.S. $=\dfrac{1}{x^2}\cdot\dfrac{x}{y}dy+\dfrac{1}{y^2}\cdot\dfrac{y}{x}dx$ **(Note)**

$\therefore \quad \dfrac{y\cdot\frac{1}{x}dx-\log x\,.dy}{y^2}+\dfrac{x\cdot\frac{1}{y}dy-\log y\,.dx}{x^2}=0$

$d\left(\dfrac{\log x}{y}\right)+d\left(\dfrac{\log y}{x}\right)=0.$

Integrating, $\quad \dfrac{\log x}{y}+\dfrac{\log y}{x}=c$

or $\quad x\log x+y\log y=cxy$

(c) Ans. (c).

Rearranging the terms of the given equation

$(y\,dx+x\,dy)+\left\{y\cdot\dfrac{1}{x}dx+\log x\,dy\right\}$
$+(\sin y\,dx+x\cos y\,dy)=0$

or $d(xy) + d(y\log x) + d(x\sin y) = 0$

Integrating, $xy + y\log x + x\sin y = c \Rightarrow$ (c)

22. (a) Divide both sides by x^2

$$\frac{x\,dy - y\,dx}{x^2} = \frac{1}{x}\sqrt{\left(1 \pm \frac{y^2}{x^2}\right)}\,dx.$$

Put $\frac{y}{x} = t \quad \therefore \quad \frac{x\,dy - y\,dx}{x^2} = dt$

$\therefore \quad dt = \frac{1}{x}\sqrt{(1 \pm t^2)}\,dx$

$$\frac{dt}{\sqrt{(1 \pm t^2)}} = \frac{1}{x}dx. \quad \text{Integrate}$$

$\sin^{-1} t = \log x + c$

or $\sinh^{-1} t = \log x + c$

$y/x = \sin(\log kx)$

or $y/x = \sinh(\log kx)$

or $y = x\sin(\log kx)$

or $y = x\sinh(\log kx)$

(b) $x^2\,dt = x^2(1 + t^2)\,dx$ where $t = y/x$

Ans. $y = x\tan(x + c)$.

(c) We know that $x\,dx + y\,dy = \frac{1}{2}d(x^2 + y^2)$

$$\frac{x\,dy - y\,dx}{x^2} = d\left(\frac{y}{x}\right)$$

The given equation can be written as

$$\frac{1}{2}\frac{d(x^2 + y^2)}{\sqrt{a^2 - (x^2 + y^2)}} = (x\,dy - y\,dx)\cdot\frac{1}{\sqrt{x^2 + y^2}}$$

$$= \frac{1}{2}\frac{d(x^2 + y^2)}{\sqrt{x^2 + y^2}\sqrt{a^2 - (x^2 + y^2)}} = \frac{x\,dy - y\,dx}{x^2(1 + y^2/x^2)}$$

Put $x^2 + y^2 = t^2$ for L.H.S. and $y/x = z$ for R.H.S.

$$\frac{1}{2}\cdot\frac{2t\,dt}{t\sqrt{a^2 - t^2}} = \frac{1}{1 + z^2}(dz) \quad \text{Integrate.}$$

$$\sin^{-1}\left(\frac{t}{a}\right) = \tan^{-1} z + c$$

or $\sin^{-1}\frac{\sqrt{x^2 + y^2}}{a} = \tan^{-1}\frac{y}{x} + c$

or $r = a\sin(\theta + c)$,

where $\theta = \tan^{-1}\frac{y}{x}$, $r = \sqrt{x^2 + y^2}$

(d) As in part (c) we have,

$$\frac{x\,dx - y\,dy}{\sqrt{(x^2 - y^2)}\sqrt{(1 + x^2 - y^2)}} = \frac{x\,dy - y\,dx}{x^2 - y^2}$$

or $\frac{1}{2}\frac{d(x^2 - y^2)}{\sqrt{(x^2 - y^2)}\sqrt{(1 + x^2 - y^2)}}$

$$= \frac{x\,dy - y\,dx}{x^2}\;\frac{1}{1 - y^2/x^2}$$

Put $x^2 - y^2 = t^2$ in L.H.S., $y/x = z$ in R.H.S.

$$\frac{t\,dt}{t\sqrt{1 + t^2}} = \frac{1}{1 - z^2}dz \quad \text{Integrate.}$$

$$\log[t + \sqrt{1 + t^2}] = \frac{1}{2}\log\frac{1 + z}{1 - z} + c$$

23. (a) The last term can be written as

$$\frac{x\,dy - y\,dx}{x^2}\Big/1 + \left(\frac{y}{x}\right)^2 \quad \text{or} \quad \frac{d(y/x)}{1 + (y/x)^2}$$

$$d\left(\frac{x^2}{2}\right) + d\left(\frac{y^2}{2}\right) + \frac{d(y/x)}{1 + (y/x)^2} = 0$$

Integrating, $\frac{x^2}{2} + \frac{y^2}{2} + \tan^{-1}\frac{y}{x} = \frac{k}{2}$

or $x^2 + y^2 + 2\tan^{-1}(y/x) = c$

(b) $\cos\left(\frac{x}{y}\right)\cdot\frac{y\,dx - x\,dy}{y^2} = xy(x\,dy + y\,dx)$

or $\cos\left(\frac{x}{y}\right).d\left(\frac{x}{y}\right) = xy\,d(xy)$.

Integrating, $\sin\left(\frac{x}{y}\right) = \frac{(xy)^2}{2} + c$

(c) $y\,dx + x\,dy = \frac{y}{x}\tan\frac{y}{x}(x\,dy - y\,dx)$

Dividing both sides by xy

$$\frac{y\,dx + x\,dy}{xy} = \tan\frac{y}{x}\cdot\frac{x\,dy - y\,dx}{x^2}$$

or $\frac{d(xy)}{xy} = \tan\frac{y}{x}\,d\left(\frac{y}{x}\right)$

Integrate both sides

$$\log xy = \log\sec\frac{y}{x} + \log k$$

$$\therefore \quad xy = k\sec\frac{y}{x}$$

(d) Ans. $\log x - \cos\left(\frac{y}{x}\right) = k$

(e) $dx + e^{x/y}\left(dx - \frac{x}{y}dy\right) + e^{x/y}\,dy = 0$

or $dx + e^{x/y}\,\frac{y\,dx - x\,dy}{y} + e^{x/y}\,dy = 0$

or $dx + ye^{x/y}\,d\left(\frac{x}{y}\right) + e^{x/y}\,dy = 0$

or $dx + d\{y.e^{x/y}\}$ by product rule.

Integrating, we get

$$x + ye^{x/y} = C$$

24. (a) $x(y\,dx + x\,dy) = y^3(x\,dy - y\,dx)$

$$x\,d(xy) = y^3x^2\,d\left(\frac{y}{x}\right)$$

$\therefore \quad \dfrac{d(xy)}{x^2y^2} = \dfrac{y}{x} d\left(\dfrac{y}{x}\right)$

Integrating, $-\dfrac{1}{xy} = \dfrac{1}{2}\left(\dfrac{y}{x}\right)^2 + c$

Pass through (4, 2)

$\therefore \quad -\dfrac{1}{8} = \dfrac{1}{8} + c \quad \therefore \; c = -\dfrac{1}{4}$

(b) $\dfrac{x\,dx + y\,dy}{y\,dx - x\,dy} = \dfrac{(x^2+y^2)^2}{x^2}$

or $\dfrac{x\,dx + y\,dy}{(x^2+y^2)^2} = \dfrac{-(x\,dy - y\,dx)}{x^2}$

or $\dfrac{1}{2}\dfrac{2x\,dx + 2y\,dy}{(x^2+y^2)^2} = -d\left(\dfrac{y}{x}\right)$

Now integrating both sides by putting $x^2 + y^2 = v$

$-\dfrac{1}{2}\cdot\dfrac{1}{x^2+y^2} = -\dfrac{y}{x} + c$

or $\dfrac{y}{x} - \dfrac{1}{2(x^2+y^2)} = c$

(c) $x\,dy + y\,dx = \dfrac{x\,dx}{(1+\log xy)^2}$

or $[1+\log(xy)]^2\, d(xy) = x\,dx$

Put $xy = t$ and integrate

$\int 1(1+\log t)^2\, dt = \int x\,dx$

or $t(1+\log t)^2 - \int t \cdot \dfrac{2(1+\log t)}{t}\, dt = \dfrac{x^2}{2} + C$

Now $\int (1+\log t)\, dt = t + [t\log t - t] = t\log t$

$\therefore \quad t(1+\log t)^2 - 2(t\log t) = \dfrac{x^2}{2} + C$

or $t[1 + (\log t)^2 + 2\log t - 2\log t] = \dfrac{x^2}{2} + C$

or $xy[1 + (\log xy)^2] = \dfrac{x^2}{2} + C$

25. (a) The given equation can be written as

$\dfrac{x\,dx + y\,dy}{(y\,dx - x\,dy)/y^2} = y^2 \cdot \dfrac{x}{y^3}\cos^2(x^2+y^2)$

or $\sec^2(x^2+y^2)\dfrac{1}{2}d(x^2+y^2) = \dfrac{x}{y}d\left(\dfrac{x}{y}\right)$

$\dfrac{1}{2}\tan(x^2+y^2) = \dfrac{1}{2}\left(\dfrac{x}{y}\right)^2 + \dfrac{c}{2}$ on integrating

or $\tan(x^2+y^2) = \dfrac{x^2}{y^2} + c$

(b) Collect the terms of e^{xy} and $e^{x/y}$

$y^2 e^{xy}(x\,dy + y\,dx) = e^{x/y}(y\,dx - x\,dy)$

$e^{xy}\, d(xy) = e^{x/y}\, d\left(\dfrac{x}{y}\right)$

Integrating both sides, we have

$e^{xy} = e^{x/y} + c$

or $xy = \log(e^{x/y} + c)$

(c) Proceed as in part (b).

$e^{x/y} = -\cos y + C$

26. (a) Put $x + y = v$; $\therefore \; 1 + \dfrac{dy}{dx} = \dfrac{dv}{dx}$

$\therefore \quad \dfrac{dv}{dx} - 1 = \dfrac{(v+a)(v-b)}{(v-a)(v+b)}$

or $\dfrac{dv}{dx} = \dfrac{(v+a)(v-b)}{(v-a)(v+b)} + 1$

$= 2\dfrac{(v^2-ab)}{v^2+(b-a)v-ab}$.

$\therefore \quad \dfrac{v^2 - ab + (b-a)v}{v^2 - ab}\, dv = 2\,dx$

or $\left(1 + \dfrac{b-a}{2}\cdot\dfrac{2v}{v^2-ab}\right)dv = 2\,dx$.

Integrating, $v + \dfrac{b-a}{2}\log(v^2 - ab) = 2x + c$

or $(b-a)\log\{(x+y)^2 - ab\} = 2(x-y) + k$.

(b) The given equation can be written as

$(x+2y)^2\dfrac{dy}{dx} - 2(x+2y) = 1$

Put $x + 2y = v \quad \therefore \; 1 + 2\dfrac{dy}{dx} = \dfrac{dv}{dx}$

$\therefore \quad \dfrac{v^2}{2}\left[\dfrac{dv}{dx} - 1\right] = 1 + 2v$

$\dfrac{dv}{dx} = \dfrac{2+4v}{v^2} + 1 = \dfrac{v^2+4v+2}{v^2}$

$\therefore$ Variables separable $\dfrac{v^2}{v^2+4v+2}dv = dx$

$v^2 = l(v^2+4v+2) + m(2v+4) + n$

Comparing coefficients $l = 1, m = -2, n = 6$

$\left[1 - 2\dfrac{(2v+4)}{v^2+4v+2} + 6\cdot\dfrac{1}{(v+2)^2 - (\sqrt{2})^2}\right]dv = dx$

Integrating

$v - 2\log(v^2+4v+2) + 6\cdot\dfrac{1}{2\sqrt{2}}\log\left|\dfrac{v+2-\sqrt{2}}{v+2+\sqrt{2}}\right| = x + c$

where $v = x + 2y$.

27. The equation can be re-written as

$y(1-\alpha y) = \dfrac{dy}{dx}x(1+\alpha x)$

$\therefore \quad \dfrac{dy}{y(1-\alpha y)} = \dfrac{dx}{x(1+\alpha x)}$, P.F's.

or $\left(\frac{1}{y}+\frac{\alpha}{1-\alpha y}\right)dy=\left(\frac{1}{x}-\frac{\alpha}{1+\alpha x}\right)dx$

$\log y-\log(1-\alpha y)=\log x-\log(1+\alpha x)+\log k$

$\therefore \quad \frac{y}{1-\alpha y}=k\cdot\frac{x}{1+\alpha x}$.

It passes through (α, α)

$\therefore \quad \frac{\alpha}{1-\alpha^2}=k\cdot\frac{\alpha}{1+\alpha^2}$

$\therefore \quad k=\frac{1+\alpha^2}{1-\alpha^2}$ Put for k

$\therefore \quad \frac{(1-\alpha^2)\,y}{(1-\alpha y)}=\frac{(1+\alpha^2)\,x}{(1+\alpha x)}$

28. $x\frac{dy}{dx}\left[\left(\frac{dy}{dx}\right)-1\right]+y\left(\frac{dy}{dx}-1\right)=0$

or $\left(\frac{dy}{dx}-1\right)\left(x\frac{dy}{dx}+y\right)=0$

$\frac{dy}{dx}=1 \Rightarrow y=x+c_1$

$x\frac{dy}{dx}+y \Rightarrow x\,dy+y\,dx=0$

$\Rightarrow d(xy)=0 \quad \therefore xy=c_2$

Hence the general solution is

$(y-x-c_1)(xy-c_2)=0$

29. (a) $(y\,dx+x\,dy)+2xy\,(y\,dx+x\,dy)+x^3y^2\,dy=0$

$(1+2xy)\,d(xy)+x^3y^2\,dy=0$

Divide both sides by x^3y^3

$\left(\frac{1}{x^3y^3}+\frac{2}{x^2y^2}\right)d(xy)+\frac{dy}{y}=0$

Put $xy=t \quad \therefore d(xy)=dt$

$\left(\frac{1}{t^3}+\frac{2}{t^2}\right)dt+\frac{dy}{y}=0.$

Now integrate $-\frac{1}{2t^2}-\frac{2}{t}+\log y=c$

or $\log y=c+\frac{1}{2x^2y^2}+\frac{2}{xy}$

(b) $\frac{dy}{dx}=\log(x+1)$

$\therefore \quad y=\int \log(x+1)\,dx$. Put $x+1=t$

$y=\int \log t\,dt=t\log t-t+c$

or $y=(x+1)\log(x+1)-(x+1)+c$

Put $x=0, y=3 \quad \therefore c=4$

$\therefore \quad y=(x+1)\log(x+1)-x+3$

30. (a) Ans. (c).

$Y-y=\frac{dy}{dx}(X-x)$

$I_x=x-\frac{y}{dy/dx}=3x$ (given)

$\therefore \quad y\frac{dx}{dy}+2x=0$ or $\frac{dx}{2x}+\frac{dy}{y}=0$

or $\frac{1}{2}\log x+\log y=k$

or $\log\sqrt{x}+\log y=k$ or $\log y\sqrt{x}=k$

$\therefore \quad y\sqrt{x}=e^k=$ constant

$\therefore \quad y=\frac{1}{\sqrt{x}}$ satisfies the above condition as it gives

$y\sqrt{x}=1=$ constant.

(b) Ans. (c), (d).

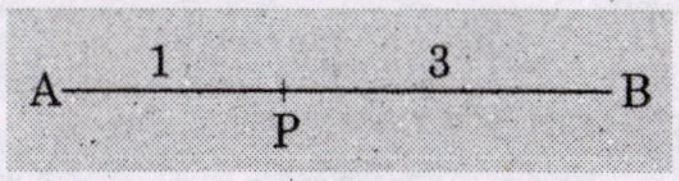

Fig. 1

$Y-y=y'(X-x)$, where $y'=\frac{dy}{dx}$

$\therefore$ A on x-axis is $\left(x-\frac{y}{y'},0\right)$, putting $Y=0$

B on y-axis is $(0, y-xy')$, putting $X=0$.

P on the curve is (x, y).

$\therefore \quad \frac{PA}{PB}=\frac{1}{3}$ or P divides AB in the ratio $1:3$.

$\therefore \quad x=\frac{1.0+3\left(x-\frac{y}{y'}\right)}{3+1}$

or $4x-3x=-\frac{3y}{y'}$

or $xy'+3y=0 \Rightarrow$ (c)

or $\frac{y'}{y}+\frac{3}{x}=0.$ Integrating

$\log y+3\log x=\log k$

$\therefore \quad yx^3=k$

It passes through $(1, 1)$

$\therefore \quad k=1$

Hence $y=\frac{1}{x^3}$.

Then point $\left(2,\frac{1}{8}\right)$ satisfies it.

(c) Ans. (c).

Let $E=$ event when each American man is seated adjacent to his wife

$A=$ event when Indian man is seated adjacent to his wife

Now $n(A\equiv E)=(4!)\times(2!)^5$

Even when each American man is seated adjcent to his wife.

Again $n(E)=(5!)\times(2!)^4$

$\Rightarrow \quad P\left(\frac{A}{E}\right)=\frac{n(A\equiv E)}{n(E)}=\frac{(4!)\times(2!)^5}{(5!)\times(2!)^4}=\frac{2}{5}$

Alternative :

Fixing four American couples and one Indian man in between any two couples; we have 5 different ways in which his wife can be seated, of which 2 cases are favourable.

$\therefore$ required probability $= \frac{2}{5} \Rightarrow$ (c).

31. From the given equation treating as a quadratic in $\frac{dy}{dx}$, we have

$$\frac{dy}{dx} = \frac{-2y\cot x \pm \sqrt{4y^2\cot^2 x + 4y^2}}{2}$$

$$= y\,[-\cot x \pm \operatorname{cosec} x]$$

$$\frac{dy}{dx} = y\,[-\cot x + \operatorname{cosec} x] \text{ or } -y\,(\cot x + \operatorname{cosec} x)$$

$$\frac{dy}{y} = [\operatorname{cosec} x - \cot x]\,dx \text{ or } -(\operatorname{cosec} x + \cot x)\,dx$$

Integrating,

$$\log y = \log\tan\frac{x}{2} - \log\sin x + \log k$$

or $\quad -\left[\log\tan\frac{x}{2} + \log\sin x\right] + \log k$

$$\log\frac{y}{k} = \log\frac{\tan\frac{x}{2}}{\sin x} = \log\frac{\tan\frac{x}{2}}{2\sin\frac{x}{2}\cos\frac{x}{2}} = \log\frac{1}{2\cos^2\frac{x}{2}}$$

$\therefore \quad y = \frac{k}{1+\cos x}$

The other result gives

$$\frac{y}{k} = -\sin x\tan\frac{x}{2} = -2\sin\frac{x}{2}\cos\frac{x}{2}\cdot\frac{\sin\frac{x}{2}}{\cos\frac{x}{2}}$$

or $\quad \frac{y}{k} = -2\sin^2\frac{x}{2} = -(1-\cos x)$

or $\quad y = -k\,(1-\cos x)$

Case II. EXACT DIFFERENTIAL EQUATIONS.

$M\,dx + N\,dy = 0$, where M and N are functions of x and y. If $\frac{\partial M}{\partial y} = \frac{\partial N}{\partial x}$, then the equation is exact and its solution is given by

$$\underset{y \text{ constant}}{\int M\,dx} + \underset{\text{only those terms of } N \text{ which are free from } x}{\int N\,dy} = c$$

Solved Examples

Ex. 1. $(x^2 - 4xy - 2y^2)\,dx + (y^2 - 4xy - 2x^2)\,dy = 0$

Above is a homogeneous equation. But it will be convenient if we solve it by exact equation.

$$\frac{\partial M}{\partial y} = -4x - 4y,\quad \frac{\partial N}{\partial x} = -4y - 4x$$

Since $\frac{\partial M}{\partial y} = \frac{\partial N}{\partial x}$ the equation is exact.

Its solution is

$$\underset{y\text{-constant}}{\int (x^2 - 4xy - 2y^2)\,dx} + \underset{\text{free of } x \text{ terms } i.e.\ y^2}{\int N\,dy} = c$$

$$\frac{x^3}{3} - 2x^2y - 2y^2x + \frac{y^3}{3} = \frac{k}{3}$$

or $\quad x^3 + y^3 - 6xy\,(x+y) = k$

Ex. 2. $\left\{y\left(1+\frac{1}{x}\right) + \cos y\right\}dx + (x + \log x - x\sin y)\,dy = 0$

$$\frac{\partial M}{\partial y} = 1 + \frac{1}{x} - \sin y = \frac{\partial N}{\partial x}$$

$$\underset{y \text{ constant}}{\int\left\{y\left(1+\frac{1}{x}\right) + \cos y\right\}dx} + \underset{\text{only free from } x\ i.e. \text{ none}}{\int N\,dy} = c$$

or $\quad y\,(x + \log x) + x\cos y = c$

Ex. 3. $(1 + e^{x/y})\,dx + e^{x/y}\left(1 - \frac{x}{y}\right)dy = 0$

$$\frac{\partial M}{\partial y} = e^{x/y}\cdot\left(-\frac{x}{y^2}\right).$$

$$\frac{\partial N}{\partial x} = e^{x/y}\cdot\frac{1}{y}\left(1 - \frac{x}{y}\right) + e^{x/y}\left(-\frac{1}{y}\right) = e^{x/y}\left(-\frac{x}{y^2}\right)$$

$\therefore \quad \frac{\partial M}{\partial y} = \frac{\partial N}{\partial x}$ *i.e.* exact

$$\underset{y \text{ constant}}{\int (1 + e^{x/y})\,dx} + \underset{\text{free from } x\ i.e. \text{ none}}{\int N\,dy} = c$$

or $\quad x + ye^{x/y} = c$

Ex. 4. $(y^2e^{xy^2} + 4x^3)\,dx + (2xye^{xy^2} - 3y^2)\,dy = 0$

Ans. $\quad e^{xy^2} + x^4 - y^3 = c$

Ex. 5. $(x^3 + 3xy^2)\,dx + (3x^2y + y^3)\,dy = 0$

Ans. $\quad x^4 + y^4 + 6x^2y^2 = c$

Ex. 6. $\cos x\,(\cos x - \sin a\sin y)\,dx + \cos y\,(\cos y - \sin a\sin x)\,dy = 0$

$$\frac{\partial M}{\partial y} = -\cos x\cos y\sin a = \frac{\partial N}{\partial x} \quad \text{(Exact)}$$

$$\underset{y \text{ constant}}{\int (\cos^2 x - \sin a\sin y\cos x)\,dx} + \underset{\text{free from } x}{\int \cos^2 y\,dy} = c$$

Ans. $2\,(x+y) + \sin 2x + \sin 2y - 4\sin a\sin x\sin y = k$

Case III. HOMOGENEOUS EQUATIONS

When $\frac{dy}{dx}$ is equal to a fraction whose numerator and denominator both are homogeneous functions of x and y of the same degree then the differential equation is said to be homogeneous equation.

$\frac{dy}{dx} = \frac{f\,(x,y)}{\phi\,(x,y)}$ where f and ϕ are both homogeneous functions of x and y of the same degree.

By homogeneous function we mean that function in which the degree of each term is the same

i.e. $\quad 4x^2y, 2xy^2, 7x^3, 3y^3, x^3 + y^3, x^2y + y^3$

are all homogeneous functions of 3rd degree.

Method of Solution :

We shall put $y = vx$. Differentiating w.r.t. x, we get

$$\frac{dy}{dx} = v + x\frac{dv}{dx}.$$

Now substitute the value of dy/dx and y in the given differential equation which will become an equation in terms of v and x in which the variables shall be separable.

Solved Examples

***Ex. 1.** Solve $(x^2 + y^2)\,dx = 2xy\,dy$

$$\frac{x^2 + y^2}{2xy} = \frac{dy}{dx} \quad \text{(Homogeneous). Put } y = vx.$$

$$\therefore \quad \frac{x^2 + v^2x^2}{2x.vx} = v + x\frac{dv}{dx},$$

$$i.e. \quad \frac{1+v^2}{2v} = v + x\frac{dv}{dx}.$$

Note : Instead of putting vx for y everywhere, then cancel out common factor like x^2 in the above; it is better to put $x = 1$ and $y = v$ and we shall get the same result. In future we shall follow this method.

$$\frac{1+v^2}{2v} - v = x\frac{dv}{dx}$$

$$\text{or} \quad \frac{1+v^2-2v^2}{2v} = x\frac{dv}{dx}$$

$$\text{or} \quad \frac{dx}{x} = \frac{2v}{1-v^2}\,dv. \quad \text{Integrate}$$

$$c + \log x = -\log(1-v^2). \text{ Put } c = \log k$$

$$\log kx + \log(1-v^2) = 0$$

$$\text{or} \quad \log kx(1-v^2) = 0; \quad \therefore \quad kx(1-v^2) = e^0 = 1$$

$$\text{or} \quad k(x^2 - y^2) = x, \qquad \because \quad v = y/x.$$

***Ex. 2.** $x^2 y\,dx - (x^3 + y^3)\,dy = 0$

$$\frac{dy}{dx} = \frac{x^2y}{x^3+y^3}. \text{ Put } y = vx.$$

$$v + x\frac{dv}{dx} = \frac{v}{1+v^3} \quad \therefore \quad x\frac{dv}{dx} = \frac{-v^4}{1+v^3}$$

$$\text{or} \quad \left(-\frac{1}{v^4} - \frac{1}{v}\right)dv = \frac{dx}{x}$$

$$\text{or} \quad \frac{1}{3v^3} - \log v = \log x + \log k$$

$$\therefore \quad \log k\,xv = \frac{1}{3v^3} = \frac{x^3}{3y^3} \quad \text{or} \quad ky = e^{x^3/3y^3}.$$

***Ex. 3.** $\dfrac{dy}{dx} + \dfrac{x^2+3y^2}{3x^2+y^2} = 0$

Proceeding as usual, we get

$$\frac{3+v^2}{(1+v)^3}\,dv = -\frac{dx}{x}.$$

$$\text{Put } v + 1 = t, \quad \therefore \quad dv = dt$$

$$\therefore \quad \frac{4+t^2-2t}{t^3}\,dt = -\frac{dx}{x}.$$

$$\text{or} \quad \left\{\frac{4}{(v+1)^3} + \frac{1}{(v+1)} - \frac{2}{(v+1)^2}\right\}dv = -\frac{dx}{x}$$

$$\text{Integrating,} \quad \frac{-2}{(v+1)^2} + \log(v+1) + \frac{2}{(v+1)} = -\log x + c$$

$$\text{or} \quad \frac{2(v+1-1)}{(v+1)^2} = \log\frac{k}{x} - \log(v+1)$$

$$\text{or} \quad \frac{2v}{(v+1)^2} = \log\frac{k}{(v+1)\,x}$$

$$\text{or} \quad \frac{2xy}{(x+y)^2} = \log\frac{k}{(x+y)}$$

***Ex. 4.(a)** $x\cos\dfrac{y}{x}(y\,dx + x\,dy) = y\sin\dfrac{y}{x}(x\,dy - y\,dx)$.

$$\text{or} \quad x\cos\frac{y}{x}\left(y + x\frac{dy}{dx}\right) = y\sin\frac{y}{x}\left(x\frac{dy}{dx} - y\right).$$

$$\frac{dy}{dx}\left(x\cos\frac{y}{x} - y\sin\frac{y}{x}\right) = -y\left(y\sin\frac{y}{x} + x\cos\frac{y}{x}\right).$$

$$\frac{dy}{dx} = \frac{y}{x}\,\frac{\left(y\sin\frac{y}{x} + x\cos\frac{y}{x}\right)}{\left(y\sin\frac{y}{x} - x\cos\frac{y}{x}\right)}. \text{ Put } y = vx \text{ etc.}$$

$$\therefore \quad v + x\frac{dv}{dx} = \frac{v}{1}\,\frac{(v\sin v + \cos v)}{(v\sin v - \cos v)}.$$

$$\text{or} \quad x\frac{dv}{dx} = \frac{v(v\sin v + \cos v)}{v\sin v - \cos v} - v,$$

$$\text{or} \quad x\frac{dv}{dx} = v\left(\frac{v\sin v + \cos v - v\sin v + \cos v}{v\sin v - \cos v}\right)$$

$$\text{or} \quad x\frac{dv}{dx} = \frac{2v\cos v}{v\sin v - \cos v};$$

$$\text{or} \quad \left(\frac{v\sin v - \cos v}{v\cos v}\right)dv = 2\frac{dx}{x}$$

$$\text{or} \quad \left(\tan v - \frac{1}{v}\right)dv = 2\frac{dx}{x}. \quad \text{Integrate}$$

$$\log\sec v - \log v = 2\log x + c,$$

$$\text{or} \quad \log\frac{\sec v}{v} = \log kx^2, \text{ where } c = \log k$$

$$\text{or} \quad \sec v = kvx^2 \quad \text{or} \quad \sec\frac{y}{x} = kxy.$$

Alternate easier method :

We know that

$$x\,dy + y\,dx = d(xy) \quad \text{and} \quad \frac{x\,dy - y\,dx}{x^2} = d\left(\frac{y}{x}\right)$$

The given equation can be written as

$$x\cos\left(\frac{y}{x}\right)d(xy)=\left(y\sin\frac{y}{x}\right)x^2\,d\left(\frac{y}{x}\right)$$

or $d(xy)=xy\tan\left(\frac{y}{x}\right)d\left(\frac{y}{x}\right)$

or $\frac{d(xy)}{xy}=\tan\left(\frac{y}{x}\right)d\left(\frac{y}{x}\right)$ Integrate.

or $\log(xy)+\log k=\log\sec(y/x)$

or $k\,xy=\sec(y/x)$

(b)* Solve the differential equation

$$y\cos\frac{y}{x}(x\,dy-y\,dx)+x\sin\frac{y}{x}(x\,dy+y\,dx)=0$$

when $y(1)=\pi/2$. **(Roorkee 1997)**

$$y\cos\frac{y}{x}\left(x\frac{dy}{dx}-y\right)+x\sin\frac{y}{x}\left(x\frac{dy}{dx}+y\right)=0$$

or $\frac{dy}{dx}\left\{xy\cos\frac{y}{x}+x^2\sin\frac{y}{x}\right\}$

$$=\left(y^2\cos\frac{y}{x}-xy\sin\frac{y}{x}\right)$$

Above is homogeneous

Put $y=vx$

$$v+x\frac{dv}{dx}=\frac{v^2\cos v-v\sin v}{v\cos v+\sin v}$$

$\therefore$ $x\frac{dv}{dx}=\frac{v^2\cos v-v\sin v}{v\cos v+\sin v}-v=\frac{-2v\sin v}{v\cos v+\sin v}$

$\therefore$ $\frac{v\cos v+\sin v}{v\sin v}dv=-\frac{2\,dx}{x}$

or $\left(\cot v+\frac{1}{v}\right)dv+\frac{2}{x}dx=0$

or $\log\sin v+\log v+\log x^2=\log k$

or $vx^2\sin v=k$ or $xy\sin\frac{y}{x}=k$

When $x=1,\ y=\frac{\pi}{2}$ $\therefore$ $k=\frac{\pi}{2}$ $\therefore$ $xy\sin\frac{y}{x}=\frac{\pi}{2}$

Alternative easier method :

The given equation can be written as

$$\frac{x\,dy-y\,dx}{x\,dy+y\,dx}=-\frac{x}{y}\tan\frac{y}{x}$$

or $\frac{(x\,dy-y\,dx)/x^2}{x\,dy+y\,dx}=-\frac{1}{xy}\tan\frac{y}{x}$

or $\cot\left(\frac{y}{x}\right)d\left(\frac{y}{x}\right)+\frac{d(xy)}{(xy)}=0$

Integrating, $\log\sin\frac{y}{x}+\log(xy)=\log k$

$\therefore$ $xy\sin\frac{y}{x}=k$

or $xy\sin\frac{y}{x}=\frac{\pi}{2}$ $\because$ $k=\frac{\pi}{2}$ at $\left(1,\frac{\pi}{2}\right)$

***Ex. 5. (a)** $x\sin\frac{y}{x}\,dy=\left(y\sin\frac{y}{x}-x\right)dx$

The given equation is $\frac{dy}{dx}=\frac{y}{x}-\frac{1}{\sin(y/x)}$

Putting $y=vx$,

$v+x\frac{dv}{dx}=v-\frac{1}{\sin v}$ $\therefore$ $-\sin v\,dv=\frac{dx}{x}$

or $\cos v=\log kx$ or $\cos(y/x)=\log kx$

(b) $\left[xe^{y/x}-y\sin\frac{y}{x}\right]dx+x\sin\frac{y}{x}\,dy=0$

Proceeding as in part (a), we have

$$\sin\frac{y}{x}\frac{dy}{dx}+xe^{y/x}-y\sin\frac{y}{x}=0$$

Homogeneous, put $y=vx$

$$\sin v\left(v+x\frac{dv}{dx}\right)+e^v-v\sin v=0$$

$\therefore$ $x\sin v\frac{dv}{dx}+e^v=0$

$\therefore$ $e^{-v}\sin v\,dx+\frac{dx}{x}=0$. Integrate ...(1)

Let $I=\int e^{-v}\sin v\,dv$

$=e^{-v}(-\cos v)-\int e^{-v}\cos v\,dv$

$=-e^{-v}\cos v-[e^{-v}\sin v+\int e^{-v}\sin v\,dv]$

$\therefore$ $I=-e^{-v}(\sin v+\cos v)-I$

$\therefore$ $I=-\frac{1}{2}e^{-v}(\sin v+\cos v)$ ...(2)

Hence from (1) and (2), we have

$$-\frac{1}{2}e^{-v}(\sin v+\cos v)+\log x+\log k=0$$

or $\frac{1}{2}e^{-y/x}\left(\sin\frac{y}{x}+\cos\frac{y}{x}\right)=\log kx$

Problem Set (3)

Homogeneous equations.

Solve the following differential equations :

1. $(x^2+y^2)\frac{dy}{dx}=xy$.
2. (a) $(x^2-y^2)\,dx+2xy\,dy=0$.

   (b) $2xy\,dy=(x^2+y^2)\,dx$.
3. $2xy\,dx+(y^2-x^2)\,dy=0$.
4. (a) $(x^2+y^2)\,dx+2xy\,dy=0$.

   (b) $(x^2-y^2)\,dx-xy\,dy=0$.
5. (a) $(x^2y-2xy^2)\,dx=(x^3-3x^2y)\,dy$.

6. (a) $(x^2 + xy)\,dy = (x^2 + y^2)\,dx$.

(b) $x(x - y)\,dy + y^2\,dx = 0$.

(c) $x(x - y)\,dy = y(x + y)\,dx$

(d) $\{x\sqrt{(x^2 + y^2)} - y^2\}\,dx + xy\,dy = 0$.

(e) $y^2 dx + (xy + x^2)\,dy = 0$.

7. (a) $(xy + y^2)\,dx + (xy - x^2)\,dy = 0$.

(b) $\dfrac{dy}{dx} = \dfrac{y(x - y)}{x(x + y)}$

(c) $\dfrac{dy}{dx} = \dfrac{y(2y - x)}{x(2y + x)}$ if $y = 1$ when $x = 1$.

(J.E.E. West Bengal 1994)

8.* $y^2 + x^2 \dfrac{dy}{dx} = xy \dfrac{dy}{dx}$ or $y^2\,dx + (x^2 - xy)\,dy = 0$.

9. $x\dfrac{dy}{dx} + \dfrac{y^2}{x} = y$.

10. (a) $x^2\,dy + y(x + y)\,dx = 0$.

(b) $\dfrac{dy}{dx} + \dfrac{y}{x} = \dfrac{y^2}{x^2}$

11. (a) $x^2 \dfrac{dy}{dx} = \dfrac{y(x + y)}{2}$

(b) $\dfrac{dy}{dx} + \dfrac{y(x + y)}{x^2} = 0$

(J.E.E. West Bengal 1995)

12. $(x^2 - y^2)\dfrac{dy}{dx} = xy$,

13. (a) $y - x\dfrac{dy}{dx} = x + y\dfrac{dy}{dx}$

(b) $(x + y)\,dx + (y - x)\,dy = 0$

14. (a) $\dfrac{dy}{dx} = \dfrac{x - y}{x + y}$ or $(x + y)\,dy - (x - y)\,dx = 0$

(b) $\dfrac{dy}{dx} + \dfrac{x - 2y}{2x - y} = 0$

15. (a)* $\dfrac{dy}{dx} = \dfrac{y^3 + 3x^2 y}{x^3 + 3xy^2}$

(b) $(x^3 - 2y^3)\,dx + 3xy^2\,dy = 0$

(c) $\dfrac{dy}{dx} = \dfrac{xy^2 - x^2 y}{x^3}$

16. $x\dfrac{dy}{dx} - y = \sqrt{(x^2 + y^2)}$.

17. $x\dfrac{dy}{dx} = y + 2\sqrt{(y^2 - x^2)}$.

18. $x\dfrac{dy}{dx} = y - x\cos^3 \dfrac{y}{x}$

19. (a)* $\dfrac{dy}{dx} = \dfrac{y}{x} + \tan\dfrac{y}{x}$ (b) $\dfrac{dy}{dx} = \dfrac{y}{x} + \sin\dfrac{y}{x}$.

20. (a)* $x\dfrac{dy}{dx} = y(\log y - \log x + 1)$.

(b) $e^{\frac{dy}{dx}} = x + 1$ given that when $x = 0, y = 3$

(c) $x\,dy = \left\{y + x\dfrac{f(y/x)}{f'(y/x)}\right\}dx$.

21. (a) $(x^2 - 2xy)\,dy + (x^2 - 3xy + 2y^2)\,dx = 0$.

(b) The solution curve of

$$\frac{dy}{dx} = \frac{y^2 - 2xy - x^2}{y^2 + 2xy - x^2},\ y(-1) = 1 \text{ is}$$

(a) st. line (b) circle

(c) parabola (d) ellipse

22. (a) $y^2 dx + (x^2 - xy + y^2)\,dy = 0$

(b) $x^2 dy + (x^2 - xy + y^2)\,dx = 0$

23. (a)* Find the equation of the curve passing through the point $(1, \pi/4)$ and tangent at any point of which makes an angle $\tan^{-1}\left(\dfrac{y}{x} - \cos^2\dfrac{y}{x}\right)$.

(b) $y\,dx + (2\sqrt{xy} - x)\,dy = 0$

(c) $x^2 y\,dy + (x^3 + x^2 y - 2xy^2 - y^3)\,dx = 0$

24.* $x^3 \dfrac{dy}{dx} = y^3 + y^2\sqrt{y^2 - x^2}$

25.* $(2x\cos y + 3x^2 y)\,dx + (x^3 - x^2 \sin y - y)\,dy = 0$

26. (a) The curve satisfying the equation $\dfrac{dy}{dx} = \dfrac{y(x + y^3)}{x(y^3 - x)}$ and passing through the point $(4, -2)$ is

(a) $y^2 = -2x$ (b) $y = -2x$

(c) $y^3 = -2x$ (d) None of these

(b) Prove that the solution of $\dfrac{x\dfrac{dy}{dx} - y}{\sqrt{x^2 - y^2}} = mx^2$ is given by $\sin^{-1}\dfrac{y}{x} = \dfrac{mx^2}{2} + c$

Solutions to Problem Set (3)

1. $\dfrac{dy}{dx} = \dfrac{xy}{x^2 + y^2}$ Put $y = vx$ ...(1)

$\therefore$ $\dfrac{dy}{dx} = v + x\dfrac{dv}{dx}$ ...(2)

$\therefore$ $v + x\dfrac{dv}{dx} = \dfrac{x.vx}{x^2 + v^2 x^2} = \dfrac{v}{1 + v^2}$ ...(3)

Note : In future step no. (2), (3) will be neglected and we shall directly come to step no. (4).

$x\dfrac{dv}{dx} = \dfrac{v}{1 + v^2} - v,$ ...(4)

$x\dfrac{dv}{dx} = \dfrac{v - v - v^3}{1 + v^2} = \dfrac{-v^3}{1 + v^2}.$

$\therefore$ $\left(\dfrac{1 + v^2}{-v^3}\right)dv = \dfrac{dx}{x}$ (Variables separable) or $\left(\frac{-1}{v^3}-\frac{1}{v}\right)dv=\frac{dx}{x}.$ Integrate both sides.

$\frac{1}{2v^2}-\log v=\log x+c,$

or $\frac{1}{2v^2}=\log vxk$, where $c=\log k$

or $\frac{1}{2}\frac{x^2}{y^2}=\log\frac{y}{x}x.k=\log ky.$

$\therefore$ $e^{x^2/2y^2}=ky.$

2. (a) $\frac{dy}{dx}=\frac{y^2-x^2}{2xy}.$ Put $y=vx$. etc.

$\therefore$ $v+x\frac{dv}{dx}=\frac{v^2-1}{2v}$ or $x\frac{dv}{dx}=-\frac{1+v^2}{2v}.$

or $\frac{2v}{1+v^2}dv+\frac{dx}{x}=0.$ Integrating

$\log(1+v^2)+\log x=\log k$

$\therefore$ $x(1+v^2)=k.$ Put $v=\frac{y}{x}.$

$x^2+y^2=k.x.$

(b) Ans. $x^3=k(x^2-y^2).$

3. Proceeding as usual, $\frac{1-v^2}{v(1+v^2)}dv=\frac{dx}{x}$

or $\left(\frac{1}{v}-\frac{2v}{1+v^2}\right)dv=\frac{dx}{x}.$ Partial Fractions.

or $\log\frac{v}{1+v^2}=\log x+\log k;$

$\therefore$ $y=k(x^2+y^2).$

4. (a) Ans. $x(x^2+3y^2)=c.$

(b) Ans. $x^2(x^2-2y^2)=k.$

5. (a) $\left(\frac{1}{v^2}-\frac{3}{v}\right)dv=\frac{1}{x}dx.$ Ans. $ky^3e^{x/y}=x^2.$

6. (a) Putting $y=vx$ etc. $\frac{1+v}{1-v}dv=\frac{dx}{x}.$

$\left(-1+\frac{2}{1-v}\right)dv=\frac{dx}{x}.$ Integrate

$k(y-x)^2=xe^{-y/x}.$

(b) $\frac{dy}{dx}=\frac{y^2}{xy-x^2}.$ Put $y=vx$

$\frac{v-1}{v}dv=\frac{dx}{x}$

or $1.dv=\frac{dv}{v}+\frac{dx}{x}$ Integrate

or $ky=e^{y/x}.$

(c) $\frac{1-v}{v^2}=2\frac{dx}{x}$ or $\left(\frac{1}{v^2}-\frac{1}{v}\right)dv=2\frac{dx}{x}$

or $k\,xy=e^{-x/y}.$

(d) $\frac{dy}{dx}+\frac{x\sqrt{(x^2+y^2)}-y^2}{xy}=0.$ Put $y=vx$

or $x\frac{dv}{dx}+\frac{\sqrt{(v^2+1)}}{v}=0$

or $\frac{1}{2}\frac{2v}{\sqrt{(1+v^2)}}dv+\frac{dx}{x}=0$

$\frac{1}{2}\cdot 2\sqrt{(1+v^2)}+\log x=\log k$

or $\sqrt{(x^2+y^2)}=x\log k/x.$

(e) $\frac{dy}{dx}=-\frac{y^2}{xy+x^2}.$ Put $y=vx.$

or $\frac{(v+1)}{v(2v+1)}dv+\frac{dx}{x}=0.$ Partial Fractions

$\left(\frac{1}{v}-\frac{1}{2v+1}\right)dv+\frac{dx}{x}=0.$ Integrate

$\log v-\frac{1}{2}\log(2v+1)+\log x=\log k$

$\frac{vx}{k}=\sqrt{(2v+1)}$ or $v^2x^2=k^2\left(2\cdot\frac{y}{x}+1\right)$

or $xy^2=c(2y+x).$

7. (a) Ans. $kxy=e^{x/y}$

(b) Ans. $kxy=e^{-x/y}.$

(c) Proceeding as usual, we have

$x\frac{dv}{dx}+\frac{2v}{2v+1}=0$

$\frac{2v+1}{2v}dv+\frac{dx}{x}=0$

$\therefore$ $\left(2+\frac{1}{v}\right)dv+2\frac{dx}{x}=0,$ Integrating,

$2v+\log v+\log x^2=\log k$

$\therefore$ $\log\frac{vx^2}{k}=-2v$

or $xy=ke^{-2y/x}$ when $x=1, y=1$

$1=ke^{-2}$ or $k=e^2$

$\therefore$ $xy=e^{2-\frac{2y}{x}}$ or $\log xy=2-\frac{2y}{x}$

or $2y=x[2-\log(xy)]$

8. $\frac{dy}{dx}=\frac{y^2}{xy-x^2}.$ Put $y=vx$

$\therefore$ $\frac{v-1}{v}dv=\frac{dx}{x}$

or $v-\log v=\log x+\log k$ or $ky=e^{y/x}.$

9. Ans. $kx=e^{1/v}=e^{x/y}$

10. (a) Ans. $y + 2x = kx^2 y.$

(b) Ans. $y - 2x = kx^2 y.$

11. (a) Ans. $(y - x)^2 = cy^2 x.$

(b) $v + x\dfrac{dv}{dx} + v + v^2 = 0$ where $y = vx$

$\therefore \quad \dfrac{dv}{v(v+2)} + \dfrac{dx}{x} = 0$

or $\left[\dfrac{1}{2v} - \dfrac{1}{2(v+2)}\right]dv + \dfrac{dx}{x} = 0$

or $\left(\dfrac{1}{v} - \dfrac{1}{v+2}\right)dv + 2\dfrac{dx}{x} = 0$, Integrating

$\log \dfrac{v}{v+2} x^2 = \log k$

$\therefore \quad vx^2 = k(v+2)$

$x^2 y = k(2x + y)$

12. Ans. $e^{-x^2/2y^2} = ky.$

13. (a) $(x+y)\,dy + (x-y)\,dx = 0$

$\dfrac{dy}{dx} = \dfrac{y-x}{y+x}.$ Put $y = vx$

$x\dfrac{dv}{dx} = \dfrac{v-1}{v+1} - v = -\dfrac{1+v^2}{v+1}$

$\therefore \quad \dfrac{v+1}{1+v^2}dv = -\dfrac{dx}{x}$

or $\dfrac{1}{2}\log(1+v^2) + \tan^{-1} v = -\log x + c$

or $\dfrac{1}{2}[\log(1+v^2) + 2\log x] + \tan^{-1} v = c$

or $\dfrac{1}{2}\log(x^2+y^2) + \tan^{-1}(y/x) = c.$

(b) Ans. $\tan^{-1}\dfrac{y}{x} - \dfrac{1}{2}\log(x^2+y^2) = c.$

14. (a) Ans. $y^2 + 2xy - x^2 = k,$

(b) Ans. $(x+y)^3 = c(x-y).$

15. (a) As usual, $\dfrac{1+3v^2}{2v(1-v)(1+v)}dv = \dfrac{dx}{x}$

Splitting into partial fractions,

$\left(\dfrac{1}{2v} + \dfrac{1}{1-v} - \dfrac{1}{1+v}\right)dv = \dfrac{dx}{x}$ Integrate.

Ans. $xy = k^2(x^2 - y^2)^2$

(b) Ans. $x^3 + y^3 = kx^2$

(c) Ans. $y - 2x = kx^2 y$

16. (a) $\dfrac{dv}{\sqrt{(1+v^2)}} = \dfrac{dx}{x}$ or $\sinh^{-1} v = \log x + c$

or $\log[v + \sqrt{(1+v^2)}] = \log kx.$

Now put $v = y/x$

or $y + \sqrt{(x^2+y^2)} = kx^2.$

17. Ans. $y + \sqrt{(y^2 - x^2)} = kx^3.$

18. Ans. $\tan\dfrac{y}{x} = \log\dfrac{k}{x}.$

19. (a) $x\cos\dfrac{y}{x}dy = \left(y\cos\dfrac{y}{x} + x\sin\dfrac{y}{x}\right)dx$

Put $y = vx \quad \therefore \quad v + x\dfrac{dv}{dx} = v + \tan v$

$\cot v\,dv = \dfrac{dx}{x}.$ Integrate

$\log\sin v = \log x + \log k$

or $\sin(y/x) = kx$

(b) $\sinh^{-1} x = \log[x + \sqrt{(1+x^2)}]$

$\tan\dfrac{y}{2x} = kx; \int \operatorname{cosec}\theta\,d\theta = \log\tan\dfrac{\theta}{2}$

20. (a) $\dfrac{dy}{dx} = \dfrac{y}{x}\left\{\log\dfrac{y}{x} + 1\right\}.$ Put $y = vx$

$v + x\dfrac{dv}{dx} = v\log v + v. \quad \therefore \quad \dfrac{dv}{v\log v} = \dfrac{dx}{x}$

$\therefore \quad \log(\log v) = \log x + \log k = \log kx$

$\therefore \quad \log v = kx$ or $v = e^{kx}$

or $y = xe^{kx}.$

(b) The given equation can be written as

$\dfrac{dy}{dx} = \log(x+1)$

$\therefore \quad dy = \log(x+1)\,dx.$ Integrating

$y = x\log(x+1) - \int \dfrac{x}{x+1}dx$

$y = x\log(x+1) - \int \left(1 - \dfrac{1}{x+1}\right)dx$

$= x\log(x+1) - x + \log(x+1) + c$

when $x = 0, y = 3 \quad \therefore \quad c = 3.$

$\therefore \quad y = (x+1)\log(x+1) - x + 3.$

(c) $\dfrac{dy}{dx} = \dfrac{y}{x} + \dfrac{f(y/x)}{f'(y/x)}$

Put $y = vx \quad \therefore \quad v + x\dfrac{dv}{dx} = v + \dfrac{f(v)}{f'(v)}$

$\therefore \quad \dfrac{f'(v)}{f(v)}dv = \dfrac{dx}{x}$ Integrating

$\log f(v) = \log x + \log k$

$\therefore \quad f(v) = kx$ or $f(y/x) = kx.$

To be more precise we may write $|f(y/x)| = k|x|$ where $k > 0$ as $\log t$ is defined only when $t > 0.$

21. (a) $x\dfrac{dv}{dx} = \dfrac{1 - 3v + 2v^2}{2v - 1} - v = \dfrac{1 - 2v}{2v - 1} = -1$

$\therefore \quad -dv = \dfrac{dx}{x}$

or $kx = e^{-v} = e^{-y/x}$

(b) Ans. (a).

Putting $y = vx$ for homogeneous equation, we have

$$v + x\frac{dv}{dx} = \frac{v^2 - 2v - 1}{v^2 + 2v - 1}$$

$$x\frac{dv}{dx} = \frac{(v^2 - 1) - 2v}{(v^2 - 1) + 2v} - v$$

or $$x\frac{dv}{dx} = \frac{(v^2 - 1)(1 - v) - 2v(1 + v)}{(v^2 - 1) + 2v}$$

or $$x\frac{dv}{dx} = \frac{(v + 1)[-(v - 1)^2 - 2v]}{v^2 - 1 + 2v}$$

or $$x\frac{dv}{dx} = \frac{-(v^2 + 1)(v + 1)}{v^2 - 1 + 2v}$$

or $$\frac{(v^2 - 1) + 2v}{(v^2 + 1)(v + 1)} dv = -\frac{dx}{x}$$

or $$\frac{2v(v + 1) - 1(v^2 + 1)}{(v^2 + 1)(v + 1)} dv = -\frac{dx}{x} \quad \text{(Note carefully)}$$

or $$\left(\frac{2v}{v^2 + 1} - \frac{1}{v + 1}\right) dv + \frac{dx}{x} = 0. \quad \text{Integrating}$$

$$\log(v^2 + 1) - \log(v + 1) + \log x = \log k$$

or $$\log\frac{x(v^2 + 1)}{v + 1} = \log k \quad \text{or} \quad \frac{y^2 + x^2}{y + x} = k$$

When $x = -1, y = 1, k = \frac{2}{0} = \infty$

$\therefore$ $y + x = 0$ which represents a straight line.

22. (a) $$\frac{dy}{dx} = -\frac{y^2}{x^2 - xy + y^2}. \quad \text{Put } y = vx$$

$\therefore$ $$x\frac{dv}{dx} = -\frac{v^2}{1 - v + v^2} - v = -\left[\frac{v + v^3}{1 - v + v^2}\right]$$

or $$\frac{1 + v^2 - v}{v(1 + v^2)} dv + \frac{dx}{x} = 0$$

or $$\left(\frac{1}{v} - \frac{1}{1 + v^2}\right) dv + \frac{dx}{x} = 0. \quad \text{Integrate}$$

$$\log v - \tan^{-1} v + \log x = \log k$$

or $$\log\frac{vx}{k} = \tan^{-1} v$$

or $$\frac{y}{k} = e^{\tan^{-1} y/x} \quad \text{or} \quad y = ke^{\tan^{-1} y/x}$$

(b) Ans. $k = xe^{\tan^{-1} y/x}$

23. (a) $$\psi = \tan^{-1}\left(\frac{y}{x} - \cos^2\frac{y}{x}\right)$$

or $$\frac{dy}{dx} = \tan\psi = \frac{y}{x} - \cos^2\frac{y}{x}$$

Put $y = vx$

$\therefore$ $$v + x\frac{dv}{dx} = v - \cos^2 v$$

$$\sec^2 v\, dv = -\frac{1}{x} dx$$

or $\tan v = \log k - \log x$

It passes through $(1, \pi/4)$ $\therefore$ $1 = \log k - 0$

$\therefore$ $\tan v = 1 - \log x = \log(e/x)$

or $$y = x\tan^{-1}\left(\log\frac{e}{x}\right)$$

(b) $$\frac{dy}{dx} = \frac{y}{x - 2\sqrt{xy}}, \quad \text{Put } y = vx$$

$\therefore$ $$v + x\frac{dv}{dx} = \frac{v}{1 - 2\sqrt{v}}$$

$\therefore$ $$x\frac{dv}{dx} = \frac{v}{1 - 2\sqrt{v}} - v = \frac{2v\sqrt{v}}{1 - 2\sqrt{v}}$$

$\therefore$ $$\frac{1 - 2\sqrt{v}}{v\sqrt{v}} dv = 2\frac{dx}{x}$$

$$\left(\frac{1}{v^{3/2}} - \frac{2}{v}\right) dv = 2\frac{dx}{x}. \quad \text{Integrate}$$

$$-\frac{2}{\sqrt{v}} - 2\log v = 2\log x + 2\log c$$

or $\log(v\, xc) = -1/\sqrt{v}$

or $cy = e^{-\sqrt{x/y}}$

(c) $$\frac{dy}{dx} = \frac{2xy^2 + y^3 - x^3 - x^2 y}{x^2 y} \quad \text{Homogeneous}$$

$$v + x\frac{dv}{dx} = \frac{2v^2 + v^3 - 1 - v}{v}$$

$\therefore$ $$x\frac{dv}{dx} = \frac{2v^2 + v^3 - 1 - v - v^2}{v}$$

or $$x\frac{dv}{dx} = \frac{v^3 + v^2 - (1 + v)}{v} = \frac{(v^2 - 1)(v + 1)}{v}$$

$\therefore$ $$\frac{v\, dv}{(v + 1)^2 (v - 1)} = \frac{dx}{x}$$

Split into partial fractions.

$$\left[\frac{1}{4(v - 1)} - \frac{1}{4(v + 1)} + \frac{1}{2(v + 1)^2}\right] dv = \frac{dx}{x}$$

$$\log\left(\frac{v - 1}{v + 1}\right) - \frac{2}{v + 1} = 4\log x + \log k$$

or $$\log\frac{v - 1}{(v + 1)kx^4} = \frac{2}{v + 1}$$

Now $v = y/x$

$\therefore$ $$\log\frac{y - x}{kx^4(y + x)} = \frac{2x}{x + y}$$

24. $$\frac{dy}{dx} = \frac{y^3 + y^2\sqrt{y^2 - x^2}}{x^3} \quad \text{(Homo.)}$$

Put $y = vx$

$$v + x\frac{dv}{dx} = \frac{v^3 + v^2\sqrt{v^2-1}}{1}$$

$$x\frac{dv}{dx} = v(v^2-1) + v^2\sqrt{v^2-1}$$

$$\frac{dv}{v\sqrt{v^2-1}\,[v+\sqrt{v^2-1}]} = dx$$

$$\frac{v-\sqrt{v^2-1}}{v\sqrt{v^2-1}}\,dv = \frac{dx}{x}$$

$$\left(\frac{1}{\sqrt{(v^2-1)}} - \frac{1}{v}\right)dv = \frac{1}{x}dx$$

$$\log(v+\sqrt{v^2-1}) = \log(v\,x\,c)$$

$$v+\sqrt{v^2-1} = v\,x\,c$$

or $\quad y+\sqrt{y^2-x^2} = x\,y\,c \quad \because \quad y = vx.$

25. It is of the form $M\,dx + N\,dy = 0$

$$\frac{\partial M}{\partial y} = -2x\sin y + 3x^2 = \frac{\partial N}{\partial x}$$

Hence it is exact and its solution is

$$\int\limits_{y\text{ constant}} M\,dx \quad + \int\limits_{\text{free from } x} N\,dy \quad = c$$

$$\int\limits_{y\text{ const.}} (2x\cos y + 3x^2 y)\,dx + \int -y\,dy = c$$

Integrating, we get $\quad x^2\cos y + x^3 y - \dfrac{y^2}{2} = c.$

26. (a) Ans. (c).

$$(xy^3 - x^2)\,dy - (xy + y^4)\,dx = 0$$

or $\quad y^3(x\,dy - y\,dx) - x(x\,dy + y\,dx) = 0$

or $\quad x^2y^3\dfrac{(x\,dy - y\,dx)}{x^2} - x(x\,dy + y\,dx) = 0$

or $\quad x^2y^3\,d\left(\dfrac{y}{x}\right) - x\,d(xy) = 0 \quad$ [Divide by x^3y^2]

or $\quad \dfrac{y}{x}\,d\left(\dfrac{y}{x}\right) - \dfrac{d(xy)}{x^2y^2} = 0$

Now Inegrating, $\quad \dfrac{1}{2}\left(\dfrac{y}{x}\right)^2 + \dfrac{1}{xy} = c$

It passess through the point $(4, -2)$

$\therefore \quad \dfrac{1}{8} - \dfrac{1}{8} = c \quad \Rightarrow \quad c = 0$

$\therefore \quad y^3 = -2x \quad \Rightarrow \quad$ (c).

(b) Do yourself.

I. Equations reducible to homogeneous form.

Consider the following equations :

$$\frac{dy}{dx} = \frac{ax+by+c}{a'x+b'y+c'} \text{ where } \frac{a}{a'} \neq \frac{b}{b'}$$

The above equation is not homogeneous. If c and c' were not present in the numerator and denominator respectively, then the equation would have been homogeneous equation of 1st degree and method of solution would have been the same as illustrated in the previous set.

In order to reduce this equation to the homogeneous form c and c' are removed as follows :

Put $\quad x = \alpha + h \qquad$ where α and β are variables
$\qquad\quad y = \beta + k \qquad$ but h and k are constants;

then $\quad \dfrac{dy}{dx} = \dfrac{d\beta}{d\alpha}$

and the above equation becomes

$$\frac{d\beta}{d\alpha} = \frac{a(\alpha+h) + b(\beta+k) + c}{a'(\alpha+h) + b'(\beta+k) + c'}$$

$$\frac{d\beta}{d\alpha} = \frac{a\alpha + b\beta + (ah+bk+c)}{a'\alpha + b'\beta + (a'h+b'k+c)}.$$

Now choose h and k such that

$$\left.\begin{aligned} ah+bk+c &= 0 \\ a'h+b'k+c' &= 0 \end{aligned}\right\} \qquad \text{...(A)}$$

From these two equations, h and k can be determined and the equation takes the form

$$\frac{d\beta}{d\alpha} = \frac{a\alpha + b\beta}{a'\alpha + b'\beta}$$

which is a homogeneous equation in α and β.

Put $\beta = v\alpha$;

$\therefore \quad \dfrac{d\beta}{d\alpha} = v + \alpha\dfrac{dv}{d\alpha}$

$$v + \alpha\frac{dv}{d\alpha} = \frac{a+bv}{a'+b'v}$$

$$\alpha.\frac{dv}{d\alpha} = \frac{a+bv}{a'+b'v} - v$$

Now the variables can be separated.

In the end put $v = \dfrac{\beta}{\alpha}$

and $\qquad \alpha = x - h,\ \beta = y - k,$

where h and k are determined from equations (A).

Solved Examples

Ex. 1. $\quad \dfrac{dy}{dx} = \dfrac{y-x+1}{y+x-5}.$

Put $\quad x = \alpha + h,\ y = \beta + k \quad \therefore \quad \dfrac{dy}{dx} = \dfrac{d\beta}{d\alpha}.$

$\therefore \quad \dfrac{d\beta}{d\alpha} = \dfrac{(\beta-\alpha) + (k-h+1)}{(\beta+\alpha) + (k+h-5)}.$

Choose h and k such that

$$\left\{\begin{aligned} k-h+1 &= 0 \\ k+h-5 &= 0 \end{aligned}\right\} \quad \therefore \quad \begin{aligned} h &= 3 \\ k &= 2 \end{aligned}$$

$\therefore \quad \dfrac{d\beta}{d\alpha} = \dfrac{\beta-\alpha}{\beta+\alpha} \qquad$ Put $\beta = v\alpha$

$\therefore \quad v + \alpha\dfrac{dv}{d\alpha} = \dfrac{v-1}{v+1}.$

$\therefore \quad \alpha \dfrac{dv}{d\alpha} = \dfrac{v-1}{v+1} - v = \dfrac{-1-v^2}{1+v}$

$\therefore \quad \dfrac{1+v}{1+v^2} dv = -\dfrac{d\alpha}{\alpha}$

or $\quad \left[\dfrac{1}{1+v^2} + \dfrac{1}{2}\dfrac{2v}{1+v^2}\right] dv = -\dfrac{d\alpha}{\alpha}$

$\tan^{-1} v + \dfrac{1}{2}\log(1+v^2) = -\log \alpha + c$

or $\quad \tan^{-1}\dfrac{\beta}{\alpha} + \dfrac{1}{2}\left[\log\left(1+\dfrac{\beta^2}{\alpha^2}\right) + \log \alpha^2\right] = c$

or $\quad \tan^{-1}\dfrac{\beta}{\alpha} + \dfrac{1}{2}\log(\alpha^2+\beta^2) = c$

where $\beta = y - k = y - 2$ and $\alpha = x - h = x - 3$.

Ex. 2. $\quad (2x + y + 3)\,dx = (2y + x + 1)\,dy$

or $\quad \dfrac{dy}{dx} = \dfrac{2x+y+3}{2y+x+1}$ or $\dfrac{d\beta}{d\alpha} = \dfrac{2\alpha+\beta}{2\beta+\alpha}$

where $\alpha = x - h = x + \dfrac{5}{3},\ \beta = y - k = y - \dfrac{1}{2}$.

Put $\beta = v\alpha$. $\quad \therefore \quad v + \alpha\dfrac{dv}{dx} = \dfrac{2+v}{2v+1}$

or $\quad \alpha\dfrac{dv}{dx} = \dfrac{2+v}{2v+1} - v = \dfrac{2(1-v^2)}{2v+1}$

or $\quad \dfrac{2v+1}{(1-v)(1+v)} dv = 2\dfrac{d\alpha}{\alpha}$ $\quad$ P.F.'s.

$\left[\dfrac{3}{2}\dfrac{1}{1-v} - \dfrac{1}{2(1+v)}\right] dv = 2\dfrac{d\alpha}{\alpha}$

Integrate

$-3\log(1-v) - \log(1+v) = 4\log\alpha - k$

$\log \alpha^4 (1+v)(1-v)^3 = k = \log c$

or $\quad \alpha^4 (1+\beta/\alpha)(1-\beta/\alpha)^3 = c$

or $\quad (\alpha+\beta)(\alpha-\beta)^3 = c$

or $\quad (x + y + 4/3)(x - y + 2)^3 = c.$

Ex. 3. $\quad (y + x + 5)\,dy = (y - x + 1)\,dx$

$\dfrac{dy}{dx} = \dfrac{y-x+1}{y+x+5}$

$\dfrac{d\beta}{d\alpha} = \dfrac{\beta-\alpha}{\beta+\alpha}$

where $\quad \begin{matrix} k - h + 1 = 0 \\ k + h + 5 = 0 \end{matrix} \quad \therefore \quad \begin{matrix} k = -3 \\ h = -2 \end{matrix}$

Put $\beta = v\alpha$

$\therefore \quad v + \alpha\dfrac{dv}{d\alpha} = \dfrac{v-1}{v+1}$

or $\quad \alpha\dfrac{dv}{d\alpha} = \dfrac{v-1}{v+1} - v = -\dfrac{(1+v^2)}{v+1}$

or $\quad \dfrac{v+1}{v^2+1} dv = -\dfrac{d\alpha}{\alpha}$

or $\quad \left(\dfrac{1}{2}\dfrac{2v}{v^2+1} + \dfrac{1}{v^2+1}\right) dv = -\dfrac{d\alpha}{\alpha}$

$\dfrac{1}{2}\log(v^2+1) + \tan^{-1} v = -\log\alpha + \log k$

or $\quad \log\dfrac{(v^2+1)\,\alpha^2}{k^2} + 2\tan^{-1} v = 0$

or $\quad \log\dfrac{\beta^2+\alpha^2}{c} + 2\tan^{-1}\dfrac{\beta}{\alpha} = 0$

where $\alpha = x - h = x + 2, \beta = y - k = y + 3.$

Ex. 4. $\quad \dfrac{dy}{dx} = \dfrac{2x-y+1}{x+2y-3}.$

We could proceed as usual but we shall give below a very simple method. It is to be noted that coefficient of y in N^r is equal to coefficient of x in D^r but with opposite sign. Such an equation is said to be exact.

$(x + 2y - 3)\,dy - (2x - y + 1)\,dx = 0$

$(x\,dy + y\,dx) + (2y - 3)\,dy - (2x + 1)\,dx = 0$

Integrating

$xy + y^2 - 3y - (x^2 + x) = c$

$\because \quad d(xy) = x\,dy + y\,dx \qquad \therefore \quad \int (x\,dy + y\,dx) = xy.$

II. A Special Case of I.

If $\quad \dfrac{dy}{dx} = \dfrac{ax+by+c}{a'x+b'y+c'}$ and $\dfrac{a}{a'} = \dfrac{b}{b'} = m$ say,

i.e. when coefficients of x and y in numerator and denominator are proportional, then the above equation can not be solved by Method No. 1 discussed before because the values of h and k given by the equations **(A) P. 1637** will be indeterminate.

In order to solve such equations, we proceed as follows :

$\dfrac{dy}{dx} = \dfrac{ax+by+c}{a'x+b'y+c'} = \dfrac{ax+by+c}{\dfrac{1}{m}(ax+by)+c'}$

Put $ax + by = v, \quad \therefore \quad a + b\dfrac{dy}{dx} = \dfrac{dv}{dx}$

$\therefore \quad \dfrac{1}{b}\left(\dfrac{dv}{dx} - a\right) = \dfrac{v+c}{\dfrac{v}{m}+c'} = \dfrac{m(v+c)}{v+mc'}$

Now the variables can be separated.

Ex. 5. Solve $\dfrac{dy}{dx} = \dfrac{2x-6y+7}{x-3y+4} = \dfrac{2(x-3y)+7}{x-3y+4}.$

Put $x - 3y = v; \quad \therefore \quad 1 - 3\dfrac{dy}{dx} = \dfrac{dv}{dx}.$

$\therefore \quad \dfrac{1}{3}\left(1 - \dfrac{dv}{dx}\right) = \dfrac{2v+7}{v+4},$

$\dfrac{dv}{dx} = 1 - \dfrac{6v+21}{v+4} = \dfrac{v+4-6v-21}{v+4} = -\dfrac{(5v+17)}{v+4}$

$\therefore \quad \dfrac{v+4}{5v+17} dv = -dx$ or $\dfrac{5v+20}{5v+17} dv = -5\,dx$

or $\left(1+\dfrac{3}{5v+17}\right)dv=-5\,dx$

Integrating, $v+\dfrac{3}{5}\log(5v+17)=-5x+c$

or $x-3y+\dfrac{3}{5}\log(5x-15y+17)=-5x+c$

or $6x-3y+\dfrac{3}{5}\log(5x-15y+17)=c$

Divide by 3.

$2x-y+\dfrac{1}{5}\log(5x-15y+17)=\dfrac{c}{3}=k.$

Note : Questions of this type are very important. Students generally forget the method of solution and begin to proceed with method no. 1.

Ex. 6. $\dfrac{dy}{dx}=\dfrac{x-y+3}{2x-2y+5}=\dfrac{x-y+3}{2(x-y)+5}$

Put $x-y=v$, $\therefore$ $1-\dfrac{dy}{dx}=\dfrac{dv}{dx}$

$\left(1-\dfrac{dv}{dx}\right)=\dfrac{v+3}{2v+5}$

$\dfrac{dv}{dx}=1-\dfrac{v+3}{2v+5}=\dfrac{v+2}{2v+5}$ (Variables separable).

$\therefore$ $\dfrac{2v+5}{v+2}dv=dx$

or $\left(2+\dfrac{1}{v+2}\right)dv=dx.$ Integrate

$2v+\log(v+2)=x+c.$

Put the value of v.

$\therefore$ $x-2y+\log(x-y+2)=c.$

Ex. 7. $\dfrac{dy}{dx}=\dfrac{x+y+1}{2x+2y+3}$

Put $x+y=v$ etc. $\therefore$ $\dfrac{dv}{dx}=\dfrac{3v+4}{2v+3}$

or $\dfrac{2v+3}{3v+4}dv=dx$

or $\dfrac{6v+9}{3v+4}dv=3\,dx$

or $\left(2+\dfrac{1}{3v+4}\right)dv=3\,dx$, Integrate

$2v+\dfrac{1}{3}\log(3v+4)=3x+k$

or $2x+2y+\dfrac{1}{3}\log(3x+3y+4)=3x+k$

$6y-3x+\log(3x+3y+4)=c.$

Problem Set (4)

Reducible to homogenous form.

Solve the following differential equations :

1. $\dfrac{dy}{dx}=\dfrac{2y-x-4}{y-3x+3}.$
2. (a) $\dfrac{dy}{dx}=\dfrac{3y-x+7}{x-7y-3}$ (b) $\dfrac{dy}{dx}=\dfrac{3y-7x+7}{3x-7y-3}$

   (c) $(x-y)\,dy-(x+y+1)\,dx=0.$
3. $(3x+5y+6)\dfrac{dy}{dx}=7y+x+2$
4. (a) $(2x+3y-5)\dfrac{dy}{dx}+3x+2y-5=0$

   (b) $\dfrac{2x^2+3y^2-7}{y}dx=\dfrac{3x^2+2y^2-8}{x}dy$
5. (a) $\dfrac{dy}{dx}=\dfrac{2x+9y-20}{6x+2y-10}$ (b) $\dfrac{dy}{dx}=\dfrac{2x+2y-2}{3x+y-5}.$
6. $\dfrac{dy}{dx}=\dfrac{x+2y-2}{2x+y-3}.$
7.* $(2x+3y-5)\,dy+(3x+2y-5)\,dx.$
8. $2(x-3y+1)\dfrac{dy}{dx}=4x-2y+1.$
9. (a) $(2x-y+1)\,dx+(2y-x-1)\,dy=0.$

   (b) $(x+2y-2)\,dx+(2x-y+3)\,dy=0.$
10. $\dfrac{dy}{dx}=\dfrac{2y+x-1}{2x+4y+3}=\dfrac{2y+x-1}{2(2y+x)+3}.$
11. (a)* $\dfrac{dy}{dx}=\dfrac{4x+6y+5}{3y+2x+4}$ (b) $\dfrac{dy}{dx}=\dfrac{3y+2x+4}{4x+6y+5}.$
12. (a) $\dfrac{dy}{dx}=\dfrac{8x+6y+12}{4x+3y+2}$

    (b) $(2x+y+1)\,dx+(4x+2y-1)\,dy=0$
13. (a) $\dfrac{dy}{dx}(2x+3y-5)+2x+3y+1=0$

    (b) $\dfrac{dy}{dx}=\dfrac{1-3x-3y}{2(x+y)}.$
14. (a)* $(x+y-1)\,dy=(x+y)\,dx.$

    (b) $\dfrac{dy}{dx}=\dfrac{x+y+1}{x+y-1}$ when $y=\dfrac{1}{3}$ at $x=\dfrac{2}{3}.$

    (c) $\dfrac{dy}{dx}=\dfrac{x+y}{x+y-2}.$
15.* $(x+y)(dx-dy)=dx+dy.$
16.* (a) $\dfrac{dy}{dx}=\dfrac{2y+x+1}{2x+4y+1}$

    (b) $(4x+6y+3)\,dx=(6x+9y+2)\,dy$

Solutions to Problem Set (4)

1. Put $x=\alpha+h,\ y=\beta+k$.

$\therefore$ $\dfrac{dy}{dx}=\dfrac{d\beta}{d\alpha}.$ $\therefore$ $\dfrac{d\beta}{d\alpha}=\dfrac{2\beta-\alpha+(2k-h-4)}{\beta-3\alpha+(k-3h+3)}$

Choose $\left\{\begin{array}{l}2k-h-4=0\\ k-3h+3=0\end{array}\right\};$ $\therefore$ $h=2,k=3$

$\therefore \quad \dfrac{d\beta}{d\alpha} = \dfrac{2\beta - \alpha}{\beta - 3\alpha}$

which is homogeneous. Put $\beta = v\alpha$,

$\therefore \quad \dfrac{d\beta}{d\alpha} = v + \alpha \dfrac{dv}{d\alpha} \quad$ or $\quad v + \alpha \dfrac{dv}{d\alpha} = \dfrac{2v-1}{v-3}$

or $\quad \alpha \dfrac{dv}{d\alpha} = \dfrac{2v-1}{v-3} - v = \dfrac{2v - 1 - v^2 + 3v}{v-3}$

or $\quad \alpha \dfrac{dv}{d\alpha} = \dfrac{5v - v^2 - 1}{v-3} \quad$ or $\quad \dfrac{v-3}{v^2 - 5v + 1} dv = -\dfrac{d\alpha}{\alpha}$

$$\left\{ \frac{2v-5}{v^2 - 5v + 1} - \frac{1}{\left(v - \frac{5}{2}\right)^2 - \left(\frac{\sqrt{21}}{2}\right)^2} \right\} dv = -\frac{d\alpha}{\alpha}$$

$$\left(\log (v^2 - 5v + 1) - \frac{1}{2\frac{\sqrt{21}}{2}} \log \frac{v - \frac{5}{2} - \frac{\sqrt{21}}{2}}{v - \frac{5}{2} + \frac{\sqrt{21}}{2}} \right) = -\log \alpha + c$$

is the required solution where $v = \dfrac{\beta}{\alpha}$

and $\quad \alpha = x - h = x - 2, \beta = y - k = y - 3.$

Note : Students can safely write down the answer in the above form.

2. (a) Ans. $\dfrac{3}{14} \log \dfrac{y - x + 1}{y + x - 1} = \log k \sqrt{[y^2 - (x-1)^2]}.$

(b) $(y - x + 1)^2 (y + x - 1)^5 = k.$

(c) $\dfrac{1 - v}{1 + v^2} dv = \dfrac{d\alpha}{\alpha}$

or $\quad \tan^{-1} v - \dfrac{1}{2} \log (1 + v^2) = \log \alpha + \log k$

Ans. $\log k \sqrt{(\beta^2 + \alpha^2)} = \tan^{-1} \dfrac{\beta}{\alpha},$

where $\alpha = x - h = x + \frac{1}{2}$ and $\beta = y - k = y + \frac{1}{2}.$

3. $\log (5v^2 - 4v + 1) - \dfrac{5}{2} \log \dfrac{5(v-1)}{5v+1} = \log \dfrac{k}{\alpha^2}$

where $\quad v = \dfrac{\beta}{\alpha} = \dfrac{y - k}{x - h} = \dfrac{y - 0}{x + 2}.$

4. (a) $\dfrac{dy}{dx} = -\dfrac{3x + 2y - 5}{2x + 3y - 5}.$

Proceeding as usual, we get

$\dfrac{3v + 2}{3v^2 + 4v + 3} dv = -\dfrac{d\alpha}{\alpha}, \quad$ where $v = \dfrac{\beta}{\alpha}$

or $\quad \dfrac{6v + 4}{3v^2 + 4v + 3} dv = -2\dfrac{d\alpha}{\alpha}.$

Integrating, $\log (3v^2 + 4v + 3) = -2 \log \alpha + c,$

$\log \dfrac{3\beta^2 + 4\alpha\beta + 3\alpha^2}{\alpha^2} + \log \alpha^2 = \log k.$

$3\beta^2 + 4\alpha\beta + 3\alpha^2 = k$

where $\beta = y - k = y - 1$ and $\alpha = x - h = x - 1.$

Ans. $3(x^2 + y^2) + 4xy - 10(x + y) = k.$

Note : For alternative easier method, see solution of Q. 7.

(b) $x^2 = X, y^2 = Y$

$\therefore \quad 2x\,dx = dX$ and $2y\,dy = dY$

The given equation is $\dfrac{dY}{dX} = \dfrac{2X + 3Y - 7}{3X + 2Y - 8}$

Now proceed as usual $X = \alpha + h, Y = \beta + k$

$\dfrac{d\beta}{d\alpha} = \dfrac{2\alpha + 3\beta}{3\alpha + 2\beta}$ ...(1)

and $2h + 3k - 7 = 0$ and $3h + 2k - 8 = 0$

Solving, we have $h = 2, k = 1$

Now solve (1) as usual by putting $\beta = v\alpha$ etc.

Ans. $x^2 + y^2 - 3 = \lambda (x^2 - y^2 - 1)^5.$

5. (a) $(\beta - 2\alpha)^2 = c(2\beta + \alpha),$

where $\alpha = x - 1$ and $\beta = y - 2.$

(b) $\dfrac{d\beta}{d\alpha} = \dfrac{2\alpha + 2\beta}{3\alpha + \beta}$

where $\alpha = x - h = x - 2, \beta = y - k = y + 1$

Ans. $(2x + y - 3) = k(x - y - 3)^4$

6. Proceeding as usual, $h = 1, k = 1$ and the equation reduces to

$\dfrac{2 + v}{(1 - v)(1 + v)} dv = \dfrac{d\alpha}{\alpha} \quad$ Partial Fractions

$\left[\dfrac{3}{2(1 - v)} + \dfrac{1}{2(1 + v)} \right] dv = \dfrac{d\alpha}{\alpha}.$ Integrate

$-3 \log (1 - v) + \log (1 + v) = 2 \log \alpha + \log k$

or $\quad \dfrac{1 + v}{(1 - v)^3} = k\alpha^2$

or $\quad \left(1 + \dfrac{\beta}{\alpha}\right) = k\alpha^2 \left(1 - \dfrac{\beta}{\alpha}\right)^3$

or $\quad (\alpha + \beta) = k(\alpha - \beta)^3$

where $\alpha = x - h = x - 1, \quad \beta = y - k = y - 1$

Ans. $(x + y - 2) = k(x - y)^3.$

Special Type.

$a(x\,dy + y\,dx) + b f(x)\,dx + c\,\phi(y)\,dy = 0$

The first bracket is differential coefficient of xy.

7.* $\dfrac{dy}{dx} = \dfrac{-3x - 2y + 5}{2x + 3y - 5}$

Coefficient of y in N^r is equal but opposite in sign to coefficient of x in D^r.

$\therefore \quad (2x + 3y - 5)\,dy + (3x + 2y - 5)\,dx = 0$

or $\quad 2(x\,dy + y\,dx) + (3y - 5)\,dy + (3x - 5)\,dx = 0.$

Integrate

$$2(xy) + 3\frac{y^2}{2} - 5y + 3\frac{x^2}{2} - 5x = c$$

or $\quad 4xy + 3(x^2 + y^2) - 10(x + y) = k.$

8. $2(x\,dy + y\,dx) + 2(1 - 3y)\,dy - (1 + 4x)\,dx = 0$

$$2xy + 2\left(y - \frac{3y^2}{2}\right) - (x + 2x^2) = c$$

or $\quad 2xy + 2y - 3y^2 - x - 2x^2 = k.$

9. (a) $(2x + 1)(dx) + (2y - 1)\,dy - (y\,dx + x\,dy) = 0$

Integrate $\quad x^2 + x + y^2 - y - xy = c$

or $\quad x^2 + y^2 - xy + (x - y) = c.$

(b) The above equation can be written as

$(x - 2)\,dx - (y - 3)\,dy + 2(y\,dx + x\,dy) = 0$

$$\frac{x^2}{2} - 2x - \frac{y^2}{2} + 3y + 2xy = c$$

Ans. $\quad x^2 - y^2 + 4xy - 4x + 6y = k.$

10. Ans. $2y - x + \frac{1}{4}\log(8y + 4x + 5) = c.$

11. (a) Put $3y + 2x = v \quad \therefore \quad 3\frac{dy}{dx} + 2 = \frac{dv}{dx}$

$$\therefore \quad \frac{1}{3}\left(\frac{dv}{dx} - 2\right) = \frac{2v + 5}{v + 4}$$

or $\quad \frac{dv}{dx} = \frac{6v + 15}{v + 4} + 2 = \frac{8v + 23}{v + 4}$

or $\quad \frac{8v + 32}{8v + 23}\,dv = 8\,dx$

or $\quad \left(1 + \frac{9}{8v + 23}\right)dv = 8\,dx$

or $\quad v + \frac{9}{8}\log(8v + 23) = 8x + c$

or $\quad 3y + 2x + \frac{9}{8}[8(3y + 2x) + 23] = 8x + c$

or $\quad y - 2x + \frac{3}{8}\log(24y + 16x + 23) = \frac{c}{3} = k.$

(b) Ans. $2y - x - \frac{3}{7}\log(14x + 21y + 22) = k.$

12. (a) Put $\quad 4x + 3y = v$

$$\therefore \quad \frac{5v + 10}{5v + 22}\,dv = 10\,dx$$

or $\quad \left(1 - \frac{12}{5v + 22}\right)dv = 10\,dx.\quad$ Integrate

$$v - \frac{12}{5}\log(5v + 22) = 10x + k$$

or $\quad 4x + 3y - \frac{12}{5}\log(20x + 15y + 22) = c.$

or $\quad 5(3y - 6x) - 12\log(20x + 15y + 22) = 10x + k$

(b) $\frac{dy}{dx} = \frac{2x + y + 1}{2(2x + y) - 1}$ etc.

Ans. $2y + x + \log(2x + y - 1) = k.$

13. (a) Ans. $x + y - 6\log(2x + 3y + 13) = \frac{c}{3} = k.$

(b) Ans. $3x + 2y + c + 2\log(1 - x - y) = 0$

14. (a) $\frac{dy}{dx} = \frac{x + y}{x + y - 1}$. Put $x + y = v$

$$\therefore \quad \left(\frac{2v - 2}{2v - 1}\right)dv = 2\,dx$$

or $\quad \left(1 - \frac{1}{2v - 1}\right)dv = 2\,dx$

or $\quad 2(y - x) - \log(2x + 2y - 1) = k.$

(b) Proceeding as above in part (a), we have

$$y - x = \log(x + y) + c.$$

Put $\quad x = \frac{2}{3}, y = \frac{1}{3}$

$$\left(\frac{1}{3} - \frac{2}{3}\right) = \log\left(\frac{2}{3} + \frac{1}{3}\right) + c$$

$$\therefore \quad -\frac{1}{3} = \log 1 + c \quad \therefore \quad c = -\frac{1}{3}$$

$$\therefore \quad y - x + \frac{1}{3} = \log(x + y).$$

(c) Ans. $y - x = \log(x + y - 1) + c.$

15. $(x + y + 1)\,dy = (x + y - 1)\,dx$

or $\quad \frac{dy}{dx} = \frac{x + y - 1}{x + y + 1}.$

Note : We can write the given equation as

$$\frac{dx + dy}{x + y} = dx - dy. \quad \text{Integrate.}$$

$$\log(x + y) = x - y + c.$$

16. (a) Ans. $4(x + 2y) - \log(4x + 8y + 3) = 8x + k.$

(b) $\frac{dy}{dx} = \frac{3(2x + 3y) + 2}{2(2x + 3y) + 3}$. Put $2x + 3y = v.$

$12(2x - 3y) + 5\log(24x + 36y + 13) = k.$

Case IV. LINEAR DIFFERENTIAL EQUATIONS.

A differential equation of the form

$$\frac{dy}{dx} + Py = Q, \qquad \text{...(1)}$$

where P and Q are functions of x (and not of y) is said to be Linear Differential Equation of the First Order.

Similarly $\frac{dx}{dy} + Px = Q$ is a linear differential equation, where P and Q are functions of y (and not of x).

Method of Solution :

In order to solve such equations we shall determine a function R of x called **Integrating factor (I.F.)**. We shall multiply both sides of the given equation (1) by R.

$$\therefore \quad R\frac{dy}{dx} + PRy = RQ. \qquad \text{...(2)}$$

Now we shall choose R such that L.H.S. of (2) is differential coefficient of $(y \times R)$.

i.e. $\quad \frac{d}{dx}(yR) = R\frac{dy}{dx} + y\frac{dR}{dx}.$

$\therefore \quad R\dfrac{dy}{dx} + PRy = \text{L.H.S.} = R\dfrac{dy}{dx} + y\dfrac{dR}{dx}.$

$\therefore \quad PRy = y\dfrac{dR}{dx}$ or $\dfrac{dR}{R} = P\,dx$. Integrating

$\log R = \int P\,dx \quad \therefore \quad R = e^{\int P\,dx} = \text{I.F.}$

Multiplying both sides by $e^{\int P\,dx}$,

$$e^{\int P\,dx}\frac{dy}{dx} + Pe^{\int P\,dx}\,y = Qe^{\int P\,dx}$$

or $\dfrac{d}{dx}(y.e^{\int P\,dx}) = Qe^{\int P\,dx}$

Now integrate both sides

$$y.e^{\int P\,dx} = c + \int Q.e^{\int P\,dx}\,dx$$

is the required solution.

Hence the method of solution is as follows :

Bring the equation in the form $\dfrac{dy}{dx} + Py = Q$

Integrate P w.r.t. x and make the integrand the power of e to get I.F.

i.e., $e^{\int P\,dx} = \text{I.F.}$

Multiply both sides by I.F.

Then L.H.S. will always be $\dfrac{d}{dx}(y \times \text{I.F.})$

$\therefore \quad \dfrac{d}{dx}(y \times \text{I.F.}) = Q \times \text{I.F.}$

Integrate both sides w.r.t. x and add a constant c to get the required solution as

$$y \times \text{I.F.} = \int Q \times \text{I.F.}\,dx + c$$

Note : If the equation be $\dfrac{dx}{dy} + Px = Q$, where P and Q are functions of y, (not of x) then $\text{I.F.} = e^{\int P\,dy}$ and solution will be

$$x \times \text{I.F.} = \int Q \times \text{I.F.}\,dy + c$$

Solved Examples

Ex. 1. $\dfrac{dy}{dx} + \dfrac{\cos x}{\sin x}y = \cos x.$

$P = \dfrac{\cos x}{\sin x};$

$\therefore \quad \int P\,dx = \int \dfrac{\cos x}{\sin x}dx = \log \sin x,$

$\therefore \quad e^{\int P\,dx} = e^{\log \sin x} = \sin x = \text{I.F.}$

Multiply both sides by $\sin x$

$\therefore \quad \sin x\dfrac{dy}{dx} + y\cos x = \sin x \cos x,$

L.H.S. you can always write at once as

$\dfrac{d}{dx}(y.\text{I.F.}),$ *i.e.*, $\dfrac{d}{dx}(y.\sin x)$

$\therefore \quad \dfrac{d}{dx}(y \sin x) = \sin x \cos x.$ Integrate.

$\therefore \quad y \sin x = \int \sin x \cos x\,dx + c = \dfrac{\sin^2 x}{2} + c.$

Ex. 2. (a) $(1 + x^2)\dfrac{dy}{dx} + 2xy - 4x^2 = 0.$

Divide by $(1 + x^2)$ to reduce to standard form

$$\frac{dy}{dx} + \frac{2x}{1 + x^2}y = \frac{4x^2}{1 + x^2} \qquad \text{...(1)}$$

$P = \dfrac{2x}{1 + x^2} \quad \therefore \quad \int P\,dx = \log(1 + x^2)$

$\therefore \quad \text{I.F.} = e^{\log(1 + x^2)} = 1 + x^2$

Multiplying both sides by I.F., we get

$(1 + x^2)\dfrac{dy}{dx} + 2x.y = 4x^2$

or $\dfrac{d}{dx}[y(1 + x^2)] = 4x^2.$ Integrating.

$y(1 + x^2) = \dfrac{4}{3}x^3 + c.$

(b) $\dfrac{dy}{dx} + \dfrac{2x}{1 + x^2}y = \dfrac{1}{(1 + x^2)^2}.$

Proceed as above Ans. $y(1 + x^2) = \tan^{-1} x + c.$

(c) $(1 + x^2)\dfrac{dy}{dx} + 2xy = \cos x.$

Ans. $y(1 + x^2) = \sin x + c.$

***Ex. 3.** $\dfrac{dy}{dx} + y\tan x = x^2 \cos^2 x.$

$\int P\,dx = \int \tan x\,dx = \log \sec x$

$\therefore \quad \text{I.F.} = e^{\log \sec x} = \sec x$

Multiplying both sides by I.F.,

$\sec x\dfrac{dy}{dx} + y\sec x \tan x = x^2 \cos^2 x \sec x$

or $\dfrac{d}{dx}(y.\sec x) = x^2 \cos x.$ Integrate

$y \sec x = \int x^2 \cos x\,dx + c.$

Integrate by parts

$= x^2(\sin x) - (2x)(-\cos x) + 2(-\sin x) + c$

or $y \sec x = x^2 \sin x + 2x \cos x - 2\sin x + c.$

***Ex. 4.** $(x + 2y^3)\dfrac{dy}{dx} = y.$

or $y\dfrac{dx}{dy} = x + 2y^3$ or $\dfrac{dx}{dy} - \dfrac{1}{y}x = 2y^2$

It is of the form $\dfrac{dx}{dy} + Px = Q$ where P and Q are functions of y. Hence

$P = -\dfrac{1}{y} \quad \therefore \quad \int P\,dy = -\log y = \log\dfrac{1}{y}$

$\therefore \quad \text{I.F.} = e^{\int P\,dy} = e^{\log(1/y)} = \dfrac{1}{y}.$

Multiplying both sides of (1) by $\dfrac{1}{y}$, we get

$$\frac{1}{y}\frac{dx}{dy}-\frac{1}{y^2}x=2y \quad \text{or} \quad \frac{d}{dy}\left(x.\frac{1}{y}\right)=2y.$$

Integrating both sides, we get $x.\frac{1}{y}=\int 2y\,dy+c.$

$$x.\frac{1}{y}=y^2+c \quad \text{or} \quad x=y^3+cy$$

Note : If the equation be $(1+x^2)\frac{dy}{dx}-xy=\frac{1}{1+x^2}$.

I. Here P is not x.

You should first bring the equation in the standard form $\frac{dy}{dx}+Py=Q$, *i.e.* coefficient of $\frac{dy}{dx}$ should be unity.

$$\frac{dy}{dx}-\frac{x}{(1+x^2)}y=\frac{1}{(1+x^2)^2}$$

Now $P\neq\frac{x}{1+x^2}$ but $=-\frac{x}{1+x^2}$.

II.* Always remember $e^{\log A}=A$,

$$e^{2\log A}=e^{\log A^2}=A^2,$$

$$e^{-\log A}=e^{\log A^{-1}}=A^{-1}, \text{ and so on.}$$

III.* $\int te^t\,dt=te^t-\int e^t\,dt=(t-1)e^t$

$$\int te^{-t}\,dt=-te^{-t}+\int e^{-t}\,dt=-(t+1)e^{-t}$$

***Ex. 5.** $\frac{dy}{dx}+y\sec x=\tan x.$

$\int P\,dx=\int \sec x\,dx=\log(\sec x+\tan x).$

$\therefore$ I.F. $=e^{\log(\sec x+\tan x)}=\sec x+\tan x.$

(1) Multiplying both sides by I.F.

(2) $(\sec x+\tan x)\frac{dy}{dx}+y\sec x(\sec x+\tan x)$

$=\tan x(\sec x+\tan x).$

(3) $\frac{d}{dx}\{y(\sec x+\tan x)\}=\sec x\tan x+\tan^2 x.$

Integrating,

(4) $y(\sec x+\tan x)=\int(\sec x\tan x+\tan^2 x)\,dx+c$

or $y(\sec x+\tan x)=\sec x+\int(\sec^2 x-1)\,dx+c$

$y(\sec x+\tan x)=\sec x+\tan x-x+c.$

Note : We know that after multiplying by the I.F. the L.H.S. is always equal to the differential coefficient of ($y\times$I.F.). Hence in future we shall omit step no. (2) and (3) and step no. (1) will be written as follows : Multiply both sides by I.F. and integrate. We shall then jump to step no. (4) in which L.H.S. will be $y\times$I.F. and R.H.S. will be $\int Q\times\text{I.F.}\,dx+c$ where Q is the given function of x in the R.H.S. in the given differential equation.

***Ex. 6.** $(1+x^2)\frac{dy}{dx}+y=e^{\tan^{-1}x}$

$$\frac{dy}{dx}+\frac{y}{(1+x^2)}=\frac{e^{\tan^{-1}x}}{1+x^2} \quad \therefore \quad \text{I.F.}=e^{\tan^{-1}x}$$

Multiplying both sides by I.F. and integrating,

$$ye^{\tan^{-1}x}=\int\frac{e^{\tan^{-1}x}}{1+x^2}e^{\tan^{-1}x}\,dx+c.$$

Put $e^{\tan^{-1}x}=t;\ \frac{e^{\tan^{-1}x}}{1+x^2}dx=dt.$

$$ye^{\tan^{-1}x}=\int t\,dt=\frac{t^2}{2}+c$$

$$2ye^{\tan^{-1}x}=e^{2\tan^{-1}x}+2c$$

***Ex. 7.** $\frac{dy}{dx}+\frac{y}{(1-x^2)^{3/2}}=\frac{x+\sqrt{(1-x^2)}}{(1-x^2)^2}$

$$\int P\,dx=\int\frac{1}{(1-x^2)^{3/2}}dx.$$

Put $x=\sin\theta;\ \therefore\ dx=\cos\theta\,d\theta$ ...(1)

$$\int P\,dx=\int\frac{1}{\cos^3\theta}\cos\theta\,d\theta$$

$$=\int\sec^2\theta\,d\theta=\tan\theta$$

$$=\frac{\sin\theta}{\cos\theta}=\frac{\sin\theta}{\sqrt{(1-\sin^2\theta)}}=\frac{x}{\sqrt{(1-x^2)}} \quad \text{[from (1)]}$$

...(2)

I.F. $=e^{x/\sqrt{(1-x^2)}}$

Multiplying both sides by I.F. and integrating,

$$ye^{x/\sqrt{(1-x^2)}}=\int\frac{x+\sqrt{(1-x^2)}}{(1-x^2)^2}e^{x/\sqrt{(1-x^2)}}\,dx$$

$$=\int\frac{\frac{x}{\sqrt{(1-x^2)}}+1}{(1-x^2)^{3/2}}e^{x/\sqrt{(1-x^2)}}\,dx \quad \text{...(3)}$$

Put $\frac{x}{\sqrt{(1-x^2)}}=t;\ \therefore\ \frac{1}{(1-x^2)^{3/2}}dx=dt$

$\left\{\begin{array}{l}\because \text{ we have done above that } \int\frac{1}{(1-x^2)^{3/2}}dx=\frac{x}{\sqrt{(1-x^2)}}\\ \therefore \text{ differentiation of } \frac{x}{\sqrt{(1-x^2)}} \text{ is } \frac{1}{(1-x^2)^{3/2}}\end{array}\right\}$

$ye^t=\int(t+1)e^t\,dt=te^t+c$ [by (3)]

$\therefore\ y=t+ce^{-t}$. Put the value of t.

***Ex. 8.** $\frac{dy}{dx}+\frac{y}{(1-x)\sqrt{x}}=1-\sqrt{x}.$

$$\int P\,dx=\int\frac{1}{(1-x)\sqrt{x}}dx. \quad \text{Put } x=t^2$$

$$=\int\frac{2t}{(1-t^2)}\frac{dt}{t}=\int\frac{2\,dt}{1-t^2}=2\cdot\frac{1}{2}\log\frac{1+t}{1-t}$$

$$\therefore \quad \text{I.F.}=e^{\log\frac{1+\sqrt{x}}{1-\sqrt{x}}}=\frac{1+\sqrt{x}}{1-\sqrt{x}}$$

Multiplying both sides by I.F. and integrating

$$y.\left(\frac{1+\sqrt{x}}{1-\sqrt{x}}\right)=\int\frac{1+\sqrt{x}}{1-\sqrt{x}}(1-\sqrt{x})\,dx+c.$$

$$y.\left(\frac{1+\sqrt{x}}{1-\sqrt{x}}\right)=x+\frac{2}{3}x^{3/2}+c$$

***Ex. 9.** $(1+x)\frac{dy}{dx}-xy=1-x.$

$$\frac{dy}{dx}-\frac{x}{1+x}y=\frac{1-x}{1+x}.$$

$$\int P\,dx=\int\frac{-x}{1+x}dx=\int\left(-1+\frac{1}{1+x}\right)dx$$

$$=-x+\log(1+x)=\log e^{-x}.(1+x).$$

$$\text{I.F.}=e^{\log e^{-x}(1+x)}=e^{-x}(1+x)$$

$\because$ $\log e^{-x}=-x\log e=-x.$

Multiplying both sides by I.F. and integrating

$$y\{e^{-x}(1+x)\}=\int e^{-x}(1+x)\cdot\frac{1-x}{1+x}dx$$

Now integrating by parts

$$ye^{-x}(1+x)=xe^{-x}+c$$

or $y(1+x)=x+ce^{x}.$

***Ex. 10.** $\sqrt{(a^2+x^2)}\frac{dy}{dx}+y=\sqrt{(a^2+x^2)}-x.$

$$\frac{dy}{dx}+\frac{y}{\sqrt{(a^2+x^2)}}=\frac{\sqrt{(a^2+x^2)}-x}{\sqrt{(a^2+x^2)}}.$$

$$\int P\,dx=\int\frac{dx}{\sqrt{(a^2+x^2)}}$$

$$=\sinh^{-1}\frac{x}{a}=\log\frac{x+\sqrt{(a^2+x^2)}}{a}$$

$\therefore$ $\text{I.F.}=\dfrac{\sqrt{(a^2+x^2)}+x}{a}$

Multiplying both sides by I.F. and integrating,

$$y.\frac{\sqrt{(a^2+x^2)}+x}{a}=\int\frac{\sqrt{(a^2+x^2)}-x}{\sqrt{(a^2+x^2)}}\cdot\frac{\sqrt{(a^2+x^2)}+x}{a}dx$$

$$=\int\frac{(a^2+x^2)-x^2}{a\sqrt{(a^2+x^2)}}dx$$

$$=\int\frac{a}{\sqrt{(a^2+x^2)}}dx=a\sinh^{-1}\frac{x}{a}+c.$$

Problem Set (5)

Linear differential equations of the form $\dfrac{dy}{dx}+Py=Q.$

Solve the following differential equations :

1. $\dfrac{ds}{dt}=-s+t$ or $\dfrac{ds}{dt}+s=t.$

2. $(x+y+1)\dfrac{dy}{dx}=1.$

3. $\dfrac{dy}{dx}+\dfrac{4x}{x^2+1}y=\dfrac{1}{(x^2+1)^3}.$

4. (a) $\dfrac{dy}{dx}+y\tan x-\sec x=0$

(b) $2\cos x\dfrac{dy}{dx}+4y\sin x=\sin 2x$

(c) $\dfrac{dy}{dx}-y\cot x=\operatorname{cosec} x.$

5. (a) $\dfrac{dy}{dx}-y\tan x=-2\sin x$

(b) $\dfrac{dy}{dx}-y\tan x=e^{x}\sec x$

(c) $\dfrac{dy}{dx}-y\tan x=e^{x}$

(d) $\sin x\dfrac{dy}{dx}+y\cos x=x\sin x.$

6. $x(x-1)\dfrac{dy}{dx}-y=x^2(x-1)^2$

(b) If $y(t)$ is solution of $(t+1)\dfrac{dy}{dt}-ty=1$, $y(0)=-1.$

At $t=1$ the solution is

(a) $e+\dfrac{1}{2}$ (b) $-\dfrac{1}{2}$

(c) $\dfrac{1}{2}$ (d) $e-\dfrac{1}{2}$ **(Screening 2003)**

7. (a) $x\dfrac{dz}{dx}+2z=\log x$ (b) $x\dfrac{dy}{dx}+2y=x^2\log x$

8. $x\,dy=(2y+2x^4+x^2)\,dx.$

9.* $(1+y^2)+(x-e^{\tan^{-1}y})\dfrac{dy}{dx}=0$ **(AIEEE 2003)**

10.* $(1+y^2)+(x-e^{-\tan^{-1}y})\dfrac{dy}{dx}=0.$

11. (a) $(1+y^2)\,dx=(\tan^{-1}y-x)\,dy.$

(b) $(1+xy)\dfrac{dy}{dx}+y^3=0$

12. (a) $(1+x^2)\dfrac{dy}{dx}+y=\tan^{-1}x$

(b) $(x^2+1)\,dy+(2y-1)\,dx=0$

(c) $y^2+\left(x-\dfrac{1}{y}\right)\dfrac{dy}{dx}=0.$

13. (a)* $x\cos x\dfrac{dy}{dx}+y(x\sin x+\cos x)=1$

(b) $x\sin x\dfrac{dy}{dx}+y(x\cos x+\sin x)=\sin x$

14. $x\log x\dfrac{dy}{dx}+y=2\log x.$

15. $(2x - 10y^3)\dfrac{dy}{dx} + y = 0.$

16. $dx + x\,dy = e^{-y}\sec^2 y\,dy.$

17.* $\dfrac{dy}{dx} + 2y\tan x = \sin x.$

18. $x\dfrac{dy}{dx} - y = 2x^2 \operatorname{cosec} 2x.$

19. $\cos x\dfrac{dy}{dx} + y\sin x = \sec^2 x$

20.* $\dfrac{dy}{dx} + 3x^2 y = x^5.$

21. $\cos^2 x\dfrac{dy}{dx} + y = \tan x.$

22. (a)* $(1 + y + x^2 y)\,dx + (x + x^3)\,dy = 0.$

(b)* Solve the differential equation

$(1 + \tan y)(dx - dy) + 2x\,dy = 0.$ **(Roorkee 1998)**

23. (a) $(1 - x^2)\dfrac{dy}{dx} + 2xy = x(1 - x^2)^{1/2}$

(b) $(1 - x^2)\dfrac{dy}{dx} - xy = \dfrac{1}{\sqrt{(1 - x^2)}}.$

24. $x(x - 1)\dfrac{dy}{dx} - (x - 2)\,y = x^3(2x - 1).$

25. $(x^2 - 1)\dfrac{dy}{dx} + 2(x + 2)\,y = 2(x + 1).$

26. (a)* $\sin 2x\dfrac{dy}{dx} - y = \tan x$

(b) $(x + \tan y)\,dy = \sin 2y\,dx.$

27. $\dfrac{dy}{dx} + y\cos x = \sin x\cos x$, I.F. $= e^{\sin x}$

28. $\sec x\dfrac{dy}{dx} = y + \sin x$ or $\dfrac{dy}{dx} - y\cos x = \sin x\cos x.$

29. (a) $\dfrac{dy}{dx} + \dfrac{2}{x}y = \sin x$, I.F. $= x^2.$

(b) $\sin x\dfrac{dy}{dx} + 2y + \sin x(1 + \cos x) = 0.$

30. $\dfrac{dy}{dx} + \dfrac{3x^2}{1 + x^3}y = \dfrac{\sin^2 x}{1 + x^3}$

31. $x^2\dfrac{dy}{dx} + y = 1.$

32. (a)* $x(x^2 + 1)\dfrac{dy}{dx} = y(1 - x^2) + x^3\log x$

(b) $(x^3 - x)\dfrac{dy}{dx} - (3x^2 - 1)\,y = x^5 - 2x^3 + x$

33. (a)* $x(1 - x^2)\,dy + (2x^2 y - y - 5x^3)\,dx = 0$ **(Roorkee 1994)**

(b) $x(1 - x^2)\,dy + (2x^2 y - y - ax^3)\,dx = 0.$

34. $x\left[\dfrac{dy}{dx} + y\right] = 1 - y.$

35. $\dfrac{dy}{dx} + \dfrac{1 - 2x}{x^2}y = 1.$

36.* $\dfrac{dy}{dx} = \dfrac{x\sqrt{(x^2 - 1)} + y}{\sqrt{(x^2 - 1)}}$

Given that $y = 1$ when $x = 1$.

37.* $y + \dfrac{d}{dx}(xy) = x(\sin x + \log x)$ **(Roorkee 1995)**

38.* Solve the differential equation

$\cos^2 x\dfrac{dy}{dx} - (\tan 2x)\,y = \cos^4 x, |x| < \dfrac{\pi}{4}$

where $y\left(\dfrac{\pi}{6}\right) = \dfrac{3\sqrt{3}}{8}.$ **(Roorkee 1996)**

39. Let $f(x)$ be differentiable on the interval $(0, \infty)$ such that

$f(1) = 1$ and $\lim_{t \to x}\dfrac{t^2 f(x) - x^2 f(t)}{t - x} = 1$

for each $x > 0$. Then $f(x)$ is

(a) $\dfrac{1}{3x} + \dfrac{2x^2}{3}$ (b) $-\dfrac{1}{3x} + \dfrac{4x^2}{3}$

(c) $-\dfrac{1}{x} + \dfrac{2}{x^2}$ (d) $\dfrac{1}{x}$ **(I.I.T. 2007)**

Solutions to Problem Set (5)

1. $P = 1 \quad \therefore \quad \int P\,dt = \int 1\,dt = t.$

I.F. $= e^t$. Multiplying both sides by I.F.

$$e^t\frac{ds}{dt} + se^t = te^t$$

or $\dfrac{d}{dt}(se^t) = te^t$. Integrate.

$\therefore \quad se^t = \int te^t\,dt + c = (t - 1)e^t + c,$

or $s = t - 1 + ce^{-t}.$

2. The given equation can be written as

$\dfrac{dx}{dy} - x = y + 1.$

$$x = ke^y - (y + 2).$$

3. I.F. $= (x^2 + 1)^2$ Ans. $y(x^2 + 1)^2 = \tan^{-1} x + c.$

4. (a) Ans. $y\sec x = \tan x + c.$

(b) $\dfrac{dy}{dx} + 2y\tan x = \sin x$, I.F.$= \sec^2 x$

Ans. $y\sec^2 x = \int \sec x\tan x + c = \sec x + c.$

(c) Ans. $y\operatorname{cosec} x = -\cot x + c.$

5. (a) $y\cos x = c - \int \sin 2x\,dx = c + \dfrac{1}{2}\cos 2x$, I.F. $= \cos x$

Similarly if $\dfrac{dy}{dx} + y\cot x = 2\cos x$ then its solution is $y\sin x = c - \dfrac{1}{2}\cos 2x.$

(b) $y\cos x = e^x + c.$

(c) $y\cos x = \dfrac{1}{2}e^x(\cos x + \sin x) + c.$

Note : $I = \int e^x\cos x\,dx$ is done by parts twice.

(d) $\frac{dy}{dx} + y \cot x = x,$ I.F. $= \sin x$

$\therefore$ $y \sin x = \int x \sin x \, dx + c$

$= c - x \cos x + \sin x$ by parts.

6. (a) $\frac{dy}{dx} - \frac{y}{x(x-1)} = x(x-1),$

$P = \frac{-1}{x(x-1)} = \left(\frac{1}{x} - \frac{1}{x-1}\right).$

I.F. $= e^{\int P \, dx} = e^{\log \frac{x}{x-1}} = \frac{x}{x-1}.$

Multiplying both sides by I.F. and integrating, we get

$\frac{yx}{x-1} = \frac{x^3}{3} + c.$

(b) Ans. (b). $\frac{dy}{dt} - \frac{t}{t+1} y = \frac{1}{t+1}$

$\int P \, dt = \int -\frac{t}{t+1} dt = \int \left(-1 + \frac{1}{t+1}\right) dt$

$= -t + \log(t+1)$

I.F. $= e^{\int P \, dt} = e^{-t}.(t+1).$

Multiplying by I.F. and integrating,

$ye^{-t}(t+1) = \int e^{-t}(t+1) \frac{1}{(t+1)} dt + c$

$= -e^{-t} + c$

$\therefore$ $y(t+1) = -1 + ce^t.$ Given at $t = 0, y = -1$

$\therefore$ $-1 = -1 + c$ or $c = 0$

$\therefore$ $y = -\frac{1}{t+1} + 0$ $\therefore$ at $t = 1, y = -\frac{1}{2}.$

7. (a) $\frac{dz}{dx} + \frac{2}{x} z = \frac{1}{x} \log x,$ I.F. $= x^2$

$zx^2 = \frac{x^2}{2} \log x - \frac{x^2}{4} + c$

(b) $yx^2 = \frac{1}{4} x^4 \log x - \frac{1}{16} x^4 + c.$

8. $\frac{dy}{dx} - \frac{2}{x} y = 2x^3 + x.$

I.F. $= e^{-2 \log x} = e^{\log x^{-2}} = x^{-2}$

$y \frac{1}{x^2} = x^2 + \log x + c.$

9. $(1+y^2) \frac{dx}{dy} + x = e^{\tan^{-1} y}$

Peoceed as in **Q. 6, P. 1644**

$2xe^{\tan^{-1} y} = e^{2 \tan^{-1} y} + k.$

10. $\frac{dx}{dy} + \frac{x}{1+y^2} = \frac{e^{-\tan^{-1} y}}{1+y^2},$ I.F. $= e^{\tan^{-1} y}$

or $xe^{\tan^{-1} y} = \int \frac{1}{1+y^2} dy + c = \tan^{-1} y + c.$

11. (a) $\frac{dx}{dy} + \frac{x}{1+y^2} = \frac{\tan^{-1} y}{1+y^2},$ $\therefore$ I.F. $= e^{\tan^{-1} y}.$

Multiply both sides by I.F. and integrate.

$xe^{\tan^{-1} y} = \int e^{\tan^{-1} y} . \frac{\tan^{-1} y}{1+y^2} dy = \int te^t \, dt$

where $\tan^{-1} y = t$ $\therefore$ $\frac{1}{1+y^2} dy = dt$

or $xe^{\tan^{-1} y} = e^t.(t-1) + c$

$= e^{\tan^{-1} y} (\tan^{-1} y - 1) + c.$

$\therefore$ $x = \tan^{-1} y - 1 + ce^{-\tan^{-1} y}.$

(b) $y^3 \frac{dx}{dy} + xy = -1$

or $\frac{dx}{dy} + x \cdot \frac{1}{y^2} = -\frac{1}{y^3}$

I.F. $= e^{\int P \, dy} = e^{\int 1/y^2 \, dy} = e^{-1/y}$

$\therefore$ $x.e^{-1/y} = \int e^{-1/y} . \left(\frac{1}{y^2}\right)\left(-\frac{1}{y}\right) dy$

$\therefore$ $xe^{-1/y} = \int t.e^t = (t-1) e^t$

$= \left(-\frac{1}{y} - 1\right) e^{-1/y} + c$

12. (a) $y = \tan^{-1} x - 1 + ce^{-\tan^{-1} x}.$

(b) $\frac{dy}{dx} + \frac{2}{x^2+1} y = \frac{1}{x^2+1}$

or $y = ce^{-2 \tan^{-1} x} + \frac{1}{2}$

(c) $\frac{dx}{dy} + \frac{1}{y^2} x = \frac{1}{y^3}.$ Linear, I.F. $= e^{-1/y}$

$x.e^{-1/y} = \int \frac{1}{y} \cdot \frac{1}{y^2} e^{-1/y} .dy + c$

$xe^t = -\int te^t \, dt + c = -(t-1) e^t + c.$

$\therefore$ $x = -(t-1) + ce^{-t}$ where $t = -1/y$

13. (a) $\frac{dy}{dx} + y\left(\tan x + \frac{1}{x}\right) = \frac{1}{x \cos x}.$

$\therefore$ I.F. $= e^{\log(x \sec x)} = x \sec x.$

Ans. $y(x \sec x) = \tan x + C$

(b) Ans. $y(x \sin x) = -\cos x + c.$

14. $\frac{dy}{dx} + \frac{y}{x \log x} = \frac{2}{x}.$

I.F. $= e^{\log(\log x)} = \log x.$

Multiplying both sides by I.F. and integrating,

$y \log x = \int \frac{2}{x} \log x \, dx + c = (\log x)^2 + c.$

15. It is not linear in the present form, but can be put as

$$(2x-10y^3)+y\frac{dx}{dy}=0$$

or $\frac{dx}{dy}+\frac{2}{y}x=10y^2,$

Ans. $x=2y^3+cy^{-2}.$

16. $\frac{dx}{dy}+x=e^{-y}\sec^2 y,$

Ans. $xe^y=\tan y+c$

17. $\int P\,dx=\int 2\tan x\,dx=2\log\sec x=\log\sec^2 x$

I.F. $=e^{\log\sec^2 x}=\sec^2 x.$

Multiplying both sides by I.F. and integrating,

$$y\sec^2 x=\int \sin x\sec^2 x\,dx+c,$$

$$y\sec^2 x=\int \tan x\sec x\,dx+c=\sec x+c.$$

$$y=\cos x+c\cos^2 x.$$

Given that $y=0$ when $x=\pi/3.$

When $x=60^o$, $y=0.$

$\therefore\quad 0=\frac{1}{2}+c\cdot\frac{1}{4}$ or $c=-2.$

$$y=\cos x-2\cos^2 x.$$

18. $\frac{dy}{dx}-\frac{1}{x}y=2x\operatorname{cosec}2x \qquad$ I.F. $=e^{-\log x}=1/x$

$\therefore\quad y=x\log\tan x+cx.$

19. $\frac{dy}{dx}+y\tan x=\sec^3 x,$ I.F. $=\sec x.$

$\therefore\quad y\sec x=\int \sec^4 x\,dx=\int (1+\tan^2 x)\sec^2 x\,dx$

$$=\tan x+\frac{1}{3}\tan^3 x+c.$$

20. $ye^{x^3}=\int x^2x^3e^{x^3}dx+c.$ Now put $x^3=t.$ I.F. $=e^{x^3}$

$$y=\frac{1}{3}(x^3-1)+ce^{-x^3}.$$

21. $\frac{dy}{dx}+y\sec^2 x=\tan x\sec^2 x,$ I.F. $=e^{\tan x}$

$$ye^{\tan x}=\int e^{\tan x}.\tan x\sec^2 x\,dx$$

Put $\tan x=t$

$\therefore\quad ye^t=\int te^t\,dt=e^t(t-1)+c$

or $\quad y=t-1+ce^{-t}$ where $t=\tan x.$

22. (a) $1+y(1+x^2)+x(1+x^2)\frac{dy}{dx}=0.$

$$xy=-\tan^{-1}x+c.$$

(b) $(1+\tan y)\frac{dx}{dy}+2x=1+\tan y$

or $\frac{dx}{dy}+\frac{2\cos y}{\sin y+\cos y}x=1$

$$\int P\,dy=\int\frac{(\cos y+\sin y)+(\cos y-\sin y)}{(\sin y+\cos y)}dy$$

$$=y+\log(\sin y+\cos y)$$

I.F. $=e^{\int P\,dy}=e^y(\sin y+\cos y)$

Multiplying both sides by I.F. and integrating,

$$x.e^y(\sin y+\cos y)=\int e^y(\sin y+\cos y)\,dy+c$$

$$=e^y\sin y+c$$

or $\quad x(\sin y+\cos y)=\sin y+ce^{-y}$

23. (a) I.F. $=\frac{1}{1-x^2},\ y=\sqrt{(1-x^2)}+c(1-x^2).$

(b) Here I.F. $=\sqrt{(1-x^2)}$

$\therefore\quad y\sqrt{(1-x^2)}=\sin^{-1}x+c.$

24. $\frac{dy}{dx}-\frac{x-2}{x(x-1)}y=\frac{x^2(2x-1)}{x-1},$ I.F. $=\frac{(x-1)}{x^2}$ (P.F.'s)

$$y=x^3+\frac{cx^2}{x-1}$$

25. I.F. is $(x-1)^3/(x+1).$ (Partial fractions)

$$\frac{y(x-1)^3}{x+1}=\left\{\frac{(x+1)^2}{2}-4(x+1)+4\log(x+1)\right\}+c.$$

26. (a) $\frac{dy}{dx}-y\operatorname{cosec}2x=\frac{\sin x}{\cos x}\cdot\frac{1}{2\sin x\cos x}=\frac{\sec^2 x}{2}$

$$\int P\,dx=\int -\operatorname{cosec}2x\,dx$$

$$=-\frac{1}{2}\log\tan x=\log(\tan x)^{-1/2}.$$

I.F. $=e^{\log(\tan x)^{-1/2}}=(\tan x)^{-1/2}.$

Multiplying throughout by I.F. and integrating,

Ans. $y=\tan x+c\sqrt{(\tan x)}.$

(b) $\sin 2y\frac{dx}{dy}-x=\tan y.$

$$x=\tan y+c\sqrt{(\tan y)}.$$

27. $ye^{\sin x}=\int \sin x\cos x\,e^{\sin x}\,dx.$

Put $\sin x=t.$

Ans. $y=(\sin x-1)+ce^{-\sin x}.$

28. Ans. $\quad y=-(\sin x+1)+ce^{\sin x}.$

29. (a) Multiplying both sides by I.F. and integrating,

$$x^2y=\int x^2\sin x\,dx+c.$$

Integrate twice by parts.

$$x^2y=(2-x^2)\cos x+2x\sin x+c.$$

(b) $\frac{dy}{dx}+2y\operatorname{cosec}x=-(1+\cos x).$

I.F. $\tan^2\frac{x}{2}=\frac{1-\cos x}{1+\cos x}.$

Multiplying both sides by I.F. and integrating,

$$y.\tan^2\frac{x}{2}=-\int(1-\cos x)\,dx$$

$$=-x+\sin x+c$$

30. $y(1+x^3)=\frac{1}{2}x-\frac{1}{4}\sin 2x+c.$

31. $\frac{dy}{dx}+\frac{1}{x^2}y=\frac{1}{x^2}$, I.F. $=e^{-1/x}$.

Ans. $y=1+ce^{1/x}$

32. (a) $\frac{dy}{dx}+\frac{x^2-1}{x(x^2+1)}y=\frac{x^2\log x}{x^2+1}$

$\int P\,dx=\int\frac{x^2-1}{x(x^2+1)}dx$

$=\int\frac{x^2-1}{x^2(x^2+1)}x\,dx.$ Put $x^2=t$.

$\therefore \int P\,dx=\frac{1}{2}\int\frac{t-1}{t(t+1)}dt=\int\left(\frac{1}{t+1}-\frac{1}{2t}\right)dt$

$=\log(t+1)-\frac{1}{2}\log t=\log\frac{t+1}{\sqrt{t}}=\log\frac{x^2+1}{x}.$

$\therefore$ I.F. $=\frac{x^2+1}{x}.$

Multiplying by I.F. and integrating,

we get $y.\frac{x^2+1}{x}=\int\frac{x^2\log x}{x^2+1}\cdot\frac{x^2+1}{x}dx$

$=\int x\log x\,dx$

or $y\cdot\frac{x^2+1}{x}=\frac{x^2}{2}\log x-\int\frac{x^2}{2}\cdot\frac{1}{x}dx$

$=\frac{x^2}{2}\log x-\frac{x^2}{4}+c.$

(b) $\frac{dy}{dx}-\frac{3x^2-1}{x^3-x}y=\frac{x(x^2-1)^2}{x(x^2-1)}=x^2-1$

$\int P\,dx=-\log(x^3-x)$

$\therefore$ I.F. $=e^{\int P\,dx}=\frac{1}{x^3-x}=\frac{1}{x(x^2-1)}$

$y\cdot\frac{1}{x(x^2-1)}=\log x+c.$

33. (a) $\frac{dy}{dx}+\frac{2x^2-1}{x(1-x^2)}y=\frac{5x^3}{x(1-x^2)}$

$\int P\,dx=\int\frac{2x^2-1}{x^2(1-x^2)}x\,dx.$ Put $x^2=t$

$\int P\,dx=\frac{1}{2}\int\frac{2t-1}{t(1-t)}dt=\frac{1}{2}\int\left(\frac{1}{1-t}-\frac{1}{t}\right)dt$

$=-\frac{1}{2}\log(1-x^2)\,x^2=\log\frac{1}{x\sqrt{(1-x^2)}},$

I.F. $=\frac{1}{x\sqrt{(1-x^2)}}$

Multiplying both sides by I.F. and integrating,

$y\cdot\frac{1}{x\sqrt{(1-x^2)}}=\int\frac{5x^3}{x(1-x^2)}\cdot\frac{1}{x\sqrt{1-x^2}}dx.$

Put $1-x^2=z$

$=-\frac{5}{2}\cdot\int\frac{dz}{z^{3/2}}=-\frac{5}{2}\cdot\frac{(-2)}{\sqrt{z}}=\frac{5}{\sqrt{(1-x^2)}}$

$\therefore y\cdot\frac{1}{x\sqrt{(1-x^2)}}=\frac{5}{\sqrt{1-x^2}}+c$

or $y=5x+cx\sqrt{1-x^2}$.

(b) The given differential equation can be put in the form

$\frac{dy}{dx}+y\cdot\frac{(2x^2-1)}{x(1-x^2)}=\frac{ax^2}{(1-x^2)}$

or $y=ax+bx\sqrt{(1-x^2)}$

34. $x\frac{dy}{dx}+y(1+x)=1$ or $\frac{dy}{dx}+\left(1+\frac{1}{x}\right)y=\frac{1}{x}.$

I.F. $=e^{x+\log x}=e^{\log(e^x.x)}=x.e^x.$

$y.(xe^x)=e^x+c$ or $xy=1+ce^{-x}.$

35. $\int P\,dx=\int\left(\frac{1}{x^2}-\frac{2}{x}\right)dx=-\frac{1}{x}-2\log x.$

$\therefore$ I.F. $=e^{-1/x}.e^{-2\log x}=\frac{1}{x^2}e^{-1/x}$ etc.

$y.\left(\frac{1}{x^2}e^{-1/x}\right)=\int\frac{1}{x^2}e^{-1/x}dx+c=e^{-1/x}+c$

or $y=x^2(1+ce^{1/x}).$

36. $\frac{dy}{dx}-y\cdot\frac{1}{\sqrt{(x^2-1)}}=x$

$\int P\,dx=\int-\frac{1}{\sqrt{(x^2-1)}}dx=-\log[x+\sqrt{(x^2-1)}]$

$\therefore$ I.F. $=\frac{1}{x+\sqrt{(x^2-1)}}$

or I.F. $=\frac{x-\sqrt{(x^2-1)}}{x^2-(x^2-1)}=x-\sqrt{(x^2-1)}$

Rationalized

Multiplying both sides by I.F. and integrating,

$y.[x-\sqrt{(x^2-1)}]=\int x[x-\sqrt{(x^2-1)}]dx+c$

$=\int[x^2-\frac{1}{2}.2x\sqrt{(x^2-1)}]dx+c$

$=\frac{1}{3}x^3-\frac{1}{2}\frac{2}{3}\cdot(x^2-1)^{3/2}+c$

or $y[x-\sqrt{(x^2-1)}]=\frac{1}{3}[x^3-(x^2-1)^{3/2}]+c$

Now when $x=1, y=1$ $\therefore$ $1=\frac{1}{3}(1)+c$ $\therefore$ $c=\frac{2}{3}$

$\therefore$ $y[x-\sqrt{(x^2-1)}]=\frac{1}{3}[x^3-(x^2-1)^{3/2}]+\frac{2}{3}$

is the solution.

37. $y+\left(y+x\frac{dy}{dx}\right)=x(\sin x+\log x)$

$\therefore \quad \frac{dy}{dx}+\frac{2y}{x}=\sin x+\log x$

Above is linear and I.F. $= e^{2\log x}=x^2$

Multiplying both sides by x^2 and integrating,

$$x^2y=\int x^2\sin x\,dx+\int x^2\log x\,dx+c$$
$$=x^2(-\cos x)-2x(-\sin x)+2\cos x$$
$$+\frac{x^3}{3}\log x-\frac{1}{3}\int x^3\cdot\frac{1}{x}\,dx+c$$

or $\quad x^2y=-x^2\cos x+2x\sin x+2\cos x$
$$+\frac{x^3}{3}\log x-\frac{x^3}{9}+c$$

We have performed successive integration by parts on first integral.

38. On dividing by $\cos^2 x$, we have

$$\frac{dy}{dx}-\frac{2\tan x}{1-\tan^2 x}\sec^2 x\,.\,y=\cos^2 x$$

$$\int P\,dx=\int -\frac{2t}{1-t^2}\,dt \qquad \text{where } t=\tan x$$

$$\int P\,dx=\log(1-t^2)$$

$\therefore \quad$ I.F. $=1-t^2=1-\tan^2 x$

Multiplying both sides by I.F. and integrating, we get

$$y(1-\tan^2 x)=\int(1-\tan^2 x)\cos^2 x\,dx+c$$
$$=\int\cos 2x\,dx+c=\frac{1}{2}\sin 2x+c$$

Given when $x=\frac{\pi}{6}$, then $y=\frac{3\sqrt{3}}{8}$

$\therefore \quad \frac{3\sqrt{3}}{8}\left(1-\frac{1}{3}\right)=\frac{1}{2}\cdot\frac{\sqrt{3}}{2}+c \quad \therefore \quad c=0$

$\therefore \quad y=\frac{1}{2}\cdot\frac{\sin 2x}{1-\tan^2 x}$ is the required solution.

39. Ans. (a).

$$\underset{t\to x}{\text{Lt}}\ \frac{t^2(f(x)-x^2 f(t))}{t-x}=1 \qquad \left(\frac{0}{0}\right)$$

Using L'Hospital Rule,

$$\text{Lt}=\underset{t\to x}{\text{Lt}}\ \frac{2t\,f(x)-x^2 f'(t)}{1}$$

or $\quad 2x\,f(x)-x^2 f'(x)=1$

If $f(x)=y$ then $f'(x)=\frac{dy}{dx}$

$\therefore \quad x^2\frac{dy}{dx}-2xy=-1$

or $\quad \frac{dy}{dx}-\frac{2}{x}y=-\frac{1}{x^2}$. $\quad$ Linear

$$\text{I.F.}=e^{\int -\frac{2}{x}x}=e^{\log 1/x^2}=1/x^2$$

Multiplying both sides by I.F. and integrating,

$$y\cdot\frac{1}{x^2}=\int -\frac{1}{x^2}\cdot\frac{1}{x^2}\,dx+c=\frac{1}{3x^3}+c$$

$\therefore \quad y=\frac{1}{3x}+cx^2$. Given $x=1$, $y=f(1)=1$

$\therefore \quad 1=\frac{1}{3}+c \qquad \therefore \qquad c=\frac{2}{3}$

$\therefore \quad y=\frac{1}{3x}+\frac{2}{3}x^2 \Rightarrow$ (a)

Extended Form of Linear Equations :

Bernoulli's Equation

$$\frac{dy}{dx}+Py=Qy^n$$

where P and Q are functions of x alone and do not contain y. Divide by y^n.

$$\frac{1}{y^n}\frac{dy}{dx}+P\frac{1}{y^{n-1}}=Q.$$

Put $\frac{1}{y^{n-1}}=v$ and differentiate w.r.t. x.

$$\frac{-(n-1)}{y^n}\frac{dy}{dx}=\frac{dv}{dx}$$

or $\quad \frac{1}{y^n}\cdot\frac{dy}{dx}=\frac{-1}{(n-1)}\frac{dv}{dx} \qquad \therefore \qquad \frac{1}{(1-n)}\frac{dv}{dx}+P.v=Q$

or $\quad \frac{dv}{dx}+P.(1-n)\,v=Q\,(1-n)$,

which is linear equation with v as independent variable and can be solved by the previous method.

Solved Examples

Solve the following differential equations :

***Ex. 1.** $\quad (y\log x-1)\,y\,dx=x\,dy$

or $\quad x\frac{dy}{dx}+y=y^2\log x.\quad$ Divide by xy^2.

$$\frac{1}{y^2}\frac{dy}{dx}+\frac{1}{x}\cdot\frac{1}{y}=\frac{1}{x}\log x.$$

Now put $\frac{1}{y}=v; \qquad \therefore \qquad \frac{-1}{y^2}\frac{dy}{dx}=\frac{dv}{dx}$

$\therefore \quad -\frac{dv}{dx}+\frac{1}{x}\cdot v=\frac{1}{x}\log x$

or $\quad \frac{dv}{dx}-\frac{1}{x}v=-\frac{1}{x}\log x$

which is linear in v.

$\therefore \quad$ I.F. $=e^{\int P\,dx}=e^{-\log x}=e^{\log(1/x)}=\frac{1}{x}$

Multiplying both sides by I.F. and integrating,

$$v\cdot\frac{1}{x}=\int -\frac{1}{x^2}\log x\,dx$$

Integrate by parts,

$$v\cdot\frac{1}{x}=\frac{1}{x}\log x-\int\frac{1}{x}\cdot\frac{1}{x}\,dx.$$

$\therefore \quad v\dfrac{1}{x}=\dfrac{1}{x}\log x+\dfrac{1}{x}+c.$

$v=\log x+1+cx=\log ex+cx, \qquad (\because \log e=1)$

or $\dfrac{1}{y}=cx+\log ex$ or $1=y\,(cx+\log ex).$

Change of variable :

Ex. 2. $\sec^2 y\dfrac{dy}{dx}+x\tan y=x^3.$

Put $\tan y=v \therefore \sec^2 y\dfrac{dy}{dx}=\dfrac{dv}{dx}$

The original equation is now

$\dfrac{dv}{dx}+x.v=x^3. \qquad \text{I.F.}=e^{x^2/2}$

$\therefore \quad \dfrac{dv}{dx}+x.v=x^3.$

$ve^{x^2/2}=\int x^3.e^{x^2/2}\,dx \qquad \text{Put } \dfrac{x^2}{2}=t \text{ etc.}$

$\therefore \quad ve^t=\int 2te^t\,dt=2e^t\,(t-1)+c;$

$\therefore \quad v=2\,(t-1)+ce^{-t}$

or $\tan y=x^2-2+ce^{-x^2/2}$

***Ex. 3.** $\dfrac{dy}{dx}(x^2y^3+xy)=1.$

$\dfrac{dx}{dy}=x^2y^3+xy.$

$\dfrac{dx}{dy}-xy=x^2y^3$, or $\dfrac{1}{x^2}\cdot\dfrac{dx}{dy}-\dfrac{1}{x}y=y^3$

Put $-\dfrac{1}{x}=v; \therefore \dfrac{1}{x^2}\dfrac{dx}{dy}=\dfrac{dv}{dy}$

$\dfrac{dv}{dy}+v.y=y^3$

which is linear and its solution (by Ex. 2) is

$v=y^2-2+ce^{-y^2/2}$, where $v=-\dfrac{1}{x}$.

$\therefore \quad 1+x\,(y^2-2+ce^{-y^2/2})=0$

is required solution.

Ex. 4. $(x^3y^2+xy)\,dx=dy.$

$\dfrac{dy}{dx}-xy=x^3y^2,$

Ans. $1+y\,(x^2-2+ce^{-x^2/2})=0$

Ex. 5. $\dfrac{dy}{dx}=x^3y^3-xy.$

or $\dfrac{1}{y^3}\dfrac{dy}{dx}+\dfrac{x}{y^2}=x^3. \qquad \text{Put } -\dfrac{1}{2y^2}=v;$

$\therefore \quad \dfrac{dv}{dx}-2xv=x^3, \qquad \text{I.F.}=e^{-x^2}$

Ans. $\dfrac{1}{y^2}=x^2+1-ce^{x^2}$

***Ex. 6. (a)** $\dfrac{dy}{dx}+\dfrac{xy}{1-x^2}=xy^{1/2}.$

or $\dfrac{1}{\sqrt{y}}\dfrac{dy}{dx}+\dfrac{x}{(1-x^2)}\sqrt{y}=x.$

Put $2\sqrt{y}=v;$

$\therefore \quad 2\dfrac{1}{2\sqrt{y}}\dfrac{dy}{dx}=\dfrac{dv}{dx}.$

$\dfrac{dv}{dx}+\dfrac{x}{2\,(1-x^2)}v=x.$

$\int P\,dx=\int\dfrac{x\,dx}{2\,(1-x^2)}$

$=-\dfrac{1}{4}\int\dfrac{-2x}{1-x^2}dx=-\dfrac{1}{4}\log\,(1-x^2).$

$\therefore \quad \text{I.F.}=(1-x^2)^{-1/4}$

Multiplying both sides by I.F. and integrating,

$v\,(1-x^2)^{-1/4}=\int x\,(1-x^2)^{-1/4}\,dx+c$

$=-\dfrac{2}{3}(1-x^2)^{3/4}+c$

or $2\sqrt{y}=-\dfrac{2}{3}(1-x^2)+c\,(1-x^2)^{1/4}$

or $\sqrt{y}=-\dfrac{1}{3}(1-x^2)+k\,(1-x^2)^{1/4}$

(b) $\dfrac{1}{y}\dfrac{dy}{dx}+\dfrac{4x}{1-x^2}=\dfrac{x}{\sqrt{y}}$

$\dfrac{2\sqrt{y}}{1-x^2}=-\dfrac{1}{2}\log\,(1-x^2)+c$

Problem Set (5)

Bernoulli's Equation $\dfrac{dy}{dx}+Py=Qy^n$

Solve the following differential equations :

1. (a) $2\dfrac{dy}{dx}-\dfrac{y}{x}=\dfrac{y^2}{x^2}$ (b) $\dfrac{dy}{dx}+\dfrac{y}{x}=\dfrac{y^2}{x^2}.$

2. $3\dfrac{dy}{dx}+\dfrac{2y}{x+1}=\dfrac{x^3}{y^2}.$

3. $\dfrac{dy}{dx}+2y\tan x=y^2.$

4. $\dfrac{dy}{dx}+\dfrac{1}{x}=\dfrac{e^y}{x^2}.$

5. $\dfrac{dy}{dx}+y\cot x=y^2\sin^2 x.$

6.* $x^3\dfrac{dy}{dx}-x^2y=-y^4\cos x$ given $y\,(0)=1$ **(M.N.R. 1996)**

7. $2xy\,dy-(x^2+y^2+1)\,dx=0.$

8. (a) $(x^2+y^2+2x)\,dx+2y\,dy=0.$

(b) $(x^2-2x+2y^2)\,dx+2xy\,dy=0$

9. $\frac{dy}{dx}+yx=y^2.e^{x^2/2}\sin x$ or $y^2 e^{x^2/2}\log x$

10. $\frac{dy}{dx}+\frac{\tan y}{1+x}=(1+x)e^x\sec y.$

11. (a) $\tan y\frac{dy}{dx}+\tan x=\cos y\cos^3 x.$

(b) $\sec^2 y\frac{dy}{dx}+\tan y=x^3.$

(c) $\frac{dy}{dx}+y=x^2y^2.$

12. (a)* $x\frac{dy}{dx}+y\log y=xye^x.$

(b) $x\frac{dy}{dx}=y(\log y-\log x+1)$

13. $y(2xy+e^x)\,dx-e^x\,dy=0.$

14. (a) $\cos x\,dy=y(\sin x-y)\,dx$

(b) $\frac{dy}{dx}+y\cot x=y^2\sin^2 x\cos^2 x.$

15. $\frac{dy}{dx}+\frac{y}{x}=y^2.$

16. (a) $\frac{dy}{dx}+\frac{1}{x}\tan y=\frac{1}{x^2}\tan y\sin y.$

(b)* $\tan y\frac{dy}{dx}+\tan x=\cos y\cos^2 x.$

17.* $\frac{dz}{dx}+\frac{z}{x}\log z=\frac{z}{x^2}(\log z)^2$

18. $\frac{dy}{dx}+x\sin 2y=x^3\cos^2 y.$

Also find the particular curve which passes through $(0,\pi/4)$.

19. (a)* $(1+x^2)\frac{dy}{dx}-4x^2\cos^2 y+x\sin 2y=0$

(b) $\frac{dy}{dx}+\frac{1}{x}\sin 2y=x^3\cos^2 y.$

20.* $x^2y\,dx-(x^3+y^3)\,dy=0.$

21. $(x^3-y^3)\,dx+xy^2\,dy=0.$

22. $\frac{dy}{dx}+y\cos x=y^n\sin 2x.$

23. (a) $(xy^2-e^{1/x^3})\,dx-x^2y\,dy=0,$

or $x^2y\frac{dy}{dx}-xy^2=-e^{1/x^3}.$

(b) $(x-y^3)+3xy^2\frac{dy}{dx}=0$

24. $\frac{dy}{dx}=(\sin x-\sin y)\frac{\cos x}{\cos y}.$

25. $\sin y\frac{dy}{dx}=\cos y(1-x\cos y)$

26.* $\frac{dy}{dx}=e^{x-y}(e^x-e^y).$

27. $\frac{dy}{dx}-2y\tan x=y^2\tan^2 x.$

28. (a) $(1-x^2)\frac{dy}{dx}+xy=xy^2.$

(b) $(1-x^2)\frac{dy}{dx}+xy=a.$

29. $y\,dx-x\,dy+3x^2y^2e^{x^3}\,dx$

30. $\frac{dy}{dx}+(2x\tan^{-1}y-x^3)(1+y^2)=0.$

31. $2\sin x\frac{dy}{dx}-y\cos x=xy^3e^x$

32.* $(1+x^2)\frac{dy}{dx}+xy=x^3y^3.$

(Bihar C.E.E. 1999)

33. $2\frac{dy}{dx}-y\sec x=y^3\tan x.$

34. (a)* $y\sin 2x\,dx-(1+y^2+\cos^2 x)\,dy=0$

(b) The solution of the differential equation $\frac{dx}{dy}-\frac{x\log x}{1+\log x}=\frac{e^y}{1+\log x}$ if $y(1)=0$, is :

(a) $x^x=e^{ye^y}$ (b) $e^y=x^{e^y}$

(c) $x^x=ye^y$ (d) none

Solutions to Problem Set (5)

1. (a) $x=y-cy\sqrt{x}.$

(b) $v\cdot\frac{1}{x}=-\frac{1}{2x^2}+c$ where $v=-1/y$

2. $y^3(1+x)^2=\frac{1}{6}x^6+\frac{2}{5}x^5+\frac{1}{4}x^4+c.$

3. Ans. $\cos^2 x+\left(\frac{1}{2}x+\frac{1}{4}\sin 2x\right)y=cy$

4. $e^{-y}\frac{dy}{dx}+\frac{1}{x}e^{-y}=\frac{1}{x^2}.$ Put $-e^{-y}=v$ etc.

or $\frac{dv}{dx}-\frac{v}{x}=\frac{1}{x^2}$ which is linear. I.F. $=\frac{1}{x}.$

$2x=-e^y(2cx^2-1)$

5. Ans. $-\frac{1}{y}(\text{cosec}\,x)=(c-\cos x)$

6. Divide by x^3y^4 and put $\frac{1}{y^3}=v$

$x^3=y^3(3\sin x+c).$

when $x=0,\ y=0\quad\therefore\ c=0$

$\therefore\quad x^3=3y^3\sin x$

7. $2xy\frac{dy}{dx}-y^2=(x^2+1).$

First divide by x and then put $y^2=v.$

$x^2-y^2-1+cx=0.$

8. (a) Ans. $e^x(x^2+y^2)=c$

(b) $2y\frac{dy}{dx}+\frac{2y^2}{x}=-\frac{x^2-2x}{x}$

Put $y^2=v$ $\quad\therefore\quad \frac{dv}{dx}+\frac{2}{x}v=-x+2$

Above is linear, I.F. $=e^{\log x^2}=x^2$

$v.x^2=\int x^2(2-x)\,dx+c$

or $\quad x^2y^2=\frac{2}{3}x^3-\frac{x^4}{4}+c$

9. Ans. $ye^{x^2/2}(c-\cos x)+1=0$

or $\quad ye^{x^2/2}(x\log x-x+c)+1=0.$

10. Ans. $\sin y=(1+x)(e^x+c)$.

11. (a) $\sec x\sec y=\frac{x}{2}+\frac{1}{4}\sin 2x+c.$

(b) Put $\tan y=v$ $\quad\therefore\quad \frac{dv}{dx}+v.1=x^3$. Linear,

I.F. $=e^x$

or $\quad \tan y=x^3-3x^2+6x-6+ce^{-x}$.

(c) $\frac{dv}{dx}-v=x^2$ $\quad$ where $\quad \frac{-1}{y}=v$, I.F. $=e^{-x}$

$ve^{-x}=\int e^{-x}x^2\,dx.$

Integrate successively by parts

$-\frac{1}{y}e^{-x}=(-e^{-x})x^2-(e^{-x})(2x)+(-e^{-x})(2)+c$

or $\quad \frac{1}{y}=(x^2+2x+2)-ce^x$.

12. (a) $\frac{1}{y}\cdot\frac{dy}{dx}+\frac{1}{x}\log y=e^x$. $\quad$ Put $\log y=v$ etc.

$x\log y=e^x(x-1)+c.$

(b) $\frac{1}{y}\frac{dy}{dx}-\frac{1}{x}\log y=\frac{1-\log x}{x}.$

Put $\log y=v$, I.F. $=\frac{1}{x}$

$\frac{1}{x}\log y=\frac{\log x}{x}+c$

or $\quad \log y-\log x=cx.$

13. $e^x\frac{dy}{dx}-ye^x=2xy^2$ $\quad$ or $\quad \frac{1}{y^2}\frac{dy}{dx}-\frac{1}{y}=2xe^{-x}$.

Put $-\frac{1}{y}=v$ $\quad\therefore\quad \frac{dv}{dx}+v=2xe^{-x}$, I.F. $=e^x$.

$y(x^2+c)+e^x=0.$

14. (a) Ans. $\sec x=y(c+\tan x)$

(b) Ans. $\frac{1}{y}\operatorname{cosec} x=\frac{1}{3}\cos^3 x+c$

15. Ans. $kx=e^{-1/xy}$

16. (a) $\cot y\operatorname{cosec} y\frac{dy}{dx}+\frac{1}{x}\operatorname{cosec} y=\frac{1}{x^2}$

Put $-\operatorname{cosec} y=v$ $\quad\therefore\quad \frac{dv}{dx}-\frac{1}{x}\cdot v=\frac{1}{x^2}$,

I.F. $=\frac{1}{x}$

Ans. $2x=\sin y(1-2cx^2)$.

(b) $\sec y\tan y\frac{dy}{dx}+\sec y\tan x=\cos^2 x.$

Put $\sec y=v$.

$\frac{dv}{dx}+v\tan x=\cos^2 x.$

Linear, I.F. $=\sec x$.

$\sec y\sec x=\sin x+c.$

17. $\frac{1}{z(\log z)^2}\cdot\frac{dz}{dx}+\frac{1}{x}\frac{1}{\log z}=\frac{1}{x^2}$

Put $-\frac{1}{\log z}=v;$ $\quad\therefore\quad \frac{1}{(\log z)^2}\frac{1}{z}\cdot\frac{dz}{dx}=\frac{dv}{dx}$

or $\quad \frac{dv}{dx}-\frac{1}{x}v=\frac{1}{x^2}$ which is linear and I.F. $=\frac{1}{x}$.

Ans. $\quad \frac{1}{x\log z}=\frac{1}{2x^2}-c.$

18. $\sec^2 y\frac{dy}{dx}+2x\tan y=x^3$ $\quad$ [$\because$ $\sin 2y=2\sin y\cos y$]

Put $\tan y=v;$ $\quad\therefore\quad \sec^2 y.\frac{dy}{dx}=\frac{dv}{dx}$.

$\therefore\quad \frac{dv}{dx}+2xv=x^3$ which is linear and I.F. $=e^{x^2}$.

Multiplying both sides by I.F. and integrating,

$v.e^{x^2}=\int x^3.e^{x^2}\,dx.$ $\quad$ Put $x^2=t$ etc.

$v.e^t=\frac{1}{2}\int te^t\,dt=\frac{1}{2}e^t(t-1)+c.$

$\tan y=\frac{1}{2}(x^2-1)+ce^{-x^2}$

If it passes through $(0,\pi/4)$, then $1=-\frac{1}{2}+c$ or $c=\frac{3}{2}$

$\therefore\quad \tan y=\frac{1}{2}(x^2-1)+\frac{3}{2}e^{-x^2}$

19. (a) $\sec^2 y\frac{dy}{dx}+\frac{2x}{1+x^2}\tan y=\frac{4x^2}{1+x^2}.$

Put $\tan y=v$

Ans. $\tan y(1+x^2)=\frac{4}{3}x^3+c.$

(b) Ans. $x^2\tan y=\frac{1}{6}x^6+c.$

20. The above equation is homogeneous and has been solved in **Ex. 2 P. 1630**. It can also be reduced to linear form.

$x^2y\frac{dx}{dy}-x^3=y^3$

or $\quad x^2\frac{dx}{dy}-\frac{1}{y}x^3=y^2,$ $\quad$ Put $x^3=v$

$v\frac{1}{y^3}=\int 3y^2\cdot\frac{1}{y^3}dy=3\log y+c$

or $\frac{x^3}{y^3}=3\log ky,$ choosing $c=3\log k$

or $e^{x^3/3y^3}=ky.$

21. Ans. $\frac{k}{x}=e^{y^3/3x^3}.$

22. $\frac{1}{y^n}\frac{dy}{dx}+\frac{1}{y^{n-1}}\cos x=2\sin x\cos x.$

Put $\frac{1}{y^{n-1}}=v;$ $\therefore$ $(1-n)\frac{1}{y^n}\frac{dy}{dx}=\frac{dv}{dx}$

$\therefore$ $\frac{1}{1-n}\frac{dv}{dx}+v\cos x=2\sin x\cos x$

or $\frac{dv}{dx}+v(1-n)\cos x=2(1-n)\sin x\cos x.$

Above is linear and I.F. $=e^{(1-n)\sin x}$

Multiplying both sides by I.F. and integrating,

$ve^{(1-n)\sin x}=\int 2(1-n)\sin x\cos x.e^{(1-n)\sin x}dx.$

Put $(1-n)\sin x=t;$

$\therefore$ $(1-n)\cos x\,dx=dt.$

$ve^t=\int 2\frac{t}{1-n}e^t dt=\frac{2}{1-n}e^t(t-1)+c$

or $v=\frac{2}{1-n}(t-1)+ce^{-t}$

or $\frac{1}{y^{n-1}}=2\sin x-\frac{2}{1-n}+ce^{(n-1)\sin x}.$

23. (a) Put $y^2=v;$ $\therefore$ $2y\frac{dy}{dx}=\frac{dv}{dx}$

or $\frac{dv}{dx}-\frac{2}{x}v=-\frac{2}{x^2}e^{1/x^3},$

which is linear and I.F. $=\frac{1}{x^2}.$

or $3y^2=2x^2e^{1/x^3}+kx^2.$

(b) $3y^2\frac{dy}{dx}-\frac{1}{x}y^3=-1.$

Put $y^3=v$, I.F. $=\frac{1}{x}.$

Ans. $y^3\frac{1}{x}=-\log x+k.$

24. Multiplying by $\cos y$, we get

$\cos y\frac{dy}{dx}+\sin y\cos x=\sin x\cos x.$

Put $\sin y=v;$ $\therefore$ $\frac{dv}{dx}+v\cos x=\sin x$, I.F. $=e^{\sin x}.$

$v.e^{\sin x}=\int e^{\sin x}\sin x\cos x\,dx$

$\therefore$ $\sin y=\sin x-1+ce^{-\sin x}.$

25. $\sec y\tan y\frac{dy}{dx}-\sec y=-x.$

Put $\sec y=v;$ $\therefore$ $\frac{dv}{dx}-v.1=-x$ (linear);

I.F. $=e^{-x}.$

$\sec y\,e^{-x}=e^{-x}(x+1)+c.$

26. $\frac{dy}{dx}=\frac{e^x}{e^y}(e^x-e^y)$

or $e^y\frac{dy}{dx}+e^x.e^y=e^x.e^x.$

Put $e^y=v,$ $\therefore$ $e^y\frac{dy}{dx}=\frac{dv}{dx}.$

$\frac{dv}{dx}+ve^x=e^xe^x,$

which is linear and I.F. $=e^{e^x}$

Multiplying both sides by I.F. and integrating,

$v.e^{e^x}=\int e^x.e^x.e^{e^x}dx$ Put $e^x=t$ etc.

$ve^t=\int te^t dt=e^t(t-1)+c;$

$\therefore$ $v=(t-1)+ce^{-t}$

$e^y=(e^x-1)+ce^{-e^x}.$

27. Ans. $-\frac{1}{y}\sec^2 x=\frac{1}{3}\tan^3 x+c.$

28. (a) $\frac{1}{y^2}\frac{dy}{dx}+\frac{1}{y}\frac{x}{1-x^2}=\frac{x}{(1-x^2)}.$

Put $-\frac{1}{y}=v$ etc. and I.F. $=\sqrt{(1-x^2)}.$

$\sqrt{(1-x^2)}.(y-1)=ky.$

(b) Proceeding as in part (a),

$y\cdot\frac{1}{\sqrt{(1-x^2)}}=\int\frac{a}{(1-x^2)^{3/2}}dx+c.$

Put $x=\sin\theta$

$=\int a\sec^2\theta\,d\theta+c=a\tan\theta+c=\frac{ax}{\sqrt{(1-x^2)}}+c,$

$y=ax+c\sqrt{(1-x^2)}.$

29. $x\frac{dy}{dx}-y=3x^2y^2.e^{x^3}$

or $\frac{1}{y^2}\frac{dy}{dx}-\frac{1}{x}\cdot\frac{1}{y}=3xe.^{x^3}$ Put $-\frac{1}{y}=v$ etc.

$-\frac{x}{y}=e^{x^3}+c.$

30. $\frac{1}{1+y^2}\frac{dy}{dx}+2x\tan^{-1}y=x^3.$

Put $\tan^{-1}y=v$ $\therefore$ $\frac{1}{1+y^2}\frac{dy}{dx}=\frac{dv}{dx}$

$\therefore$ $\frac{dv}{dx}+2xv=x^3$ which is linear and I.F. $=e^{x^2}$ etc.

$ve^{x^2}=\frac{1}{2}e^{x^2}(x^2-1)+c.$

or $\quad 2\tan^{-1} y = x^2 - 1 + 2ce^{-x^2}$

31. $\dfrac{2}{y^3}\dfrac{dy}{dx} - \dfrac{1}{y^2}\cot x = \dfrac{xe^x}{\sin x}$

Put $-\dfrac{1}{y^2} = v \quad \therefore \quad \dfrac{dv}{dx} + \cot x = \dfrac{xe^x}{\sin x}, \quad$ I.F. $= \sin x$

$-\dfrac{1}{y^2}\sin x = e^x(x-1) + c.$

32. $\dfrac{1}{y^3}\dfrac{dy}{dx} + \dfrac{x}{1+x^2}\cdot\dfrac{1}{y^2} = \dfrac{x^3}{1+x^2}.$

Put $-\dfrac{1}{2}\cdot\dfrac{1}{y^2} = v; \quad \therefore \quad \dfrac{1}{y^3}\dfrac{dy}{dx} = \dfrac{dv}{dx}.$

$\therefore \quad \dfrac{dv}{dx} - \dfrac{2x}{1+x^2}v = \dfrac{x^3}{1+x^2}$

I.F. $= \dfrac{1}{1+x^2}$

$v\cdot\dfrac{1}{(1+x^2)} = \displaystyle\int \dfrac{x^3}{(1+x^2)^2}dx + c$

Put $1 + x^2 = t$

$\therefore \quad v\cdot\dfrac{1}{t} = \dfrac{1}{2}\left[\log t + \dfrac{1}{t}\right] + c$ etc.

33. $\dfrac{2}{y^3}\dfrac{dy}{dx} - \dfrac{1}{y^2}\sec x = \tan x. \quad$ Put $-\dfrac{1}{y^2} = v$

$\dfrac{dv}{dx} + v\sec x = \tan x.$

Linear I.F. $= \sec x + \tan x$

$v.(\sec x + \tan x) = \int \tan x(\sec x + \tan x)\,dx + c$

or $\quad -\dfrac{1}{y^2}(\sec x + \tan x) = \sec x + \tan x - x + c$

$\because \quad \tan^2 x = (\sec^2 x - 1).$

34. (a) $y\sin 2x\dfrac{dx}{dy} - \cos^2 x = (1+y^2)$

or $\quad \sin 2x\dfrac{dx}{dy} - \dfrac{1}{y}\cos^2 x = \dfrac{1}{y} + y.$

Put $-\cos^2 x = v$

$\dfrac{dv}{dy} + \dfrac{1}{y}v = \dfrac{1}{y} + y.$ Linear I.F. $= e^{\log y} = y$

$v.y = \int (1+y^2)\,dy + c$

or $\quad -y\cos^2 x = y + \dfrac{1}{3}y^3 + c$

(b) Ans. (a).

The given equation can be re-written as

$(1+\log x)\dfrac{dx}{dy} - x\log x = e^y$

Put $x\log x = t \quad \therefore \quad (1+\log x)\dfrac{dx}{dy} = \dfrac{dt}{dy}$

$\therefore \quad \dfrac{dt}{dy} - t.1 = e^y$

Above is a linear differential equation.

$\therefore \quad$ I.F. $= e^{\int P\,dy} = e^{\int -1\,dy} = e^{-y}$

Multiplying both sides by I.F. and integrating

$t.e^{-y} = \int e^{-y}.e^y\,dy + c$

or $\quad t.e^{-y} = y + c \quad$ or $\quad x\log x = (y+c)e^y$

Now $y(1) = 0$, *i.e.*, when $x = 1, y = 0$

$\therefore \quad 1\log 1 = 0 + ce^0 \quad$ or $\quad 0 = c$

$\therefore \quad x\log x = ye^y \quad$ or $\quad \log x^x = ye^y$

$\therefore \quad x^x = e^{ye^y} \Rightarrow$ (a)

Clairaut form of differential equations.

A differential equation of the form $y = px + f(p)$ where $p = \dfrac{dy}{dx}$ is called Clairaut form of differential equation whose solution is obtained by replacing p by c as shown below :

Differentiate both sides w.r.t. x and put $\dfrac{dy}{dx} = p$

$\therefore \quad p = p + x\dfrac{dp}{dx} + f'(p)\dfrac{dp}{dx} = 0$

or $\quad [x + f'(p)]\dfrac{dp}{dx} = 0$

$\therefore \quad \dfrac{dp}{dx} = 0 \Rightarrow p = c$

Putting $p = c$ the required solution is $y = cx + f(c)$.

35. Solution of $\left(\dfrac{dy}{dx}\right)^2 - x\dfrac{dy}{dx} + y = 0$ is

(a) $y = 2$ (b) $y = 2x$

(c) $y = 2x - 4$ (d) $y = 2x^2 - 4$ **(I.I.T. 1999)**

Ans. (c).

Putting $\dfrac{dy}{dx} = p$, the above equation is $y = px - p^2$. It is Clairaut form.

Hence its solution is $y = cx - c^2$ where c is any arbitrary constant. Choosing $c = 2$, the required solution is $y = 2x - 4 \Rightarrow$ (c).

36. Solve the following equations :

(a) $(y - px)(p - 1) = p$

$y = px + \dfrac{p}{p-1}$ **Clairaut form**

Solution is $y = cx + \dfrac{c}{c-1}$

(b) $\sin px\cos y = \cos px\sin y + p$

$\sin(px - y) = p$

or $\quad y = px - \sin^{-1} p$ **Clairaut form**

Solution is $y = cx - \sin^{-1} c.$

(c) $p = \log(px - y)$

$y = px - e^p$ **Clairaut form**

$y = cx - e^c$ is the solution.

(d) $p^2(x^2-a^2)-2pxy+y^2-b^2=0$

$$(y-px)^2=a^2p^2+b^2$$

$\therefore \quad y=px\pm\sqrt{a^2p^2+b^2}$

Clairaut form Solution is

$$y=cx\pm\sqrt{a^2c^2+b^2}$$

or $\quad (y-cx)^2=a^2c^2+b^2.$

Case V. EQUATION SOLVABLE FOR *x* OR *y*

$y=f(x,p)$ or $x=f(y,p)$ where, $p=\dfrac{dy}{dx}$

Rule. Differentiate w.r.t. x and put $\dfrac{dy}{dx}=p$ or $\dfrac{dx}{dy}=\dfrac{1}{p}$ and then solve. If the solutions be $g(x,p,c)$ or $f(y,p,c)$, then eliminate p between given equation and above and we get a relation between x, y and c which is the required solution.

Ex. 1. (a) $y+px=x^4p^2$ ...(1)

$y=-px+x^4p^2$. Diff. w.r.t. x

$$p=-p-x\frac{dp}{dx}+x^4\,2p\frac{dp}{dx}+p^2\,4x^3$$

$$\therefore \quad \left(2p+x\frac{dp}{dx}\right)=2px^3\left(2p+x\frac{dp}{dx}\right)$$

or $\quad \left(2p+x\dfrac{dp}{dx}\right)(1-2px^3)=0$

$2p+x\dfrac{dp}{dx}=0$ or $2\dfrac{dx}{x}+\dfrac{dp}{p}=0$

or $\log x^2+\log p=\log c$ or $px^2=c$ ...(2)

Eliminating p between (1) and (2), we get

$xy=-c+c^2x$ as the required solution.

(b) $y=2px+p^4x^2$

Proceeding as in (a), $\quad p+2x\dfrac{dp}{dx}=0$

or $p^2x=c$ or $p^2=\dfrac{c}{x}$. Eliminate p

$\therefore \quad y-c^2=2px$

$(y-c^2)^2=4p^2x^2=4cx$

(c) $xp^2-2yp+x=0$

or $\quad 2y=x\left(p+\dfrac{1}{p}\right)$. Diff. w.r.t. x

$$2p=p+\frac{1}{p}+x\left(1-\frac{1}{p^2}\right)\frac{dp}{dx}$$

or $\quad p\left(1-\dfrac{1}{p^2}\right)=x\left(1-\dfrac{1}{p^2}\right)\dfrac{dp}{dx}$

or $\quad p=x\dfrac{dp}{dx}$ or $\dfrac{dp}{p}=\dfrac{dx}{x}$

or $\quad p=cx$. Now eliminate p

$2cy=c^2x^2+1$

Ex. 2 (a). $y^2\log y=xyp+p^2$

$$x=y\frac{\log y}{p}-\frac{p}{y}$$

Differentiate w.r.t. y and put $\dfrac{dx}{dy}=\dfrac{1}{p}$

Use quotient formula and simplify

$$\frac{1}{y}\frac{dp}{dy}\left(1+\frac{y^2}{p^2}\log y\right)=\frac{p}{y^2}\left(1+\frac{y^2}{p^2}\log y\right)$$

or $\quad \dfrac{dp}{p}=\dfrac{dy}{y}$. Integrate $p=ky$

Eliminating p, we get

$$\log y=kx+x^2$$

(b) $y=2px+y^2p^3$

or $\quad 2x=\dfrac{y}{p}-y^2p^2$. Proceeding as in part (a).

$$\left(\frac{1}{p}+2yp^2\right)=-\frac{y}{p}\frac{dp}{dy}\left(\frac{1}{p}+2yp^2\right)=0$$

or $\quad \dfrac{dp}{p}+\dfrac{dy}{y}=0.$ Integrate $py=c$ or $p=\dfrac{c}{y}$

Eliminate p $\quad \therefore \quad y^2=2cx+c^2$

Case VI. EQUATIONS SOLVABLE FOR *p*

If this case resolve the given equation into linear factors of the type.

$$(p-\beta_1)(p-\beta_2)\ \ldots\ldots\ (p-\beta_n)=0$$

Solve each of the above n equations of the type $p-\beta_k=0$ and let their solution be

$$f_1(x,y,c_1)=0,\ f_2(x,y,c_2)=0,\ldots.\ f_n(x,y,c_n)=0$$

We may replace different constants occurring in above by the same constant say k.

Hence the complete solution will be

$$f_1(x,y,k),\ f_2(x,y,k),\ldots.\ f_n(x,y,k)=0$$

Ex. 3 (a). $x^2\left(\dfrac{dy}{dx}\right)^2+xy\dfrac{dy}{dx}-6y^2=0$

$x^2p^2+xyp-6y^2=0$ or $(px+3y)(px-2y)=0$

$\therefore \quad \dfrac{dy}{dx}=-\dfrac{3y}{x}$ or $\dfrac{dy}{dx}=\dfrac{2y}{x}$

Their solutions by variables separable is

$$(yx^3-c_1)=0 \text{ and } (y-c_2x^2)=0$$

Replacing c_1 and c_2 by k, the required solution is

$$(yx^3-k)(y-kx^2)=0.$$

(b) $p^2+2py\cot x-y^2=0$

Solving as a quadratic in p,

$$\frac{dy}{dx}=-y\left(\frac{1+\cos x}{\sin x}\right)=-y\frac{1-\cos^2 x}{\sin x(1-\cos x)}$$

$$=-y\frac{1+\cos x}{\sin x}$$

or $\quad \dfrac{dy}{dx}=\dfrac{-y(\cos x-1)}{\sin x}=\dfrac{y(1-\cos^2 x)}{\sin x(1+\cos x)}=\dfrac{y(\sin x)}{1+\cos x}$

Integrating above by variables separable,

$y(1\pm\cos x)=k$ is required solution.

Geometrical Problems

In the figure below, TM = sub-tangent and MG is sub-normal where PT is a tangent and PG is normal at $P(x, y)$ and PM is ordinate of the point P.

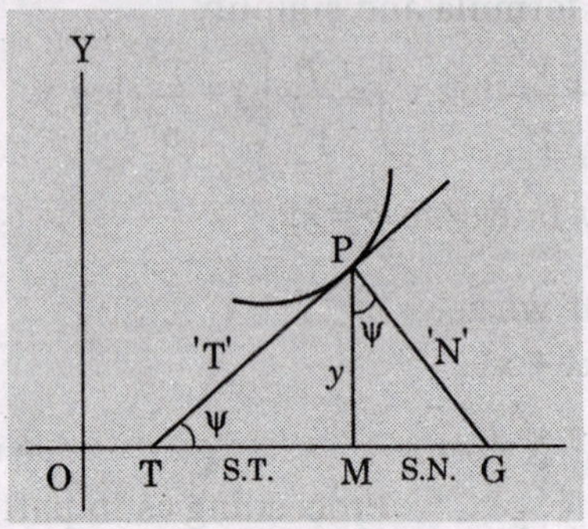

Fig. 92

Also $\tan\psi = \dfrac{dy}{dx} = y', \cot\psi = \dfrac{1}{y'}$,

Equations of tangent and normal are

$$Y - y = \frac{dy}{dx}(X - x) \qquad ...(1)$$

$$Y - y = -\frac{1}{\left(\dfrac{dy}{dx}\right)}[X - x] \qquad ...(2)$$

Putting $Y = 0$ in the above, we get intercept on x-axis made by tangents and normal

$$X = OT = x - y\bigg/\frac{dy}{dx} = x - \frac{y}{y'}$$

$$X = OG = x + y\frac{dy}{dx} = x + yy'$$

$$\text{S.T.} = TM = y\cot\psi = y\bigg/\frac{dy}{dx} = \frac{y}{y'}$$

$$\text{S.N.} = MG = y\tan\psi = y\frac{dy}{dx} = yy'$$

$$\text{Normal} = PG = y\sec\psi = y\sqrt{1+y'^2}$$

$$\text{Tangent} = PT = y\,\text{cosec}\,\psi = \frac{y}{y'}\sqrt{1+y'^2}$$

Problem Set (6)

Geometrical Problems.

Ex. 1. Find the equations of the curve for which

(i) (a) Cartesian sub-tangent is constant, or
(b) it varies as the abscissa.

(ii) Cartesian sub-normal is (a) constant, or
(b) equal to abscissa

(i) (a) By knowledge of differential calculus, we know that Cartesian sub-tangent

$$= y\bigg/\frac{dy}{dx} = \text{const.} = a \text{ say}$$

$$\therefore \quad y = a\frac{dy}{dx} \quad \text{or} \quad \frac{dx}{a} = \frac{1}{y}dy.$$

Integrating, we get

$$\log y = x/a + \log k; \quad \therefore \quad y = ke^{x/a}$$

(b) In this case $y\bigg/\dfrac{dy}{dx} = kx$ or $y = kx\dfrac{dy}{dx}$

or $\dfrac{dx}{x} = k\dfrac{dy}{y}$

or $\log x + \log c = k\log y$

or $cx = y^k$.

(ii) (a) Cartesian sub-normal is $y\dfrac{dy}{dx} = a$ say.

$\therefore \quad y\,dy = a\,dx; \quad \therefore \quad y^2 = 2ax + k$, i.e. a parabola.

(b) Ans. $x^2 - y^2 = a^2$.

Ex. 2. The tangent at any point P of a curve meets the axis of x in T. Find the curve for which $OP = PT$, O being the origin.

Since $OP = PT$, $\quad\therefore\quad \Delta OPT$ is isosceles.

$$\angle POT = \angle PTO = 180^o - \psi.$$

If P be the point (x, y), then

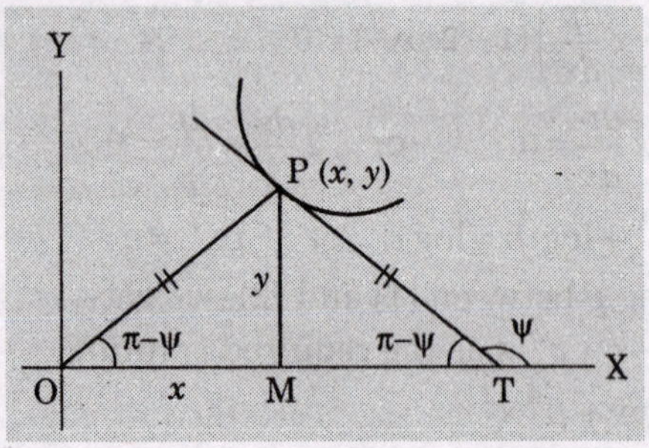

Fig. 2

$$\frac{y}{x} = \tan(180° - \psi) = -\tan\psi$$

$$\frac{y}{x} = -\frac{dy}{dx} \quad \text{or} \quad \frac{dx}{x} = -\frac{dy}{y}. \text{ Integrate}$$

$$\log x + \log y = k;$$

$\therefore \quad xy = a^2$ (A rectangular hyperbola).

***Ex. 3.** A curve is such that any point P on it is as far from the origin as from the point in which the normal at P meets the x-axis. Show that it must be either an equilateral hyperbola or a circle.

Another form :

Find the equation of family of curves for which the length of the normal is equal to the radius vector.

From Differential Calculus we know that PG = length of normal or from **Fig. 92 above.**

$$\frac{y}{PG} = \cos\psi.$$

$$\therefore \quad PG = y\sec\psi = r = \sqrt{[x^2 + y^2]} \quad \text{(given)}$$

$\therefore \quad y^2 \sec^2 \psi = x^2 + y^2$

or $\quad y^2 (1 + \tan^2 \psi) = x^2 + y^2$

or $\quad y^2 + y^2 \left[\dfrac{dy}{dx}\right]^2 = x^2 + y^2$

or $\quad y\,dy \pm x\,dx = 0 \quad$ or $\quad y^2 \pm x^2 = k^2$.

This represents a circle or equilateral hyperbola according as we take + or – sign.

***Ex. 4.** A normal is drawn at a point $P(x, y)$ of a curve. It meets x-axis at G. If PG is of constant length k, then show that the differential equation describing such curves is $y\dfrac{dy}{dx} = \pm\sqrt{k^2 - y^2}$. Find the equation of such a curve passing through $(0, k)$. **(I.I.T. 1994)**

Refer **Ex. 3**. $PG^2 = y^2 + y^2\left(\dfrac{dy}{dx}\right)^2 = k^2$ given

$\therefore \quad y\dfrac{dy}{dx} = \pm\sqrt{(k^2 - y^2)} \qquad ...(1)$

or $\quad \dfrac{-2y}{\sqrt{(k^2 - y^2)}}\,dy = \pm 2\,dx$. Integrating

$2\sqrt{k^2 - y^2} = c \pm 2x$. If it passes through $(0, k)$, then

$0 = c \pm 0 \quad \therefore \quad c = 0$. Hence

$2\sqrt{k^2 - y^2} = \pm 2x \quad$ or $\quad x^2 = k^2 - y^2$

or $\quad x^2 + y^2 = k^2$ *i.e.*, a circle.

Ex. 5. Find the curve in which the sub-tangent is always bisected at the origin.

If T be the point where tangent meets x-axis and M is foot of perpendicular, then TM is sub-tangent where

T is $\left(x - y\dfrac{dx}{dy}, 0\right)$, M is $(x, 0)$.

By given condition mid-point of TM is (0, 0)

$\dfrac{1}{2}\left[x - y\dfrac{dx}{dy} + x\right] = 0 \quad$ or $\quad 2x - y\dfrac{dx}{dy} = 0$

or $\quad 2\dfrac{dy}{y} = \dfrac{dx}{x}$. Integrate

$\log y^2 = \log x + \log k$

$\therefore \quad y^2 = kx \quad$ *i.e.*, parabola

Ex. 6. Show that the curve for which the normal at every point passes through a fixed point is a circle.

Equation of the normal at any point (x, y) is

$Y - y = -\dfrac{dx}{dy}(X - x)$.

It passes through a fixed point say (h, k)

$\therefore \quad (k - y) = -\dfrac{dx}{dy}(h - x)$

or $\quad (x - h)\,dx = -(y - k)\,dy$.

Variables separable

Integrate $\dfrac{(x - h)^2}{2} = -\dfrac{(y - k)^2}{2} + c$

Choose $c = \dfrac{r^2}{2}$ and it becomes $(x - h)^2 + (y - k)^2 = r^2$ which is a circle.

***Ex. 7.** Find the curve for which the intercept cut off by a tangent on x-axis is equal to four times the ordinate of the point of contact.

$Y - y = \dfrac{dy}{dx}(X - x)$

Put $Y = 0$, we get $X = x - y\dfrac{dx}{dy}$.

By given condition,

$x - y\dfrac{dx}{dy} = 4y \quad$ or $\quad \dfrac{dy}{dx} = \dfrac{y}{x - 4y}$

Homogeneous.

Putting $y = vx$ etc., it reduces to $\dfrac{1 - 4v}{v^2}\,dv = \dfrac{4dx}{x}$

or $\quad \left(\dfrac{1}{v^2} - \dfrac{4}{v}\right)dv = \dfrac{4dx}{x}$. Integrate

$-\dfrac{1}{v} = 4 \log xvk = \log (yk)^4$

$\therefore \quad y^4 k^4 = e^{-x/y} \quad$ or $\quad cy^4 = e^{-x/y}$.

Ex. 8. The normal PG to a curve meets the axis in G. If the distance of G from the origin is twice the abscissa of P, prove that the curve is a rectangular hyperbola.

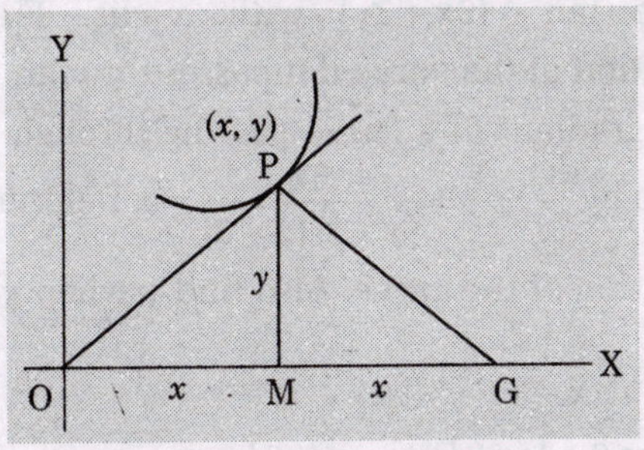

Fig. 3

$OG = 2x \quad$ or $\quad OM + MG = 2x$

or $\quad x + MG = 2x; \quad \therefore \quad MG = x$.

But MG is sub-normal $= y\dfrac{dy}{dx}$.

$\therefore \quad y\dfrac{dy}{dx} = x \quad$ or $\quad y\,dy = x\,dx$. Integrate.

$\therefore \quad x^2 - y^2 = a^2$ which is a rectangular hyperbola.

Ex. 9. The normal at each point of a curve and the line from that point to the origin form an isosceles triangle with the base on the x-axis. Find the equation of the curve. If the normal makes equal angles with the radius vector and the initial line find the curve.

Refer fig. of Q. 8 above; since $\Delta\, OPG$ is isosceles, PM will bisect the base.

$\therefore \quad OM = MG =$ sub-normal

or $\quad x = y\dfrac{dy}{dx}; \quad \therefore \; x^2 - y^2 = a^2.$

***Ex. 10. (a)** The slope of the curve at any point is the reciprocal of twice the ordinate at the point. The curve also passes through the point (4, 3). Find the equation.

Slope of the curve = slope of tangent

$$= \tan\psi = \frac{dy}{dx} = \frac{1}{2y} \text{ (given)}$$

$\therefore \quad 2y\,dy = dx$ i.e. $y^2 = x + c.$

It passes through (4, 3).

$\therefore \quad 9 = 4 + c \quad$ i.e., $\quad c = 5.$

$\therefore \quad$ Equation is $y^2 = x + 5.$

(b) Show that the equation of the curve whose slope at any point is equal to $y + 2x$ and which passes through origin is

$y = 2(e^x - x - 1).$

$$\frac{dy}{dx} = y + 2x$$

or $\quad \dfrac{dy}{dx} - y = 2x;$ Linear, I.F. $= e^{-x}$

$$ye^{-x} = -2e^{-x}(x + 1) + c.$$

It passes through (0, 0).

$\therefore \; c = 2,\; y = 2(e^x - x - 1).$

(c) The tangent at any point (x, y) of a curve makes an angle $\tan^{-1}(2x + 3y)$ with x-axis. Find the equation of the curve if it passes through (1, 2).

(d) The gradient of a curve passing through (4, 0) is given by $\dfrac{dy}{dx} - \dfrac{y}{x} + \dfrac{5x}{(x+2)(x-3)} = 0.$ Determine the equation of the curve. Also find y when $x = 5.$

$$\frac{y}{x} = \log\frac{x+2}{x-3} \cdot k$$

where $0 = \log 6k \qquad \therefore \quad 6k = 1$

Also $\dfrac{y}{5} = \log\dfrac{7}{2}k \quad \therefore \quad y = 5\log\dfrac{7}{2}\cdot\dfrac{1}{6} = 5\log\dfrac{7}{12}.$

***Ex. 11.** Find the curve which is such that portion of x-axis cut off between the origin and the tangent at any point is proportional to the ordinate of the point.

$Y - y = \dfrac{dy}{dx}(X - x)$ is the equation of the tangent

Putting $Y = 0$, we get

$$X = x - \frac{y}{y'} = ky \qquad \text{(given)}$$

or $\quad y\dfrac{dx}{dy} - x = -ky$

or $\quad \dfrac{dx}{dy} - \dfrac{x}{y} = -k.$ It is linear

and I.F. $= e^{-\log y} = \dfrac{1}{y}$

Its solution is $x \cdot \dfrac{1}{y} = -k\log y + c.$

or $\quad -\dfrac{x}{ky} = \log y - \log a \quad$ or $\quad y = ae^{-x/ky}.$

***Ex. 12.** The tangent at a point P of a curve meets the axis of y in N the parallel through P to the axis of y meets the axis of x at M; O is the origin. If the area of the triangle MON is constant, show that the curve is a hyperbola.

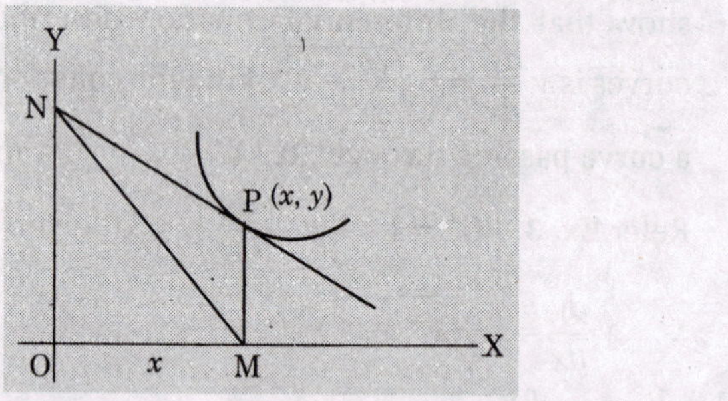

Fig. 4

Tangent is $\quad Y - y = \dfrac{dy}{dx}(X - x).$

If it meets y-axis in N, then putting $X = 0$,

$$Y = ON = y - x\frac{dy}{dx}$$

Also $\quad OM = x$

$\therefore \quad \Delta MON = \dfrac{1}{2}OM.ON = \text{constant}$

$\therefore \quad \dfrac{1}{2}x\left(y - x\dfrac{dy}{dx}\right) = \text{constant}$

or $\quad x^2\dfrac{dy}{dx} - xy = c \quad$ or $\quad \dfrac{dy}{dx} - \dfrac{1}{x}y = \dfrac{c}{x^2}.$

Above is linear and I.F. $= e^{-\log x} = \dfrac{1}{x}.$

$\therefore \quad y \cdot \dfrac{1}{x} = \displaystyle\int \dfrac{c}{x^3}\,dx + k = -\dfrac{c}{2x^2} + k$

or $\quad 2k.x^2 - 2xy + c = 0.$

$$H^2 - AB = (-1)^2 - (2k)(0) = +1, \text{ i.e. } +\text{ive}$$

Hence the above represents a hyperbola

$$ax^2 + 2hxy + by^2 + 2gx + 2fy + c = 0$$

represents a hyperbola if $h^2 - ab > 0.$

Ex. 13. The normal at any point P of a curve cuts OX, in G and N is the foot of the ordinate of P. If NG varies as the square of the radius vector from O, find the curve.

Clearly $NG =$ sub-normal $= y\dfrac{dy}{dx}$

Radius vector $OP = \sqrt{(x^2 + y^2)}.$

By the given condition, $y\dfrac{dy}{dx} = k(x^2 + y^2)$

or $y\dfrac{dy}{dx}-ky^2=kx^2$

Put $\dfrac{y^2}{2}=v.\quad\therefore\quad y\dfrac{dy}{dx}=\dfrac{dv}{dx}\quad\therefore\quad\dfrac{dv}{dx}-2kv=kx^2$

which is linear and I.F. $=e^{-2k.x}$

$$v.e^{-2k.x}=k\int x^2e^{-2k.x}\,dx+c.$$

Integrating successively by parts,

$$\frac{y^2}{2}e^{-2k.x}=k\left[\left(\frac{e^{-2k.x}}{-2k}\right)x^2-\left(\frac{e^{-2k.x}}{4k^2}\right)2x+\left(\frac{e^{-2k.x}}{-8k^3}\right)2+c\right]$$

or $y^2=-x^2-\dfrac{x}{k}-\dfrac{1}{2k^2}+2ce^{2kx}$

***Ex. 14. (a)** A curve is such that the length of perpendicular from origin on the tangent at any point P of the curve is equal to the abscissa of P. Prove that the differential equation of the curve is $y^2-2xy\dfrac{dy}{dx}-x^2=0$ and hence find the curve.

Tangent is $Y-y-\dfrac{dy}{dx}(X-x)=0$. If p be perpendicular from origin, then

$$p=\frac{x\dfrac{dy}{dx}-y}{\sqrt{\left[1+\left(\dfrac{dy}{dx}\right)^2\right]}}=x\text{ given. Square}$$

$$x^2\left(\frac{dy}{dx}\right)^2-2xy\frac{dy}{dx}+y^2=x^2+x^2\left(\frac{dy}{dx}\right)^2$$

or $y^2-2xy\dfrac{dy}{dx}-x^2=0$

or $\dfrac{dy}{dx}=\dfrac{y^2-x^2}{2xy}$ (Homogeneous)

or $2xy\dfrac{dy}{dx}-y^2=-x^2$

or $2y\dfrac{dy}{dx}-\dfrac{y^2}{x}=-x.$ Put $y^2=v.$

$\therefore\quad\dfrac{dv}{dx}-\dfrac{v}{x}=-x.$ Linear, I.F. is $e^{\log 1/x}=\dfrac{1}{x}$

Multiplying by I.F. and integrating, we get

$$v\cdot\frac{1}{x}=\int -x\cdot\frac{1}{x}dx+c=-x+c$$

or $\dfrac{y^2}{x}=-x+c$ or $x^2+y^2=cx$

is the required equation to the curve.

(b) A curve passing through the point (1, 1) has the property that the perpendicular distance of the origin from the normal at any point P of the curve is equal to the distance of P from the x-axis. Determine the equation of the curve. **(I.I.T. 1999)**

Normal is $Y-y=-\dfrac{1}{y'}(X-x)$ or $y'Y+X=yy'+x$

Perp. from $(0,0)=y$ (given)

$\therefore\quad\dfrac{yy'+x}{\sqrt{(1+y'^2)}}=y$

or $x^2+2xy\dfrac{dy}{dx}+y^2\left(\dfrac{dy}{dx}\right)^2=y^2+y^2\left(\dfrac{dy}{dx}\right)^2$

or $\dfrac{dy}{dx}=\dfrac{y^2-x^2}{2xy}$ Homogeneous.

Put $y=vx\quad\therefore\quad v+x\dfrac{dv}{dx}=\dfrac{v^2-1}{2v}$

or $x\dfrac{dv}{dx}=\dfrac{v^2-1}{2v}-v=-\dfrac{1+v^2}{2v}$

$\therefore\quad\dfrac{2v}{1+v^2}dv=-\dfrac{dx}{x}$

$\log(1+v^2)+\log x=\log k$

or $x\left(1+\dfrac{y^2}{x^2}\right)=k$ or $x^2+y^2=kx$

It passes through (1, 1) $\therefore\ 2=k$

$\therefore\quad x^2+y^2=2x$ is the required equation.

Ex. 15. A particle P moves so that its velocities parallel to the axes of x and y are respectively $-ky$ and kx where k is a constant different from zero. Find the parth of the particle, if it passes through the point (3, 4).

$\dfrac{dy}{dt}=kx$ and $\dfrac{dx}{dt}=-ky$ given

$\therefore\quad\dfrac{dy}{dx}=\dfrac{dy}{dt}\div\dfrac{dx}{dt}=-\dfrac{x}{y}$

$\therefore\quad y\,dy+x\,dx=0$. Integrating, we get

$\dfrac{y^2}{2}+\dfrac{x^2}{2}=c$ or $x^2+y^2=2c$

It passes through (3, 4) $\therefore\ 9+16=2c$

Hence the path is $x^2+y^2=25$.

Ex. 16. Find the family of curves whose tangent form an angle of $\pi/4$ with the hyperbola $xy=c$.

Let the slope of tangent of required family be $\dfrac{dy}{dx}=m_1$

Also $\quad y=\dfrac{c}{x}\quad\therefore\quad\dfrac{dy}{dx}=-\dfrac{c}{x^2}=m_2$, say.

By given condition, $\tan\dfrac{\pi}{4}=\dfrac{m_1-m_2}{1+m_1m_2}=1$

or $\dfrac{dy}{dx}+\dfrac{c}{x^2}=1-\dfrac{c}{x^2}\dfrac{dy}{dx}$

or $\left(1+\dfrac{c}{x^2}\right)\dfrac{dy}{dx}=1-\dfrac{c}{x^2}$

or $\frac{dy}{dx} = \frac{x^2 - c}{x^2 + c} = 1 - \frac{2c}{x^2 + c}$.

Integrating $y + k = x - 2c \frac{1}{\sqrt{c}} \tan^{-1} \frac{x}{\sqrt{c}}$.

Above represents the required family of curves in which k is parameter.

Ex. 17. Find the equation of the curve which passes through the origin and the tangent to which at every point (x, y) has slope equal to $\frac{x^4 + 2xy - 1}{1 + x^2}$. **(Roorkee 2001)**

Sol. $\tan \psi = \frac{dy}{dx} = \frac{x^4 + 2xy - 1}{1 + x^2} = x^2 - 1 + \frac{2xy}{x^2 + 1}$

$\therefore \quad \frac{dy}{dx} - \frac{2x}{1 + x^2} y = x^2 - 1;$ Linear

$\text{I.F.} = -\log(1 + x^2) = \frac{1}{1 + x^2}$

Multiplying both sides by I.F. and integrating,

$$y \cdot \frac{1}{x^2 + 1} = \int \frac{x^2 - 1}{x^2 + 1} dx + c = \int \left(1 - \frac{2}{x^2 + 1}\right) dx + c$$

or $y \cdot \frac{1}{x^2 + 1} = x - 2\tan^{-1} x + c$

Since it passes through $(0, 0)$ $\therefore$ $c = 0$

Hence $y = (x^2 + 1)(x - 2\tan^{-1} x)$.

Ex. 18. A curve passes through $(2, 0)$ and the slope of tangent at point $P(x, y)$ equals $\frac{(x+1)^2 + y - 3}{(x+1)}$. Find the equation of the curve and area enclosed by the curve and the x-axis in the fourth quadrant. **(I.I.T. 2004)**

Given slope of tangent at (x, y)

$$= \frac{(x+1)^2 + (y - 3)}{x + 1} = \frac{dy}{dx}$$

Put $x + 1 = X, y - 3 = Y$ $\quad \therefore \quad \frac{dy}{dx} = \frac{dY}{dX}$

$\therefore \quad \frac{dY}{dX} = X + \frac{Y}{X}$ or $\frac{dY}{dX} - \frac{Y}{X} = X.$

Above is linear differential equation.

$\therefore \quad \text{I.F.} = e^{\int -\frac{1}{X} dX} = e^{-\log X} = \frac{1}{X}$

Multiplying both sides by I.F. and integrating

$$Y \cdot \frac{1}{X} = \int X \cdot \frac{1}{X} dX + c = X + c$$

or $\frac{y - 3}{x + 1} = (x + 1) + c.$

The curve passes through the point $(2, 0)$.

$\therefore \quad -\frac{3}{3} = 3 + c$ or $c = -4.$

Hence the required equation is

$$y - 3 = (x + 1)^2 - 4(x + 1)$$

or $y = x^2 - 2x$ or $y + 1 = (x - 1)^2$

Above represents a parabola with vertex at $(1, -1)$ which meets the x-axis at the points $(0, 0)$ and $(2, 0)$. Its shape is as shown in the figure below.

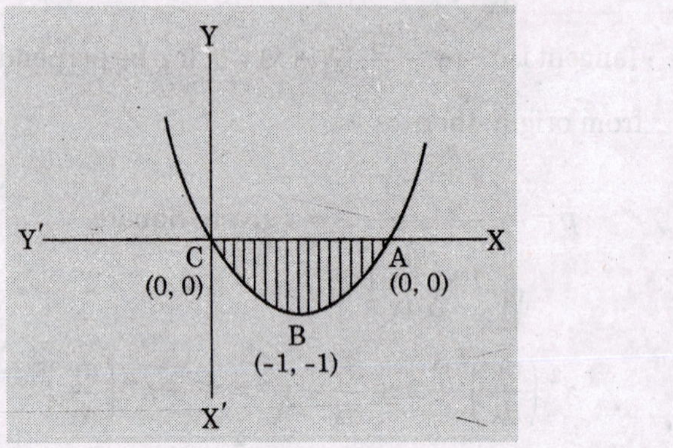

Fig. 5

Required area in fourth quadrant is

$$\int_0^2 y\, dx = \int_0^2 (x^2 - 2x)\, dx = \left(\frac{x^3}{3} - x^2\right)_0^2 = \frac{4}{3} \text{ sq. units}$$

Miscellaneous Problem Set (7)

1. The differential equation which represent the family of curves $y = c_1 e^{c_2 x}$, c_1 and c_2 are constants is

(a) $y' = y^2$ (b) $y'' = y' y$

(c) $yy'' = y'$ (d) $yy' = (y')^2$

(AIEEE 2009, WB JEE 2011)

2. The differential equation of the family of circles with fixed radius 5 units and centre on the line $y = 2$ is

(a) $(y - 2) y'^2 = 25 - (y - 2)^2$

(b) $(y - 2)^2 y'^2 = 25 - (y - 2)^2$

(c) $(x - 2)^2 y'^2 = 25 - (y - 2)^2$

(d) $(x - 2) y'^2 = 25 - (y - 2)^2$

(AIEEE 2008)

3. The solution of the differential equation $\frac{dy}{dx} = \frac{x + y}{x}$ satisfying the conditions $y(1) = 1$ is

(a) $y = x \log x + x^2$ (b) $y = xe^{(x-1)}$

(c) $y = x \log x + x$ (d) $y = \log x + x$

(AIEEE 2008)

4. Solution of the differential equation

$$\cos x\, dy = y(\sin x - y)\, dx, 0 < x < \frac{\pi}{2} \text{ is}$$

(a) $\sec x = (\tan x + c) y$ (b) $y \sec x = \tan x + c$

(c) $y \tan x = \sec x + c$ (d) $\tan x = (\sec x + c) . y$

(AIEEE 2010)

5. Let I be the purchase value of an equipment and $V(t)$ be the value after it has been used for t years. The value $V(t)$ depreciates at a rate given by differential equation $\frac{d}{dt}(vt) = -k(T-t)$ $k > 0$ is a constant and T is the total life in years of the equipment. Then the scrap value $V(T)$ of the equipment is

(a) $T^2 - \frac{1}{k}$ (b) $I = \frac{kT^2}{2}$

(c) $I - \frac{k(T-t)^2}{2}$ (d) e^{-kT}

(AIEEE 2011)

6. If $y(x)$ satisfies the differential equation $y' - y\tan x = 2x\sec x$ and $y(0) = 0$ then

(a) $y\left(\frac{\pi}{4}\right) = \frac{\pi^2}{8\sqrt{2}}$ (b) $y'\left(\frac{\pi}{4}\right) = \frac{\pi^2}{18}$

(c) $y\left(\frac{\pi}{3}\right) = \frac{\pi^2}{9}$ (d) $y'\left(\frac{\pi}{3}\right) = \frac{4\pi}{3} + \frac{2\pi^2}{3\sqrt{3}}$

(IIT-JEE 2012)

7. Let $f : [1, \infty[\to [2, \infty[$ be a differentiable function such that $f(1) = 2$ if $6\int_1^x f(t)\,dt = 3x f(x) - x^3 - 5$ for all $x \geq 1$. Then the value of $f(x)$ is

(a) 6 (b) 4 (c) $\frac{1}{4}$ (d) $\frac{1}{6}$

(IIT-JEE 2011)

8. Let $y'(x) + y(x)g'(x) = g(x)g'(x)$, $y(0) = 0$, $x \in \mathbf{R}$ where $f'(x)$ denotes $\frac{d(f(x))}{dx}$ and $g(x)$ is a given non-constant differentiable function on $\mathbf{R}$ with $g(0) = g(z) = 0$. Then $y(2)$ is equal to

(a) 0 (b) 1 (c) 2 (d) −1

(IIT-JEE 2011)

9. Let f be a real valued differentiable function on $\mathbf{R}$ such that $f(1) = 1$. If the y-intercept of the tangent at any point $P(x, y)$ on the curve $y = f(x)$ is equal to the cube of the abscissa of P, then the value of $f(-3)$ is equal to

(a) 9 (b) 10 (c) −9 (d) 10

(IIT-JEE 2010)

10. The differential equation representing the family of curves $y^2 = 2c(x + \sqrt{c})$ where c is a positive parameter, is of

(a) order 1 (b) order 2

(c) degree 3 (d) degree 4

(IIT 1999; AIEEE 2005)

Hints / Solution the Problems Set (7)

1. Ans. (d).

$y = C_1 e^{C_2 x} \Rightarrow y' = c_1 c_2 e^{c_2 x}$

$\Rightarrow y'' = c_1 c_2 . c_2 e^{c_2 x} \Rightarrow y'' = c_2 y'$

$\therefore yy'' = c_2 yy'' \Rightarrow yy'' = (y')^2$

2. Ans. (b).

Circle $(x-h)^2 + (y-2)^2 = 25$

$\Rightarrow 2(x-h) + 2(y-2)y' = 0$

$\Rightarrow 2(y-2)y' = -2(x-h)$

$\Rightarrow (y-2)^2 y'^2 = (x-h)^2$

$\Rightarrow (y-2)^2 y'^2 = 25 - (y-2)^2$

3. Ans. (c).

$\frac{dy}{dx} = \frac{x+y}{x} \Rightarrow x\,dy = (x+y)dx$

$\Rightarrow x\,dy - y\,dx = x\,dx$

$\Rightarrow \frac{x\,dy - y\,dx}{x^2} = \frac{1}{x}dx \Rightarrow d\left(\frac{y}{x}\right) = \frac{1}{x}dx$

On integrating we get

$\frac{y}{x} = \log x + c$

given $y(1) = 1$ $\therefore c = 1 \Rightarrow y = x\log x + x$

4. Ans. (a).

$\cos x\,dy = y(\sin x - y)\,dx$

$\Rightarrow \frac{dy}{dx} = \frac{y\sin x - y^2}{\cos x} = y\tan x - y^2\sec x$

$\Rightarrow \frac{1}{y^2}.\frac{dy}{dx} - \frac{1}{y}\tan x = -\sec x$

$\Rightarrow -\frac{1}{y^2}\frac{dy}{dx} + \frac{1}{y}\tan x = \sec x$ ...(1)

Let $\frac{1}{y} = t \Rightarrow \frac{-1}{y^2}\frac{dy}{dx} = \frac{dt}{dx}$ ...(2)

From (1) and (2) we get

$\frac{dt}{dx} + t.\tan x = \sec x$

$\therefore$ I.F. $= e^{\int \tan x\,dx} = e^{\log|\sec x|} = \sec x$

Hence the required solution is

$t.\sec x = \int \sec x.\sec x\,dx + c$

$\Rightarrow \frac{1}{y}\sec x = \tan x = c \Rightarrow \sec x = y(\tan x + c)$

5. Ans. (b).

$\frac{dV(t)}{dt} = k(T-t) \Rightarrow \int dV(t) = \int(-kT)\,dt + \int kt\,dt$

$\Rightarrow v(t) = -kT.t + k.\frac{t^2}{2} + c$

At $t = 0$, $c = v(t) = I$

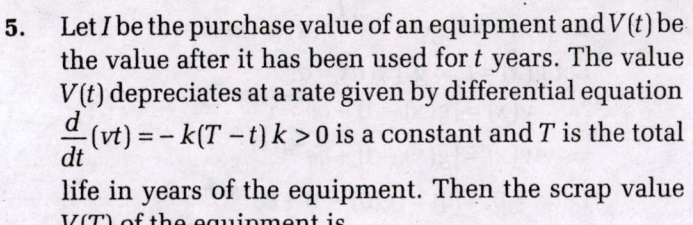

$\therefore \quad v(t) = -kTt + \dfrac{kt^2}{2} + I$

At $t = T$

$V(T) = -kT^2 + k.\dfrac{T^2}{2} + I \Rightarrow V(t) = I - \dfrac{1}{2}kT^2$

6. Ans. (a) and (d).

$\dfrac{dy}{dx} - y\tan x = 2x\sec x$

$P = -\tan x \qquad \therefore \qquad \text{I.F.} = e^{\int P dx}$

$\Rightarrow \quad e^{-\int \tan dx} = e^{\log\cos x} = \cos x$

$\therefore$ Solution is given by

$y.\cos x = x^2 + c$

$\because \; y(0) = 0 \qquad \Rightarrow \quad c = 0$

$\therefore \quad y = x^2 \sec x$

$y\left(\dfrac{\pi}{4}\right) = \dfrac{\pi^2}{8\sqrt{2}},\; y\left(\dfrac{\pi}{3}\right) = \dfrac{2\pi^2}{9}$

$y'(\pi) = 2x\sec x + x^2 \sec x\tan x$

$y'\left(\dfrac{\pi}{4}\right) = \dfrac{\pi}{\sqrt{2}} + \dfrac{\pi^2}{16}\sqrt{2} = \dfrac{\pi}{\sqrt{2}} + \dfrac{\pi^2}{8\sqrt{2}} = \dfrac{9\pi^2}{8\sqrt{2}}$

$y'\left(\dfrac{\pi}{3}\right) = \dfrac{2\pi}{3} \times 2 + \dfrac{\pi^2}{9} \times 2\sqrt{3}$

7. Ans. (a).

Given : $6\int_1^x f(t)\,dt = 3x f(x) - x^3 - 5$

Differentiating, we get $6f(x) = 3f(x) + 3xf'(x) - 3x^2$

$f'(x) - \dfrac{1}{x}f(x) = x$

Put $y = f(x)$

$\therefore \quad \dfrac{dy}{dx} - \dfrac{1}{x}y = x$, which is linear

$\Rightarrow \quad \text{I.F.} = \dfrac{1}{x}$

Solution is $y\dfrac{1}{x} = x + c$

Put $x = 1, y = 2 \Rightarrow c = 1$

$\Rightarrow \quad y = x^2 + x$

$\Rightarrow \quad f(x) = x^2 + x = 4 + 2 = 6$

8. Ans. (a).

$y'(x) + y(x)g'(x) = g(x)g'(x),\; y(0) = 0,\; \forall\, x \in \mathbf{R}$

$\Rightarrow \quad \dfrac{d}{dx}(y(x)) + y(x)g'(x) = g(x)\,g'(x),\; g(0) = g(2) = 0$

$\text{I.F.} = e^{\int g'(x)dx} = e^{g(x)}$

so $y(x)\,e^{g(x)} = \int e^{g(x)}.g(x)\,g'(x)\,dx + c$

Let $g(x) = t \Rightarrow g'(x)\,dx = dt$

$\therefore \quad y(x) = (g(x) - 1) + ce^{-g(x)}$

$\Rightarrow \quad y(x) = (g(x) - 1) + ce^{-g(x)}$

Let $x = 0$, $y(0) = (g(0) - 1) + ce^{-g(0)}$

$\Rightarrow \quad 0 = (0 - 1) + c \Rightarrow c = 1$

$\Rightarrow \quad y(x) = (g(x) - 1) + e^{-g(x)}$

$\Rightarrow \quad y(2) = (g(2) - 1) + e^{-g(2)}$

$\Rightarrow \quad y(2) = (0 - 1) + e^{-(0)} = -1 + 1 = 0$

9. Ans. (a).

$Y - y = m(X - x)$

y-intercept $(X = 0)$

$Y = y - mx$

given that $y - mx = x^3 \Rightarrow x\dfrac{dy}{dx} - y = -x^3$

$\Rightarrow \quad \dfrac{dy}{dx} - \dfrac{y}{x} = -x^2$

$\text{I.F.} = e^{-\int \frac{1}{x}dx} = \dfrac{1}{x}$

$\therefore \quad$ solution is $y.\dfrac{1}{x} = \int \dfrac{1}{x}(-x^2)\,dx$

$\Rightarrow \quad f(x) = y = \dfrac{-x^3}{2} + cx$

given that $f(1) = 1 \Rightarrow c = \dfrac{3}{2}$

Hence, $f(x) = \dfrac{-x^3}{2} + \dfrac{3x}{2} \Rightarrow f(-3) = 9$

10. Ans. (a) and (c).

$y^2 = 2c(x + \sqrt{c})$

$\Rightarrow \quad 2y\dfrac{dy}{dx} = 2c \Rightarrow c = y.\dfrac{dy}{dx}$

$\therefore \quad$ differential equation is $y^2 = 2y.\dfrac{dy}{dx}\left(x + \sqrt{y\dfrac{dy}{dx}}\right)$

$\Rightarrow \quad \dfrac{y}{2.\dfrac{dy}{dx}} - x = \sqrt{y\dfrac{dy}{dx}}$

Squaring and multiplying by $\left(\dfrac{dy}{dx}\right)^2$, we get

$y\left(\dfrac{dy}{dx}\right)^3 - x^2\left(\dfrac{dy}{dx}\right)^2 + xy\left(\dfrac{dy}{dx}\right) - \dfrac{y^2}{4} = 0$

Hence order is 1 and degree is 3.

MISCELLANEOUS EXERCISE

Matching Entries

Match the entries of List-A and List-B.

1.

List-A	List-B
(a) The order and degree of the differential equation $\frac{d^4y}{dx^4} = y + \left(\frac{dy}{dx}\right)^4$	1. $\sin^{-1}\frac{y}{x} = \frac{mx^2}{2} + c$
(b) If $\frac{2+\sin x}{y+1}\frac{dy}{dx} = -\cos x$ and $y = 1$ at $x = 0$, then the value of y at $x = \frac{\pi}{2}$ is	2. 4, 1
(c) Solution of $x.\frac{dy}{dx} = y + x\tan\frac{y}{x}$ is	3. $\frac{1}{3}$
(d) Solution of $\frac{x\frac{dy}{dx} - y}{\sqrt{x^2 - y^2}} = mx^2$ is	4. $\sin\frac{y}{x} = cx$

2.

List-A	List-B
(a) Solution of differential equation $x\log x.\frac{dy}{dx} + y = 2\log x$ is	1. $y = ce^{2x}$
(b) Solution of differential equation $\sin 2x\frac{dy}{dx} - y = \tan x$ is	2. $y = \log x + \frac{c}{\log x}$
(c) If in any curve subnormal is twice the square of ordinate, then the curve is	3. $y = \tan x + c\sqrt{\tan x}$

Answers

1. (a) $\rightarrow$ 2.
(b) $\rightarrow$ 3. **Q. 3 (c) P. 1624-25**
(c) $\rightarrow$ 4. **Q. 19 (a) P. 1633-35**
(d) $\rightarrow$ 1. **Q. 26 (b) P. 1644-35**

2. (a) $\rightarrow$ 2. **Q. 14 P. 1644-46**
(b) $\rightarrow$ 3. **Q. 26 (a) P. 1645-47**
(c) $\rightarrow$ 1.

$$y\frac{dy}{dx} = 2y^2 \qquad \therefore \frac{dy}{y} = 2\,dx$$

or $\log y = 2x + c$

Now c can be chosen in any form to give the answers (b) and (c).

CHAPTER 33

Statistics

Measures of Central Tendency and Dispersion

§1. Measures of Central tendency or Measures of Location

The jumbled up data for any distribution has no significance and are dark to us. To grasp their significance, we have to fall back upon some kind of measure called averages, which shall highlight the entire data. Averages really are statistical constants which enable one to comprehend easily the significance of the whole. The five measures of central tendency in common use are :

(i) Arithmetic mean (ii) Geometric mean
(iii) Harmonic mean (iv) Median
(v) Mode

§2. Arithmetic mean

The arithmetic mean $\bar{x}$ of n observations is given by $\bar{x} = \frac{1}{n}(x_1 + x_2 + \ldots + x_n)$ or by $\frac{1}{n}\sum_{i=1}^{n} x_i$.

If the frequency of the random variable x_i is f_i in a distribution, then

$$\bar{x} = \frac{f_1x_1 + f_2x_2 + \ldots + f_ix_i + \ldots + f_nx_n}{f_1 + f_2 + \ldots + f_n} = \frac{1}{N}\sum_{i=1}^{n} f_ix_i$$

where $N = \sum_{i=1}^{n} f_i$ = total frequency.

we can write this as $\bar{x} = \frac{1}{N}\Sigma f_i (x_i - 0)$ *i.e.* deviations are measured from the origin.

Now, if deviations are measured from any fixed arbitrary point A, then

$$\bar{X} = \frac{1}{N}\Sigma f_i (x_i - A) = \frac{1}{N}\Sigma f_i x_i - A\frac{1}{N}\sum_i f_i = \bar{x} - A$$

$$\Rightarrow \quad \bar{x} = \bar{X} + A \quad \text{as} \quad \sum_{i=1}^{n} f_i = N$$

Note : This helps in shortening calculation work for finding the mean.

Alternatively $\bar{x} = A + \frac{1}{N}\Sigma f_i d_i$ where $d_i = x_i - A$

In case of grouped or continuous frequency distribution the x's are values at mid-points of different class-intervals. If the width of each class interval is h, then we take $d_i = \frac{x_i - A}{h}$

so that $x_i = A + hd_i$

and hence $\bar{x} = \frac{1}{N}\sum_i f_i x_i = \frac{1}{N}\sum_i f_i \{A + hd_i\}$

$$\bar{x} = A + \frac{h}{N}\sum_i f_i d_i \qquad \because \sum_{i=1}^{n} f_i = N$$

Symbols for moments :

$$\mu_0 = \frac{1}{N}\Sigma f_i (x_i - \bar{x})^0 = 1$$

$$\mu_1 = \frac{1}{N}\Sigma f_i (x_i - \bar{x}) = 0$$

In general $\mu_1' = \frac{1}{N}\Sigma f_i (x_i - a) = \bar{x} - a$

$$\mu_n = \frac{1}{N}\sum_i f_i (x_i - \bar{x})^n$$

and $\mu_n' = \frac{1}{N}\sum_i f_i (x_i - a)^n$

Properties of A.M.

I. **Algebraic sum of the deviations of a set of values from their arithmetic mean is zero**

i.e. $\sum_{i=1}^{n} f_i (x_i - \bar{x}) = 0$

Since $\sum_i f_i (x_i - \bar{x}) = \sum_i f_i x_i - \bar{x}\sum_i f_i = N\bar{x} - \bar{x}N = 0$

II. **The sum of the squares of the deviations of a set of values is minimum about their mean $\bar{x}$.**

We consider squares of deviations about any number A *i.e.* $S = \sum_{i=1}^{n} f_i (x_i - A)^2$

Here A is any variable, therefore for S to be minimum

$$\frac{dS}{dA} = 0 \text{ and } \frac{d^2S}{dA^2} > 0$$

These give $\sum_{i=1}^{n} 2f_i (x_i - A)(-1) = 0$

and $\sum_{i=1}^{n} 2f_i = 2N > 0 \quad \Rightarrow \quad \sum_{i=1}^{n} f_i (x_i - A) = 0$

$\Rightarrow \sum_i f_i x_i = A\sum_i f_i = AN$

$\Rightarrow \frac{\sum_i f_i x_i}{N} = A$ or $\bar{x} = A$ *i.e.* the assumed number A is equal to the mean $\bar{x}$.

III. **The grand mean of k-component series of sizes $n_1, n_2, \ldots, n_k$ with respective means $\overline{x_1}, \overline{x_2}, \ldots, \overline{x_k}$, is given by**

$$\bar{x} = \frac{n_1 \overline{x_1} + n_2 \overline{x_2} + \ldots + n_k \overline{x_k}}{n_1 + n_2 + \ldots + n_k} = \frac{\sum_{i=1}^{k} n_i \overline{x_i}}{\sum_i n_i}$$

Merits and demerits of Arithmetic mean

Merits :

(1) It is rigidly defined.
(2) It is based on all observations.
(3) It is easily understood and followed.
(4) It is calculated rapidly and with reasonable ease.
(5) It is least affected by fluctuations of sampling.
(6) It is easily amenable to algebraic treatment.
(7) It has minimal property. The second moment about any number a *i.e.* $\mu_2' = \frac{1}{N}\sum f_i (x_i - a)^2$ is least when measured about the mean value.

Demerits :

(1) In practice, the calculated value of mean differs from the actually observed values.
(2) It is seriously affected by the extreme values.
(3) Its position can not be located on the graph by inspection.
(4) It can not be calculated for the qualitative observations.
(5) If fails to average the ratios and percentages properly.

§3. Geometic Mean

We know, G.M. of two positive numbers x_1 and x_2 is givien by $(x_1 x_2)^{1/2}$. This when extended to n positive numbers gives the geometric mean

$$G = (x_1 \, x_2 \, x_3 \ldots x_n)^{1/n}$$

or $\log G = \frac{1}{n}[\log x_1 + \log x_2 + \ldots + \log x_n]$

$$= \frac{1}{n}\sum_{i=1}^{n} \log x_i$$

$$\Rightarrow \quad G = \text{antilog}\left[\frac{1}{n}\sum_{i=1}^{n} \log x_i\right]$$

In case x_i is repeated f_i times

then $G = (x_1^{f_1} \, x_2^{f_2} \ldots x_i^{f_i} \ldots x_n^{f_n})^{1/\sum_{i=1}^{n} f_i}$

or $\log G = \frac{1}{N}\sum_{i=1}^{n} f_i \log x_i$

$\because \sum_{i=1}^{n} f_i = N$

$$\Rightarrow \quad G = \text{antilog}\left[\frac{1}{N}\sum_{i=1}^{n} f_i \log x_i\right]$$

Thus the logarithm of the geometric mean of a series of values is the arithmetic mean of their logarithms.

The geometric mean of the combined two series of sizes n_1 and n_2 with respective geometric means G_1 and G_2 is given by

$$\log G = \frac{n_1 \log G_1 + n_2 \log G_2}{n_1 + n_2}$$

§4. Harmonic Mean

We know that if x_1, H, x_2 are in harmonic progression, then $\frac{1}{x_1}, \frac{1}{H}, \frac{1}{x_2}$ are in A.P. so that

$$\frac{1}{H} = \frac{1}{2}\left(\frac{1}{x_1} + \frac{1}{x_2}\right) \quad \text{or} \quad H = \frac{1}{\frac{1}{2}\left(\frac{1}{x_1} + \frac{1}{x_2}\right)}$$

i.e. harmonic mean of two non-zero numbers x_1 and x_2 is the reciprocal of the arithmetic mean of the reciprocals of the given set of values.

Generalizing over n values $x_1, x_2, \ldots, x_n$ with frequencies $f_1, f_2, \ldots, f_n$ respectively their harmonic mean is given by

$$H = \frac{1}{\frac{1}{N}\sum_{i=1}^{n} \frac{f_i}{x_i}} \quad \text{where } N = \sum_{i=1}^{n} f_i$$

This is the formula for weighted Harmonic mean with weights f_1, f_2, ¼, f_n.

Ex. A cyclist covers his first three miles at an average speed of 8 m.p.h., another two miles at 3 m.p.h. and the last two miles at 3 m.p.h. Find his average speed for the entire journey.

Sol. The average speed for the entire journey is the weighted harmonic mean of reciprocal speeds with distances travelled as weights.

$\therefore$ Average speed for the entire journey

$$= \frac{3+2+2}{3 \cdot \frac{1}{8} + 2 \cdot \frac{1}{3} + 2 \cdot \frac{1}{3}} = \frac{(7)\,(24)}{9+32} = \frac{168}{41}$$

$= 4 \cdot 1$ m.p.h.

Ex. If in a distribution probability of a random variable X taking the particluar value x is ${}^nC_x \, p^x \, q^{n-x}$ where $p + q = 1$, and $x = 0, 1, 2, \ldots, n$, find its mean.

Sol. We have

$$\overline{X} = E(X) = \sum_{x=0}^{n} x . P(X=x) = \sum_{0}^{n} x . {}^{n}C_x\, p^x\, q^{n-x}$$

$$= \sum_{x=0}^{n} n . {}^{n-1}C_{x-1}\, p^x\, q^{n-x}$$

$$\because x . {}^{n}C_x = n\, {}^{n-1}C_{x-1}$$

$$= np \sum_{x=1}^{n} {}^{n-1}C_{x-1}\, p^{x-1}\, q^{(n-1)-(x-1)}$$

$$\because \sum_{x=0}^{n} {}^{n}C_x\, p^x q^{n-x} = (p+q)^n$$

$$= np\,(p+q)^{n-1} = np \qquad \because p+q=1$$

Ex. 1. The geometric mean G of the product of n series of data with geometric means $G_1, G_2, ..., G_n$ respectively, is given by $G = G_1 G_2 ... G_n$.

Sol. Let $X_1, X_2, ..., X_n$ be the variates corresponding to n sets of data, each having the same number of observations say K, and X be their product.

Then $X = X_1\, X_2 ... X_n$

i.e. $\log X = \log X_1 + \log X_2 + ... + \log X_n$

or $\dfrac{\Sigma \log X}{K} = \dfrac{\Sigma \log X_1}{K} + \dfrac{\Sigma \log X_2}{K} + ... + \dfrac{\Sigma \log X_n}{K}$

or $\log G = \log G_1 + \log G_2 + ... + \log G_n$

$\Rightarrow G = G_1 G_2 ... G_n$.

Ex. 2. Show that for a set of positive values of the variate, the arithmetic, geometric and harmonic means are the special cases of the pth root of the mean of the pth powers of the variates.

Sol. Let $x_1, x_2, ..., x_n$ be the n values of some random variate X.

If S be the pth root of the mean of the pth powers of the variate values.

Then, $S = \left(\dfrac{x_1{}^p + x_2{}^p + ... + x_n{}^p}{n} \right)^{\frac{1}{p}}$ ...(1)

(i) If $p = 1$,

then $S = \left(\dfrac{x_1 + x_2 + ... + x_n}{n} \right)$ = Arithmetic mean

(ii) If $p = -1$,

then $S = \left(\dfrac{x_1^{-1} + x_2^{-1} + ... + x_n^{-1}}{n} \right)^{-1}$

$$= \frac{n}{\frac{1}{x_1} + \frac{1}{x_2} + ... + \frac{1}{x_n}} = \text{H.M.}$$

(iii) Taking logarithm of (1), we have

$$\log S = \frac{1}{p} \log \left(\frac{1}{n} \sum_{i=1}^{n} x_i^p \right) = \log \sum_{i=1}^{n} \frac{x_i^p}{n} \Big/ p$$

Applying the limit $p \to 0$ on both sides, we get

$$\lim_{p\to 0} \log S = \lim_{p \to 0} \frac{\log \sum_{i=1}^{n} \frac{x_i^p}{n}}{p} \quad \left(\text{form } \frac{0}{0}\right)$$

Differentiating Numerator and Denominator separately with respect to p, we have

$$= \lim_{p\to 0} \frac{\frac{1}{\sum_i \frac{x_i^p}{n}} \times \sum_{i=1}^{n} \frac{1}{n} x_i^p \log x_i}{1}$$

$$= \lim_{p\to 0} \frac{n}{1+1+...+n \text{ terms}} \times \frac{1}{n}(x_1^p \log x_1 + x_2^p \log x_2 + ... + x_n^p \log x_n)$$

$$= \frac{1}{n} \sum_i \log x_i = \text{G.M.} = \lim_{p\to 0} \log S$$

Hence, for a set of positive values of the variate, the arithmetic, geometric and harmonic means are the special cases of the pth root of the pth powers of the variate, when $p = 1$, $p \to 0$ and $p = -1$ respectively.

Ex 3. A motor car when travelling from rest travels the first twentieth of a mile at 6 m.p.h. the next three twentieths of the mile at 8, 12, 24 m.p.h. respectively. But its average speed over the first one-fifth of a mile is not 12·5 m.p.h., but 9·6 m.p.h. Explain the apparent paradox.

Sol. Let A and H be the arithmetic and harmonic means of speeds

so $A = \dfrac{6+8+12+24}{4} = \dfrac{50}{4} = 12{\cdot}5$ m.p.h.

and $H = \dfrac{4}{\frac{1}{6} + \frac{1}{8} + \frac{1}{12} + \frac{1}{24}} = \dfrac{4 \times 24}{10} = \dfrac{48}{5} = 9{\cdot}6$ m.p.h.

It is obvious from the data that the average speed would not be arithmetic mean, but it is the harmonic mean, because

$$\text{The average speed} = \frac{\text{Total distance travelled}}{\text{Total time of journey}}$$

$$= \frac{\frac{1}{20} + \frac{3}{20}}{\frac{1}{20} \times \frac{1}{6} + \frac{1}{20} \times \frac{1}{8} + \frac{1}{20} \times \frac{1}{12} + \frac{1}{20} \times \frac{1}{24}}$$

$$= \frac{480}{5 \times 10} = 9{\cdot}6 = \text{H.M.}$$

Ex. 4. Find the average rate of (a) motion in the case of a person who rides the first mile at 10 m.p.h., the next mile at 8 m.p.h., and the third mile at 6 m.p.h.; (b) increase in population which in the first decade has increased 20%, in the next 25% and in the third 44%.

Sol. (a) In this case, the harmonic mean is the suitable average

The average rate of motion is,

$$H = \frac{3}{\frac{1}{10}+\frac{1}{8}+\frac{1}{6}} = \frac{3\times 120}{47} = 7\cdot 66 \text{ m.p.h.}$$

$$= \frac{\text{Total distance}}{\text{Total time taken}}$$

(b) Here G.M. is the appropriate average

$$G = (20\times 25\times 44)^{1/3}$$

$$\Rightarrow \quad \log G = \frac{1}{3}[\log 20 + \log 25 + \log 44]$$

$$= \frac{1}{3}[1\cdot 3010 + 1\cdot 3979 + 1\cdot 6435]$$

$$= \frac{1}{3}\times 4\cdot 3424 = 1\cdot 4475$$

$\therefore \quad G = 28\cdot 02 =$ the average increase in population.

Ex. 5. A man motors from A to B. In motoring a distance uphill, he gets a mileage of only 10 miles per gallon of gasoline. On the return trip, he makes 15 miles per gallon. Find the harmonic mean of his mileage. Verify that this is the proper average to be used here, assuming that the distance from A to B is 60 miles.

Sol. The harmonic mean

$$H = \frac{2}{\frac{1}{10}+\frac{1}{15}} = \frac{2\times 30}{5} = 12 \text{ miles per gallon}$$

Let us verify it. The distance between A and B is 60 miles. He has consumed $\frac{60}{10} = 6$ gallons of gasoline in going uphill and $\frac{60}{15} = 4$ gallons in returning i.e., 10 gallons in all.

The total distance covered $= (60+60)$ (both ways) $= 120$ miles

$\therefore$ The average consumption $= \frac{120}{10} = 12$ gallons per mile = H.M.

Hence harmonic mean is the proper average here.

§5. Median and other partition values

Median is the value of the variate which divides the total frequency into two equal halves. Thus if n values are arranged in ascending order of magnitude in an ungrouped frequency distribution, the median is the middle value if n is odd, and the mean of the two middle values, if n is even.

In case of grouped frequency distribution with total frequency N, the class corresponding to the cumulative frequency just greater than $\frac{N}{2}$ is called median class and the value of the median is obtained by the following **formula** :

$$\text{Median} = l + \frac{h}{f}\left(\frac{N}{2} - C\right)$$

where $l =$ lower limit of the median class
$f =$ frequency of the median class
$h =$ magnitude of the median class
$C =$ cumulative frequency of the class preceding the median class
$N = \Sigma f$, the total frequency.

Uses of the Median

It is used

(i) If the data is skewed or heterogeneous.
(ii) If there are extreme deviations.
(iii) If the data is qualitative.
(iv) If a quick estimate of an average is desired.

Ex. Obtain the median for the frequency distribution

Class intervals	Frequency	Cumulative frequency
100—119	8	8
120—139	10	18
140—159	16	34
160—179	15	49
180—199	10	59
200—239	8	67
240—259	3	70

Median = value of (70/2)th *i.e.* 35th item which lies in class interval 160—179.

Since class intervals are of inclusive type, the real limits of the class are $159\cdot 5$ to $179\cdot 5$

$$\therefore \quad \text{Median} = 159\cdot 5 + \frac{20}{15}(35-34) = 160\cdot 83$$

§6. Quartiles

Quartiles are those values of the variate which divide the total frequency into four equal parts; **deciles** and **percentiles**, those values that divide into **ten** and **one hundred** equal parts respectively. **First quartile** is denoted by Q_1 and **third quartile** by Q_3 and $Q_3 - Q_1$ is called **interquartile range.**

The formulae for calculating quartiles, deciles and percentiles are :

$$Q_i = l + \frac{\left(\frac{iN}{4} - C\right)}{f}\times h, i = 1, 2, 3$$

$$D_j = l + \frac{\left(\frac{jN}{10} - C\right)}{f}\times h, j = 1, 2, 3, \ldots, 9$$

$$P_k = l + \frac{\left(\frac{kN}{100} - C\right)}{f}\times h, k = 1, 2, \ldots, 99$$

where $l =$ lower limit of the class in which the particular quartile lies
$f =$ frequency of this class

h = width of this class

C = cumulative frequency of the class preceding the class in which a particular quartile lies.

N = total frequency

§7. Mode.

It is the value of the variate in the frequency distribution for which the frequency is maximum. **Formula** for calculating mode is :

$$\text{Mode} = l + \frac{f_m - f_1}{2f_m - f_1 - f_2} \times h$$

where l = lower limit of the modal class

f_m = maximum frequency

f_1 = frequency of the class preceding the modal class

f_2 = frequency of the class succeeding the modal class

h = width of the modal class

Remark : (1) For a moderately asymmetrical distribution, the relation connecting mean, median and mode is

Mean – Mode = 3 (Mean – Median)

(2) For a symmetrical distribution Mean, Median and Mode coincide.

Measures of Dispersion

Measures of central tendency are inadequate to give us complete idea of the distribution. So it is imperative to know how the observations are spread round the central value. This means, we should determine the degree of scatteredness of the data. Dispersion measures the extent of the variation of the given data. Commonly used measures of dispersion are :

(i) Range

(ii) Quartile deviation or semi-quartile range

(iii) Mean deviation and

(iv) Standard deviation

Range : It is the difference between the greatest and least values of the variable.

Quartile deviation : The difference between the upper and lower quartiles *i.e.* $Q_3 - Q_1$ is called **interquartile range** and $Q = \frac{Q_3 - Q_1}{2}$ is called **quartile deviation** or **semi-interquartile range.**

Coefficient of quartile deviation is $\frac{Q_3 - Q_1}{Q_3 + Q_1}$, it is independent of the unit of measurement.

Mean deviation : It is the arithmetic mean of the absolute deviations of the values from an average A which may be mean, median or mode.

Mean deviation about the mean

$$= \frac{1}{N} \sum_{i=1}^{n} f_i \, |(x_i - \bar{x})|, N = \Sigma f_i$$

§8 Mean deviation is least when measured from the median

Standard deviation and Root Mean Square deviation.

Standard deviation (S.D.) usually denoted by σ is the positive square root of the arithmetic mean of the squares of the deviations of the given values from their arithmetic mean. For the frequency distribution x_i / f_i, $i = 1, 2, \ldots, n$

$$\sigma = \sqrt{\frac{1}{N} \sum_i f_i \, (x_i - \bar{x})^2} \text{ where } \bar{x} = \text{A.M.}, N = \sum_i f_i$$

or $\sigma^2 = \frac{1}{N} \Sigma_i f_i \, (x_i - \bar{x})^2$

σ^2 is called the **variance** of the distribution. **Root mean square deviation** about any arbitrary A usually denoted by s is given by

$$s = \sqrt{\frac{1}{N} \sum_i f_i \, (x_i - A)^2}$$

or $s^2 = \frac{1}{N} \sum_i (x_i - A)^2$

is called mean square deviation.

Relation between S.D. and Root mean square deviation We have

$$s^2 = \frac{1}{N} \sum_i f_i \, (x_i - A)^2$$

$$= \frac{1}{N} \sum_i f_i \, (x_i - \bar{x} + \bar{x} - A)^2.$$

Putting $\bar{x} - A = d$, we get

$$s^2 = \frac{1}{N} \sum_i f_i \, [(x_i - \bar{x}) + d]^2$$

$$= \frac{1}{N} \sum_i [f_i \, (x_i - \bar{x})^2 + 2d \sum_i f_i \, (x_i - \bar{x}) + f_i d^2]$$

$$= \frac{1}{N} \sum_i f_i \, (x_i - \bar{x})^2 + d^2 \frac{1}{N} \sum_i f_i \because \Sigma f_i \, (x_i - \bar{x}) = 0$$

$$= \sigma^2 + d^2 \quad \text{or} \quad \sigma^2 = s^2 - d^2$$

Obviously s^2 is minimum when $d = 0$, *i.e.* when $A = \bar{x}$ and its minimum value is σ^2.

Different formulae for calculating variance σ^2

We have

$$\sigma^2 = \frac{1}{N} \sum_i f_i \, (x_i - \bar{x})^2$$

$$= \frac{1}{N} \sum_i f_i \, (x_i^2 - 2x_i \, \bar{x} + \bar{x}^2)$$

$$= \frac{1}{N} \sum_i f_i \, x_i^2 - 2\bar{x} \cdot \frac{1}{N} \sum_i f_i x_i + \bar{x}^2 \ldots \sum_i f_i = N$$

$$= \frac{1}{N} \sum_i f_i x_i^2 - (2\bar{x}) \cdot \bar{x} + \bar{x}^2$$

$$= \frac{1}{N} \sum_i f_i x_i^2 - \bar{x}^2 = \frac{1}{N} \sum_i f_i x_i^2 - \left(\frac{1}{N} \sum_i f_i x_i\right)^2$$

In case, when the calculation involves large figures, we take deviations of the values from an arbitrary point A.

So $\sigma^2 = \frac{1}{N} \sum_i f_i \, (x_i - \bar{x})^2$

$$= \frac{1}{N} \sum_i f_i (x_i - A + A - \bar{x})^2$$

Taking $x_i - A = d_i$ and $\bar{x} - A = d$,

we have $\sigma^2 = \frac{1}{N} \sum_i f_i (d_i - d)^2 \qquad \because \frac{1}{N} \sum_i f_i d_i$

$$= \frac{1}{N} \sum_i f_i (x_i - A) = \bar{x} - A = d$$

$$= \frac{1}{N} \sum_i f_i d_i^2 - 2d \left(\frac{1}{N} \sum_i f_i d_i \right) + d^2$$

$$= \frac{1}{N} \sum_i f_i d_i^2 - d^2$$

or $\sigma^2 = \frac{1}{N} \sum_i f_i d_i^2 - \left(\frac{1}{N} \sum_i f_i d_i \right)^2$

This result is independent of A. Hence variance and consequently S.D. are **independent of the change of origin.** We can expect still further easy calculation of σ_x^2, if we change the random variable x into a random variable u by means of changing the origin and the scale by the transforming equation

$$u_i = \frac{x_i - a}{h} \text{ where } i = 1, 2, 3, \ldots, n$$

a is change of origin and h is change of scale and these are constants.

or $x_i = a + u_i h$ ...(1)

$\Rightarrow E(x_i) = E(a + u_i h) = E(a) + h E(u_i)$

where operator E is defined as

$$E(x_i) = \frac{1}{n} \sum_{i=1}^{n} x_i = \bar{x}$$

or $\bar{x} = a + h \bar{u}$ ...(2)

$\therefore$ (1) – (2) $\Rightarrow x_i - \bar{x} = h(u_i - \bar{u})$

or $\frac{1}{N} \sum_{i=1}^{n} f_i (x_i - \bar{x})^2 = h^2 \frac{1}{N} \sum_{i=1}^{n} f_i (u_i - \bar{u})^2$,

where f_i is the frequency of x_i

$\Rightarrow \sigma_x^2 = h^2 \sigma_u^2$, thus variance is not independent of the change of scale.

This formula makes calculation of σ^2 easy and simple.

Standard deviation of first n natural numbers

Mean $\bar{x} = \frac{1 + 2 + \ldots + n}{n} = \frac{n(n+1)}{2n} = \frac{n+1}{2}$

Taking the assumed mean $A = 0$, we get

$$d = \bar{x} - A = \frac{n+1}{2}$$

and $s^2 = \frac{1^2 + 2^2 + \ldots + n^2}{n} = \frac{n(n+1)(2n+1)}{6n}$

$\therefore \sigma^2 = s^2 - d^2 = \frac{(n+1)(2n+1)}{6} - \left(\frac{n+1}{2} \right)^2$

$$= \frac{n+1}{2} \left[\frac{2n+1}{3} - \frac{n+1}{2} \right] = \frac{n+1}{2} \cdot \frac{n-1}{6}$$

$$= \frac{n^2 - 1}{12}$$

Variance of the combined series.

If we are given two series with sizes n_1, n_2 with means $\overline{x_1}, \overline{x_2}$ and standard deviations σ_1, σ_2 then the variance of the combined series is given by

$$\sigma^2 = \frac{1}{n_1 + n_2} [n_1 (\sigma_1^2 + d_1^2) + n_2 (\sigma_2^2 + d_2^2)]$$

where $d_1 = \overline{x_1} - \bar{x}, d_2 = \overline{x_2} - \bar{x}$

and $\bar{x}$ being the mean of the combined series is given by

$$\bar{x} = \frac{n_1 \overline{x_1} + n_2 \overline{x_2}}{n_1 + n_2}$$

Empirical Relations between measures of Dispersion

$$\frac{1}{N} \Sigma f |(x - M)| = \text{Mean deviation}$$

$$= \frac{4}{5} \text{ (Standard deviation)}$$

$$\frac{1}{2}(Q_3 - Q_1) = \text{Quartile deviation}$$

$$= \frac{2}{3} \text{ (Standard deviation)}$$

and $Q.D. = \frac{5}{6} (M.D.)$ approx.

Coefficient of dispersion

The ratio of standard deviation and arithmetic mean *i.e.* $\frac{\sigma}{M}$ is defined as the **coefficient of dispersion.**

Coefficient of Variation $= 100 \times \frac{\sigma}{M}$

For quartile deviation

Coefficient of dispersion $= \frac{Q_3 - Q_1}{Q_3 + Q_1}$

Symmetrical and Skew distributions

In a symmetrical distribution frequencies are symmetrically distributed about the mean and in that mean, median and mode coincide.

Skewness means lack of symmetry or departure from symmetry. Skewness is **positive** if the curve is more elongated towards the right and **negative** if more elongated towards the left.

[**Note :** For positive skewness, mode < median < mean and for negative skewness, mean < median < mode]

Coefficient of skewness $= \frac{\text{Mean-Mode}}{\text{Standard deviation}}$

or $= \frac{3\,(\text{Mean-median})}{\text{Standard deviation}}$

This is a pure number as numerator and denominator have same dimensions. It is zero for a symmetrical distribution.

In case standard deviation is not known, a rough measure of coefficient of skewness is given by $\frac{Q_3 + Q_1 - 2Q_2}{Q_3 - Q_1}$.

In a symmetrical distribution $\bar{x} \pm 2\sigma$ covers approximately 95% area of the curve and $\bar{x} \pm 3\sigma$ covers 99% area of the curve.

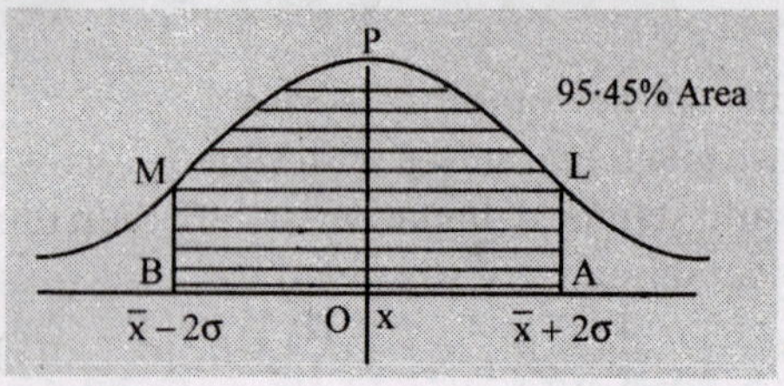

Fig. 1

Ex. 1. Compute the mean of the following data by using both direct and short-cut methods.

x = Height in inches :	73	72	71	70	69	68	67	66	65
freq. = Students :	2	4	6	10	11	7	5	4	1

Hint : Direct Method. $M = \frac{\Sigma xf}{n}$ where $\Sigma f = n$

$$= \frac{3459}{50} = 69 \cdot 18$$

Let the assumed mean be $(A) = 69$ inches, then by short-cut method

$$M = A + \frac{\Sigma fd}{n} \qquad \text{where } d = (x - A)$$

So, $M = 69 + \frac{9}{50}$ inches $= 69 \cdot 18$ inches

Ex. 2. Compute the mean (M) from the frequency distribution

Monthly wages Rs.	Freq. (f)	Mid Value (x)	xf	$\xi = (x - A)$	$f\xi$
12.5–17.5	2	15	30	− 15	− 30
17.5–22.5	22	20	440	− 10	− 220
22.5–27.5	19	25	475	− 5	− 95
27.5–32.5	14	30	420	0	0
32.5–37.5	3	35	105	+ 5	+ 15
37.5–42.5	4	40	160	+ 10	+ 40
42.5–47.5	6	45	270	+ 15	+ 90
47.5–52.5	1	50	50	+ 20	+ 20
	$n = 71$		$\Sigma xf = 1950$	$A = 30$	$\Sigma f\xi = -180$

$$M = A + \frac{\Sigma f\xi}{n} = 30 + \left[\frac{-180}{71}\right]$$

$$= 30 - 2 \cdot 53 = 27 \cdot 47 \text{ Rs. approx.}$$

Ex. 3 (a). The following table gives the marks obtained by a batch of 25 students in a certain class test in Economics. Compute the median from the following table :

Roll No. of the Students	Economics	Roll No. of the Students	Economics
1	29	14	47
2	65	15	60
3	33	16	30
4	45	17	32
5	51	18	52
6	72	19	54
7	48	20	56
8	33	21	58
9	42	22	49
10	25	23	39
11	28	24	40
12	35	25	46
13	46		

Note : For calculating median of an individual series, it is essential that the series is placed in an arranged order (ascending or descending)

$$\text{Median} = \text{size of the} \left(\frac{n+1}{2}\right) \text{th item}$$

If it comes in the fraction, say it is equal to $5 \cdot 5$th item, then it is located as,

$$\frac{\text{size of the 5th item} + \text{size of the 6th item}}{2}$$

For finding out the median, here it is arranged in the descending order.

Roll No. of the Students	Economics	Roll No. of the Students	Economics
1	72	14	45
2	65	15	42
3	60	16	40
4	58	17	38
5	56	18	35
6	54	19	33
7	52	20	33
8	51	21	32
9	49	22	30
10	48	23	29
11	47	24	28
12	46	25	25
13	46		

$$\text{Median} = \left(\frac{n+1}{2}\right)^{\text{th}} \text{item} = \left(\frac{25+1}{2}\right)^{\text{th}} \text{item}$$

$$= 13^{\text{th}} \text{ item} = 46 \text{ marks}$$

Ex. 3 (b). Calculate the median of the following series of marks obtained by 10 candidates in an examination

22, 26, 14, 30, 18, 11, 35, 41, 12, 32

Sol. Arranging marks in ascending order of magnitude, we have

Serial Number	Marks
1	11
2	12
3	14
4	18
5	22
6	26
7	30
8	32
9	35
10	41

$$\text{Median} = \text{size of } \frac{10+1}{2} \quad i.e., \ (5 \cdot 5)\text{th item}$$

$$= \text{size of 5th item}$$

$$+ \cdot 5 \times (\text{size of 6th item} - \text{size of 5th item})$$

$= 22 + \cdot 5\,(26 - 22)$
$= 22 + 2 = 24$ marks

Note : For grouped freq. distribution, median is calculated by the formula :

$$\text{Median} = l_1 + \left\{ \frac{l_2 - l_1}{f_1} (m - c) \right\}$$

where l_1 and l_2 = lower and upper limit of the median group,

f_1 = frequency of the median group

m = size of $\left(\frac{n+1}{2}\right)^{\text{th}}$ item

$C = cmf$ (cumulative frequency) of the next lower group than the median group

Ex. 4. Calculate the median and mode of the following grouped distribution

Wages in Rs.	No. of workers	Wages in Rs.	No. of workers
20	8	25	25
21	10	26	16
22	11	27	9
23	16	28–29	6
24	20		

Sol.

Wages in Rs.	No. of workers (f)	Cumulative frequency (cmf)
20–21	8	8
21–22	10	18
22–23	11	29
23–24	16	45
24–25	20	65
25–26	25	90
26–27	16	106
27–28	9	115
28–29	6	121

Here m = size of $\left(\frac{n+1}{2}\right)^{\text{th}}$ item $= \frac{121+1}{2} = 61$

c = cumulative frequency of the next lower group than the median group = 45

$l_1 = 24, l_2 = 25, f_1 = 20$

Hence median

$$= 24 + \left\{ \frac{25 - 24}{20} (61 - 45) \right\} = 24 \cdot 8 \text{ approx.}$$

Note : Mode in the continuous series is computed by the formula :

$$M_0 = l_1 + \frac{f_1 - f_0}{2f_1 - f_0 - f_2} (l_2 - l_1)$$

where M_0 = Mode, l_1 and l_2 = lower and upper limits of the modal group, f_1 = frequency of the modal group, f_0 = frequency of the next lower group than the modal group, f_2 = frequency of the next higher group than the modal group.

Here 25 – 26 with frequency 25 is the modal group

$l_1 = 25, l_2 = 26, f_1 = 25, f_0 = 20, f_2 = 16$

$$\therefore \quad M_0 = 25 + \frac{25 - 20}{50 - 20 - 16} (26 - 25) = 25 \cdot 35 \text{ approx.}$$

Ex. 5. Calculate the modal size in the following series by the method of grouping.

Size of item :	2	3	4	5	6	7	8	9	10	11	12	13
Frequency :	3	8	10	12	16	14	10	8	17	5	4	1

Sol. Grouping table :

Size of item	Frequency I	II	III	IV	V	VI
2	3	11		21		
3	8		18		30	
4	10	22				38
5	12		28	42		
6	16	30			40	
7	14		24			32
8	10	18		35		
9	8		25		30	
10	17	22				26
11	5		9	16		
12	4	5				
13	1					

Analysis of grouping in various columns :

In column II frequencies are shown in the range of curled brackets by grouping in two's the frequencies in column I.

In column III grouping is done in two's after leaving the first frequency in column I.

In column IV grouping is done in three's of the frequencies of the column I.

In column V grouping is done in three's after leaving the first frequency in column I.

In column VI grouping is done in three's after leaving the first two frequencies of column I.

Maximum frequencies in columns II, III, IV, V, VI are ticked.

Analysis table :

Columns	Size of items having max. freq.
I	10
II	6, 7
III	5, 6
IV	5, 6, 7
V	6, 7, 8
VI	4, 5, 6

Here we observe that occurs maximum number of times *i.e.*, five times. Hence the is the mode.

Ex. 6. Calculate the Mean, Median and Mode of the following distribution :

Marks	Frequency	Marks	Frequency
10–25	6	50–70	26
25–40	20	70–85	3
40–55	44	85–100	1

Ans. $M = 47\cdot 95$ approx, $Md = 48\cdot 35$ approx, $M_0 = 48\cdot 57$ approx.

Ex. 7. Find the mode of the following series by grouping :

Height	Frequency	Height	Frequency
5′6″	1	5′11″	1
5′7″	2	6′0″	2
5′8″	4	6′1″	1
5′9″	3	6′2″	1
5′10″	2	6′3″	1

Ans : Convert heights in inches and find that 68 occurs greatest viz 5, number of times, therefore mode is located at 5′8″.

Ex. 8. Determine Mode and the Median from the following figures :

25, 15, 23, 40, 27, 25, 23, 25, 20

Ans : $Md = 25,\ M_0 = 25$

Ex. 9. Calculate the values of (a) the mode (b) the median from the following :

Wages in Rs.	No. of workers
20	8
21	10
22	11
23	16
24	20
25	25
26	15
27	9
28–29	6

Ans : Mode $= 25\cdot 333$ approx, Median $= 24\cdot 75$ approx.

Ex. 10. Recast the following cumulative table in the form of an ordinary frequency distribution and determine the value of the mode by using the formula :
mode = 3 median - 2 mean

No. of days absent	No. of students	No. of days absent	No. of students
Less than 5	29	Less than 30	644
Less than 10	224	Less than 35	650
Less than 15	465	Less than 40	653
Less than 20	582	Less than 45	655
Less than 25	634		

Ans : Mean $= 12\cdot 87$ days $\left[\text{use, Mean} = a + \dfrac{\Sigma fd}{\Sigma f} \times i\right]$

$$\text{Median} = \text{size of} \left(\frac{n+1}{2}\right)^{\text{th}} \text{item} = 328^{\text{th}} \text{ item}$$

which lies in the group 10–15.

$$\text{Median} = 10 + \frac{328 - 224}{241} \times (15 - 10)$$

$$= 12\cdot 15 \text{ days}$$

$$\text{Mode} = 10\cdot 71 \text{ days}$$

Problems on Measures of Dispersion

Ex. 1. Calculate the mean deviation from the arithmatic mean of the following series of marks :

20, 22, 27, 30, 31, 32, 35, 40, 45, 48

Serial No.	Marks x	Deviation from 33, $\|d\|$ (sign ignored)
1	20	13
2	22	11
3	27	6
4	30	3
5	31	2
6	32	1
7	35	2
8	40	7
9	45	12
10	48	15
$n = 10$	$\Sigma x = 330$	$\Sigma\|d\| = 72$

$$\text{A.M.} = \frac{\Sigma x}{n} = \frac{330}{10} = 33 \text{ marks}$$

Mean deviation from mean

$$= \frac{\Sigma|d|}{n} = \frac{72}{10} = 7\cdot 2 \text{ marks}$$

Ex. 2. Calculate the mean deviation from the median and from the mean for the following distribution of the scores of 50 college students.

Scores	140–	150–	160–	170–	180–	190–200
Freq.	4	6	10	18	9	3

Sol.

Score groups	Mid-value (x)	Freq. (f)	Dev. from ass. mean 175 *i.e.* $d' = \frac{x\ 17\cdot 5}{10}$	$f \times d'$	Cum. freq	$\|d_m\|$	$f \times \|d_m\|$
140–150	145	4	– 3	– 12	4	26·2	104·8
150–160	155	6	– 2	– 12	10	16·2	97·2
160–170	165	10	– 1	– 10	20	6·2	62·0
170–180	175	18	0	0	38	3·8	68·4
180–190	185	9	1	9	47	13·8	124·2
190–200	195	3	2	6	50	23·8	71·4
Total		$n = 50$		– 19			528·0

Ans : $|d_m| = |$deviations from mean $171\cdot 2|$

Arithmetic mean $= a + \dfrac{\Sigma fd'}{\Sigma f} \times i$

[here $a = 175, i = 10$ length of each class interval]

$$= 175 + \frac{(-19)}{50} \times 10 = 171 \cdot 2$$

Here median = size of $\left(\dfrac{n+1}{2}\right)^{\text{th}}$ item

$$= \left(\frac{50+1}{2}\right)^{\text{th}} \text{ item} = 25 \cdot 5^{\text{th}} \text{ item}$$

So median group = 170 – 186

Hence Median

$$= l + \frac{i}{f}\left(\frac{n}{2} - c\right) = 170 + \frac{10}{18}(25 - 20) = 172.8$$

as f = freq. of median group, $c = cmf$ of previous group.

∴ Mean deviation from mean

$$= \frac{\Sigma f\,|d_m|}{\Sigma f} = \frac{528}{50} = 10 \cdot 56$$

Similarly find $|d_{me}|$

i.e., values $|x - 172 \cdot 8|$

and so $\Sigma f \times |d_{me}| = 512 \cdot 0$

∴ Mean deviation from median

$$= \frac{\Sigma f\,|d_{me}|}{\Sigma f} = \frac{512 \cdot 0}{50} = 10 \cdot 24$$

Ex. 3. Find the standard deviation for the following frequency distribution

Variable	2	3	4	5	9	10	12	13	15
Freq.	25	37	44	59	68	43	31	23	12

Sol.

x	f	$\xi = x - 9$	$f\xi$	$f\xi^2$
2	25	– 7	– 175	1225
3	37	– 6	– 222	1332
4	44	– 5	– 220	1100
5	59	– 4	– 236	944
9	68	0	0	0
10	43	1	43	43
12	31	3	93	279
13	23	4	92	368
15	12	6	72	432

Here $n = \Sigma f = 342, \Sigma f\xi = -553, \Sigma f\xi^2 = 5723$

$$\therefore \quad \text{S.D.} = \sigma = \sqrt{\frac{\Sigma f\xi^2}{n} - \left(\frac{\Sigma f\xi}{n}\right)^2}$$

$$\text{or} \quad \sigma^2 = \text{variance} = \sqrt{\frac{5723}{342} - \left(\frac{-553}{342}\right)^2}$$

or σ = positive square root = 3 · 76

Ex. 4. Calculate the standard deviation and the coeff. of variation from the following data :

Age	No. of members
20–30	3
30–40	61
40–50	132
50–60	153
60–70	140
70–80	51
80–90	2

Sol.

Age group years	Mid-values x	No. of members f	Step dev. from a = 55 d'	fd'	fd'^2
20–30	25	3	– 3	– 9	27
30–40	35	61	– 2	– 122	244
40–50	45	132	– 1	– 132	132
50–60	55	153	0	0	0
60–70	65	140	+ 1	+ 140	140
70–80	75	51	+ 2	+ 102	204
80–90	85	2	+ 3	+ 6	18
		$n = \Sigma f$ = 542		$\Sigma fd'$ = – 15	$\Sigma fd'^2$ = 765

Mean $\bar{x} = a + \dfrac{\Sigma fd'}{n} \times i$ where i = length of common interval = 10

$$= 55 + \frac{-15}{542} \times 10 = 54 \cdot 7 \text{ years approx.}$$

$$\text{Standard deviation, } \sigma = \sqrt{\frac{\Sigma fd'^2}{n} - \left(\frac{\Sigma fd'}{n}\right)^2} \times i$$

$$= \sqrt{\frac{765}{542} - \left(\frac{-15}{542}\right)^2} \times 10$$

$$= \sqrt{1 \cdot 4107} \times 10 = 11 \cdot 6 \text{ years approx.}$$

Coeff. of variation

$$= 100 \times \frac{\sigma}{\bar{x}} = 100 \times \frac{11 \cdot 6}{54 \cdot 7} = 21 \cdot 7$$

Ex. 5. Calculate the mean, median and the coeff. of variation from the following freq. table :

No. of letters	No. of words	No. of letters	No. of words
2	9	7	4
3	6	8	3
4	2	9	3
5	2	10	2
6	2	11	3

Ans : Mean = 5 · 5, S.D., σ = 3 · 12, Coeff. of variation = 56 · 7, Median = 5

Ex. 6. Calculate the arithmetic average and the standard deviation of the following series :

Expenditure	No. of students
Below Rs. 5	6
Below Rs. 10	16
Below Rs. 15	28
Below Rs. 20	38
Below Rs. 25	46

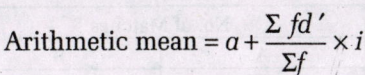

Ans : Mean = Rs. 12.94

S.D., σ = Rs. 6.5 approx

Ex. 7. Calculate the arithmetic average, mean deviation and the standard deviation from the data in the following series :

Size of item	Frequency
3–4	3
4–5	7
5–6	22
6–7	60
7–8	85
8–9	32
9–10	8

Ans : Mean = $6\cdot5$ approx.

Mean deviation $= \frac{218}{217} = 1\cdot004$ approx

S.D., $\sigma = \sqrt{\frac{362}{217}} = \sqrt{1\cdot66} = 1\cdot2$ approx.

Ex. 8. Goals scored by two teams A and B in a foot ball season were as follows :

No. of goals scored in a Match	No. of Matches	
	A	B
0	27	17
1	9	9
2	8	6
3	5	5
4	4	3

By calculating the coeff. of variation in each case, find which team may be considered the more consistent.

Ans : For team $A\ \sigma = \sqrt{\frac{138}{53}} = 1\cdot6$,

coeff. of variation = 80 ,

For team $B\ \sigma = \sqrt{\frac{94}{40}} = 1\cdot53$,

coeff. of variation = $76\cdot5$

Since $76.5 < 80$, the team B is more consistent.

Ex. 9. Find the mean, mode and S.D. for the following :

Year under :	10	20	30	40	50	60
No. of persons :	15	32	51	78	97	109

Ans : Mean = $39\cdot95$ years,

S.D. $\sigma = 15\cdot49$ years, Mode = 35 years

Problem Set (1)

Measures of Central Tendency

1. The algebraic sum of the deviations of x_i / f_i from the mean is :
(a) zero (b) maximum
(c) least (d) none of these

2. The sum of squares of deviations of a set of values about the mean is :
(a) zero (b) maximum
(c) least (d) none of these

3. The mean marks of 100 students were found to be 40. Later on it was discovered that a score of 53 was misread as 83. The corrected mean corresponding to the corrected score is :
(a) 37·5 (b) 35·6 (c) 39·7 (d) 38·7

4. The median of the following items
25, 15, 23, 40, 27, 25, 23, 25 and 20 is
(a) 27 (b) 40 (c) 25 (d) 23

5. The median of the variables $x+4$, $x-7/2$, $x-5/2$, $x-3, x-2$, $x+1/2$, $x-1/2$, $x+5$, $(x>0)$ is
(a) $x-3$ (b) $x-2$
(c) $x+5/4$ (d) $x-5/4$

6. The algebraic sum of deviations of ten observations about 15 is 70. The mean is
(a) 22 (b) 25
(c) 20 (d) none of these

7. A distribution has mean $= 8\cdot7$, median $= 8\cdot5$ and mode $= 7\cdot3$. The distribution is
(a) positively skewed (b) negatively skewed
(c) symmetrical (d) none of these

8. The average of daily wages for the workers of the two factories combined is

No. of wage earners	Factory A 250	Factory B 200
Average daily wage	Rs. 2·00	Rs. 2·50

(a) 2·22 (b) 3·15
(c) 4.10 (d) none of these

9. Marks obtained by four students are : 25, 35, 45, 55. The average deviations from the mean is
(a) 10 (b) 9
(c) 7 (d) none of these

10. The quartile deviation of the income of a certain person given in rupees for 12 months in a year : 129, 150, 151, 151, 157, 158, 160, 161, 162, 162, 173, 175
(a) 4·5 (b) 5·5
(c) 6·2 (d) none of these

11. The weighted mean of first n natural numbers whose weights are equal to the corresponding number is equal to
(a) $\frac{1}{3}(2n+1)$ (b) $\frac{1}{2}(n+4)$
(c) $\frac{1}{5}(2n+3)$ (d) none of these

12. The arithmetic mean of n numbers of a series is $\bar{x}$. The sum of the first $(n-1)$ numbers is k. The nth number is

(a) $\frac{n}{2}\bar{x}-k$ (b) $n\bar{x}-k$

(c) $\frac{1}{n}\bar{x}-k$ (d) none of these

13. If a variate takes values $a, ar, ar^2, \dots, ar^{n-1}$ which of the relation between means hold

(a) $AH = G^2$ (b) $\frac{A+H}{2} = G$

(c) $A > G > H$ (d) $A = G = H$

14. A population of values is symmetrically distributed about the constant k. Test which statements are correct

(a) the mean is k

(b) the mean coincides with the mode

(c) the distribution cannot be bimodal

(d) $\frac{1}{2}$ (upper quartile + lower quartile) is equal to k

(e) the median coincides with mean

15. The geometric mean of the series $1, 2, 4, 8, \dots, 2^n$ is

(a) $2^{n/2}$ (b) $2^{n/4}$

(c) 2^{2n} (d) none of these

16. An aeroplane flies round a squares, the sides of which measure 100 miles each. The aeroplane covers at a speed of 100 m. p.h. the first side, at 200 m.p.h. the second side, at 300 m.p.h. the third side and 400 m.p.h. the fourth side. The average speed of the aeroplane around the square is

(a) 190 (b) 195 (c) 192 (d) 200

17. A group of 10 items has mean equal to 6. If the mean of 4 of these items is 7·5, the mean of the remaining items is

(a) 6·5 (b) 5·5 (c) 5 (d) 4·5

18. If the mean of a variate x is m, the mean of $\frac{ax+b}{c}$ where a, b, c are constants is

(a) $\frac{am+b}{c}$ (b) $\left(\frac{2b+a}{c}\right)m$

(c) $\frac{a+b}{mc}$ (d) none of these

19. The numbers 3, 5, 7, 4 have frequencies x, $x+4$, $x-3$, $x+8$. If their arithmetic mean is 4, the value of x is

(a) $\frac{5}{3}$ (b) $\frac{7}{4}$

(c) $\frac{2}{3}$ (d) none of these

20. If $\bar{x}$ denotes the mean of n values $x_1, x_2, \dots, x_n$ then mean of the values $x_i + 2i$, where $i = 1, 2, 3, \dots, n$ is

(a) $\bar{x}+2$ (b) $\bar{x}+n$ (c) $\bar{x}+2n$ (d) $\bar{x}+n+1$

21. If the mode and mean of a moderately asymmetrical series are 16 inches and 15·6 inches respectively, then most probable median is

(a) 15·73 (b) 14·60

(c) 16·02 (d) none of these

22. The results of two colleges are as follows :

		M.A.	M.Sc.	B.A.	B.Sc.	Total
A	Appeared	100	60	120	200	480
	Passed	90	45	75	150	360
B	Appeared	240	200	160	200	800
	Passed	200	160	100	140	600

then

(a) A is better than B

(b) none is better than the other

(c) A is inferior to B

(d) can not say

23. If g_1 and g_2 be the geometric means of two series of n_1 and n_2 items. Then the G.M. of the series obtained on combining them is

(a) $\left[(g_1)^{n_1} \cdot (g_2)^{n_2}\right]^{\frac{1}{n_1+n_2}}$ (b) $(g_1\, g_2)^{\frac{n_1}{n_1+n_2}}$

(c) $(g_1\, g_2)^{\frac{n_2}{n_1+n_2}}$ (d) $(g_1\, g_2)^{\frac{n_1 n_2}{n_1+n_2}}$

24. For a symmetrical distribution lower quartile is 20 and upper quartile is 40. The value of 50th percentile is

(a) 20 (b) 40

(c) 30 (d) none of these

25. For a symmetrical distribution P_{25} and P_{75} are 30 and 70 respectively. The value of median is

(a) 50 (b) 30

(c) 40 (d) none of these

Measures of Dispersion

26. If in a series which is not highly skewed the mean deviation is 7·8, the approximate value of its standard deviation is

(a) 9·75 (b) 8·37

(c) 10·2 (d) none of these

27. If mean of a series is 40 and variance 148·6, then coefficient of variation is

(a) 30·5 (b) 29·6

(c) 28·7 (d) none of these

28. In a final examination in Statistics the mean marks of a group of 150 students were 78 and the s.d. was 8·0. In Economics, however, the mean marks were 73 and the s.d. was 7·6. The variability in the two subjects respectively is

(a) 10·3%, 10·4% (b) 9·5%, 7·9%

(c) 11·2%, 10·1% (d) none of these

29. If the variable takes values $0, 1, 2, 3, \dots, n$ with frequencies proportional to nc_0, nc_1, $nc_2 \dots, nc_n$ respectively, the variance is

(a) $n/4$ (b) $n/3$

(c) $2n/5$ (d) none of these

30. The sum of the squares of deviations of 10 items about mean 50 is 250. The coefficient of variation is

(a) 10% (b) 50%
(c) 30% (d) none of these

31. If s.d. of X is σ, then s.d. of the variable $U = \dfrac{aX+b}{c}$ where a, b, c are constants is

(a) $\left|\dfrac{c}{a}\right|\sigma$ (b) $\left|\dfrac{a}{c}\right|\sigma$
(c) $\left|\dfrac{b}{c}\right|\sigma$ (d) $\dfrac{c^2}{a^2}\sigma$

32. The mean of five observations is 44 and the variance is 8·24. Three of the five observations are 1, 2 and 6. The remaining two are

(a) 9, 4 (b) 7, 6 (c) 6, 5 (d) 10, 3

33. Mean deviations of the series $a, a+d, a+2d, \ldots, a+2nd$ from its mean is

(a) $\dfrac{n(n+1)\,d}{(2n+1)}$ (b) $\dfrac{nd}{2n+1}$
(c) $\dfrac{(n+1)\,d}{2n+1}$ (d) $\dfrac{(2n+1)\,d}{n(n+1)}$

34. A sample of 35 observations has the mean 80 and s.d. 4. A second sample of 65 observations from the same population has mean 70 and s.d. 3. The s.d. of the combined sample is

(a) 5·85 (b) 37·2
(c) 5·58 (d) none of these

35. The first of two samples has 100 items with mean 15 and s.d. 3. If the whole group has 250 items with mean 15·6 and s.d. $= \sqrt{13 \cdot 44}$ the s.d. of the second group is

(a) 5 (b) 4 (c) 6 (d) 3·52

36. The mean and s.d. of 63 children on an arithmetic test are repectively 27·6 and 7·1. To them are added a new group of 26 who had less training and whose mean is 19·2 and s.d. 6·2. The values of the combined group differ from the original as to (i) the mean and (ii) the s.d.

(a) 2·5, 0·7 (b) 2·3, 0·8
(c) 1·5, 0·9 (d) none of these

37. Coefficient of skewness for the values

Median $= 18 \cdot 8''$
$Q_1 = 14 \cdot 6''$
$Q_3 = 25 \cdot 2''$ is

(a) 0·2 (b) 0·5
(c) 0·7 (d) none of these

38. For a series the value of mean deviation is 15. The most likely value of its quartile deviation is

(a) 12·5 (b) 11·6 (c) 13 (d) 9·7

39. Karl Pearson's coefficient of skewness of a distribution is 0·32. Its s.d. is 6·5 and mean is 29·6. The mode and median of the distribution are

(a) 27·52, 28.91 (b) 26·92, 27·23
(c) 25·67, 26·34 (d) none of these

40. Which of the following are dimensionless

(a) S.D. (b) M.D.
(c) variance
(d) coefficient of variation

41. The variance of the first n natural numbers is

(a) $\dfrac{n^2+1}{12}$ (b) $\dfrac{n^2-1}{12}$
(c) $\dfrac{n(n+1)(2n+1)}{6}$ (d) none of these

42. An incomplete frequency distribution is given below

Variate	Frequency
10–20	12
20–30	30
30–40	?
40–50	65
50–60	45
60–70	25
70–80	18
Total	229

Median value is 46, the missing frequency is

(a) 33 (b) 35 (c) 34 (d) 26

43. Mean deviation about the mean $\bar{x}$ of the variate x is

$$\frac{2}{N}\left[\bar{x}\sum_{x_i<\bar{x}} f_i - \sum_{x_i<\bar{x}} f_i\,x_i\right]$$ True/False

44. If r be the range and $S = \left\{\dfrac{1}{n-1}\sum_i (x_i-\bar{x})^2\right\}^{1/2}$ be the s.d. of a set of observations $x_1, x_2, \ldots, x_n$ then $S \le r\left(\dfrac{n}{n-1}\right)^{1/2}$ True/False

45. The scores of two golfers for 10 rounds each are

A: 58, 59, 60, 54, 65, 66, 52, 75, 69, 52
B: 84, 56, 92, 65, 86, 78, 44, 54, 78, 68

B is a more consistent player than A. True/False

46. If the variable takes the values $0, 1, 2, \ldots, n$ with frequencies proportional to $q^n, {}^nC_1 q^{n-1} p, {}^nC_2 q^{n-2} p^2, \ldots, p^n$ where $p+q=1$, then mean square deviation is $n^2p^2 + npq$ and variance is npq. True/False

47. A student obtained the mean and s.d. of 100 observations as 40 and 5·1 respectively. It was later on discovered that he had wrongly copied down an observation as 50 instead of 40. The correct mean and s.d. is 39·9 and 5 respectively. True/False

48. The S.D. is not less than the mean deviation. True/False

Answers to Problem Set (1)

MULTIPLE CHOICE QUESTIONS

1. (a)	**2.** (c)	**3.** (c)	**4.** (c)	**5.** (d)	**6.** (a)	**7.** (a)	**8.** (a)	**9.** (a)	**10.** (b)
11. (a)	**12.** (b)	**13.** (a)	**14.** (a,d)	**15.** (a)	**16.** (c)	**17.** (c)	**18.** (a)	**19.** (a)	**20.** (d)
21. (a)	**22.** (b)	**23.** (a)	**24.** (c)	**25.** (a)	**26.** (a)	**27.** (a)	**28.** (a)	**29.** (a)	**30.** (a)
31. (b)	**32.** (a)	**33.** (a)	**34.** (a)	**35.** (b)	**36.** (a)	**37.** (a)	**38.** (a)	**39.** (a)	**40.** (d)
41. (b)	**42.** (c)	**43.** True	**44.** True	**45.** True	**46** True	**47.** True	**48.** True		

Hints / Solutions to Problem Set (1)

4. First arrange figures in ascending order

Median = size of $\left(\frac{9+1}{2}\right)$th item = 5th item = 25

5. Arrange values in ascending order of magnitude.

$x-\frac{7}{2}, x-3, x-\frac{5}{2}, x-2, x-\frac{1}{2}, x+\frac{1}{2}, x+4, x+5$

$$\text{Median} = \frac{1}{2}\left\{(x-2)+\left(x-\frac{1}{2}\right)\right\} = x-\frac{5}{4}$$

13. $A = \frac{a(1+r+r^2+\ldots+r^{n-1})}{n} = \frac{a}{n}\frac{1-r^n}{1-r}$

$$G = (a\,.\,ar\,.\,ar^2\ldots ar^{n-1})^{1/n}$$

$$= a\,.\,r^{\frac{1+2+\ldots+(n-1)}{n}} = ar^{\frac{n-1}{2}}$$

$$\frac{1}{H} = \frac{1}{na}\left\{1+\frac{1}{r}+\frac{1}{r^2}+\ldots+\frac{1}{r^{n-1}}\right\} = \frac{1}{na}\cdot\frac{1-\frac{1}{r^n}}{1-\frac{1}{r}}$$

$$\Rightarrow \quad H = \frac{na(1-r)\,r^{n-1}}{1-r^n}$$

$$\therefore \quad AH = a^2\,r^{n-1} = G^2$$

16. Using the weighted H.M. formula

$$\frac{1}{H} = \frac{1}{N}\sum_{i=1}^{n}\frac{f_i}{x_i} \quad \text{or} \quad H = \frac{1}{\frac{1}{N}\sum_i \frac{f_i}{x_i}}$$

$$\therefore \text{ Average speed} = \frac{400}{100\left(\frac{1}{100}+\frac{1}{200}+\frac{1}{300}+\frac{1}{900}\right)}$$

$$= 192$$

21. Use : mean – mode = 3 (mean – median)

22. Since number of students appearing for different examinations widely differ, simple arithmetic average of pass percentage will not do. Here we should take the weighted average of pass percentages with the number of students appearing as weights for each examination.

Thus for college A, pass percentage

$$= \frac{90\times100+75\times60+62\cdot5+120\times75\times200}{100+60+120+200} = 75\%$$

Similarly for college B, pass percentage

$$= \frac{\frac{250}{3}\times240+80\times200+(62\cdot5)\times160\times70\times200}{240+200+160+200}$$

$= 75\%$

$\therefore$ None is better than the other

23. Let $g_1 = (x_1x_2\ldots x_{n_1})^{\frac{1}{n_1}}, g_2 = (y_2y_2\ldots y_{n_2})^{\frac{1}{n_2}}$

If g is the G.M. of the combined series

$$g = \left\{(x_1x_2\ldots x_{n_1})\times(y_1y_2\ldots y_{n_2})\right\}^{\frac{1}{n_1+n_2}}$$

$$= \left\{g_1^{n_1}\,.\,g_2^{n_2}\right\}^{\frac{1}{n_1+n_2}}$$

26. Use : M.D. $= \frac{4}{5}$(S.D.)

29. $$\mu_1' = \frac{\sum_0^n r\,.\,{}^nC_r}{\sum_0^n {}^nC_r} = \frac{\Sigma\, r\,.\frac{n}{r}\,{}^{n-1}C_{r-1}}{\Sigma\,{}^nC_r}$$

$$= \frac{n\sum_{r=1}^{n}{}^{n-1}C_{r-1}}{\sum_{r=0}^{n}{}^nC_r} = \frac{n\,.\,2^{n-1}}{2^n} = \frac{n}{2}$$

$$\mu_2' = \frac{\sum_0^n r^2\,.\,{}^nC_r}{\sum_{r=0}^{n}{}^nC_r} = \frac{1}{2^n}\sum_0^n\{r(r-1)+r\}\,{}^nC_r$$

$$= \frac{1}{2^n}\sum_0^n r(r-1)\,{}^nC_r + \frac{n}{2}$$

$$= \frac{1}{2^n}\sum_0^n r(r-1)\frac{n(n-1)}{r(r-1)}\,{}^{n-2}C_{r-2} + \frac{n}{2}$$

$$= \frac{n(n-1)}{2^n}\cdot2^{n-2} + \frac{n}{2}$$

$$= \frac{n(n-1)}{4} + \frac{n}{2}$$

Variance $\mu_2 = \mu_2' - (\mu_1')^2$

$$= \frac{n(n-1)}{4} + \frac{n}{2} - \left(\frac{n}{2}\right)^2 = \frac{n}{4}$$

31. Make use of the results

$E(aX+b) = a\,E(X)+b$

$\text{var}(aX+b) = a^2\ \text{var}(x)$

we have $\text{var}\left\{\dfrac{aX+b}{c}\right\} = \dfrac{a^2}{c^2}\text{var}\,X = \dfrac{a^2}{c^2}\sigma^2$

$\Rightarrow$ S.D. $\left\{\dfrac{aX+b}{c}\right\} = \left|\dfrac{a}{c}\right|\sigma$

33. Mean $= \dfrac{1}{2}\{a + \overline{a+2nd}\} = a+nd$

Mean deviation about mean $= \dfrac{1}{2n+1}\Sigma|x-\bar{x}|$

$= \dfrac{1}{2n+1}\cdot 2d\,(1+2+3+\ldots+n)$

$= \dfrac{n(n+1)\,d}{2n+1}$

34. Use the formula :

$$\sigma^2 = \frac{n^2\sigma_1^2 + n_2\sigma_2^2}{n_1+n_2} + \frac{n_1 n_2}{(n_1+n_2)^2}(m_1-m_2)^2$$

35. Use : $\sigma^2 = \dfrac{n_1\sigma_1^2+n_2\sigma_2^2}{n_1+n_2} + \dfrac{n_1 d_1^2 + n_2 d_2^2}{n_1+n_2}$

where $d_1 = m_1 - a, d_2 = m_2 - a$, a being the mean of the whole group. Let m_2 = mean of the second group

$\therefore\quad 15\cdot 6 = \dfrac{100\times 15 + 150\times m_2}{250} \Rightarrow m_2 = 16$

Thus $13\cdot 44 = \dfrac{(100\times 9 + 150\times\sigma^2) + 100\times(0\cdot 6)^2 + 150\times(0\cdot 4)^2}{250}$

$\Rightarrow\ \sigma = 4$

36. Mean and s.d. σ of the combined group are

$m = \dfrac{63\times 27\cdot 6 + 26\times 19\cdot 2}{63+26} = 25\cdot 1$

Thus A.M. is decreased by $27\cdot 6 - 25\cdot 1 = 2\cdot 5$

$$\sigma^2 = \frac{63\times(7\cdot 1)^2 + 26\times(6\cdot 2)^2}{89} + \frac{63\,(25\cdot 1 - 27\cdot 6)^2 + 26\,(25\cdot 1 - 19\cdot 2)^2)}{89}$$

$\Rightarrow\ \sigma = 7\cdot 8$ approx

37. Use : coefficient of skewness

$= \dfrac{Q_3 + Q_1 - 2\,(\text{Med})}{Q_3 - Q_1}$

38. Use : M.D. $= \dfrac{4}{4}\sigma$, Q.D. $= \dfrac{2}{3}\sigma$

$\Rightarrow\ \dfrac{M.D.}{Q.D.} = \dfrac{6}{5}\ \Rightarrow$ Q.D. $= \dfrac{5}{6}$(M.D.)

39. Karl Pearson's coefficient of skewness

$= \dfrac{\text{Mean-Mode}}{\text{S.D.}}$

$\therefore\quad 0\cdot 32 = \dfrac{29\cdot 6 - \text{Mode}}{6\cdot 5} \Rightarrow \text{Mode} = 27\cdot 52$

Also Karl Pearson's coeff.of skewness

$= \dfrac{3\,(\text{Mean-Median})}{\text{S.D.}}$

$\because\quad 0\cdot 32 = \dfrac{3\,(29\cdot 6 - \text{Median})}{6\cdot 5}$

$\Rightarrow$ Median $= 28\cdot 91$

41. Remember $\mu_2 = \mu_2' - (\mu_1')^2$

$\Rightarrow\ \sigma^2 = \dfrac{1}{n}\{1^2+2^2+\ldots+n^2\} - \left[\dfrac{1}{n}(1+2+\ldots+n)\right]^2$

$= \dfrac{1}{n}\cdot\dfrac{(n(n+1)(2n+1)}{6} - \left(\dfrac{n+1}{2}\right)^2 = \dfrac{n^2-1}{12}$

42. Median = 46 which lies in 40–50 class

Median $= l + h\dfrac{\left\{\dfrac{N}{2} - C\right\}}{f}$

where f = freq. of median class
C = cumulative freq. of the class preceding the median class.

$\therefore\quad 46 = 40 + 10\dfrac{\left[\dfrac{229}{2} - (x+42)\right]}{65}$

where x = freq. of class 30–40

$\Rightarrow\ x = 33\cdot 5 = 34$

43. S = M.D. about the mean $= \dfrac{1}{N}\sum_i f_i|x_i - \bar{x}|$

Since $\sum_i f_i(x - \bar{x}) = 0$

$\Rightarrow\ \sum_{x_i<\bar{x}} f_i(x_i-\bar{x}) + \sum_{x_i>\bar{x}} f_i(x_i - \bar{x}) = 0$

$\Rightarrow\ \sum_{x_i>\bar{x}} f_i(x_i-\bar{x}) = \sum_{x_i<\bar{x}} f_i(\bar{x}-x_i)$

$\therefore\quad S = \dfrac{2}{N}\sum_{x_i<\bar{x}} f_i(\bar{x}-x_i)$ where $N = \sum_i f_i$

$= \dfrac{2}{N}\left[\bar{x}\sum_{x_i<\bar{x}} f_i - \sum_{x_i<\bar{x}} f_i x_i\right]$

44. Let $x_r = \max(x_1, x_2, \ldots, x_n)$

$x_k = \min(x_1, x_2, \ldots, x_n)$

$\therefore\quad r = x_r - x_k$

$\Rightarrow\ (x_i - \bar{x})^2 \le (x_i - x_k)^2 \qquad \because \bar{x} \ge x_k$

$\therefore\quad S^2 = \dfrac{1}{n-1}\sum_{i=1}^{n}(x_i-\bar{x})^2 \le \dfrac{1}{n-1}\sum_{i=1}^{n}(x_i - x_k)^2$

$\le \dfrac{1}{n-1}\sum_{i=1}^{n}(x_r - x_k)^2$

$\Rightarrow\ S^2 \le \dfrac{nr^2}{n-1}$ or $S \le r\left[\dfrac{n}{n-1}\right]^{1/2}$

45. Hint : Compare coefficients of variation of golfers A and B i.e. $100 \times \dfrac{\sigma}{M}$

46. $\mu_1' = E(x) = \sum_{x=0}^{n} x\binom{n}{x} p^x q^{n-x}$

$$\binom{n}{x} = {}^nC_x = \frac{n}{x}\binom{n-1}{x-1}$$

$$= np \sum_{x=1}^{n} \binom{n-1}{x-1} p^{x-1} q^{(n-1)-(x-1)}$$

$$= np\,(p+q)^{n-1} = np$$

$\because\ p+q=1$

mean square deviation about $x=0$ is

$$\mu_2' = E(X^2) = \sum_{x=0}^{n} x^2\binom{n}{x} p^x q^{n-x}$$

$$= \sum_{x=0}^{n} [x(x-1)+x]\binom{n}{x} p^x q^{n-x}$$

$$= \sum_{x=0}^{n} x(x-1)\binom{n}{x} p^x q^{n-x} + \sum_{x=0}^{n} x\binom{n}{x} p^x q^{n-x}$$

$$= n(n-1)p^2 \sum_{x=2}^{n}\binom{n-2}{x-2} p^{x-2} q^{(n-2)-(x-2)} + np$$

$$= n(n-1)p^2 (q+p)^{n-2} + np$$

$$= n(n-1)p^2 + np = n^2p^2 + np(1-p)$$

$$= n^2p^2 + npq \qquad \because\ p+q=1$$

$$\text{variance} = \mu_2 = \mu_2^1 - (\mu_1')^2$$

$$= n^2p^2 + npq - (np)^2 = npq$$

47. $\bar{x} = \dfrac{1}{n}\sum_{i=1}^{n} x_i$

$\Rightarrow\ \Sigma x_i = n\bar{x} = 100 \times 40 = 4000$

$\sigma_x^2 = \dfrac{1}{n}\sum_i x_i^2 - (\bar{x})^2$

$\Rightarrow\ \Sigma x_i^2 = n(\sigma^2 + \bar{x}^2) = 100\,(2601 + 1600) = 162601$

Corrected $\Sigma x_i = 4000 - 50 + 40 = 3990$

Corrected $\Sigma x_i^2 = 162601 - (50)^2 + (40)^2 = 161701$

$\therefore$ Corrected mean $= \dfrac{3990}{100} = 39\cdot 9$

Corrected $\sigma_x^2 = \dfrac{161701}{100} - (39\cdot 9)^2 = 25$

or Corrected S.D. $= 5$

48. We take $\dfrac{1}{N}\sum_i f_i (x_i - \bar{x})^2 \ge \left\{\dfrac{1}{N}\sum_i f_i |x_i - \bar{x}|\right\}^2$

put $|x_i - \bar{x}| = z_i$

$\therefore\ \dfrac{1}{N}\sum_i f_i z_i^2 \ge \left\{\dfrac{1}{N}\sum_i f_i z_i\right\}^2$

or $\dfrac{1}{N}\Sigma f_i z_i^2 - \bar{z}^2 \ge 0$

$\Rightarrow\ \sigma_Z^2 \ge 0$ which is always true.

Problem Set (2)

Multiple Choice Question

1. If the mean deviation about the median of the numbers $a, 2a, \ldots, 50a$ is 50. then $|a|$ equals
   (a) 2 (b) 3 (c) 4 (d) 5
   (AIEEE 2011)

2. For two data sets, each of size 5, the variances are given to be 4 and 5 and the corresponding means are given to be 2 and 4 respectively. The variance of the combined data set is
   (a) $\frac{5}{2}$ (b) $\frac{11}{2}$ (c) 6 (d) $\frac{13}{2}$
   (AIEEE 2010)

3. If the mean deviation of the number $1, 1+d, 1+2d, \ldots 1+100d$ from their mean is 255 then d is equal to
   (a) 10.0 (b) 20.0 (c) 10.1 (d) 20.2
   (AIEEE 2009)

4. If the average of the number, $1, 2, 3, \ldots 98, 99, x$ is $100x$ then the value of x is
   (a) $\frac{51}{100}$ (b) $\frac{50}{99}$ (c) $\frac{50}{101}$ (d) $\frac{51}{99}$
   (Kerala Engg 2011)

Solution to Problem Set (2)

1. Median $= 25.5\,a$
   Mean deviation about mean $= 50$
   Therefore $\dfrac{\Sigma|x_i - 25.5\,a|}{50} = 50$
   $\Rightarrow\ 24.5\,a + 23.5a + \ldots + 0.5a + 0.5a + \ldots + 2.45a = 2500$
   $\Rightarrow\ a + 3a + 5a + \ldots + 49a = 250$

2. Ans. (b)
   $\sigma_x^2 = 4 \quad \Rightarrow \quad \dfrac{\Sigma x_i^2}{n} - \left(\dfrac{\Sigma x_i}{n}\right)^2 = 4$
   $\Rightarrow\ \dfrac{\Sigma x_i^2}{5} - (2)^2 = 4 \quad \Rightarrow\ \Sigma x_i^2 = 40$
   Similarly $\Sigma y_i^2 = 105$
   $\therefore\ \sigma^2 = \dfrac{\Sigma x_i^2 + \Sigma y_i^2}{10} - \left(\dfrac{\Sigma x_i - \Sigma y_i}{10}\right)^2$
   $= \dfrac{145}{10} - \left(\dfrac{10+20}{10}\right) = \dfrac{11}{2}$

3. Ans. (c).
   $\Sigma x = 101 + d\,(1 + 25 \ldots + 100) = 101 + d\left(\dfrac{100 \times 101}{2}\right)$

$$\bar{x} = \frac{\Sigma x}{101} = 1 + 50d$$

$$\text{M.D.} = \frac{\Sigma|x - \bar{x}|}{101}$$

$$\Rightarrow 255 = \frac{50 \times 51d}{101} = \frac{2550\,d}{101}$$

$$\Rightarrow 101 = 10d \Rightarrow d = 10.1$$

4. Ans. (c).

$$\frac{1+2+3+\ldots 99 + x}{100} = 100x$$

$$\Rightarrow 10000x = \frac{99 \times 100}{2} + x$$

$$\Rightarrow 9999x = \frac{99 \times 100}{2}$$

$$\Rightarrow 101x = \frac{100}{2} \Rightarrow x = \frac{50}{101}$$

Assertion / Reason

1. Let $x_1, x_2, \ldots, x_n$ be n observations and let $\bar{x}$ be their arithmetic mean and σ^2 be the variance

Statements 1. Variance $2x_1, 2x_2, \ldots$ of $2x_n$ is $4\sigma^2$

Statement 2. Arithmetic mean $2x_1, 2x_2, \ldots, 2x_n$ is $4\bar{x}$

(AIEEE 2012)

Sol. Ans. (c)

$$\text{A.M. of } 2x_1, 2x_2, \ldots, 2x_n \; \frac{2x_1 + 2x_2 + \ldots + 2x_n}{n}$$

$$2\left(\frac{nx_1 + x_2 + \ldots + x_n}{n}\right) 2\bar{x}$$

$\Rightarrow$ Statement –2 is false

Variance $(2x_i) = 2^2$. Variance $(x_i) = 4\sigma^2 \Rightarrow$ Statement –1 is true.

2. **Statement-1** The variance of first n even natural number is $\frac{n^2 - 1}{4}$

Statement-2 the sum of first n natural numbers is $\frac{n(n+1)(2n+1)}{6}$

(AIEEE 2009)

Sol. Ans. (d)

It is a fundamental result.

❑

CHAPTER **34**

Probability

§1. Some Definitions

1.1 Sample Space. The Set S of all possible outcomes of an experiment (or observation) is called a sample space provided no two or more of these outcomes can occur simultaneously and exactly one of the outcomes **must** occur whenever the experiment is performed.

It should be noted that with one experiment we may succeed in associating more than one sample space. To determine a sample space, we must know precisely the aim of the experiment.

For example, consider the 'experiment' of tossing two coins. If we are interested in whether each coin falls heads (H) or tails (T), then the possible outcomes are

$$(H, H),\ (H, T),\ (T, H),\ (T, T) \quad ...(1)$$

On the other hand, we may be interested in whether the coins fall alike (A) or different (D). Then the possible outcomes are (A), (D).

1.2 Event. An **event** is a subset of a sample space. For example, for the sample space given by (1), the subset

$$A = \{(H, H),\ (H, T),\ (T, H)\}$$

is the event that at least one head occurs. An event consisting of a single point is called a **simple event.**

1.3 Mutually Exclusive Events. If two or more events have no point in common (*i.e.* if they cannot occur simultaneously), the events are said to be mutually exclusive.

Thus the events A and B are mutually exclusive if $A \cap B = \phi$.

1.4 Equally Likely Events. Two events are said to be equally likely if one of them cannot be expected to occur in preference to the other.

1.5 Exhaustive Events. A set of events is said to be totally exhaustive (or simply exhaustive) if no event outside this set occurs and at least one of these events must happen as a result of an experiment.

Thus when we toss a coin, either it must fall head or tail (the possibility of standing on the edge is ruled out).

§ 2. Classical Definition of Probability

If there are n exhaustive, mutually exclustive and equally likely outcomes of an experiment and m of them are favourable to an event A, then the mathematical probability of A is defined as the ratio m / n.

Odds in favour and odds against an event.

If a of the outcomes are **favourable** to an event A and b of the outcomes are **against** it as a result of an experiment, then we say that *odds are a to b in favour of A, or odds are b to a against A.*

§ 3. Axiomatic approach to Probability Theory.

We shall be mainly concerned with **discrete** sample spaces, that is, with those spaces which contain only a finite number of sample points or an infinite number of points which can be arranged as a sequence $a_1, a_2, a_3, ...$

Axioms of Probability.

Let the sample space S be the set

$$S = \{a_1, a_2, a_3 \ ..... \} = A_1 \cup A_2 \cup A_3 \cup ......$$

where $A_i = \{a_i\}$ are the simple events in S.

Then to each event A in S, we assign a **non-negative real number** $P(A)$, called the probability of A satisfying the following axioms :

$\mathbf{P_1}$: $P(A) \geq 0$ for every event A,

$\mathbf{P_2}$: $P(S) = 1$ for the certain event S,

$\mathbf{P_3}$: Probability $P(A)$ of any event A is the sum of the probabilities of the simple events whose union is A.

Remark 1.

(i) If the sample space S is the union of the distinct simple events $A_1, A_2, A_3, ...$, then it follows from axioms $\mathbf{P_2}$ and $\mathbf{P_3}$ that

$$P(S) = P(A_1) + P(A_2) + P(A_3) + ... = 1. \quad ...(1)$$

(ii) From axiom P_3, we easily conclude that if A and B are mutually exclusive events, so that $A \cap B = \phi$, then

$$P(A \cup B) = P(A) + P(B). \quad ...(2)$$

In general, if $A_1, A_2, A_3, \ldots\ldots\ldots$ are mutually exclusive events, then

$$P(A_1 \cup A_2 \cup A_3 \cup \ldots\ldots) = P(A_1) + P(A_2) + P(A_3) + \ldots\ldots \quad ...(3)$$

We now state theorems without proof.

Theorem 1. *Probability of an impossible event is zero i.e.,* $P(\phi) = 0$.

Theorem 2. $P(A \cap \overline{B}) = P(A) - P(A \cap B)$

where $\overline{B}$ denotes the event complementary to event B, that is, $\overline{B}$ contains the sample points of S not in B.

Theorem 3. $P(\overline{A}) = 1 - P(A)$.

Theorem 4. (Addition theorem) : *Probability of A or B.*

$$P(A \cup B) = P(A) + P(B) - P(A \cap B).$$

Remark 2. By theorem 2,

$$P(A) = P(A \cap B) + P(A \cap \overline{B})$$

and $P(B) = P(A \cap B) + P(\overline{A} \cap B)$.

Hence theorem 4 may be restated as

$P(A \cup B) = P(A \cap B) + P(A \cap \overline{B}) + P(\overline{A} \cap B)$.

i.e., $P(A \cup B)$ denotes the probability that at least one of the events A and B will occur.

Cor. If A and B are mutually exclusive, that is, if $A \cap B = \phi$, then

$$P(A \cup B) = P(A) + P(B).$$

The extension of addition rule to three or more events is the following theorem.

Theorem 5. (i) $P(A \cup B \cup C) = P(A) + P(B) + P(C)$.

$- P(A \cap B) - P(A \cap C) - P(B \cap C) + P(A \cap B \cap C)$.

(ii) $P(A_1 \cup A_2 \cup \ldots\ldots \cup A_n)$

$= P(A_1) + P(A_2) + \ldots\ldots + P(A_n)$

$- P(A_1 \cap A_2) - P(A_1 \cap A_3) - \ldots\ldots$

$- P(A_{n-1} \cap A_n) + P(A_1 \cap A_2 \cap A_3)$

$+ P(A_1 \cap A_2 \cap A_4) + \ldots\ldots$

$+ P(A_{n-2} \cap A_{n-1} \cap A_n)$

$+ \ldots. + (-1)^{n-1} P(A_1 \cap A_2 \cap \ldots \cap A_n)$.

Cor. If $A_1, A_2, A_3, \ldots., A_n$ are mutually exclusive, then

$P(A_1 \cup A_2 \cup A_3 \cup \ldots. \cup A_n)$

$= P(A_1) + P(A_2) + \ldots. + P(A_n)$.

Note. For $A \cup B$, we often use the symbol $A + B$ and for $A \cap B$, we use AB.

Remark 3. Since probability of an event is a non-negative number, it follows from theorem 4 that

$$P(A \cup B) \le P(A) + P(B) \quad ...(4)$$

The inequality (4) holds in general. Thus for arbitrary events $A_1, A_2, A_3, \ldots\ldots$, we have

$$P(A_1 \cup A_2 \cup A_3 \cup \ldots..) \le P(A_1) + P(A_2) + P(A_3) + \ldots.. \quad ...(5)$$

The inequality (5) is known as **Boole's inequality.**

§ 4. Conditional Probability.

A word of explanation is necessary to understand conditional probability. Suppose a pair of dice is thrown. Here the sample space S consists of 36 points $(1, 1), (1, 2), \ldots., (1, 6);\ (2, 1), (2, 2), \ldots\ (2, 6); \ldots;\ (6, 1)\ (6, 2), (6, 6)$. Suppose that we now ask the question, "If a pair of dice shows an even sum, what is the probability that this sum is less than 6 ?" Here we are restricting the sample space to a subset of points corresponding to even sum only (18 such points) and asking, "Which of these possible points (outcomes) represents a sum less than 6 ?" There are four such points *viz.*, (1, 1), (1, 3), (3, 1), (2, 2). Since all these outcomes are equally likely, the required probability $P = \frac{4}{18} = \frac{2}{9}$.

Observe that here we have **imposed the condition** that the sum, $x + y$, is even (event A), and then asked the probability for $x + y$ to be less than 6 (event B). We denote this conditional probability by the symbol $P(B/A)$, which is read "the probability of the event B under the condition that the event A has already happened. A little consideration will show that the probability $\frac{2}{9}$ was obtained when we divided the number $n(A \cap B)$ of points in the subset

$$A \cap B = \{(x, y) :\ x + y \text{ is even and} < 6\}$$

by the number, $n(A)$, of points in the subset $A = \{(x, y) :\ x + y \text{ is even}\}$, so that

$$P(B / A) = \frac{n(A \cap B)}{n(A)} = \frac{n(A \cap B) / n(S)}{n(A) / n(S)} = \frac{P(A \cap B)}{P(A)} \quad ...(1)$$

where $n(S)$ is the number of points in the entire sample space. Note that here it is assumed that

$$P(A) \neq 0.$$

Although the equation (1) has been obtained for the special case where all points of S have the same probability $\frac{1}{36}$, it will be found to hold in those cases as well where the equality of probability does not hold. *Thus equation (1) constitutes our formal definition of conditional probability of B on the hypothesis A (or for given A).*

Multiplication Theorem.

$P(A \cap B) = P(A)\ P(B / A)$, *i.e.*, the probability of the simultaneous occurrence of the events A and B equals the probability of A multiplied by the conditional probability of B that A has already occurred.

Independent events. *If the happening of the event B is not influenced or conditioned by a second event* $A\ (P(A) \neq 0)$ *so that*

$$P(B/A) = P(B) \quad ...(2)$$

then B is said to be independent of A.

Theorem 1. If $P(A) \neq 0$ and $P(B) \neq 0$ and B is independent of A, then A is independent of B. In this case, we say that A and B are mutually independent.

Theorem 2. Two events A and B are mutually independent if and only if

$$P(A \cap B) = P(A)\ P(B)$$

provided $P(A) \neq 0$ and $P(B) \neq 0$.

The generalization of this theorem is as follows : The events $A_1, A_2, ..., A_n$ *are mutually independent (or simply independent) if and only if the multiplication rule*

$$P(A_1 \cap A_2 \cap .... \cap A_k) = P(A_1)\ P(A_2) .... P(A_k) \quad ...(3)$$

holds for every k-tuples of events; $k = 2, 3, ..., n$.

If (3) holds for $k = 2$ and may or may not hold for $k = 3, 4, ..., n$, then events $A_1, A_2, ..., A_n$ are said to be pairwise independent. Thus mutually independent events are pairwise independent but not conversely.

Theorem 3. If the events A and B are mutually independent then the events A and $\overline{B}$ are also mutually independent.

Theorem 4. If A and B are mutually independent events such that $P(A) \neq 0$ and $P(B) \neq 0$, then the events A and B have atleast one common sample point.

Important Note. The reader will do well to note *difference between mutually exclusive events and independent events.* Mutually exclusive events in general are not independent. For example, in the case of toss of two coins for which the sample space is

$$S = \{(H, H),\ (H, T),\ (T, H),\ (T, T)\},$$

let A be the event that there are two heads and B the event that there are two tails. Thus $A = \{(H, H)\}$ and $B = \{(T, T)\}$. Here $A \cap B = \phi$ so that A and B are mutually exclusive. But A and B are not independent.

since $P(A) = \frac{1}{4} = P(B)$ and $P(A \cap B) = 0$

so that $P(A \cap B) \neq P(A)\ P(B)$ in this case.

Also we know from Theorem 4 above that independent events are not in general mutually exclusive.

In fact, events are 'independent' if the probability of any one of them is not **affected** by supplementary knowledge concerning the materialization of any number of the remaining events. For example, if A and B represent white balls drawn from two different urns, the probability of A is the same whether the colour of the ball drawn from the other urn is known or not. Similarly, for an unbiased coin, head at the first and head at the second throw are independent events but they are not mutually exclusive events. As an example of dependent events, consider an urn containing 2 white balls and 3 black ones. Two balls are drawn in succession without replacement. Let A be the event consisting in the white colour of the first ball and B the event consisting in the white colour of second ball. Evidently, here A and B are dependent events.

Important Remarks.

(a) Let E_1 and E_2 be two independent events with respective probabilities p_1 and p_2, then the probability p of the event E_1 to occur and that of E_2 not to occur is given by $p = p_1\ (1 - p_2)$.

(b) If there are n mutually independent events $E_1, E_2, ..., E_n$ with respective probabilities $p_1, p_2, ..., p_n$, then the probability of m events $E_1, E_2, ..., E_m$ to occur and that of the remaining $(n - m)$ events E_{m+1}, $E_{m+2}, ..., E_n$ not to occur is given by $p_1\ p_2 .... p_m\ (1 - p_{m+1})\ (1 - p_{m+2}) .... (1 - p_n)$

(c) The probability that none of the n events occurs is given by $(1 - p_1)(1 - p_2) ..... (1 - p_n)$.

(d) The probability that at least one of the n events will occur is given by $1 - (1 - p_1)(1 - p_2) .... (1 - p_n)$.

§ 5. Partition of a Sample Space.

Let $A_1, A_2, ... A_n$ *be subsets of a sample space S. Then these subsets are said to form a partition of S if the following conditions hold :*

(i) Each A_i is a proper subset of S, that is $A_i \subset S,\ i = 1, 2, ... n$ and $A_i \neq S$.

(ii) $A_1 \cup A_2 \cup ...... \cup A_n = S$.

(iii) The subsets A_i are pairwise disjoint, that is, $A_i \cap A_j = \phi,\ i, j = 1, 2, 3, ... n,\ i \neq j$.

Theorem of Total Probability for Compound Events.

Theorem 1. Let $\{A_1, A_2, ..., A_n\}$ be any partition of a sample space S and let A be any event. Then

$$P(A) = \sum_{i=1}^{n} P(A_i)\ P(A / A_i) \qquad ...(1)$$

provided $P(A_i) \neq 0,\ i = 1, 2, \ldots\ldots, n.$

Proof. If S is the sample space, then

$S = \bigcup_{i=1}^{n} A_i$ and therefore

$$A = A \cap S = A \cap (\bigcup_{i=1}^{n} A_i) = \bigcup_{i=1}^{n} [A \cap A_i], \qquad ...(2)$$

[By distributive law].

Since $A_i \cap A_j = \phi$ for $i \neq j$, it follows that $(A \cap A_i) \cap (A \cap A_j) = \phi$ for $i \neq j$.

Hence $P(A) = P[\bigcup_{i=1}^{n} (A \cap A_i)] + \sum_{i=1}^{n} P(A \cap A_i)$

[By Cor. of Theorem 5 of §3]

$$= \sum_{i=1}^{n} P(A_i)\ P(A / A_i)$$

Theorem 2. **(Baye's Rule).** *Let the set of events $\{A_1, A_2, \ldots\ldots, A_n\}$ form a partition of the sample space S, where $P(A_i) \neq 0,\ i = 1, 2, \ldots n$. Then for any event A for which $P(A) \neq 0$ and for $1 \leq k \leq n$.*

$$P(A_k / A) = \frac{P(A_k)\ P(A/A_k)}{\sum_{i=1}^{n} P(A_i)\ P(A/A_i)}$$

Baye's theorem can be put in the following useful form.

Let $S = A_1 \cup A_2 \cup \ldots\ldots \cup A_n$ *where* A_i, *are* **simple events**. *Then clearly A_i form a partition of S. If A is any non-empty subset of S, then for each integer $k\ (1 \leq k \leq n)$,*

$$P(A_k / A) - \frac{P(A/A_k)\ P(A_k)}{\sum_{i=1}^{n} P(A/A_i)\ P(A_i)} \qquad ...(3)$$

Proof. By Theorem 1,

$$P(A) = \sum_{i=1}^{n} P(A_i)\ P(A/A_i) \qquad ...(1)$$

Also $\quad P(A \cap A_k) = P(A_k)\ P(A/A_k) \qquad ...(2)$

$$\therefore \quad P(A_k / A) = \frac{P(A \cap A_k)}{P(A)} = \frac{P(A_k)\ P(A/A_k)}{\sum_{i=1}^{n} P(A_i)\ P(A/A_i)}$$

by (1) and (2).

Note—Baye's theorem serves to connect the conditional probability of A_k, given A, with the conditional probability of A, given A_i and the probability of the A_i themselves. If the events A_i are called 'causes' then (2) or (3) can be regarded as a formula for the probability that the event A, which has occurred, is the result of the cause A_k.

The probabilities $P(A_i),\ i = 1, 2, \ldots., n$ are called the '*a priori probabilities*' because they exist before we get any information from the experiment itself.

The probabilities $P(A_i / A),\ i = 1, 2, \ldots, n$ are called '*posteriori probabilities;* because they are determined after the results of the experiment are known.

The probabilities $P(A/A_i),\ i = 1, 2, \ldots, n$ are called '*likelihoods*' because they show how likely the event A under consideration is to occur given a priori probabilities.

For the application of Baye's theorem, it is essential that the events $A_i = 1, 2, \ldots.., n$ are mutually exclusive and sum of their probabilities equal to 1.

§ 6. Binomial Distributions.

When we know the probability of the happening of an event in one trial, the probability of the happening exactly once, twice, thrice etc. in n trials can be found as shown below.

If p is the probability of happening (success) of an event in one trial, then the probability of its non-happening (failure) is $1 - p = q$, say. Hence, by the multiplication theorem, the probability of its happening r times and failing to happen $(n - r)$ times in a *prescribed order is* $p^r\ q^{n-r}$. But the number of orders is equal to the number of combinations of n things taken r at a time, *i.e.* ${}^nC_r$ and these orders are all mutually exclusive and equally likely. Hence the probability of the event happening r times (*i.e.* probability of r successes) exactly in n trials *in any order is* ${}^nC_r\ p^r\ q^{n-r}$ which is the $(r + 1)$th term in the binomial expansion of $(p + q)^n$. Thus probabilities of 0, 1, 2, ..., n successes are respectively

$$q^n,\ {}^nC_1\ q^{n-1}\ p,\ {}^nC_2\ q^{n-2}\ p^2, \ldots\ldots,$$
$$ {}^nC_r\ q^{n-r}\ p^r, \ldots.., p^n$$

n and p are called parameters of the binomial distribution; sometimes denoted by $B(n, p)$ we usually write $X \sim B(n, p)$

Probability of at least r successes in n independent trials is given by

$$P(X \geq r) = \sum_{x=r}^{n} {}^nC_x\ q^{n-x}\ p^x$$

$$= 1 - \sum_{x=0}^{r-1} {}^nC_x\ q^{n-x}\ p^x$$

$$\because \quad \sum_{x=0}^{n} {}^nC_x\ q^{n-x}\ p^x = (q + p)^n = 1$$

Probability of at most r successes is given by

$$P(X \leq r) = \sum_{x=0}^{r} {}^nC_x\ q^{n-x}\ p^x.$$

We now find the value of r so that $p(X=r)$ is maximum. Let B_r denote the $(r+1)^{th}$ term in the binomial expansion of the expression $(p+q)^n$ i.e., $B_r = {}^nC_r\, p^r q^{n-r}$. If B_r is the greatest term, then

$$B_r \geq B_{r-1} \text{ and } B_r \geq B_{r+1}$$

Taking $B_r \geq B_{r-1}$ or $B_{r-1} \leq B_r$

$$\Rightarrow \quad {}^nC_{r-1}\, p^{r-1} q^{n-(r-1)} \leq {}^nC_r\, p^r q^{n-r}$$

$$\text{or} \quad \frac{n!}{(r-1)!\,(n-r+1)!} p^{r-1} q^{n-r+1} \leq \frac{n!}{r!\,(n-r)!} p^r q^{n-r}$$

$$\text{or} \quad q \leq \frac{n-r+1}{r} p, \quad \text{i.e., } qr \leq (n-r+1)\,p$$

$$\Rightarrow \quad r \leq p\,(n+1) \qquad \because\ p+q=1 \qquad \ldots(1)$$

Similarly from $B_r \geq B_{r+1}$, we have

$$r \geq p\,(n+1) - 1 \qquad \ldots(2)$$

Thus $p\,(n+1) - 1 \leq r \leq p\,(n+1)$ from (1) and (2).

Now if $p\,(n+1)$ is not an integer then it is the greatest integer in $p\,(n+1)$ i.e., if $p\,(n+1) = 3\frac{1}{4}$ then we take $r = 3$

and if $p\,(n+1)$ is an integer, that is, say $= 4$ then r can be both 4 as well as 3.

The expression $p\,(n+1) - 1 \leq r \leq p\,(n+1)$ gives us the **modal** or **maximum** value of r in the binomial probability distribution, where n denotes the number of trials and p the probability of success in a single trial, which remains constant from trial to trial.

Ex. Find the most probable number (modal value) of heads in 99 tossings of a biased coin, given that the probability of a head in a single tossing is $\frac{3}{5}$.

Sol. Here $n = 99$, $p = \frac{3}{5}$

Hence using the formula for the modal value r we have

$$p\,(n+1) - 1 \leq r \leq p\,(n+1)$$

$$\Rightarrow \quad \frac{3}{5}(99+1) - 1 \leq r \leq \frac{3}{5}(99+1)$$

$$\Rightarrow \quad 59 \leq r \leq 60$$

Hence $r = 60$

Remark : From modal formula, we have

$$p - \frac{q}{n} \leq \frac{r}{n} \leq p + \frac{p}{n}$$

$$\because \quad p+q=1 \Rightarrow p-1=-q$$

Hence, when n is increased indefinitely the mode tends to np.

Theorem : If X is a random binomial variate, then $X \sim B\,(n, p)$, n, p being the parameters of the binomial probability distribution.

Then expected value of X i.e., $E\,(X) = np$ and variance of X i.e., $\text{var}\,(X) = npq$

Proof. $E\,(X) = \sum_{r=0}^{n} r \,.\, {}^nC_r\, p^r q^{n-r}$

$$= np \sum_{r-1=0}^{n} {}^{n-1}C_{r-1}\, p^{r-1} q^{(n-1)-(r-1)}$$

$$= np\,(p+q)^{n-1} = np; \text{ using the result}$$

$$\sum_{r=0}^{n} {}^nC_r\, p^r q^{n-r} = (p+q)^n \text{ and } p+q=1$$

$$E\,(X^2) = \sum_{r=0}^{n} r^2\, {}^nC_r\, p^r q^{n-r}$$

$$= np \sum_{r-1=0}^{n} r \,.\, {}^{n-1}C_{r-1}\, p^{r-1} q^{n-r}$$

$$= np \sum_{r-1=0}^{n} (r-1+1)\ {}^{n-1}C_{r-1}\, p^{r-1} q^{n-r}$$

$$= np \left[\sum_{r-1=0}^{n} (r-1)\ {}^{n-1}C_{r-1}\, p^{r-1} q^{n-r} + \sum_{r-1=0}^{n} {}^{n-1}C_{r-1}\, p^{r-1} q^{n-r} \right]$$

$$= np\,[(n-1)\,p + (p+q)^{n-1}]$$

using result (1) and $p+q=1$

$$= n\,(n-1)\,p^2 + np$$

We have, $\text{Var}\,(X) = E\,(X^2) - [E\,(X)]^2$

$$= n\,(n-1)\,p^2 + np - (np)^2$$

$$np\,(p-1) = npq \qquad \because\ p+q=1$$

Ex. It is given that mean and variance of a binomial variate X are 2 and 1 respectively. Find the probability that X takes a value greater or equal to 1.

Sol. Here we have $E\,(X) = np = 2$

and $\text{Var}\,(X) = npq = 1$

These give $q = \frac{1}{2}$, $p = \frac{1}{2}$, $n = 4$

Thus $P\,(X \geq 1) = 1 - P\,(X = 0)$

Since $P\,(X = r) = {}^nC_r\, p^r q^{n-r}$

$$= 1 - {}^4C_0 \left(\frac{1}{2}\right)^4 = 1 - \frac{1}{16} = \frac{15}{16}$$

§ 7. Use of Multinomial Theorem.

Suppose a die has m faces marked with the numbers 1, 2, 3, ... , m and such n dices are thrown.

Then the probability that the sum of the numbers shown on the upper faces is equal to s is given by

the coefficient of x^s in the expansion of $\dfrac{(x+x^2+x^3+\ldots\ldots+x^m)^n}{m^n}$.

Ex. Four dice are thrown. Find the chance that the sum of the numbers appearing will be 18.

Sol. Probability = Coefficient of x^{18} in the expansion of

$$\frac{(x+x^2+x^3+x^4+x^5+x^6)^4}{6^4}$$

Now coefficient of x^{18} in

$$x^4(1+x+x^2+x^3+x^4+x^5)^4$$

or in $x^4\left(\dfrac{1-x^6}{1-x}\right)^4$

$$= \text{coefficient of } x^{14} \text{ in } (1-x^6)^4(1-x)^{-4}$$

$$= \text{coefficient of } x^{14} \text{ in}$$

$$(1-4x^6+6x^{12}+\ldots)(1+{}^4C_1x+{}^5C_2x^2 + {}^{11}C_8x^8+\ldots+{}^{17}C_{14}x^{14}+\ldots)$$

$$=6\times{}^5C_2-4\times{}^{11}C_8+{}^{17}C_{14}$$

$$=6\times10-4\times\frac{11.10.9}{1.2.3}+\frac{17.16.15}{1.2.3}$$

$$=60-660+680=80$$

Thus, required chance $=\dfrac{80}{6\times6\times6\times6}=\dfrac{5}{81}$

§ 8. Alternative Concept of Inverse Probability (Baye's rule)

Sometimes in probability Theory, we come across quite often, the problems of the following nature. Suppose when an event has happened, it may be due to some one of the n causes. The **apriori probability** of these causes is estimated as $P_1, P_2, \ldots, P_n$.

Let p_r denote the probability of the happening of the event due to the rth cause, then the **antecedent probability** that the event follows from the rth cause is $p_r\,P_r$.

Let Q_r denote the a **posteriori** probability that the rth cause was the true one, then Q_r is proportional to the probability given by

$$\frac{Q_1}{p_1P_1}=\frac{Q_2}{p_2P_2}\ldots=\frac{Q_r}{p_rP_r}=\ldots=\frac{Q_n}{p_nP_n}$$

$$=\frac{\sum_{r=1}^{n}Q_r}{\sum_{r=1}^{n}p_r\,P_r}=\frac{1}{\sum_{r=1}^{n}p_r\,P_r}$$

Thus $Q_r=\dfrac{p_r\,P_r}{\sum_{r=1}^{n}p_r\,P_r}$.

If $P_1, P_2, P_3, \ldots$ are all equal, calculation work is much simplified.

Ex. In a bag there are six balls of unknown colours, three balls are drawn and found to be black; find the chance that no black ball is left in the bag.

Sol. Here we can formulate four hypotheses, that the bag contains 6 or 5 or 4 or 3 black balls which are all equally likely *i.e.*, $P_1=P_2=P_3=P_4$

Hypothesis

p_1 (all balls black) = 1,

Hypothesis

p_2 (5B and 1 of other colour) $=\dfrac{5}{6}\cdot\dfrac{4}{5}\cdot\dfrac{3}{4}$

Hypothesis

p_3 (4B and 2 of other colours) $=\dfrac{4}{6}\cdot\dfrac{3}{5}\cdot\dfrac{2}{4}$

Hypothesis

p_4 (3B and 3 of other colours) $=\dfrac{3}{6}\cdot\dfrac{2}{5}\cdot\dfrac{1}{4}$

$$\therefore\quad \frac{Q_1}{p_1P_1}=\frac{Q_2}{p_2P_2}=\frac{Q_3}{p_3P_3}=\frac{Q_4}{p_4P_4}$$

gives $\dfrac{Q_1}{1}=\dfrac{Q_2}{60/120}=\dfrac{Q_3}{24/120}=\dfrac{Q_4}{6/120}$

or $\dfrac{Q_1}{20}=\dfrac{Q_2}{10}=\dfrac{Q_3}{4}=\dfrac{Q_4}{1}=\dfrac{\Sigma Q}{35}=\dfrac{1}{35}$

This implies that the probability of the fourth hypothesis being the true one is $Q_4=\dfrac{1}{35}$.

Problem Set (1)

1. An urn contains 3 white and 5 black balls. One ball is drawn. What is the probability that it is black ?
2. From a pack of 52 cards, four cards are drawn. Find the chance that they will be the four honours of the same suit.
3. (a) In a hand at whist what is the chance that the 4 kings are held by a specified player ?

   (b) In bridge game of playing cards, 4 players are distributed one card each by turn so that each player gets 13 cards. Find out the probability of a specified player getting a black ace and a king.
4. What is the chance that a leap year selected at random will contain 53 Sundays ?

5. (a) Two dice are thrown simultaneously. What is the probability of obtaining a total score of seven ?
(b) Six dice are thrown simultaneously. Find the probability that all dice show different faces.

6. (a) Six boys and six girls sit in a row randomly. Find the probability that
(i) The six girls sit together.
(ii) The boys and girls sit alternately.
(b) Seven students are to sit at one side of a straight table. Find the probability of two particular students sitting together.
(c) Twenty people sit around at random at a round table. Find the probability that two people A, B sit with four people between them.

7. (i) Five persons entered the lift cabin on the ground floor of an 8-floor house. Suppose that each of them independently and with equal probability, can leave the cabin at any floor beginning with the first. Find out the probability of all five persons leaving at different floors. **(Roorkee 1990)**
(ii) M telegrams are distributed at random over N communication channels $(N > M)$. Find the probability that not more than one telegram will be sent over each channel.

8. (a) A die is loaded so that the probability of face i is proportional to i, $i = 1, 2, \ldots, 6$. What is the probability of an even number occurring when the die is rolled ?
(b) Three faces of a fair die are yellow, two faces red and one blue. The die is tossed three times. The probability that the colours, yellow, red and blue appear in the first, second and the third tosses respectively is .... **(I.I.T. 1992)**
(c) A die is loaded so that the probability of face showing even number is twice the probability of odd number. If the biased die is thrown twice, find the probability that
(i) the sum is even
(ii) the sum is odd.

9. A coin is tossed twice. Events E and F are defined as follows : E = heads on first toss, F = heads on second toss.
Find the probability of $E \cup F$.

10. (a) There are three events A, B, C one of which must, and only one can happen ; the odds are 8 to 3 against A, 5 to 2 against B ; find the odds against C.
(b) The odds against the player A to win are 5 : 2 and odds in favour of another player to win are 6 : 5. If the two events are independent, find the probability that at least one player will win.
(c) A person has to go through three successive tests. Probability of his passing first exam is P. Probability of passing successive tests is P or $P/2$ according as he passed the last test or not. He is selected if he passes at least two tests. Find the probability of his selection. **(IIT 2003)**

11. The odds that a book will be reviewed favourably by three independent critics are 5 to 2, 4 to 3, and 3 to 4 respectively ; what is the probability that of three reviews a majority will be favourable ?

12. (i) Given the probability that A can solve a problem is 2/3 and the probability that B can solve a problem is 3/5, find the probability that (a) at least one of A and B will be able to solve the problem (b) none of the two will be able to solve the problem.
(ii) A man and a woman appear in an interview for two vacancies in the same post. The probability of man's selection is 1/4 and that of the woman's selection is 1/3, what is the probability that
(a) both of them will be selected
(b) only one of them will be selected
(c) none of them will be selected.
(iii) Three rifle-men take one shot each at the same target. The probability of the first rifle-man hitting the target is $0 \cdot 4$, the probability of the second rifle-man hitting the target is $0 \cdot 5$ and the probability of the third rifle-man hitting the target is 0·8. Find the probability that exactly two of them hit the target. **(M.N.R. 1997)**

13. (i) A problem in mathematics is given to three students whose chances of solving it are respectively $\frac{1}{2}, \frac{1}{3}$ and $\frac{1}{4}$. What is the probability that the problem will be solved ?
(ii) An anti-aircraft gun can take a maximum of four shots at an enemy plane moving away from it. The probabilities of hitting the plane at the first, second, third and fourth shot are $0 \cdot 4, 0 \cdot 3, 0 \cdot 2$ and $0 \cdot 1$ respectively. What is the probability that the gun hits the plane ?
(iii) A worker attends three machines each of which operates independently of the other two. The probabilities of the event that the machines will not require operator's intervention during a shift are equal to $p_1 = 0 \cdot 4$, $p_2 = 0 \cdot 3$, $p_3 = 0 \cdot 2$. Find the probability of the event that at least one machine will require worker's intervention during a shift.

14. Four different objects A, B, C, D are distributed at random on four places marked 1, 2, 3, 4 respectively.

What is the probability that none of the objects occupies the place correpsonding to its number ?

15. In a group of equal number of men and women, 10% men and 45% women are unemployed. What is the probability that person selected at random is employed ?

16. A candidate is selected for interview for three posts. For the first there are 3 candidates, for the second there are 4 and for the third there are 2. What are the chances of his getting at least one post ?

17. An article manufactured by a company consists of two parts X and Y. In the process of manufacture of part X, 9 out of 104 parts may be defective. Similarly, 5 out of 100 are likely to be defective in the manufacture of the part Y. Calculate the probability that the assembled product will not be defective.

18. If p is the probability that a man aged x years will die in a year, find the probability that out of n men $A_1, A_2, \ldots\ldots, A_n$ each aged x years, A_1 will die in a year and will be the first to die.

19. (a) Three groups of children contain 3 girls and one boy; 2 girls and 2 boys, one girl and 3 boys. One child is selected at random from each group. Show that the chance that the three selected consist of 1 girl and 2 boys is $\frac{13}{32}$.

(b) If from each of the three boxes containing 3 white and 1 black, 2 white and 2 black, 1 white and 3 black balls, one ball is drawn at random, then the probability that 2 white and 1 black ball will be drawn is

(a) $\frac{13}{32}$ (b) $\frac{1}{4}$

(c) $\frac{1}{32}$ (d) $\frac{3}{16}$ **(I.I.T. 1998)**

(c) A group contains 10 men and 4 women. Three member committee is formed which must contain at least one woman. Find the probability that the committee so formed has more women than men.

20. (a) A coin is tossed n times ; what is the chance that the head will present itself an odd number of times ?

(b) Two persons A and B toss a coin 50 times each together. Find the probability that both of them get tails at the same time.

21. A student is given a true-false exam. with 10 questions. If he gets 8 or more correct answers he passes the exam. Given that he guesses at the answer to each question, compute the probability that he passes the exam.

22. (a) A, B, C in order cut a pack of cards, replacing them after each cut, on the condition that the first who cuts a spade shall win a prize; find their respective chances. **(Roorkee 1992)**

(b) Three players, A, B and C, toss a coin cyclically in that order (that is $A, B, C, A, B, C, A, B\ldots$) till a head shows. Let p be the probability that the coin shows a head. Let α, β and γ be, respectively, the probabilities that A, B and C gets the first head. Prove that $\beta = (1-p)\,\alpha$. Determine α, β and γ (in terms of p). **(I.I.T. 1998)**

23. If a fair coin is tossed 15 times, what is the probability of getting head as many times in the first ten throws as in the last five ?

24. A is one of 6 horses entered for a race, and is to be ridden by one of two jockeys B and C. It is 2 to 1 that B rides A, in which case all the horses are equally likely to win ; if C rides A, his chance is trebled ; what are the odds against his winning ?

25. (i) A speaks truth in 75 percent cases, and B in 80 percent of the cases. In what percentage of cases are they likely to contradict each other in stating the same fact ?

(ii) A and B are two independent witnesses (*i.e.* there is no collusion between them) in a case. The probability that A will speak the truth is x and the probability that B will speak the truth is y. A and B agree in a certain statement. Show that the probability that the statement is true is $\frac{xy}{1-x-y+2xy}$.

26. A speaks the truth 2 out of 3 times and B 4 times out of 5, they agree in the assertion that from a bag containing 6 balls of different colours a red ball has been drawn; find the probability that the statement is true.

27. There are 5 pairs of shoes in a shoe rack. Four shoes are drawn one by one at random. Find the probability that at least one pair of shoes is drawn.

28. There are four machines and it is known that exactly two of them are faulty. They are tested, one by one, in a random order till both the faulty machines are identified. Then the probability that only two tests are needed is

(A) $\frac{1}{3}$ (B) $\frac{1}{6}$ (C) $\frac{1}{2}$ (D) $\frac{1}{4}$

(I.I.T. 1998)

29. If four whole numbers taken at random are multiplied together, show that chance that the last-digit in the product is $1, 3, 7$ or 9 is $\frac{16}{625}$.

30. A and B play a match to be decided as soon as either has won two games. The chance of either winning a game is $\frac{1}{20}$ and of its being drawn $\frac{9}{10}$. What is the chance that the match is finished in 10 or less games ?

31. A pair of fair dice is rolled together till a sum of either 5 or 7 is obtained. What is the chance that 5 comes before 7 ?

32. A factory A produces 10% defective valves and another factory B produces 20% defective. A bag contains 4 valves of factory A and 5 valves of factory B. If two valves are drawn at random from the bag, find the probability that atleast one valve is defective. Give your answer upto two places of decimals. **(Roorkee 1995)**

33. A person is assigned to 3 jobs A, B and C. The probabilities of his doing the jobs A, B, C respectively are p, q and 1/2. He gets the full payment only if he either does the jobs A and B or the jobs A and C. If the probability of his getting the full payment is 1/2, find the relation satisfied by p and q. **(M.N.R. 1996)**

34. Two friends Ashok and Baldev have equal number of sons. There are 3 tickets for a cricket match which are to be distributed among the sons. The probability that 2 tickets go to the sons of the one and one ticket go to the sons of the other is 6/7. Find how many sons each of the two friends have. **(M.N.R. 1996)**

35. Sixteen players $S_1, S_2, ..., S_{16}$ play in a tournament. They are divided into eight pairs at random. From each pair a winner is decided on the basis of a game played between the two players of the pair. Assume that all the players are of equal strength.

(a) Find the probability that the player S_1 is among the eight winners.

(b) Find the probability that exactly one of the two players S_1 and S_2 is among the eight winners. **(I.I.T. 1997)**

36. (a) If the integers m and n are chosen at random between 1 and 100, then the probability that a number of the form $7^m + 7^n$ is divisible by 5 equals

(a) $\frac{1}{4}$ (b) $\frac{1}{7}$

(c) $\frac{1}{8}$ (d) $\frac{1}{49}$ **(I.I.T. 1999)**

(b) If 3 distinct numbers are chosen randomly from {1, 2, ...100}, then probability that all are divisible by both 2 and 3 is

(a) 4/25 (b) 4/35

(c) 4/33 (d) 4/1155 **(Screening 2004)**

37. (a) An urn contains m white and n black balls. A ball is drawn at random and is put back into the urn along with k additional balls of the same colour as that of the ball drawn. A ball is again drawn at random. What is the probability that the ball drawn now is white ? **(I.I.T. 2001)**

(b) A bag contains 12 red balls and 6 white balls. Six balls are drawn one by one without replacement of which atleast 4 balls are white. Find the probability that in the next two draws exactly one white ball is drawn.

(leave the answer in terms of ^nC_r). **(I.I.T. 2004)**

38. Eight players $P_1, P_2, ... P_8$ play a knock-out tournament. It is known that whenever the players P_i and P_j play, the player P_i will win if $i < j$. Assuming that the players are paired at random in each round, what is the probability that the player P_4 reaches the final ? **(IIT 1999)**

39. Four cards are drawn from a pack of 52 playing cards. Find the probability (correct upto two places of decimals) of drawing exactly one pair. **(Roorkee 1999)**

40. An unbiased die, with faces numbered 1, 2, 3, 4, 5, 6 is thrown n times and the list of n numbers showing up is noted. What is the probability that among the numbers 1, 2, 3, 4, 5, 6, only three numbers appear in this list ? **(I.I.T. 2001)**

41. The probabilities that a student passes in Mathematics, Physics and Chemistry are M, P and C respectively. Of these subjects, the student has a 75% chance of passing in atleast one, a 50% chance of passing in atleast two, and a 40% chance of passing in exactly two. Which of the following relations are true ?

(a) $P + M + C = \frac{19}{20}$ (b) $P + M + C = \frac{27}{20}$

(c) $PMC = \frac{1}{10}$ (d) $PMC = \frac{1}{4}$ **(I.I.T. 1999)**

42. Three newspapers A, B, C are published in a certain city, and a survey shows that of the adult population; 20% read A, 16% read B, 14% read C, 8% read both A and B, 5% read both A and C, 4% read both B and C, and 2% read all three.

What percentage reads at least one of the papers ? Of those that read at least one, what percentage reads both A and B ?

43. Two sets of candidates are competing for the positions on the board of directors of a company. The probabilities that the first and second sets will win are $0 \cdot 6$ and $0 \cdot 4$ respectively. If the first set wins the probability of introducing a new product is 0 · 8 and the corresponding probability if the second set wins is 0 · 3. What is the probability that the new product will be introduced ?

44. (a) If p and q are chosen randomly from the set {1, 2, 3, 4, 5, 6, 7, 8, 9, 10}, with replacement, determine the probability that the roots of the equation $x^2 + px + q = 0$ are real. **(I.I.T. Re-ex. 1997)**

(b) Each coefficient in the equation $ax^2 + bx + c = 0$ is determined by throwing an ordinary die. Find the probability that the equation will have equal roots. **(Roorkee 1998)**

(c) Two numbers are chosen from {1, 2, 3, 4, 5, 6} one after another without replacement. Find the probability that one of the smaller value of two is less than 4

(a) 4/5 (b) 1/15

(c) 1/5 (d) 14/15 **(Screening 2003)**

45. *(The birthday problem).* What is the probability that in a group of N people, at least two of them will have the same birthday ?

46. (i) One card is drawn from each of two ordinary sets of 52 cards. Find the probability that at least one of them will be Ace of hearts.

(ii) If two dice are thrown, what is the probability that at least one of the dice shows a number greater than 3 ?

47. (a) Two cards are drawn simultaneously from the same set. Find the probability that at least one of them will be the Ace of hearts.

(b) Two cards are drawn one by one from a pack of well shuffled cards with replacement. Find the probability of at least two kings but none of the cards is of clubs.

48. (i) A has 3 shares in a lottery containing 3 prizes and 9 blanks. B has two shares in a lottery containing 2 prizes and 6 blanks; compare their chances of success.

(ii) In a multiple choice question there are four alternative answers, of which one or more are correct. A candidate will get marks in the question only if he ticks all the correct answers. The candidate decides to tick answers at random. If he is allowed upto three chances to answer the question, find the probability that he will get marks in the question.

49. A bag contains n red and n white balls. Two balls at a time are drawn at random from the bag till all the balls are drawn. Find the probability that in each draw there is one white and one red ball.

50. A and B throw with a pair of dice. A wins if he throws 6 before B throws 7 and B if he throws 7 before A throws 6. If A begins, show that his chance of winning is 30/61. **(M.N.R. 1995)**

51. Three white balls and five black balls are placed in a bag, and three men draw a ball in succession (the balls drawn not being replaced) until a white ball is drawn : show that their respective chances are as 27 : 18 : 11.

52. (i) A box contains 2 black, 4 white and 3 red balls. One ball is drawn at random from the box, and kept aside. From the remaining balls in the box, another ball is drawn at random and kept besides the first. This process is repeated till all the balls are drawn from the box. Find the probability that the balls drawn are in the sequence of 2 black, 4 white and 3 red.

(ii) A bag contains 3 black and 2 red balls. One by one three balls are drawn without replacing them. Find the probability that the third ball is red. **(M.N.R. 1994)**

53. The chance of an event happening is the square of the chance, of a second event but the odds against the first are the cubes of the odds against the second. Find the chance of each.

54. There is 30% chance that it rains on any particular day. What is the probability that there is at least one rainy day within a period of 7 days ? Given that there is at least one rainy day, what is the probability that there are at least two rainy days ? **(Roorkee 1997)**

55. In a purse there are 10 coins, all five nP's except one which is a rupee; in another there are 10 coins all five nP's. Nine coins are taken from the former and put into the latter and then nine coins are taken from the latter and put into the former, find the chance that the rupee is still in the first purse.

56. If n biscuits are distributed among N different beggars, what is the probability that a particular beggar gets exactly r biscuits ?

57. There are ten pairs of gloves in a bag. First A draws one glove from the bag, then B draws one glove, then A draws one glove and finally B draws one glove, drawn gloves being not replaced. Show that the chance of A drawing a pair is the same as that of B drawing a pair. Also find the probability that neither draws a pair.

58. Two coins are tossed. What is the conditional probability that two heads result, given that there is at least one head ?

59. A die is thrown three times, and sum of three numbers thrown is 15. Find the chance that the first throw was a four.

60. Two dice are thrown together first and secondly three dice are thrown together. Find the probability that the total in the first throw is 4 or more and at the same time the total in the second throw is 6 or more.

61. A, B, C are events such that

$P_r(A) = 0\cdot 3,\ P_r(B) = 0\cdot 4,\ P_r(C) = 0\cdot 8$
$P_r(AB) = 0\cdot 08,\ P_r(AC) = 0\cdot 28$
$P_r(ABC) = 0\cdot 09.$

If $P_r(A \cup B \cup C) \geq 0\cdot 75$, then show that $P_r(BC)$ lies in the interval $0\cdot 23 \leq x \leq 0\cdot 48$.

62. (i) Cards are dealt one-by-one from a well-shuffled pack until an ace appears. Show that the probability that exactly n cards are dealt before the first ace appears is $\dfrac{4(51-n)(50-n)(49-n)}{52.51.50.49}$.

(ii) Cards are drawn one-by-one at random from a well-shuffled full pack of 52 playing cards until 2 aces are obtained for the first time. If N is the number of cards required to be drawn, then show that $P_r(N = n) = \dfrac{(n-1)(52-n)(51-n)}{50 \times 49 \times 17 \times 13}$

where $2 \leq n \leq 50$.

(iii) A person draws cards one by one from a pack. Show that the probability that exactly n cards are drawn until all the aces appear is $\dfrac{4(n-1)(n-2)(n-3)}{52.51.50.49}$.

63. K balls are distributed at random and independently of one another among N cells which lie in a straight line $(N > K)$. Find the probability that they will occupy K adjacent cells.

64. A coin is tossed $(m+n)$ times $(m > n)$; show that the probability of at least m consecutive heads is $\dfrac{n+2}{2^{m+1}}$.

65. (a) If three squares are chosen at random on a chess board, show that the chance that they should be in a diagonal line is $\dfrac{7}{744}$.

(b) There is a key-ring which has n keys of which only one is the right key of the lock. A person tries to open the lock at random. If he discards the key already tried, what is the probability that he opens the lock at k^{th} trial ?

66. (a) n letters to each of which corresponds an addressed envelope are placed in the envelopes at random. What is the probability that no letter is placed in the right envelope ?

(b) There are n different objects 1, 2, 3, ... n distributed at random in n boxes $A_1, A_2, A_3, \dots A_n$. Find the probability that two objects are placed in the boxes corresponding to their number.

67. A set A has n elements. A subset P of A is selected at random. Returning the elements of P, the set Q is formed again and then a subset Q is selected from it. Find the probability that P and Q have no common elements. **(I.I.T. 1990)**

68. A box contains 2 fifty paise coins, 5 twenty five paise coins and a certain fixed number $N\ (\geq 2)$ of 10 and five paise coins. Five coins are taken out of the box at random. Find the probability that the total value of these 5 coins is less than one rupee and fifty paise.

69. (i) A five digit number is formed by the digits 1, 2, 3, 4, 5 without repetition. Find the probability that the number formed is divisible by 4.

(ii) A ten digit number is formed using the digits from zero to nine, every digit being used exactly once. Find the probability that the number is divisible by four. **(Roorkee 1991)**

70. (i) Out of $3n$ consecutive integers, three are selected at random. Find the chance that their sum is divisible by 3.

(ii) Two numbers are selected at random from 1, 2, 3, ..., 100 and are multiplied. Find the probability correct to two places of decimals that the product thus obtained, is divisible by 3. **(Roorkee 1993)**

71. (i) Out of $(2n+1)$ tickets consecutively numbered, three are drawn at random. Find the chance that the numbers on them are in A.P.

(ii) Out of 21 tickets marked with numbers from 1 to 21, three are drawn at random, find the probability that the three numbers on them are in A.P.

72. If $6n$ tickets numbered 0, 1, 2, ..., $(6n-1)$ are placed in a bag, and three are drawn out, show that the chance that the sum of the numbers on them is equal to $6n$ is $\dfrac{3n}{(6n-1)(6n-2)}$.

73. (a) The probabilities of three events A, B and C are $P(A) = 0\cdot 6$, $P(B) = 0\cdot 4$ and $P(C) = 0\cdot 5$. If $P(A \cup B) = 0\cdot 8, P(A \cap C) = 0\cdot 3,$
$P(A \cap B \cap C) = 0\cdot 2$ and $P(A \cup B \cup C) \geq 0\cdot 85$, find $P(B \cap C)$. **(Roorkee 1996)**

(b) $P(B) = \dfrac{3}{4}, P(\overline{A} \cap B \cap \overline{C}) = \dfrac{1}{3}$

$P(A \cap B \cap \overline{C}) = \frac{1}{3}$ then $P(B \cap C)$

(a) 1/12 (b) 3/4

(c) 5/12 (d) 23/36 **(Screening 2003)**

74. For two events A, B prove the following relations :

(i) $P(\overline{A}/B) = 1 - P(A/B)$

(ii) $P(\overline{A} \cup \overline{B}) = 1 - P(A)\, P(B/A)$.

75. A and B are two candidates seeking admission in I.I.T. The probability that A is selected is 0·5 and the probability that both A and B are selected is at most 0·3. Is it possible that the probability of B getting selected is 0·9 ?

76. (i) Let A and B be two independent events such that the probability is $\frac{1}{8}$ that they will occur simultaneously and $\frac{3}{8}$ that neither of them will occur. Find $P(A)$ and $P(B)$.

(ii) A and B are two independent events. The probability that both occur simultaneously is 1/6 and the probability that neither occurs is 1/3. Find the probabilities of occurrence of the events A and B separately. **(Roorkee 2000)**

77. (a) If A and B are two events and $P(B) \neq 1$, prove that $P(A|\overline{B}) = \dfrac{P(A) - P(A \cap B)}{1 - P(B)}$ and hence deudce that $P(A \cap B) \geq P(A) + P(B) - 1$

Also show that $P(A) >$ or $< P(A|B)$ according as $P(A|\overline{B}) >$ or $< P(A)$.

(b) If A and B are two independent events, prove that $P(A \cup B)$.

$P(A' \cap B') \leq P(C)$, where C is an event defined that exactly one of A and B occurs. **(I.I.T. 2004)**

78. An urn contains 52 balls, numbered from 1 to 52. Let the balls be drawn one at a time and divided among four players A, B, C, D. The player A gets the ball drawn on the first, fifth, ninth draws, ... etc., player B gets the balls drawn on the second, sixth, tenth, ... draws and so on.

Suppose that the balls numbered 1, 11, 31 and 41 are considered "Lucky". What is the probability that each player will have a 'Lucky' ball ?

79. A man takes a step forward with probability 0 · 4 and backward with probability 0 · 6. Find the probability that at the end of eleven steps he is one step away from the starting point.

80. (a) If on an average 1 vessel in every 10 is wrecked, find the chance that out of 5 vessels expected 4 at least will arrive safely.

(b) In a certain experiment the probability of success is twice the probability of failure. Find the probability of at least four successes in six trials.

(c) A shopkeeper has five customers who take cycle on rent. He has three cycles and the probability that customer will hire a cycle is $\frac{3}{4}$. If he charges Rs. 2 for a cycle as a rent, find the probability that he earns exactly Rs. 6 per day.

81. If m things are distributed among a men and b women, show that the chance that the number of things received by men is odd is $\frac{1}{2} \cdot \dfrac{(b+a)^m - (b-a)^m}{(b+a)^m}$.

82. A lot of 100 bulbs from manufacturing process is known to contain 10 defective and 90 non-defective bulbs. If a sample of 8 bulbs is selected at random, what is the probability that

(a) The sample has 3 defective and 5 non-defective bulbs.

(b) The sample has at least one defective bulb ?

83. (i) In five throws with a single die what is the chance of throwing (1) three aces *exactly*, (2) three aces at least ?

(ii) Numbers are selected at random, one at a time, from the two-digit numbers 00, 01, 02, ..., 99 with replacement. An event E occurs if and only if the product of the two digits of a selected number is 18. If four numbers are selected, find the probability that the event E occurs at least 3 times. **(I.I.T. 1993)**

84. A and B play a match in which the chances of their winning a game is $\frac{1}{4}$ for both of them and $\frac{1}{2}$ is the probability that match is being drawn. Match is finished as soon as either player wins two games. Find the probability that the match will be finished in 4 or less games.

85. A bag contains a certain number of balls, some of which are white; a ball is drawn and replaced, another is then drawn and replaced; and so on. If p be the chance of drawing a white ball in a single trial, find the number of white balls that is most likely to have been drawn in n trials. For $p = \frac{1}{2}$ and $n = 12$, calculate the number of white balls.

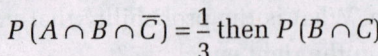

86. (a) *The problem of points.* Two players A and B want respectively m and n points of winning a set of games; their chances of winning a single game are p and q respectively where $p + q = 1$. The stake is to belong to the player who first makes up his set; find the probabilities in favour of each player.

(b) Find the minimum number of tosses required of an unbiased coin so that probability of at least one head is 0·8.

87. A seed merchant finds that 90% of his cucumber seeds germinate under standard conditions. He accordingly claims 90% germination when he sells them in packets of 10. Show that about one quarter of his customers will be entitled to complain that seeds in their packets do not reach the standard of germination.

88. (i) The probability of at least one double-six being thrown in n throws with two ordinary dice is greater than 99 percent. Calculate the least numerical value of n.

Given $\log 36 = 1 \cdot 5563$ and $\log 35 = 1 \cdot 5441$.

(ii) Find the minimum number of tosses of a pair of dice so that the probability of getting the sum of the digits on the dice equal to 7 on at least one toss is greater than 0·95.

$(\log_{10} 2 = 0 \cdot 3010, \log_{10} 3 = 0 \cdot 4771)$ **(Roorkee 1993)**

89. In each of a set of games it is 2 to 1 in favour of the winner of the previous game. What is the chance that the player who wins the first game shall win three at least of the next four ?

90. One bag contains 2 white balls and 2 black balls and another contains 3 white and 5 black balls. A bag and one ball from that bag is chosen at random and ball is replaced. This trial is repeated five times. Find the probability that there are exactly four white balls drawn.

91. If the mean and the variance of a binomial variate X are 2 and 1 respectively, then the probability that X takes a value greater than one is equal to .... **(I.I.T. 1991)**

92. The probability that a family has exactly n children is $\alpha p^n, n \geq 1$ and $p_0 = 1 - \alpha p (1 + p + p^2 + ...)$ is the probability that a family has no children. All sex distributions of n children in a family have the same probability.

(i) Show that the probability that a family contains exactly k boys is $2\alpha p^k \, (2 - p)^{-k-1}, k \geq 1$

(ii) Given that a family includes at least one boy, show that the probability that there are two or more boys is $\dfrac{p}{2 - p}$.

93. Suppose the probability for A to win a game against B is $0 \cdot 4$. A has two options of playing matches against B. One 'the best of 3 games' and the other 'the best of 5 games'. Which of the options, A should choose ? (No game ends in a draw).

94. A coin whose faces are marked 3 and 5 is tossed 4 times; what are the odds against the sum of the numbers thrown being less than 15 ?

95. A and B throw with 3 dice; if A throws 8, what is B's chance of throwing a higher number ?

96. A person throws two dice, one the common cube and the other a regular tetrahedron, the number on the lowest face being taken in the case of the tetrahedron. What is the chance that the sum of the numbers thrown is not less than 5 ?

97. In a bag there are three tickets numbered 1, 2, 3. A ticket is drawn at random and put back; and this is done four times. Show that it is 41 to 40 that the sum of the numbers drawn is even.

98. A bag contains four tickets with numbers 00, 01, 10, 11. A ticket is drawn and replaced. In this way five tickets are drawn. Find the probability that the sum of the numbers on the ticket drawn is 23.

99. An urn contains, a white and b black balls and a second urn, c white and d black balls. One ball is transferred from the first urn into the second and one ball is then drawn from the second urn. What is the probability that it is a white ball ?

100. An urn contains 2 white and 2 black balls. A ball is drawn at random. If it is white, it is not replaced into the urn, otherwise it is replaced along with another ball of the same colour. The process is repeated. Find the probability that the third ball drawn is black.

101. (a) In a certain city two newspapers A and B are published. It is known that 25% of the city population reads A and 20% reads B while 8% reads both A and B. It is also known that 30% of those who read A but not B look into advertisements and 40% of those who read B but not A look advertisements while 50% of those who read both A and B look into advertisements. What is the percentage of the population who reads an advertisement ?

(b) A bag A contains 3 white and 2 black balls and another bag B contains 2 white and 4 black balls. A bag and a ball out of it are picked at random. What is the probability that the ball is white ?

102. (a) There are two groups of subjects one of which consists of 5 science subjects and 3 engineering subjects and the other consists of 3 science and 5 engineering subjects. An unbaised die is cast. If number 3 or number 5 turns up, a subject is selected at random from the first group, otherwise the subject is selected at random from the second group. Find the probability that an engineering subject is selected ultimately.

(b) Three groups A, B and C are competing for positions on the Board of Directors of a company. The probabilities of their winning are $0 \cdot 5, 0 \cdot 3, 0 \cdot 2$ respectively. If the group A wins, the probability of introducing a new product is $0 \cdot 7$ and the corresponding probabilities for groups B and C are $0 \cdot 6$ and $0 \cdot 5$ respectively. Find the probability that the new product will be introduced.

(Roorkee 1994)

103. (i) An unbiased coin is tossed. If the result is a head, a pair of unbiased dice is rolled and the number obtained by adding the numbers on the two faces is noted. If the result is a tail, a card from a well shuffled pack of eleven cards numbered 2, 3, 4, ... 12 is picked and the number on the card is noted. What is the probability that the noted number is either 7 or 8 ? **(I.I.T. 1994)**

(ii) There are two bags, one of which contains three black and four white balls while the other contains four black and three white balls. A die is cast : if the face 1 or 3 turns up, a ball is taken from the first bag ; and if any other face turns up, a ball is chosen from the second bag. Find the probability of choosing a black ball.

(iii) A box contains N coins, m of which are fair and the rest are biased. The probability of getting a head when a fair coin is tossed is 1/2, while it is 2/3 when a biased coin is tossed. A coin is drawn from the box at random and is tossed twice. The first time it shows head and the second time it shows tail. What is the probability that the coin drawn is fair ? **(I.I.T. 2002)**

104. Suppose there are three urns containing 2 white and 3 black balls : 3 white and 2 black balls, and 4 white and one black ball respectively. There is equal probability of each urn being chosen. One ball is drawn from an urn chosen at random. What is the probability that a white ball is drawn ?

105. If in Q. 104, we are told that a white ball has been drawn, find the probability that it was drawn from the first urn.

106. A lot contains 20 articles. The probability that the lot contains exactly 2 defective articles is $0 \cdot 4$ and the probability that the lot contains exactly 3 defective articles is $0 \cdot 6$. Articles are drawn from the lot at random one by one without replacement and tested till all the defective articles are found. What is the probability that the testing procedure ends at the twelfth testing ?

107. (i) A bag A contains 2 white and 3 red balls and a bag B contains 4 white and 5 red balls. One ball is drawn at random from one of the bags and is found to be red. Find the probability that it was drawn from bag B.

(ii) We have two boxes, B_1 and B_2. Box B_1 contains one red and one white marble. Box B_2 contains three red marbles and one green marble. A box is selected by the toss of a fair coin and one marble is drawn at random from the box selected. Given that a red marble is obtained, what is the probability that the marble was drawn from B_1 ?

108. A pack of playing cards was found to contain only 51 cards. If the first 13 cards which are examined are all red, what is probability that the missing card is black ?

(M.N.R. 1992)

109. (a) In a test an examinee either guesses or copies or knows the answer to a multiple choice question with four choices. The probability that he makes a guess is $\frac{1}{3}$ and the probability that he copies the answer is $\frac{1}{6}$. The probability that his answer is correct given that he copied it, is $\frac{1}{8}$. Find the probability that he knew the answer to the question given that he correctly answered it.

(I.I.T. 1991)

(b) An employer sends a letter to his employee but he does not receive the reply (It is certain that employee would have replied if he did receive the letter). It is known that one out of n letters does not reach its destination. Find the probability that employee does not receive the letter.

(c) In a combat between A, B and C, A tries to hit B and C, and B and C try to hit A. Probability of A, B and C hitting the targets are 2/3, 1/2 and 1/3 respectively. If A is hit, find the probability that B hits A and C does not. **(I.I.T. 2003)**

110. In a bolt factory, machines A, B and C manufacture 25%, 35%, 40% respectively. Of the total of their output 5, 4 and 2% are defective. A bolt is drawn and is found to be defective. What are the probabilities that it was manufactured by the machines A, B and C ?

111. An urn contains five balls. Two balls are drawn and are found to be white. What is the probability that all the balls are white ?

112. It is known that an urn containing altogether 10 balls was filled in the following manner :

A coin was tossed 10 times, and according as it showed heads or tails, one white or one black ball was put into the urn. Balls are drawn from this urn one at a time, 10 times in succession (with replacements) and every one turns out to be white. Find the chance that the urn contains nothing but white balls.

113. A purse contains four coins; two coins having been drawn are found to be 2 Rupee coins; find the chance (i) that all coins are 2 Rupee coins (ii) that if the coins are replaced, another drawing will give a 2 Rupee coin.

114. A bag contains 5 balls of unknown colours, a ball is drawn and replaced twice and in each case is found to be red. If two balls are now drawn simultaneously, find the chance that both are red.

115. From each of two equal lines of length l a portion is cut off at random, and removed. What is the chance that the sum of the remainders is less than l?

116. Three tangents are drawn at random to a given circle. Show that the odds are 3 to 1 against the circle being inscribed in the triangle formed by them.

117. Two dice are tossed. If (m, n) denotes a typical sample point, find whether the following two events A and B are independent

$$A = \{(m, n) : m + n = 11\}, \quad B = \{(m, n) : n \neq 5\}.$$

118. Assume that two coins are tossed : one a rupee and the other an eight anna piece. Let A be the event that rupee shows heads and B the event that the coins show different faces. Are A and B independent ?

119. An urn contains five balls alike in every respect save colour. If three of these balls are white and two are black and we draw two balls at random from this urn without replacing them. If A is the event that the first ball drawn is white and B the event that the second ball drawn is black, are A and B independent ?

120. An urn contains four tickets with numbers 112, 121, 211, 222 and one ticket is drawn. Let A_i $(i = 1, 2, 3)$ be the event that the ith digit of the number of tickets drawn is 1. Discuss the independence of the events A_1, A_2, A_3.

121. A lot contains 50 defective and 50 non-defective bulbs. Two bulbs are drawn at random, one at a time, with replacement. The events A, B, C are defined as

$A = \{$The first bulb is defective$\}$

$B = \{$The second bulb is non-defective$\}$

$C = \{$The two bulbs are both defective or both non-defective$\}$

Determine whether

(i) A, B, C are pairwise independent,

(ii) A, B, C are independent. **(I.I.T. 1992)**

122. Prove that if A, B and C are random events in a sample space, and if A, B, C are pairwise independent and A is independent of $(B \cup C)$, then A, B and C are mutually independent.

123. An event A is known to be independent of the events $B, B \cup C$ and $B \cap C$. Show that it is also independent of C.

Solutions to Problem Set (1)

1. Total no. of ways $n = {}^8C_1 = 8$

and favourable no. of ways $m = {}^5C_1 = 5$.

Hence required probability $= \dfrac{m}{n} = \dfrac{5}{8}$.

2. Here $n =$ Total no.of ways $m = {}^{52}C_4$

$$= \frac{52 \times 51 \times 50 \times 49}{1 \times 2 \times 3 \times 4} = 13 \times 17 \times 25 \times 49 = 270725.$$

There are four honours (ace, king, queen and knave) in each suit and so there are 4 sets of 4 honours each. To obtain the favourable number of ways, we have to select one suit of four honours from these four sets

$\therefore \quad m = {}^4C_1 = 4$

$\therefore \quad p =$ required probability $= \dfrac{m}{n} = \dfrac{4}{270725}$.

3. (a) We know that 13 cards are delivered to a hand at whist so that $n =$ total no. of ways

$$= {}^{52}C_{13} = \frac{52!}{13!\ 39!}.$$

Since 4 kings are held by a specified player, 9 more cards are to be delivered to him from the remaining 48 cards so that

$m =$ favourable no. of ways

$$= {}^{48}C_9 = \frac{48!}{9!\ 39!}$$

Hence required probability,

$$p = \frac{m}{n} = \frac{48!}{9!\ 39!} \times \frac{13!\ 39!}{52!} = \frac{13.12.11.10}{52.51.50.49} = \frac{11}{4165}.$$

(b) This problem is similar to Problem 3.

Here $n = {}^{52}C_{13}$ and $m = {}^2C_1 \times {}^4C_1 \times {}^{46}C_{11}$, since one black ace out of 2 black aces can be chosen in ${}^2C_1$ ways, one king out of 4 kings in ${}^4C_1$ ways and the remaining 11 cards from the remaining 46 cards in ${}^{46}C_{11}$ ways.

∴ The required probability

$$p=\frac{m}{n}=\frac{{}^{2}C_1 \times {}^{4}C_1 \times {}^{46}C_{11}}{{}^{52}C_{13}}=\frac{164502}{978775}$$

[Calculate yourself]

4. A leap year consists of 366 days and so it shall have 52 complete weeks and two extra days. These two days can be

(i) Monday and Tuesday

(ii) Tuesday and Wednesday

(iii) Wednesday and Thursday

(iv) Thursday and Friday

(v) Friday and Saturday

(vi) Saturday and Sunday

(vii) Sunday and Monday

Of these 7 cases, the last two are favourable and hence the required probability $=\frac{2}{7}$.

5. (a) There are 6 numbers (1, 2, 3, 4, 5, 6) written on the six faces of each die. Thus there are six possible ways as to the number of points on the first die ; and to each of these ways, there correspond 6 possible numbers of points on the second die. Hence the total no. of ways $n = 6 \times 6 = 36$

We now find out how many ways are favourable to the total of 7 points. This may happen only in the following ways : (1, 6), (6, 1), (2, 5), (5, 2), (3, 4), and (4, 3), that is, in 6 ways, where first member of each ordered pair denotes the number on the first die and second member denotes the number of the second die.

∴ $m = 6$.

Hence required probability $=\frac{m}{n}=\frac{6}{36}=\frac{1}{6}$.

(b) Total ways $= 6^6$

Different faces can occur in 6 ! ways as different permutations of occurrence of number on faces of dice.

Hence required probability $=\frac{6!}{6^6}=\frac{5}{324}$.

6. (a) (i) n = total no. of ways = 12 !

and m = favourable no. of ways = 7 ! 6 !,

since 7 objects (considering 6 boys as different objects and all the six girls together as one object) can be arranged in 7 ! ways corresponding to each of these ways, the six girls can be arranged amongst themselves in 6 ! ways.

Hence $p=\frac{m}{n}=\frac{7!\ 6!}{12!}=\frac{1}{132}$.

(ii) Here $n = 12!$ and $m = 2 \times 6!\ 6!$,

since the boys and girls can sit alternately in 6 ! 6 ! ways if we begin with a boy and similarly they can sit alternately in 6 ! 6 ! ways if we begin with a girl.

Hence $p=\frac{m}{n}=\frac{2\times 6!\ 6!}{12!}=\frac{1}{462}$.

(b) 7 students can sit in 7 ! ways.

∴ Total ways = 7 !

Now consider two particular students as one, then they can sit in 6 ! ways.

But these two students can interchange their seats.

∴ Favourable cases $= 2 \times 6!$

Hence probability $=\frac{2\times 6!}{7!}=\frac{2}{7}$.

(c) Suppose we fix any seat for A then B can sit in other 19 seats, so total ways = 19.

Now favourable cases = 2, as B can sit on the left or on the right of A with four persons between them.

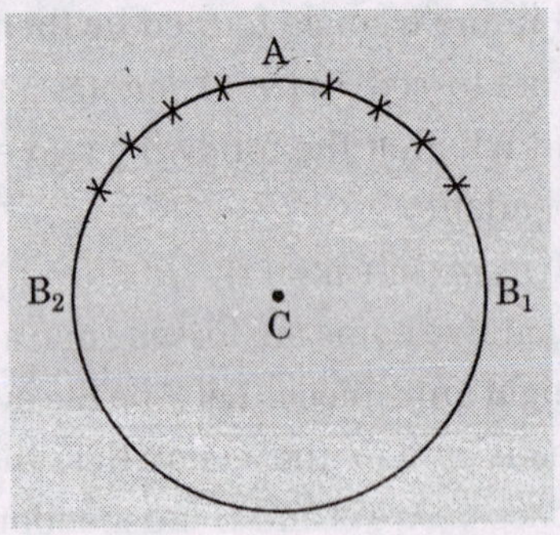

Fig. 1

Hence required probability $=\frac{2}{19}$.

7. (i) Besides the ground floor, there are seven floors. The total number of ways in which each of the five persons can leave cabin at any of the 7 floors $= 7^5$.

And the favourable number of ways, that is, the number of ways in which the 5 persons leave at different floors is ${}^{7}P_5$.

∴ The required probability $= {}^{7}P_5/7^5$.

(ii) n = the total number of ways of distributing M telegrams over N channels $= N^M$. The number of ways of choosing M channels out of N in order to send one telegram over each channel is ${}^{N}C_M$ and corresponding to each of these ways of choosing M channels, there are $M!$ ways of sending the M telegrams. Hence

$m=$ the favourable number of ways $= {}^N C_m . M!$

$\therefore$ The required probability $= \dfrac{{}^N C_M\, M!}{N^M}$.

8. (a) Since the probability of the faces are proportional to the numbers on them, we can take the probabilities of faces 1, 2, 6 as $k, 2k, ..., 6k$, respectively.

Since one of the faces must occur, we have

$$k+2k+3k+4k+5k+6k=1$$

or $k=\dfrac{1}{21}$.

$\therefore$ The probability of an even number

$$=2k+4k+6k$$

$$=12k=12\times\frac{1}{21}=\frac{4}{7}.$$

(b) Ans. $\dfrac{1}{36}$.

$P(Y)=\dfrac{3}{6}$; $P(R)=\dfrac{2}{6}$; $P(B)=\dfrac{1}{6}$

$\because$ Outcomes are independent in each toss.

$$P(Y\,R\,B)=P(Y)\cdot P(R)\cdot P(B)=\frac{3}{6}\cdot\frac{2}{6}\cdot\frac{1}{6}=\frac{1}{36}$$

(c) The probability of even number $=\dfrac{2}{3}$.

The probability of odd number $=\dfrac{1}{3}$.

(i) Now the sum of two numbers will be even if both results show either odd numbers or both show even numbers.

Hence the required probability $=\dfrac{2}{3}.\dfrac{2}{3}+\dfrac{1}{3}.\dfrac{1}{3}=\dfrac{5}{9}$

(ii) Similarly the sum is odd when one number is odd and another is even.

Hence the required probability $={}^2C_1\cdot\left(\dfrac{2}{3}\right).\left(\dfrac{1}{3}\right)=\dfrac{4}{9}$

9. We denote the appearance of head by H and of tail by T. The sample space S consists of four points, that is,

$$S=\{(H,H),\ (H,T),\ (T,H),\ (T,T)\}.$$

Then $E=\{(H,H),\ (H,T)\}$

and $F=\{(H,H),\ (T,H)\}$.

so that $E\cup F=\{(H,H),\ (H,T),\ (T,H)\}$.

Hence $n=n(S)=$ the number of points in $S=4$.

and $m=n(E\cup F)=3$.

Hence $P(E\cup F)=\dfrac{n(E\cup F)}{n(S)}=\dfrac{3}{4}$.

10. (a) Since odds against A are as $8:3$, the probability of A's occurring, $P(A)=\dfrac{3}{8+3}=\dfrac{3}{11}$.

Similarly $P(B)=\dfrac{2}{5+2}=\dfrac{2}{7}$

Since the events A, B, C are mutually exclusive and totally exhaustive, the sum of their probabilities must be unity, that is,

$P(A)+P(B)+P(C)=1$

or $\dfrac{3}{11}+\dfrac{2}{7}+P(C)=1$

$\therefore$ $P(C)=1-\dfrac{3}{11}-\dfrac{2}{7}=\dfrac{34}{77}$.

Hence the odds against C are as

$(77-34):34$ *i.e.,* $43:34$.

(b) If A is the event the player A wins, then

$$P(A)=\frac{2}{5+2}=\frac{2}{7}\ \Rightarrow\ P(\bar{A})=\frac{5}{7}$$

If B be the event that player B wins, then

$$P(B)=\frac{6}{11}\ \Rightarrow P(\bar{B})=\frac{5}{11}$$

The probability of happening of at least one event is

$$=1-P(\bar{A}).P(\bar{B})$$

$$=1-\frac{5}{7}.\frac{5}{11}=1-\frac{25}{77}=\frac{52}{77}$$

(c) According to given condition, the person is selected if he either (a) passes all the tests or (b) exactly two of the tests.

(a) P (passing all the tests) $=P.P.P=P^3$ ...(1)

(b) P (Ist and IInd) $+P$ (Ist and IIIrd) $+P$ (IInd and IIIrd)

$$=P.P(1-P)+P(1-P)\frac{P}{2}+(1-P).\frac{P}{2}.P$$

$$=\frac{1}{2}P^2(1-P)[2+1+1]=2P^2(1-P)$$

$$=2P^2-2P^3 \qquad ...(2)$$

Hence the required probability by (1) and (2) is

$$P^3+2P^2-2P^3=2P^2-P^3.$$

11. Let p_1, p_2, p_3 denote the probabilities that first, second and third critics review the book favourably. Then

$$p_1=\frac{5}{5+2}=\frac{5}{7},\ p_2=\frac{4}{4+3}=\frac{4}{7}, p_3=\frac{3}{3+4}=\frac{3}{7}$$

$$\therefore\quad \overline{p_1}=1-\frac{5}{7}=\frac{2}{7},\ \overline{p_2}=1-\frac{4}{7}=\frac{3}{7}, \overline{p_3}=1-\frac{3}{7}=\frac{4}{7}.$$

Now the majority will be favourable if any of the two critics is favourable and third is unfavourable or all the three critics are favourable.

Hence the required probability

$p = p_1\ p_2\ \overline{p_3} + p_1\ \overline{p_2}\ p_3 + \overline{p_1}\ p_2\ p_3 + p_1\ p_2\ p_3$
$= \frac{5}{7}.\frac{4}{7}.\frac{4}{7} + \frac{5}{7}.\frac{3}{7}.\frac{3}{7} + \frac{2}{7}.\frac{4}{7}.\frac{3}{7} + \frac{5}{7}.\frac{4}{7}.\frac{3}{7} = \frac{209}{343}.$

12. (i) Let E_1 be the event that A can solve a problem and E_2 the event that B can solve the same problem. Then $P(E_1) = \frac{2}{3}$ and $P(\overline{E_1}) = 1 - \frac{2}{3} = \frac{1}{3}$,

$P(E_2) = \frac{3}{5}$ and $P(\overline{E_2}) = 1 - \frac{3}{5} = \frac{2}{5}$.

(a) **First Method.** Here we want the probability $P(E_1 \cup E_2)$.

Now $P(E_1 \cup E_2) = P(E_1) + P(E_2) - P(E_1 \cap E_2)$
$= P(E_1) + P(E_2) - P(E_1)\ P(E_2)$

$[P(E_1 \cap E_2) = P(E_1)\ P(E_2)$ since the events E_1 and E_2 are independent]

$= \frac{2}{3} + \frac{3}{5} - \frac{2}{3} \times \frac{3}{5} = \frac{2}{3} + \frac{3}{5} - \frac{2}{5} = \frac{13}{15}.$

Second Method. $P(E_1 \cup E_2)$ = Probability that A solves and B does not solve or B solves and A does not solve or both A and B solve the problem.

$= P(E_1 \cap \overline{E_2}) + P(E_2 \cap \overline{E_1}) + P(E_1 \cap E_2)$
$= P(E_1)\ P(\overline{E_2}) + P(E_2)\ P(\overline{E_1}) + P(E_1)\ P(E_2)$

[$\because$ Events are independent]

$= \frac{2}{3}.\frac{2}{5} + \frac{3}{5}.\frac{1}{3} + \frac{2}{3}.\frac{3}{5} = \frac{13}{15}.$

(b) Here we have to find the probability of the event $\overline{E_1} \cap \overline{E_2}$. We have

$P(\overline{E_1} \cap \overline{E_2}) = P(\overline{E_1})\ P(\overline{E_2}) = \frac{1}{3}.\frac{2}{5} = \frac{2}{15}.$

Remark. Probability of case (i) can be deduced from that of case (ii).

$\because\ P(\overline{E_1} \cap \overline{E_2}) = P(\overline{E_1 \cup E_2}) = 1 - P(E_1 \cup E_2)$

$\therefore\ P(E_1 \cup E_2) = 1 - P(\overline{E_1} \cap \overline{E_2}) = 1 - \frac{2}{15} = \frac{13}{15}$

(ii) Let E_1 be the event that man will be selected and E_2 the event that woman will be selected. Then

$P(E_1) = \frac{1}{4},\ P(\overline{E_1}) = 1 - \frac{1}{4} = \frac{3}{4}.$

$P(E_2) = \frac{1}{3},\ P(\overline{E_2}) = 1 - \frac{1}{3} = \frac{2}{3}.$

clearly events, E_1, E_2 are independent. Hence

(a) $P(E_1 \cap E_2) = P(E_1)\ P(E_2) = \frac{1}{4} \times \frac{1}{3} = \frac{1}{12}$

(b) $P(E_1 \cap \overline{E_2}) + P(\overline{E_1} \cap E_2)$
$= P(E_1)\ P(\overline{E_2}) + P(\overline{E_1})\ P(E_2) = \frac{1}{4} \times \frac{2}{3} + \frac{3}{4} \times \frac{1}{3} = \frac{5}{12}.$

(c) $P(\overline{E_1} \cap \overline{E_2}) = P(\overline{E_1})\ P(\overline{E_2}) = \frac{3}{4} \times \frac{2}{3} = \frac{1}{2}$

(iii) Let A, B, C be the three rifle-men and we are given the probability of their hitting the right target as

$P(A) = 0 \cdot 4 = \frac{2}{5}, \quad P(B) = 0 \cdot 5 = \frac{1}{2}$

and $P(C) = 0 \cdot 8 = \frac{4}{5}$

$\therefore\ P(\overline{A}) = \frac{3}{5}, P(\overline{B}) = \frac{1}{2}, P(\overline{C}) = \frac{1}{5}.$

Now the probability that exactly two of them hit the target is

$P(A \cap B \cap \overline{C}) + P(A \cap \overline{B} \cap C) + P(\overline{A} \cap B \cap C)$
$\left(\frac{2}{5}\right)\left(\frac{1}{2}\right)\left(\frac{1}{5}\right) + \left(\frac{2}{5}\right)\left(\frac{1}{2}\right)\left(\frac{4}{5}\right) + \left(\frac{3}{5}\right)\left(\frac{1}{2}\right)\left(\frac{4}{5}\right)$
$= \frac{2+8+12}{50} = \frac{22}{50} = \frac{11}{25} = 0 \cdot 44$

13. (i) We have

$P(E_1) = \frac{1}{2},\ P(E_2) = \frac{1}{3}$ and $P(E_3) = \frac{1}{4}.$

$\therefore\ P(E_1 \cup E_2 \cup E_3) = 1 - P(\overline{E_1})\ P(\overline{E_2})\ P(\overline{E_3})$
$= 1 - \left(1 - \frac{1}{2}\right)\left(1 - \frac{1}{3}\right)\left(1 - \frac{1}{4}\right)$
$= 1 - \frac{1}{2} \times \frac{2}{3} \times \frac{3}{4} = \frac{3}{4}.$

(ii) Let E_i = the event that ith shot from the guns hits the enemy $i = 1, 2, 3, 4$. Then according to the question,

$P(E_1) = 0 \cdot 4,\ P(E_2) = 0 \cdot 3, P(E_3) = 0 \cdot 2$ and $P(E_4) = 0 \cdot 1$.

We have to find $P(E_1 \cup E_2 \cup E_3 \cup E_4)$.

As in Problem 17, we have

$P(E_1 \cup E_2 \cup E_3 \cup E_4)$
$= 1 - P(\overline{E_1})\ P(\overline{E_2})\ P(\overline{E_3})\ P(\overline{E_4})$.
$= 1 - (1 - 0 \cdot 4)(1 - 0 \cdot 3)(1 - 0 \cdot 2)(1 - 0 \cdot 1)$
$= 1 - 0 \cdot 6 \times 0 \cdot 7 \times 0 \cdot 8 \times 0 \cdot 9$
$= 1 - 0 \cdot 3024 = \cdot 6976.$

(iii) Ans. $p = 1 - p_1 p_2 p_3 = 1 - \cdot 4 \times \cdot 3 \times \cdot 2 = 0 \cdot 976$.

14. Total number of ways of distributing 4 objects on 4 places = 4! = 24.

Number of ways in which all the **four objects** can occupy their places = 1

If **three objects** occupy their places, 4th will also do so. This is included in the above case.

If **two objects** occupy their places, remaining two can go wrong by occupying each other's position in only one way.

So number of ways in which only two objects can occupy their places = ${}^4C_2 \times 1 = 6$.

If **one object** occupies its position, any one of the remaining three can go wrong in 2 ways by occupying the positions of the other two.

So number of ways in which only one object can occupy its place = $^4C_1 \times 2 = 8$.

∴ Total number of ways in which at least one object can occupy its place = $1 + 6 + 8 = 15$.

Hence total number of ways in which none of the objects occupies the place corresponding to its number $= 24 - 15 = 9$

∴ Required prob. $= \frac{9}{24} = \frac{3}{8}$.

15. Let A denote that a man is unemployed, so

∴ $P(A) = \frac{10}{100} = \frac{1}{10}$ and $P(\bar{A}) = 1 - \frac{1}{10} = \frac{9}{10}$

Also let B denote that a woman is unemployed, so

$P(B) = \frac{45}{100} = \frac{9}{20}$ and $P(\bar{B}) = 1 - \frac{9}{20} = \frac{11}{20}$

Since the group contains equal number of men and women, probability of selecting a man or a woman $= \frac{1}{2}$

∴ Probability of selecting an employed man

$= \frac{1}{2} \times \frac{9}{10}$

and probability of selecting an employed woman

$= \frac{1}{2} \times \frac{11}{20}$

The selected person may be either a man or woman. Hence by the theorem of total probability, probability of selecting an employed person

$= \frac{1}{2} \times \frac{9}{10} + \frac{1}{2} \times \frac{11}{20} = \frac{29}{40}$.

16. Let A, B and C denote the events that the candidate gets the first, second and third post respectively

∴ $P(A) = \frac{1}{3}$ and $P(\bar{A}) = 1 - P(A) = \frac{2}{3}$

$P(B) = \frac{1}{4} \Rightarrow P(\bar{B}) = \frac{3}{4}$

$P(C) = \frac{1}{2} \Rightarrow P(\bar{C}) = \frac{1}{2}$

Now P (candidate will get at least one post)

$= P(A \cup B \cup C) = 1 - P(\bar{A} \cap \bar{B} \cap \bar{C})$

$= 1 - P(\bar{A})\, P(\bar{B})\, P(\bar{C})$

Since events A, B, C are independent

$\Rightarrow$ $\bar{A}, \bar{B}, \bar{C}$ are also independent $= 1 - \frac{2}{3} \times \frac{3}{4} \times \frac{1}{2} = \frac{3}{4}$.

17. Since in the process of manufacture of part X, 9 out of 104 parts may be defective, therefore the Probability of X to be defective $= 9/104$ and so its not being defective $= 1 - (9/104) = 95/104$.

Similarly the probability of the part Y to be defective $= 5/100 = 1/20$

and not to be defective $= 1 - (1/20) = 19/20$.

Now the assembled product will not be defective if both the parts are not defective and hence the probability of this event

$= \frac{95}{104} \times \frac{19}{20} = \frac{19 \times 19}{104 \times 4} = \frac{361}{416}$,

by the multiplication theorem.

18. Since the probability that a man aged x years will die in a year is p, therefore the probability of that man not to die in a year $= 1 - p$. Hence the probability that none out of n men aged x year will die in a year $= (1-p)^n$. It follows that the probability that out of n men, at least one dies in a year $= 1 - (1-p)^n$.

Also, the probability that out of n men the man to die first is $A_1 = 1/n$.

∴ The required probability $= (1/n)\,[1 - (1-p)^n]$.

19. (a) Selection can be made in the following manner :

(i) Boy, boy, girl Probability $p_1 = \frac{1}{4} \cdot \frac{2}{4} \cdot \frac{1}{4} = \frac{1}{32}$

(ii) Boy, girl, boy Probability $p_2 = \frac{1}{4} \cdot \frac{2}{4} \cdot \frac{3}{4} = \frac{3}{32}$

(iii) Girl, boy, boy Probability $p_3 = \frac{3}{4} \cdot \frac{2}{4} \cdot \frac{3}{4} = \frac{9}{32}$.

Since these are mutually exclusive cases, therefore the required probability

$= p_1 + p_2 + p_3 = \frac{13}{32}$.

(b) Ans. (a).

(c) Total no. of ways in which three members are selected of which at least one is woman

$= {^4C_1} \times s C_2 + {^4C_2} \times s C_1 + {^4C_3} = 244$.

The favourable ways in which there are more women than men

$= {^4C_2} \times s C_1 + {^4C_3} = 64$

Hence required probability $= \frac{64}{244} = \frac{16}{61}$.

20. (a) In one throw of a coin, the number of possible ways is 2 since either head (H) or tail (T) may appear. In two throws of a coin, the total no. of ways is 2×2 *i.e.* 4 since corresponding to each way of the first coin there are 2 ways of second. Similarly in three throws of a coin, the number of ways is 2^3 and thus in n throws, the number of ways $N = 2^n$.

And $M =$ the favourable no. of ways
$=$ the number of ways in which head will occur once or thrice or 5 times or 7 times and so on,
$= {^nC_1} + {^nC_3} + {^nC_5} + \dots\dots\dots = 2^{n-1}$.

Hence required probability $p=\frac{M}{N}=\frac{2^{n-1}}{2^n}=\frac{1}{2}$.

Alternative. Probability of tail (T) in one trial

$=\frac{1}{2}=q$, say,

and probability of head (H) in one trial $=\frac{1}{2}=p$, say.

Then the required probability
= sum of even terms in the expansion $(q+p)^n$

$$={q^n}+{}^nC_1\,q^{n-1}\,p+{}^nC_2\,q^{n-2}\,p^2+{}^nC_3\,q^{n-3}\,p^3+\dots+p^n$$

$$={}^nC_1\,q^{n-1}\,p+{}^nC_3\,q^{n-3}\,p^3+{}^nC_5\,q^{n-5}\,p^5+\dots$$

$$={}^nC_1\left(\frac{1}{2}\right)^{n-1}\frac{1}{2}+{}^nC_3\left(\frac{1}{2}\right)^{n-3}\left(\frac{1}{2}\right)^3+{}^nC_5\left(\frac{1}{2}\right)^{n-5}\left(\frac{1}{2}\right)^5+\dots$$

$$=\left(\frac{1}{2}\right)^n[{}^nC_1+{}^nC_3+{}^nC_5+\dots]=\frac{2^{n-1}}{2^n}=\frac{1}{2}.$$

(b) When A and B toss a coin we can get following results :

$\{HH, HT, TH, TT\}$

So the probability of getting tail on both coins $=\frac{1}{4}$.

Hence the required probability in 50 trials

$$=\frac{1}{4}\cdot\frac{1}{4}\dots 50 \text{ times}=\left(\frac{1}{4}\right)^{50}.$$

21. n = total no. of ways $=2^{10}=1024$.

Since each answer can be true or false.

and m = favourable number of ways

$$={}^{10}C_8+{}^{10}C_9+{}^{10}C_{10}=45+10+1=56.$$

Since to pass the exam, he must give 8 or 9 or 10 true answers,

Hence $p=\frac{m}{n}=\frac{56}{1024}=\frac{7}{128}$.

22. (a) Let p be the chance of cutting a spade and q the chance of not cutting a spade from a pack of 52 cards.

Then $p=\frac{{}^{13}C_1}{{}^{52}C_1}=\frac{1}{4}$ and $q=1-\frac{1}{4}=\frac{3}{4}$.

Now A will win a prize if he cuts spade at 1st, 4th, 7th, 10th turns, etc. Note that A will get a second chance if A, B, C all fail to cut a spade once and then A cuts a spade at the 4th turn.

Similarly he will cut a spade at the 7th turn when A, B, C fail to cut spade twice, etc.

Hence A's chance of winning the prize

$$=p+q^3p+q^6p+q^9p+\dots$$

$$=\frac{p}{1-q^3}=\frac{\frac{1}{4}}{1-(\frac{3}{4})^3}=\frac{16}{37}.$$

Similarly B's chance $=(qp+q^4p+q^7p+\dots)$

$$=q\,(p+q^3p+q^6p+\dots)$$

$$=\frac{3}{4}\cdot\frac{16}{37}=\frac{12}{37}$$

and C's chance $=\frac{3}{4}$ of B's chance $=\frac{3}{4}\cdot\frac{12}{37}=\frac{9}{37}$.

(b) It is same as part (a).

$q=1-p$ whose p is prob. of success.

$$\alpha=p+(1-p)^3\,p+(1-p)^6\,p+\dots\infty$$

$$=\frac{p}{1-(1-p)^3} \quad \text{sum of a G.P.}$$

$$\beta=(1-p)\,p+(1-p)^4\,p+\dots\infty=\frac{p(1-p)}{1-(1-p)^3}$$

$$\gamma=(1-p)^2\,p+(1-p)^5\,p+\dots\infty=\frac{(1-p)^2\,p}{1+(1-p)^3}$$

Above gives the values of α, β, γ in terms of p. It is clear that $b\eta=(1-p)\,\alpha$.

23. In the last five throws there can be 0, 1, 2, 3, 4 or 5 heads and the same should be the case in the first ten throws. Hence the favourable number of cases

$$m={}^5C_0\,{}^{10}C_0+{}^5C_1\,{}^{10}C_1+{}^5C_2\,{}^{10}C_2+{}^5C_3\,{}^{10}C_3+{}^5C_4\,{}^{10}C_4+{}^5C_5\,{}^{10}C_5$$

$$=1+50+450+1200+1050+252=3003.$$

And the total number of ways $n=2^{15}=32768$.

Hence the required probability $=\frac{m}{n}=\frac{3003}{32768}$.

24. Let E_1 be the event that B rides A, E_2, the event that C rides A and E the event that A wins. Then according to the question,

$$P(E_1)=\frac{2}{3},\quad P(E_2)=1-\frac{2}{3}=\frac{1}{3}$$

$$P(E/E_1)=\frac{1}{6}$$

(since all the 6 horses are equally likely to win when B rides A).

$$P(E/E_2)=3\times\frac{1}{6}=\frac{1}{2}$$

(since A's chance of winning is trebled when C rides A).

$$\therefore \quad P(E)=P(E_1)\,P(E/E_1)+P(E_2)\,P(E/E_2)$$

$$=\frac{2}{3}\cdot\frac{1}{6}+\frac{1}{3}\cdot\frac{1}{2}=\frac{5}{18}.$$

Hence probability of A's win is 5/18 so that odds against A's win are as $(18-5):5$, that is $13:5$.

25. (i) If E_1 denotes the event that A speaks the truth, then $\overline{E_1}$ is the event that A does not speak the truth. Similarly, we define the events E_2 and $\overline{E_2}$ for B.

Let E be the event that A and B contradict each other.

Then according to the question, we have

$$P(E_1) = \frac{75}{100} = \frac{3}{4} \text{ and } P(\overline{E_1}) = 1 - \frac{3}{4} = \frac{1}{4},$$

$$P(E_2) = \frac{80}{100} = \frac{4}{5} \text{ and } P(\overline{E_2}) = 1 - \frac{4}{5} = \frac{1}{5}.$$

They will contradict each other if one speaks the truth and other does not.

Hence $E = E_1 \overline{E_2} + \overline{E_1} E_2$.

Now $P(E_1 \overline{E_2})$ = the probability that A speaks the truth and B tells a lie

$$= P(E_1)\, P(\overline{E_2}) = \frac{3}{4} \times \frac{1}{5} = \frac{3}{20}.$$

Similarly $P(\overline{E_1} E_2) = \frac{1}{4} \times \frac{4}{5} = \frac{1}{5}$.

[Note the E_1 and E_2 are independent events and so are $\overline{E_1}$ and E_2].

Since $E_1 \overline{E_2}$ and $\overline{E_1} E_2$ are mutually exclusive events, we have

$$P(E) = P(E_1 \overline{E_2} + \overline{E_1} E_2) = P(E_1 \overline{E_2} + \overline{E_1} E_2)$$

$$= \frac{3}{20} + \frac{1}{5} = \frac{7}{20} = \frac{35}{100} \quad i.e., 35\%.$$

Hence in 35% cases, A and B will contradict each other.

Note. Here we have used the notation

$E_1 \overline{E_2}$ for $E_1 \cap \overline{E_2}$ and $E_1 \overline{E_2} + \overline{E_1} E_2$ for $(E_1 \cap \overline{E_2}) \cup (\overline{E_1} \cap E_2)$. We shall make use of both the notations so that the students may be familiar with both of them.

(ii) A and B both agree when either both of them speak truth or both make false statements. Hence the total number of cases of agreeing is proportional to $xy + (1-x)(1-y)$ and the number of cases of speaking truth is proportional to xy.

Hence the required probability

$$= \frac{xy}{xy + (1-x)(1-y)} = \frac{xy}{1 - x - y + 2xy}.$$

26. There are two hypotheses (i) their coincident testimony is true (ii) it is false.

$\therefore \quad P_1 = \frac{1}{6}$ (red ball), $P_2 = \frac{5}{6}$ (no red ball)

$$p_1 = \frac{2}{3} \times \frac{4}{5}, \quad p_2 = \left(\frac{1}{5} \times \frac{1}{5}\right) \times \frac{1}{3} \times \frac{1}{5}$$

for in estimating p_2 we must take into account the chance that A and B will both select the red ball, when it has not been drawn.

Thus $P_1 p_1 : P_2\, p_2 = 8 : \frac{1}{5} = 40 : 1$

Hence the probability that the statement is true is $\frac{40}{41}$.

27. The probability that at least one pair is drawn $= 1 -$ (None of them is a pair)

$$= 1 - \frac{10}{10} \cdot \frac{8}{9} \cdot \frac{6}{8} \cdot \frac{4}{7} = 1 - \frac{8}{21} = \frac{13}{21}.$$

28. Ans. (B). $A =$ event that two defective machines are identified in first two tests out of four machines.

$$\therefore \quad P(A) = \frac{{}^2C_2}{{}^4C_2} = \frac{1}{6}$$

29. Total number of digits used in any number at the last (*i.e.* at unit's) place is 10 since 0, 1, 2, 3, 4, 5, 6, 7, 8, or 9 can occur at that place. It is clear that if the last digit in any of the four numbers is 0, 2, 4, 5, 6 or 8, then the last digit in the product of the four numbers cannot be 1, 3, 7 or 9. Hence in order that the last digit in the product may be 1, 3, 7 or 9, it is necessary that the last digit in each number must be 1, 3, 7 or 9. Hence for any one number, we have $n = 10$ and $m = 4$.

$\therefore \quad p =$ The probability that the last digit in any number is 1, 3, 7 or 9

$$= \frac{m}{n} = \frac{4}{10} = \frac{2}{5}.$$

Hence the required probability $= p^4 = \left(\frac{2}{5}\right)^4 = \frac{16}{625}$.

30. If the match is not finished in 10 games, either of the following events will possibly occur :

(i) All the games are drawn

(ii) A and B each win one game and the rest 8 games are drawn.

(iii) A or B wins one game and the rest 9 games are drawn.

The corresponding probabilities of the above events are

(i) $\left(\frac{9}{10}\right)^{10}$,

(ii) $2 \cdot {}^{10}C_2 \left(\frac{1}{20}\right)^2 \left(\frac{9}{10}\right)^8$,

(iii) $2 \cdot {}^{10}C_1 \left(\frac{1}{20}\right) \left(\frac{9}{10}\right)^9$

Since these events are mutually exclusive, the probability of the game not being finished in 10 games

$$= \left(\frac{9}{10}\right)^{10} + 2.\,{}^{10}C_2 \left(\frac{1}{20}\right)^2 \left(\frac{9}{10}\right)^8$$

$$+ 2.\,{}^{10}C_1 \left(\frac{1}{20}\right)\left(\frac{9}{10}\right)^9$$

$$= \frac{9^8 \times 387}{2 \times 10^{10}}$$

Hence the probability that the match is finished in 10 or less number of games

$$= 1 - \frac{9^8 \times 387}{2 \times 10^{10}} = 0 \cdot 17 \text{ approx.}$$

31. A sum of 5 is possible with (1, 4), (4, 1), (2, 3), (3, 2) *i.e.*, in 4 ways. Similarly sum 7 is made with (1, 6), (6, 1), (2, 5), (5, 2), (3, 4) and (4, 3) *i.e.*, in all 6 ways. Now neither a sum of 5 nor a sum of 7 occurs in $36 - (4 + 6) = 26$ ways.

Let A denote the event that a sum of 5 occurs, B the event that a sum of 7 occurs and C the event that neither a sum of 5 nor a sum of 7 occurs. So

$$P(A) = \frac{4}{36} = \frac{1}{9}, P(B) = \frac{6}{36} = \frac{1}{6}$$

$$P(C) = \frac{26}{36} = \frac{13}{18} \cdot \text{Thus}$$

P (A occurs before B)

$$= P[A \text{ or } CA \text{ or } C^2 A \text{ or } \ldots]$$

$$= P(A) + P(CA) + P(C^2 A) + \ldots$$

$$= P(A) + P(C)\,P(A) + P^2(C)\,P(A) + \ldots$$

as A and C are independent.

$$= \frac{P(A)}{1 - P(C)} = \frac{1/9}{1 - \frac{13}{18}} = \frac{2}{5}.$$

32. Let E_1 and E_2 denote the events that defective valves are produced by factory A and B respectively, then

$$P(E_1) = \frac{10}{100} = \frac{1}{10} \text{ and } P(E_2) = \frac{20}{100} = \frac{1}{5}$$

Out of 9 valves (4 valves from factory A and 5 valves from factory B) 2 valves can be drawn in ${}^9C_2$ ways. We are interested in the probability that at least one valve is defective; so this event (at least one valve is defective) can happen in three mutually exclusive ways

(i) Two defective valves from factory A

(ii) Two defective valves from factory B

(iii) One defective valve from each factory

(iv) One defective valve from factory A but non-defective from factory B

(v) One defective valve from factory B but non-defective from factory A.

$$\therefore \quad P(i) = \frac{{}^4C_2}{{}^9C_2} \times \left(\frac{1}{10}\right)^2 = \frac{4.3}{9.8} \cdot \left(\frac{1}{10}\right)^2 = \frac{1}{600}$$

$$P(ii) = \frac{{}^5C_2}{{}^9C_2} \times \left(\frac{1}{5}\right)^2 = \frac{5.4}{9.8}\left(\frac{1}{5}\right)^2 = \frac{1}{90}$$

$$P(iii) = \frac{{}^4C_1 \times {}^5C_1}{{}^9C_2} \times \left(\frac{1}{10}\right) \times \left(\frac{1}{5}\right)$$

$$= \frac{4.5}{36} \cdot \frac{1}{10} \cdot \frac{1}{5} = \frac{1}{90}$$

$$P(iv) = \frac{1}{5} \times \frac{9}{10} \times \frac{{}^5C_1 \times {}^4C_1}{{}^9C_2} = \frac{1}{10}$$

$$P(v) = \frac{4}{5} \times \frac{1}{10} \times \frac{{}^5C_1 + {}^4C_1}{{}^9C_2} = \frac{2}{45}$$

Hence P [at least one defective valve]

$$= P(i) + P(ii) + P(iii)$$

$$= \frac{1}{600} + \frac{1}{90} + \frac{1}{90} + \frac{1}{10} + \frac{2}{45}$$

$$= \frac{3 + 20 + 20 + 180 + 80}{1800} = \frac{303}{1800} = 0 \cdot 168 \text{ app.}$$

33. The man will get full payment if he either does the jobs A and B or jobs A or C or does all the three jobs A, B and C. Given that the probability of getting full payment is

$$p(AB\overline{C}) + p(AC\overline{B}) + p(ABC) = \frac{1}{2}. \quad \ldots(1)$$

It is given that $p(A) = p, P(B) = q$

$$\therefore \quad p(\overline{B}) = 1 - q,$$

$$p(C) = \frac{1}{2}, \quad \therefore \quad p(\overline{C}) = 1 - \frac{1}{2} = \frac{1}{2}.$$

Hence from (1),

$$p.q.\frac{1}{2} + p.\frac{1}{2}(1 - q) + p.q.\frac{1}{2} = \frac{1}{2}$$

$$\therefore \quad pq + p - pq + pq = 1 \quad \therefore \quad p(1 + q) = 1$$

is the required relation between p and q.

34. Let each of them have n sons each. Hence we have to distribute 3 tickets amongst the sons of Ashok and Baldev, in such a manner that one ticket goes to the sons of one and two tickets to the sons of other.

1 to Ashok's sons and 2 to Baldev's son

+ 2 to Ashok's son and 1 to Baldev's son

= Total number of ways of distributing the tickets as per directions

$${}^nC_1 \,.\, {}^nC_2 + {}^nC_2 \; {}^nC_1 = 2.\, {}^nC_1 \; {}^nC_2 = m$$

But in all 3 tickets are to be distributed amongst $2n$ sons of both.

Hence total number of ways is ${}^{2n}C_3 = n$

Hence required probability $= \frac{m}{n} = \frac{6}{7}$ given.

$\therefore \quad 2.\frac{^nC_1\ ^nC_2}{^{2n}C_3} = \frac{6}{7}$

$7.\frac{n(n-1)}{2}.n = 3.\frac{2n(2n-1)(2n-2)}{6}$

Cancel $n(n-1)$ from both sides.

or $7n = 4(2n-1)$ or $n = 4$.

Hence both Ashok and Baldev have four sons each.

35. (a) Here the probability of winning is $\frac{1}{2}\lambda$ for each player in a pair as all players are of equal strength.

So the player S_1 will be among 8 winners as there are 8 pairs.

Hence the required probability $P(S_1) = \frac{1}{8}.\frac{1}{2} = \frac{1}{16}$

(b) Here the required probability

$= P(S_1).P(\bar{S}_2) + P(S_2).P(\bar{S}_1)$

The probability of winning is same for each player so

$P(S_2) = \frac{1}{16}$

Putting the values, we get

$= \frac{1}{16}.\frac{15}{16} + \frac{1}{16}.\frac{15}{16} = \frac{15}{128}$

36. (a) Ans. (c). $7^2 = 49$, $7^4 = 49 \times 49 = 2401$

$\therefore \quad 7^6, 7s, 7^{14}$ all end with 9.

$7^8, 7^{12}, 7^{16}$ all end with 1.

Now $7^m + 7^n$ will be divisible by 5 if one ends with 9 and other ends with 1 so that the sum has 0 in the end.

$\therefore$ m can be 2, 6, 10, 14, ... 98 (25)

n can be 4, 8, 12, 16, ... 100 (25)

$\therefore$ But m and n can inter change.

$P = 2.\frac{25 \times 25}{100 \times 100} = \frac{1}{8}$.

(b) Ans. (d). The number of numbers divisible by 6 from the numbers 1 to 100 are 6, 12, ..., 96 or $96 = 6 + (n-1)6 \quad \therefore \quad n = 16$

$\therefore \quad$ Probability $= \frac{^{16}C_3}{^{100}C_3} = \frac{4}{1155}$

37. (a) Total ways $= {}^{52}C_4$

Condition is exactly one pair ...(1)

Now out of 13 different cards one card say 7 is selected in $^{13}C_1$ ways. Then a pair can be formed if out of four sevens, two sevens are selected in $^4C_2$ ways. Now we have to draw two more cards out of these none should be 7. Hence we are left with 48 cards out of which we choose any one say 8 in $^{48}C_1$ ways. The fourth card should not be either 7 or 8 because of condition (1). Hence we are left with 44 possible cards (4 sevens and 4 eights excluded) out of which 1 can be drawn in $^{44}C_1$ ways. Hence by fundamental theorem, number of favourable ways is

$^{13}C_1 . 4C_2 . {}^{48}C_1 . {}^{44}C_1 = 13.6.48.44$

Required probabilities is

$= 13 \times 6 \times 48 \times 44 \ \frac{52.51.50.49}{1.2.3.4}$

$= \frac{(13 \times 6 \times 48 \times 44) \times 24}{52.51.50.49} = \frac{6 \times 48 \times 44 \times 12}{100(50+1)(50-1)}$ etc.

(b) Let $P(A)$ be the probability that **at least 4 white balls** are drawn and $P(B)$ be the probability that **exactly one white** is drawn from two draws. Also $P(A_1), P(A_2)$ and $P(A_3)$ stand for the probability that **exactly 4 or 5 or 6** balls have been drawn respectively.

$\therefore \quad P\left(\frac{B}{A}\right) = \frac{\sum_{i=1}^{3} P(A_i)P(B/A_i)}{\sum_{i=1}^{3} P(A_i)}$

$= \frac{\frac{^{12}C_2\ ^6C_4}{^{18}C_6}.\frac{sC_1 . {}^2C_1}{^{12}C_2} + \frac{^{12}C_1 . {}^6C_5}{^{18}C_6}.\frac{^{11}C_1 . {}^1C_1}{^{12}C_2}}{\frac{^{12}C_2\ ^6C_4}{^{18}C_6} + \frac{^{12}C_1 . {}^6C_5}{^{18}C_6} + \frac{^{12}C_0 . {}^6C_6}{^{18}C_6}}$

$= \frac{^{12}C_2\ ^6C_4\ sC_1\ ^2C_1 + {}^{12}C_1\ ^6C_5\ ^{11}C_1\ ^1C_1}{^{12}C_2\ [^{12}C_2\ ^6C_4 + {}^{12}C_1\ ^6C_2 + {}^{12}C_0\ ^6C_6]}$

38. m white and n black balls

Event (a) = White ball is drawn in Ist draw

Event (b) = Black ball is drawn in Ist draw

Event (c) = White ball is drawn in the 2nd draw.

Hence the required probability is

$P(c) = P(a).P\left(\frac{c}{a}\right) + P(b).P\left(\frac{c}{b}\right)$

$= \frac{m}{m+n}.\frac{m+k}{m+n+k} + \frac{n}{m+n}.\frac{m}{m+n+k}$

$= \frac{m(m+k)+mn}{(m+n)(m+n+k)} = \frac{m(m+n+k)}{(m+n)(m+n+k)}$

$= \frac{m}{m+n}$.

39. Let us divide the players into two pools A and B each containing 4 players.

Pool A $\quad P_1, P_2, P_3, P_4$

Pool B $\quad P_5, P_6, P_7, P_8$

Let P_4 be in pool A. Now P_4 will reach the final if we fill the remaining three of pool A by any of P_5, P_6, P_7 or P_8 as P_i, P_j play, P_i wins when $i < j$

$\therefore$ Probability is $\dfrac{{}^4C_3}{{}^7C_3} = \dfrac{4.3.2}{7.6.5} = \dfrac{4}{35}$.

40. Total number of ways $= 6^n$ ...(1)

Now we shall calculate the number of ways of having only three numbers out of six.

= Number of ways in which any three numbers can appear − number of ways in which only two appear − number in which only one number appears

$= {}^6C_3 \,.\, 3^n - {}^6C_3 \,.\, {}^3C_2\,(2^n - 2) - {}^6C_3 \,.\, {}^3C_1 \,.\, 1$

$= {}^6C_3\,[3^n - 3.2^n + 6 - 3]$

$= {}^6C_3\,[3^n - 3.2^n + 3]$ ...(2)

$\therefore$ Required probability $= \dfrac{{}^6C_3\,(3^n - 3.2^n + 3)}{6^n}$

by (1) and (2)

41. Ans. (b) and (c).

At least one $\Rightarrow$ Any one, any two, all the three $= 0 \cdot 75 = \dfrac{3}{4}$

At least two $\Rightarrow$ Any two, all the three $= 50\% = \dfrac{1}{2}$

Exactly two $\Rightarrow$ Any two $= 40\% = \dfrac{2}{5}$

$\Sigma M\,(1-P)\,(1-C) + \Sigma\, MP\,(1-C) + MPC = \dfrac{3}{4}$ ...(1)

$\Sigma\, MP\,(1-C) + MPC = \dfrac{1}{2}$ ...(2)

$\Sigma\, MP\,(1-C) = \dfrac{2}{5}$ ...(3)

Solving (2) and (3),

$MPC = \dfrac{1}{10} \Rightarrow$ (c) ...(4)

Solving (2) and (4),

$M + P + C = \dfrac{27}{20}$

42. Let $P\,(A) = \dfrac{20}{100}, P\,(B) = \dfrac{16}{100}, P\,(C) = \dfrac{14}{100}$

$P\,(AB) = \dfrac{8}{100}, P\,(AC) = \dfrac{5}{100}, P\,(BC) = \dfrac{4}{100}$,

$P\,(ABC) = \dfrac{2}{100}$

$\because \quad P\,(A \cup B \cup C) = \Sigma P\,(A) - \Sigma P\,(AB) + P\,(ABC)$

$= \dfrac{50}{100} - \dfrac{17}{100} + \dfrac{2}{100} = \dfrac{35}{100}$

(i) Hence 35% of the adult population reads at least one of the newspapers.

(ii) $P\,[(A \cap B) \mid (A \cup B \cup C)]$

$= \dfrac{P\,[(A \cap B) \cap (A \cup B \cup C)]}{P\,[(A \cup B \cup C)]} = \dfrac{P\,(A \cap B)}{P\,(A \cup B \cup C)} = \dfrac{8}{35}$

Thus, of those that read at least one, $\dfrac{8}{35} \times 100 = 22\dfrac{6}{7}\%$ read both A and B.

43. Let $P\,(A_1)$ = probability that the first set wins $= 0 \cdot 6$

$P\,(A_2)$ = probability that the second set wins $= 0 \cdot 4$

$P\,(B)$ = probability that a new product is introduced

$\therefore \quad P\,(B) = P\,(B \cap A_1) + P\,(B \cap A_2)$

$= P\,(A_1)\,P\,(B \mid A_1) + P\,(A_2) \,.\, P\,(B \mid A_2)$ ...(1)

Now as per hypothesis

$P\,(B \mid A_1) = 0 \cdot 8, P\,(B \mid A_2) = 0 \cdot 3$

Hence from (1), $P\,(B) = 0 \cdot 6 \times 0 \cdot 8 + 0 \cdot 4 \times 0 \cdot 3 = 0 \cdot 60$

44. (a) If roots of $x^2 + px + q = 0$ are real,

then $\quad p^2 - 4q \geq 0$ ...(1)

Both p, q belong to set $S = \{1, 2, 3, \ldots.\, 10\}$ when $p = 1$, no value of q from S will satisfy (1)

$p = 2$	$q = 1$ will satisfy	1 value
$p = 3$	$q = 1, 2$	2 values
$p = 4$	$q = 1, 2, 3, 4$	4 values
$p = 5$	$q = 1, 2, 3, 4, 5, 6$	6 values
$p = 6$	$q = 1, 2, 3, 4, 5, 6, 7, 8, 9$	9 values

For $p = 7, 8, 9, 10$ all the ten values of q will satisfy.

Sum of these selections is

$1 + 2 + 4 + 6 + 9 + 10 + 10 + 10 + 10 = 62$

But the total number of selections of p and q without any order is $10 \times 10 = 100$

Hence the required probability is

$= \dfrac{62}{100} = 0 \cdot 62.$

(b) Roots equal $\quad \Rightarrow b^2 - 4ac = 0$

$\therefore \quad \left(\dfrac{b}{2}\right)^2 = ac$ ...(1)

Each coefficient is an integer, so we consider the following cases :

$b = 1 \quad \therefore \dfrac{1}{4} = ac,\quad$ No integral values of a and c

$b = 2 \quad 1 = ac \quad \therefore (1, 1)$

$b = 3 \quad 9/2 = ac,\quad$ No integral values of a and c

$b = 4 \quad 4 = ac \quad \therefore (1, 4), (2, 2), (4, 1)$

$b = 5 \quad 25/2 = ac,$

No integral values of a and c

$b = 6 \quad 9 = ac \quad \therefore 3, 3$

Thus we have 5 favavurable ways for $b = 2, 4, 6$

Total number of equations is $6.6.6 = 216$.

$\therefore$ Required probability is $\frac{5}{216}$.

(c) Ans. (a).

Total number of selection of two out of six is ${}^6C_2 = \frac{6.5}{1.2} = 15$. Now for favourable ways, we have the following :

If smaller is chosen as 3 then greater can be 4, 5, 6 *i.e.*, 3 choices.

Similarly for 2 we have 4 choices *i.e.*, 3, 4, 5, 6 and for 1 we have 5 choices *i.e.*, 2, 3, 4, 5, 6.

$\therefore$ Total favourable choices is $3 + 4 + 5 = 12$

Hence required probability is $\frac{12}{15} = \frac{4}{5}$.

45. We first find the probability that no two persons have the same birthday and then subtract the result from 1. Excluding leap years, there are 365 different birthdays possible. Any person might have any one of the 365 days of the year as a birthday. A second person may likewise have any one of 365 birthday : and so on. Hence the total number of ways is given by

$$n = 365^N.$$

And the number of possible ways for none of the N birthdays to coincide is

$$m = 365.364 \ldots\ldots (365 - N - 1)$$
$$= \frac{365!}{(365 - N)!}$$

$\therefore$ The probability that no two birthdays coincide is

$$\frac{m}{n} = \frac{365!/(365 - N)!}{365^N}$$

Hence the required probability

$$= 1 - \frac{m}{n} = 1 - \frac{365!/(365 - N)!}{365^N}.$$

46. (i) We denote by A the event that the first card is the ace of hearts and B the corresponding event in respect of the second card.

We have to find $P(A \cup B)$. But by addition theorem,

$$P(A \cup B) = P(A) + P(B) - P(A \cap B) \quad \ldots(1)$$

Now $P(A) = P(B) = \frac{1}{52}$,

since there is only ace of hearts in each suit of 52 cards. To find $P(A \cap B)$, we see that there are in all 52^2 cases which are represented by all possible pairs consisting of one card from first and one from the second. Only one of these cases is favourable to the event $A \cap B$, so that

$$P(A \cap B) = \frac{1}{52^2}.$$

Hence from (1), we obtain

$$P(A \cup B) = \frac{1}{52} + \frac{1}{52} - \frac{1}{52^2} = \frac{103}{2704}.$$

(ii) Let A be the event that the first die shows a number greater than 3 and B the event that the second die shows a number greater than 3. Then $P(A) = \frac{3}{6} = \frac{1}{2}$ and $P(B) = \frac{3}{6} = \frac{1}{2}$. To find $P(A \cap B)$, we see that there are in all 36 cases which are represented by all possible pairs (x, y), $1 \le x \le 6$, $1 \le y \le 6$ and only 9 of these cases are favourable to the event $A \cap B$, so that $P(A \cap B) = \frac{9}{36} = \frac{1}{4}$.

Hence $P(A \cup B) = P(A) + P(B) - P(A \cap B)$

$$= \frac{1}{2} + \frac{1}{2} - \frac{1}{4} = \frac{3}{4}.$$

47. (a) Let $A =$ event the first card is an ace of hearts, and $B =$ event that second card is an ace of hearts. Since here both the cards are drawn from the same set, they both cannot be the ace of hearts so that here events A and B are mutually exclusive.

$\therefore$ $P(A \cup B) = P(A) + P(B)$

and $P(A) = P(B) = \frac{1}{52}$ as in example 12.

Hence $P(A \cup B) = \frac{1}{52} + \frac{1}{52} = \frac{2}{52} = \frac{1}{26}$.

(b) Out of 52 cards there are 13 cards of clubs so the two cards must be drawn from remaining cards. The probability of a king being chosen $p = \frac{3}{52}$ (As one king of club is to be omitted)

Now out of 39 cards 36 are non-clubs, so the probability of non-club card is being chosen $q = \frac{36}{52}$.

Now the probability of at least one king and no club card being chosen

$$= {}^2C_1\, p.q + {}^2C_2\, .p^2$$

$$= 2 \times \frac{3}{52} \times \frac{36}{52} + \left(\frac{3}{52}\right)^2 = \frac{3}{(52)^2}[216 + 9] = \frac{225}{2704}.$$

48. (i) Since A has three shares in a lottery, his chance of success means that he gets at least one prize, that is, he gets either one prize or 2 prizes or 3 prizes and his chance of failure means that he gets no prize. It is certain that either he succeeds or fails.

If p denotes his chance of success and q the chance of his failure, then

$$p+q=1 \quad \text{or} \quad p=1-q$$

We now find q.

$$n = \text{total no. of ways}$$

$$= {}^{12}C_3 = \frac{12\times 11\times 10}{1\times 2\times 3} = 220$$

since out of 12 tickets in the lottery, he can draw any three tickets by virtue of his having three shares in the lottery and

$$m = \text{favourable number of ways}$$

$$= {}^{9}C_3 = \frac{9\times 8\times 7}{1\times 2\times 3} = 84,$$

Since he will fail to draw a prize if all the tickets drawn by him are blanks.

$$\therefore \quad q = \frac{m}{n} = \frac{84}{220} = \frac{21}{55}.$$

$$\therefore \quad p = A\text{'s chance of success} = 1 - \frac{21}{55} = \frac{34}{55}.$$

Similarly B's chance of success

$$p' = 1 - q' = 1 - \frac{{}^6C_2}{{}^8C_2} = 1 - \frac{6\times 5}{8\times 7} = 1 - \frac{15}{28} = \frac{13}{28}.$$

$\therefore$ A's chance of success : B's chance of success

$$= p : p' = \frac{34}{55} : \frac{13}{28} = \frac{952}{1540} : \frac{715}{1540} = 952 : 715.$$

(ii) The total number of ways of ticking the answers in any one attempt $= 2^4 - 1 = 15$ the student is taking chance at ticking the correct solution, the case of his not ticking any answer is ruled out.)

It is reasonable to assume that in order to derive maximum benefit, the three solutions which he will submit must be all different.

$$\therefore \quad n = \text{total no. of ways} = {}^{15}C_3$$

m = the no. of ways in which the correct solution is excluded $= {}^{14}C_3$.

Hence the required probability

$$= 1 - \frac{{}^{14}C_3}{{}^{15}C_3} = 1 - \frac{4}{5} = \frac{1}{5}.$$

49. In the bag there are $2n$ balls out of which two balls at a time are drawn till all the balls are drawn.

So total no. of cases

$$= {}^{2n}C_2 \cdot {}^{2n-2}C_2 \cdot {}^{2n-4}C_2 \dots {}^{2}C_2$$

$$= \frac{(2n)!}{(2n-2)!\,2!} \cdot \frac{(2n-2)!}{(2n-4)!\,2!} \dots \frac{2!}{2!\,0!} = \frac{(2n)!}{2^n}$$

Now favourable ways.

In first draw white ball can be drawn in n ways and red ball in n ways.

So both can be drawn in $n\times n = n^2$ ways

Similarly when 2nd pair is drawn white in $(n-1)$ ways and red in $(n-1)$ ways.

So both in $(n-1)(n-1) = (n-1)^2$ ways, so on.

$$\text{Hence favourable cases} = n^2 . (n-1)^2 \dots 1^2$$

$$= [n(n-1)\dots 1]^2 = (n!)^2$$

$$\therefore \quad \text{The required probability} = \frac{(n!)^2}{(2n)!/2^n}$$

$$= \frac{2^n\, n!\, n!}{(2n)!} = \frac{2^n}{{}^{2n}C_n}.$$

50. Let E_1 denote the event of A's throwing '6' and E_2 the event of B's throwing '7' with a pair of dice. Then $\bar{E}_1, \bar{E}_2$ are the complementary events.

There are 5 ways of obtaining 6 namely (1, 5), (2, 4), (3, 3), (4, 2), (5, 1) and similarly there are 6 ways of getting 7 namely (1, 6), (2, 5), (3, 4), (4, 3), (5, 2), (6, 1)

$$\therefore \quad P(E_1) = \frac{5}{36} \text{ and } P(\bar{E}_1) = 1 - \frac{5}{36} = \frac{31}{36}$$

$$P(E_2) = \frac{6}{36} = \frac{1}{6} \text{ and } P(\bar{E}_2) = 1 - \frac{1}{6} = \frac{5}{6}$$

It is given that A starts the game and he will win in the following mutually exclusive ways.

(i) E_1 happens *i.e.* A wins at the first draw.

(ii) $\bar{E}_1 \cap \bar{E}_2 \cap E_1$ happens *i.e.* A wins at the third draw when both A and B fail at 1st and 2nd draw.

(iii) $\bar{E}_1 \cap \bar{E}_2 \cap \bar{E}_1 \cap \bar{E}_2 \cap E_1$ happens *i.e.* A wins at the fifth draw when both A and B fail at Ist, IInd, IIIrd and IVth draw and so on ....

Hence the required probability of 'A' winning say $P(A)$ is given by

$$P(A) = P(i) + P(ii) + P(iii) + \dots$$

$$= P(E_1) + P(\bar{E}_1 \cap \bar{E}_2 \cap E_1)$$

$$+ P(\bar{E}_1 \cap \bar{E}_2 \cap \bar{E}_1 \cap \bar{E}_2 \cap E) + \dots$$

$$= P(E_1) + P(\bar{E}_1)P(\bar{E}_2)$$

$$+ P(\bar{E}_1)P(\bar{E}_2)P(\bar{E}_1)P(\bar{E}_2)P(E_1)$$

$$= \frac{5}{36} + \frac{31}{36}.\frac{5}{6}.\frac{5}{36} + \frac{31}{36}.\frac{5}{6}.\frac{31}{36}.\frac{5}{6}.\frac{5}{36} + \dots$$

$$= \frac{5}{36} + \left(\frac{31}{36}.\frac{5}{6}\right).\frac{5}{36} + \left(\frac{31}{36}.\frac{5}{6}\right)^2.\frac{5}{36} + \dots$$

$$= \frac{5}{36} . \frac{1}{1-\left(\frac{31}{36}.\frac{5}{6}\right)} = \frac{5}{36}.\frac{216}{61} = \frac{30}{61}$$

51. Let A, B, C be the three men. This problem is different from problem 32 since here the balls are not replaced.

To find A's chance, we must find the sum of probabilities of his drawing a white ball at 1st, 4th draw. (He will not need to draw at the 7th turn since the number of black balls is 5 which is less than 6).

Hence $p_1 = A\text{'s chance} = \frac{3}{8} + \frac{5}{8} \cdot \frac{4}{7} \cdot \frac{3}{6} \cdot \frac{3}{5} = \frac{27}{56}$.

[Note that A will get a second chance when A, B, C in this order draw black balls the probabilities for which are clearly $\frac{5}{8}, \frac{4}{7}$ and $\frac{3}{6}$ and at the fourth turn the chance of A's drawing white ball is $\frac{3}{5}$].

Similarly,

$p_2 = B\text{'s chance}$

$= \frac{5}{8} \cdot \frac{3}{7} + \frac{5}{8} \cdot \frac{4}{7} \cdot \frac{3}{6} \cdot \frac{2}{5} \cdot \frac{3}{4} = \frac{18}{56}$,

and $p_3 = C\text{'s chance}$

$= \frac{5}{8} \cdot \frac{4}{7} \cdot \frac{3}{6} + \frac{5}{8} \cdot \frac{4}{7} \cdot \frac{3}{6} \cdot \frac{2}{5} \cdot \frac{1}{4} \cdot 1 = \frac{11}{56}$.

$\therefore \quad p_1 : p_2 : p_3 = \frac{27}{56} : \frac{18}{56} : \frac{11}{56} = 27 : 18 : 11.$

52. (i) Let $p_1, p_2, p_3, \ldots, p_9$ denote the probabilities of drawing black, black, white, white, white, white, red, red and red respectively in this order without replacement. Then

$p =$ the required probability $= p_1 \, p_2 \, p_3 \cdots p_9$.

$$p_1 = \frac{{}^2C_1}{{}^9C_1} = \frac{2}{9},$$

since one black ball can be drawn out of 2 in ${}^2C_1$ ways and total number of ways is ${}^9C_1$.

$$p_2 = \frac{{}^1C_1}{{}^8C_1} = \frac{1}{8}$$

since one black ball remains after the first draw.

$$p_3 = \frac{{}^4C_1}{{}^7C_1} = \frac{4}{7},$$

since in the remaining 7 balls 4 are white.

Similarly,

$$p_4 = \frac{{}^3C_1}{{}^6C_1} = \frac{3}{6} = \frac{1}{2}, \quad p_5 = \frac{{}^2C_1}{{}^5C_1} = \frac{2}{5}, \quad p_6 = \frac{1}{4}$$

Now the remaining three balls are all red so that

$p_7 = p_8 = p_9 = 1$.

Hence $p = \frac{2}{9} \cdot \frac{1}{8} \cdot \frac{4}{7} \cdot \frac{1}{2} \cdot \frac{2}{5} \cdot \frac{1}{4} = \frac{1}{1260}$.

(ii) Let R stand for drawing red ball B for drawing black ball and W for drawing white ball. Then required probability is

$= P(WWR) + P(BBR) + P(WBR)$
$\quad + P(BWR) + P(WRR) + P(BRR)$
$\quad + P(RWR) + P(RBR)$

$$= \frac{3 \cdot 2 \cdot 2}{8 \cdot 7 \cdot 6} + \frac{3 \cdot 2 \cdot 2}{8 \cdot 7 \cdot 6} + \frac{3 \cdot 3 \cdot 2}{8 \cdot 7 \cdot 6} + \frac{3 \cdot 3 \cdot 2}{8 \cdot 7 \cdot 6} + \frac{3 \cdot 2 \cdot 1}{8 \cdot 7 \cdot 6} + \frac{3 \cdot 2 \cdot 1}{8 \cdot 7 \cdot 6} + \frac{2 \cdot 3 \cdot 1}{8 \cdot 7 \cdot 6} + \frac{2 \cdot 3 \cdot 1}{8 \cdot 7 \cdot 6}$$

$$= \frac{2}{56} + \frac{2}{56} + \frac{3}{56} + \frac{3}{56} + \frac{1}{56} + \frac{1}{56} + \frac{1}{56} = \frac{1}{4} \text{ Ans.}$$

53. Let the chance of the second event be p. Then the chance of the first event is p^2.

$\therefore$ Odds against the first event are as $1 - p^2 : p^2$

and odds against the second event are $1 - p : p$

Hence according to the condition given in the question, we have

$$\frac{1-p^2}{p^2} = \left(\frac{1-p}{p}\right)^3$$

or $\frac{(1-p)(1+p)}{p^2} = \frac{(1-p)^3}{p^3}$ or $p(p+1) = (1-p)^2$

or $p^2 + p = p^2 - 2p + 1$ or $3p = 1$

$\therefore \quad p = \frac{1}{3}$ and $p^2 = \frac{1}{9}$.

Hence the probability of the first event $= \frac{1}{9}$

and the probability of the second event $= \frac{1}{3}$.

54. $p(r) = \frac{3}{10}$ so $p(\bar{r}) = \frac{7}{10}$

The probability of at least one rainy day in 7 days

$$P(A) = 1 - \left(\frac{7}{10}\right)^7$$

Now the probability that at least two rainy days in 7 days

$$P(B) = 1 - \left(\frac{7}{10}\right)^7 - {}^7C_1 \left(\frac{3}{10}\right)\left(\frac{7}{10}\right)^6$$

Hence

$$P(B/A) = \frac{P(B \cap A)}{P(A)} = \frac{1 - \left(\frac{7}{10}\right)^7 - {}^7C_1 \left(\frac{3}{10}\right)\left(\frac{7}{10}\right)^6}{1 - \left(\frac{7}{10}\right)^7}$$

55. **First Method.** The rupee will be in the first purse if

(i) either it does not go from the purse at all.

or (ii) it goes to the second purse and comes back

The probability of case (i) $= \frac{{}^9C_9}{{}^{10}C_9} \times 1 = \frac{1}{10}$.

and the probability of case

(ii) $= \dfrac{{}^9C_8 \times {}^1C_1}{{}^{10}C_9} \times \dfrac{{}^{18}C_8 \times {}^1C_1}{{}^{19}C_9} = \dfrac{81}{190}$.

Since the events in case (i) and (ii) are mutually exclusive, the required probability

$$= \frac{1}{10} + \frac{81}{190} = \frac{100}{190} = \frac{10}{19}.$$

Second Method. We find the probability of the event that the rupee goes to the second purse and does not return and subtract it from 1.

Hence required probability

$$= 1 - \frac{{}^9C_8 \times {}^1C_1}{{}^{10}C_9} \times \frac{{}^{18}C_9}{{}^{19}C_9}$$

$$= 1 - \frac{9}{10} \times \frac{18!}{9!\ 9!} \times \frac{9!\ 10!}{19!} = 1 - \frac{9}{19} = \frac{10}{19}.$$

56. Total no. of ways $= N^n$.

[**Note.** That first biscuit can be given to any of the N beggars. Similarly second biscuit can also be given to any of the N beggars and so on]. Favourable no. of ways is ${}^nC_r \cdot (N-1)^{n-r}$. Out of n biscuits, r biscuits can be given to a particular beggar in ${}^nC_r$ ways and the remaining $n - r$ biscuits can be distributed among the remaining $N - 1$ beggars in $(N-1)^{n-r}$ ways. Hence the required probability $= \dfrac{{}^nC_r (N-1)^{n-r}}{N^n}$.

57. Let A denote the event that A draws a pair and B the event that B draws a pair. Then

$$P(A) = 1 \times \frac{{}^{18}C_1}{{}^{19}C_1} \times \frac{1}{{}^{18}C_1} \times 1 = \frac{1}{19}$$

Observe that at first draw A may draw any glove which is a certainty. Then B at the second draw, draws a glove out of the remaining 19 gloves, 18 of which are favourable since B must not draw the remaining one glove of the pair one of which was already drawn by A. Now 18 gloves are left. Since A has to draw a pair, at the third draw he must draw the remaining glove of the pair one of which was already drawn by him. At the fourth draw, B may draw any glove. Note that we have to ensure only that A draws a pair; B may or may not draw a pair.

Arguing as before, it is easy to see that

$$P(B) = 1 \times \frac{{}^{18}C_1}{{}^{19}C_1} \times \frac{{}^{17}C_1}{{}^{18}C_1} \times \frac{1}{{}^{17}C_1} = \frac{1}{19}.$$

Thus $P(A) = P(B) = \dfrac{1}{19}$.

This proves the first part.

For the second part, we have to find $P(\bar{A} \cap \bar{B})$.

But $P(\bar{A} \cap \bar{B}) = P[\overline{(A \cup B)}] = 1 - P(A \cup B)$

$= 1 - \{P(A) + P(B) - P(A \cap B)\}$ ...(1)

Now $P(A \cap B) =$ Prob. that both A and B draw a pair.

$$= 1 \times \frac{{}^{18}C_1}{{}^{19}C_1} \times \frac{1}{{}^{18}C_1} \times \frac{1}{{}^{17}C_1} = \frac{1}{19 \times 17} = \frac{1}{323}.$$

Substituting in (1), we get

$$P(\bar{A} \cap \bar{B}) = 1 - \frac{1}{19} - \frac{1}{19} + \frac{1}{323} = \frac{290}{323}.$$

58. Let A be the event that two heads result and B the event that there is at least one head. If S denote the sample space, then

$S = \{(H,H),\ (H,T),\ (T,H),\ (T,T)\}$.

$A = \{(H,H)\}$,

$B = \{(H,H),\ (H,T),\ (T,H)\}$

and so $A \cap B = \{H, H\}$,

$$P(B) = \frac{N(B)}{N(S)} = \frac{3}{4},$$

$$P(A \cap B) = \frac{N(A \cap B)}{N(S)} = \frac{1}{4}.$$

Hence $P(A/B) = \dfrac{P(A \cap B)}{P(B)} = \dfrac{1/4}{3/4} = \dfrac{1}{3}$.

59. We have to find the conditional probability of obtaining a sum of 15 when the first throw was a four. Let A be the event that the sum of the three numbers thrown is 15 and B the event that the first throw was a four. So we have to find $P(A/B)$.

But $P(A/B) = \dfrac{n(A \cap B)}{n(B)}$ [See (1) of § 4]

where $n(A \cap B)$ and $n(B)$ denote the number of points in $A \cap B$ and B respectively.

Now $n(B) = 36$, since first throw being a four, the other two throws can occur in 6×6 *i.e.* 36 ways. There are only two throws of three dice beginning with a four giving a total of 15, namely, (4, 5, 6), (4, 6, 5).

Hence $n(A \cap B) = 2$.

$\therefore\quad P(A/B) = \dfrac{2}{36} = \dfrac{1}{18}$.

60. In the first throw a number less than 4 can come as (1, 1), (1, 2), (2, 1), that is, in 3 ways and so 4 or more can come in $36 - 3$ *i.e.* in 33 ways since two dice can come up in 36 ways.

Hence the probability of this case $= \dfrac{33}{36} = \dfrac{11}{12}$.

In the second case, three dice are thrown. In this case, the total of 3, 4 or 5 can come as

(1, 1, 1), (2, 1, 1), (1, 2, 1), (1, 1, 2),

(1, 1, 3), (3, 1, 1), (1, 3, 1), (1, 2, 2), (2, 1, 2) and (2, 2, 1) *i.e.* in 10 ways.

Hence the number 6 or more can come in $216 - 10 = 206$ ways.

Hence the probability of this case $= \frac{206}{216} = \frac{103}{108}$.

$\therefore$ The required probability $= \frac{11}{12} \times \frac{103}{108} = \frac{1133}{1296}$.

61. Let $P_r\,(B \cap C) = x$.

Then we have $P_r\,(A \cup B \cup C) \geq 0 \cdot 75$

$\Rightarrow P_r\,(A) + P_r\,(B) + P_r\,(C) - P_r\,(B \cap C) - P_r\,(C \cap A) - P_r\,(A \cap B) + P_r\,(A \cap B \cap C) \geq 0 \cdot 75$

$\Rightarrow 0 \cdot 3 + 0 \cdot 4 + 0 \cdot 8 - x - 0 \cdot 28 - 0 \cdot 08 + 0 \cdot 09 \geq 0 \cdot 75$

$\Rightarrow 0 \cdot 48 - x \geq 0 \Rightarrow 0 \cdot 48 \geq x \Rightarrow x \leq 0 \cdot 48.$ ...(1)

Again similarly $P_r\,(A \cup B \cup C) \leq 1 \Rightarrow 0 \cdot 23 - x \leq 0$

$\Rightarrow 0 \cdot 23 \leq x.$ ...(2)

$\therefore$ From (1) and (2), we get, $0 \cdot 23 \leq x \leq 0 \cdot 48$.

Remark. In our opinion some data in the question appears to be wrong since $P_r\,(A \cap B \cap C)$ cannot be greater than $P_r\,(A \cap B)$

62. (i) Probability of not drawing an ace in the first n draws is ${}^{48}C_n / {}^{52}C_n$ and to drawing an ace in $(n+1)^{th}$ draw is ${}^4C_1 / {}^{(52-n)}C_n = \frac{4}{52-n}$.

Hence the required probability

$= ({}^{48}C_n / {}^{52}C_n)\,\{4/(52-n)\}$

$= \frac{48!}{n!\,(48-n)!} \times \frac{n!.(52-n)!}{52!} \times \frac{4}{52-n}$

$= \frac{4\,(51-n)\,(50-n)\,(49-n)}{52.51.50.49}$.

(ii) We must have one ace in $(n-1)$ attempts and one ace in the nth attempt. The probability of one ace in first $(n-1)$ attempts is ${}^4C_1 \times {}^{48}C_{n-2} / {}^{52}C_{n-1}$ and of one ace in the nth attempt is ${}^3C_1 / [52-(n-1)] = \frac{3}{53-n}$. Hence the required probability

$= \frac{4.48!}{(n-2)!\,(50-n)!} \times \frac{(n-1)!\,(53-n)!}{52!} \times \frac{3}{53-n}$

$= \frac{(n-1)\,(52-n)\,(51-n)}{50.49.17.13}$

(iii) Proceed as in (b).

63. $n =$ the total number of ways of distributing K balls over N cells $= N^K$

Now we find the favourable no. of ways. K adjacent cells out of N can be chosen in $N - K + 1$ ways. For if we denote the N cells by $C_1, C_2, C_3, \ldots, C_N$ then the following groupings of K consecutive cells are possible.

$C_1C_2 \,........\, C_K$

$C_2C_3 \,......\, C_{K+1}$

$C_3C_4 \,....\, C_{K+2}$

....

$C_{N-K}, C_{N-K+1}, \,.....\, C_{N-1}$

$C_{N-K+1}, C_{N-K+2}, \,.....,\, C_N$.

Now K balls can be distributed over each of these groups of K consecutive cells in $K!$ ways. Hence

$m =$ the favourable no. of ways $= (N - K + 1)\,K!$

$\therefore$ The required probability $= \frac{(N-K+1)\,K!}{N^K}$

64. We denote by H the appearance of head and T the appearance of tail and let X denote the appearance of head or tail.

Then $P(H) = P(T) = \frac{1}{2}$ and $P(X) = 1$.

If the sequence of m consecutive heads starts from the first throw, we have

$(H\,H\,H \ldots\ldots m \text{ times})\ (X\,X\,X \ldots\ldots n \text{ times})$

$\therefore$ The chance of this event

$= \frac{1}{2} \cdot \frac{1}{2} \cdot \frac{1}{2} \ldots\ldots m \text{ times} = \frac{1}{2^m}$

[Note that $(m+1)$ and subsequent throws may be head or tail since we are considering at least m consecutive heads].

If the sequence of m consecutive heads starts from the second throw, the first must be a tail and we have

$T\,(H\,H\,H \ldots\ldots m \text{ times})\ (X\,X\,X \ldots\ldots \overline{1-n} \text{ times})$

The chance of this event $= \frac{1}{2} \cdot \frac{1}{2^m} = \frac{1}{2^{m+1}}$.

If the sequence of heads starts with the $(r+1)^{th}$ throw, then the first $(r-1)$ throws may be head or tail but r^{th} throw must be tail and we have

$(X\,X \ldots\ldots \overline{r-1} \text{ times})\ T\ (H\,H\,H \ldots\ldots m \text{ times})\ (X\,X \ldots (n-m-r) \text{ times})$

$\therefore$ The probability of this event also

$= \frac{1}{2} \cdot \frac{1}{2^m} = \frac{1}{2^{m+1}}$.

Since all the above cases are mutually exclusive, the required probability

$= \frac{1}{2^m} + \left(\frac{1}{2^{m+1}} + \frac{1}{2^{m+1}} + \ldots \text{to } n \text{ terms}\right)$

$= \frac{1}{2^m} + \frac{n}{2^{m+1}} = \frac{2+n}{2^{m+1}}$.

65. (a) A chess board is a square divided into 64 equal squares parallel to the sides of the outer square as shown in the figure. We can choose three squares in a diagonal line parallel to BD in the $\Delta\, ABD$ along the dotted lines. It can be seen that in one of the dotted lines, there are only three squares and hence the selection can be in ${}^3C_3$ ways. In the next lower dotted line, the selection can be in ${}^4C_3$ ways and so on. Similarly in the $\Delta\, BCD$ three squares can be chosen in an equal number of ways.

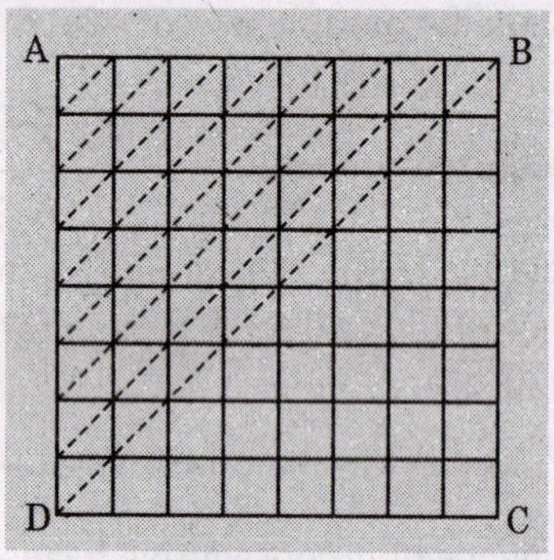

Fig. 2

Hence the number of ways in which 3 squares can be chosen parallel to BD and along BD itself is

$$2({}^3C_3 + {}^4C_3 + {}^5C_3 + {}^6C_3 + {}^7C_3) + {}^8C_3.$$

[Note that we do not have $2.{}^8C_3$ since the line BD is common to both the Δ^s ABD and ACD]

The same argument applies to squares parallel to AC. Hence the total number of favourable ways

$$m = 4({}^3C_3 + {}^4C_3 + {}^5C_3 + {}^6C_3 + {}^7C_3) + 2.{}^8C_3 = 392.$$

And $n =$ total number of ways

$$= {}^{64}C_3 = \frac{64.63.62}{1.2.3} = 32.21.62$$

Hence the required probability

$$= \frac{m}{n} = \frac{392}{32.21.62} = \frac{7}{744}.$$

(b) We have to find the probability that the person unlocks the lock at k^{th} trial. It means that he fails in first $(k-1)$ trials.

$= P$ (he fails in $k-1$ trials)

$\times P$ (he succeeds in k^{th} trial)

$$= \left[\frac{n-1}{n}\cdot\frac{n-2}{n-1}\cdot\frac{n-3}{n-2}\cdots\frac{n-(k-1)}{n-(k-2)}\right] \times \left[\frac{1}{n-(k-1)}\right]$$

$$= \frac{1}{n}$$

66. (a) Let A_i denote the event that the ith letter is placed in the right envelope. Then the required probability is

$$P(\overline{A_1} \cap \overline{A_2} \cap \ldots.. \cap \overline{A_n})$$

$$= P(\overline{A_1 \cup A_2 \cup \ldots\ldots A_n}) \quad \text{[By De-Morgan law]}$$

$$= 1 - P(A_1 \cup A_2 \cup \ldots.. \cup A_n)$$

$$= 1 - [\Sigma\, P(A_i) - \underset{i \ne j}{\Sigma}\, P(A_i \cap A_j) + \underset{i \ne j \ne k}{\Sigma}\, P(A_i \cap A_j \cap A_k) - \ldots. + (-1)^{n-1}\, P(A_1 \cap A_2 \cap \ldots.. \cap A_n)]$$

Now $P(A_i) = \dfrac{(n-1)!}{n!}$ as having placed i^{th} letter in the right envelope, the remaining letters can be placed in $(n-1)!$ ways.

Similarly, $P(A_1 \cap A_2 \cap \ldots\ldots \cap A_r)$

$=$ Prob. of r particular letters in right envelopes

$$= \frac{(n-r)!}{n!}$$

$$\therefore \quad \Sigma\, P(A_1 \cap A_2 \cap \ldots.. \cap A_r)$$

$$= {}^nC_r \cdot \frac{(n-r)!}{n!} = \frac{1}{r!},$$

where $r = 1, 2, 3, \ldots., n.$

$$\therefore \quad \Sigma\,(\overline{A_1} \cap \overline{A_2} \cap \ldots. \cap \overline{A_n})$$

$$= 1 - \left\{\frac{1}{1!} - \frac{1}{2!} + \frac{1}{3!} - \ldots + (-1)^{n-1}\cdot\frac{1}{n!}\right\}$$

$$= \frac{1}{2!} - \frac{1}{3!} + \frac{1}{4!} - \ldots.. + (-1)^n \cdot \frac{1}{n!}$$

which is equal to first $n-2$ terms in the expansion of e^{-1}.

(b) Let E_i be the event that ith object is placed in ith box.

$$P(E_i) = 1.\frac{(n-1)!}{n!} = \frac{1}{n}, i = 1, 2, \ldots, n.$$

Now the probability that two boxes contain right objects.

$$P(E_i \cap E_j) = 1.\frac{(n-2)!}{n!}$$

and these two objects can be out of n objects in ${}^nC_2$ ways.

So the probability that two objects are in right boxes.

$$= {}^nC_2 \cdot \frac{(n-2)!}{n!} = \frac{n!}{2!(n-2)!}\cdot\frac{(n-2)!}{n!} = \frac{1}{2}.$$

67. The set P be the empty set, or one element set or two elements set .... or n elements set. Then the set Q will be chosen from amongst the remaining n elements or $n-1$ elements or $n-2$ elements .... or no elements. Now if P is the empty set, then the probability of its choosing is $^nC_0/2^n$, if it is one element set, then probability of its choosing is $^nC_1/2^n$ and in general if P is r element set, then probability of its choosing is $^nC_r/2^n$.

When the set P consisting of r elements is chosen from A, then the probability of choosing the set Q from amongst the remaining $n-r$ elements is $2^{n-r}/2^n$.

Hence the probability that P and Q have no common elements is given by

$$\sum_{r=0}^{n} \frac{^nC_r}{2^n} \cdot \frac{2^{n-r}}{2^n} = \frac{1}{4^n} \sum_{r=0}^{n} {^nC_r} \cdot 2^{n-r}$$

$$= \frac{1}{4^n}(1+2)^n = \left(\frac{3}{4}\right)^n. \quad \text{[By binomial theorem]}$$

68. Since there are in all $N+7$ coins, the total number of ways of drawing 5 coins $= {^{N+7}C_5}$.

We have to find the probability that the total value of 5 coins is < one rupee and fifty paisé. We first find the probability that the total value is ≥ one rupee and fifty paisa.

Now the total value will be equal or more than one rupee and fifty paisa in three ways only :

(i) one fifty paisa coin and 4 twenty five paise coins.
(ii) 2 fifty paise coins and 3 twenty five paise coins
(iii) 2 fifty paise coins, 2 twenty five paise coins and one ten paise or five paise coin.

So the favourable ways

$$= {^2C_2} \cdot {^5C_3} \cdot {^NC_0} + {^2C_2} \cdot {^5C_2} \cdot {^NC_1} + {^2C_1} \cdot {^5C_4}$$

$$= 10N + 20$$

So the probability $= \dfrac{10N+20}{^{N+7}C_5}$

Hence the required probability $= 1 - \dfrac{10N+20}{^{N+7}C_5}$

69. (i) $n =$ Total no. of five digit numbers $= 5! = 120$. Now a number will be divisible by 4 if the last two digits are divisible by 4. Therefore the last two digits can be 12, 24, 32, 52, that is, they can be filled in 4 ways. Corresponding to each of these ways there are $3! = 6$ ways of filling the remaining three places.

Hence $m =$ favourable no. of ways $= 4 \times 6 = 24$

∴ The required probability $= \dfrac{24}{120} = \dfrac{1}{5}$

(ii) $n =$ Total number of ways $= 10! - 9!$

To find the favourable number of ways, we observe that a number is divisible by 4 if the last-two digits are divisible by 4. Hence the last two digits can be

20, 40, 60, 80, 12, 32, 52, 72, 92, 04, 24, 64, 84, 16, 36, 56, 76, 96, 08, 28, 48, 68 corresponding to each of 20, 40, 60, 80, 04, 08 the remaining 8 places can be filled up in $8!$ ways so that the number of ways in this case $= 6.8!$

And corresponding to remaining 16 possibilities the number of ways $= 16\,(8! - 7!)$

Hence $m =$ favourable number of ways.

$$= 22.8! - 16.7!$$

∴ The required probability $= \dfrac{m}{n}$

$$= \frac{22.8! - 16.7}{10! - 9!} = \frac{22.8 - 16}{10.9.8 - 9.8} = \frac{160}{648} = \frac{20}{81}.$$

70. (i) Let the sequence of numbers start with the integer m so that the $3n$ consecutive integers are

$$m, m+1, m+2, m+3, \ldots\ldots, m+3n-1.$$

Now they can be classified as

$$m,\ m+3,\ m+6, \ldots\ldots, m+3n-3,$$
$$m+1,\ m+4,\ m+7, \ldots\ldots, m+3n-2,$$
$$m+2,\ m+5,\ m+8, \ldots\ldots, m+3n-1.$$

The sum of the three numbers shall be divisible by 3 if either all the three numbers are from the same row or all the three numbers are from different rows. The number of ways that the three numbers are from the same row is $3 \cdot {^nC_3}$ and the number of ways that the numbers are from different rows is $n \times n \times n = n^3$ since a number can be selected from each row in n ways.

Hence the favourable no. of ways

$$M = 3 \cdot {^nC_3} + n^3$$

And the total number of ways $N = {^{3n}C_3}$

∴ The required probability

$$= \frac{M}{N} = \frac{3 \cdot {^nC_3} + n^3}{^{3n}C_3} = \frac{3n^2 - 3n + 2}{(3n-1)(3n-2)}.$$

(ii) Ans. 0·55. Total number of ways of selecting two numbers out of 100

$$n = {^{100}C_2} = \frac{100.99}{1.2} = 4950$$

Now to obtain favourable number of ways, let lowest one number drawn be 1. Then other selected number which gives the product divisible by 3 can be following :

3, 6, 9, ..., 99.

These give 33 favourable ways. Similarly when lower selected number is 2, other numbers should be

3, 6, 9, ..., 99.

These give another set of 33 favourable ways. When lower number selected is 3, then other numbers should be

4, 5, 6, ..., 99

These give set of $100 - 3 = 97$ favourable ways and so on.

Thus total favourable ways are

$$m = 2[33 + 32 + 31 + \ldots + 2 + 1] + [97 + 94 + 91 + \ldots + 4 + 1]$$

$$= 2 \cdot \frac{33.34}{2} + \frac{33}{2}[97 + 1] = 33.34 + 33.49$$

$$m = 33.83 = 2739$$

$$P(E) = \frac{m}{n} = \frac{2739}{4950} = 0 \cdot 55$$

71. (i) If the smallest number is 1, the groups of three numbers in A.P. are as 1, 2, 3 ; 1, 3, 5 ; 1, 4, 7 ; ......; $1, n+1, 2n+1$; and they are n in number.

If the smallest number selected is 2, the possible groupings are 2, 3, 4 ; 2, 4, 6 ; 2, 5, 8 ; ......; $2, n+1, 2n$; and their number is $n - 1$.

If the lowest number is 3, the groupings are 3, 4, 5 ; 3, 5, 7 ; 3, 6, 9 ; ......; $3, n+2, 2n+1$; their number being $n-1$.

Similarly it can be seen that if the lowest number selected are 4, 5, 6, $2n-2, 2n-1$, the numbers of selections respectively are $n-2$, $n-2$, $n-3$, $n-3, \ldots\ldots, 2, 2, 1, 1$. Thus the favourable ways for 2, 3 are the same and similarly they are the same for 4, 5 and so on.

Hence number of favourable ways

$$M = 2(1 + 2 + 3 + \ldots . n - 1) + n$$

$$= 2 . \frac{(n-1)\, n}{2} + n = n^2 - n + n = n^2.$$

Also the total number of ways

$$N = {}^{2n+1}C_3 = \frac{(2n+1) . 2n . (2n-1)}{1.2.3} = \frac{n(4n^2 - 1)}{3}.$$

Hence the required probability

$$= \frac{M}{N} = \frac{3n^2}{n(4n^2 - 1)} = \frac{3n}{4n^2 - 1}.$$

(ii) Ans. The required prob. $= \frac{10}{133}$.

[**Hint :** Put $n = 10$ in part (i). But students are advised to do it independently].

72. Total number of ways

$$N = {}^{6n}C_3 = \frac{6n(6n-1)(6n-2)}{1.2.3}$$

$$= n(6n-1)(6n-2).$$

We now obtain the favourable number of ways. Let the lowest number drawn be 0. Then the remaining two tickets are to be drawn from the tickets numbered 1, 2, 3, ..., $3n-2, 3n-1, 3n, 3n+1, \ldots\ldots, 6n-2, 6n-1$ such that their sum is $6n$. In this case, there are the following $(3n-1)$ triples of tickets having the sum $6n$.

$(0, 1, 6n-1)$, $(0, 2, 6n-2)$, $(0, 3, 6n-3)$,......, $(0, 3n-1, 3n+1)$.

If the lowest number drawn is 1, then the other two tickets will be chosen from the tickets numbered

2, 3, 4,.... $3n-1, 3n, . 3n+1, \ldots\ldots, 6n-1$

such that the sum of all the three tickets is $6n$. There are the following $(3n-2)$ triplets with their sum $6n$.

$(1, 2, 6n-3), (1, 3, 6n-4), (1, 4, 6n-5), \ldots.., (1, 3n-1, 3n)$

Similarly if the lowest number drawn is 2, then the other two tickets can be chosen from the tickets numbered 3, 4, 5, ..., $3n-1, 3n, 3n+1, \ldots.., (6n-1)$ in $(3n-4)$ ways and so on.

There is only one way with the lowest number $2n-1$. It is the triplet $(2n-1, 2n, 2n+1)$.

∴ Favourable number of ways

$$M = [(3n-1) + (3n-2)] + [(3n-4) + (3n-5)] + (5 + 4) + (2 + 1)$$

$$= 3 + 9 + 15 + \ldots . + (6n-9) + (6n-3)$$

$$= 3[1 + 3 + 5 + \ldots .. + (2n-1)]$$

$$= 3 . \frac{n}{2}[2.1 + (n-1)2] = 3n^2.$$

Hence the required probability

$$= \frac{M}{N} = \frac{3n^2}{n(6n-1)(6n-3)} = \frac{3n}{(6n-1)(6n-2)}.$$

73. (a) $P(A \cup B) = P(A) + P(B) - P(A \cap B)$

$0 \cdot 8 = 0 \cdot 6 + 0 \cdot 4 - P(A \cap B)$

∴ $P(A \cap B) = 0 \cdot 2$

Now $P(A \cup B \cup C) = S_1 - S_2 + S_3$

$= (0 \cdot 6 + 0 \cdot 4 + 0 \cdot 5) - (0 \cdot 2 + P(B \cap C) + 0 \cdot 3) + 0 \cdot 2$

$= 1 \cdot 5 - 0 \cdot 3 - P(B \cap C)$

We know $0 \cdot 85 \le P(A \cup B \cup C) \le 1$

or $0 \cdot 85 \le 1 \cdot 2 - P(B \cap C) \le 1$

∴ $0 \cdot 2 \le P(B \cap C) \le 0 \cdot 35$.

(b) Ans. (a).

$P(B \cap \overline{C}) = Q(A \cap B \cap \overline{C}) + P(\overline{A} \cap B \cap \overline{C})$

or $P(B \cap \overline{C}) = \frac{1}{3} + \frac{1}{3} = \frac{2}{3}$ ...(1)

Again $P(B \cap \bar{C}) = P(B) - P(B \cap C)$

$\therefore \quad P(B \cap C) = P(B) - P(B \cap \bar{C}) = \frac{3}{4} - \frac{2}{3} = \frac{1}{12}$

74. (i) $P(\bar{A}/B) = \frac{P(\bar{A} \cap B)}{P(B)}$,

by definition of conditional probability

$= \frac{P(B) - P(A \cap B)}{P(B)}$, by theorem 2 of §3.

$= 1 - \frac{P(A \cap B)}{P(B)} = 1 - P(A / B).$

(ii) $P(\bar{A} \cup \bar{B}) = P(\overline{A \cap B})$ by De-Morgan laws.

$= 1 - P(A \cap B)$, by theorem 3 of §3.

$= 1 - P(A)\, P(B/A).$

75. Let A denote the event that the candidate A is selected and B the event that B is selected. It is given that

$P(A) = \cdot 5$ ...(1)

$P(A \cap B) \le \cdot 3$ ...(2)

Now $P(A) + P(B) - P(A \cap B) = P(A \cup B) \le 1$

or $\cdot 5 + P(B) - P(A \cap B) \le 1$, by (1)

or $P(B) \le \cdot 5 + P(A \cap B) \le \cdot 5 + \cdot 3$, by (2)

or $P(B) \le \cdot 8$

Hence probability of B cannot be 9.

76. (i) We are given, $P(A \cap B) = \frac{1}{8}$ ...(1)

and $P(\bar{A} \cap \bar{B}) = \frac{3}{8}$ ...(2)

We have to find $P(A)$ and $P(B)$.

Let $P(A) = x$ and $P(B) = y$.

Since the events are independent, we have from (1),

$P(A)\, P(B) = \frac{1}{8}$ i.e. $xy = \frac{1}{8}$. ...(3)

And from (2), we have

$P(\bar{A} \cap \bar{B}) = P(\overline{A \cup B}) + \frac{3}{8}$

or $1 - P(A \cup B) = \frac{3}{8}$

or $1 - P(A) - P(B) + P(A \cap B) = \frac{3}{8}$

or $1 - P(A) - P(B) + P(A)\, P(B) = \frac{3}{8}$

or $1 - x - y + xy = \frac{3}{8}$. ...(4)

Subtracting (3) from (4), we get

$1 - x - y = \frac{1}{4}$ or $x + y = \frac{3}{4}$ ...(5)

Now $(x - y)^2 = (x + y)^2 - 4xy = \frac{9}{16} - 4 \times \frac{1}{8} = \frac{1}{16}$

or $x - y = \pm \frac{1}{4}$. ...(6)

Solving (5) and (6), we get

$x = \frac{1}{2}$ and $y = \frac{1}{4}$

or $x = \frac{1}{4}$ and $y = \frac{1}{2}$.

Hence $P(A) = \frac{1}{2}$ and $P(B) = \frac{1}{4}$.

or $P(A) = \frac{1}{4}$ and $P(B) = \frac{1}{2}$.

(ii) Let $P(A) = x$ and $P(B) = y$ where A and B are independent events

$\Rightarrow \quad P(A) \,.\, P(B) = \frac{1}{6}$

Now $P(A \cap B) = \frac{1}{6}, P(A \cup B)' = \frac{1}{3}$

$\therefore \quad 1 - P(A \cup B) = \frac{1}{3} \quad \therefore P(A \cup B) = \frac{2}{3}$

or $P(A) + P(B) - P(A \cap B) = \frac{2}{3}$

or $x + y = \frac{2}{3} + \frac{1}{6} = \frac{5}{6}$. Also $xy = \frac{1}{6}$

Solving, we get

$x = \frac{1}{3} = P(A), y = \frac{1}{2} = P(B).$

77. (a) We have

$P(A \mid \bar{B}) = \frac{P(A \cap \bar{B})}{P(\bar{B})} = \frac{P(A) - P(A \cap B)}{1 - P(B)}$

Since $P(A \mid \bar{B}) \le 1$, we have

$P(A) - P(AB) \le 1 - P(B)$

$\Rightarrow \quad P(AB) \ge P(A) + P(B) - 1$

Also $\frac{P(A \mid \bar{B})}{P(A)} = \frac{P(\bar{B} \mid A)}{P(\bar{B})} = \frac{1 - P(B \mid A)}{1 - P(B)}$

Hence $P(A \mid \bar{B}) > P(A)$

if $1 - P(B \mid A) > 1 - P(B)$

or if $P(B \mid A) < P(B)$

i.e., if $P(A \mid B) < P(A)$

Since $\frac{P(A \mid B)}{P(A)} = \frac{P(B \mid A)}{P(B)}$

Hence the result.

(b) Let $P(A) = x$ so that $P(A') = 1 - x < 1$,

and $P(B) = y$ so that $P(B') = 1 - y < 1$

then by definition

$P(A \cup B) = x + y - xy$ ...(1)

$P(A' \cap B') = P(A') \cdot P(B') = (1 - x)(1 - y)$ ...(2)

as events are independent

$P(C) = P(A \cap B') + P(A' \cap B)$

$= x(1 - y) + y(1 - x)$ ...(3)

$P(A \cup B) \cdot P(A' \cap B') = (x + y - xy)(1 - x)(1 - y)$

by (1), (2)

$= x(1 - x)(1 - y) + y(1 - x)(1 - y) - xy(1 - x)(1 - y)$

$\le x(1 - y) + y(1 - x) = P(C)$ by (3)

78. Total number of ways in which each player will get 13 balls is

$$({}^{52}C_{13})({}^{39}C_{13})({}^{26}C_{13})({}^{13}C_{13}) = \frac{52!}{(13!)^4} \quad \text{...(1)}$$

Number of ways in which each of the four players will get exactly one 'Lucky' ball

$$= 4!({}^{48}C_{12})({}^{36}C_{12})({}^{24}C_{12})({}^{12}C_{12}) = 4!\frac{48!}{(12!)^4} \quad \text{...(2)}$$

$$\text{Reqd. probability} = \frac{4! \times 48!}{(12!)^4} \times \frac{(13!)^4}{52!} \text{ by (1), (2)}$$

$$= \frac{4!(13)^4}{49.50.51.52} \text{ etc.}$$

79. The man will be one step away from the starting point if (i) either he is one step ahead or (ii) one step behind the starting point.

Now if at the end of eleven steps the man is one step ahead the starting point, thus he must take six steps forward and five steps backwards.

The probability of this event

$$= {}^{11}C_6 \times (0\cdot4)^6 \times (0\cdot6)^5$$

$$= 462 \times (0\cdot4)^6 \times (0\cdot6)^5$$

Again if at the end of eleven steps, the man is one step behind the starting point, then out of 11 steps he must have taken six steps backward and five steps forward.

The probability of this event

$$= {}^{11}C_6 \times (0\cdot6)^6 \times (0\cdot4)^5$$

$$= 462 \times (0\cdot6)^6 \times (0\cdot4)^5$$

Since the events (i) and (ii) are mutually exclusive therefore the probability that one of these events happens

$$= 462 \times (0\cdot4)^6 \times (0\cdot6)^5 + 462 \times (0\cdot6)^6 \times (0\cdot4)^5$$

$$= 462 \times (0\cdot4)^5 \times (0\cdot6)^5 [0\cdot4 + 0\cdot6]$$

$$= 462 \times (0\cdot4 \times 0\cdot6)^5 \times 1 = 462 \times (0\cdot24)^5$$

80. (a) Let the probability of a vessel wrecking be q and of safe arrival be p so that

$$q = \frac{1}{10} \text{ and } p = 1 - \frac{1}{10} = \frac{9}{10}.$$

The probabilities of no vessel, one vessel, two vessels, etc., arriving safely are the first, second, third terms, etc., in the binomial expansion

$$(q+p)^5 = q^5 + {}^5C_1 q^4 p + {}^5C_2 q^3 p^2 + {}^5C_3 q^2 p^3 + {}^5C_4 qp^4 + p^5.$$

$\therefore$ The probability of at least 4 vessels arriving safely is the sum of last two terms.

Hence the required probability $= {}^5C_4 qp^4 + p^5$

$$= 5 \cdot \frac{1}{10} \cdot \left(\frac{9}{10}\right)^4 + \left(\frac{9}{10}\right)^5 = \frac{45927}{50000}.$$

(b) If p is the probability of success and q the probability of failure, then it is given that $p = 2q$ and $p + q = 1$

$$\Rightarrow 2q + q = 1 \Rightarrow q = \frac{1}{3} \quad \therefore \quad p = \frac{2}{3}$$

Now the probability of at least four successes in six trials

$$= {}^6C_4 p^4 q^2 + {}^6C_5 p^5 q + {}^6C_6 p^6$$

$$= 15\left(\frac{1}{3}\right)^2\left(\frac{2}{3}\right)^4 + 6\left(\frac{2}{3}\right)^5\left(\frac{1}{3}\right) + \left(\frac{2}{3}\right)^6$$

$$= \frac{1}{3^6}[240 + 192 + 64] = \frac{496}{729}.$$

(c) A is the event that the cycle is hired, so

$$P(A) = \frac{3}{4}, P(\bar{A}) = \frac{1}{4}$$

To earn Rs 6 per day his all the three cycles must be hired. His cycles can be hired by 5 customers. Hence the required probability

$$= {}^5C_3 \cdot \left(\frac{3}{4}\right)^3 \cdot \left(\frac{1}{4}\right)^2 = \frac{135}{512}.$$

81. Let p denote the probability that a thing goes to a man and q the probability that it goes to a woman. Then

$$p = \frac{a}{a+b} \text{ and } q = \frac{b}{a+b}.$$

Now the probabilities of 0, 1, 2, 3,..... things going to men are the first, second, third terms etc. in the binomial expansion.

$$(q+p)^m = q^m + {}^mC_1 q^{m-1} p + {}^mC_2 q^{m-2} p^2 + \ldots\ldots + p^m. \quad \text{...(1)}$$

But men are to receive an odd number of things. Hence the required probability is the sum of even terms in (1).

To obtain the sum of even terms, we write the expansion

$$(q-p)^m = q^m - {}^mC_1 q^{m-1} p + {}^mC_2 q^{m-2} p^2 - \ldots\ldots + (-1)^m p^m \quad \text{...(2)}$$

Subtracting (2) from (1), we get

$$(q+p)^m - (q-p)^m = 2 \times \text{ sum of even terms in (1).}$$

$$\text{Hence required probability} = \frac{1}{2}[(q+p)^m - (q-p)^m]$$

$$= \frac{1}{2}\left[1 - \left(\frac{b-a}{b+a}\right)^m\right] \quad [\because q + p = 1]$$

$$= \frac{1}{2} \cdot \frac{(b+a)^m - (b-a)^m}{(b+a)^m}$$

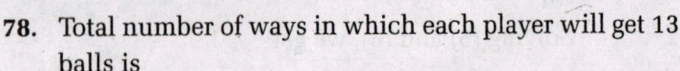

82. We have

q = prob. of a bulb being defective $= \dfrac{10}{100} = \dfrac{1}{10}$

and p = prob. of the bulb being non-defective $= \dfrac{9}{10}$.

The probabilities of no defective, one defective, two defective bulbs, etc., are the first, second, third terms, etc., in the binomial expansion

$$(p+q)^8 = p^8 + {}^8C_1\, p^7 q + {}^8C_2\, p^6 q^2 + \ldots + q^8.$$

∴ (a) The probability of 3 defective and 5 non-defective bulbs

$$= {}^8C_3\, p^5 q^3 = 56 \times \left(\frac{9}{10}\right)^5 \left(\frac{1}{10}\right)^3 = \frac{413343}{12500000}$$

(b) The prob. of at least one defective bulb

$$= 1 - p^8 = 1 - \left(\frac{9}{10}\right)^8 = 1 - 4\frac{3046721}{100000000}$$

$$= \frac{56953279}{100000000}.$$

83. (i) Let p be the chance of throwing an ace (*i.e.* 1) and q the chance of not throwing an ace in a single throw with one die.

Then $p = \dfrac{1}{6}$ and $q = \dfrac{5}{6}$ (why ?)

Now the chances of throwing no ace, one ace, two aces, etc., in five throws with a single die are the first, second, third terms, etc., in the binomial expansion

$$(q+p)^5 = q^5 + {}^5C_1\, q^4 p + {}^5C_2\, q^3 p^2 + {}^5C_3\, q^2 p^3 + {}^5C_4\, q\, p^4 + p^5.$$

Hence (1) chance of three aces exactly

$$= {}^5C_3\, q^2 p^3 = 10 \cdot \left(\frac{5}{6}\right)^2 \left(\frac{1}{6}\right)^3 = \frac{125}{3888}.$$

(2) Chance of throwing three aces at least

$$= {}^5C_3\, q^2 p^3 + {}^5C_4\, q\, p^4 + p^5$$

$$= 10\left(\frac{5}{6}\right)^2 \left(\frac{1}{6}\right)^3 + 5\left(\frac{5}{6}\right)\left(\frac{1}{6}\right)^4 + \left(\frac{1}{6}\right)^5$$

$$= \frac{1}{6^5}[250 + 25 + 1] = \frac{276}{7776} = \frac{23}{648}.$$

(ii) Favourable ways for event E when one number is selected are (2, 9), (3, 6), (6, 3) and (9, 2). These are 4 and total ways are 100.

$$\therefore\quad p = \frac{4}{100} = \frac{1}{25}$$

$$\therefore\quad q = 1 - \cdot 04 = 1 - \frac{1}{25} = \frac{24}{25}$$

Here $n = 4$

Prob. of occurrence for at least 3 successes

= Prob. occurrence for 3 successes + Prob. for 4 successes

$$= {}^4C_3\, p^3 q + {}^4C_4\, p^4$$

$$= 4\left(\frac{1}{25}\right)^3 \left(\frac{24}{25}\right) + \left(\frac{1}{25}\right)^4$$

$$= \left(\frac{1}{25}\right)^3 \left[\frac{96}{25} + \frac{1}{25}\right] = \frac{97}{(25)^4}.$$

84. We have to find the probability that match will be finished in 4 or less games. First let us find the ways in which match is not finished in 4 games.

There are following 4 mutually exculsive ways :

(1) All the 4 games are drawn.

(2) A and B both win one game each and remaining two are drawn.

(3) A wins one game and remaining three are drawn.

(4) B wins one game and remaining three are drawn.

So the probability that match is not finished in 4 games is equal to the sum of probabilities of 4 ways.

$$= \left(\frac{1}{2}\right)^4 + {}^4C_2\left(\frac{1}{4}\right)^2\left(\frac{1}{2}\right)^2 + {}^4C_1\left(\frac{1}{4}\right)\left(\frac{1}{2}\right)^3 + {}^4C_1\left(\frac{1}{4}\right)\left(\frac{1}{2}\right)^3$$

$$= \frac{1}{16} + \frac{3}{16} + \frac{1}{8} + \frac{1}{8} = \frac{1}{2}$$

Hence the required probability $= 1 - \dfrac{1}{2} = \dfrac{1}{2}$.

85. The probability of drawing exactly r white balls in n trials is ${}^nC_r\, p^r q^{n-r}$, and it is required to find for what value of r this expression is greatest.

Now ${}^nC_r\, p^r q^{n-r} > {}^nC_{r-1}\, p^{r-1} q^{n-(r-1)}$

so long as $\dfrac{n!}{r!\,(n-r)!}\, p > \dfrac{n!}{(r-1)!\,(n-r+1)!}\, q$

or $(n - r + 1)\, p > r q$

or $(n+1)\, p > (p+q)\, r$.

or $np + p > r$ $\quad [\because\ p + q = 1]$

or $r < np + p$.

Hence the required value of r is the greatest integer in $np + p$.

If n is such that np is an integer, the most likely case is that of np successes and nq failures.

For the numerical part, we have $p = \dfrac{1}{3}$ and $n = 12$.

∴ In this case, $r < 12 \times \dfrac{1}{3} + \dfrac{1}{3}$ or $r < 4 + \dfrac{1}{3}$.

Hence 4 white balls are most likely to be drawn.

86. (a) Suppose A wins in excatly $m + r$ games. To do so he must win the last game and $m - 1$ out of the preceding $m + r - 1$ games. The chance of this is ${}^{m+r-1}C_{m-1}\, p^{m-1} q^r\, p$, i.e.

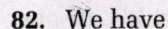

${}^{m+r-1}C_{m-1}\, p^m q^r$. Now the set will definitely be decided in $m+n-1$ games, and A may win these m games in exactly m games, or $m+1$ games,...., or $m+n-1$ games. Hence we shall obtain the chance of A's winning the set by giving to r the values 0, 1, 2, ..., $n-1$ in succession in the expression ${}^{m+r-1}C_{m-1}\, p^m q^r$. Hence A's probability to win the set is

$$p^m \left[1 + mq + \frac{m(m+1)}{1.2} q^2 + \ldots + \frac{(m+n-2)!}{(m-1)!\,(n-1)!} q^{n-1}\right];$$

Similarly B's probability to win the set is

$$q^n \left[1 + np + \frac{n(n+1)}{1.2} p^2 + \ldots\ldots + \frac{(m+n-2)!}{(m-1)!\,(n-1)!} p^{m-1}\right]$$

(b) Suppose it requires n tosses of a coin. The probability of throwing at least one head in n trials $= 1 - P$ (not a single head in n trials)

This probability should be greater than or equal to 0·8.

Here probability of head $p = \frac{1}{2}$

and probability of tail $q = \frac{1}{2}$

$\Rightarrow \quad 1 - {}^nC_0\, p^0 q^n \geq 0\cdot 8$

$\Rightarrow \quad 1 - \left(\frac{1}{2}\right)^n \geq 0\cdot 8 \quad \Rightarrow \quad 0\cdot 2 \geq \left(\frac{1}{2}\right)^n$

$\Rightarrow \quad \frac{1}{5} \geq \left(\frac{1}{2}\right)^n \quad \Rightarrow 2^n \geq 5$

This shows that least value of n should be 3.

87. Here $p = \frac{90}{100} = \frac{9}{10}$ and $q = 1 - \frac{9}{10} = \frac{1}{10}$ and $n = 10$.

Let N be the number of customers to whom packets are sold.

The frequency that success will be less than 90% is equal to

$N\,(sC_2\, p^8 q^2 + \ldots.. + {}^{10}C_9\, p q^9 + qs)$

$= N\,(p+q)s - N\,(ps + {}^{10}C_1\, p^9 q)$

$= N\,[1 - ps - 10\,p^9 q]$

$= N\,[1 - (\cdot 9)s - 10\,(\cdot 9)^9\,(\cdot 1)]$

$= N\,[1 - \cdot 3483 - \cdot 3871] = \cdot 2646\, N = \frac{1}{4} N$ nearly.

88. (i) The probability of getting a double six in one throw with two dice $= \frac{1}{6} \times \frac{1}{6} = \frac{1}{36}$.

$\therefore$ The probability of not throwing a double six

$$= 1 - \frac{1}{36} = \frac{35}{36}$$

Let $p = \frac{1}{36}$ and $q = \frac{35}{36}$

$\therefore$ The probability of not throwing a double six in any of the n throws $= q^n$.

Hence the probability of throwing a double six at least once in n throws $= 1 - q^n = 1 - \left(\frac{35}{36}\right)^n$.

Now according to the question,

$$1 - \left(\frac{35}{36}\right)^n > 0\cdot 99$$

or $\left(\frac{35}{36}\right)^n < 0\cdot 01$ ...(1)

Since both sides of (1) are +ive, the inequality will not be affected by taking logarithm to the base 10 (which is greater than 1).

or $n\,[\log_{10} 35 - \log_{10} 36] < \log_{10} 0\cdot 01$

or $n\,[1\cdot 5441 - 1\cdot 5563] < -2$

or $-0\cdot 0122\, n < -2$

or $0\cdot 0122\, n > 2$

or $n > \frac{2}{0\cdot 0122} = 163\cdot 9$

$\therefore$ The least value of n is 164.

(ii) The probability of getting a sum of 7 is $\frac{6}{36} = \frac{1}{6}$

$(\because\ n = 36, m = 6)$

$\therefore$ The probability of not throwing seven $= 1 - \frac{1}{6} = \frac{5}{6}$

Let $p = \frac{1}{6}$ and $q = \frac{5}{6}$

The probability of not throwing seven in any of the n throws $= q^n$.

Hence the probability of throwing seven at least once in n throws

$$= 1 - q^n = 1 - \left(\frac{5}{6}\right)^n$$

Now according to the question,

$1 - \left(\frac{5}{6}\right)^n > \cdot 95$ or $\left(\frac{5}{6}\right)^n < \cdot 05$ ...(1)

Since both sides of (1) are +ive, the inequality will not be affected by taking logarithm to the base 10.

or $n\log_{10}\left(\frac{5}{6}\right) < \log_{10} \cdot 05$

$n\log_{10}\left(\frac{10}{12}\right) < \log_{10} \frac{10^{-1}}{2}$

or $n[\log 10 - \log_{10} 4 - \log_{10} 3]$

$< \log_{10} 10^{-1} - \log_{10} 2$

or $n[1 - 2\times\cdot 3010 - \cdot 4771] < -1 - \cdot 3010$

or $n[-0\cdot 0791] < [-1\cdot 3010]$

or $n > \frac{1\cdot 3010}{0\cdot 0791}$ or $n > 16\cdot 4$

$\therefore$ Least value of n is 17.

89. Let w stand for the winning of a game and l for losing it. Then there are 4 mutually exclusive possibilities

(i) $w, w, w,$ (ii) $w, w, l, w,$

(iii) $w, l, w, w,$ (iv) $l, w, w, w.$

[Note that case (i) includes both the cases whether he loses or wins the fourth game].

According to the conditions of the question, the probabilities for (i), (ii), (iii) and (iv) are respectively

$\frac{2}{3}.\frac{2}{3}.\frac{2}{3}, \ \frac{2}{3}.\frac{2}{3}.\frac{1}{3}.\frac{1}{3}, \ \frac{2}{3}.\frac{1}{3}.\frac{1}{3}.\frac{2}{3}$ and $\frac{1}{3}.\frac{1}{3}.\frac{2}{3}.\frac{2}{3}.$

Hence the required probability

$$=\frac{8}{27}+\frac{4}{81}+\frac{4}{81}+\frac{4}{81}=\frac{36}{81}=\frac{4}{9}.$$

90. First we will find the probability of drawing white ball in a single trial. There is equal probability of each bag being chosen.

So the probability of white ball being chosen from either bag

$$p=\frac{1}{2}.\frac{2}{4}+\frac{1}{2}.\frac{3}{8}=\frac{1}{4}+\frac{3}{16}=\frac{7}{16}.$$

And the probability of black ball being chosen

$$=1-\frac{7}{16}=\frac{9}{16}.$$

Now the probability of 4 balls in 5 trials

$$= {}^5C_4 \, . \, p^4 \, . q$$

$$=5\times\left(\frac{7}{16}\right)^4\times\frac{9}{16}=\frac{108045}{1048576}=0\cdot 103.$$

91. Ans. 11/16. This question is out of syllabus. However, we are giving the solution of this question . The binomial distribution of X is given by

$$(q+p)^n = \Sigma \ {}^nC_X \, q^{n-X} \, p^X,$$

where $X = 0, 1, 2, \ldots\ldots n$ and $p + q = 1$.

The mean of this distribution $= np$ and its variance $= npq$.

As given in this question, we have

$np = 2$ and $npq = 1$, whence $q = \frac{1}{2}$,

Then $p = 1 - q = \frac{1}{2}$ and $n = 4$.

So in this case, the distribution is

$$1=\left(\frac{1}{2}+\frac{1}{2}\right)^4 = {}^4C_0\left(\frac{1}{2}\right)^4 + {}^4C_1\left(\frac{1}{2}\right)^3\left(\frac{1}{2}\right)$$

$$+ {}^4C_2\left(\frac{1}{2}\right)^2\left(\frac{1}{2}\right)^2 + {}^4C_3\,\frac{1}{2}\left(\frac{1}{2}\right)^3 + {}^4C_4\left(\frac{1}{2}\right)^4 \quad \ldots(1)$$

Now the probability that X takes a value greater than 1 is the sum of last three terms on the L.H.S. of (1).

Hence the required probability

$$=6\left(\frac{1}{2}\right)^4+4\left(\frac{1}{2}\right)^4+\left(\frac{1}{2}\right)^4=\frac{11}{16}.$$

92. (i) If the family of n children contains exactly k boys, then by Binomial probability theorem its probability is ${}^nC_k\left(\frac{1}{2}\right)^k\left(\frac{1}{2}\right)^{n-k}$

Hence by compound probability law, the probability of a family of n children having exactly k boys is given by

$\alpha \, p^n \, . \, {}^nC_k\left(\frac{1}{2}\right)^k\left(\frac{1}{2}\right)^{n-k}$, where $n \geq k$

$\therefore$ By addition theorem, the required probability is

$$\sum_{n=k}^{\infty} \alpha \, p^n \, . \, {}^nC_k\left(\frac{1}{2}\right)^k\left(\frac{1}{2}\right)^{n-k}$$

$$=\alpha\left(\frac{1}{2}\right)^k p^k \sum_{n=k}^{\infty} {}^nC_k\left(\frac{p}{2}\right)^{n-k}$$

$$=\alpha\left(\frac{1}{2}\right)^k p^k\left[1+(k+1)\left(\frac{p}{2}\right)\right.$$

$$\left.+(k+1)(k+2)\left(\frac{p}{2}\right)^2+\ldots\right]$$

$$=\alpha\left(\frac{1}{2}\right)^k p^k\left(1-\frac{p}{2}\right)^{-(k+1)}$$

$$=2\alpha p^k\,(2-p)^{-(k+1)}=\frac{2\alpha}{2-p}\left(\frac{p}{2-p}\right)^k, \ k\geq 1$$

(ii) Let A denote the event of a family including at least one boy, then

$$p(A)=\frac{2\alpha}{2-p}\sum_{k=1}^{\infty}\left(\frac{p}{2-p}\right)^k$$

$$=\frac{2\alpha}{2-p}\cdot\frac{p/(2-p)}{1-p/(2-p)} \text{ by } S_\infty \text{ of G.P.}$$

$$=\frac{\alpha p}{(2-p)(1-p)}$$

Let B denote the event of a family including at least two or more boys, then

$$P(B) = \frac{2\alpha}{2-p} \sum_{k=2}^{\infty} \left(\frac{p}{2-p}\right)^k = \frac{\alpha p^2}{(2-p)^2 (1-p)}$$

Thus, $P(B \mid A) = \frac{P(A \cap B)}{P(A)} = \frac{P(B)}{P(A)}$,

as $B \subset A = \frac{p}{2-p}$.

Note : $p_0 + p_1 + p_2 + \ldots = 1$.

93. Suppose X denotes the number of games A wins against B. Then X follows the binomial probability law with parameters 3, p in the first case and 5, p in the second case, where $p = 0 \cdot 4$ and $q = 1 - 0 \cdot 4 = 0 \cdot 6$

Case I : P (A wins the match)

$= P(X \geq 2) = P(X = 2) + P(X = 3)$

$= {}^3C_2\, p^2 q + {}^3C_3\, p^3 = 3(0 \cdot 4)^2 (0 \cdot 6) + (0 \cdot 4)^3$

$= 0 \cdot 352$

Case II : P (A wins the match)

$= P(X \geq 3) = P(X = 3) + P(X = 4) + P(X = 5)$

$= {}^5C_3\, p^3 q^2 + {}^5C_4\, p^4 q + {}^5C_5\, p^5$

$= 10(0 \cdot 4)^3 (0 \cdot 6)^2 + 5(0 \cdot 4)^4 (0 \cdot 6) + (0 \cdot 4)^5$

$= 0 \cdot 31744$.

Since $0.352 > 0 \cdot 31744$

So the probability of A winning the match is higher in the first case.

Alt. $p_1 =$ probability of winning the 'best of 3 games'

= last two terms in the expansion of $(0 \cdot 6 + 0 \cdot 4)^3$

$= {}^3C_2\, (0 \cdot 6) . (0 \cdot 4)^2 + (0 \cdot 4)^3$

$= 0 \cdot 288 + 0 \cdot 064$

$= 0 \cdot 35200$

and $p_2 =$ probability of winning the 'best of 5 games'

= last three terms in the expansion of $(0 \cdot 6 + 0 \cdot 4)^5$

$= {}^5C_3\, (0 \cdot 6)^2 . (0 \cdot 4)^3 + {}^5C_4\, (0 \cdot 6) . (0 \cdot 4)^4 + (0 \cdot 4)^5$

$= \cdot 2304 + \cdot 0768 + 01024$

$= 0 \cdot 31744$.

Since $p_1 > p_2$, the first option *i.e.* the option of best of 3 games', has a higher probability of winning the match.

94. Here total number of ways $n = 2^4 = 16$ and favourable number of ways is m where

$m =$ sum of coefficients of powers of x less than 15 in the expansion of $(x^3 + x^5)^4$.

Now $(x^3 + x^5)^4 = x^{12} (1 + x^2)^4$

$= x^{12} [1 + 4x^2 + 6x^4 + 4x^6 + x^8]$

$\therefore \quad m =$ sum of coefficients of x^{12} and $x^{14} = 1 + 4 = 5$.

Hence the required probability $= \frac{m}{n} = \frac{5}{16}$.

$\therefore$ The odds against are as $(16 - 5) : 5$ or $11 : 5$.

95. Here total number of ways $n = 6^3 = 216$. To find favourable number of ways, we have to find the sum of coefficients of powers of x less than 9 in the expansion $(x + x^2 + x^3 + x^4 + x^5 + x^6)^3$ and subtract this sum from 216.

Now $(x + x^2 + x^3 + x^4 + x^5 + x^6)^3$

$= x^3 (1 + x + x^2 + x^3 + x^4 + x^5)^3$

$= \frac{x^3 (1 + x + x^2 + x^3 + x^4 + x^5)^3 (1 - x)^3}{(1 - x)^3}$

$= x^3 (1 - x^6)^3 (1 - x)^{-3}$

$= x^3 [1 - 3x^6 + 3x^{12} - x^{18}]$

$\times \left[1 + 3x + 6x^2 + \ldots .. + \frac{(r+1)(r+2)}{2} x^r + \ldots ..\right]$

$= [x^3 - 3x^9 + 3x^{15} - x^{21}]$

$\times \left[1 + 3x + 6x^2 + \ldots . + \frac{(r+1)(r+2)}{2} x^r + \ldots ..\right]$ ...(1)

It is evident from (1) that

Coeff. of $x^8 = 1 \times \frac{(5+1)(5+2)}{2} = 21$

Coeff. of $x^7 = 1 \times \frac{(4+1)(4+2)}{2} = 15$

Coeff. of $x^6 = 1 \times \frac{(3+1)(3+2)}{2} = 10$

Coeff. of $x^5 = 1 \times \frac{(2+1)(2+2)}{2} = 6$

Coeff. of $x^4 = 1 \times \frac{(1+1)(1+2)}{2} = 3$

and Coeff. of $x^3 = 1$.

[Note that to obtain the coefficient of x^3, we put $r = 5$ in the second bracket and multiply this coeff. of x^5 with the coefficient of x^3 (*i.e.* 1) in the first bracket etc.]

Sum of these coefficients = 56

Hence the favourable number of ways.

$m = 216 - 56 = 160$.

Hence the required probability $= \frac{m}{n} = \frac{160}{216} = \frac{20}{27}$.

96. Total number of ways $n = 6 \times 4 = 24$, because in a tetrahedron there are four faces and in a cube there are six faces. To obtain the favourable number of ways, we find the sum of coefficients of powers of x less than 5 in the expansion

$(x + x^2 + x^3 + x^4)(x + x^2 + x^3 + x^4 + x^5 + x^6)$ ...(1)

and subtract this sum from 24.

Now the coeff. of x^4 in (1) = 3,

the coeff. of x^3 in (1) = 2,

and coeff. of x^2 in (1) = 1.

sum of these coefficients = 6.

$\therefore$ $m=$ Favourable number of ways $= 24 - 6 = 18$

$\therefore$ The required probability $= \dfrac{m}{n} = \dfrac{18}{24} = \dfrac{3}{4}$.

97. Total number of ways $= 3^4 = 81$.

Favourable number of ways is the sum of the coefficients of $x^2, x^4, x^6, x^8, x^{10}$ and x^{12} in the expansion of $(x + x^2 + x^3)^4$.

Now $(x + x^2 + x^3)^4 = x^4 (1 + x + x^2)^4$

$= x^4 [1 + 4(x + x^2) + 6(x + x^2)^2 + 4(x + x^2)^3 + (x + x^2)^4]$

$\therefore$ Coeff. of $x^2 = 0$, Coeff. of $x^4 = 1$,

Coeff. of $x^6 = 10$,

Coeff. of $x^8 = 6 + 12 + 1 = 19$,

Coeff. of $xs^{10} = 4 + 6 = 10$

and Coeff. of $x^{12} = 1$

Hence the favourable number of ways

$= 0 + 1 + 10 + 19 + 10 + 1 = 41$.

$\therefore$ The required probability $= \dfrac{41}{81}$ and so the odds in favour are as $41 : 81 - 41$ or $41 : 40$.

98. The total ways of drawing 5 tickets with replacement out of 4 tickets $n = 4^5$.

Now the following are the favourable cases of sum being 23 of the 5 tickets drawn :

(1) 00, 00, 01, 11, 11

(2) 00, 01, 01, 10, 11

(3) 01, 01, 01, 10, 10.

In each case numbers can come in different orders.

Hence the required probability

$$= \frac{5!}{2!\,2!\,1!}\left(\frac{1}{4}\right)^5 + \frac{5!}{2!\,1!\,1!\,1!}\left(\frac{1}{4}\right)^5 + \frac{5!}{3!\,2!}\left(\frac{1}{4}\right)^5$$

$$= 5!\left(\frac{1}{4}\right)^5 \left[\frac{1}{4} + \frac{1}{2} + \frac{1}{12}\right] = \frac{1}{4^5}.120\left[\frac{10}{12}\right] = \frac{100}{4^5}.$$

99. Let E_1 denote the event that first transferred ball is white and E_2 the event that it is black. Also let E denote the event consisting in the white colour of the ball drawn from the second urn. Clearly E_1, E_2 are mutually exclusive events.

Hence

$P(E) = P(E_1)\, P(E/E_1) + P(E_2)\, P(E/E_2)$. ...(1)

Now $P(E_1) = \dfrac{a}{a+b}$ and $P(E_2) = \dfrac{b}{a+b}$.

$P(E/E_1) = \dfrac{c+1}{c+d+1}$; because before the drawing there were $c+1$ white and d black balls in the second urn.

Similarly, $P(E/E_2) = \dfrac{c}{c+d+1}$.

Substituting in (1), we get

$$P(E) = \frac{a}{a+b}\cdot\frac{c+1}{c+d+1} + \frac{b}{a+b}\cdot\frac{c}{c+d+1}$$

$$= \frac{ac + bc + a}{(a+b)\,(c+d+1)}.$$

100. The first ball can be drawn in the following four possible ways :

(i) Both the first and the second balls drawn are white.

(ii) The first ball drawn is white and the second ball drawn is black.

(iii) The first ball drawn is black and the second ball drawn is white.

(iv) Both the first and the second balls drawn are black. Let the events in (i), (ii), (iii) and (iv) be respectively denoted by E_1, E_2, E_3 and E_4. Also let E denote the event that the third ball drawn is black. Then

$P(E_1) = \dfrac{2}{4} \times \dfrac{1}{3} = \dfrac{1}{6}$, $P(E_{2)} = \dfrac{2}{4} \times \dfrac{2}{3} = \dfrac{1}{3}$,

$P(E_3) = \dfrac{2}{4} \times \dfrac{2}{5} = \dfrac{1}{5}$, $P(E_4) = \dfrac{2}{4} \times \dfrac{3}{5} = \dfrac{3}{10}$.

Also $P(E/E_1) = \dfrac{2}{2} = 1$, since when the event E_1 has already happened, *i.e.*, the first two balls drawn are both white, they are not replaced and so there are left 2 black balls in the urn so that the probability that the third ball drawn in this case is black $= 2/2 = 1$.

Again $P(E/E_r) = 3/4$. Note that when the event E_2 has already happened there are 3 black and one white balls in the urn. So in this case the probability that the third ball drawn is black $= 3/4$.

Similarly $P(E/E_3) = 3/4$ and $P(E/E_4) = 2/3$.

Now by the theorem of total probability for compound events, we have

$$P(E) = P(E_1)\, P(E/E_1) + P(E_2)\, P(E/E_2) + P(E_3)\, P(E/E_3) + P(E_4)\, P(E/E_4)$$

$$= \frac{1}{6} \times 1 + \frac{1}{3} \times \frac{3}{4} + \frac{1}{5} \times \frac{3}{4} + \frac{3}{10} \times \frac{2}{3}$$

$$= \frac{1}{6} + \frac{1}{4} + \frac{3}{20} + \frac{1}{5} = \frac{23}{30}.$$

101. (a) Let $P(A)$ and $P(B)$ denote the percentage of city population who read newspapers A and B. Then from given data, we have

$P(A) = 25\% = \frac{1}{4}, \quad P(B) = 20\% = \frac{1}{5}.$

$P(A \cap B) = 8\% = \frac{2}{25}.$

$\therefore$ Percentage of those who read A but not B

$= P(A \cap \bar{B}) = P(A) - P(A \cap B)$ [see theorem 2 of §3]

$= \frac{1}{4} - \frac{2}{25} = \frac{17}{100} = 17\%$

Similarly, $P(\bar{A} \cap B) = P(B) - P(A \cap B)$

$= \frac{1}{5} - \frac{2}{25} = \frac{3}{25} = 12\%$

If $P(C)$ denotes the percentage of those who look into advertisement, then from the given data we obtain

$P(C) = 30\%$ of $P(A \cap \bar{B}) + 40\%$ of $P(\bar{A} \cap B) + 50\%$ of $P(A \cap B)$

$= \frac{3}{10} \times \frac{17}{100} + \frac{2}{5} \times \frac{3}{25} + \frac{1}{2} \times \frac{2}{25}$

$= \frac{51 + 48 + 40}{1000} = \frac{139}{1000} = 13 \cdot 9\%$

Thus the percentage of population who read an advertisement is 13·9%

(b) Let A be the event that bag A is selected and B be the event that bag B is selected. W be the event that white ball is selected, then

$P(W) = P[A \cap W] + P[B \cap W]$

($\because$ two events are mutually exclusive)

$\Rightarrow \quad P(W) = P[A].P[W/A] + P[B].P[W/B]$

$= \frac{1}{2} \cdot \frac{3}{5} + \frac{1}{2} \cdot \frac{2}{6}$

Hence the total probability of white ball being selected $P(W) = \frac{3}{10} + \frac{1}{6} = \frac{7}{15}$.

102. (a) Let E_1 be the event that a subject is selected from first group, E_2 the event that a subject is selected from the second group and E the event that an engineering subject is selected.

It is given that subject is selected from first group if the die shows 3 or 5 otherwise it is selected from the second group.

Now the probability that die shows 3 or 5 $= \frac{2}{6} = \frac{1}{3}$

$\therefore \quad P(E_1) = \frac{1}{3}$

and $P(E_2) = P(\overline{E_1}) = 1 - P(E_1) = 1 - \frac{1}{3} = \frac{2}{3}$.

Now $P(E/E_1) =$ Prob. of choosing an engineering subject from first group $= \frac{{}^3C_1}{{}^8C_1} = \frac{3}{8}$.

Similarly, $P(E/E_2) = \frac{{}^5C_1}{{}^8C_1} = \frac{5}{8}$.

Hence $P(E) = P(E_1)\,P(E/E_1) + P(E_2)\,P(E/E_2)$

$= \frac{1}{3} \cdot \frac{3}{8} + \frac{2}{3} \cdot \frac{5}{8} = \frac{13}{24}$.

(b) Let E be the event that a new product is introduced.

Then $P(A) = \cdot 5; \quad P(B) = \cdot 3; \quad P(C) = \cdot 2$

and $P(E/A) = \cdot 7; P(E/B) = \cdot 6; P(E/C) = \cdot 5$

$\because$ A, B and C are mutually exclusive and exhaustive events.

$P(E) = P(A) \cdot P(E/A) + P(B) \cdot P(E/B) + P(C) \cdot P(E/C)$

$= \cdot 5 \times \cdot 7 + \cdot 3 \times \cdot 6 + \cdot 2 \times \cdot 5$

$= \cdot 35 + \cdot 18 + \cdot 10 = \cdot 63$

103. (i) Let E_1 be the event of getting head, E_2 be the event of getting tail and let E be the event that noted number is 7 or 8 then

$P(E_1) = \frac{1}{2}; P(E_2) = \frac{1}{2}$

$P(E/E_1) = P$

(getting either 7 or 8 when pair of unbaised dice is thrown)

$= \frac{11}{36}$

$P(E/E_2) = P$

(getting either 7 or 8 when a card is picked from the pack of 11 cards.)

$= \frac{2}{11}$

$\because$ E_1 and E_2 are mutually exclusive and exhaustive events

$P(E) = P(E_1) \cdot P(E/E_1) + P(E_2) \cdot P(E/E_2)$

$= \frac{1}{2} \cdot \frac{11}{36} + \frac{1}{2} \cdot \frac{2}{11} = \frac{11}{72} + \frac{1}{11} = \frac{193}{792}$

(ii) Let E_1 be the event that a ball is drawn from first bag, E_2 the event that a ball is drawn from the second bag and E the event a black ball is chosen. Then as in Problem 24, we have

$P(E) = P(E_1)\,P(E/E_1) + P(E_2)\,P(E/E_2)$

$= \frac{1}{3} \cdot \frac{3}{7} + \frac{2}{5} \cdot \frac{4}{7} = \frac{11}{21}$.

[Students are advised to write the detailed solution as in Problem 24].

(iii) Let E_1 be the event that the coin drawn is fair and E_2 be the event that the coin drawn is biased.

$\therefore \quad P(E_1) = \frac{m}{N}$ and $P(E_2) = \frac{N-m}{N}$.

A is the event that on tossing the coin the head appears first and then appears tail.

$$\therefore \quad P(A) = P(E_1 A) + P(E_2 A)$$
$$= P(E_1)\, P(A/E_1) + P(E_2)\, P(A/E_2)$$
$$= \frac{m}{N}\left(\frac{1}{2}\right)^2 + \left(\frac{N-m}{N}\right)\left(\frac{2}{3}\right)\left(\frac{1}{3}\right) \quad \ldots(1)$$

We have to find the probability that A has happened because of E_1

$$P\left(\frac{E_1}{A}\right) = \frac{P(E_1 A)}{P(A)} = \frac{\frac{m}{N}\left(\frac{1}{2}\right)^2}{\frac{m}{N}\left(\frac{1}{2}\right)^2 + \frac{N-m}{N}\left(\frac{2}{3}\right)\left(\frac{1}{3}\right)}, \quad \text{by (1)}$$

$$= \frac{m/4}{\frac{m}{4} + \frac{2(N-m)}{9}} = \frac{9m}{m+8N}.$$

104. Let A_i $(i = 1, 2, 3)$ be the event that ith urn is chosen and B the event that a white ball is drawn.

Since all the urns are equally likely to be selected, we have

$$P(A_1) = P(A_2) = P(A_3) = \frac{1}{3}$$

and $P(B/A_1) = \frac{2}{5}$, $P(B/A_2) = \frac{3}{5}$, $P(B/A_3) = \frac{4}{5}$.

Hence $P(B) = P(A_1)\, P(B/A_1) + P(A_2)\, P(B/A_2) + P(A_3)\, P(B/A_3)$

$$= \frac{1}{3}.\frac{2}{5} + \frac{1}{3}.\frac{3}{5} + \frac{1}{3}.\frac{4}{5} = \frac{9}{15} = \frac{3}{5}.$$

105. Here we have to find $P(A_1/B)$.

By Baye's theorem

$$P(A_1/B) = \frac{P(A_1)\, P(B/A_1)}{P(A_1)\, P(B/A_1) + P(A_2)\, P(B/A_2) + P(A_3)\, P(B/A_3)}$$

$$= \frac{\frac{1}{3}.\frac{2}{5}}{\frac{3}{5}}, \text{ from Q. 104.}$$

$$= \frac{2}{9}.$$

106. Let A_1 be the event that the lot contains 2 defective articles and A_2 the event the lot contains 3 defective articles. Also let A be the event that the testing procedure ends at the twelfth testing. Then according to the question :

$$P(A_1) = 0 \cdot 4 \text{ and } P(A_2) = 0 \cdot 6$$

Since $0 < P(A_1) < 1$, $0 < P(A_2) < 1$,

and $P(A_1) + P(A_2) = 1$

the events A_1, A_2 form a partition of the sample space. Hence by the theorem of total probability for compound events, we have

$$P(A) = P(A_1)\, P(A/A_1) + P(A_2)\, P(A/A_2) \quad \ldots(1)$$

$$\text{But } P(A/A_1) = \left(\frac{{}^{18}C_{10} \times {}^{2}C_1}{{}^{20}C_{11}}\right) \times \left(\frac{1}{9}\right) \quad \ldots(2)$$

$$= \frac{2}{9} \times \frac{18!}{10!\ 8!} \times \frac{11! \times 9!}{20!} = \frac{11}{190}.$$

[Note that out of 20 articles, first 11 draws must contain 10 non-defective and 1 defective article and the 12th draw must give a defective article. Probabilities of these two events are shown in separate parantheses in (2)].

$$\text{Similarly, } P(A/A_2) = \frac{{}^{17}C_9 \times {}^{3}C_1}{{}^{20}C_{11}} \times \frac{1}{9}$$

$$= \frac{1}{3} \times \frac{17!}{9!\ 8!} \times \frac{11!.9!}{20!} = \frac{11}{228}.$$

Now substituting the values of $P(A_1)$, $P(A_2)$, $P(A/A_1)$ and $P(A/A_2)$ in (1), we get

$$P(A) = 0 \cdot 4 \times \frac{11}{190} + 0 \cdot 6 \times \frac{11}{228}$$

$$= \frac{11}{475} + \frac{11}{380} = \frac{99}{1900}.$$

Alt. Let A denote the event that the lot contains 2 defective articles and B the event that the lot contains 3 defective articles.

$$\therefore \quad P(A) = 0 \cdot 4, P(B) = 0 \cdot 6.$$

Suppose C denotes the event that all the defective articles are found by the twelfth test, *i.e.*, all but one defective article must be found in the first eleven tests and the last defective article must be found at the twelfth test.

$$\therefore \quad P(C \mid A) = \frac{({}^{2}C_1)({}^{18}C_{10})}{{}^{20}C_{11}} \times \frac{1}{9} = \frac{11}{190}$$

$$P(C \mid B) = \frac{({}^{3}C_2)({}^{17}C_9)}{{}^{20}C_{11}} \times \frac{1}{9} = \frac{11}{228}$$

$$\therefore \quad P(C) = P(C \cap A) + P(C \cap B)$$
$$= P(A)\, P(C \mid A) + P(B)\, P(C \mid B)$$
$$= 0 \cdot 4 \times \frac{11}{190} + 0 \cdot 6 \times \frac{11}{228} = \frac{99}{1900}.$$

107. (i) Let E_1 be the event that the ball is drawn from bag A, E_2 the event that it is drawn from bag B and E that the ball is red.

We have to find $P(E_2/E)$.

Since both the bags are equally likely to be selected, we have

$$P(E_1) = P(E_2) = \frac{1}{2}.$$

Also $P(E/E_1) = 3/5$ and $P(E/E_2) = 5/9$.

Hence by Baye's theorem, we have

$$P(E_2/E) = \frac{P(E_2)\, P(E/E_2)}{P(E_1)\, P(E/E_1) + P(E_2)\, P(E/E_2)}$$

$$= \frac{\frac{1}{2}\cdot\frac{5}{9}}{\frac{1}{2}\cdot\frac{3}{5}+\frac{1}{2}\cdot\frac{5}{9}} = \frac{25}{52}.$$

Note. If in the problem, you read 'is found to be' then it is the problem on Baye's Theorem.

(ii) Same type as (i). Ans. $\frac{2}{5}$.

108. Let A_1 be the event that black card is lost, A_2 be the event that red card is lost and let A denote occurrence of first 13 cards which are examined are found all red.

Then we have to find $P(A_1/A)$.

Now since black and red were initially equal in the pack,

$$P(A_1) = P(A_2) = \frac{1}{2}$$

Also $P(A/A_1) = \dfrac{^{26}C_{13}}{^{51}C_{13}}$

and $P(A/A_2) = \dfrac{^{25}C_{13}}{^{51}C_{13}}$

Then by Baye's Rule

$$P(A_1/A) = \frac{P(A_1)\cdot P(A/A_1)}{P(A_1)\cdot P(A/A_1) + P(A_2)\cdot P(A/A_2)}$$

$$= \frac{\frac{1}{2}\cdot\frac{^{26}C_{13}}{^{51}C_{13}}}{\frac{1}{2}\cdot\frac{^{26}C_{13}}{^{51}C_{13}} + \frac{1}{2}\cdot\frac{^{25}C_{13}}{^{51}C_{13}}}$$

$$= \frac{^{26}C_{13}}{^{26}C_{13} + {}^{25}C_{13}} = \frac{\frac{26!}{13!\,13!}}{\frac{26!}{13!\,13!} + \frac{25!}{13!\,12!}}$$

$$= \frac{\frac{26.25!}{13.12!\,13!}}{\frac{26.25!}{13.12!\,13!} + \frac{25!}{13!\,12!}} = \frac{2}{2+1} = \frac{2}{3}.$$

109. (a) Let A_1 be the event that the examinee guesses the answer; A_2 the event that he copies the answer and A_3 the event that he knows the answer. Also let A be the event that he answers correctly. Then as given, we have

$$P(A_1) = \frac{1}{3},\ P(A_2) = \frac{1}{6},\ P(A_3) = 1 - \frac{1}{3} - \frac{1}{6} = \frac{1}{2}.$$

[We have assumed here that the events A_1, A_2 and A_3 are mutually exclusive and totally exhaustive.]

Now $P(A/A_1) = \frac{1}{4}$, $P(A/A_2) = \frac{1}{8}$ (as given).

Again it is reasonable to take the probability of answering correctly given that he knows the answer as 1, that is, $P(A/A_3) = 1$

We have to find $P(A_3/A)$.

By Baye's theorem, we have

$$P(A_3/A) = \frac{P(A_3)\, P(A/A_3)}{P(A_1)\, P(A/A_1) + P(A_2)\, P(A/A_2) + P(A_3)\, P(A/A_3)}$$

$$= \frac{(1/2)\cdot 1}{(1/3)(1/4) + (1/6)(1/8) + (1/2)\cdot 1} = \frac{24}{29}.$$

(b) Let E be the event that employee received the letter and A that employer received the reply, then

$$P(E) = \frac{n-1}{n} \quad \text{and} \quad P(\bar{E}) = \frac{1}{n}$$

$$P(A/E) = \frac{n-1}{n} \quad \text{and} \quad P(A/\bar{E}) = 0$$

$$\text{Now } P(A) = P(E \cap A) + P(\bar{E} \cap A)$$

$$= P(E).P(A/E) + P(\bar{E}).P(A/\bar{E})$$

$$= \left(\frac{n-1}{n}\right)\left(\frac{n-1}{n}\right) + \frac{1}{n}.0$$

$$P(A) = \left(\frac{n-1}{n}\right)^2$$

$$P(\bar{A}) = 1 - \left(\frac{n-1}{n}\right)^2 = \frac{n^2 - n^2 - 1 + 2n}{n^2} = \frac{2n-1}{n^2}$$

Now the required probability

$$P(E/\bar{A}) = \frac{P(E \cap \bar{A})}{P(\bar{A})} = \frac{P(E) - P(E \cap A)}{P(\bar{A})}$$

$$= \frac{P(E) - P(E).P(A/E)}{P(\bar{A})}$$

Putting the values, we get

$$= \frac{\frac{n-1}{n} - \frac{n-1}{n} \cdot \frac{n-1}{n}}{\frac{2n-1}{n^2}}$$

$$\therefore \quad P(E/\bar{A}) = \frac{n-1}{2n-1}.$$

(c) We have to find the probability of A being hit by B but not by C *i.e.*, $P(BC' \mid A)$

$$= \frac{P(A \mid BC')\,P(BC')}{P(A \mid BC')\,P(BC') + P(A \mid BC')\,P(B'C) + P(A \mid BC)\,P(BC) + P(A \mid B'C')\,P(R'C')}$$

Now putting the values from the given data, we have

$$P(BC' \mid A) = \frac{1 . \frac{1}{2} . \frac{2}{3}}{1 \cdot \frac{1}{2} \cdot \frac{2}{3} + 1 \cdot \frac{1}{2} \cdot \frac{1}{3} + 1 \cdot \frac{1}{2} \cdot \frac{1}{3} + 0 \cdot \frac{1}{2} \cdot \frac{2}{3}}$$

$$= \frac{\frac{1}{3}}{\frac{1}{3} + \frac{1}{6} + \frac{1}{6}} = \frac{1}{2}.$$

110. Do yourself.

Ans. $\frac{25}{69}, \frac{28}{69}, \frac{16}{69}$.

111. Let A_i $(i = 1, 2, 3, 4)$ be the event that the urn contains 2, 3, 4 or 5 white balls and B the event that two white balls are drawn.

We have to find $P(A_4/B)$.

Since the four events A_1, A_2, A_3, A_4 are equally likely, we have $P(A_1) = P(A_2) = P(A_3) = P(A_4) = \frac{1}{4}$.

$P(B/A_1)$ is the probability of event that the urn contains 2 white balls and both have been drawn.

Hence $\quad P(B/A_1) = \frac{^2C_2}{^5C_2} = \frac{1}{10}$.

Similarly, $\quad P(B/A_2) = \frac{^3C_2}{^5C_2} = \frac{3}{10}$.

$P(B/A_3) = \frac{^4C_2}{^5C_2} = \frac{6}{10} = \frac{3}{5}$. and $P(B/A_4) = \frac{^5C_2}{^5C_2} = 1$.

$\therefore$ By Baye's theorem

$$P(A_4/B) = \frac{P(A_4)\,P(B/A_4)}{\sum_{i=1}^{4} P(A_i)\,P(B/A_i)}$$

$$= \frac{\frac{1}{4} . 1}{\frac{1}{4}\left(\frac{1}{10} + \frac{3}{10} + \frac{3}{5} + 1\right)} = \frac{1}{2}.$$

112. Let B_k denote the event that the urn contains k white balls, where k assumes values from 0 to 10.

In 10 throws, if the coin shows k heads and $10 - k$ tails, then

$$P(B_k) = {}^{10}C_k \left(\frac{1}{2}\right)^k \left(\frac{1}{2}\right)^{10-k} = {}^{10}C_k \frac{1}{2^{10}}$$

Let A denote the event of drawing a white ball, then

$P(A \mid B_k) = \frac{k}{10}$ where $k = 0, 1, 2, \ldots, 10$

Hence using Baye's formula

$$P(B_{10} \mid A) = \frac{P(B_{10})\,P(A \mid B_{10})}{\sum_{k=0}^{10} P(B_k)\,P(A \mid B_k)}$$

$$= \frac{\left({}^{10}C_{10} \cdot \frac{1}{2^{10}}\right)\frac{10}{10}}{\sum_{k=0}^{10} {}^{10}C_k \frac{1}{2^{10}} \frac{k}{10}} = \frac{10}{10 . 2^{10-1}} = \frac{1}{2^9}$$

applying the formula in the denominator $n . 2^{n-1} = \sum_{k=1}^{n} k . {}^nC_k$ of binomial theorem with $n = 10$.

113. The purse may contain 2 or 3 or 4 two-rupee coins. All these three hypotheses are equally likely *i.e.*, $P_1 = P_2 = P_3$

Hence $p_1 = \frac{2}{4} \times \frac{1}{3} = \frac{1}{6}$, $p_2 = \frac{3}{4} \times \frac{2}{3}$, $p_3 = \frac{4}{4} \times \frac{3}{3} = 1$

$\therefore$ The chance that all are two-rupee coins

$$= \frac{p_3}{\Sigma(p)} = \frac{1}{\frac{1}{6} + \frac{1}{2} + 1} = \frac{6}{10} = \frac{3}{5}$$

Again $\frac{p_1}{1} = \frac{p_2}{3} = \frac{p_3}{6} = \frac{\Sigma(p)}{10}$

$\therefore \quad Q_1 = \frac{1}{10}, Q_2 = \frac{3}{10}, Q_3 = \frac{6}{10}$

$\therefore$ The chance that another drawing will give a two rupee coin

$$= \left(Q_1 \times \frac{2}{4}\right) + \left(Q_2 \times \frac{3}{4}\right) + (Q_3 \times 1)$$

$$= \frac{1}{20} + \frac{9}{40} + \frac{6}{10} = \frac{7}{8}.$$

114. Bag may contain 1 or 2 or 3 or 4 or 5 red balls. These five are equally likely hypotheses *i.e.*,

$P_1 = P_2 = P_3 = P_4 = P_5$

Now $p_1 = \left(\frac{1}{5}\right)^2, p_2 = \left(\frac{2}{5}\right)^2, p_3 = \left(\frac{3}{5}\right)^2,$

$p_4 = \left(\frac{4}{5}\right)^2, p_5 = \left(\frac{5}{5}\right)^2$

(posteriori probabilities) *i.e.*, either first, second, ... or fifth hypotheses are true

$$\frac{Q_1}{p_1P_1}=\frac{Q_2}{p_2P_2}=\ldots=\frac{Q_5}{p_5P_5}=\frac{1}{\Sigma pP}$$

i.e., $\frac{Q_1}{1^2}=\frac{Q_2}{2^2}=\frac{Q_3}{3^2}=\frac{Q_4}{4^2}=\frac{Q_5}{5^2}=\frac{1}{55}$

The chance of now drawing two red balls

$$=(Q_1\times 0)+\left(Q_2\times\frac{2}{5}\cdot\frac{1}{4}\right)+\left(Q_3\times\frac{3}{5}\cdot\frac{2}{4}\right)+\left(Q_4\times\frac{4}{5}\cdot\frac{3}{4}\right)+(Q_5\times 1)$$

$$=\frac{1}{55}\left\{\frac{2}{5}+\frac{27}{10}+\frac{48}{5}+25\right\}=\frac{377}{550}.$$

115. We place the two lines parallel to one another. Suppose that after cutting the lines the right hand portions are removed. Then the problem is equivalent to asking : "what is the chance that the sum of the left hand portions is less than the sum of right hand portions. It is equally likely that the first sum is equally likely to be less or greater than the second".

Hence the required probability is $\frac{1}{2}$.

116. We draw three lines L, M, N at random in the same plane as the circle and then draw the six tangents parallel to these lines (see the figure)

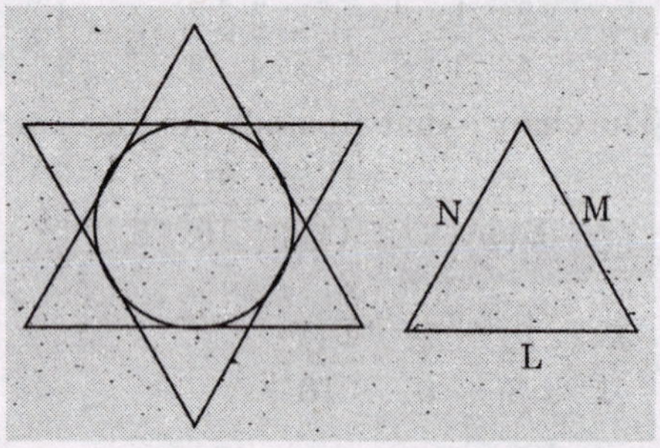

Fig. 3

Then the total number of triangles so formed is 8. Out of these eight triangles, the circle is escribed to 6 and inscribed in 2 and this is true whatever be the original direction of L, M, N. Hence the odds against the circle being inscribed in the triangle formed by the lines are as 6 : 2 or 3 : 1 as required.

117. Here A consists of two elements (6, 5) and (5, 6) only whereas B consists of 30 elements of all the elements of sample space except the elements (1, 5), (2, 5), (3, 5), (4, 5), (5, 5), (6, 5) Hence $A\cap B$ consists of a single element (5, 6) only.

Therefore $P(A)=\frac{2}{36}=\frac{1}{18}$.

$P(B)=\frac{30}{36}=\frac{5}{6}$ and $P(A\cap B)=\frac{1}{36}$.

Thus here $P(A)\,P(B)=\frac{1}{18}\times\frac{5}{6}=\frac{5}{108}$.

giving $P(A\cap B)\neq P(A)\,P(B)$.

Hence A and B are dependent events.

118. Let S denote the sample space. Then

$$S=\{(H,H),\ (H,T),\ (T,H),\ (T,T)\}$$

where the first letter of each pair refers to the outcome for the rupee, and the second to the eight-anna piece. We have

$$A=\{(H,T),\ (H,T)\}\ \text{so that}\ P(A)=\frac{1}{2}$$

$$B=\{(H,T),\ (T,H)\}\ \text{so that}\ P(B)=\frac{1}{2}$$

and $A\cap B=\{(H,T)\}$, so that $P(A\cap B)=\frac{1}{4}$.

Since here $P(A\cap B)=P(A)\,P(B)$, the events A and B are independent.

119. Here $P(A)=\frac{3}{5}$.

$$P(B)=P(B/A)+P(B/B)=\frac{2}{4}+\frac{1}{4}=\frac{3}{4}.$$

Also $P(A\cap B)=\frac{3}{5}\cdot\frac{2}{4}=\frac{3}{10}$

and $P(A)\,P(B)=\frac{3}{5}\cdot\frac{3}{4}=\frac{9}{20}$.

Hence $P(A\cap B)\neq P(A)\,P(B)$.

Therefore A and B are not independent events.

120. We have $P(A_1)=\frac{2}{4}=\frac{1}{2}=P(A_2)=P(A_3)$.

[Note that $P(A_1)$ is the probability of the event that the first digit is 1 and since there are two numbers having 1 at the first place out of four, we have $P(A_1)=\frac{2}{4}=\frac{1}{2}$.

Similarly for $P(A_2)$ and $P(A_3)$].

$A_1\cap A_2$ is the event that the first two digits in the numbers drawn are each equal to 1 and so

$$P(A_1\cap A_2)=\frac{1}{4}=\frac{1}{2}\cdot\frac{1}{2}=P(A_1)\,P(A_2).$$

Similarly, $P(A_2\cap A_3)=P(A_2)\,P(A_3)$

and $P(A_3\cap A_1)=P(A_3)\,P(A_1)$.

Thus the events A_1, A_2 and A_3 are equal to 1 and since there is no such number, we have

$$P(A_1\cap A_2\cap A_3)=0$$
$$\neq P(A_1)\,P(A_2)\,P(A_3).$$

Hence the events A_1, A_2, A_3 are not mutually independent although they are pairwise independent.

121. Ans. (i) Pairwise independent.

(ii) Not mutually independent.

We have $P(A)=\frac{50}{100}\cdot 1=\frac{1}{2}$

$$P(B) = 1 \cdot \frac{50}{100} = \frac{1}{2}$$

$$P(C) = \frac{50}{100} \cdot \frac{50}{100} + \frac{50}{100} \cdot \frac{50}{100} = \frac{1}{2}$$

$A \cap B$ is the event that first bulb is defective and second is non-defective.

$\therefore \quad P(A \cap B) = \frac{1}{2} \cdot \frac{1}{2} = \frac{1}{4}$

$A \cap C$ is the event that the first bulb is defective and second is also defective.

$\therefore \quad P(A \cap C) = \frac{1}{2} \frac{1}{2} = \frac{1}{4}$

Similarly, $P(B \cap C) = \frac{1}{4}$

Thus we have

$P(A \cap B) = P(A) \cdot P(B)$;

$P(A \cap C) = P(A) \cdot P(C)$;

$P(B \cap C) = P(B) \cdot P(C)$

$\therefore$ A, B and C are pairwise independent.

There is no element in $A \cap B \cap C$

$\therefore \quad P(A \cap B \cap C) = 0$

$\therefore \quad P(A \cap B \cap C) \neq P(A) \cdot P(B) \cdot P(C)$

Hence A, B and C are not mutually independent.

122. Since A, B, C are pairwise independent, we have

$P(A \cap B) = P(A) P(B)$,

$P(B \cap C) = P(B) P(C)$,

$P(A \cap C) = P(A) P(C)$

and $P\{A \cap (B \cup C)\} = P(A) P(B \cup C)$ ...(1)

Now $P[A \cap (B \cup C)] = P[(A \cap B) \cup (A \cap C)]$

$= P(A \cap B) + P(A \cap C) - P\{(A \cap B) \cap (A \cap C)\}$

$= P(A) P(B) + P(A) P(C) - P(A \cap B \cap C)$

Also right-hand side of (1)

$P(A) P(B \cup C)$

$= P(A) [P(B) + P(C) - P(B \cap C)]$

$= P(A) P(B) + P(A) P(C) - P(A) P(B \cap C)$

$\therefore$ From (1)

$P(A) P(B) + P(A) P(C) - P(A \cap B \cap C)$

$= P(A) P(B) + P(A) P(C) - P(A) P(B \cap C)$

$\Rightarrow \quad p(A \cap B \cap C) = P(A) P(B \cap C)$

$= P(A) P(B) P(C)$ from (1)

$\Rightarrow$ A, B, C are mutually independent.

$\because \quad P(B \cap C) = P(B) P(C)$

123. Since A and B are independent,

$P(A \cap B) = P(A) P(B)$

Similarly $P[A \cap (B \cup C)] = P(A) P(B \cup C)$

$P[A \cap (B \cap C)] = P(A) P(B \cap C)$ ...(1)

$\therefore \quad P(A \cap B) + P(A \cap C) - P(A \cap B \cap C)$

$= P[A \cap (B \cup C)]$

$= P(A) [P(B) + P(C) - P(B \cap C)]$

$\Rightarrow \quad P(A) P(B) + P(A \cap C) - P(A \cap B \cap C)$

$= P(A) P(B) + P(A) P(C)) - P(A) P(B \cap C)$

$\Rightarrow \quad P(A \cap C) = P(A) P(C)$

$\Rightarrow$ A and C are independent.

Problem Set (2)

Objective Questions

1. The probability of getting heads in both trials, when a balanced coin is tossed twice, will be

(a) $\frac{1}{4}$ (b) $\frac{1}{2}$ (c) 1 (d) $\frac{3}{4}$.

2. (i) Two cards are drawn at random from a pack of 52 cards. The probability of these two being aces is

(a) $\frac{1}{26}$ (b) $\frac{1}{221}$

(c) $\frac{1}{2}$ (d) none of those.

(ii) A bag contains 5 brown and 4 white socks. A man pulls out two socks. The probability that they are of the same colour is

(a) $\frac{5}{108}$ (b) $\frac{1}{6}$ (c) $\frac{5}{18}$ (d) $\frac{4}{9}$

(M.N.R. 1993)

3. A and B throw with 2 dice; if A throws 9, then B's chance of throwing a higher number is $\frac{1}{6}$.

(a) True (b) False

4. (i) Two cards are drawn successively with replacement from a well shuffled deck of 52 cards. The probability of drawing two aces is

(a) $\frac{1}{13} \times \frac{1}{13}$ (b) $\frac{1}{13} \times \frac{1}{17}$

(c) $\frac{1}{52} \times \frac{1}{51}$ (d) $\frac{1}{13} \times \frac{4}{51}$

(ii) A pack of cards contains 4 aces, 4 kings, 4 queens and 4 jacks. Two cards are drawn at random. The probability that at least one of them is an ace is

(a) $\frac{1}{5}$ (b) $\frac{3}{16}$

(c) $\frac{1}{6}$ (d) $\frac{1}{9}$

(M.N.R. 1991)

5. Three urns contain respectively 3 white and 1 black balls, 2 white and 2 black; 1 white and 3 black. One ball is selected at random from each urn. Find the chance

that the three selected comprise 1 white and 2 black balls.

6. Two dice are thrown. What is the probability of scoring either a double, or a sum greater than 9 ?

7. An integer is chosen at random from the first two hundred digits. What is the probability that the integer chosen is divisible by 6 or 8 ?

8. A person draws a card from a pack of playing cards, replaces it and shuffles the pack. He continues doing this until he shows a spade. The chance that he will fail the first two times is

(a) $\frac{9}{64}$ (b) $\frac{1}{64}$

(c) $\frac{1}{16}$ (d) $\frac{9}{16}$

9. (i) Two mutually exclusive events are always independent.

(a) True (b) False.

(ii) Two independent events are always mutually exclusive.

(a) True (b) False.

10. Three letters are written to different persons, and addresses on three envelopes are also written. Without looking at the addresses, the probability that the letters go into right envelopes is

(a) $\frac{1}{27}$ (b) $\frac{1}{6}$

(c) $\frac{1}{9}$ (d) none of these

11. The probability that a student is not a swimmer is $\frac{1}{5}$. Then the probability that out of five students, four are swimmers is

(a) ${}^5C_4\left(\frac{4}{5}\right)^4\frac{1}{5}$ (b) $\left(\frac{4}{5}\right)^4\frac{1}{5}$

(c) ${}^5C_1\frac{1}{5}\left(\frac{4}{5}\right)^4$ (d) none of these.

12. (i) The chance of throwing an ace is the first only of two successive throws with an ordinary die is

(a) $\frac{1}{36}$ (b) $\frac{5}{36}$

(c) $\frac{25}{36}$ (d) $\frac{1}{6}$

(ii) A fair coin is tossed repeatedly. If tail appears on first four tosses, then the probability of head appearing on fifth toss equals

(a) $\frac{1}{2}$ (b) $\frac{1}{32}$

(c) $\frac{31}{32}$ (d) $\frac{1}{5}$ **(I.I.T. 1998)**

13. There are three works, one consisting of 3 volumes, one of 4, and the other of 1 volume. They are placed on a shelf at random. Find the chance that volumes of the same works are all together.

14. A bag contains 4 white, 5 red and 6 black balls. Three are drawn at random. Find the probability that (i) no ball drawn is black, (ii) exactly 2 are black (iii) all are of the same colour.

15. An urn contains 11 balls numbered from 1 to 11. If a ball is selected at random, what is the probability of having a ball with a number which is mutliple of either 2 or 3 ?

16. The probability that a certain beginner at golf gets a good shot if he uses the correct club is $\frac{1}{3}$, and the probability of a good shot with an incorrect club is $\frac{1}{4}$. In his bag are 5 different clubs, only one of which is correct for the shot in question. If he chooses a club at random and takes a stroke, the probability that he gets a good shot is

(a) $\frac{1}{3}$ (b) $\frac{1}{12}$ (c) $\frac{4}{15}$ (d) $\frac{7}{12}$

17. (i) The probability that in the toss of two dice we obtain the sum 7 or 11 is

(a) $\frac{1}{6}$ (b) $\frac{1}{18}$

(c) $\frac{2}{9}$ (d) $\frac{23}{108}$

(ii) Two dice are thrown. The probability that the sum of the points on two dice will be 7 is

(a) $\frac{5}{36}$ (b) $\frac{6}{36}$

(c) $\frac{7}{36}$ (d) $\frac{8}{36}$ **(M.N.R. 1991)**

(iii) Two dice are thrown simultaneously. The probability of obtaining a total score of 5 is

(a) $\frac{1}{18}$ (b) $\frac{1}{12}$

(c) $\frac{1}{9}$ (d) none of these **(M.N.R. 1993)**

18. *A* can solve 75% of the problems of Mathematics and *B* can solve 70%. What is the probability that either *A* or *B* can solve a problem chosen at random ?

19. A room has three lamp sockets. From a collection of 10 light bulbs of which only six are good, three bulbs are selected at random and placed in the sockets. What is the probability that there will be light in the room ?

20. One of the two events must occur. If the chance of one is $\frac{2}{3}$ of the other, then odds in favour of the other are

(a) 1:3 (b) 3:1

(c) 2:3 (d) none of these

21. An ordinary cube has four blank faces, one face marked 2, another marked 3. Then the probability of obtaining a total of exactly 12 in 5 throws is

(a) $\frac{5}{1296}$ (b) $\frac{5}{1944}$

(c) $\frac{5}{2592}$ (d) none of these

22. An experiment succeeds twice as often as it fails. Find the chance that in the next six trials, there shall be at least four successes.

23. (i) The probability that a marksman will hit a target is given as 1/5. Then his probability at least one hit in 10 shots is

(a) $1-\left(\frac{4}{5}\right)s,$ (b) $\frac{1}{5}s$

(c) $1-\frac{1}{5}s,$ (d) none of these.

(ii) The probability that a man can hit a target is $\frac{3}{4}$. He tries 5 times. The probability that he will hit the target at least three times is

(a) $\frac{291}{364}$ (b) $\frac{371}{464}$

(c) $\frac{471}{502}$ (d) $\frac{459}{512}$ **(M.N.R. 1994)**

24. The probability of n independent events are $p_1, p_2, \ldots p_n$. Find an expression for the probability that at least one of the events will happen.

25. A's skill is to B as 1 : 3, to C's as 3 : 2 and to D's as 4 : 3; find the chance that A in three trials, one with each person, will succeed twice at least.

26. Five persons A, B, C, D, E throw a dice in the order specified until one of them throws an ace, find their relative chances of winning, supposing the throws to continue till an ace appears.

27. Three urns contain respectively 1 white, 2 black balls; 2 W and 1 B balls, 2 W and 2 B balls. One ball is transferred from the first urn into the second; then one from the latter is transferred into the third. Finally one ball is drawn from the third urn. What is the probability of its being white ?

28. Suppose there is a set A containing 11 elements $a_1, a_2, a_3, \ldots, a_{11}$. A subset P of A is chosen at random. The set A is reconstructed by replacing the elements of the subset of P. A subset Q of A is again chosen at random. What is the probability that P and Q are non-intersecting sets ?

29. The odds in favour of A winning a game of chess against B are 5 : 2. If three games are to be played, then the odds in favour of A's winning at least one game are 355 : 8.

(a) True (b) False.

30. A number is chosen at random among the first 120 natural numbers. The probability of the number chosen being a multiple of 5 or 15 is

(a) 1/5 (b) 1/8

(c) 1/6 (d) none of these

31. The probability of an event A occurring is $0 \cdot 5$ and of B occuring is $0 \cdot 3$. If A and B are mutually exclusive events, then the probability of neither A nor B occurring is

(a) $0 \cdot 6$ (b) $0 \cdot 5$

(c) $0 \cdot 7$ (d) none of these

32. The probability that an event A happens in one trial of an experiment is $0 \cdot 4$. Three independent trials of the experiment are formed. The probability that the event A happens at least once is

(a) $0 \cdot 936$ (b) $0 \cdot 784$,

(c) $0 \cdot 904$ (d) none of these

33. A single letter is selected at random from the word "PROBABILITY".

The probability that it is a vowel is :

(a) 3/11 (b) 4/11 (c) 2/11 (d) 0

34. In a box containing 100 bulbs, 10 are defective. What is the probability that out of a sample of 5 bulbs, none is defective ?

(a) 10^{-5} (b) $(1/2)^5$

(c) $(9/10)^5$ (d) 9/10.

35. If the probability of A to fail in an examination is $0 \cdot 2$ and that for B is $0 \cdot 3$, then the probability that either A or B is $0 \cdot 5$.

(a) True (b) False.

36. The probability of having at least one tail in 4 throws with a coin is

(a) 15/16 (b) 1/16 (c) 1/4 (d) 1

37. (a) From a pack of cards two are drawn, the first being replaced before the second is drawn. The probability that the first is a diamond and the second is a king will be

(a) 13/4 (b) 4/13

(c) 1/52 (d) 52.

(b) Two cards are drawn at random from a pack of playing cards. Find the probability that one card is a heart and the other is an ace. **(Roorkee 2001)**

38. Two uniform dice marked 1 to 6 are tossed together. The probability of the total 7 in a single throw is

(a) 5/36 (b) 5/12
(c) 2/31 (d) 1/6.

39. Three of the six vertices of a regular hexagon are chosen at random. The possibility that the triangle with three vertices is equilateral equals to

(a) $\frac{1}{2}$ (b) $\frac{1}{5}$ (c) $\frac{1}{10}$ (d) $\frac{1}{20}$

(I.I.T. 1995)

40. The probability of India winning a test match against West Indies is 1/2. Assuming independence from match to match, the probability that in a 5 match series India's win occurs at third test is

(a) 1/8 (b) 1/4 (c) 1/2 (d) 2/3

(I.I.T. 1995)

41. A coin is tossed $(m+n)$ times $(m>n)$. Find the probability of at least m consecutive heads.

42. Each coefficient in the equation $ax^2+bx+c=0$ is determined by throwing an ordinary die. Find the probability that the equation will have real roots.

43. A, B, C in order cut a pack of cards replacing them after each cut; on condition that the first who cuts a spade shall win a prize; find their respective chances.

44. One bag contains 5 white and 3 red balls, and a second bag contains 4 white and 5 red balls. From one of them chosen at random two balls are drawn; find the chance that they are of different colours.

45. Supposing that it is 9 to 7 against a person A who is now 35 years of age living till he is 65, and 3 to 2 against a person B now 45 till he is 75; find the chance that one at least of these persons will be alive 30 years hence.

46. In shuffling a pack of cards; four are accidently dropped; find the chance that the missing cards should be one from each suit.

47. The probability that Krishna will be alive 10 years hence is $\frac{7}{15}$ and that Hari will be alive is $\frac{7}{10}$. What is the probability that both Krishna and Hari will be dead 10 years hence

(a) $\frac{21}{150}$ (b) $\frac{24}{150}$ (c) $\frac{49}{150}$ (d) $\frac{56}{150}$

(M.N.R. 1993)

48. A bag has 13 red, 14 green and 15 black balls. The probability of getting exactly 2 blacks on pulling out 4 balls is P_1. Now the number of each colour ball is doubled and 8 balls are pulled out. The probability of getting exactly 4 blacks is P_2. Then

(a) $P_1 = P_2$ (b) $P_1 > P_2$
(c) $P_1 < P_2$.

49. A purse contains 4 copper coins, 3 silver coins, the second purse contains 6 copper coins and 2 silver coins. A coin is taken out of any purse, the probability that it is a copper coin is

(a) $\frac{4}{7}$ (b) $\frac{3}{4}$ (c) $\frac{3}{7}$ (d) $\frac{37}{56}$

50. Two persons A and B, have respectively $n+1$ and n coins, which they toss simultaneously. Then the probability that A will have more heads than B is

(a) $\frac{1}{2}$ (b) $>\frac{1}{2}$ (c) $<\frac{1}{2}$.

51. (i) Fifteen coupons are numbered 1, 2,...., 15 respectively. Seven coupons are selected at random one at a time with replacement. The probability that the largest number appearing on a selected coupon is 9, is

(a) $\left(\frac{9}{10}\right)^6$ (b) $\left(\frac{8}{15}\right)^7$
(c) $\left(\frac{3}{5}\right)^7$ (d) none of these

(ii) An unbiased die with faces marked 1, 2, 3, 4, 5 and 6 is rolled four times. Out of four face values obtained, the probability that the minimum face value is not less than 2 and the maximum face value is not greater than 5 is then

(a) 16/81 (b) 1/81
(c) 80/81 (d) 65/81 **(I.I.T. 1993)**

52. A box contains 100 tickets, numbered 1, 2, ..., 100. Two tickets are chosen at random. It is given that the maximum number on the two chosen tickets is not more than 10. The minimum number of them is 2 with probability ....

53. A student appears for tests I, II and III. The student is successful if he passes either in tests I and II or tests I and III. The probabilities of the student passing in tests I, II and III are p, q and $\frac{1}{2}$ respectively. If the probability that the student is successful is $\frac{1}{2}$, then

(a) $p=q=1$ (b) $p=q=\frac{1}{2}$
(c) $p=1,\ q=0$ (d) $p=1,\ q=\frac{1}{2}$
(e) none of these

54. (i) If $\frac{1+3p}{3}$, $\frac{1-p}{4}$ and $\frac{1-2p}{2}$ are the probabilities of three mutually exclusive events, then the set of all values of p is ......

(ii) If $\frac{1-3p}{2}$, $\frac{1+4p}{3}$ and $\frac{1+p}{6}$ are the probabilities of three mutually exclusive and exhaustive events, then the set of all values of p is ......

(a) $(0, 1)$ (b) $\left(-\frac{1}{4}, \frac{1}{3}\right)$

(c) $\left(0, \frac{1}{3}\right)$ (d) $(0, \infty)$ **(M.N.R. 1992)**

55. Urn A contains 6 red and 4 black balls and urn B contains 4 red and 6 black balls, one ball is drawn at random from urn A and placed in urn B. Then one ball drawn at random from urn B and placed in urn A. If one ball is now drawn from urn A, the probability that it is found to be red is ....

56. One hundred identical coins, each with probability p, of showing up heads are tossed. If $0 < p < 1$ and the probability of heads showing on 50 coins is equal to that of the heads showing in 51 coins, then the value of p is

(a) $\frac{1}{2}$ (b) $\frac{49}{101}$ (c) $\frac{50}{101}$ (d) $\frac{51}{101}$

57. India plays two matches each with West Indies and Australia. In any match the probabilities of India getting points 0, 1 and 2 are $0 \cdot 45$, $0 \cdot 05$ and $0 \cdot 50$ respectively. Assuming that the outcomes are independent, the probability of India getting at least 7 points is

(a) $0 \cdot 8750$ (b) $\cdot 0875$

(c) $0 \cdot 0625$ (d) $0 \cdot 0250$ **(I.I.T. 1992)**

58. There are 3 bags each containing 5 white balls and 2 black balls and 2 bags each containing 1 white ball and 4 black balls, a black ball having been drawn, find the chance that it came from the first group.

59. Consider a family with two children. Assume that each child is as likely to be a boy as it is to be a girl. Find the conditional probability that both children are boys, given that (i) the older child is a boy, (ii) at least one of the children is a boy.

60. (i) A coin is tossed 3 times. The probability of obtaining two heads will be

(a) 3/8 (b) 1/2

(c) 1 (d) 2

(ii) 8 coins are tossed simultaneously. The probability of getting at least 6 heads is

(a) 57/64 (b) 229/256

(c) 7/64 (d) 37/256

61. A sample of size 4 is drawn with replacement (without replacement) from an urn containing 12 balls, of which 8 are white, what is the conditional probability that the ball drawn on the third draw was white, given that the sample contains 3 white balls ?

62. If two events A and B are such that $P(A^c) = 0 \cdot 3$. $P(B) = 0 \cdot 4$ and $P(AB^c) = 0 \cdot 5$ then $P[B/(A \cup B^c)] =$ .... **(I.I.T. 1994)**

63. (i) If A and B are two events such that $P(A \cup B) = \frac{5}{6}$, $P(A \cap B) = \frac{1}{3}$, $P(\overline{B}) = \frac{1}{2}$, then the events A and B are

(a) dependent

(b) independent

(c) mutually exclusive

(d) none of these.

(ii) A and B each throws a die. Then it is 7 : 5 that A's throw is not greater than B's.

(a) True (b) False.

64. Two persons each makes a single throw with a die. The probability they get equal value is P_1. Four persons each makes a single throw and probability of three being equal is P_2. Then

(a) $P_1 = P_2$, (b) $P_1 < P_2$,

(c) $P_1 > P_2$.

65. A cricket team has 15 members, of whom only 5 can bowl. If the names of the 15 members are put into a hat and 11 drawn random, then the chance of obtaining an eleven containing at least 3 bowlers is

(a) $\frac{7}{13}$ (b) $\frac{11}{15}$

(c) $\frac{12}{13}$ (d) none of these.

66. (i) On a toss of two dice, A throws a total of 5. Then the probability that he will throw another 5 before he throws 7 is

(a) $\frac{1}{9}$ (b) $\frac{1}{6}$

(c) $\frac{2}{5}$ (d) $\frac{5}{36}$

(ii) Pair of dice is rolled together till a sum of either 5 or 7 is obtained. Then the probability that 5 comes before 7 is ....

67. For any three events A, B and C prove that

(i) $P(A+B|C) = P(A|C) + P(B|C) - P(AB|C)$

(ii) $P(A\bar{B}|C) + P(AB|C) = P(A|C)$

68. (a) For any two events A and B, prove that
$P[(A \cap \bar{B}) \cup (B \cap \bar{A})] = P(A) + P(B) - 2P(A \cap B)$

(b) $P(B) = \frac{3}{4}, P(\bar{A} \cap B \cap \bar{C}) = \frac{1}{3}$

$P(A \cap B \cap \bar{C}) = \frac{1}{3}$ then $P(B \cap C)$

(a) 1/12 (b) 3/4
(c) 5/12 (d) 23/36 **(IIT-Sc. 2003)**

69. (i) If A and B are independent events, then $P(A \cap B)$ equals

(a) $P(A) + P(B)$ (b) $P(A)\,P(B)$
(c) $P(A/B)$ (d) $P(B/A)$.

(ii) If A and B are mutually exclusive events, then $P(A \cap B)$ equals

(a) 0 (b) $\frac{1}{2}$
(c) 1 (d) $\frac{1}{4}$

70. (i) If A and B are such events that $P(A) > 0$ and $P(B) \neq 1$, then $P(\overline{A/B})$ is equal to

(a) $1 - P(A/B)$ (b) $1 - P(\bar{A}/B)$
(c) $\frac{1 - P(A \cup B)}{P(\bar{B})}$ (d) $\frac{P(\bar{A})}{P(\bar{B})}$.

(ii) $P(A \cup B) = P(A \cap B)$ if and only if the relation between $P(A)$ and $P(B)$ is ......

71. If A and B are arbitrary events, then

(a) $P(A \cap B) \geq P(A) + P(B) - 1$
(b) $P(A \cap B) \leq P(A) + P(B) - 1$.
(c) $P(A \cap B) = P(A) + P(B) - 1$.

72. (i) If A and B are arbitrary events, then

(a) $P(A \cap B) \geq P(A) + P(B)$,
(b) $P(A \cap B) \leq P(A) + P(B)$,
(c) $P(A \cap B) = P(A) + P(B)$.

(ii) For two events A and B, $P(A \cap B)$ is

(a) not less than $P(A) + P(B) - 1$
(b) not greater than $P(A) + P(B)$
(c) equal to $P(A) + P(B) - P(A \cup B)$
(d) equal to $P(A) + P(B) + P(A \cup B)$.

73. If M and N are any two events, the probability that the exactly one of them occurs is

(a) $P(M) + P(N) - 2P(M \cap N)$
(b) $P(M) + P(N) - P(M \cap N)$
(c) $P(M^c) + P(N^c) - 2P(M^c \cap N^c)$
(d) $P(M \cap N^c) + P(M^c \cap N)$.

74. If E and F are independent events such that $0 < P(E) < 1$, and $0 < P(F) < 1$, then

(a) E and F are mutually exclusive
(b) E and F^c (complement of the event F) are independent
(c) E^c and F^c are independent
(d) $P(E/F) + P(E^c/F) = 1$.

75. Let E and F be two independent events. The probability that both E and F happen is 1/12 and the probability that neither E nor F happens is 1/2. Then,

(a) $P(E) = 1/3, P(F) = 1/4$ (b) $P(E) = 1/2, P(F) = 1/6$
(c) $P(E) = 1/6, P(F) = 1/2$ (d) $P(E) = 1/4, P(F) = 1/3$
(I.I.T. 1993)

76. (i) If the events A and B be mutually exclusive, then $P(A + B)$ will be equal to

(a) $P(A) + P(B)$ (b) $P(A) - P(B)$
(c) $P(A) \,.\, P(B)$ (d) $P(A) / P(B)$.

(ii) If A and B are two independent events in a sample space, then $P(\bar{A}/\bar{B})$ equals :

(a) $1 - P(A/\bar{B})$ (b) $1 - P(\bar{A}/B)$
(c) $1 - P(B)$ (d) $1 - P(A)$ **(M.N.R. 1992)**

77. For any two events A and B in a sample space

(a) $P(A/B) \geq \frac{P(A) + P(B) - 1}{P(B)}$, $P(B) \neq 0$, is always true.
(b) $P(A \cap \bar{B}) = P(A) - P(A \cap B)$ does not hold.
(c) $P(A \cup B) = 1 - P(\bar{A})\,P(\bar{B})$, if A and B are independent.
(d) $P(A \cup B) = 1 - P(\bar{A})\,P(\bar{B})$, if A and B are disjoint.
(I.I.T. 1991)

78. (i) The probabilities of three mutually exclusive events A, B, C are : $P(A) = 2/3$, $P(B) = 1/4$, $P(C) = 1/6$. Is the statement

(a) true (b) wrong
(c) could be either (d) do not know

(ii) The probability that at least one of the events A and B occurs is $0 \cdot 6$. If A and B occur simultaneously with probability $0 \cdot 2$, then $P(\bar{A}) + P(\bar{B})$ is

(a) $0 \cdot 4$ (b) $0 \cdot 8$
(c) $1 \cdot 2$ (d) $1 \cdot 4$
(e) none of these

79. Let $0 < P(A) < 1, 0 < P(B) < 1$ and $P(A \cup B) = P(A) + P(B) - P\,P(A) \,.\, P(B)$, then

(a) $P(B/A) = P(B) - P\ (A)$
(b) $P(A^c - B^c) = P(A^c) - P(B^c)$
(c) $P(A \cup B)^c = P(A^c) \,.\, P(B^c)$
(d) $P(A/B) = P(A)$ **(I.I.T. 1995)**

80. For the three events A, B and C, P (exactly one of the events A or B occurs) $= P$ (exactly one of the events B or C occurs) $= P$ (exactly one of the events C or A occurs) $= p$ and P (all the three events occur simultaneously) $= p^2$, where $0 < p < \frac{1}{2}$. Then the probability of at least one of the three events A, B and C occurring is

(a) $\frac{3p+2p^2}{2}$ (b) $\frac{p+3p^2}{4}$

(c) $\frac{p+3p^2}{2}$ (d) $\frac{3p+2p^2}{4}$ **(I.I.T. 1996)**

81. (a) For a biased die the probabilities for different faces to turn up are given below :

Face	1	2	3	4	5	6
Probability	0·1	0·32	0·21	0·15	0·05	0·17

The die is tossed and you are told that either face 1 or 2 has turned up. Then the probability that it is face 1 is ....

(b) A biased die is tossed and the respective probabilities for various faces to turn up are

Face	1	2	3	4	5	6
Probability	0·1	0·24	0·19	0·18	0·15	0·14

If an even face has turned up, then the probability that it is face 2 or face 4 is

(a) 0·25 (b) 0·42

(c) 0·75 (d) 0·9 **(M.N.R. 1992)**

82. Three identical dice are rolled. The probability that the same number will appear on each of them is

(a) 1/6 (b) 1/36 (c) 1/18 (d) 3/28

83. A letter is known to have come either from London or Clifton; on the post only the consecutive letters *ON* are legible; what is the chance that it came from London ?

84. One of a pack of 52 cards has been lost; from the remainder of the pack two cards are drawn and are found to be spades; find the chance that the missing card is a spade.

85. The probability that in the toss of two dice we obtain an even sum or a sum less than 5 is

(a) $\frac{1}{2}$ (b) $\frac{1}{6}$ (c) $\frac{2}{3}$ (d) $\frac{5}{9}$

86. A determinant is chosen at random from the set of all determinants of order 2 with elements 0 or 1 only. The probability that value of the determinant chosen is positive is ....

87. (a) An experiment has 10 equally likely outcomes. Let A and B be two non-empty events of the experiment. If A consists of 4 outcomes, the number of outcomes that B must have so that A and B are independent, is

(a) 2, 4 or 8 (b) 3, 6 or 9

(c) 4 or 8 (d) 5 or 10 **(I.I.T. 2008)**

(b) One ticket is selected at random from 50 tickets numbered 00, 01, 02, ..., 49. Then the probability that the sum of the digits on the selected ticket is 8, given that the product of these digits is zero, equals

(a) $\frac{1}{50}$ (b) $\frac{1}{14}$

(c) $\frac{1}{7}$ (d) $\frac{5}{14}$ **(AIEEE 2009)**

(c) In a binomial distribution $B\left(n, p=\frac{1}{4}\right)$, if the probability of at least one success is greater than or equal to $\frac{9}{10}$, then n is greater than :

(a) $\frac{4}{\log_{10} 4 - \log_{10} 3}$ (b) $\frac{1}{\log_{10} 4 - \log_{10} 3}$

(c) $\frac{1}{\log_{10} 4 + \log_{10} 3}$ (d) $\frac{9}{\log_{10} 4 - \log_{10} 3}$

(AIEEE 2009)

88. Four fair dice D_1, D_2, D_3 and D_4 each having six faces numbered 1, 2, 3, 4, 5 and 6 are rolled simultaneously. the probability that D_4 shows a number appearing on one of D_1, D_2 and D_3 is

(a) $\frac{91}{216}$ (b) $\frac{108}{216}$ (c) $\frac{125}{216}$ (d) $\frac{127}{216}$

(IIT-JEE 2012)

89. An urn contains nine balls of which three are red, four are blue and two are green. Three balls are drawn at random without replacement from the urn. The probability that the three balls have different colours is :

(a) $\frac{1}{3}$ (b) $\frac{2}{7}$ (c) $\frac{1}{21}$ (d) $\frac{2}{23}$

(AIEEE 2010)

90. Three numbers are chosen at random without replacement from {1, 2, 3, ... 8}. The probability that their minimum is 3, given that their maximum is 6 is

(a) $\frac{3}{8}$ (b) $\frac{1}{5}$ (c) $\frac{1}{4}$ (d) $\frac{2}{5}$

(AIEEE 2012)

91. A signal which can be green or red with probability $\frac{4}{5}$ and $\frac{1}{5}$ respectively, is received by station A and then transmitted to station B. The probasility of each station receiving the signal correctly is $\frac{3}{4}$. If the signal received at station B is green then the probability that the original signal was green is

(a) $\frac{3}{5}$ (b) $\frac{6}{7}$

(c) $\frac{20}{23}$ (d) $\frac{9}{20}$ **(IIT-JEE 2010)**

92. Consider 5 independent Bernoullis trials each with probability of success p. It the probability of at least one failure is greater than or equal to $\frac{31}{32}$, then p lies in the interval

(a) $\left(\frac{1}{2}, \frac{3}{4}\right)$ (b) $\left(\frac{3}{4}, \frac{11}{12}\right)$

(c) $\left(0, \frac{1}{2}\right)$ (d) $\left(\frac{11}{12}, 1\right)$ **(AIEEE 2011)**

93. If ω be a complex cube root of unity with $\omega \neq 1$. A fair die is thrown three times. If r_1, r_2 and r_3 are the numbers obtained on the die then the probability that $\omega^{r_1} + \omega^{r_2} + \omega^{r_2} = 0$ is

(a) $\frac{1}{18}$ (b) $\frac{1}{9}$

(c) $\frac{2}{9}$ (d) $\frac{1}{36}$ **(IIT-JEE 2010)**

94. Let E and F be two independent events. The probability that the exactly one of them occurs is $\frac{11}{25}$ and the probability of none of them occuring is $\frac{2}{25}$. If $P(T)$ denotes the probability of occurance of the event T, then

(a) $P(E) = \frac{4}{5}, P(F) = \frac{3}{5}$ (b) $P(E) = \frac{1}{5}, P(F) = \frac{2}{5}$

(c) $P(E) = \frac{2}{5}, P(F) = \frac{1}{5}$ (d) $P(E) = \frac{3}{5}, P(F) = \frac{4}{5}$

(IIT-JEE 2011)

95. A ship is fitted with three engines E_1, E_2 and E_3. The engine function independently of each other with respective probabilities $\frac{1}{2}, \frac{1}{4}$ and $\frac{1}{4}$. For the ship to be operational at least two of its engines must function. Let X denote the event that the ship is operational and let $X_1 X_2$ and X_3 denote respectively the events that the engines E_1, E_2 and E_3 are functioning which of the following is true.

(a) $P[X_1^c \mid X] = \frac{3}{16}$

(b) P [Exactly two engines of the ship are functioning $\mid X] = \frac{7}{8}$

(c) $P[X \mid X_2] = \frac{5}{16}$

(d) $P[X \mid X_1] = \frac{7}{16}$ **(IIT-JEE 2012)**

96. Let X and Y be two events such that $P(X \mid Y) = \frac{1}{2}$, $P(Y \mid X) = \frac{1}{3}$ and $P(X \cap Y) = \frac{1}{6}$ which of the following is correct

(a) $P(X \cup Y) = \frac{2}{3}$

(b) X and Y are independent

(c) X and Y are not independent

(d) $P(X' \cap Y) = \frac{1}{3}$ **(IIT-JEE 2012)**

Comprehension

Paragraph for Question (97) to (98)

Let U_1 and U_2 be two urns such that U_1 contains 3 white and 2 red balls and U_2 contains only 1 white ball. A fair coin is tossed. If head appears then 1 ball is drawn at random from U_1 and put into U_2. However, if tail appears then 2 balls are drawn at random from U_1 and put into U_2. Now 1 ball is drawn at random from U_2 **(IIT-JEE 2011)**

97. The probability of the drawn ball from U_2 being white is

(a) $\frac{13}{30}$ (b) $\frac{23}{30}$ (c) $\frac{19}{30}$ (d) $\frac{11}{30}$

98. Given that the drawn ball from U_2 is white, the probability that head appeared on the coin is

(a) $\frac{17}{23}$ (b) $\frac{11}{23}$ (c) $\frac{15}{23}$ (d) $\frac{12}{23}$

Paragraph for Question No. 99 : A fair die is tossed repeatedly until a six is obtained. Let X denote the number of tosses required. **(I.I.T. 2009)**

99. (a) The probability that $X = 3$ equals

(a) $\frac{25}{216}$ (b) $\frac{25}{36}$

(c) $\frac{5}{36}$ (d) $\frac{125}{216}$

(b) The probability that $x \geq 3$ equals

(a) $\frac{125}{216}$ (b) $\frac{25}{36}$

(c) $\frac{5}{36}$ (d) $\frac{25}{216}$

(c) The conditional probability that $X \geq 6$ given $X > 3$ equals

(a) $\frac{125}{216}$ (b) $\frac{25}{216}$

(c) $\frac{5}{36}$ (d) $\frac{25}{36}$

Solutions to Problem Set (2)

1. **Ans. (a).**

Probability of getting head in one trial $= \frac{1}{2}$

$\therefore$ Probability of getting heads in both the trials

$= \frac{1}{2} \times \frac{1}{2} = \frac{1}{4}.$

2. (i) Ans. (b).

Required probability $= \frac{^4C_2}{^{52}C_2} = \frac{4 \times 3}{52 \times 51} = \frac{1}{221}$

(ii) Ans. (d). Total socks are $5 + 4 = 9$

Two socks are pulled $\therefore$ $n = {}^9C_2 = \frac{9.8}{1.2} = 36$

Same colour can be either brown or white

$\therefore$ $m = {}^5C_2 + {}^4C_2 = \frac{5.4}{1.2} + \frac{4.3}{1.2} = 10 + 6 = 16$

$\therefore$ Probability $= \frac{m}{n} = \frac{16}{36} = \frac{4}{9}.$

3. Ans. (a). $n =$ Total no. of ways $= 6 \times 6 = 36$.

The numbers higher than 9 are 10, 11, 12 in the case of two dice.

$\therefore$ $m =$ favourable no. of ways $= 3 + 2 + 1 = 6$ (why ?).

Hence $p = \frac{m}{n} = \frac{6}{36} = \frac{1}{6}.$

4. (i) Ans. (a). Required probability

$= \frac{^{13}C_1}{^{52}C_1} \times \frac{^4C_1}{^{52}C_1} = \frac{13 \times 4}{52 \times 52} = \frac{1}{52}.$

(ii) Ans. (a).

$n =$ Total number of ways $= {}^{16}C_2 = 120.$

$m =$ Favourable number of ways

$= {}^2C_1 . {}^{12}C_1 = 24$

$\therefore$ Required probability $= \frac{24}{120} = \frac{1}{5}.$

Note. Hindi version of the question is correct which when translated into English means that the ace is drawn least number of times, that is, once.

5. The event may happen in any of the following mutually exclusive ways :

WBB, BWB, BBW

The probabilities of these are

$\frac{3}{4}.\frac{2}{4}.\frac{3}{4}$; $\frac{1}{4}.\frac{2}{4}.\frac{3}{4}$; $\frac{1}{4}.\frac{2}{4}.\frac{1}{4}$ respectively.

Required probability is their sum $= \frac{26}{64} = \frac{13}{32}$

6. Let $A = \{(1,1), (2,2), (3,3), (4,4), (5,5), (6,6)\}$

$B = \{(4,6), (5,5), (6,4), (5,6), (6,5), (6,6)\}$

$\therefore$ $A \cap B = \{(5,5), (6,6)\}$

$\therefore$ $P(A \cup B) = P(A) + P(B) - P(A \cap B)$

$= \frac{6}{36} + \frac{6}{36} - \frac{2}{36} = \frac{10}{36} = \frac{5}{18}.$

7. Let $A = \{$the integer is divisible by 6$\}$

$B = \{$the integer is divisible by 8$\}$

The set A contains 33 integers and the set B, 25 integers.

Number of integers which are divisible by 6 and 8 both $= \frac{200}{24} = 8$ where L.C.M. of 6 and 8 is 24

$\therefore$ $P(A \cup B) = P(A) + P(B) - P(AB)$

$= \frac{33}{200} + \frac{25}{200} - \frac{8}{200} = \frac{1}{4}.$

8. Ans. (a). Required probability

$= \frac{^{39}C_1}{^{52}C_1} \times \frac{^{39}C_1}{^{52}C_1} \times \frac{^{13}C_1}{^{52}C_1} = \frac{3}{4} \times \frac{3}{4} \times \frac{1}{4} = \frac{9}{64}.$

9. (i) Ans. (b). (See the 'Important Note' of § 4)

(ii) Ans. (b). (See the 'Important Note' of § 4).

10. Ans. (b). $\because$ Total no. of ways $= 3! = 6$ and favourable no. of ways $= 1$.

11. Ans. (a).

12. (i) Ans. (b). Probability of throwing an ace $= 1/6$, and of not throwing ace $= 5/6$.

Hence required probability $= \frac{1}{6} \times \frac{5}{6} = \frac{5}{36}.$

(ii) Ans. (a). Since tossing of a coin is an independent event, therefore the result of fifth trial is independent of the outcome of previous four trials.

$\therefore$ $P(H) = \frac{1}{2}.$

13. Since the three works can be placed in 3 ! ways so required probability $= \frac{3!\,3!\,4!}{8!} = \frac{3}{140}$

14. In all there are 15 balls in the bag. So the three balls can be drawn in $^{15}C_3$ ways. Excluding black balls we are left with 9 other balls, from which three balls can be drawn in $^9C_3$ ways. Hence prob. for (a) is $\frac{^9C_3}{^{15}C_3} = \frac{12}{65}$

Similarly for (b) prob. $= \frac{^6C_2 \times {}^9C_1}{^{15}C_3} = \frac{27}{91}.$

Since along with two black balls, the third may be any one from remaining nine balls. For (c) the balls drawn may be white or red or black.

These are mutually exclusive events, hence required prob.

$= \frac{^4C_3 + {}^5C_3 + {}^6C_3}{^{15}C_3} = \frac{4 + 10 + 20}{(15.14.13)\ (3!)} = \frac{34}{455}$

15. Let A denote the event that the ball No. is a multiple of 2 and B denote the event that the ball No. is a multiple of 3

i.e., set $A = \{2, 4, 6, 8, 10\}$ and set $B = \{3, 6, 9\}$

$\therefore$ set $A \cap B = \{6\}$

Thus $p(A \cup B) = P(A) + P(B) - P(A \cap B)$

$$= \frac{5}{11} + \frac{3}{11} - \frac{1}{11} = \frac{7}{11}$$

16. Ans. (c).

Required probability = Prob. of right club and good shot or prob. of wrong club and good shot

$$= \frac{1}{5} \cdot \frac{1}{3} + \frac{4}{5} \cdot \frac{1}{4} = \frac{4}{15}$$

17. (i) Ans. (c).

Here $n = 36$ and $m = 8$ since 7 can be thrown in 6 ways and 11 in 2 ways

$\therefore \quad p = \frac{m}{n} = \frac{8}{36} = \frac{2}{9}.$

(ii) Ans. (b).

(iii) Ans. (c). n = Total no. of ways $= 6 \times 6 = 36$

Favourable ways are (1, 4), (2, 3), (3, 2) and (4, 1)

$\therefore$ Favourable no. of ways = 4

Hence Probability $= \frac{m}{n} = \frac{4}{36} = \frac{1}{9}.$

18. Since $P(A \cup B) + P(\overline{A \cup B}) = 1$

or $P(A \cup B) = 1 - P(\overline{A \cup B}) = 1 - P(\bar{A} \cap \bar{B})$

where $p(A) = \frac{75}{100} = \frac{3}{4}, P(B) = \frac{70}{100} = \frac{7}{10}$

$$= 1 - P(\bar{A})\,P(\bar{B}) = 1 - \left(1 - \frac{3}{4}\right)\left(1 - \frac{7}{10}\right) = \frac{37}{40}$$

Since A and B are independent, then complementary events $\bar{A}$ and $\bar{B}$ are also independent.

19. There will be light in the room, if at least one good bulb is selected.

$\therefore$ Reqd. prob. $= \frac{{}^6C_1 \times {}^4C_2 + {}^6C_2 \times {}^4C_1 + {}^6C_3}{sC_3} = \frac{29}{30}.$

20. Ans. (d). Let p be the probability of the other event. Then the probability of the first event is $\frac{2}{3}p$. Since two events are totally exclusive, we have $p + (2/3)\,p = 1$ or $p = 3/5$

Hence odds in favour of the other are $3 : (5 - 3)$ *i.e.* $3 : 2$.

21. Ans. (c). n = Total no. of ways $= 6^5$.

To find the favourable no. of ways, a total of 12 in 5 throws can be obtained in the following two ways only :

(i) One blank and four 3's.

or (ii) Three 2's and two 3's.

The no. of ways in case (i) $= {}^5C_1 = 5$.

and the no. of ways in case (ii) $= {}^5C_2 = 10$.

$\therefore$ m = the favourable no. of ways $= 5 + 10 = 15$

Hence the required probability $= \frac{15}{6^5} = \frac{5}{2592}.$

22. If p denotes prob. of success and q prob. of failure, then $p + q = 1$ and $p = 2q$

Thus $p = \frac{2}{3}, \quad q = \frac{1}{3}$

Hence prob. of at least four successes in the next six trials $= {}^6C_4\, p^4 q^2 + {}^6C_5\, p^5 q + {}^6C_6\, p^6$

$$= 15\left(\frac{2}{3}\right)^4\left(\frac{1}{3}\right)^2 + 6\left(\frac{2}{3}\right)^5\left(\frac{1}{3}\right) + \left(\frac{2}{3}\right)^6 = \frac{426}{729}.$$

23. (i) Ans. (a).

(ii) Ans. (d). We have $p = \frac{3}{4}$ $\therefore$ $q = \frac{1}{4}$ and $n = 5$

$\therefore$ Required probability

$$= {}^5C_3\left(\frac{3}{4}\right)^3\left(\frac{1}{4}\right)^2 + {}^5C_4\left(\frac{3}{4}\right)^4\left(\frac{1}{4}\right) + {}^5C_5\left(\frac{3}{4}\right)^5$$

$$= \frac{10.27}{4^5} + \frac{5.81}{4^5} + \frac{243}{4^5} = \frac{270 + 405 + 243}{1024} = \frac{459}{512}$$

24. The chance that all the events fail

$$= (1 - p_1)(1 - p_2) \ldots (1 - p_n)$$

Leaving this case, in other cases some one of the events must happen. So using the formula

$$P(A) + P(\bar{A}) = 1$$

we have the reqd. chance as

$$1 - (1 - p_1)(1 - p_2) \ldots (1 - p_n)$$

25. We have $A = \frac{1}{4}, \; B = \frac{3}{4}; \; A = \frac{3}{5}; \; C = \frac{2}{5}; A = \frac{4}{7}, D = \frac{3}{7}.$

A may either win with all three or fail with B or fail with C or fail with D. The chance of these four cases are

$$\frac{1}{4} \cdot \frac{3}{5} \cdot \frac{4}{7}, \quad \frac{3}{4} \cdot \frac{3}{5} \cdot \frac{4}{7}, \quad \frac{1}{4} \cdot \frac{2}{5} \cdot \frac{4}{7}, \quad \frac{1}{4} \cdot \frac{3}{5} \cdot \frac{3}{7}$$

The sum of these four gives the reqd. chance

$$\frac{12 + 36 + 8 + 9}{140} = \frac{55}{140} = \frac{11}{28}.$$

26. A may throw an ace in the first chance or 6th chance or 11th chance and so on.

$\therefore$ A's chance $= \frac{1}{6}\left\{1 + \left(\frac{5}{6}\right)^5 + \left(\frac{5}{6}\right)^{10} + \ldots\right\} = S,$ suppose

Similarly B's chance

$$= \frac{5}{6} \cdot \frac{1}{6}\left\{1 + \left(\frac{5}{6}\right)^5 + \left(\frac{5}{6}\right)^{10} + \ldots\right\} = \frac{5}{6} S,$$

C's chance $= \left(\frac{5}{6}\right)^2 S$, D's chance $= \left(\frac{5}{6}\right)^3 S$,

E's chance $= \left(\frac{5}{6}\right)^4 S$

$\therefore$ Respective chances are as

$$= 1 : \frac{5}{6} : \left(\frac{5}{6}\right)^2 : \left(\frac{5}{6}\right)^3 : \left(\frac{5}{6}\right)^4.$$

27. Urns I II III

1 W, 2 B 2 W, 1B 2W, 2B

There are four possibilities in transference.

(i) W ball goes from I to II; and W goes from II to III So prob. of drawing a W ball from urn III $= \frac{1}{3} \times \frac{3}{4} \times \frac{3}{5} = \frac{9}{60}$

(ii) W goes from I to II, B goes from II to III then prob. of W from III $= \frac{1}{3} \times \frac{1}{4} \times \frac{2}{5} = \frac{2}{60}$

(iii) B goes from I to II, W goes from II to III, then prob. of W from III $= \frac{2}{3} \times \frac{2}{4} \times \frac{3}{5} = \frac{12}{60}$

(iv) B goes from I to II, B goes from II to III, then prob of W from III $= \frac{2}{3} \times \frac{2}{4} \times \frac{2}{5} = \frac{8}{60}$

These are mutually exclusive events, so required prob.

$$= \text{sum of these} = \frac{9}{60} + \frac{2}{60} + \frac{12}{60} + \frac{8}{60} = \frac{31}{60}$$

28. Let $A = \{a_1, a_2, ..., a_{11}\}$. For each a_i $(1 \le i \le 11)$ we have following four cases :

(1) $a_i \in P, a_i \in Q$ (2) $a_i \notin P, a_i \in Q$

(3) $a_i \in P, a_i \notin Q$ (4) $a_i \notin P, a_i \notin Q$

Non-intersecting set of P and Q is possible from the cases (2), (3) and (4)th

$\therefore$ Reqd. prob. $= \frac{3^{11}}{4^{11}} = \left(\frac{3}{4}\right)^{11}$

29. Ans. (a).

We have $p = 1 - \left(\frac{2}{7}\right)^3 = \frac{335}{343}$. Hence odds in favour are as $335 : 343 - 335$ or $335 : 8$.

30. Ans. (a). $n =$ Total no. of ways $= {}^{120}C_1 = 120$.

$m =$ Favourable no. of ways is the number of terms in the arithmetical series 5, 10, 15, 20, 25, 30, ..., 120.

$\therefore$ $120 = 4 + (m-1)5$ or $m = 24$.

Hence $P = \frac{m}{n} = \frac{24}{120} = \frac{1}{5}$.

31. Ans. (d). $P(\bar{A} \cap \bar{B}) = P(\overline{A \cup B})$

$= 1 - P(A \cup B) = 1 - [P(A) + P(B)]$

[$\because$ Events A, B are mutually exclusive, we have $P(A \cup B) = P(A) + P(B)$]

$= 1 - 0 \cdot 5 - 0 \cdot 3 = 0 \cdot 2$.

32. Ans. (b). Here $P(A) = 0 \cdot 4$ and $P(\bar{A}) = 0 \cdot 6$

$\therefore$ Required probability $= 1 - [P(\bar{A})]^3 = 1 - (0 \cdot 6)^3$

$= 1 - 0 \cdot 216 = 0 \cdot 784$.

33. Ans. (a).

34. Ans. (c).

35. Ans. (b). Since A and B are independent events, we have $P(A \cap B) = P(A)\, P(B)$

$\therefore$ $P(A \cup B) = P(A) + P(B) - P(A \cap B)$

$= P(A) + P(B) - P(A)\, P(B)$

$= 0 \cdot 2 + 0 \cdot 3 - 0 \cdot 2 \times 0 \cdot 3$

$= 0 \cdot 50 - 0 \cdot 06 = 0 \cdot 44$

36. Ans. (a).

The probability of no tail in 4 throws of a coin $= (1/2)^4 = 1/16$. Hence the probability of at least one tail in four throws

$= 1 - (1/16) = 15/16$.

37. (a) Ans. (c).

The required pobability

$$= \frac{{}^{13}C_1}{{}^{52}C_1} \cdot \frac{{}^{4}C_1}{{}^{52}C_1} = \frac{13}{52} \cdot \frac{4}{52} = \frac{1}{52}.$$

(b) Ans: $\frac{4}{52} \cdot \frac{4}{51}$.

38. Ans. (d).

In a single throw with two dice, 7 can be obtained in the following 6 ways :

$(6,1), (1,6), (5,2), (2,5), (4,3), (3,4)$

and total no. of ways $= 6^2 = 36$.

$\therefore$ The required probability $= \frac{6}{36} = \frac{1}{6}$.

39. Ans. (c).

Three vertices out of 6 can be chosen in ${}^6C_3$ ways. So total ways $= {}^6C_3 = 20$.

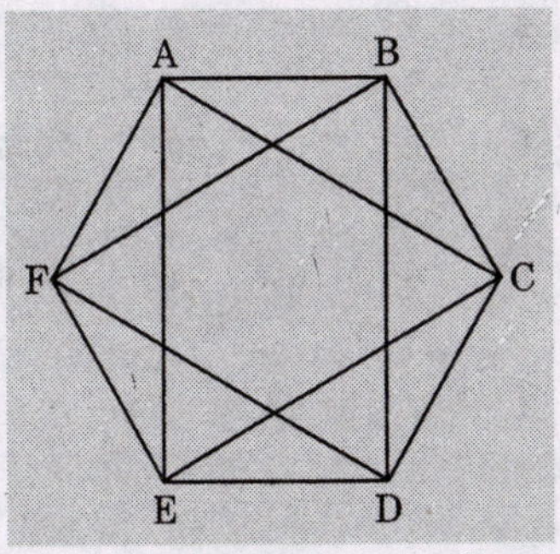

Fig. 4

Only two equilateral triangles can be formed ΔAEC and ΔBED. So favourable ways = 2

So required prob. $= \frac{2}{20} = \frac{1}{10}$

40. Ans. (b).

Prob. of India winning the match is $\frac{1}{2}$

Prob. of losing a match is also $\frac{1}{2}$.

Now in two ways India can win 2nd time in 3rd match

(i) *LWL* (ii) *WLW*

41. If the sequence of m consecutive heads starts from the first head *i.e.*, $H\ H\ H \ldots m$ times $\times$ throws may be tail or head. Prob. of this event $= \frac{1}{2^m}$

Similarly if the sequence starts after the first tail, then its prob. $= \frac{1}{2} \times \frac{1}{2^m} = \frac{1}{2^{m+1}}$.

If the sequence starts from $(r+1)^{\text{th}}$ throw, $r \geq 1$, the first r throws may be heads or tails, but the rth throw must be a tail followed by m consecutive heads. The prob. for this $= \frac{1}{2} \times \frac{1}{2^m} = \frac{1}{2^{m+1}}$

Hence reqd. prob.

$$= \frac{1}{2^m} + \left(\frac{1}{2^{m+1}} + \frac{1}{2^{m+1}} + \ldots + n \text{ times} \right) = \frac{2+n}{2^{m+1}}.$$

42. The roots will be real, if $b^2 \geq 4ac$.

Now a, b, c can assume any value from 1 to 6.

Since there are 3 coefficients, total number of cases $= 6 \times 6 \times 6 = 216$

Now various possibilities in which $b^2 \geq 4ac$ are

	a	c	ac	$4ac$	b	No. of cases ($b^2 \geq 4ac$)
One case	1	1	1	4	2, 3, 4, 5, 6	5 × 1 = 5
Two cases	2	1	2	8	3, 4, 5, 6	4 × 2 = 8
	1	2				
Two cases	1	3	3	12	4, 5, 6	3 × 2 = 6
	3	1				
Three cases	1	4	4	16	4, 5, 6	3 × 3 = 9
	2	2				
	4	1				
Two cases	1	5	5	20	5, 6	2 × 2 = 4
	5	1				
Four cases	1	6	6	24	5, 6	2 × 4 = 8
	2	3				
	3	2				
	6	1				
Two cases	2	4	8	32	6	1 × 2 = 2
	4	2				
One case	3	3	9	36	6	1 × 1 = 1

$\therefore$ Total No. of favourable cases = 43

$\therefore$ Reqd. prob. $= \frac{43}{216}$

43. Prob. of cutting a spade card $= \frac{13}{52} = \frac{1}{4}$.

and of not cutting it $= 1 - \frac{1}{4} = \frac{3}{4}$

Let x denote the prob. of cutting a spade card in the long run by A, then

$x + \frac{3}{4}x + \left(\frac{3}{4}\right)^2 x = 1$, as it is certain that one of A, B, C will cut a spade card and B and C in their chances cut the spade card under exactly similar conditions.

$\therefore$ their respective probabilities are

$$\frac{16}{37}, \frac{3}{4} \times \frac{16}{37}, \left(\frac{3}{4}\right)^2 \frac{16}{37}$$

or respective chances are $\frac{16}{37}, \frac{12}{37}, \frac{9}{37}$.

44. Prob. of first bag chosen = 1/2 and then the chance of 1 white and 1 red ball is $\frac{5 \times 3}{{}^8C_2}$

Again prob. of second bag $= \frac{1}{2}$ and the chance of choosing one of each colour is $\frac{4 \times 5}{{}^9C_2}$

Required chance $= \frac{1}{2} \cdot \frac{15}{28} + \frac{1}{2} \cdot \frac{20}{36} = \frac{275}{504}$.

45. The chance that A will die within 30 years $= \frac{9}{16}$

The chance that B will die within 30 years $= \frac{3}{5}$

$\therefore$ the chance that both will die is $\frac{9}{16} \times \frac{3}{5} = \frac{27}{80}$

$\therefore$ the chance that both will not be dead, that is, one at least will be alive is $1 - \frac{27}{80} = \frac{53}{80}$

46. One card from each suit may be dropped in $(13)^4$ ways, and any four cards may be dropped in ${}^{52}C_4$ ways.

$\therefore$ The reqd. chance $= \frac{(13)^4}{{}^{52}C_4}$.

47. Ans. (b). Let K denote event Krishna will be alive 10 years hence, then $\overline{K}$ denotes Krishna will be dead 10 years hence.

$\therefore$ $P(K) = \frac{7}{15}$ and $P(\overline{K}) = 1 - P(K)$

i.e., $P(\overline{K}) = 1 - \frac{7}{15} = \frac{8}{15}$

Similarly for Hari $P(H) = \frac{7}{10}, P(\overline{H}) = \frac{3}{10}$

Hence $P(\overline{K} \cap \overline{H}) = P(\overline{K}).P(\overline{H}) = \frac{8}{15} \times \frac{3}{10} = \frac{24}{150}$.

48. Ans. (b). $P_1 = \frac{{}^{15}C_2 \times {}^{27}C_2}{{}^{42}C_4}$

$$= \frac{15 \times 14 \times 27 \times 26 \times 1 \times 2 \times 3 \times 4}{1 \times 2 \times 1 \times 2 \times 42 \times 41 \times 40 \times 39} = \frac{27}{82}.$$

$$P_2 = \frac{{}^{30}C_4 \times {}^{54}C_4}{{}^{84}C_8}$$

$$= \frac{30.29.28.27.54.53.52.51.8!}{4!\ 4!\ .84.83.82.81.80.79.78.77}$$

$$= \frac{17.29.45.53}{11.79.82.83}, \quad \text{after simplification.}$$

$$\therefore \quad \frac{P_1}{P_2} = \frac{27}{82} \times \frac{11.79.82.83}{17.29.45.53} = \frac{33.79.83}{29.53.85} = \frac{216381}{130645} > 1.$$

Hence $P_1 > P_2$.

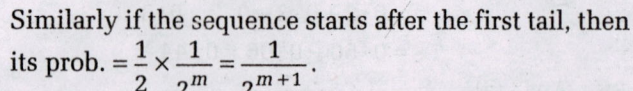

49. Ans. (d).

Required prob. $= \frac{1}{2} \cdot \frac{4}{7} + \frac{1}{2} \cdot \frac{6}{8} = \frac{37}{56}$.

50. Ans. (a).

Let λ, μ and λ', μ' be the numbers of heads and tails thrown by A and B respectively, so that $\lambda + \lambda' = n+1$ and $\mu + \mu' = n$.

The required probability P is the probability of the inequality $\lambda > \mu$. The probability $1-P$ of the opposite event $\lambda \le \mu$ is at the same time the probability of the inequality $\lambda' > \mu'$, that is, $1-P$ is the probability that A will throw more tails than B.

[Reason : $\lambda \le \mu \Rightarrow n+1-\lambda' \le n-\mu'$

$\Rightarrow \quad 1-\lambda' \le -\mu' \Rightarrow \lambda' - 1 \ge \mu'$

$\Rightarrow \quad \lambda' \ge \mu' + 1 > \mu'$]

By reason of symmetry, $1-P = P$ or $P = \frac{1}{2}$.

51. (i) Ans. (c).

Hint. On trial, $n = 15$ since any of the 15 numbers can be on the selected coin and $m = 9$ since the largest, number is 9 and so it can be 1 or 2 or 3, ... or 9.

Since seven trials are performed with replacement, we have the required probability $= \left(\frac{9}{15}\right)^7 = \left(\frac{3}{5}\right)^7$.

(ii) Ans. (a). In a single throw, favourable points are 2, 3, 4 and 5. Their number is 4. All possible outcomes are 6. $\therefore \quad p = \frac{4}{6} = \frac{2}{3}$

Since the die is rolled four times and all results are independent

$\therefore$ Required Probability $= \left(\frac{2}{3}\right)^4 = \frac{16}{81}$.

52. Let A be the event that the maximum number on the two chosen tickets is not more than 10, that is, the no. on them ≤ 10 and B the event that the minimum no. on them is 5, that is, the no. on them is ≥ 5. We have to find $P(B/A)$.

Now $P(B/A) = \frac{P(A \cap B)}{P(A)} = \frac{n(A \cap B)}{n(A)}$.

Now the number of ways of getting a number r on the two tickets is the coeff. of x^r in the expansion of

$(x^1 + x^2 + ... + x^{100})^2 = x^2 \ (1 + x + ... + x^{99})^2$

$= x^2 \left(\frac{1-x^{100}}{1-x}\right)^2 = x^2 \ (1 - 2x^{100} + x^{200}) \ (1-x)^{-2}$

$= x^2 \ (1 - 2x^{100} + x^{200}) \ (1 + 2x + 3x^2 + ... (r+1) \ x^r + ...)$

Thus coeff. of $x^2 = 1$, of $x^3 = 2$, of $x^4 = 3$,...., of x^{10} is 9.

Hence $n(A) = 1+2+3+4+5+6+7+8+9 = 45$ and $n(A \cap B) = 4+5+6+7+8+9 = 39$.

[Note that in finding $n(A)$, we have to add the coefficients of $x^2, x^3, ..., x^{10}$ and in $n(A \cap B)$ we add the coefficients of $x^5, x^6, ..., x^{10}$].

Hence required prob. $= P(B/A) = \frac{39}{45} = \frac{13}{15}$.

53. Ans. (c).

Let A, B, C denote the events of passing the tests I, II and III respectively. Evidently A, B, C are independent events. Now according to the question,

$\frac{1}{2} = P[(A \cap B) \cup (A \cap C)]$

$= P(A \cap B) + P(A \cap C) - P(A \cap B \cap C)$

$= P(A)\, P(B) + P(A)\, P(C) - P(A)\, P(B)\, P(C)$

$= pq + p \cdot \frac{1}{2} - pq \cdot \frac{1}{2}$

or $\quad 1 = 2pq + p - pq = p(q+1)$.

Of the given values, values in (c) satisfy (1). Hence (c) is the required answer.

[In fact, the equality (1) is satisfied for infinite no. of values of p and q. For, if we take any value of q such that $0 \le q \le 1$, then p takes the value $1/(q+1)$. It is evident that $0 < 1/(q+1) \le 1$ *i.e.* $0 < p \le 1$. But we have to correct the answer from given ones].

54. (i) Ans. $\frac{1}{3} \le p \le \frac{1}{2}$.

Let A, B, C denote the mutually exclusive events so that $P(A) = \frac{1+3p}{3}, P(B) = \frac{1-p}{4}$, $P(C) = \frac{1-2p}{2}$. Since A, B, C are mutually exclusive, we have

$0 \le P(A) + P(B) + P(C) = P(A \cup B \cup C) \le 1$

or $\quad 0 \le \frac{1+3p}{3} + \frac{1-p}{4} + \frac{1-2p}{2} \le 1$

or $\quad 0 \le 13 - 3p \le 12$ or $-13 \le -3p \le -1$

or $\quad 13 \ge 3p \ge 1$ or $\frac{1}{3} \le p \le \frac{13}{3}$. ...(1)

Also $\quad 0 \le P(A) \le 1 \Rightarrow 0 \le \frac{1+3p}{3} \le 1$

$\Rightarrow \quad 0 \le 1 + 3p \le 3 \Rightarrow -1 \le 3p \le 2$

$\Rightarrow \quad -\frac{1}{3} \le p \le \frac{2}{3}$.

But $p \ge 0$, hence $0 \le p \le \frac{2}{3}$ ...(2)

Again $0 \le P(B) \le 1 \Rightarrow 0 \le \frac{1-p}{4} \le 1$

$\Rightarrow \quad 0 \le 1 - p \le 4 \Rightarrow -1 \le -p \le 3$

$\Rightarrow \quad 1 \ge p \ge -3$

$\therefore \quad 0 \le p \le 1 \quad (\because \ p \ge 0)$. ...(3)

Similarly from $0 \le P(C) \le 1$, we shall easily get

$0 \le p \le \frac{1}{2}$ ...(4)

Now the set of values of p which satisfy all the inequalities from (1) to (4) is given by $\frac{1}{3} \le p \le \frac{1}{2}$.

(ii) Ans. (b). $\left(-\frac{1}{4}, \frac{1}{3}\right)$

Let A, B and C denote mutually exclusive and exhaustive events so that

$$P(A) = \frac{1-3p}{2},\ P(B) = \frac{1+4p}{3},\ P(C) = \frac{1+p}{6}.$$

$\because$ Events are mutually exclusive and exhaustive.

$\therefore$ $P(A) + P(B) + P(C) = 1$

$\Rightarrow$ $\frac{1-3p}{2} + \frac{1+4p}{3} + \frac{1+p}{6} = 1$ ...(i)

Also $0 \le P(A) \le 1,\ 0 \le P(B) \le 1,\ 0 \le P(C) \le 1$

$\therefore$ $0 \le \frac{1-3p}{2} \le 1 \Rightarrow -1 \le -3p \le 1$

$\Rightarrow$ $\frac{1}{3} \ge p \ge -\frac{1}{3} \Rightarrow -\frac{1}{3} \le p \le \frac{1}{3}$ ...(ii)

$0 \le \frac{1+4p}{3} \le 1 \Rightarrow -1 \le 4p \le 2$

$\Rightarrow$ $-\frac{1}{4} \le p \le \frac{1}{2}$ ...(iii)

$0 \le \frac{1+p}{6} \le 1 \Rightarrow 0 \le 1+p \le 6$

$\Rightarrow$ $-1 \le p \le 5$ ...(iv)

Now set of values of p which satisfy all the above inequalities is $\left(-\frac{1}{4}, \frac{1}{3}\right)$.

55. Let R stand for drawing a red ball and B for drawing a black ball. Then required probability

$= RRR + RBR + BRR + BBR$

$$= \frac{5}{11} \times \frac{5}{11} \times \frac{6}{10} + \frac{6}{10} \times \frac{6}{11} \times \frac{5}{10} + \frac{4}{10} \times \frac{4}{11} \times \frac{7}{10} + \frac{4}{10} \times \frac{7}{11} \times \frac{6}{10} = \frac{640}{1100} = \frac{32}{55}.$$

56. Ans. (d).

We have

$$^{10}C_{50}\, p^{50} (1-p)^{50} = {}^{100}C_{51}\, p^{51} (1-p)^{49}$$

or $\frac{1-p}{p} = \frac{100!}{51!\ 49!} \times \frac{50!\ 50!}{100!} = \frac{50}{51}$

or $51 - 51p = 50p$ giving $p = \frac{51}{101}$.

57. Ans. (b). Matches played by India are four.

Maximum points in any match are two.

$\therefore$ Maximum points in four matches can be 8 only.

$\therefore$ At least 7 points means 7 or 8 points.

$\therefore$ Required Probability $= P(7) + P(8)$

$$P(7) = {}^4C_1\,(\cdot 05)(\cdot 5)^3 = \cdot 0250$$

$$P(8) = (\cdot 5)^4 = \cdot 0625$$

$\therefore$ Required Probability $= \cdot 0250 + \cdot 0625 = \cdot 0875$

58. Out of five bags, 3 belong to the first group and 2 to the second; hence

$$P_1 = \frac{3}{5},\ P_2 = \frac{2}{5}$$

If a bag is selected from the first group, the chance of drawing a black ball is $\frac{2}{7}$; if from the second group, the chance is $\frac{4}{5}$, thus

$$p_1 = \frac{2}{7},\quad p_2 = \frac{4}{5}$$

$\therefore$ $p_1 P_1 = \frac{6}{35},\quad p_2 P_2 = \frac{8}{25}$

Hence the chance that the black ball came from one of the first group $= \frac{6/35}{\left(\frac{6}{35} + \frac{8}{25}\right)} = \frac{15}{43}$.

59. Let A denote the event that the older child is a boy and B denote the event that the younger child is a boy.

(i) $\therefore$ $P[AB \mid A] = \frac{P[AB]}{P(A)} = \frac{P(A)\,P(B)}{P(A)}$

$$= \frac{(1/2) \times (1/2)}{1/2} = \frac{1}{2}$$

(ii) $P[AB \mid A \cup B] = \frac{P[AB]}{P(A \cup B)} = \frac{P[AB]}{1 - P(\bar{A} \cap \bar{B})}$

$$= \frac{P(A)\,P(B)}{1 - P(\bar{A})\ P(\bar{B})} = \frac{\frac{1}{2} \times \frac{1}{2}}{1 - \frac{1}{2} \times \frac{1}{2}} = \frac{1}{3}$$

60. (a) Ans (b). The required probability

$$= {}^3C_2 \left(\frac{1}{2}\right)^2 \cdot \frac{1}{2} + {}^3C_3 \left(\frac{1}{2}\right)^3 = \frac{1}{2}.$$

(b) Ans. (d). The required probability

$$= {}^8C_6 \left(\frac{1}{2}\right)^6 \left(\frac{1}{2}\right)^2 + {}^8C_7 \left(\frac{1}{2}\right)^7 \left(\frac{1}{2}\right) + {}^8C_8 \left(\frac{1}{2}\right)^8.$$

$$= \frac{1}{256}(28 + 8 + 1) = \frac{37}{256}.$$

61. Let A denote the event that the sample contains exactly three white balls and let B be the event that the ball drawn on the third draw was white.

To find $P[B \mid A]$

Now $P[A] = ({}^4C_3)\,\frac{8}{12} \times \frac{8}{12} \times \frac{8}{12} \times \frac{4}{12}$

$$P[AB] = ({}^3C_2)\,\frac{8}{12} \times \frac{8}{12} \times \frac{8}{12} \times \frac{4}{12}$$

$\therefore$ $P[B \mid A] = \frac{P[AB]}{P(A)} = \frac{{}^3C_2}{{}^4C_3} = \frac{3}{4}$

In the case of sampling without replacement,

$P[A] = ({}^4C_3)\frac{8}{12}\times\frac{7}{11}\times\frac{6}{10}\times\frac{4}{9}$

$P[AB] = ({}^3C_2)\frac{8}{12}\times\frac{7}{11}\times\frac{6}{10}\times\frac{4}{9}$

$\therefore\quad P[B\mid A] = \frac{{}^3C_2}{{}^4C_3} = \frac{3}{4}$

62. Ans. $\frac{1}{4}$. Given that $P(A^c) = \cdot 3 \Rightarrow P(4) = \cdot 7$

$P(B) = \cdot 4 \Rightarrow P(B^c) = \cdot 6$

$P(AB^c) = \cdot 5 \Rightarrow P(A) - P(AB) = \cdot 5$

$\Rightarrow\quad P(AB) = \cdot 7 - \cdot 5 = \cdot 2$ By **§4 Page 1682.**

$P[B/(A\cup B^c)] = \frac{P[B\cap(A\cup B^c)]}{P(A\cup B^c)}$ ...(1)

Now $B\cap(A\cup B^c) = A\cap B$

$\therefore\quad P[B\cap(A\cup B^c)] = P(A\cap B) = .2$ ...(2)

and $P(A\cup B^c) = P(A) + P(B^c) - P(A\cap B^c)$

$= \cdot 7 + \cdot 6 - \cdot 5 = \cdot 8$ ...(3)

Substituting values of (2) and (3) in (1), we get required probability.

$= \frac{\cdot 2}{\cdot 8} = \frac{1}{4}$

63. (i) Ans. (b).

$P(B) = 1 - P(\bar{B}) = 1 - \frac{1}{2} = \frac{1}{2}$

and $P(A\cup B) = P(A) + P(B) - P(A\cap B)$

or $\frac{5}{6} = P(A) + \frac{1}{2} - \frac{1}{3}$ or $P(A) = \frac{2}{3}$.

$\therefore\quad P(A)\,P(B) = \frac{2}{3}\times\frac{1}{2} = \frac{1}{3} = P(A\cap B)$.

Hence A and B are independent.

(ii) Ans. (a).

Let (p, q) denote a typical throw in which first number is thrown by A and second by B. Then A can throw a higher number than B in the following 15 ways :

$(2,1), (3,2), (3,1), (4,3), (4,2), (4,1), (5,4),$
$(5,3), (5,2), (5,1), (6,5), (6,4), (6,3), (6,2), (6,1)$

Hence the number of ways in which A's throw is greater than B's $= 36 - 15 = 21$.

Hence odds in favour of A not throwing a number greater than B are as $21:15$, *i.e.,* $7:5$.

64. Ans. (c).

$P_1 = \frac{6}{36} = \frac{1}{6}$

[$\because$ Out of total of 36 ways, both the persons can throw equal values in 6 ways]

To find P_2, the total no. of ways $n = 6^4$ and the favourable no. of ways $m = 15\times 8 = 120$.

Since any two numbers out of 6 can be selected in ${}^6C_2$ *i.e.,* 15 ways and corresponding to each of these ways, there are 8 ways *e.g.,* corresponding to the numbers 1 and 2 the eight ways are : $(1,1,1,2), (1,1,2,1), (1,2,1,1), (2,1,1,1), (2,2,2,1), (2,2,1,2), (2,1,2,2) (1,2,2,2)$.

Hence $p_2 = \frac{120}{6^4} = \frac{5}{54}$.

Since $\frac{1}{6} > \frac{5}{54}$, we have $P_1 > P_2$.

65. Ans. (c).

Required probability

$= \frac{{}^5C_3\times{}^{10}C_8}{{}^{15}C_{11}} + \frac{{}^5C_4\times{}^{10}C_7}{{}^{15}C_{11}} + \frac{{}^5C_5\times{}^{10}C_6}{{}^{15}C_{11}}$

$= \frac{1}{{}^{15}C_{11}}[10\times 45 + 5\times 120 + 1\times 210]$

$= \frac{1260\times 1\times 2\times 3\times 4}{15\times 14\times 13\times 12} = \frac{12}{15}$.

66. (i) Ans. (c).

5 can be thrown in 4 ways and 7 can be thrown in 6 ways in a single throw with a pair of dice. Hence no. of ways of throwing neither 5 nor 7 is $36 - (4+6) = 26$.

$\therefore$ Probability of throwing a five in a single throw with a pair of dice is $4/36 = 1/9$.

And probability of throwing neither 5 nor 7 is $26/36 = 13/18$.

Hence the required probability

$= \frac{1}{9} + \frac{13}{18}\cdot\frac{1}{9} + \left(\frac{13}{18}\right)^2\frac{1}{9} + \left(\frac{13}{18}\right)^3\frac{1}{9} + \ldots\ldots$

$= \frac{(1/9)}{1-(13/18)} = \frac{2}{5}$.

Explanation. Since he has already thrown a five (*i.e.* a number different from 7), he may throw 5 at the next attempt the probability for which is $\frac{1}{9}$ or he may throw 5 at the second attempt when he fails to throw either 5 or 7 at the first attempt, the probability for which is $\frac{13}{18}\times\frac{1}{9}$ or at the third attempt the probability for which is $\left(\frac{13}{18}\right)^2\times\frac{1}{9}$ and so on.

(ii) same as part (1).

67. (i) We have $P(A+B) = P(A) + P(B) - P(AB)$

Replace A by AC and B by BC

$\therefore\quad P(AC+BC) = P(AC) + P(BC) - P(ABC)$

$\Rightarrow\quad \frac{P(AC+BC)}{P(C)} = \frac{P(AC)}{P(C)} + \frac{P(BC)}{P(C)} - \frac{P(ABC)}{P(C)}$

$\Rightarrow\quad P(A+B\mid C) = P(A\mid C) + P(B\mid C) - P(AB\mid C)$

(ii) $P(A\bar{B}\mid C) + P(AB\mid C)$

$$= \frac{P(A\bar{B}C)}{P(C)} + \frac{P(ABC)}{P(C)} = \frac{P(AC)}{P(C)} = P(A|C)$$

68. (a) Since events $A \cap \bar{B}$ and $B \cap \bar{A}$ are mutually exclusive

$P[(A \cap \bar{B}) \cup (B \cap \bar{A})]$
$= P(A \cap \bar{B}) + P(B \cap \bar{A})$
$= P(A) - P(A \cap B) + P(B) - P(A \cap B)$
$= P(A) + P(B) - 2P(A \cap B)$

(b) Ans. (a).

$P(B \cap \bar{C}) = Q(A \cap B \cap \bar{C}) + P(\bar{A} \cap B \cap \bar{C})$

or $P(B \cap \bar{C}) = \frac{1}{3} + \frac{1}{3} = \frac{2}{3}$ ...(1)

Again $P(B \cap \bar{C}) = P(B) - P(B \cap C)$

$\therefore$ $P(B \cap C) = P(B) - P(B \cap \bar{C}) = \frac{3}{4} - \frac{2}{3} = \frac{1}{12}$

69. (a) Ans. (b). (see definition).

(b) Ans. (a).

$\because$ Here $A \cap B = \phi$ and so $P(\phi) = 0$.

70. (i) Ans. (c).

$$P(\bar{A}/\bar{B}) = \frac{P(\bar{A} \cap \bar{B})}{P(\bar{B})} = \frac{P(\overline{A \cup B})}{P(\bar{B})} = \frac{1 - P(A \cup B)}{P(\bar{B})}$$

(ii) $P(A \cup B) = P(A \cap B)$ iff

$P(A) + P(B) - P(A \cap B) = P(A \cap B)$

if $P(A) + P(B) = 2P(A \cap B)$ iff

$P(A) + P(B) = 2P(A)P(B/A)$

which is the required relation.

Note that we may write

$P(B)P(A/B)$ for $P(A \cap B)$ instead of $P(A)P(B/A)$.

71. Ans. (a).

For arbitrary events A, B, we have

$P(A \cup B) = P(A) + P(B) - P(A \cap B)$. ...(1)

Since probability of an event is less than or equal to 1, we have

$P(A \cup B) \le 1$ and so (1) gives

$P(A) + P(B) - P(A \cap B) \le 1$

or $P(A) + P(B) - 1 \le P(A \cap B)$

or $P(A \cap B) \ge P(A) + P(B) - 1$.

72. (i) Ans. (b).

Since probability of an event is a non-negative quantity, equation (1) of Q. 71 gives

$P(A) + P(B) - P(A \cap B) \ge 0$

or $P(A) + P(B) \ge P(A \cap B)$

or $P(A \cap B) \le P(A) + P(B)$.

(ii) Ans. (a), (b), (c).

73. Ans. (a), (b), (d). The required probability = Prob. that M occurs and N does not occur or N occurs and M does not occur.

$= P(M \cap N^c) + P(M^c \cap N)$ [This is (d)]

$= P(M) - P(M \cap N) + P(N) - P(M \cap N)$ [Theorem 2, §3]

$= P(M) + P(N) - 2P(M \cap N)$ [This is (a)].

$= 1 - P(M^c) + 1 - P(N^c) - 2[1 - P(M \cap N)^c]$ [By Theorem 3, §3].

$= 2P(M^c \cup N^c) - P(M^c) - P(N^c)$ [By De-Morgan law].

$= 2[P(M^c) + P(N^c) - P(M^c \cup N^c) - P(M^c) - P(N^c)]$

$= P(M^c) + P(N^c) - 2p(M^c \cap N^c)$ [This is (c)].

74. Ans. (b), (c) and (d). Since E, F are independent, we have

$P(E \cap F) = P(E)P(F)$ ...(i)

Now $P(E \cap F^c) = P(E) - P(E \cap F)$

$= P(E) - P(E)P(F)$, by (i)

$= P(E)[1 - P(F)] = P(E)P(F^c)$

$\therefore$ E and F^c are independent.

Again, $P(E^c \cap F^c) = P(E \cup F)^c$

$= 1 - P(E \cup F)$

$= 1 - P(E) - P(F) + P(E \cap F)$

$= 1 - P(E) - P(F) + P(E)P(F)$, by (i)

$= P(E^c) - P(F)[1 - P(E)]$

$= P(E^c) - P(F)P(E^c)$

$= P(E^c)[1 - P(F)] = P(E^c)P(F^c)$.

Hence E^c and F^c are also independent.

Finally, $P(E/F) + P(E^c/F)$

$$= \frac{P(E \cap F)}{P(F)} + \frac{P(E^c \cap F)}{P(F)}$$

$$= \frac{P(E \cap F) + P(E^c \cap F)}{P(F)} = \frac{P(F)}{P(F)} = 1$$

75. Ans. (a) and (d). Since E and F are independent, we have

$P(E \cap F) = P(E) = P(E).P(F)$

$\therefore$ $P(E).P(F) = \frac{1}{12}$ ...(1)

E and F are independent

$\therefore$ E^c and F^c are also independent

$\therefore$ $P(E^c \cap F^c) = P(E^c).P(F^c) = \frac{1}{2}$

$\Rightarrow$ $(1 - P(E)).(1 - P(F)) = \frac{1}{2}$

$\Rightarrow$ $1 - P(E) - P(F) + P(E)P(F) = \frac{1}{2}$

$\Rightarrow$ $1 - P(E) - P(F) + \frac{1}{12} = \frac{1}{2}$

$\Rightarrow$ $P(E) + P(F) = \frac{7}{12}$ ...(2)

Solving (1) and (2), we get $P(E) = \frac{1}{4}, \frac{1}{3}$

then $P(F) = \frac{1}{3}, \frac{1}{4}$ $\therefore$ Ans. (a) and (b) both.

76. (i) Ans. (a). For mutually exclusive events A and B, we have $A \cap B = \phi$ so that $P(A \cap B) = 0$. So in this case, we have

$$P(A \cup B) \text{ or } P(A + B) = P(A) + P(B).$$

(ii) Ans. (d). We know that

$$P(\bar{A}/\bar{B}) = \frac{P(\bar{A} \cap \bar{B})}{P(\bar{B})} = \frac{P(\bar{A})\, P(\bar{B})}{P(\bar{B})}$$

$$= P(\bar{A}) = 1 - P(A)$$

as the events A and B being independent implies that $\bar{A}$ and $\bar{B}$ are also independent and hence we can write $P(\bar{A} \cap \bar{B}) = P(\bar{A})\, P(\bar{B})$.

77. Ans. (a) and (c).

By definition of conditional probability,

$$P(A/B) = \frac{P(A \cap B)}{P(B)}, P(B) \neq 0 \qquad ...(1)$$

Now $P(A \cup B) = P(A) + P(B) - P(A \cap B)$

But $P(A \cup B) \leq 1$. Hence

$$P(A) + P(B) - P(A \cap B) \leq 1$$

or $P(A) + P(B) - 1 \leq P(A \cap B)$.

Then (1) gives $P(A/B) \geq \frac{P(A) + P(B) - 1}{P(B)}$

Thus (a) is correct.

If A, B are independent, then

$$P(A \cap B) = P(A)\, P(B) \qquad ...(2)$$

Now $P(A \cup B) = P(A) + P(B) - P(A \cap B)$

$= P(A) + P(B) - P(A)\, P(B)$, by (2)

and $1 - P(\bar{A}).P(\bar{B}) = 1 - [1 - P(A)][1 - P(B)]$

$= 1 - 1 + P(A) + P(B) - P(A \cap B)$

$= P(A) + P(B) - P(A \cap B)$

It follows that $P(A \cup B) = 1 - P(\bar{A})\, P(\bar{B})$

$\therefore$ (c) is also correct.

Observe that the equality

$P(A \cap \bar{B}) = P(A) - P(A \cap B)$ always holds. So (b) is false. Again if A and B are disjoint, then

$$P(A \cup B) = P(A) + P(B)$$

But $1 - P(\bar{A})\, P(\bar{B}) = P(A) + P(B) - P(A)\, P(B)$ as in part (c).

Hence $P(A \cup B) \neq 1 - P(\bar{A})\, P(\bar{B})$, if A, B are disjoint.

78. (a) Ans. (b). Since the events A, B, C are mutually exclusive, we have

$$P(A \cup B \cup C) = P(A) + P(B) + P(C)$$

$$= \frac{2}{3} + \frac{1}{4} + \frac{1}{6} = \frac{13}{12} > 1$$

which is impossible since the probability of any event cannot be greater than 1.

(b) Ans. (c). We are given that $P(A \cup B) = 0 \cdot 6$, and $P(A \cap B) = 0 \cdot 2$. We know that if A and B are any two events, then

$$P(A \cup B) = P(A) + P(B) - P(A \cap B)$$

or $0 \cdot 6 = 1 - P(\bar{A}) + 1 - P(\bar{B}) - 0 \cdot 2$

or $P(\bar{A}) + P(\bar{B}) = 2 - 0 \cdot 2 - 0 \cdot 6 = 1 \cdot 2$.

79. Ans. (c) and (d). Since $P(A \cap B) = P(A).P(B)$

It means A and B are independent events so A^c and B^c will also be independent

So $P(A \cup B)^c = P(A^c \cup B^c) = P(A^c).P(B^c)$

as A is independent of B.

So $P(A/B) = P(A)$

80. Ans. (a). $p_A + p_B = p_B + p_C = p_C + p_A = p$

From (1) and (2), $p_A = p_C$

From (2) and (3), $p_B = p_A$

$\therefore$ $p_A = p_B = p_c = \frac{1}{2} p$

$\therefore$ $p(A \cup B \cup C) = S_1 - S_2 + S_3$

$$= \frac{3}{2} p - 0 + p^2 = \frac{3p + p^2}{2}$$

81. (a) Ans. $\frac{5}{21}$.

Let A be the event that face 1 turns up and B the event that face 2 turns up.

Then $P(A) = 0 \cdot 10$ and $P(B) = 0 \cdot 32$.

Since A, B are mutually exclusive, we have

$P(A \cup B) = P(A) + P(B) = 0 \cdot 10 + 0 \cdot 32 = 0 \cdot 42$.

We are to find $P(A/A \cup B)$

But $P(A/A \cup B) = \frac{P[A \cap (A \cup B)]}{P(A \cup B)} = \frac{P(A)}{P(A \cup B)}$.

Hence $P(A/A \cup B) = \frac{0 \cdot 10}{0 \cdot 42} = \frac{5}{21}$.

(b) Ans. 75.

Let A be the event that an even face turns up and B be the event that it is 2 or 4

Then $P(A) = P(2) + P(4) + P(6)$

$= \cdot 24 + \cdot 18 + \cdot 14 = \cdot 56$

and $P(B) = P(2) + P(4) = \cdot 24 + \cdot 18 = \cdot 42$

We have to find $P(B/A)$

But $P(B/A) = \frac{P(B \cap A)}{P(A)} = \frac{P(B)}{P(A)}$

[$\because$ B is subset of A]

$$= \frac{\cdot 42}{\cdot 56} = \frac{3}{4} = 0 \cdot 75$$

82. Ans. (b).

Total number of ways $n = 6^3 = 216$, since each die can fall in 6 ways.

We now find the number m of favourable ways. Now the same number on each die can appear in the following six ways :

(1, 1, 1), (2, 2, 2), (3, 3, 3), (4, 4, 4), (5, 5, 5), (6, 6, 6),

i.e. in 6 ways so that $m = 6$.

Hence the required probability $= \frac{m}{n} = \frac{6}{216} = \frac{1}{36}$.

83. If letter came from Clifton there are 6 pairs of consecutive letters *i.e.*, cl, li, if, ft, to, ON in which *ON* appears only once.

$\therefore$ the chance that this was the legible couple on the Clifton hypothesis $= \frac{1}{6}$

pairs of consecutive letters in the word London are lo, on, nd, do, ON in which *ON* occurs twice.

$\therefore$ the chance that this was the legible couple on the London hypothesis $= 2/5$.

$\therefore$ The a posteriori chances that the letter was from Clifton or London are

$$\frac{1/6}{\frac{1}{6}+\frac{2}{5}} \text{ and } \frac{2/5}{\frac{1}{6}+\frac{2}{5}} \text{ respectively.}$$

Thus the reqd. chance $= \frac{12}{17}$.

84. The antecedent chance that the lost card is a spade is $\frac{13}{52} = \frac{1}{4}$, and the chance that is not a spade is $\frac{3}{4}$.

Thus $P_1 = \frac{1}{4}, P_2 = \frac{3}{4}$

Also $p_1 = \frac{12}{51} \times \frac{11}{50}, p_2 = \frac{13}{51} \times \frac{12}{50}$

$\therefore \quad \frac{Q_1}{p_1 P_1} = \frac{Q_2}{p_2 P_2} = \frac{(Q_1 + Q_2 = 1)}{p_1 P_1 + p_2 P_2}$ yields

$$\frac{Q_1}{11} = \frac{Q_2}{3 \times 13} = \frac{1}{50}$$

$\therefore \quad Q_1 = \frac{11}{50}$ = the chance that the missing card was a spade.

85. Ans. (d). Let *A* be the event of obtaining an even sum and *B* the event of obtaining a sum less than five. Then we have to find $P(A \cup B)$. Since *A*, *B* are not mutually exclusive, we have

$$P(A \cup B) = P(A) + P(B) - P(A \cap B)$$
$$= \frac{18}{36} + \frac{6}{36} - \frac{4}{36} = \frac{5}{9}.$$

since there are 18 ways to get an even sum and 6 ways to get a sum < 5, *viz.* (1, 3), (3, 1), (2, 2), (1, 2), (2, 1), (1, 1) and 4 ways to get an even sum less than 5, namely, (1, 3), (3, 1), (2, 2), (1, 1).

86. Ans. $\frac{3}{16}$.

n = total no. of ways $= 2^4 = 16$, since each of the four places in a determinant of order 2 can be filled in two ways by 0 or 1. m = favourable no. of ways = 3 since the value of the determinant is positive when it is

$$\begin{vmatrix} 1 & 0 \\ 0 & 1 \end{vmatrix} \text{ or } \begin{vmatrix} 1 & 0 \\ 1 & 1 \end{vmatrix} \text{ or } \begin{vmatrix} 1 & 1 \\ 0 & 1 \end{vmatrix}.$$

Hence $p = \frac{m}{n} = \frac{3}{16}$.

87. (a) Ans. (d).

$$n(B) = x, P(A) = \frac{4}{10}, P(B) = \frac{x}{10}$$

$$P(A \cap B) = \frac{y}{10} = P(A) \cdot P(B) = \frac{4x}{100} \quad \therefore \quad y = \frac{2x}{5}$$

Since y is an integer, we must have $x = 5$ or 10.

(b) Ans. (b).

Let $S = \{00, 01, 02, \ldots, 49\}$

Any number of set S consists of two digits ab where $a \in \{0, 1, 2, 3, 4\}$ and $b \in \{0, 1, 2, 3, \ldots, 9\}$

For the product of digits to be zero, the number should be of the form $x0$ which are 5 in number as $x \in a$, or of the form $0x$ which are 10 in number as $x \in b$. The only number common to both is 00. Hence, the number of numbers in S, the product of whose digits is zero $= 10 + 5 - 1 = 14$.

Of these numbers whose sum of digits is 8 just one, *i.e.*, 08.

$\therefore$ Required probability $= \frac{1}{14}$.

(c) Ans. (b).

P = Probability of at least one success

= 1 – Probability of all failures

or $\quad 1 - \left(\frac{3}{4}\right)^n \geq \frac{9}{10} \Rightarrow 1 - \frac{9}{10} \geq \left(\frac{3}{4}\right)^n$

$\Rightarrow \quad \frac{1}{10} \geq \left(\frac{3}{4}\right)^n$

or $\quad$ Take log of both sides to the base 10

$\therefore \quad -1 \geq n [\log_{10} 3 - \log_{10} 4]$

or $\quad \frac{1}{n} \leq [\log_{10} 4 - \log_{10} 3]$

Taking reciprocal and hence changing the sign of inequality.

$$n \geq \frac{1}{\log_{10} 4 - \log_{10} 3} \Rightarrow \text{(b)}$$

88. Ans. (a).

Favourable : D_4 shows a number and only 1 of D_1, D_2, D_3 shows same number or all 3 of D_1, D_2, D_3 shows same number

$\therefore$ Required probability

$$= \frac{{}^6C_1 ({}^3C_1 \times 5 \times 5 + {}^3C_2 \times 5 + {}^3C_3)}{216 \times 6}$$

$$= \frac{6 \times (75 + 15 + 1)}{216 \times 6} = \frac{6 \times 91}{216 \times 6} = \frac{91}{216}$$

89. Ans. (b).

$$\text{Required probability} = \frac{{}^3C_1}{{}^9C_1} \cdot \frac{{}^4C_1}{{}^8C_1} \cdot \frac{{}^2C_1}{{}^7C_1} \cdot 3! = \frac{2}{7}$$

90. Ans. (b).

Let A : maximum of three numbers is 6

B : minimum of three numbers is 3

$\therefore \quad P\left(\frac{B}{A}\right) = \frac{P(B \cup A)}{P(A)} = \frac{{}^2C_1}{{}^5C_2} = \frac{2}{10} = \frac{1}{5}$

91. Ans. (c).

$$P = \frac{P(GGG) + P(GRG)}{P(GGG) + P(GRG) + P(RGG) + P(RRG)}$$

$$= \frac{\frac{4}{5}\times\frac{3}{4}\times\frac{3}{4}+\frac{4}{5}\times\frac{1}{4}\times\frac{1}{4}}{\frac{4}{5}\times\frac{3}{4}\times\frac{3}{4}+\frac{4}{5}\times\frac{1}{4}\times\frac{1}{4}+\frac{1}{5}\times\frac{1}{4}\times\frac{3}{4}+\frac{1}{5}\times\frac{3}{4}\times\frac{1}{4}}$$

$$= \frac{36+4}{36+4+3+3} = \frac{40}{46} = \frac{20}{23}$$

92. Ans. (c).

$1 - p^5 \geq \frac{31}{32} \quad \Rightarrow \quad p^5 \leq \frac{1}{32} \Rightarrow p \leq \frac{1}{2}$

$\therefore \quad p \in \left[0, \frac{1}{2}\right]$

93. Ans. (c).

$\omega^{r_1} + \omega^{r_2} + \omega^{r_3} = 0$; r_1, r_2, r_3 are to be selected from $\{1, 2, 3, 4, 5, 6\}$

$\because \quad 1 + \omega + \omega^2 = 0$, No from r_1, r_2, r_3 one has remainder 1, other has remainder 2 and third has remainder 0 when divided by 3

$\therefore$ We have to select r_1, r_2, r_3 from {1, 4} or {2, 5] or {3, 5]

Which can be done in ${}^2C_1 \times {}^2C_1 \times {}^2C_1$ ways and value of r_1, r_2, r_3 can be interchanged in 3 ! ways

$\therefore$ required probability $= \frac{({}^2C_1 \times {}^2C_1 \times {}^2C_1) \times 3!}{6 \times 6 \times 6} = \frac{2}{9}$

94. Ans. (a) and (d).

$P(E \cap F) = P(E) . P(F)$

$P(E \cap \bar{F}) + P(\bar{E} \cap F) = \frac{11}{25}, \quad P(\bar{E} \cap \bar{F}) = \frac{2}{25}$

$\Rightarrow \quad P(F) + P(E) - 2P(E \cap F) = \frac{11}{25}$

and $1 - [P(E) + P(F) - P(E \cap F)] = \frac{2}{25}$ ...(1)

$\Rightarrow \quad [P(E) + P(F) - P(E \cap F)] = \frac{23}{25}$ ...(2)

$\therefore \quad P(E) + P(F) = \frac{7}{25}$ ...(3)

$\therefore$ on solving (1), (2) and (3) we get

$P(E) = \frac{4}{5}, \ P(F) = \frac{3}{5}$, or $P(E) = \frac{3}{5}, P(F) = \frac{4}{5}$

95. Ans. (b) and (d).

$P(X_1) = \frac{1}{2}, P(X_2) = \frac{1}{4}, P(X_3) = \frac{1}{4}$

$P(X) = P(E_1 \ E_2 E_3) + P(\bar{E}_1 E_2 E_3) + P(E_1 \bar{E}_2 E_3) + P(E_1 E_2 \bar{E}_3)$

$= \frac{1}{2}.\frac{1}{4}.\frac{1}{4} + \frac{1}{2}.\frac{1}{4}.\frac{1}{4} + \frac{1}{2}.\frac{3}{4}.\frac{1}{4} + \frac{1}{2}.\frac{1}{4}.\frac{3}{4}$

$= \frac{1}{4}$

(a) $P\left(\frac{X_1'}{X}\right) = \frac{P(X_1' nx)}{P(X)} = \frac{\frac{1}{2}.\frac{1}{4}.\frac{1}{4}}{\frac{1}{4}} = \frac{1}{8}$

(b) P(exactly two engines are functioning $| x$]

$= \frac{P(\text{exactly two engines } \cap X]}{P(X)}$

$= \frac{\frac{1}{2}\times\frac{1}{4}\times\frac{1}{4}+\frac{1}{2}\times\frac{3}{4}\times\frac{1}{4}+\frac{1}{2}\times\frac{1}{4}\times\frac{3}{4}}{1/4} = \frac{7}{8}$

(c) $P(X | X_2) = \frac{P(X \cap X_2)}{P(X_2)}$

$= \frac{\frac{1}{2}.\frac{1}{4}.\frac{1}{4}+\frac{1}{2}.\frac{1}{4}.\frac{1}{4}+\frac{1}{2}.\frac{1}{4}.\frac{3}{4}}{\frac{1}{4}} = \frac{5}{8}$

(d) $P(X | X_1) = \frac{P(X \cap X_1)}{P(X_1)}$

$= \frac{\frac{1}{2}.\frac{1}{4}.\frac{1}{4}+\frac{1}{2}.\frac{3}{4}.\frac{1}{4}+\frac{1}{2}.\frac{1}{4}.\frac{3}{4}}{\frac{1}{2}} = \frac{7}{16}$

96. Ans. (a) and (b). $P(X|Y) = \frac{1}{2}$

$\frac{P(X \cap Y)}{P(Y)} = \frac{1}{2} \quad \Rightarrow P(Y) = \frac{1}{3}$

$P(Y | X) = \frac{1}{3}, \qquad \frac{P(X \cap Y)}{P(X)} = \frac{1}{3} \Rightarrow P(X) = \frac{1}{2}$

$P(X \cup Y) = P(X) + P(Y) - P(X \cap Y) = \frac{2}{3} \Rightarrow$ (a) is correct

$P(X \cap Y) = P(X) \, P(Y) \Rightarrow X$ and Y are independent $\Rightarrow$ (b) is correct

$P(X' \cap Y) = P(Y) - P(X \cap Y) = \frac{1}{3} - \frac{1}{6} = \frac{1}{6} \Rightarrow$ (d) is not correct

97. Ans. (b).

P (white) $= P(H \cap \text{white}) + P(T \cap \text{white})$

$= \frac{1}{2}\left[\frac{3}{5} \times 1 + \frac{2}{5} \times \frac{1}{2}\right]$

$+ \frac{1}{2}\left[\frac{{}^3C_2}{{}^5C_2} \times 1 + \frac{{}^2C_2}{{}^5C_2} \times \frac{1}{3} + \frac{{}^3C_1 \cdot {}^2C_1}{{}^5C_2} \times \frac{2}{3}\right]$

$= \frac{1}{2} \times \frac{8}{10} \times \frac{1}{2} \times \left[\frac{3}{10} + \frac{1}{30} + \frac{12}{30}\right] = \frac{4}{10} + \frac{1}{2} \times \frac{22}{30} = \frac{23}{30}$

98. Ans. (d). $P(\text{Head} \mid \text{white}) = \frac{P(\text{Head} \cap \text{white})}{P(\text{white})}$

$$= \frac{\frac{1}{2}\times\left\{\frac{3}{5}\times 1+\frac{2}{5}\times\frac{1}{2}\right\}}{\frac{23}{30}} = \frac{\frac{4}{10}}{\frac{23}{30}} = \frac{12}{23}$$

99. (a) Ans. (a). $P(X=3)=\frac{5}{6}\cdot\frac{5}{6}\cdot\frac{1}{6}=\frac{25}{216}$

(b) Ans. (b). $P(X\le 2)=\frac{1}{6}+\frac{5}{6}\cdot\frac{1}{6}=\frac{11}{36}$

$\therefore$ Reqd. probability is $\left(1-\frac{11}{36}\right)=\frac{25}{36}$

(c) Ans. (d). For $X\ge 6$, the probability is

$$\frac{5^5}{6^6}+\frac{5^6}{6^7}+\ldots\infty=\frac{5^5}{6^6}\left(\frac{1}{1-(5/6)}\right)=\left(\frac{5}{6}\right)^5$$

For $X>3$,

$$\frac{5^3}{6^4}+\frac{5^4}{6^5}+\frac{5^5}{6^6}+\ldots\infty=\frac{5^3}{6^4}\left(\frac{1}{1-(5/6)}\right)=\left(\frac{5}{6}\right)^3$$

Hence conditional probability is

$$\left(\frac{5}{6}\right)^5\div\left(\frac{5}{6}\right)^3=\frac{25}{36}$$

MISCELLANEOUS EXERCISE

Comphresion

1. One Indian and four American men and their wives are to be seated randomly around a cicular table. Then the conditional probability that the Indian man is seated adjacent to his wife given that each American man is seated adjacent to his wife is

(1) 1/2 (b) 1/3 (c) 2/5 (d) 1/5

(I.I.T. 2007)

Sol. Ans. (c). Let E = event when each American man is seated adjacent to his wife

A = event when Indian man is seated adjacent to his wife

Now $n(A\cap E)=(4!)\times(2!)^5$

Event when each American man is seated adjacent to his wife.

Again $n(E)=(5!)\times(2!)^4$

$$\Rightarrow\quad P\left(\frac{A}{E}\right)=\frac{n(A\cap E)}{n(E)}=\frac{(4!)\times(2!)^5}{(5!)\times(2!)^4}=\frac{2}{5}$$

Alternative :

Fixing four American couples and one Indian man in between any two couples; we have 5 different ways in which his wife can be seated, of which 2 cases are favourable.

$\therefore$ required probability $=\frac{2}{5}\Rightarrow$ (c).

2. Let $H_1, H_2, \ldots, H_n$ be mutually exclusive and exhaustive events with $P(H_i)>0, i=1,2,\ldots n$. Let E be any other event with $0<P(E)<1$.

STATEMENT-1 :

$P(H_i\,|\,E)>P(E\,|\,H_1)\,.\,P(H_i)$ for $i=1,2,\ldots n$

because

STATEMENT-2 : $\sum_{i=1}^{n} P(H_i)=1$

(I.I.T. 2007)

Sol. Ans. (d).

If $P(H_i\cap E)=0$ for some i, then $P\left(\frac{H_i}{E}\right)=P\left(\frac{E}{H_i}\right)=0$

If $P(H_i\cap E)\ne 0$ for $\forall\ i=1,2\ldots n$, then

$$P\left(\frac{H_i}{E}\right)=\frac{P(H_i\cap E)}{P(H_i)}\times\frac{P(H_i)}{P(E)}$$

$$=\frac{P\left(\frac{E}{H_i}\right)\times P(H_i)}{P(H)}>P\left(\frac{E}{H_i}\right).P(H_i)$$

[as $0<P(E)<1$]

Hence statement 1 may not always be true.

Statement 2 :

Clearly $H_1\cup H_2\ldots\cup H_n=S$ (sample space)

$\Rightarrow\quad P(H_1)+P(H_2)+\ldots+P(H_n)=1$

3. Let E^c denote the complement of an event E. Let E, F, G be pairwise independent events with $P(G)>0$ and $P(E\cap F\cap G)=0$. Then $P(E^C\cap F^C\,|\,G)$ equals

(a) $P(E^C)+P(F^C)$ (b) $P(E^C)-P(F^C)$

(c) $P(E^C)-P(F)$ (d) $P(E)-P(F^C)$

(I.I.T. 2007)

Sol. Ans. (c).

$$P\left(\frac{E^C\cap F^C}{G}\right)=\frac{P(E^C\cap F^C\cap G)}{P(G)}$$

$$=\frac{P(G)-P(E\cap G)-P(G\cap F)}{P(G)}$$

$$=\frac{P(G)(1-P(E)-P(F))}{P(G)}\qquad[\because P(G)\ne 0]$$

$$=1-P(E)-P(F)=P(E^C)-P(F)$$

4. **Read** : There are n urns U_i, $(i=1,\ldots,n)$ which contains i white and $(n+1-i)$ black balls. U_i is event of selecting the ith urn, W event of getting white ball from the selected urn, E is event of getting even number of balls from selected urn.

Now answer following questions :

5. If $P(U_i)\ \alpha\ i; \{i=1,2,3,\ldots,n\}$, then $\lim_{n\to\infty} P(W)$ is :

(a) $\frac{2}{3}$ (b) $\frac{1}{3}$ (c) $\frac{1}{2}$ (d) $\frac{3}{4}$

Sol. Ans. (a).

$P(U_1) = \lambda, P(U_2) = 2\lambda, ..., P(U_n) = n\lambda$

$\Rightarrow \quad \lambda + 2\lambda + ... + n\lambda = 1 \quad \Rightarrow \lambda = \frac{2}{n(n+1)}$

$\Rightarrow \quad P(W) = \lim_{n\to\infty} \left(\frac{2\times 1}{n(n+1)}\right)\times\left(\frac{1}{n+1}\right)$

$+ \frac{2\times 2}{n(n+1)}\times\frac{2}{n+1} + ... = \lim_{n\to\infty} \frac{2n+1}{3(n+1)} = \frac{2}{3}$

6. If $P(U_i) = C$ (constant), then $P\left(\frac{U_n}{W}\right)$, where n is even :

(a) $\frac{1}{2}$ (b) $\frac{n}{n+1}$ (c) $\frac{n+2}{2(n+1)}$ (d) $\left(\frac{n+1}{n+2}\right)$

Sol. Ans. (c).

$$P\left(\frac{U_i}{E}\right) = \frac{C\left[\frac{2}{n+1} + \frac{4}{n+1} + ... + \frac{2(n/2)}{n+1}\right]}{c + c + ... + c \quad (n/2 \text{ times})} = \frac{n+2}{2(n+1)}$$

7. $P(U_i) = \frac{1}{n}$, and one urn is selected at random, then $P(W)$ is :

(a) $\frac{1}{2}$ (b) $\frac{1}{n}$ (c) $\frac{n}{n+1}$ (d) $\frac{n+1}{n+2}$

Sol. Ans. (a).

$$P(W) = \frac{1}{n}\times\left(\frac{1}{n+1}\right) + \frac{1}{n}\times\left(\frac{2}{n+1}\right) + ... + \frac{1}{n}\times\left(\frac{n}{n+1}\right) = \frac{1}{2}$$

8. Probabilities of Ramesh using car, scooter, bus and train are 1/7, 2/7, 3/7 and 1/7 respectively. Probabilities of him reaching office late with these vehicles are 2/9, 4/9, 1/9 and 1/9 respectively. If he reaches office on time, find the probability that he went by car. **(I.I.T. 2005)**

Sol. Let C = Car, B = Bus, S = Scooter, T = Train, E = reaching office in time.

Given $P(C) = \frac{1}{7}, P(B) = \frac{3}{7}, P(S) = \frac{2}{7}, P(T) = \frac{1}{7}$

Also $P(E/C) = \frac{2}{9}, P(E/B) = \frac{1}{9}, P(E/S) = \frac{4}{9}, P(E/T) = \frac{1}{9}$

$$P(C/E) = \frac{P(C).P(E/C)}{P(C)P(E/C) + P(B).P(E/B) + P(S)P(E/S) + P(T).P(E/T)}$$

$$= \frac{\frac{1}{7}\times\frac{2}{9}}{\left(\frac{1}{7}\times\frac{2}{9}\right) + \left(\frac{3}{7}\times\frac{1}{9}\right) + \left(\frac{2}{7}\times\frac{4}{9}\right) + \left(\frac{1}{7}\times\frac{1}{9}\right)} = \frac{2}{14} = \frac{1}{7}.$$

9. Four number are choose at random (without replacement) from the set {1, 2, 3, ... 20)

Statement-1 : The probability that the choose numbers when arranged in same order will form an A.P. is $\frac{1}{85}$

Statement-2 : If the four chosen numbers forms an A.P., then the set of all possible values of common difference is $\{\pm 1, \pm 2, \pm 3, \pm 4, \pm 5\}$ **(AIEEE 2010)**

Sol. Ans. (c).

Let the terms of an A.P., $a, a+d, a+2d, a+3d$

$\because \quad a > 1 \Rightarrow a + 3d \le 20, 3d \le 19 \Rightarrow d \le \frac{19}{3}$

$\therefore \quad d = \pm 1, \pm 2, \pm 3, \pm 4, \pm 5$ and ± 6

$\Rightarrow$ statement (2) is not correct.

If $d = 1$, then $a + 3d \le 20 \Rightarrow a \le 17 \Rightarrow 17$ cases will be there. Similarly if $d = -1$. In this case for $d = \pm 1$ is 34. Similarly

d	± 1	± 2	± 3	± 4	± 5	± 6
Cases	34	28	22	16	10	14

$\therefore$ total favourable cases 114, total exhaustive the case $= {}^{20}C_4 \times 2!$

$\therefore$ Required probability $= \frac{114}{{}^{20}C_4 \times 2!} = \frac{1}{85}$

$\Rightarrow$ statement-1 is true.

❑

CHAPTER

35

Algebra

Mathematical Reasoning

§1. Mathematical Logic

Statement :

Definition. *A sentence which is either true or false but not both is called a statement and are generally denoted by letters p, q, r, s, ...*

For Example :

(a) Chandigarh is capital of Punjab.

(b) Sum of the angles of a triangle is two right angles.

The above are sentences which are true and hence are statements. Now below we shall give examples of sentences which are false and they will also be called statements.

(c) 5 is greater than 7. **false.**

(d) Mount Everest is a river. **false.**

Now we shall give examples of sentences which are not statements.

(e) When will you come back?

(f) How do you do?

(g) The liar says, "I always tell a lie."

§2. Logical Connectives

(i) Conjunction.

A compound statement joining two statements by 'And' is called a conjunction and is denoted by Λ. *If p and q are two statements then* $p \Lambda q$ *(p and q) is a conjunction.*

For example : Consider the statement

$x^3 = -27$ has three integral roots.

Above is a false statement which is combination of two statements.

$p : x^3 = -27$ has three roots (True)

q : These three roots are integral (False)

$p \Lambda q : x^2 = -27$ has three integral roots. (False)

Again consider the statements

p : Earth is a planet (True)

p : Earth is centre of universe (False)

$p \wedge q$: Earth is a planet and is centre of universe (False)

Now consider the statements

$p : 7 > 4$ (True), $q : 9 < 15$ (True)

then $p \Lambda q : 7 > 4$ and $9 < 15$ (True).

From above examples it is clear that the **conjunction** $p \wedge q$ **is a true statement if and only if both *p* and *q* are true.** In case either of p and q or both are false then $p \wedge q$ is also false. We shall express this in tabular form given below.

(ii) Disjunctions. *A compound statement joining two statements by 'or' is called a disjunction and is denoted by* $\vee$.

If p and q are two statements then $p \vee q$ (p or q) is a disjunction.

For example : Consider the statements

p : Prof. Khanna teaches Mathematics (True)

q : Prof. Khanna teaches Biology (False)

$p V q$: Prof. Khanna teaches Mathematics or Biology (True)

p : Delhi is capital of India (True)

q : Mount Everest is a river (False)

$p V q$: Delhi is capital of India or Mount Everest is a river (True)

From above example it is clear that a disjunction $p V q$ is a false statement if and only if both p and q are false and true otherwise *i.e.*, if either of these or both be true then $p V q$ is also true.

We can express both $p \Lambda q$ and $p V q$ in tabular form as under. T stands for true and F stands for false.

Truth Table

p	q	$p \wedge q$	$p \vee q$
T	T	T	T
T	F	F	T
F	T	F	T
F	F	F	F

(iii) Implications $p \Rightarrow q$. One way implication *i.e.*, p implies q which means 'if p then q' or 'q if p'.

$p : x = 2 \quad q : x^2 = 4 \quad \therefore \quad p \Rightarrow q.$

$p : x = y \quad q : x^3 = y^3 \quad \therefore \quad p \Rightarrow q$

A true statement cannot imply a false statement.

This statement $p \Rightarrow q$ is always true except when p is true q is false.

(iv) Two way Implication : $p \Leftrightarrow q$, p implies and is implied by q or "p if and only if q".

$x \pm 4 \Leftrightarrow x^2 = 16$ because it is true both ways

i.e., if $= \pm 4$ then $x^2 = 16$ and if $x^2 = 16$ then $x = \pm 4$.

The statement $p \Leftrightarrow q$ is true if both p and q are true or both false and is false when one of the statements is true and the other is false.

p	q	$p \Rightarrow q$	$q \Rightarrow q$	$p \Leftrightarrow q$
T	T	T	T	T
T	F	F	T	F
F	T	T	F	F
F	F	F	T	T

(v) Negation : If p is a statement then negation p is written as $\sim p$ *i.e.*, if p : It is raining then $\sim p$: it is not raining or if p : Delhi is a capital of India then $\sim p$: Delhi is not capital of India. If p is true then $\sim p$ is false. If p is false then $\sim p$ is true.

We can now have the following truth table.

p	q	$p \wedge q$	$\sim(p \wedge q)$	$\sim p$	$\sim q$	$\sim p \vee \sim q$	$\sim(p \wedge q) \Rightarrow (\sim p \wedge \sim q)$
T	T	T	F	F	F	F	T
T	F	F	T	F	T	T	T
F	T	F	T	T	F	T	T
F	F	F	T	T	T	T	T

(vi) Conditional : Let us suppose p and q are two statements. Then the statement "$p \Rightarrow q$" which is read as if "p then q" or "p implies q" is called conditional statements. Here 'p' is called antecedent and 'q' is called consequent. The conditional statement '$p \Rightarrow q$' has four possibilities depends on p and q.

Case I. If p is true, q is false, then "$p \Rightarrow q$" is false.
Case II. If p is true, q is true, then "$p \Rightarrow q$" is true
Case III. If p is false, q is true, then "$p \Rightarrow q$" is true.
Case IV. If p is false, q is false, then "$p \Rightarrow q$" is true.

(vii) Bi-Conditional : Let p and q be two statements, then $p \Leftrightarrow q$ is called bi-conditional statement. This statement can also be written as

$(p \Rightarrow q)$ and $(q \Rightarrow p)$ *i.e.* $(p \Rightarrow q) \wedge (q \Rightarrow p)$.

This bi-conditional statement is true only if both the statement p and q have same truth values.

(viii) Joint Denial : The word "NOR" is a combination of NOT and OR where NOT and OR stands for negation and disjunction. Let p and q be two statements. The "$p \downarrow q$" is called Joint Denial or "NOR" statement and read as "Neither p nor q". This "$p \downarrow q$" can also be written as

$p \downarrow q \Leftrightarrow \urcorner(p \vee q)$

The Joint Denial statement $p \downarrow q$ is true only when p and q both are false.

(ix) NAND Statement : The word "NAND" is a combination of NOT and AND where NOT and AND stand for negation and conjunction respectively. Then the statement "$p \uparrow q$" is called NAND statement and this can be written as

$p \uparrow q \Leftrightarrow \urcorner(p \wedge q)$

This statement is false only if both p and q are true.

(x) Types of Conditional Statement : Let p and q be any two statements, then there are some other conditional statements which are related to the conditional $p \Rightarrow q$.

(i) Converse Implication : The statement $q \Rightarrow p$ is called converse implication of the statement of $p \Rightarrow q$.

(ii) Inverse Implication : The statement $\urcorner p \Rightarrow \urcorner q$ is called inverse implication of the statement $p \Rightarrow q$.

(iii) Contrapositive Implication : The statement $\urcorner q \Rightarrow \urcorner p$ is called contrapositive of the statement $p \Rightarrow q$.

Use of Brackets.

The use of brackets in the statements has an important role. By using brackets in the statements, the meaning or explanation of the statements are completely different. There are some rules related to the brackets.

(i) If the negation (*i.e.*, $\urcorner$) is repeated in the statement then there is no need of bracket.

For Example : $\urcorner\urcorner p$ and $(\urcorner(\urcorner p))$ both have same meaning.

(ii) If in a statement, the connectives of same type are present, then brackets are applied from the left. For example : $p \vee q \vee r \vee s = [\{(p \vee q) \vee r\} \vee s]$.

(iii) If the different connectives are used in the statement, then we remove the bracket of lower order connective, but we can not remove the bracket of higher order connective.

For example : $p \Rightarrow (q \wedge r) = p \Rightarrow q \wedge r$.

Here order of $\wedge$ is less than the order of $\Rightarrow$. Hence bracket is removed. Let us consider another example

$$p \vee (q \Rightarrow r) \neq p \vee q \Rightarrow r$$

In this example, bracket can not be removed.

§3. Types of Sentences

There are two type of sentences or statements.

(i) Simple Sentence : A statement which has no connectives is called simple sentence or simple statement (or Atomic statement).

For example : He is a boy or she is a girl. Both are simple.

(ii) Compound Sentence : A statement which is formed by two simple statement through the connective is called compound sentence or molecular sentence.

For Example :

(a) If you work hard, then you will get success.

(b) Suresh will play or he will leave ground.

Statement Form

This is a form obtained by simple statements, using finite number of connectives, is called statement form.

For example : Let p, q and r be three simple statements, then the statement $(p \wedge q) \Rightarrow r$ is a statement form. The connective which is used at the end of the statement form is called principal connective.

Principal connective.

Thus in the above example, $\Rightarrow$ is the principal connective. The statements on both sides of the principal connective are called **Arguments.** Therefore, in the above example, the statement $(p \wedge q)$ and r are arguments. The statement form is also known as **Truth function.**

Use of Venn Diagrams in Checking Truth and Falsity of Statements

In this section, we shall discuss the usage of Venn diagrams to represent truth and falsity of statement of propositions.

Solved Examples

Example 1. Give the venn diagram for the truth of the following statement "Equivalent triangles are isosceles triangles.

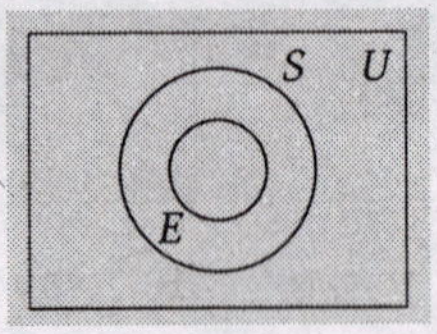

Fig. 1

Sol. Let U, E and S denotes the set of triangles in a plane, the set of equilateral triangles in a plane and the set of all isosceles triangles in a plane respectively.

Then, $E \subset U$ and $S \subset U$

It is also clear that $E \subset S$. Hence, we have the following Venn diagram to represent the truth of the given statement.

Example 2. Let U, P and T denotes respectively the set of human beings, the set of policemen and the set of all thieves. Write the truth value of the following statements from the Venn diagram given below :

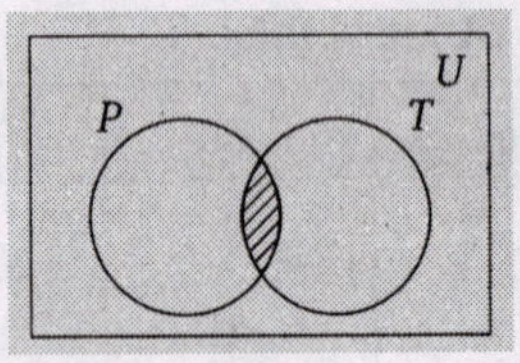

Fig. 2

(i) No policeman is a thief.

(ii) Thieves are not policeman.

(iii) Men who are not policemen are thieves.

(iv) Some policemen are thieves.

Sol. (i) From Venn diagram, it is clear that the policemen x is a thief also. Therefore, the given statement is not true. Hence, the truth value is F.

(ii) We find that $P \cap T \neq \phi$, therefore, there are some thieves who are also policemen. Hence, the statement is not true and the truth value is F.

(iii) From Venn diagram, it is clear that there are some human beings who are neither policemen nor thieves. Hence, the above statement is not true and the truth value is F.

(iv) Here, it is clear that the policemen x is a thief also. Hence, the given statement is true and the truth value is T.

Example 3. Use Venn diagrams to check the validity of the following argument

S_1 : If a man is a bachelor, he is unhappy.

S_2 : If a man is unhappy, he dies young.

... ...

S : All bachelors die young.

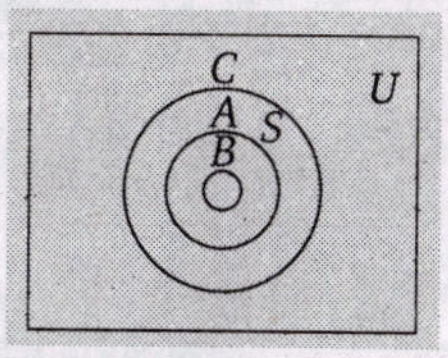

Fig. 3

Sol. Define the following sets

A = set of all unhappy men

B = set of all bachelors

and C = set of all men who die young.

Then, the truth of the hypothesis S_1 is represented by placing the B inside the set A, *i.e.*, $B \subset A$.

Now, the truth of statement S_2 is represented by placing the set A completely inside the set C, *i.e.*, $A \subset C$.

Now, S_1 and S_2 are true

$\Rightarrow$ $B \subset A$ and $A \subset C$.

$\Rightarrow$ $B \subset C$, *i.e.*, all bachelors die young.

$\therefore$ S is true.

Hence, the given argument is a valid argument.

§4. Truth values and Truth Table

Since we know that every statement has a unique value. This unique value is called **Truth value.** These truth values are 'True' or 'False'. Hence the truth value of every statement form is obtained by the truth values of its components. The range of statement form (or Truth function) is $\{T, F\}$. Hence we can say that there will be 2^n truth function having n statements. T and F represent the truth value, True and False respectively. These truth values are also represented by 1 and 0.

To show that the set of statement and the operations of conjunction, disjunction and negation, it is necessary first to define them equal. Let us consider two statement forms 'f' and 'g' having two component statements p and q each. These two statement forms are said to be equal if both have same truth values for each of the four possible ways.

(i) p false and q true. (ii) p true and q false.

(iii) p and q both are true. (iv) p and q both are false.

If in anyone of above possible ways, the truth values differ, then f and g are not equal. To understand the meaning and uses of different types of connectives, we analyse the truth values with the help of a table. This table is called truth table.

(1) Truth Table for Negation

Let p be any statement, then $\sim p$ is negation of p. The truth value of negation of p is opposite of truth value of p. Suppose p = Delhi is a capital of India.

Then, $\sim p$ = Delhi is not a capital of India.

The truth table is given below :

p	$\sim P(\rceil p)$
T	F
F	T

Or

p	$\sim P(\rceil p)$
1	0
0	1

(2) Truth Table for Conjunction

Let p and q be two simple statements, then $p \wedge q$ is conjunction of p and q. Thus $p \wedge q$ has a true value if both p and q have true values. Let us consider

p = Lucknow is a capital of Uttar Pradesh.

q = Delhi is a capital of India.

Then $p \wedge q$ means that Lucknow is a capital of Uttar Pradesh and Delhi is a capital of India. The truth table is given below :

p	q	$p \wedge q$
T	T	T
T	F	F
F	T	F
F	F	F

Or

p	q	$p \wedge q$
1	1	1
1	0	0
0	1	0
0	0	0

(3) Truth Table for Disjunction

Let p and q be any two simple statements, then $p \vee q$ is called disjunction of p and q which is read as p or q. Let us consider

p = Mathematics is very hard subject;

q = Commerce is very easy subject.

Then $p \vee q$ can be written as

$p \vee q$ = Mathematics is very hard subject or commerce is very easy subject. The statement $p \vee q$ has the truth value false only if both are false. Thus truth table is given below :

p	q	$p \vee q$
T	T	T
T	F	T
F	T	T
F	F	F

Or

p	q	$p \vee q$
1	1	1
1	0	1
0	1	1
0	0	0

(4) Truth Table for conditional

Let p and q be two simple statements, then $p \Rightarrow q$ is the statement which is conditional. This statement has the truth value false only if antecedent p is true and consequent q is false. The truth table for $p \Rightarrow q$ is given below :

p	q	$p \Rightarrow q$
T	T	T
T	F	F
F	T	T
F	F	T

Or

p	q	$p \Rightarrow q$
1	1	1
1	0	0
0	1	1
0	0	1

(5) Truth Table for Bi-Conditional

Let p and q be any two simple statements. The statement of the type $p \Leftrightarrow q$ is called bi-conditional. This can also be written as $p \Leftrightarrow q = (p \Rightarrow q) \wedge (q \Rightarrow p)$. This statement has the truth value true only if both p and q have same truth values.

Thus the truth table is given below :

p	q	$p \Leftrightarrow q$
T	T	T
T	F	F
F	T	F
F	F	T

Or

p	q	$p \Leftrightarrow q$
1	1	1
1	0	0
0	1	0
0	0	1

(6) Truth table for Joint Denial

Let p and q be two statements. The statement $p \downarrow q$ is called Joint Denial statement, which is read as 'Neither p nor q'. The statement $p \downarrow q$ has truth value 'True' when both p and q are false. Thus the truth table for $p \downarrow q$ is given below :

p	q	$p \downarrow q$
T	T	F
T	F	F
F	T	F
F	F	T

Or

p	q	$p \downarrow q$
1	1	0
1	0	0
0	1	0
0	0	1

(7) Truth Table for NAND Statement

Let p and q be two statements. The statement $p \uparrow q$ is called NAND statement. This statement is false only when both p and q are true. The truth table for NAND statement is given below :

p	q	$p \uparrow q$
T	T	F
T	F	T
F	T	T
F	F	T

Or

p	q	$p \uparrow q$
1	1	0
1	0	1
0	1	1
0	0	1

(8) Table for Symbols

To understand and then to write any statement into symbols there is a table given below :

(i)	If p then q	$p \Rightarrow q$
(ii)	p if q	$q \Rightarrow p$
(iii)	p only if q	$q \Rightarrow p$
(iv)	p unless q	$\rceil q \Rightarrow p$
(v)	p is a sufficient condition for q	$p \Rightarrow q$
(vi)	p is a necessary condition for q	$q \Rightarrow p$
(vii)	A sufficient condition for p is q	$q \Rightarrow p$
(viii)	A necessary condition for p is q	$p \Rightarrow q$
(ix)	In order that p is sufficient that q	$q \Rightarrow p$
(x)	In order that p is necessary that q	$p \Rightarrow q$
(xi)	p if and only if q	$p \Leftrightarrow q$
(xii)	p is a necessary and sufficient condition for q	$p \Leftrightarrow q$

Solved Examples

Example 1. Which of the following expression are statements :

(i) $1+2+3=1\times 2\times 3$ (ii) $\{2,3\} \subset \{2,4,6\}$
(iii) May you live long. (iv) 7 is a prime number
(v) $5 \in \{1,4,5\}$ (vi) All roses are white
(vii) What is your Name ?
(viii) The girls are beautiful.
(ix) Go to your home.
(x) Blood is red.

Sol. (i) Since $1+2+3=1\times 2\times 3$ or $6=6$.
Thus (i) is true. Hence, (i) is a statement.

(ii) $\{2,3\} \subset \{2,4,6\}$.
This expression is false. Hence, it is a statement.

(iii) "May you live long" is not a declarative sentence. Hence, it is not a statement.

(iv) "7 is a prime number" which is declarative sentence having truth value 'True'.
Hence, it is a statement.

(v) $5 \in \{1,4,5\}$ is true. Hence, it is a statement.

(vi) "All roses are white". This is a declarative sentence and having truth value 'False'.
Hence, it is a statement.

(vii) "What is your name?" It is not a declarative sentence. Hence, it is not a statement.

(viii) "The girls are beautiful" This sentence is not declarative. Hence, it is not a statement.

(ix) "Go to your home". This is not a declarative sentence. Hence, it is not a statement.

(x) "Blood is red." It is a declarative sentence. Its truth value is True. Hence, it is a statement.

Example 2. Which of the following sentences are propositions ? What are the truth values of those that are propositions (statement) ?

(i) Do you speak Hindi ? (ii) Four is even.
(iii) Please submit your proposal as soon as possible.
(iv) Do you speak English ?
(v) $4 - x = 8$.
(vi) Please try to solve the problem.

Sol. We know that a statement is a declarative sentence which is either true or false, but not both. These two values are 'true' and 'false' denoted by symbolical T and F. Thus

(i) not statement (ii) statement
(iii) not statement (iv) not statement
(v) not statement (vi) not statement

Example 3. If $P \equiv$ He is a carpenter and $q =$ He is making a table.

Then write down the following statement into symbols :

(i) He is a carpenter and making a table.
(ii) He is a carpenter but is not making a table.
(iii) It is false that he is a carpenter or making a table.
(iv) Neither he is a carpenter nor he is making a table.
(v) He is not a carpenter and he is making a table.
(vi) It is false that he is not a carpenter or is not making a table.
(vii) He is a carpenter or making a table.

Sol. The solution of above compound statements in terms of p and q are given below :

(i) $p \wedge q$ (ii) $p \wedge \rceil q$
(iii) $\rceil(p \vee q)$ (iv) $\rceil p \wedge \rceil q$
(v) $\rceil p \wedge q$ (vi) $(\rceil p \vee \rceil q)$
(vii) $p \vee q$

Example 4. Consider the following :

p : This computer is good.
q : This computer is cheap.

Write each of the following statements in symbolic forms :

(i) This computer is good and cheap.
(ii) This computer is not good but cheap.
(iii) This computer is costly but good.
(iv) This computer is neither good nor cheap.
(v) This computer is good or cheap.

Sol. (i) $p \wedge q$ (ii) $p' \wedge q$
(iii) $p \vee q'$ (iv) $p' \vee q'$
(v) $p \vee q$.

Example 5. Consider the following :

p : Question paper is hard.
p : I will fail in the examination.

Then translate the following sentences into symbols :

(i) Question paper is hard then I will fail in the examination.
(ii) If I will not fail in the examination, then question paper is not hard.
(iii) Question paper is not hard if and only if I will fail in the examination.
(iv) If question paper is not hard then I will pass in the examination.

Sol. (i) $p \Rightarrow q$ (ii) $\rceil p \Rightarrow \rceil q$
(iii) $\rceil p \Leftrightarrow q$ (iv) $\rceil p \Rightarrow \rceil q$

Example 6. Write the following in symbols :

(i) Sachin will go out of station or will remain in his house and he will repair his radio.
(ii) The necessary and sufficient condition for an infinite series Σu_n to be convergent is that limit of u_n as n tending to infinity must be zero.
(iii) We shall go to Delhi, but we shall not see the Red Fort.
(iv) Not only the children, but also Mothers and Fathers were killed.
(v) If teams do not arrive or the weather is bad, then there will be no match.

Sol. (i) Let $p \equiv$ Sachin will go out of station.
$q \equiv$ Sachin will remain in his house.
$r \equiv$ Sachin will repair his radio.
Thus the statement has the symbol $p \vee (q \wedge r)$.

(ii) $p \equiv$ An infinite series Σu_n to be convergent.
$q \equiv$ limit of u_n must be zero as n tending to infinity.
Thus the statement has the symbol $p \Leftrightarrow q$.

(iii) $p \equiv$ We shall go to Delhi.
$q \equiv$ We shall not see the Red Fort.
Thus the statement is $p \wedge \rceil q$.

(iv) $p \equiv$ children were killed.
$q \equiv$ Mothers were killed.
$r \equiv$ Fathers were killed.
Thus the statement is $p \wedge (q \wedge r)$.

(v) $p \equiv$ The teams do not arrive.
$q \equiv$ Whether is bad.
$r \equiv$ There will be no match.
Thus the statement is $(p \vee q) \Rightarrow r$.

Example 7. If $p =$ Ramesh is a player, $q \equiv$ Mohan is an intelligent boy, then write the following symbols into sentences :

(i) $p \wedge q$ (ii) $\rceil(p \vee q)$

(iii) $p \wedge \rceil q$ (iv) $\rceil(p \wedge q)$

(v) $\rceil p \Leftrightarrow q$ (vi) $p \Rightarrow \rceil q$

Sol. (i) Ramesh is a player and Mohan is an intelligent boy.

(ii) Neither Ramesh is a player nor Mohan is an intelligent boy.

(iii) Ramesh is a player and Mohan is not an intelligent boy.

(iv) It is false that Ramesh is a player and Mohan is an intelligent boy.

(v) Ramesh is not a player if and only if Mohan is an intelligent boy.

(vi) If Ramesh is a player, then Mohan is not an intelligent boy.

Example 8. If $p \equiv$ Money is evil, $q \equiv$ Wise men are poor, $r \equiv$ beggars are failures. Then translate each of the following statements into symbols :

(i) Wise men are poor only if money is evil.

(ii) Money is evil unless wise men are poor.

(iii) That beggars are failures is a sufficient condition that money is evil.

(iv) A necessary condition for money to be evil is that beggars are failures.

(v) Money is evil and beggars are failures if wise men are poor.

(vi) Unless beggars are failures, wise men are not poor and money is not evil.

Sol. (i) $p \Rightarrow q$ (ii) $\rceil q \Rightarrow p$

(iii) $r \Rightarrow p$ (iv) $p \Rightarrow r$

(v) $q \Rightarrow (p \wedge r)$ (vi) $\rceil r \Rightarrow \rceil p \wedge \rceil q$.

Example 9. Write the negation of each of the following statements in terms of symbols :

(i) It will rain unless the barometer rises.

(ii) I grow fat only if I eat too much.

(iii) A necessary condition that two triangles are equivalent is that they have the same area.

(iv) In order to live well, it is sufficient to be wealthy.

Sol. (i) Let $p \equiv$ It will rain, $q \equiv$ Barometer rises.
Then the statement (i) can be written as $\rceil q \Rightarrow p$.
Thus the negation is $\rceil(\rceil q \Rightarrow p)$.

(ii) Let $p \equiv$ I grow fat, and $q \equiv$ I eat too much.
Then the statement (ii) can be written as $q \Rightarrow p$.
Thus its negation is $\rceil(q \Rightarrow p)$

(iii) Let $p \equiv$ Two triangles are equivalent, and $q \equiv$ They have the same area.
Then the statement (iii) can be written as $p \Rightarrow q$.
Thus its negation is $\rceil(p \Rightarrow q)$

(iv) Let $p \equiv$ Live well, and $q \equiv$ To be wealthy.
Then the statement (iv) can be put as $q \Rightarrow p$.
Thus its negation is $\rceil(q \Rightarrow p)$.

Example 10. Write the negation of the following :

(i) If she studies, she will pass in exam.

(ii) If it rains, then they will not go for picnic.

(iii) Every even integer greater than 4 is the sum of two primes.

(iv) Some people have no scooter.

(v) No one wants to buy my house.

Sol. (i) If she will not study, she will not pass in exam.

(ii) If it will not rain, then they will go for picnic.

(iii) Every odd integer greater than 4 is the sum of two primes.

(iv) Some people have scooter.

(v) Everyone wants to buy my house.

Example 11. Write the negation of the following :

(i) Anil is not rich and Kanchan is poor.

(ii) A cow is an animal.

(iii) If the determinant of a system of linear equations is zero, then either the system has no solution or it has an infinite number of solution.

Sol. (i) Anil is rich and Kanchan is not poor.

(ii) A cow is not an animal.

(iii) p : Determinant of a system of linear equation is zero.

q : System has no solution.

r : System has an infinite number of solution.

Its negation is $\rceil p \rightarrow \rceil q \vee \rceil r$.

Example 12. Write in words the converse, inverse, contrapositive and negation of the implication "If 2 is less then 3, then 1/3 is less than 1/2.

Sol. Let $p \equiv 2$ is less than 3. $q \equiv 1/3$ is less than 1/2.

Then implication is $p \Rightarrow q$:

(i) Converse of $p \Rightarrow q$ is $q \Rightarrow p$. In words $q \Rightarrow p$ means "If 1/3 is less than 1/2, then 2 is less than 3".

(ii) Inverse of $p \Rightarrow q$ is $\rceil p \Rightarrow \rceil q$. Thus in words, $\rceil p \Rightarrow \rceil q$ means "If 2 is not less than 3, then 1/3 is not less than 1/2".

(iii) Contrapositive of $p \Rightarrow q$ is $\rceil q \Rightarrow \rceil p$. Thus in words $\rceil q \Rightarrow \rceil p$ means "If 1/3 is not less than 1/2, then 2 is not less than 3".

(iv) Negation of $p \Rightarrow q$ is $\rceil(p \Rightarrow q)$. Thus in words $\rceil(p \Rightarrow q)$ means "It is false than p implies q".

Example 13. Let p be a statement "Eight is an even number", and let q be a statement "Candy is sweet".

Write in words (i) the implication $p \Rightarrow q$, (ii) its converse, (iii) its inverse, (iv) its contrapositive, (v) its negation.

Sol. (i) $p \Rightarrow q$ means "If eight is an even number, then candy is sweet."

(ii) Converse of $p \Rightarrow q$ is $q \Rightarrow p$ it means "If candy is sweet, then eight is an even number."

(iii) Inverse of $p \Rightarrow q$ is $\rceil p \Rightarrow \rceil q$. It means "If eight is not an even number, then candy is not sweet".

(iv) ontrapositive of $p \Rightarrow q$ is $\rceil q \Rightarrow \rceil p$. It means "If candy is not sweet, then eight is odd number."

(v) Negation of $p \Rightarrow q$ is $\rceil(p \Rightarrow q)$. In words, we can write "It is false that p implies q" or "Eight is an even number, and candy is not sweet".

Remark : $\rceil(p \Rightarrow q) = \rceil(\rceil p \vee q) = p \wedge \rceil q$.

Example 14. If $p \equiv$ Missiles are costly and $q \equiv$ Grandma chews gum. Write in words, the following statement given in symbol :

(i) $p \vee \rceil q$ (ii) $\rceil p \wedge \rceil q$

(iii) $(p \wedge \rceil q) \vee (\rceil p \wedge q)$

Sol. (i) $p \vee \rceil q \equiv$ Either missiles are costly or Grandma does not chew gum.

(ii) $\rceil p \wedge \rceil q \equiv$ Missiles are not costly and Grandma does not chew gum.

(iii) Either missiles are costly and Grandma does not chew gum, or missiles are not costly and Grandma chews gum.

Example 15. If $p \equiv$ Mathematics is easy and $q \equiv$ Two is less than three. Write in words the following statement given in symbols :

(i) $\rceil(p \wedge q)$ (ii) $\rceil(p \vee q)$

(iii) $\rceil p \vee q$ (iv) $(p \wedge \rceil q) \vee (\rceil p \wedge q)$

Sol. (i) It is false that mathematics is easy and two is less than three.

(ii) It is false that either mathematics is easy or two is less than three.

(iii) Either mathematics is not easy or two is not less than three.

(iv) Either mathematics is easy and two is not less than three or mathematics is not easy and two is less than three.

Example 16. If $p \equiv$ It is 10 o' clock, $q \equiv$ the train is late, then state in words the following resultants :

(i) $q \vee \rceil p$ (ii) $\rceil p \wedge q$ (iii) $p \wedge \rceil q$

(iv) $\rceil(p \wedge q) = \rceil p \vee \rceil q$ (v) $\rceil p \wedge \rceil q$

Sol. (i) $q \vee \rceil p$: The train is late or it is not 10 o' clock.

(ii) $\rceil p \wedge q$: It is not 10 o' clock and the train is late.

(iii) $p \wedge \rceil q$: It is 10 o' clock and the train is not late.

(iv) $\rceil(p \wedge q) = \rceil p \vee \rceil q$: It is not 10 o' clock, or the train is not late.

(v) $\rceil p \wedge \rceil q$: It is not 10 o' clock and the train is not late.

Example 17. Consider the following :

p : You take a course in Discrete Mathematics.

q : You understand logic.

r : You get an A grade on the final exam.

Write in simple sentences the meaning of the following :

(i) $q \Rightarrow r$ (ii) $\rceil p \Rightarrow \rceil q$

(iii) $(p \wedge q) \Rightarrow r$ (iv) $(p \wedge q) \Rightarrow r$

Sol. (i) If you understand logics, then you get an A grade in the final exam.

(ii) If you will not take a course in Discrete Mathematics, then you will not understand logic.

(iii) If you take a course in Discrete Mathematics and understand logic, then you may not get an A grade in the final exam.

(iv) If you take a course in Discrete Mathematics and you understand logic, then you get an A grade in the final exam.

Example 18. Construct a truth table for each of the following functions :

(i) $(p \wedge q \wedge r) \vee (\rceil p \wedge q \wedge \rceil r) \vee (\rceil p \wedge \rceil q \wedge \rceil r)$

(ii) $(p \vee q \vee r) \wedge (\rceil p \vee q \vee \rceil r) \wedge (\rceil p \vee \rceil q \vee \rceil r)$

(iii) $\rceil(\rceil p \vee (q \wedge r) \wedge \{(p \wedge q) \vee (\rceil q \wedge r)\}$

Sol. (i) Truth table

p	q	r	$\rceil p$	$\rceil q$	$\rceil r$	$(p \wedge q \vee r)$	$(\rceil p \wedge q \wedge \rceil r)$	$(\rceil p \wedge \rceil q \wedge \rceil r)$	(i)
T	T	T	F	F	F	T	F	F	T
T	T	F	F	F	T	F	F	F	F
T	F	T	F	T	F	F	F	F	F
F	T	T	T	F	F	F	F	F	F
T	F	F	F	T	T	F	F	F	F
F	T	F	T	F	T	F	T	F	T
F	F	T	T	T	F	F	F	F	F
F	F	F	T	T	T	F	F	T	T

(ii) Truth table

p	q	r	$\neg p$	$\neg q$	$\neg r$	$(p \vee q \vee r)$	$(\neg p \vee q \vee \neg r)$	$(\neg p \vee \neg q \vee \neg r)$	(ii)
T	T	T	F	F	F	T	T	F	F
T	T	F	F	F	T	T	T	T	T
T	F	T	F	T	F	T	F	T	F
F	T	T	T	F	F	T	T	T	T
T	F	F	F	T	T	T	T	T	T
F	T	F	T	F	T	T	T	T	T

(iii) Truth table

p	q	r	$\neg p$	$\neg q$	$p \wedge q$	$(q \wedge r)$	$\neg q \wedge r$	$\neg p \vee (q \wedge r)$	$\neg\{\neg p \vee (q \wedge r)\}$	$\{(p \wedge q) \vee (\neg q \wedge r)\}$	(iii)
T	T	T	F	F	T	T	F	T	F	T	F
T	T	F	F	F	T	F	F	F	T	T	T
T	F	T	F	T	F	F	T	F	T	T	T
F	T	T	T	F	F	T	F	T	F	F	F
T	F	F	F	T	F	F	F	F	T	F	F
F	T	F	T	F	F	F	F	T	F	F	F
F	F	T	T	T	F	F	T	T	F	T	F
F	F	F	T	T	F	F	F	T	F	F	F

Example 19. Construct the truth table of the following :

(a) $(p \wedge q) \wedge (q \wedge r) \wedge (r \wedge s)$

(b) $\neg(\neg(p \wedge \neg q)$

Sol. (a)

p	q	r	s	$p \wedge q$	$q \wedge r$	$r \wedge s$	$(p \wedge q) \wedge (q \wedge r) \wedge (r \wedge s)$
T	T	T	T	T	T	T	T
T	T	T	F	T	T	F	F
T	T	F	T	T	F	F	F
T	F	T	T	F	F	T	F
F	T	T	T	F	T	T	F
T	T	F	F	T	F	F	F
T	F	F	T	F	F	F	F
F	T	F	T	F	F	F	F
F	F	T	T	F	F	T	F
T	F	T	F	F	F	F	F
F	T	T	F	F	T	F	F
T	F	F	F	F	F	F	F

(b)

p	q	$\rceil p$	$\rceil q$	$\rceil p \wedge \rceil q$	$\rceil(\rceil p \wedge \rceil q)$
T	T	F	F	F	T
T	F	F	T	F	T
F	T	T	F	F	T
F	F	T	T	T	F

Example 20. Write the negation for the statement $\forall \in R, x > 3 \Rightarrow x^2 > 9$

20. Let $P(x)$ and $Q(x)$ denote '$x > 3$' and $x^2 > 9$.

Then the given statement can be written as $\forall \; x(P(x) \Rightarrow Q(x))$

The negation of this statement is $\exists \, x(P(x) \wedge -Q(x))$

i.e., there exist a real number x such that $x \leq 3$ and $x^2 \leq 9$.

§4. Tautology

We have already discussed about the compound statements which formed with the help of simple statements using connectives. The truth values of this compound statement depend on the truth values of simple statement substituted for the variables. Thus the truth table of a resulting compound statement gives the summary of all its truth values for all possible choice of values of the variables. Therefore sometimes the truth values of the compound statement may, be "True (T)" and sometimes "False (F)". But there are some compound statements whose truth values are always T or always F irrespective of all possible truth values given to the variables.

Definition : *A statement whose truth value is always T (i.e., True) is called a* ***"Tautology"*** *and the statement whose truth value is always False (i.e., F) is called a* ***"Contradiction".***

Remark : Negation of a tautology is a contradiction while negation of contradiction is a tautology.

Logical Equivalence.

The two compound statements are said to be logically equivalents if both have same truth values for all possible assignments given to the variables. This logically equivalent is also known as tautologically equivalent.

§5. Duality

The two compound statements are said to be dual of each other if either one can be obtained from other by interchanging $\wedge$ and $\vee$ provided both remain valid.

For example :

The dual of $(p \vee q) \wedge r$ is $(p \wedge q) \vee r$ and the dual of $\rceil(p \vee q) \wedge \{p \vee \rceil(q \wedge \rceil s)\}$ is $\rceil(p \wedge q) \vee \{p \wedge \rceil(q \vee \rceil s)\}$.

Algebra of statements

(1) Commutative laws :

(i) $(p \vee q) \Leftrightarrow (q \vee p)$

(ii) $(p \wedge q) \Leftrightarrow (q \wedge p)$

(2) Associative laws :

(i) $p \vee (q \vee r) \Leftrightarrow (p \vee q) \vee r$

(ii) $p \wedge (q \wedge r) \Leftrightarrow (p \wedge q) \wedge r$

(3) Distributive laws :

(i) $p \wedge (q \vee r) \Leftrightarrow (p \wedge q) \vee (p \wedge r)$

(ii) $p \vee (q \wedge r) \Leftrightarrow (p \vee q) \wedge (p \vee r)$

(4) Idempotent laws :

(i) $(p \vee p) \Leftrightarrow p$

(ii) $(p \wedge p) \Leftrightarrow p$

(5) Absorption laws :

(i) $p \vee (p \wedge q) \Leftrightarrow p$

(ii) $p \wedge (p \vee q) \Leftrightarrow p$

(6) De'morgan's laws :

(i) $\sim(p \vee q) \Leftrightarrow (\sim p \wedge \sim q)$

(ii) $\sim(p \wedge q) \Leftrightarrow (\sim p \vee \sim q)$

(7) Detachement law $[(p \Rightarrow q) \wedge p] \Rightarrow q$

(8) Chain laws $[(p \Rightarrow q) \wedge (q \Rightarrow p)] \Rightarrow (p \Rightarrow r)$

(9) Identity laws : If t stands for tautology and f for contradiction then

(i) $p \wedge t = t \wedge p = p$

(ii) $p \vee f = f \vee p = p$

(10) Compliment law :

(i) $p \vee \sim p = t$

(ii) $p \wedge \sim p = f$

Problem Set (1)

Multiple Choice Questions

1. The order of the connective "$\Rightarrow$" is :

(a) 1 (b) 2
(c) 4 (d) 3

2. Which of these connectives is conjunction :

(a) $\vee$ (b) $\Rightarrow$
(c) $\rceil$ (d) $\wedge$

3. Which is the following is true :

(a) $p \wedge q = p \vee q$
(b) $(p \wedge q \vee r) \Leftrightarrow (p \vee q) \wedge r$
(c) $\rceil(p \wedge q) \Leftrightarrow \rceil p \vee \rceil q$
(d) $\rceil p = \rceil q$

4. the contrapositive of $p \Rightarrow q$ is :

(a) $\rceil q \Rightarrow \rceil p$ (b) $\rceil p \Rightarrow \rceil q$
(c) $q \Rightarrow p$ (d) $p \Rightarrow q$

5. If p is true, q is false and r is false, the which of the following is true :

(a) $(p \vee q) \Rightarrow r$ (b) $p \wedge \rceil(q \vee r)$
(c) $(p \vee q) \wedge r$ (d) $p \Rightarrow \rceil(q \Rightarrow r)$

6. $p \wedge (q \vee r) \equiv (p \wedge q) \vee (p \wedge r)$ is :

(a) Associative law (b) Distributive
(c) Identity law (d) Absorption

7. If $p \equiv$ "She goes to market" and
$q \equiv$ "She buys some fruits".
then choose the correct symbol for the given statements :

(i) Either She goes to market or she buys some fruits :

(a) $p \vee q$ (b) $p \wedge q$
(c) $\rceil p \vee q$ (d) $p \vee \rceil q$

(ii) If She goes to market, then she buys some fruits :

(a) $\rceil p \wedge q$ (b) $p \Rightarrow q$
(c) $p \wedge q$ (d) $\rceil p \vee q$

(iii) Neither She go to market nor she buy some fruits :

(a) $\rceil p \vee \rceil q$ (b) $p \Rightarrow q$
(c) $p \vee q$ (d) $\rceil p \wedge \rceil q$

(iv) She does not go to market and she buys some fruits :

(a) $\rceil p \wedge q$ (b) $\rceil(p \vee q)$
(c) $p \wedge \rceil q$ (d) $p \Rightarrow q$

(v) She does not go to market unless she buys some fruits :

(a) $p \Rightarrow q$ (b) $q \Rightarrow p$
(c) $\rceil q \Rightarrow \rceil p$ (d) $p \vee q$

8. $p \wedge \rceil p$ is :

(a) False (b) True
(c) p (d) q

9. True stands for :

(a) 0 (b) 1
(c) −1 (d) 2

10. The negation of $p \Rightarrow q$ is :

(a) $p \wedge \rceil q$ (b) $p \Rightarrow q$
(c) $q \Rightarrow p$ (d) $p \vee \rceil q$

11. $(p \Rightarrow q) \vee p$ is :

(a) $p \Rightarrow q$ (b) q
(c) $p \vee q$ (d) $p \wedge q$

12. $(p \Rightarrow q) \wedge (q \Rightarrow p)$ is :

(a) $p \Rightarrow q$ (b) $p \Leftrightarrow q$
(c) $p \vee q$ (d) q

13. $p \Rightarrow q$ is false if :

(a) p is false, q is true (b) p is false, q is false
(c) p is true, q is false (d) p is true, q is true

14. The dual of $(p \vee q) \wedge r$ is :

(a) $(p \wedge q) \wedge r$ (b) $(p \wedge q) \vee r$
(c) $(p \vee q) \vee r$ (d) $p \wedge r$

15. Which of these is a tautology :

(a) $p \vee \rceil p$ (b) $p \wedge \rceil p$
(c) $p \vee q$ (d) $p \wedge q$

16. Which of these is a tautology :

(a) $p \Rightarrow q$ (b) $\rceil p \wedge q$
(c) $(p \wedge q) \Rightarrow q$ (d) $p \wedge q$

17. The inverse of $p \Rightarrow \rceil q$ is :

(a) $\rceil q \Rightarrow p$ (b) $\rceil p \Rightarrow q$
(c) $p \Rightarrow q$ (d) $q \Rightarrow p$

18. Which of these is false :

(a) $\rceil p \wedge p$ (b) $p \vee q$
(c) $p \wedge q$ (d) $p \Rightarrow q$

19. If p is true and q is false, then $p \Leftrightarrow q$ is :

(a) True (b) False
(c) p (d) $\rceil p$

20. Conditional is represented by :

(a) $\wedge$ (b) $\Rightarrow$
(c) $\Leftrightarrow$ (d) $\vee$

21. $p \Leftrightarrow p$ is :

(a) Tautology (b) Logic Equivalence
(c) Contradiction (d) None of these

22. If p is true, q is also true, then $(p \Rightarrow q) \Rightarrow \rceil q$ is :

(a) True (b) p
(c) False (d) q

23. $p \Rightarrow q$ is logically equivalent to :

(a) $\rceil(p \vee q) \vee (p \wedge q)$ (b) $p \vee q$
(c) q (d) $p \Rightarrow q$

24. The dual of $p \Rightarrow q$ is :

(a) $\rceil p \vee q$ (b) $p \vee q$
(c) $p \wedge q$ (d) $\rceil p \wedge q$

25. $(p \vee p) \Leftrightarrow p, (p \wedge p) \Leftrightarrow p$ are under :

(a) Idempotent laws (b) Absorption laws
(c) Chain rule (d) Commutative laws.

Fill in the Blanks

1. A declarative sentence which is either true or false is called ......
2. "Grass is Yellow". This statement........
3. The expression $3x + y = 7$ is a ....
4. To form new statement with the help of two or more than two statements using ....
5. The combination of two or more than two statement using connectives gives a ....
6. The negative of $p \vee q$ is ....
7. The disjunction of p and q is ....
8. The truth values are ....
9. A statement is a .... sentence.
10. The truth values 'T' and 'F' can also be denoted by ....
11. If a statement is always true, then it is a ....
12. If a statement is not always true, then it is a ....
13. The dual of $(p \wedge q) \vee r$ is ....
14. $(p \vee q) \wedge q =$ is ....
15. $(p \wedge q) \vee r = (p \vee r) \wedge$ ....
16. $(p \Rightarrow q) \wedge p \Leftrightarrow$ ....
17. $(p \Rightarrow q) \Leftrightarrow$ ....
18. $(p \Leftrightarrow q) \Leftrightarrow (p \Rightarrow q) \wedge$ ....
19. If p is true, and q is false, then $\rceil(p \vee \rceil q)$ is ....
20. The converse of $p \Rightarrow q$ is ....
21. the contrapositive of $p \Rightarrow q$ is ....
22. $\rceil(p \vee q) =$ ....

True or False

Write 'T' for True and 'F' for False.

1. The negation of $p \Rightarrow q$ is $p \wedge \rceil q$.
2. A statement is not a declarative sentence.
3. The equation of $4x + 2 = 6$ is an open statement.
4. p unless q means $\rceil q \Rightarrow p$.
5. "If you read" then you will pass" is a compound statement.
6. $\rceil(p \Rightarrow q) = p \wedge \rceil q$.
7. $(p \vee q) \wedge q = p$.
8. $(p \wedge q) \wedge p = p$ is an absorption law.
9. $(p \Leftrightarrow q) \Leftrightarrow (p \Rightarrow q) \wedge (q \Rightarrow p)$.
10. If p is false and q is true, then $\rceil(p \wedge q)$ is true.
11. Always true statement is called contradiction.
12. 1 stands for true and 0 stands for false.
14. If $(p \wedge q) \Rightarrow r$ in this statement '$\Rightarrow$' is a principal connective.
15. If $p \equiv q$, then $p \Leftrightarrow q$ will be a tautology.
16. $p \vee (q \wedge r) \equiv (p \vee q) \wedge (p \vee r)$ is an associative law.
17. $\rceil(p \Leftrightarrow q) \equiv p \Leftrightarrow \rceil q \equiv \rceil p \Leftrightarrow q$ is under De-Morgan's law.
18. $(p \Rightarrow q) \vee (r \Rightarrow p)$ is a tautology.
19. $(p \vee q) \wedge r$ is a dual of $(p \vee q) \vee r$.
20. $(p \wedge q) \Rightarrow q$ is not tautology.
21. $\rceil(p \Rightarrow q) \vee r$ is a dual of $\rceil(p \Rightarrow q) \wedge r$.
22. $p \wedge (p \Rightarrow q) = q$ is under the law of detachment.

Answers

Mulitiple Choice Questions

1. (c) **2.** (d) **3.** (c) **4.** (a) **5.** (b) **6.** (b)
7. (i) (a) (ii) (b) (iii) (d) (iv) (a) (v) (c) **8.** (a) **9.** (b) **10.** (a) **11.** (c) **12.** (b)
13. (c) **14.** (b) **15.** (a) **16.** (c) **17.** (b) **18.** (a) **19.** (b) **20.** (b) **21.** (c) **22.** (c)
23. (a) **24.** (d) **25.** (a)

Fill in the Blanks

1. Statement
2. False
3. An open statement
4. Connectives
5. Compound statement
6. $\rceil(p \vee q)$
7. $p \vee q$
8. T and F
9. Declarative
10. 1 and 0
11. Tautology
13. $(p \vee q) \wedge r$
14. q
15. $q \vee r$
16. $q \wedge p$
17. $\rceil p \vee q$
18. $q \Rightarrow p$
19. False
20. $q \Rightarrow p$
21. $q \Rightarrow \rceil p$
22. $\rceil p \wedge \rceil q$

True or False

1. Ture 2. False 3. True 4. True 5. True 6. True 7. True 8. True 9. True 10. True
11. False 12. True 13. True 14. True 15. True 16. False 17. True 18. True 19. False 20. True
21. False 22. True

Problem Set (2)

1. $\sim(p \vee q) \vee (\sim p \wedge q)$ is logical equivalent to
(a) $\sim p$ (b) p
(c) q (d) $\sim q$ **(Kerela Engg. 2010)**

2. Let p : roses are red and q : the sun is a star. Then the verbal translation is $(\sim p) \vee q$ is
(a) Roses are not red and the sun is not a star
(b) it is not true that roses are red or the sun is not a star.
(c) it is not true that roses are red and the sun is not a star.
(d) roses are not red or the sun is a star
(e) it is not true that roses are red and the sun is a star.
(Kerela Engg. 2011)

3. Let S be a non-empty subset of **R**. Consider the following statement p : there is a rational number $x \in S$ such that $x > 0$
The negation of p is
(a) There is a rational number $x \in S$ such that $x \leq 0$
(b) There is no rational number $x \in S$ such that $x \leq 0$
(c) Every rational number $x \in S$ such that $x \leq 0$
(d) $x \in S$ and $x \leq 0 \Rightarrow x$ is not rational **(AIEEE 2010)**

4. The statement $p \to (q \to p)$ is equivalent to
(a) $p \to (p \vee q)$ (b) $p \to (p \wedge q)$
(c) $p \to (p \leftrightarrow q)$ (d) $p \to (p \to q)$
(AIEEE 2008)

5. Which of the following statement is a tautology
(a) $(\sim q \wedge p) \wedge q$ (b) $(\sim q \wedge p) \wedge (p \wedge \sim p)$
(c) $(\sim q \wedge p) \vee (p \vee \sim p)$ (d) $(p \wedge q) \wedge (\sim(p \wedge q))$
(DCE 2009)

6. Consider the following statement.
p : Suman is brilliant,
q : Suman is rich
r : Suman is honest
The negation of the statement "Suman is brilliant and dishonest if and Suman is rich "Can be expressed as
(a) $\sim p \wedge (q \leftrightarrow \sim r)$ (b) $\sim (q \leftrightarrow (p \wedge \sim r)$
(c) $\sim q \leftrightarrow \sim p \wedge r$ (d) $\sim (p \wedge \sim r) \leftrightarrow q$
(AIEEE 2011)

7. Ram secures 100 marks in maths, then he will get a mobile. Then converse is
(a) If Ram gets a mobile, then he will not secures 100 marks
(b) If Ram does not get a mobile, then he will secures 100 marks.
(c) If Ram will get a mobile, then he secures 100 marks in maths.
(d) None of these **(Orissa JEE 2010)**

8. The negation of $(p \vee \sim q) \wedge q$ is
(a) $(\sim p \vee q) \wedge \sim q$ (b) $(p \wedge \sim q) \vee q$
(c) $(\sim p \wedge q) \wedge \sim q$ (d) $(p \wedge \sim q) \wedge \sim q$
(e) $(\sim p \wedge \sim q) \wedge \sim q$ **(Kerela Engg. 2011)**

9. $\sim p \wedge q$ is logically equivalent to
(a) $p \to q$ (b) $q \to p$
(c) $\sim (p \to q)$ (d) $\sim (q \to q)$

10. $\sim (p \Leftrightarrow q)$ is
(a) $\sim p \wedge \sim q$ (b) $\sim p \vee \sim q$
(c) $(p \wedge \sim q) \vee (\sim p \wedge q)$ (d) none of these

11. Which of the following is logically equivalent to $\sim(\sim p \Rightarrow q)$

(a) $p \wedge q$ (b) $p \wedge \sim q$

(c) $\sim p \wedge q$ (d) $\sim p \wedge \sim q$

12. If $(p \wedge \sim r) \Rightarrow (q \vee r)$ is false and q and r are both false, then p is

(a) true (b) false

(c) may be true or false (d) data insufficient

13. If $S(p,q,r) = (\sim p) \vee [\sim(q \wedge r)]$ is a compound statement then $S(\sim p, \sim q, \sim r)$ is

(a) $\sim S(p,q,r)$ (b) $S(p,q,r)$ (c) $p \vee (q \wedge r)$

(d) $p \wedge (q \vee r)$ (e) $S(p,q,\sim r)$

(Kerela Engg. 2010)

14. Negation of $q \vee \sim(p \wedge r)$ is

(a) $\sim q \wedge \sim(p \wedge r)$ (b) $\sim q \wedge (p \wedge r)$

(c) $\sim q \vee (p \wedge r)$ (d) none of these

15. If it is raining, then I will not come, give its contrapositive.

(a) If I will come, then it is not raining

(b) If *I* will not came, then it is raining

(c) If *I* will not came, then it is not raining

(d) If *I* will came, then it is raining. **(Orissa Jee 2011)**

Hints / Solution to Problem Set (2)

1. And (a).

$\sim(p \vee q) \vee (\sim p \vee q)$

$= (\sim p \wedge \sim q) \vee (\sim p \wedge q)$

$= (\sim p \vee \sim q) \vee (\sim p \vee q)$

$= \sim p \wedge (\sim q \vee p) = \sim p$

2. And (d).

p : roses are red; $\sim p$: roses are not red

$(\sim p) \vee q$: roses are not red or sum is a star.

3. And (c).

For every rational number $x \in S$ satisfies $x \le 0$

4. And (a).

$p \to (q \to p) = \sim p \vee (q \to p)$

$= \sim p \vee (\sim q \vee p)$

since $p \vee \sim p$ is always true

$= \sim p \vee p \vee q = p \to (p \vee q)$

5. Ans. (c).

$f \equiv (\sim q \wedge p) \vee (p \vee \sim p)$

q	$\sim q$	p	$\sim p$	$\sim q \wedge p$	$p \wedge \sim p$	f
T	F	T	F	F	T	T
T	F	F	T	F	T	T
F	T	T	F	T	T	T
F	T	F	T	F	T	T

6. Ans. (b).

negation of $(p \vee \sim r) \leftrightarrow q$ is $\sim((p \wedge \sim r) \leftrightarrow q)$ which can also be written is $\sim(q \leftrightarrow (p \wedge \sim r))$

7. Ans. (c).

Let p : Ram secures 100 marks in mathematics

q : Ram will get a mobile

Converse of statement p and q. If p then $q \Rightarrow$ if q then p

$\therefore$ Converse of above statement is

If Ram will get a mobile, then he secures 100 marks in mathematics.

8. Ans. (c).

$\sim\{(p \vee (\sim q)) \wedge q\} = (\sim(\sim p \vee (\sim q)) \vee (\sim q)$

(By De-Morgan's law)

$= ((\sim p) \wedge \sim(\sim q)) \vee \sim q$

(Again by De-Morgan's law)

$= (\sim p \wedge q) \vee (\sim q)$

9. Ans. (d).

$\sim p \wedge q = \sim(q \to p)$

10. Ans. (c).

$\sim(p \Leftrightarrow q) = (p \wedge \sim q) \vee (q \wedge \sim p)$

1. Ans. (d).

Since $\sim(p \Rightarrow q) = p \wedge \sim q$

$\sim(\sim p \Rightarrow q) = \sim p \wedge \sim q$

12. Ans. (a).

Given result means $p \wedge \sim r$ is true, $q \vee r$ is false.

13. Ans. (d).

$\because$ $S(p,q,r) = (\sim p) \vee (\sim(q \wedge r))$

$S(p,q,r) = (\sim p) \vee [(\sim q) \vee (\sim r)]$

$\therefore$ $S(\sim p, \sim q, \sim r) = (\sim(\sim p)) \vee (\sim(\sim q) \vee \sim(\sim r)]$

$= p \vee [q \vee r]$

14. Ans. (b).

$\sim(q \vee \sim(p \wedge r)) = \sim q \wedge (\sim(\sim(p \wedge r)) = \sim q \wedge (p \wedge r)$

15. Ans. (a).

The given statement can be written as $a \to b$ where $a \equiv$ it is raining $b =$ I will not come

The contra positive for $a \to b$, $(\sim b) \to (\sim a)$

Now $\sim b$ – is will come

$\sim a$ = it is not raining

so $\sim b \to \sim a$ can be written as

"If I will come, then it is not raining"

Assertion / Reason

1. **Statement-1 :** $\sim(p \leftrightarrow \sim q)$ is equivalent to $p \leftrightarrow q$.

   Statement-2 : $\sim(p \leftrightarrow q)$ is a tautology. **(AIEEE 2009)**

Sol. Ans. (c)

p	q	$\sim q$	$(p \leftrightarrow \sim q)$	$\sim(p \leftrightarrow \sim q)$	$p \leftrightarrow q$
T	T	F	F	T	T
T	F	T	T	F	F
F	F	T	F	T	T
F	T	F	T	F	F

Clearly, statement-1 is true but statement-2 is false.

2. Let p be the statement "x is an irrational number", q be the statement "y is a transcendental number" and r be the statement "x is a rational number if y is a transcendental number **(AIEEE 2008)**

   Statement-1 : r is equivalent to either p or q.

   Statement-2 : r is equivalent to $\sim(p \leftrightarrow \sim q)$.

Sol. Ans. (c).

Given statement $r = \sim p \leftrightarrow q$

Statement-1 : $r_1 = (p \wedge \sim q) \vee (\sim p \wedge q)$

Statement-2 : $r_2 = \sim(p \leftrightarrow \sim q) = (p \wedge q) \vee (q \wedge \sim p)$

using truth table, we can easily verify that $r = r_1$

Hence, statement – 1 is true and statement–2 is false.

❑

Fun in Mathematics

1. A. Who is this HE sitting between two MATs preparing for the ICS examination ?

Ans.

	HE		
MAT	HE	MAT	
MAT	HE	MAT	ICS

MATHEMATICS

Note : ICS of British days is **IAS** of present day.

B. Prof. M.L. Khanna when he goes to his new class for the first time establishes the relation between himself and his students by reciting the following :

Fifty before zero
Five before E
This is the relation
Between you and me.

Can you tell the relation ?

Ans. Fifty before zero *i.e.* ℒO
Five before E *i.e.* VE

This is the relation betwen you and me *i.e.* **LOVE.**

C. **Mathematical definition of GOD.**

GOD is a circle
With its centre everywhere
And circumference, nowhere.

—Swami Ram Tirath.

D. **Define life in mathematical language.**

Ans. Life : 0 + − × ÷ ∞

Emerging from zero and during the life time performs the four fundamental operations of + − × ÷ and ultimately vanishes to infinity. This is life.

जिन्दगी

शून्य से उत्पन्न होकर जीवन काल में जोड़, घटाव, गुणा, भाग, गणित के चार सूत्रों में उलझकर अनन्त में विलीन हो जाना ही जिन्दगी है।
अंकगणित की सुबह मेरी, बीजगणित की शाम।
× गुणा ÷ भाग एवं + जमा − घटाव में बीती उमर तमाम।।

E. (+) = दोस्त, (−) = दुश्मन, (•) = का, तब

+ · + = + दोस्त का दोस्त, दोस्त होता है

+ · − = − दोस्त का दुश्मन, दुश्मन होता है

− · + = − दुश्मन का दोस्त, दुश्मन होता है

− · − = + दुश्मन का दुश्मन, दोस्त होता है।

F. +, +, +, +, ... = +

किन्तु − (+, +, +, +, ...) = −

अर्थात् आप ने अनेकों अच्छे काम किये हों तो आपकी वाह-वाही होती है, परन्तु एक गलत काम से सारी वाह-वाही घुल जाती है और आप बदनाम हो जाते है।

G. **Blessing to my students,**

Friends to multiply,
Enemies to divide,
Joys to add,
Sorrows to subtract.

H. (a) **This date will never come again.**

Hour	Minute	Sec	Date	Month	Year
02	03	04	05	06	07

2 बजकर, 3 मिनट, 4 सैकेण्ड, 5 तारीख, छठे (जून) का महीना, सन सात (2007)

(b) **The most auspicious time.**

01 02 03 04 05 06

सुबह के एक बजकर, 2 मिनट, 3 सैकेण्ड, 4 तारीख, 5वाँ महीना (मई), सन 06 was the most auspicious time.

(c) **777, the most auspicious day.**

सन 7 के सातवें महीने (जुलाई) की 7 तारीख अति शुभ दिन था।

(d) **786, the most pious number of Mohammedans.**

सात तारीख, आठवाँ (अगस्त) का महीना, सन 2006 will come after 1000 years in the same way *i.e.* in 3006.

2. **The Magic of numbers.**

A.

$$1 \times 9 + 2 = 11$$
$$12 \times 9 + 3 = 111$$
$$123 \times 9 + 4 = 1111$$
$$1234 \times 9 + 5 = 11111$$
$$12345 \times 9 + 6 = 111111$$
$$123456 \times 9 + 7 = 1111111$$
$$1234567 \times 9 + 8 = 11111111$$
$$12345678 \times 9 + 9 = 111111111$$

B.

$9\times9+7=88$

$98\times9+6=888$

$987\times9+5=8888$

$9876\times9+4=88888$

$98765\times9+3=888888$

$987654\times9+2=8888888$

$9876543\times9+1=88888888$

$98765432\times9+0=888888888$

C.

$1\times8+1=9$

$12\times8+2=98$

$123\times8+3=987$

$1234\times8+4=9876$

$12345\times8+5=98765$

$123456\times8+6=987654$

$1234567\times8+7=9876543$

$12345678\times8+8=98765432$

$123456789\times8+9=987654321$

D.

$12345679\times8=98765432$

$12345679\times9=111111111$

$12345679\times18=222222222$

$12345679\times27=333333333$

$12345679\times36=444444444$ etc. etc.

E.

$(11)^2=121$

$(111)^2=12321$

$(1111)^2=1234321$

$(11111)^2=123454321$

$(111111)^2=12345654321$

$(1111111)^2=1234567654321$

$(11111111)^2=123456787654321$

$(111111111)^2=12345678987654321$

3. **The magic of number 45.**

(a) **Addition**

1 2 3 4 5 6 7 8 9	Sum of digits = 45
1 2 3 4 5 6 7 8 9	Sum of digits = 45
2 4 6 9 1 3 5 7 8	Sum of digits = 45

(b) **Subtraction**

9 8 7 6 5 4 3 2 1	Sum of digits = 45
1 2 3 4 5 6 7 8 9	Sum of digits = 45
8 6 4 1 9 7 5 3 2	Sum of digits = 45

(c) **Multiplication**

1 2 3 4 5 6 7 8 9	Sum of digits = 45
2	
2 4 6 9 1 3 5 7 8	Sum of digits = 45
9 8 7 6 5 4 3 2 1	Sum of digits = 45
2	
1 9 7 5 3 0 8 6 4 2	Sum of digits = 45

(d) **Division**

```
     6 1 7 2 8 3 9 4 5              4 9 3 8 2 7 1 6 0 5
2) 1 2 3 4 5 6 7 8 9 0 (        2) 9 8 7 6 5 4 3 2 1 0 (
   1 2 3 4 5 6 7 8 9 0             9 8 7 6 5 4 3 2 1 1
           ×                               ×
```

Sum of digits in each dividend = 45

Sum of digits in each quotient = 45

Add the quotients 6 1 7 2 8 3 9 4 5 Sum of digits = 45

4 9 3 8 2 7 1 6 0 5 Sum of digits = 45

5 5 5 5 5 5 5 5 5 0 Sum of digits = 45

4. **Do you know**

(a) That 8712 and 9801 are the only 4 digit numbers which are integral multiples of their reversals.

i.e. $8712=2178\times4$

$9801=1089\times9$

(b) There are no numbers below 10,000 which have the following property.

$312\times221=68952$ (Now reverse each number)

$213\times122=25986$ (digits reversed)

(c) There are only 4 numbers (after 1) which are sums of their cubes of their digits.

$153=1^3+5^3+3^3$ *i.e.* $1+125+27=153$

$370=3^3+7^3+0^3$ *i.e.* $27+343+0=370$

$371=3^3+7^3+1^3$ *i.e.* $27+343+1=371$

Peculiar Multiplication

5. No. of digits

3.	$6\times21=126$,	$51\times3=153$	(Same digits)
4.	$15\times93=1395$,	$35\times41=1435$	(" ")
5.	$3\times4281=12843$,	$24\times651=15624$	(" ")

Can you add few more numbers to the above ?

Ans. Yes.

Using 4 digits,

$21\times87=1827$, $27\times81=2187$

$8\times473=3784$, $9\times351=3159$

Using 5 digits,

$2\times8714=17428$, $9\times7461=67149$

$3\times7125=21375$, $6\times2541=15246$

$8\times4973=39784$, $8\times6521=52168$

$42\times678=28476$, $24\times651=15624$

$57\times834=47538$, $87\times435=37845$

6. **Using 9 digits.**

(i) $51,249,876\times3=153,749,628$

(ii) $16,583,742\times9=149,253,678$

Both in (i) and (ii) all the nine digits are used only once in the left or right hand side.

Can you try if the multiplier be 6 instead of 3 or 9 and the result is same 9 digits used only once ?

Ans. $325,478,91\times6=195,287,346$.

7. Consider the 10 digits separated in three groups a, b, c.

715 — 46 — 32890

(a) (b) (c)

Observe that $a\times b=c$.

8. **The Great century 100. Same digits 1 to 9.**

Do it in as many possible ways as you can :

1 2 3 4 5 6 7 8 9 = 100

On the left hand side you have to place arithmetical signs between the nine digits so that the reslut is 100. You are not to change the order of the digits.

A couple of possible solutions are given below.

(a) $1+2+3+4+5+6+7+(8\times 9)=100$

(b) $123+4-5+67-89=100$

How many more arrangements of the above type you can give ?

Ans. $-(1\times 2)-3-4-5+(6\times 7)+(8\times 9)=100$

$1+(2\times 3)+(4\times 5)-6+7+(8\times 9)=100$

$(1+2-3-4)(5-6-7-8-9)=100$

$1+(2\times 3)+4+5+67+8+9=100$

$12+3-4+5+67+8+9=100$

$123-4-5-6-7+8-9=100$

$123+45-67+8-9=100$

$123-45-67+89=100$

9. Again a question of 9 digits 1 to 9 using all the nine digits 1 to 9 and the sign of multiplication. *e.g.*,

1. $4\times 1738=6952$ (all nine digits)
2. $48\times 159=7632$ (" ")
3. $39\times 186=7254$ (" ")
4. $4\times 1963=7852$ (" ")
5. $42\times 138=5796$ (" ")
6. $28\times 157=4396$ (" ")
7. $12\times 483=5796$ (" ")
8. $18\times 297=5346$ (" ")
9. $27\times 198=5346$ (" ")

10. Again a question of 9 non-repetitive digits. Write the digits 1, 2, 3, ... 9 in the sides of a triangle so that sum of digits in sides of the triangle is

(i) 20 **(ii) 17.**

Ans.

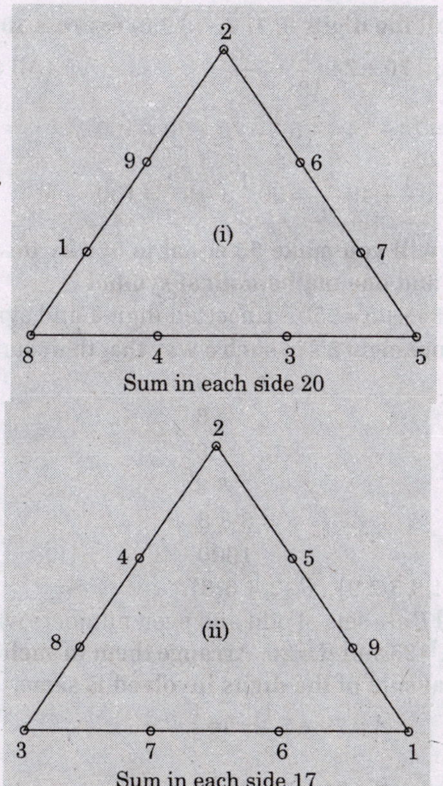

Sum in each side 20

Sum in each side 17

Fig. 01

11. Magic of Number 9.

(A)	(B)
$9\times 1=09$	$0+9=9$
$9\times 2=18$	$1+8=9$
$9\times 3=27$	$2+7=9$
$9\times 4=36$	$3+6=9$
$9\times 5=45$	$4+5=9$
$9\times 6=54$	$5+4=9$
$9\times 7=63$	$6+3=9$
$9\times 8=72$	$7+2=9$
$9\times 9=81$	$8+1=9$
$9\times 10=90$	$9+0=9$

What do you observe in the above table?

(1) The two columns in (A) are in reverse order.
i.e., 0, 1, 2 ... 9 is Ist col. of (A) and 9, 8,7... 1, 0 is 2nd col. of (A).

(2) The digits in numbers equidistant from top and bottom are interchanged in (A).
i.e., 2nd from top = 18, 2nd from bottom = 81
4th from top = 36, 4th from bottom = 63

(3) The sum of all the digits in column (A) is 9 as is clear from (B).

12. The magic number 9801.

You will always be coorect in your answer.

Insert one 9, two 9 or three 9, ... any number of 9's between 98 and 01. **The number thus obtained will be multiple of 9 with the given number with digits reversed.**

$98901=9\times 10989$ (digits reversed of given number)

$989901=9\times 109989$ (" " ")

$9899901=9\times 1099989$ (" " ")

13. The Magic Number 1089.

Given any number of three digits not ending with zero and also the difference between the extreme two digits is not less than two.

i.e., 541, not ending with zero and difference between extreme digits $=5-1=4$.

It is not less than 2.

$$\begin{array}{rl} 541 & \text{Reverse 145} \\ -\,145 & \\ \hline 396 & \text{Add it to reverse of 396.} \\ +\,693 & \\ \hline 1089 & \text{always.} \end{array}$$

$$\begin{array}{rl} \text{Again, } 732 & \text{Reverse 237} \\ -\,237 & \\ \hline 495 & \text{Add it to reverse of 495} \\ +\,594 & \\ \hline 1089 & \end{array}$$

Another number $8712=4\times 2178$ (Reversed).

14. Arithmatical Trick.

(i) Write down any three digit number, say 582.

(ii) Now write the same number along side the original, *i.e.,* 582582

$$582582 = 582000 + 582 = 582\,(1000 + 1) = 582 \times 1001$$

(iii) Now divide the number by 7, 11, 13 successively

$$= \frac{582 \times 1001}{7} = 582 \times 143$$

(iv) Now divide by 11

$$= \frac{582 \times 143}{11} = 582 \times 13$$

(v) Now divide by 13 $= \frac{582 \times 13}{13} = 582$, the original number.

15. Multiplication Table of 9.

Write triplets of natural numbers starting with 2 and add the number in each triplet.

$2 + 3 + 4 = 9 \quad = 9.1$

$5 + 6 + 7 = 18 \quad = 9.2$

$8 + 9 + 10 = 27 \quad = 9.3$

$11 + 12 + 13 = 36 \quad = 9.4$ and so on.

The result is multiplication table of 9, *i.e.,* 9, 18, 27, 36, 45, ...

16. The Magic Number 37037037.

Multiply the above number by 3, 6, 9 successively. The numbers obtained are

1111111111 ...

2222222222 ...

3333333333 ...

17. How you add to show $a + a^2 = a$?

Consider the numbers 12, 15, 18, 24 and 27.

a	a^2	$a + a^2 = a$
12	144	$1+2+1+4+4=12$
15	225	$1+5+2+2+5=15$
18	324	$1+8+3+2+4=18$
24	576	$2+4+5+7+6=24$
27	729	$2+7+7+2+9=27$

18. Peculiar Numbers

(1) $\mathbf{a, \frac{a}{a-1}}$

The product and sum of these numbers is same.

i.e., $a \cdot \frac{a}{a-1} = \frac{a^2}{a-1}$ and $a + \frac{a}{a-1} = \frac{a^2}{a-1}$

(2) $\mathbf{a, \frac{a}{a+1}}$

The product and difference of these numbers is same.

i.e., $a \cdot \frac{a}{a+1} = \frac{a^2}{a+1}$ and $a - \frac{a}{a+1} = \frac{a^2}{a+1}$

(3) $\mathbf{\frac{a^2}{1-a}}$

If you divide by a or add a to the above number you get the same number $\frac{a}{a-1}$.

i.e., $\frac{1}{a}\left[\frac{a^2}{1-a}\right] = \frac{a}{1-a}$ and $\left[\frac{a^2}{1-a} + a\right] = \frac{a}{1-a}$

(4) If you divide by a or subtract a from the above number you get the same number a as in (3).

19. How will you represent number 1 by using all the digits from 0 to 9 ?

Ans. $\frac{35}{70} = \frac{1}{2}$ (used 4 digits 0, 3, 5, 7)

$\frac{148}{296} = \frac{1}{2}$ (used remaining 6 digits 1, 2, 4, 6, 8, 9)

$\therefore \frac{35}{70} + \frac{148}{296} = \frac{1}{2} + \frac{1}{2} = 1$ (used all the ten digits)

20. How will you represent 10 with the help of same digit used five times ?

Ans. $\frac{99}{9} - \frac{9}{9} = 11 - 1 = 10$(digit 9 used five times)

$\frac{66}{6} - \frac{6}{6} = 11 - 1 = 10$ (digit 6 used five times)

21. How will you represent the number 24 by using the same digit three times ?

Ans. $8 + 8 + 8 = 24$, $3^3 - 3 = 24$

$22 + 2 = 24.$

22. Three identical digits to make 30.

$5 \times 5 + 5 = 30$, $6 \times 6 - 6 = 30$

$3^3 + 3 = 30$, $33 - 3 = 30$

23. Write 100 by using same digit 5 times.

Ans. $111 - 11 = 100$, $(5 \times 5 \times 5) - (5 \times 5) = 100$

$(5 + 5 + 5 + 5) \times 5 = 100$

$33 \times 3 + \frac{3}{3} = 100$

24. Use all the digits 0, 1, 2, ..., 9 to express 100.

Ans. (i) $70 + 24\frac{9}{18} + 5\frac{3}{6}$ (All ten digits)

$= 70 + 24\frac{1}{2} + 5\frac{1}{2} = 70 + 30 = 100$

(ii) $50\frac{1}{2} + 49\frac{38}{76} = 50\frac{1}{2} + 49\frac{1}{2} = 100$

25. How will you make 55 equal to 550 by inserting one digit and one mathematical symbol ?

Ans. $545 + 5 = 550$ (Inserted digit 4 and symbol +)

26. Arrange eight 8's in such a way that their sum is 1000.

Ans.

```
    8
    8
    8
   88
  888
 ----
 1000
```

27. $A = \{1, 3, 5, 7, 9\}$, $B\,\{2, 4, 6, 8\}$.

A and B are sets of odd and even numbers whose sums are $A = 25$ and $B = 20$. **Arrange them in such a manner so that sum of the digits involved is same.**

Ans. $A = 79 + 5\frac{1}{3} = 84\frac{1}{3}$

$B = 84 + \frac{2}{6} = 84\frac{1}{3}$

28. Printing Mistake but still correct.

(a) The number of permutations in a certain question was 2592 but the compositor printed this number as $2^5 9^2 = 32 \times 81 = 2592$, the same number.

(b) If you take any number, double it. Add 10 and divide by 2 and subtract your original number the answer will always be 5. Let the number be 374.

374×2	218×2
$748 + 10$	$436 + 10$
$758 \div 2$	$446 \div 2$
379 – original	223 – original
374	218
5 Always	5 Always

29. Nine digit problems.

(a) In the adjoining figure, the nine digits from 1 to 9 are arranged in such a manner such that the number in R_2 *i.e.,* 654 is twice the number 327 of R_1 and the number in number in R_3 *i.e.,* 981 is thrice the number in R_1 *i.e.* 981 is thrice the number 327 of R_1.

3	2	7
6	5	4
9	8	1

Fig. 02

Can you give some more examples like above such that $R_2 = 2R_1$ and $R_3 = 3R_1$?

Ans.			
R_1	192	219	273
R_2	384	438	546
R_3	576	657	819

(b) **Try if you can fill the boxes with numbers as instructed.**

In the adjoining figure 03 there are eight boxes and we have 8 numbers from 1 to 8. you have to fill these 8 numbers in these eight boxes under the following conditions. No two consecutive numbers be together in neighbouring boxes either horizontally or vertically or diagonally. In other words, placement of numbers as shown below in figure 04 is not permitted.

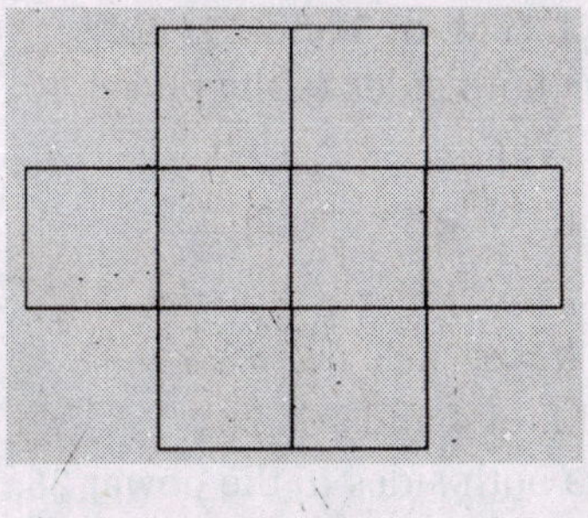

Fig. 03

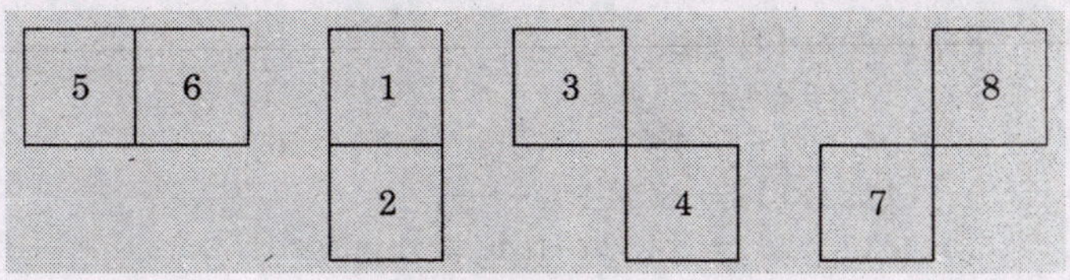

Fig.04

Ans.

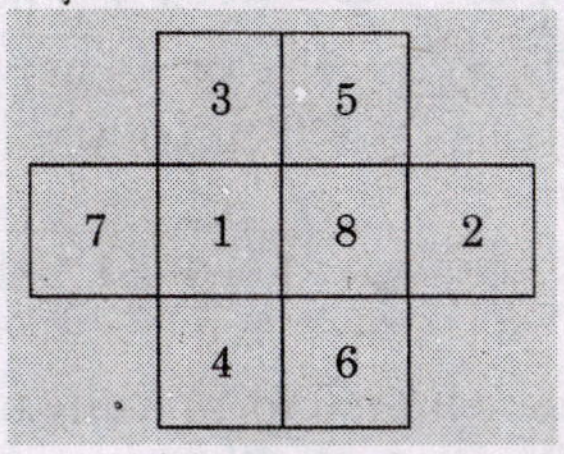

Fig. 05

30. Again the nine digit problem

Can you name four square numbers which contain all the nine digits 1 to 9 ?

Ans. 9 81 324 576 (all nine digits)

i.e., 3^2 9^2 18^2 24^2

31. Can you do it with four sevens ?

The students were not in a mood to listen to the usual boring lecture of the professor and requested him to talk about something interesting. Look here boys I arrange four 5^s with simple arithmetical signs so as to represent 100 and similarly I arrange four 9^s,

$$(5+5) \times (5+5) = 100$$

$$99\frac{9}{9} = 100$$

Can you do the same thing with four sevens ?

The Professor was relaxing whereas the students got lost in the problem.

Ans. $\frac{7}{\cdot 7} \times \frac{7}{\cdot 7} = 100.$

32. Perfect Square Numbers

The two digit number $x = 48$ has the property that

$$x + 1 = 48 + 1 = 49 = 7^2$$

$$\frac{x}{2} + 1 = 24 + 1 = 25 = 5^2$$

Can you give a four digit number satisfying the above criteria ?

Ans. Yes. $x = 1680$

$$x + 1 = 1680 + 1 = 1681 = (41)^2$$

$$\frac{x}{2} + 1 = 840 \quad + 1 = \ 841 = (29)^2$$

33. Positive power of given number with last digit as 5, 6 or 9.

(a) 5 will have last digit 5

$(15)^2 = 225$

(b) 6 will have last digit 6

$(6)^2 = 36, \quad (16)^2 = 256, \ldots$

(c) 9 then even power will have 1 and odd power will have 9.

$9^2 = 81, \qquad$ but $9^3 = 729$ etc.

34. Reversal of digits

(i) $13 \times 13 = 169$

but $31 \times 31 = 961$ (digits reversed)

(ii) $112 \times 112 = 12544$

$211 \times 211 = 44521$ (digits reversed)

35. All the sevens

```
  1 2 3 4 5 6 7 9
          × 6 3
  3 7 0 3 7 0 3 7
7 4 0 7 4 0 7 4
7 7 7 7 7 7 7 7
```

All the ones

```
      4 6 4 9
      × 2 3 9
    4 1 8 4 1
    1 3 9 4 7
    9 2 9 8
1 1 1 1 1 1 1
```

36. Four fours

Express numbers from 3 to 18 using only four 4's e.g.,

$$7 = \frac{44}{4} - 4 = 11 - 4 = 7$$

Ans.

$3 = \dfrac{4+4+4}{4}$ $\quad 4 = 4(4-4)+4$

$5 = \dfrac{(4 \times 4)+4}{4}$ $\quad 6 = 4 + \dfrac{4+4}{4}$

$7 = \dfrac{44}{4} - 4$ $\quad 8 = 4+4+4-4$

$9 = 4+4+\dfrac{4}{4}$ $\quad 10 = \dfrac{44-4}{4}$

$11 = \dfrac{44}{\sqrt{4}+\sqrt{4}}$ $\quad 12 = \dfrac{44+4}{4}$

$13 = \dfrac{44}{4} + \sqrt{4}$ $\quad 14 = 4+4+4+\sqrt{4}$

$15 = \dfrac{44}{4} + 4$ $\quad 16 = 4+4+4+4$

$17 = (4 \times 4) + \dfrac{4}{4}$ $\quad 18 = (4 \times 4) + 4 - \sqrt{4}$

37. Very Interesting Result

$(1 \times 8) + 1 \quad = 9$

$(12 \times 8) + 2 \quad = 98$

$(123 \times 8) + 3 \quad = 987$

$(1234 \times 8) + 4 = 9876$

$(12345 \times 8) + 5 = 98765$

38. Arithmetical Truth

Number	digits reversed
987654321	123456789
87654321	12345678
7654321	1234567
654321	123456
54321	12345
4321	1234
321	123
21	12
1	1
Sum = 1083676269	**Sum = 1083676269**

39. Criteria for divisibility of a given number by 0, 2, 3, 4, 5, 6, 7, 8, 9, 10, 11 and 99.

Ans.

÷ 0. Never divide any number by 0.

÷ 2. All those numbers whose last digit is any of 0, 2, 4, 6, 8, are divisible by 2.

÷ 3. Sum of whose digits is divisible by 3, e.g., 123, 7428, ... Sum of the digits are 6, 21, ... i.e., divisible by 3.

÷ 4. Numbers whose last two digits are multiple of 4, e.g., 724, 8132, 97564, ... are all divisible by 4.

÷ 5. Whose last digit is either 0 or 5, e.g., 725, 4530, 97325, ... are all divisible by 5.

÷ 6. Whose last digit is even i.e., ÷ 2, and sum of whose digits is divisible by 3 i.e., ÷ 3, are divisible by $(2 \times 3) = 6$. e.g. 4386 last digit 6 is divisible by 2 and sum of digits is 21 which is divisible by 3.

÷ 7. There is no rule for divisibility by 7.

÷ 8. Whose last three digits form a number divisible by 8 are ÷ 8. e.g., 128, 1408, 15624, ... are all ÷ 8, because 128, 408, 624 i.e., last three digits are ÷ 8.

÷ 9. Sum of whose digits is divisible by 9 are all ÷ 9, e.g., 18, 324, 7524, 53217, ... are all ÷ 9 because sum of the digits, i.e. 9, 9, 18, 18,... are divisible by 9.

÷ 10. Numbers whose last digit is 0, i.e., 20, 540, 6320, ... are all ÷ 10.

÷ 11. Take the sum of digits placed at odd places and even places i.e., S_1 and S_2. If $S_1 - S_2 = 0$ or ÷ by 11 then the given number is divisible by 11, e.g., 147521

$\underbrace{(1+7+2)}_{\text{odd places}} - \underbrace{(4+5+1)}_{\text{even places}} = 0 \quad \therefore \quad \div 11$

or 125792018

$\underbrace{(1+5+9+0+8)}_{\text{odd places}} - \underbrace{(2+7+2+1)}_{\text{even places}} = 23 - 12 = 11$

$\therefore \quad \div 11$

40. In how many ways can you express four 2's in exponential form ?

Ans. $2222,\ 2^{222},\ (2^2)^{2^2},\ (2^2)^{22},\ 2^{(22)^2},\ (222)^2,$

$(22)^{22},\ (22)^{2^2}$, i.e., 8 forms.

41. Below are the pairs of numbers a and b. Which is greater a or b ?

(i) $a = \sqrt[5]{5}$, $\qquad\qquad b = \sqrt{2}$

(ii) $a = \sqrt[4]{4}$, $\qquad\qquad b = \sqrt[7]{7}$

(iii) $a = \sqrt{7} + \sqrt{10}$, $\qquad b = \sqrt{3} + \sqrt{19}$

Ans. (i) L.C.M. of 5 and 2 is 10.

Raise both sides to the power 10.

$\qquad (\sqrt[5]{5})^{10}$, $\qquad\qquad (\sqrt[2]{2})^{10}$

or $\quad (5)^{10/5}$, $\qquad\qquad (2)^{10/2}$

or $\quad 5^2$, $\qquad\qquad 2^5$ i.e., 25, 32.

$\therefore \quad b > a$ i.e., $\sqrt{2} > \sqrt[5]{5}$

(ii) L.C.M. of 4 and 7 is 28.

Raise both sides to the power 28.

$\therefore \quad (4)^{28/4}$, $\qquad\qquad (7)^{28/7}$

or $\quad 4^7$, $\qquad\qquad 7^4$

or $\quad 2^7 \cdot 2^7$, $\qquad\qquad 7^2 \cdot 7^2$

or $\quad (128)^2$, $\qquad\qquad (49)^2$

Naturally $a > b$

i.e., $\sqrt[4]{4} > \sqrt[7]{7}$

(iii) $a^2 = 17 + 2\sqrt{70}, b^2 = 22 + 2\sqrt{57}$

Subtract 17 from both

$\therefore \quad p = 2\sqrt{70}, \quad q = 5 + 2\sqrt{57}$

$p^2 = 280, \quad q^2 = 253 + 20\sqrt{57}$

$p^2 - 253 = 27, q^2 - 253 = 20\sqrt{57}$

Now $\sqrt{57} > 2 \quad \therefore \quad 20\sqrt{57} > 40$

$\therefore \quad q^2 - 253 > p^2 - 253 \quad \therefore q^2 > p^2$

or $q > p$ or $b^2 > a^2$ or $b > a$

i.e, $\sqrt{3} + \sqrt{19} > \sqrt{7} + \sqrt{10}$

42. Magic number 142857.

Its cyclic permutations are

(1) 142857 (2) 428571 (3) 285714 (4) 857142
(4) 571428 (6) 714285

Note that all these cyclic permutations are obtained by multiplying the given number by 1, 2, 3, 4, 5, 6.

e.g., $142857 \times 4 = 571428$ *i.e.,* (5) of the above list.

Similarly by multiplying with 1, 2, 3, 4, 5, 6 you will get all the above six cyclic permutations.

43. (a) **Square of any number ending with 5.**

i.e., $(15)^2, (25)^2, (35)^2, (45)^2, \ldots, (95)^2, (105)^2$

The last two digits will always be 25 and the digits before 25 will be $(a + 1)\, a$.

$(25)^2 = 625 = [(2+1).2]\, 25 = (3.2)\, 25 = 625$

$(55)^2 = 3025 = [(5+1).5]\, 25 = (6.5)\, 25 = 3025$

$(95)^2 = 9025 = [(9+1).9]\, 25 = (10.9)\, 25 = 9025$

$(105)^2 = 11025 = [(10+1).10]\, 25 = (11.10)\, 25 = 11025$

In a similar manner, we can write

$(15)^2 = 225, \quad (35)^2 = 1225, \quad (45)^2 = 2025,$

$(65)^2 = 4225, \quad (75)^2 = 5625$ etc. ...(A)

(b) **Square root of any perfect square number ending with 5.**

In the list (A) above part (a), we have perfect square numbers ending with 5. Their square root will be $a\,5$ where a is found by the rule given below :

625 is a perfect square number ending with 5, Leave 25 and we are left with 6. Now choose a such that a^2 is just less than 6.

$\therefore \quad 2^2 = 4 < 6$ but $3^2 = 9$ is > 6 and $1^2 = 1$

is not just less than 6 $\therefore \; a = 2$. Hence square root of $625 = a\,5 = 25$, as $a = 2$.

Another example :

9025 is a perfect square being $(95)^2$. Leave 25 and we are left with 90. Now choose a such that a^2 is just less than 90.

$\therefore \quad 9^2 = 81 < 90$, but $(10)^2 = 100 > 90$,

$8^2 = 64$ is not just less than 90.

$\therefore \quad a\,5 = 95$, as $a = 9$.

44. What is half of twelve ? 6 or 7 ?

Half of rectangle *ABCD* is *ABEF* or *DCEF* where *EF* is a line joining the mid-points of *BC* and *AD* (Fig. 06). Now

Fig.06

consider the figure 07.

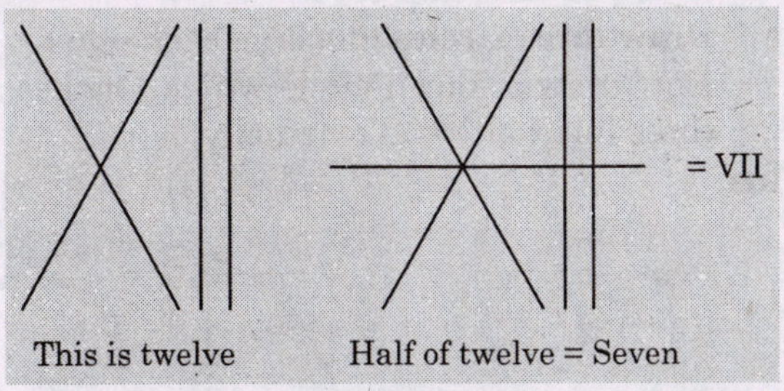

Fig.07

45. An engagement letter in Mathematics.

Proposal for marriage of Mr. Algebra's son to Mrs. Trigonometry's daughter.

My dear Trigonometry,

With due calculation and measurement, given a thought to your notation about the engagement of my son **Master Zero** with your daughter **Miss Infinity**, I have already taken the argeement of Mr. Solid Geometry. Mr Analysis did not have any objection. Mr. Statistics and Miss Astronomy predicated that their stars promise a happy and prosperous life. Moreover Mr. Zero is famous and well known to all because it is usually found in many results after exam. He is such a stiff fellow that inspite of quarelling ($\times$ or $-$) it remains unaffected. As regard to Infinity, she is not very beautiful and moreover when she walks she never stops, so many intellectual giants have tried to check her but all in vain.

Would you kindly inform me, after consulting formulae and log tables the suitable day for matrimonial ?

Thanking you.

Yours correctly,
ALGEBRA
MATHEMATICS TOWN,
ARITHMETIC STREET,
45 degree 15 minute
and 20 second.

Astrologers have predicated that the newly married couple will be blessed with six sons. Two of them will be 'Loolos' who will not stir out of their house either from front door or back door. They will be named as

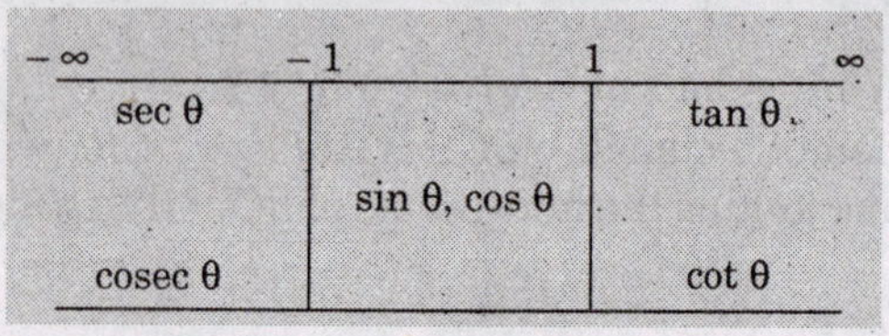

Fig. 8

sin θ and **cos** θ. The other two will be **'scoundrels'** who will never enter their house but will always be roaming outside their house to any extent. Whenever their pocket is empty they will knock at the house but will never enter it. Their names will be **sec** θ and **cosec** θ. By God's grace the remaining two will be renowned internationally and also visit their parents and will roam from one corner of the world to the other. Their names will be **tan** θ and **cot** θ.

46. (a) **Draw three circles touching each other.**

Now draw a fourth circle which touches all the three internally and externally.

Ans.

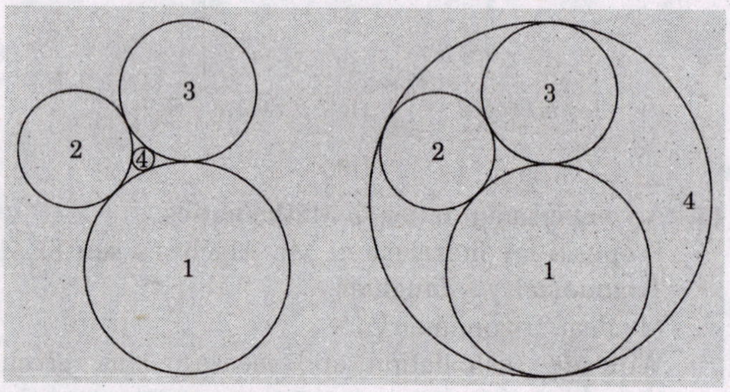

Fig. 9

(b) **Very interesting.**

Prove in two ways the following :

(i) $\dfrac{a^2-b^2}{a+b}=a-b$

(ii) $\dfrac{a^2-b^2}{a-b}=a+b$

(iii) $\sin(A+B)\sin(A-B)=\sin^2 A-\sin^2 B$

Ans. (i) $\dfrac{a^2-b^2}{a+b}=\dfrac{(a+b)(a-b)}{a+b}=a-b$

$\dfrac{a^2}{a}=a,\ \dfrac{-}{+}=-,\ \dfrac{b^2}{b}=b\ \ \therefore\ a-b$

(ii) As in (i)

(iii) $\sin(A+B)\sin(A-B)=\sin^2 A-\sin^2 B$

Above is a trigonometrical formula.

Again, $\sin(A+B)=\sin A+\sin B$ opening

$\sin(A-B)=\sin A-\sin B$ bracket

$\therefore\ \sin(A+B)\sin(A-B)=\sin^2 A-\sin^2 B$

47. (a) **Why these 10 numbers 0, 1, 2, 3, 4, 5, 6, 7, 8, 9 are written like this ?**

Ans. Above is the natural order of the 10 numbers. But one of my students wrote them as under : 8, 5, 4, 9, 1, 7, 6, 3, 2, 0 and asked me in which order are these numbers written now. I could not find any answer to his query. Then I started writing them in English :

Eight, (Five, Four), Nine, One, (Seven, Six), (Three, Two) and Zero.

i.e., e, f, f, n, o, s, s, t, t, z.

Now it struck to me that these numbers are in alphabetical order.

(b) The difference between the differences of two consecutive numbers is always 2.

Ans. True. $1^2, 2^2, 3^2, 4^2, 5^2, 6^2, \ldots$

1st Diff. 3 5 7 9 11 ...

2nd Diff. 2 2 2 2 ...

48. Befooling of a king by his officer who knew a little of mathematics.

A king who was fond of horses pruchased 40 Arabian horses and appointed an officer incharge of the stable who arranged the horses in the order as shown (15 in each line). The king was happy to see the arrangement. After a few months the officer stole 8 horses and sold them to another king. The matter was reported to the king who was very furious and called the officer. The

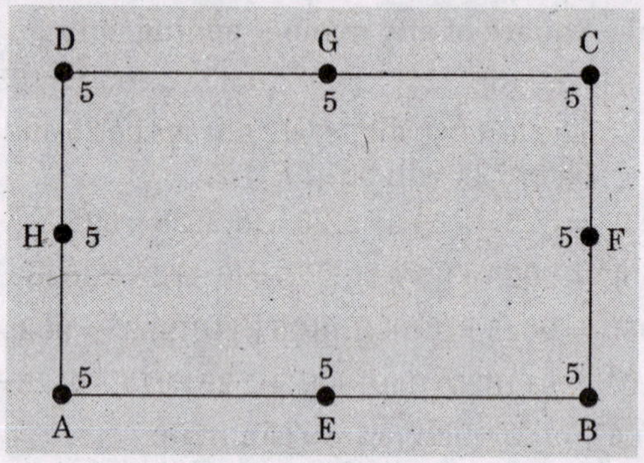

Fig 10

clever officer denied having stolen the horses and took the king to the stable. He showed him that there were 15 horses in each line of the stable as were in the beginning. The king was very happy and gave a prize to the officer for his sense of honesty.

But the fact is that he did steal 8 horses and befooled the king. Can you say how ?

Ans. The clever officer placed seven horses at each of the four corners and one each at the mid-points and

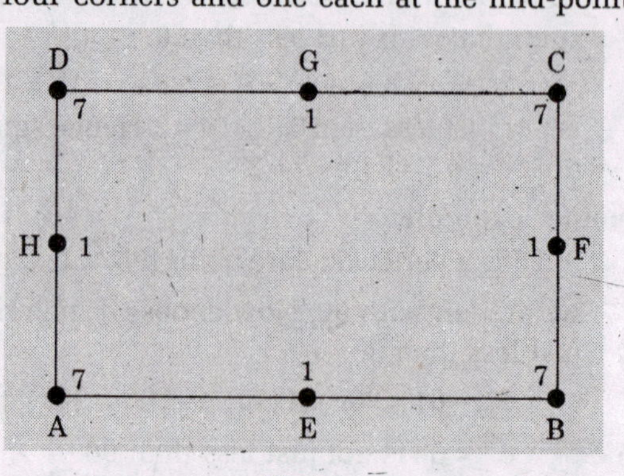

Fig. 11

showed the king that as before there are 15 horses in each line.

49. Believe it or not ?

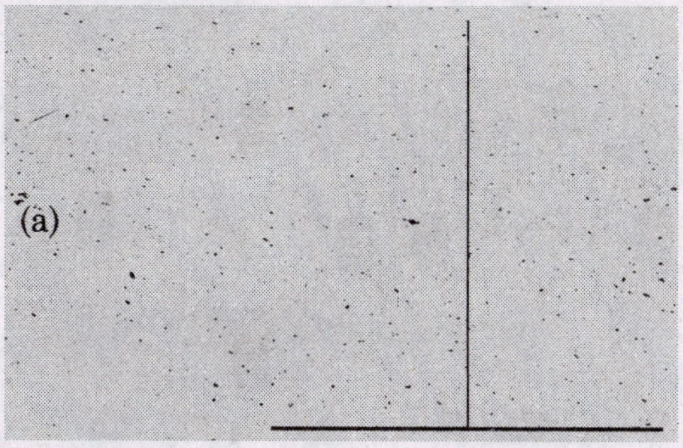

The vertical line and the horizontal one are of equal length.

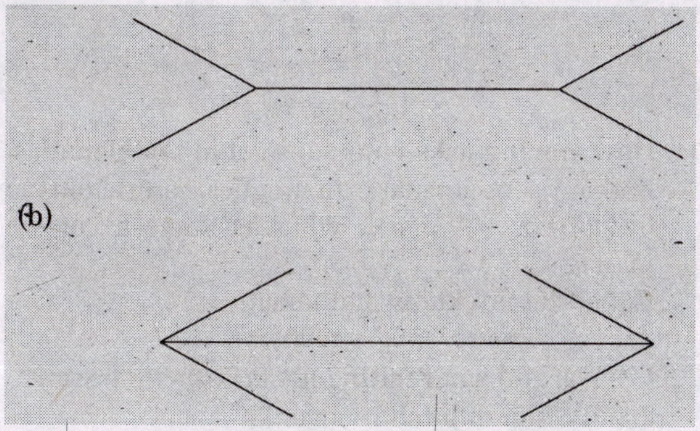

The two horizontal lines are of equal length.

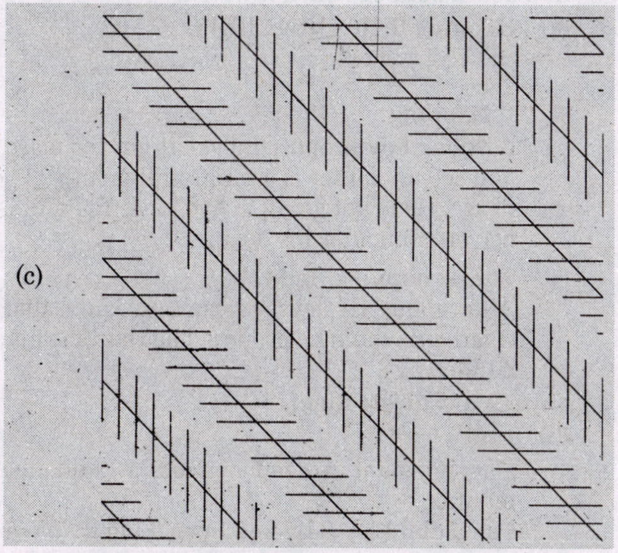

Fig. 12

The thick diagonal lines are really all parallel.

50. (a) **Five One-Rupee Coins.**

In the adjoining figure 13, I have arranged four, one-rupee coins in such a way that each coin touches the remaining three. Can you do the same thing with five coins and arrange them in such a way that each coin touches the remaining four ?

Fig. 13

Ans. First lay three coins as in figure 13 then place the remaining two coins in the position as shown in fig. 14 so that each of them touches the three horizontally placed coins and also touch each other at the top as in fig. 14.

Fig. 14

(b) **Yes, one of my students Lt. Col. Ranbir Singh did it in a P.O.W. (Prisoner of War) Camp. Can you do it on the paper ?**

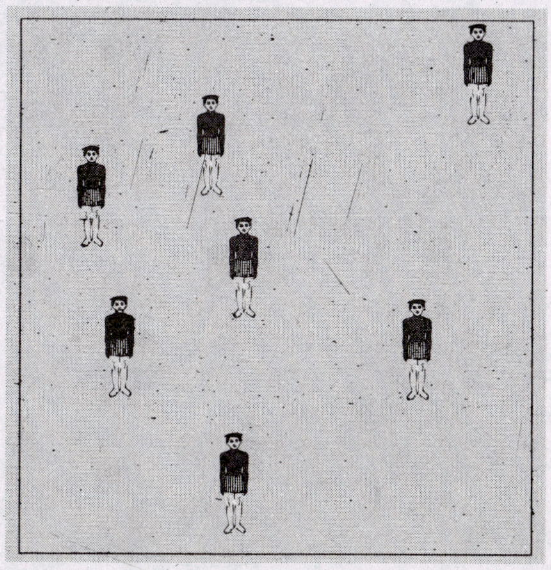

Fig. 15

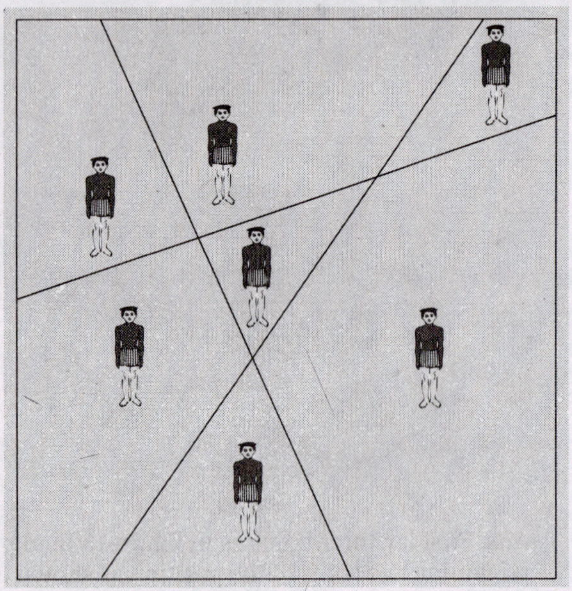

Fig. 15(a)

Lt. Col. Ranbir Singh was officer-in-charge of a P.O.W. Camp where the chief came on an inspection. In one of the camps there were ten P.O.W. standing in the position as shown in the circular camp (Fig. 15). They started shouting seeing the chief. The guards took position and ordered them 'Hands up'. The chief asked the Col. to put three circular fences in the camp so that each P.O.W. is in a separate enclosure. He did it at once [Fig. 15(a)].

A similar thing happened in the adjoining rectangular camp (Fig. 16) in which there were seven P.O.W. and the chief asked the Col. to separate them out by placing three straight fences so that each P.O.W. is in a separate enclosure [Fig. 16(a)].

Ans.

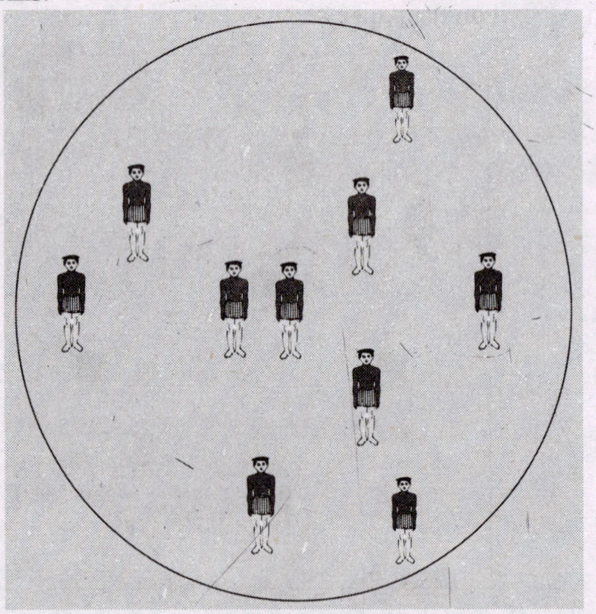

Fig. 16

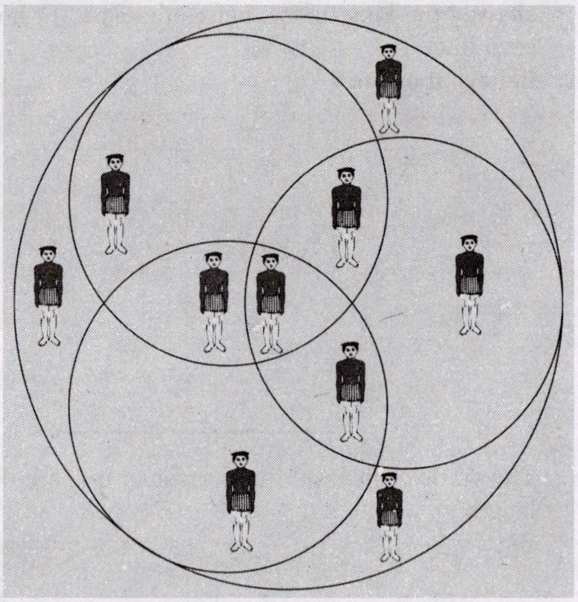

Fig. 16(a)

51. How much marks your sons got in mathematics ?

Both my sons got marks in nineties. Paresh told me that he got cos 90° marks whereas Ramesh got sin 90° marks.

Father did not know mathematics, *i.e.*

$$\cos 90° = 0, \quad \sin 90° = 1$$

52. Little grand son reciting his arithmetic lesson :

2 and 5 **son** of **bitch** is seven,
2 and 5 **son** of **bitch** is seven, ...
in place of **sum** of **which** is seven.

53. (a) **Hopping flight-Direct flight.**

$$\vec{AB} + \vec{BC} = \vec{AC}$$

Hopping Direct

A young boy proposed a smart girl for marriage. You see my father is a multi-millionaire 93 years of age. He is not going to live long. You and I will be very rich after his death.

This is hopping flight.

After about 10 days he came to know that the smart girl whom he proposed has become his step mother.

This is direct flight.

(b) $1 \times 9 = 9 \times 1$

One pregnant woman delivers a child in nine months.

Can a child be delivered by making nine women pregnant in one month ?

Ans. Certainly not.

(c) **Mathematician goes to post office.**

He asked the clerk, "What is the value of stamps to be affixed on this inland ?" "Fifteen Paisa", replied the clerk. But he thought that the clerk was saying "fifty".

He went to the stamp counter and purchased a stamp for 50 Paisa and after affixing it showed it to the clerk.

Clerk : No sir, I told you only fifteen and not fifty.
He again went to stamp counter and purchased stamps for 35 Paisa and affixed it along with 50 Paisa stamp and inserted a minus sign in between. "Is it all-right now?" he asked the clerk.
"What is all this!", remarked the clerk laughingly. "It seems you do not understand mathematics", said the mathematician, "I will make it clear" and he again rushed to the stamp counter and purchased another stamp of 15 Paisa and affixed it along with the other stamps and placed a sign of equality in between and posted the letter.

50 − 35 = 15 (fifteen)

54. Which is the barrel of Beer ?

A wine contractor purchased an odd lot of wine in barrels and one barrel contained beer. The barrels are shown in figure with the number of gallons each contains clearly marked on it. He wanted to bribe both the police and excise officials.

Fig. 17

Accordingly he instructed his salesman as under. "Do not temper with the seal of any of the barrels. Send some barrels of wine to the police officials and rest to excise people keeping in mind that police gets double the quantity of wine than the excise people get. Send the barrel of beer home for my daily use." He further ordered that his order must be carried out by the evening or else he will be dismissed."

Can you help him and point out how he should distribute the barells ?

Ans. Barrel of 20 gal. contained beer.

Barrel containing 15 gal. and 18 gal. (total 33) were sent to excise people. Barrel containing 31 gal., 19 gal. and 16 gal. (total 66) were sent to police. Thus police got 66 gal. of wine whereas excise people got 33 gal. The remaining 6th barrel contained 20 gallons of beer.

55. Mathematical Test

(a) **Fill in the blanks :**

OTTFFSS _ _ _

Ans. ENT

Given letters represent the first letters of one, two, three, four, five, six, seven and ENT for remaining eight, nine and ten.

(b) **Amusing Facts.**

Will you believe that ?

Letters *a,b,c* and *d* do not appear anywhere in the spellings of 1 to 99. Only the letter *d* comes for the first time in hundered.

Letters *a,b* and *c* do not appear anywhere in the spellings of 1 to 999. Only the letter *a* comes for the first time in thousand.

Letters *b* and *c* do not appear anywhere in the spellings of 1 to 999,999,999. Only the letter *b* comes for the first time in billion.

Letter *c* does not appear anywhere in the spellings of the entire English counting.

(c) **Ten horses have 24 legs. True or False ?**

Ans. True. Ten horses have twenty **fore** legs (front legs).

(d) **If there are 4 plants in each row, how many plants will be there in 5 rows ?**

Ans. I know you will say $5 \times 4 = 20$ but actually only 10. See the figure 18 below.

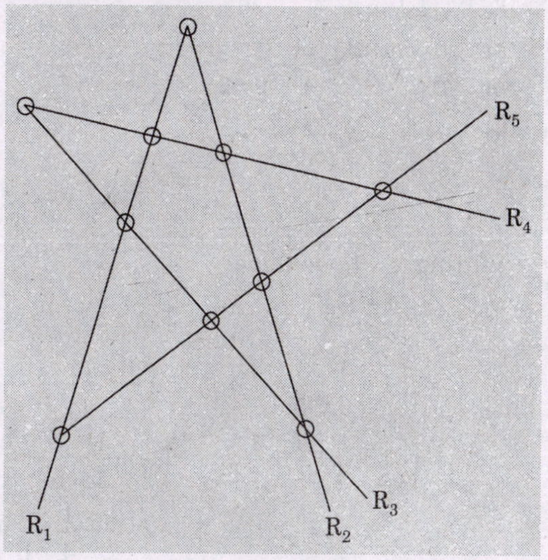

Fig. 18

$R_1, R_2, \ldots$ stands for rows and *O* stands for plants.
You now count the plants in the five rows $R_1, R_2 \ldots R_5$ of above figure 16. Their number is 10 only and not $5 \times 4 = 20$.

56. Another method of multiplication :

(A mystifying property of the number 2)

Example.

$$\begin{array}{r} 40 \\ \times 35 \\ \hline 1400 \end{array}$$

Method

(i) Divide the top number by 2 successively (ignoring the remainders if any) till we get the last quotient 1., *i.e.* quotients 20, 10, 5, 2, 1 (five).

(ii) Multiply the second number successively by 2 as many times as the number of quotients in (a), *i.e.* 70, 140, 280, 560, 1120 (five)

(iii) Add those numbers in (b) which appear below odd quotients in (a) and you get the required product.

(a) 20, 10, 5, 2, 1 (40 divided by 2)
(b) 70 140 280 560 1120 (35 multiplied by 2 successively).
(c) $280 + 1120 = 1400$ (Adding the numbers in 2nd row which are below odd quotients 5 and 1).

Another example.

$$\begin{array}{r} 72 \\ \times 12 \\ \hline 864 \end{array}$$

(i) 36 18 9 4 2 1
(ii) 24 48 96 192 384 768
(iii) $96 + 768 = 864$ (Adding numbers below odd quotients 9 and 1)

57. Will you believe that 2 = 1 ?

(a) Let $a = b$.

$ab = b^2$ or $ab - a^2 = b^2 - a^2$

or $a(b-a) = (b-a)(b+a)$

$\therefore$ $a = b + a$.

or $a = a + a$ $(\because a = b)$

or $a = 2a$ or $1 = 2$.

(b) $\log(1+x) = x - \frac{1}{2}x^2 + \frac{1}{3}x^3 - \frac{1}{4}x^4 + \frac{1}{5}x^5 - \frac{1}{6}x^6 + \dots$

Putting $x = 1$, we have

$$\log 2 = 1 - \frac{1}{2} + \frac{1}{3} - \frac{1}{4} + \frac{1}{5} - \frac{1}{6} + \frac{1}{7} - \frac{1}{8} + \dots \quad \dots(I)$$

$$= \left\{\left(1 + \frac{1}{3} + \frac{1}{5} + \frac{1}{7} + \dots\right) - \left(\frac{1}{2} + \frac{1}{4} + \frac{1}{6} + \frac{1}{8} \dots\right)\right\}$$

$$= \left\{\left(1 + \frac{1}{3} + \frac{1}{5} + \frac{1}{7} \dots\right) + \left(\frac{1}{2} + \frac{1}{4} + \frac{1}{6} + \frac{1}{8} \dots\right)\right\} - 2\left(\frac{1}{2} + \frac{1}{4} + \frac{1}{6} + \frac{1}{8} + \dots\right)$$

$$= \left(1 + \frac{1}{2} + \frac{1}{3} + \frac{1}{4} + \frac{1}{5} + \dots\right) - \left(1 + \frac{1}{2} + \frac{1}{3} + \frac{1}{4} + \dots\right)$$

$= 0$

$\therefore$ $2 = e^0 = 1$. Hence $2 = 1$.

(c) Multiplying both sides of (I) by 2, we get

$$2\log 2 = 2 - 1 + \frac{2}{3} - \frac{1}{2} + \frac{2}{5} - \frac{1}{3} + \frac{2}{7} - \frac{1}{4} + \dots$$

Taking those terms together which have a common denominator, we have

$$2\log 2 = (2-1) + \left(\frac{2}{3} - \frac{1}{3}\right) - \frac{1}{2} + \left(\frac{2}{5} - \frac{1}{5}\right) + \left(\frac{2}{7} - \frac{1}{7}\right) - \frac{1}{4} + \dots$$

or $2\log 2 = 1 - \frac{1}{2} + \frac{1}{3} - \frac{1}{4} + \frac{1}{5} - \dots$

$= \log 2$ by (1)

Hence $2 = 1$.

58. A father gave Rs. 150 to his son. Another father gave Rs. 100 to his son. But total money with both the sons is only Rs. 150 instead of Rs. (150 + 100) = Rs. 250. It is possible ?

Ans. A is father of B and B is father of C. B is son of A but father of C.

$$\underset{}{\overset{\text{F}}{A}} \xrightarrow{150} \underset{\substack{\text{(Son of A)} \\ 150 - 100 = 50}}{\overset{\text{F}}{B}} \xrightarrow{100} \underset{\substack{\text{(Son of B)} \\ 100}}{C}$$

Thus total money with both the sons B and C is $50 + 100 = 150$.

59. Even the richest king could not fulfil his promise.

A group of 64 sadhus were camping at the ouskirts of the capital of a very rich king whose only son was ailing and there was no hope of his survival. On hearing of the arrival of the sadhus he rushed to them to seek their blessings for his son. The son became all-right and there were lot of festivities in the kingdom.

The king approached the leader of the group of sadhus and requested him to ask for anything. The leader refused to have anything in return of the blessings he gave, but the king insisted and promised that he will fulfil their wish at every cost.

The leader said, "Our demand is very simple. We are 64 sadhus, give one grain of wheat to one of us today, 2 grains of wheat to the second, 4 grains of wheat to the third, 8 grains of wheat to the fourth and so so on to all the 64 sadhus. The king was rather disappointed at such a simple and petty demand of the Sadhus. He ordered his Ministers to fulfil their demand. They immediately rushed with few bags of wheat to be given to them in accordance with the promise but they had hardly given the wheat to about 25 sadhus when they ran short of it. Orders were issued to procure wheat from the whole of the kingdom but even with this they could give only to a few sadhus more."

Will you believe that even if the king had collected the entire wheat of his kingdom it would not have been sufficient for distribution amongst the sadhus in the manner they desired. The number of grains of wheat required was $\frac{2^{64} - 1}{2 - 1}$ (Sum of a G.P.).

60. Be quick to answer.

A boy says, "I have as many brothers as sisters." His sister answers, "I have twice as many brothers as sisters."

How many brothers and sisters are in the family ?

Ans. 4 brothers and 3 sisters.

1 brother says, "3 brothers, 3 sisters" (Equal)
1 sister says, "4 brothers, 2 sisters" (Twice)

61. Is there really any difference ?

"My property is exactly a **mile square**", said one land owner to another.

"Curiously enough, mine is a **square mile**" was the reply.

"Then there is no difference", said the farmer. Was he right ?

Ans. No difference from the point of view of area but there is clearly a difference in shape. A mile square is certainly a square whereas a square mile may be of any shape.

62. I am sure you will give a wrong answer.

Our society had arranged a picnic for the members at the time of annual conference and a bus was requisitioned for this purpose. We had gone at the rate of 30 miles an hour while on return journey over the same route we travelled at the rate of 40 m.p.h. as the roads were quite clear of traffic. What was our average speed ?

Ans. $\frac{30+40}{2} = 35$ (wrong). Average speed is $34\frac{2}{7}$ m.p.h. Suppose the distance be 120 miles, then time taken in onward journey is 4 hours and in backward journey is 3 hours. Hence in a total time of 7 hours distance covered is $120 + 120 = 240$ miles so that the average speed is $\frac{240}{7} = 34\frac{2}{7}$ m.p.h. You may choose any distance what so ever you like.

Family

63. How was he related to Asha ?

Mrs. Chandra saw Asha talking to a man and enquired if he was related to her.

Asha : "Yes, of course, you see his mother was my mother's mother-in-law, but he is not on talking terms with my papa."

Mrs. Chandra just nodded as if she understood the relationship of Asha with that man, but actually she could not follow. Can you help Mrs. Chandra ?

Ans. He was Asha's uncle.

A = Ram	C = Mother of	E = Mrs. Chandra
B = Shyam	both A & B and	w/o A
(Brothers)	M.I.L. of both	D = Asha d/o B
	E & F	F = Mother of D

Asha (D) said his (Ram's) mother C was M.I.L . of my mother F but he (Ram) is not on talking terms with my papa Shyam.

64. Can you count the number of persons in the family party ?

At a family party the following were persent :

1 Grand father, 1 Grand mother, 2 Fathers, 2 Mothers, 4 Children, 3 Grand children, 1 Brother, 2 Sisters, 2 Sons, 2 Daughters, 1 Father-in-law, 1 Mother-in-law and 1 Daughter-in-law.

I am sure you will say that there is no problem. Evidently the number of persons present is twenty three. You are absolutely wrong.

Can you give the correct answer ?

Ans. There were only following seven persons in the party as explained.

From above chart it is clear that the family party included the following :

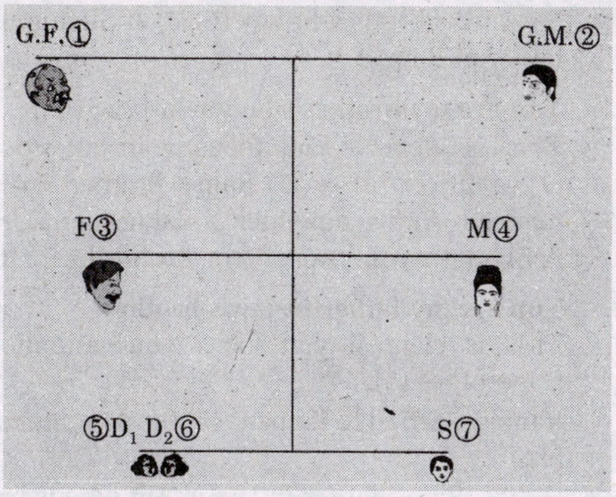

Fig. 19

1 Grand father	(1),	1 Grand mother	(2)
2 Fathers	(1, 3),	2 Mothers	(2, 4)
4 Children	(3, 5, 6, 7),	3 Grand children	(5, 6, 7)
1 Brother	(7),	2 Sisters	(5, 6)
2 Sons	(3, 7)	2 Daughters	(5, 6)
1 Father-in-law	(1 of 4),	1 Mother-in-law	(2 of 4)
1 Daughter-in-law	(4 of 2),		

65. What the relationship ? Can you clarify ?

Mr. Anil Bhatter met Mr. Ram Kakkar by chance in the college and said, "It appears I have seen you somewhere, my boy".

"Seen you, we are related to each other, Sir", said Mr. Ram Kakkar.

'How?', enquired Mr. Anil Bhatter.

'Listen', said Mr. Ram Kakkar, "You happen to be my father's brother-in-law, my brother's father-in-law and also my father-in-law's brother."

"What is all this, I can't make out anything", said Mr. Anil Bhatter.

Can you explain to him the relationship ?

Ans.

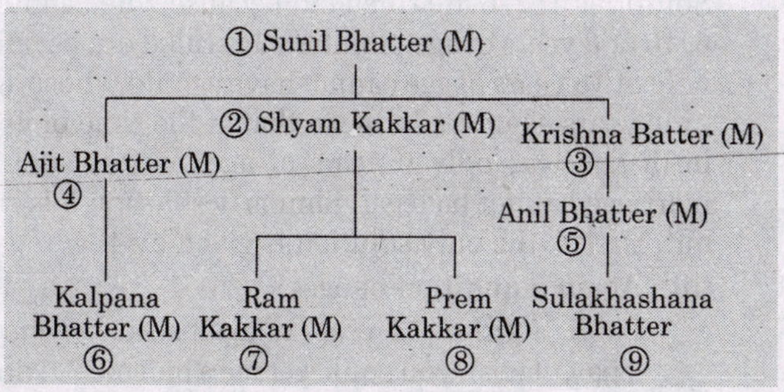

Fig. 20

Ram Kakkar said to Anil Bhatter :

1. You are my father's bother-in-law.

This is clear if you focus your attention on (7) → (2) → (5) (Krishna (3), Anil (5) are sister and brother being the daughter and son of Sunil (1)).

So Anil is brother-in-law (साला) of Shyam who is father of Ram.

2. **You are my brother's father-in-law.**
This is clear if you focus your attention on (7) → (8) → (9) → (5) Ram's brother Prem has married Anil's daughter Sulakhashana. Hence Anil is father-in-law of Prem, the brother of Ram.

3. **You are my father-in-law's brother.**
This is clear if you focus your attention on (7) → (4) → (5).
Ram is married to Kalpana (6) the daughter of Ajit (4).
Hence, Ram's father-in-law is Ajit who is brother of Anil.

Ages

66. Can you tell their ages ?

(a) Mr. Paul is **legally** married and has reached a square age. The product of the digits of his age is his wife's age. The age of their daughter is the sum of the digits of her father's age and the age of their son is the sum of the digits of his mother's age. How old are they ?

Ans. The words **legally married** should be carefully noted. As Mr. Paul has reached a square age so his age could be

16, 25, 36, 49, 64, 81 .....

We will compute the ages of oher members under given conditions and then see which is the solution keeping in view the words legally married.

	×	×	×	√	×	×
No. of Sol.	1	2	3	4	5	6
Age of Paul	16	25	36	49	64	81
Age of Wife	6	10	18	36	24	8
Age of Daughter	×	×	9	13	10	×
Age of Son	×	×	9	9	6	×

Solutions 1, 2, 6 are ruled out because wife can not be 6, 10 or 8 years of age. Solution 3 is ruled out because a wife of 18 years of age cannot have a child whose age is nine years as it would mean that at the time of giving birth she was only 9 years of age, and as such the marriage cannot be legal. Similarly solution 5 is ruled out. Hence, the only solution is given by 4.

(b) **Again a question of ages.**
Babli, a girl of 12 years of age asked her mother Vijay, "I wish you could get me a bicycle." "I do not think you are old enough to have a cycle. When I am three times as old as you are you shall have one", replied her mother.
Now the mother's age is 45 years. When may the young Babli get the cycle ?

Ans. After $4\frac{1}{2}$ years.

$$45 + x = 3(12 + x) \Rightarrow 9 = 2x \quad \therefore \quad x = 4\frac{1}{2}$$

(c) The ages of Lata and her husband Kishore are represented by the reverse order of the digits of either's age. But the difference in their ages is one-eleventh of their sum. Can you tell their ages ?

Ans. Kishore 54, Lata 45

Husband $xy = 10x + y$ as $59 = 10.5 + 9$

Wife $yx = 10y + x$ as $95 = 10.9 + 5$

Difference $= 9(x - y)$, Sum $= 11(x + y)$

By given condition,

$$9(x - y) = \frac{1}{11}.11(x + y) = x + y$$

or $8x = 10y$ or $\frac{x}{5} = \frac{y}{4} = 1, 2, \ldots$

$\therefore \quad x = 5, y = 4 \quad$ or $\quad x = 10, y = 8$

Husband $= xy = 10.5 + 4 = 54, \quad 10 \times 10 + 8 = 108$

Wife $= yx = 10.4 + 5 = 45 \quad 10 \times 8 + 10 = 90$

Hence correct answer is 54, 45 as difference 9 is $\frac{1}{11}$ of sum 99. The second set does not satisfy the given condition.

67. (a) **Again a question of their ages.**
Kishore was married to Lata 18 years ago and the age of Kishore was thrice the age of Lata. But today Kishore is just twice as old as Lata. What were their ages at the time of their wedding ?

Ans. Kishore 54, Lata 18

Kishore x, Lata y, where $x = 3y$ at wedding time

Today after 18 years

Kishore $x + 18$, Lata $y + 18$

where $\quad x + 18 = 2(y + 18)$

or $\quad x - 2y = 18$

But $x = 3y \therefore 3y - 2y = 18$, *i.e.*, $y = 18$ and hence $x = 54$.

Another form :

Again a question of ages.

Eighteen years ago a father was three times as old as his son. Presently he is twice as old now.

Ans. Son's age x, then father's age $2x$ presently

18 years ago, son's age $x - 18$ and father's age is $2x - 18$

By given condition,

$2x - 18 = 3(x - 18) \quad \therefore \quad x = 36$

Son's age is 36 and father's age is $2 \times 36 = 72$

18 years ago their ages are son 18, father 54, *i.e.*, three times son's age.

(b) Sankalp says that in 1932 he was as old as the last digits of birth year 1932. When Sankalp said it to his grand father M.L.K. he said the same was applicable to him. Can you give the correct ages of Sankalp and M.L.K. ?

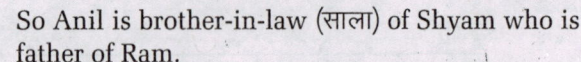

Ans. First of all it should be observed that Sankalp was born in 20th century *i.e.*, 1932. Naturally, his grandfather was born in 19th century, *i.e.* some year like $18ab$. Now ab must be equal to $\frac{1}{2}(132) = 66$. Hence the grand father was born in 1866 so that in 1932 he was 66 years of age represented by the last two digits of his year of birth.

(c) **What is your age now ?**

Reply : Take may age three years after today. Multiply it by three. Subtract it from three times my age three years ago and you will know my age.

Ans. Suppose my age is x years, then my age three years after will be $x+3$ and three years ago it was $x-3$.

By given condition,

$$3(x+3)-3(x-3)=x$$

$$\therefore \quad x=18$$

Verification. My age three years after and three years before are 21 and 15.

$\therefore \quad 3(21-15)=3.6=18$ years.

68. How charitable was he ?

Mr. Sharma was a man of charitable disposition. He was approached by a sadhu as soon as he came out of his house and gave him one paisa more than half the money he had in his pocket. On the way he met a leper who appealed to him for charity. To the leper he gave two paisa more than half the money he then had in his pocket. While he was entering his office a widow appealed to him for some alms to get the medicine for his only son who was ill. To her he gave three paisa more than half of what was left with him.

He could not even have a pan in the office as he had only one paisa left in his pocket.

Can you tell how much money Mr. Sharma had in his pocket when he started from his house ?

Ans. Suppose he had x paisa when he left home.

	Charity	Left
Sadhu	$\frac{x}{2}+1$	$\frac{x}{2}-1=y$ say
Leper	$\frac{y}{2}+2$	$\frac{y}{2}-2=z$ say
Widow	$\frac{z}{2}+3$	$\frac{z}{2}-3=1$ given

$\therefore \quad z=8,\ y=20,\ x=42.$

Hence he had 42 paisa when he left home.

69. Was he a gainer or a loser ?

Mr. Singh bought two second hand scooters, one for himself and the other for his wife and later on they changed their mind and decided to go in for an old car. So he sold them for Rs. 1200/- each, making a profit of 20 percent on one and a loss of 20 percent on the other. Was Mr. Singh a gainer or a loser on the whole transaction and by how much ?

Ans. Certainly a loser. He must have paid Rs. 1500/- for the scooter on wich he suffered a loss of 20% by selling at Rs. 1200/-. For the second one he paid Rs. 1000/- on which he gained 20% by selling at Rs. 1200/-. Thus he actually paid Rs. 2500/- and got only Rs. 2400/- and hence suffered a loss of Rs. 100/- only.

Questions on Will

70. (a) **The Lawyer did not know simple mathematics.**

A rich man was on death bed when his wife was about to deliver a child. He called his lawyer and asked him to write his will and he gave the following instructions.

Two thirds of his estate will go to his son (if the new born is a boy) and one third to the mother (*i.e.* rich man's widow). But if the child is a girl then two thirds should go to the mother and one third to the daughter. After his death his wife delivered twins a boy and a girl. The Lawyer was at a loss to understand as to how the estate be distributed now amongst the three in accordance with the spirit of dead man's will.

Can you help him ?

Ans. The rich man desired that his wife should get twice as much as his daughter and the son should get twice as much as his wife. Hence if his daughter's share is x, then that of mother is $2x$ and of son is $4x$, so that total estate is $7x$. Hence daughter gets one seventh, mother gets two sevenths and son gets four sevenths of his estate.

(b) **Will of a mathematics teacher.**

A school teacher of mathematics had a very large family of 4 sons, 5 daughters and one wife. He used to live very miserly and had saved about three lakh fifty one thousand with him at the age of 75 when he wrote his will as under :

Each of my daughters should get twice as much as my wife would receive and each of my son should get thrice as much as each of my daughter receives. Can you say how much money each received ?

Ans. W = 9000, D = 18000, S = 54000

W	D	S
x	$2x$	$6x$

$$\therefore \quad x.1+2x.4+6x.5=351000$$

$$39x=351000$$

$$\therefore \quad x=9000$$

(c) **Again a question of will.**

A farmer had 112 acres of land and he wrote the will for the distribution amongst his three sons—Ram, Shyam and Mohan in the proportion of $\frac{1}{3}$rd, $\frac{1}{4}$th and $\frac{1}{5}$th respectively. In the mean time both the farmer and his youngest son Mohan died in a road accident. How the property be now distributed between the two sons in accordance with the wishes of the farmer ?

Ans. 64 acres to Ram and 48 acres to Shyam

$$\frac{1}{3}:\frac{1}{4}::\frac{4}{12}:\frac{3}{12}.$$

Hence the property is to be distributed in the ratio 4:3

$\therefore \quad \frac{x}{4} = \frac{y}{3} = \frac{x+y}{4+3} = \frac{112}{7} = 16$

$\therefore \quad x = 64,\ y = 48$

(d) A rich man made his will distributing his property cash, farm house and seventeen horses between his three sons A, B, C as under : A to get $\frac{1}{2}$ of the share, B to get $\frac{1}{3}$rd and C to get $\frac{1}{4}$th of the share. He also entrusted his friend Prof. M.L. Khanna to distribute the property in the manner he desired. How was it settled ?

Ans. There was no problem in distributing the cash and farm land in accordance with the provision of the will. But division of 17 horses was a real problem. Prof. Khanna asked some of his friends to take one horse and mix them with the 17 in the farm house, thus making the total number of horses 18. He gave $\frac{1}{2}$ *i.e.* 9 horses to A, $\frac{1}{3}$rd *i.e.* 6 horses to B and $\frac{1}{9}$th *i.e.* 2 horses to C. Thus $9 + 6 + 2 = 17$ horses were given to the sons and remaining one horse which Prof. Khanna's friend had brought was given to him.

71. Yes, it happened with me. Can you say how I managed?

Myself, my wife and my two sons Ajay, Atul along with our dog Tipsy were out on a tour in our car. On the way we came across a river which we had to cross by a boat in order to visit the temple on the other side. There was only one boat which was capable of carrying only 150 lbs weight. My weight and that of my wife is each 150 lbs whereas each of my son weighs 75 lbs. The sweet Tipsy had also to be carried on to the other side. My son immediately said, "Ladies first, so Dad send mummy first". "Don't be foolish sonny. What will be the use, she will have to come back with the boat. Yes, Dad you are right, my son realized. Then I guided the operations. Can you say how I did it and in how many trips ?

Ans. In eleven trips. I sent both Atul and Ajay (both 150 lbs. wt) in the boat. Ajay returned back leaving Atul there. In the next trip I (150 lbs) went in the boat and sent back Atul who was on the other bank. Again both Atul and Ajay went in the boat and Ajay returned back. Now my wife goes in the boat and again Atul is sent back. Now Atul and Ajay cross again and leaves Atul there and Ajay returns. Ajay now takes doggie Tipsy with him and thus all of us are now there on the other bank. In all there are eleven to and fro trips in the boat.

72. A primitive way of bartering animals.

Three villagers A, B, C met at a cattle market. A said to B "I will give you six of my donkeys for one of your horses and then you will have twice as many animals here as I have got." C said to A, "I will give you fourteen of my sheep for a horse and then you will have three times as many animals as I." B said to C, "I will give you four cows for a horse and then you will have six times as many animals as I have got here."

Can you tell the number of animals each of A, B, C had when they went to the cattle market ?

Ans.	A	B	C
Animals	x	y	z
	Donkey	Horse	Sheep

A's offer to B $\quad 2(x - 6 + 1) = y - 1 + 6 \quad \therefore\ 2x - y = 15$

C's offer to A $\quad 3(z - 14 + 1) = x - 1 + 14 \therefore\ x - 3z = -52$

B's offer to C $\quad 6(y - 4 + 1) = (z - 1 + 4) \therefore\ 6y - z = 21$

Solving the above three equations, we have

$$x = 11,\ y = 7,\ z = 21$$

73. The horse and donkey.

Heavily loaded horse and donkey were going side by side. The donkey complained of heavy load. The horse replied, "If I take one sack of your back then my load will be twice as of yours. But if you remove one sack from my back, then our loads will be equal". How many sacks each was carrying ?

Ans. 7 and 5.

Let horse carry x sacks and donkey y sacks.

By the given condition,

$x + 1 = 2(y - 1)$ or $x - 2y = -3$

and $x - 1 = y + 1$ or $x - y = 2$

Solving the above two equations, we get $x = 7$ and $y = 5$.

74. 1 foot = 144 inches. True or false ?

Ans. False.

2 foot = 24 inches Divide by 4

$\therefore \quad \frac{1}{2}$ foot = 6 inches. Multiply

$\therefore \quad \left(2 \times \frac{1}{2}\right)$ foot $= 24 \times 6$ inches

or $\quad$ 1 foot = 144 inches ...(A)

Seems to be true. But actually you have to write result (A) as

$\left(2 \times \frac{1}{2}\right)$ sq. ft = 144 sq. inches

or $\quad$ 1 sq. ft = 144 sq. inches

Taking square root of both sides,

1 ft = 12 inches.

75. Indeterminate form.

When, where and how you will die is indeterminate.

76. The Game of doubling and halving.

(A) Sharing one's joys doubles the joy. Sharing one's sorrows halves it.

(B) When, where and how you talk either doubles your beauty or halves it.

❑

EXAMINATION PAPER-2016

IIT-JEE (Main)

Mathematics

1. If $f(x) + 2f\left(\frac{1}{x}\right) = 3x, x \neq 0$ and

$S = \{x \in R : f(x) = f(-x)\}$; then S :

(a) is an empty set

(b) contains exactly one element

(c) contains exactly two elements

(d) contains more than two elements

Sol. Ans. (c)

$\because \quad f(x) + 2f\left(\frac{1}{x}\right) = 3x \quad$ ...(i)

Replace x by $\frac{1}{x}$, then

$f\left(\frac{1}{x}\right) + 2f(x) = \frac{3}{x} \quad$ ...(ii)

From Eqs. (i) and (ii), we get $f(x) = \frac{2}{x} - x$

given $f(x) = f(-x)$, we get

$x = \pm\sqrt{2}$

2. A value of θ for which $\frac{2 + 3i\sin\theta}{1 - 2i\sin\theta}$ is purely imaginary, is :

(a) $\frac{\pi}{3}$ (b) $\frac{\pi}{6}$

(c) $\sin^{-1}\left(\frac{\sqrt{3}}{4}\right)$ (d) $\sin^{-1}\left(\frac{1}{\sqrt{3}}\right)$

Sol. Ans. (b)

Let $z = \frac{2 + 3i\sin\theta}{1 - 2i\sin\theta}$

$\Rightarrow \bar{z} = -z$

We get $\sin\theta = \frac{1}{3} \Rightarrow \theta = \sin^{-1}\left(\frac{1}{\sqrt{3}}\right)$

3. The sum of all real values of x satisfying the equation $(x^2 - 5x + 5)^{x^2+4x-60} = 1$ is :

(a) 3 (b) -4

(c) 6 (d) 5

Sol. Ans. (a)

Case (1) : $x^2 - 5x + 5 = 1$

$\Rightarrow x^2 - 5x + 4 = 0, x = 1, 4$

Case (2) : $x^2 + 4x - 60 = 0$

$x = -10, 6$

Case (3) : $x^2 - 5x + 5 = -1$

$x^2 - 5x + 6 = 0$

$x = 2, 3$

for $x = 2$

power is –ive and even.

for $x = 3$

power is –ve and odd.

Hence $x = 2$ is final and $x \neq 3$.

Sum of all values of x

$= 1 + 4 + (-10) + 6 + 2$

$= 5 - 10 + 8 = 3$

4. If $A = \begin{bmatrix} 5a & -b \\ 3 & 2 \end{bmatrix}$ and A adj $A = AA^T$, then $5a + b$ is equal to :

(a) -1 (b) 5 (c) 4 (d) 13

Sol. Ans. (a)

Given A adj $A = AA^T$

$\Rightarrow \begin{bmatrix} 10a + 3b & 0 \\ 0 & 3b + 10a \end{bmatrix} = \begin{bmatrix} 25a^2 + b^2 & 15a - 2b \\ 15a - 2b & 13 \end{bmatrix}$

$\Rightarrow 15a - 2b = 0$

$25a^2 + b^2 = 13$

or $(5a)^2 + b^2 = 2^2 + 3^2 \quad \therefore b = 3, 5a = 2$

Hence, $5a + b = 5$

5. The system of linear equations

$x + \lambda y - z = 0$

$\lambda x - y - z = 0$

$z + y - \lambda z = 0$

has a non-trivial solution for :

(a) infinitely many values of λ

(b) exactly one value of λ

(c) exactly two values of λ

(d) exactly three values of λ

Sol. Ans. (d)

$\begin{vmatrix} 1 & \lambda & -1 \\ \lambda & -1 & -1 \\ 1 & 1 & -\lambda \end{vmatrix} = 0 \Rightarrow \lambda^3 - \lambda = 0 \Rightarrow \lambda = -1, 0, 1$

6. If all the words (with or without meaning) having five letters, formed using the letters of the word SMALL and arranged as in a dictionary; then the position of the word SMALL is :

(a) 46th (b) 59th

(c) 52th (d) 58th

Sol. Ans. (d)

A, L, L, M, S

$A \to \frac{4!}{2!} = 12, \quad L \to 4! = 24, \quad M \to \frac{4!}{2!} = 12$

$SA \to \frac{3!}{2!} = 3, \quad SL \to 3! = 6$

SMALL $\to 1$

Hence required position $= 12 + 24 + 12 + 3 + 6 + 1 = 58$

7. If the number of terms in the expansion of $\left(1 - \frac{2}{x} + \frac{4}{x^2}\right)^n, x \neq 0$, is 28, then the sum of the coefficients of all the terms in this expansion, is :

(a) 64 (b) 2187

(c) 243 (d) 729

Sol. Ans. (d)

$^{n+2}C_2 = 28 = {}^8C_2 \Rightarrow n + 2 = 8$

$\therefore \quad n = 6$

$\therefore$ Sum of coefficient $= (1 - 2 + 4)^n = 3^n = 3^6 = 729$

8. If the 2nd, 5th and 9th terms of a non-constant A.P. are in G.P., then the common ratio of this G.P. is :

(a) $\frac{8}{5}$ (b) $\frac{4}{3}$ (c) 1 (d) $\frac{7}{4}$

Sol. Ans. (b)

$\because \quad (a + 4d)^2 = (a + d)(a + 8d) \Rightarrow d = \frac{a}{8}$

$\therefore$ Common ratio $= \frac{a + 4d}{a + d} = \frac{a + \frac{a}{2}}{a + \frac{a}{8}} = \frac{4}{3}$

9. If the sum of the first ten terms of the series $\left(1\frac{3}{5}\right)^2 + \left(2\frac{2}{5}\right)^2 + \left(3\frac{1}{5}\right)^2 + 4^2 + \left(4\frac{4}{5}\right)^2 + \ldots$, is $\frac{16}{5}m$, then m is equal to :

(a) 102 (b) 101 (c) 100 (d) 99

Sol. Ans. (b)

$\frac{16}{25}(2^2 + 3^2 + 4^2 + \ldots + 11^2) = \frac{11}{5}m$

$\Rightarrow \frac{16}{25}(22 \times 23 - 1) = \frac{16}{5}m \Rightarrow m = 101.$

10. Let $p = \lim_{x \to 0^+} (1 + \tan^2 \sqrt{x})^{\frac{1}{2x}}$ then $\log^p$ is equal to :

(a) 2 (b) 1 (c) $\frac{1}{2}$ (d) $\frac{1}{4}$

Sol. Ans. (c)

$p = \lim_{h \to 0} (1 + \tan^2 \sqrt{h})^{1/2h}$

$= e^{\lim_{h \to 0} \frac{\tan^2 \sqrt{h}}{2h}} = e^{1/2}$

$\therefore \quad \log_e p = \frac{1}{2}$

11. For $x \in R$, $f(x) = |\log 2 - \sin x|$ and $g(x) = f(f(x))$, then :

(a) g is not differentiable at $x = 0$

(b) $g'(0) = \cos(\log 2)$

(c) g is differentiable at $x = 0$

(d) $g'(0) = -\sin(\log 2)$

Sol. Ans. (b)

At $x = 0$

$\ln 2 > \sin x$

$\therefore \quad f(x) = \ln 2 - \sin x$

$\Rightarrow \quad g(x) = f(f(x)) = \ln 2 - \sin(\ln 2 - \sin x)$

$g'(x) = -\cos(\ln 2 - \sin x)(-\cos x)$

$g'(0) = \cos(\ln 2)$

12. Consider $f(x) = \tan^{-1}\left(\sqrt{\frac{1 + \sin x}{1 - \sin x}}\right), x \in \left(0, \frac{\pi}{2}\right)$

A normal to $y = f(x)$ at $x = \frac{\pi}{6}$ also passes through the point :

(a) (0, 0) (b) $\left(0, \frac{2\pi}{3}\right)$ (c) $\left(\frac{\pi}{6}, 0\right)$ (d) $\left(\frac{\pi}{4}, 0\right)$

Sol. Ans. (b)

$f(x) = \tan^{-1}\left(\sqrt{\frac{1 + \cos\left(\frac{\pi}{2} - x\right)}{1 - \cos\left(\frac{\pi}{2} - x\right)}}\right)$

$= \tan^{-1} \cot\left(\frac{\pi}{4} - \frac{x}{2}\right) \qquad \left(\because f\left(\frac{\pi}{6}\right) = \frac{\pi}{3}\right)$

$\therefore \quad f'(x) = \frac{1}{2}$

Equation of normal $y - \frac{\pi}{3} = -2\left(x - \frac{\pi}{6}\right)$ which is passed through $\left(0, \frac{2\pi}{3}\right)$.

13. A wire of length 2 units is cut into two parts which are bent respectively to form a square of side = x units and a circle of radius = r units. If the sum of areas of the square and the circle so formed is minimum then :

(a) $2x = (\pi + 4)r$ (b) $(4 - \pi)x = \pi r$

(c) $x = 2r$ (d) $2x = r$

Sol. Ans. (c)

$\because \quad 4x + 2\pi r = 2 \Rightarrow r = \frac{1 - 2x}{\pi}$ ...(i)

$\therefore \quad A = x^2 + \pi r^2 = x^2 + \frac{(1 - 2x)^2}{\pi}$

For max. or min. $\frac{dA}{dx} = 0$

$x = \frac{2(1 - 2x)}{\pi}$ ...(ii)

From Eqs. (i) and (ii), $x = 2r$

14. The integral $\int \frac{2x^{12} + 5x^9}{(x^5 + x^3 + 1)^3} dx$ is equal to :

(a) $\frac{-x^5}{(x^5 + x^3 + 1)^2} + C$ (b) $\frac{x^{10}}{2(x^5 + x^3 + 1)^2} + C$

(c) $\frac{x^5}{2(x^5 + x^3 + 1)^2} + C$ (d) $\frac{-x^{10}}{2(x^5 + x^3 + 1)^2} + C$

Sol. Ans. (b)

$\int \frac{\frac{2}{x^3} + \frac{5}{x^6}}{\left(1 + \frac{1}{x^2} + \frac{1}{x^5}\right)^3} dx = \frac{1}{2\left(1 + \frac{1}{x^2} + \frac{1}{x^5}\right)^2} + C$

$= \frac{x^{10}}{2(x^5 + x^3 + 1)^2} + C$

15. $\lim_{n \to \infty} \left(\frac{(n + 1)(n + 2) \ldots 3n}{n^{2n}}\right)^{1/n}$ is equal to :

(a) $\frac{18}{e^4}$ (b) $\frac{27}{e^2}$

(c) $\frac{9}{e^2}$ (d) $3 \log 3 - 2$

Sol. Ans. (b)

$P = \lim_{n \to \infty} \left(\frac{n + 1}{n} \cdot \frac{n + 2}{n} \cdot \frac{n + 3}{n} \ldots \frac{n + 2n}{n}\right)^{1/n}$

$= \lim_{n \to \infty} \prod_{r=1}^{2n} \left(\frac{n + r}{n}\right)^{1/n}$

$\therefore \quad \ln p = \lim_{n \to \infty} \sum_{r=1}^{2n} \frac{1}{n} \log\left(1 + \frac{r}{n}\right)$

$$= \int_0^2 \ln(1+x)\,dx = \int_1^3 \ln x\,dx$$

$$= \ln 27 - 2 = \ln\left(\frac{27}{e^2}\right)$$

$$\Rightarrow \quad p = \frac{27}{e^2}$$

16. The area (in sq. units) of the region $\{(x, y) : y^2 \geq 2x$ and $x^2 + y^2 \leq 4x, x \geq 0, y \geq 0\}$ is :

(a) $\pi - \frac{4}{3}$ (b) $\pi - \frac{8}{3}$ (c) $\pi - \frac{4\sqrt{2}}{3}$ (d) $\frac{\pi}{2} - \frac{2\sqrt{2}}{3}$

Sol. Ans. (b)

Required area $= \frac{1}{4}\pi(2)^2 - \int_0^2 \sqrt{2}\sqrt{x}\,dx$

$= \pi - \frac{8}{3}$

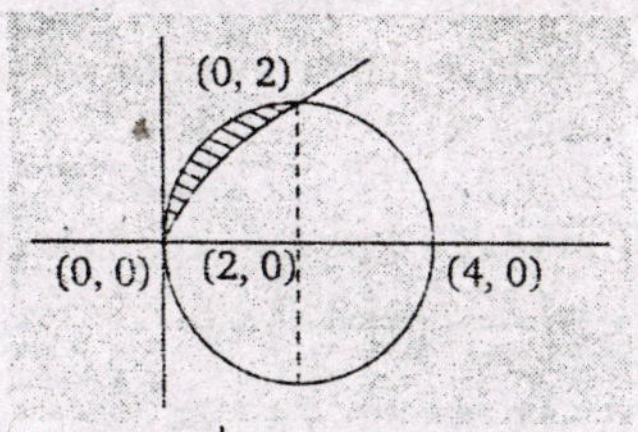

17. If a curve $y = f(x)$ passes through the point $(1, -1)$ and satisfies the differential equation, $y(1 + xy)\,dx = x\,dy$, the $f\left(-\frac{1}{2}\right)$ is equal to :

(a) $-\frac{2}{5}$ (b) $-\frac{4}{5}$ (c) $\frac{2}{5}$ (d) $\frac{4}{5}$

Sol. Ans. (d)

$$\left(\frac{y\,dx - x\,dy}{y^2}\right) + x\,dx = 0$$

$$\Rightarrow d\left(\frac{x}{y}\right) + x\,dx = 0 \quad \Rightarrow \quad \frac{x}{y} + \frac{x^2}{2} = C$$

which passes through $(1, -1)$

$\therefore \quad C = -\frac{1}{2} \qquad \frac{x}{y} + \frac{x^2}{2} = -\frac{1}{2}$

at $x = -\frac{1}{2}, y = \frac{4}{5} \quad \therefore \quad f\left(-\frac{1}{2}\right) = \frac{4}{5}$

18. Two sides of a rhombus are along the lines, $x - y + 1 = 0$ and $7x - y - 5 = 0$. If its diagonals intersect at $(-1, -2)$, then which one of the following is a vertex of this rhombus ?

(a) $(-3, -9)$ (b) $(-3, -8)$

(c) $\left(\frac{1}{3}, -\frac{8}{3}\right)$ (d) $\left(-\frac{10}{3}, -\frac{7}{3}\right)$

Sol. Ans. (c)

$$\alpha - \beta + 1 = 0 \qquad \text{...(i)}$$

and $7(-2 - \alpha) - (-4 - \beta) - 5 = 0$ ...(ii)

Solving Eqs. (i) and (ii), we get

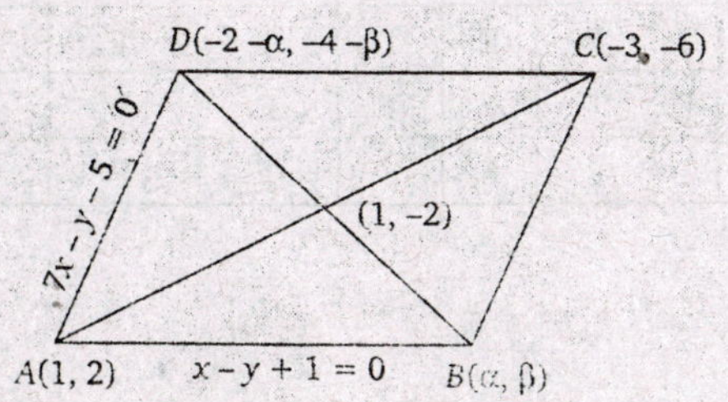

$$\alpha = -\frac{7}{3}, \beta = -\frac{4}{3}$$

$$D = \left(\frac{1}{3}, \frac{-8}{3}\right)$$

19. The centres of those circles which touch the circle, $x^2 + y^2 - 8x - 8y - 4 = 0$, externally and also touch the x-axis, lie on :

(a) a circle

(b) an ellipse which is not a circle

(c) a hyperbola

(d) a parabola

Sol. Ans. (d)

$$\Rightarrow \sqrt{(x-4)^2 + (y-4)^2} = (6 + y)$$

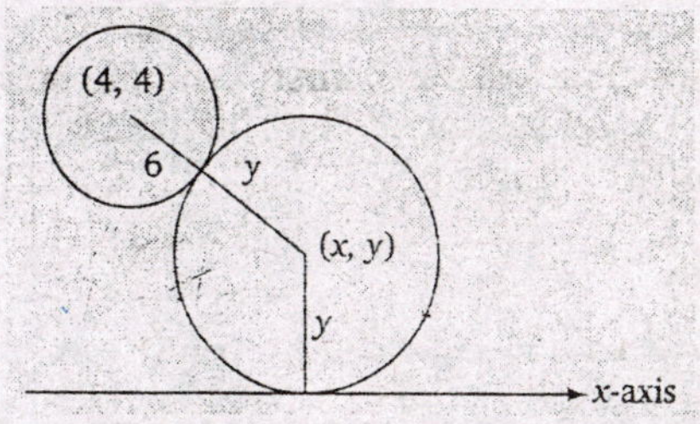

$$\Rightarrow \quad x^2 - 8x - 20y - 4 = 0 \quad \text{(parabola)}$$

20. If one of the diameters of the circle, given by the equation, $x^2 + y^2 - 4x + 6y - 12 = 0$ is a chord of a circle S, whose centre is $(-3, 2)$, then the radius of S is :

(a) $5\sqrt{2}$ (b) $5\sqrt{3}$

(c) 5 (d) 10

Sol. Ans. (b)

$$\therefore \quad r = \sqrt{(50 + 25)} = 5\sqrt{3}$$

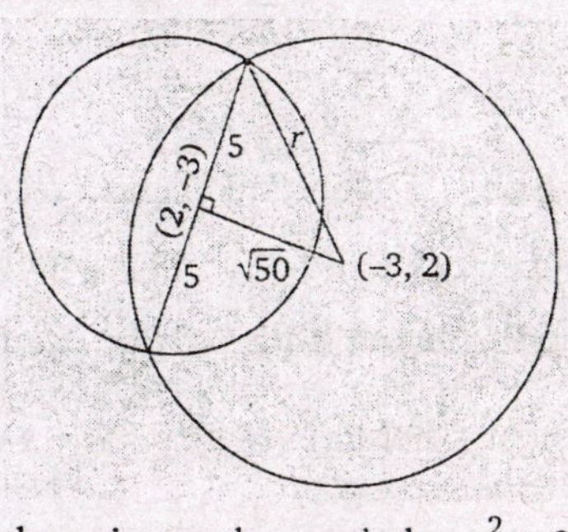

21. Let P be the point on the parabola, $y^2 = 8x$, which is at a minimum distance from the centre C of the circle, $x^2 + (y + 6)^2 = 1$. Then the equation of the circle, passing through C and having its centre at P is :

(a) $x^2 + y^2 - 4x + 8y + 12 = 0$

(b) $x^2 + y^2 - x + 4y - 12 = 0$

(c) $x^2 + y^2 - \frac{x}{4} + 2y - 24 = 0$

(d) $x^2 + y^2 - 4x + 9y + 18 = 0$

Sol. Ans. (a)

Let $P(2t^2, 4t)$ and $C(0, -6)$

$\therefore \quad (CP)^2 = 4t^4 + (4t + 6)^2 = z$ (say)

$\therefore \quad \frac{dz}{dt} = 0 \quad \Rightarrow \quad t = -1 \quad \Rightarrow \quad P(2, -4)$

Equation of circle is

$$(x-2)^2 + (y+4)^2 = (2-0)^2 + (-4+6)^2$$
$$\Rightarrow x^2 + y^2 - 4x + 8y + 12 = 0$$

22. The eccentricity of the hyperbola whose length of the latus rectum is equal to 8 and the length of its conjugate axis is equal to half of the distance between its foci, is :

(a) $\frac{4}{3}$ (b) $\frac{4}{\sqrt{3}}$ (c) $\frac{2}{\sqrt{3}}$ (d) $\sqrt{3}$

Sol. Ans. (c)

$$\frac{2b^2}{a} = 8 \Rightarrow b^2 = 4a \quad \text{and} \quad 2b = ae$$
$$\therefore \quad b^2 = a^2(e^2 - 1)$$
We get $a = 12, b^2 = 48$
$$e = \frac{2b}{a} = \frac{2 \times 4\sqrt{3}}{12} = \frac{2}{\sqrt{3}}$$

23. The distance of the point $(1, -5, 9)$ from the plane $x - y + z = 5$ measured along the line $x = y = z$ is :

(a) $3\sqrt{10}$ (b) $10\sqrt{3}$ (c) $\frac{10}{\sqrt{3}}$ (d) $\frac{20}{3}$

Sol. Ans. (b)

$$\frac{x-1}{1} = \frac{y+5}{1} = \frac{z-9}{1} = \lambda \quad \text{(say)}$$
$\therefore$ $P(1+\lambda, \lambda-5, \lambda+9)$ lie on given plane, then $\lambda = -10$

$\therefore$ $P(-9, -15, -1)$ and point $(1, -5, 9)$

Required distance $= \sqrt{100+100+100} = 10\sqrt{3}$

24. If the line, $\frac{x-3}{2} = \frac{y+2}{-1} = \frac{z+4}{3}$ lies in the plane, $lx + my - z = 9$, then $l^2 + m^2$ is equal to :

(a) 26 (b) 18 (c) 5 (d) 2

Sol. Ans. (d)

$$3l - 2m + 4 = 9 \Rightarrow 3l - 2m = 5$$
and $\quad 2l - m - 3 = 0$

We get $\quad l = 1, m = -1$

$\therefore \quad l^2 + m^2 = 2$

25. Let **a**, **b** and **c** be three unit vectors such that $\mathbf{a} \times (\mathbf{b} \times \mathbf{c}) = \frac{\sqrt{3}}{2}(\mathbf{b} + \mathbf{c})$. If **b** is not parallel to **c**, then the angle between **a** and **b** is :

(a) $\frac{3\pi}{4}$ (b) $\frac{\pi}{2}$ (c) $\frac{2\pi}{3}$ (d) $\frac{5\pi}{6}$

Sol. Ans. (d)

$$(\mathbf{a}\cdot\mathbf{c})\,\mathbf{b} - (\mathbf{a}\cdot\mathbf{b})\,\mathbf{c} = \frac{\sqrt{3}}{2}(\mathbf{b} + \mathbf{c})$$
$$\therefore \quad \mathbf{a}\cdot\mathbf{b} = -\frac{\sqrt{3}}{2} \Rightarrow |\mathbf{a}||\mathbf{b}|\cos\theta = -\frac{\sqrt{3}}{2}$$
$$\Rightarrow \cos\theta = -\frac{\sqrt{3}}{2} \qquad \therefore \theta = \frac{5\pi}{6}$$

26. If the standard deviation of the numbers 2, 3, a and 11 is 3.5, then which of the following is true ?

(a) $3a^2 - 26a + 55 = 0$ (b) $3a^2 - 32a + 84 = 0$

(c) $3a^2 - 34a + 91 = 0$ (d) $3a^2 - 23a + 44 = 0$

Sol. Ans. (b)

$$3.5 = \sqrt{\left(\frac{4+9+a^2+121}{4}\right) - \left(\frac{16+a}{4}\right)^2}$$
$$\Rightarrow 3a^2 - 32a + 84 = 0$$

27. Let two fair six faced dice A and B be thrown simultaneously. If E_1 is the event that die A shows up four, E_2 is the event that die B shows up two and E_3 is the event that the sum of numbers on both dice is odd, then which of the following statements is NOT true?

(a) E_1 and E_2 are independent

(b) E_2 and E_3 are independent

(c) E_1 and E_3 are independent

(d) E_1, E_2 and E_3 are independent

Sol. Ans. (d)

$$\because \quad E_1 \cap E_2 \cap E_3 = \phi$$
$$P(E_1 \cap E_2 \cap E_3) = 0$$
$$\neq P(E_1)P(E_2)P(E_3)$$

28. If $0 \le x < 2\pi$, then the number of real values of x, which satisfy the equation

$$\cos x + \cos 2x + \cos 3x + \cos 4x = 0 \text{ is :}$$

(a) 3 (b) 5 (c) 7 (d) 9

Sol. Ans. (c)

$$(\cos x + \cos 4x) + (\cos 2x + \cos 3x) = 0$$
$$\Rightarrow 4\cos x \cos\left(\frac{x}{2}\right)\cos\left(\frac{5x}{2}\right) = 0$$
$$\therefore \quad x = \frac{\pi}{2}, \pi, \frac{3\pi}{2}, \frac{\pi}{5}, \frac{3\pi}{5}, \frac{7\pi}{5}, \frac{9\pi}{5}$$

29. A man is walking towards a vertical pillar in a straight path, at a uniform speed. At a certain point A on the path, he observes that the angle of elevation of the top of the pillar is 30°. After walking for 10 minutes from A in the same direction, at a point B he observes that the angle of elevation of the top of the pillar is 60°. Then the time taken (in minutes) by him, from B to reach the pillar, is :

(a) 6 (b) 10 (c) 20 (d) 5

Sol. Ans. (d)

$$\therefore \quad OB = 10v\cos 60° = 5v$$

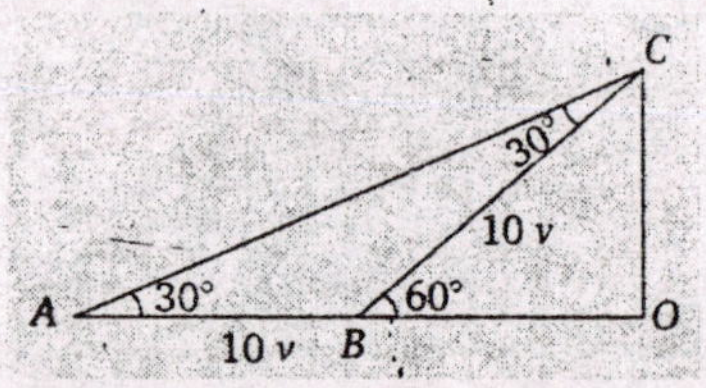

$$\text{time} = \frac{5v}{v} = 5 \text{ min}$$

30. The Boolean Expression $(p \wedge \sim q) \vee q \vee (\sim p, q)$ is equivalent to :

(a) $\sim p \wedge q$ (b) $p \wedge q$

(c) $p \vee q$ (d) $p \vee \sim q$

Sol. Ans. (c)

p	q	$\sim p$	$\sim q$	$\sim p \wedge q$	$p \wedge q$	$p \vee q$	$p \vee \sim q$	$p \wedge \sim q$	$(p \wedge \sim q) \vee q \vee (\sim p, q)$
T	T	F	F	F	T	T	T	F	T
T	F	F	T	F	F	T	T	T	T
F	T	T	F	T	F	T	F	F	T
F	F	T	T	F	F	F	T	F	F